GLENCOE
MATHEMATICS

Algebra 2

Solutions Manual

D1296913

Mc Graw Hill **Glencoe
McGraw-Hill**

New York, New York
Columbus, Ohio
Chicago, Illinois
Peoria, Illinois
Woodland Hills, California

The *McGraw-Hill* Companies

Send all inquiries to:
Glencoe/McGraw-Hill
8787 Orion Place
Columbus, OH 43240-4027

ISBN: 0-07-828028-1

Algebra 2
Solutions Manual

1 2 3 4 5 6 7 8 9 10   045   07 06 05 04 03 02

CONTENTS

Chapter 1 Solving Equations and Inequalities 1

Chapter 2 Linear Relations and Functions .42

Chapter 3 Systems of Equations and Inequalities 92

Chapter 4 Matrices 149

Chapter 5 Polynomials 199

Chapter 6 Quadratic Functions and Inequalities 241

Chapter 7 Polynomial Functions 315

Chapter 8 Conic Sections 368

Chapter 9 Rational Expressions and Equations 439

Chapter 10 Exponential and Logarithmic Relations 484

Chapter 11 Sequences and Series 520

Chapter 12 Probability and Statistics 568

Chapter 13 Trigonometric Functions 629

Chapter 14 Trigonometric Graphs and Identities 670

Chapter 1 Solving Equations and Inequalities

Page 5   Getting Started

1. $20 - 0.16 = 19.84$

2. $12.2 + (-8.45) = +(|12.2| - |-8.45|)$
$$= +(12.2 - 8.45)$$
$$= 3.75$$

3. $-3.01 - 14.5 = -3.01 + (-14.5)$
$$= -(|-3.01| + |-14.5|)$$
$$= -(3.01 + 14.5)$$
$$= -17.51$$

4. $-1.8 + 17 = +(|17| - |-1.8|)$
$$= +(17 - 1.8)$$
$$= 15.2$$

5. $\frac{1}{4} - \frac{2}{3} = \frac{1}{4} + \left(-\frac{2}{3}\right)$
$$= \frac{3}{12} + \left(-\frac{8}{12}\right)$$
$$= -\left(\left|-\frac{8}{12}\right| - \left|\frac{3}{12}\right|\right)$$
$$= -\left(\frac{8}{12} - \frac{3}{12}\right)$$
$$= -\frac{5}{12}$$

6. $\frac{3}{5} + (-6) = -\left(|-6| - \left|\frac{3}{5}\right|\right)$
$$= -\left(6 - \frac{3}{5}\right)$$
$$= -5\frac{2}{5}$$

7. $-7\frac{1}{2} + 5\frac{1}{3} = -7\frac{3}{6} + 5\frac{2}{6}$
$$= -\left(\left|-7\frac{3}{6}\right| - \left|5\frac{2}{6}\right|\right)$$
$$= -\left(7\frac{3}{6} - 5\frac{2}{6}\right)$$
$$= -2\frac{1}{6}$$

8. $-11\frac{5}{8} - \left(-4\frac{3}{7}\right) = -11\frac{5}{8} + \left(+4\frac{3}{7}\right)$
$$= -11\frac{35}{56} + 4\frac{24}{56}$$
$$= -\left(\left|-11\frac{35}{56}\right| - \left|4\frac{24}{56}\right|\right)$$
$$= -\left(11\frac{35}{56} - 4\frac{24}{56}\right)$$
$$= -7\frac{11}{56}$$

9. $(0.15)(3.2) = 0.48$

10. $2 \div (-0.4) = -5$

11. $(-1.21) \div (-1.1) = 1.1$

12. $(-9)(0.036) = -0.324$

13. $-4 \div \frac{3}{2} = -4 \cdot \frac{2}{3}$
$$= \frac{-8}{3}$$
$$= -2\frac{2}{3}$$

14. $\left(\frac{5}{4}\right)\left(-\frac{3}{10}\right) = -\frac{15}{40}$
$$= -\frac{3}{8}$$

15. $\left(-2\frac{3}{4}\right)\left(-3\frac{1}{5}\right) = \left(-\frac{11}{4}\right)\left(-\frac{16}{5}\right)$
$$= \frac{176}{20}$$
$$= 8\frac{4}{5}$$

16. $7\frac{1}{8} \div (-2) = 7\frac{1}{8} \cdot \left(\frac{1}{-2}\right)$
$$= \frac{57}{8} \cdot \frac{1}{-2}$$
$$= \frac{57}{-16}$$
$$= -3\frac{9}{16}$$

17. $2^3 = 2 \cdot 2 \cdot 2$
$$= 8$$

18. $5^3 = 5 \cdot 5 \cdot 5$
$$= 125$$

19. $(-7)^2 = (-7)(-7)$
$$= 49$$

20. $(-1)^3 = (-1)(-1)(-1)$
$$= -1$$

21. $(-0.8)^2 = (-0.8)(-0.8)$
$$= 0.64$$

22. $-(1.2)^2 = -(1.2)(1.2)$
$$= -1.44$$

23. $\left(\frac{2}{3}\right)^2 = \left(\frac{2}{3}\right)\left(\frac{2}{3}\right)$
$$= \frac{4}{9}$$

24. $\left(-\frac{4}{11}\right)^2 = \left(-\frac{4}{11}\right)\left(-\frac{4}{11}\right)$
$$= \frac{16}{121}$$

25. False, -5 is greater than -7.

26. True, 6 is greater than -8.

27. True, -2 equals -2.

28. True, -3 is greater than -3.01.

29. False, -9.02 is greater than -9.2.

30. False, $\frac{1}{5}$ is greater than $\frac{1}{8}$.

31. True, $\frac{2}{5}$ equals $\frac{16}{40}$.

32. False, $\frac{3}{4}$ is less than 0.8.

1-1   Expressions and Formulas

Page 7   Graphing Calculator Investigation

1. KEYSTROKES: 8 $-$ 2 $\times$ 4 $+$ 5 ENTER
   The result is 5.

2. The calculator multiplies 2 by 4, subtracts the result from 8, and then adds 5.

3a. $8 - 2 \times (4 + 5) = -10$
   Therefore, place the parentheses around $4 + 5$.

3b. $(8 - 2) \times (4 + 5) = 29$
   Therefore, place the parentheses around $8 - 2$.

3c. $8 - (2 \times 4 + 5) = -5$
   Therefore, place the parentheses around $2 \times 4 + 5$.

4. KEYSTROKES: 18 x^2 $\div$ (2 $\times$ 3) ENTER
   The result is 54.
   The calculator found the square of 18 and divided it by the product of 2 and 3.

5. No; you would square 18 and then divide it by 2. The result would then be multiplied by 3.

Pages 8–9 Check for Understanding

1. First, find the sum of c and d. Divide this sum by e. Multiply the quotient by b. Finally, add a.

2. Sample answer: $\dfrac{14 - 4}{5}$

3. b; the sum of the cost of adult and children tickets should be subtracted from 50.
   Therefore, parentheses need to be inserted around this sum to insure that this addition is done before subtraction.

4. $8(3 + 6) = 8(9)$
   $\qquad\qquad = 72$
   The value is 72.

5. $10 - 8 \div 2 = 10 - 4$
   $\qquad\qquad\quad = 6$
   The value is 6.

6. $14 \cdot 2 - 5 = 28 - 5$
   $\qquad\qquad\quad = 23$
   The value is 23.

7. $[9 + 3(5 - 7)] \div 3 = [9 + 3(-2)] \div 3$
   $\qquad\qquad\qquad\quad = [9 + (-6)] \div 3$
   $\qquad\qquad\qquad\quad = 3 \div 3$
   $\qquad\qquad\qquad\quad = 1$
   The value is 1.

8. $[6 - (12 - 8)^2] \div 5 = [6 - (4)^2] \div 5$
   $\qquad\qquad\qquad\qquad = (6 - 16) \div 5$
   $\qquad\qquad\qquad\qquad = -10 \div 5$
   $\qquad\qquad\qquad\qquad = -2$
   The value is -2.

9. $\dfrac{17(2 + 26)}{4} = \dfrac{17(28)}{4}$
   $\qquad\qquad\quad = \dfrac{476}{4}$
   $\qquad\qquad\quad = 119$
   The value is 119.

10. $z - x + y = 6 - 4 + (-2)$
    $\qquad\qquad\ = 2 + (-2)$
    $\qquad\qquad\ = 0$
    The value is 0.

11. $x + (y - 1)^3 = 4 + (-2 - 1)^3$
    $\qquad\qquad\quad = 4 + (-3)^3$
    $\qquad\qquad\quad = 4 + (-27)$
    $\qquad\qquad\quad = -23$
    The value is -23.

12. $x + [3(y + z) - y] = 4 + [3(-2 + 6) - (-2)]$
    $\qquad\qquad\qquad\quad = 4 + [3(4) - (-2)]$
    $\qquad\qquad\qquad\quad = 4 + [12 - (-2)]$
    $\qquad\qquad\qquad\quad = 4 + (12 + 2)$
    $\qquad\qquad\qquad\quad = 4 + 14$
    $\qquad\qquad\qquad\quad = 18$
    The value is 18.

13. Substitute each value given into the formula. Then evaluate the expression using the order of operations.
    $I = prt$
    $\quad = (1800)(0.06)(4)$
    $\quad = (108)(4)$
    $\quad = 432$
    The simple interest is $432.

14. Substitute each value given into the formula. Then evaluate the expression using the order of operations.
    $I = prt$
    $\quad = (5000)(0.0375)(10)$
    $\quad = (187.5)(10)$
    $\quad = 1875$
    The simple interest is $1875.

15. Substitute each value given into the formula. Then evaluate the expression using the order of operations.
    $I = prt$
    $\quad = (31{,}000)(0.025)(1.5)$
    $\quad = (775)(1.5)$
    $\quad = 1162.5$
    The simple interest is $1162.50.

Pages 9–10 Practice and Apply

16. $18 + 6 \div 3 = 18 + 2$
    $\qquad\qquad\quad = 20$
    The value is 20.

17. $7 - 20 \div 5 = 7 - 4$
    $\qquad\qquad\quad = 3$
    The value is 3.

18. $3(8 + 3) - 4 = 3(11) - 4$
    $\qquad\qquad\qquad = 33 - 4$
    $\qquad\qquad\qquad = 29$
    The value is 29.

19. $(6 + 7)2 - 1 = (13)2 - 1$
    $\qquad\qquad\qquad = 26 - 1$
    $\qquad\qquad\qquad = 25$
    The value is 25.

20. $2(6^2 - 9) = 2(36 - 9)$
    $\qquad\qquad\ = 2(27)$
    $\qquad\qquad\ = 54$
    The value is 54.

21. $-2(3^2 + 8) = -2(9 + 8)$
    $\qquad\qquad\quad = -2(17)$
    $\qquad\qquad\quad = -34$
    The value is -34.

22. $2 + 8(5) \div 2 - 3 = 2 + 40 \div 2 - 3$
    $\qquad\qquad\qquad\qquad = 2 + 20 - 3$
    $\qquad\qquad\qquad\qquad = 22 - 3$
    $\qquad\qquad\qquad\qquad = 19$
    The value is 19.

23. $4 + 64 \div (8 \times 4) \div 2 = 4 + 64 \div 32 \div 2$
    $\qquad\qquad\qquad\qquad\qquad = 4 + 2 \div 2$
    $\qquad\qquad\qquad\qquad\qquad = 4 + 1$
    $\qquad\qquad\qquad\qquad\qquad = 5$
    The value is 5.

24. $[38 - (8 - 3)] \div 3 = (38 - 5) \div 3$
    $\qquad\qquad\qquad\qquad = 33 \div 3$
    $\qquad\qquad\qquad\qquad = 11$
    The value is 11.

25. $10 - [5 + 9(4)] = 10 - (5 + 36)$
    $\qquad\qquad\qquad\ = 10 - 41$
    $\qquad\qquad\qquad\ = -31$
    The value is -31.

26. $1 - \{30 \div [7 + 3(-4)]\} = 1 - \{30 \div [7 + (-12)]\}$
$= 1 - [30 \div (-5)]$
$= 1 - (-6)$
$= 7$

The value is 7.

27. $12 + \{10 \div [11 - 3(2)]\} = 12 + [10 \div (11 - 6)]$
$= 12 + (10 \div 5)$
$= 12 + 2$
$= 14$

The value is 14.

28. $\frac{1}{3}(4 - 7^2) = \frac{1}{3}(4 - 49)$
$= \frac{1}{3}(-45)$
$= -15$

The value is -15.

29. $\frac{1}{2}[9 + 5(-3)] = \frac{1}{2}[9 + (-15)]$
$= \frac{1}{2}(-6)$
$= -3$

The value is -3.

30. $\frac{16(9 - 22)}{4} = \frac{16(-13)}{4}$
$= -\frac{208}{4}$
$= -52$

The value is -52.

31. $\frac{45(4 + 32)}{10} = \frac{45(36)}{10}$
$= \frac{1620}{10}$
$= 162$

The value is 162.

32. $0.3(1.5 + 24) \div 0.5 = 0.3(25.5) \div 0.5$
$= 7.65 \div 0.5$
$= 15.3$

The value is 15.3.

33. $1.6(0.7 + 3.3) \div 2.5 = 1.6(4) \div 2.5$
$= 6.4 \div 2.5$
$= 2.56$

The value is 2.56.

34. $\frac{1}{5} - \frac{20(81 \div 9)}{25} = \frac{1}{5} - \frac{20(9)}{25}$
$= \frac{1}{5} - \frac{180}{25}$
$= \frac{1}{5} - \frac{36}{5}$
$= -\frac{35}{5}$
$= -7$

The value is -7.

35. $\frac{12(52 \div 2^2)}{6} - \frac{2}{3} = \frac{12(52 \div 4)}{6} - \frac{2}{3}$
$= \frac{12(13)}{6} - \frac{2}{3}$
$= \frac{156}{6} - \frac{2}{3}$
$= \frac{78}{3} - \frac{2}{3}$
$= \frac{76}{3}$
$= 25\frac{1}{3}$

The value is $25\frac{1}{3}$.

36. $\frac{(52.84 \times 10) + (5.955 \times 50)}{454} = \frac{528.4 + 297.75}{454}$
$= \frac{826.15}{454}$
≈ 1.8

About 1.8 pounds of pollutants are created.

37. $\frac{1500 \times 15}{12 \times 60} = \frac{22{,}500}{720}$
$= 31.25$

The IV flow rate is 31.25 drops per minute.

38. $w + x + z = 6 + 0.4 + (-3)$
$= 6.4 + (-3)$
$= 3.4$

The value is 3.4.

39. $w + 12 \div z = 6 + 12 \div (-3)$
$= 6 + (-4)$
$= 2$

The value is 2.

40. $w(8 - y) = 6\left(8 - \frac{1}{2}\right)$
$= 6\left(7\frac{1}{2}\right)$
$= 45$

The value is 45.

41. $z(x + 1) = -3(0.4 + 1)$
$= -3(1.4)$
$= -4.2$

The value is -4.2.

42. $w - 3x + y = 6 - 3(0.4) + \frac{1}{2}$
$= 6 - 1.2 + \frac{1}{2}$
$= 4.8 + \frac{1}{2}$
$= 5.3$

The value is 5.3.

43. $5x + 2z = 5(0.4) + 2(-3)$
$= 2 + 2(-3)$
$= 2 + (-6)$
$= -4$

The value is -4.

44. $z^4 - w = (-3)^4 - 6$
$= 81 - 6$
$= 75$

The value is 75.

45. $(5 - w)^2 - x = (5 - 6)^2 + 0.4$
$= (-1)^2 + 0.4$
$= 1 + 0.4$
$= 1.4$

The value is 1.4.

46. $\frac{5wx}{z} = \frac{5(6)(0.4)}{-3}$
$= \frac{30(0.4)}{-3}$
$= \frac{12}{-3}$
$= -4$

The value is -4.

47. $\dfrac{2z - 15x}{3y} = \dfrac{2(-3) - 15(0.4)}{3\left(\frac{1}{2}\right)}$

$\qquad = \dfrac{-6 - 6}{\frac{3}{2}}$

$\qquad = -\dfrac{12}{\frac{3}{2}}$

$\qquad = -12\left(\dfrac{2}{3}\right)$

$\qquad = \dfrac{-24}{3}$

$\qquad = -8$

The value is -8.

48. $(x - y)^2 - 2wz = \left(0.4 - \dfrac{1}{2}\right)^2 - 2(6)(-3)$

$\qquad = (-0.1)^2 - 2(6)(-3)$

$\qquad = 0.01 - 2(6)(-3)$

$\qquad = 0.01 - 12(-3)$

$\qquad = 0.01 - (-36)$

$\qquad = 36.01$

The value is 36.01.

49. $\dfrac{1}{y} + \dfrac{1}{w} = \dfrac{1}{\frac{1}{2}} + \dfrac{1}{6}$

$\qquad = 2 + \dfrac{1}{6}$

$\qquad = 2\dfrac{1}{6}$

The value is $2\dfrac{1}{6}$.

50. Substitute the expression given into the formula.

$A = \pi\left(\dfrac{d}{2}\right)^2$

$\quad = \pi\left(\dfrac{y + 5}{2}\right)^2$

The area of the circle is $\pi\left(\dfrac{y + 5}{2}\right)^2$.

51. Substitute each value given into the formula. Then evaluate the expression using order of operations.

$ab^n = 2000\left(-\dfrac{1}{5}\right)^3$

$\quad = 2000\left(-\dfrac{1}{125}\right)$

$\quad = -\dfrac{2000}{125}$

$\quad = -16$

The value is -16.

52. Substitute each value given into the formula. Then evaluate the expression using order of operations.

$n = 24d \div [8(b \times 15 \div 125)]$

$\quad = 24(30) \div [8(25 \times 15 \div 125)]$

$\quad = 24(30) \div [8(375 \div 125)]$

$\quad = 24(30) \div [8(3)]$

$\quad = 24(30) \div 24$

$\quad = 720 \div 24$

$\quad = 30$

The amount needed for a 30-day supply is 30 tablets.

53. Substitute each value given into the formula. Then evaluate the expression using order of operations.

$V = \dfrac{A}{S}C$

$\quad = \dfrac{2000}{42.1}(174.0)$

$\quad = 47.50594(174.0)$

$\quad = 8266.03356$

Buying a car for \$2000 in 1950 is like buying a car for \$8266.03 in 2000.

54. Substitute each value given into the formula. Then evaluate the expression using order of operations.

$w = 20At$

$\quad = 20(4)(5)$

$\quad = 80(5)$

$\quad = 400$

The width of the firework display is 400 feet.

55. Sample answer: $4 - 4 + 4 \div 4 = 1$

$4 \div 4 + 4 \div 4 = 2$

$(4 + 4 + 4) \div 4 = 3$

$4 \times (4 - 4) + 4 = 4$

$(4 \times 4 + 4) \div 4 = 5$

$(4 + 4) \div 4 + 4 = 6$

$44 \div 4 - 4 = 7$

$(4 + 4) \times (4 \div 4) = 8$

$4 + 4 + 4 \div 4 = 9$

$(44 - 4) \div 4 = 10$

56. Nurses use formulas to calculate a drug dosage given a supply dosage and a doctor's drug order. They also use formulas to calculate IV flow rates. Answers should include the following.

- A table of IV flow rates is limited to those situations listed, while a formula can be used to find any IV flow rate.
- If a formula used in a nursing setting is applied incorrectly, a patient could die.

57. C; $1 + 3(5 - 17) \div 2 \times 6 = 1 + 3(-12) \div 2 \times 6$

$\qquad = 1 + (-36) \div 2 \times 6$

$\qquad = 1 + (-18) \times 6$

$\qquad = 1 + (-108)$

$\qquad = -107$

The value is -107.

58. D; $A = \dfrac{1}{2}bh$

$\quad = \dfrac{1}{2}(4)(10)$

$\quad = 2(10)$

$\quad = 20$

The area of the triangle is 20 square feet.

$A = lw$

$\quad = 50(0.4)$

$\quad = 20$

The area of the 0.4 ft by 50 ft rectangle is 20 square feet.

Page 10 Maintain Your Skills

59. $\sqrt{9}$ represents the positive square root of 9.

$9 = 3^2 \rightarrow \sqrt{9} = 3$

60. $\sqrt{16}$ represents the positive square root of 16.
$16 = 4^2 \rightarrow \sqrt{16} = 4$

61. $\sqrt{100}$ represents the positive square root of 100.
$100 = 10^2 \rightarrow \sqrt{100} = 10$

62. $\sqrt{169}$ represents the positive square root of 169.
$169 = 13^2 \rightarrow \sqrt{169} = 13$

63. $-\sqrt{4}$ represents the negative square root of 4.
$4 = 2^2 \rightarrow -\sqrt{4} = -2$

64. $-\sqrt{25}$ represents the negative square root of 25.
$25 = 5^2 \rightarrow -\sqrt{25} = -5$

65. $\sqrt{\frac{4}{9}}$ represents the positive square root of $\frac{4}{9}$.
$\frac{4}{9} = \left(\frac{2}{3}\right)^2 \rightarrow \sqrt{\frac{4}{9}} = \frac{2}{3}$

66. $\sqrt{\frac{36}{49}}$ represents the positive square root of $\frac{36}{49}$.
$\frac{36}{49} = \left(\frac{36}{49}\right)^2 \rightarrow \sqrt{\frac{36}{49}} = \frac{6}{7}$

1-2 | Properties of Real Numbers

Page 13   Algebra Activity

1. The equation is false.

To find the product $4(x + 2)$, model a rectangle with a width of 4 and a length of $x + 2$.

The rectangle has 4 x tiles and 8 1 tiles. The area of the rectangle is $x + x + x + x + 1 + 1 + 1 + 1 + 1 + 1 + 1 + 1$ or $4x + 8$. Thus $4(x + 2) = 4x + 8$.

2. The equation is false.

To find the product $3(2x + 4)$, model a rectangle with a width of 3 and a length of $2x + 4$.

The rectangle has 6 x tiles and 12 1 tiles. The area of the rectangle is $x + x + x + x + x + x + 1 + 1 + 1 + 1 + 1 + 1 + 1 + 1 + 1 + 1 + 1 + 1$ or $6x + 12$. Thus, $3(2x + 4) = 6x + 12$.

3. The equation is true.

To find the product $2(3x + 5)$, model a rectangle with a width of 2 and a length of $3x + 5$.

The rectangle has 6 x tiles and 10 1 tiles. The area of the rectangle is $x + x + x + x + x + x + 1 + 1 + 1 + 1 + 1 + 1 + 1 + 1 + 1 + 1$ or $6x + 10$. Thus $2(3x + 5) = 6x + 10$.

4. The equation is false.

To find the product $(4x + 1)5$, model a rectangle with a width of $4x + 1$ and a length of 5.

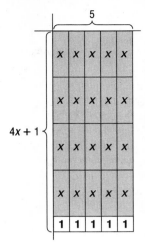

The rectangle has 20 x tiles and 5 1 tiles. The area of the rectangle is $x + x + x + x + x + x + x + x + x + x + x + x + x + x + x + x + x + x + x + x + 1 + 1 + 1 + 1 + 1$ or $20x + 5$. Thus, $(4x + 1)5 = 20x + 5$.

Pages 14–15   Check for Understanding

1a. Sample answer: 2

1b. Sample answer: 5

1c. Sample answer: -11

1d. Sample answer: 1.3

1e. Sample answer: $\sqrt{2}$

1f. Sample answer: -1.3

2. A rational number is the ratio of two integers. Since $\sqrt{3}$ is not an integer, $\sqrt{\frac{3}{2}}$ is not a rational number.

3. 0; zero does not have a multiplicative inverse since $\frac{1}{0}$ is undefined.

4. integers (Z), rationals (Q) and reals (R)

5. naturals (N), wholes (W), integers (Z), rationals (Q), and reals (R)

6. rationals (Q) and reals (R)

7. Multiplicative Inverse Property—the product of a number and its multiplicative inverse is equal to 1

8. Associative Property of Addition—the way you group three numbers when adding does not change the sum.

9. Additive Identity Property—the sum of any number and 0 is equal to the number

10. Since $-8 + 8 = 0$, the additive inverse of -8 is 8. Since $(-8)\left(-\frac{1}{8}\right) = 1$, the multiplicative inverse of -8 is $-\frac{1}{8}$.

11. Since $\frac{1}{3} + \left(-\frac{1}{3}\right) = 0$, the additive inverse of $\frac{1}{3}$ is $-\frac{1}{3}$.

Since $\left(\frac{1}{3}\right)(3) = 1$, the multiplicative inverse of $\frac{1}{3}$ is 3.

12. Since $1.5 + (-1.5) = 0$, the additive inverse of 1.5 is -1.5.

The multiplicative inverse of 1.5 is $\frac{1}{1.5}$ or $\frac{2}{3}$.

13. $3x + 4y - 5x = 3x - 5x + 4y$
$ = (3 - 5)x + 4y$
$ = -2x + 4y$

14. $9p - 2n + 4p + 2n = 9p + 4p - 2n + 2n$
$ = 9p + 4p + 2n - 2n$
$ = (9 + 4)p + (2 - 2)n$
$ = 13p + 0n$
$ = 13p$

15. $3(5c + 4d) + 6(d - 2c)$
$ = 3(5c) + 3(4d) + 6(d) + 6(-2c)$
$ = 15c + 12d + 6d - 12c$
$ = 15c - 12c + 12d + 6d$
$ = (15 - 12)c + (12 + 6)d$
$ = 3c + 18d$

16. $\frac{1}{2}(16 - 4a) - \frac{3}{4}(12 + 20a)$
$ = \frac{1}{2}(16) + \frac{1}{2}(-4a) - \frac{3}{4}(12) - \frac{3}{4}(20a)$
$ = 8 - 2a - 9 - 15a$
$ = 8 - 9 - 2a - 15a$
$ = (8 - 9) + (-2 - 15)a$
$ = -1 + (-17)a$
$ = -1 - 17a$
$ = -17a - 1$

17. **Method 1**
Multiply the number of chocolate bars sold each day by $1.50 and then add.
$1.5(10) + 1.5(15) + 1.5(12) + 1.5(8) + 1.5(19) + 1.5(22) + 1.5(31)$
Method 2
Add the number of chocolate bars sold for all days and then multiply the total by $1.50.
$1.5(10 + 15 + 12 + 8 + 19 + 22 + 31)$

18. $T = 1.5(10 + 15 + 12 + 8 + 19 + 22 + 31)$
$ = 1.5(10) + 1.5(15) + 1.5(12) + 1.5(8) +$
$ 1.5(19) + 1.5(22) + 1.5(31)$
$ = 15 + 22.5 + 18 + 12 + 28.5 + 33 + 46.5$
$ = 175.5$

The total money raised by Ashley was $175.50.

Pages 15–18 Practice and Apply

19. wholes (W), integers (Z), rationals (Q), and reals (R)

20. rationals (Q) and reals (R)

21. $\sqrt{121} = 11$; naturals (N), wholes (W), integers (Z), rationals (Q), and reals (R)

22. rationals (Q) and reals (R)

23. $\sqrt{10}$ lies between 3 and 4 so it is not a whole number. irrationals (I) and reals (R)

24. integers (Z), rationals (Q), and reals (R)

25. $\frac{12}{2} = 6$ naturals (N), wholes (W), integers (Z), rationals (Q), and reals (R)

26. $\frac{3\pi}{2}$ lies between 4 and 5 so it is not a whole number. irrationals (I) and reals (R)

27. rationals (Q), and reals (R)
Write each number in decimal notation.
$2.\overline{49} = 2.49494949\ldots$ or about 2.495
$2.4\overline{9} = 2.49999999\ldots$ or about 2.500
$2.4 = 2.400$
$2.49 = 2.490$
$2.\overline{9} = 2.999999999\ldots$ or about 3.000
$2.400 < 2.490 < 2.495 < 2.500 < 3.000$
Therefore, $2.4 < 2.49 < 2.\overline{49} < 2.4\overline{9} < 2.\overline{9}$.

28. Additive Inverse Property—the sum of a number and its additive inverse is equal to 0

29. Associative Property of Multiplication—the way you group three numbers when multiplying does not change the product

30. Additive Identity Property—the sum of any number and 0 is equal to the number

31. Associative Property of Addition—the way you group three numbers when adding does not change the sum

32. Commutative Property of Addition—the order in which you add does not change the sum

33. Multiplicative Inverse Property—the product of a number and its multiplicative inverse is equal to 1

34. Distributive Property—the product of a number and a sum is equal to the sum of the products of the number and each addend

35. Multiplicative Identity Property—the product of any number and 1 is equal to the number

36. Since $m + 0 = m$, $n = 0$.

37. Since $m + (-m) = 0$, $n = -m$. Therefore, n is the additive inverse of m.

38. Since $m\left(\frac{1}{m}\right) = 1$, $n = \frac{1}{m}$. Therefore, n is the multiplicative inverse of m.

39. Since $m(1) = m$, $n = 1$.

40. The positive integers make up the set of natural numbers.

41. $c = \sqrt{2s^2}$
$ = \sqrt{2(1)^2}$
$ = \sqrt{2(1)}$
$ = \sqrt{2}$

The length of the hypotenuse is $\sqrt{2}$ units.

42. The square root of 2 is irrational, and therefore, cannot be described by a natural number.

43. Since $-10 + 10 = 0$, the additive inverse of -10 is 10.
Since $(-10)\left(-\frac{1}{10}\right) = 1$, the multiplicative inverse of -10 is $-\frac{1}{10}$.

44. Since $2.5 + (-2.5) = 0$, the additive inverse of 2.5 is -2.5.

The multiplicative inverse of 2.5 is $\frac{1}{2.5}$ or 0.4.

45. Since $-0.125 + 0.125 = 0$, the additive inverse of -0.125 is 0.125.

The multiplicative inverse of -0.125 is $-\frac{1}{0.125}$ or -8.

46. Since $-\frac{5}{8} + \frac{5}{8} = 0$, the additive inverse of $-\frac{5}{8}$ is $\frac{5}{8}$. Since $\left(-\frac{5}{8}\right)\left(-\frac{8}{5}\right) = 1$, the multiplicative inverse of $-\frac{5}{8}$ is $-\frac{8}{5}$.

47. Since $\frac{4}{3} + \left(-\frac{4}{3}\right) = 0$, the additive inverse of $\frac{4}{3}$ is $-\frac{4}{3}$.

Since $\left(\frac{4}{3}\right)\left(\frac{3}{4}\right) = 1$, the multiplicative inverse of $\frac{4}{3}$ is $\frac{3}{4}$.

48. Since $-4\frac{3}{5} + 4\frac{3}{5} = 0$, the additive inverse of $-4\frac{3}{5}$ is $4\frac{3}{5}$.

Since $-4\frac{3}{5} = -\frac{23}{5}$ and $\left(-\frac{23}{5}\right)\left(-\frac{5}{23}\right) = 1$, the multiplicative inverse of $-4\frac{3}{5}$ is $-\frac{5}{23}$.

49. $7a + 3b - 4a - 5b = 7a - 4a + 3b - 5b$
$= (7 - 4)a + (3 - 5)b$
$= 3a + (-2)b$
$= 3a - 2b$

50. $3x + 5y + 7x - 3y = 3x + 7x + 5y - 3y$
$= (3 + 7)x + (5 - 3)y$
$= 10x + 2y$

51. $3(15x - 9y) + 5(4y - x)$
$= 3(15x) + 3(-9y) + 5(4y) + 5(-x)$
$= 45x - 27y + 20y - 5x$
$= 45x - 5x + 20y - 27y$
$= (45 - 5)x + (20 - 27)y$
$= 40x + (-7)y$
$= 40x - 7y$

52. $2(10m - 7a) + 3(8a - 3m)$
$= 2(10m) + 2(-7a) + 3(8a) + 3(-3m)$
$= 20m - 14a + 24a - 9m$
$= 20m - 9m + 24a - 14a$
$= (20 - 9)m + (24 - 14)a$
$= 11m + 10a$

53. $8(r + 7t) - 4(13t + 5r)$
$= 8(r) + 8(7t) - 4(13t) - 4(5r)$
$= 8r + 56t - 52t - 20r$
$= 8r - 20r + 56t - 52t$
$= -12r + 4t$

54. $4(14c - 10d) - 6(d + 4c)$
$= 4(14c) + 4(-10d) - 6(d) - 6(4c)$
$= 56c - 40d - 6d - 24c$
$= 56c - 24c - 40d - 6d$
$= (56 - 24)c + (-40 - 6)d$
$= 32c + (-46d)$
$= 32c - 46d$

55. $4(0.2m - 0.3n) - 6(0.7m - 0.5n)$
$= 4(0.2m) + 4(-0.3n) - 6(0.7m) - 6(-0.5n)$
$= 0.8m - 1.2n - 4.2m + 3n$
$= 0.8m - 4.2m + 3n - 1.2n$
$= (0.8 - 4.2)m + (3 - 1.2)n$
$= -3.4m + 1.8n$

56. $7(0.2p - 0.3q) + 5(0.6p - q)$
$= 7(0.2p) + 7(0.3q) + 5(0.6p) + 5(-q)$
$= 1.4p + 2.1q + 3p - 5q$
$= 1.4p + 3p + 2.1q - 5q$
$= (1.4 + 3)p + (2.1 - 5)q$
$= 4.4p + (-2.9q)$
$= 4.4p - 2.9g$

57. $\frac{1}{4}(6 + 20y) - \frac{1}{2}(19 - 8y)$
$= \frac{1}{4}(6) + \frac{1}{4}(20y) - \frac{1}{2}(19) - \frac{1}{2}(-8y)$
$= \frac{3}{2} + 5y - \frac{19}{2} + 4y$
$= \frac{3}{2} - \frac{19}{2} + 5y + 4y$
$= \left(\frac{3}{2} - \frac{19}{2}\right) + (5 + 4)y$
$= -8 + 9y$

58. $\frac{1}{6}(3x + 5y) + \frac{2}{3}\left(\frac{3}{5}x - 6y\right)$
$= \frac{1}{6}(3x) + \frac{1}{6}(5y) + \frac{2}{3}\left(\frac{3}{5}x\right) + \frac{2}{3}(-6y)$
$= \frac{1}{2}x + \frac{5}{6}y + \frac{2}{5}x - 4y$
$= \frac{1}{2}x + \frac{2}{5}x + \frac{5}{6}y - 4y$
$= \left(\frac{1}{2} + \frac{2}{5}\right)x + \left(\frac{5}{6} - 4\right)y$
$= \frac{9}{10}x + \left(-\frac{19}{6}y\right)$
$= \frac{9}{10}x - \frac{19}{6}y$

59. True

60. False; -3 is a counterexample.

61. False; 6 is a counterexample.

62. True

63. Method 1
Multiply the number of hours worked each day by $6.50 and then add.
$6.5(0) + 6.5(4.5) + 6.5(0) + 6.5(4.25) + 6.5(5.25) + 6.5(6.5) + 6.5(5.0)$
Method 2
Add the number of hours worked for all days and then multiply the total by $6.50.
$6.5(0 + 4.5 + 0 + 4.25 + 5.25 + 6.5 + 5.0)$

64. mean $= \frac{0 + 4.5 + 0 + 4.25 + 5.25 + 6.5 + 5.0}{7}$
$= \frac{25.5}{7}$ or 3.643

The average number of hours Andrea worked each day is 3.6. There are 14 days in 2 weeks. Therefore, multiply 3.6 by 14 to determine how many hours she worked in a two week period.
$T = 6.5[3.6(14)]$
$= 6.5(50.4)$
$= 327.6$

Her pay would be $327.60.

65. $3\left(2\frac{1}{4}\right) + 2\left(1\frac{1}{8}\right)$

$\qquad = 3\left(2 + \frac{1}{4}\right) + 2\left(1 + \frac{1}{8}\right)$ Definition of a mixed number

$\qquad = 3(2) + 3\left(\frac{1}{4}\right) + 2(1) + 2\left(\frac{1}{8}\right)$ Distributive Property

$\qquad = 6 + \frac{3}{4} + 2 + \frac{1}{4}$ Multiply.

$\qquad = 6 + 2 + \frac{3}{4} + \frac{1}{4}$ Commutative Property of Addition

$\qquad = 8 + \frac{3}{4} + \frac{1}{4}$ Add.

$\qquad = 8 + \left(\frac{3}{4} + \frac{1}{4}\right)$ Associative Property of Addition

$\qquad = 8 + 1$ Add.

$\qquad = 9$ Add.

She needs 9 cups of flour.

66. Method 1
Multiply the length of each half-court by the width and then add.
$50(47) + 50(47)$

Method 2
Add the length of the two half-courts and then multiply the total by the width.
$50(47 + 47)$

67. $T = 50(47 + 47)$
$\qquad = 50(47) + 50(47)$
$\qquad = 2350 + 2350$
$\qquad = 4700$

The area of the basketball court is 4700 square feet.

68. Method 1
Multiply the percents of money spent at each store by $113 and then add.
$113(0.36) + 113(0.19)$

Method 2
Add the percent spent at both stores and then multiply the total by $113.
$113(0.36 + 0.19)$

69. $T = 113(0.36 + 0.19)$
$\qquad = 113(0.36) + 113(0.19)$
$\qquad = 40.68 + 21.47$
$\qquad = 62.15$

The amount students spend at specially stores and department stores is $62.15.

70. Yes; $\frac{6 + 8}{2} = \frac{6}{2} + \frac{8}{2} = 7$;

Dividing by a number is the same as multiplying by its reciprocal.

71. Answers should include the following.
- Instead of doubling each coupon value and then adding these values together, the Distributive Property could be applied allowing you to add the coupon values first and then double the sum.

- If a store had a 25% off sale on all merchandise, the Distributive Property could be used to calculate these savings. For example, the savings on a $15 shirt, $40 pair of jeans, and $25 pair of slacks could be calculated as $0.25(15) + 0.25(40)$ and $0.25(25)$ or as $0.25(15 + 40 + 25)$ using the Distributive Property.

72. B; The product of two natural numbers is a natural number. Let $a = 1$ and $b = 2$. Then
$\qquad a - b = 1 - 2$ or -1 and $\frac{a}{b} = \frac{1}{2}$.

73. C; $27(x + 1.2) - 26(x + 1.2)$
$\qquad = 27(1.4 + 1.2) - 26(1.4 + 1.2)$
$\qquad = 27(2.6) - 26(1.4 + 1.2)$
$\qquad = 27(2.6) - 26(2.6)$
$\qquad = (27 - 26)2.6$
$\qquad = 1(2.6)$
$\qquad = 2.6$

74. True

75. False; $0 - 1 = -1$; which is not a whole number.

76. True

77. False; $2 \div 3 = \frac{2}{3}$, which is not a whole number.

Page 18   Maintain Your Skills

78. $9(4 - 3)^5 = 9(1)^5$
$\qquad\qquad\quad = 9(1)$
$\qquad\qquad\quad = 9$
The value is 9.

79. $5 + 9 \div 3(3) - 8 = 5 + 3(3) - 8$
$\qquad\qquad\qquad\qquad = 5 + 9 - 8$
$\qquad\qquad\qquad\qquad = 14 - 8$
$\qquad\qquad\qquad\qquad = 6$
The value is 6.

80. $a + 2b - c = -5 + 2(0.25) - \frac{1}{2}$

$\qquad\qquad\quad = -5 + 0.5 - \frac{1}{2}$

$\qquad\qquad\quad = -4.5 - \frac{1}{2}$

$\qquad\qquad\quad = -5$
The value is -5.

81. $b + 3(a + d)^3 = 0.25 + 3(-5 + 4)^3$
$\qquad\qquad\qquad\quad = 0.25 + 3(-1)^3$
$\qquad\qquad\qquad\quad = 0.25 + 3(-1)$
$\qquad\qquad\qquad\quad = 0.25 + (-3)$
$\qquad\qquad\qquad\quad = -2.75$
The value is -2.75.

82. $SA = 2lw + 2lh + 2wh$
$\qquad = 2(12)(5) + 2(12)(7) + 2(5)(7)$
$\qquad = 120 + 168 + 70$
$\qquad = 358$
The surface area of the prism is 358 square inches.

83. $8b - 5 = 8\left(-\frac{3}{4}\right) - 5$
$\qquad\qquad = -6 - 5$
$\qquad\qquad = -11$
The value is -11.

84. $\frac{2}{5}b + 1 = \frac{2}{5}\left(-\frac{3}{4}\right) + 1$

$\qquad = -\frac{3}{10} + 1$

$\qquad = \frac{7}{10}$

The value is $\frac{7}{10}$.

85. $1.5c - 7 = 1.5(1.8) - 7$

$\qquad = 2.7 - 7$

$\qquad = -4.3$

The value is -4.3.

86. $-9(a - 6) = -9(2 - 6)$

$\qquad = -9(-4)$

$\qquad = 36$

The value is 36.

Page 18   Practice Quiz 1

1. $18 - 12 \div 3 = 18 - 4$

$\qquad = 14$

The value is 14.

2. $-4 + 5(7 - 2^3) = -4 + 5(7 - 8)$

$\qquad = -4 + 5(-1)$

$\qquad = -4 + (-5)$

$\qquad = -9$

The value is -9.

3. $\frac{18 + 3 \times 4}{13 - 8} = \frac{18 + 12}{5}$

$\qquad = \frac{30}{5}$

$\qquad = 6$

The value is 6.

4. $a^3 + b(9 - c) = (-2)^3 + \frac{1}{3}[9 - (-12)]$

$\qquad = (-2)^3 + \frac{1}{3}(21)$

$\qquad = -8 + \frac{1}{3}(21)$

$\qquad = -8 + 7$

$\qquad = -1$

5. $I = \frac{E}{R + r}$

$\qquad = \frac{2.5}{1.05 + 0.2}$

$\qquad = \frac{2.5}{1.25}$

$\qquad = 2$

The amount of current is 2 amperes.

6. rationals (Q) and reals (R)

7. $\sqrt{100} = 10$

naturals (N), wholes (W), integers (Z), rationals (Q), and reals (R)

8. Additive Inverse Property—the sum of a number and its additive inverse is equal to 0.

9. Since $\frac{6}{7} + \left(-\frac{6}{7}\right) = 0$, the additive inverse of $\frac{6}{7}$ is $-\frac{6}{7}$.

Since $\left(\frac{6}{7}\right)\left(\frac{7}{6}\right) = 1$, the multiplicative inverse of $\frac{6}{7}$ is $\frac{7}{6}$.

10. $4(14x - 10y) - 6(x + 4y)$

$\qquad = 4(14x) + 4(-10y) - 6(x) - 6(4y)$

$\qquad = 56x - 40y - 6x - 24y$

$\qquad = 56x - 6x - 40y - 24y$

$\qquad = (56 - 6)x + (-40 - 24)y$

$\qquad = 50x + (-64y)$

$\qquad = 50x - 64y$

Page 19   Algebra Activity
(Follow-Up of Lesson 1-2)

1.

Figure Name	Sides (n)	Diagonals	Diagonals From One Vertex
triangle	3	0	0
quadrilateral	4	2	1
pentagon	5	5	
hexagon	6	9	
heptagon	7	14	
octagon	8	20	

triangle   quadrilateral   pentagon

hexagon   heptagon   octagon

2. Beginning with 2, you add the next consecutive integer to obtain the next number of diagonals: $0 + 2 = 2$, $2 + 3 = 5$, $5 + 4 = 9$, $9 + 5 = 14$, and so on.

3.

Figure Name	Sides (n)	Diagonals	Diagonals From One Vertex
triangle	3	0	0
quadrilateral	4	2	1
pentagon	5	5	2
hexagon	6	9	3
heptagon	7	14	4
octagon	8	20	5

4. The number of diagonals from one vertex is always 3 less than the number of sides of the figure. Therefore, if n is the number of sides, the expression is $n - 3$.

5. A polygon has the same number of vertices as sides. Therefore, the number of vertices is n.

6. A diagonal is drawn from a vertex to a vertex. Therefore, one diagonal connects 2 vertices.

7. There are n vertices in a polygon with $n - 3$ diagonals off each vertex. Since each vertex connects 2 diagonals, the formula is found by multiplying the number of vertices by the number of diagonals off each vertex and then dividing by 2 or $[n(n - 3)] \div 2$.

8. See students' work. A decagon has 35 diagonals because $10(10 - 3) \div 2 = 35$.

9. A generic polygon has n sides and n vertices. From each vertex, $n - 3$ diagonals can be drawn. So $n(n - 3)$ is the number of diagonals except that this formula counts each diagonal twice, since one diagonal connect 2 vertices. Therefore you must divide the expression by 2. So the formula is $y = n(n - 3) \div 2$.

10. Sample answer: 3 lines connect 3 dots, 6 lines connect 4 dots, 10 lines connect 5 dots.

11.

Dots (x)	Connection Lines (y)
3	3
4	6
5	10
6	15
7	21
8	28

12. The number of lines y is found by multiplying the number of dots x by the number of lines from each dot. Since there is a line connecting each dot with every other dot, the number of lines from each dot is $x - 1$. Also, since each line connects two dots, the product must then be divided by 2. Therefore, the formula is $y = [x(x - 1)] \div 2$ or $y = 0.5x^2 - 0.5x$.

13. There are two possible answers. One answer is that the number of dots is x. From each dot $x - 1$ lines can be drawn to other dots, but then the lines are counted twice, so the formula is $y = x(x - 1) \div 2$. A second answer is that you can see that the number of lines needed to connect the dots is the number of diagonals for a polygon with that number of vertices or sides plus the number of sides. So,
$$y = [x(x - 3) \div 2] + x$$
$$= (0.5x^2 - 1.5x) + x$$
$$= 0.5x^2 - 0.5x$$
or $y = 0.5x^2 - 0.5x$.

Page 24 **Check for Understanding**

1. Sample answer: $2x = -14$

2. Sometimes true; only when the expression you are dividing by does not equal zero

3. Jamal; his method can be confirmed by solving the equation using an alternative method.
$$C = \frac{5}{9}(F - 32)$$
$$C = \frac{5}{9}F - \frac{5}{9}(32)$$
$$C + \frac{5}{9}(32) = \frac{5}{9}F$$
$$\frac{9}{5}\left[C + \frac{5}{9}(32)\right] = F$$
$$\frac{9}{5}C + 32 = F$$

4. $5 + 4n$

5. $2n - n^3$

6. Sample answer: 9 times a number decreased by 3 is 6.

7. Sample answer: 5 plus 3 times the square of a number is twice that number.

8. Reflexive Property of Equality

9. Addition Property of Equality

10.
$$y + 14 = -7$$
$$y + 14 - 14 = -7 - 14$$
$$y = -21$$
The solution is -21.
Check: $y + 14 = -7$
$$-21 + 14 \stackrel{?}{=} -7$$
$$-7 = -7 \checkmark$$

11.
$$7 + 3x = 49$$
$$7 + 3x - 7 = 49 - 7$$
$$3x = 42$$
$$\frac{3x}{3} = \frac{42}{3}$$
$$x = 14$$
The solution is 14.
Check: $7 + 3x = 49$
$$7 + 3(14) \stackrel{?}{=} 49$$
$$7 + 42 \stackrel{?}{=} 49$$
$$49 = 49 \checkmark$$

12.
$$-4(b + 7) = -12$$
$$-4b - 28 = -12$$
$$-4b - 28 + 28 = -12 + 28$$
$$-4b = 16$$
$$\frac{-4b}{-4} = \frac{16}{-4}$$
$$b = -4$$
The solution is -4.
Check: $-4(b + 7) = -12$
$$-4(-4 + 7) \stackrel{?}{=} -12$$
$$-4(3) \stackrel{?}{=} -12$$
$$-12 = -12 \checkmark$$

13. $7q + q - 3q = -24$

$\quad\quad 8q - 3q = -24$

$\quad\quad\quad\quad 5q = -24$

$\quad\quad\quad\dfrac{5q}{5} = -\dfrac{24}{5}$

$\quad\quad\quad\quad q = -4.8$

The solution is -4.8.

Check: $\quad\quad 7q + q + -3q = -24$

$7(-4.8) + (-4.8) - 3(-4.8) \stackrel{?}{=} -24$

$-33.6 - 4.8 + 14.4 \stackrel{?}{=} -24$

$-38.4 + 14.4 \stackrel{?}{=} -24$

$-24 = -24\ \checkmark$

14. $\quad\quad 1.8a - 5 = -2.3$

$\quad 1.8a - 5 + 5 = -2.3 + 5$

$\quad\quad\quad 1.8a = 2.7$

$\quad\quad\quad\dfrac{1.8a}{1.8} = \dfrac{2.7}{1.8}$

$\quad\quad\quad\quad a = 1.5$

The solution is 1.5.

Check: $1.8a - 5 = -2.3$

$1.8(1.5) - 5 \stackrel{?}{=} -2.3$

$2.7 - 5 \stackrel{?}{=} -2.3$

$-2.3 = -2.3\ \checkmark$

15. $\quad\quad -\dfrac{3}{4}n + 1 = -11$

$\quad -\dfrac{3}{4}n + 1 - 1 = -11 - 1$

$\quad\quad\quad -\dfrac{3}{4}n = -12$

$\quad -\dfrac{4}{3}\left(-\dfrac{3}{4}n\right) = -\dfrac{4}{3}\left(-12\right)$

$\quad\quad\quad\quad n = 16$

The solution is 16.

Check: $\quad -\dfrac{3}{4}n + 1 = -11$

$\quad -\dfrac{3}{4}(16) + 1 \stackrel{?}{=} -11$

$\quad -12 + 1 \stackrel{?}{=} -11$

$\quad -11 = -11\ \checkmark$

16. $\quad\quad 4y - 2n = 9$

$\quad 4y - 2n + 2n = 9 + 2n$

$\quad\quad\quad 4y = 9 + 2n$

$\quad\quad\quad\dfrac{4y}{4} = \dfrac{9 + 2n}{4}$

$\quad\quad\quad\quad y = \dfrac{9 + 2n}{4}$

17. $I = prt$

$\quad \dfrac{I}{rt} = \dfrac{prt}{rt}$

$\quad \dfrac{I}{rt} = p$

18. D; Solve $4x + 7 = 18$

$\quad\quad 4x + 7 = 18$

$\quad 4x + 7 - 7 = 18 - 7$

$\quad\quad\quad 4x = 11$

$\quad\quad\quad\dfrac{4x}{4} = \dfrac{11}{4}$

$\quad\quad\quad\quad x = \dfrac{11}{4}$

Evaluate $12x + 21$ for $x = \dfrac{11}{4}$.

$12x + 21 = 12\left(\dfrac{11}{4}\right) + 21$

$\quad\quad\quad = 33 + 21$

$\quad\quad\quad = 54$

19. $5 + 3n$

20. $10n + 7$

21. $n^2 - 4$

22. $-6n^3$

23. $5(9 + n)$

24. $2(n + 8)$

25. $\left(\dfrac{n}{4}\right)^2$

26. $(n - 7)^3$

27. $2\pi rh + 2\pi r^2$

28. $2\pi rh + 2\pi r^2 = 2\pi r(h + r)$

29. Sample answer: 5 less than a number is 12.

30. Sample answer: Twice a number plus 3 is -1.

31. Sample answer: A number squared is equal to 4 times the number.

32. Sample answer: Three times the cube of a number is equal to the number plus 4.

33. Sample answer: A number divided by 4 is equal to twice the sum of that number and 1.

34. Sample answer: 7 minus half a number is equal to 3 divided by the square of the number.

35. Substitution Property of Equality

36. Subtraction Property of Equality

37. Transitive Property of Equality

38. Addition Property of Equality

39. Symmetric Property of Equality

40. Multiplication Property of Equality

Exercises 41–56 For checks, see students' work.

41. $\quad\quad 2p + 15 = 29$

$\quad 2p + 15 - 15 = 29 - 15$

$\quad\quad\quad 2p = 14$

$\quad\quad\quad\dfrac{2p}{2} = \dfrac{14}{2}$

$\quad\quad\quad\quad p = 7$

The solution is 7.

42. $\quad\quad 14 - 3n = -10$

$\quad 14 - 3n - 14 = -10 - 14$

$\quad\quad\quad -3n = -24$

$\quad\quad\quad\dfrac{-3n}{-3} = \dfrac{-24}{-3}$

$\quad\quad\quad\quad n = 8$

The solution is 8.

43. $7a - 3a + 2a - a = 16$

$\quad 4a + 2a - a = 16$

$\quad\quad 6a - a = 16$

$\quad\quad\quad 5a = 16$

$\quad\quad\quad\dfrac{5a}{5} = \dfrac{16}{5}$

$\quad\quad\quad\quad a = 3.2$

The solution is 3.2.

44. $x + 9x - 6x + 4x = 20$

$10x - 6x + 4x = 20$

$4x + 4x = 20$

$8x = 20$

$\frac{8x}{8} = \frac{20}{8}$

$x = 2.5$

The solution is 2.5.

45. $\frac{1}{9} - \frac{2}{3}b = \frac{1}{18}$

$\frac{1}{9} - \frac{2}{3}b - \frac{1}{9} = \frac{1}{18} - \frac{1}{9}$

$-\frac{2}{3}b = -\frac{1}{18}$

$-\frac{3}{2}\left(-\frac{2}{3}b\right) = -\frac{3}{2}\left(-\frac{1}{18}\right)$

$b = \frac{1}{12}$

The solution is $\frac{1}{12}$.

46. $\frac{5}{8} + \frac{3}{4}x = \frac{1}{16}$

$\frac{5}{8} + \frac{3}{4}x - \frac{5}{8} = \frac{1}{16} - \frac{5}{8}$

$\frac{3}{4}x = -\frac{9}{16}$

$\frac{4}{3}\left(\frac{3}{4}x\right) = \frac{4}{3}\left(-\frac{9}{16}\right)$

$x = -\frac{3}{4}$

The solution is $-\frac{3}{4}$.

47. $27 = -9(y + 5)$

$27 = -9y - 45$

$27 + 45 = -9y - 45 + 45$

$72 = -9y$

$\frac{72}{-9} = \frac{-9y}{-9}$

$-8 = y$

The solution is -8.

48. $-7(p + 8) = 21$

$-7p - 56 = 21$

$-7p - 56 + 56 = 21 + 56$

$-7p = 77$

$\frac{-7p}{-7} = \frac{77}{-7}$

$p = -11$

The solution is -11.

49. $3f - 2 = 4f + 5$

$3f - 2 - 4f = 4f + 5 - 4f$

$-f - 2 = 5$

$-f - 2 + 2 = 5 + 2$

$-f = 7$

$\frac{-f}{-1} = \frac{7}{-1}$

$f = -7$

The solution is -7.

50. $3d + 7 = 6d + 5$

$3d + 7 - 6d = 6d + 5 - 6d$

$-3d + 7 = 5$

$-3d + 7 - 7 = 5 - 7$

$-3d = -2$

$\frac{-3d}{-3} = \frac{-2}{-3}$

$d = \frac{2}{3}$

The solution is $\frac{2}{3}$.

51. $4.3n + 1 = 7 - 1.7n$

$4.3n + 1 + 1.7n = 7 - 1.7n + 1.7n$

$6n + 1 = 7$

$6n + 1 - 1 = 7 - 1$

$6n = 6$

$\frac{6n}{6} = \frac{6}{6}$

$n = 1$

The solution is 1.

52. $1.7x - 8 = 2.7x + 4$

$1.7x - 8 - 2.7x = 2.7x + 4 - 2.7x$

$-x - 8 = 4$

$-x - 8 + 8 = 4 + 8$

$-x = 12$

$\frac{-x}{-1} = \frac{12}{-1}$

$x = -12$

The solution is -12.

53. $3(2z + 25) - 2(z - 1) = 78$

$3(2z) + 3(25) - 2(z) - 2(-1) = 78$

$6z + 75 - 2z + 2 = 78$

$4z + 77 = 78$

$4z + 77 - 77 = 78 - 77$

$4z = 1$

$\frac{4z}{4} = \frac{1}{4}$

$z = \frac{1}{4}$

The solution is $\frac{1}{4}$.

54. $4(k + 3) + 2 = 4.5(k + 1)$

$4(k) + 4(3) + 2 = 4.5(k) + 4.5(1)$

$4k + 12 + 2 = 4.5k + 4.5$

$4k + 14 = 4.5k + 4.5$

$4k + 14 - 4.5k = 4.5k + 4.5 - 4.5k$

$-0.5k + 14 = 4.5$

$-0.5k + 14 - 14 = 4.5 - 14$

$-0.5k = -9.5$

$\frac{-0.5k}{-0.5} = \frac{-9.5}{-0.5}$

$k = 19$

The solution is 19.

55. $\frac{3}{11}a - 1 = \frac{7}{11}a + 9$

$\frac{3}{11}a - 1 - \frac{7}{11}a = \frac{7}{11}a + 9 - \frac{7}{11}a$

$-\frac{4}{11}a - 1 = 9$

$-\frac{4}{11}a - 1 + 1 = 9 + 1$

$-\frac{4}{11}a = 10$

$-\frac{11}{4}\left(-\frac{4}{11}a\right) = -\frac{11}{4}(10)$

$a = -\frac{55}{2}$

The solution is $-\frac{55}{2}$.

56.
$$\frac{2}{5}x + \frac{3}{7} = 1 - \frac{4}{7}x$$
$$\frac{2}{5}x + \frac{3}{7} + \frac{4}{7}x = 1 - \frac{4}{7}x + \frac{4}{7}x$$
$$\frac{34}{35}x + \frac{3}{7} = 1$$
$$\frac{34}{35}x + \frac{3}{7} - \frac{3}{7} = 1 - \frac{3}{7}$$
$$\frac{34}{35}x = \frac{4}{7}$$
$$\frac{35}{34}\left(\frac{34}{35}x\right) = \frac{35}{34}\left(\frac{4}{7}\right)$$
$$x = \frac{10}{17}$$

The solution is $\frac{10}{17}$.

57. $d = rt$
$$\frac{d}{t} = \frac{rt}{t}$$
$$\frac{d}{t} = r$$

58.
$$x = \frac{-b}{2a}$$
$$a(x) = a\left(\frac{-b}{2a}\right)$$
$$ax = \frac{-b}{2}$$
$$\frac{1}{x}(ax) = \frac{1}{x}\left(\frac{-b}{2}\right)$$
$$a = \frac{-b}{2x}$$

59.
$$V = \frac{1}{3}\pi r^2 h$$
$$\frac{3}{\pi r^2}(V) = \frac{3}{\pi r^2}\left(\frac{1}{3}\pi r^2 h\right)$$
$$\frac{3V}{\pi r^2} = h$$

60.
$$A = \frac{1}{2}h(a + b)$$
$$\frac{2}{h}(A) = \frac{2}{h}\left(\frac{1}{2}h\right)(a + b)$$
$$\frac{2A}{h} = a + b$$
$$\frac{2A}{h} - a = a + b - a$$
$$\frac{2A}{h} - a = b$$

61.
$$\frac{a(b - 2)}{c - 3} = x$$
$$(c - 3)\frac{a(b - 2)}{c - 3} = (c - 3)x$$
$$a(b - 2) = x(c - 3)$$
$$\frac{a(b - 2)}{a} = \frac{x(c - 3)}{a}$$
$$b - 2 = \frac{x(c - 3)}{a}$$
$$b - 2 + 2 = \frac{x(c - 3)}{a} + 2$$
$$b = \frac{x(c - 3)}{a} + 2$$

62.
$$x = \frac{y}{y + 4}$$
$$(y + 4)x = (y + 4)\frac{y}{y + 4}$$
$$x(y + 4) = y$$
$$x(y) + x(4) = y$$
$$xy + 4x = y$$
$$xy + 4x - xy = y - xy$$
$$4x = y - xy$$
$$4x = y(1 - x)$$
$$\frac{4x}{1 - x} = \frac{y(1 - x)}{1 - x}$$
$$\frac{4x}{1 - x} = y$$

63. Explore: Let n represent the number of games played.

Plan: Write and solve an equation to find the value of n.

The number of shoe rentals	times	the cost of shoe rental	plus
2	·	1.50	+

the number of games	times	the cost of a game	equals	the total cost.
n	·	2.50	=	16.75

Solve:
$$2(1.50) + n(2.50) = 16.75$$
$$3 + 2.50n = 16.75$$
$$3 + 2.50n - 3 = 16.75 - 3$$
$$2.50n = 13.75$$
$$\frac{2.50n}{2.50} = \frac{13.75}{2.50}$$
$$n = 5.5$$

They can bowl 5 games each.

64. Explore: Let s represent the length of a side.

Plan: Write and solve an equation to find the value of s.

The number of sides	times	the length of a side	equals	the perimeter.
8	·	s	=	124

Solve:
$$8s = 124$$
$$\frac{8s}{8} = \frac{124}{8}$$
$$s = 15.5$$

The length of each side is 15.5 inches.

65. Explore: Let x represent the cost of gasoline per mile.

Plan: Write and solve an equation to find the value of x.

The cost of insurance	plus	the cost of registration	plus	the cost of maintenance
972	+	114	+	105

plus	the number of miles	times	the cost per mile	equals	the total cost.
+	7600	·	x	=	1837

Solve:
$$972 + 114 + 105 + 7600x = 1837$$
$$1191 + 7600x = 1837$$
$$1191 + 7600x - 1191 = 1837 - 1191$$
$$7600x = 646$$
$$\frac{7600x}{7600} = \frac{646}{7600}$$
$$x = 0.085$$

The average cost was \$0.085 or 8.5¢ per mile.

66. Explore: Let n represent the number of students that can attend each meeting.

Plan: Write and solve an equation to find the value of n.

The number of people per student	times	the number of students	plus
2	$\cdot$	n	+

the number of administrators	equals	the total number of people.
3	=	83

Solve:
$$2n + 3 = 83$$
$$2n + 3 - 3 = 83 - 3$$
$$2n = 80$$
$$\frac{2n}{2} = \frac{80}{2}$$
$$n = 40$$

40 students can attend each meeting.

67. Explore: Let a represent Chun-Wei's age. Then $2a + 8$ represents his mother's age, and $2a + 8 + 3$ represents his father's age.

Plan: Write and solve an equation to find the value of a.

Chun-Wei's age	plus	his mother's age	plus
a	+	$2a + 8$	+

his father's age	equals	the number of years lived.
$2a + 8 + 3$	=	94

Solve:
$$a + 2a + 8 + 2a + 8 + 3 = 94$$
$$5a + 19 = 94$$
$$5a + 19 - 19 = 94 - 19$$
$$5a = 75$$
$$\frac{5a}{5} = \frac{75}{5}$$
$$a = 15$$

Chun-Wei is 15 years old. His mother is 38 years old, and his father is 41 years old.

68. Explore: Let c represent the cost per student paid by the student. Then $30 - c$ represents the cost per student paid by the PTO.

Plan: Write and solve an equation to find the value of c.

The number of students	times	cost per student paid by PTO	plus
50	$\cdot$	$30 - c$	+

the number of adults	times	cost per adult	equals
$\frac{50}{0}$	$\cdot$	45	=

total amount raised.
1800

Solve:
$$50(30 - c) + \frac{50}{5}(45) = 1800$$
$$50(30) - 50(c) + 10(45) = 1800$$
$$1500 - 50c + 450 = 1800$$
$$-50c + 1950 = 1800$$
$$-50c + 1950 - 1950 = 1800 - 1950$$
$$-50c = -150$$
$$\frac{-50c}{-50} = \frac{-150}{-50}$$
$$c = 3$$

The cost per student would be \$3.

69. Explore: Let n represent the number of lamps broken.

Plan: Write and solve an equation to find the value of n.

the number of lamps	times	change per lamp	minus
125	$\cdot$	12	−

the cost per lamp	times	the number of lamps broken	equals
45	$\cdot$	n	=

the total payment.
1365

Solve:
$$125(12) - 45n = 1365$$
$$1500 - 45n = 1365$$
$$1500 - 45n - 1500 = 1365 - 1500$$
$$-45n = -135$$
$$\frac{-45n}{-45} = \frac{-135}{-45}$$
$$n = 3$$

The can break 3 lamps.

70. Explore: Let h represent the height of can A.

Plan: Write and solve an equation to find the value of h.

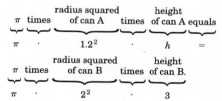

π	times	radius squared of can A	times	height of can A	equals
π	$\cdot$	1.2^2	$\cdot$	h	=

π	times	radius squared of can B	times	height of can B.
π	$\cdot$	2^2	$\cdot$	3

Solve:
$$\pi(1.2^2)h = \pi(2^2)3$$
$$\pi(1.44)h = \pi(4)3$$
$$1.44\pi h = 12\pi$$
$$\frac{1.44\pi h}{1.44\pi} = \frac{12\pi}{1.44\pi}$$
$$h = \frac{10}{1.2}$$
$$h = 8\frac{1}{3}$$

The height of can A is $8\frac{1}{3}$ units.

71. Explore: Let x represent the average number of miles of track laid per month by the Union Pacific.

Plan: Write and solve an equation to find the value of x.

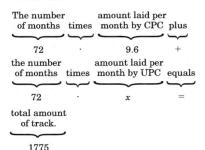

The number of months times amount laid per month by CPC plus

72 · 9.6 +

the number of months times amount laid per month by UPC equals

72 · x =

total amount of track.

1775

Solve:
$$72(9.6) + 72x = 1775$$
$$691.2 + 72x = 1775$$
$$691.2 + 72x - 691.2 = 1775 - 691.2$$
$$72x = 1083.8$$
$$\frac{72x}{72} = \frac{1083.8}{72}$$
$$x \approx 15.053$$

The Union Pacific laid an average of 15.1 miles of track per month.

72. The number of miles of track laid by the Central Pacific Company was about $72(9.6)$ or about 690 miles. The number of miles of track laid by the Union Pacific Company was about $72(15.1)$ or about 1085 miles.

73. The Central Pacific had to lay their track through the Rocky Mountains, while the Union Pacific mainly built track over flat prairie.

74. Explore: Let x represent the price of the system.

Plan: Write and solve an equation to find the value of x.

The amount saved the first week plus the amount saved the second week plus

$\frac{2}{5}x - 8$ + $\frac{1}{2}x - 8$ +

the amount short equals the price of the system.

37 = 295

Solve:
$$\frac{2}{5}x - 8 + \frac{1}{2}x + 0.5 + 37 = 295$$
$$\frac{9}{10}x + 29.5 = 295$$
$$\frac{9}{10}x + 29.5 - 29.5 = 295 - 29.5$$
$$\frac{9}{10}x = 265.5$$
$$\frac{10}{9}\left(\frac{9}{10}x\right) = \frac{10}{9}(265.5)$$
$$x = 295$$

The price of the system was \$295.

75. the product of 3 and the difference of a number and 5 added to the product of four times the number and the sum of the number and 1

76. To find the most effective level of intensity for your workout, you need to use your age and 10-second pulse count. You must also be able to solve the formula given for A. Answers should include the following.

- Substitute 0.80 for I and 27 for P in the formula $I = 6 \times P \div (220 - A)$ and solve for A. To solve this equation, divide the product of 6 and 28 by 0.8. Then subtract 220 and divide by -1. The result is 17.5. This means that this person is $17\frac{1}{2}$ years old.

- To find the intensity level for different values for A and P would require solving a new equation but using the same steps as described above. Solving for A would mean that for future calculations for A you would only need to simplify an expression, $220 - \frac{6p}{I}$, rather than solve an equation.

77. B; Since you are not required to find the value of x, use the Multiplication Property of Equality on the given equation to find the value of $3x - 5$.
$$-6x + 10 = 17$$
$$\frac{-6x + 10}{-2} = \frac{17}{-2}$$
$$3x - 5 = -\frac{17}{2}$$

78. D; **Explore:** Let x represent the number of degrees in angle QSR.

Plan: Write and solve an equation to find the value of x.

The measure of angle QSR plus the measure of angle RQS plus

x + $\frac{1}{2}\left(\frac{180 - 74}{2}\right)$ +

the measure of angle SRQ equals 180.

$\frac{1}{2}\left(\frac{180 - 74}{2}\right)$ = 180

Solve:
$$x + \frac{1}{2}\left(\frac{180 - 74}{2}\right) + \frac{1}{2}\left(\frac{180 - 74}{2}\right) = 180$$
$$x + \frac{1}{2}(53) + \frac{1}{2}(53) = 180$$
$$x + 26.5 + 26.5 = 180$$
$$x + 53 = 180$$
$$x + 53 - 53 = 180 - 53$$
$$x = 127$$

The measure of angle QSR is $127°$.

Page 27   Maintain Your Skills

79. $2x + 9y + 4z - y - 8x = 2x - 8x + 9y - y + 4z$
$$= (2 - 8)x + (9 - 1)y + 4z$$
$$= -6x + 8y + 4z$$

80. $4(2a + 5b) - 3(4b - a)$
$$= 4(2a) + 4(5b) - 3(4b) - 3(-a)$$
$$= 8a + 20b - 12b + 3a$$
$$= 8a + 3a + 20b - 12b$$
$$= (8 + 3)a + (20 - 12)b$$
$$= 11a + 8b$$

81. $a - [b(a - c)] = 3 - [-2(3 - 1.2)]$
$$= 3 - [-2(1.8)]$$
$$= 3 - (-3.6)$$
$$= 3 + (+3.6)$$
$$= 6.6$$
The value is 6.6.

82. $c^2 - ab = (1.2)^2 - 3(-2)$
$$= 1.44 - 3(-2)$$
$$= 1.44 - (-6)$$
$$= 1.44 + (+6)$$
$$= 7.44$$
The value is 7.44.

83. $S = \frac{1}{2}P\ell + B$
$$= \frac{1}{2}(20)8 + 5^2$$
$$= \frac{1}{2}(20)8 + 25$$
$$= 10(8) + 25$$
$$= 80 + 25$$
$$= 105$$
The surface area of the square-based pyramid is 105 cm^2.

84. Since $5 + (-5) = 0$, the additive inverse of 5 is -5.

85. Since $-3 + 3 = 0$, the additive inverse of -3 is 3.

86. Since $2.5 + (-2.5) = 0$, the additive inverse of 2.5 is -2.5.

87. Since $\frac{1}{4} + \left(-\frac{1}{4}\right) = 0$, the additive inverse of $\frac{1}{4}$ is $-\frac{1}{4}$.

88. Since $-3x + 3x = 0$, the additive inverse of $-3x$ is $3x$.

89. Since $(5 - 6y) + -(5 - 6y) = 0$, the additive inverse of $5 - 6y$ is $-(5 - 6y)$ or $-5 + 6y$.

1–4 Solving Absolute Value Equations

Page 30   Check for Understanding

1. $|a| = -a$ when a is a negative number and the opposite of a negative number is positive.

2a. On the number line, each answer is 4 units away from 0. Therefore, the equation is $|x| = 4$.

2b. On the number line, each answer is 2 units away from 6. Therefore, the equation is $|x - 6| = 2$.

3. Always; since the opposite of 0 is still 0, this equation has only one case, $ax + b = 0$. The solution is $\frac{-b}{a}$.

4. Sample answer: $|4 - 6|$
$$|4 - 6| = |-2|$$
$$= 2$$

5. $|a + 12| = |-4 + 12|$
$$= |8|$$
$$= 8$$
The value is 8.

6. $|-6b| = |-6(1.5)|$
$$= |-9|$$
$$= 9$$
The value is 9.

7. $-|a + 21| = -|-4 + 21|$
$$= -|17|$$
$$= -17$$
The value is -17.

8. Case 1: $a = b$ or Case 2: $a = -b$
$$x + 4 = 17 \qquad\qquad x + 4 = -17$$
$$x + 4 - 4 = 17 - 4 \qquad x + 4 - 4 = -17 - 4$$
$$x = 13 \qquad\qquad\qquad x = -21$$
Check: $|x + 4| = 17$ or $|x + 4| = 17$
$$|13 + 4| \stackrel{?}{=} 17 \qquad\qquad |-21 + 4| \stackrel{?}{=} 17$$
$$17 \stackrel{?}{=} 17 \qquad\qquad\qquad |17| \stackrel{?}{=} 17$$
$$17 = 17 \checkmark \qquad\qquad\qquad 17 = 17 \checkmark$$
The solutions are 13 or -21. Thus, the solution set is $\{-21, \; 13\}$.

9. Case 1: $a = b$ or Case 2: $a = -b$
$$b + 15 = 3 \qquad\qquad b + 15 = -3$$
$$b + 15 - 15 = 3 - 15 \quad b + 15 - 15 = -3 - 15$$
$$b = -12 \qquad\qquad\qquad b = -18$$
Check: $|b + 15| = 3$ or $|b + 15| = 3$
$$|-12 + 15| \stackrel{?}{=} 3 \qquad\qquad |-18 + 15| \stackrel{?}{=} 3$$
$$|3| \stackrel{?}{=} 3 \qquad\qquad\qquad |-3| \stackrel{?}{=} 3$$
$$3 = 3 \checkmark \qquad\qquad\qquad 3 = 3 \checkmark$$
The solutions are -12 or -18. Thus, the solution set is $\{-18, -12\}$.

10. Case 1: $a = b$ or Case 2: $a = -b$
$$a - 9 = 20 \qquad\qquad a - 9 = -20$$
$$a - 9 + 9 = 20 + 9 \qquad a - 9 + 9 = -20 + 9$$
$$a = 29 \qquad\qquad\qquad a = -11$$
Check: $|a - 9| = 20$ or $|a - 9| = 20$
$$|29 - 9| \stackrel{?}{=} 20 \qquad\qquad |-11 - 9| \stackrel{?}{=} 20$$
$$|20| \stackrel{?}{=} 20 \qquad\qquad\qquad |-20| \stackrel{?}{=} 20$$
$$20 = 20 \checkmark \qquad\qquad\qquad 20 = 20 \checkmark$$
The solutions are 29 or -11. Thus, the solution set is $\{-11, 29\}$.

11. Case 1: $a = b$ or Case 2: $a = -b$
$$y - 2 = 34 \qquad\qquad y - 2 = -34$$
$$y - 2 + 2 = 34 + 2 \qquad y - 2 + 2 = -34 + 2$$
$$y = 36 \qquad\qquad\qquad y = -32$$
Check: $|y - 2| = 34$ $|y - 2| = 34$
$$|36 - 2| \stackrel{?}{=} 34 \qquad\qquad |-32 - 2| \stackrel{?}{=} 34$$
$$|34| \stackrel{?}{=} 34 \qquad\qquad\qquad |-34| \stackrel{?}{=} 34$$
$$34 = 34 \checkmark \qquad\qquad\qquad 34 = 34 \checkmark$$
The solutions are 36 or -32. Thus, the solution set is $\{-32, 36\}$.

12. $|2w + 3| + 6 = 2$
$$|2w + 3| = -4$$
This sentence is never true. So the solution set is $\varnothing$.

13. Case 1: $a = b$ or Case 2: $a = -b$
$$c - 2 = 2c - 10 \qquad\qquad c - 2 = -(2c - 10)$$
$$-2 = c - 10 \qquad\qquad c - 2 = -2c + 10$$
$$8 = c \qquad\qquad\qquad 3c - 2 = 10$$
$$3c = 12$$
$$c = 4$$

Check: $|c - 2| = 2c - 10$ $|c - 2| = 2c - 10$
$|8 - 2| \overset{?}{=} 2(8) - 10$ $|4 - 2| = 2(4) - 10$
$|6| \overset{?}{=} 16 - 10$ $|2| = 8 - 10$
$6 = 6$ ✓ $2 \neq -2$ ✓

Since $2 \neq -2$, the only solution is 8. Thus, the solution set is {8}.

14. The least and greatest temperatures will be 2 units away from 160. Therefore, the equation is $|x - 160| = 2$.

15. Case 1: $a = b$ or Case 2: $a = -b$
$$x - 160 = 2 \qquad\qquad x - 160 = -2$$
$$x - 160 + 160 = 2 + 160 \qquad x - 160 + 160 = -2 + 160$$
$$x = 162 \qquad\qquad\qquad x = 158$$

Check: $|x - 160| = 2$ $|x - 160| = 2$
$|162 - 160| \overset{?}{=} 2$ $|158 - 160| \overset{?}{=} 2$
$|2| \overset{?}{=} 2$ $|-2| = 2$
$2 = 2$ ✓ $2 = 2$ ✓

The least temperature is 158°F, and the greatest temperature is 162°F.

16. Since the thermometers are accurate to within plus or minus 2°F, the ham should be baked to a minimum of 2°F higher than 160°F or to 162°F. This would ensure a minimum internal temperature of 160°F.

Pages 30–32   Practice and Apply

17. $|-3a| = |-3(-5)|$
$$= |15|$$
$$= 15$$
The value is 15.

18. $|-4b| = |-4(6)|$
$$= |-24|$$
$$= 24$$
The value is 24.

19. $|a + 5| = |-5 + 5|$
$$= |0|$$
$$= 0$$
The value is 0.

20. $|2 - b| = |2 - 6|$
$$= |-4|$$
$$= 4$$
The value is 4.

21. $|2b - 15| = |2(6) - 15|$
$$= |12 - 15|$$
$$= |-3|$$
$$= 3$$
The value is 3.

22. $|4a + 7| = |4(-5) + 7|$
$$= |-20 + 7|$$
$$= |-13|$$
$$= 13$$
The value is 13.

23. $-|18 - 5c| = -|18 - 5(2.8)|$
$$= -|18 - 14|$$
$$= -|4|$$
$$= -4$$
The value is −4.

24. $-|c - a| = -|2.8 - (-5)|$
$$= -|2.8 + 5|$$
$$= -|7.8|$$
$$= -7.8$$
The value is −7.8.

25. $6 - |3c + 7| = 6 - |3(2.8) + 7|$
$$= 6 - |8.4 + 7|$$
$$= 6 - |15.4|$$
$$= 6 - 15.4$$
$$= -9.4$$
The value is −9.4.

26. $9 - |-2b + 8| = 9 - |-2(6) + 8|$
$$= 9 - |-12 + 8|$$
$$= 9 - |-4|$$
$$= 9 - 4$$
$$= 5$$
The value is 5.

27. $3|a - 10| + |2a| = 3 - |-5 - 10| + |2(-5)|$
$$= 3|-15| + |-10|$$
$$= 3(15) + 10$$
$$= 45 + 10$$
$$= 55$$
The value is 55.

28. $|a - b| - |10c - a|$
$$= |-5 - 6| - |10(2.8) - (-5)|$$
$$= |-11| - |28 - (-5)|$$
$$= 11 - |28 + (+5)|$$
$$= 11 - |33|$$
$$= 11 - 33$$
$$= -22$$
The value is −22.

29. Case 1: $a = b$ or Case 2: $a = -b$
$$x - 25 = 17 \qquad\qquad x - 25 = -17$$
$$x - 25 + 25 = 17 + 25 \qquad x - 25 + 25 = -17 + 25$$
$$x = 42 \qquad\qquad\qquad x = 8$$

Check: $|x - 25| = 17$ $|x - 25| = 17$
$|42 - 25| \overset{?}{=} 17$ $|8 - 25| \overset{?}{=} 17$
$|17| \overset{?}{=} 17$ $|-17| \overset{?}{=} 17$
$17 = 17$ ✓ $17 = 17$ ✓

The solutions are 42 or 8. Thus, the solution set is {8, 42}.

30. Case 1: $a = b$ or Case 2: $a = -b$
$$y + 9 = 21 \qquad\qquad y + 9 = -21$$
$$y + 9 - 9 = 21 - 9 \qquad y + 9 - 9 = -21 - 9$$
$$y = 12 \qquad\qquad\qquad y = -30$$

Check: $|y + 9| = 21$ $|y + 9| = 21$
$|12 + 9| \overset{?}{=} 21$ $|-30 + 9| \overset{?}{=} 21$
$|21| \overset{?}{=} 21$ $|-21| \overset{?}{=} 21$
$21 = 21$ ✓ $21 = 21$ ✓

The solutions are 12 or −30. Thus, the solution set is {−30, 12}.

31. Case 1: $\quad a = b \quad$ or Case 2: $\quad a = -b$

$$a + 12 = 33 \qquad\qquad a + 12 = -33$$
$$a + 12 - 12 = 33 - 12 \quad a + 12 - 12 = -33 - 12$$
$$a = 21 \qquad\qquad a = -45$$

Check: $|a + 12| = 33 \qquad |a + 12| = 33$
$$|21 + 12| \stackrel{?}{=} 33 \qquad |-45 + 12| \stackrel{?}{=} 33$$
$$|33| \stackrel{?}{=} 33 \qquad\qquad |-33| \stackrel{?}{=} 33$$
$$33 = 33 \checkmark \qquad\qquad 33 = 33 \checkmark$$

The solutions are 21 or -45. Thus, the solution set is $\{-45, 21\}$.

32. $2|b + 4| = 48$
$$|b + 4| = 24$$

Case 1: $\quad a = b \quad$ or Case 2: $\quad a = -b$
$$b + 4 = 24 \qquad\qquad b + 4 = -24$$
$$b + 4 - 4 = 24 - 4 \qquad b + 4 - 4 = -24 - 4$$
$$b = 20 \qquad\qquad b = -28$$

Check: $\quad 2|b + 4| = 48 \qquad 2|b + 4| = 48$
$$2|20 + 4| \stackrel{?}{=} 48 \qquad 2|-28 + 4| \stackrel{?}{=} 48$$
$$2|24| \stackrel{?}{=} 48 \qquad\quad 2|-24| \stackrel{?}{=} 48$$
$$2(24) \stackrel{?}{=} 48 \qquad\quad 2(24) \stackrel{?}{=} 48$$
$$48 = 48 \checkmark \qquad\qquad 48 = 48 \checkmark$$

The solutions are 20 or -28. Thus, the solution set is $\{-28, 20\}$.

33. $8|w - 7| = 72$
$$|w - 7| = 9$$

Case 1: $a = b \qquad$ or Case 2: $\quad a = -b$
$$w - 7 = 9 \qquad\qquad w - 7 = -9$$
$$w - 7 + 7 = 9 + 7 \qquad w - 7 + 7 = -9 + 7$$
$$w = 16 \qquad\qquad w = -2$$

Check: $8|w - 7| = 72 \qquad 8|w - 7| = 72$
$$8|16 - 7| \stackrel{?}{=} 72 \qquad 8|-2 - 7| \stackrel{?}{=} 72$$
$$8|9| \stackrel{?}{=} 72 \qquad\quad 8|-9| \stackrel{?}{=} 72$$
$$8(9) \stackrel{?}{=} 72 \qquad\quad 8(9) \stackrel{?}{=} 72$$
$$72 = 72 \checkmark \qquad\quad 72 = 72 \checkmark$$

The solutions are 16 or -2. Thus, the solution set is $\{-2, 16\}$

34. Case 1: $a = b \qquad$ or Case 2: $a = -b$
$$3x + 5 = 11 \qquad\qquad 3x + 5 = -11$$
$$3x + 5 - 5 = 11 - 5 \qquad 3x + 5 - 5 = -11 - 5$$
$$3x = 6 \qquad\qquad 3x = -16$$
$$\frac{3x}{3} = \frac{6}{3} \qquad\qquad \frac{3x}{3} = \frac{-16}{3}$$
$$x = 2 \qquad\qquad x = \frac{-16}{3}$$

Check: $|3x + 5| = 11 \qquad |3x + 5| = 11$
$$|3(2) + 5| \stackrel{?}{=} 11 \qquad \left|3\left(-\frac{16}{3}\right) + 5\right| \stackrel{?}{=} 11$$
$$|6 + 5| \stackrel{?}{=} 11 \qquad\quad |-16 + 5| \stackrel{?}{=} 11$$
$$|11| \stackrel{?}{=} 11 \qquad\qquad |-11| \stackrel{?}{=} 11$$
$$11 = 11 \checkmark \qquad\qquad 11 = 11 \checkmark$$

The solutions are 2 or $-\frac{16}{3}$. Thus, the solution set is $\left\{-\frac{16}{3}, 2\right\}$.

35. Case 1: $\quad a = b \qquad$ or Case 2: $\quad a = -b$
$$2z - 3 = 0 \qquad\qquad 2z - 3 = -0$$
$$2z - 3 + 3 = 0 + 3 \qquad 2z - 3 + 3 = 0$$
$$2z = 3 \qquad\qquad 2z = 3$$
$$\frac{2z}{2} = \frac{3}{2} \qquad\qquad \frac{2z}{2} = \frac{3}{2}$$
$$z = \frac{3}{2} \qquad\qquad z = \frac{3}{2}$$

Check: $\quad |2z - 3| = 0$
$$\left|2\left(\frac{3}{2}\right) - 3\right| \stackrel{?}{=} 0$$
$$|3 - 3| \stackrel{?}{=} 0$$
$$|0| \stackrel{?}{=} 0$$
$$0 = 0 \checkmark$$

The solution is $\frac{3}{2}$. Thus, the solution set is $\left\{\frac{3}{2}\right\}$.

36. $|6c - 1| = -2$
This sentence is never true. So the solution set is $\varnothing$.

37. $7|4x - 13| = 35$
$$|4x - 13| = 5$$

Case 1: $\quad a = b \qquad$ or Case 2: $\quad a = -b$
$$4x - 13 = 5 \qquad\qquad 4x - 13 = -5$$
$$4x - 13 + 13 = 5 + 13 \qquad 4x - 13 + 13 = -5 + 13$$
$$4x = 18 \qquad\qquad 4x = 8$$
$$\frac{4x}{4} = \frac{18}{4} \qquad\qquad \frac{4x}{4} = \frac{8}{4}$$
$$x = \frac{9}{2} \qquad\qquad x = 2$$

Check: $7|4x - 13| = 35 \qquad 7|4x - 13| = 35$
$$7\left|4\left(\frac{9}{2}\right) - 13\right| \stackrel{?}{=} 35 \qquad 7|4(2) - 13| \stackrel{?}{=} 35$$
$$7|18 - 13| \stackrel{?}{=} 35 \qquad 7|8 - 13| \stackrel{?}{=} 35$$
$$7|5| \stackrel{?}{=} 35 \qquad\quad 7|-5| \stackrel{?}{=} 35$$
$$7(5) \stackrel{?}{=} 35 \qquad\quad 7(5) \stackrel{?}{=} 35$$
$$35 = 35 \checkmark \qquad\quad 35 = 35 \checkmark$$

The solutions are $\frac{9}{2}$ or 2. Thus, the solution set is $\left\{2, \frac{9}{2}\right\}$.

38. $-3|2n + 5| = -9$
$$|2n + 5| = 3$$

Case 1: $\quad a = b \qquad$ or Case 2: $\quad a = -b$
$$2n + 5 = 3 \qquad\qquad 2n + 5 = -3$$
$$2n + 5 - 5 = 3 - 5 \qquad 2n + 5 - 5 = -3 - 5$$
$$2n = -2 \qquad\qquad 2n = -8$$
$$\frac{2n}{2} = \frac{-2}{2} \qquad\qquad \frac{2n}{2} = \frac{-8}{2}$$
$$n = -1 \qquad\qquad n = -4$$

Check: $-3|2n + 5| = -9 \qquad -3|2n + 5| = -9$
$$-3|2(-1) + 5| \stackrel{?}{=} -9 \quad -3|2(-4) + 5| \stackrel{?}{=} -9$$
$$-3|-2 + 5| \stackrel{?}{=} -9 \qquad -3|-8 + 5| \stackrel{?}{=} -9$$
$$-3|3| \stackrel{?}{=} -9 \qquad\quad -3|-3| \stackrel{?}{=} -9$$
$$-3(3) \stackrel{?}{=} -9 \qquad\quad -3(3) \stackrel{?}{=} -9$$
$$-9 = -9 \checkmark \qquad\qquad -9 = -9 \checkmark$$

The solutions are -1 or -4. Thus, the solution set is $\{-4, -1\}$.

39. $-12|9x + 1| = 144$
$$|9x + 1| = -12$$
This sentence is never true. So the solution set is $\varnothing$.

40. $|5x + 9| + 6 = 1$
$$|5x + 9| = -5$$
This sentence is never true. So the solution set is $\varnothing$.

41. $|a - 3| - 14 = -6$
$|a - 3| = 8$

Case 1: $a = b$ or Case 2: $a = -b$
$a - 3 = 8$ $a - 3 = -8$
$a - 3 + 3 = 8 + 3$ $a - 3 + 3 = -8 + 3$
$a = 11$ $a = -5$

Check: $|a - 3| - 14 = -6$ $|a - 3| - 14 = -6$
$|11 - 3| - 14 \stackrel{?}{=} -6$ $|-5 - 3| - 14 \stackrel{?}{=} -6$
$|8| - 14 \stackrel{?}{=} -6$ $|-8| - 14 \stackrel{?}{=} -6$
$8 - 14 \stackrel{?}{=} -6$ $8 - 14 \stackrel{?}{=} -6$
$-6 = -6$ ✓ $-6 = -6$ ✓

The solutions are 11 or -5. Thus, the solution set is $\{-5, 11\}$.

42. $3|p - 5| = 2p$
$|p - 5| = \frac{2}{3}p$

Case 1: $a = b$ or Case 2: $a = -b$

$p - 5 = \frac{2}{3}p$ $p - 5 = -\frac{2}{3}p$
$p - 5 - p = \frac{2}{3}p - p$ $p - 5 - p = -\frac{2}{3}p - p$
$-5 = -\frac{1}{3}p$ $-5 = -\frac{5}{3}p$
$-3(-5) = -3\left(-\frac{1}{3}p\right)$ $-\frac{3}{5}(-5) = -\frac{3}{5}\left(-\frac{5}{3}p\right)$
$15 = p$ $3 = p$

Check: $3|p - 5| = 2p$ $3|p - 5| = 2p$
$3|15 - 5| \stackrel{?}{=} 2(15)$ $3|3 - 5| \stackrel{?}{=} 2(3)$
$3|10| \stackrel{?}{=} 30$ $3|-2| \stackrel{?}{=} 6$
$3(10) \stackrel{?}{=} 30$ $3(2) \stackrel{?}{=} 6$
$30 = 30$ ✓ $6 = 6$ ✓

The solutions are 15 or 3. Thus, the solution set is $\{3, 15\}$.

43. $3|2a + 7| = 3a + 12$
$|2a + 7| = a + 4$

Case 1: $a = b$ or Case 2: $a = -b$
$2a + 7 = a + 4$ $2a + 7 = -(a + 4)$
$2a + 7 - a = a + 4 - a$ $2a + 7 = -a - 4$
$a + 7 = 4$ $2a + 7 + a = -a - 4 + a$
$a + 7 - 7 = 4 - 7$ $3a + 7 = -4$
$a = -3$ $3a + 7 - 7 = -4 - 7$
                  $3a = -11$
                  $\frac{3a}{3} = \frac{-11}{3}$
                  $a = \frac{-11}{3}$

Check: $3|2a + 7| = 3a + 12$ $3|2a + 7| = 3a + 12$
$3|2(-3) + 7| \stackrel{?}{=} 3(-3) + 12$ $3\left|2\left(-\frac{11}{3}\right) + 7\right| \stackrel{?}{=} 3\left(-\frac{11}{3}\right) + 12$
$3|-6 + 7| \stackrel{?}{=} -9 + 12$ $3\left|-\frac{22}{3} + 7\right| \stackrel{?}{=} -11 + 12$
$3|1| \stackrel{?}{=} 3$ $3\left|-\frac{1}{3}\right| \stackrel{?}{=} 1$
$3(1) \stackrel{?}{=} 3$ $3\left(\frac{1}{3}\right) \stackrel{?}{=} 1$
$3 = 3$ ✓ $1 = 1$ ✓

The solutions are -3 or $-\frac{11}{3}$. Thus, the solution set is $\left\{-\frac{11}{3}, -3\right\}$.

44. $|3x - 7| - 5 = -3$
$|3x - 7| = 2$

Case 1: $a = b$ or Case 2: $a = -b$
$3x - 7 = 2$ $3x - 7 = -2$
$3x - 7 + 7 = 2 + 7$ $3x - 7 + 7 = -2 + 7$
$3x = 9$ $3x = 5$
$\frac{3x}{3} = \frac{9}{3}$ $\frac{3x}{3} = \frac{5}{3}$
$x = 3$ $x = \frac{5}{3}$

Check: $|3x - 7| - 5 = -3$ $|3x - 7| - 5 = -3$
$|3(3) - 7| - 5 \stackrel{?}{=} -3$ $\left|3\left(\frac{5}{3}\right) - 7\right| - 5 \stackrel{?}{=} -3$
$|9 - 7| - 5 \stackrel{?}{=} -3$ $|5 - 7| - 5 \stackrel{?}{=} -3$
$|2| - 5 \stackrel{?}{=} -3$ $|-2| - 5 \stackrel{?}{=} -3$
$2 - 5 \stackrel{?}{=} -3$ $2 - 5 \stackrel{?}{=} -3$
$-3 = -3$ ✓ $-3 = -3$ ✓

The solutions are 3 or $\frac{5}{3}$. Thus, the solution set is $\left\{\frac{5}{3}, 3\right\}$.

45. $4|3t + 8| = 16t$
$|3t + 8| = 4t$

Case 1: $a = b$ or Case 2: $a = -b$
$3t + 8 = 4t$ $3t + 8 = -4t$
$3t + 8 - 3t = 4t - 3t$ $3t + 8 - 3t = -4t - 3t$
$8 = t$ $8 = -7t$
                $\frac{8}{-7} = \frac{-7t}{-7}$
                $-\frac{8}{7} = t$

Check: $4|3t + 8| = 16t$ $4|3t + 8| = 16t$
$4|3(8) + 8| \stackrel{?}{=} 16(8)$ $4\left|3\left(-\frac{8}{7}\right) + 8\right| \stackrel{?}{=} 16\left(-\frac{8}{7}\right)$
$4|24 + 8| \stackrel{?}{=} 128$ $4\left|-\frac{24}{7} + 8\right| \stackrel{?}{=} -\frac{128}{7}$
$4|32| \stackrel{?}{=} 128$ $4\left|\frac{32}{7}\right| \stackrel{?}{=} -\frac{128}{7}$
$4(32) \stackrel{?}{=} 128$ $4\left(\frac{32}{7}\right) \stackrel{?}{=} -\frac{128}{7}$
$128 = 128$ ✓ $\frac{128}{7} \neq -\frac{128}{7}$ ✓

Since $\frac{128}{7} \neq -\frac{128}{7}$, the only solution is 8. Thus, the solution set is $\{8\}$.

46. Case 1: $a = b$ or Case 2: $a = -b$
$15 + m = -2m + 3$ $15 + m = (-2m + 3)$
$15 + m + 2m = -2m + 3 + 2m$ $15 + m = 2m - 3$
$15 + 3m = 3$ $15 + m - m = 2m - 3 - m$
$15 + 3m - 15 = 3 - 15$ $15 = m - 3$
$3m = -12$ $15 + 3 = m - 3 + 3$
$\frac{3m}{3} = \frac{-12}{3}$ $18 = m$
$m = -4$

Check: $|15 + m| = -2m + 3$ $|15 + m| = -2m + 3$
$|15 + (-4)| \stackrel{?}{=} -2(-4) + 3$ $|15 + 18| \stackrel{?}{=} -2(18) + 3$
$|11| \stackrel{?}{=} 8 + 3$ $|33| \stackrel{?}{=} -36 + 3$
$11 = 11$ ✓ $33 \neq -33$

Since $33 \neq -33$, the only solution is -4. Thus, the solution set is $\{-4\}$.

47. The maximum and minimum temperatures will be 5 units away from 200. Therefore, the equation is $|x - 200| = 5$.

Case 1: $a = b$ or Case 2: $a = -b$
$$x - 200 = 5 \qquad\qquad x - 200 = -5$$
$$x - 200 + 200 = 5 + 200 \quad x - 200 + 200 = -5 + 200$$
$$x = 205 \qquad\qquad\qquad x = 195$$

Check: $\quad |x - 200| = 5 \qquad\qquad |x - 200| = 5$
$$|205 - 200| \stackrel{?}{=} 5 \qquad\qquad |195 - 200| \stackrel{?}{=} 5$$
$$|5| \stackrel{?}{=} 5 \qquad\qquad\qquad |-5| \stackrel{?}{=} 5$$
$$5 = 5 \checkmark \qquad\qquad\qquad 5 = 5 \checkmark$$

The maximum temperature is 205°F, and the minimum temperature is 195°F.

48. The heaviest and lightest weights will be 0.3 units away from 16. Therefore, the equation is $|x - 16| = 0.3$.

Case 1: $a = b$ or Case 2: $a = -b$
$$x - 16 = 0.3 \qquad\qquad x - 16 = -0.3$$
$$x - 16 + 16 = 0.3 + 16 \quad x - 16 + 16 = -0.3 + 16$$
$$x = 16.3 \qquad\qquad\qquad x = 15.7$$

Check: $|x - 16| = 0.3 \qquad\qquad |x - 16| = 0.3$
$$|16.3 - 16| \stackrel{?}{=} 0.3 \qquad\qquad |15.7 - 16| \stackrel{?}{=} 0.3$$
$$|0.3| \stackrel{?}{=} 0.3 \qquad\qquad\qquad |-0.3| \stackrel{?}{=} 0.3$$
$$0.3 = 0.3 \checkmark \qquad\qquad\qquad 0.3 = 0.3 \checkmark$$

The heaviest weight is 16.3 oz, and the lightest weight is 15.7 oz.

49. The maximum and minimum heights will be 5 units away from 13. Therefore, the equation is $|x - 13| = 5$.

Case 1: $a = b$ or Case 2: $a = -b$
$$x - 13 = 5 \qquad\qquad x - 13 = -5$$
$$x - 13 + 13 = 5 + 13 \quad x - 13 + 13 = -5 + 13$$
$$x = 18 \qquad\qquad\qquad x = 8$$

Check: $|x - 13| = 5 \qquad\qquad |x - 13| = 5$
$$|18 - 13| \stackrel{?}{=} 5 \qquad\qquad |8 - 13| \stackrel{?}{=} 5$$
$$|5| \stackrel{?}{=} 5 \qquad\qquad\qquad |-5| \stackrel{?}{=} 5$$
$$5 = 5 \checkmark \qquad\qquad\qquad 5 = 5 \checkmark$$

The maximum height is 18 km, and the minimum height is 8 km.

50. Sometimes; true only if $a \geq 0$ and $b \geq 0$ or if $a \leq 0$ and $b \leq 0$

51. Sometimes; true only if $c \geq 0$

52. Answers should include the following.
- This equation needs to show that the difference of the estimate E from the originally stated magnitude of 6.1 could be plus 0.3 or minus 0.3, as shown in the graph below. Instead of writing two equations, $E - 6.1 = 0.3$ and $E - 6.1 = -0.3$, absolute value symbols can be used to account for both possibilities, $|E - 6.1| = 0.3$.

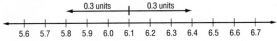

- Using an original magnitude of 5.9, the equation to represent the estimated extremes would be $|E - 5.9| = 0.3$.

53. B; $|x - 3| - 4 = 0$
$$|x - 3| = 4$$
Thus, the number line should show the two points that are 4 units away from 3 or points at -1 and 7.

54. A; $-|-9| - |4| - 3|5 - 7|$
$$= -|-9| - |4| - 3|-2|$$
$$= -9 - 4 - 3(2)$$
$$= -9 - 4 - 6$$
$$= -19$$
The value is -19.

55. Case 1: $a = b$ or Case 2: $a = -b$
$$|x + 1| + 2 = x + 4 \qquad |x + 1| + 2 = -(x + 4)$$

56. For $|x + 1| + 2 = x + 4$

Case 1: $x + 1 + 2 = x + 4$ or Case 2: $-(x + 1) + 2 = x + 4$
$$-x - 1 + 2 = x + 4$$

For $|x + 1| + 2 = -(x + 4)$

Case 1: $x + 1 + 2 = -(x + 4)$ or Case 2: $(x + 1) + 2 = -(x + 4)$
$$x + 1 + 2 = -x - 4 \qquad\qquad -x - 1 + 2 = -x - 4$$

57. Solve $x + 1 + 2 = x + 4$.
$$x + 1 + 2 = x + 4$$
$$x + 3 = x + 4$$
$$x + 3 - x = x + 4 - x$$
$$3 \neq 4$$
Since $3 \neq 4$ there is no solution to this equation.

Solve: $-x - 1 + 2 = x + 4$.
$$-x - 1 + 2 = x + 4$$
$$-x + 1 = x + 4$$
$$-2x + 1 = 4$$
$$-2x = 3$$
$$x = -\frac{3}{2}$$
The solution is $-\frac{3}{2}$ or -1.5.

Check: $|x + 1| + 2 = |x + 4|$
$$|-1.5 + 1| + 2 \stackrel{?}{=} |-1.5 + 4|$$
$$|-0.5| + 2 \stackrel{?}{=} |2.5|$$
$$0.5 + 2 \stackrel{?}{=} 2.5$$
$$2.5 = 2.5 \checkmark$$

Solve $x + 1 + 2 = -x - 4$.
$$x + 1 + 2 = -x - 4$$
$$x + 3 = -x - 4$$
$$2x + 3 = -4$$
$$2x = -7$$
$$x = -\frac{7}{2}$$
The solution is $-\frac{7}{2}$ or -3.5.

Check: $|x + 1| + 2 = |x + 4|$
$$|-3.5 + 1| + 2 \stackrel{?}{=} |-3.5 + 4|$$
$$|-2.5| + 2 \stackrel{?}{=} |0.5|$$
$$2.5 + 2 \stackrel{?}{=} 0.5$$
$$4.5 \neq 0.5$$

Solve $-x - 1 + 2 = -x - 4$.
$$-x - 1 + 2 = -x - 4$$
$$-x + 1 = -x - 4$$
$$-x + 1 + x = -x - 4 + x$$
$$1 \neq -4$$
Since $1 \neq -4$, there is no solution to this equation.

Thus, the solution set for $|x + 1| + 2 = |x + 4|$ is $\{-1.5\}$.

58. The pattern seems to be 2 raised to the number of sets of absolute value symbols. Thus, for an equation with 3 sets of absolute value symbols, the number of cases that needs to be checked is 2^3 or 8.

Page 32   Maintain Your Skills

59. $2(n - 11)$

60. $5n^2$

61.
$$3x + 6 = 22$$
$$3x + 6 - 6 = 22 - 6$$
$$3x = 16$$
$$\frac{3x}{3} = \frac{16}{3}$$
$$x = \frac{16}{3}$$
The solution is $\frac{16}{3}$.

62.
$$7p - 4 = 3(4 + 5p)$$
$$7p - 4 = 3(4) + 3(5p)$$
$$7p - 4 = 12 + 15p$$
$$7p - 4 - 15p = 12 + 15p - 15p$$
$$-8p - 4 = 12$$
$$-8p - 4 + 4 = 12 + 4$$
$$-8p = 16$$
$$\frac{-8p}{-8} = \frac{16}{-8}$$
$$p = -2$$
The solution is -2.

63.
$$\frac{5}{7}y - 3 = \frac{3}{7}y + 1$$
$$\frac{5}{7}y - 3 - \frac{3}{7}y = \frac{3}{7}y + 1 - \frac{3}{7}y$$
$$\frac{2}{7}y - 3 = 1$$
$$\frac{2}{7}y - 3 + 3 = 1 + 3$$
$$\frac{2}{7}y = 4$$
$$\frac{7}{2}\left(\frac{2}{7}y\right) = \frac{7}{2}(4)$$
$$y = 14$$
The solution is 14.

64. Commutative Property of Addition—the order in which you add does not change the sum

65. Distributive Property—the product of a number and a sum is equal to the sum of the products of the number and each addend

66. Multiplicative Inverse Property—the product of a number and its multiplicative inverse is equal to 1

67. Additive Identity Property—the sum of any number and 0 is equal to the number

68. False; $\sqrt{3}$ is a counterexample.

69. True

70. True

71. False; 1.2 is a counterexample.

72. $A = \frac{1}{2}bh$
$$= \frac{1}{2}(x + 5)(x + 3)$$

73. $\frac{1}{2}(x + 5)(x + 3) = \frac{1}{2}(23 + 5)(23 + 3)$
$$= \frac{1}{2}(28)(26)$$
$$= 14(26)$$
$$= 364$$
The area of the triangle would be 364 square feet.

74.
$$14y - 3 = 25$$
$$14y - 3 + 3 = 25 + 3$$
$$14y = 28$$
$$\frac{14y}{14} = \frac{28}{14}$$
$$y = 2$$
The solution is 2.

75.
$$4.2x + 6.4 = 40$$
$$4.2x + 6.4 - 6.4 = 40 - 6.4$$
$$4.2x = 33.6$$
$$\frac{4.2x}{4.2} = \frac{33.6}{4.2}$$
$$x = 8$$
The solution is 8.

76.
$$7w + 2 = 3w - 6$$
$$7w + 2 - 3w = 3w - 6 - 3w$$
$$4w + 2 = -6$$
$$4w + 2 - 2 = -6 - 2$$
$$4w = -8$$
$$\frac{4w}{4} = -\frac{8}{4}$$
$$w = -2$$
The solution is -2.

77.
$$2(a - 1) = 8a - 6$$
$$2(a) - 2(1) = 8a - 6$$
$$2a - 2 = 8a - 6$$
$$2a - 2 - 8a = 8a - 6 - 8a$$
$$-6a - 2 = -6$$
$$-6a - 2 + 2 = -6 + 2$$
$$-6a = -4$$
$$\frac{-6a}{-6} = \frac{-4}{-6}$$
$$a = \frac{2}{3}$$
The solution is $\frac{2}{3}$.

78.
$$48 + 5y = 96 - 3y$$
$$48 + 5y + 3y = 96 - 3y + 3y$$
$$48 + 8y = 96$$
$$48 + 8y - 48 = 96 - 48$$
$$8y = 48$$
$$\frac{8y}{8} = \frac{48}{8}$$
$$y = 6$$
The solution is 6.

79.
$$\frac{2x+3}{5} = \frac{3}{10}$$
$$10\left(\frac{2x + 3}{5}\right) = 10\left(\frac{3}{10}\right)$$
$$2(2x + 3) = 3$$
$$2(2x) + 2(3) = 3$$
$$4x + 6 = 3$$
$$4x + 6 - 6 = 3 - 6$$
$$4x = -3$$
$$\frac{4x}{4} = \frac{-3}{4}$$
$$x = -\frac{3}{4}$$
The solution is $-\frac{3}{4}$.

Page 36   Graphing Calculator Investigation

1.

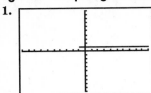

The graph is the horizontal line $y = 1$ for $x > -1$.

2. The values of x on the graph are all real numbers. The values of y on the graph are 0 and 1.

3. Since the calculator graphs 1 when the inequality is true and 0 when it is false, the inequality must be true for values of x greater than or equal to -1. Thus, the inequality is $x \geq -1$.

4.
$$11x + 3 \geq 2x - 6$$
$$11x + 3 - 2x \geq 2x - 6 - 2x$$
$$9x + 3 \geq -6$$
$$9x + 3 - 3 \geq -6 - 3$$
$$9x \geq -9$$
$$\frac{9x}{9} \geq \frac{-9}{9}$$
$$x \geq -1$$

The solution set is $\{x \mid x \geq -1\}$ or $[-1, \infty)$.
The solutions are the same.

Page 37   Check for Understanding

1. Dividing by a number is the same as multiplying by its inverse.

2. Sample answer: $-2n > -6$

3. Sample answer: $x + 2 < x + 1$

4.
$$a + 2 < 3.5$$
$$a + 2 - 2 < 3.5 - 2$$
$$a < 1.5$$

The solution set is $\{a \mid a < 1.5\}$ or $(-\infty, 1.5)$.

5. $5 \geq 3x$
$$\frac{5}{3} \geq \frac{3x}{3}$$
$$\frac{5}{3} \geq x$$

The solution set is $\left\{x \mid x \leq \frac{5}{3}\right\}$ or $\left(-\infty, \frac{5}{3}\right]$.

6.
$$11 - c \leq 8$$
$$11 - c - 11 \leq 8 - 11$$
$$-c \leq -3$$
$$\frac{-c}{-1} \geq \frac{-3}{-1}$$
$$c \geq 3$$

The solution set is $\{c \mid c \geq 3\}$ or $[3, +\infty)$.

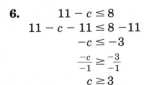

7.
$$4y + 7 > 31$$
$$4y + 7 - 7 > 31 - 7$$
$$4y > 24$$
$$\frac{4y}{4} > \frac{24}{4}$$
$$y > 6$$

The solution set is $\{y \mid y > 6\}$ or $(6, +\infty)$.

8.
$$2w + 19 < 5$$
$$2w + 19 - 19 < 5 - 19$$
$$2w < -14$$
$$\frac{2w}{2} < \frac{-14}{2}$$
$$w < -7$$

The solution set is $\{w \mid w < -7\}$ or $(-\infty, -7)$.

9. $-0.6p < -9$
$$\frac{-0.6p}{-0.6} > \frac{-9}{-0.6}$$
$$p > 15$$

The solution set is $\{p \mid p > 15\}$ or $(15, +\infty)$.

10.
$$\frac{n}{12} + 15 \leq 13$$
$$\frac{n}{12} + 15 - 15 \leq 13 - 15$$
$$\frac{n}{12} \leq -2$$
$$12\left(\frac{n}{12}\right) \leq 12(-2)$$
$$n \leq -24$$

The solution set is $\{n \mid n \leq -24\}$ or $(-\infty, -24]$.

11.
$$\frac{5z + 2}{4} < \frac{5z}{4} + 2$$
$$4\left(\frac{5z + 2}{4}\right) < 4\left(\frac{5z}{4} + 2\right)$$
$$5z + 2 < 4\left(\frac{5z}{4}\right) + 4(2)$$
$$5z + 2 < 5z + 8$$
$$5z + 2 - 5z < 5z + 8 - 5z$$
$$2 < 8$$

The sentence is always true. So the solution set is $\{z \mid z \text{ is any real number}\}$ or $(-\infty, +\infty)$.

12. Let $n =$ the number.

The product of 12 and a number | is greater than | 36.
$12n$ | $>$ | 36

$$12n > 36$$
$$\frac{12n}{12} > \frac{36}{12}$$
$$n > 3$$

The solution set is $\{n \mid n > 3\}$.

13. Let n = the number.

Twice a number minus three is at most 5.

$$2n \quad - \quad 3 \quad \leq \quad 5$$

$$2n - 3 \leq 5$$
$$2n - 3 + 3 \leq 5 + 3$$
$$2n \leq 8$$
$$\frac{2n}{2} \leq \frac{8}{2}$$
$$n \leq 4$$

The solution set is $\{n \mid n \leq 4\}$.

14. Explore: Let x = the score on the final exam. A final grade of at least 80 means that the final grade must be greater than or equal to 80.

Plan: The portion of the final grade from the final exam score is $0.25x$. The portion of the final grade from the average test scores plus the portion of the final grade from the final exam must be greater than or equal to 80. Write an inequality.

Final grade from average test scores plus final grade from final exam score is greater than or equal to 80.

$$0.75(76) \quad + \quad 0.25x \quad \geq \quad 80$$

Solve:
$$0.75(76) + 0.25x \geq 80$$
$$57 + 0.25x \geq 80$$
$$57 + 0.25x - 57 \geq 80 - 57$$
$$0.25x \geq 23$$
$$\frac{0.25x}{0.25} \geq \frac{23}{0.25}$$
$$x \geq 92$$

Examine: The student must make at least 92 on the final exam to have a final grade of at least 80.

Pages 37–39   Practice and Apply

15.
$$n + 4 \geq -7$$
$$n + 4 - 4 \geq -7 - 4$$
$$n \geq -11$$
The solution set is $\{n \mid n \geq -11\}$ or $[-11, +\infty)$.

16.
$$b - 3 \leq 15$$
$$b - 3 + 3 \leq 15 + 3$$
$$b \leq 18$$
The solution set is $\{b \mid b \leq 18\}$ or $(-\infty, 18]$.

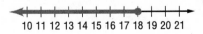

17. $5x < 35$
$$\frac{5x}{5} < \frac{35}{5}$$
$$x < 7$$
The solution set is $\{x \mid x < 7\}$ or $(-\infty, 7)$.

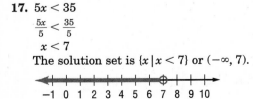

18.
$$\frac{d}{2} > -4$$
$$2\left(\frac{d}{2}\right) > 2(-4)$$
$$d > -8$$
The solution set is $\{d \mid d > -8\}$ or $(-8, +\infty)$.

19.
$$\frac{g}{-3} \geq -9$$
$$-3\left(\frac{g}{-3}\right) \leq -3(-9)$$
$$g \leq 27$$
The solution set is $\{g \mid g \leq 27\}$ or $(-\infty, 27]$.

20. $-8p \geq 24$
$$\frac{-8p}{-8} \leq \frac{24}{-8}$$
$$p \leq -3$$
The solution set is $\{p \mid p \leq -3\}$ or $(-\infty, -3]$.

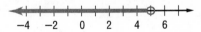

21.
$$13 - 4k \leq 27$$
$$13 - 4k - 13 \leq 27 - 13$$
$$-4k \leq 14$$
$$\frac{-4k}{-4} \geq \frac{14}{-4}$$
$$k \geq -3.5$$
The solution set is $\{k \mid k \geq -3.5\}$ or $[-3.5, +\infty)$.

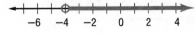

22.
$$14 > 7y - 21$$
$$14 + 21 > 7y - 21 + 21$$
$$35 > 7y$$
$$\frac{35}{7} > \frac{7y}{7}$$
$$5 > y$$
The solution set is $\{y \mid y < 5\}$ or $(-\infty, 5)$.

23.
$$-27 < 8m + 5$$
$$-27 - 5 < 8m + 5 - 5$$
$$-32 < 8m$$
$$\frac{-32}{8} < \frac{8m}{8}$$
$$-4 < m$$
The solution set is $\{m \mid m > -4\}$ or $(-4, +\infty)$.

24.
$$6b + 11 \geq 15$$
$$6b + 11 - 11 \geq 15 - 11$$
$$6b \geq 4$$
$$\frac{6b}{6} \geq \frac{4}{6}$$
$$b \geq \frac{2}{3}$$
The solution set is $\left\{b \mid b \geq \frac{2}{3}\right\}$ or $\left[\frac{2}{3}, +\infty\right)$.

25.
$$2(4t + 9) \le 18$$
$$2(4t) + 2(9) \le 18$$
$$8t + 18 \le 18$$
$$8t + 18 - 18 \le 18 - 18$$
$$8t \le 0$$
$$\frac{8t}{8} \le \frac{0}{8}$$
$$t \le 0$$
The solution set is $\{t \mid t \le 0\}$ or $(-\infty, 0]$.

26.
$$90 \ge 5(2r + 6)$$
$$90 \ge 5(2r) + 5(6)$$
$$90 \ge 10r + 30$$
$$90 - 30 \ge 10r + 30 - 30$$
$$60 \ge 10r$$
$$\frac{60}{10} \ge \frac{10r}{10}$$
$$6 \ge r$$
The solution set is $\{r \mid r \le 6\}$ or $(-\infty, 6]$.

27.
$$14 - 8n \le 0$$
$$14 - 8n - 14 \le 0 - 14$$
$$-8n \le -14$$
$$\frac{-8n}{-8} \ge \frac{-14}{-8}$$
$$n \ge 1.75$$
The solution set is $\{n \mid n \ge 1.75\}$ or $[1.75, +\infty)$.

28.
$$-4(5w - 8) < 33$$
$$-4(5w) - 4(-8) < 33$$
$$-20w + 32 - 32 < 33 - 32$$
$$-20w < 1$$
$$\frac{-20w}{-20} > \frac{1}{-20}$$
$$w > -\frac{1}{20}$$
The solution set is $\left\{w \mid w > -\frac{1}{20}\right\}$ or $\left(-\frac{1}{20}, +\infty\right)$.

29.
$$0.02x + 5.58 < 0$$
$$0.02x + 5.58 - 5.58 < 0 - 5.58$$
$$0.02x < -5.58$$
$$\frac{0.02x}{0.02} < \frac{-5.58}{0.02}$$
$$x < -279$$
The solution set is $\{x \mid x < -279\}$ or $(-\infty, -279)$.

30.
$$1.5 - 0.25c < 6$$
$$1.5 - 0.25c - 1.5 < 6 - 1.5$$
$$-0.25c < 4.5$$
$$\frac{-0.25c}{-0.25} > \frac{4.5}{-0.25}$$
$$c > -18$$
The solution set is $\{c \mid c > -18\}$ or $(-18, +\infty)$.

31.
$$6d + 3 \ge 5d - 2$$
$$6d + 3 - 5d \ge 5d - 2 - 5d$$
$$d + 3 \ge -2$$
$$d + 3 - 3 \ge -2 - 3$$
$$d \ge -5$$
The solution set is $\{d \mid d \ge -5\}$ or $[-5, +\infty)$.

32.
$$9z + 2 > 4z + 15$$
$$9z + 2 - 4z > 4z + 15 - 4z$$
$$5z + 2 > 15$$
$$5z + 2 - 2 > 15 - 2$$
$$5z > 13$$
$$\frac{5z}{5} > \frac{13}{5}$$
$$z > 2.6$$
The solution set is $\{z \mid z > 2.6\}$ or $(2.6, +\infty)$.

33.
$$2(g + 4) < 3g - 2(g - 5)$$
$$2(g) + 2(4) < 3g - 2(g) - 2(-5)$$
$$2g + 8 < 3g - 2g + 10$$
$$2g + 8 < g + 10$$
$$2g + 8 - g < g + 10 - g$$
$$g + 8 < 10$$
$$g + 8 - 8 < 10 - 8$$
$$g < 2$$
The solution set is $\{g \mid g < 2\}$ or $(-\infty, 2)$.

34.
$$3(a + 4) - 2(3a + 4) \le 4a - 1$$
$$3(a) + 3(4) - 2(3a) - 2(4) \le 4a - 1$$
$$3a + 12 - 6a - 8 \le 4a - 1$$
$$-3a + 4 \le 4a - 1$$
$$-3a + 4 - 4a \le 4a - 1 - 4a$$
$$-7a + 4 \le -1$$
$$-7a + 4 - 4 \le -1 - 4$$
$$-7a \le -5$$
$$\frac{-7a}{-7} \ge \frac{-5}{-7}$$
$$a \ge \frac{5}{7}$$
The solution set is $\left\{a \mid a \ge \frac{5}{7}\right\}$ or $\left[\frac{5}{7}, +\infty\right)$.

35.
$$y < \frac{-y + 2}{9}$$
$$9(y) < 9\left(\frac{-y + 2}{9}\right)$$
$$9y < -y + 2$$
$$9y + y < -y + 2 + y$$
$$10y < 2$$
$$\frac{10y}{10} < \frac{2}{10}$$
$$y < \frac{1}{5}$$
The solution set is $\left\{y \mid y < \frac{1}{5}\right\}$ or $\left(-\infty, \frac{1}{5}\right)$.

36.
$$\frac{1-4p}{5} < 0.2$$
$$5\left(\frac{1-4p}{5}\right) < 5(0.2)$$
$$1 - 4p < 1$$
$$1 - 4p - 1 < 1 - 1$$
$$-4p < 0$$
$$\frac{-4p}{-4} > \frac{0}{-4}$$
$$p > 0$$
The solution set is $\{p \mid p > 0\}$ or $(0, +\infty)$.

```
←――――+――――――――――――――→
 -6  -4  -2   0   2   4   6
```

37.
$$\frac{4x+2}{6} < \frac{2x+1}{3}$$
$$6\left(\frac{4x+2}{6}\right) < 6\left(\frac{2x+1}{3}\right)$$
$$4x + 2 < 2(2x+1)$$
$$4x + 2 < 2(2x) + 2(1)$$
$$4x + 2 < 4x + 2$$
$$4x + 2 - 4x < 4x + 2 - 4x$$
$$2 < 2$$
This sentence is never true. So the solution set is $\varnothing$.

```
←――――+――――+――――+――――→
 -6  -4  -2   0   2   4
```

38.
$$12\left(\frac{1}{4} - \frac{n}{3}\right) \leq -6n$$
$$12\left(\frac{1}{4}\right) - 12\left(\frac{n}{3}\right) \leq -6n$$
$$3 - 4n \leq -6n$$
$$3 - 4n + 4n \leq -6n + 4n$$
$$3 \leq -2n$$
$$\frac{3}{-2} \geq \frac{-2n}{-2}$$
$$-\frac{3}{2} \geq n$$
The solution set is $\left\{n \mid n \leq -\frac{3}{2}\right\}$ or $\left(-\infty, -\frac{3}{2}\right]$.

```
←――――――――――●――――+――――→
 -4  -3  -2  -1   0   1
```

39. $5.6x - 0.25(5.6x) \geq 105$
$$5.6x - 1.4x \geq 105$$
$$4.2x \geq 105$$
$$\frac{4.2x}{4.2} \geq \frac{105}{4.2}$$
$$x \geq 25$$
David must work at least 25 hours a week.

40.
$$1.5n + 13.25 \leq 35$$
$$1.5n + 13.25 - 13.25 \leq 35 - 13.25$$
$$1.5n \leq 21.75$$
$$\frac{1.5n}{1.5} \leq \frac{21.75}{1.5}$$
$$n \leq 14.5$$
Just can afford no more than 14 rides.

41. Let n = the number.

$$n + 8 > 2$$
$$n + 8 - 8 > 2 - 8$$
$$n > -6$$
The solution set is $\{n \mid n > -6\}$.

42. Let n = the number.

-4 times	a number	is at least	35.
$-4 \quad \cdot$	n	$\geq$	35

$$-4n \geq 35$$
$$\frac{-4n}{-4} \leq \frac{35}{-4}$$
$$n \leq -8.75$$
The solution set is $\{n \mid n \leq -8.75\}$.

43. Let n = the number.

One half of a number	minus	7	is greater than or equal to	5.
$\frac{1}{2}n$	$-$	7	$\geq$	5

$$\frac{1}{2}n - 7 \geq 5$$
$$\frac{1}{2}n - 7 + 7 \geq 5 + 7$$
$$\frac{1}{2}n \geq 12$$
$$2\left(\frac{1}{2}n\right) \geq 2(12)$$
$$n \geq 24$$
The solution set is $\{n \mid n \geq 24\}$.

44. Let n = the number.

The product of -3 and a number	plus	1	is less than	16.
$-3n$	$+$	1	$<$	16

$$-3n + 1 < 16$$
$$-3n + 1 - 1 < 16 - 1$$
$$-3n < 15$$
$$\frac{-3n}{-3} > \frac{15}{-3}$$
$$n > -5$$
The solution set is $\{n \mid n > -5\}$.

45. Let n = the number.

Twice the sum of a number and 5	is no more than	3	times	that same number	increased by	11.
$2(n+5)$	$\leq$	3	$\cdot$	n	$+$	11

$$2(n+5) \leq 3n + 11$$
$$2(n) + 2(5) \leq 3n + 11$$
$$2n + 10 \leq 3n + 11$$
$$2n + 10 - 2n \leq 3n + 11 - 2n$$
$$10 \leq n + 11$$
$$10 - 11 \leq n + 11 - 11$$
$$-1 \leq n$$
The solution set is $\{n \mid n \geq -1\}$

46. Let n = the number.

A number	minus	9	is at most	that same number divided by 2.
n	$-$	9	$\leq$	$\frac{n}{2}$

$$n - 9 \leq \frac{n}{2}$$
$$n - 9 - n \leq \frac{n}{2} - n$$
$$-9 \leq -\frac{n}{2}$$
$$-2(-9) \geq -2\left(-\frac{n}{2}\right)$$
$$18 \geq n$$
The solution set is $\{n \mid n \leq 18\}$.

47. Explore: Let m = the number of staff members required. Twice the maximum of 7 toddlers per 1 staff member means that the product of 2 and 7 times the number of staff members is greater than or equal to 17.

Plan: Write an inequality.

Two	times	the product of 7 and the number of staff members
2	$\cdot$	$7m$

is greater than or equal to	17.
$\geq$	17

Solve:
$$2(7m) \geq 17$$
$$14m \geq 17$$
$$\frac{14m}{14} \geq \frac{17}{14}$$
$$m \geq \frac{17}{14}$$

Examine: Since you cannot have a fraction of a staff member present, there must be at least 2 child care staff members present.

48. Explore: Let n = the number of cars she sells. At least $40,000 means that her annual income is greater than or equal to $40,000.

Plan: The portion of her annual income earned from commission is $0.015(30,500n)$. Mrs. Lucas's salary plus her commission must be greater than or equal to $40,000. Write an inequality.

Mrs. Lucas's salary	plus	her commission
24,000	+	$0.015(30,500n)$

is greater than or equal to	$40,000.
$\geq$	40,000

49. Solve:
$$24,000 + 0.015(30,500n) \geq 40,000$$
$$24,000 + 457.5n \geq 40,000$$
$$24,000 + 457.5n - 24,000 \geq 40,000 - 24,000$$
$$457.5n \geq 16,000$$
$$\frac{457.5\,n}{457.5} \geq \frac{16,000}{457.5}$$
$$n \geq \frac{6400}{183} \approx 34.97$$

Examine: Since she cannot sell a fraction of a car, she must sell at least 35 cars. •

50. Explore: Let s = Ahmik's score on the fifth test. At least 90 means that Ahmik's test average must be greater than or equal to 90.

Plan: The sum of the five test scores divided by 5 must be greater than or equal to 90. Write an inequality.

The sum of the test scores divided by 5	is greater than or equal to	90.
$\frac{85 + 91 + 89 + 94 + s}{5}$	$\geq$	90

51. Solve:
$$\frac{85 + 91 + 89 + 94 + s}{5} \geq 90$$
$$5\left(\frac{85 + 91 + 89 + 94 + s}{5}\right) \geq 5(90)$$
$$85 + 91 + 89 + 94 + s \geq 450$$
$$359 + s \geq 450$$
$$359 + s - 359 \geq 450 - 359$$
$$s \geq 91$$

Examine: Ahmik must score at least 91 on her next test to have an A test average.

52a. The Reflexive Property holds for $\leq$ or $\geq$. The Reflexive Property does not hold for $<$ or $>$. The number 2 is a counterexample; $2 \not< 2$

52b. The Symmetric Property does not hold for inequalities. The numbers 1 and 2 are a counterexample; $1 < 2$ but $2 \not< 1$

52c. The Transitive Property holds for inequalities. For all real numbers a, b, and c, if $a < b$ and $b < c$, then $a < c$.

53. Answers should include the following.
- $150 < 400$
- Let n equal the number of minutes used. Write an expression representing the cost of Plan 1 and for Plan 2 for n minutes. The cost for Plan 1 would include a monthly access fee plus 40 cents for each minute over 150 minutes or $35 + 0.4(n - 150)$. The cost for Plan 2 for 400 minutes or less would be $55. To find where Plan 2 would cost less than Plan 1, solve $55 < 35 + 0.4(n - 150)$ for n. The solution set is $\{n \mid n > 200\}$, which means that for more than 200 minutes of calls, Plan 2 is cheaper.

54. D;
$$4 - 5n \geq -1$$
$$4 - 5n - 4 \geq -1 - 4$$
$$-5n \geq -5$$
$$\frac{-5n}{-5} \leq \frac{-5}{-5}$$
$$n \leq 1$$
Thus, $2 \not\leq 1$.

55. D; If $a < b$ and $c < 0$, then adding or subtracting c to both sides of the inequality, $a < b$, does not change the direction of the inequality. But, multiplying or dividing both sides of the inequality by c does change the direction of the inequality. Therefore, $ac > bc$, $a + c < b + c$, and $a - c < b - c$.

56. Clear the Y= list. Enter $-5x - 8 < 7$ as Y1. Put your calculator in DOT mode. Then, graph in the standard viewing window. The calculator graphs $y = 1$ for $x > -3$. Therefore, the solution set is $\{x \mid x > -3\}$.

57. Clear the Y = list. Enter $-4(6x - 3) \leq 60$ as Y1. Put your calculator in DOT mode. Then, graph in the standard viewing window. The calculator graphs $y = 1$ for $x \geq -2$. Therefore, the solution set is $\{x \mid x \geq -2\}$.

58. Clear the Y = list. Enter $3(x + 3) \geq 2(x + 4)$ as Y1. Put your calculator in DOT mode. Then, graph in the standard viewing window. The calculator graphs $y = 1$ for $x \geq -1$. Therefore, the solution set is $\{x \mid x \geq -1\}$.

Page 39 Maintain Your Skills

59. Case 1: $a = b$ or Case 2: $a = -b$
$$\begin{array}{ll} x - 3 = 17 & x - 3 = -17 \\ x - 3 + 3 = 17 + 3 & x - 3 + 3 = -17 + 3 \\ x = 20 & x = -14 \end{array}$$

Check: $|x - 3| = 17$ $|x - 3| = 17$
$|20 - 3| \stackrel{?}{=} 17$ $|-14 - 3| \stackrel{?}{=} 17$
$|17| \stackrel{?}{=} 17$ $|-17| \stackrel{?}{=} 17$
$17 = 17$ ✓ $17 = 17$ ✓

The solutions are 20 or -14. Thus, the solution set is $\{-14, 20\}$.

60. $8|4x - 3| = 64$
$|4x - 3| = 8$

Case 1: $a = b$ or Case 2: $a = -b$
$$\begin{array}{ll} 4x - 3 = 8 & 4x - 3 = -8 \\ 4x - 3 + 3 = 8 + 3 & 4x - 3 + 3 = -8 + 3 \\ 4x = 11 & 4x = -5 \\ \dfrac{4x}{4} = \dfrac{11}{4} & \dfrac{4x}{4} = \dfrac{-5}{4} \\ x = \dfrac{11}{4} & x = -\dfrac{5}{4} \end{array}$$

Check: $8|4x - 3| = 64$ $8|4x - 3| = 64$

$8\left|4\left(\frac{11}{4}\right) - 3\right| \stackrel{?}{=} 64$ $8\left|4\left(-\frac{5}{4}\right) - 3\right| \stackrel{?}{=} 64$

$8|11 - 3| \stackrel{?}{=} 64$ $8|-5 - 3| \stackrel{?}{=} 64$
$8|8| \stackrel{?}{=} 64$ $8|-8| \stackrel{?}{=} 64$
$8(8) \stackrel{?}{=} 64$ $8(8) \stackrel{?}{=} 64$
$64 = 64$ ✓ $64 = 64$ ✓

The solutions are $\frac{11}{4}$ or $-\frac{5}{4}$. Thus, the solution set is $\left\{-\frac{5}{4}, \frac{11}{4}\right\}$.

61. Case 1: $a = b$ or Case 2: $a = -b$
$$\begin{array}{ll} x + 1 = x & x + 1 = -x \\ x + 1 - x = x - x & x + 1 - x = -x - x \\ 1 = 0 & 1 = -2x \\ & \dfrac{1}{-2} = \dfrac{-2x}{-2} \\ & -\dfrac{1}{2} = x \end{array}$$

This statement is never true.

Check: $|x + 1| = x$
$\left|-\frac{1}{2} + 1\right| \stackrel{?}{=} -\frac{1}{2}$
$\left|\frac{1}{2}\right| \stackrel{?}{=} -\frac{1}{2}$
$\frac{1}{2} \neq -\frac{1}{2}$

Since $\frac{1}{2} \neq -\frac{1}{2}$, there is no solution. So the solution set is $\varnothing$.

62. Explore: Let b represent the increase in the number of online browsers each year.

Plan: Write and solve an equation to find the value of b.

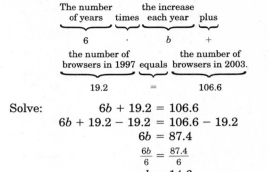

The number of years	times	the increase each year	plus	
6	$\cdot$	b	$+$	
the number of browsers in 1997	equals	the number of browsers in 2003.		
19.2	$=$	106.6		

Solve: $6b + 19.2 = 106.6$
$6b + 19.2 - 19.2 = 106.6 - 19.2$
$6b = 87.4$
$\dfrac{6b}{6} = \dfrac{87.4}{6}$
$b \approx 14.6$

The average increase was about 14.6 million browsers each year.

63. naturals (N), wholes (W), integers (Z), rationals (Q), and reals (R)

64. rationals (Q) and reals (R)

65. $\sqrt{7}$ lies between 2 and 3, so it is not a whole number. irrationals (I) and reals (R)

66. **Method 1**
Multiply each day's hours by the charge per hour and then add.
$4.25(5.5) + 4.25(8)$
Method 2
Add the number of hours worked for both days and then multiply the total by $4.25.
$4.25(5.5 + 8)$

67. Case 1: $a = b$ or   Case 2: $a = -b$
$$\begin{array}{ll} x = 7 & x = -7 \end{array}$$
Check: $|x| = 7$ $|x| = 7$
$|7| \stackrel{?}{=} 7$ $|-7| \stackrel{?}{=} 7$
$7 = 7$ ✓ $7 = 7$ ✓

The solutions are 7 or -7. Thus, the solution set is $\{-7, 7\}$.

68. Case 1: $a = b$ or Case 2: $a = -b$
$$\begin{array}{ll} x + 5 = 18 & x + 5 = -18 \\ x + 5 - 5 = 18 - 5 & x + 5 - 5 = -18 - 5 \\ x = 13 & x = -23 \end{array}$$
Check: $|x + 5| = 18$ $|x + 5| = 18$
$|13 + 5| \stackrel{?}{=} 18$ $|-23 + 5| \stackrel{?}{=} 18$
$|18| \stackrel{?}{=} 18$ $|-18| \stackrel{?}{=} 18$
$18 = 18$ ✓ $18 = 18$ ✓

The solutions are 13 or -23. Thus, the solution set is $\{-23, 13\}$.

69. Case 1: $a = b$ or Case 2: $a = -b$

$$5y - 8 = 12 \qquad\qquad 5y - 8 = -12$$
$$5y - 8 + 8 = 12 + 8 \qquad 5y - 8 + 8 = -12 + 8$$
$$5y = 20 \qquad\qquad 5y = -4$$
$$\frac{5y}{5} = \frac{20}{5} \qquad\qquad \frac{5y}{5} = \frac{-4}{5}$$
$$y = 4 \qquad\qquad y = -\frac{4}{5}$$

Check: $|5y - 8| = 12$ $|5y - 8| = 12$

$|5(4) - 8| \overset{?}{=} 12$ $\left|5\left(-\frac{4}{5}\right) - 8\right| \overset{?}{=} 12$

$|20 - 8| \overset{?}{=} 12$ $|-4 - 8| \overset{?}{=} 12$

$|12| \overset{?}{=} 12$ $|-12| \overset{?}{=} 12$

$12 = 12$ ✓ $12 = 12$ ✓

The solutions are 4 or $-\frac{4}{5}$. Thus, the solution set is $\left\{-\frac{4}{5}, 4\right\}$.

70. Case 1: $a = b$ or Case 2: $a = -b$

$$2x - 36 = 14 \qquad\qquad 2x - 36 = -14$$
$$2x - 36 + 36 = 14 + 36 \qquad 2x - 36 + 36 = -14 + 36$$
$$2x = 50 \qquad\qquad 2x = 22$$
$$\frac{2x}{2} = \frac{50}{2} \qquad\qquad \frac{2x}{2} = \frac{22}{2}$$
$$x = 25 \qquad\qquad x = 11$$

Check: $|2x - 36| = 14$ $|2x - 36| = 14$

$|2(25) - 36| \overset{?}{=} 14$ $|2(11) - 36| \overset{?}{=} 14$

$|50 - 36| \overset{?}{=} 14$ $|22 - 36| \overset{?}{=} 14$

$|14| \overset{?}{=} 14$ $|-14| \overset{?}{=} 14$

$14 = 14$ ✓ $14 = 14$ ✓

The solutions are 25 or 11. Thus, the solution set is {11, 25}.

71. $2|w + 6| = 10$
$|w + 6| = 5$

Case 1: $a = b$ or Case 2: $a = -b$

$$w + 6 = 5 \qquad\qquad w + 6 = -5$$
$$w + 6 - 6 = 5 - 6 \qquad w + 6 - 6 = -5 - 6$$
$$w = -1 \qquad\qquad w = -11$$

Check: $2|w + 6| = 10$ $2|w + 6| = 10$

$2|-1 + 6| \overset{?}{=} 10$ $2|-11 + 6| \overset{?}{=} 10$

$2|5| \overset{?}{=} 10$ $2|-5| \overset{?}{=} 10$

$2(5) \overset{?}{=} 10$ $2(5) \overset{?}{=} 10$

$10 = 10$ ✓ $10 = 10$ ✓

The solutions are -1 or -11. Thus, the solution set is {$-11, -1$}.

72. $|x + 4| + 3 = 17$
$|x + 4| = 14$

Case 1: $a = b$ or Case 2: $a = -b$

$$x + 4 = 14 \qquad\qquad x + 4 = -14$$
$$x + 4 - 4 = 14 - 4 \qquad x + 4 - 4 = -14 - 4$$
$$x = 10 \qquad\qquad x = -18$$

Check: $|x + 4| + 3 = 17$ $|x + 4| + 3 = 17$

$|10 + 4| + 3 \overset{?}{=} 17$ $|-18 + 4| + 3 \overset{?}{=} 17$

$|14| + 3 \overset{?}{=} 17$ $|-14| + 3 \overset{?}{=} 17$

$14 + 3 \overset{?}{=} 17$ $14 + 3 \overset{?}{=} 17$

$17 = 17$ ✓ $17 = 17$ ✓

The solutions are 10 or -18. Thus, the solution set is {$-18, 10$}.

Page 39   Practice Quiz 2

1.
$$2d + 5 = 8d + 2$$
$$2d + 5 - 8d = 8d + 2 - 8d$$
$$-6d + 5 = 2$$
$$-6d + 5 - 5 = 2 - 5$$
$$-6d = -3$$
$$\frac{-6d}{-6} = \frac{-3}{-6}$$
$$d = \frac{1}{2}$$

The solution is $\frac{1}{2}$.

2. $\quad s = \frac{1}{2}gt^2$

$$\frac{2}{t^2}(s) = \frac{2}{t^2}\left(\frac{1}{2}gt^2\right)$$
$$\frac{25}{t^2} = g$$

3. $|x - 3y| = |-8 - 3(2)|$
$$= |-8 - 6|$$
$$= |-14|$$
$$= 14$$

The value is 14.

4. $3|3x + 2| = 51$
$|3x + 2| = 17$

Case 1: $a = b$ or Case 2: $a = -b$

$$3x + 2 = 17 \qquad\qquad 3x + 2 = -17$$
$$3x + 2 - 2 = 17 - 2 \qquad 3x + 2 - 2 = -17 - 2$$
$$3x = 15 \qquad\qquad 3x = -19$$
$$\frac{3x}{3} = \frac{15}{3} \qquad\qquad \frac{3x}{3} = \frac{-19}{3}$$
$$x = 5 \qquad\qquad x = -\frac{19}{3}$$

Check: $3|3x + 2| = 51$ $3|3x + 2| = 51$

$3|3(5) + 2| \overset{?}{=} 51$ $3\left|3\left(-\frac{19}{3}\right) + 2\right| \overset{?}{=} 51$

$3|15 + 2| \overset{?}{=} 51$ $3|-19 + 2| \overset{?}{=} 51$

$3|17| \overset{?}{=} 51$ $3|-17| \overset{?}{=} 51$

$3(17) \overset{?}{=} 51$ $3(17) \overset{?}{=} 51$

$51 = 51$ ✓ $51 = 51$ ✓

The solutions are 5 or $-\frac{19}{3}$. Thus, the solution set is $\left\{-\frac{19}{3}, 5\right\}$.

5.
$$2(m - 5) - 3(2m - 5) < 5m + 1$$
$$2(m) + 2(-5) - 3(2m) - 3(-5) < 5m + 1$$
$$2m - 10 - 6m + 15 < 5m + 1$$
$$-4m + 5 < 5m + 1$$
$$-4m + 5 - 5m < 5m + 1 - 5m$$
$$-9m + 5 < 1$$
$$-9m + 5 - 5 < 1 - 5$$
$$-9m < -4$$
$$\frac{-9m}{-9} > \frac{-4}{-9}$$
$$m > \frac{4}{9}$$

The solution set is $\left\{m \middle| m > \frac{4}{9}\right\}$ or $\left(\frac{4}{9}, +\infty\right)$.

1-6 Solving Compound and Absolute Value Inequalities

Pages 43–44 Check for Understanding

1. Let c = the cost of the present. At least \$5 means \$5 is less than or equal to c.

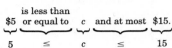

$$5 \leq c \leq 15$$

2. Sample answer: $x < -3$ and $x > 2$

3. Sabrina; an absolute value inequality of the form $|a| > b$ should be rewritten as an *or* compound inequality, $a > b$ or $a < -b$.

4. All numbers between -8 and 8 are less than 8 units from 0. Thus, the inequality is $|n| < 8$. The solution set is $\{n \mid -8 < n < 8\}$.

5. All numbers greater than 3 or less than -3 are not between -3 and 3, and are greater than 3 units from 0. Thus, the inequality is $|n| > 3$. The solution set is $\{n \mid n > 3 \text{ or } n < -3\}$.

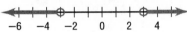

6. The graph shows all numbers whose distance is greater than or equal to 4 units from 0. Thus, the inequality is $|n| \geq 4$.

7. The graph shows all numbers whose distance is less than 2 units from 0. Thus, the inequality is $|n| < 2$.

8. Solve each inequality separately.

$$\begin{array}{lll} y - 3 > 1 & \text{or} & y + 2 < 1 \\ y > 4 & & y < -1 \end{array}$$

The solution set is $\{y \mid y > 4 \text{ or } y < -1\}$.

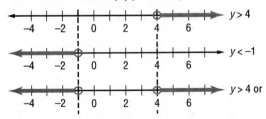

9. Solve both parts at the same time.

$$\begin{array}{l} 3 < d + 5 < 8 \\ -2 < d < 3 \end{array}$$

The solution set is $\{d \mid -2 < d < 3\}$.

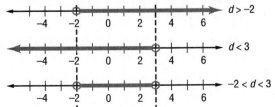

10. $|a| \geq 5$ is equivalent to $a \geq 5$ or $a \leq -5$. The solution set is $\{a \mid a \geq 5 \text{ or } a \leq -5\}$.

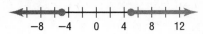

11. $|g + 4| \leq 9$ is equivalent to $-9 \leq g + 4 \leq 9$. Solve both parts at the same time.

$$\begin{array}{l} -9 \leq g + 4 \leq 9 \\ -13 \leq g \leq 5 \end{array}$$

The solution set is $\{g \mid -13 \leq g \leq 5\}$.

12. $|4k - 8| < 20$ is equivalent to $-20 < 4k - 8 < 20$. Solve both parts at the same time.

$$\begin{array}{l} -20 < 4k - 8 < 20 \\ -12 < 4k < 28 \\ -3 < k < 7 \end{array}$$

The solution set is $\{k \mid -3 < k < 7\}$.

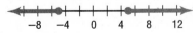

13. $|w| > -2$ is equivalent to $w > -2$ or $w < 2$. The solution set is $\{w \mid w \text{ is all real numbers}\}$.

14. Let c = the cost of the tile. Then $\frac{c}{6.25}$ is the number of tiles.

$$55 \leq \frac{c}{6.25} \leq 60$$

Solve both parts of the inequality at the same time.

$$55 \leq \frac{c}{6.25} \leq 60$$
$$343.75 \leq c \leq 375$$

The solution set is $\{c \mid 343.75 \leq c \leq 375\}$. Thus, The cost of the tile will fall between \$343.75 and \$375.

Pages 44–46 Practice and Apply

15. All numbers greater than or equal to 5 or less than or equal to -5 are not between -5 and 5, and are greater than 5 units from 0. Thus, the inequality is $|n| \geq 5$. The solution set is $\{n \mid n \geq 5 \text{ or } n \leq -5\}$.

16. All numbers less than 7 and greater than -7 are less than 7 units from 0. Thus, the inequality is $|n| < 7$. The solution set is $\{n \mid -7 < n < 7\}$.

17. All numbers between -4 and 4 are less than 4 units from 0. Thus, the inequality is $|n| < 4$. The solution set is $\{n \mid -4 < n < 4\}$.

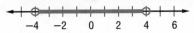

18. All numbers less than or equal to -6 or greater than or equal to 6 are not between -6 and 6, and are greater than 6 units from 0. Thus, the inequality is $|n| \mid n \ge 6$. The solution set is $\{n \mid n \ge 6 \text{ or } n \le -6\}$.

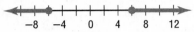

19. All numbers greater than 8 or less than -8 are not between -8 and 8, and are greater than 8 units from 0. Thus, the inequality is $|n| \mid n > 8$. The solution set is $\{n \mid n > 8 \text{ or } n < -8\}$.

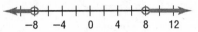

20. All numbers less than or equal to 1.2 and greater than or equal to -1.2 are less than or equal to 1.2 units from 0. Thus, the inequality is $|n| \le 1.2$. The solution set is $\{n \mid -1.2 \le n \le 1.2\}$.

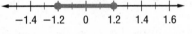

21. The graph shows all numbers whose distance is greater than 1 unit from 0. Thus the inequality is $|n| > 1$.

22. The graph shows all numbers whose distance is less than or equal to 5 units from 0. Thus, the inequality is $|n| \le 5$.

23. The graph shows all numbers whose distance is greater than or equal to 1.5 units from 0. Thus, the inequality is $|n| \ge 1.5$.

24. The graph shows all numbers whose distance is less than 6 units from 0. Thus the inequality is $|n| < 6$.

25. The graph shows all numbers whose distance is greater than 1 unit from -1. Thus, the inequality is $|n - (-1)| > 1$ or $|n + 1| > 1$.

26. The graph shows all numbers whose distance is less than or equal to 3 units from 1. Thus, the inequality is $|n - 1| \le 3$.

27. Solve each inequality separately.

$$3p + 1 \le 7 \quad \text{or} \quad 2p - 9 \ge 7$$
$$3p \le 6 \qquad\qquad 2p \ge 16$$
$$p \le 2 \qquad\qquad p \ge 8$$

The solution set is $\{p \mid p \le 2 \text{ or } p \ge 8\}$.

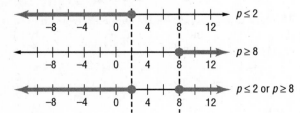

28. Solve both parts at the same time.

$$9 < 3t + 6 < 15$$
$$3 < \quad 3t \quad < 9$$
$$1 < \quad t \quad < 3$$

The solution set is $\{t \mid 1 < t < 3\}$.

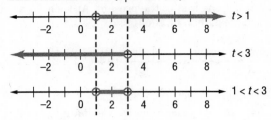

29. Solve both parts at the same time.

$$-11 < -4x + 5 < 13$$
$$-16 < \quad -4x \quad < 8$$
$$4 > \quad x \quad > -2$$

The solution set is $\{x \mid -2 < x < 4\}$.

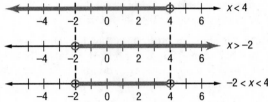

30. Solve each inequality separately.

$$2c - 1 < -5 \qquad \text{or} \qquad 3c + 2 \ge 5$$
$$2c < -4 \qquad\qquad\qquad 3c \ge 3$$
$$c < -2 \qquad\qquad\qquad c \ge 1$$

The solution set is $\{c \mid c < -2 \text{ or } c \ge 1\}$.

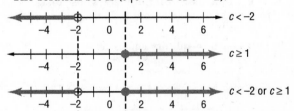

31. Solve both parts at the same time.

$$-4 < 4f + 24 < 4$$
$$-28 < \quad 4f \quad < -20$$
$$-7 < \quad f \quad < -5$$

The solution set is $\{f \mid -7 < f < -5\}$.

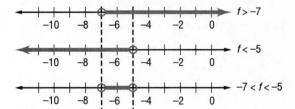

32. Solve each inequality separately.

$a + 2 > -2$ or $a - 8 < 1$
$a > -4$ $a < 9$

The solution set is $\{a \mid a$ is all real numbers$\}$.

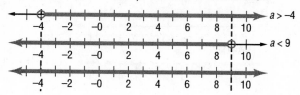

33. $|g| \leq 9$ is equivalent to $-9 \leq g \leq 9$. The solution set is $\{g \mid -9 \leq g \leq 9\}$.

34. $|2m| \geq 8$ is equivalent to $2m \geq 8$ or $2m \leq -8$. Solve each inequality separately.

$2m \geq 8$ or $2m \leq -8$
$m \geq 4$ $m \leq -4$

The solution set is $\{m \mid m \geq 4$ or $m \leq -4\}$.

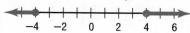

35. $|3k| < 0$ is equivalent to $0 < 3k < 0$. The solution set is $\varnothing$.

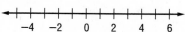

36. $|-5y| < 35$ is equivalent to $-35 < -5y < 35$. Solve both parts at the same time.

$-35 < -5y < 35$
$7 > y > -7$

The solution set is $\{y \mid -7 < y < 7\}$.

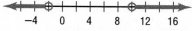

37. $|b - 4| > 6$ is equivalent to $b - 4 > 6$ or $b - 4 < -6$. Solve each inequality separately.

$b - 4 > 6$ or $b - 4 < -6$
$b > 10$ $b < -2$

The solution set is $\{b \mid b > 10$ or $b < -2\}$.

38. $|6r - 3| < 21$ is equivalent to $-21 < 6r - 3 < 21$. Solve both parts at the same time.

$-21 < 6r - 3 < 21$
$-18 < 6r < 24$
$-3 < r < 4$

The solution set is $\{r \mid -3 < r < 4\}$.

39. $|3w + 2| \leq 5$ is equivalent to $-5 \leq 3w + 2 \leq 5$. Solve both parts at the same time.

$-5 \leq 3w + 2 \leq 5$
$-7 \leq 3w \leq 3$
$-\frac{7}{3} \leq w \leq 1$

The solution set is $\left\{w \mid -\frac{7}{3} \leq w \leq 1\right\}$.

40. $|7x| + 4 < 0$
$|7x| < -4$
$|7x| < -4$ is equivalent to $4 < 7x < -4$. The solution set is $\varnothing$.

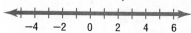

41. $|n| \geq n$ is equivalent to $n \geq n$ or $n \leq -n$. Solve each inequality separately.

$n \geq n$ or $n \leq -n$
$0 \geq 0$ $2n \leq 0$
                $n \leq 0$

The solution set is $\{n \mid n$ is all real numbers$\}$.

42. $|n| \leq n$ is equivalent to $n \leq n$ and $n \geq -n$. Solve each inequality separately.

$n \leq n$ and $n \geq -n$
$0 \leq 0$ $2n \geq 0$
                $n \geq 0$

The solution set is $\{n \mid n \geq 0\}$.

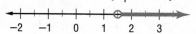

43. $|2n - 7| \leq 0$ is equivalent to $0 \leq 2n - 7 \leq 0$. Solve both parts at the same time.

$0 \leq 2n - 7 \leq 0$
$7 \leq 2n \leq 7$
$\frac{7}{2} \leq n \leq \frac{7}{2}$

The solution set is $\left\{n \mid n = \frac{7}{2}\right\}$.

44. $|n - 3| < n$ is equivalent to $n - 3 < n$ and $n - 3 > -n$. Solve each inequality separately.

$n - 3 < n$ and $n - 3 > -n$
$-3 < 0$ $-3 > -2n$
              $1.5 < n$

The solution set is $\{n \mid n > 1.5\}$.

45. Let $x =$ the water pH level.

6.8 is less than the water pH level is less than 7.4.

$6.8 < x < 7.4$

46. Let $s =$ the speed of the car.

45 is less than or equal to the speed of the car is less than or equal to 65.

$45 \leq s \leq 65$

47. Let $s =$ the speed of the tractor-trailer.

45 is less than or equal to the speed of the tractor-trailer is less than or equal to 55.

$45 \leq s \leq 55$

48. Let b = the temperature.

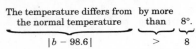

The temperature differs from the normal temperature | by more than | $8°$.
$|b - 98.6|$ | $>$ | 8

Rewrite the absolute value inequality as a compound inequality. Then solve for b.

$b - 98.6 > 8$ or $b - 98.6 < -8$
   $b > 106.6$ $b < 90.6$

The solution set is $\{b \mid b > 106.6 \text{ or } b < 90.6\}$. Thus, body temperatures that are less than $90.6°\text{F}$ or greater than $106.6°\text{F}$ are considered potentially dangerous.

49.

108 inches | is less than | the sum of the length and the distance around the thickest part | is less than or equal to | 130 inches.
108 | $<$ | $L + D$ | $\leq$ | 130

50. Evaluate $108 < L + D \leq 130$ with $D = 24$.

$108 < L + D \leq 130$
$108 < L + 24 \leq 130$
$84 < L \leq 106$

The solution set is $\{L \mid 84 < L \leq 106\}$. Thus, the length is greater than 84 inches and less than or equal to 106 inches.

51.

The sum of the measures of side a and b | is greater than | the measure of side c.
$a + b$ | $>$ | c

The sum of the measures of side a and c | is greater than | the measure of side b.
$a + c$ | $>$ | b

The sum of the measures of side b and c | is greater than | the measure of side a.
$b + c$ | $>$ | a

52. The three inequalities are $a + b > c$, $a + c > b$, and $b + c > a$. Solve the compound inequality $a + c > b$ or $b + c > a$ for c.

$a + c > b$ or $b + c > a$
  $c > b - a$ $c > a - b$

Since $a > b$, $a - b$ is greater than $b - a$. Thus, the measure of $a - b$ must be less than c and c must be less than $a + b$ or $a - b < c < a + b$.

53a. Graph the solution set for each inequality and find their intersection.

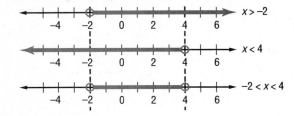

53b. Graph the solution set for each inequality and find their intersection.

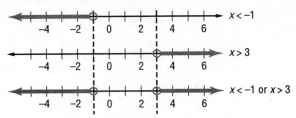

53c. Graph the solution set for each compound inequality and find their intersection.

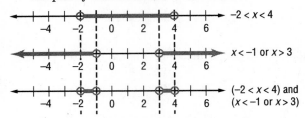

53d. $3 < |x + 2| \leq 8$ is equivalent to $|x + 2| > 3$ and $|x + 2| \leq 8$.

Solve each absolute value inequality.

$|x + 2| > 3$ is equivalent to $x + 2 > 3$ or $x + 2 < -3$.

Solve each inequality.

$x + 2 > 3$ or $x + 2 < -3$
    $x > 1$ $x < -5$

The solution set for this compound inequality is $\{x \mid x > 1 \text{ or } x < -5\}$.

$|x + 2| \leq 8$ is equivalent to $-8 \leq x + 2 \leq 8$.

Solve both parts at the same time.

$-8 \leq x + 2 \leq 8$
$-10 \leq x \leq 6$

The solution set for this compound inequality is $\{x \mid -10 \leq x \leq 6\}$.

Therefore, the union of these two sets is $(x > 1 \text{ or } x < -5)$ and $(-10 \leq x \leq 6)$. The union of the graph of $x > 1$ or $x < -5$ and the graph of $-10 \leq x \leq 6$ is shown below. From this we can see that the solution can be rewritten as $(-10 \leq x < -5)$ or $(1 < x \leq 6)$.

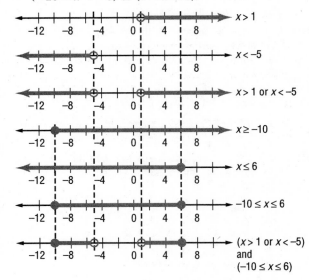

54. Compound inequalities can be used to describe the acceptable time frame for the fasting state before a glucose tolerance test is administered to a patient suspected of having diabetes. Answers should include the following.

- Use the word *and* when both inequalities must be satisfied. Use the word *or* when only one or the other of the inequalities must be satisfied.
- $10 \leq h \leq 16$
- 12 hours would be an acceptable fasting state for this test since it is part of the solution set of $10 \leq h \leq 16$ as indicated on the graph below.

55. $|2x + 11| > 1$ is equivalent to $2x + 11 > 1$ or $2x + 11 < -1$. Solve each inequality.

$$
\begin{array}{lll}
2x + 11 > 1 & \text{or} & 2x + 11 < -1 \\
2x > -10 & & 2x < -12 \\
x > -5 & & x < -6
\end{array}
$$

The solution set is $\{x \mid x > -5 \text{ or } x < -6\}$.

56. D; Since $5 < a < 7$, then $\frac{5}{7} < \frac{a}{7} < 1$ and $\frac{5}{14} < \frac{a}{14} < \frac{1}{2}$. Since $7 < b < 14$, then $\frac{1}{14} < \frac{1}{b} < \frac{1}{7}$. So, $\frac{a}{14} < \frac{a}{b} < \frac{a}{7}$. Therefore, using the Transitive Property of Inequality, $\frac{5}{14} < \frac{a}{14} < \frac{a}{b} < \frac{a}{7} < 1$ or $\frac{5}{14} < \frac{a}{b} < 1$.

57.

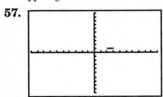

58. The calculator graphed $y = 1$ for values of x between 2 and 3. Thus, the inequality is $2 < x < 3$.

59. Clear the Y = list. Enter $(5x + 2 \geq 3)$ or $(5x + 2 \leq -3)$ as Y1. With your calculator in DOT mode and using the standard viewing window, press $\boxed{\text{GRAPH}}$. The calculator graphed $y = 1$ for values of x less than or equal to -1 and for values of x greater than or equal to 0.2. Thus, the solution set is $\{x \mid x \geq 0.2 \text{ or } x \leq -1\}$.

60. Clear the Y = list. Enter abs$(2x - 6) > 10$ as Y1. With your calculator in DOT mode and using the standard viewing window, press $\boxed{\text{GRAPH}}$. The calculator graphed $y = 1$ for values of x less than -2 and for values of x greater than 8. Thus, the solution set is $\{x \mid x < -2 \text{ or } x > 8\}$.

Page 46   Maintain Your Skills

61.
$$
\begin{aligned}
2d + 15 &\geq 3 \\
2d + 15 - 15 &\geq 3 - 15 \\
2d &\geq -12 \\
\frac{2d}{2} &\geq \frac{-12}{2} \\
d &\geq -6
\end{aligned}
$$
The solution set is $\{d \mid d \geq -6\}$ or $[-6, +\infty)$.

62.
$$
\begin{aligned}
7x + 11 &> 9x + 3 \\
7x + 11 - 9x &> 9x + 3 - 9x \\
-2x + 11 &> 3 \\
-2x + 11 - 11 &> 3 - 11 \\
-2x &> -8 \\
\frac{-2x}{-2} &< \frac{-8}{-2} \\
x &< 4
\end{aligned}
$$
The solution set is $\{x \mid x < 4\}$ or $(-\infty, 4)$.

63.
$$
\begin{aligned}
3n + 4(n + 3) &< 5(n + 2) \\
3n + 4(n) + 4(3) &< 5(n) + 5(2) \\
3n + 4n + 12 &< 5n + 10 \\
7n + 12 &< 5n + 10 \\
7n + 12 - 5n &< 5n + 10 - 5n \\
2n + 12 &< 10 \\
2n + 12 - 12 &< 10 - 12 \\
2n &< -2 \\
\frac{2n}{2} &< \frac{-2}{2} \\
n &< -1
\end{aligned}
$$
The solution set is $\{n \mid n < -1\}$ or $(-\infty, -1)$.

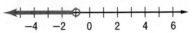

64. The highest and lowest number of keys will be 5 units away from 587. Therefore, the equation is $|x - 587| = 5$.

$$
\begin{array}{ll}
\text{Case 1:} \quad a = b & \text{or Case 2:} \quad a = -b \\
x - 587 = 5 & x - 587 = -5 \\
x - 587 + 587 = 5 + 587 & x - 587 + 587 = -5 + 587 \\
x = 592 & x = 582 \\
\text{Check:} \ |x - 587| = 5 & |x - 587| = 5 \\
|592 - 587| \stackrel{?}{=} 5 & |582 - 587| \stackrel{?}{=} 5 \\
|5| \stackrel{?}{=} 5 & |-5| \stackrel{?}{=} 5 \\
5 = 5 \ \checkmark & 5 = 5 \ \checkmark
\end{array}
$$

The highest number of keys is 592, and the lowest number of keys is 582.

65.
$$
\begin{aligned}
5|x - 3| &= 65 \\
|x - 3| &= 13
\end{aligned}
$$

$$
\begin{array}{ll}
\text{Case 1} \quad a = b & \text{or Case 2:} \quad a = -b \\
x - 3 = 13 & x - 3 = -13 \\
x - 3 + 3 = 13 + 3 & x - 3 + 3 = -13 + 3 \\
x = 16 & x = -10 \\
\text{Check:} \ 5|x - 3| = 65 & 5|x - 3| = 65 \\
5|16 - 3| \stackrel{?}{=} 65 & 5|-10 - 3| \stackrel{?}{=} 65 \\
5|13| \stackrel{?}{=} 65 & 5|-13| \stackrel{?}{=} 65 \\
5(13) \stackrel{?}{=} 65 & 5(13) \stackrel{?}{=} 65 \\
65 = 65 \ \checkmark & 65 = 65 \ \checkmark
\end{array}
$$

The solutions are 16 or -10. Thus, the solution set is $\{-10, 16\}$.

66. Case 1: $a = b$ or Case 2: $a = -b$

$$2x + 7 = 15 \qquad\qquad 2x + 7 = -15$$
$$2x + 7 - 7 = 15 - 7 \qquad 2x + 7 - 7 = -15 - 7$$
$$2x = 8 \qquad\qquad 2x = -22$$
$$\frac{2x}{2} = \frac{8}{2} \qquad\qquad \frac{2x}{2} = \frac{-22}{2}$$
$$x = 4 \qquad\qquad x = -11$$

Check: $|2x + 7| = 15 \qquad |2x + 7| = 15$
$$|2(4) + 7| \overset{?}{=} 15 \qquad |2(-11) + 7| \overset{?}{=} 15$$
$$|8 + 7| \overset{?}{=} 15 \qquad |-22 + 7| \overset{?}{=} 15$$
$$|15| \overset{?}{=} 15 \qquad |-15| \overset{?}{=} 15$$
$$15 = 15 \checkmark \qquad\qquad 15 = 15 \checkmark$$

The solutions are 4 or -11. Thus, the solution set is $\{-11, 4\}$.

67. $|8c + 7| = -4$

This sentence is never true. So the solution set is $\varnothing$.

68. Addition Property of Equality

69. Symmetric Property of Equality

70. Transitive Property of Equality

71. $6a - 2b - 3a + 9b = 6a - 3a + 9b - 2b$
$$= (6 - 3)a + (9 - 2)b$$
$$= 3a + 7b$$

72. $-2(m - 4n) - 3(5n + 6)$
$$= -2(m) - 2(-4n) - 3(5n) - 3(6)$$
$$= -2m + 8n - 15n - 18$$
$$= -2m + (8 - 15)n - 18$$
$$= -2m + (-7)n - 18$$
$$= -2m - 7n - 18$$

73. $6(5 - 8) \div 9 + 4 = 6(-3) \div 9 + 4$
$$= -18 \div 9 + 4$$
$$= -2 + 4$$
$$= 2$$

The value is 2.

74. $(3 + 7)^2 - 16 \div 2 = (10)^2 - 16 \div 2$
$$= 100 - 16 \div 2$$
$$= 100 - 8$$
$$= 92$$

The value is 92.

75. $\dfrac{7(1 - 4)}{8 - 5} = \dfrac{7(-3)}{8 - 5}$
$$= \frac{-21}{8 - 5}$$
$$= \frac{-21}{3}$$
$$= -7$$

The value is -7.

Chapter 1 Study Guide and Review

Page 47   Vocabulary and Concept Check

1. This example is a compound inequality since it consists of two inequalities joined by the word *or*.

2. This is an example of the Identity Property of Addition. The Identity Property says that the sum of any number and zero equals the number.

3. This is an example of the Commutative Property of Multiplication. The Commutative Property says that the order in which you multiply does not change the product.

4. This is an example of the Distributive Property. The Distributive Property says that the product of a number and a sum is equal to the sum of the products of the number and each addend.

5. This is an example of the Reflexive Property of Equality since it says an expression is equal to itself.

6. This is an example of the Transitive Property since it says that one expression equal to two other expressions means the two other expressions are equal.

7. This is an example of Multiplicative Inverse Property. The Multiplicative Inverse Property says that the product of a number and its Inverse is one.

8. This is an example of the Associative Property of Addition. The Associative Property says that the way you group three numbers when adding does not change the sum.

9. This example is an absolute value expression since it consists of an expression inside the absolute value symbol.

10. This example is an algebraic expression since it consists of an expression that contains at least one variable.

Pages 47–50   Lesson-by-Lesson Review

11. $10 + 16 \div 4 + 8 = 10 + 4 + 8$
$$= 14 + 8$$
$$= 22$$

The value is 22.

12. $[21 - (9 - 2)] \div 2 = [21 - 7] \div 2$
$$= 14 \div 2$$
$$= 7$$

The value is 7.

13. $\dfrac{14(8 - 15)}{2} = \dfrac{14(-7)}{2}$
$$= \frac{-98}{2}$$
$$= -49$$

The value is -49.

14. $6b - 5c = 6(0.5) - 5(-3)$
$$= 3 - 5(-3)$$
$$= 3 + 15$$
$$= 18$$

The value is 18.

15. $c^3 + ad = (-3)^3 + 12\left(\frac{1}{3}\right)$
$$= -27 + 4$$
$$= -23$$

The value is -23.

16. $\dfrac{9c + ab}{c} = \dfrac{9(-3) + 12(0.5)}{-3}$
$$= \frac{-27 + 6}{-3}$$
$$= \frac{-21}{-3}$$
$$= 7$$

The value is 7.

17. $a[b^2(b + a)] = 12[0.5^2(0.5 + 12)]$
$$= 12[0.5^2(12.5)]$$
$$= 12[0.25(12.5)]$$
$$= 12[3.125]$$
$$= 37.5$$
The value is 37.5.

18. $-\sqrt{9} = -3$
integers (Z), rationals (Q), and reals (R)

19. rationals (Q) and reals (R)

20. $\frac{35}{7} = 5$
naturals (N), wholes (W), integers (Z), rationals (Q), and reals (R)

21. $\sqrt{18}$ lies between 4 and 5 so it is not a whole number.
irrationals (I) and reals (R)

22. $2m + 7n - 6m - 5n = 2m - 6m + 7n - 5n$
$$= (2 - 6)m + (7 - 5)n$$
$$= -4m + 2n$$

23. $-5(a - 4b) + 4b = -5(a) - 5(-4b) + 4b$
$$= -5a + 20b + 4b$$
$$= -5a + (20 + 4)b$$
$$= -5a + 24b$$

24. $2(5x + 4y) - 3(x + 8y) = 2(5x) + 2(4y) - 3(x) - 3(8y)$
$$= 10x + 8y - 3x - 24y$$
$$= 10x - 3x + 8y - 24y$$
$$= (10 - 3)x + (8 - 24)y$$
$$= 7x + (-16y)$$
$$= 7x - 16y$$

Exercises 25–30 For checks, see student's work.

25. $x - 6 = -20$
$$x - 6 + 6 = -20 + 6$$
$$x = -14$$
The solution is -14.

26. $-\frac{2}{3}a = 14$
$$-\frac{3}{2}\left(-\frac{2}{3}a\right) = -\frac{3}{2}(14)$$
$$a = -21$$
The solution is -21.

27. $7 + 5n = -58$
$$7 + 5n - 7 = -58 - 7$$
$$5n = -65$$
$$n = -13$$
The solution is -13.

28. $3w + 14 = 7w + 2$
$$3w + 14 - 7w = 7w + 2 - 7w$$
$$-4w + 14 = 2$$
$$-4w + 14 - 14 = 2 - 14$$
$$-4w = -12$$
$$w = 3$$
The solution is 3.

29. $5y + 4 = 2(y - 4)$
$$5y + 4 = 2(y) + 2(-4)$$
$$5y + 4 = 2y - 8$$
$$5y + 4 - 2y = 2y - 8 - 2y$$
$$3y + 4 = -8$$
$$3y + 4 - 4 = -8 - 4$$
$$3y = -12$$
$$y = -4$$
The solution is -4.

30. $\frac{n}{4} + \frac{n}{3} = \frac{1}{2}$
$$12\left(\frac{n}{4} + \frac{n}{3}\right) = 12\left(\frac{1}{2}\right)$$
$$12\left(\frac{n}{4}\right) + 12\left(\frac{n}{3}\right) = 6$$
$$3n + 4n = 6$$
$$7n = 6$$
$$n = \frac{6}{7}$$
The solution is $\frac{6}{7}$.

31. $Ax + By = C$
$$Ax + By - By = C - By$$
$$Ax = C - By$$
$$x = \frac{C - By}{A}$$

32. $\frac{a - 4b^2}{2c} = d$
$$2c\left(\frac{a - 4b^2}{2c}\right) = 2c(d)$$
$$a - 4b^2 = 2cd$$
$$a - 4b^2 + 4b^2 = 2cd + 4b^2$$
$$a = 2cd + 4b^2$$

33. $A = p + prt$
$$A = p(1 + rt)$$
$$\frac{A}{1 + rt} = p$$

34. Case 1: $\quad a = b \quad$ or Case 2: $\quad a = -b$
$$x + 11 = 42 \qquad\qquad x + 11 = -42$$
$$x + 11 - 11 = 42 - 11 \quad x + 11 - 11 = -42 - 11$$
$$x = 31 \qquad\qquad\qquad x = -53$$
Check: $\quad |x + 11| = 42 \qquad |x + 11| = 42$
$$|31 + 11| \overset{?}{=} 42 \qquad |-53 + 11| \overset{?}{=} 42$$
$$|42| \overset{?}{=} 42 \qquad\quad |-42| \overset{?}{=} 42$$
$$42 = 42 ✓ \qquad\qquad 42 = 42 ✓$$
The solutions are 31 or -53. Thus, the solution set is $\{-53, 31\}$.

35. $3|x + 6| = 36$
$$|x + 6| = 12$$
Case 1: $a = b \qquad$ or Case 2: $\quad a = -b$
$$x + 6 = 12 \qquad\qquad x + 6 = -12$$
$$x + 6 - 6 = 12 - 6 \qquad x + 6 - 6 = -12 - 6$$
$$x = 6 \qquad\qquad\qquad x = -18$$
Check: $\quad 3|x + 6| = 36 \qquad 3|x + 6| = 36$
$$3|6 + 6| \overset{?}{=} 36 \qquad 3|-18 + 6| \overset{?}{=} 36$$
$$3|12| \overset{?}{=} 36 \qquad\quad 3|-12| \overset{?}{=} 36$$
$$3(12) \overset{?}{=} 36 \qquad\quad 3(12) \overset{?}{=} 36$$
$$36 = 36 ✓ \qquad\qquad 36 = 36 ✓$$
The solutions are 6 or -18. Thus, the solution set is $\{-18, 6\}$.

36. $|4x - 5| = -25$
This sentence is never true. So the solution set is $\varnothing$.

37. Case 1: $a = b$ or Case 2: $a = -b$

$x + 7 = 3x - 5$ $\qquad$ $x + 7 = -(3x - 5)$

$x + 7 - 3x = 3x - 5 - 3x$ $\qquad$ $x + 7 = -3x + 5$

$-2x + 7 = -5$ $\qquad$ $x + 7 + 3x = -3x + 5 + 3x$

$-2x + 7 - 7 = -5 - 7$ $\qquad$ $4x + 7 = 5$

$-2x = -12$ $\qquad$ $4x + 7 - 7 = 5 - 7$

$x = 6$ $\qquad$ $4x = -2$

$\qquad\qquad\qquad\qquad\qquad x = -\frac{1}{2}$

Check: $|x + 7| = 3x - 5$ $\qquad$ $|x + 7| = 3x - 5$

$|6 + 7| \overset{?}{=} 3(6) - 5$ $\qquad$ $\left|-\frac{1}{2} + 7\right| \overset{?}{=} 3\left(-\frac{1}{2}\right) - 5$

$|13| \overset{?}{=} 18 - 5$ $\qquad$ $\left|\frac{13}{2}\right| \overset{?}{=} -\frac{3}{2} - 5$

$13 = 13 \checkmark$ $\qquad$ $\frac{13}{2} \neq -\frac{13}{2}$

Since $\frac{13}{2} \neq -\frac{13}{2}$, the only solution is 6. Thus, the solution set is {6}.

38. $|y - 5| - 2 = 10$

$|y - 5| = 12$

Case 1: $a = b$ or Case 2: $a = -b$

$y - 5 = 12$ $\qquad$ $y - 5 = -12$

$y - 5 + 5 = 12 + 5$ $\qquad$ $y - 5 + 5 = -12 + 5$

$y = 17$ $\qquad$ $y = -7$

Check: $|y - 5| - 2 = 10$ $\qquad$ $|y - 5| - 2 = 10$

$|17 - 5| - 2 \overset{?}{=} 10$ $\qquad$ $|-7 - 5| - 2 \overset{?}{=} 10$

$|12| - 2 \overset{?}{=} 10$ $\qquad$ $|-12| - 2 \overset{?}{=} 10$

$12 - 2 \overset{?}{=} 10$ $\qquad$ $12 - 2 \overset{?}{=} 10$

$10 = 10 \checkmark$ $\qquad$ $10 = 10 \checkmark$

The solutions are 17 or -7. Thus, the solution set is $\{-7, 17\}$.

39. $4|3x + 4| = 4x + 8$

$|3x + 4| = x + 2$

Case 1: $a = b$ or Case 2: $a = -b$

$3x + 4 = x + 2$ $\qquad$ $3x + 4 = -(x + 2)$

$3x + 4 - x = x + 2 - x$ $\qquad$ $3x + 4 = -x - 2$

$2x + 4 = 2$ $\qquad$ $3x + 4 + x = -x - 2 + x$

$2x + 4 - 4 = 2 - 4$ $\qquad$ $4x + 4 = -2$

$2x = -2$ $\qquad$ $4x + 4 - 4 = -2 - 4$

$x = -1$ $\qquad$ $4x = -6$

$\qquad\qquad\qquad\qquad\qquad x = -\frac{3}{2}$

Check: $4|3x + 4| = 4x + 8$ $\qquad$ $4|3x + 4| = 4x + 8$

$4|3(-1) + 4| \overset{?}{=} 4(-1) + 8$ $\qquad$ $4\left|3\left(-\frac{3}{2}\right) + 4\right| \overset{?}{=} 4\left(-\frac{3}{2}\right) + 8$

$4|-3 + 4| \overset{?}{=} -4 + 8$ $\qquad$ $4\left|-\frac{9}{2} + 4\right| \overset{?}{=} -6 + 8$

$4|1| \overset{?}{=} 4$ $\qquad$ $4\left|-\frac{1}{2}\right| \overset{?}{=} 2$

$4(1) \overset{?}{=} 4$ $\qquad$ $4\left(\frac{1}{2}\right) \overset{?}{=} 2$

$4 = 4 \checkmark$ $\qquad$ $2 = 2 \checkmark$

The solutions are -1 or $-\frac{3}{2}$. Thus, the solution set is $\left\{-\frac{3}{2}, -1\right\}$.

40. $-7w > 28$

$\frac{-7w}{-7} < \frac{28}{-7}$

$w < -4$

The solution set is $\{w \mid w < -4\}$ or $(-\infty, -4)$.

41. $3x + 4 \geq 19$

$3x + 4 - 4 \geq 19 - 4$

$3x \geq 15$

$\frac{3x}{3} \geq \frac{15}{3}$

$x \geq 5$

The solution set is $\{x \mid x \geq 5\}$ or $[5, +\infty)$.

42. $\frac{n}{12} + 5 \leq 7$

$\frac{n}{12} + 5 - 5 \leq 7 - 5$

$\frac{n}{12} \leq 2$

$12\left(\frac{n}{12}\right) \leq 12(2)$

$n \leq 24$

The solution set is $\{n \mid n \leq 24\}$ or $(-\infty, 24]$.

43. $3(6 - 5a) < 12a - 36$

$3(6) - 3(5a) < 12a - 36$

$18 - 15a < 12a - 36$

$18 - 15a - 12a < 12a - 36 - 12a$

$-27a + 18 < -36$

$-27a + 18 - 18 < -36 - 18$

$-27a < -54$

$\frac{-27a}{-27} > \frac{-54}{-27}$

$a > 2$

The solution set is $\{a \mid a > 2\}$ or $(2, +\infty)$.

44. $2 - 3z \geq 7(8 - 2z) + 12$

$2 - 3z \geq 7(8) - 7(2z) + 12$

$2 - 3z \geq 56 - 14z + 12$

$2 - 3z \geq 68 - 14z$

$2 - 3z + 14z \geq 68 - 14z + 14z$

$11z + 2 \geq 68$

$11z + 2 - 2 \geq 68 - 2$

$11z \geq 66$

$\frac{11z}{11} \geq \frac{66}{11}$

$z \geq 6$

The solution set is $\{z \mid z \geq 6\}$ or $[6, +\infty)$.

45. $8(2x - 1) > 11x - 17$

$8(2x) + 8(-1) > 11x - 17$

$16x - 8 > 11x - 17$

$16x - 8 - 11x > 11x - 17 - 11x$

$5x - 8 > -17$

$5x - 8 + 8 > -17 + 8$

$5x > -9$

$\frac{5x}{5} > \frac{-9}{5}$

$x > -1.8$

The solution set is $\{x \mid x > -1.8\}$ or $(-1.8, +\infty)$.

46. $-1 < 3a + 2 < 14$
$-3 < 3a < 12$
$-1 < a < 4$
The solution set is $\{a \mid -1 < a < 4\}$.

47. $-1 < 3(y - 2) \le 9$
$-1 < 3y - 6 \le 9$
$5 < 3y \le 15$
$\frac{5}{3} < y \le 5$
The solution set is $\left\{y \mid \frac{5}{3} < y \le 5\right\}$.

48. $|x| + 1 > 12$
$|x| > 11$
$|x| > 11$ is equivalent to $x > 11$ or $x < -11$.
The solution set is $\{x \mid x > 11 \text{ or } x < -11\}$.

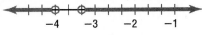

49. $|2y - 9| \le 27$ is equivalent to $-27 \le 2y - 9 \le 27$.
$-27 \le 2y - 9 \le 27$
$-18 \le 2y \le 36$
$-9 \le y \le 18$
The solution set is $\{y \mid -9 \le y \le 18\}$.

50. $|5n - 8| > -4$ is equivalent to $5n - 8 > -4$ or $5n - 8 < 4$.
$5n - 8 > -4 \qquad \text{or} \qquad 5n - 8 < 4$
$5n > 4 \qquad\qquad\qquad 5n < 12$
$n > \frac{4}{5} \qquad\qquad\qquad n < \frac{12}{5}$
The solution set is $\{n \mid n \text{ is all real numbers}\}$.

51. $|3b + 11| > 1$ is equivalent to $3b + 11 > -1$ or $3b + 11 < -1$.
$3b + 11 > 1 \qquad\qquad \text{or} \qquad 3b + 11 < -1$
$3b > -10 \qquad\qquad\qquad 3b < -12$
$b > -\frac{10}{3} \qquad\qquad\qquad b < -4$
The solution set is $\left\{b \mid b > -\frac{10}{3} \text{ or } b < -4\right\}$.

Chapter 1 Practice Test

Page 51
1. equation
2. Whole numbers
3. Symmetric

4. $[(3 + 6)^2 \div 3] \times 4 = [(9)^2 \div 3] \times 4$
$= [81 \div 3] \times 4$
$= 27 \times 4$
$= 108$
The value is 108.

5. $\dfrac{20 + 4 \times 3}{11 - 3} = \dfrac{20 + 12}{11 - 3}$
$\phantom{\dfrac{20 + 4 \times 3}{11 - 3}} = \dfrac{32}{11 - 3}$
$\phantom{\dfrac{20 + 4 \times 3}{11 - 3}} = \dfrac{32}{8}$
$\phantom{\dfrac{20 + 4 \times 3}{11 - 3}} = 4$
The value is 4.

6. $0.5(2.3 + 25) \div 1.5 = 0.5(27.3) \div 1.5$
$= 13.65 \div 1.5$
$= 9.1$
The value is 9.1.

7. $\dfrac{db + 4c}{a} = \dfrac{-6\left(\frac{2}{3}\right) + 4(8)}{-9}$
$\phantom{\dfrac{db + 4c}{a}} = \dfrac{-4 + 32}{-9}$
$\phantom{\dfrac{db + 4c}{a}} = \dfrac{28}{-9}$
$\phantom{\dfrac{db + 4c}{a}} = -\dfrac{28}{9}$
The value is $-\dfrac{28}{9}$.

8. $\dfrac{a}{b^2} + c = \dfrac{-9}{\left(\frac{2}{3}\right)^2} + 8$
$\phantom{\dfrac{a}{b^2} + c} = \dfrac{-9}{\frac{4}{9}} + 8$
$\phantom{\dfrac{a}{b^2} + c} = -\dfrac{81}{4} + 8$
$\phantom{\dfrac{a}{b^2} + c} = -\dfrac{49}{4}$
$\phantom{\dfrac{a}{b^2} + c} = -12.25$
The value is -12.25.

9. $2b(4a + a^2) = 2\left(\frac{2}{3}\right)[4(-9) + (-9)^2]$
$ = 2\left(\frac{2}{3}\right)[4(-9) + 81]$
$ = 2\left(\frac{2}{3}\right)[-36 + 81]$
$ = 2\left(\frac{2}{3}\right)[45]$
$ = \frac{4}{3}[45]$
$ = 60$
The value is 60.

10. $\sqrt{17}$ lies between 4 and 5 so it is not a whole number. irrationals (I) and reals (R)

11. rationals (Q) and reals (R)

12. $\sqrt{64} = 8$
naturals (N), wholes (W), integers (Z), rationals (Q), and reals (R)

13. Associative Property of Multiplication—the way you group three numbers when multiplying does not change the product

14. Symmetric Property of Equality—if two expressions are equal, the order in which they are written does not change the equality

15. Reflexive Property of Equality—an expression is always equal to itself

16. Substitution Property of Equality—equivalent expressions can be substituted for each other into an equation

17. Commutative Property of Addition—the order in which you add does not change the sum

18. Transitive Property of Equality—if an expression is equivalent to two other expressions, then those two other expressions are equivlent

Exercises 19–21 For checks see student's work.

19.
$$5t - 3 = -2t + 10$$
$$5t - 3 + 2t = -2t + 10 + 2t$$
$$7t - 3 = 10$$
$$7t - 3 + 3 = 10 + 3$$
$$7t = 13$$
$$t = \frac{13}{7}$$
The solution set is $\frac{13}{7}$.

20. $2x - 7 - (x - 5) = 0$
$$2x - 7 - x + 5 = 0$$
$$x - 2 = 0$$
$$x - 2 + 2 = 0 + 2$$
$$x = 2$$
The solution set is 2.

21. $5m - (5 + 4m) = (3 + m) - 8$
$$5m - 5 - 4m = 3 + m - 8$$
$$m - 5 = m - 5$$
This sentence is always true. So the solution set is all real numbers.

22. $|8w + 2| + 2 = 0$
$$|8w + 2| = -2$$
This sentence is never true. So the solution set is $\varnothing$.

23. $12\left|\frac{1}{2}y + 3\right| = 6$
$$\left|\frac{1}{2}y + 3\right| = \frac{1}{2}$$

Case 1: $a = b$ or Case 2: $a = -b$

$\frac{1}{2}y + 3 = \frac{1}{2}$ $\frac{1}{2}y + 3 = -\frac{1}{2}$

$\frac{1}{2}y + 3 - 3 = \frac{1}{2} - 3$ $\frac{1}{2}y + 3 - 3 = -\frac{1}{2} - 3$

$\frac{1}{2}y = -\frac{5}{2}$ $\frac{1}{2}y = -\frac{7}{2}$

$2\left(\frac{1}{2}y\right) = 2\left(-\frac{5}{2}\right)$ $2\left(\frac{1}{2}y\right) = 2\left(-\frac{7}{2}\right)$

$y = -5$ $y = -7$

Check: $12\left|\frac{1}{2}y + 3\right| = 6$ $12\left|\frac{1}{2}y + 3\right| = 6$

$12\left|\frac{1}{2}(-5) + 3\right| \overset{?}{=} 6$ $12\left|\frac{1}{2}(-7) + 3\right| \overset{?}{=} 6$

$12\left|-\frac{5}{2} + 3\right| \overset{?}{=} 6$ $12\left|-\frac{7}{2} + 3\right| \overset{?}{=} 6$

$12\left|\frac{1}{2}\right| \overset{?}{=} 6$ $12\left|-\frac{1}{2}\right| \overset{?}{=} 6$

$12\left(\frac{1}{2}\right) \overset{?}{=} 6$ $12\left(\frac{1}{2}\right) \overset{?}{=} 6$

$6 = 6 \checkmark$ $6 = 6 \checkmark$

The solutions are -5 or -7. Thus, the solution set is $\{-7, -5\}$.

24. $2|2y - 6| + 4 = 8$
$$2|2y - 6| = 4$$
$$|2y - 6| = 2$$

Case 1: $a = b$ or Case 2: $a = -b$
   $2y - 6 = 2$ $2y - 6 = -2$
$2y - 6 + 6 = 2 + 6$ $2y - 6 + 6 = -2 + 6$
   $2y = 8$ $2y = 4$
   $y = 4$ $y = 2$

Check: $2|2y - 6| + 4 = 8$ $2|2y - 6| + 4 = 8$
$2|2(4) - 6| + 4 \overset{?}{=} 8$ $2|2(2) - 6| + 4 \overset{?}{=} 8$
$2|8 - 6| + 4 \overset{?}{=} 8$ $2|4 - 6| + 4 \overset{?}{=} 8$
$2|2| + 4 \overset{?}{=} 8$ $2|-2| + 4 \overset{?}{=} 8$
$2(2) + 4 \overset{?}{=} 8$ $2(2) + 4 \overset{?}{=} 8$
$4 + 4 \overset{?}{=} 8$ $4 + 4 \overset{?}{=} 8$
$8 = 8 \checkmark$ $8 = 8 \checkmark$

The solutions are 4 or 2. Thus, the solution set is $\{2, 4\}$.

25.
$$4 > b + 1$$
$$4 - 1 > b + 1 - 1$$
$$3 > b$$
The solution set is $\{b \mid b < 3\}$ or $(-\infty, 3)$.

26.
$$3q + 7 \geq 13$$
$$3q + 7 - 7 \geq 13 - 7$$
$$3q \geq 6$$
$$\frac{3q}{3} \geq \frac{6}{3}$$
$$q \geq 2$$
The solution set is $\{q \mid q \geq 2\}$ or $[2, +\infty)$.

27.
$$5(3x - 5) + x < 2(4x - 1) + 1$$
$$5(3x) + 5(-5) + x < 2(4x) + 2(-1) + 1$$
$$15x - 25 + x < 8x - 2 + 1$$
$$16x - 25 < 8x - 1$$
$$16x - 25 - 8x < 8x - 1 - 8x$$
$$8x - 25 < -1$$
$$8x - 25 + 25 < -1 + 25$$
$$8x < 24$$
$$\frac{8x}{8} < \frac{24}{8}$$
$$x < 3$$
The solution set is $\{x \mid x < 3\}$ or $(-\infty, 3)$.

28. $|5 + k| \leq 8$ is equivalent to $-8 \leq 5 + k \leq 8$.
$$-8 \leq 5 + k \leq 8$$
$$-13 \leq \quad k \quad \leq 3$$
The solution set is $\{k \mid -13 \leq k \leq 3\}$ or $[-13, 3]$.

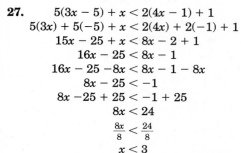

29. $-12 < 7d - 5 \leq 9$
$$-7 < \quad 7d \quad \leq 14$$
$$-1 < \quad d \quad \leq 2$$
The solution set is $\{d \mid -1 < d \leq 2\}$ or $(-1, 2]$.

30. $|3y - 1| > 5$ is equivalent to $3y - 1 > 5$ or $3y - 1 < -5$.

$$3y - 1 > 5 \qquad \text{or} \qquad 3y - 1 < -5$$
$$3y > 6 \qquad\qquad\qquad 3y < -4$$
$$y > 2 \qquad\qquad\qquad y < -\frac{4}{3}$$

The solution set is $\left\{y \,\middle|\, y > 2 \text{ or } y < -\frac{4}{3}\right\}$ or $\left(-\infty, -\frac{4}{3}\right) \cup (2, +\infty)$.

31. Let m represent the number of miles traveled.

The rental charge per day	plus	the cost per mile	times	the number of miles	equals	the amount reimbursed.
19.50	+	0.18	·	m	=	33

$$19.50 + 0.18\,m = 33$$
$$19.50 + 0.18m - 19.50 = 33 - 19.50$$
$$0.18m = 13.50$$
$$\frac{0.18m}{0.18} = \frac{13.50}{0.18}$$
$$m = 75$$

Her company will pay for 75 miles.

32. Let s = his score on the last test.

The sum of the test scores divided by 5	is greater than or equal to	80.
$\frac{87 + 89 + 76 + 77 + s}{5}$	$\geq$	80

$$\frac{87 + 89 + 76 + 77 + s}{5} \geq 80$$
$$5\left(\frac{87 + 89 + 76 + 77 + s}{5}\right) \geq 5(80)$$
$$87 + 89 + 76 + 77 + s \geq 400$$
$$329 + s \geq 400$$
$$329 + s - 329 \geq 400 - 329$$
$$s \geq 71$$

Nick must score at least 71 on his next test to have a B in his English class.

33. B; Solve $\frac{a}{b} = 8$ for b.

$$\frac{a}{b} = 8$$
$$b\left(\frac{a}{b}\right) = b(8)$$
$$a = 8b$$
$$\frac{a}{8} = \frac{8b}{8}$$
$$\frac{a}{8} = b$$

Solve $ac - 5 = 11$ for c.

$$ac - 5 = 11$$
$$ac = 16$$
$$\frac{ac}{a} = \frac{16}{a}$$
$$c = \frac{16}{a}$$

Evaluate bc if $b = \frac{a}{8}$ and $c = \frac{16}{a}$.

$$bc = \frac{a}{8}\left(\frac{16}{a}\right)$$
$$= 2$$

The value is 2.

Chapter 1 Standardized Test Practice

Pages 52–53

1. B; Solve $5x = x + 8$.

$$5x = x + 8$$
$$5x - x = x + 8 - x$$
$$4x = 8$$
$$\frac{4x}{4} = \frac{8}{4}$$
$$x = 2$$

The solution is 2.

2. D; Let x = the total number of students.

30%	of	the total	is	18.
0.3	·	x	=	18

$$0.3x = 18$$
$$\frac{0.3x}{0.3} = \frac{18}{0.3}$$
$$x = 60$$

3. D; mean $= \dfrac{7(87) + 79}{7 + 1}$

$$= \frac{688}{8}$$
$$= 86$$

4. D; $\quad 4 + 6 + PR = 3(PQ)$
$$4 + 6 + PR = 3(6)$$
$$10 + PR = 18$$
$$10 + PR - 10 = 18 - 10$$
$$PR = 8$$

5. C; Chose 6 from R, 4 from S, and 7 from T.
$$6 + 4 + 7 = 10 + 7$$
$$= 17$$

6. C;

The amount in the pitcher	minus	the amount in each glass	times	the number of glasses
a	−	b	·	c

7. D; Let n = the least of the three integers. Then $n + 1$ = the next consecutive integer, and $n + 2$ = the greatest of the three integers.

The sum of three consecutive integers	is	135.
$n + (n + 1) + (n + 2)$	=	135

$$n + (n + 1) + (n + 2) = 135$$
$$n + n + 1 + n + 2 = 135$$
$$3n + 3 = 135$$
$$3n + 3 - 3 = 135 - 3$$
$$3n = 132$$
$$\frac{3n}{3} = \frac{132}{3}$$
$$n = 44$$

$n + 1 = 44 + 1$ or 45 and $n + 2 = 44 + 2$ or 46
The greatest of the three integers is 46.

8. A; Let g = the number of girls.
Then $27 - g$ = the number of boys.

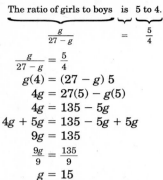

$$\frac{g}{27 - g} = \frac{5}{4}$$

$$g(4) = (27 - g)\,5$$
$$4g = 27(5) - g(5)$$
$$4g = 135 - 5g$$
$$4g + 5g = 135 - 5g + 5g$$
$$9g = 135$$
$$\frac{9g}{9} = \frac{135}{9}$$
$$g = 15$$

There are 15 girls in the class.

9. D; $x + y \overset{?}{>} 3 \qquad x - y \overset{?}{<} -2$
$2 + 5 \overset{?}{>} 3 \qquad 2 - 5 \overset{?}{<} -2$
$7 > 3 \; \checkmark \qquad -3 < -2 \; \checkmark$

10. B; Use the formula for the area of a triangle to find the length of $\overline{AD}$.

$$A = \tfrac{1}{2}bh$$
$$280 = \tfrac{1}{2}(AD)(16)$$
$$280 = 8(AD)$$
$$\frac{280}{8} = \frac{8(AD)}{8}$$
$$35 = AD$$

Use the formula for the area of a parallelogram with the given information.

$$A = \tfrac{1}{2}(b_1 + b_2)h$$
$$= \tfrac{1}{2}(16 + 20)(35)$$
$$= \tfrac{1}{2}(36)(35)$$
$$= 18(35)$$
$$= 630$$

The area of polygon $ABCD$ is 630 units.

11. Solve $x + 2y = 180$ if $y = 26$.
$$x + 2y = 180$$
$$x + 2(26) = 180$$
$$x + 52 = 180$$
$$x = 128$$

Solve $x + 2y = 180$ if $y = 27$.
$$x + 2y = 180$$
$$x + 2(27) = 180$$
$$x + 54 = 180$$
$$x = 126$$

Solve $x + 2y = 180$ if $y = 28$.
$$x + 2y = 180$$
$$x + 2(28) = 180$$
$$x + 56 = 180$$
$$x = 124$$

Solve $x + 2y = 180$ if $y = 29$.
$$x + 2y = 180$$
$$x + 2(29) = 180$$
$$x + 58 = 180$$
$$x = 122$$

Therefore, the value of x can be 122, 124, 126, or 128.

12. Evaluate $3n + 4p$ if $n = 1$ and $p = 3$.
$$3n + 4p = 3(1) + 4(3)$$
$$= 3 + 12$$
$$= 15$$

Evaluate $3n + 4p$ if $n = 3$ and $p = 1$.
$$3n + 4p = 3(3) + 4(1)$$
$$= 9 + 4$$
$$= 13$$

The possible values are 13 or 15.

13. Solve $2x + 70 = 180$.
$$2x + 70 = 180$$
$$2x + 70 - 70 = 180 - 70$$
$$2x = 110$$
$$\frac{2x}{2} = \frac{110}{2}$$
$$x = 55$$

The value of x is 55.

14. Lemonade concentrate varies directly as the number of people. Find the value of k.

$$y = kx$$
$$\tfrac{1}{2} = k(6)$$
$$\frac{\frac{1}{2}}{6} = \frac{k(6)}{6}$$
$$\frac{1}{12} = k$$

Find y when $x = 21$.
$$y = \tfrac{1}{12}x$$
$$y = \tfrac{1}{12}(21)$$
$$y = \tfrac{7}{4}$$

Therefore, for 21 people, $\frac{7}{4}$ or 1.75 quarts of lemonade concentrate are needed.

15. 25% of 300 is equal to 500% of t.
$$0.25 \cdot 300 = 5.00 \cdot t$$
$$0.25(300) = 5.00(t)$$
$$75 = 5t$$
$$\frac{75}{5} = \frac{5t}{5}$$
$$15 = t$$

The solution is 15.

16. Let x = the length of a side of the shaded square. Then $x = \sqrt{3^2 + 2^2}$ or $\sqrt{13}$. Use the formula for the area of a square.
$$A = x^2$$
$$= (\sqrt{13})^2$$
$$= 13$$

The area is 13 square units.

17. $\dfrac{2}{5} = \dfrac{\text{the number of brass players}}{\text{the total number of students in the band}}$

Let x = the number of brass players.
$$\frac{2}{5} = \frac{x}{140}$$
$$2(140) = 5(x)$$
$$280 = 5x$$
$$\frac{280}{5} = \frac{5x}{5}$$
$$56 = x$$

There are 56 brass players.

18. Let n = the number of cans. We know that $n < 50$ and n is a multiple of 5. Thus n is 5, 10, 15, 20, 25, 30, 35, 40, or 45. Since $n - 1$ is a multiple of 3, evaluate $\frac{n-1}{3}$ from the largest possible value to the smallest possible value until the value of the expression is an integer.

For $n = 45$: $\frac{n-1}{3} = \frac{45-1}{3}$ or $\frac{44}{3}$

For $n = 40$: $\frac{n-1}{3} = \frac{40-1}{3}$ or 13

Therefore, 40 is the greatest number of cans.

19. C; $\dfrac{\frac{3}{4}}{\left(\frac{3}{4}\right)^2} = \dfrac{\frac{3}{4}}{\frac{9}{16}}$

$\qquad = \dfrac{3}{4} \cdot \dfrac{16}{9}$

$\qquad = \dfrac{4}{3}$

20. B; $13 < 14$. Thus, $13 + x < 14 + x$ for all real values of x.

21. D; $\quad 0 < \quad s \quad < \dfrac{3}{4}$

$3(0) < 3(s) < 3\left(\dfrac{3}{4}\right)$

$\quad 0 < \quad 3s \quad < \dfrac{9}{4}$

Thus, the relationship cannot be determined.

22. C; $\quad 120 + a = 180$

$120 + a - 120 = 180 - 120$

$\qquad\qquad a = 60$

$\qquad 2(a) = 2(60)$

$\qquad\quad 2a = 120$

23. B; $\dfrac{s+t}{2} > \dfrac{s+w}{2}$

$2\left(\dfrac{s+t}{2}\right) > 2\left(\dfrac{s+w}{2}\right)$

$\qquad s + t > s + w$

$s + t - s > s + w - s$

$\qquad\quad t > w$

Chapter 2 Linear Relations and Functions

1. $(-3, 3)$

2. $(2, 3)$

3. $(-3, -1)$

4. $(2, 0)$

5. $(0, -4)$

6. $(3, -2)$

7. $c + d = -2 + 0$
$= -2$

8. $4c - b = 4(-2) - 3$
$= -8 - 3$
$= -11$

9. $a^2 - 5a + 3 = (-1)^2 - 5(-1) + 3$
$= 1 + 5 + 3$
$= 9$

10. $2b^2 + b + 7 = 2(3)^2 + 3 + 7$
$= 2 \cdot 9 + 3 + 7$
$= 18 + 3 + 7$
$= 28$

11. $\frac{a - b}{c - d} = \frac{-1 - 3}{-2 - 0}$
$= \frac{-4}{-2}$
$= 2$

12. $\frac{a + c}{b + c} = \frac{-1 + (-2)}{3 + (-2)}$
$= \frac{-3}{1}$
$= -3$

13. $x - (-1) = x + 1$

14. $x - (-5) = x + 5$

15. $2[x - (-3)] = 2[x + 3]$
$= 2x + 2(3)$
$= 2x + 6$

16. $4[x - (-2)] = 4[x + 2]$
$= 4x + 4(2)$
$= 4x + 8$

17. $\frac{1}{2}[x - (-4)] = \frac{1}{2}[x + 4]$
$= \frac{1}{2}x + \frac{1}{2}(4)$
$= \frac{1}{2}x + 2$

18. $\frac{1}{3}[x - (-6)] = \frac{1}{3}[x + 6]$
$= \frac{1}{3}x + \frac{1}{3}(6)$
$= \frac{1}{3}x + 2$

19. $|x| = |-3|$
$= 3$

20. $|y| = |4|$
$= 4$

21. $|5x| = |5(-3)|$
$= |-15|$
$= 15$

22. $-|2z| = -|2(-4.5)|$
$= -|-9|$
$= -(9)$
$= -9$

23. $5|y + z| = 5|4 + (-4.5)|$
$= 5|-0.5|$
$= 5(0.5)$
$= 2.5$

24. $-3|x + y| - |x + z|$
$= -3|-3 + 4| - |-3 + (-4.5)|$
$= -3|1| - |-7.5|$
$= -3(1) - 7.5$
$= -10.5$

2-1 Relations and Functions

Page 60 Check for Understanding

1. Sample answer: $\{(-4, 3), (-2, 3), (1, 5), (-2, 1)\}$; This relation is not a function because the element -2 in the domain is paired with two different elements, 1 and 3, in the range.

2. Sample answer:

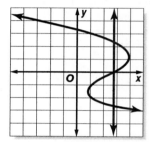

The graph does not represent a function because the vertical line drawn intersects the graph in more than one point.

3. Molly; to find $g(2a)$, replace x with $2a$. Teisha found $2g(a)$, not $g(2a)$.

4. Yes; each member of the domain is paired with exactly one member of the range.

5. Yes; each member of the domain is paired with exactly one member of the range.

6. No; the element 2 in the domain is paired with two different elements, 2 and 3, in the range.

7.

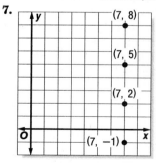

The domain is $\{7\}$. The range is $\{-1, 2, 5, 8\}$. The relation is not a function because the element 7 in the domain is paired with four different elements, $-1, 2, 5,$ and 8, in the range.

8.

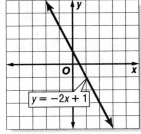

The domain is {3, 4, 6}. The range is {2.5}. The relation is a function because each member of the domain is paired with exactly one member of the range.

9. $y = -2x + 1$

x	y
-1	3
0	1
1	-1
2	-3

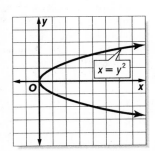

$y = -2x + 1$

Every real number is the x-coordinate of some point on the line, and every real number is the y-coordinate of some point on the line. Thus, the domain and range are both all real numbers. No vertical line intersects the graph in more than one point. The graph passes the vertical line test, so the relation is a function.

10. $x = y^2$

x	y
4	-2
1	-1
0	0
1	1
4	2

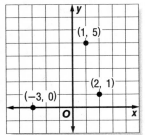

$x = y^2$

Only real numbers greater than or equal to 0 are x-coordinates of points on the graph, so the domain is $\{x \mid x \geq 0\}$. Every real number is the y-coordinate of some point on the graph, so the range is all real numbers. Many vertical lines may be drawn that intersect the graph in more than one point. The relation is not a function since its graph does not pass the vertical line test.

11. $f(x) = x^2 - 3x$
$f(5) = 5^2 - 3(5)$
$ = 25 - 15$
$ = 10$

12. $h(x) = x^3 + 1$
$h(-2) = (-2)^3 + 1$
$ = -8 + 1$
$ = -7$

13. The domain is {70, 72, 88}. The range is {95, 97, 105, 114}.

14. {(88, 97), (70, 114), (88, 95), (72, 105)}

15. **Record High Temperatures**

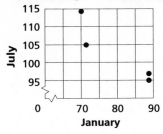

16. No, the domain value 88 is paired with two range values, 95 and 97.

Pages 60–62   Practice and Apply

17. Yes; each element of the domain is paired with exactly one element of the range.

18. No; the element 2 in the domain is paired with two different elements, 3 and 5, in the range.

19. No; the element 0.5 in the domain is paired with two different elements, -3 and 8, in the range.

20. Yes; each element of the domain is paired with exactly one element of the range.

21. Yes; no vertical line intersects the graph in more than one point. The graph passes the vertical line test, so the relation is a function.

22. No; many vertical lines may be drawn that intersect the graph in more than one point. The relation is not a function since its graph does not pass the vertical line test.

23.

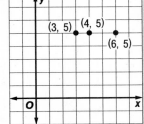

The domain is $\{-3, 1, 2\}$. The range is {0, 1, 5}. Each element of the domain is paired with exactly one element of the range, so the relation is a function.

24.

The domain is {3, 4, 5}. The range is {5}. Each element of the domain is paired with exactly one element of the range, so the relation is a function.

25.

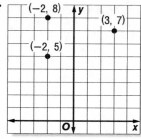

The domain is {−2, 3}. The range is {5, 7, 8}. The relation is not a function because the element −2 in the domain is paired with two different elements, 5 and 8, in the range.

26.

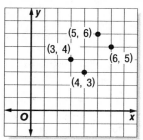

The domain is {3, 4, 5, 6}. The range is {3, 4, 5, 6}. Each element of the domain is paired with exactly one element of the range, so the relation is a function.

27.

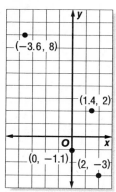

The domain is {−3.6, 0, 1.4, 2}. The range is {−3, −1.1, 2, 8}. Each element of the domain is paired with exactly one element of the range, so the relation is a function.

28.

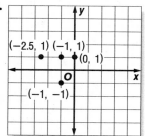

The domain is {−2.5, −1, 0}. The range is {−1, 1}. The relation is not a function because the element −1 in the domain is paired with two different elements, −1 and 1, in the range.

29. $y = -5x$

x	y
−1	5
0	0
1	5

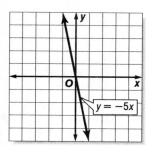

Every real number is the x-coordinate of some point on the line, and every real number is the y-coordinate of some point on the line. Thus, the domain and range are both all real numbers. No vertical line intersects the graph in more than one point. The graph passes the vertical line test, so the relation is a function.

30. $y = 3x$

x	y
−1	−3
0	0
1	3

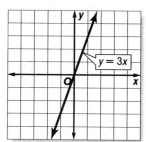

Every real number is the x-coordinate of some point on the line, and every real number is the y-coordinate of some point on the line. Thus, the domain and range are both all real numbers. No vertical line intersects the graph in more than one point. The graph passes the vertical line test, so the relation is a function.

31. $y = 3x - 4$

x	y
0	−4
1	−1
2	2

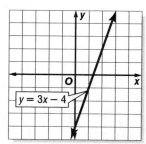

Every real number is the x-coordinate of some point on the line, and every real number is the y-coordinate of some point on the line. Thus, the domain and range are both all real numbers. No vertical line intersects the graph in more than one point. The graph passes the vertical line test, so the relation is a function.

32. $y = 7x - 6$

x	y
0	-6
1	1

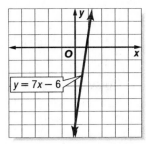

Every real number is the x-coordinate of some point on the line, and every real number is the y-coordinate of some point on the line. Thus, the domain and range are both all real numbers. No vertical line intersects the graph in more than one point. The graph passes the vertical line test, so the relation is a function.

33. $y = x^2$

x	y
-2	4
-1	1
0	0
1	1
2	4

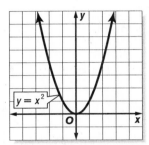

Every real number is the x-coordinate of some point on the graph, so the domain is all real numbers. Only real numbers greater than or equal to 0 are y-coordinates of points on the graph, so the range is $\{y \mid y \geq 0\}$. No vertical line intersects the graph in more than one point. The graph passes the vertical line test, so the relation is a function.

34. $x = 2y^2 - 3$

x	y
5	-2
-1	-1
-3	0
-1	1
5	2

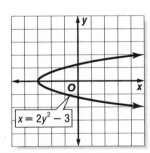

Only real numbers greater than or equal to −3 are x-coordinates of points on the graph, so the domain is $\{x \mid x \geq -3\}$. Every real number is the y-coordinate of some point on the graph, so the range is all real numbers. Many vertical lines may be drawn that intersect the graph in more than one point. The relation is not a function since its graph does not pass the vertical line test.

35.

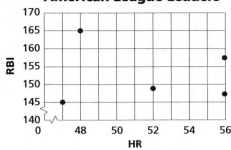

American League Leaders

36. The domain consists of the numbers of home runs: {47, 48, 52, 56}. The range consists of the numbers of runs batted in: {145, 147, 148, 157, 165}.

37. No; the element 56 in the domain is paired with two elements, 147 and 157, in the range.

38. {(1997, 39), (1998, 43), (1999, 48), (2000, 55), (2001, 61), (2002, 52)}

39.

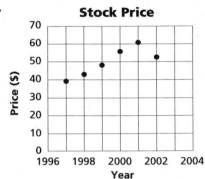

Stock Price

40. The domain consists of the years: {1997, 1998, 1999, 2000, 2001, 2002}. The range consists of the prices: {39, 43, 48, 52, 55, 61}.

41. Yes; each year is paired with exactly one price, so the relation is a function.

42. {(1987, 12), (1989, 13), (1991, 11), (1993, 12), (1995, 9), (1997, 6), (1999, 3)}

43.

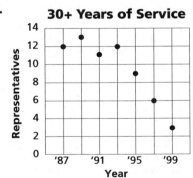

30+ Years of Service

44. The domain consists of the years: {1987, 1989, 1991, 1993, 1995, 1997, 1999}. The range consists of the numbers of representatives: {3, 6, 9, 11, 12, 13}.

45. Yes; the relation is a function since each domain value is paired with only one range value. No; the function is not one-to-one since the range value 12 is paired with two domain values, 1987 and 1993.

46. $f(x) = 3x - 5$
$f(-3) = 3(-3) - 5$
$\qquad = -9 - 5$
$\qquad = -14$

47. $g(x) = x^2 - x$
$g(3) = 3^2 - 3$
$\qquad = 9 - 3$
$\qquad = 6$

48. $g(x) = x^2 - x$
$g\left(\dfrac{1}{3}\right) = \left(\dfrac{1}{3}\right)^2 - \dfrac{1}{3}$
$\qquad = \dfrac{1}{9} - \dfrac{3}{9}$
$\qquad = -\dfrac{2}{9}$

49. $f(x) = 3x - 5$
$f\left(\dfrac{2}{3}\right) = 3\left(\dfrac{2}{3}\right) - 5$
$\qquad = 2 - 5$
$\qquad = -3$

50. $f(x) = 3x - 5$
$f(a) = 3a - 5$

51. $g(x) = x^2 - x$
$g(5n) = (5n)^2 - 5n$
$\qquad = 25n^2 - 5n$

52. $f(x) = -3x + 2$
$f(2) = -3(2) + 2$
$\qquad = -6 + 2$
$\qquad = -4$

53. $g(x) = x^2 - 5$
$g(4) = 4^2 - 5$
$\qquad = 16 - 5$
$\qquad = 11$

54. $C(t) = 15 + 3t$
$C(8) = 15 + 3(8)$
$\qquad = 15 + 24$
$\qquad = 39$
After 8 trips to the music store, Chaz has 39 CDs.

55. Set $x = 3a - 1$ and solve for a.
$\qquad x = 3a - 1$
$\qquad x + 1 = 3a$
$\qquad \dfrac{x+1}{3} = a$
Use $f(3a - 1) = 12a - 7$ and substitute x for $3a - 1$ on the left side and substitute $\dfrac{x+1}{3}$ for a on the right side.
$f(3a - 1) = 12a - 7$
$\qquad f(x) = 12\left(\dfrac{x+1}{3}\right) - 7$
$\qquad f(x) = 4(x + 1) - 7$
$\qquad f(x) = 4x + 4 - 7$
$\qquad f(x) = 4x - 3$

56. Relations and functions can be used to represent biological data. Answers should include the following.
- If the data are written as ordered pairs, then those ordered pairs are a relation.
- The maximum lifetime of an animal is not a function of its average lifetime.

57. B; $f(x) = 2x - 5$
$f(0) = 2(0) - 5$
$\qquad = 0 - 5$
$\qquad = -5$

58. C; $g(x) = x^2$
$g(x + 1) = (x + 1)^2$
$\qquad = x^2 + 2x + 1$

59. The graph consists of disconnected points, so the function is discrete.

60. You can draw the graph without lifting your pencil, so the function is continuous.

61. The graph consists of disconnected points, so the function is discrete.

62. You can draw the graph without lifting your pencil, so the function is continuous.

Page 62   Maintain Your Skills

63. $|y + 1| < 7$
$-7 < y + 1 < 7$
$-8 < \quad y \quad < 6$
The solution set is $\{y \mid -8 < y < 6\}$.

64. $|5 - m| < 1$
$-1 < 5 - m < 1$
$-6 < \quad -m \quad < -4$
$6 > \quad -m \quad > 4$
The solution set is $\{m \mid 4 < m < 6\}$.

65. $x - 5 < 0.1$
$\qquad x < 5.1$
The solution set is $\{x \mid x < 5.1\}$.

66. $27.89 - 25.04 = 2.85$
Javier borrowed \$2.85.

67. $32.67 - 2.85 = 29.82$
Sally still had \$29.82.

68. $3^2(2^2 - 1^2) + 4^2 = 9(4 - 1) + 16$
$\qquad = 9(3) + 16$
$\qquad = 27 + 16$
$\qquad = 43$

69. $3(5a + 6b) + 8(2a - b)$
$= 3(5a) + 3(6b) + 8(2a) - 8(b)$
$= 15a + 18b + 16a - 8b$
$= 15a + 16a + 18b - 8b$
$= (15 + 16)a + (18 - 8)b$
$= 31a + 10b$

70. $\qquad x + 3 = 2$
$x + 3 - 3 = 2 - 3$
$\qquad x = -1$
Check: $x + 3 = 2$
$\qquad -1 + 3 \overset{?}{=} 2$
$\qquad 2 = 2 \checkmark$

71. $\qquad -4 + 2y = 0$
$-4 + 2y + 4 = 0 + 4$
$\qquad 2y = 4$
$\qquad \dfrac{2y}{2} = \dfrac{4}{2}$
$\qquad y = 2$
Check: $-4 + 2y = 0$
$\qquad -4 + 2(2) \overset{?}{=} 0$
$\qquad -4 + 4 \overset{?}{=} 0$
$\qquad 0 = 0 \checkmark$

72.
$$0 = \frac{1}{2}x - 3$$
$$0 + 3 = \frac{1}{2}x - 3 + 3$$
$$3 = \frac{1}{2}x$$
$$2(3) = 2\left(\frac{1}{2}x\right)$$
$$6 = x$$

Check: $0 = \frac{1}{2}x - 3$

$0 \stackrel{?}{=} \frac{1}{2}(6) - 3$

$0 \stackrel{?}{=} 3 - 3$

$0 = 0 ✓$

73.
$$\frac{1}{3}x - 4 = 1$$
$$\frac{1}{3}x - 4 + 4 = 1 + 4$$
$$\frac{1}{3}x = 5$$
$$3\left(\frac{1}{3}x\right) = 3(5)$$
$$x = 15$$

Check: $\frac{1}{3}x - 4 = 1$

$\frac{1}{3}(15) - 4 \stackrel{?}{=} 1$

$5 - 4 \stackrel{?}{=} 1$

$1 = 1 ✓$

2-2 Linear Equations

Pages 65–66 Check for Understanding

1. The function can be written as $f(x) = \frac{1}{2}x + 1$, so it is of the form $f(x) = mx + b$, where $m = \frac{1}{2}$ and $b = 1$.

2. The graph crosses the x-axis at $(5, 0)$, so the x-intercept is 5. The graph crosses the y-axis at $(0, -2)$, so the y-intercept is -2.

3. Sample answer: $x + y = 2$
Let $y = 0$.
$x + y = 2$
$x + 0 = 2$
$x = 2$

The x-intercept is 2.

4. No; the variables have an exponent other than 1.

5. Yes; the function can be written as $h(x) = -2x + 1.1$, so it is of the form $h(x) = mx + b$, where $m = -2$ and $b = 1.1$.

6.
$$y = 3x - 5$$
$$-3x + y = -5$$
$$3x - y = 5$$
$$A = 3, B = -1, C = 5$$

7.
$$4x = 10y + 6$$
$$4x - 10y = 6$$
$$2x - 5y = 3$$
$$A = 2, B = -5, C = 3$$

8.
$$y = \frac{2}{3}x + 1$$
$$-\frac{2}{3}x + y = 1$$
$$2x - 3y = -3$$
$$A = 2, B = -3, C = -3$$

9. x-intercept:
$$y = -3x - 5$$
$$0 = -3x - 5$$
$$5 = -3x$$
$$-\frac{5}{3} = x$$

The x-intercept is $-\frac{5}{3}$.

y-intercept:
$$y = -3x - 5$$
$$y = -3(0) - 5$$
$$y = -5$$

The y-intercept is -5.

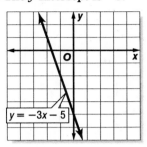

$y = -3x - 5$

10. x-intercept:
$$x - y - 2 = 0$$
$$x - 0 - 2 = 0$$
$$x = 2$$

The x-intercept is 2.

y-intercept:
$$x - y - 2 = 0$$
$$0 - y - 2 = 0$$
$$-2 = y$$

The y-intercept is -2.

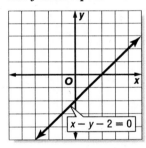

$x - y - 2 = 0$

47

11. x-intercept:
$$3x + 2y = 6$$
$$3x + 2(0) = 6$$
$$3x = 6$$
$$x = 2$$
y-intercept:
$$3x + 2y = 6$$
$$3(0) + 2y = 6$$
$$2y = 6$$
$$y = 3$$
The y-intercept is 3.

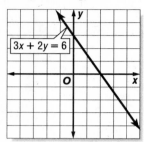

12. x-intercept:
$$4x + 8y = 12$$
$$4x + 8(0) = 12$$
$$4x = 12$$
$$x = 3$$
The x-intercept is 3.
y-intercept:
$$4x + 8y = 12$$
$$4(0) + 8y = 12$$
$$8y = 12$$
$$y = \frac{12}{8} \text{ or } \frac{3}{2}$$
The y-intercept is $\frac{3}{2}$.

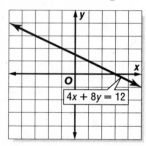

13. $d(x) = 0.8881x$
$d(200) = 0.8881(200)$
$= 177.62$
On March 22, 2001, 200 euros were worth $177.62.

14. $d(x) = 0.8881x$
$500 = 0.8881x$
$\frac{500}{0.8881} = x$
$563.00 \approx x$
On March 22, 2001, $500 was equivalent to about 563 euros.

Pages 66–67 Practice and Apply

15. Yes; this is a linear function because it can be written as $y = -x + 5$. $m = -1, b = 5$

16. No; x appears in a denominator.

17. No; y is inside a square root.

18. No; x has exponents other than 1.

19. No; x appears in a denominator.

20. Yes; this is a linear function because it is written as $f(x) = 6x - 19$. $m = 6, b = -19$

21. No; x has an exponent other than 1.

22. No; x is inside a square root.

23. The equation $x^2 + 5y = 0$ is not linear because x has an exponent other than 1.

24. The function $h(x) = x^3 - x^2 + 3x$ is not linear because x has exponents other than 1.

25. $y = 1440x$
$y = 1440(5)$
$= 7200$
Sound travels 7200 meters in 5 seconds underwater.

26. $y = 343x$
$y = 343(5)$
$= 1715$
Sound travels only 1715 meters in 5 seconds in air, so it travels faster underwater.

27. $y = -3x + 4$
$3x + y = 4$
$A = 3, B = 1, C = 4$

28. $y = 12x$
$-12x + y = 0$
$12x - y = 0$
$A = 12, B = -1, C = 0$

29. $x = 4y - 5$
$x - 4y = -5$
$A = 1, B = -4, C = -5$

30. $x = 7y + 2$
$x - 7y = 2$
$A = 1, B = -7, C = 2$

31. $5y = 10x - 25$
$-10x + 5y = -25$
$2x - y = 5$
$A = 2, B = -1, C = 5$

32. $4x = 8y - 12$
$4x - 8y = -12$
$x - 2y = -3$
$A = 1, B = -2, C = -3$

33. $\frac{1}{2}x + \frac{1}{2}y = 6$
$x + y = 12$
$A = 1, B = 1, C = 12$

34. $\frac{1}{3}x - \frac{1}{3}y = -2$
$x - y = -6$
$A = 1, B = -1, C = -6$

35. $0.5x = 3$
$x = 6$
$A = 1, B = 0, C = 6$

36. $0.25y = 10$
$y = 40$
$A = 0, B = 1, C = 40$

37. $\frac{5}{6}x + \frac{1}{15}y = \frac{3}{10}$

$30\left(\frac{5}{6}x + \frac{1}{15}y\right) = 30\left(\frac{3}{10}\right)$

$25x + 2y = 9$

$A = 25, B = 2, C = 9$

38. $0.25x = 0.1 + 0.2y$

$0.25x - 0.2y = 0.1$

$20(0.25x - 0.2y) = 20(0.1)$

$5x - 4y = 2$

$A = 5, B = -4, C = 2$

39. x-intercept:

$5x + 3y = 15$

$5x + 3(0) = 15$

$5x = 15$

$x = 3$

The x-intercept is 3.

y-intercept:

$5x + 3y = 15$

$5(0) + 3y = 15$

$3y = 15$

$y = 5$

The y-intercept is 5.

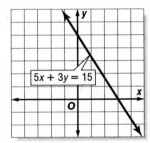

40. x-intercept:

$2x - 6y = 12$

$2x - 6(0) = 12$

$2x = 12$

$x = 6$

The x-intercept is 6.

y-intercept:

$2x - 6y = 12$

$2(0) - 6y = 12$

$-6y = 12$

$y = -2$

The y-intercept is -2.

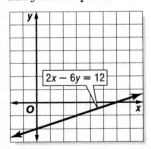

41. x-intercept:

$3x - 4y - 10 = 0$

$3x - 4(0) - 10 = 0$

$3x = 10$

$x = \frac{10}{3}$

The x-intercept is $\frac{10}{3}$.

y-intercept:

$3x - 4y - 10 = 0$

$3(0) - 4y - +10 = 0$

$-4y = 10$

$y = \frac{10}{-4}$ or $-\frac{5}{2}$

The y-intercept is $-\frac{5}{2}$.

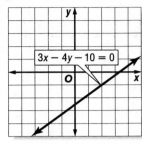

42. x-intercept:

$2x + 5y - 10 = 0$

$2x + 5(0) - 10 = 0$

$2x = 10$

$x = 5$

The x-intercept is 5.

y-intercept:

$2x + 5y - 10 = 0$

$2(0) + 5y - 10 = 0$

$5y = 10$

$y = 2$

The y-intercept is 2.

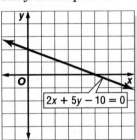

Chapter 2

43. x-intercept:

$y = x$

$0 = x$

The x-intercept is 0.

y-intercept:

$y = x$

$y = 0$

The y-intercept is 0.

Since the intercepts are the same point, find another point to graph the line.

Let $x = 1$.

$y = x$

$y = 1$

The point $(1, 1)$ is also on the graph.

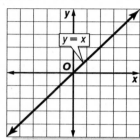

44. x-intercept:

$y = 4x - 2$

$0 = 4x - 2$

$-4x = -2$

$x = \frac{-2}{-4}$ or $\frac{1}{2}$

The x-intercept is $\frac{1}{2}$.

y-intercept:

$y = 4x - 2$

$y = 4(0) - 2$

$y = -2$

The y-intercept is -2.

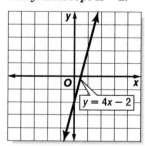

45. x-intercept:

$y = -2$

$0 = -2$, false

There is no x-intercept.

y-intercept:

$y = -2$

The y-intercept is -2.

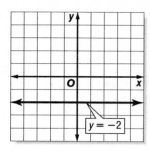

46. x-intercept:

$y = 4$

$0 = 4$, false

There is no x-intercept.

y-intercept:

$y = 4$

The y-intercept is 4.

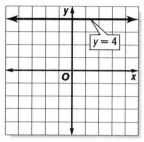

47. x-intercept:

$x = 8$

The x-intercept is 8.

y-intercept:

$x = 8$

$0 = 8$, false

There is no y-intercept.

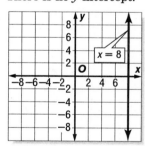

48. x-intercept:

$x = 1$

The x-intercept is 1.

y-intercept:

$x = 1$

$0 = 1$, false

There is no y-intercept.

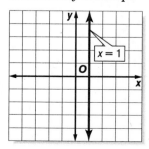

49. x-intercept:
$$f(x) = 4x - 1$$
$$0 = 4x - 1$$
$$1 = 4x$$
$$\frac{1}{4} = x$$

The x-intercept is $\frac{1}{4}$.

y-intercept:
$$f(x) = 4x - 1$$
$$f(0) = 4(0) - 1$$
$$= -1$$

The y-intercept is -1.

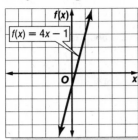

50. x-intercept:
$$g(x) = 0.5x - 3$$
$$0 = 0.5x - 3$$
$$3 = 0.5x$$
$$6 = x$$

The x-intercept is 6.

y-intercept:
$$g(x) = 0.5x - 3$$
$$g(0) = 0.5(0) - 3$$
$$= -3$$

The y-intercept is -3.

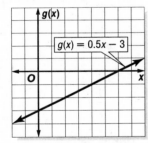

51.

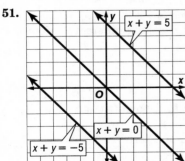

The lines are parallel but have different y-intercepts.

52. Sample answer: $x + y = 2$

53. $T(d) = 35d + 20$
$$T(2) = 35(2) + 20$$
$$= 70 + 20$$
$$= 90$$

At a depth of 2 kilometers, the temperature is 90°C.

54. $T(d) = 35d + 20$
$$160 = 35d + 20$$
$$140 = 35d$$
$$4 = d$$

The temperature is 160°C at a depth of 4 kilometers.

55. Use the points (2, 90) and (4, 160) to graph the equation.

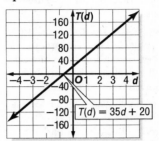

56. Let b represent the number of beverages and c the number of pieces of candy.
$$1.75b + 1.5c = 525$$

57. b-intercept:
$$1.75b + 1.5c = 525$$
$$1.75b + 1.5(0) = 525$$
$$1.75b = 525$$
$$b = 300$$

c-intercept:
$$1.75b + 1.5c = 525$$
$$1.75(0) + 1.5c = 525$$
$$1.5c = 525$$
$$c = 350$$

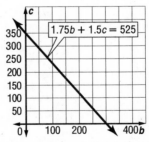

58. Yes; no vertical line intersects the graph in more than one point. Thus, by the vertical line test, the graph represents a function.

59. $1.75b + 1.5c = 1.75(100) + 1.5(200)$
$$= 175 + 300$$
$$= 475$$

No; the boosters will not meet their goal of $525 if they sell 100 beverages and 200 pieces of candy.

60. The shaded region is a trapezoid with bases of length 2 and 5 and height 3.

$$A = \frac{1}{2}h(b_1 + b_2)$$
$$= \frac{1}{2}(3)(2 + 5)$$
$$= \frac{21}{2}$$

The area of the shaded region is $\frac{21}{2}$ square units.

61. A linear equation can be used to relate the amounts of time that a student spends on each of two subjects if the total amount of time is fixed. Answers should include the following.

- x and y must be nonnegative because Lolita cannot spend a negative amount of time studying a subject.
- The intercepts represent Lolita spending all of her time on one subject. The x-intercept represents her spending all of her time on math, and the y-intercept represents her spending all of her time on chemistry.

62. B; We can eliminate answer choice A because x has an exponent other than 1. We can eliminate answer choices C and D because in each of these, x is inside a square root. This leaves answer choice B.

63. B;
$$10 - x = 2y$$
$$10 - 0 = 2y$$
$$10 = 2y$$
$$5 = y$$

Page 67   Maintain Your Skills

64. The domain is $\{-1, 1, 2, 4\}$. The range is $\{-4, 3, 5\}$. The relation is a function since each member of the domain is paired with only one member of the range.

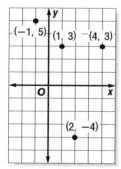

65. The domain is $\{0, 1, 2\}$. The range is $\{-1, 0, 2, 3\}$. The relation is not a function since the element 1 in the domain is paired with two elements, 0 and 3, in the range.

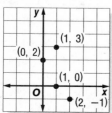

66. $-2 < 3x + 1 < 7$
$$-3 < \quad 3x \quad < 6$$
$$-1 < \quad x \quad < 2$$

The solution set is $\{x \mid -1 < x < 2\}$.

67. $|x + 4| > 2$

$\quad x + 4 > 2 \quad$ or $\quad x + 4 < -2$
$\quad\quad x > -2 \quad\quad\quad\quad x < -6$

The solution set is $\{x \mid x < -6 \text{ or } x > -2\}$.

68. Let p be the price of the book before tax.
$$p + 0.06p = 8.43$$
$$(1 + 0.06)p = 8.43$$
$$1.06p = 8.43$$
$$p \approx 7.95$$

Before tax, the price of the book is \$7.95.

69. $(9s - 4) - 3(2s - 6) = 9s - 4 - 6s + 18$
$$= 9s - 6s - 4 + 18$$
$$= 3s + 14$$

70. $[19 - (8 - 1)] \div 3 = [19 - 7] \div 3$
$$= 12 \div 3$$
$$= 4$$

71. $\frac{1}{3}$

72. $-\frac{1}{4}$

73. 2

74. $-\frac{3}{2}$

75. -5

76. $3\frac{3}{4} = \frac{15}{4}$

The reciprocal of $\frac{15}{4}$ is $\frac{4}{15}$.

77. $2.5 = \frac{5}{2}$

The reciprocal of $\frac{5}{2}$ is $\frac{2}{5}$ or 0.4.

78. $-1.25 = -\frac{5}{4}$

The reciprocal of $-\frac{5}{4}$ is $-\frac{4}{5}$ or -0.8.

2-3   Slope

Page 70   Graphing Calculator Investigation

1. The parent function is $y = 3x$. The graphs are parallel lines, but they have different y-intercepts.

2. Each line has slope 3.

3. Sample answer: $y = 3x - 4$

Pages 71–72   Check for Understanding

1. Sample answer: $y = 1$
   The graph of $y = 1$ is a horizontal; a horizontal line has slope 0.

2. Sometimes; the slope of a vertical line is undefined.

3. Luisa is correct; Mark did not subtract in a consistent manner when using the slope formula. If $y_2 = 5$ and $y_1 = 4$, then x_2 must be -1 and x_1 must be 2, not vice versa.

4. $m = \dfrac{y_2 - y_1}{x_2 - x_1}$

$= \dfrac{1 - 1}{3 - 1}$

$= \dfrac{0}{2}$

$= 0$

5. $m = \dfrac{y_2 - y_1}{x_2 - x_1}$

$= \dfrac{-2 - 0}{3 - (-1)}$

$= \dfrac{-2}{4}$

$= -\dfrac{1}{2}$

6. $m = \dfrac{y_2 - y_1}{x_2 - x_1}$

$= \dfrac{2 - 4}{1 - 3}$

$= \dfrac{-2}{-2}$

$= 1$

7. Graph the ordered pair $(2, -1)$. Then go down 3 units and right 1 unit. Plot the new point $(3, -4)$.

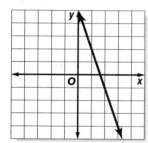

8. Graph the ordered pair $(-3, -4)$. Then go up 3 units and right 2 units. Plot the new point $(-1, -1)$.

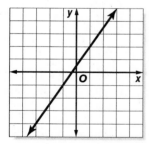

9. Use the intercepts to graph $6y - 10x = 30$. The x-intercept is -3, and the y-intercept is 5. The line rises 5 units for every 3 units it moves to the right, so its slope is $\dfrac{5}{3}$. The slope of the parallel line is also $\dfrac{5}{3}$.

Now use the slope and the point at $(0, 3)$ to graph the line.

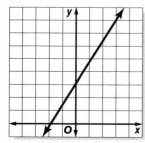

10. Use the intercepts to graph $3x - 2y = 6$. The x-intercept is 2, and the y-intercept is -3. The line rises 3 units for every 2 units it moves to the right, so its slope is $\dfrac{3}{2}$. The slope of the perpendicular line is the opposite reciprocal of $\dfrac{3}{2}$, or $-\dfrac{2}{3}$.

Now use the slope and the point at $(4, -2)$ to graph the line.

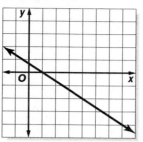

11. Use the intercepts to graph $5x - 3y - 3 = 0$. The x-intercept is $\dfrac{3}{5}$, and the y-intercept is -1.

The line rises 1 unit for every $\dfrac{3}{5}$ unit it moves to the right, so its slope is $\dfrac{1}{\frac{3}{5}}$ or $\dfrac{5}{3}$. The slope of the perpendicular line is the opposite reciprocal of $\dfrac{5}{3}$, or $-\dfrac{3}{5}$.

Now use the slope and the point at $(-1, 5)$ to graph the line.

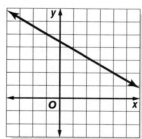

12. Use the slope formula with the ordered pairs $(8, 36)$ and $(10, 47)$.

$m = \dfrac{y_2 - y_1}{x_2 - x_1}$

$= \dfrac{47 - 36}{10 - 8}$

$= \dfrac{11}{2}$

$= 5.5$

Between 8:00 A.M. and 10:00 A.M., the temperature changed at an average rate of 5.5°F per hour.

13. Use the slope formula with the ordered pairs $(12, 55)$ and $(16, 60)$.

$m = \dfrac{y_2 - y_1}{x_2 - x_1}$

$= \dfrac{60 - 55}{16 - 12}$

$= \dfrac{5}{4}$

$= 1.25$

Between 12:00 P.M. and 4:00 P.M., the temperature changed at an average rate of 1.25°F per hour.

14. Use the slope formula to find the average rate of change during each 2-hour time period.

Time Period	Rate of Change
8:00–10:00	5.5° per hour
10:00–12:00	4° per hour
12:00–2:00	1.5° per hour
2:00–4:00	1° per hour

The least rate of change occurred in the 2:00 P.M. − 4:00 P.M. time period.

Pages 72–74   Practice and Apply

15. $m = \dfrac{y_2 - y_1}{x_2 - x_1}$

$= \dfrac{-4 - 1}{8 - 6}$

$= \dfrac{-5}{2}$ or $-\dfrac{5}{2}$

16. $m = \dfrac{y_2 - y_1}{x_2 - x_1}$

$= \dfrac{-5 - 8}{5 - 6}$

$= \dfrac{-13}{-1}$ or 13

17. $m = \dfrac{y_2 - y_1}{x_2 - x_1}$

$= \dfrac{1 - (-5)}{4 - (-6)}$

$= \dfrac{6}{10}$ or $\dfrac{3}{5}$

18. $m = \dfrac{y_2 - y_1}{x_2 - x_1}$

$= \dfrac{1 - (-7)}{4 - 2}$

$= \dfrac{8}{2}$ or 4

19. $m = \dfrac{y_2 - y_1}{x_2 - x_1}$

$= \dfrac{8 - 8}{1 - 7}$

$= \dfrac{0}{-6}$ or 0

20. $m = \dfrac{y_2 - y_1}{x_2 - x_1}$

$= \dfrac{-5 - (-3)}{0 - (-2)}$

$= \dfrac{-2}{2}$ or -1

21. $m = \dfrac{y_2 - y_1}{x_2 - x_1}$

$= \dfrac{-9 - 3}{1 - 2.5}$

$= \dfrac{-12}{-1.5}$ or 8

22. $m = \dfrac{y_2 - y_1}{x_2 - x_1}$

$= \dfrac{4.5 - (-1.5)}{4 - 4}$

$= \dfrac{6}{0}$

undefined

23. $m = \dfrac{y_2 - y_1}{x_2 - x_1}$

$= \dfrac{\frac{2}{3} - \left(-\frac{1}{3}\right)}{\frac{1}{4} - \frac{1}{2}}$

$= \dfrac{1}{-\frac{1}{4}}$ or -4

24. $m = \dfrac{y_2 - y_1}{x_2 - x_1}$

$= \dfrac{\frac{1}{4} - \frac{2}{3}}{\frac{5}{6} - \frac{1}{2}}$

$= \dfrac{-\frac{5}{12}}{\frac{1}{3}}$ or $-\dfrac{5}{4}$

25. $m = \dfrac{y_2 - y_1}{x_2 - x_1}$

$= \dfrac{-2 - 2}{a - a}$

$= \dfrac{-4}{0}$

undefined

26. $m = \dfrac{y_2 - y_1}{x_2 - x_1}$

$= \dfrac{b - b}{-5 - 3}$

$= \dfrac{0}{-8}$

$= 0$

27. $m = \dfrac{y_2 - y_1}{x_2 - x_1}$

$\dfrac{1}{3} = \dfrac{2 - r}{9 - 6}$

$\dfrac{1}{3} = \dfrac{2 - r}{3}$

$1 = 2 - r$

$-1 = -r$

$1 = r$

28. $m = \dfrac{y_2 - y_1}{x_2 - x_1}$

$2 = \dfrac{3 - r}{2 - 5}$

$2 = \dfrac{3 - r}{-3}$

$-6 = 3 - r$

$-9 = -r$

$9 = r$

29. The pyramid reaches its maximum height over a horizontal distance of 350 feet.

$m = \dfrac{210}{350}$

$= \dfrac{3}{5}$ or 0.6

30. The pyramid reaches its maximum height over a horizontal distance of 378 feet.

$m = \dfrac{481}{378}$

≈ 1.3

31. Graph the ordered pair (2, 6). Then go up 2 units and right 3 units. Plot the new point (5, 8).

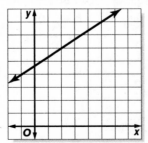

32. Graph the ordered pair $(-3, -1)$. Then go down 1 unit and right 5 units. Plot the new point $(2, -2)$.

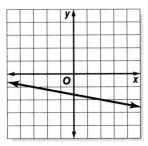

33. Graph the ordered pair $(3, -4)$. Then go up 2 units and right 1 unit. Plot the new point $(4, -2)$.

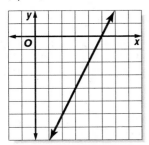

34. Graph the ordered pair $(1, 2)$. Then go down 3 units and right 1 unit. Plot the new point $(2, -1)$.

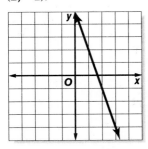

35. Graph the ordered pair $(6, 2)$. Since the slope is 0, the graph is the horizontal line through this point.

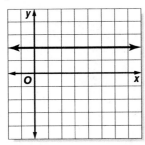

36. Graph the ordered pair $(-2, -3)$. Since the slope is undefined, the graph is the vertical line through this point.

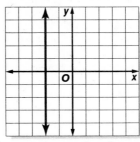

37. From the graph, it appears that about 350 million CDs were shipped in 1991 and about 960 million were shipped in 2000. Use the slope formula and the ordered pairs (1991, 350) and (2000, 960).

$$m = \frac{y_2 - y_1}{x_2 - x_1}$$
$$= \frac{960 - 350}{2000 - 1991}$$
$$= \frac{610}{9} \text{ or about } 68$$

From 1999 to 2000, the number of CDs shipped changed an average of about 68 million per year.

38. From the graph, it appears that about 370 million cassette tapes were shipped in 1991 and about 80 million were shipped in 2000. Use the slope formula and the ordered pairs (1991, 370) and (2000, 80).

$$m = \frac{y_2 - y_1}{x_2 - x_1}$$
$$= \frac{80 - 370}{2000 - 1991}$$
$$= \frac{-290}{9} \text{ or about } -32$$

From 1999 to 2000, the number of cassette tapes shipped changed an average of about -32 million per year.

39. The number of cassette tapes shipped has been decreasing.

40. Use the slope formula and the ordered pairs $(1, 55)$ and $(3, 165)$.

$$m = \frac{y_2 - y_1}{x_2 - x_1}$$
$$= \frac{165 - 55}{3 - 1}$$
$$= \frac{110}{2} \text{ or } 55$$

Between 1 and 3 hours after leaving home, the Wellmans traveled an average of 55 miles per hour.

41. Use the slope formula and the ordered pairs $(0, 0)$ and $(5, 225)$.

$$m = \frac{y_2 - y_1}{x_2 - x_1}$$
$$= \frac{225 - 0}{5 - 0}$$
$$= \frac{225}{5} \text{ or } 45$$

Between 0 and 5 hours after leaving home, the Wellmans traveled an average of 45 miles per hour.

42. speed or velocity

43. The parallel line also has slope -1.
Use the slope and the point at $(-2, 2)$ to graph the line.

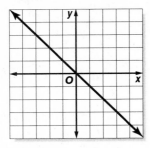

44. The slope of the perpendicular line is the opposite reciprocal of $-\frac{3}{2}$, or $\frac{2}{3}$.

Now use the slope and the point at $(-4, 1)$ to graph the line.

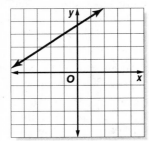

45. The graph of $y = 3$ is a horizontal line; a line perpendicular to it is vertical.
Draw the vertical line through the point $(3, 3)$.

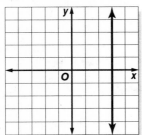

46. The graph of $x = 4$ is a vertical line; a line parallel to it is also vertical.
Draw the vertical line through the point $(2, -5)$.

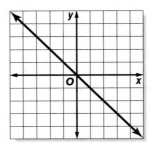

47. Use the intercepts to graph $2x + 3y = 6$. The x-intercept is 3, and the y-intercept is 2.
The line falls 2 units for every 3 units it moves to the right, so its slope is $-\frac{2}{3}$. The slope of the parallel line is also $-\frac{2}{3}$.

Now use the slope and the point at $(2, -1)$ to graph the line.

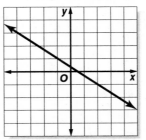

48. Use the intercepts to graph $x + y = 10$. The x-intercept is 10, and the y-intercept is 10.
The line falls 10 units for every 10 units it moves to the right, so its slope is -1. The slope of the parallel line is also -1.
Now use the slope and the point at $(0, 0)$ to graph the line.

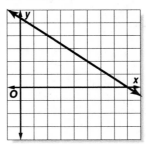

49. Use the intercepts to graph $3x - 2y = 24$. The x-intercept is 8, and the y-intercept is -12.
The line rises 12 units for every 8 units it moves to the right, so its slope is $\frac{3}{2}$. The slope of the perpendicular line is the opposite reciprocal of $\frac{3}{2}$, or $-\frac{2}{3}$.

Now use the slope and the point at $(8, 0)$ to graph the line.

50. Use the intercepts to graph $2x + 5y = 10$. The x-intercept is 5, and the y-intercept is 2.
The line falls 2 units for every 5 units it moves to the right, so its slope is $-\frac{2}{5}$. The slope of the perpendicular line is the opposite reciprocal of $-\frac{2}{5}$, or $\frac{5}{2}$.
Now use the slope and the point at $(0, 2)$ to graph the line.

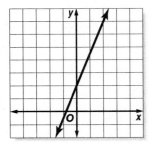

51. Find the slope of each side of the quadrilateral.

slope of $\overline{AB}$: $m = \frac{1 - (-1)}{1 - (-2)}$ or $\frac{2}{3}$

slope of $\overline{BC}$: $m = \frac{-2 - 1}{3 - 1}$ or $-\frac{3}{2}$

slope of $\overline{CD}$: $m = \frac{-4 - (-2)}{0 - 3}$ or $\frac{2}{3}$

slope of $\overline{AD}$: $m = \frac{-4 - (-1)}{0 - (-2)}$ or $-\frac{3}{2}$

The slopes show that adjacent sides are perpendicular. Thus, quadrilateral $ABCD$ is a rectangle.

52. Find the slope of each line.

Two points on the line $ax + 3y = 9$ are $\left(\frac{9}{a}, 0\right)$ and $(0, 3)$.

slope of $ax + 3y = 9$: $m = \frac{3 - 0}{0 - \frac{9}{a}}$ or $-\frac{a}{3}$

Two points on the line $3x + y = -4$ are $\left(-\frac{4}{3}, 0\right)$ and $(0, -4)$.

slope of $3x + y = -4$: $m = \frac{-4 - 0}{0 - \left(-\frac{4}{3}\right)}$ or -3

Since the graphs are perpendicular, the slopes are opposite reciprocals.

$-\frac{a}{3} = -\frac{1}{(-3)}$

$a = -1$

53. The grade or steepness of a road can be interpreted mathematically as a slope. Answers should include the following.
- Think of the diagram at the beginning of the lesson as being in a coordinate plane. Then the rise is a change in y-coordinates, and the hoizontal distance is a change in x-coordinates. Thus, the grade is a slope expressed as a percent.

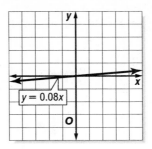

54. D; The line rises 3 units for every 2 units it moves to the right. The slope is $\frac{3}{2}$.

55. D; The opposite reciprocal of $-\frac{1}{2}$ is 2.

56. The graphs have the same y-intercept. As the slopes increase, the lines get steeper.

57. The graphs have the same y-intercept. As the slopes increase in absolute value, the lines get steeper.

Page 74 Maintain Your Skills

58. x-intercept:

$-2x + 5y = 20$

$-2x + 5(0) = 20$

$-2x = 20$

$x = -10$

y-intercept:

$-2x + 5y = 20$

$-2(0) + 5y = 20$

$5y = 20$

$y = 4$

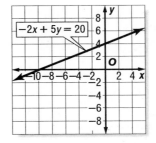

59. x-intercept:
$$4x - 3y + 8 = 0$$
$$4x - 3(0) + 8 = 0$$
$$4x = -8$$
$$x = -2$$
y-intercept:
$$4x - 3y + 8 = 0$$
$$4(0) - 3y + 8 = 0$$
$$-3y = -8$$
$$y = \frac{8}{3}$$

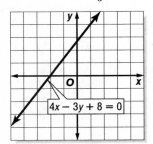

60. x-intercept:
$$y = 7x$$
$$0 = 7x$$
$$0 = x$$
y-intercept:
$$y = 7x$$
$$y = 7(0)$$
$$y = 0$$
Since the intercepts are the same point, find another point to graph the line.
Let $x = 1$.
$$y = 7x$$
$$y = 7(1) \text{ or } 7$$

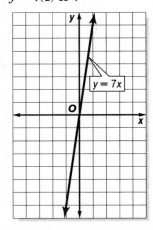

61. $f(x) = 3x - 4$
$$f(-1) = 3(-1) - 4$$
$$= -3 - 4$$
$$= -7$$

62. $f(x) = 3x - 4$
$$f(3) = 3(3) - 4$$
$$= 9 - 4$$
$$= 5$$

63. $f(x) = 3x - 4$
$$f\left(\frac{1}{2}\right) = 3\left(\frac{1}{2}\right) - 4$$
$$= \frac{3}{2} - \frac{8}{2}$$
$$= -\frac{5}{2}$$

64. $f(x) = 3x - 4$
$$f(a) = 3a - 4$$

65.
$$5 < 2x + 7 < 13$$
$$-2 < 2x < 6$$
$$-1 < x < 3$$
The solution set is $\{x \mid -1 < x < 3\}$.

66.
$$2z + 5 \geq 1475$$
$$2z \geq 1470$$
$$z \geq 735$$
The solution set is $\{z \mid z \geq 735\}$.

67. Let x represent the number of true-false questions Marco must answer correctly.
$$4(14) + 3x \geq 80$$
$$56 + 3x \geq 80$$
$$3x \geq 24$$
$$x \geq 8$$
He must answer at least 8 correctly.

68. $\frac{1}{3}(15a + 9b) - \frac{1}{7}(28b - 84a)$
$$= \frac{1}{3}(15a) + \frac{1}{3}(9b) - \frac{1}{7}(28b) - \frac{1}{7}(-84a)$$
$$= 5a + 3b - 4b + 12a$$
$$= 5a + 12a + 3b - 4b$$
$$= 17a - b$$

69. $3 + (21 \div 7) \times 8 \div 4 = 3 + 3 \times 8 \div 4$
$$= 3 + 24 \div 4$$
$$= 3 + 6$$
$$= 9$$

70. $x + y = 9$
$$y = 9 - x$$

71. $4x + y = 2$
$$y = -4x + 2$$

72. $-3x - y + 7 = 0$
$$-y = 3x - 7$$
$$y = -3x + 7$$

73. $5x - 2y - 1 = 0$
$$-2y = -5x + 1$$
$$y = \frac{5}{2}x - \frac{1}{2}$$

74. $3x - 5y + 4 = 0$
$$-5y = -3x - 4$$
$$y = \frac{3}{5}x + \frac{4}{5}$$

75. $2x + 3y - 11 = 0$
$$3y = -2x + 11$$
$$y = -\frac{2}{3}x + \frac{11}{3}$$

Page 74   Practice Quiz 1

1. domain : $\{-7, -3, 0, 2\}$
range : $\{-2, 1, 2, 4, 5\}$

2. $f(x) = 100x - 5x^2$
$$f(15) = 100(15) - 5(15)^2$$
$$= 100(15) - 5(225)$$
$$= 1500 - 1125$$
$$= 375$$

3.
$$y = -6x + 4$$
$$6x + y = 4$$

4. x-intercept:
$$3x + 5y = 30$$
$$3x + 5(0) = 30$$
$$3x = 30$$
$$x = 10$$
y-intercept:
$$3x + 5y = 30$$
$$3(0) + 5y = 30$$
$$5y = 30$$
$$y = 6$$

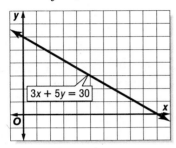

5. Use the intercepts to graph $2x + 5y = 10$. The x-intercept is 5, and the y-intercept is 2.

The line falls 2 units for every 5 units it moves to the right, so its slope is $-\frac{2}{5}$. The slope of the parallel line is also $-\frac{2}{5}$.

Now use the slope and the point at $(4, -3)$ to graph the line.

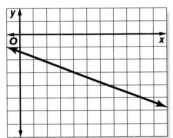

2-4 Writing Linear Equations

Page 78 Check for Understanding

1. Sample answer: $y = 3x + 2$

2. The equation $y = 6x$ can be written as $y = 6x + 0$, where $m = 6$ and $b = 0$. The slope is 6, and the y-intercept is 0.

3. Solve the equation for y to get $y = \frac{3}{5}x - \frac{2}{5}$. The slope of the line is $\frac{3}{5}$. The slope of a parallel line is the same.

4. The equation is written in slope-intercept form. The slope is 2, and the y-intercept is -5.

5. Write the equation in slope-intercept form.
$$3x + 2y - 10 = 0$$
$$2y = -3x + 10$$
$$y = -\frac{3}{2}x + 5$$
The slope is $-\frac{3}{2}$, and the y-intercept is 5.

6. First find b.
$$y = mx + b$$
$$4 = 0.5(6) + b$$
$$4 = 3 + b$$
$$1 = b$$
Now write the equation.
$$y = mx + b$$
$$y = 0.5x + 1$$

7. First find b.
$$y = mx + b$$
$$\frac{1}{2} = -\frac{3}{4}(2) + b$$
$$\frac{1}{2} = -\frac{3}{2} + b$$
$$2 = b$$
Now write the equation.
$$y = mx + b$$
$$y = -\frac{3}{4}x + 2$$

8. First find the slope.
$$m = \frac{y_2 - y_1}{x_2 - x_1}$$
$$= \frac{-4 - 1}{8 - 6}$$
$$= \frac{-5}{2} \text{ or } -\frac{5}{2}$$
Then use the point-slope form.
$$y - y_1 = m(x - x_1)$$
$$y - 1 = -\frac{5}{2}(x - 6)$$
$$y - 1 = -\frac{5}{2}x + 15$$
$$y = -\frac{5}{2}x + 16$$

9. First find the slope.
$$m = \frac{y_2 - y_1}{x_2 - x_1}$$
$$= \frac{2 - 5}{2 - (-3)}$$
$$= \frac{-3}{5} \text{ or } -\frac{3}{5}$$
Then use the point-slope form.
$$y - y_1 = m(x - x_1)$$
$$y - 5 = -\frac{3}{5}[x - (-3)]$$
$$y - 5 = -\frac{3}{5}x - \frac{9}{5}$$
$$y = -\frac{3}{5}x + \frac{16}{5}$$

10. The slope of $y = x - 2$ is 1. The slope of the perpendicular line is the opposite reciprocal of 1, or -1.

The slope is -1, and the y-intercept is -2. Use the slope-intercept form.
$$y = mx + b$$
$$y = -x - 2$$

59

11. First find the slope
$$m = \frac{y_2 - y_1}{x_2 - x_1}$$
$$= \frac{7 - 2}{0 - (-4)}$$
$$= \frac{5}{4}$$

The slope is $\frac{5}{4}$, and the y-intercept is 7. Use the slope-intercept form.
$$y = mx + b$$
$$y = \frac{5}{4}x + 7$$

12. B; First find the slope.
$$m = \frac{y_2 - y_1}{x_2 - x_1}$$
$$= \frac{-1 - (-4)}{-3 - 2}$$
$$= -\frac{3}{5}$$

Now find the y-intercept.
$$y = mx + b$$
$$-4 = -\frac{3}{5}(2) + b$$
$$-4 = -\frac{6}{5} + b$$
$$-\frac{14}{5} = b$$

The equation is $y = -\frac{3}{5}x - \frac{14}{5}$.

Pages 78–80   Practice and Apply

13. The equation is written in slope-intercept form.
The slope is $-\frac{2}{3}$, and the y-intercept is -4.

14. The equation $y = \frac{3}{4}x$ can be written as $y = \frac{3}{4}x + 0$.
The slope is $\frac{3}{4}$, and the y-intercept is 0.

15. Write the equation in slope-intercept form.
$$2x - 4y = 10$$
$$-4y = -2x + 10$$
$$y = \frac{1}{2}x - \frac{5}{2}$$

The slope is $\frac{1}{2}$, and the y-intercept is $-\frac{5}{2}$.

16. Write the equation in slope-intercept form.
$$3x + 5y - 30 = 0$$
$$5y = -3x + 30$$
$$y = -\frac{3}{5}x + 6$$

The slope is $-\frac{3}{5}$, and the y-intercept is 6.

17. The graph of $x = 7$ is a vertical line. The slope is undefined. There is no y-intercept.

18. Write the equation in slope-intercept form.
$$cx + y = d$$
$$y = -cx + d$$
The slope is $-c$, and the y-intercept is d.

19. First find the slope.
$$m = \frac{y_2 - y_1}{x_2 - x_1}$$
$$= \frac{2 - 0}{2.5 - 0}$$
$$= \frac{2}{2.5}$$
$$= 0.8$$

The slope is 0.8, and the y-intercept is 0. Use the slope-intercept form.
$$y = mx + b$$
$$y = 0.8x + 0$$
$$y = 0.8x$$

20. First find the slope.
$$m = \frac{y_2 - y_1}{x_2 - x_1}$$
$$= \frac{3 - (-2)}{4 - 7}$$
$$= -\frac{5}{3}$$

Then use the point-slope form.
$$y - y_1 = m(x - x_1)$$
$$y - (-2) = -\frac{5}{3}(x - 7)$$
$$y + 2 = -\frac{5}{3}x + \frac{35}{3}$$
$$y = -\frac{5}{3}x + \frac{29}{3}$$

21. The line is horizontal, so the slope is 0. The y-intercept is -4. Use the slope-intercept form.
$$y = mx + b$$
$$y = 0x - 4$$
$$y = -4$$

22. The line is horizontal, so the slope is 0. The y-intercept is 2. Use the slope-intercept form.
$$y = mx + b$$
$$y = 0x + 2$$
$$y = 2$$

23. Use the slope-intercept form.
$$y = mx + b$$
$$y = 3x - 6$$

24. Use the slope-intercept form.
$$y = mx + b$$
$$y = 0.25x + 4$$

25. Use the point-slope form.
$$y - y_1 = m(x - x_1)$$
$$y - 3 = -\frac{1}{2}(x - 1)$$
$$y - 3 = -\frac{1}{2}x + \frac{1}{2}$$
$$y = -\frac{1}{2}x + \frac{7}{2}$$

26. Use the point-slope form.
$$y - y_1 = m(x - x_1)$$
$$y - 1 = \frac{3}{2}[x - (-5)]$$
$$y - 1 = \frac{3}{2}x + \frac{15}{2}$$
$$y = \frac{3}{2}x + \frac{17}{2}$$

27. Use the point-slope form.
$$y - y_1 = m(x - x_1)$$
$$y - (-3) = -0.5(x - 2)$$
$$y + 3 = -0.5x + 1$$
$$y = -0.5x - 2$$

28. Use the slope-intercept form.
$$y = mx + b$$
$$y = 4x + 0$$
$$y = 4x$$

29. First find the slope.
$$m = \frac{y_2 - y_1}{x_2 - x_1}$$
$$= \frac{1 - 5}{3 - (-2)}$$
$$= \frac{-4}{5} \text{ or } -\frac{4}{5}$$
Now use the point-slope form.
$$y - y_1 = m(x - x_1)$$
$$y - 5 = -\frac{4}{5}[x - (-2)]$$
$$y - 5 = -\frac{4}{5}x - \frac{8}{5}$$
$$y = -\frac{4}{5}x + \frac{17}{5}$$

30. First find the slope.
$$m = \frac{y_2 - y_1}{x_2 - x_1}$$
$$= \frac{8 - 1}{7 - 7}$$
$$= \frac{7}{0}$$
The slope is undefined; this is a vertical line with equation $x = 7$. This equation has no slope-intercept form.

31. First find the slope.
$$m = \frac{y_2 - y_1}{x_2 - x_1}$$
$$= \frac{0 - 0}{3 - (-4)}$$
$$= 0$$
Use the point-slope form.
$$y - y_1 = m(x - x_1)$$
$$y - 0 = 0[x - (-4)]$$
$$y = 0$$

32. First find the slope.
$$m = \frac{y_2 - y_1}{x_2 - x_1}$$
$$= \frac{0 - (-3)}{0 - (-2)}$$
$$= \frac{3}{2}$$
Use the slope-intercept form.
$$y = mx + b$$
$$y = \frac{3}{2}x + 0$$
$$y = \frac{3}{2}x$$

33. First find the slope.
$$m = \frac{y_2 - y_1}{x_2 - x_1}$$
$$= \frac{4 - 0}{0 - (-4)}$$
$$= 1$$
Use the slope-intercept form.
$$y = mx + b$$
$$y = x + 4$$

34. First find the slope.
$$m = \frac{y_2 - y_1}{x_2 - x_1}$$
$$= \frac{-\frac{1}{4} - 0}{0 - \frac{1}{3}}$$
$$= \frac{3}{4}$$
Use the slope-intercept form.
$$y = mx + b$$
$$y = \frac{3}{4}x - \frac{1}{4}$$

35. The slope is $\frac{2}{3}$. Use the point-slope form.
$$y - y_1 = m(x - x_1)$$
$$y - 6 = \frac{2}{3}(x - 4)$$
$$y - 6 = \frac{2}{3}x - \frac{8}{3}$$
$$y = \frac{2}{3}x + \frac{10}{3}$$

36. The slope is the opposite reciprocal of $\frac{1}{4}$ or -4.
Use the point-slope form.
$$y - y_1 = m(x - x_1)$$
$$y - (-5) = -4(x - 2)$$
$$y + 5 = -4x + 8$$
$$y = -4x + 3$$

37. Write the equation of the given line in slope-intercept form.
$$3x - \frac{1}{5}y = 3$$
$$-\frac{1}{5}y = -3x + 3$$
$$y = 15x - 15$$
The slope of this line is 15. The slope of a line perpendicular to it is $-\frac{1}{15}$. Use the point-slope form.
$$y - y_1 = m(x - x_1)$$
$$y - (-5) = -\frac{1}{15}(x - 6)$$
$$y + 5 = -\frac{1}{15}x + \frac{2}{5}$$
$$y = -\frac{1}{15}x - \frac{23}{5}$$

38. First find the slope.
$$m = \frac{y_2 - y_1}{x_2 - x_1}$$
$$= \frac{6 - 3}{0 - 3}$$
$$= -1$$
Use the point-slope form.
$$y - y_1 = m(x - x_1)$$
$$y - (-1) = -1[x - (-3)]$$
$$y + 1 = -x - 3$$
$$y = -x - 4$$

39. First find the slope.
$$m = \frac{y_2 - y_1}{x_2 - x_1}$$
$$= \frac{7 - 1}{3 - 1}$$
$$= \frac{6}{2} \text{ or } 3$$
Use the point-slope form.
$$y - y_1 = m(x - x_1)$$
$$y - 1 = 3(x - 1)$$
$$y - 1 = 3x - 3$$
$$y = 3x - 2$$

40. First find the slope.
$$m = \frac{y_2 - y_1}{x_2 - x_1}$$
$$= \frac{-2 - 2}{4 - 2}$$
$$= \frac{-4}{2} \text{ or } -2$$
Use the point-slope form.
$$y - y_1 = m(x - x_1)$$
$$y - 2 = -2(x - 2)$$
$$y - 2 = -2x + 4$$
$$y = -2x + 6$$

41. $d = 180(c - 2)$
$d = 180c - 360$

42. The slope is 180, and the y-intercept is -360.

43. $d = 180(c - 2)$
$\quad = 180(5 - 2)$
$\quad = 180(3)$
$\quad = 540$

There are $540°$ in a pentagon.

44. The slope is 75, and the y-intercept is 6000. Use the slope-intercept form.
$y = mx + b$
$y = 75x + 6000$

45. Let x represent the number of miles.
$3x + 20 = 2x + 30$
$\quad x + 20 = 30$
$\quad\quad\quad x = 10$

The stores charge the same amount at a distance of 10 miles.

46. Find the slope of the line through the points $(0, 32)$ and $(100, 212)$.
$m = \frac{y_2 - y_1}{x_2 - x_1}$
$\quad = \frac{212 - 32}{100 - 0}$
$\quad = \frac{180}{100}$ or $\frac{9}{5}$

Use the slope-intercept form.
$y = mx + b$
$y = \frac{9}{5}x + 32$

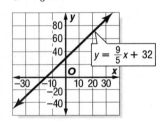

47. $y = \frac{9}{5}x + 32$
$y = \frac{9}{5}(20) + 32$
$\quad = 36 + 32$
$\quad = 68$

$68°$F corresponds to $20°$C.

48. Substitute x for y.
$y = \frac{9}{5}x + 32$
$x = \frac{9}{5}x + 32$
$-\frac{4}{5}x = 32$
$\quad\quad x = -40$

The temperature is the same on both scales at $-40°$.

49. Find the slope of the line through $(4, 2.65)$ and $(10, 4.75)$.
$m = \frac{y_2 - y_1}{x_2 - x_1}$
$\quad = \frac{4.75 - 2.65}{10 - 4}$
$\quad = \frac{2.10}{6}$ or 0.35

Use the point-slope form.
$y - y_1 = m(x - x_1)$
$y - 2.65 = 0.35(x - 4)$
$y - 2.65 = 0.35x - 1.4$
$\quad\quad\quad y = 0.35x + 1.25$

50. $y = 0.35x + 1.25$
$y = 0.35(30) + 1.25$
$\quad = 10.50 + 1.25$
$\quad = 11.75$

It would cost $11.75 to talk for half an hour.

51. Find the slope of $\overline{BC}$.
$m = \frac{y_2 - y_1}{x_2 - x_1}$
$\quad = \frac{10 - 4}{-6 - 6}$
$\quad = \frac{6}{-12}$ or $-\frac{1}{2}$

The slope of the altitude is the opposite reciprocal of $-\frac{1}{2}$ or 2.

Use the point-slope form.
$y - y_1 = m(x - x_1)$
$y - (-8) = 2[x - (-6)]$
$\quad\quad y + 8 = 2x + 12$
$\quad\quad\quad\quad y = 2x + 4$

52. A linear equation can sometimes be used to relate a company's cost to the number they produce of a product. Answers should include the following.
- The y-intercept, 5400, is the cost the company must pay if they produce 0 units, so it is the fixed cost. The slope, 1.37, means that it costs $1.37 to produce each unit. The variable cost is $1.37x$.
- $6770

53. C; Find the slope.
$m = \frac{y_2 - y_1}{x_2 - x_1}$
$\quad = \frac{1 - (-3)}{4 - 0}$
$\quad = \frac{4}{4}$ or 1

Use the slope-intercept form.
$y = mx + b$
$y = x - 3$

54. A; Find the slope.
$m = \frac{y_2 - y_1}{x_2 - x_1}$
$\quad = \frac{\frac{1}{2} - \left(-\frac{3}{2}\right)}{-\frac{1}{2} - \frac{1}{2}}$
$\quad = \frac{2}{-1}$ or -2

We can eliminate answer choices B, C, and D because none of these has slope -2. This leaves answer choice A.

55. x-intercept:
$$2x - y - 5 = 0$$
$$2x - 0 - 5 = 0$$
$$2x = 5$$
$$x = \frac{5}{2}$$

y-intercept:
$$2x - y - 5 = 0$$
$$2(0) - y - 5 = 0$$
$$-y = 5$$
$$y = -5$$

equation:
$$\frac{x}{a} + \frac{y}{b} = 1$$
$$\frac{x}{\frac{5}{2}} + \frac{y}{-5} = 1$$
$$\frac{x}{\frac{5}{2}} - \frac{y}{5} = 1$$

56. The x-intercept is $\frac{5}{2}$, and the y-intercept is -5.

Page 80 Maintain Your Skills

57. $m = \frac{y_2 - y_1}{x_2 - x_1}$
$$= \frac{6 - 2}{5 - 7}$$
$$= \frac{4}{-2}$$
$$= -2$$

58. $m = \frac{y_2 - y_1}{x_2 - x_1}$
$$= \frac{3 - (-3)}{3 - 1}$$
$$= \frac{6}{2}$$
$$= 3$$

59. $m = \frac{y_2 - y_1}{x_2 - x_1}$
$$= \frac{0 - 0}{4 - (-5)}$$
$$= \frac{0}{9}$$
$$= 0$$

60. $t(n) = 0.005n + 0.3$
$$t(50) = 0.005(50) + 0.3$$
$$= 0.25 + 0.3$$
$$= 0.55$$

When 50 people are connecting, it takes about 0.55 second to connect.

61. $|x - 2| \le -99$

The absolute value of a real number is never negative. There are no solutions; the solution set is $\varnothing$.

62. $-4x + 7 \le 31$
$$-4x \le 24$$
$$x \ge -6$$

The solution set is $\{x \mid x \ge -6\}$.

63. $2(r - 4) + 5 \ge 9$
$$2r - 8 + 5 \ge 9$$
$$2r - 3 \ge 9$$
$$2r \ge 12$$
$$r \ge 6$$

The solution set is $\{r \mid r \ge 6\}$.

64. List the numbers from least to greatest.
1, 2, 3, 3, 4, 4, 8
The median is the middle number or 3.

65. List the numbers from least to greatest.
3, 3, 5, 6, 7, 7, 9, 9
The median is the mean of the middle two numbers.
The median is $\frac{6 + 7}{2}$ or 6.5.

66. List the numbers from least to greatest.
138, 230, 235, 412, 466, 976
The median is the mean of the middle two numbers.
The median is $\frac{235 + 412}{2}$ or 323.5.

67. List the numbers from least to greatest.
2.3, 2.5, 5.5, 6.2, 7.8, 7.8
The median is the mean of the middle two numbers.
The median is $\frac{5.5 + 6.2}{2}$ or 5.85.

2-5 Modeling Real-World Data: Using Scatter Plots

Page 83 Algebra Activity

1–5. See students' work.

Page 83 Check for Understanding

1. d; The points are closest to lying on a straight line.

2. domain: $\{-1, 1, 2, 4\}$
range: $\{0, 2, 3\}$
Sample answer: Using $(-1, 0)$ and $(2, 2)$, find the slope.
$$m = \frac{y_2 - y_1}{x_2 - x_1}$$
$$= \frac{2 - 0}{2 - (-1)}$$
$$= \frac{2}{3}$$

Use the point-slope form.
$$y - y_1 = m(x - x_1)$$
$$y - 0 = \frac{2}{3}[x - (-1)]$$
$$y = \frac{2}{3}x + \frac{2}{3}$$

Make the prediction.
$$y = \frac{2}{3}x + \frac{2}{3}$$
$$y = \frac{2}{3}(5) + \frac{2}{3}$$
$$= \frac{12}{3} \text{ or } 4$$

3. Sample answer: Using $(4, 130.0)$ and $(6, 140.0)$, find the slope.
$$m = \frac{y_2 - y_1}{x_2 - x_1}$$
$$= \frac{140 - 130}{6 - 4}$$
$$= \frac{10}{2} \text{ or } 5$$

Use the point-slope form.
$$y - y_1 = m(x - x_1)$$
$$y - 130 = 5(x - 4)$$
$$y - 130 = 5x - 20$$
$$y = 5x + 110$$

4a.

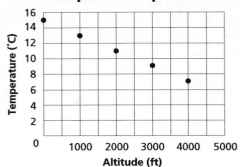

Atmospheric Temperature

4b. Sample answer: Using (2000, 11.0) and (3000, 9.1), find the slope.

$$m = \frac{y_2 - y_1}{x_2 - x_1}$$
$$= \frac{9.1 - 11.0}{3000 - 2000}$$
$$= \frac{-1.9}{1000} \text{ or } -0.0019$$

Use the point-slope form.
$$y - y_1 = m(x - x_1)$$
$$y - 11.0 = -0.0019(x - 2000)$$
$$y - 11.0 = -0.0019x + 3.8$$
$$y = -0.0019x + 14.8$$

4c. Sample answer:
$$y = -0.0019x + 14.8$$
$$y = -0.0019(5000) + 14.8$$
$$= 5.3$$

At 5000 feet, the temperature should be 5.3°C.

5a.

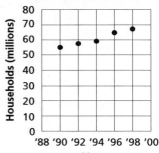

Cable Television

5b. Sample answer: Using (1992, 57) and (1998, 67), find the slope.

$$m = \frac{y_2 - y_1}{x_2 - x_1}$$
$$= \frac{67 - 57}{1998 - 1992}$$
$$= \frac{10}{6} \text{ or about } 1.67$$

Use the point-slope form.
$$y - y_1 = m(x - x_1)$$
$$y - 57 = 1.67(x - 1992)$$
$$y - 57 = 1.67x - 3326.64$$
$$y = 1.67x - 3269.64$$

5c. Sample answer:
$$y = 1.67x - 3269.64$$
$$y = 1.67(2010) + 3269.64$$
$$\approx 87$$

In 2010, about 87 million households will have cable service.

6a.

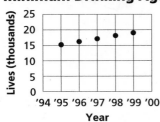

Lives Saved by Minimum Drinking Age

6b. Sample answer: Using (1996, 16.5) and (1998, 18.2), find the slope.

$$m = \frac{y_2 - y_1}{x_2 - x_1}$$
$$= \frac{18.2 - 16.5}{1998 - 1996}$$
$$= \frac{1.7}{2} \text{ or } 0.85$$

Use the point-slope form.
$$y - y_1 = m(x - x_1)$$
$$y - 16.5 = 0.85(x - 1996)$$
$$y - 16.5 = 0.85x - 1696.6$$
$$y = 0.85x - 1680.1$$

6c. Sample answer:
$$y = 0.85x - 1680.1$$
$$y = 0.85(2010) - 1680.1$$
$$= 28.4$$

The model predicts that about 28.4 thousand lives will have been saved by 2010.

7a.

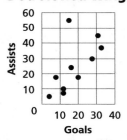

2000–2001 Detroit Red Wings

7b. Sample answer: Using (4, 5) and (32, 37), find the slope.

$$m = \frac{y_2 - y_1}{x_2 - x_1}$$
$$= \frac{37 - 5}{32 - 4}$$
$$= \frac{32}{28} \text{ or about } 1.14$$

Use the point-slope form.
$$y - y_1 = m(x - x_1)$$
$$y - 5 = 1.14(x - 4)$$
$$y - 5 = 1.14x - 4.56$$
$$y = 1.14x + 0.44$$

7c. Sample answer:
$$y = 1.14x + 0.44$$
$$15 = 1.14x + 0.44$$
$$14.56 = 1.14x$$
$$13 \approx x$$

The model predicts that a player with 15 assists will score about 13 goals.

8a. **Bottled Water Consumption**

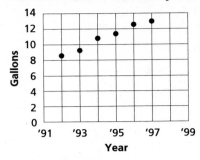

8b. Sample answer: Using (1993, 9.4) and (1996, 12.5), find the slope.

$m = \dfrac{y_2 - y_1}{x_2 - x_1}$

$\quad = \dfrac{12.5 - 9.4}{1996 - 1993}$

$\quad = \dfrac{3.1}{3}$ or about 1.03

Use the point-slope form.

$y - y_1 = m(x - x_1)$

$y - 9.4 = 1.03(x - 1993)$

$y - 9.4 = 1.03x - 2052.79$

$\quad\quad y = 1.03x - 2043.39$

8c. Sample answer:

$y = 1.03x - 2043.39$

$y = 1.03(2010) - 2043.39$

$\quad \approx 26.9$

The model predicts that about 26.9 gallons of bottled water will be consumed per person in 2010.

9a. **Broadway Play Revenue**

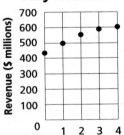

9b. Sample answer: Let x represent the number of seasons since the '95–'96 season. Using (1,499) and (3,588), find the slope.

$m = \dfrac{y_2 - y_1}{x_2 - x_1}$

$\quad = \dfrac{588 - 499}{3 - 1}$

$\quad = \dfrac{89}{2}$ or 44.5

Use the point-slope form.

$y - y_1 = m(x - x_1)$

$y - 499 = 44.5(x - 1)$

$y - 499 = 44.5x - 44.5$

$\quad\quad y = 44.5x - 454.5$

9c. Sample answer:

$y = 44.5x + 454.5$

$y = 44.5(14) + 454.5$

$\quad \approx 1078$

The model predicts that the total revenue of all Broadway plays will be about $1078 million or about $1.1 billion in the 2009–2010 season.

10. Sample answer: Using (1990, 563) and (1995, 739), find the slope.

$m = \dfrac{y_2 - y_1}{x_2 - x_1}$

$\quad = \dfrac{739 - 563}{1995 - 1990}$

$\quad = \dfrac{176}{5}$ or 35.2

Use the point-slope form.

$y - y_1 = m(x - x_1)$

$y - 563 = 35.2(x - 1990)$

$y - 563 = 35.2x - 70,048$

$\quad\quad y = 35.2x - 69,485$

11. Sample answer:

$y = 35.2x - 69,485$

$y = 35.2(2005) - 69,485$

$\quad = 1091$

The model predicts that Americans will spend $1091 on doctors' visits in 2005.

12. The value predicted by the equation is somewhat lower than the one given in the graph.

13. Sample answer: Using the data for August and November, a prediction equation for Company 1 is $y = -0.86x + 25.13$, where x is the number of months since August. The negative slope suggests that the value of Company 1's stock is going down. Using the data for October and November, a prediction equation for Company 2 is $y = 0.38x + 31.3$, where x is the number of months since August. The positive slope suggests that the value of Company 2's stock is going up. Since the value of Company 1's stock appears to be going down, and the value of Company 2's stock appears to be going up, Della should buy Company 2 stock.

14. No. Past performance is no guarantee of the future performance of a stock. Other factors that should be considered include the companies' earnings data and how much debt they have.

15. **World Cities**

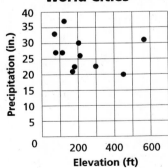

16. Sample answer: Using the points (213, 26) and (298, 23), find the slope.

$$m = \frac{y_2 - y_1}{x_2 - x_1}$$
$$= \frac{23 - 26}{298 - 213}$$
$$= \frac{-3}{85} \text{ or about } -0.04$$

Use the point slope form.

$$y - y_1 = m(x - x_1)$$
$$y - 26 = -0.04(x - 213)$$
$$y - 26 = -0.04x + 8.52$$
$$y = -0.04x + 34.52$$

17. Sample answer:

$$y = -0.04x + 34.52$$
$$y = -0.04(279) + 34.52$$
$$\approx 23$$

The model predicts that Dublin, Ireland, has an average annual precipitation of about 23 inches.

18. Sample answer: The predicted value differs from the actual value by more than 20%, possibly because no line fits the data very well.

19. Sample answer: Using (1975, 62.5) and (1995, 81.7) find the slope.

$$m = \frac{y_2 - y_1}{x_2 - x_1}$$
$$= \frac{81.7 - 62.5}{1995 - 1975}$$
$$= \frac{19.2}{20}$$
$$= 0.96$$

Use the point-slope form.

$$y - y_1 = m(x - x_1)$$
$$y - 62.5 = 0.96(x - 1975)$$
$$y - 62.5 = 0.96x - 1896$$
$$y = 0.96x - 1833.5$$

Now make the prediction.

$$y = 0.96x - 1833.5$$
$$y = 0.96(2010) - 1833.5$$
$$= 1929.6 - 1833.5$$
$$= 96.1$$

The model predicts that 96.1% of people over 25 will have a high school diploma in 2010.

20. Sample answer: The predicted percent is almost certainly too high. Since the percent cannot exceed 100%, it cannot continue to increase indefinitely at a linear rate.

21. See students' work.

22. Sample answer: Data can be used to write a linear equation that approximates the number of Calories burned per hour in terms of the speed that a person runs. Answers should include the following.

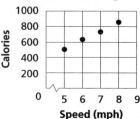

Calories Burned While Running

• Using (5, 508) and (8, 858), find the slope.

$$m = \frac{y_2 - y_1}{x_2 - x_1}$$
$$= \frac{858 - 508}{8 - 5}$$
$$= \frac{350}{3} \text{ or about } 116.67$$

Use the point-slope form.

$$y - y_1 = m(x - x_1)$$
$$y - 508 = 116.67(x - 5)$$
$$y - 508 = 116.67x - 583.35$$
$$y = 116.67x - 75.35$$

Now make the prediction.

$$y = 116.67x - 75.35$$
$$y = 116.67(9) - 75.35$$
$$\approx 975$$

The model predicts that a 140-pound person running at 9 miles per hour will burn 975 Calories.
The actual value is 953. The predicted value differs from the actual value by only about 2%.

23. D; The slope is positive so the answer must be either A or D. By inspection, except for point (1, 0.5), the slope between any two other points is 0.5.

24. A; $y = 0.63x + 4.51$
$$6.4 = 0.63x + 4.51$$
$$1.89 = 0.63x$$
$$3 = x$$

25. group 1: (1986, 217), (1988, 247), (1990, 297)
group 2: (1992, 332), (1994, 389)
group 3: (1996, 427), (1998, 461), (1999, 476)
medians of x-values:
$$x_1 = 1988$$
$$x_2 = \frac{1992 + 1994}{2} \text{ or } 1993$$
$$x_3 = 1988$$
medians of y-values:
$$y_1 = 247$$
$$y_2 = \frac{332 + 389}{2} \text{ or } 360.5$$
$$y_3 = 461$$

26. First find the slope $(x_1, y_1) = (1988, 247)$ and $(x_3, y_3) = (1998, 461)$.

$$m = \frac{y_3 - y_1}{x_3 - x_1}$$
$$= \frac{461 - 247}{1998 - 1988}$$
$$= \frac{214}{10} \text{ or } 21.4$$

Then use the point-slope form.

$$y - y_1 = m(x - x_1)$$
$$y - 247 = 21.4(x - 1988)$$
$$y - 247 = 21.4x - 42,543.2$$
$$y = 21.4x - 42,296.2$$

27. $Y = 21.4x_2 - 42,296.2$
$$Y = 21.4(1993) - 42,296.2$$
$$= 354$$

28. $\frac{2}{3}Y + \frac{1}{3}y_2 = \frac{2}{3}(354) + \frac{1}{3}(360.5)$
$$\approx 356.17$$
The ordered pair is (1993, 356.17).

29. The slope is 21.4. Use the point-slope form.

$$y - 356.17 = 21.4(x - 1993)$$
$$y - 356.17 = 21.4x - 42{,}650.2$$
$$y = 21.4x - 42{,}294.03$$

30. $y = 21.4x - 42{,}294.03$

$$y = 21.4(2005) - 42{,}294.03$$
$$\approx 613$$

There will be about 613 prisoners per 100,000 citizens in 2005.

$$y = 21.4x - 42{,}294.03$$
$$y = 21.4(2010) - 42{,}294.03$$
$$\approx 720$$

There will be about 720 prisoners per 100,000 citizens in 2010.

Page 86   Maintain Your Skills

31. Use slope-intercept form.

$$y = mx + b$$
$$y = 4x + 6$$

32. First find the slope.

$$m = \frac{y_2 - y_1}{x_2 - x_1}$$
$$= \frac{0 - (-3)}{-2 - 5}$$
$$= -\frac{3}{7}$$

Then use the point-slope form.

$$y - y_1 = m(x - x_1)$$
$$y - (-3) = -\frac{3}{7}(x - 5)$$
$$y + 3 = -\frac{3}{7}x + \frac{15}{7}$$
$$y = -\frac{3}{7}x - \frac{6}{7}$$

33. $g(x) = -\frac{4x}{3} + 7$

$$g(3) = -\frac{4(3)}{3} + 7$$
$$= -4 + 7$$
$$= 3$$

34. $g(x) = -\frac{4x}{3} + 7$

$$g(0) = -\frac{4(0)}{3} + 7$$
$$= 0 + 7$$
$$= 7$$

35. $g(x) = -\frac{4x}{3} + 7$

$$g(-2) = -\frac{4(-2)}{3} + 7$$
$$= \frac{8}{3} + 7$$
$$= \frac{29}{3}$$

36. $g(x) = -\frac{4x}{3} + 7$

$$g(-4) = -\frac{4(-4)}{3} + 7$$
$$= \frac{16}{3} + 7$$
$$= \frac{37}{3}$$

37. $|x + 4| > 3$

$$x + 4 > 3 \qquad \text{or} \qquad x + 4 < -3$$
$$x + 4 - 4 > 3 - 4 \qquad\qquad x + 4 - 4 < -3 - 4$$
$$x > -1 \qquad\qquad\qquad x < -7$$

The solution set is $\{x \,|\, x < -7 \text{ or } x > -1\}$.

38. $|-3| = 3$

39. $|11| = 11$

40. $|0| = 0$

41. $\left|-\frac{2}{3}\right| = \frac{2}{3}$

42. $|-1.5| = 1.5$

Page 88   Graphing Calculator Investigation (Follow-Up of Lesson 2-5)

1. Enter the population in L1 and the number of representatives in L2.

KEYSTROKES: [STAT] [ENTER] 29.8 [ENTER] 18 [ENTER] 17 [ENTER] 12.9 [ENTER] 6.6 [ENTER] 5.5 [ENTER] 4 [ENTER] [▶] 52 [ENTER] 31 [ENTER] 30 [ENTER] 23 [ENTER] 12 [ENTER] 10 [ENTER] 7 [ENTER]

Then: graph the scatter plot.

KEYSTROKES: [2nd] 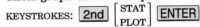 [ENTER] [ENTER] [GRAPH] [ZOOM] 9

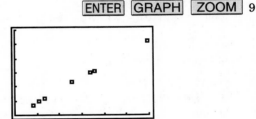

[0, 30] scl: 5 by [0, 60] scl: 10

2. KEYSTROKES: [STAT] [▶] 4 [ENTER]

The regression equation is $y = 1.73x + 0.39$.

3. Graph the regression equation.

KEYSTROKES: [y=] [VARS] 5 [▶] [▶] 1 [GRAPH]

Calculate the number of representatives for Oregon.

KEYSTROKES: [2nd] [CALC] 1 2.8 [ENTER]

Oregon has about 5 representatives.

4. Enter the year in L1 and the attendance in L2.

KEYSTROKES: STAT ENTER 1985 ENTER 1990 ENTER 1995 ENTER 2000 ENTER ▶

18.4 ENTER 25.2 ENTER 33.1 ENTER 37.6 ENTER

Then graph the scatter plot.

KEYSTROKES: 2nd [STAT PLOT] ENTER

ENTER GRAPH ZOOM 9

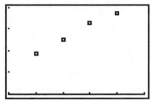

[1980, 2005] scl: 5 by [0, 40] scl: 10

5. KEYSTROKES: STAT ▶ 4 ENTER

The regression equation is $y = 11.3x - 2581.6$.

6. Graph the regression equation.

KEYSTROKES: y= VARS 5 ▶ ▶ 1 GRAPH

Calculate the attendance in 2010.

KEYSTROKES: 2nd [CALC] 1 2010 ENTER

The attendance in 2010 will be about 51.5 million or 51,500,000.

7. Enter the year in L1 and the number of vehicles sold in L2.

KEYSTROKES: STAT ENTER 1992 ENTER 1993 ENTER 1994 ENTER 1995 ENTER 1996 ENTER 1997 ENTER 1998 ENTER 1999 ENTER ▶

13118 ENTER 14199 ENTER 15413 ENTER 15118 ENTER 15456 ENTER 15498 ENTER 15963 ENTER 17414 ENTER

Graph the scatter plot.

KEYSTROKES: 2nd [STAT PLOT] ENTER

ENTER GRAPH ZOOM 9

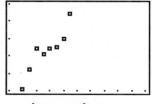

[1990, 2000] scl: 2 by [13,000, 18,000] scl: 1000

8. KEYSTROKES: STAT ▶ 4 ENTER

The regression equation is $y = 470.06x - 922,731.40$.

9. About 470,000 vehicles more per year

10. Graph the regression equation.

KEYSTROKES: y= VARS 5 ▶ ▶ 1 GRAPH

Calculate the sales in 2010.

KEYSTROKES: 2nd [CALC] 1 2010 ENTER

About 22,089,000 vehicles will be sold in 2010.

11. The prediction may not be accurate because different parts of the data could be represented by lines with different slopes. The sales could drop, as they did in 1995, or they could level out, as they did in 1996 and 1997.

12. Enter the year in L1 and the sales in L2.

KEYSTROKES: STAT ENTER 1993 ENTER 1994 ENTER 1995 ENTER 1996 ENTER 1997 ENTER 1998 ENTER 1999 ENTER ▶

315 ENTER 322 ENTER 328 ENTER 340 ENTER 332 ENTER 345 ENTER 363 ENTER

Find the regression equation.

KEYSTROKES: STAT ▶ 4 ENTER

The regression equation is $y = 6.93x - 13,494.43$.

13. Re-enter the data set without the data point for 1997.
Find the new regression equation.

KEYSTROKES: STAT ▶ 4 ENTER

The new regression equation is $y = 7.36x - 14,354.33$.

14. Graph the regression equation.

KEYSTROKES: y= VARS 5 ▶ ▶ 1 GRAPH ZOOM 0

Calculate the sales in 2010.

KEYSTROKES: 2nd [CALC] 1 2010 ENTER

In 2010, sales will be about $440 million or $440,000,000.

15. The correlation coefficient, 0.9761660092, is closer to 1. The new regression line fits the data better.

2-6 Special Functions

Page 91 Graphing Calculator Investigation

1. All the graphs have a corner point at the origin.

2. The graph becomes narrower.

3. Sample answer: $y = 2.5|x|$

4. KEYSTROKES: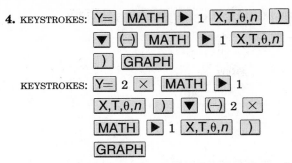

The graphs are reflections of each other about the *x*-axis.

5. The graph opens downward.

Pages 92–93 Check for Understanding

1. Sample answer: 1.9 rounded to the nearest integer is 2 but $[\![1.9]\!] = 1$.

2. $g(x) = [\![x - 5]\!]$
$g(4.3) = [\![4.3 - 5]\!]$
$\quad\quad = [\![-0.7]\!]$
$\quad\quad = -1$

3. Sample answer: $f(x) = |x - 1|$
$f(-2) = |-2 - 1|$
$\quad\quad = |-3|$
$\quad\quad = 3$

4. A; The graph has a V-shape.

5. S; This graph consists of multiple horizontal segments.

6. $f(x) = -[\![x]\!]$

x	f(x)
$-3 \le x < -2$	3
$-2 \le x < -1$	2
$-1 \le x < 0$	1
$0 \le x < 1$	0
$1 \le x < 2$	-1
$2 \le x < 3$	-2
$3 \le x < 4$	-3

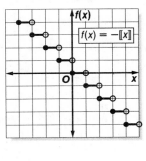

The domain is all real numbers.
The range is all integers.

7. $g(x) = [\![2x]\!]$

x	g(x)
$-1.5 \le x < -1$	-3
$-1 \le x < -0.5$	-2
$-0.5 \le x < 0$	-1
$0 \le x < 0.5$	0
$0.5 \le x < 1$	1
$1 \le x < 1.5$	2
$1.5 \le x < 2$	3

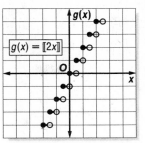

The domain is all real numbers.
The range is all integers.

8. $h(x) = |x - 4|$

x	h(x)
1	3
2	2
3	1
4	0
5	1
6	2
7	3

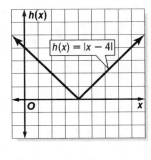

The domain is all real numbers.
The range is all nonnegative real numbers.

9. $f(x) = |3x - 2|$

x	f(x)
$-\frac{1}{3}$	3
0	2
$\frac{1}{3}$	1
$\frac{2}{3}$	0
1	1
$\frac{4}{3}$	2
$\frac{5}{3}$	3

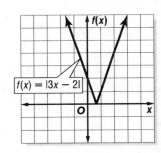

The domain is all real numbers.
The range is all nonnegative real numbers.

10. $g(x) = \begin{cases} -1 & \text{if } x < 0 \\ -x + 2 & \text{if } x \ge 0 \end{cases}$

x	g(x)
-3	-1
-2	-1
-1	-1
0	2
1	1
2	0
3	-1

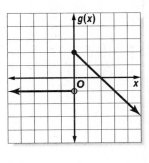

The domain is all real numbers.
The range is $\{y \mid y \le 2\}$.

11. $h(x) = \begin{cases} x + 3 \text{ if } x \leq -1 \\ 2x \text{ if } x < -1 \end{cases}$

x	$h(x)$
-4	-1
-3	0
-2	1
-1	2
0	0
1	2
2	4

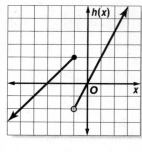

The domain is all real numbers.
The range is all real numbers.

12. The cost of parking must be an integer greater than or equal to 2, so the function is a step function.

13.

Time (hr)	Cost ($)
$0 \leq t < 1$	2
$1 \leq t < 2$	3
$2 \leq t < 3$	4
$3 \leq t < 4$	5
$4 \leq t < 5$	6
$5 \leq t < 6$	7

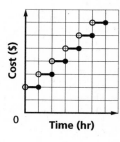

14. When the time is $4\frac{1}{2}$ hours, the cost is $6.

Pages 93–95   Practice and Apply

15. C; The graph is a horizontal line.

16. A; The graph has a V-shape.

17. S; The graph consists of multiple horizontal segments.

18. S; The graph consists of multiple horizontal segments.

19. A; The graph has a V-shape.

20. P; The graph consists of different rays and segments.

21.

x	y
$0 < x \leq 60$	1
$60 < x \leq 120$	2
$120 < x \leq 180$	3
$180 < x \leq 240$	4
$240 < x \leq 300$	5

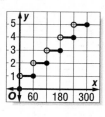

22.

Minutes	Cost($)
$0 < m \leq 1$	0.10
$1 < m \leq 2$	0.20
$2 < m \leq 3$	0.30
$3 < m \leq 4$	0.40
$4 < m \leq 5$	0.50
$5 < m \leq 6$	0.60
$6 < m \leq 7$	0.70

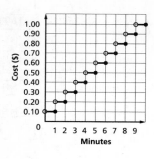

23. The call cost $1.

24. $f(x) = [\![x + 3]\!]$

x	$f(x)$
$-5 \leq x < -4$	-2
$-4 \leq x < -3$	-1
$-3 \leq x < -2$	0
$-2 \leq x < -1$	-1
$-1 \leq x < 0$	2
$0 \leq x < 1$	3
$1 \leq x < 2$	4

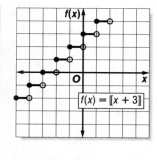

The domain is all real numbers.
The range is all integers.

25. $g(x) = [\![x - 2]\!]$

x	$g(x)$
$-2 \leq x < -1$	-4
$-1 \leq x < 0$	-3
$0 \leq x < 1$	-2
$1 \leq x < 2$	-1
$2 \leq x < 3$	0
$3 \leq x < 4$	1
$4 \leq x < 5$	2

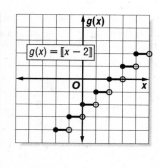

The domain is all real numbers.
The range is all integers.

26. $f(x) = 2 [\![x]\!]$

x	$f(x)$
$-2 \leq x < -1$	-4
$-1 \leq x < 0$	-2
$0 \leq x < 1$	0
$1 \leq x < 2$	2
$2 \leq x < 3$	4

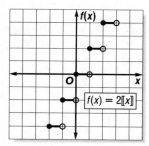

The domain is all real numbers.
The range is all even integers.

27. $h(x) = -3 \llbracket x \rrbracket$

x	$h(x)$
$-3 \le x < -2$	9
$-2 \le x < -1$	6
$-1 \le x < 0$	3
$0 \le x < 1$	0
$1 \le x < 2$	-3
$2 \le x < 3$	-6
$3 \le x < 4$	-9

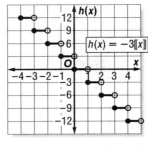

The domain is all real numbers.
The range is all integer multiples of 3 or $\{3a \mid a$ is an integer$\}$.

28. $g(x) = \llbracket x \rrbracket + 3$

x	$g(x)$
$-5 \le x < -4$	-2
$-4 \le x < -3$	-1
$-3 \le x < -2$	0
$-2 \le x < -1$	1
$-1 \le x < 0$	2
$0 \le x < 1$	3
$1 \le x < 2$	4

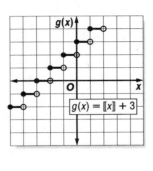

The domain is all real numbers.
The range is all integers.

29. $f(x) = \llbracket x \rrbracket - 1$

x	$f(x)$
$-3 \le x < -2$	-4
$-2 \le x < -1$	-3
$-1 \le x < 0$	-2
$0 \le x < 1$	-1
$1 \le x < 2$	0
$2 \le x < 3$	1
$3 \le x < 4$	2

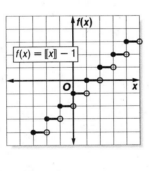

The domain is all real numbers.
The range is all integers.

30. $f(x) = |2x|$

x	$f(x)$
-1.5	3
-1	2
-0.5	1
0	0
0.5	1
1	2
1.5	3

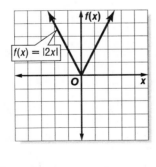

The domain is all real numbers.
The range is all nonnegative real numbers.

31. $h(x) = |-x|$

x	$h(x)$
-3	3
-2	2
-1	1
0	0
1	1
2	2
3	3

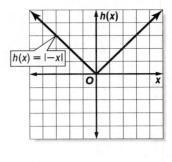

The domain is all real numbers.
The range is all nonnegative real numbers.

32. $g(x) = |x| + 3$

x	$g(x)$
-3	6
-2	5
-1	4
0	3
1	4
2	5
3	6

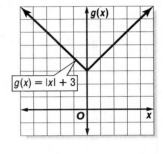

The domain is all real numbers.
The range is $\{y \mid y \ge 3\}$.

33. $g(x) = |x| + 4$

x	$g(x)$
-3	-1
-2	-2
-1	-3
0	-4
1	-3
2	-2
3	-1

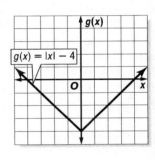

The domain is all real numbers.
The range is $\{y \mid y \ge -4\}$.

34. $h(x) = |x + 3|$

x	$h(x)$
-6	3
-5	2
-4	1
-3	0
-2	1
-1	2
0	3

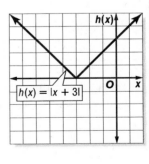

The domain is all real numbers.
The range is all nonnegative real numbers.

35. $f(x) = |x + 2|$

x	$f(x)$
−4	2
−3	1
−2	0
−1	1
0	2
1	3
2	4

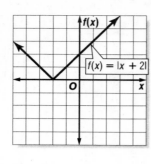

The domain is all real numbers.
The range is all nonnegative real numbers.

36. $f(x) = \left| x - \frac{1}{4} \right|$

x	$f(x)$
−2	$2\frac{1}{4}$
−1	$1\frac{1}{4}$
0	$\frac{1}{4}$
$\frac{1}{4}$	0
1	$\frac{3}{4}$
2	$1\frac{3}{4}$
3	$2\frac{3}{4}$

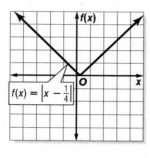

The domain is all real numbers.
The range is all nonnegative real numbers.

37. $f(x) = \left| x + \frac{1}{2} \right|$

x	$f(x)$
−3	$2\frac{1}{2}$
−2	$1\frac{1}{2}$
−1	$\frac{1}{2}$
$-\frac{1}{2}$	0
0	$\frac{1}{2}$
1	$1\frac{1}{2}$
2	$2\frac{1}{2}$

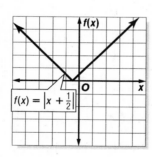

The domain is all real numbers.
The range is all nonnegative real numbers.

38. $f(x) = \begin{cases} -x \text{ if } x \le 3 \\ 2 \text{ if } x > 3 \end{cases}$

Graph the linear equation $f(x) = -x$ for $x \le 3$.
Since 3 satisfies the inequality $x \le 3$, stop with a closed circle at $x = 3$.
Graph the constant equation $f(x) = 2$ for $x > 3$.
Since 3 does not satisfy the inequality $x > 3$, start with an open circle at $x = 3$.

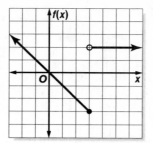

The domain is all real numbers.
The range is $\{y \mid y \ge -3\}$.

39. $h(x) = \begin{cases} -1 \text{ for } x < -2 \\ 1 \text{ for } x > 2 \end{cases}$

Graph the constant function $h(x) = -1$ for $x < -2$.
Since −2 does not satisfy the inequality $x < -2$, stop with an open circle at $x = -2$.
Graph the constant function $h(x) = 1$ for $x > 2$.
Since 2 does not satisfy the inequality $x > 2$, begin with an open circle at $x = 2$.

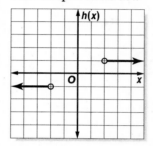

The domain is $\{x \mid x < -2 \text{ or } x > 2\}$.
The range is $\{-1, 1\}$.

40. $f(x) = \begin{cases} x \text{ if } x < -3 \\ 2 \text{ if } -3 \le x < 1 \\ -2x + 2 \text{ if } x \ge 1 \end{cases}$

Graph the linear equation $f(x) = x$ for $x < -3$.
Since −3 does not satisfy the inequality $x < -3$, end with an open circle at $x = -3$.
Graph the constant function $f(x) = 2$ for $-3 \le x < 1$. Since −3 does satisfy the inequality $-3 \le x < 1$ but 1 does not, begin with a closed circle at −3 and end with an open circle at 1.
Graph the linear equation $f(x) = -2x + 2$ for $x \ge 1$. Since 1 satisfies the inequality $x \ge 1$, begin with a closed circle at $x = 1$.

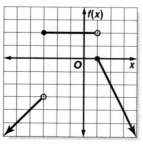

The domain is all real numbers.
The range is $\{y \mid y \le 0 \text{ or } y = 2\}$.

41. $g(x) = \begin{cases} \end{cases}$

Graph the constant equation $g(x) = -1$ for $x \leq -2$. Since x satisfies the inequality $x \leq -2$, stop with a closed circle at $x = -2$.
Graph the linear equation $g(x) = x$ for $-2 < x < 2$. Since neither -2 nor 2 satisfies the inequality $-2 < x < 2$, begin with an open circle at $x = -2$ and stop with an open circle at $x = 2$.
Graph the linear equation $g(x) = -x + 1$ for $x \geq 2$. Since 2 satisfies the inequality $x \geq 2$, begin with a closed circle at $x = 2$.

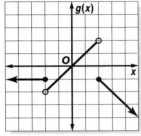

The domain is all real numbers.
The range is $\{y \mid y < 2\}$.

42. $f(x) = [\![\, |x| \,]\!]$

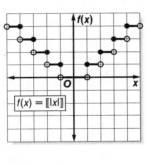

x	$f(x)$
$-4 < x \leq -3$	3
$-3 < x \leq -2$	2
$-2 < x \leq -1$	1
$-1 < x < 1$	0
$1 \leq x < 2$	1
$2 \leq x < 3$	2
$3 \leq x < 4$	3

The domain is all real numbers.
The range is all nonnegative whole numbers.

43. $g(x) = |[\![x]\!]|$

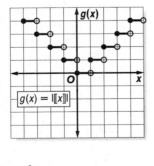

x	$g(x)$
$-3 \leq x < 2$	3
$-2 \leq x < 1$	2
$-1 \leq x < 0$	1
$0 \leq x < 1$	0
$1 \leq x < 2$	1
$2 \leq x < 3$	2
$3 \leq x < 4$	3

The domain is all real numbers.
The range is all nonnegative whole numbers.

44. For $x < -1$, the function is the constant function $f(x) = 2$.
For $-1 \leq x \leq 1$, the function is the line with slope 2 and y-intercept 0, so $f(x) = 2x$.
For $x > 1$, the function is the line with slope -1 passing through $(2, 2)$. Use the point-slope form to find that $f(x) = -x$ for $x > 1$.

$f(x) = \begin{cases} 2 & \text{if } x < -1 \\ 2x & \text{if } -1 \leq x \leq 1 \\ -x & \text{if } x > 1 \end{cases}$

45. $f(x) = |x - 2|$

46. Since you cannot eat a negative number of micrograms of vitamin C, the appropriate domain for the function is $\{x \mid x \geq 0\}$.

47.

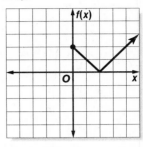

x	$f(x)$
0	2
1	1
2	0
3	1
4	2
5	3

48. $f(x) = \begin{cases} 0 & \text{if } 0 \leq x \leq 300 \\ 0.8(x - 300) & \text{if } x > 300 \end{cases}$

49. $|x| + |y| = 3$

Use trail and error to find ordered pairs that satisfy the equation.

x	y
0	3
1	2
2	1
3	0
0	-3

x	y
1	-2
2	-1
-1	2
-2	1
-3	0

x	y
-2	-1
-1	-2

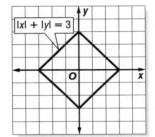

50. A step function can be used to model the cost of a letter in terms of its weight. Answers should include the following.

- Since the cost of a letter must be one of the values $0.34, $0.55, $0.76, $0.97, and so on, a step function is the best model for the cost of mailing a letter. The gas mileage of a car can be any real number in an interval of real numbers, so it cannot be modeled by a step function. In other words, gas mileage is a continuous function of time.

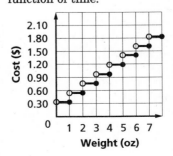

51. B; $f(x) = |-2x|$

$$f\left(-\frac{1}{2}\right) = \left|-2\left(-\frac{1}{2}\right)\right|$$
$$= |1| \text{ or } 1$$

52. D; We can eliminate answer choice A since $f(-1) = -(-1)$ or 1. We can eliminate answer choice B since $f(1) = [\![1]\!]$ or 1. We can eliminate answer choice C since $f(1) = |1|$ or 1. Only answer choice D remains.

Page 95   Maintain Your Skills

53.

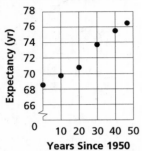

Life Expectancy

Expectancy (yr) vs. Years Since 1950

54. Sample answer:

Using the points $(10, 69.7)$ and $(47, 76.5)$ find the slope.

$$m = \frac{y_2 - y_1}{x_2 - x_1}$$
$$= \frac{76.5 - 69.7}{47 - 10}$$
$$= \frac{6.8}{37} \text{ or about } 0.18$$

Use the point-slope form.

$$y - y_1 = m(x - x_1)$$
$$y - 69.7 = 0.18(x - 10)$$
$$y - 69.7 = 0.18x - 1.8$$
$$y = 0.18x + 67.9$$

55. Sample answer:

$$y = 0.18x + 67.9$$
$$y = 0.18(60) + 67.9$$
$$= 78.7$$

The model predicts that the life expectancy of a person born in 2010 will be 78.7 years.

56. Use the point-slope form.

$$y - y_1 = m(x - x_1)$$
$$y - 4 = 3[x - (-2)]$$
$$y - 4 = 3x + 6$$
$$y = 3x + 10$$

57. First find the slope.

$$m = \frac{y_2 - y_1}{x_2 - x_1}$$
$$= \frac{2 - (-2)}{4 - 0}$$
$$= \frac{4}{4} \text{ or } 1$$

Then use the slope-intercept form.

$$y = mx + b$$
$$y = 1x + (-2)$$
$$y = x - 2$$

58. $3x - 5 \geq 4$

$$3x \geq 9$$
$$x \geq 3$$

The solution set is $\{x \mid x \geq 3\}$.

59. $28 - 6y < 23$

$$-6y < -5$$
$$y > \frac{5}{6}$$

The solution set is $\left\{y \mid y > \frac{5}{6}\right\}$.

60. $y < 2x + 3$

$$0 < 2(0) + 3$$
$$0 < 3, \text{ true}$$

Yes; $(0, 0)$ satisfies the inequality.

61. $y \geq -x + 1$

$$0 \geq -0 + 1$$
$$0 \geq 1, \text{ false}$$

No; $(0, 0)$ does not satisfy the inequality.

62. $y \leq \frac{3}{4}x - 5$

$$0 \leq \frac{3}{4}(0) - 5$$
$$0 \leq -5, \text{ false}$$

No; $(0, 0)$ does not satisfy the inequality.

63. $2x + 6y + 3 > 0$

$$2(0) + 6(0) + 3 > 0$$
$$0 + 0 + 3 > 0$$
$$3 > 0, \text{ true}$$

Yes; $(0, 0)$ satisfies the inequality.

64. $y > |x|$

$$0 > |0|$$
$$0 > 0, \text{ false}$$

No; $(0, 0)$ does not satisfy the inequality.

65. $|x| + y \leq 3$

$$|0| + 0 \leq 3$$
$$0 \leq 3, \text{ true}$$

Yes; $(0, 0)$ satisfies the inequality.

Page 95   Practice Quiz 2

1. Use the point-slope form.

$$y - y_1 = m(x - x_1)$$
$$y - 5 = -\frac{2}{3}[x - (-2)]$$
$$y - 5 = -\frac{2}{3}x - \frac{4}{3}$$
$$y = -\frac{2}{3}x + \frac{11}{3}$$

2.

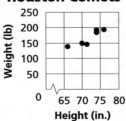

Houston Comets

Weight (lb) vs. Height (in.)

3. Sample answer: Using the points (66, 138) and (74, 178), find the slope.

$$m = \frac{y_2 - y_1}{x_2 - x_1}$$
$$= \frac{178 - 138}{74 - 66}$$
$$= \frac{40}{8} \text{ or } 5$$

Use the point-slope form.

$$y - y_1 = m(x - x_1)$$
$$y - 138 = 5(x - 66)$$
$$y - 138 = 5x - 330$$
$$y = 5x - 192$$

4. $y = 5x - 192$
$y = 5(72) - 192$
$\quad = 360 - 192$
$\quad = 168$

The model predicts that a 72 in. player weighs 168 lb.

5. $f(x) = |x - 1|$

x	$f(x)$
-3	4
-2	3
-1	2
0	1
1	0
2	1
3	2

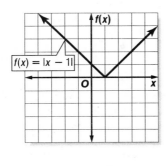

The domain is all real numbers.
The range is all nonnegative real numbers.

2-7 Graphing Inequalities

Page 98 Check for Understanding

1. The slope of the line is -3, and the y-intercept is 4. Thus, the equation of the boundary line is $y = -3x + 4$. Since the boundary line is solid, the inequality is either $y \geq -3x + 4$ or $y \leq -3x + 4$.

The point (0, 0) satisfies only the second of these two inequalities.

$y \leq -3x + 4$
$0 \leq -3(0) + 4$
$0 \leq 0 + 4$
$0 \leq 4$

Therefore, the inequality is $y \leq -3x + 4$.

2. Substitute the coordinates of a point not on the boundary into the inequality. If the inequality is satisfied, shade the region containing the point. If the inequality is not satisfied, shade the region that does not contain a point.

3. Sample answer: $y \geq |x|$

4. $y < 2$

The boundary is the graph of $y = 2$. Since the inequality symbol is $<$, the boundary is dashed.

Test the point (0, 0).
$y < 2$
$0 < 2$, true
Shade the region that contains (0, 0).

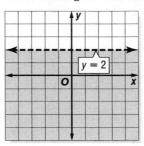

5. $y > 2x - 3$.
The boundary is the graph of $y = 2x - 3$. Since the inequality symbol is $>$, the boundary is dashed.

Test the point (0, 0).
$y > 2x - 3$
$0 > 2(0) - 3$
$0 > -3$, true
Shade the region that contains (0, 0).

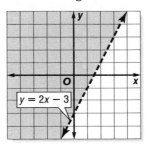

6. $x - y \geq 0$
The boundary is the graph of $x - y = 0$. Since the inequality symbol is $\geq$, the boundary is solid.

Test the point (0, 1).
$x - y \geq 0$
$0 - 1 \geq 0$
$-1 \geq 0$, false
Shade the region that does not contain (0, 1).

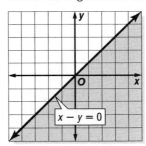

7. $x - 2y \leq 5$

The boundary is the graph of $x - 2y = 5$. Since the inequality symbol is $\leq$, the boundary is solid.

Test the point $(0, 0)$.

$x - 2y \leq 5$
$0 - 2(0) \leq 5$
$\qquad 0 \leq 5$, true

Shade the region that contains $(0, 0)$.

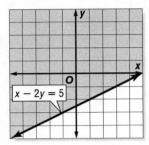

8. $y > |2x|$

The boundary is the graph of $y = |2x|$. Since the inequality symbol is $>$, the boundary is dashed.

Test the point $(0, 1)$.

$1 > |2(0)|$
$1 > 0$, true

Shade the region that contains $(0, 1)$.

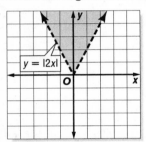

9. $y \leq 3|x| - 1$

The boundary is the graph of $y = 3|x| - 1$. Since the inequality symbol is $\leq$, the boundary is solid.

Now test the point $(0, 0)$.

$y \leq 3|x| - 1$
$0 \leq 3|0| - 1$
$0 \leq 0 - 1$
$0 \leq -1$, false

Shade the region that does not contain $(0, 0)$.

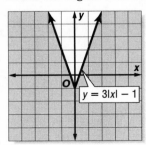

10. $10c + 13d \leq 40$

11. The boundary is the graph of $10c + 13d = 40$. Since the inequality symbol is $\leq$, the boundary is solid.

Test the point $(0, 0)$.

$10c + 13d \leq 40$
$10(0) + 13(0) \leq 40$
$\qquad\qquad 0 \leq 40$, true

Shade the region that contains $(0, 0)$.
Because there cannot be a negative number of cassettes or CDs, any region outside the first quadrant cannot be shaded.

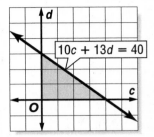

12. No; $(3, 2)$ is not in the shaded region.

Pages 98–99   Practice and Apply

13. The boundary is the graph of $x + y = -5$. Since the inequality symbol is $>$, the boundary is dashed.

Test the point $(0, 0)$.

$x + y > -5$
$0 + 0 > -5$
$\qquad 0 > -5$, true

Shade the region that contains $(0, 0)$.

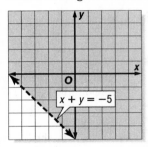

14. The boundary is the graph of $3 = x - 3y$. Since the inequality symbol is $\geq$, the boundary is solid.

Test the point $(0, 0)$.

$3 \geq x - 3y$
$3 \geq 0 - 3(0)$
$3 \geq 0$, true

Shade the region that contains $(0, 0)$.

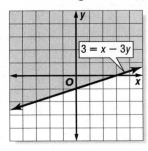

15. The boundary is the graph of $y = 6x - 2$. Since the inequality symbol is $>$, the boundary is dashed.

Test the point $(0, 0)$.
$y > 6x - 2$
$0 > 6(0) - 2$
$0 > -2$, true

Shade the region that contains $(0, 0)$.

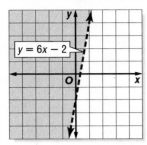

16. The boundary is the graph of $x - 5 = y$. Since the inequality symbol is $\leq$, the boundary is solid.

Test the point $(0, 0)$.
$x - 5 \leq y$
$0 - 5 \leq 0$
$-5 \leq 0$, true

Shade the region that contains $(0, 0)$.

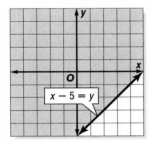

17. The boundary is the graph of $y = -4x + 3$. Since the inequality symbol is $\geq$, the boundary is solid.

Test the point $(0, 0)$.
$y \geq -4x + 3$
$0 \geq -4(0) + 3$
$0 \geq 3$, false

Shade the region that does not contain $(0, 0)$.

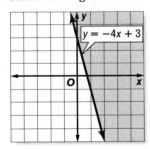

18. The boundary is the graph of $y - 2 = 3x$. Since the inequality symbol is $<$, the boundary is dashed.

Test the point $(0, 0)$.
$y - 2 < 3x$
$0 - 2 < 3(0)$
$-2 < 0$, true

Shade the region that contains $(0, 0)$.

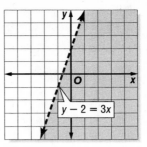

19. The boundary is the graph of $y = 1$. Since the inequality symbol is $\geq$, the boundary is solid.

Test the point $(0, 0)$.
$y \geq 1$
$0 \geq 1$, false

Shade the region that does not contain $(0, 0)$.

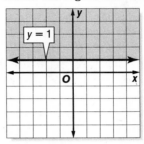

20. The boundary is the graph of $y + 1 = 4$. Since the inequality symbol is $<$, the boundary is dashed.

Test the point $(0, 0)$.
$y + 1 < 4$
$0 + 1 < 4$
$1 < 4$, true

Shade the region that contains $(0, 0)$.

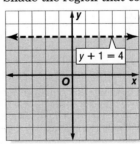

21. The boundary is the graph of $4x - 5y - 10 = 0$. Since the inequality symbol is $\leq$, the boundary is solid.

Test the point $(0, 0)$.
$$4x - 5y - 10 \leq 0$$
$$4(0) - 5(0) - 10 \leq 0$$
$$0 - 0 - 10 \leq 0$$
$$-10 \leq 0, \text{ true}$$

Shade the region that contains $(0, 0)$.

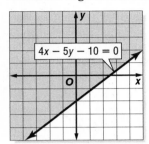

22. The boundary is the graph of $x - 6y + 3 = 0$. Since the inequality symbol is $>$, the boundary is dashed.

Test the point $(0, 0)$.
$$x - 6y + 3 > 0$$
$$0 - 6(0) + 3 > 0$$
$$0 - 0 + 3 > 0$$
$$3 > 0, \text{ true}$$

Shade the region that contains $(0, 0)$.

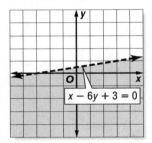

23. The boundary is the graph of $y = \frac{1}{3}x + 5$. Since the inequality symbol is $>$, the boundary is dashed.

Test the point $(0, 0)$.
$$y > \frac{1}{3}x + 5$$
$$0 > \frac{1}{3}(0) + 5$$
$$0 > 0 + 5$$
$$0 > 5, \text{ false}$$

Shade the region that does not contain $(0, 0)$.

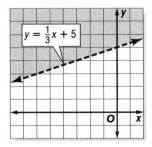

24. The boundary is the graph of $y = \frac{1}{2}x - 5$. Since the inequality symbol is $\geq$, the boundary is solid.

Test the point $(0, 0)$.
$$y \geq \frac{1}{2}x - 5$$
$$0 \geq \frac{1}{2}(0) - 5$$
$$0 \geq 0 - 5$$
$$0 \geq -5, \text{ false}$$

Shade the region that contains $(0, 0)$.

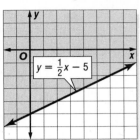

25. The boundary is the graph of $y = |x|$. Since the inequality symbol is $\leq$, the boundary is solid.

Test the point $(0, 1)$.
$$y \leq |x|$$
$$1 \leq |0|$$
$$1 \leq 0, \text{ false}$$

Shade the region that does not contain $(0, 1)$.

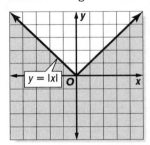

26. The boundary is the graph of $y = |4x|$. Since the inequality symbol is $>$, the boundary is dashed.

Test the point $(0, 1)$.
$$y > |4x|$$
$$1 > |4(0)|$$
$$1 > |0|$$
$$1 > 0, \text{ true}$$

Shade the region that contains $(0, 1)$.

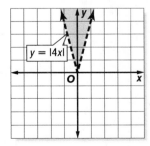

27. The boundary is the graph of $y + |x| = 3$. Since the inequality symbol is $<$, the boundary is dashed.

Test the point $(0, 0)$.
$y + |x| < 3$
$0 + |0| < 3$
$0 + 0 < 3$
$0 < 3$, true

Shade the region that contains $(0, 0)$.

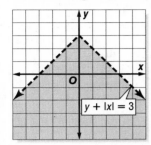

28. The boundary is the graph of $y = |x - 1| - 2$. Since the inequality symbol is $\geq$, the boundary is solid.

Test the point $(0, 0)$.
$y \geq |x - 1| - 2$
$0 \geq |0 - 1| - 2$
$0 \geq |-1| - 2$
$0 \geq 1 - 2$
$0 \geq -1$, true

Shade the region that contains $(0, 0)$.

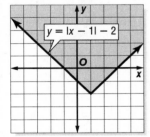

29. The boundary is the graph of $|x + y| = 1$. The absolute value equation $|x + y| = 1$ is equivalent to $x + y = 1$ or $x + y = -1$. Graph both lines. Since the inequality symbol is $>$, the boundary is dashed.

The graph is divided into three regions. Test one point from each region.

Test $(-1, -1)$:
$|x + y| > 1$
$|(-1) + (-1)| > 1$
$|2| > 1$
$2 > 1$, true

Test $(0, 0)$:
$|x + y| > 1$
$|0 + 0| > 1$
$0 > 1$, false

Test $(1, 1)$:
$|x + y| > 1$
$|1 + 1| > 1$
$|2| > 1$
$2 > 1$, true

Shade the regions that contain $(1, 1)$ and $(-1, -1)$.

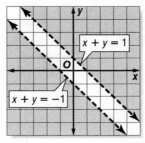

30. The boundary is the graph of $|x| = |y|$. The absolute value equation $|x| = |y|$ is equivalent to $x = y$ or $x = -y$. Graph both lines. Since the inequality symbol is $\leq$, the boundary is solid.

The graph is divided into four regions. Test one point from each region.

Test $(1, 0)$:
$|x| \leq |y|$
$|1| \leq |0|$
$1 \leq 0$, false

Test $(0, 1)$:
$|x| \leq |y|$
$|0| \leq |1|$
$0 \leq 1$, true

Test $(-1, 0)$:
$|x| \leq |y|$
$|-1| \leq |0|$
$1 \leq 0$, false

Test $(0, -1)$:
$|x| \leq |y|$
$|0| \leq |-1|$
$0 \leq 1$, true

Shade the regions that contain $(0, 1)$ and $(0, -1)$.

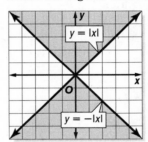

31.

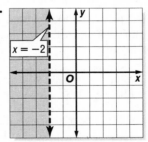

Since the graph only contains points to the left of $x = -2$, the boundary is dashed. Thus, the inequality is either $x < -2$ or $x > -2$. The point $(-3, 0)$ is in the shaded region. Since $-3 < -2$, the inequality $x < -2$ describes the region.

32.

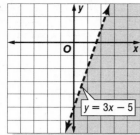

Since the graph only contains points below the graph of $y = 3x - 5$, the boundary is dashed. Thus, the inequality is either $y < 3x - 5$ or $y > 3x - 5$. The point $(3, 0)$ is in the shaded region. Since $0 < 3(3) - 5$, the inequality $y < 3x - 5$ describes the region.

33. The boundary is the graph of $0.4x + 0.6y = 90$. Since the inequality symbol is $\geq$, the boundary is solid.

Test the point $(0, 0)$.
$$0.4x + 0.6y \geq 90$$
$$0.4(0) + 0.6(0) \geq 90$$
$$0 \geq 90, \text{ false}$$

Shade the region that does not contain $(0, 0)$. Since the variables cannot be negative, shade only the part in the first quadrant.

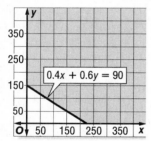

34. Yes; the point $(85, 95)$ is in the shaded region.

35. Let a represent the number of adult tickets and s the number of student tickets.
$$4a + 3s \geq 2000$$

36. The boundary is the graph of $4a + 3s = 2000$. Since the inequality symbol is $\geq$, the boundary is solid.

Test the point $(0, 0)$.
$$4a + 3s \geq 2000$$
$$4(0) + 3(0) \geq 2000$$
$$0 \geq 2000, \text{ false}$$

Shade the region that does not contain $(0, 0)$. Since the variables cannot be negative, shade only the part in the first quadrant.

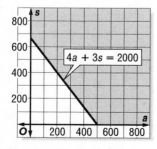

37. Yes; $(180, 465)$ lies in the shaded region.

38. Let a represent the number of shares of Able Rentals and b the number of shares of Best Bikes.
$$1.20a + 1.80b \geq 9000$$

The boundary is the graph of $1.2a + 1.8b = 9000$. Since the inequality symbol is $\geq$, the boundary is solid.

Test the point $(0, 0)$.
$$1.2a + 1.8b \geq 9000$$
$$1.2(0) + 1.8(0) \geq 9000$$
$$0 \geq 9000, \text{ false}$$

Shade the region that does not contain $(0, 0)$. Since the variables cannot be negative, shade only the part in the first quadrant.

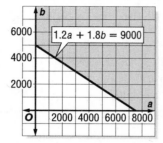

39. Yes; the point $(3000, 3000)$ is on the line.

40. The boundary is the graph of $|y| = x$. Since the inequality symbol is $<$, the boundary is dashed.

Test the point $(1, 0)$.
$$|y| < x$$
$$|0| < 1$$
$$0 < 1, \text{ true}$$

Shade the region that contains the point $(1, 0)$.

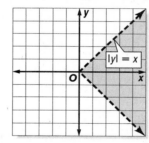

41. Linear inequalities can be used to track the performance of players in fantasy football leagues. Answers should include the following.

- Let x be the number of receiving yards and let y be the number of touchdowns. The number of points Dana gets from receiving yards is $5x$, and the number of points he gets from touchdowns is $100y$. His total number of points is $5x + 100y$. He wants at least 1000 points, so the inequality $5x + 100y \geq 1000$ represents the situation.

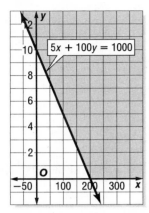

- The first game qualifies as a good game because its statistics lie in the shaded region.

42. A; We can eliminate answer choices B and D because the boundary is dashed. We can eliminate answer choice C because $(0, 0)$ is a point in the shaded region but does not satisfy $y > 3x + 2$.

43. B;
$y > 5|x| - 3$
$y > 5|1| - 3$
$3 > 5 - 3$
$3 > 2$, true

44. KEYSTROKES: [2nd] [DRAW] 7 3 [,] 10 [)] [ENTER]

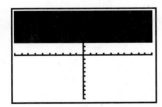

[−10, 10] scl: 1 by [−10, 10] scl: 1

45. KEYSTROKES: [2nd] [DRAW] 7 [(−)] 10 [,] [X,T,θ,n] [+] 2 [)] [ENTER]

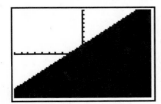

[−10, 10] scl: 1 by [−10, 10] scl: 1

46. KEYSTROKES: [2nd] [DRAW] 7 [(−)] 10 [,] [(−)] 2 [X,T,θ,n] [−] 4 [)] [ENTER]

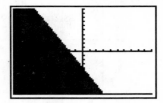

[−10, 10] scl: 1 by [−10, 10] scl: 1

47. KEYSTROKES: [2nd] [DRAW] 7 [X,T,θ,n] [(−)] 7 [,] 10 [)] [ENTER]

[−10, 10] scl: 1 by [−10, 10] scl: 1

Page 99   Maintain Your Skills

48. $f(x) = [\![x]\!] - 4$

x	$f(x)$
$0 \leq x < 1$	-4
$1 \leq x < 2$	-3
$2 \leq x < 3$	-2
$3 \leq x < 4$	-1
$4 \leq x < 5$	0

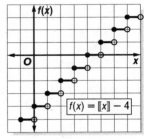

The domain is all real numbers.
The range is all integers.

49. $g(x) = |x| - 1$

x	y
-2	1
-1	0
0	-1
1	0
2	1

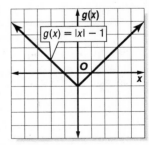

The domain is all real numbers.
The range is $\{y \mid y \geq -1\}$.

50. $h(x) = |x - 3|$

x	y
0	3
1	2
2	1
3	0
4	1

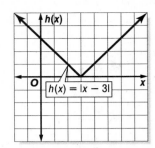

The domain is all real numbers. The range is all nonnegative reals.

51.

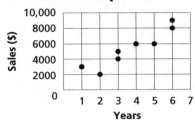

Sales vs. Experience

52. Sample answer: Using the points (4, 6000) and (6, 8000), find the slope.

$m = \dfrac{y_2 - y_1}{x_2 - x_1}$

$= \dfrac{8000 - 6000}{6 - 4}$

$= \dfrac{2000}{2}$ or 1000

Use the point-slope form.
$y - 6000 = 1000(x - 4)$
$y - 6000 = 1000x - 4000$
$\qquad y = 1000x + 2000$

53. $y = 1000x + 2000$
$y = 1000(8) + 2000$
$\quad = 10{,}000$

According to the model, a representative with 8 years of experience will have $10,000 in sales.

54. $4x - 9 = 23$
$\quad 4x = 32$
$\quad\ x = 8$

Check: $4x - 9 = 23$
$\quad 4(8) - 9 \stackrel{?}{=} 23$
$\quad\ 32 - 9 \stackrel{?}{=} 23$
$\qquad\qquad 23 = 23$ ✓

55. $11 - 2y = 5$
$\quad -2y = -6$
$\qquad y = 3$

Check: $11 - 2y = 5$
$\quad 11 - 2(3) \stackrel{?}{=} 5$
$\quad\ 11 - 6 \stackrel{?}{=} 5$
$\qquad\qquad 5 = 5$ ✓

56. $2z - 3 = -6z + 1$
$\quad 8z - 3 = 1$
$\qquad 8z = 4$
$\qquad\ z = \dfrac{4}{8}$ or $\dfrac{1}{2}$

Check: $2z - 3 = -6z + 1$
$\quad 2\left(\dfrac{1}{2}\right) - 3 \stackrel{?}{=} -6\left(\dfrac{1}{2}\right) + 1$
$\qquad\ 1 - 3 \stackrel{?}{=} -3 + 1$
$\qquad\qquad -2 = -2$ ✓

Chapter 2 Study Guide and Review

Page 100 Vocabulary and Concept Check

1. identity
2. absolute value
3. standard
4. parallel
5. domain
6. range
7. slope
8. vertical line test

Pages 100–104 Lesson-by-Lesson Review

9.

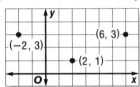

The domain is $\{-2, 2, 6\}$. The range is $\{1, 3\}$. Each element of the domain is paired with exactly one element of the range, so the relation is a function.

10.

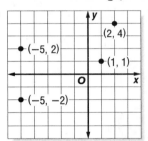

The domain is $\{-5, 1, 2\}$. The range is $\{-2, 1, 2, 4\}$. The relation is not a function because the element -5 in the domain is paired with two different elements, -2 and 2, in the range.

11. $y = 0.5x$

x	y
-2	-1
0	0
2	1

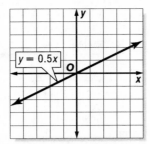

Every real number is the x-coordinate of some point on the line, and every real number is the y-coordinate of some point on the line. Thus, the domain and range are both all real numbers. No vertical line intersects the graph in more than one point, so the relation is a function.

12. $y = 2x + 1$

x	y
-1	-1
0	1
1	3

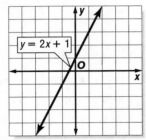

Every real number is the x-coordinate of some point on the line, and every real number is the y-coordinate of some point on the line. Thus, the domain and range are both all real numbers. No vertical line intersects the graph in more than one point, so the relation is a function.

13. $f(x) = 5x - 9$
$f(6) = 5(6) - 9$
$\quad = 30 - 9$
$\quad = 21$

14. $f(x) = 5x - 9$
$f(-2) = 5(-2) - 9$
$\quad = -10 - 9$
$\quad = -19$

15. $f(x) = 5x - 9$
$f(y) = 5y - 9$

16. $f(x) = 5x - 9$
$f(-2v) = 5(-2v) - 9$
$\quad = -10v - 9$

17. No; x has an exponent other than 1.

18. Yes; this is a linear function because it can be written as $y = -2x + 11$. $m = -2$, $b = 11$

19. No; x is inside a square root.

20. $y = 7x + 15$
$-7x + y = 15$
$7x - y = -15.$
$A = 7, B = -1, C = -15$

21. $0.5x = -0.2y - 0.4$
$0.5x + 0.2y = -0.4$
$5x + 2y = -4$
$A = 5, B = 2, C = -4$

22. $\frac{2}{3}x - \frac{3}{4}y = 6$
$8x - 9y = 72$
$A = 8, B = -9, C = 72$

23. x-intercept:
$-\frac{1}{5}y = x + 4$
$-\frac{1}{5}(0) = x + 4$
$0 = x + 4$
$-4 = x$

y-intercept:
$-\frac{1}{5}y = x + 4$
$-\frac{1}{5}y = 0 + 4$
$-\frac{1}{5}y = 4$
$y = -20$

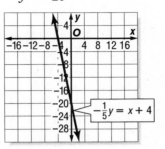

24. x-intercept:
$6x = -12y + 48$
$6x = -12(0) + 48$
$6x = 48$
$x = 8$

y-intercept:
$6x = -12y + 48$
$6(0) = -12y + 48$
$0 = -12y + 48$
$12y = 48$
$y = 4$

25. x-intercept:
$$y - x = -9$$
$$0 - x = -9$$
$$-x = -9$$
$$x = 9$$

y-intercept:
$$y - x = -9$$
$$y - 0 = -9$$
$$y = -9$$

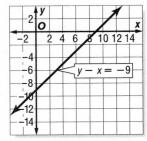

26. $m = \dfrac{y_2 - y_1}{x_2 - x_1}$

$\quad = \dfrac{7 - (-3)}{6 - (-6)}$

$\quad = \dfrac{10}{12}$ or $\dfrac{5}{6}$

27. $m = \dfrac{y_2 - y_1}{x_2 - x_1}$

$\quad = \dfrac{-7 - (-5.5)}{11 - 5.5}$

$\quad = \dfrac{-1.5}{5.5}$ or $-\dfrac{3}{11}$

28. $m = \dfrac{y_2 - y_1}{x_2 - x_1}$

$\quad = \dfrac{-41 - 24}{10 - (-3)}$

$\quad = \dfrac{-65}{13}$ or -5

29. Plot the ordered pair $(0, 1)$. Then go up 2 units and right 1 unit. Plot the new point $(1, 3)$.

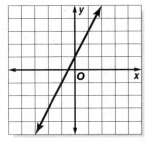

30. Plot the ordered pair $(3, -2)$. Then go up 5 units and right 2 units. Plot the new point $(5, 3)$.

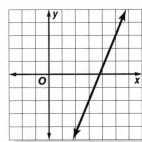

31. Plot the ordered pair $(-5, 2)$. Then go down 1 unit and right 4 units. Plot the new point $(-1, 1)$.

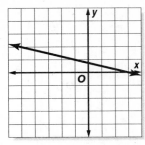

32. The parallel line also has slope 3.

Use the slope and the point at $(2, 0)$ to graph the line.

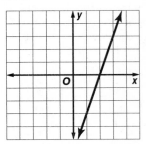

33. The slope of the perpendicular line is the opposite reciprocal of $\frac{1}{2}$, or -2.

Use the slope and the point at $(-1, -2)$ to graph the line.

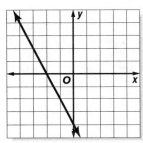

34. Use the intercepts to graph $2x + 3y = 1$. The x-intercept is $\frac{1}{2}$, and the y-intercept is $\frac{1}{3}$.

The line falls 2 units for every 3 units it moves to the right, so its slope is $-\frac{2}{3}$. The slope of the perpendicular line is the negative reciprocal of $-\frac{2}{3}$, or $\frac{3}{2}$.

Use the slope and the point at $(4, 1)$ to graph the line.

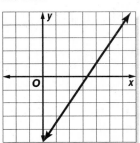

35. Use the intercepts to graph $-2x + y = 4$. The x-intercept is -2, and the y-intercept is 4.

The line rises 4 units for every 2 units it moves to the right, so its slope is $\frac{4}{2}$ or 2. The parallel line also has slope 2.

Use the slope and the point at $(-2, 2)$ to graph the line.

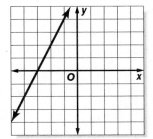

36. Use point-slope form.
$$y - y_1 = m(x - x_1)$$
$$y - 9 = \frac{3}{4}[x - (-6)]$$
$$y - 9 = \frac{3}{4}x + \frac{9}{2}$$
$$y = \frac{3}{4}x + \frac{27}{2}$$

37. Find the slope.
$$m = \frac{y_2 - y_1}{x_2 - x_1}$$
$$= \frac{2 - (-8)}{-3 - 3}$$
$$= \frac{10}{-6} \text{ or } -\frac{5}{3}$$

Use the point-slope form.
$$y - y_1 = m(x - x_1)$$
$$y - (-8) = -\frac{5}{3}(x - 3)$$
$$y + 8 = -\frac{5}{3}x + 5$$
$$y = -\frac{5}{3}x - 3$$

38. Write the equation of the given line in slope-intercept form.
$$x - 3y = 14$$
$$-3y = -x + 14$$
$$y = \frac{1}{3}x - \frac{14}{3}$$

The slope of this line is $\frac{1}{3}$. The slope of the parallel line is also $\frac{1}{3}$.

Use the point-slope form.
$$y - y_1 = m(x - x_1)$$
$$y - 2 = \frac{1}{3}[x - (-1)]$$
$$y - 2 = \frac{1}{3}x + \frac{1}{3}$$
$$y = \frac{1}{3}x + \frac{7}{3}$$

39. Write the equation of the given line in slope-intercept form.
$$4x - 3y = 12$$
$$-3y = -4x + 12$$
$$y = \frac{4}{3}x - 4$$

The slope of this line is $\frac{4}{3}$. The slope of the perpendicular line is $-\frac{3}{4}$.

Use the point-slope form.
$$y - y_1 = m(x - x_1)$$
$$y - 2 = -\frac{3}{4}(x - 3)$$
$$y - 2 = -\frac{3}{4}x + \frac{9}{4}$$
$$y = -\frac{3}{4}x + \frac{17}{4}$$

40.

People Below Poverty Level

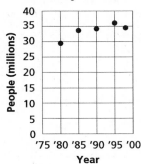

41. Sample answer: Using the points (1980, 29.3) and (1990, 33.6), find the slope.
$$m = \frac{y_2 - y_1}{x_2 - x_1}$$
$$= \frac{33.6 - 29.3}{1990 - 1980}$$
$$= 0.43$$

Use the point-slope form.
$$y - y_1 = m(x - x_1)$$
$$y - 29.3 = 0.43(x - 1980)$$
$$y - 29.3 = 0.43x - 851.4$$
$$y = 0.43x - 822.1$$

42. Sample answer:
$$y = 0.43x - 822.1$$
$$y = 0.43(2010) - 822.1$$
$$= 42.2$$

The model predicts that 42.2 million people will live below the poverty level in 2010.

43. $f(x) = [\![x]\!] - 2$.

x	$f(x)$
$-2 \le x < -1$	-4
$-1 \le x < 0$	-3
$0 \le x < 1$	-2
$1 \le x < 2$	-1
$2 \le x < 3$	0

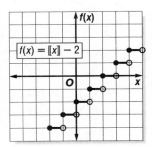

The domain is all real numbers.
The range is all integers.

44. $h(x) = [\![2x - 1]\!]$

x	$h(x)$
$-0.5 \le x < 0$	-2
$0 \le x < 0.5$	-1
$0.5 \le x < 1$	0
$1 \le x < 1.5$	1
$1.5 \le x < 2$	2

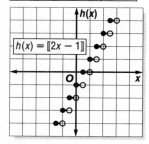

The domain is all real numbers.
The range is all integers.

45. $g(x) = |x| + 4$

x	$g(x)$
-2	6
-1	5
0	4
1	5
2	6

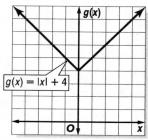

The domain is all real numbers.
The range is $\{y \mid y \ge 4\}$.

46. $h(x) = |x - 1| - 7$

x	$h(x)$
-1	-5
0	-6
1	-7
2	-6
3	-5

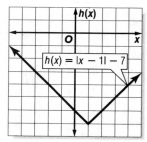

The domain is all real numbers.
The range is $\{y \mid y \ge -7\}$.

47. $f(x) = \begin{cases} 2 & \text{if } x < -1 \\ -x - 1 & \text{if } x \ge -1 \end{cases}$

Graph the constant function $f(x) = 2$ for $x < -1$. Stop with an open circle at $x = -1$ since -1 does not satisfy the inequality $x < -1$.

Graph the linear equation $f(x) = -x - 1$ for $x \ge -1$. Start with a closed circle at $x = -1$ since -1 satisfies the inequality $x \ge -1$.

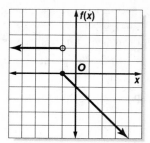

The domain is all real numbers.
The range is $\{y \mid y \le 0 \text{ or } y = 2\}$.

48. $g(x) = \begin{cases} -2x - 3 & \text{if } x < 1 \\ x - 4 & \text{if } x > 1 \end{cases}$

Graph the linear equation $g(x) = -2x - 3$ for $x < 1$. Stop with an open circle at $x = 1$ since 1 does not satisfy the inequality $x < 1$.

Graph the linear equation $g(x) = x - 4$ for $x > 1$. Start with an open circle at $x = 1$ since 1 does not satisfy the inequality $x > 1$.

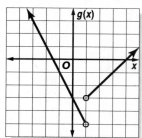

The domain is $\{x \mid x \ne 1\}$.
The range is $\{y \mid y > -5\}$.

49. The boundary is the graph of $y = 3x - 5$. Since the inequality symbol is $\le$, the boundary is solid.
Test the point $(0, 0)$.
$y \le 3x - 5$
$0 \le 3(0) - 5$
$0 \le -5$, false
Shade the region that does not contain $(0, 0)$.

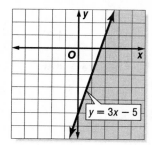

50. The boundary is the graph of $x = y - 1$. Since the inequality symbol is $>$, the boundary is dashed.

Test the point $(0, 0)$.
$x > y - 1$
$0 > 0 - 1$
$0 > -1$, true
Shade the region that contains $(0, 0)$.

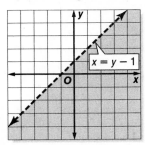

51. The boundary is the graph of $y + 0.5x = 4$. Since the inequality symbol is $<$, the boundary is dashed.

Test the point $(0, 0)$.
$y + 0.5x < 4$
$0 + 0.5(0) < 4$
$0 + 0 < 4$
$0 < 4$, true
Shade the region that contains $(0, 0)$.

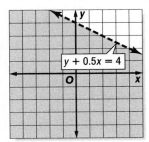

52. The boundary is the graph of $2x + y = 3$. Since the inequality symbol is $\geq$, the boundary is solid.
Test the point $(0, 0)$.
$2x + y \geq 3$
$2(0) + 0 \geq 3$
$0 \geq 3$, false
Shade the region that does not contain $(0, 0)$.

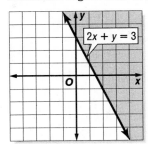

53. The boundary is the graph of $y = |x| + 2$. Since the inequality symbol is $\geq$, the boundary is solid.
Test the point $(0, 0)$.
$y \geq |x| + 2$
$0 \geq |0| + 2$
$0 \geq 2$, false

Shade the region that does not contain $(0, 0)$.

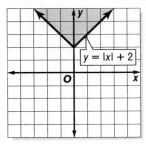

54. The boundary is the graph of $y = |x - 3|$. Since the inequality symbol is $>$, the boundary is dashed.
Test the point $(0, 0)$.
$0 > |0 - 3|$
$0 > |-3|$
$0 > 3$, false
Shade the region that does not contain $(0, 0)$.

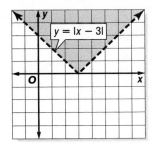

Chapter 2 Practice Test

Page 105

1. independent
2. x-intercept
3. $y = mx + b$
4.

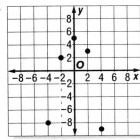

The domain is $\{-4, -2, 0, 2, 4\}$.
The range is $\{-9, -8, 2, 3, 5\}$.
Every element in the domain is paired with exactly one element in the range, so the relation is a function.

5. $y = 3x - 3$

x	y
0	−3
1	0
2	3

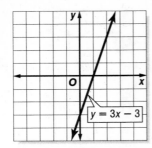

The domain and range are both all real numbers. No vertical line intersects the graph in more than one point, so the relation is a function.

6. $f(x) = 7 - x^2$
$f(3) = 7 - 3^2$
$\quad\;\; = 7 - 9$
$\quad\;\; = -2$

7. $f(x) = x - 3x^2$
$f(0) = 0 - 3(0)^2$
$\quad\;\; = 0$

8. x-intercept:
$y = \frac{3}{5}x - 4$
$0 = \frac{3}{5}x - 4$
$-\frac{3}{5}x = -4$
$x = \frac{20}{3}$ or $6\frac{2}{3}$

y-intercept:
$y = \frac{3}{5}x - 4$
$y = \frac{3}{5}(0) - 4$
$y = -4$

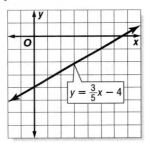

9. x-intercept:
$4x - y = 2$
$4x - 0 = 2$
$\quad\;\; 4x = 2$
$\quad\;\; x = \frac{2}{4}$ or $\frac{1}{2}$

y-intercept:
$4x - y = 2$
$4(0) - y = 2$
$\quad\; -y = 2$
$\quad\;\;\; y = -2$

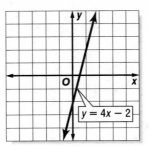

10. $x = -4$ is a vertical line passing through $(-4, 0)$.

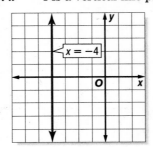

11. x-intercept:
$y = 2x - 5$
$0 = 2x - 5$
$5 = 2x$
$\frac{5}{2} = x$

y-intercept:
$y = 2x - 5$
$y = 2(0) - 5$
$y = -5$

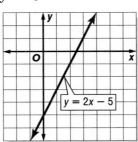

12. x-intercept:
$f(x) = 3x - 1$
$0 = 3x - 1$
$1 = 3x$
$\frac{1}{3} = x$

y-intercept:
$f(x) = 3x - 1$
$f(0) = 3(0) - 1$
$\quad\;\; = -1$

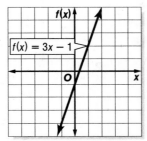

13. $f(x) = [\![3x]\!] + 3$

x	$f(x)$
$-\frac{4}{3} \leq x < -1$	-1
$-1 \leq x < -\frac{2}{3}$	0
$-\frac{2}{3} \leq x < -\frac{1}{3}$	1
$-\frac{1}{3} \leq x < 0$	2
$0 \leq x < \frac{1}{3}$	3

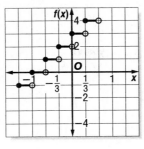

14. $g(x) = |x + 2|$

x	$g(x)$
-4	2
-3	1
-2	0
-1	1
0	2

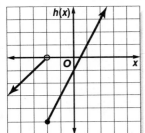

15. $f(x) = \begin{cases} x + 2 \text{ if } x < -2 \\ 2x - 1 \text{ if } x \geq -2 \end{cases}$

Graph the linear function $h(x) = x + 2$ for $x < -2$.
Stop with an open circle at $x = -2$ since -2 does not satisfy the inequality $x < -2$.
Graph the linear function $h(x) = 2x - 1$ for $x \geq -2$. Start with a closed circle at $x = -2$ since -2 satisfies the inequality $x \geq -2$.

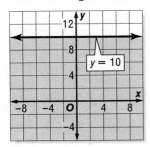

16. The boundary is the graph of $y = 10$. Since the inequality symbol is $\leq$, the boundary is solid. Test the point $(0, 0)$.
$y \leq 10$
$0 \leq 10$, true
Shade the region that contains $(0, 0)$.

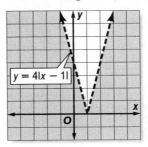

17. The boundary is the graph of $x = 6$. Since the inequality symbol is $>$, the boundary is dashed. Test the point $(0, 0)$.
$x > 6$,
$0 > 6$, false
Shade the region that does not contain $(0, 0)$.

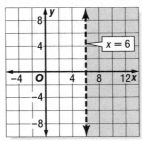

18. The boundary is the graph of $-2x + 5 = 3y$. Since the inequality symbol is $\leq$, the boundary is solid. Test the point $(0, 0)$.
$-2x + 5 \leq 3y$
$-2(0) + 5 \leq 3(0)$
$5 \leq 0$, false
Shade the region that does not contain $(0, 0)$.

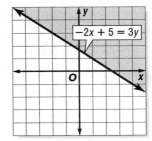

19. The boundary is the graph of $y = 4|x - 1|$. Since the inequality symbol is $<$, the boundary is dashed.
Test the point $(0, 0)$.
$y < 4|x - 1|$
$0 < 4|0 - 1|$
$0 < 4|-1|$
$0 < 4(1)$
$0 < 4$, true
Shade the region that contains $(0, 0)$.

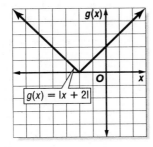

20. $m = \frac{y_2 - y_1}{x_2 - x_1}$
$= \frac{1 - (-4)}{6 - 8}$
$= \frac{5}{-2}$ or $-\frac{5}{2}$

21. $m = \frac{y_2 - y_1}{x_2 - x_1}$
$= \frac{5 - 5}{4 - (-2)}$
$= \frac{0}{6}$ or 0

22. $m = \dfrac{y_2 - y_1}{x_2 - x_1}$

$= \dfrac{-6 - 7}{4 - 5}$

$= \dfrac{-13}{-1}$ or 13

23. Plot the ordered pair $(1, -3)$. Then go up 2 units and right 1 unit. Plot the new point $(2, -1)$.

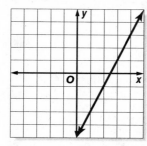

24. Plot the ordered pair $(-2, 2)$. Then go down 1 unit and right 3 units. Plot the new point $(1, 1)$.

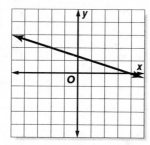

25. A line with undefined slope is vertical. Graph the vertical line through the point $(3, -2)$.

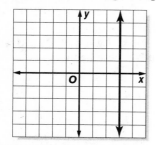

26. Use the slope-intercept form.

$y = mx + b$

$y = -5x + 11$

27. Find the slope using $(9, 0)$ and $(0, -4)$.

$m = \dfrac{y_2 - y_1}{x_2 - x_1}$

$= \dfrac{-4 - 0}{0 - 9}$

$= \dfrac{-4}{-9}$ or $\dfrac{4}{9}$

Use the slope-intercept form.

$y = mx + b$

$y = \dfrac{4}{9}x + (-4)$

$y = \dfrac{4}{9}x - 4$

28. Write the given equation in slope-intercept form.

$2x + 3y = 1$

$3y = -2x + 1$

$y = -\dfrac{2}{3}x + \dfrac{1}{3}$

The slope of this line is $-\dfrac{2}{3}$.

The slope of the parallel line is also $-\dfrac{2}{3}$.

Use the point-slope form.

$y - y_1 = m(x - x_1)$

$y - 15 = -\dfrac{2}{3}[x - (-6)]$

$y - 15 = -\dfrac{2}{3}x - 4$

$y = -\dfrac{2}{3}x + 11$

29. Write the given equation in slope-intercept form.

$x + 3y = 7$

$3y = -x + 7$

$y = -\dfrac{1}{3}x + \dfrac{7}{3}$

The slope of this line is $-\dfrac{1}{3}$.

The slope of the perpendicular line is the opposite reciprocal of $-\dfrac{1}{3}$, or 3.

Use the point slope form.

$y - y_1 = m(x - x_1)$

$y - 2 = 3(x - 5)$

$y - 2 = 3x - 15$

$y = 3x - 13$

30.

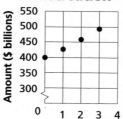

Money Spent on Recreation

31. Sample answer:

Using the points $(0, 401.6)$ and $(1, 429.6)$, find the slope.

$m = \dfrac{y_2 - y_1}{x_2 - x_1}$

$= \dfrac{429.6 - 401.6}{1 - 0}$

$= 28$

Use the point-slope form.

$y - y_1 = m(x - x_1)$

$y - 401.6 = 28(x - 0)$

$y - 401.6 = 28x$

$y = 28x + 401.6$

32. Sample answer:

$y = 28x + 401.6$

$y = 28(15) + 401.6$

$= 821.6$

The model predicts that Americans will spend $821.6 billion on recreation in 2010.

33. D; The line $y - 2 = 4(x + 1)$ is in point-slope form. Therefore the slope is 4. Any line parallel to this line will also have slope of 4.

Chapter 2 Standardized Test Practice

Pages 106–107

1. A; $A = \frac{1}{2}bh$
   $ = \frac{1}{2}(8)(9)$
   $ = 36$

2. B; $-1 + 3 = 2$ is an even integer, so x could be equal to -1.

3. B; $m = \frac{y_2 - y_1}{x_2 - x_1}$
   $ = \frac{4 - 7}{6 - 15}$
   $ = \frac{-3}{-9}$ or $\frac{1}{3}$

4. D; Matt currently has $30 - 2 + 6 - 3 + 4$ or 35 CDs. This is an increase of 5 CDs.
   $\frac{5}{30} = \frac{r}{100}$
   $500 = 30r$
   $\frac{500}{30} = r$
   $16\frac{2}{3} = r$

5. B; $(2 + 3)(3 + 4)(4 + 5) = 3(40 + x)$
   $5 \cdot 7 \cdot 9 = 120 + 3x$
   $315 = 120 + 3x$
   $195 = 3x$
   $65 = x$

6. A; The length of the third side must be less than the sum of the lengths of the other two sides. Only $3s$ is less than $4s$.

7. D; The product of two positive numbers is positive. The product of two even numbers is even. However, the product of two prime numbers is not prime. For example, 2 and 3 are prime numbers, but their product, 6, is not prime.

8. D; $\frac{3 + x}{7 + x} = \frac{3}{7} + \frac{3}{7}$
   $\frac{3 + x}{7 + x} = \frac{6}{7}$
   $7(3 + x) = 6(7 + x)$
   $21 + 7x = 42 + 6x$
   $7x = 21 + 6x$
   $x = 21$

9. D; Since $\frac{x + y}{2} = 4$, we have $x + y = 8$.
   $\frac{r + s + x + y}{4} = 8$
   $r + s + x + y = 32$
   $r + s + 8 = 32$
   $r + s = 24$
   $\frac{r + s}{2} = 12$

10. $2n > 19 \geq \frac{7}{8}n$

    $2n > 19$ and $19 \geq \frac{7}{8}n$
    $n > \frac{19}{2}$ $\frac{152}{7} \geq n$
    $n > 9\frac{1}{2}$ $21\frac{5}{7} \geq n$
    $9\frac{1}{2} < n \leq 21\frac{5}{7}$

    The prime numbers satisfying this inequality are 11, 13, 17, and 19.

11. $3t + 5t = 2$
    $8t = 2$
    $t = \frac{2}{8}$ or $\frac{1}{4}$

12. $0.85x = 8.5$
    $x = 10$
    $\frac{1}{x} = \frac{1}{10}$

13. $w + x + 60 = 180$, so $w + x = 120$.
    $y + z + 60 = 180$, so $y + z = 120$.
    $w + x + y + z = 120 + 120$
    $ = 240$

14. Since candidate C received 800 votes, together A and B received $4000 - 800$ or 3200 votes. Since A received more votes than B, then A received more than half of the 3200 votes. Thus, A received at least 1601 votes.

15. Points P and R are on the same horizontal line. Points Q and R are on the same vertical line. Thus, $\triangle PQR$ has a right angle at R. The length of $\overline{PR}$ is 4, and the length of $\overline{QR}$ is 2.
    $A = \frac{1}{2}bh$
    $ = \frac{1}{2}(4)(2)$
    $ = 4$

16. List the numbers.
    7, 17, 27, 37, 47, 57, 67, 70, 71, 72, 73, 74, 75, 76, 77, 78, 79, 87, 97
    There 19 numbers.

17. The sum of the lengths of the other two sides must be greater than 17. Since the sum is an integer, the least it can be is 18. Thus, the length of each side is at least 9.

18. A; $m > 3$
    $\frac{1}{m} < \frac{1}{3}$
    $\frac{1}{m} - \frac{1}{4} < \frac{1}{3} - \frac{1}{4}$
    $\frac{1}{m} - \frac{1}{4} < \frac{1}{12}$
    Since $\frac{1}{12} < \frac{1}{4}$, it follows that $\frac{1}{m} - \frac{1}{4} < \frac{1}{12}$.

19. C; The x-coordinate of Q is 2, and the y-coordinate of P is 2.

20. D

21. B; $\frac{x + y + z}{3} = 30$
    $x + y + z = 90$
    Thus,
    $\frac{x + y + z + 29}{4} = \frac{90 + 29}{4}$
    $\phantom{\frac{x + y + z + 29}{4}} = 29.25$

22. A; The slope of the line is $\frac{k - 0}{0 - (1 - k)}$ or $\frac{k}{k - 1}$.
    Since $1 - k$ is negative, $k - 1$ is positive.
    $k - 1 < k$
    $1 < \frac{k}{k - 1}$

Chapter 3 Systems of Equations and Inequalities

Page 109   Getting Started

1. Write the equation in slope-intercept form.

$2y = x$

$y = \frac{1}{2}x$

$y = \frac{1}{2}x + 0$

The y-intercept is 0. Graph the ordered pair $(0, 0)$. The slope is $\frac{1}{2}$. From $(0, 0)$ move up 1 unit and right 2 units. Plot a new point at $(2, 1)$. Draw the line containing the points.

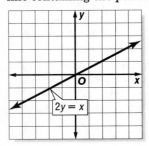

2. Find the x-intercept and y-intercept of the graph of $y = x - 4$.

$0 = x - y - 4$

$0 = x - (0) - 4$

$4 = x$

The graph crosses the x-axis at $(4, 0)$.

$0 = x - y - 4$

$\quad = 0 - y - 4$

$4 = -y$

$-4 = y$

The graph crosses the y-axis at $(0, -4)$.

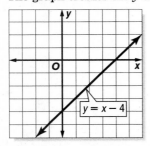

3. Find the x-intercept and y-intercept of the graph of $y = 2x - 3$.

$0 = 2x - y - 3$

$0 = 2x - (0) - 3$

$\quad = 2x - 3$

$3 = 2x$

$\frac{3}{2} = x$ or $1\frac{1}{2} = x$

The graph crosses the x-axis at $\left(1\frac{1}{2}, 0\right)$.

$0 = 2x - y - 3$

$0 = 2(0) - y - 3$

$\quad = -y - 3$

$-3 = -y$

$3 = y$

The graph crosses the y-axis at $(0, 3)$.

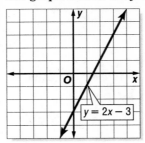

4. Find the x-intercept and the y-intercept of the graph of $x + 3y = 6$.

$x + 3y - 6 = 0$

$x + 3(0) - 6 = 0$

$\quad x - 6 = 0$

$\quad x = 6$

The graph crosses the x-axis at $(6, 0)$.

$x + 3y - 6 = 0$

$(0) + 3y - 6 = 0$

$\quad 3y - 6 = 0$

$\quad 3y = 6$

$\quad y = 2$

The graph crosses the y-axis at $(0, 2)$.

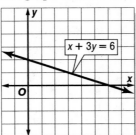

5. Find the x-intercept and the y-intercept of the graph of $2x + 3y = -12$.

$2x + 3y + 12 = 0$

$2x + 3(0) + 12 = 0$

$\quad 2x + 12 = 0$

$\quad 2x = -12$

$\quad x = -6$

The graph crosses the x-axis at $(-6, 0)$.

$2x + 3y + 12 = 0$

$2(0) + 3y + 12 = 0$

$\quad 3y + 12 = 0$

$\quad 3y = -12$

$\quad y = -4$

The graph crosses the y-axis at $(0, -4)$.

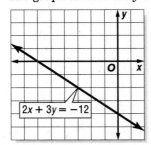

6. Find the x-intercept and the y-intercept of the graph of $4y - 5x = 10$.
$$4y - 5x = 10$$
$$-5x + 4y = 10$$
$$5x - 4y = -10$$
$$5x - 4y + 10 = 0$$
$$5x - 4(0) + 10 = 0$$
$$5x + 10 = 0$$
$$5x = -10$$
$$x = -2$$
The graph crosses the x-axis at $(-2, 0)$.
$$5x - 4y + 10 = 0$$
$$5(0) - 4y + 10 = 0$$
$$-4y + 10 = 0$$
$$-4y = -10$$
$$y = \frac{10}{4} \text{ or } 2\frac{1}{2}$$
The graph crosses the y-axis at $\left(0, -2\frac{1}{2}\right)$.

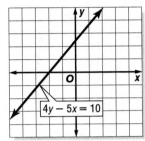

7.
$$2x + y = 0$$
$$2x + y - 2x = 0 - 2x$$
$$y = -2x$$

8.
$$x - y = -4$$
$$x - y - x = -4 - x$$
$$-y = -x - 4$$
$$\frac{-y}{-1} = \frac{-x - 4}{-1}$$
$$y = x + 4$$

9.
$$6x + 2y = 12$$
$$6x + 2y - 6x = 12 - 6x$$
$$2y = -6x + 12$$
$$\frac{2y}{2} = \frac{-6x + 12}{2}$$
$$y = -3x + 6 \text{ or } y = 6 - 3x$$

10.
$$8 - 4y = 5x$$
$$8 - 4y - 8 = 5x - 8$$
$$-4y = 5x - 8$$
$$\frac{-4y}{-4} = \frac{5x - 8}{-4}$$
$$y = -\frac{5}{4}x + 2 \text{ or } y = 2 - \frac{5}{4}x$$

11.
$$\frac{1}{2}y + 3x = 1$$
$$\frac{1}{2}y + 3x - 3x = 1 - 3x$$
$$\frac{1}{2}y = -3x + 1$$
$$2\left(\frac{1}{2}y\right) = 2(-3x + 1)$$
$$y = 2(-3x) + 2(1)$$
$$y = -6x + 2 \text{ or } y = 2 - 6x$$

12.
$$\frac{1}{3}x - 2y = 8$$
$$\frac{1}{3}x - 2y - \frac{1}{3}x = 8 - \frac{1}{3}x$$
$$-2y = -\frac{1}{3}x + 8$$
$$\frac{-2y}{-2} = \frac{-\frac{1}{3}x + 8}{-2}$$
$$y = \frac{1}{6}x - 4$$

13. The boundary is the graph of $y = -2$. Since the inequality symbol is $\geq$, the boundary will be solid. Use the slope-intercept form, $y = 0x - 2$. Now test the point $(0, 0)$.
$$y \geq -2$$
$$0 \geq -2 \quad \text{true}$$
Shade the region that includes $(0, 0)$.

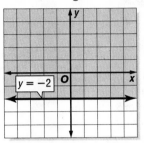

14. The boundary is the graph of $x + y = 0$. Since the inequality symbol is $\leq$, the boundary will be solid. Use the slope-intercept form, $y = -x + 0$. Now test the point $(1, 0)$.
$$x + y \leq 0$$
$$1 + 0 \leq 0$$
$$1 \leq 0 \quad \text{false}$$
Shade the region that does not contain $(1, 0)$.

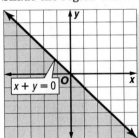

15. The boundary is the graph of $y = 2x - 2$. Since the inequality symbol is $<$, the boundary will be dashed. Use the slope-intercept form, $y = 2x - 2$. Now test the point $(0, 0)$.
$$y < 2x - 2$$
$$0 < 2(0) - 2$$
$$0 < 0 - 2$$
$$0 < -2 \quad \text{false}$$
Shade the region that does not contain $(0, 0)$.

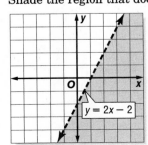

16. The boundary is the graph of $x + 4y = 3$. Since the inequality symbol is $<$, the boundary will be dashed. Use the slope-intercept form, $y = -\frac{1}{4}x + \frac{3}{4}$.

Now test the point $(0, 0)$.

$$x + 4y < 3$$
$$0 + 4(0) < 3$$
$$0 + 0 < 3$$
$$0 < 3 \quad \text{true}$$

Shade the region that includes $(0, 0)$.

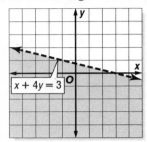

17. The boundary is the graph of $2x - y = 6$. Since the inequality symbol is $\geq$, the boundary will be solid. Use the slope-intercept form, $y = 2x - 6$. Now test the point $(0, 0)$.

$$2x - y \geq 6$$
$$2(0) - 0 \geq 6$$
$$0 - 0 \geq 6$$
$$0 \geq 6 \quad \text{false}$$

Shade the region that does not contain $(0, 0)$.

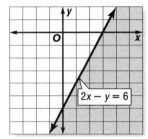

18. The boundary is the graph of $3x - 4y = 10$. Since the inequality symbol is $<$, the boundary will be dashed. Use the slope-intercept form, $y = \frac{3}{4}x - \frac{5}{2}$.

Now test the point $(0, 0)$.

$$3x - 4y < 10$$
$$3(0) - 4(0) < 10$$
$$0 - 0 < 10$$
$$0 < 10 \quad \text{true}$$

Shade the region that includes $(0, 0)$.

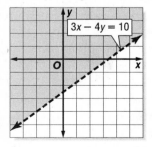

19.
$$3x + 2y - z = 3(-3) + 2(1) - 2$$
$$= -9 + 2(1) - 2$$
$$= -9 + 2 - 2$$
$$= -7 - 2$$
$$= -9$$

The value is -9.

20.
$$3y - 8z = 3(1) - 8(2)$$
$$= 3 - 8(2)$$
$$= 3 - 16$$
$$= -13$$

The value is -13.

21.
$$x - 5y + 4z = -3 - 5(1) + 4(2)$$
$$= -3 - 5 + 8$$
$$= 0$$

The value is 0.

22.
$$2x + 9y + 4z = 2(-3) + 9(1) + 4(2)$$
$$= -6 + 9 + 8$$
$$= 11$$

The value is 11.

23.
$$2x - 6y - 5z = 2(-3) - 6(1) - 5(2)$$
$$= -6 - 6 - 10$$
$$= -12 - 10$$
$$= -22$$

The value is -22.

24.
$$7x - 3y + 2z = 7(-3) - 3(1) + 2(2)$$
$$= -21 - 3 + 4$$
$$= -24 + 4$$
$$= -20$$

The value is -20.

3-1	Solving Systems of Equations by Graphing

Pages 112–113 Check for Understanding

1. Two lines cannot intersect in exactly two points.

2. Sample answer: $x + y = 4$, $x - y = 2$

3. A graph is used to estimate the solution. To determine that the point lies on both lines, you must check that it satisfies both equations.

4. Write each equation in slope-intercept form.
$$y = 2x + 9$$
$$y = -x + 3$$

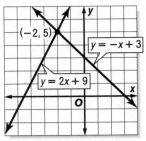

The graph appears to intersect at $(-2, 5)$.

Check: Substitute the coordinates into each equation.

$$\begin{array}{ll} y = 2x + 9 & y = -x + 3 \\ 5 \stackrel{?}{=} 2(-2) + 9 & 5 \stackrel{?}{=} -(-2) + 3 \\ 5 = 5 \checkmark & 5 = 5 \checkmark \end{array}$$

The solution of the system is $(-2, 5)$.

5. Write each equation in slope-intercept form.

$$3x + 2y = 10 \rightarrow y = -\frac{3}{2}x + 5$$

$$2x + 3y = 10 \rightarrow y = -\frac{2}{3}x + \frac{10}{3}$$

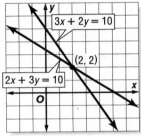

The graphs appear to intersect at $(2, 2)$.

Check: Substitute the coordinates into each equation.

$$\begin{array}{ll} 3x + 2y = 10 & 2x + 3y = 10 \\ 3(2) + 2(2) \stackrel{?}{=} 10 & 2(2) + 3(2) \stackrel{?}{=} 10 \\ 10 = 10 \checkmark & 10 = 10 \checkmark \end{array}$$

The solution of the system is $(2, 2)$.

6. Write each equation in slope-intercept form.

$$4x - 2y = 22 \rightarrow y = 2x - 11$$

$$6x + 9y = -3 \rightarrow y = -\frac{2}{3}x - \frac{1}{3}$$

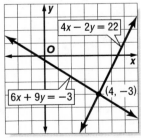

The graphs appear to intersect at $(4, -3)$.

Check: Substitute the coordinates into each equation.

$$\begin{array}{ll} 4x - 2y = 22 & 6x + 9y = -3 \\ 4(4) - 2(-3) \stackrel{?}{=} 22 & 6(4) + 9(-3) \stackrel{?}{=} -3 \\ 22 = 22 \checkmark & -3 = -3 \checkmark \end{array}$$

The solution of the system is $(4, -3)$.

7. $y = 6 - x \rightarrow y = -x + 6$
$$y = x + 4$$

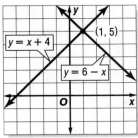

The graphs intersect at $(1, 5)$. Since there is one solution, this system is *consistent and independent*.

8. $x + 2y = 2 \quad \rightarrow y = -\frac{1}{2}x + 1$

$$2x + 4y = 8 \rightarrow y = -\frac{1}{2}x + 2$$

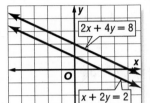

The lines do not intersect. Their graphs are parallel lines. So, there are no solutions that satisfy both equations. This system is *inconsistent*.

9. $x - 2y = 8 \rightarrow y = \frac{1}{2}x - 4$

$$\frac{1}{2}x - y = 4 \rightarrow y = \frac{1}{2}x - 4$$

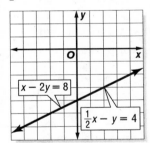

Since the equations are equivalent, their graphs are the same line. Any ordered pair representing a point on that line will satisfy both equations. So, there are infinitely many solutions to this system. This system is *consistent and dependent*.

10. Let $x =$ the number of prints, and let $y =$ the cost of developing film.

Cost of developing	is	cost for the prints	plus	cost for one roll.
y	$=$	$0.08x$	$+$	3.20

Cost of developing	is	cost for the prints	plus	cost for one roll.
y	$=$	$0.10x$	$+$	2.60

11. $y = 0.08x + 3.2$
$y = 0.1x + 2.6$

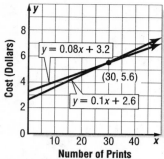

The graphs intersect at $(30, 5.6)$. The cost is \$5.60 for both stores to develop a roll with 30 prints.

12. You should use Specialty Photos if you are developing a roll with less than 30 prints, and you should use The Photo Lab if you are developing more than 30 prints.

Pages 113–115 Practice and Apply

13. Write each equation in slope-intercept form.
$y = 2x - 4$
$y = -3x + 1$

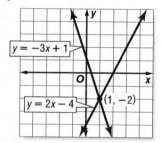

The graphs appear to intersect at $(1, -2)$.

Check: Substitute the coordinates into each equation.

$\quad y = 2x - 4 \qquad\qquad y = -3x + 1$
$-2 \stackrel{?}{=} 2(1) - 4 \qquad -2 \stackrel{?}{=} -3(1) + 1$
$\quad -2 = -2 \checkmark \qquad\qquad -2 = -2 \checkmark$

The solution of the system is $(1, -2)$.

14. Write each equation in slope-intercept form.
$y = 3x - 8$
$y = x - 8$

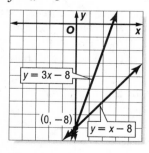

The graphs appear to intersect at $(0, -8)$.

Check: Substitute the coordinates into each equation.

$\quad y = 3x - 8 \qquad\qquad y = x - 8$
$-8 \stackrel{?}{=} 3(0) - 8 \qquad -8 \stackrel{?}{=} 0 - 8$
$\quad -8 = -8 \checkmark \qquad\qquad -8 = -8 \checkmark$

The solution of the system is $(0, -8)$.

15. Write each equation in slope-intercept form.

$x + 2y = 6 \rightarrow y = -\frac{1}{2}x + 3$
$2x + y = 9 \rightarrow y = -2x + 9$

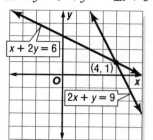

The graphs appear to intersect at $(4, 1)$.

Check: Substitute the coordinates into each equation.

$\quad x + 2y = 6 \qquad\qquad 2x + y = 9$
$4 + 2(1) \stackrel{?}{=} 6 \qquad 2(4) + 1 \stackrel{?}{=} 9$
$\qquad\quad 6 = 6 \checkmark \qquad\qquad\quad 9 = 9 \checkmark$

The solution of the system is $(4, 1)$.

16. Write each equation in slope-intercept form.

$2x + 3y = 12 \rightarrow y = -\frac{2}{3}x + 4$
$2x - y = 4 \quad \rightarrow y = 2x - 4$

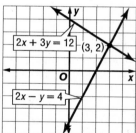

The graphs appear to intersect at $(3, 2)$.

Check: Substitute the coordinates into each equation.

$\quad 2x + 3y = 12 \qquad\qquad 2x - y = 4$
$2(3) + 3(2) \stackrel{?}{=} 12 \qquad 2(3) - 2 \stackrel{?}{=} 4$
$\qquad\quad 12 = 12 \checkmark \qquad\qquad\quad 4 = 4 \checkmark$

The solution of the system is $(3, 2)$.

17. Write each equation in slope-intercept form.

$3x - 7y = -6 \rightarrow y = \frac{3}{7}x + \frac{6}{7}$

$x + 2y = 11 \quad \rightarrow y = -\frac{1}{2}x + \frac{11}{2}$

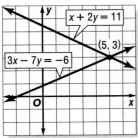

The graphs appear to intersect at $(5, 3)$.
Check: Substitute the coordinates into each
    equation.

$3x - 7y = -6$	$x + 2y = 11$
$3(5) - 7(3) \stackrel{?}{=} -6$	$5 + 2(3) \stackrel{?}{=} 11$
$-6 = -6$ ✓	$11 = 11$ ✓

The solution of the system is $(5, 3)$.

18. Write each equation in slope-intercept form.

$5x - 11 = 4y \rightarrow y = \frac{5}{4}x - \frac{11}{4}$

$7x - 1 = 8y \quad \rightarrow y = \frac{7}{8}x - \frac{1}{8}$

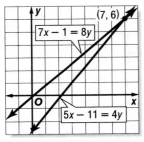

The graphs appear to intersect at $(7, 6)$.
Check: Substitute the coordinates into each
    equation.

$5x - 11 = 4y$	$7x - 1 = 8y$
$5(7) - 11 \stackrel{?}{=} 4(6)$	$7(7) - 1 \stackrel{?}{=} 8(6)$
$24 = 24$ ✓	$48 = 48$ ✓

The solution of the system is $(7, 6)$.

19. Write each equation in slope-intercept form.

$2x + 3y = 7 \rightarrow y = -\frac{2}{3}x + \frac{7}{3}$

$2x - 3y = 7 \rightarrow y = \frac{2}{3}x - \frac{7}{3}$

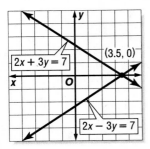

The graphs appear to intersect at $(3.5, 0)$.
Check: Substitute the coordinates into each
    equation.

$2x + 3y = 7$	$2x - 3y = 7$
$2(3.5) + 3(0) \stackrel{?}{=} 7$	$2(3.5) - 3(0) \stackrel{?}{=} 7$
$7 = 7$ ✓	$7 = 7$ ✓

The solution of the system is $(3.5, 0)$.

20. Write each equation in slope-intercept form.

$8x - 3y = -3 \rightarrow y = \frac{8}{3}x + 1$

$4x - 2y = -4 \rightarrow y = 2x + 2$

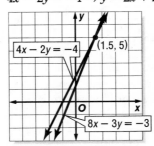

The graphs appear to intersect at $(1.5, 5)$.
Check: Substitute the coordinates into each
    equation.

$8x - 3y = -3$	$4x - 2y = -4$
$8(1.5) - 3(5) \stackrel{?}{=} -3$	$4(1.5) - 2(5) \stackrel{?}{=} -4$
$-3 = -3$ ✓	$-4 = -4$ ✓

The solution of the system is $(1.5, 5)$.

21. Write each equation in slope-intercept form.

$\frac{1}{4}x + 2y = 5 \rightarrow y = -\frac{1}{8}x + \frac{5}{2}$

$2x - y = 6 \quad \rightarrow y = 2x - 6$

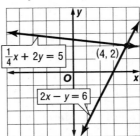

The graphs appear to intersect at $(4, 2)$.
Check: Substitute the coordinates into each
    equation.

$\frac{1}{4}x + 2y = 5$	$2x - y = 6$
$\frac{1}{4}(4) + 2(2) \stackrel{?}{=} 5$	$2(4) - 2 \stackrel{?}{=} 6$
$5 = 5$ ✓	$6 = 6$ ✓

The solution of the system is $(4, 2)$.

22. Write each equation in slope-intercept form.

$\frac{2}{3}x + y = -3 \rightarrow y = -\frac{2}{3}x - 3$

$y - \frac{1}{3}x = 6 \rightarrow y = \frac{1}{3}x + 6$

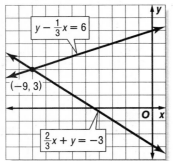

The graphs appear to intersect at $(-9, 3)$.

Check: Substitute the coordinates into each equation.

$\frac{2}{3}x + y = -3 \qquad\qquad y - \frac{1}{3}x = 6$

$\frac{2}{3}(-9) + 3 \stackrel{?}{=} -3 \qquad 3 - \frac{1}{3}(-9) \stackrel{?}{=} 6$

$-3 = -3 \checkmark \qquad\qquad 6 = 6 \checkmark$

The solution of the system is $(-9, 3)$.

23. Write each equation in slope-intercept form.

$\frac{1}{2}x - y = 0 \quad\rightarrow y = \frac{1}{2}x$

$\frac{1}{4}x + \frac{1}{2}y = -2 \rightarrow y = -\frac{1}{2}x - 4$

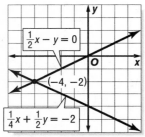

The graphs appear to intersect at $(-4, -2)$.

Check: Substitute the coordinates into each equation.

$\frac{1}{2}x - y = 0 \qquad\qquad \frac{1}{4}x + \frac{1}{2}y = -2$

$\frac{1}{2}(-4) - (-2) \stackrel{?}{=} 0 \quad \frac{1}{4}(-4) + \frac{1}{2}(-2) \stackrel{?}{=} -2$

$0 = 0 \checkmark \qquad\qquad -2 = -2 \checkmark$

The solution of the system is $(-4, -2)$.

24. Write each equation in slope-intercept form.

$\frac{4}{3}x + \frac{1}{5}y = 3 \rightarrow y = -\frac{20}{3}x + 15$

$\frac{2}{3}x - \frac{3}{5}y = 5 \rightarrow y = \frac{10}{9}x - \frac{75}{9}$

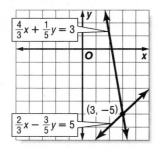

The graphs appear to intersect at $(3, -5)$.

Check: Substitute the coordinates into each equation.

$\frac{4}{3}x + \frac{1}{5}y = 3 \qquad\qquad \frac{2}{3}x - \frac{3}{5}y = 5$

$\frac{4}{3}(3) + \frac{1}{5}(-5) \stackrel{?}{=} 3 \qquad \frac{2}{3}(3) - \frac{3}{5}(-5) \stackrel{?}{=} 5$

$3 = 3 \checkmark \qquad\qquad 5 = 5 \checkmark$

The solution of the system is $(3, -5)$.

25. $y = x + 4$

$\quad\; y = x - 4$

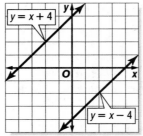

The lines do not intersect. Their graphs are parallel lines. So, there are no solutions that satisfy both equations. This system is *inconsistent*.

26. $y = x + 3$

$\quad\; y = 2x + 6$

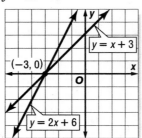

The graphs intersect at $(-3, 0)$. Since there is one solution, this system is *consistent and independent*.

27. $x + y = 4 \quad \rightarrow y = -x + 4$

$\quad -4x + y = 9 \rightarrow y = 4x + 9$

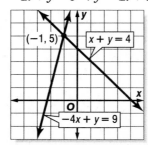

The graphs intersect at $(-1, 5)$. Since there is one solution, this system is *consistent and independent*.

28. $3x + y = 3 \quad \rightarrow y = -3x + 3$
$6x + 2y = 6 \rightarrow y = -3x + 3$

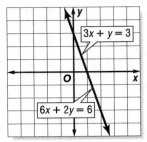

Since the equations are equivalent, their graphs are the same line. Any ordered pair representing a point on that line will satisfy both equations. So, there are infinitely many solutions to this system. This system is *consistent and dependent*.

29. $y - x = 5 \quad \rightarrow y = x + 5$
$2y - 2x = 8 \rightarrow y = x + 4$

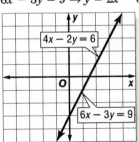

The lines do not intersect. Their graphs are parallel lines. So, there are no solutions that satisfy both equations. This system is *inconsistent*.

30. $4x - 2y = 6 \rightarrow y = 2x - 3$
$6x - 3y = 9 \rightarrow y = 2x - 3$

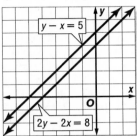

Since the equations are equivalent, their graphs are the same line. Any ordered pair representing a point on that line will satisfy both equations. So, there are infinitely many solutions to this system. This system is *consistent and dependent*.

31. $2y = x \qquad \rightarrow y = \frac{1}{2}x$
$8y = 2x + 1 \rightarrow y = \frac{1}{4}x + \frac{1}{8}$

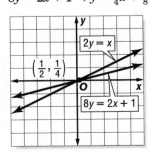

The graphs intersect at $\left(\frac{1}{2}, \frac{1}{4}\right)$. Since there is one solution, this system is *consistent and independent*.

32. $2y = 5 - x \quad \rightarrow y = -\frac{1}{2}x + \frac{5}{2}$
$6y = 7 - 3x \rightarrow y = -\frac{1}{2}x + \frac{7}{6}$

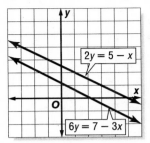

The lines do not intersect. Their graphs are parallel lines. So, there are no solutions that satisfy both equations. This system is *inconsistent*.

33. $0.8x - 1.5y = -10 \rightarrow y = \frac{8}{15}x + \frac{20}{3}$
$1.2x + 2.5y = 4 \quad \rightarrow y = -\frac{12}{25}x + \frac{8}{5}$

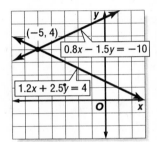

The graphs intersect at $(-5, 4)$. Since there is one solution, this system is *consistent and independent*.

34. $1.6y = 0.4x + 1 \quad \rightarrow y = \frac{1}{4}x + \frac{5}{8}$
$0.4y = 0.1x + 0.25 \rightarrow y = \frac{1}{4}x + \frac{5}{8}$

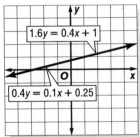

Since the equations are equivalent, their graphs are the same line. Any ordered pair representing a point on that line will satisfy both equations. So, there are infinitely many solutions to this system. This system is *consistent and dependent*.

35. $3y - x = -2 \rightarrow y = \frac{1}{3}x - \frac{2}{3}$

$y - \frac{1}{3}x = 2 \rightarrow y = \frac{1}{3}x + 2$

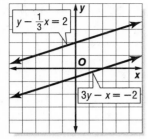

The lines do not intersect. Their graphs are parallel lines. So, there are no solutions that satisfy both equations. This system is *inconsistent*.

36. $2y - 4x = 3 \rightarrow y = 2x + \frac{3}{2}$

$\frac{4}{3}x - y = -2 \rightarrow y = \frac{4}{3}x + 2$

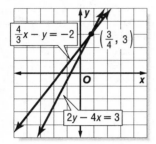

The graphs intersect at $\left(\frac{3}{4}, 3\right)$. Since there is one solution, this system is *consistent and independent*.

37. Write each equation in slope-intercept form.

$2y + 3x = -7 \rightarrow y = -\frac{3}{2}x - \frac{7}{2}$

$3y - 2x = 9 \rightarrow y = \frac{2}{3}x + 3$

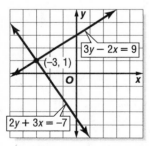

The graphs appear to intersect at $(-3, 1)$.
Check: Substitute the coordinates into each equation.

$$
\begin{array}{ll}
2y + 3x = -7 & 3y - 2x = 9 \\
2(1) + 3(-3) \stackrel{?}{=} -7 & 3(1) - 2(-3) \stackrel{?}{=} 9 \\
\qquad\qquad -7 = -7 \checkmark & \qquad\qquad 9 = 9 \checkmark
\end{array}
$$

The vertex is at the point $(-3, 1)$.

38. Write each equation in slope-intercept form.

$y - 2x = 1 \rightarrow y = 2x + 1$

$4x + y = 7 \rightarrow y = -4x + 7$

$2y - x = -4 \rightarrow y = \frac{1}{2}x - 2$

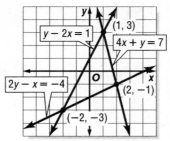

The graphs of $y - 2x = 1$ and $4x + y = 7$ appear to intersect at $(1, 3)$.

Check: Substitute the coordinates into each equation.

$$
\begin{array}{ll}
y - 2x = 1 & 4x + y = 7 \\
3 - 2(1) \stackrel{?}{=} 1 & 4(1) + 3 \stackrel{?}{=} 7 \\
\qquad 1 = 1 \checkmark & \qquad 7 = 7 \checkmark
\end{array}
$$

The graphs of $4x + y = 7$ and $2y - x = -4$ appear to intersect at $(2, -1)$.

Check: Substitute the coordinates into each equation.

$$
\begin{array}{ll}
4x + y = 7 & 2y - x = -4 \\
4(2) + (-1) \stackrel{?}{=} 7 & 2(-1) - 2 \stackrel{?}{=} -4 \\
\qquad\qquad 7 = 7 \checkmark & \qquad\quad -4 = -4 \checkmark
\end{array}
$$

The graphs of $y - 2x = 1$ and $2y - x = -4$ appear to intersect at $(-2, -3)$.

Check: Substitute the coordinates into each equation.

$$
\begin{array}{ll}
y - 2x = 1 & 2y - x = -4 \\
-3 - 2(-2) \stackrel{?}{=} 1 & 2(-3) - (-2) \stackrel{?}{=} -4 \\
\qquad\qquad 1 = 1 \checkmark & \qquad\quad -4 = -4 \checkmark
\end{array}
$$

The vertices are at the points $(1, 3)$, $(2, -1)$, and $(-2, -3)$.

39. Let $x =$ the number of miles, and let $y =$ the cost of renting a car.

Cost of renting a car	is	cost for miles driven	plus	cost for one day.
y	$=$	$0.23x$	$+$	52

Cost of renting a car	is	cost for one day.
y	$=$	80

40. $y = 0.23x + 52$

$y = 80$

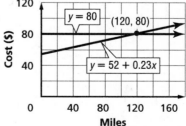

The graphs intersect at approximately $(120, 80)$. The cost is \$80 for both plans if you drive 120 miles.

41. The cost of the two plans is the same for 120 miles. The Deluxe Rental Plan is more expensive if the mileage is less than 120, but the Standard Rental Plan is more expensive if the mileage is more than 120. Therefore, the Adam's family should choose the Deluxe Rental Plan.

42. The point (200, 8) is a point on the supply curve. Thus, the supply would be 200,000 units. The point (300, 8) is a point on the demand curve. Thus, the demand would be 300,000 units. Prices will tend to rise.

43. The point (300, 12) is a point on the supply curve. Thus, the supply would be 300,000 units. The point (200, 12) is a point on the demand curve. Thus, the demand would be 200,000 units. Prices will tend to fall.

44. The graphs intersect at (250, 10). Therefore, the quantity will stabilize at 250,000 units. The equilibrium price is $10.

45. Let x = the number of years after 2000, and let y = the population in thousands.

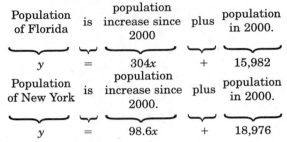

Population of Florida	is	population increase since 2000	plus	population in 2000.
y	=	$304x$	+	15,982

Population of New York	is	population increase since 2000.	plus	population in 2000.
y	=	$98.6x$	+	18,976

46. $y = 304x + 15{,}982$
$y = 98.6x + 18{,}976$

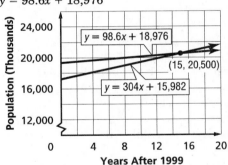

The graphs appear to intersect at (15, 20,500). Therefore, the population of both states will be about 20,500,000 in 2015.

47. Florida will probably be ranked third by 2020. The graphs intersect in the year 2015, so New York will still have a higher population in 2010, but Florida will have a higher population in 2020.

48. Write each equation in slope-intercept form.
$$ax + by = c \rightarrow y = -\frac{a}{b}x + \frac{c}{b}$$
$$dx + ey = f \rightarrow y = -\frac{d}{e}x + \frac{f}{e}$$

48a. A system is consistent and dependent if it has an infinite number of solutions. This occurs when the graphs of the equations are the same line. This occurs when the slopes are equal and the y-intercepts are equal or when $\frac{a}{b} = \frac{d}{e}$ and $\frac{c}{b} = \frac{f}{e}$.

48b. A system is consistent and independent if it has exactly one solution. This occurs when the graphs of the equations are intersecting lines. This occurs when the slopes are not equal or when $\frac{a}{b} \neq \frac{d}{e}$.

48c. A system is inconsistent if it has no solution. This occurs when the graphs of the equations are parallel lines. This occurs when the slopes are equal and the y-intercepts are not equal or when $\frac{a}{b} = \frac{d}{e}$ and $\frac{c}{b} \neq \frac{f}{e}$.

49. You can use a system of equations to track sales and make predictions about future growth based on past performance and trends in the graphs. Answers should include the following.
- The coordinates (6, 54) represent that 6 years after 1999 both the in-store sales and online sales will be $54,000.
- The in-store sales and the online sales will never be equal and in-store sales will continue to be higher than online sales.

50. A; Write each equation in slope-intercept form.
$$2x + 3y = 12 \rightarrow y = -\frac{2}{3}x + 4$$
$$2x - y = 4 \quad \rightarrow y = 2x - 4$$

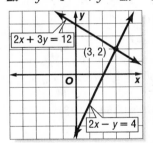

The graphs appear to intersect at (3, 2).
Check: Substitute the coordinates into each equation.

$2x + 3y = 12$	$2x - y = 4$
$2(3) + 3(2) \stackrel{?}{=} 12$	$2(3) - 2 \stackrel{?}{=} 4$
$12 = 12$ ✓	$4 = 4$ ✓

The solution of the system is (3, 2).

51. C; Write each equation in slope-intercept form.
$$4x + 8y = 12 \rightarrow y = -\frac{1}{2}x + \frac{3}{2}$$
$$x + y = 3 \quad \rightarrow y = -x + 3$$
$$2x + y = 3 \quad \rightarrow y = -2x + 3$$
$$x + 2y = 3 \quad \rightarrow y = -\frac{1}{2}x + \frac{3}{2}$$
$$2x + 2y = 6 \quad \rightarrow y = -x + 3$$
Since $4x + 8y = 12$ and $x + 2y = 3$ are equivalent, their graphs are the same line.

52. $y = 0.125x - 3.005$
$y = -2.58$
Clear the Y= list. Enter $0.125x - 3.005$ as Y$_1$ and -2.58 as Y$_2$. Graph in the standard viewing window. The solution of the system is $(3.40, -2.58)$.

53. $3.6x - 2y = 4 \rightarrow y = 1.8x - 2$
$-2.7x + y = 3 \rightarrow y = 2.7x + 3$
Clear the Y= list. Enter $1.8x - 2$ as Y$_1$ and $2.7x + 3$ as Y$_2$. Graph in the window X$_{min}$ = -10, X$_{max}$ = 10, Y$_{min}$ = -15, and Y$_{max}$ = 5. The solution of the system is $(-5.56, 12)$.

54. $y = 0.18x + 2.7$
$y = -0.42x + 5.1$
Clear the Y= list. Enter $0.18x + 2.7$ as Y$_1$ and $-0.42x + 5.1$ as Y$_2$. Graph in the standard viewing window. The solution of the system is $(4, 3.42)$.

55. $1.6x + 3.2y = 8 \rightarrow y = -0.5x + 2.5$
$1.2x + 2.4y = 4 \rightarrow y = -0.5x + 1.667$
Clear the Y= list. Enter $-0.5x + 2.5$ as Y$_1$ and $-0.5x + 1.667$ as Y$_2$. Graph in the standard viewing window. The intersect feature yields an error message. The lines are parallel. There are no solutions that satisfy both equations.

56. $y - \frac{1}{4}x = 6 \rightarrow y = \frac{1}{4}x + 6$
$2y + \frac{1}{2}x = 3 \rightarrow y = -\frac{1}{4}x + \frac{3}{2}$
Clear the Y= list. Enter $\frac{1}{4}x + 6$ as Y$_1$ and $-\frac{1}{4}x + \frac{3}{2}$ as Y$_2$. Graph in the standard viewing window. The solution of the system is $(-9, 3.75)$.

57. $\frac{1}{2}y - 5x = 8 \rightarrow y = 10x + 16$
$\frac{1}{3}y - 8x = -7 \rightarrow y = 24x - 21$
Clear the Y= list. Enter $10x + 16$ as Y$_1$ and $24x - 21$ as Y$_2$. Graph in the window X$_{min}$ = -10, X$_{max}$ = 10, Y$_{min}$ = -50, and Y$_{max}$ = 50. The solution of the system is $(2.64, 42.43)$.

Page 115   Maintain Your Skills

58. The boundary is the graph of $y = 5 + 3x$. Since the inequality symbol is $\geq$, the boundary will be solid. Use the slope-intercept form, $y = 3x + 5$. Now test the point $(0, 0)$.
$y \geq 5 + 3x$
$0 \geq 5 + 3(0)$
$0 \geq 5$ false
Shade the region that does not contain $(0, 0)$.

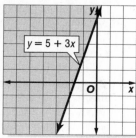

59. The boundary is the graph of $2x + y = -4$. Since the inequality symbol is $>$, the boundary will be dashed. Use the slope-intercept form, $y = -2x - 4$. Now test the point $(0, 0)$.
$2x + y > -4$
$2(0) + 0 > -4$
$0 > -4$ true
Shade the region that includes $(0, 0)$.

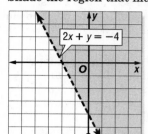

60. The boundary is the graph of $2y - 1 = x$. Since the inequality symbol is $\leq$, the boundary will be solid. Use the slope-intercept form, $y = \frac{1}{2}x + \frac{1}{2}$. Now test the point $(0, 0)$.
$2y - 1 \leq x$
$2(0) - 1 \leq 0$
$-1 \leq 0$ true
Shade the region that includes $(0, 0)$.

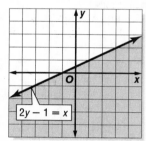

61. Since this graph consists of a V-shape graph, it represents an absolute value function (A).

62. Since this graph is a horizontal line, it represents a constant function (C).

63. Since this graph consists of multiple line segments that are not horizontal, it represents a piecewise function (P).

64. $|x| - 5 = 8$
$|x| = 13$
Case 1: $a = b$ or   Case 2: $a = -b$
    $x = 13$ $x = -13$
Check: $|x| - 5 = 8$ $|x| - 5 = 8$
      $|13| - 5 \stackrel{?}{=} 8$ $|-13| - 5 \stackrel{?}{=} 8$
        $13 - 5 \stackrel{?}{=} 8$ $13 - 5 \stackrel{?}{=} 8$
             $8 = 8$ ✓ $8 = 8$ ✓
The solutions are 13 or -13. Thus, the solution set is $\{-13, 13\}$.

65. Case 1: $a = b$ or   Case 2: $a = -b$
$$w + 3 = 12 \qquad\qquad w + 3 = -12$$
$$w = 9 \qquad\qquad\quad w = -15$$
Check: $|w + 3| = 12 \qquad |w + 3| = 12$
$|9 + 3| \stackrel{?}{=} 12 \qquad |-15 + 3| \stackrel{?}{=} 12$
$|12| \stackrel{?}{=} 12 \qquad\quad |-12| \stackrel{?}{=} 12$
$12 = 12 \ \checkmark \qquad\quad 12 = 12 \ \checkmark$

The solutions are 9 or -15. Thus, the solution set is $\{-15, 9\}$.

66. This sentence is never true. So the solution set is $\varnothing$.

67. $3|2t - 1| = 15$
$|2t - 1| = 5$

Case 1: $a = b$ or   Case 2: $a = -b$
$$2t - 1 = 5 \qquad\qquad 2t - 1 = -5$$
$$2t - 1 + 1 = 5 + 1 \qquad 2t - 1 + 1 = -5 + 1$$
$$2t = 6 \qquad\qquad\quad 2t = -4$$
$$\frac{2t}{2} = \frac{6}{2} \qquad\qquad\quad \frac{2t}{2} = \frac{-4}{2}$$
$$t = 3 \qquad\qquad\quad t = -2$$
Check: $3|2t - 1| = 15 \qquad 3|2t - 1| = 15$
$3|2(3) - 1| \stackrel{?}{=} 15 \qquad 3|2(-2) - 1| \stackrel{?}{=} 15$
$3|6 - 1| \stackrel{?}{=} 15 \qquad 3|-4 - 1| \stackrel{?}{=} 15$
$3|5| \stackrel{?}{=} 15 \qquad\quad 3|-5| \stackrel{?}{=} 15$
$3(5) \stackrel{?}{=} 15 \qquad\quad 3(5) \stackrel{?}{=} 15$
$15 = 15 \ \checkmark \qquad\quad 15 = 15 \ \checkmark$

The solutions are 3 or -2. Thus, the solution set is $\{-2, 3\}$.

68. $|4r + 3| - 7 = 10$
$|4r + 3| = 17$

Case 1: $a = b$ or   Case 2: $a = -b$
$$4r + 3 = 17 \qquad\qquad 4r + 3 = -17$$
$$4r + 3 - 3 = 17 - 3 \qquad 4r + 3 - 3 = -17 - 3$$
$$4r = 14 \qquad\qquad\quad 4r = -20$$
$$\frac{4r}{4} = \frac{14}{4} \qquad\qquad\quad \frac{4r}{4} = \frac{-20}{4}$$
$$r = \frac{7}{2} \qquad\qquad\quad r = -5$$
Check:
$|4r + 3| - 7 = 10 \qquad |4r + 3| - 7 = 10$
$\left|4\left(\frac{7}{2}\right) + 3\right| - 7 \stackrel{?}{=} 10 \qquad |4(-5) + 3| - 7 \stackrel{?}{=} 10$
$|14 + 3| - 7 \stackrel{?}{=} 10 \qquad |-20 + 3| - 7 \stackrel{?}{=} 10$
$|17| - 7 \stackrel{?}{=} 10 \qquad\quad |-17| - 7 \stackrel{?}{=} 10$
$17 - 7 \stackrel{?}{=} 10 \qquad\quad 17 - 7 \stackrel{?}{=} 10$
$10 = 10 \ \checkmark \qquad\quad 10 = 10 \ \checkmark$

The solutions are $\frac{7}{2}$ or -5. Thus, the solution set is $\left\{-5, \frac{7}{2}\right\}$.

69. Case 1: $a = b$ or Case 2: $a = -b$
$$k + 7 = 3k - 11 \qquad\qquad k + 7 = -(3k - 11)$$
$$k + 7 - 3k = 3k - 11 - 3k \qquad k + 7 = -3k + 11$$
$$-2k + 7 = -11 \qquad\qquad k + 7 + 3k = -3k + 11 + 3k$$
$$-2k + 7 - 7 = -11 - 7 \qquad 4k + 7 = 11$$
$$-2k = -18 \qquad\qquad 4k + 7 - 7 = 11 - 7$$
$$k = 9 \qquad\qquad\qquad 4k = 4$$
$$\qquad\qquad\qquad\qquad\qquad k = 1$$
Check: $|k + 7| = 3k - 11 \qquad |k + 7| = 3k - 11$
$|9 + 7| \stackrel{?}{=} 3(9) - 11 \qquad |1 + 7| \stackrel{?}{=} 3(1) - 11$
$|16| \stackrel{?}{=} 27 - 11 \qquad\quad |8| \stackrel{?}{=} 3 - 11$
$16 = 16 \ \checkmark \qquad\qquad 8 \neq -8$

Since $8 \neq -8$, the only solution is 9. Thus, the solution set is $\{9\}$.

70. $8 + 2n$

71. $x^2 - 6$

72. $4(a + 5)$

73. $\frac{z}{3} + 1$

74. $(3x + 5) - (2x + 3) = 3x + 5 - 2x - 3$
$= 3x - 2x + 5 - 3$
$= (3 - 2)x + (5 - 3)$
$= 1x + 2$
$= x + 2$

75. $(3y - 11) + (6y + 12) = 3y - 11 + 6y + 12$
$= 3y + 6y + 12 - 11$
$= (3 + 6)y + (12 - 11)$
$= 9y + 1$

76. $(5x - y) + (-8x + 7y) = 5x - y - 8x + 7y$
$= 5x - 8x + 7y - y$
$= (5 - 8)x + (7 - 1)y$
$= -3x + 6y$

77. $6(2x + 3y - 1) = 6(2x) + 6(3y) + 6(-1)$
$= 12x + 18y + (-6)$
$= 12x + 18y - 6$

78. $5(4x + 2y - x + 2) = 5(4x) + 5(2y) + 5(-x) + 5(2)$
$= 20x + 10y + (-5x) + 10$
$= 20x + 10y - 5x + 10$
$= 20x - 5x + 10y + 10$
$= (20 - 5)x + 10y + 10$
$= 15x + 10y + 10$

79. $3(x + 4y) - 2(x + 4y) = 3(x) + 3(4y) - 2(x) - 2(4y)$
$= 3x + 12y - 2x - 8y$
$= 3x - 2x + 12y - 8y$
$= (3 - 2)x + (12 - 8)y$
$= 1x + 4y$
$= x + 4y$

3-2	**Solving Systems of Equations Algebraically**

Pages 119–120 Check for Understanding

1. See students' work; for substitution one equation should have a variable with a coefficient of 1.

2. There are infinitely many solutions.

3. Vincent; Juanita subtracted the two equations incorrectly; $-y - y = -2y$, not 0.

4. Substitute $3x - 4$ for y in the second equation and solve for x.
$$y = 4 + x$$
$$3x - 4 = 4 + x$$
$$2x - 4 = 4$$
$$2x = 8$$
$$x = 4$$
Now, substitute the value for x in either original equation and solve for y.
$$y = 4 + x$$
$$y = 4 + 4$$
$$y = 8$$
The solution of the system is $(4, 8)$.

5. Solve the second equation for c in terms of d.

$$c + 3d = 10$$
$$c = 10 - 3d$$

Substitute $10 - 3d$ for c in the first equation and solve for d.

$$4c + 2d = 10$$
$$4(10 - 3d) + 2d = 10$$
$$40 - 12d + 2d = 10$$
$$-10d = -30$$
$$d = 3$$

Now, substitute the value for d in either original equation and solve for c.

$$c + 3d = 10$$
$$c + 3(3) = 10$$
$$c + 9 = 10$$
$$c = 1$$

The solution of the system is $(1, 3)$.

6. In each equation, the coefficient of r is 2. If one equation is subtracted from the other, the variable r will be eliminated.

$$2r - 3s = 11$$
$$(-)\ \underline{2r + 2s = \ \ \ 6}$$
$$-5s = \ \ \ 5$$
$$s = -1$$

Now find r by substituting -1 for s in either original equation.

$$2r - 3s = 11$$
$$2r - 3(-1) = 11$$
$$2r + 3 = 11$$
$$2r = 8$$
$$r = 4$$

The solution is $(4, -1)$.

7. Multiply the first equation by 3 and the second equation by 2. Then add the equations to eliminate the q variable.

$$2p + 4q = 18 \qquad\qquad 6p + 12q = 54$$
$$3p - 4q = 3 \qquad\qquad (+)\ \underline{6p - 12q = \ \ 6}$$
$$\qquad\qquad\qquad\qquad\qquad 12p \qquad\quad = 60$$
$$\qquad\qquad\qquad\qquad\qquad\qquad p = 5$$

Replace p with 5 and solve for q.

$$2p + 4q = 18$$
$$2(5) + 4q = 18$$
$$10 + 4q = 18$$
$$4q = 8$$
$$q = 2$$

The solution is $(5, 2)$.

8. Multiply the first equation by 2. Then add the equations to eliminate the a variable.

$$a - b = 2 \qquad\qquad 2a - 2b = 4$$
$$-2a + 3b = 3 \qquad\qquad (+)\ \underline{-2a + 3b = 3}$$
$$\qquad\qquad\qquad\qquad\qquad\qquad b = 7$$

Replace b with 7 and solve for a.

$$a - b = 2$$
$$a - 7 = 2$$
$$a = 9$$

The solution is $(9, 7)$.

9. In each equation, the coefficient of n is 1. If one equation is subtracted from the other, the variable n will be eliminated.

$$5m + n = 10$$
$$(-)\ \underline{4m + n = \ \ 4}$$
$$m \quad\ \ \ = \ \ 6$$

Now find n by substituting 6 for m in either original equation.

$$5m + n = 10$$
$$5(6) + n = 10$$
$$30 + n = 10$$
$$n = -20$$

The solution is $(6, -20)$.

10. Solve the second equation for h in terms of g.

$$8h = 5 + 12g$$
$$h = \frac{5}{8} + \frac{3}{2}g$$

Substitute $\frac{5}{8} + \frac{3}{2}g$ for h in the first equation and solve for g.

$$3g - 2h = -1$$
$$3g - 2\left(\frac{5}{8} + \frac{3}{2}g\right) = -1$$
$$3g - \frac{5}{4} - 3g = -1$$
$$-\frac{5}{4} = -1$$

Since there are no values of g and h that will make the equation $-\frac{5}{4} = -1$ true, there are no solutions for this system of equations.

11. Multiply the second equation by 2. Then add the equations to eliminate the y variable.

$$\frac{1}{4}x + y = \frac{7}{2} \qquad\qquad \frac{1}{4}x + y = \frac{7}{2}$$
$$x - \frac{1}{2}y = 2 \qquad\qquad (+)\ \underline{2x - y = 4}$$
$$\qquad\qquad\qquad\qquad\qquad \frac{9}{4}x \qquad\ = \frac{15}{2}$$
$$\qquad\qquad\qquad\qquad\qquad\qquad x = \frac{10}{3}$$

Replace x with $\frac{10}{3}$ and solve for y.

$$x - \frac{1}{2}y = 2$$
$$\frac{10}{3} - \frac{1}{2}y = 2$$
$$-\frac{1}{2}y = -\frac{4}{3}$$
$$y = \frac{8}{3}$$

The solution is $\left(\frac{10}{3}, \frac{8}{3}\right)$ or $\left(3\frac{1}{3}, 2\frac{2}{3}\right)$.

12. C; Solve the second equation for y in terms of x.
$$2x + y = 1$$
$$y = 1 - 2x$$
Substitute $1 - 2x$ for y in the first equation.
$$4x + 3y = 7$$
$$4x + 3(1 - 2x) = 7$$
$$4x + 3 - 6x = 7$$
$$3 - 2x = 7$$
$$-2x = 4$$
$$x = -2$$
Now replace x with -2 in either equation to find the value of y.
$$2x + y = 1$$
$$2(-2) + y = 1$$
$$-4 + y = 1$$
$$y = 5$$
Evaluate $2x + 2y$ to answer the original problem.
$$2x + 2y = 2(-2) + 2(5)$$
$$= -4 + 10$$
$$= 6$$
So, $2x + 2y = 6$.
The answer is C.

Pages 120–122 Practice and Apply

13. Solve the second equation for j in terms of k.
$$j + k = 14$$
$$j = 14 - k$$
Substitute $14 - k$ for j in the first equation and solve for k.
$$2j - 3k = 3$$
$$2(14 - k) - 3k = 3$$
$$28 - 2k - 3k = 3$$
$$-5k = -25$$
$$k = 5$$
Now substitute the value for k in either original equation and solve for j.
$$j + k = 14$$
$$j + 5 = 14$$
$$j = 9$$
The solution of the system is $(9, 5)$.

14. Solve the first equation for s in terms of r.
$$2r + s = 11$$
$$s = 11 - 2r$$
Substitute $11 - 2r$ for s in the second equation and solve for r.
$$6r - 2s = -2$$
$$6r - 2(11 - 2r) = -2$$
$$6r - 22 + 4r = -2$$
$$10r = 20$$
$$r = 2$$
Now substitute the value for r in either original equation and solve for s.
$$2r + s = 11$$
$$2(2) + s = 11$$
$$4 + s = 11$$
$$s = 7$$
The solution of the system is $(2, 7)$.

15. Solve the first equation for b in terms of a.
$$5a - b = 17$$
$$-b = 17 - 5a$$
$$b = 5a - 17$$
Substitute $5a - 17$ for b in the second equation and solve for a.
$$3a + 2b = 5$$
$$3a + 2(5a - 17) = 5$$
$$3a + 10a - 34 = 5$$
$$13a = 39$$
$$a = 3$$
Now substitute the value for a in either original equation and solve for b.
$$5a - b = 17$$
$$5(3) - b = 17$$
$$15 - b = 17$$
$$-b = 2$$
$$b = -2$$
The solution of the system is $(3, -2)$.

16. Solve the first equation for w in terms of z.
$$-w - z = -2$$
$$-w = z - 2$$
$$w = 2 - z$$
Substitute $2 - z$ for w in the second equation and solve for z.
$$4w + 5z = 16$$
$$4(2 - z) + 5z = 16$$
$$8 - 4z + 5z = 16$$
$$z = 8$$
Now substitute the value for z in either original equation and solve for w.
$$-w - z = -2$$
$$-w - 8 = -2$$
$$-w = 6$$
$$w = -6$$
The solution of the system is $(-6, 8)$.

17. Solve the second equation for d in terms of c.
$$2c = 8 - d$$
$$d + 2c = 8$$
$$d = 8 - 2c$$
Substitute $8 - 2c$ for d in the first equation and solve for c.
$$6c + 3d = 12$$
$$6c + 3(8 - 2c) = 12$$
$$6c + 24 - 6c = 12$$
$$24 = 12$$
Since there are no values of c and d that will make the equation $24 = 12$ true, there are no solutions for this system of equations.

18. Solve the first equation for x in terms of y.
$$2x + 4y = 6$$
$$2x = 6 - 4y$$
$$x = 3 - 2y$$
Substitute $3 - 2y$ for x in the second equation and solve for y.
$$7x = 4 + 3y$$
$$7(3 - 2y) = 4 + 3y$$
$$21 - 14y = 4 + 3y$$
$$21 - 17y = 4$$
$$-17y = -17$$
$$y = 1$$
Now substitute the value for y in either original equation and solve for x.
$$7x = 4 + 3y$$
$$7x = 4 + 3(1)$$
$$7x = 4 + 3$$
$$7x = 7$$
$$x = 1$$
The solution of the system is $(1, 1)$.

19. In each equation, the coefficient of v is 1. If one equation is subtracted from the other, the variable v will be eliminated.
$$\begin{array}{rl} u + v = & 7 \\ (-)\ 2u + v = & 11 \\ \hline -u\quad\ = & -4 \\ u = & 4 \end{array}$$
Now find v by substituting 4 for u in either original equation.
$$u + v = 7$$
$$4 + v = 7$$
$$v = 3$$
The solution is $(4, 3)$.

20. Multiply the first equation by 2. Then add the equations to eliminate the n variable.
$$m - n = -9 \qquad\quad 2m - 2n = -18$$
$$7m + 2n = 9 \qquad \underline{(+)\ 7m + 2n = \quad 9}$$
$$\qquad\qquad\qquad\quad 9m\quad\ = -9$$
$$\qquad\qquad\qquad\qquad\quad m = -1$$

Replace m with -1 and solve for n.
$$m - n = -9$$
$$-1 - n = -9$$
$$-n = -8$$
$$n = 8$$
The solution is $(-1, 8)$.

21. Multiply the first equation by 2 and the second equation by 3. Then subtract the equations to eliminate the p variable.
$$3p - 5q = 6 \qquad\quad 6p - 10q = 12$$
$$2p - 4q = 4 \qquad \underline{(-)\ 6p - 12q = 12}$$
$$\qquad\qquad\qquad\qquad\quad 2q = 0$$
$$\qquad\qquad\qquad\qquad\quad\ q = 0$$
Replace q with 0 and solve for p.
$$3p - 5q = 6$$
$$3p - 5(0) = 6$$
$$3p = 6$$
$$p = 2$$
The solution is $(2, 0)$.

22. Multiply the first equation by 4 and the second equation by 5. Then add the equations to eliminate the y variable.

$$4x - 5y = 17 \qquad\qquad 16x - 20y = 68$$
$$3x + 4y = 5 \qquad\qquad \underline{(+)\ 15x + 20y = 25}$$
$$\qquad\qquad\qquad\qquad\quad 31x\qquad\ = 93$$
$$\qquad\qquad\qquad\qquad\qquad\quad x = 3$$

Replace x with 3 and solve for y.
$$4x - 5y = 17$$
$$4(3) - 5y = 17$$
$$12 - 5y = 17$$
$$-5y = 5$$
$$y = -1$$
The solution is $(3, -1)$.

23. Multiply the second equation by 2. Then add the equations to eliminate the d variable.
$$2c + 6d = 14 \qquad\qquad 2c + 6d = 14$$
$$\tfrac{1}{2}c - 3d = 8 \qquad\qquad \underline{(+)\ c - 6d = 16}$$
$$\qquad\qquad\qquad\qquad\quad 3c\quad\ = 30$$
$$\qquad\qquad\qquad\qquad\qquad c = 10$$

Replace c with 10 and solve for d.
$$2c + 6d = 14$$
$$2(10) + 6d = 14$$
$$20 + 6d = 14$$
$$6d = -6$$
$$d = -1$$
The solution is $(10, -1)$.

24. Multiply the second equation by 3. Then subtract the equations to eliminate the s variable.
$$3s + 2t = -3 \qquad\qquad 3s + 2t = \quad -3$$
$$s + \tfrac{1}{3}t = -4 \qquad\qquad \underline{(-)\ 3s + \ t = -12}$$
$$\qquad\qquad\qquad\qquad\qquad\quad t = 9$$
Replace t with 9 and solve for s.
$$3s + 2t = -3$$
$$3s + 2(9) = -3$$
$$3s + 18 = -3$$
$$3s = -21$$
$$s = -7$$
The solution is $(-7, 9)$.

25. Multiply the first equation by 3. Then subtract the equations to eliminate the r variable.
$$r + 4s = -8 \qquad\qquad 3r + 12s = -24$$
$$3r + 2s = 6 \qquad\qquad \underline{(-)\ 3r + \ 2s = \quad 6}$$
$$\qquad\qquad\qquad\qquad\quad 10s = -30$$
$$\qquad\qquad\qquad\qquad\qquad\ s = -3$$
Replace s with -3 and solve for r.
$$r + 4s = -8$$
$$r + 4(-3) = -8$$
$$r - 12 = -8$$
$$r = 4$$
The solution is $(4, -3)$.

26. Multiply the second equation by 2. Then subtract the equations to eliminate the m variable.
$$10m - 9n = 15 \qquad\qquad 10m - 9n = \ 15$$
$$5m - 4n = 10 \qquad\qquad \underline{(-)\ 10m - 8n = \ 20}$$
$$\qquad\qquad\qquad\qquad\qquad\ -n = -5$$
$$\qquad\qquad\qquad\qquad\qquad\quad n = 5$$

Replace n with 5 and solve for m.
$$5m - 4n = 10$$
$$5m - 4(5) = 10$$
$$5m - 20 = 10$$
$$5m = 30$$
$$m = 6$$
The solution is $(6, 5)$.

27. Multiply the first equation by 6 and the second equation by 7. Then add the equations to eliminate the d variable.

$$3c - 7d = -3 \qquad\qquad 18c - 42d = -18$$
$$2c + 6d = -34 \qquad \underline{(+)\ 14c + 42d = -238}$$
$$\qquad\qquad\qquad\qquad\quad 32c \qquad\quad = -256$$
$$\qquad\qquad\qquad\qquad\qquad\qquad\quad c = -8$$

Replace c with -8 and solve for d.
$$3c - 7d = -3$$
$$3(-8) - 7d = -3$$
$$-24 - 7d = -3$$
$$-7d = 21$$
$$d = -3$$
The solution is $(-8, -3)$.

28. Multiply the first equation by 3 and the second equation by 4. Then add the equations to eliminate the h variable.

$$6g - 8h = 50 \qquad\qquad 18g - 24h = 150$$
$$4g + 6h = 22 \qquad \underline{(+)\ 16g + 24h = \ \ 88}$$
$$\qquad\qquad\qquad\qquad\quad 34g \qquad\qquad = 238$$
$$\qquad\qquad\qquad\qquad\qquad\qquad\quad g = 7$$

Replace g with 7 and solve for h.
$$6g - 8h = 50$$
$$6(7) - 8h = 50$$
$$42 - 8h = 50$$
$$-8h = 8$$
$$h = -1$$
The solution is $(7, -1)$.

29. Solve the first equation for q in terms of p.
$$2p = 7 + q$$
$$2p - 7 = q$$
Substitute $2p - 7$ for q in the second equation and solve for p.
$$6p - 3q = 24$$
$$6p - 3(2p - 7) = 24$$
$$6p - 6p + 21 = 24$$
$$21 = 24$$
Since there are no values of p and q that will make the equation $21 = 24$ true, there are no solutions for this system of equations.

30.
$$3x = -31 + 2y \rightarrow 3x - 2y = -31$$
$$5x + 6y = 23 \qquad\qquad 5x + 6y = 23$$
Multiply the first equation by 3. Then add the equations to eliminate the y variable.
$$3x - 2y = -31 \qquad\qquad 9x - 6y = -93$$
$$5x + 6y = 23 \qquad \underline{(+)\ 5x + 6y = \ \ \ 23}$$
$$\qquad\qquad\qquad\qquad\quad 14x \qquad\quad = -70$$
$$\qquad\qquad\qquad\qquad\qquad\qquad x = -5$$

Replace x with -5 and solve for y.
$$5x + 6y = 23$$
$$5(-5) + 6y = 23$$
$$-25 + 6y = 23$$
$$6y = 48$$
$$y = 8$$
The solution is $(-5, 8)$.

31. Multiply the first equation by 2 and the second equation by 3. Then subtract the equations to eliminate the u variable.

$$3u + 5v = 6 \qquad\qquad 6u + 10v = \ \ \ 12$$
$$2u - 4v = -7 \qquad \underline{(-)\ 6u - 12v = -21}$$
$$\qquad\qquad\qquad\qquad\qquad 22v = \ \ \ 33$$
$$\qquad\qquad\qquad\qquad\qquad\quad v = \frac{3}{2}$$

Replace v with $\frac{3}{2}$ and solve for u.
$$3u + 5v = 6$$
$$3u + 5\left(\frac{3}{2}\right) = 6$$
$$3u + \frac{15}{2} = 6$$
$$3u = -\frac{3}{2}$$
$$u = -\frac{1}{2}$$
The solution is $\left(-\frac{1}{2}, \frac{3}{2}\right)$.

32. Multiply the second equation by 2. Then add the equations to eliminate the b variable.

$$3a - 2b = -3 \qquad\qquad 3a - 2b = -3$$
$$3a + b = 3 \qquad \underline{(+)\ 6a + 2b = \ \ \ 6}$$
$$\qquad\qquad\qquad\qquad\quad 9a \qquad\quad = 3$$
$$\qquad\qquad\qquad\qquad\qquad\quad a = \frac{1}{3}$$

Replace a with $\frac{1}{3}$ and solve for b.
$$3a + b = 3$$
$$3\left(\frac{1}{3}\right) + b = 3$$
$$1 + b = 3$$
$$b = 2$$
The solution is $\left(\frac{1}{3}, 2\right)$.

33. Multiply the second equation by 2. Then subtract the equations to eliminate the s variable.

$$s + 3t = 27 \qquad\qquad s + 3t = \ \ \ 27$$
$$\tfrac{1}{2}s + 2t = 19 \qquad \underline{(-)\ s + 4t = \ \ \ 38}$$
$$\qquad\qquad\qquad\qquad\qquad -t = -11$$
$$\qquad\qquad\qquad\qquad\qquad\ \ t = 11$$

Replace t with 11 and solve for s.
$$s + 3t = 27$$
$$s + 3(11) = 27$$
$$s + 33 = 27$$
$$s = -6$$
The solution is $(-6, 11)$.

34. Substitute $6 - 2g$ for f in the second equation and solve for g.
$$\frac{1}{6}f + \frac{1}{3}g = 1$$
$$\frac{1}{6}(6 - 2g) + \frac{1}{3}g = 1$$
$$1 - \frac{1}{3}g + \frac{1}{3}g = 1$$
$$1 = 1$$
Since the equation $1 = 1$ is true for all values of f and g, there are infinitely many solutions for this system of equations.

35. Multiply the first equation by 2. Then subtract the equations to eliminate the x variable.

$$0.25x + 1.75y = 1.25 \qquad 0.5x + 3.5y = 2.5$$
$$0.5x + 2.5y = 2 \qquad \underline{(-)\ 0.5x + 2.5y = \ \ \ 2}$$
$$\qquad\qquad\qquad\qquad\qquad\qquad\qquad y = 0.5$$

Replace y with 0.5 and solve for x.
$$0.5x + 2.5y = 2$$
$$0.5x + 2.5(0.5) = 2$$
$$0.5x + 1.25 = 2$$
$$0.5x = 0.75$$
$$x = 1.5$$
The solution is $(1.5, 0.5)$.

36. Multiply the first equation by 3. Then subtract the equations to eliminate the m variable.

$$0.4m + 1.8n = 8 \qquad 1.2m + 5.4n = 24$$
$$1.2m + 3.4n = 16 \qquad \underline{(-)\ 1.2m + 3.4n = 16}$$
$$2n = 8$$
$$n = 4$$

Replace n with 4 and solve for m.

$$0.4m + 1.8n = 8$$
$$0.4m + 1.8(4) = 8$$
$$0.4m + 7.2 = 8$$
$$0.4m = 0.8$$
$$m = 2$$

The solution is (2, 4).

37. Let x = one number, and y = another number.

$$3x + 5y = 54$$
$$y = x - 2$$

Substitute $x - 2$ for y in the first equation and solve for x.

$$3x + 5y = 54$$
$$3x + 5(x - 2) = 54$$
$$3x + 5x - 10 = 54$$
$$8x = 64$$
$$x = 8$$

Now, substitute the value for x in either original equation and solve for y.

$$y = x - 2$$
$$y = 8 - 2$$
$$y = 6$$

The solution is (8, 6). Thus, the numbers are 8 and 6.

38. Let x = one number, and y = the other number.

$$\frac{x + y}{2} = 7$$
$$3x = \frac{1}{2}y$$

Solve the first equation for x in terms of y.

$$\frac{x + y}{2} = 7$$
$$x + y = 14$$
$$x = 14 - y$$

Substitute $14 - y$ for x in the second equation and solve for y.

$$3x = \frac{1}{2}y$$
$$3(14 - y) = \frac{1}{2}y$$
$$42 - 3y = \frac{1}{2}y$$
$$42 = \frac{7}{2}y$$
$$12 = y$$

Now, substitute the value for y in either original equation and solve for x.

$$3x = \frac{1}{2}y$$
$$3x = \frac{1}{2}(12)$$
$$3x = 6$$
$$x = 2$$

The solution is (2, 12). Thus, the numbers are 2 and 12.

39. Let x = the number of members who rented skis, and y = the number of members who rented snowboards.

$$x + y = 28$$
$$16x + 19y = 478$$

40. Solve the first equation for x in terms of y.

$$x + y = 28$$
$$x = 28 - y$$

Substitute $28 - y$ for x in the second equation and solve for y.

$$16x + 19y = 478$$
$$16(28 - y) + 19y = 478$$
$$448 - 16y + 19y = 478$$
$$3y = 30$$
$$y = 10$$

Now, substitute the value for y in either original equation and solve for x.

$$x + y = 28$$
$$x + 10 = 28$$
$$x = 18$$

18 members rented skis and 10 members rented snowboards.

41. Let x = the number of 2-bedroom apartments and y = the number of 3-bedroom apartments.

$$x + y = 6$$
$$700x + 900y = 4600$$

Multiply the first equation by 700. Then subtract the equations to eliminate the x variable.

$$x + y = 6 \qquad\qquad 700x + 700y = 4200$$
$$700x + 900y = 4600 \qquad \underline{(-)\ 700x + 900y = 4600}$$
$$-200y = -400$$
$$y = 2$$

Replace y with 2 and solve for x.

$$x + y = 6$$
$$x + 2 = 6$$
$$x = 4$$

There were four 2-bedroom apartments and two 3-bedroom apartments vacant.

42. Solve $2x + y = -12$
$2x - y = -8$.
Add the equations to eliminate the y variable.

$$\begin{array}{r} 2x + y = -12 \\ (+)\ 2x - y = \ -8 \\ \hline 4x \qquad = -20 \\ x = -5 \end{array}$$

Replace x with -5 and solve for y.
$$\begin{array}{l} 2x + y = -12 \\ 2(-5) + y = -12 \\ -10 + y = -12 \\ y = -2 \end{array}$$
The solution is $(-5, -2)$.
Solve $2x - y = -8$
$4x + 2y = 24$.
Multiply the first equation by 2. Then add the equations to eliminate the y variable.

$2x - y = -8 \qquad\qquad 4x - 2y = -16$
$4x + 2y = 24 \qquad\quad (+)\ 4x + 2y = \ \ 24$
$$\begin{array}{r} \hline 8x \qquad = \ \ 8 \\ x = 1 \end{array}$$

Replace x with 1 and solve for y.
$$\begin{array}{l} 2x - y = -8 \\ 2(1) - y = -8 \\ 2 - y = -8 \\ -y = -10 \\ y = 10 \end{array}$$
The solution is $(1, 10)$.
Solve $\quad 2x + y = -12$ or $2x + y = -12$
$2x - y - 4 = 0 \qquad 2x - y = 4$.
Add the equations to eliminate the y variable.

$$\begin{array}{r} 2x + y = -12 \\ (+)\ 2x - y = \quad 4 \\ \hline 4x \qquad = \ -8 \\ x = -2 \end{array}$$

Replace x with -2 and solve for y.
$$\begin{array}{l} 2x + y = -12 \\ 2(-2) + y = -12 \\ -4 + y = -12 \\ y = -8 \end{array}$$
The solution is $(-2, -8)$.
Solve $2x - y - 4 = 0$ or $2x - y = 4$
$4x + 2y = 24 \qquad 4x + 2y = 24$.
Multiply the first equation by 2. Then add the equations to eliminate the y variable.

$2x - y = 4 \qquad\qquad 4x - 2y = \ \ 8$
$4x + 2y = 24 \qquad\quad (+)\ 4x + 2y = 24$
$$\begin{array}{r} \hline 8x \qquad = 32 \\ x = 4 \end{array}$$

Replace x with 4 and solve for y.
$$\begin{array}{l} 2x - y = 4 \\ 2(4) - y = 4 \\ 8 - y = 4 \\ -y = -4 \\ y = 4 \end{array}$$
The solution is $(4, 4)$.
The vertices are $(-5, -2)$, $(1, 10)$, $(-2, -8)$, and $(4, 4)$.

43. Let $x =$ the number of printers, and $y =$ the number of monitors.
$x + y = 30$
$700x + 200y = 15{,}000$

44. Multiply the first equation by 700. Then subtract the equations to eliminate the x variable.

$x + y = 30 \qquad\qquad\quad 700x + 700y = 21{,}000$
$700x + 200y = 15{,}000 \quad (-)\ 700x + 200y = 15{,}000$
$$\begin{array}{r} \hline 500y = \ \ 6000 \\ y = 12 \end{array}$$

Replace y with 12 and solve for x.
$$\begin{array}{l} x + y = 30 \\ x + 12 = 30 \\ x = 18 \end{array}$$
There were 18 laser printers and 12 color monitors.

45. Let $x =$ the number of true/false questions, and $y =$ the number of multiple-choice questions.
$2x + 4y = 100$
$y = 2 \cdot x$

46. Substitute $2x$ for y in the first equation and solve for x.
$$\begin{array}{l} 2x + 4y = 100 \\ 2x + 4(2x) = 100 \\ 2x + 8x = 100 \\ 10x = 100 \\ x = 10 \end{array}$$
Now, substitute the value for x in either original equation and solve for y.
$$\begin{array}{l} y = 2x \\ y = 2(10) \\ y = 20 \end{array}$$
There will be 10 true/false questions and 20 multiple-choice questions.

47. $10(1) + 20\left(1\frac{1}{2}\right) = 10 + 30$
$= 40$
Yes, they should finish the test within 40 minutes.

48. Let $a =$ the number of minutes of step aerobics, and $s =$ the number of minutes of stretching.
$a + s = 40$
$11a + 4s = 335$

49. Multiply the first equation by 4. Then subtract the equations to eliminate the s variable.

$a + s = 40 \qquad\qquad\quad 4a + 4s = \quad 160$
$11a + 4s = 335 \qquad\quad (-)\ 11a + 4s = \quad 335$
$$\begin{array}{r} \hline 7a \qquad = -175 \\ a = 25 \end{array}$$

Replace a with 25 and solve for b.
$$\begin{array}{l} a + s = 40 \\ 25 + s = 40 \\ s = 15 \end{array}$$
She should do step aerobics for 25 minutes and stretch for 15 minutes.

50. Let $m = \frac{1}{x}$ and $n = \frac{1}{y}$.

$\frac{1}{x} + \frac{3}{y} = \frac{3}{4} \rightarrow m + 3n = \frac{3}{4}$

$\frac{3}{x} - \frac{2}{y} = \frac{5}{12} \quad 3m - 2n = \frac{5}{12}$

Multiply the first equation by 3. Then subtract the equations to eliminate the m variable.

$m + 3n = \frac{3}{4} \qquad\qquad 3m + 9n = \frac{9}{4}$

$3m - 2n = \frac{5}{12} \qquad (-)\ 3m - 2n = \frac{5}{12}$

$\qquad\qquad\qquad\qquad\qquad\qquad 11n = \frac{11}{6}$

$\qquad\qquad\qquad\qquad\qquad\qquad\quad n = \frac{1}{6}$

Replace n with $\frac{1}{6}$ and solve for m.

$m + 3n = \frac{3}{4}$

$m + 3\left(\frac{1}{6}\right) = \frac{3}{4}$

$m + \frac{1}{2} = \frac{3}{4}$

$m = \frac{1}{4}$

Replace m with $\frac{1}{4}$ and solve for x.

$m = \frac{1}{x}$

$\frac{1}{4} = \frac{1}{x}$

$x = 4$

Replace n with $\frac{1}{6}$ and solve for y.

$n = \frac{1}{y}$

$\frac{1}{6} = \frac{1}{y}$

$y = 6$

The solution for the original system of equations is $(4, 6)$.

51. You can use a system of equations to find the monthly fee and rate per minute charged during the months of January and February. Answers should include the following.
- The coordinates of the point of intersection are $(0.08, 3.5)$.
- Currently, Yolanda is paying a monthly fee of $3.50 and an additional 8¢ per minute. If she graphs $y = 0.08x + 3.5$ (to represent what she is paying currently) and $y = 0.10x + 3$ (to represent the other long-distance plan) and finds the intersection, she can identify which plan would be better for a person with her level of usage.

52. C; Replace x with 10 and solve for y.

$x + y = 6$

$10 + y = 6$

$y = -4$

Replace x with 10, y with -4, and solve for z.

$x = y + z$

$10 = -4 + z$

$14 = z$

53. A; Solve $2y = 4x$

$\qquad\quad 4y + 8x = 48.$

Solve the first equation for y in terms of x.

$2y = 4x$

$y = 2x$

Substitute $2x$ for y in the second equation and solve for x.

$4y + 8x = 48$

$4(2x) + 8x = 48$

$8x + 8x = 48$

$16x = 48$

$x = 3$

Page 122   Maintain Your Skills

54. $y = x + 2$

$\quad\ y = x - 1$

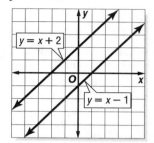

The lines do not intersect. Their graphs are parallel lines. So, there are no solutions that satisfy both equations. This system is *inconsistent*.

55. $4y - 2x = 4 \rightarrow y = \frac{1}{2}x + 1$

$\quad y - \frac{1}{2}x = 1 \ \rightarrow y = \frac{1}{2}x + 1$

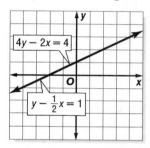

Since the equations are equivalent, their graphs are the same line. Any ordered pair representing a point on that line will satisfy both equations. So, there are infinitely many solutions to this system. This system is *consistent and dependent*.

56. $3x + y = 1 \rightarrow y = -3x + 1$

$\quad y = 2x - 4 \qquad y = \ \ 2x - 4$

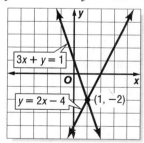

The graphs intersect at $(1, -2)$. Since there is one solution, this system is *consistent and independent*.

57. The boundary is the graph $x + y = 3$. Since the inequality symbol is $\leq$, the boundary will be solid. Use the slope-intercept form $y = -x + 3$. Now test the point $(0, 0)$.

$x + y \leq 3$
$0 + 0 \leq 3$
$\quad 0 \leq 3$ true

Shade the region that includes $(0, 0)$.

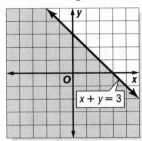

58. The boundary is the graph of $5y - 4x = -20$. Since the inequality symbol is $<$, the boundary will be dashed. Use the slope-intercept form, $y = \frac{4}{5}x - 4$. Now test the point $(0, 0)$.

$5y - 4x < -20$
$5(0) - 4(0) < -20$
$\quad 0 - 0 < -20$
$\quad\quad 0 < -20$ false

Shade the region that does not contain $(0, 0)$.

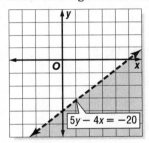

59. The boundary is the graph of $3x + 9y = -15$. Since the inequality symbol is $\geq$, the boundary will be solid. Use the slope-intercept form, $y = -\frac{1}{3}x - \frac{5}{3}$. Now test the point $(0, 0)$.

$3x + 9y \geq -15$
$3(0) + 9(0) \geq -15$
$\quad 0 + 0 \geq -15$
$\quad\quad 0 \geq -15$ true

Shade the region that includes $(0, 0)$.

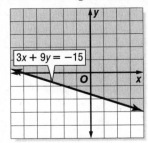

60. $\quad y = 7x + 4$
$-7x + y = 4$
$\;\; 7x - y = -4$
So, $A = 7$, $B = -1$, and $C = -4$.

61. $\quad x = y$
$x - y = 0$
So, $A = 1$, $B = -1$, and $C = 0$.

62. $\quad 3x = 2 - 5y$
$3x + 5y = 2$
So, $A = 3$, $B = 5$, and $C = 2$.

63. $\quad 6x = 3y - 9$
$6x - 3y = -9$
$\;\; 2x - y = -3$
So, $A = 2$, $B = -1$, and $C = -3$.

64. $\quad y = \frac{1}{2}x - 3$
$-\frac{1}{2}x + y = -3$
$\quad x - 2y = 6$
So, $A = 1$, $B = -2$, and $C = 6$.

65. $\frac{2}{3}y - 6 = 1 - x$
$\quad \frac{2}{3}y = 7 - x$
$\quad x + \frac{2}{3}y = 7$
$3x + 2y = 21$
So, $A = 3$, $B = 2$, and $C = 21$.

66. Substitute each value given into the formula. Then evaluate the expression using the order of operations.

$I = \frac{E}{R + r}$
$\;= \frac{1.5}{2.35 + 0.15}$
$\;= \frac{1.5}{2.5}$
$\;= 0.6$

The current is 0.6 ampere.

67. Test the point in the inequality.
$\quad 3x + 2y \leq 10$
$3(2) + 2(-1) \leq 10$
$\quad\quad 6 - 2 \leq 10$
$\quad\quad\quad\; 4 \leq 10$ true

Yes, $(2, -1)$ is a solution.

68. Test the point in the inequality.
$\quad 4x - 2y > 6$
$4(3) - 2(3) > 6$
$\quad 12 - 6 > 6$
$\quad\quad\; 6 > 6$ false

No, $(3, 3)$ is not a solution.

69. Test the point in the inequality.
$\quad 7x + 4y \geq -15$
$7(-4) + 4(2) \geq -15$
$\quad -28 + 8 \geq -15$
$\quad\quad -20 \geq -15$ false

No, $(-4, 2)$ is not a solution.

70. Test the point in the inequality.
$\quad 7y + 6x < 50$
$7(5) + 6(-5) < 50$
$\quad 35 - 30 < 50$
$\quad\quad\quad 5 < 50$ true

Yes, $(-5, 5)$ is a solution.

1. Write each equation in slope-intercept form.

$y = 3x + 10$
$y = -x + 6$

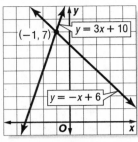

The graphs appear to intersect at $(-1, 7)$.

Check: $y = 3x + 10$ $y = -x + 6$
     $7 \overset{?}{=} 3(-1) + 10$ $7 \overset{?}{=} -(-1) + 6$
     $7 = 7$ ✓ $7 = 7$ ✓

The solution of the system is $(-1, 7)$.

2. Write each equation in slope-intercept form.

$2x + 3y = 12 \rightarrow y = -\frac{2}{3}x + 4$

$2x - y = 4 \quad \rightarrow y = 2x - 4$

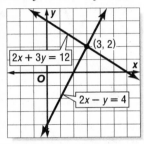

The graphs appear to intersect at $(3, 2)$.

Check: $2x + 3y = 12$ $2x - y = 4$
     $2(3) + 3(2) \overset{?}{=} 12$ $2(3) - 2 \overset{?}{=} 4$
     $12 = 12$ ✓ $4 = 4$ ✓

The solution of the system is $(3, 2)$.

3. Substitute $x + 5$ for y in the second equation and solve for x.

     $x + y = 9$
$x + x + 5 = 9$
       $2x = 4$
        $x = 2$

Now, substitute the value for x in either original equation and solve for y.

$y = x + 5$
$y = 2 + 5$
$y = 7$

The solution of the system is $(2, 7)$.

4. Multiply the second equation by 3. Then subtract the equations to eliminate the y variable.

$2x + 6y = 2$ $2x + 6y = 2$
$3x + 2y = 10$ $(-)\ 9x + 6y = 30$
               $-7x = -28$
                       $x = 4$

Replace x with 4 and solve for y.

     $2x + 6y = 2$
$2(4) + 6y = 2$
   $8 + 6y = 2$
       $6y = -6$
        $y = -1$

The solution is $(4, -1)$.

5. Let $x =$ the number of passengers at Hartsfield, and $y =$ the number of passengers at O'Hare.

$x + y = 150.5$
    $x = 5.5 + y$

Substitute $5.5 + y$ for x in the first equation and solve for y.

        $x + y = 150.5$
$5.5 + y + y = 150.5$
          $2y = 145$
           $y = 72.5$

Now, substitute the value for y in either original equation and solve for x.

$x = 5.5 + y$
$x = 5.5 + 72.5$
$x = 78$

Hartsfield had 78 million passengers and O'Hare had 72.5 million passengers.

3-3   **Solving Systems of Inequalities by Graphing**

Page 125   Check for Understanding

1. Sample answer: $y > x + 3, y < x - 2$

2. The statement is true.

3a. Solution of $y \geq x \quad \rightarrow$ regions 1 and 4
    Solution of $y \leq -x \rightarrow$ regions 3 and 4
    The intersection of these regions is Region 4.

3b. Solution of $y \leq x \quad \rightarrow$ regions 2 and 3
    Solution of $y \geq -x \rightarrow$ regions 1 and 2
    The intersection of these regions is Region 2.

3c. Solution of $y \geq x \quad \rightarrow$ regions 1 and 4
    Solution of $y \geq -x \rightarrow$ regions 1 and 2
    The intersection of these regions is Region 1.

3d. Solution of $y \leq x \quad \rightarrow$ regions 2 and 3
    Solution of $y \leq -x \rightarrow$ regions 3 and 4
    The intersection of these regions is Region 3.

4. Graph all of the inequalities on the same coordinate plane and shade the region or regions that are common to all.

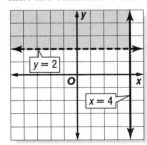

---

5. Graph all of the inequalities on the same coordinate plane and shade the region or regions that are common to all.

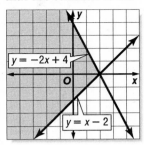

6. The inequality $|x - 1| \leq 2$ can be written as $x - 1 \leq 2$ and $x - 1 \geq -2$.
Graph all of the inequalities on the same coordinate plane and shade the region or regions that are common to all.

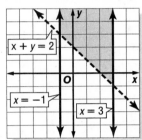

7. Graph all of the inequalities on the same coordinate plane and shade the region or regions that are common to all.

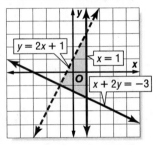

8. Graph each inequality. The intersection of the graphs forms a triangle.

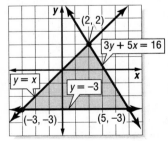

The coordinates $(-3, -3)$, $(2, 2)$, and $(5, -3)$ can be determined from the graph. The vertices of the triangle are at $(-3, -3)$, $(2, 2)$, and $(5, -3)$.

9. Graph each inequality. The intersection of the graphs forms a rectangle.

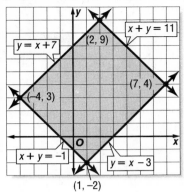

The coordinates $(2, 9)$, $(7, 4)$, $(1, -2)$, and $(-4, 3)$ can be determined from the graph. The vertices of the rectangle are at $(2, 9)$, $(7, 4)$, $(1, -2)$, and $(-4, 3)$.

10. Let b = the number of packages of bagels.
$b \geq 2$
Let m = the number of packages of muffins.
$m \geq 3$
The cost restriction can be written
$2.5b + 3.5m \leq 28$.
Graph all of the inequalities. Any ordered pair in the intersection of the graphs is a solution of the system.

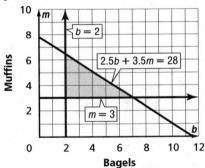

11. Sample answer: 3 packages of bagels and 4 packages of muffins; 4 packages of bagels and 4 packages of muffins; 3 packages of bagels and 5 packages of muffins

Pages 126–127   Practice and Apply

12. Graph all of the inequalities on the same coordinate plane and shade the region or regions that are common to all.

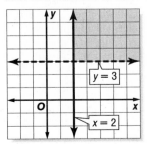

13. Graph all of the inequalities on the same coordinate plane and shade the region or regions that are common to all.

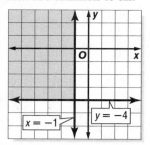

$x = -1$ $y = -4$

14. Graph all of the inequalities on the same coordinate plane and shade the region or regions that are common to all.

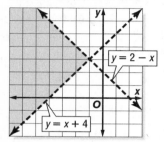

$y = 2 - x$ $y = x + 4$

15. The inequality $|y| \leq 2$ can be written as $y \leq 2$ and $y \geq -2$. Graph all of the inequalities on the same coordinate plane and shade the region or regions that are common to all.

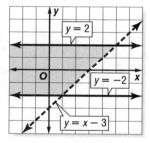

$y = 2$ $y = -2$ $y = x - 3$

16. Graph all of the inequalities on the same coordinate plane and shade the region or regions that are common to all.

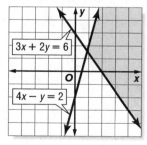

$3x + 2y = 6$ $4x - y = 2$

17. Graph all of the inequalities on the same coordinate plane and shade the region or regions that are common to all.

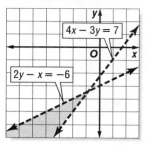

$4x - 3y = 7$ $2y - x = -6$

18. Graph all of the inequalities on the same coordinate plane and shade the region or regions that are common to all.

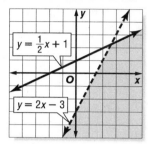

$y = \frac{1}{2}x + 1$ $y = 2x - 3$

19. Graph both inequalities.

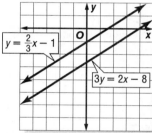

$y = \frac{2}{3}x - 1$ $3y = 2x - 8$

The graphs do not overlap, so the solutions have no points in common. The solution set is $\varnothing$.

20. The inequality $|x| \leq 3$ can be written as $x \leq 3$ and $x \geq -3$. The inequality $|y| > 1$ can be written as $y > 1$ or $y < -1$.
Graph all of the inequalities on the same coordinate plane and shade the region or regions that are common to all.

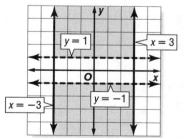

$y = 1$ $x = 3$ $x = -3$ $y = -1$

21. The inequality $|x + 1| \leq 3$ can be written as $x + 1 \leq 3$ and $x + 1 \geq -3$.
Graph all of the inequalities on the same coordinate plane and shade the region or regions that are common to all.

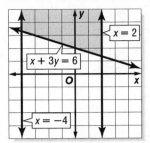

22. Graph all of the inequalities.

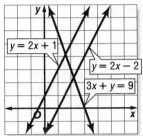

The graphs of $y \geq 2x + 1$ and $y \leq 2x - 2$ do not overlap, so the solutions have no points in common. The solution set is $\varnothing$.

23. Graph all of the inequalities on the same coordinate plane and shade the region or regions that are common to all.

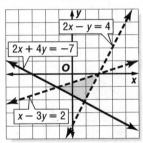

24. Graph each inequality. The intersection of the graphs forms a triangle.

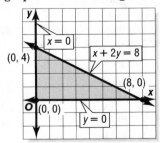

The coordinates $(0, 0)$, $(0, 4)$, and $(8, 0)$ can be determined from the graph. The vertices of the triangle are at $(0, 0)$, $(0, 4)$, and $(8, 0)$.

25. Graph each inequality. The intersection of the graphs forms a triangle.

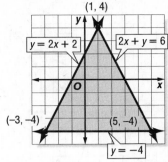

The coordinates $(-3, -4)$, $(1, 4)$, and $(5, -4)$ can be determined from the graph. The vertices of the triangle are at $(-3, -4)$, $(1, 4)$, and $(5, -4)$.

26. Graph each inequality. The intersection of the graphs forms a triangle.

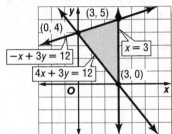

The coordinates $(0, 4)$, $(3, 0)$, and $(3, 5)$ can be determined from the graph. The vertices of the triangle are at $(0, 4)$, $(3, 0)$, and $(3, 5)$.

27. Graph each inequality. The intersection of the graphs forms a triangle.

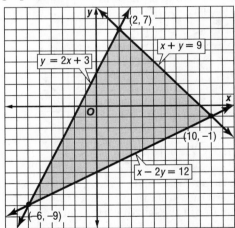

The coordinates $(-6, -9)$, $(2, 7)$, and $(10, -1)$ can be determined from the graph. The vertices of the triangle are at $(-6, -9)$, $(2, 7)$, and $(10, -1)$.

28. Graph each inequality. The intersection of the graphs forms a quadrilateral.

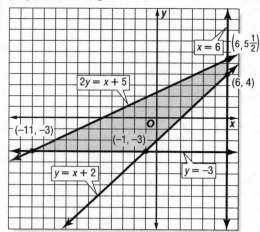

The coordinates $(-11, -3)$, $(-1, -3)$, and $(6, 4)$ can be determined from the graph. To find the coordinates of the fourth vertex, solve the system of equations $x = 6$ and $2y = x + 5$.
Find y by substituting 6 for x in the second equation.
$$2y = x + 5$$
$$2y = 6 + 5$$
$$2y = 11$$
$$y = 5\tfrac{1}{2}$$
The vertices of the quadrilateral are at $(-11, -3)$,

$(-1, -3)$, $(6, 4)$, and $\left(6, 5\tfrac{1}{2}\right)$.

29. Graph each inequality. The intersection of the graphs forms a quadrilateral.

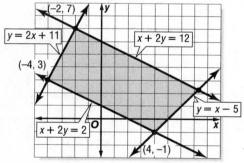

The coordinates $(-4, 3)$, $(-2, 7)$, and $(4, -1)$ can be determined from the graph. To find the coordinates of the fourth vertex, solve the system of equations $y = x - 5$ and $x + 2y = 12$.
Substitute $x - 5$ for y in the second equation and solve for x.
$$x + 2y = 12$$
$$x + 2(x - 5) = 12$$
$$x + 2x - 10 = 12$$
$$3x = 22$$
$$x = 7\tfrac{1}{3}$$

Now find y by substituting $7\tfrac{1}{3}$ for x in the first equation.
$$y = x - 5$$
$$y = 7\tfrac{1}{3} - 5$$
$$y = 2\tfrac{1}{3}$$
The vertices of the quadrilateral are at $(-4, 3)$, $(-2, 7)$, $(4, -1)$, and $\left(7\tfrac{1}{3}, 2\tfrac{1}{3}\right)$.

30. Graph each inequality. The intersection of the graphs forms a triangle.

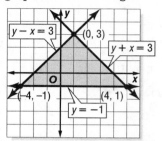

From the graph we can determine that the height of the triangle is 4 units and the base is 8 units.
$$A = \tfrac{1}{2}bh$$
$$= \tfrac{1}{2}(8)(4)$$
$$= 16$$

31. Graph each inequality. The intersection of the graphs forms a triangle.

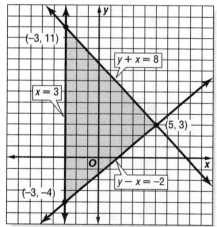

From the graph we can determine that the height of the triangle is 8 units and the base is 16 units.
$$A = \tfrac{1}{2}bh$$
$$= \tfrac{1}{2}(16)(8)$$
$$= 64$$
The area is 64 square units.

32. Let x represent the number of hours cutting grass. Let y represent the number of hours raking leaves. He cannot work for a negative number of hours. We can write this information as $x \geq 0$ and $y \geq 0$. He cannot work more than 15 hours per week. This information can be written as $x + y \leq 15$. Bryan wants to earn at least $120 per week. This information can be written as $10x + 12y \geq 120$. Graph all of the inequalities. Any ordered pair in the intersection of the graphs is a solution of the system.

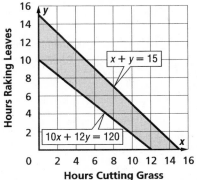

33. A category 3 hurricane has wind speeds between 111 mph and 130 mph. This information can be written as $111 \leq s$ and $s \leq 130$. A category 3 hurricane has storm surges between 9 ft and 12 ft. This information can be written as $9 \leq h$ and $h \leq 12$.

Graph all of the inequalities. Any ordered pair in the intersection of the graphs is a solution of the system.

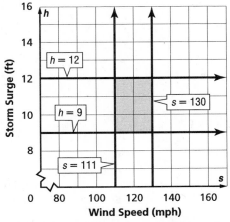

34. Since 140 mph is between 131 mph and 155 mph, Hurricane Floyd was a category 4 hurricane. From the chart we can determine that its storm surges were between 13 ft and 18 ft.

35. Let x represent the number of loaves of pumpkin bread. Let y represent the number of loaves of Swedish soda bread. The number of loaves cannot be negative. We can write this as $x \geq 0$ and $y \geq 0$. They only have 24 cups of flour and 26 teaspoons of baking powder. We can write this as $2x + 1\frac{1}{2}y \leq 24$ and $x + 2\frac{1}{2}y \leq 26$. Graph all of the inequalities. Any ordered pair in the intersection of the graphs is a solution of the system.

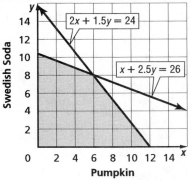

36. Sample answer: 2 loaves of pumpkin bread and 8 loaves of soda bread; 4 loaves of pumpkin bread and 6 loaves of soda bread; 8 loaves of pumpkin bread and 4 loaves of soda bread

37. The intersection point is the only point that is a solution to $2x + 1.5y = 24$ and $x + 2.5y = 26$. Thus, 6 loaves of pumpkin bread and 8 loaves of soda bread uses all of the ingredients.

38. $|x| + |y| \le 5 \rightarrow |y| \le 5 - |x|$

The inequality $|y| \le 5 - |x|$ can be written as
$y \le 5 - |x|$ and $y \ge -(5 - |x|)$.
$$y \le 5 - |x| \quad \rightarrow |x| \le 5 - y$$
$$y \ge -(5 - |x|) \rightarrow |x| \le 5 + y$$
The inequality $|x| \le 5 - y$ can be written as
$x \le 5 - y$ and $x \ge -(5 - y)$.
The inequality $|x| \le 5 + y$ can be written as
$x \le 5 + y$ and $x \ge -(5 + y)$.
Therefore, the inequality $|x| + |y| \le 5$ can be
written as $-5 \le x + y \le 5$ and $-5 \le x - y \le 5$.
Likewise, the inequality $|x| + |y| \ge 2$ can be
written as $x + y \ge 2$ or $x + y \le -2$ or $x - y \ge 2$ or
$x - y \le -2$. Graph all of the inequalities.

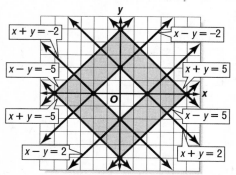

From the graph we can determine that the side
length of the outer square is $5\sqrt{2}$ and the side
length of the inner square is $2\sqrt{2}$.
$$A = S_1^2 - S_2^2$$
$$= (5\sqrt{2})^2 - (2\sqrt{2})^2$$
$$= 50 - 8$$
$$= 42$$
The area is 42 square units.

39. The range for normal blood pressure satisfies four
inequalities that can be graphed to find their
intersection. Answers should include the following.

- Graph the blood pressure as an ordered pair; if
the point lies in the shaded region, it is in the
normal range.

- High systolic pressure is represented by the
region to the right of $x = 140$ and high diastolic
pressure is represented by the region above
$y = 90$.

40. B; The dashed line is $x = -3$ and the regions to
the right of the dashed line satisfy $x > -3$. The
solid line is $y = -2$ and the regions below the
solid line satisfy $y \le -2$. Therefore, the shaded
region satisfies the system
$x > -3$
$y \le -2$.

41. Sample answer: $y \le 6, y \ge 2, x \le 5, x \ge 1$

Page 127 **Maintain Your Skills**

42. Multiply the first equation by 2. Then add the
equations to eliminate the y variable.

$$4x - y = -20 \qquad\qquad 8x - 2y = -40$$
$$x + 2y = 13 \qquad\qquad \underline{(+)\ x + 2y = \ \ \ 13}$$
$$9x \qquad\quad = -27$$
$$x = -3$$

Replace x with -3 and solve for y.
$$4x - y = -20$$
$$4(-3) - y = -20$$
$$-12 - y = -20$$
$$-y = -8$$
$$y = 8$$
The solution is $(-3, 8)$.

43. Multiply the second equation by 2. Then add the
equations to eliminate the y variable.

$$3x - 4y = -2 \qquad\qquad 3x - 4y = \ -2$$
$$5x + 2y = 40 \qquad\qquad \underline{(+)\ 10x + 4y = \ \ 80}$$
$$13x \qquad\quad = \ 78$$
$$x = 6$$

Replace x with 6 and solve for y.
$$3x - 4y = -2$$
$$3(6) - 4y = -2$$
$$18 - 4y = -2$$
$$-4y = -20$$
$$y = 5$$
The solution is $(6, 5)$.

44. Multiply the first equation by 3 and the second
equation by 4. Then subtract the equations to
eliminate the x variable.

$$4x + 5y = 7 \qquad\qquad 12x + 15y = \ \ \ \ 21$$
$$3x - 2y = 34 \qquad\qquad \underline{(-)12x - \ 8y = \ \ 136}$$
$$23y = -115$$
$$y = -5$$

Replace y with -5 and solve for x.
$$4x + 5y = 7$$
$$4x + 5(-5) = 7$$
$$4x - 25 = 7$$
$$4x = 32$$
$$x = 8$$
The solution is $(8, -5)$.

45. Write each equation in slope-intercept form.
$y = 2x + 1$
$y = -\frac{1}{2}x - 4$

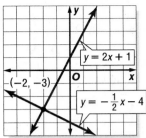

The graphs appear to intersect at $(-2, -3)$.
Check: Substitute the coordinates into each equation.

$y = 2x + 1$	$y = -\frac{1}{2}x - 4$
$-3 \stackrel{?}{=} 2(-2) + 1$	$-3 \stackrel{?}{=} -\frac{1}{2}(-2) - 4$
$-3 = -3$ ✓	$-3 = -3$ ✓

The solution of the system is $(-2, -3)$.

46. Write each equation in slope-intercept form.
$x + y = -3 \rightarrow y = -2x - 3$
$6x + 3y = -9 \rightarrow y = -2x - 3$

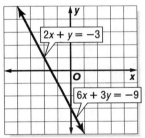

Since the equations are equivalent, their graphs are the same line. Any ordered pair representing a point on that line will satisfy both equations. So, there are infinitely many solutions to this system.

47. Write each equation in slope-intercept form.
$2x - y = 6 \quad\rightarrow y = 2x - 6$
$-x + 8y = 12 \rightarrow y = \frac{1}{8}x + \frac{3}{2}$

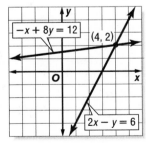

The graphs appear to intersect at $(4, 2)$.
Check: Substitute the coordinates into each equation.

$2x - y = 6$	$-x + 8y = 12$
$2(4) - 2 \stackrel{?}{=} 6$	$-4 + 8(2) \stackrel{?}{=} 12$
$6 = 6$ ✓	$12 = 12$ ✓

The solution of the system is $(4, 2)$.

48. Find the slope of the line.
$$m = \frac{y_2 - y_1}{x_2 - x_1}$$
$$= \frac{9 - 4}{6 - (-4)}$$
$$= \frac{5}{10}$$
$$= \frac{1}{2}$$

Substitute for m, x and y in the slope-intercept form.
$y = mx + b$
$4 = \frac{1}{2}(-4) + b$
$4 = -2 + b$
$6 = b$
The y-intercept is 6. So, the equation in slope-intercept form is $y = \frac{1}{2}x + 6$.

49. $f(x) = 4x + 3$
$f(-2) = 4(-2) + 3$
$\quad\quad = -8 + 3$
$\quad\quad = -5$

50. $g(x) = 5x - 7$
$g(-1) = 5(-1) - 7$
$\quad\quad = -5 - 7$
$\quad\quad = -12$

51. $g(x) = 5x - 7$
$g(3) = 5(3) - 7$
$\quad\quad = 15 - 7$
$\quad\quad = 8$

52. $f(x) = 4x + 3$
$f(6) = 4(6) + 3$
$\quad\quad = 24 + 3$
$\quad\quad = 27$

53. $f(x) = 4x + 3$
$f(0.5) = 4(0.5) + 3$
$\quad\quad = 2 + 3$
$\quad\quad = 5$

54. $g(x) = 5x - 7$
$g(-0.25) = 5(-0.25) - 7$
$\quad\quad = -1.25 - 7$
$\quad\quad = -8.25$

**Page 128   Graphing Calculator Investigation
(Follow-Up of Lesson 3-3)**

1. Step 1: Enter 4 as Y_1. Since y is greater than 4, shade above the line.

Step 2: Enter $-x$ as Y_2. Since y is less than $-x$, shade below the line.

Step 3: Display the graphs by pressing $\boxed{\text{GRAPH}}$.

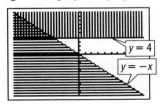

$[-10, 10]$ scl: 1 by $[-10, 10]$ scl: 1

2. Step 1: Enter $-2x$ as Y_1. Since y is greater than $-2x$, shade above the line.

Step 2: Enter -3 as Y_2. Since y is less than -3, shade below the line.

Step 3: Display the graphs by pressing $\boxed{\text{GRAPH}}$.

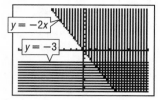

$[-10, 10]$ scl: 1 by $[-10, 10]$ scl: 1

3. Step 1: Enter $1 - x$ as Y_1. Since y is greater than $1 - x$, shade above the line.

Step 2: Enter $x + 5$ as Y_2. Since y is less than $x + 5$, shade below the line.

Step 3: Display the graphs by pressing $\boxed{\text{GRAPH}}$.

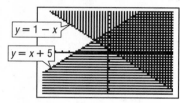

$[-10, 10]$ scl: 1 by $[-10, 10]$ scl: 1

4. Step 1: Enter $x + 2$ as Y_1. Since y is greater than $x + 2$, shade above the line.

Step 2: Enter $-2x - 1$ as Y_2. Since y is less than $-2x - 1$, shade below the line.

Step 3: Display the graphs by pressing $\boxed{\text{GRAPH}}$.

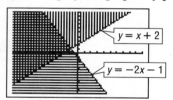

$[-10, 10]$ scl: 1 by $[-10, 10]$ scl: 1

5. $3y \geq 6x - 15 \rightarrow y \geq 2x - 5$

$2y \leq -x + 3 \rightarrow y \leq -\frac{1}{2}x + \frac{3}{2}$

Step 1: Enter $2x - 5$ as Y_1. Since y is greater than $2x - 5$, shade above the line.

Step 2: Enter $-\frac{1}{2}x + \frac{3}{2}$ as Y_2. Since y is less than $-\frac{1}{2}x + \frac{3}{2}$, shade below the line.

Step 3: Display the graphs by pressing $\boxed{\text{GRAPH}}$.

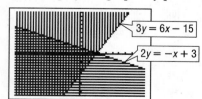

$[-10, 10]$ scl: 1 by $[-10, 10]$ scl: 1

6. $y + 3x \geq 6 \rightarrow y \geq -3x + 6$

$y - 2x \leq 9 \rightarrow y \leq 2x + 9$

Step 1: Enter $-3x + 6$ as Y_1. Since y is greater than $-3x + 6$, shade above the line.

Step 2: Enter $2x + 9$ as Y_2. Since y is less than $2x + 9$, shade below the line.

Step 3: Display the graphs by pressing $\boxed{\text{GRAPH}}$.

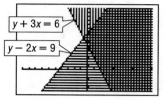

$[-10, 10]$ scl: 1 by $[-5, 15]$ scl: 1

7. $6y + 4x \geq 12 \rightarrow y \geq -\frac{2}{3}x + 2$

$5y - 3x \leq -10 \rightarrow y \leq \frac{3}{5}x - 2$

Step 1: Enter $-\frac{2}{3}x + 2$ as Y_1. Since y is greater than $-\frac{2}{3}x + 2$, shade above the line.

Step 2: Enter $\frac{3}{5}x - 2$ as Y_2. Since y is less than $\frac{3}{5}x - 2$, shade below the line.

Step 3: Display the graphs by pressing $\boxed{\text{GRAPH}}$.

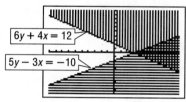

$[-10, 10]$ scl: 1 by $[-10, 10]$ scl: 1

8. $\frac{1}{4}y - x \geq -2 \rightarrow y \geq 4x - 8$

$\frac{1}{3}y + 2x \leq 4 \rightarrow y \leq -6x + 12$

Step 1: Enter $4x - 8$ as Y_1. Since y is greater than $4x - 8$, shade above the line.

Step 2: Enter $-6x + 12$ as Y_2. Since y is less than $-6x + 12$, shade below the line.

Step 3: Display the graphs by pressing $\boxed{\text{GRAPH}}$.

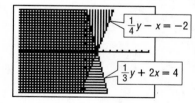

$[-10, 10]$ scl: 1 by $[-10, 10]$ scl: 1

$\boxed{\textbf{3-4}}$ **Linear Programming**

Pages 132 Check for Understanding

1. The statement is sometimes true. Some feasible regions are not bounded.

2. Sample answer: $y \geq -x, y \geq x - 5, y \leq 0$

120

3. Step 1: Find the vertices of the region. Graph the inequalities.

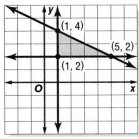

The polygon formed is a triangle with vertices at (1, 2), (1, 4), and (5, 2).

Step 2: Use a table to find the maximum and minimum values of $f(x, y)$. Substitute the coordinates of the vertices into the function.

(x, y)	$2x - 3y$	$f(x, y)$
(1, 2)	$2(1) - 3(2)$	-4
(1, 4)	$2(1) - 3(4)$	-10
(5, 2)	$2(5) - 3(2)$	4

The maximum value is 4 at (5, 2).
The minimum value is -10 at (1, 4).

4. Graph the system of inequalities.

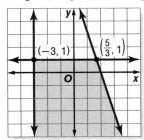

There are only two points of intersection, $(-3, 1)$ and $\left(\frac{5}{3}, 1\right)$.

(x, y)	$(5x - 2y)$	$f(x, y)$
$(-3, 1)$	$5(-3) - 2(1)$	-17
$\left(\frac{5}{3}, 1\right)$	$5\left(\frac{5}{3}\right) - 2(1)$	$\frac{19}{3}$

The minimum is -17 at (3, 1).

Although $f\left(\frac{5}{3}, 1\right)$ is $\frac{19}{3}$, it is not the maximum value since there are other points in the solution that produce greater values. For example, $f(2, 0) = 10$ and $f(-3, -20) = 25$. It appears that because the region is unbounded, $f(x, y)$ has no maximum value.

5. Step 1: Find the vertices of the region. Graph the inequalities.

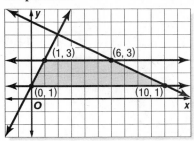

The polygon formed is a quadrilateral with vertices at (0, 1), (1, 3), (6, 3), and (10, 1).

Step 2: Use a table to find the maximum and minimum values of $f(x, y)$. Substitute the coordinates of the vertices into the function.

(x, y)	$3x + y$	$f(x, y)$
(0, 1)	$3(0) + 1$	1
(1, 3)	$3(1) + 3$	6
(6, 3)	$3(6) + 3$	21
(10, 1)	$3(10) + 1$	31

The maximum value is 31 at (10, 1).
The minimum value is 1 at (0, 1).

6. Step 1: Find the vertices of the region. Graph the inequalities.

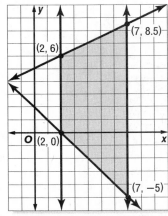

The polygon formed is a quadrilateral with vertices at (2, 0), (2, 6) (7, 8.5), and (7, −5).

Step 2: Use a table to find the maximum and minimum values of $f(x, y)$. Substitute the coordinates of the vertices into the function.

(x, y)	$8x + 3y$	$f(x, y)$
(2, 0)	$8(2) + 3(0)$	16
(2, 6)	$8(2) + 3(6)$	34
(7, 8.5)	$8(7) + 3(8.5)$	81.5
(7, −5)	$8(7) + 3(-5)$	41

The maximum value is 81.5 at (7, 8.5).
The minimum value is 16 at (2, 0).

7. Step 1: Find the vertices of the region. Graph the inequalities.

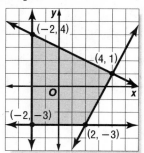

The polygon formed is a quadrilateral with vertices at $(-2, -3)$, $(-2, 4)$, $(2, -3)$, and $(4, 1)$.

Step 2: Use a table to find the maximum and minimum values of $f(x, y)$. Substitute the coordinates of the vertices into the function.

(x, y)	$x - y$	$f(x, y)$
$(-2, -3)$	$-2 - (-3)$	1
$(-2, 4)$	$-2 - 4$	-6
$(2, -3)$	$2 - (-3)$	5
$(4, 1)$	$4 - 1$	3

The maximum value is 5 at $(2, -3)$.
The minimum value is -6 at $(-2, 4)$.

8. Step 1: Find the vertices of the region. Graph the inequalities.

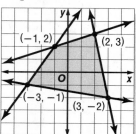

The polygon formed is a quadrilateral with vertices at $(-3, -1)$, $(-1, 2)$, $(2, 3)$, and $(3, -2)$.

Step 2: Use a table to find the maximum and minimum values of $f(x, y)$. Substitute the coordinates of the vertices into the function.

(x, y)	$x - y$	$f(x, y)$
$(-3, -1)$	$-3 - (-1)$	-2
$(-1, 2)$	$-1 - 2$	-3
$(2, 3)$	$2 - 3$	-1
$(3, -2)$	$3 - (-2)$	5

The maximum value is 5 at $(3, -2)$.
The minimum value is -3 at $(-1, 2)$.

9. Since the number of tote bags cannot be negative, c and ℓ must be nonnegative numbers.
$c \geq 0$ and $\ell \geq 0$
A canvas tote bag uses 1 yard of leather, and a leather tote bag uses 3 yards of leather.
$c + 3\ell \leq 56$
A canvas tote bag uses 4 yards of canvas, and a leather tote bag uses 2 yards of canvas.
$4c + 2\ell \leq 104$

10. Graph the system of inequalities.

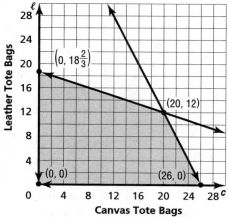

11. From the graph three of the vertices are at $(0, 0)$, $(26, 0)$, and $(20, 12)$. To find the fourth vertex solve the system $c = 0$ and $c + 3\ell = 56$. Substitute 0 for c in the second equation.
$c + 3\ell = 56$
$0 + 3\ell = 56$
$3\ell = 56$
$\ell = 18\frac{2}{3}$

The four vertices are at $(0, 0)$, $(26, 0)$, $(20, 12)$, and $\left(0, 18\frac{2}{3}\right)$.

12. The function that describes the income is $f(c, \ell) = 20c + 35\ell$.

13. Substitute the coordinates of the vertices into the function.

(c, ℓ)	$20c + 35\ell$	$f(c, \ell)$
$(0, 0)$	$20(0) + 35(0)$	0
$(26, 0)$	$20(26) + 35(0)$	520
$(20, 12)$	$20(20) + 35(12)$	820
$\left(0, 18\frac{2}{3}\right)$	$20(0) + 35\left(18\frac{2}{3}\right)$	$653\frac{1}{3}$

The maximum value for the function is 820 at $(20, 12)$. This means that the maximum profit is $820 when they make 20 canvas tote bags and 12 leather tote bags.

14. The maximum profit is $820.

15. Step 1: Find the vertices of the region. Graph the inequalities.

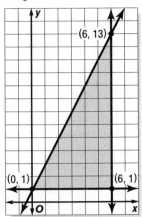

The polygon formed is a triangle with vertices at $(0, 1)$, $(6, 1)$, and $(6, 13)$.

Step 2: Use a table to find the maximum and minimum values of $f(x, y)$. Substitute the coordinates of the vertices into the function.

(x, y)	$x - y$	$f(x, y)$
$(0, 1)$	$0 + 1$	1
$(6, 1)$	$6 + 1$	7
$(6, 13)$	$6 + 13$	19

The maximum value is 19 at $(6, 13)$.
The minimum value is 1 at $(0, 1)$.

16. Step 1: Find the vertices of the region. Graph the inequalities.

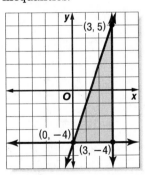

The polygon formed is a triangle with vertices at $(0, -4)$, $(3, -4)$, and $(3, 5)$.

Step 2: Use a table to find the maximum and minimum values of $f(x, y)$. Substitute the coordinates of the vertices into the function.

(x, y)	$x - y$	$f(x, y)$
$(0, -4)$	$0 - (-4)$	4
$(3, -4)$	$3 - (-4)$	7
$(3, 5)$	$3 - 5$	-2

The maximum value is 7 at $(3, -4)$.
The minimum value is -2 at $(3, 5)$.

17. Step 1: Find the vertices of the region. Graph the inequalities.

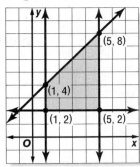

The polygon formed is a quadrilateral with vertices at $(1, 2)$, $(1, 4)$, $(5, 2)$, and $(5, 8)$.

Step 2: Use a table to find the maximum and minimum values of $f(x, y)$. Substitute the coordinates of the vertices into the function.

(x, y)	$3x - 2y$	$f(x, y)$
$(1, 2)$	$3(1) - 2(2)$	-1
$(1, 4)$	$3(1) - 2(4)$	-5
$(5, 2)$	$3(5) - 2(2)$	11
$(5, 8)$	$3(5) - 2(8)$	-1

The maximum value is 11 at $(5, 2)$.
The minimum value is -5, at $(1, 4)$.

18. Step 1: Find the vertices of the region. Graph the inequalities.

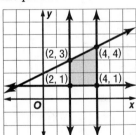

The polygon formed is a quadrilateral with vertices at $(2, 1)$, $(2, 3)$, $(4, 1)$, and $(4, 4)$.

Step 2: Use a table to find the maximum and minimum values of $f(x, y)$. Substitute the coordinates of the vertices into the function.

(x, y)	$3y - x$	$f(x, y)$
$(2, 1)$	$3(1) + 2$	5
$(2, 3)$	$3(3) + 2$	11
$(4, 1)$	$3(1) + 4$	7
$(4, 4)$	$3(4) + 4$	16

The maximum value is 16 at $(4, 4)$.
The minimum value is 5 at $(2, 1)$.

19. Graph the system of inequalities.

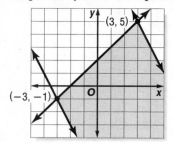

There are only two points of intersection, $(-3, -1)$ and $(3, 5)$.

(x, y)	$4x - 3y$	$f(x, y)$
$(-3, -1)$	$4(-3) - 3(-1)$	-9
$(3, 5)$	$4(3) - 3(5)$	-3

The minimum is -9 at $(-3, -1)$.
Although $f(3, 5)$ is -3, it is not the maximum value since there are other points in the solution that produce greater values. For example, $f(-1, -2) = 2$ and $f(-3, -6) = 6$. It appears that because the region is unbounded, $f(x, y)$ has no maximum value.

20. Step 1: Find the vertices of the region. Graph the inequalities.

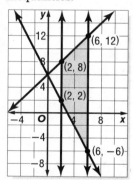

The polygon formed is a quadrilateral with vertices at $(2, 2)$, $(2, 8)$, $(6, -6)$, and $(6, 12)$.

Step 2: Use a table to find the maximum and minimum values of $f(x, y)$. Substitute the coordinates of the vertices into the function.

(x, y)	$-x + 3y$	$f(x, y)$
$(2, 2)$	$-2 + 3(2)$	4
$(2, 8)$	$-2 + 3(8)$	22
$(6, -6)$	$-6 + 3(-6)$	-24
$(6, 12)$	$-6 + 3(12)$	30

The maximum value is 30 at $(6, 12)$.
The minimum value is -24 at $(6, -6)$.

21. Step 1: Find the vertices of the region. Graph the inequalities.

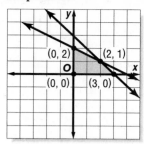

The polygon formed is a quadrilateral with vertices at $(0, 0)$, $(0, 2,)$, $(3, 0)$, and $(2, 1)$.

Step 2: Use a table to find the maximum and minimum values of $f(x, y)$. Substitute the coordinates of the vertices into the function.

(x, y)	$3y - 4x$	$f(x, y)$
$(0, 0)$	$3(0) - 4(0)$	0
$(0, 2)$	$3(2) - 4(0)$	6
$(3, 0)$	$3(0) - 4(3)$	-12
$(2, 1)$	$3(1) - 4(2)$	-5

The maximum value is 6 at $(0, 2)$. The minimum value is -12 at $(3, 0)$.

22. Step 1: Find the vertices of the region. Graph the inequalities.

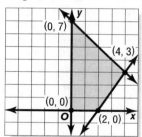

The polygon formed is a quadrilateral with vertices at $(0, 0)$, $(0, 7)$, $(2, 0)$, and $(4, 3)$.

Step 2: Use a table to find the maximum and minimum values of $f(x, y)$. Substitute the coordinates of the vertices into the function.

(x, y)	$5x - 2y$	$f(x, y)$
$(0, 0)$	$5(0) - 2(0)$	0
$(0, 7)$	$5(0) - 2(7)$	-14
$(2, 0)$	$5(2) - 2(0)$	10
$(4, 3)$	$5(4) - 2(3)$	14

The maximum value is 14 at $(4, 3)$.
The minimum value is -14 at $(0, 7)$.

23. Graph the system of inequalities.

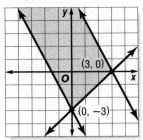

There are only two points of intersection, $(0, -3)$ and $(3, 0)$.

(x, y)	$3x + 4y$	$f(x, y)$
$(0, -3)$	$3(0) + 4(-3)$	-12
$(3, 0)$	$3(3) + 4(0)$	9

The minimum is -12 at $(0, -3)$.
Although $f(3, 0)$ is 9, it is not the maximum value since there are other points in the solution that produce greater values. For example, $f(0, 5) = 20$ and $f(-3, 9) = 27$. It appears that because the region is unbounded, $f(x, y)$ has no maximum value.

24. Step 1: Find the vertices of the region. Graph the inequalities.

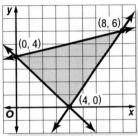

The polygon formed is a triangle with vertices at $(4, 0)$, $(0, 4)$, and $(8, 6)$.

Step 2: Use a table to find the maximum and minimum values of $f(x, y)$. Substitute the coordinates of the vertices into the function.

(x, y)	$x - 2y$	$f(x, y)$
$(4, 0)$	$4 - 2(0)$	4
$(0, 4)$	$0 - 2(4)$	-8
$(8, 6)$	$8 - 2(6)$	-4

The maximum value is 4 at $(4, 0)$.
The minimum value is -8 at $(0, 4)$.

25. Step 1: Find the vertices of the region. Graph the inequalities.

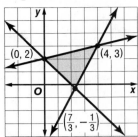

The polygon formed is a triangle with vertices at $(0, 2)$, $(4, 3)$, and $\left(\frac{7}{3}, -\frac{1}{3}\right)$.

Step 2: Use a table to find the maximum and minimum values of $f(x, y)$. Substitute the coordinates of the vertices into the function.

(x, y)	$4x + 3y$	$f(x, y)$
$(0, 2)$	$4(0) + 3(2)$	6
$(4, 3)$	$4(4) + 3(3)$	25
$\left(\frac{7}{3}, -\frac{1}{3}\right)$	$4\left(\frac{7}{3}\right) + 3\left(-\frac{1}{3}\right)$	$\frac{25}{3}$

The maximum value is 25 at $(4, 3)$. The minimum value is 6 at $(0, 2)$.

26. Step 1: Find the vertices of the region. Graph the inequalities.

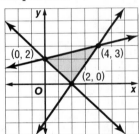

The polygon formed is a triangle with vertices at $(0, 2)$, $(2, 0)$, and $(4, 3)$.

Step 2: Use a table to find the maximum and minimum values of $f(x, y)$. Substitute the coordinates of the vertices into the function.

(x, y)	$3y + x$	$f(x, y)$
$(0, 2)$	$3(2) + 0$	6
$(2, 0)$	$3(0) + 2$	2
$(4, 3)$	$3(3) + 4$	13

The maximum value is 13 at $(4, 3)$. The minimum value is 2 at $(2, 0)$.

27. Graph the system of inequalities.

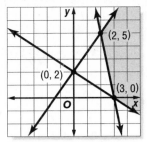

There are only two points of intersection, (3, 0) and (2, 5).

(x, y)	$x + 3y$	$f(x, y)$
(3, 0)	$3 + 3(0)$	3
(2, 5)	$2 + 3(5)$	17

Although $f(2, 5)$ is 17, it is not the maximum value since there are other points in the solution that produce greater values. For example, $f(3, 5) = 18$ and $f(10, 10) = 40$. Although $f(3, 0)$ is 3, it is not the minimum value since there are other points in the solution that produce lesser values. For example, $f(5, -1) = 2$ and $f(10, -4) = -2$. It appears that because the region is unbounded, $f(x, y)$ has no maximum or minimum value.

28. Step 1: Find the vertices of the region. Graph the inequalities.

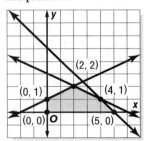

The polygon formed is a pentagon with vertices at (0, 0), (0, 1), (2, 2), (4, 1), and (5, 0).

Step 2: Use a table to find the maximum and minimum values of $f(x, y)$. Substitute the coordinates of the vertices into the function.

(x, y)	$3x - 5y$	$f(x, y)$
(0, 0)	$3(0) - 5(0)$	0
(0, 1)	$3(0) - 5(1)$	-5
(2, 2)	$3(2) - 5(2)$	-4
(4, 1)	$3(4) - 5(1)$	7
(5, 0)	$3(5) - 5(0)$	15

The maximum value is 15 at (5, 0).
The minimum value is -5 at (0, 1).

29. Step 1: Find the vertices of the region. Graph the inequalities.

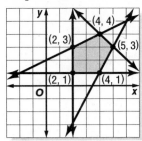

The polygon formed is a pentagon with vertices at (2, 1), (2, 3), (4, 4), (5, 3), and (4, 1).

Step 2: Use a table to find the maximum and minimum values of $f(x, y)$. Substitute the coordinates of the vertices into the function.

(x, y)	$x - 4y$	$f(x, y)$
(2, 1)	$2 - 4(1)$	-2
(2, 3)	$2 - 4(3)$	-10
(4, 4)	$4 - 4(4)$	-12
(5, 3)	$5 - 4(3)$	-7
(4, 1)	$4 - 4(1)$	0

The maximum value is 0 at (4, 1).
The minimum value is -12 at (4, 4).

30a. Sample answer: Write a function, $f(x, y)$, such that $f(1, 2) > f(1, 4) > f(5, 2)$.
$f(x, y) = -2x - y$

30b. Sample answer: Write a function, $f(x, y)$, such that $f(1, 4) > f(1, 2) > f(5, 2)$.
$f(x, y) = 3y - 2x$

30c. Sample answer: Write a function, $f(x, y)$, such that $f(5, 2) > f(1, 4) > f(1, 2)$.
$f(x, y) = x + y$

30d. Sample answer: Write a function, $f(x, y)$, such that $f(1, 2) > f(5, 2) > f(1, 4)$.
$f(x, y) = -x - 3y$

30e. Sample answer: Write a function, $f(x, y)$, such that $f(5, 2) = f(1, 4) > f(1, 2)$.
$f(x, y) = x + 2y$

31. Since the number of calculators cannot be negative, c and g must be nonnegative numbers.
$c \geq 0$ and $g \geq 0$.

A graphing calculator uses $1\frac{1}{2}$ hours of production time, and a CAS calculator uses 1 hour of production time.
$c + 1.5g \leq 85$
A graphing calculator uses 2 hours for encasement and quality control, and a CAS calculator uses $\frac{1}{2}$ hour for encasement and quality control.
$0.5c + 2g \leq 40$
A system of inequalities is $c \geq 0, g \geq 0$, $1.5g + c \leq 85$, and $2g + 0.5c \leq 40$.

32. Graph the system of inequalities.

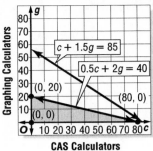

CAS Calculators

33. From the graph, the vertices of the feasible region are at $(0, 0)$, $(0, 20)$, and $(80, 0)$.

34. The function that describes the profit is
$f(c, g) = 65c + 50g$.

35. Substitute the coordinates of the vertices into the function.

(c, g)	$66c + 50g$	$f(c, g)$
$(0, 0)$	$65(0) + 50(0)$	0
$(0, 20)$	$65(0) + 50(20)$	1000
$(80, 0)$	$65(80) + 50(0)$	5200

The maximum value for the function is 5200 at $(80, 0)$.
This means that the maximum profit is $5200 when they make 80 CAS calculators and 0 graphing calculators.

36. The maximum profit is $5200.

37. See students' work.

38. Since the number of acres cannot be negative, c and s must be nonnegative numbers.
$c \geq 0$, $s \geq 0$
There are 4500 acres available for planting these two crops.
$c + s \leq 4500$
The corn can be planted at a rate of 250 acres per day and soybeans at a rate of 200 acres per day, and Dean has 20 days in which to plant.
$\frac{c}{250} + \frac{s}{200} \leq 20 \rightarrow 4c + 5s \leq 20{,}000$

39. Graph the system of inequalities.

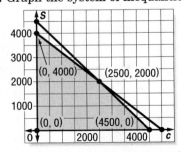

From the graph, the vertices of the feasible region are at $(0, 0)$, $(0, 4000)$, $(4500, 0)$, and $(2500, 2000)$.

40. The function that describes the profit is
$f(c, s) = 26c + 30s$.
Substitute the coordinates of the vertices into the function.

(c, s)	$26c + 30s$	$f(c, s)$
$(0, 0)$	$26(0) + 30(0)$	0
$(0, 4000)$	$26(0) + 30(4000)$	$120{,}000$
$(4500, 0)$	$26(4500) + 30(0)$	$117{,}000$
$(2500, 2000)$	$26(2500) + 30(2000)$	$125{,}000$

The maximum value for the function is 125,000 at $(2500, 2000)$. This means that the maximum profit is $125,000 when he plants 2500 acres of corn and 2000 acres of soybeans.

41. The function that describes the profit is
$f(c, s) = 29c + 24s$.
Substitute the coordinates of the vertices into the function.

(c, s)	$29c + 24s$	$f(c, s)$
$(0, 0)$	$29(0) + 24(0)$	0
$(0, 4000)$	$29(0) + 24(4000)$	$96{,}000$
$(4500, 0)$	$29(4500) + 24(0)$	$130{,}500$
$(2500, 2000)$	$29(2500) + 24(2000)$	$120{,}500$

The maximum value for the function is 130,500 at $(4500, 0)$. This means that the maximum profit is $130,500 when he plants 4500 acres of corn and 0 acres of soybeans.

42. Let c = the number of chocolate chip cookies, and p = the number of peanut butter cookies.
At least three of each type of cookie should be in each package.
$c \geq 3$ and $p \geq 3$
The packages will contain between 6 and 12 cookies, inclusively.
$6 \leq c + p$ and $c + p \leq 12$
Graph the system of inequalities.

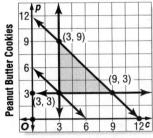

Chocolate Chip Cookies

From the graph, the vertices of the feasible region are at $(3, 3)$, $(3, 9)$, and $(9, 3)$.
The function that describes the profit is
$f(c, p) = 0.25c + 0.26p$
Substitute the coordinates of the vertices into the function.

(c, p)	$0.25c + 0.26p$	$f(c, p)$
$(3, 3)$	$0.25(3) + 0.26(3)$	1.53
$(3, 9)$	$0.25(3) + 0.26(9)$	3.09
$(9, 3)$	$0.25(9) + 0.26(3)$	3.03

The maximum value of the function is 3.09 at $(3, 9)$. This means that the maximum profit is $3.09 when they package 3 chocolate chip cookies and 9 peanut butter cookies.

43. There are many variables in scheduling tasks. Linear programming can help make sure that all the requirements are met. Answers should include the following.
  - Let x = the number of buoy replacements and let y = the number of buoy repairs. Then, $x \geq 0$, $y \geq 0$, $x \leq 8$, and $x + 2.5y \leq 24$.
  - The captain would want to maximize the number of buoys that a crew could repair and replace; so $f(x, y) = x + y$.
  - Graph the inequalities and find the vertices of the intersection of the graphs. The coordinates $(0, 24)$ maximize the function. So the crew can service the maximum number of buoys if they replace 0 and repair 24 buoys.

44. A; Substitute the coordinates of the vertices into the function.

(x, y)	$x + 3y$	$f(x, y)$
$(0, 0)$	$0 + 3(0)$	0
$(4, 0)$	$4 + 3(0)$	4
$(5, 5)$	$5 + 3(5)$	20
$(0, 8)$	$0 + 3(8)$	24

The maximum value is 24 at $(0, 8)$.
The minimum value is 0 at $(0, 0)$.

45. C; The length of side $\overline{AB}$ is $\sqrt{5^2 + 2^2}$ or $\sqrt{29}$ units.
$$A = s^2$$
$$= (\sqrt{29})^2$$
$$= 29$$

The area is 29 square units.

Page 135   Maintain Your Skills

46. Graph all of the inequalities on the same coordinate plane and shade the region or regions that are common to all.

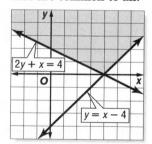

47. Graph both inequalities.

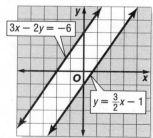

The graphs do not overlap, so the solutions have no points in common. The solution set is $\varnothing$.

48. Multiply the first equation by 5 and the second equation by 4. Then, subtract equations to eliminate the x variable.

$4x + 5y = 20$ $20x + 25y = 100$
$5x + 4y = 7$ $(-)\ 20x + 16y = \ \ 28$
$$9y = 72$$
$$y = 8$$

Replace y with 8 and solve for x.
$$4x + 5y = 20$$
$$4x + 5(8) = 20$$
$$4x + 40 = 20$$
$$4x = -20$$
$$x = -5$$
The solution is $(-5, 8)$.

49. Multiply the first equation by 4. Then, add equations to eliminate the y variable.

$6x + y = 15$ $24x + 4y = \ \ \ \ 60$
$x - 4y = -10$ $(+)\ \ x - 4y = -10$
$$25x \ \ \ \ \ \ = 50$$
$$x = 2$$

Replace x with 2 and solve for y.
$$6x + y = 15$$
$$6(2) + y = 15$$
$$12 + y = 15$$
$$y = 3$$
The solution is $(2, 3)$.

50. Multiply the second equation by 8. Then, add equations to eliminate the y variable.

$3x + 8y = 23$ $3x + 8y = \ \ \ 23$
$5x - y = 24$ $(+)\ 40x - 8y = 192$
$$43x \ \ \ \ \ \ = 215$$
$$x = 5$$

Replace x with 5 and solve for y.
$$3x + 8y = 23$$
$$3(5) + 8y = 23$$
$$15 + 8y = 23$$
$$8y = 8$$
$$y = 1$$
The solution is $(5, 1)$.

51. Let c represent the average cost per pupil per year.

The number of years	times	the average cost per year	plus	the cost in 1986	equals	the cost in 2001.
15	$\cdot$	c	$+$	3479	$=$	7489

52.
$$15c + 3479 = 7489$$
$$15c + 3479 - 3479 = 7489 - 3479$$
$$15c = 4010$$
$$\frac{15c}{15} = \frac{4010}{15}$$
$$c \approx 267.33$$

The average cost per pupil increased about $267 per year.

53. Additive Inverse Property
The Inverse Property says that the sum of a number and its additive inverse is 0.

54. Associative Property of Multiplication
The Associative Property says that the way you group three numbers when multiplying does not change the product.

55. Multiplicative Inverse Property
The Inverse Property says that the product of a number and its multiplicative inverse is 1.

56. Distributive Property
The Distributive Property says that the product of a number and a sum is equal to the sum of the products of the number and each addend.

57. $x + y + z = -2 + 6 + 5$
$\quad\quad\quad\quad = 9$
The value is 9.

58. $2x - y + 3z = 2(-2) - 6 + 3(5)$
$\quad\quad\quad\quad\quad = -4 - 6 + 3(5)$
$\quad\quad\quad\quad\quad = -10 + 15$
$\quad\quad\quad\quad\quad = 5$
The value is 5.

59. $-x + 4y - 2z = -(-2) + 4(6) - 2(5)$
$\quad\quad\quad\quad\quad\quad = 2 + 4(6) - 2(5)$
$\quad\quad\quad\quad\quad\quad = 2 + 24 - 10$
$\quad\quad\quad\quad\quad\quad = 16$
The value is 16.

60. $5x + 2y - z = 5(-2) + 2(6) - 5$
$\quad\quad\quad\quad\quad = -10 + 12 - 5$
$\quad\quad\quad\quad\quad = -3$
The value is -3.

61. $3x - y + 4z = 3(-2) - 6 + 4(5)$
$\quad\quad\quad\quad\quad = -6 - 6 + 20$
$\quad\quad\quad\quad\quad = 8$
The value is 8.

62. $-2x - 3y + 2z = -2(-2) - 3(6) + 2(5)$
$\quad\quad\quad\quad\quad\quad = 4 - 18 + 10$
$\quad\quad\quad\quad\quad\quad = -4$
The value is -4.

Page 135   Practice Quiz 2

1. Graph all of the inequalities on the same coordinate plane and shade the region or regions that are common to all.

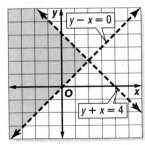

2. Graph all of the inequalities on the same coordinate plane and shade the region or regions that are common to all.

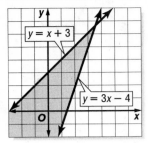

3. Graph all of the inequalities on the same coordinate plane and shade the region or regions that are common to all.

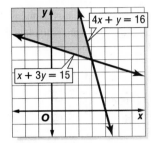

4. Step 1: Find the vertices of the region. Graph the inequalities.

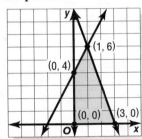

The polygon formed is a quadrilateral with vertices at $(0, 0)$, $(0, 4)$, $(3, 0)$ and $(1, 6)$.

Step 2: Use a table to find the maximum and minimum values of $f(x, y)$. substitute the coordinates of the vertices into the function.

$f(x, y)$	$2x + y$	$f(x, y)$
$(0, 0)$	$2(0) + 0$	0
$(0, 4)$	$2(0) + 4$	4
$(3, 0)$	$2(3) + 0$	6
$(1, 6)$	$2(1) + 6$	8

The maximum value is 8 at $(1, 6)$.
The minimum value is 0 at $(0, 0)$.

5. Step 1: Find the vertices of the region. Graph the inequalities.

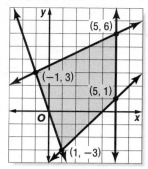

The polygon formed is a quadrilateral with vertices at $(-1, 3)$, $(1, -3)$, $(5, 1)$, and $(5, 6)$.

Step 2: Use a table to find the maximum and minimum values of $f(x, y)$ Substitute the coordinates of the vertices into the function.

(x, y)	$4x - 3y$	$f(x, y)$
$(-1, 3)$	$4(-1) - 3(3)$	-13
$(1, -3)$	$4(1) - 3(-3)$	13
$(5, 1)$	$4(5) - 3(1)$	17
$(5, 6)$	$4(5) - 3(6)$	2

The maximum value is 17 at $(5, 1)$.
The minimum value is -13 at $(-1, 3)$.

Page 137   Algebra Activity
(Preview of Lesson 3-5)

1. Draw the x-, y-, and z-axes. Begin by finding the point $(5, 3, 0)$ in the xy-plane.
The z-coordinate is 6, so move the point up 6 units parallel to the z-axis. The point lies in octant 1.

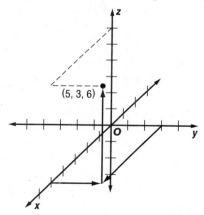

2. Draw the x-, y-, and z-axes. Begin by finding the point $(-2, 4, 0)$ in the xy-plane.
The z-coordinate is 3, so move the point up 3 units parallel to the z-axis
The point lies in octant 5.

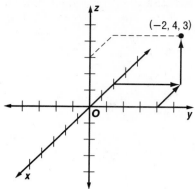

3. Draw the x-, y-, and z-axes.
Begin by finding the point $(1, -5, 0)$ in the xy-plane.
The z-coordinate is 7, so move the point up 7 units parallel to the z-axis.
The point lies in octant 2.

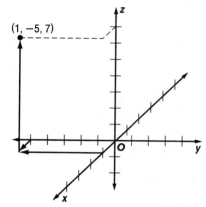

4. Begin by finding the x-, y-, and z-intercepts.

x-intercept
Let $y = 0$ and $z = 0$.
$3x = 6$
$x = 2$

y-intercept
Let $x = 0$ and $z = 0$.
$6y = 6$
$y = 1$

z-intercept
Let $x = 0$ and $y = 0$.
$z = 6$

To sketch the plane, graph the intercepts, which have coordinates $(2, 0, 0)$, $(0, 1, 0)$, and $(0, 0, 6)$.
Then connect the points.

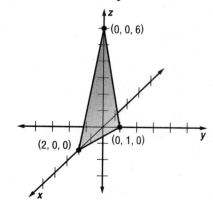

5. Begin by finding the x-, y-, and z-intercepts.

x-intercept
Let $y = 0$ and $z = 0$.
$2x = 20$
$x = 10$

y-intercept
Let $x = 0$ and $z = 0$.
$-5y = 20$
$y = -4$

z-intercept
Let $x = 0$ and $y = 0$.
$4z = 20$
$z = 5$

To sketch the plane, graph the intercepts, which have coordinates $(10, 0, 0)$, $(0, -4, 0)$, and $(0, 0, 5)$. Then connect the points.

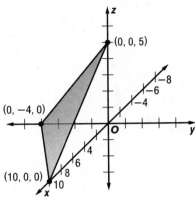

6. Begin by finding the x-, y-, and z-intercepts.

x-intercept
Let $y = 0$ and $z = 0$.
$x = 3$

y-intercept
Let $x = 0$ and $z = 0$.
$3y = 3$
$y = 1$

z-intercept
Let $x = 0$ and $y = 0$.
$-6z = 3$
$z = -\dfrac{1}{2}$

To sketch the plane, graph the intercepts, which have coordinates $(3, 0, 0)$, $(0, 1, 0)$, and $\left(0, 0, -\dfrac{1}{2}\right)$. Then connect the points.

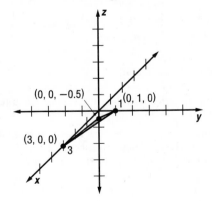

7. Begin by finding the x-, y-, and z-intercepts.

x-intercept
Let $y = 0$ and $z = 0$.
$-3x = 15$
$x = -5$

y-intercept
Let $x = 0$ and $z = 0$.
$5y = 15$
$y = 3$

z-intercept
Let $x = 0$ and $y = 0$.
$10z = 15$
$z = \dfrac{3}{2}$

To sketch the plane, graph the intercepts, which have coordinates $(-5, 0, 0)$, $(0, 3, 0)$, and $\left(0, 0, \dfrac{3}{2}\right)$.
Then connect the points. Remember this is only a portion of the plane that extends indefinitely.

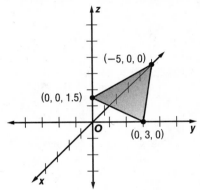

8. Begin by finding the x- and z- intercepts.

x-intercept
Let $y = 0$ and $z = 0$.
$6x = 18$
$x = 3$

z-intercept
Let $x = 0$ and $y = 0$.
$9z = 18$
$z = 2$

There is no y-intercept. The equation $6x + 9z = 18$ represents a plane that does not intersect the y-axis. To sketch the plane, graph the intercepts, which have coordinates $(3, 0, 0)$ and $(0, 0, 2)$. Connect the points, and shade half the plane.

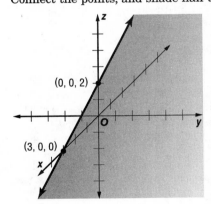

9. Begin by finding the x- and y-intercepts.

x-intercept	y-intercept
Let $y = 0$ and $z = 0$.	Let $x = 0$ and $z = 0$.
$4x = 24$	$-6y = 24$
$x = 6$	$y = -4$

There is no z-intercept. The equation $4x - 6y = 24$ represents a plane that does not intersect the z-axis. To sketch the plane, graph the intercepts, which have coordinates $(6, 0, 0)$ and $(0, -4, 0)$. Connect the points, and shade half the plane.

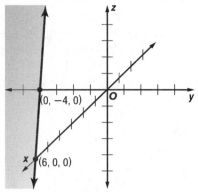

10. The equation can be written in the form $Ax + By + z = C$. D is the lowest common multiple of 8, 3, and 6. So, $D = 24$.
$A = \frac{D}{8}$ or 3. $B = \frac{D}{-3}$ or -8. $C = \frac{D}{6}$ or 4.
Therefore, the equation is $3x - 8y + 4z = 24$.

11. The equation can be written in the form $Ax + By + Cz = D$. D is the lowest common multiple of 10, 4, and 5. So, $D = 20$.
$A = \frac{D}{10}$ or 2. $B = \frac{D}{4}$ or 5. $C = \frac{D}{-5}$ or -4.
Therefore, the equation is $2x + 5y - 4z = 20$.

12. The equation can be written in the form $Ax + By + Cz = D$. D is the lowest common multiple of 4 and 12 that is also divisible by $\frac{1}{2}$.
So, $D = 12$.
$A = \frac{D}{\frac{1}{2}}$ or 24. $B = \frac{D}{4}$ or 3. $C = \frac{D}{-12}$ or -1.
Therefore, the equation is $24x + 3y - z = 12$.

13. In octant 1, x is positive, y is positive, and z is positive. In octant 2, x is positive, y is negative, and z is positive. In octant 3, x is positive, y is negative, and z is negative. In octant 4, x is positive, y is positive, and z is negative. In octant 5, x is negative, y is positive, and z is positive. In octant 6, x is negative, y is negative, and z is positive. In octant 7, x is negative, y is negative, and z is negative. In octant 8, x is negative, y is positive, and z is negative.

14a. The graph of $x = -3$ on a number line is the point at -3.

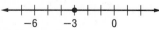

14b. The graph of $x = -3$ on a coordinate plane is the vertical line through the point $(-3, 0)$.

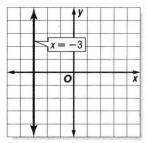

14c. The graph of $x = -3$ on a three-dimensional space is the plane through the point $(-3, 0, 0)$ that is parallel to the yz-plane.

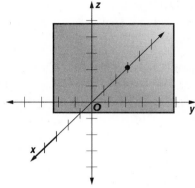

14d. One is a point (one-dimensional), one is a line (two-dimensional), and one is a plane (three-dimensional).

14e. The graph of $x > -3$ in one dimension includes all of the numbers that lie to the right of the point $x = -3$ on a number line. The graph of $x > -3$ in two dimensions is a half-plane and includes all of the ordered pairs that lie to the right of the line $x = -3$. The graph of $x > -3$ in three dimensions includes all of the space that lies in front of the plane $x = -3$.

3-5 | **Solving Systems of Equations in Three Variables**

Page 142   Check for Understanding

1. You can use elimination or substitution to eliminate one of the variables. Then you can solve two equations in two variables.

2. No; the first two equations do represent the same plane, however they do not intersect the third plane, so there is no solution of this system.

3. Sample answer:
$$x + y + z = 4$$
$$2x - y + z = -9$$
$$x + 2y - z = 5$$

Check:
$$x + y + z = 4$$
$$-3 + 5 + 2 \stackrel{?}{=} 4$$
$$4 = 4 ✓$$
$$2x - y + z = -9$$
$$2(-3) - 5 + 2 \stackrel{?}{=} -9$$
$$-9 = -9 ✓$$
$$x + 2y - z = 5$$
$$-3 + 2(5) - 2 \stackrel{?}{=} 5$$
$$5 = 5 ✓$$

4. Step 1: Use elimination to make a system of two equations in two variables.
$$x + 2y \qquad = 12$$
$$\underline{(-)\ x + 6y + z = 20}$$
$$-4y - z = -8$$

Step 2: Solve the system of two equations.
$$3y - 4z = 25 \qquad 3y - 4z = \quad 25$$
$$-4y - z = -8 \quad \underline{(-) -16y - 4z = -32}$$
$$19y \qquad = \quad 57$$
$$y = 3$$

Substitute 3 for y in one of the equations with two variables and solve for z.
$$-4y - z = -8$$
$$-4(3) - z = -8$$
$$-12 - z = -8$$
$$z = -4$$
The result is $y = 3$ and $z = -4$.

Step 3: Substitute 3 for y and -4 for z in one of the original equations with three variables.
$$x + 6y + z = 20$$
$$x + 6(3) + (-4) = 20$$
$$x + 18 - 4 = 20$$
$$x = 6$$
The solution is $(6, 3, -4)$.

5. Step 1: Use elimination to make a system of two equations in two variables.
$$9a + 7b = -30$$
$$-3a + 10c = 73$$

$$9a + 7b \qquad = -30$$
$$\underline{(+) -9a \qquad + 30c = 219}$$
$$7b + 30c = 189$$

Step 2: Solve the system of two equations.
$$8b + 5c = 11 \qquad 48b + 30c = \quad 66$$
$$7b + 30c = 189 \quad \underline{(-)\ 7b + 30c = \quad 189}$$
$$41b \qquad = -123$$
$$b = -3$$

Substitute -3 for b in one of the equations with two variables and solve for c.
$$8b + 5c = 11$$
$$8(-3) + 5c = 11$$
$$-24 + 5c = 11$$
$$5c = 35$$
$$c = 7$$
The result is $b = -3$ and $c = 7$.

Step 3: Substitute -3 for b and 7 for c in one of the original equations.
$$9a + 7b = -30$$
$$9a + 7(-3) = -30$$
$$9a - 21 = -30$$
$$9a = -9$$
$$a = -1$$
The solution is $(-1, -3, 7)$.

6. Step 1: Use elimination to make a system of two equations in two variables.
$$r - 3s + t = 4 \qquad 3r - 9s + 3t = 12$$
$$3r - 6s + 9t = 5 \quad \underline{(-)\ 3r - 6s + 9t = \quad 5}$$
$$-3s - 6t = \quad 7$$

$$r - 3s + t = 4 \qquad 4r - 12s + 4t = 16$$
$$4r - 9s + 10t = 9 \ \underline{(-)\ 4r - \quad 9s + 10t = \quad 9}$$
$$-3s - 6t = \quad 7$$

Step 2: Solve the system of two equations.
$$-3s - 6t = 7$$
$$\underline{(-)-3s - 6t = 7}$$
$$0 = 0$$

The equation $0 = 0$ is always true. This indicates that there are an infinite number of solutions of the system of two equations. The system has an infinite number of solutions.

7. Step 1: Use elimination to make a system of two equations in two variables.
$$2r + 3s - 4t = 20$$
$$4r - s + 5t = 13$$

$$2r + 3s - \quad 4t = 20$$
$$\underline{(+) 12r - 3s + 15t = 39}$$
$$14r \qquad + 11t = 59$$

$$4r - s + 5t = 13$$
$$3r + 2s + 4t = 15$$

$$8r - 2s + 10t = 26$$
$$\underline{(+) 3r + 2s + \quad 4t = 15}$$
$$11r \qquad + 14t = 41$$

Step 2: Solve the system of two equations.
$$14r + 11t = 59 \qquad 154r + 121t = 649$$
$$11r + 14t = 41 \quad \underline{(-) 154r + 196t = 574}$$
$$-75t = \quad 75$$
$$t = -1$$

Substitute -1 for t in one of the equations with two variables and solve for r.
$$14r + 11t = 59$$
$$14r + 11(-1) = 59$$
$$14r - 11 = 59$$
$$14r = 70$$
$$r = 5$$
The result is $r = 5$ and $t = -1$.

Step 3: Substitute 5 for r and -1 for t in one of the original equations.
$$2r + 3s - 4t = 20$$
$$2(5) + 3s - 4(-1) = 20$$
$$10 + 3s + 4 = 20$$
$$3s = 6$$
$$s = 2$$
The solution is $(5, 2, -1)$.

8. Step 1: Use elimination to make a system of two equations in two variables.

$$2x - y + z = 1 \qquad 2x - y + z = 1$$
$$x + 2y - 4z = 3 \qquad (-)\,2x + 4y - 8z = 6$$
$$\overline{ -5y + 9z = -5}$$

$$x + 2y - 4z = 3$$
$$4x + 3y - 7z = -8$$

$$4x + 8y - 16z = 12$$
$$(-)\,4x + 3y - 7z = -8$$
$$\overline{5y - 9z = 20}$$

Step 2: Solve the system of two equations.

$$-5y + 9z = -5$$
$$(+)\,5y - 9z = 20$$
$$\overline{\,0 = 15}$$

The equation $0 = 15$ is never true. So, there is no solution of the system of two equations. The system has no solution.

9. Step 1: Use elimination to make a system of two equations in two variables.

$$x + y + z = 12$$
$$(+)\,6x - 2y - z = 16$$
$$\overline{7x - y = 28}$$

$$x + y + z = 12$$
$$3x + 4y + 2z = 28$$

$$2x + 2y + 2z = 24$$
$$(-)\,3x + 4y + 2z = 28$$
$$\overline{-x - 2y = -4}$$

Step 2: Solve the system of two equations.

$$7x - y = 28 \qquad 14x - 2y = 56$$
$$-x - 2y = -4 \qquad (-)\,-x - 2y = -4$$
$$\overline{15x = 60}$$
$$x = 4$$

Substitute 4 for x in one of the equations with two variables and solve for y.

$$7x - y = 28$$
$$7(4) - y = 28$$
$$28 - y = 28$$
$$y = 0$$

The result is $x = 4$ and $y = 0$.

Step 3: Substitute 4 for x and 0 for y in one of the original equations.

$$x + y + z = 12$$
$$4 + 0 + z = 12$$
$$z = 8$$

The solution is $(4, 0, 8)$.

10. Read the problem and define the variables.

$c =$ the amount of chicken.
$s =$ the amount of sausage.
$r =$ the amount of rice.

Simone buys $13\frac{1}{2}$ pounds of food.

$$c + s + r = 13\frac{1}{2}$$

She spends \$42. Chicken costs \$6 per pound, sausage costs \$3 per pound, and rice costs \$1 per pound.

$$6c + 3s + r = 42$$

She buys twice as much rice as sausage.

$$r = 2s$$

11. Substitute $r = 2s$ in each of the first two equations.

$$c + s + r = 13\frac{1}{2}$$
$$c + s + 2s = 13\frac{1}{2}$$
$$c + 3s = 13\frac{1}{2}$$

$$6c + 3s + r = 42$$
$$6c + 3s + 2s = 42$$
$$6c + 5s = 42$$

Now solve the system of two equations in two variables.

$$c + 3s = 13\frac{1}{2} \qquad\qquad 6c + 18s = 81$$
$$6c + 5s = 42 \qquad\qquad (-)\,6c + 5s = 42$$
$$\overline{13s = 39}$$
$$s = 3$$

Substitute 3 for s in one of the equations.

$$c + 3s = 13\frac{1}{2}$$
$$c + 3(3) = 13\frac{1}{2}$$
$$c + 9 = 13\frac{1}{2}$$
$$c = 4\frac{1}{2}$$

Substitute 3 for s and $4\frac{1}{2}$ for c in one of the original equations.

$$c + s + r = 13\frac{1}{2}$$
$$4\frac{1}{2} + 3 + r = 13\frac{1}{2}$$
$$r = 6$$

So, Simone used $4\frac{1}{2}$ pounds of chicken, 3 pounds of sausage, and 6 pounds of rice.

Pages 142–144 Practice and Apply

12. Step 1: Solve the second equation for z.

$$3z = 21$$
$$z = 7$$

Step 2: Substitute 7 for z in the third equation and solve for x.

$$4x + z = 19$$
$$4x + 7 = 19$$
$$4x = 12$$
$$x = 3$$

Step 3: Substitute 3 for x in the first equation and solve for y.

$$2x - y = 2$$
$$2(3) - y = 2$$
$$6 - y = 2$$
$$y = 4$$

The solution is $(3, 4, 7)$.

13. Step 1: Solve the first equation for a.
$$-4a = 8$$
$$a = -2$$

Step 2: Substitute -2 for a in the second equation and solve for c.
$$5a + 2c = 0$$
$$5(-2) + 2c = 0$$
$$-10 + 2c = 0$$
$$2c = 10$$
$$c = 5$$

Step 3: Substitute 5 for c in the third equation and solve for b.
$$7b + 3c = 22$$
$$7b + 3(5) = 22$$
$$7b + 15 = 22$$
$$7b = 7$$
$$b = 1$$
The solution is $(-2, 1, 5)$.

14. Step 1: Use elimination to make a system of two equations in two variables.
$$3x + 4y + 2z = 6$$
$$7x + 3y + 4z = 29$$

$$\begin{array}{r} 6x + 8y + 4z = 12 \\ (-)\ 7x + 3y + 4z = 29 \\ \hline -x + 5y = -17 \end{array}$$

Step 2: Solve the system of two equations.
$$\begin{array}{ll} 5x + 2y = 4 & \ 5x + 2y = 4 \\ -x + 5y = -17 & (+)\ -5x + 25y = -85 \\ & \ 27y = -81 \\ & y = -3 \end{array}$$

Substitute -3 for y in one of the equations with two variables and solve for x.
$$5x + 2y = 4$$
$$5x + 2(-3) = 4$$
$$5x - 6 = 4$$
$$5x = 10$$
$$x = 2$$
The result is $x = 2$ and $y = -3$.

Step 3: Substitute 2 for x and -3 for y in one of the original equations.
$$3x + 4y + 2z = 6$$
$$3(2) + 4(-3) + 2z = 6$$
$$6 - 12 + 2z = 6$$
$$2z = 12$$
$$z = 6$$
The solution is $(2, -3, 6)$.

15. Step 1: Use elimination to make a system of two equations in two variables.
$$\begin{array}{ll} 2x - 5y + 3z = 5 & 4x - 10y + 6z = 10 \\ x + 10y - 4z = 8 & (+)\ x + 10y - 4z = 8 \\ & 5x \ + 2z = 18 \end{array}$$

Step 2: Solve the system of two equations.
$$\begin{array}{ll} 8x - 6z = 38 & 8x - 6z = 38 \\ 5x + 2z = 18 & (+)\ 15x + 6z = 54 \\ & 23x \ = 92 \\ & x \ = 4 \end{array}$$

Substitute 4 for x in one of the equations with two variables and solve for z.
$$5x + 2z = 18$$
$$5(4) + 2z = 18$$
$$20 + 2z = 18$$
$$2z = -2$$
$$z = -1$$
The result is $x = 4$ and $z = -1$.

Step 3: Substitute 4 for x and -1 for z in one of the original equations.
$$2x - 5y + 3z = 5$$
$$2(4) - 5y + 3(-1) = 5$$
$$8 - 5y - 3 = 5$$
$$-5y = 0$$
$$y = 0$$
The solution is $(4, 0, -1)$.

16. Eliminate a in the first two equations.
$$\begin{array}{ll} 4a + 2b - 6c = 2 & 12a + 6b - 18c = 6 \\ 6a + 3b - 9c = 3 & (-)\ 12a + 6b - 18c = 6 \\ & \ 0 = 0 \end{array}$$

The equation $0 = 0$ is always true. This indicates that the first two equations represent the same plane. Check to see if this plane intersects the third plane.
$$\begin{array}{ll} 4a + 2b - 6c = 2 & 8a + 4b - 12c = 4 \\ 8a + 4b - 12c = 6 & (-)\ 8a + 4b - 12c = 6 \\ & \ 0 = -2 \end{array}$$

The equation $0 = -2$ is never true. So there is no solution of this system.

17. Step 1: Use elimination to make a system of two equations in two variables.

$2r + s + t = 14$
$-r - 3s + 2t = -2$

$$\begin{array}{r} 2r + s + t = 14 \\ (+) -2r - 6s + 4t = -4 \\ \hline -5s + 5t = 10 \end{array}$$

$-r - 3s + 2t = -2$
$4r - 6s + 3t = -5$

$$\begin{array}{r} -4r - 12s + 8t = -8 \\ (+) 4r - 6s + 3t = -5 \\ \hline -18s + 11t = -13 \end{array}$$

Step 2: Solve the system of two equations.

$$\begin{array}{ll} -5s + 5t = 10 & -55s + 55t = 110 \\ -18s + 11t = -13 & (-) -90s + 55t = -65 \\ & \hline \quad 35s = 175 \\ & \qquad s = 5 \end{array}$$

Substitute 5 for s in one of the equations with two variables and solve for t.
$-5s + 5t = 10$
$-5(5) + 5t = 10$
$-25 + 5t = 10$
$5t = 35$
$t = 7$
The result is $s = 5$ and $t = 7$.

Step 3: Substitute 5 for s and 7 for t in one of the original equations.
$2r + s + t = 14$
$2r + 5 + 7 = 14$
$2r = 2$
$r = 1$
The solution is $(1, 5, 7)$.

18. Step 1: Use elimination to make a system of two equations in two variables.

$$\begin{array}{ll} 3x + y + z = 4 & 6x + 2y + 2z = 8 \\ 2x + 2y + 3z = 3 & (-) 2x + 2y + 3z = 3 \\ & \hline 4x \qquad - z = 5 \end{array}$$

$$\begin{array}{ll} 3x + y + z = 4 & 9x + 3y + 3z = 12 \\ x + 3y + 2z = 5 & (-) x + 3y + 2z = 5 \\ & \hline 8x \qquad + z = 7 \end{array}$$

Step 2: Solve the system of two equations.

$$\begin{array}{r} 4x - z = 5 \\ (+) 8x + z = 7 \\ \hline 12x = 12 \\ x = 1 \end{array}$$

Substitute 1 for x in one of the equations with two variables and solve for z.
$4x - z = 5$
$4(1) - z = 5$
$4 - z = 5$
$z = -1$
The result is $x = 1$ and $z = -1$.

Step 3: Substitute 1 for x and -1 for z in one of the original equations.
$3x + y + z = 4$
$3(1) + y + (-1) = 4$
$3 + y - 1 = 4$
$y = 2$
The solution is $(1, 2, -1)$.

19. Eliminate a in the first and third equations.

$$\begin{array}{ll} 4a - 2b + 8c = 30 & 4a - 2b + 8c = 30 \\ 2a - b + 4c = 15 & (-) 4a - 2b + 8c = 30 \\ & \hline 0 = 0 \end{array}$$

The equation $0 = 0$ is always true. This indicates that the first and third equations represent the same plane. Check to see if this plane intersects the second plane.

$$\begin{array}{r} 4a - 2b + 8c = 30 \\ (+) a + 2b - 7c = -12 \\ \hline 5a \quad + c = 18 \end{array}$$

The planes intersect in the line. So, there are infinitely many solutions.

20. Step 1: Use elimination to make a system of two equations in two variables.

$$\begin{array}{r} 2r + s + t = 7 \\ (-) r + 2s + t = 8 \\ \hline r - s = -1 \end{array}$$

$$\begin{array}{ll} 2r + s + t = 7 & 4r + 2s + 2t = 14 \\ r + s + 2t = 11 & (-) r + s + 2t = 11 \\ & \hline 3r + s = 3 \end{array}$$

Step 2: Solve the system of two equations.

$$\begin{array}{r} r - s = -1 \\ (+) 3r + s = 3 \\ \hline 4r = 2 \\ r = \frac{1}{2} \end{array}$$

Substitute $\frac{1}{2}$ for r in one of the equations with two variables and solve for s.
$r - s = -1$
$\frac{1}{2} - s = -1$
$s = \frac{3}{2}$
The result is $r = \frac{1}{2}$ and $s = \frac{3}{2}$.

Step 3: Substitute $\frac{1}{2}$ for r and $\frac{3}{2}$ for s in one of the original equations.
$2r + s + t = 7$
$2\left(\frac{1}{2}\right) + \frac{3}{2} + t = 7$
$1 + \frac{3}{2} + t = 7$
$t = \frac{9}{2}$
The solution is $\left(\frac{1}{2}, \frac{3}{2}, \frac{9}{2}\right)$.

21. Step 1: Use elimination to make a system of two equations in two variables.

$6x + 2y + 4z = 2$
$3x + 4y - 8z = -3$

$6x + 2y + 4z = 2$
$\underline{(-)\ 6x + 8y - 16z = -6}$
$\qquad -6y + 20z = 8$

$6x + 2y + 4z = 2$
$-3x - 6y + 12z = 5$

$6x + 2y + 4z = 2$
$\underline{(+) -6x - 12y + 24z = 10}$
$\qquad -10y + 28z = 12$

Step 2: Solve the system of two equations.

$-6y + 20z = 8$
$-10y + 28z = 12$

$-30y + 100z = 40$
$\underline{(-) -30y + 84z = 36}$
$\qquad 16z = 4$
$\qquad z = \frac{1}{4}$

Substitute $\frac{1}{4}$ for z in one of the equations with two variables and solve for y.

$-6y + 20z = 8$
$-6y + 20\left(\frac{1}{4}\right) = 8$
$-6y + 5 = 8$
$-6y = 3$
$y = -\frac{1}{2}$

The result is $y = -\frac{1}{2}$ and $z = \frac{1}{4}$.

Step 3: Substitute $-\frac{1}{2}$ for y and $\frac{1}{4}$ for z in one of the original equations.

$6x + 2y + 4z = 2$
$6x + 2\left(-\frac{1}{2}\right) + 4\left(\frac{1}{4}\right) = 2$
$6x - 1 + 1 = 2$
$6x = 2$
$x = \frac{1}{3}$

The solution is $\left(\frac{1}{3}, -\frac{1}{2}, \frac{1}{4}\right)$.

22. Step 1: Use elimination to make a system of two equations in two variables.

$r + s + t = 5 \qquad\qquad 2r + 2s + 2t = 10$
$2r - 7s - 3t = 13 \qquad \underline{(-)\ 2r - 7s - 3t = 13}$
$\qquad\qquad\qquad\qquad\qquad\qquad 9s + 5t = -3$

$r + s + t = 5 \qquad\qquad\quad r + s + t = 5$
$\frac{1}{2}r - \frac{1}{3}s + \frac{2}{3}t = -1 \qquad \underline{(-)\ r - \frac{2}{3}s + \frac{4}{3}t = -2}$
$\qquad\qquad\qquad\qquad\qquad\qquad\quad \frac{5}{3}s - \frac{1}{3}t = 7$

Step 2: Solve the system of two equations.

$9s + 5t = -3 \qquad\qquad 9s + 5t = -3$
$\frac{5}{3}s - \frac{1}{3}t = 7 \qquad \underline{(+)\ 25s - 5t = 105}$
$\qquad\qquad\qquad\qquad\qquad 34s = 102$
$\qquad\qquad\qquad\qquad\qquad\quad s = 3$

Substitute 3 for s in one of the equations with two variables and solve for t.

$9s + 5t = -3$
$9(3) + 5t = -3$
$27 + 5t = -3$
$5t = -30$
$t = -6$

The result is $s = 3$ and $t = -6$.

Step 3: Substitute 3 for s and -6 for t in one of the original equations.

$r + s + t = 5$
$r + 3 + (-6) = 5$
$r + 3 - 6 = 5$
$r = 8$

The solution is $(8, 3, -6)$.

23. Step 1: Use elimination to make a system of two equations in two variables.

$2a - b + 3c = -7$
$4a + 5b + c = 29$

$4a - 2b + 6c = -14$
$\underline{(-)\ 4a + 5b + c = 29}$
$\qquad -7b + 5c = -43$

$2a - b + 3c = -7$
$a - \frac{2b}{3} + \frac{c}{4} = -10$

$2a - b + 3c = -7$
$\underline{(-)\ 2a - \frac{4}{3}b + \frac{1}{2}c = -20}$
$\qquad\quad \frac{1}{3}b + \frac{5}{2}c = 13$

Step 2: Solve the system of two equations.

$-7b + 5c = -43 \qquad\qquad -7b + 5c = -43$
$\frac{1}{3}b + \frac{5}{2}c = 13 \qquad \underline{(-)\ \frac{2}{3}b + 5c = 26}$
$\qquad\qquad\qquad\qquad\qquad -\frac{23}{3}b = -69$
$\qquad\qquad\qquad\qquad\qquad\quad b = 9$

Substitute 9 for b in one of the equations with two variables and solve for c.

$-7b + 5c = -43$
$-7(9) + 5c = -43$
$-63 + 5c = -43$
$5c = 20$
$c = 4$

The result is $b = 9$ and $c = 4$.

Step 3: Substitute 9 for b and 4 for c in one of the original equations.

$2a - b + 3c = -7$
$2a - 9 + 3(4) = -7$
$2a - 9 + 12 = -7$
$2a = -10$
$a = -5$

The solution is $(-5, 9, 4)$.

24. Read the problem and define the variables.
x = the first number.
y = the second number.
z = the third number.
The sum of three numbers is 20.
$x + y + z = 20$
The second number is 4 times the first.
$y = 4x$
The sum of the first and third is 8.
$x + z = 8$
Substitute $y = 4x$ in the first equation.
$x + y + z = 20$
$x + 4x + z = 20$
$5x + z = 20$
Now solve the system of two equations in two variables.

$$\begin{array}{rl} x + z = & 8 \\ (-)\ 5x + z = & 20 \\ \hline -4x \quad\quad = & -12 \\ x = & 3 \end{array}$$

Substitute 3 for x in one of the equations.
$x + z = 8$
$3 + z = 8$
$z = 5$
Substitute 3 for x and 5 for z in one of the original equations.
$x + y + z = 20$
$3 + y + 5 = 20$
$y = 12$
The three numbers are 3, 12, and 5.

25. Read the problem and define the variables.
x = the first number.
y = the second number.
z = the third number.
The sum of three numbers is 12.
$x + y + z = 12$
The first number is twice the sum of the second and third.
$x = 2(y + z) \rightarrow x = 2y + 2z$
The third number is 5 less than the first.
$z = x - 5$
Substitute $z = x - 5$ in each of the first two equations.
$$\begin{array}{l} x + y + z = 12 \\ x + y + x - 5 = 12 \\ 2x + y - 5 = 12 \\ 2x + y = 17 \end{array}$$
$$\begin{array}{l} x = 2y + 2z \\ x = 2y + 2(x - 5) \\ x = 2y + 2x - 10 \\ 10 = 2y + x \end{array}$$
$x + 2y = 10$
Now solve the system of two equations in two variables.

$$\begin{array}{ll} 2x + y = 17 & \\ x + 2y = 10 & \end{array} \quad \begin{array}{rl} 2x + y = & 17 \\ (-)\ 2x + 4y = & 20 \\ \hline -3y = & -3 \\ y = & 1 \end{array}$$

Substitute 1 for y in one of the equations.
$x + 2y = 10$
$x + 2(1) = 10$
$x + 2 = 10$
$x = 8$
Substitute 8 for x and 1 for y in one of the original equations.
$x + y + z = 12$
$8 + 1 + z = 12$
$z = 3$
The three numbers are 8, 1, and 3.

26. Read the problem and define the variables.
x = the number of \$20 travelers checks.
y = the number of \$50 travelers checks.
z = the number of \$100 travelers checks.
Jonathan purchased 10 travelers checks.
$x + y + z = 10$
The denominations are \$20, \$50, and \$100, and the checks total \$370.
$20x + 50y + 100z = 370$
He has twice as many \$20 checks as \$50 checks.
$x = 2y$
Substitute $x = 2y$ in each of the first two equations.
$$\begin{array}{l} x + y + z = 10 \\ 2y + y + z = 10 \\ 3y + z = 10 \end{array}$$
$$\begin{array}{l} 20x + 50y + 100z = 370 \\ 20(2y) + 50y + 100z = 370 \\ 40y + 50y + 100z = 370 \\ 90y + 100z = 370 \end{array}$$
Now solve the system of two equations in two variables.

$$\begin{array}{ll} 3y + z = 10 & \\ 90y + 100z = 370 & \end{array} \quad \begin{array}{rl} 90y + 30z = & 300 \\ (-)\ 90y + 100z = & 370 \\ \hline -70z = & -70 \\ z = & 1 \end{array}$$

Substitute 1 for z in one of the equations.
$3y + z = 10$
$3y + 1 = 10$
$3y = 9$
$y = 3$
Substitute 3 for y and 1 for z in one of the original equations.
$x + y + z = 10$
$x + 3 + 1 = 10$
$x = 6$
So, Jonathan has 6 \$20 checks, 3 \$50 checks, and 1 \$100 check.

27. Read the problem and define the variables.
x = the price of an enchilada.
y = the price of a taco.
z = the price of a burrito.
Two tacos and one burrito costs $6.55.
$2y + z = 6.55$
One enchilada, one taco, and one burrito costs $7.10.
$x + y + z = 7.10$
Two enchiladas and two tacos costs $8.90.
$2x + 2y = 8.90$
Use elimination to make a system of two equations in two variables.

$$\begin{array}{r} 2y + z = 6.55 \\ (-)\,\underline{x + y + z = 7.10} \\ -x + y = -0.55 \end{array}$$

Solve the system of two equations in two variables.

$$\begin{array}{ll} 2x + 2y = 8.90 & 2x + 2y = 8.90 \\ -x + y = -0.55 & (+)\,\underline{-2x + 2y = -1.10} \\ & 4y = 7.80 \\ & y = 1.95 \end{array}$$

Substitute 1.95 for y in one of the equations.

$$\begin{array}{r} -x + y = -0.55 \\ -x + 1.95 = -0.55 \\ x = 2.50 \end{array}$$

Substitute 2.50 for x and 1.95 for y in one of the original equations.

$$\begin{array}{r} x + y + z = 7.10 \\ 2.50 + 1.95 + z = 7.10 \\ z = 2.65 \end{array}$$

So, enchiladas cost $2.50, tacos cost $1.95, and burritos cost $2.65.

28. Burritos cost $2.65 and enchiladas cost $2.50.

$$\begin{array}{r} 2(2.65) + 2.50 = 5.30 + 2.50 \\ = 7.80 \end{array}$$

Maka should plan to spend $7.80.

29. Read the problem and define the variables.
x = the number of free-throws made.
y = the number of 2-point field goals made.
z = the number of 3-point field goals made.
Katie made 355 shots.
$x + y + z = 355$
She scored 646 points.
$x + 2y + 3z = 646$
She made 27 more 2-point field goals than 3-point field goals.
$y = z + 27$

30. Substitute $y = z + 27$ in each of the first two equations.

$$\begin{array}{r} x + y + z = 355 \\ x + z + 27 + z = 355 \\ x + 2z + 27 = 355 \\ x + 2z = 328 \end{array}$$

$$\begin{array}{r} x + 2y + 3z = 646 \\ x + 2(z + 27) + 3z = 646 \\ x + 2z + 54 + 3z = 646 \\ x + 5z + 54 = 646 \\ x + 5z = 592 \end{array}$$

Now solve the system of two equations in two variables.

$$\begin{array}{r} x + 2z = 328 \\ (-)\,\underline{x + 5z = 592} \\ -3z = -264 \\ z = 88 \end{array}$$

Substitute 88 for z in one of the equations.

$$\begin{array}{r} x + 2z = 328 \\ x + 2(88) = 328 \\ x + 176 = 328 \\ x = 152 \end{array}$$

Substitute 152 for x and 88 for z in one of the original equations.

$$\begin{array}{r} x + y + z = 355 \\ 152 + y + 88 = 355 \\ y = 115 \end{array}$$

So, Katie made 152 free throws, 115 2-point field goals, and 88 3-point field goals.

31. The equation passes through the points $(-2, 9)$, $(0, 3)$, and $(2, 9)$. Therefore, each of these three points satisfies the equation.

$$\begin{array}{l} y = ax^2 + bx + c \\ 9 = a(-2)^2 + b(-2) + c \rightarrow 9 = 4a - 2b + c \\ 3 = a(0)^2 + b(0) + c \rightarrow 3 = c \\ 9 = a(2)^2 + b(2) + c \rightarrow 9 = 4a + 2b + c \end{array}$$

Substitute $c = 3$ in each of the other two equations.

$$\begin{array}{l} 9 = 4a - 2b + c \\ 9 = 4a - 2b + 3 \\ 6 = 4a - 2b \\ 9 = 4a + 2b + c \\ 9 = 4a + 2b + 3 \\ 6 = 4a + 2b \end{array}$$

Now solve the system of two equations in two variables.

$$\begin{array}{r} 6 = 4a - 2b \\ (+)\,\underline{6 = 4a + 2b} \\ 12 = 8a \\ \frac{3}{2} = a \end{array}$$

Substitute $\frac{3}{2}$ for a in one of the equations.

$$\begin{array}{l} 6 = 4a + 2b \\ 6 = 4\left(\frac{3}{2}\right) + 2b \\ 6 = 6 + 2b \\ 0 = 2b \\ 0 = b \end{array}$$

So, $a = \frac{3}{2}$, $b = 0$, and $c = 3$. The equation is $y = \frac{3}{2}x^2 + 0x + 3$ or $y = \frac{3}{2}x^2 + 3$.

32. You can write a system of three equations in three variables to find the number of each type of medal.

Answers should include the following.

- You can substitute $b + 6$ for g and $b - 8$ for s in the equation $g + s + b = 97$. This equation is now in terms of b. Once you find b, you can substitute again to find g and s. The U. S. Olympians won 39 gold medals, 25 silver medals, and 33 bronze medals.

- Another situation involving three variables is winning times of the first, second, and third place finishers of a race.

33. D;
$$\begin{array}{r} a + b = 16 \\ (-)\, a - c = 4 \\ \hline b + c = 12 \end{array}$$

$$\begin{array}{r} a - c = 4 \\ (-) b - c = -4 \\ \hline a - b = 8 \end{array}$$

$$\begin{array}{r} a + b = 16 \\ (-) b - c = -4 \\ \hline a + c = 20 \end{array}$$

34. A;
$$\begin{array}{r} x + y = 1 \\ y + z = 10 \\ (+)\, x + z = 3 \\ \hline 2x + 2y + 2z = 14 \\ x + y + z = 7 \end{array}$$

Page 144   Maintain Your Skills

35. Define the variables.
x = the number of units of notebook paper.
y = the number of units of newspaper.
Write a system of inequalities.
Regular customers require at least 10 units of notebook paper and 80 units of newspaper.
$x \geq 10$ and $y \geq 80$
The Paper Mill can produce at most 200 units of paper a day.
$x + y \leq 200$
Graph the system of inequalities.

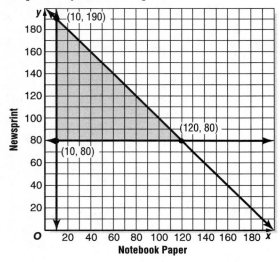

From the graph, the vertices of the feasible region are at (10, 80), (10, 190), and (120, 80). The function that describes the profit is $f(x, y) = 500x + 350y$. Find the maximum value for this function. Substitute the coordinates of the vertices into the function.

(x, y)	$500x + 350y$	$f(x, y)$
(10, 80)	500(10) + 350(80)	33,000
(10, 190)	500(10) + 350(190)	71,500
(120, 80)	500(120) + 350(80)	88,000

The maximum value of the function is 88,000 at (120, 80). This means that the maximum profit is $88,000 when they produce 120 units of notebook paper and 80 units of newsprint.

36. Graph all of the inequalities on the same coordinate plane and shade the region or regions that are common to all.

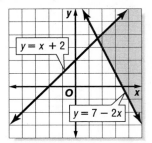

37. Graph all of the inequalities on the same coordinate plane and shade the region or regions that are common to all.

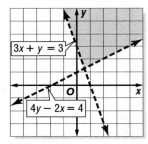

38. Graph all of the inequalities on the same coordinate plane and shade the region or regions that are common to all.

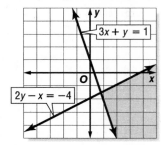

39. Find an equation of the line through $(7, 15)$ and $(14, 22)$. Begin by finding the slope.

$$m = \frac{y_2 - y_1}{x_2 - x_1}$$
$$= \frac{22 - 15}{14 - 7}$$
$$= \frac{7}{7}$$
$$= 1$$

$$y - y_1 = m(x - x_1)$$
$$y - 15 = 1(x - 7)$$
$$y - 15 = x - 7$$
$$y = x + 8$$

One prediction equation is $y = x + 8$.

40. The year 2010 is 39 years after 1971, so use the prediction equation to find the value of y when $x = 39$.

$$y = x + 8$$
$$y = 39 + 8$$
$$y = 47$$

The model predicts that the price for a first-class stamp in 2010 will be about 47¢.

41. $5x + 2y - 4x + y = 5x - 4x + 2y + y$
$$= (5 - 4)x + (2 + 1)y$$
$$= x + 3y$$

42. $(4z + 1) - (6z - 7) = 4z + 1 - 6z + 7$
$$= 4z - 6z + 1 + 7$$
$$= (4 - 6)z + (1 + 7)$$
$$= -2z + 8$$

43. $(8s - 5t) + (9t + s) = 8s - 5t + 9t + s$
$$= 8s + s + 9t - 5t$$
$$= (8 + 1)s + (9 - 5)t$$
$$= 9s + 4t$$

44. $4(6a + 5b) - 2(3a + 2b)$
$$= 4(6a) + 4(5b) - 2(3a) - 2(2b)$$
$$= 24a + 20b - 6a - 4b$$
$$= 24a - 6a + 20b - 4b$$
$$= (24 - 6)a + (20 - 4)b$$
$$= 18a + 16b$$

Chapter 3 Study Guide and Review

Page 145 Vocabulary and Concept Check

1. c; constraints

2. b; dependent system

3. f; feasible region

4. i; substitution method

5. a; consistent system

6. e; elimination method

7. h; ordered triple

8. g; linear programming

9. d; inconsistent system

10. j; unbounded region

11. Graph both equations on the same coordinate plane.

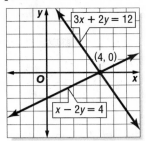

The solution of the system is $(4, 0)$.

12. Graph both equations on the same coordinate plane.

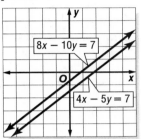

The lines are parallel, and do not intersect. Therefore, there is no solution for the system.

13. Graph both equations on the same coordinate plane.

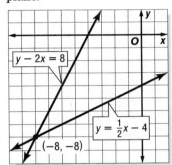

The solution of the system is $(-8, -8)$.

14. Graph both equations on the same coordinate plane.

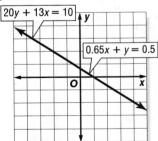

The lines are the same. Each point on the line is a solution of the system. There are infinitely many solutions of the system.

15. Add the equations to eliminate the y variable.

$$\begin{array}{r} x + y = 5 \\ (+)\ 2x - y = 4 \\ \hline 3x \quad\ = 9 \\ x = 3 \end{array}$$

Replace x with 3 and solve for y.

$$x + y = 5$$
$$3 + y = 5$$
$$y = 2$$

The solution is $(3, 2)$.

16. Multiply the first equation by 2. Then subtract the equations to eliminate the x variable.

$$\begin{array}{ll} 2x - 3y = 9 & 4x - 6y = \ \ 18 \\ 4x + 2y = -22 & \underline{(-)\ 4x + 2y = -22} \\ & \qquad\ -8y = \ \ 40 \\ & \qquad\quad\ y = -5 \end{array}$$

Replace y with -5 and solve for x.

$$2x - 3y = 9$$
$$2x - 3(-5) = 9$$
$$2x + 15 = 9$$
$$2x = -6$$
$$x = -3$$

The solution is $(-3, -5)$.

17. Multiply the second equation by 2. Then add the equations to eliminate the x variable.

$$\begin{array}{ll} 7y - 2x = 10 & 7y - 2x = \ \ 10 \\ -3y + x = -3 & \underline{(+)\ -6y + 2x = -6} \\ & \qquad\quad\ y = \ \ \ 4 \end{array}$$

Replace y with 4 and solve for x.

$$7y - 2x = 10$$
$$7(4) - 2x = 10$$
$$28 - 2x = 10$$
$$-2x = -18$$
$$x = 9$$

The solution is $(9, 4)$.

18. Multiply the first equation by 3, and the second equation by 2. Then add the equations to eliminate the x variable.

$$\begin{array}{ll} -2x - 6y = 0 & -6x - 18y = 0 \\ 3x + 11y = 4 & \underline{(+)\ 6x + 22y = 8} \\ & \qquad\quad\ 4y = 8 \\ & \qquad\quad\ \ y = 2 \end{array}$$

Replace y with 2 and solve for x.

$$-2x - 6y = 0$$
$$-2x - 6(2) = 0$$
$$-2x - 12 = 0$$
$$-2x = 12$$
$$x = -6$$

The solution is $(-6, 2)$.

19. Multiply the first equation by 2, and the second equation by 5. Then add the equations to eliminate the y variable.

$$\begin{array}{ll} 3x - 5y = -13 & 6x - 10y = -26 \\ 4x + 2y = 0 & \underline{(+)\ 20x + 10y = \quad\ 0} \\ & \qquad 26x \qquad\ = -26 \\ & \qquad\quad\ x = -1 \end{array}$$

Replace x with -1 and solve for y.

$$3x - 5y = -13$$
$$3(-1) - 5y = -13$$
$$-3 - 5y = -13$$
$$-5y = -10$$
$$y = 2$$

The solution is $(-1, 2)$.

20. Add the equations to eliminate the y variable.

$$\begin{array}{r} x + y = \ \ 4 \\ (+)\ x - y = \ \ 8.5 \\ \hline 2x \qquad = 12.5 \\ x = 6.25 \end{array}$$

Replace x with 6.25 and solve for y.

$$x + y = 4$$
$$6.25 + y = 4$$
$$y = -2.25$$

The solution is $(6.25, -2.25)$.

21. Graph each inequality and shade the intersection.

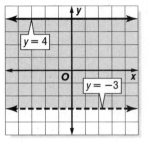

22. $|y| > 3$ can be written as $y > 3$ or $y < -3$.
Graph each inequality and shade the intersection.

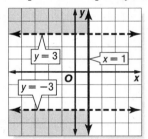

23. Graph each inequality and shade the intersection.

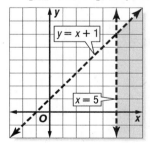

24. Graph each inequality and shade the intersection.

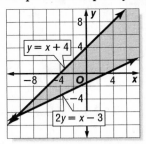

25. Let x = the number of My First Babies and y = the number of My Real Babies.
$x \geq 0, y \geq 0, 5x + 2y \leq 1920,$ and $x \geq 2y$
Graph the inequalities.

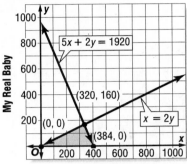

The vertices of the feasible region are $(0, 0)$, $(320, 160)$, and $(384, 0)$.
The profit function is $f(x, y) = 3x + 7.5y$.
The maximum value of $2160 occurs at $(320, 160)$.
So the company should produce 320 of the My First Baby dolls and 160 of the My Real Baby dolls.

26. Use elimination to make a system of two equations in two variables.
$x + 4y - z = 6$
$3x + 2y + 3z = 16$

$3x + 12y - 3z = 18$
$\underline{(+) 3x + 2y + 3z = 16}$
$\quad 6x + 14y \qquad = 34$

$\quad x + 4y - z = 6$
$\underline{(+) 2x - y + z = 3}$
$\quad 3x + 3y \qquad = 9$

Solve the system of two equations.
$6x + 14y = 34$
$3x + 3y = 9$

$6x + 14y = 34$
$\underline{(-) 6x + 6y = 18}$
$\qquad\qquad 8y = 16$
$\qquad\qquad\; y = 2$

Substitute 2 for y in one of the equations with two variables and solve for x.
$6x + 14y = 34$
$6x + 14(2) = 34$
$6x + 28 = 34$
$\quad 6x = 6$
$\qquad x = 1$

Substitute 1 for x and 2 for y in one of the original equations.
$x + 4y - z = 6$
$1 + 4(2) - z = 6$
$\quad 1 + 8 - z = 6$
$\qquad\qquad z = 3$
The solution is $(1, 2, 3)$.

27. Use elimination to make a system of two equations in two variables.
$\quad 2a + b - c = 5$
$\underline{(+) a - b + 3c = 9}$
$\quad 3a \qquad + 2c = 14$

Solve the system of two equations.
$\quad 3a - 6c = 6$
$\underline{(-) 3a + 2c = 14}$
$\qquad -8c = -8$
$\qquad\quad c = 1$

Substitute 1 for c in one of the equations with two variables and solve for a.
$3a - 6c = 6$
$3a - 6(1) = 6$
$\quad 3a - 6 = 6$
$\qquad 3a = 12$
$\qquad\; a = 4$

Substitute 4 for a and 1 for c in one of the original equations.
$2a + b - c = 5$
$2(4) + b - 1 = 5$
$\quad 8 + b - 1 = 5$
$\qquad\qquad b = -2$
The solution is $(4, -2, 1)$.

28. Solve the third equation for e.
$3e = -3$
$\quad e = -1$

Substitute -1 for e in the first equation and solve for f.
$e + f = 4$
$-1 + f = 4$
$\qquad f = 5$

Substitute -1 for e and 5 for f in the second equation and solve for d.
$2d + 4e - f = -3$
$2d + 4(-1) - 5 = -3$
$\quad 2d - 4 - 5 = -3$
$\qquad\qquad 2d = 6$
$\qquad\qquad\; d = 3$
The solution is $(3, -1, 5)$.

Chapter 3 Practice Test

Page 149
1. linear
2. elimination
3. point
4. Subtract the equations to eliminate the y variable.
$\quad -4x + y = -5$
$\underline{(-) 2x + y = 7}$
$\quad -6x \qquad = -12$
$\qquad\quad x = 2$

Replace x with 2 and solve for y.
$-4x + y = -5$
$-4(2) + y = -5$
$\quad -8 + y = -5$
$\qquad\quad y = 3$
The solution is $(2, 3)$.

5. Multiply the first equation by 3. Then add the equations to eliminate the x variable.

$x + y = -8$
$-3x + 2y = 9$

$\begin{aligned} 3x + 3y &= -24 \\ (+)\ -3x + 2y &= 9 \\ \hline 5y &= -15 \\ y &= -3 \end{aligned}$

Replace y with -3 and solve for x.
$x + y = -8$
$x + (-3) = -8$
$x = -5$
The solution is $(-5, -3)$.

6. Substitute $6x - 6$ for y in the first equation and solve for x.

$3x + 2y = 18$
$3x + 2(6x - 6) = 18$
$3x + 12x - 12 = 18$
$15x = 30$
$x = 2$

Substitute 2 for x in one of the equations and solve for y.
$y = 6x - 6$
$y = 6(2) - 6$
$y = 12 - 6$
$y = 6$
The solution is $(2, 6)$.

7. Multiply the second equation by 3. Then subtract the equations to eliminate the y variable.

$-6x + 3y = 33$
$-4x + y = 16$

$\begin{aligned} -6x + 3y &= 33 \\ (-)\ -12x + 3y &= 48 \\ \hline 6x &= -15 \\ x &= -2.5 \end{aligned}$

Replace x with -2.5 and solve for y.
$-6x + 3y = 33$
$-6(-2.5) + 3y = 33$
$15 + 3y = 15$
$3y = 18$
$y = 6$
The solution is $(-2.5, 6)$.

8. Multiply the first equation by 3 and the second equation by 7. Then add the equations to eliminate the x variable.

$-7x + 6y = 42$
$3x + 4y = 28$

$\begin{aligned} -21x + 18y &= 126 \\ (+)\ 21x + 28y &= 196 \\ \hline 46y &= 322 \\ y &= 7 \end{aligned}$

Replace y with 7 and solve for x.
$-7x + 6y = 42$
$-7x + 6(7) = 42$
$-7x + 42 = 42$
$-7x = 0$
$x = 0$
The solution is $(0, 7)$.

9. Solve the first equation for y in terms of x.
$2y = 5x - 1$
$y = \frac{5}{2}x - \frac{1}{2}$

Substitute $\frac{5}{2}x - \frac{1}{2}$ for y in the second equation and solve for x.

$x + y = -1$
$x + \frac{5}{2}x - \frac{1}{2} = -1$
$\frac{7}{2}x = -\frac{1}{2}$
$x = -\frac{1}{7}$

Substitute $-\frac{1}{7}$ for x in one of the equations and solve for y.

$2y = 5x - 1$
$2y = 5\left(-\frac{1}{7}\right) - 1$
$2y = -\frac{5}{7} - 1$
$2y = -\frac{12}{7}$
$y = -\frac{6}{7}$

The solution is $\left(-\frac{1}{7}, -\frac{6}{7}\right)$.

10. Graph each inequality and shade the intersection.

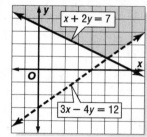

11. Graph each inequality and shade the intersection.

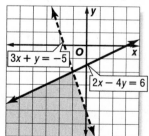

12. Graph each inequality and shade the intersection.

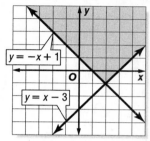

13. Find the vertices of the region. Graph the inequalities.

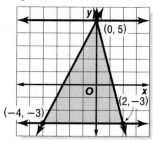

The polygon formed is a triangle with vertices at $(-4, -3)$, $(0, 5)$, and $(2, -3)$.

Use a table to find the maximum and minimum values of $f(x, y)$. Substitute the coordinates of the vertices into the function.

(x, y)	$4x - 3y$	$f(x, y)$
$(-4, -3)$	$4(-4) - 3(-3)$	-7
$(0, 5)$	$4(0) - 3(5)$	-15
$(2, -3)$	$4(2) - 3(-3)$	17

The maximum value is 17 at $(2, -3)$.
The minimum value is -15 at $(0, 5)$.

14. Find the vertices of the region. Graph the inequalities.

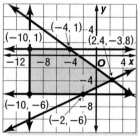

The polygon formed is a pentagon with vertices at $(-10, -6)$, $(-10, 1)$, $(-4, 1)$, $(-2, -6)$ and $(2.4, -3.8)$.

Use a table to find the maximum and minimum values of $f(x, y)$. Substitute the coordinates of the vertices into the function.

(x, y)	$2x + y$	$f(x, y)$
$(-10, -6)$	$2(-10) + (-6)$	-26
$(-10, 1)$	$2(-10) + 1$	-19
$(-4, 1)$	$2(-4) + 1$	-7
$(-2, -6)$	$2(-2) + (-6)$	-10
$(2.4, -3.8)$	$2(2.4) + (-3.8)$	1

The maximum value is 1 at $(2.4, -3.8)$.
The minimum value is -26 at $(-10, -6)$.

15. Define the variables.
$x = $ the number of soccer balls.
$y = $ the number of volleyballs.
Write a system of inequalities.
Since the number of balls cannot be negative, x and y must be nonnegative numbers.
$x \geq 0$ and $y \geq 0$
Cutting requires 2 hours to make 75 soccer balls and 3 hours to make 60 volleyballs. Cutting has 500 hours available.
$$2\left(\frac{x}{75}\right) + 3\left(\frac{y}{60}\right) \leq 500 \rightarrow 8x + 15y \leq 150{,}000$$
Sewing needs 3 hours to make 75 soccer balls and 2 hours to make 60 volleyballs. Sewing has 450 hours available.
$$3\left(\frac{x}{75}\right) + 2\left(\frac{y}{60}\right) \leq 450 \rightarrow 6x + 5y \leq 67{,}500$$
Graph the system of inequalities.

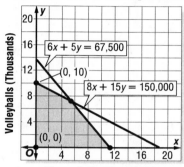

Soccer Balls (Thousands)

From the graph, vertices at $(0, 0)$ and $(0, 10{,}000)$ can be determined. Solve the system $y = 0$ and $6x + 5y = 67{,}500$ to find the vertex at $(11{,}250, 0)$. Solve the system $6x + 5y = 67{,}500$ and $8x + 15y = 150$ to find the vertex at $(5250, 7200)$.

The function that describes the profit is $f(x, y) = 5x + 4y$. Find the maximum value for this function. Substitute the coordinates of the vertices into the function.

(x, y)	$5x + 4y$	$f(x, y)$
$(0, 0)$	$5(0) + 4(0)$	0
$(0, 10{,}000)$	$5(0) + 4(10{,}000)$	$40{,}000$
$(11{,}250, 0)$	$5(11{,}250) + 4(0)$	$56{,}250$
$(5250, 7200)$	$5(5250) + 4(7200)$	$55{,}050$

The maximum value of the function is 56,250 at $(11{,}250, 0)$. This means that the maximum profit is \$56,250 when they make 11,250 soccer balls and 0 volleyballs.

16. The maximum profit is \$56,250.

17. Use elimination to make a system of two equations in two variables.

$x + y + z = -1$
$2x + 4y + z = 1$

$\begin{array}{r} 2x + 2y + 2z = -2 \\ (-)\ 2x + 4y + z = 1 \\ \hline -2y + z = -3 \end{array}$

$\begin{array}{r} x + y + z = -1 \\ (-)\ x + 2y - 3z = -3 \\ \hline -y + 4z = 2 \end{array}$

Solve the system of two equations.

$-2y + z = -3$
$-y + 4z = 2$

$\begin{array}{r} -2y + z = -3 \\ (-)\ -2y + 8z = 4 \\ \hline -7z = -7 \\ z = 1 \end{array}$

Substitute 1 for z in one of the equations with two variables and solve for y.

$-2y + z = -3$
$-2y + 1 = -3$
$ -2y = -4$
$ y = 2$

Substitute 2 for y and 1 for z in one of the original equations.

$x + y + z = -1$
$x + 2 + 1 = -1$
$ x = -4$

The solution is $(-4, 2, 1)$.

18. Use elimination to make a system of two equations in two variables.

$\begin{array}{r} x + z = 7 \\ (+)\ -x - 3y + 2z = 11 \\ \hline -3y + 3z = 18 \end{array}$

Solve the system of two equations.

$2y - z = -3$
$-3y + 3z = 18$

$\begin{array}{r} 6y - 3z = -9 \\ (+)\ -3y + 3z = 18 \\ \hline 3y = 9 \\ y = 3 \end{array}$

Substitute 3 for y in one of the equations with two variables and solve for z.

$2y - z = -3$
$2(3) - z = -3$
$ 6 - z = -3$
$ z = 9$

Substitute 3 for y and 9 for z in one of the original equations.

$-x - 3y + 2z = 11$
$-x - 3(3) + 2(9) = 11$
$-x - 9 + 18 = 11$
$ x = -2$

The solution is $(-2, 3, 9)$.

19. Read the problem and define the variables.
Let x = the price of a shirt.
Let y = the price of a pair of pants.
Let z = the price of a pair of shoes.
Carla: $3x + 4y + 2z = 149.79$
Beth: $5x + 3y + 3z = 183.19$
Kayla: $6x + 5y + z = 181.14$
Use elimination to make a system of two equations in two variables.
$3x + 4y + 2z = 149.79$
$5x + 3y + 3z = 183.19$

$\begin{array}{r} 9x + 12y + 6z = 449.37 \\ (-)\ 10x + 6y + 6z = 366.38 \\ \hline -x + 6y = 82.99 \end{array}$

$3x + 4y + 2z = 149.79$
$6x + 5y + z = 181.14$

$\begin{array}{r} 3x + 4y + 2z = 149.79 \\ (-)\ 12x + 10y + 2z = 362.28 \\ \hline -9x -6y = -212.49 \end{array}$

Solve the system of two equations.

$\begin{array}{r} -x + 6y = 82.99 \\ (+)\ -9x - 6y = -212.49 \\ \hline -10x = -129.50 \\ x = 12.95 \end{array}$

Substitute 12.95 for x in one of the equations with two variables and solve for y.

$-x + 6y = 82.99$
$-12.95 + 6y = 82.99$
$ 6y = 95.94$
$ y = 15.99$

Substitute 12.95 for x and 15.99 for y in one of the original equations.

$6x + 5y + z = 181.14$
$6(12.95) + 5(15.99) + z = 181.14$
$77.70 + 79.95 + z = 181.14$
$ z = 23.49$

So, the price of a shirt is $12.95, the price of a pair of pants is $15.99, and a price of a pair of shoes is $23.49.

20. Multiply the first equation by 3 and the second equation by 2. Then subtract the equations to eliminate the x variable.

$2x + 3y = 7$
$3x - 4y = 2$

$\begin{array}{r} 6x + 9y = 21 \\ (-)\ 6x - 8y = 4 \\ \hline 17y = 17 \\ y = 1 \end{array}$

Replace y with 1 and solve for x.

$2x + 3y = 7$
$2x + 3(1) = 7$
$ 2x = 4$
$ x = 2$

The solution is $(2, 1)$.

Chapter 3 Standardized Test Practice

Pages 150–151

1. B; Find the slope of $6x + 5y = 9$.

$6x + 5y = 9$
$6x + 5y - 6x = 9 - 6x$
$5y = -6x + 9$
$\dfrac{5y}{5} = \dfrac{-6x + 9}{5}$
$y = -\dfrac{6}{5}x + 9$

The slope of the equation is $-\dfrac{6}{5}$. Therefore, the slope of any line parallel to the graph of $6x + 5y = 9$ is $-\dfrac{6}{5}$.

2. D; $\dfrac{NO}{MO} = \dfrac{NP}{MQ}$

$\dfrac{6}{14} = \dfrac{9}{MQ}$

$6(MQ) = 14(9)$

$6(MQ) = 126$

$\dfrac{6(MQ)}{6} = \dfrac{126}{6}$

$MQ = 21$

The length of $\overline{MQ}$ is 21.

3. D; Multiply the second equation by 3. Then subtract the equations to eliminate the x variable.

$3x - y = -3$ $3x - y = -3$

$x + 5y = 15$ $\underline{(-)\ 3x + 15y = \quad 45}$

                           $-16y = -48$

                                  $y = 3$

The value of y is 3.

4. D; $3x + 4 < 16$

     $3x + 4 - 4 < 16 - 4$

             $3x < 12$

               $x < 4$

5. C; Find the distance between two adjacent vertices.

$d = \sqrt{(x_2 - x_1)^2 + (y_2 - y_1)^2}$

   $= \sqrt{[-1 - (-4)]^2 + (5 - 2)^2}$

   $= \sqrt{3^2 + 3^2}$

   $= \sqrt{18}$

Find the area.

$A = s^2$

   $= \left(\sqrt{18}\right)^2$

   $= 18$

The area is 18 square units.

6. B; If twenty-seven white cubes are put together to form a cube, the cube would be a stack of 3 by 3 by 3 cubes. The cubes that have exactly one red face are the cubes located in the center of each face of the larger cube. Since each face has only one such cube, and there are six faces on the large cube, there are 6 smaller cubes with exactly one red face.

7. D; $|-4| \cdot |3| = 4 \cdot 3$

               $= 12$

8. A; Let $x =$ the length of the third side. Use the triangle inequality to determine which is not the possible length of x.

$60 + 30 > x$ and $30 + x > 60$

     $90 > x$ $x > 30$

Since $x > 30$, then $x \neq 30$.

9. D; $S \div 7 = \dfrac{S}{8} + 12$

     $\dfrac{S}{7} = \dfrac{S}{8} + 12$

$\dfrac{S}{7} - 12 = \dfrac{S}{8}$

10. C; $15 - 3(x + 1) = 15 - 3(-2 + 1)$

                     $= 15 - 3(-1)$

                     $= 15 - (-3)$

                     $= 15 + 3$

                     $= 18$

11. If 6 are boys, then $13 - 6$ or 7 are girls.

The ratio of girls to boys is $\dfrac{7}{6}$ or 7:6.

12. k is 2 more than a multiple of 8. The numbers between 50 and 100 that satisfy this statement are 58, 66, 74, 82, 90, and 98. k is also 1 more than a multiple of 3. The numbers from the previous list that satisfy this second statement are 58 and 82.

13. The dimensions of the base are 5 units by 7 units. Since 56 is not divisible by 5, the dimensions of the face are 7 units by 8 units. Thus, the volume is $V = 5(7)(8)$ or 280 cubic units.

14. The sum of the 8 angles would be 360°. Thus, the measure of one angle would be $\dfrac{360}{8}$ or 45°.

15. Let $n =$ the least of the five consecutive integers. Then $n + 1, n + 2, n + 3$, and $n + 4$ represent the next 4 consecutive integers.

$n + (n + 1) + (n + 2) + (n + 3) + (n + 4) = 135$

$n + (n + 1) + (n + 2) + (n + 3) + (n + 4) = 135$

                                    $5n + 10 = 135$

                                        $5n = 125$

                                           $n = 25$

$n + 1 = 25 + 1$ or 26

$n + 2 = 25 + 2$ or 27

$n + 3 = 25 + 3$ or 28

$n + 4 = 25 + 4$ or 29

The greatest of the five integers is 29.

16. $p = 2\ell + 2w$ and $p = 12w$

$2\ell + 2w = 12w$

      $2\ell = 10w$

        $\ell = 5w$

The length is 5 times the width.

17. $AC = AB + BC$ and $AC = \dfrac{4}{3}AB$

$AB + BC = \dfrac{4}{3}AB$

       $BC = \dfrac{1}{3}AB$

     $BD = BC + CD$ and $BD = 6BC$

$BC + CD = 6BC$

      $CD = 5BC$

$BC = \dfrac{1}{3}AB$ and $CD = 5BC$

$CD = 5\left(\dfrac{1}{3}AB\right)$

$CD = \dfrac{5}{3}AB$

$\dfrac{AB}{CD} = \dfrac{AB}{\frac{5}{3}AB}$

    $= \dfrac{1}{\frac{5}{3}}$

    $= \dfrac{3}{5}$ or 0.6

18. Use a weighted average formula.

$\dfrac{x(74) + y(88)}{x + y} = 76$

$74x + 88y = 76(x + y)$

$74x + 88y = 76x + 76y$

      $12y = 2x$

        $6y = x$

         $6 = \dfrac{x}{y}$

The value is 6.

19. A; $\dfrac{100 - 75}{75} = \dfrac{25}{75}$

$\qquad\qquad\quad \approx 0.33$ or 33%

$\qquad \dfrac{100 - 75}{100} = \dfrac{25}{100}$

$\qquad\qquad\qquad = 0.25$ or 25%

20. A; $3x + 12 = 5x - 3$

$\qquad 3x + 15 = 5x$

$\qquad\qquad 15 = 2x$

21. D; $2 + 3 = 5 \ \ < 10 = 4 + 6$

$\qquad 5 + 7 = 12 > 10 = 4 + 6$

22. C; $u - p = 40 \rightarrow u = p + 40$

If the integers are equally spaced, then
$q = p + 8, r = p + 16, s = p + 24,$ and
$t = p + 32.$
Therefore, $t - s\ = (p + 32) - (p + 24)$ or 8.

Chapter 4 Matrices

Page 153 Getting Started

1. $3x = 18$

$\dfrac{3x}{3} = \dfrac{18}{3}$

$x = 6$

2. $2a - 3 = -11$

$2a - 3 + 3 = -11 + 3$

$2a = -8$

$\dfrac{2a}{2} = \dfrac{-8}{2}$

$a = -4$

3. $4t - 5 = 14$

$4t - 5 + 5 = 14 + 5$

$4t = 19$

$\dfrac{4t}{4} = \dfrac{19}{4}$

$t = 4\dfrac{3}{4}$

4. $\dfrac{1}{3}y + 5 = 9$

$\dfrac{1}{3}y + 5 - 5 = 9 - 5$

$\dfrac{1}{3}y = 4$

$3\left(\dfrac{1}{3}y\right) = 3(4)$

$y = 12$

5. $3k + 5 = 2k - 8$

$3k + 5 - 2k - 5 = 2k - 8 - 2k - 5$

$k = -13$

6. $5m - 6 = 7m - 8$

$5m - 6 - 7m + 6 = 7m - 8 - 7m + 6$

$-2m = -2$

$\dfrac{-2m}{-2} = \dfrac{-2}{-2}$

$m = 1$

7. additive inverse: -3

multiplicative inverse: $\dfrac{1}{3}$

8. additive inverse: 11

multiplicative inverse: $-\dfrac{1}{11}$

9. additive inverse: -8

multiplicative inverse: $\dfrac{1}{8}$

10. additive inverse: 0.5

multiplicative inverse: $\dfrac{1}{-0.5}$ or -2

11. additive inverse: -1.25

multiplicative inverse: $\dfrac{1}{1.25}$ or 0.8

12. additive inverse: $-\dfrac{5}{9}$

multiplicative inverse: $\dfrac{1}{\frac{5}{9}}$ or $\dfrac{9}{5}$

13. additive inverse: $\dfrac{8}{3}$

multiplicative inverse: $\dfrac{1}{-\frac{8}{3}}$ or $-\dfrac{3}{8}$

14. additive inverse: $1\dfrac{1}{5}$ or $\dfrac{6}{5}$

multiplicative inverse: $\dfrac{1}{-\frac{6}{5}}$ or $-\dfrac{5}{6}$

15. Graph $\{(0, 0), (1, 3), (-2, 4)\}$.

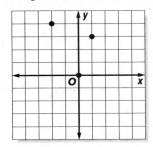

16. Graph $\{(-1, 5), (2, -3), (4, 0)\}$.

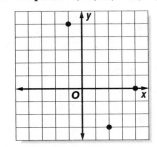

17. Graph $\{(-3, -3), (-1, 2), (1, -3), (3, -6)\}$.

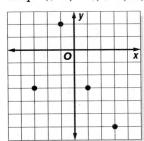

18. Graph $\{(-2, 5), (1, 3), (4, -2), (4, 7)\}$.

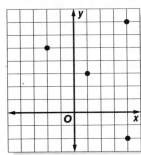

19. $x = y + 5$

$3x + y = 19$

Substitute $y + 5$ for x in the second equation, and solve for y.

$$3x + y = 19$$
$$3(y + 5) + y = 19$$
$$3y + 15 + y = 19$$
$$4y + 15 - 15 = 19 - 15$$
$$4y = 4$$
$$\frac{4y}{4} = \frac{4}{4}$$
$$y = 1$$

Substitute 1 for y in the first equation, and solve for x.

$$x = y + 5$$
$$x = 1 + 5$$
$$x = 6$$

The solution is $(6, 1)$.

20. $3x - 2y = 1$

$4x + 2y = 20$

Add the equations and then solve for x.

$$\begin{array}{r} 3x - 2y = 1 \\ (+)\ 4x + 2y = 20 \\ \hline 7x = 21 \end{array}$$
$$\frac{7x}{7} = \frac{21}{7}$$
$$x = 3$$

Substitute 3 for x in the first equation, and solve for y.

$$3x - 2y = 1$$
$$3(3) - 2y = 1$$
$$9 - 2y = 1$$
$$-9 + 9 - 2y = -9 + 1$$
$$-2y = -8$$
$$\frac{-2y}{-2} = \frac{-8}{-2}$$
$$y = 4$$

The solution is $(3, 4)$.

21. $5x + 3y = 25$

$4x + 7y = -3$

Multiply by 4.
Multiply by -5.
$$\begin{array}{r} 20x + 12y = 100 \\ (+)\ -20x - 35y = 15 \\ \hline -23y = 115 \end{array}$$
$$\frac{-23y}{-23} = \frac{115}{-23}$$
$$y = -5$$

Substitute -5 for y in the first equation, and solve for x.

$$5x + 3y = 25$$
$$5x + 3(-5) = 25$$
$$5x - 15 + 15 = 25 + 15$$
$$5x = 40$$
$$\frac{5x}{5} = \frac{40}{5}$$
$$x = 8$$

The solution is $(8, -5)$.

22. $y = x - 7$

$2x - 8y = 2$

Substitute $x - 7$ for y in the second equation, and solve for x.

$$2x - 8y = 2$$
$$2x - 8(x - 7) = 2$$
$$2x - 8x + 56 = 2$$
$$-6x + 56 - 56 = 2 - 56$$
$$-6x = -54$$
$$\frac{-6x}{-6} = \frac{-54}{-6}$$
$$x = 9$$

Substitute 9 for x in the first equation, and solve for y.

$$y = x - 7$$
$$y = 9 - 7$$
$$y = 2$$

The solution is $(9, 2)$.

23. $5x - 3y = 16$

$x - 3y = 8$

Subtract the second equation from the first and then solve for x.

$$\begin{array}{r} 5x - 3y = 16 \\ (-)\ x - 3y = 8 \\ \hline 4x = 8 \end{array}$$
$$\frac{4x}{4} = \frac{8}{4}$$
$$x = 2$$

Substitute 2 for x in the second equation, and solve for y.

$$x - 3y = 8$$
$$2 - 3y = 8$$
$$-2 + 2 - 3y = -2 + 8$$
$$-3y = 6$$
$$\frac{-3y}{-3} = \frac{6}{-3}$$
$$y = -2$$

The solution is $(2, -2)$.

24. $9x + 4y = 17$

$3x - 2y = 29$

Multiply by 2.
$$\begin{array}{r} 9x + 4y = 17 \\ (+)\ 6x - 4y = 58 \\ \hline 15x = 75 \end{array}$$
$$\frac{15x}{15} = \frac{75}{15}$$
$$x = 5$$

Substitute 5 for x in the first equation, and solve for y.

$$9x + 4y = 17$$
$$9(5) + 4y = 17$$
$$-45 + 45 + 4y = -45 + 17$$
$$4y = -28$$
$$\frac{4y}{4} = \frac{-28}{4}$$
$$y = -7$$

The solution is $(5, -7)$.

Introduction to Matrices

Page 156 Check for Understanding

1. The matrices must have the same dimensions and each element of one matrix must be equal to the corresponding element of the other matrix.

2. Sample answers: row matrix, $[1 \ 2 \ 3]$, 1×3;

   column matrix, $\begin{bmatrix} 1 \\ 2 \end{bmatrix}$, 2×1;

   square matrix, $\begin{bmatrix} 1 & 2 \\ 3 & 4 \end{bmatrix}$, 2×2;

   zero matrix, $\begin{bmatrix} 0 & 0 \\ 0 & 0 \end{bmatrix}$, 2×2

3. Corresponding elements are elements in the same row and column positions.

4. 1×5

5. 3×4

6. Write the corresponding system of equations.
$$x + 4 = 9$$
$$2y = 12$$
Solve the first equation for x.
$$x + 4 = 9$$
$$x + 4 - 4 = 9 - 4$$
$$x = 5$$
Solve the second equation for y.
$$2y = 12$$
$$\frac{2y}{2} = \frac{12}{2}$$
$$y = 6$$
The solution is $(5, 6)$.

7. Write the corresponding system of equations.
$$9 = x + 2y$$
$$13 = 4x + 1$$
Solve the second equation for x.
$$13 = 4x + 1$$
$$13 - 1 = 4x + 1 - 1$$
$$12 = 4x$$
$$\frac{12}{4} = \frac{4x}{4}$$
$$3 = x$$
Substitute 3 for x in the first equation.
$$9 = x + 2y$$
$$9 = 3 + 2y$$
$$-3 + 9 = -3 + 3 + 2y$$
$$6 = 2y$$
$$\frac{6}{2} = \frac{2y}{2}$$
$$3 = y$$
The solution is $(3, 3)$.

8.
	Fri	Sat	Sun	Mon	Tue
High	88	88	90	86	85
Low	54	54	56	53	52

9. 2×5

Pages 156–158 Practice and Apply

10. 2×3

11. 3×1

12. 4×3

13. 3×3

14. 2×5

15. 3×2

16. Write the corresponding system of equations.
$$2x = 5$$
$$3 = 3y$$
$$3z = 9$$
Solve the first equation for x.
$$2x = 5$$
$$\frac{2x}{2} = \frac{5}{2}$$
$$x = 2.5$$
Solve the second equation for y.
$$3 = 3y$$
$$\frac{3}{3} = \frac{3y}{3}$$
$$1 = y$$
Solve the third equation for z.
$$3z = 9$$
$$\frac{3z}{3} = \frac{9}{3}$$
$$z = 3$$
The solution is $(2.5, 1, 3)$.

17. Write the corresponding system of equations.
$$4x = 12$$
$$3y = -1$$
Solve the first equation for x.
$$4x = 12$$
$$\frac{4x}{4} = \frac{12}{4}$$
$$x = 3$$
Solve the second equation for y.
$$3y = -1$$
$$\frac{3y}{3} = \frac{-1}{3}$$
$$y = -\frac{1}{3}$$
The solution is $\left(3, -\frac{1}{3}\right)$.

18. Write the corresponding system of equations.
$$4x = 15 + x$$
$$5 = 2y - 1$$
Solve the first equation for x.
$$4x = 15 + x$$
$$4x - x = 15 + x - x$$
$$3x = 15$$
$$\frac{3x}{3} = \frac{15}{3}$$
$$x = 5$$
Solve the second equation for y.
$$5 = 2y - 1$$
$$5 + 1 = 2y - 1 + 1$$
$$6 = 2y$$
$$\frac{6}{2} = \frac{2y}{2}$$
$$3 = y$$
The solution is $(5, 3)$.

19. Write the corresponding system of equations.

$4x - 3 = 9$
$3y = -15$
$7 = 7$
$13 = 2z + 1$

Solve the first equation for x.

$$4x - 3 = 9$$
$$4x - 3 + 3 = 9 + 3$$
$$4x = 12$$
$$\frac{4x}{4} = \frac{12}{4}$$
$$x = 3$$

Solve the second equation for y.

$$3y = -15$$
$$\frac{3y}{3} = \frac{-15}{3}$$
$$y = -5$$

Solve the fourth equation for z.

$$13 = 2z + 1$$
$$13 - 1 = 2z + 1 - 1$$
$$12 = 2z$$
$$\frac{12}{2} = \frac{2z}{2}$$
$$6 = z$$

The solution is $(3, -5, 6)$.

20. Write the corresponding system of equations.

$x + 3y = -13$
$3x + y = 1$

Solve the second equation for y.

$$3x + y = 1$$
$$-3x + 3x + y = -3x + 1$$
$$y = -3x + 1$$

Substitute $-3x + 1$ for y in the first equation and solve for x.

$$x + 3y = -13$$
$$x + 3(-3x + 1) = -13$$
$$x - 9x + 3 = -13$$
$$-8x + 3 = -13$$
$$-8x + 3 - 3 = -13 - 3$$
$$-8x = -16$$
$$\frac{-8x}{-8} = \frac{-16}{-8}$$
$$x = 2$$

Substitute 2 for x in the second equation and solve for y.

$$3x + y = 1$$
$$3(2) + y = 1$$
$$6 + y = 1$$
$$-6 + 6 + y = -6 + 1$$
$$y = -5$$

The solution is $(2, -5)$.

21. Write the corresponding system of equations.

$2x + y = 5$
$x - 3y = 13$

Solve the second equation for x.

$$x - 3y = 13$$
$$x - 3y + 3y = 13 + 3y$$
$$x = 13 + 3y$$

Substitute $13 + 3y$ for x in the first equation and solve for y.

$$2x + y = 5$$
$$2(13 + 3y) + y = 5$$
$$26 + 6y + y = 5$$
$$26 + 7y = 5$$
$$-26 + 26 + 7y = -26 + 5$$
$$7y = -21$$
$$\frac{7y}{7} = \frac{-21}{7}$$
$$y = -3$$

Substitute -3 for y in the second equation and solve for x.

$$x - 3y = 13$$
$$x - 3(-3) = 13$$
$$x + 9 = 13$$
$$x + 9 - 9 = 13 - 9$$
$$x = 4$$

The solution is $(4, -3)$.

22. Write the corresponding system of equations.

$2x = y$
$2x + 3y = 12$

Substitute $2x$ for y in the second equation and solve for x.

$$2x + 3y = 12$$
$$2x + 3(2x) = 12$$
$$2x + 6x = 12$$
$$8x = 12$$
$$\frac{8x}{8} = \frac{12}{8}$$
$$x = 1.5$$

Substitute 1.5 for x in the first equation and solve for y.

$$2x = y$$
$$2(1.5) = y$$
$$3 = y$$

The solution is $(1.5, 3)$.

23. Write the corresponding system of equations.

$4x = 11 + 3y$
$y - 1 = x$

Substitute $y - 1$ for x in the first equation and solve for y.

$$4x = 11 + 3y$$
$$4(y - 1) = 11 + 3y$$
$$4y - 4 = 11 + 3y$$
$$4y - 4 + 4 - 3y = 11 + 3y + 4 - 3y$$
$$y = 15$$

Substitute 15 for y in the second equation and solve for x.

$$y - 1 = x$$
$$15 - 1 = x$$
$$14 = x$$

The solution is $(14, 15)$.

24. Write the corresponding system of equations.

$x^2 + 1 = 5$
$5 - y = x$
$x + y = 5$
$y - 4 = 3$

Solve the fourth equation for y.

$y - 4 = 3$
$y - 4 + 4 = 3 + 4$
$y = 7$

Substitute 7 for y in the second equation and solve for x.

$5 - y = x$
$5 - 7 = x$
$-2 = x$

A possible solution is $(-2, 7)$. Check whether this solution satisfies the first and third equations. Substitute -2 for x in the first equation.

$x^2 + 1 = 5$
$(-2)^2 + 1 = 5$
$4 + 1 = 4$ true

Substitute -2 for x and 7 for y in the third equation.

$x + y = 5$
$-2 + 7 = 5$
$5 = 5$ true

The solution is $(-2, 7)$.

25. Write the corresponding system of equations.

$3x - 5 = 10$
$x + y = 8$
$12 = 12$
$9z = 3x + y$

Solve the first equation for x.

$3x - 5 = 10$
$3x - 5 + 5 = 10 + 5$
$3x = 15$
$\frac{3x}{3} = \frac{15}{3}$
$x = 5$

Substitute 5 for x in the second equation and solve for y.

$x + y = 8$
$5 + y = 8$
$-5 + 5 + y = -5 + 8$
$y = 3$

Substitute 5 for x and 3 for y in the fourth equation and solve for z.

$9z = 3x + y$
$9z = 3(5) + 3$
$9z = 15 + 3$
$\frac{9z}{9} = \frac{18}{9}$
$z = 2$

The solution is $(5, 3, 2)$.

26.

	Evening	Matinee	Twilight
Adult	7.50	5.50	3.75
Child	4.50	4.50	3.75
Senior	5.50	5.50	3.75

27. 3×3

28.

	Cost	Service	Atmosphere	Location
Catalina Grill	**	*	*	*
Oyster Club	***	**	*	**
Casa di Pasta	****	***	***	***
Mason's Steakhouse	**	****	****	***

29. Sample answer: Mason's Steakhouse; it was given the highest rating possible for service and atmosphere, location was given one of the highest ratings, and it is moderately priced.

30.

	Weekday	Weekend
Single	60	79
Double	70	89
Suite	75	95

31.

	Single	Double	Suite
Weekday	60	70	75
Weekend	79	89	95

32. The matrix contains the natural numbers ordered consecutively along diagonals beginning in the first column, moving up and to the right, and ending in the first row. You can use this pattern to extend the matrix indefinitely.

To find the number that follows 15 in the first row, follow the diagonal that begins in the first column with 16. As you follow the consecutive natural numbers along the diagonal, you will see that the next number is 21. So the number to the right of 15 in the first row is 21. Since this diagonal ends in the first row with 21, the next diagonal begins in the first column with 22. Then you can complete this diagonal by moving up and to the right and filling in missing numbers with the next natural number.

Continue this process until you have added one more row and column to the given matrix.

```
 1   3   6  10  15  21 | 28  36  45  55  66
 2   5   9  14  20  27 | 35  44  54  65
 4   8  13  19  26  34 | 43  53  64
 7  12  18  25  33  42 | 52  63
11  17  24  32  41  51 | 62
16  23  31  40  50  61 |
22  30  39  49  60  72 |
-----------------------
29  38  48  59  71       |
37  47  58  70           |
46  57  69               |
56  68                   |
67                       |
```

The matrix with 6 columns and 7 rows is shown below.

$$\begin{bmatrix} 1 & 3 & 6 & 10 & 15 & 21 \\ 2 & 5 & 9 & 14 & 20 & 27 \\ 4 & 8 & 13 & 19 & 26 & 34 \\ 7 & 12 & 18 & 25 & 33 & 42 \\ 11 & 17 & 24 & 32 & 41 & 51 \\ 16 & 23 & 31 & 40 & 50 & 61 \\ 22 & 30 & 39 & 49 & 60 & 72 \end{bmatrix}$$

33. If you continue adding to the matrix using the pattern in Exercise 32, you will find that 100 is in row 6 and column 9.

```
 1   3   6  10  15  21  28  36   45  55  66  78  91
 2   5   9  14  20  27  35  44   54  65  77  90
 4   8  13  19  26  34  43  53   64  76  89
 7  12  18  25  33  42  52  63   75  88
11  17  24  32  41  51  62  74   87
16  23  31  40  50  61  73  86  100
22  30  39  49  60  72  85  99
29  38  48  59  71  84  98
37  47  58  70  83  97
46  57  69  82  96
56  68  81  95
67  80  94
79  93
92
```

34. Matrices are used to organize information so it can be read and compared more easily. Answers should include the following.

- If you want the least expensive vehicle, the compact SUV has the best price; the large SUV has the most horsepower, towing capacity and cargo space, and the standard SUV has the best fuel economy.

- Sample answer: Matrices are used to report stock prices in the newspaper.

35. B

36. C; Write the corresponding system of equations.

$3x = 9 + y$

$y + 5 = x$

Substitute $y + 5$ for x in the first equation and solve for y.

$$3x = 9 + y$$
$$3(y + 5) = 9 + y$$
$$3y + 15 = 9 + y$$
$$-y - 15 + 3y + 15 = -y - 15 + 9 + y$$
$$2y = -6$$
$$\frac{2y}{2} = \frac{-6}{2}$$
$$y = -3$$

Page 158   Maintain Your Skills

37. Solve the second equation for y.

$$-6y = -30$$
$$\frac{-6y}{-6} = \frac{-30}{-6}$$
$$y = 5$$

Substitute 5 for y in the first equation and solve for x.

$$3x - 3y = 6$$
$$3x - 3(5) = 6$$
$$3x - 15 = 6$$
$$3x - 15 + 15 = 6 + 15$$
$$3x = 21$$
$$\frac{3x}{3} = \frac{21}{3}$$
$$x = 7$$

Substitute 7 for x in the third equation and solve for z.

$$5z - 2x = 6$$
$$5z - 2(7) = 6$$
$$5z - 14 = 6$$
$$5z - 14 + 14 = 6 + 14$$
$$5z = 20$$
$$\frac{5z}{5} = \frac{20}{5}$$
$$z = 4$$

The solution is $(7, 5, 4)$.

38. Use the second and third equations to eliminate C.

$5a - 7b + c = 5$

$-2a + 10b + 5c = -29$

Multiply by -5.

$$\begin{array}{r} -25a + 35b - 5c = -25 \\ (+)\ -2a + 10b + 5c = -29 \\ \hline -27a + 45b = -54 \end{array}$$

The resulting equation has a common factor of 9 and, therefore, can be rewritten as $-3a + 5b = -6$.

Add this equation to the first equation to eliminate a and solve for b.

$$\begin{array}{r} 3a + 2b = 27 \\ (+)\ -3a + 5b = -6 \\ \hline 7b = 21 \end{array}$$
$$\frac{7b}{7} = \frac{21}{7}$$
$$b = 3$$

Substitute into the first equation to find a.

$$3a + 2b = 27$$
$$3a + 2(3) = 27$$
$$3a + 6 = 27$$
$$3a = 21$$
$$a = 7$$

Substitute 7 for a and 3 for b into the second equation to find c.

$$5a - 7b + c = 5$$
$$5(7) - 7(3) + c = 5$$
$$35 - 21 + c = 5$$
$$14 + c = 5$$
$$c = -9$$

The solution is $(7, 3, -9)$.

39. Eliminate r using the first and second equations.

$3r - 15s + 4t = -57$
$9r + 45s - t = 26$

Multiply by -3. $\begin{array}{r} -9r + 45s - 12t = 171 \\ (+)\ 9r + 45s - \quad t = \ 26 \\ \hline 90s - 13t = 197 \end{array}$

Eliminate r again using the first and third equations.

$3r - 15s + 4t = -57$
$-6r + 10s + 3t = -19$

Multiply by 2. $\begin{array}{r} 6r - 30s + 8t = -114 \\ (+)\ -6r + 10s + 3t = \ -19 \\ \hline -20s + 11t = -133 \end{array}$

Solve the resulting system of two equations.

$90s - 13t = 197$
$-20s + 11t = -133$

Multiply by 2. $\begin{array}{r} 180s - 26t = \quad 394 \end{array}$
Multiply by 9. $\begin{array}{r} (+) - 180s + 99t = -1197 \\ \hline 73t = \ -803 \\ \frac{73t}{73} = -\frac{803}{73} \\ t = -11 \end{array}$

Substitute -11 for t.

$90s - 13t = 197$
$90s - 13(-11) = 197$
$90s + 143 = 197$
$90s = 54$
$s = \frac{54}{90}$ or $\frac{3}{5}$

Substitute $\frac{3}{5}$ for s and -11 for t into any original equation.

$3r - 15s + 4t = -57$
$3r - 15\left(\frac{3}{5}\right) + 4(-11) = -57$
$3r - 9 - 44 = -57$
$3r - 53 = -57$
$3r = -4$
$r = -\frac{4}{3}$

The solution is $\left(-\frac{4}{3}, \frac{3}{5}, -11\right)$.

40.

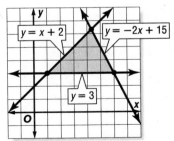

The vertices of the feasible region are $(1, 3)$, $(6, 3)$, and $\left(\frac{13}{3}, \frac{19}{3}\right)$. Make a table to find the maximum and minimum values of $f(x, y)$.

(x, y)	$2x + 3y$	$f(x, y)$
$(1, 3)$	$2(1) + 3(3)$	11
$(6, 3)$	$2(6) + 3(3)$	21
$\left(\frac{13}{3}, \frac{19}{3}\right)$	$2\left(\frac{13}{3}\right) + 3\left(\frac{19}{3}\right)$	$\frac{83}{3}$

The maximum value is $f\left(\frac{13}{3}, \frac{19}{3}\right) = \frac{83}{3}$.
The minimum value is $f(1, 3) = 11$.

41.

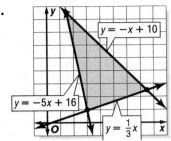

The vertices of the feasible region are $(3, 1)$, $\left(\frac{15}{2}, \frac{5}{2}\right)$, $\left(\frac{3}{2}, \frac{17}{2}\right)$. Make a table to find the maximum and minimum values of $f(x, y)$.

(x, y)	$5x - y$	$f(x, y)$
$(3, 1)$	$5(3) - 1$	14
$\left(\frac{15}{2}, \frac{5}{2}\right)$	$5\left(\frac{15}{2}\right) - \frac{5}{2}$	35
$\left(\frac{3}{2}, \frac{17}{2}\right)$	$5\left(\frac{3}{2}\right) - \frac{17}{2}$	-1

The maximum value is $f\left(\frac{15}{2}, \frac{5}{2}\right) = 35$.
The minimum value is $f\left(\frac{3}{2}, \frac{17}{2}\right) = -1$.

42.

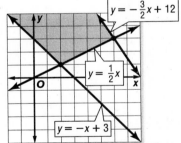

The vertices of the feasible region are $(2, 1)$ and $(6, 3)$. Make a table to find the value of $f(x, y)$ at the vertices.

(x, y)	$3y - x$	$f(x, y)$
$(2, 1)$	$3(1) - 2$	1
$(6, 3)$	$3(3) - 6$	3

The minimum value is $f(2, 1) = 1$.
Although $f(6, 3)$ is 3, it is not the maximum value since there are other points in the solution, that produce larger values. Because the region is unbounded, $f(x, y)$ has no maximum value.

43.

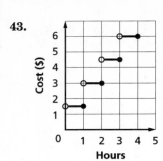

44. step function

45. Jada had to pay for two hours and a fraction of a third, so she had to pay 3 · $1.50 or $4.50 for parking.

46. $f(x) = x^2 - 3x + 2$
$f(3) = 3^2 - 3(3) + 2$
$\quad\ = 9 - 9 + 2$
$\quad\ = 2$

47. $f(x) = x^2 - 3x + 2$
$f(0) = 0^2 - 3(0) + 2$
$\quad\ = 0 - 0 + 2$
$\quad\ = 2$

48. $f(x) = x^2 - 3x + 2$
$f(2) = 2^2 - 3(2) + 2$
$\quad\ = 4 - 6 + 2$
$\quad\ = 0$

49. $f(x) = x^2 - 3x + 2$
$f(-3) = (-3)^2 - 3(-3) + 2$
$\qquad = 9 + 9 + 2$
$\qquad = 20$

50. $8 + (-5) = 8 - 5 = 3$

51. $-2 - 8 = -10$

52. $3.5 + 2.7 = 6.2$

53. $6(-3) = -18$

54. $\frac{1}{2}(34) = 17$

55. $6(4) + 3(-9) = 24 - 27$ or -3

56. $-5(3 - 18) = -5(-15)$ or 75

57. $14\left(\frac{1}{4}\right) - 12\left(\frac{1}{6}\right) = \frac{7}{2} - 2$
$\qquad\qquad\qquad = \frac{7}{2} - \frac{4}{2}$
$\qquad\qquad\qquad = \frac{3}{2}$

Page 159 Spreadsheet Investigation (Follow-Up of Lesson 4-1)

1.

	A	B	C	D	E	F
1		Base Price	Horse-Power	Towing Capacity (lb)	Cargo Capacity (ft³)	Fuel Economy (mpg)
2	Large	$32,450	285	12,000	46	17
3	Standard	$29,115	275	8700	16	17.5
4	Mid-size	$27,975	190	5700	34	20
5	Compact	$18,180	127	3000	15	26.5

2. Both use rows and columns. In a spreadsheet, the rows are designated by numbers and the columns are designated by letters. In a matrix, both rows and columns are designated by numbers.

4-2 Operations with Matrices

Page 163 Graphing Calculator Investigation

1. KEYSTROKES: MATRX ▶ ▶ 1 2 ENTER 2 ENTER 3 ENTER (−) 2 ENTER 5 ENTER 4 ENTER

Elements are entered row by row.

2. The first number represents the row, and the second represents the column of the element being entered.

3. KEYSTROKES: 18 × MATRX 1 ENTER
$$\begin{bmatrix} 54 & -36 \\ 90 & 72 \end{bmatrix}$$

4. Enter B.
KEYSTROKES: MATRX ▶ ▶ 2 2 ENTER 3 ENTER 1 ENTER 9 ENTER (−) 3 ENTER 8 ENTER 6 ENTER (−) 5 ENTER

Find $A + B$.
KEYSTROKES: MATRX 1 + MATRX 2 ENTER

There is an error on the screen because the dimensions are not equal.

Pages 163–164 Check for Understanding

1. They must have the same dimensions.

2. Sample answer: $[-3, 1]$ and $[3, -1]$
$[-3, 1] + [3, -1] = [-3 + 3 \quad 1 + (-1)]$
$\qquad\qquad\qquad\quad = [0, 0]$

3. $\begin{bmatrix} 4 & 4 \\ 4 & 4 \\ 4 & 4 \end{bmatrix}$

4. Impossible; the matrices have different dimensions.

5. $\begin{bmatrix} 3 & 7 \\ -2 & 1 \end{bmatrix} - \begin{bmatrix} 2 & -3 \\ 5 & -4 \end{bmatrix} = \begin{bmatrix} 3 - 2 & 7 - (-3) \\ -2 - 5 & 1 - (-4) \end{bmatrix}$
$\qquad\qquad\qquad\qquad\qquad = \begin{bmatrix} 1 & 10 \\ -7 & 5 \end{bmatrix}$

6. $3\begin{bmatrix} 6 & -1 & 5 & 2 \\ 7 & 3 & -2 & 8 \end{bmatrix} = \begin{bmatrix} 3(6) & 3(-1) & 3(5) & 3(2) \\ 3(7) & 3(3) & 3(-2) & 3(8) \end{bmatrix}$
$\qquad\qquad\qquad\qquad = \begin{bmatrix} 18 & -3 & 15 & 6 \\ 21 & 9 & -6 & 24 \end{bmatrix}$

7. $4\begin{bmatrix} 2 & 7 \\ -3 & 6 \end{bmatrix} + 5\begin{bmatrix} -6 & -4 \\ 3 & 0 \end{bmatrix}$

$= \begin{bmatrix} 4(2) & 4(7) \\ 4(-3) & 4(6) \end{bmatrix} + \begin{bmatrix} 5(-6) & 5(-4) \\ 5(3) & 5(0) \end{bmatrix}$

$= \begin{bmatrix} 8 & 28 \\ -12 & 24 \end{bmatrix} + \begin{bmatrix} -30 & -20 \\ 15 & 0 \end{bmatrix}$

$= \begin{bmatrix} 8 + (-30) & 28 + (-20) \\ -12 + 15 & 24 + 0 \end{bmatrix}$

$= \begin{bmatrix} -22 & 8 \\ 3 & 24 \end{bmatrix}$

8. $A + B + C = \begin{bmatrix} 2 & 3 \\ 5 & 6 \end{bmatrix} + \begin{bmatrix} -1 & 7 \\ 0 & -4 \end{bmatrix} + \begin{bmatrix} 9 & -4 \\ -6 & 5 \end{bmatrix}$

$= \begin{bmatrix} 2 + (-1) + 9 & 3 + 7 + (-4) \\ 5 + 0 + (-6) & 6 + (-4) + 5 \end{bmatrix}$

$= \begin{bmatrix} 10 & 6 \\ -1 & 7 \end{bmatrix}$

9. $3B - 2C = 3\begin{bmatrix} -1 & 7 \\ 0 & -4 \end{bmatrix} - 2\begin{bmatrix} 9 & -4 \\ -6 & 5 \end{bmatrix}$

$= \begin{bmatrix} 3(-1) & 3(7) \\ 3(0) & 3(-4) \end{bmatrix} - \begin{bmatrix} 2(9) & 2(-4) \\ 2(-6) & 2(5) \end{bmatrix}$

$= \begin{bmatrix} -3 & 21 \\ 0 & -12 \end{bmatrix} - \begin{bmatrix} 18 & -8 \\ -12 & 10 \end{bmatrix}$

$= \begin{bmatrix} -3 - 18 & 21 - (-8) \\ 0 - (-12) & -12 - 10 \end{bmatrix}$

$= \begin{bmatrix} -21 & 29 \\ 12 & -22 \end{bmatrix}$

10. $4A + 2B - C$

$= 4\begin{bmatrix} 2 & 3 \\ 5 & 6 \end{bmatrix} + 2\begin{bmatrix} -1 & 7 \\ 0 & -4 \end{bmatrix} - \begin{bmatrix} 9 & -4 \\ -6 & 5 \end{bmatrix}$

$= \begin{bmatrix} 4(2) & 4(3) \\ 4(5) & 4(6) \end{bmatrix} + \begin{bmatrix} 2(-1) & 2(7) \\ 2(0) & 2(-4) \end{bmatrix} - \begin{bmatrix} 9 & -4 \\ -6 & 5 \end{bmatrix}$

$= \begin{bmatrix} 8 & 12 \\ 20 & 24 \end{bmatrix} + \begin{bmatrix} -2 & 14 \\ 0 & -8 \end{bmatrix} - \begin{bmatrix} 9 & -4 \\ -6 & 5 \end{bmatrix}$

$= \begin{bmatrix} 8 + (-2) - 9 & 12 + 14 - (-4) \\ 20 + 0 - (-6) & 24 + (-8) - 5 \end{bmatrix}$

$= \begin{bmatrix} -3 & 30 \\ 26 & 11 \end{bmatrix}$

11. Males $= \begin{bmatrix} 16{,}763 & 549{,}499 \\ 14{,}620 & 477{,}960 \\ 14{,}486 & 455{,}305 \\ 9041 & 321{,}416 \\ 5234 & 83{,}411 \end{bmatrix}$

Females $= \begin{bmatrix} 16{,}439 & 456{,}873 \\ 14{,}545 & 405{,}163 \\ 12{,}679 & 340{,}480 \\ 7931 & 257{,}586 \\ 5450 & 133{,}235 \end{bmatrix}$

12. $\begin{bmatrix} 549{,}499 + 456{,}873 \\ 477{,}960 + 405{,}163 \\ 455{,}305 + 340{,}480 \\ 321{,}416 + 257{,}586 \\ 83{,}411 + 133{,}235 \end{bmatrix} = \begin{bmatrix} 1{,}006{,}372 \\ 883{,}123 \\ 795{,}785 \\ 579{,}002 \\ 216{,}646 \end{bmatrix}$

13. No; many schools offer the same sport for males and females, so those schools would be counted twice.

Pages 164–166   Practice and Apply

14. $\begin{bmatrix} 4 \\ 1 \\ -3 \end{bmatrix} + \begin{bmatrix} 6 \\ -5 \\ 8 \end{bmatrix} = \begin{bmatrix} 4 + 6 \\ 1 + (-5) \\ -3 + 8 \end{bmatrix}$

$= \begin{bmatrix} 10 \\ -4 \\ 5 \end{bmatrix}$

15. Impossible; the matrices have different dimensions.

16. $\begin{bmatrix} 12 & 0 & 8 \\ 9 & 15 & -11 \end{bmatrix} - \begin{bmatrix} -3 & 0 & 4 \\ 9 & 2 & -6 \end{bmatrix}$

$= \begin{bmatrix} 12 - (-3) & 0 - 0 & 8 - 4 \\ 9 - 9 & 15 - 2 & -11 - (-6) \end{bmatrix}$

$= \begin{bmatrix} 15 & 0 & 4 \\ 0 & 13 & -5 \end{bmatrix}$

17. $-2\begin{bmatrix} 2 & -4 & 1 \\ -3 & 5 & 8 \\ 7 & 6 & -2 \end{bmatrix} = \begin{bmatrix} -2(2) & -2(-4) & -2(1) \\ -2(-3) & -2(5) & -2(8) \\ -2(7) & -2(6) & -2(-2) \end{bmatrix}$

$= \begin{bmatrix} -4 & 8 & -2 \\ 6 & -10 & -16 \\ -14 & -12 & 4 \end{bmatrix}$

18. $5[0 \ -1 \ 7 \ 2] + 3[5 \ -8 \ 10 \ -4]$

$= [5(0) \ 5(-1) \ 5(7) \ 5(2)] + [3(5) \ 3(-8) \ 3(10) \ 3(-4)]$

$= [0 \ -5 \ 35 \ 10] + [15 \ -24 \ 30 \ -12]$

$= [0 + 15 \quad -5 + (-24) \ 35 + 30 \ 10 + (-12)]$

$= [15 \ -29 \ 65 \ -2]$

19. $5\begin{bmatrix} 1 \\ -1 \\ -3 \end{bmatrix} + 6\begin{bmatrix} -4 \\ 3 \\ 5 \end{bmatrix} - 2\begin{bmatrix} -3 \\ 8 \\ -4 \end{bmatrix}$

$= \begin{bmatrix} 5(1) \\ 5(-1) \\ 5(-3) \end{bmatrix} + \begin{bmatrix} 6(-4) \\ 6(3) \\ 6(5) \end{bmatrix} - \begin{bmatrix} 2(-3) \\ 2(8) \\ 2(-4) \end{bmatrix}$

$= \begin{bmatrix} 5 \\ -5 \\ -15 \end{bmatrix} + \begin{bmatrix} -24 \\ 18 \\ 30 \end{bmatrix} - \begin{bmatrix} -6 \\ 16 \\ -8 \end{bmatrix}$

$= \begin{bmatrix} 5 + (-24) - (-6) \\ -5 + 18 - 16 \\ -15 + 30 - (-8) \end{bmatrix}$

$= \begin{bmatrix} -13 \\ -3 \\ 23 \end{bmatrix}$

20. $\begin{bmatrix} 1.35 & 5.80 \\ 1.24 & 14.32 \\ 6.10 & 35.26 \end{bmatrix} + \begin{bmatrix} 0.45 & 3.28 \\ 1.94 & 16.72 \\ 4.31 & 21.30 \end{bmatrix}$

$= \begin{bmatrix} 1.35 + 0.45 & 5.80 + 3.28 \\ 1.24 + 1.94 & 14.32 + 16.72 \\ 6.10 + 4.31 & 35.26 + 21.30 \end{bmatrix}$

$= \begin{bmatrix} 1.80 & 9.08 \\ 3.18 & 31.04 \\ 10.41 & 56.56 \end{bmatrix}$

21. $8 \begin{bmatrix} 0.25 & 0.5 \\ 0.75 & 1.5 \end{bmatrix} - 2 \begin{bmatrix} 0.25 & 0.5 \\ 0.75 & 1.5 \end{bmatrix}$

$= \begin{bmatrix} 8(0.25) & 8(0.5) \\ 8(0.75) & 8(1.5) \end{bmatrix} - \begin{bmatrix} 2(0.25) & 2(0.5) \\ 2(0.75) & 2(1.5) \end{bmatrix}$

$= \begin{bmatrix} 2 & 4 \\ 6 & 12 \end{bmatrix} - \begin{bmatrix} 0.5 & 1 \\ 1.5 & 3 \end{bmatrix}$

$= \begin{bmatrix} 2 - 0.5 & 4 - 1 \\ 6 - 1.5 & 12 - 3 \end{bmatrix}$

$= \begin{bmatrix} 1.5 & 3 \\ 4.5 & 9 \end{bmatrix}$

22. $\frac{1}{2} \begin{bmatrix} 4 & 6 \\ 3 & 0 \end{bmatrix} - \frac{2}{3} \begin{bmatrix} 9 & 27 \\ 0 & 3 \end{bmatrix} = \begin{bmatrix} \frac{1}{2}(4) & \frac{1}{2}(6) \\ \frac{1}{2}(3) & \frac{1}{2}(0) \end{bmatrix} - \begin{bmatrix} \frac{2}{3}(9) & \frac{2}{3}(27) \\ \frac{2}{3}(0) & \frac{2}{3}(3) \end{bmatrix}$

$= \begin{bmatrix} 2 & 3 \\ \frac{3}{2} & 0 \end{bmatrix} - \begin{bmatrix} 6 & 18 \\ 0 & 2 \end{bmatrix}$

$= \begin{bmatrix} 2 - 6 & 3 - 18 \\ \frac{3}{2} - 0 & 0 - 2 \end{bmatrix}$

$= \begin{bmatrix} -4 & -15 \\ \frac{3}{2} & -2 \end{bmatrix}$

23. $5 \begin{bmatrix} \frac{1}{2} & 0 & 1 \\ 2 & \frac{1}{3} & -1 \end{bmatrix} + 4 \begin{bmatrix} -2 & \frac{3}{4} & 1 \\ \frac{1}{6} & 0 & \frac{5}{8} \end{bmatrix}$

$= \begin{bmatrix} 5\left(\frac{1}{2}\right) & 5(0) & 5(1) \\ 5(2) & 5\left(\frac{1}{3}\right) & 5(-1) \end{bmatrix} + \begin{bmatrix} 4(-2) & 4\left(\frac{3}{4}\right) & 4(1) \\ 4\left(\frac{1}{6}\right) & 4(0) & 4\left(\frac{5}{8}\right) \end{bmatrix}$

$= \begin{bmatrix} \frac{5}{2} & 0 & 5 \\ 10 & \frac{5}{3} & -5 \end{bmatrix} + \begin{bmatrix} -8 & 3 & 4 \\ \frac{2}{3} & 0 & \frac{5}{2} \end{bmatrix}$

$= \begin{bmatrix} \frac{5}{2} + (-8) & 0 + 3 & 5 + 4 \\ 10 + \frac{2}{3} & \frac{5}{3} + 0 & -5 + \frac{5}{2} \end{bmatrix}$

$= \begin{bmatrix} -5\frac{1}{2} & 3 & 9 \\ 10\frac{2}{3} & 1\frac{2}{3} & -2\frac{1}{2} \end{bmatrix}$

24. $A + B = \begin{bmatrix} 5 & 7 \\ -1 & 6 \\ 3 & -9 \end{bmatrix} + \begin{bmatrix} 8 & 3 \\ 5 & 1 \\ 4 & 4 \end{bmatrix}$

$= \begin{bmatrix} 5 + 8 & 7 + 3 \\ -1 + 5 & 6 + 1 \\ 3 + 4 & -9 + 4 \end{bmatrix}$

$= \begin{bmatrix} 13 & 10 \\ 4 & 7 \\ 7 & -5 \end{bmatrix}$

25. $D - B = \begin{bmatrix} 6 & 2 \\ 9 & 0 \\ -3 & 0 \end{bmatrix} - \begin{bmatrix} 8 & 3 \\ 5 & 1 \\ 4 & 4 \end{bmatrix}$

$= \begin{bmatrix} 6 - 8 & 2 - 3 \\ 9 - 5 & 0 - 1 \\ -3 - 4 & 0 - 4 \end{bmatrix}$

$= \begin{bmatrix} -2 & -1 \\ 4 & -1 \\ -7 & -4 \end{bmatrix}$

26. $4C = 4 \begin{bmatrix} 0 & 4 \\ -2 & 5 \\ 7 & -1 \end{bmatrix}$

$= \begin{bmatrix} 4(0) & 4(4) \\ 4(-2) & 4(5) \\ 4(7) & 4(-1) \end{bmatrix}$

$= \begin{bmatrix} 0 & 16 \\ -8 & 20 \\ 28 & -4 \end{bmatrix}$

27. $6B - 2A = 6 \begin{bmatrix} 8 & 3 \\ 5 & 1 \\ 4 & 4 \end{bmatrix} - 2 \begin{bmatrix} 5 & 7 \\ -1 & 6 \\ 3 & -9 \end{bmatrix}$

$= \begin{bmatrix} 6(8) & 6(3) \\ 6(5) & 6(1) \\ 6(4) & 6(4) \end{bmatrix} - \begin{bmatrix} 2(5) & 2(7) \\ 2(-1) & 2(6) \\ 2(3) & 2(-9) \end{bmatrix}$

$= \begin{bmatrix} 48 & 18 \\ 30 & 6 \\ 24 & 24 \end{bmatrix} - \begin{bmatrix} 10 & 14 \\ -2 & 12 \\ 6 & -18 \end{bmatrix}$

$= \begin{bmatrix} 48 - 10 & 18 - 14 \\ 30 - (-2) & 6 - 12 \\ 24 - 6 & 24 - (-18) \end{bmatrix}$

$= \begin{bmatrix} 38 & 4 \\ 32 & -6 \\ 18 & 42 \end{bmatrix}$

28. $3C - 4A + B$

$$= 3\begin{bmatrix} 0 & 4 \\ -2 & 5 \\ 7 & -1 \end{bmatrix} - 4\begin{bmatrix} 5 & 7 \\ -1 & 6 \\ 3 & -9 \end{bmatrix} + \begin{bmatrix} 8 & 3 \\ 5 & 1 \\ 4 & 4 \end{bmatrix}$$

$$= \begin{bmatrix} 3(0) & 3(4) \\ 3(-2) & 3(5) \\ 3(7) & 3(-1) \end{bmatrix} - \begin{bmatrix} 4(5) & 4(7) \\ 4(-1) & 4(6) \\ 4(3) & 4(-9) \end{bmatrix} + \begin{bmatrix} 8 & 3 \\ 5 & 1 \\ 4 & 4 \end{bmatrix}$$

$$= \begin{bmatrix} 0 & 12 \\ -6 & 15 \\ 21 & -3 \end{bmatrix} - \begin{bmatrix} 20 & 28 \\ -4 & 24 \\ 12 & -36 \end{bmatrix} + \begin{bmatrix} 8 & 3 \\ 5 & 1 \\ 4 & 4 \end{bmatrix}$$

$$= \begin{bmatrix} 0 - 20 + 8 & 12 - 28 + 3 \\ -6 - (-4) + 5 & 15 - 24 + 1 \\ 21 - 12 + 4 & -3 - (-36) + 4 \end{bmatrix}$$

$$= \begin{bmatrix} -12 & -13 \\ 3 & -8 \\ 13 & 37 \end{bmatrix}$$

29. $C + \frac{1}{3}D = \begin{bmatrix} 0 & 4 \\ -2 & 5 \\ 7 & -1 \end{bmatrix} + \frac{1}{3}\begin{bmatrix} 6 & 2 \\ 9 & 0 \\ -3 & 0 \end{bmatrix}$

$$= \begin{bmatrix} 0 & 4 \\ -2 & 5 \\ 7 & -1 \end{bmatrix} + \begin{bmatrix} \frac{1}{3}(6) & \frac{1}{3}(2) \\ \frac{1}{3}(9) & \frac{1}{3}(0) \\ \frac{1}{3}(-3) & \frac{1}{3}(0) \end{bmatrix}$$

$$= \begin{bmatrix} 0 & 4 \\ -2 & 5 \\ 7 & -1 \end{bmatrix} + \begin{bmatrix} 2 & \frac{2}{3} \\ 3 & 0 \\ -1 & 0 \end{bmatrix}$$

$$= \begin{bmatrix} 0 + 2 & 4 + \frac{2}{3} \\ -2 + 3 & 5 + 0 \\ 7 + (-1) & -1 + 0 \end{bmatrix}$$

$$= \begin{bmatrix} 2 & 4\frac{2}{3} \\ 1 & 5 \\ 6 & -1 \end{bmatrix}$$

30. Friday: $\begin{bmatrix} 120 & 97 & 64 & 75 \\ 80 & 59 & 36 & 60 \\ 72 & 84 & 29 & 48 \end{bmatrix}$,

Saturday: $\begin{bmatrix} 112 & 87 & 56 & 74 \\ 84 & 65 & 39 & 70 \\ 88 & 98 & 43 & 60 \end{bmatrix}$

31. $\begin{bmatrix} 120 & 97 & 64 & 75 \\ 80 & 59 & 36 & 60 \\ 72 & 84 & 29 & 48 \end{bmatrix} + \begin{bmatrix} 112 & 87 & 56 & 74 \\ 84 & 65 & 39 & 70 \\ 88 & 98 & 43 & 60 \end{bmatrix}$

$$= \begin{bmatrix} 120 + 112 & 97 + 87 & 64 + 56 & 75 + 74 \\ 80 + 84 & 59 + 65 & 36 + 39 & 60 + 70 \\ 72 + 88 & 84 + 98 & 29 + 43 & 48 + 60 \end{bmatrix}$$

$$= \begin{bmatrix} 232 & 184 & 120 & 149 \\ 164 & 124 & 75 & 130 \\ 160 & 182 & 72 & 108 \end{bmatrix}$$

32. $\begin{bmatrix} 112 & 87 & 56 & 74 \\ 84 & 65 & 39 & 70 \\ 88 & 98 & 43 & 60 \end{bmatrix} - \begin{bmatrix} 120 & 97 & 64 & 75 \\ 80 & 59 & 36 & 60 \\ 72 & 84 & 29 & 48 \end{bmatrix}$

$$= \begin{bmatrix} 112 - 120 & 87 - 97 & 56 - 64 & 74 - 75 \\ 84 - 80 & 65 - 59 & 39 - 36 & 70 - 60 \\ 88 - 72 & 98 - 84 & 43 - 29 & 60 - 48 \end{bmatrix}$$

$$= \begin{bmatrix} -8 & -10 & -8 & -1 \\ 4 & 6 & 3 & 10 \\ 16 & 14 & 14 & 12 \end{bmatrix}$$

33. $\begin{bmatrix} 52 \\ 42 \\ 44 \\ 46 \\ 51 \end{bmatrix} + \begin{bmatrix} 25 \\ 67 \\ 130 \\ 94 \\ 29 \end{bmatrix} + \begin{bmatrix} 131 \\ 118 \\ 136 \\ 68 \\ 37 \end{bmatrix} + \begin{bmatrix} 37 \\ 1 \\ 9 \\ 19 \\ 0 \end{bmatrix}$

$$= \begin{bmatrix} 52 + 25 + 131 + 37 \\ 42 + 67 + 118 + 1 \\ 44 + 130 + 136 + 9 \\ 46 + 94 + 68 + 19 \\ 51 + 29 + 37 + 0 \end{bmatrix}$$

$$= \begin{bmatrix} 245 \\ 228 \\ 319 \\ 227 \\ 117 \end{bmatrix}$$

34. $\begin{bmatrix} 52 \\ 42 \\ 44 \\ 46 \\ 51 \end{bmatrix} - \begin{bmatrix} 37 \\ 1 \\ 9 \\ 19 \\ 0 \end{bmatrix} = \begin{bmatrix} 52 - 37 \\ 42 - 1 \\ 44 - 9 \\ 46 - 19 \\ 51 - 0 \end{bmatrix}$

$$= \begin{bmatrix} 15 \\ 41 \\ 35 \\ 27 \\ 51 \end{bmatrix}$$

35. In 1996−1998, floods accounted for the most deaths.
In 1999, tornadoes accounted for the most deaths.
In 2000, lightning accounted for the most deaths.

36. Residents:

	Child	Adult
Before 6 PM	3.00	4.50
After 6 PM	2.00	3.50

Nonresidents:

	Child	Adult
Before 6 PM	4.50	6.75
After 6 PM	3.00	5.25

37. $\begin{bmatrix} 4.50 & 6.75 \\ 3.00 & 5.25 \end{bmatrix} - \begin{bmatrix} 3.00 & 4.50 \\ 2.00 & 3.50 \end{bmatrix}$

$$= \begin{bmatrix} 4.50 - 3.00 & 6.75 - 4.50 \\ 3.00 - 2.00 & 5.25 - 3.50 \end{bmatrix}$$

$$= \begin{bmatrix} 1.50 & 2.25 \\ 1.00 & 1.75 \end{bmatrix}$$

38. Before 6:00PM:
$$\begin{array}{c} \text{Child} \ \ \text{Adult} \end{array}$$
$$\begin{array}{l} \text{Residents} \\ \text{Nonresidents} \end{array} \begin{bmatrix} 3.00 & 4.50 \\ 4.50 & 6.75 \end{bmatrix}$$

After 6:00PM:
$$\begin{array}{c} \text{Child} \ \ \text{Adult} \end{array}$$
$$\begin{array}{l} \text{Residents} \\ \text{Nonresidents} \end{array} \begin{bmatrix} 2.00 & 3.50 \\ 3.00 & 5.25 \end{bmatrix}$$

39. $\begin{bmatrix} 3.00 & 4.50 \\ 4.50 & 6.75 \end{bmatrix} - \begin{bmatrix} 2.00 & 3.50 \\ 3.00 & 5.25 \end{bmatrix}$

$= \begin{bmatrix} 3.00 - 2.00 & 4.50 - 3.50 \\ 4.50 - 3.00 & 6.75 - 5.25 \end{bmatrix}$

$= \begin{bmatrix} 1.00 & 1.00 \\ 1.50 & 1.50 \end{bmatrix}$

40. Since $d = 1$ and $e = 4d$, $e = 4(1)$ or 4.
Now since $z + d = e$, $z + 1 = 4$ or $z = 3$.
Since $x = \frac{d}{2}$, $x = \frac{1}{2}$ or 0.5.
Since $f = \frac{x}{5}$, $f = \frac{0.5}{5}$ or 0.1.
Since $y = x + \frac{x}{2}$, $y = 0.5 + \frac{0.5}{2}$ or 0.75.
Finally, since $ay = 1.5$, $a(0.75) = 1.5$, so $a = 2$.
$2\begin{bmatrix} 0.5 & 0.75 & 3 \\ 1 & 4 & 0.1 \end{bmatrix} = \begin{bmatrix} 1 & 1.5 & 6 \\ 2 & 8 & 0.2 \end{bmatrix}$

41. You can use matrices to track dietary requirements and add them to find the total each day or each week. Answers should include the following.

- Breakfast = $\begin{bmatrix} 566 & 18 & 7 \\ 482 & 12 & 17 \\ 530 & 10 & 11 \end{bmatrix}$,

Lunch = $\begin{bmatrix} 785 & 22 & 19 \\ 622 & 23 & 20 \\ 710 & 26 & 12 \end{bmatrix}$,

Dinner = $\begin{bmatrix} 1257 & 40 & 26 \\ 987 & 32 & 45 \\ 1380 & 29 & 38 \end{bmatrix}$

- Add the three matrices: $\begin{bmatrix} 2608 & 80 & 52 \\ 2091 & 67 & 82 \\ 2620 & 65 & 61 \end{bmatrix}$.

42. D; $\begin{bmatrix} 5 & -2 \\ -3 & 7 \end{bmatrix} - \begin{bmatrix} 3 & 4 \\ -5 & 6 \end{bmatrix} = \begin{bmatrix} 5 - 3 & -2 - 4 \\ -3 - (-5) & 7 - 6 \end{bmatrix}$

$= \begin{bmatrix} 2 & -6 \\ 2 & 1 \end{bmatrix}$

43. A; The equation corresponding to the second row is $7 - x = 12$.
$$7 - x = 12$$
$$7 - x - 7 = 12 - 7$$
$$-x = 5$$
$$x = -5$$
We can eliminate answer choices B, C, and D since the x-coordinate of each is not -5.

44. 2×2

45. 1×4

46. 2×4

47. 3×3

48. 3×2

49. 4×3

50. Solve the second equation for a.
$$5a = 15$$
$$\frac{5a}{5} = \frac{15}{5}$$
$$a = 3$$
Substitute 3 for a in the first equation to find b.
$$2a + b = 2$$
$$2(3) + b = 2$$
$$6 + b = 2$$
$$b = -4$$
Substitute 3 for a and -4 for b in the third equation.
$$a + b + c = -1$$
$$3 + (-4) + c = -1$$
$$-1 + c = -1$$
$$c = 0$$
The solution is $(3, -4, 0)$.

51. Use the first and second equation to eliminate r.
$$\begin{array}{r} r + s + t = 15 \\ (-) \ r \quad\ + t = 12 \\ \hline s \quad\quad = 3 \end{array}$$
Substitute 3 for s into the third equation to find t.
$$s + t = 10$$
$$3 + t = 10$$
$$t = 7$$
Substitute 7 for t into the second equation to find r.
$$r + t = 12$$
$$r + 7 = 12$$
$$r = 5$$
The solution is $(5, 3, 7)$.

52. Use the first and second equation to eliminate z.

$6x - 2y - 3z = -10$
$-6x + y + 9z = 3$

Multiply by 3.
$$18x - 6y - 9z = -30$$
$$\underline{(+) - 6x + y + 9z = 3}$$
$$12x - 5y = -27$$

Use this resulting equation and the third equation to eliminate y.

$12x - 5y = -27$
$8x - 3y = -16$

Multiply by -3. $-36x + 15y = 81$
Multiply by 5. $\underline{(+) 40x - 15y = -80}$
$$4x = 1$$
$$x = \tfrac{1}{4}$$

Substitute $\tfrac{1}{4}$ for x in the third equation to find y.

$8x - 3y = -16$
$8\left(\tfrac{1}{4}\right) - 3y = -16$
$2 - 3y = -16$
$-3y = -18$
$\dfrac{-3y}{-3} = \dfrac{-18}{-3}$
$y = 6$

Substitute $\tfrac{1}{4}$ for x and 6 for y in the first equation.

$6x - 2y - 3z = -10$
$6\left(\tfrac{1}{4}\right) - 2(6) - 3z = -10$
$\tfrac{3}{2} - 12 - 3z = -10$
$3 - 24 - 6z = -20$
$-21 - 6z = -20$
$-6z = 1$
$z = -\tfrac{1}{6}$

The solution is $\left(\tfrac{1}{4}, 6, -\tfrac{1}{6}\right)$.

53. $2s + 7t = 39$
$5s - t = 5$

$$2s + 7t = 39$$
Multiply by 7. $\underline{(+) 35s - 7t = 35}$
$$37s = 74$$
$$\dfrac{37s}{37} = \dfrac{74}{37}$$
$$s = 2$$

Substitute 2 for s in the second equation.

$5s - t = 5$
$5(2) - t = 5$
$-10 + 10 - t = -10 + 5$
$-t = -5$
$t = 5$

The solution is $(2, 5)$.

54. $3p + 6q = -3$
$2p - 3q = -9$

$$3p + 6q = -3$$
Multiply by 2. $\underline{(+) 4p - 6q = -18}$
$$7p = -21$$
$$p = -3$$

Substitute -3 for p in the first equation.

$3p + 6q = -3$
$3(-3) + 6q = -3$
$-9 + 6q + 9 = -3 + 9$
$6q = 6$
$\dfrac{6q}{6} = \dfrac{6}{6}$
$q = 1$

The solution is $(-3, 1)$.

55. Solve the first equation for a.

$a + 5b = 1$
$a + 5b - 5b = 1 - 5b$
$a = 1 - 5b$

Substitute $1 - 5b$ for a in the second equation.

$7a - 2b = 44$
$7(1 - 5b) - 2b = 44$
$7 - 35b - 2b = 44$
$-7 + 7 - 37b = -7 + 44$
$-37b = 37$
$\dfrac{-37b}{-37} = \dfrac{37}{-37}$
$b = -1$

Substitute -1 for b in the first equation and solve for a.

$a + 5b = 1$
$a + 5(-1) = 1$
$a - 5 = 1$
$a - 5 + 5 = 1 + 5$
$a = 6$

The solution is $(6, -1)$.

56. An inequality that describes this situation is $0.30p + 0.15s \leq 6$ where p is the number of printed sheets and s is the number of solid color sheets.

57. The boundary is the graph of $0.30p + 0.15s = 6$. Since the inequality symbol is $\leq$ the boundary is solid.

Test the point $(0, 0)$.

$0.3p + 0.15s \leq 6$
$0.3(0) + 0.15(0) \leq 6$
$0 + 0 \leq 6$
$0 \leq 6$ true

Shade the region that contains the point $(0, 0)$. Since the variable must be nonnegative, only shade the portion of the region in the first quadrant.

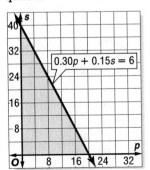

58. No; $0.30p + 0.15s \leq 6$
$0.30(14) + 0.15(14) \leq 6$
$4.2 + 2.1 \leq 6$
$6.3 \leq 6$ false

59. Multiplicative Inverse

60. Associative Property of Addition

61. Distributive Property

62. Commutative Property of Multiplication

4-3 Multiplying Matrices

Page 171 Check for Understanding

1. Sample answer: $\begin{bmatrix} 1 & 2 \\ 3 & 4 \\ 5 & 6 \end{bmatrix} \cdot \begin{bmatrix} 7 & 8 \\ 9 & 10 \end{bmatrix}$

2. Never; the inner dimensions will never be equal.

3. The Right Distributive Property says that $(A + B)C = AC + BC$, but $AC + BC \neq CA + CB$ since the Commutative Property does not hold for matrix multiplication in most cases.

4. 3×2

5. Undefined; the inner dimensions are not equal.

6. $[3 \quad -5] \cdot \begin{bmatrix} 3 & 5 \\ -2 & 0 \end{bmatrix}$

$= [3(3) + (-5)(-2) \quad 3(5) + (-5)(0)]$

$= [19 \quad 15]$

7. $\begin{bmatrix} 5 \\ 8 \end{bmatrix} \cdot [3 \quad -1 \quad 4] = \begin{bmatrix} 5(3) & 5(-1) & 5(4) \\ 8(3) & 8(-1) & 8(4) \end{bmatrix}$

$= \begin{bmatrix} 15 & -5 & 20 \\ 24 & -8 & 32 \end{bmatrix}$

8. Not possible; the inner dimensions are not equal.

9. $\begin{bmatrix} 4 & -1 \\ 3 & 5 \end{bmatrix} \cdot \begin{bmatrix} 7 \\ 4 \end{bmatrix} = \begin{bmatrix} 4(7) + (-1)(4) \\ 3(7) + 5(4) \end{bmatrix}$

$= \begin{bmatrix} 24 \\ 41 \end{bmatrix}$

10. Yes; $A(BC) = (AB)C$ for the given matrices.

$A(BC) = \begin{bmatrix} 2 & -1 \\ 3 & 5 \end{bmatrix} \cdot \left(\begin{bmatrix} -4 & 1 \\ 8 & 0 \end{bmatrix} \cdot \begin{bmatrix} 3 & 2 \\ -1 & 2 \end{bmatrix} \right)$

$= \begin{bmatrix} 2 & -1 \\ 3 & 5 \end{bmatrix} \cdot \begin{bmatrix} -13 & -6 \\ 24 & 16 \end{bmatrix}$

$= \begin{bmatrix} -50 & -28 \\ 81 & 62 \end{bmatrix}$

$(AB)C = \left(\begin{bmatrix} 2 & -1 \\ 3 & 5 \end{bmatrix} \cdot \begin{bmatrix} -4 & 1 \\ 8 & 0 \end{bmatrix} \right) \cdot \begin{bmatrix} 3 & 2 \\ -1 & 2 \end{bmatrix}$

$= \begin{bmatrix} -16 & 2 \\ 28 & 3 \end{bmatrix} \cdot \begin{bmatrix} 3 & 2 \\ -1 & 2 \end{bmatrix}$

$= \begin{bmatrix} -50 & -28 \\ 81 & 62 \end{bmatrix}$

11. Registration fees: $R = [45 \quad 55 \quad 65]$

Number of players: $P = \begin{bmatrix} 350 & 280 \\ 320 & 165 \\ 180 & 120 \end{bmatrix}$

12. $RP = [45 \quad 55 \quad 65] \cdot \begin{bmatrix} 350 & 280 \\ 320 & 165 \\ 180 & 120 \end{bmatrix}$

$= [45(350) + 55(320) + 65(180) \quad 45(280) + 55(165) + 65(120)]$

$= [45{,}050 \quad 29{,}475]$

The league received \$45,050 from baseball and \$29,475 from softball for a total of \$74,525.

Pages 172–173 Practice and Apply

13. 4×2

14. 2×2

15. Undefined; the inner dimensions are not equal.

16. 1×5

17. Undefined; the inner dimensions are not equal.

18. 3×5

19. $[2 \quad -1] \cdot \begin{bmatrix} 5 \\ 4 \end{bmatrix} = [2(5) + (-1)(4)]$

$= [6]$

20. $\begin{bmatrix} 3 & -2 \\ 5 & 1 \end{bmatrix} \cdot \begin{bmatrix} 4 & 1 \\ 2 & 7 \end{bmatrix} = \begin{bmatrix} 3(4) + (-2)(2) & 3(1) + (-2)(7) \\ 5(4) + 1(2) & 5(1) + 1(7) \end{bmatrix}$

$= \begin{bmatrix} 8 & -11 \\ 22 & 12 \end{bmatrix}$

21. Not possible; the inner dimensions are not equal.

22. $\begin{bmatrix} 4 & -2 & -7 \\ 6 & 3 & 5 \end{bmatrix} \cdot \begin{bmatrix} -2 \\ 5 \\ 3 \end{bmatrix} = \begin{bmatrix} 4(-2) + (-2)(5) + (-7)(3) \\ 6(-2) + 3(5) + 5(3) \end{bmatrix}$

$= \begin{bmatrix} -39 \\ 18 \end{bmatrix}$

23. $\begin{bmatrix} 2 & -1 \\ 3 & 4 \end{bmatrix} \cdot \begin{bmatrix} 3 & -9 & -2 \\ 5 & 7 & -6 \end{bmatrix}$

$= \begin{bmatrix} 2(3) + (-1)(5) & 2(-9) + (-1)(7) & 2(-2) + (-1)(-6) \\ 3(3) + 4(5) & 3(-9) + 4(7) & 3(-2) + 4(-6) \end{bmatrix}$

$= \begin{bmatrix} 1 & -25 & 2 \\ 29 & 1 & -30 \end{bmatrix}$

24. Not possible; the inner dimensions are not equal.

25. $\begin{bmatrix} 4 & 0 \\ -3 & 7 \\ -5 & 9 \end{bmatrix} \cdot \begin{bmatrix} 6 & 4 \\ -2 & 1 \end{bmatrix}$

$= \begin{bmatrix} 4(6) + 0(-2) & 4(4) + 0(1) \\ -3(6) + 7(-2) & -3(4) + 7(1) \\ -5(6) + 9(-2) & -5(4) + 9(1) \end{bmatrix}$

$= \begin{bmatrix} 24 & 16 \\ -32 & -5 \\ -48 & -11 \end{bmatrix}$

26. $\begin{bmatrix} 0 & 8 \\ 3 & 1 \\ -1 & 5 \end{bmatrix} \cdot \begin{bmatrix} 3 & 1 & -2 \\ 0 & 8 & -5 \end{bmatrix}$

$= \begin{bmatrix} 0(3) + 8(0) & 0(1) + 8(8) & 0(-2) + 8(-5) \\ 3(3) + 1(0) & 3(1) + 1(8) & 3(-2) + 1(-5) \\ -1(3) + 5(0) & -1(1) + 5(8) & -1(-2) + 5(-5) \end{bmatrix}$

$= \begin{bmatrix} 0 & 64 & -40 \\ 9 & 11 & -11 \\ -3 & 39 & -23 \end{bmatrix}$

27. Yes; $AC + BC = (A + B)C$ for the given matrices.

$AC + BC = \begin{bmatrix} 1 & -2 \\ 4 & 3 \end{bmatrix} \cdot \begin{bmatrix} 5 & 1 \\ 2 & -4 \end{bmatrix} + \begin{bmatrix} -5 & 2 \\ 4 & 3 \end{bmatrix} \cdot \begin{bmatrix} 5 & 1 \\ 2 & -4 \end{bmatrix}$

$= \begin{bmatrix} 1 & 9 \\ 26 & -8 \end{bmatrix} + \begin{bmatrix} -21 & -13 \\ 26 & -8 \end{bmatrix}$

$= \begin{bmatrix} -20 & -4 \\ 52 & -16 \end{bmatrix}$

$(A + B)C = \left(\begin{bmatrix} 1 & -2 \\ 4 & 3 \end{bmatrix} + \begin{bmatrix} -5 & 2 \\ 4 & 3 \end{bmatrix} \right) \cdot \begin{bmatrix} 5 & 1 \\ 2 & -4 \end{bmatrix}$

$= \begin{bmatrix} -4 & 0 \\ 8 & 6 \end{bmatrix} \cdot \begin{bmatrix} 5 & 1 \\ 2 & -4 \end{bmatrix}$

$= \begin{bmatrix} -20 & -4 \\ 52 & -16 \end{bmatrix}$

28. Yes; $c(AB) = A(cB)$ for the given matrices.

$c(AB) = 3 \left(\begin{bmatrix} 1 & -2 \\ 4 & 3 \end{bmatrix} \cdot \begin{bmatrix} -5 & 2 \\ 4 & 3 \end{bmatrix} \right)$

$= 3 \begin{bmatrix} -13 & -4 \\ -8 & 17 \end{bmatrix}$

$= \begin{bmatrix} -39 & -12 \\ -24 & 51 \end{bmatrix}$

$A(cB) = \begin{bmatrix} 1 & -2 \\ 4 & 3 \end{bmatrix} \cdot \left(3 \begin{bmatrix} -5 & 2 \\ 4 & 3 \end{bmatrix} \right)$

$= \begin{bmatrix} 1 & -2 \\ 4 & 3 \end{bmatrix} \begin{bmatrix} -15 & 6 \\ 12 & 9 \end{bmatrix}$

$= \begin{bmatrix} -39 & -12 \\ -24 & 51 \end{bmatrix}$

29. No; $C(A + B) \neq AC + BC$ for the given matrices.

$C(A + B) = \begin{bmatrix} 5 & 1 \\ 2 & -4 \end{bmatrix} \cdot \left(\begin{bmatrix} 1 & -2 \\ 4 & 3 \end{bmatrix} + \begin{bmatrix} -5 & 2 \\ 4 & 3 \end{bmatrix} \right)$

$= \begin{bmatrix} 5 & 1 \\ 2 & -4 \end{bmatrix} \cdot \begin{bmatrix} -4 & 0 \\ 8 & 6 \end{bmatrix}$

$= \begin{bmatrix} -12 & 6 \\ -40 & -24 \end{bmatrix}$

$AC + BC = \begin{bmatrix} 1 & -2 \\ 4 & 3 \end{bmatrix} \cdot \begin{bmatrix} 5 & 1 \\ 2 & -4 \end{bmatrix} + \begin{bmatrix} -5 & 2 \\ 4 & 3 \end{bmatrix} \cdot \begin{bmatrix} 5 & 1 \\ 2 & -4 \end{bmatrix}$

$= \begin{bmatrix} 1 & 9 \\ 26 & -8 \end{bmatrix} + \begin{bmatrix} -21 & -13 \\ 26 & -8 \end{bmatrix}$

$= \begin{bmatrix} -20 & -4 \\ 52 & -16 \end{bmatrix}$

30. No; $ABC \neq CBA$ for the given matrices.

$ABC = \begin{bmatrix} 1 & -2 \\ 4 & 3 \end{bmatrix} \cdot \begin{bmatrix} -5 & 2 \\ 4 & 3 \end{bmatrix} \cdot \begin{bmatrix} 5 & 1 \\ 2 & -4 \end{bmatrix}$

$= \begin{bmatrix} -13 & -4 \\ -8 & 17 \end{bmatrix} \cdot \begin{bmatrix} 5 & 1 \\ 2 & -4 \end{bmatrix}$

$= \begin{bmatrix} -73 & 3 \\ -6 & -76 \end{bmatrix}$

$CBA = \begin{bmatrix} 5 & 1 \\ 2 & -4 \end{bmatrix} \cdot \begin{bmatrix} -5 & 2 \\ 4 & 3 \end{bmatrix} \cdot \begin{bmatrix} 1 & -2 \\ 4 & 3 \end{bmatrix}$

$= \begin{bmatrix} -21 & 13 \\ -26 & -8 \end{bmatrix} \cdot \begin{bmatrix} 1 & -2 \\ 4 & 3 \end{bmatrix}$

$= \begin{bmatrix} 31 & 81 \\ -58 & 28 \end{bmatrix}$

31. $F = \begin{bmatrix} 290 & 165 & 210 \\ 175 & 240 & 190 \\ 110 & 75 & 0 \end{bmatrix}$

32. $C = \begin{bmatrix} 22 \\ 25 \\ 18 \end{bmatrix}$

33. $FC = \begin{bmatrix} 290 & 165 & 210 \\ 175 & 240 & 190 \\ 110 & 75 & 0 \end{bmatrix} \begin{bmatrix} 22 \\ 25 \\ 18 \end{bmatrix}$

$= \begin{bmatrix} 290(22) + 165(25) + 210(18) \\ 175(22) + 240(25) + 190(18) \\ 110(22) + 75(25) + 0(18) \end{bmatrix}$

$= \begin{bmatrix} 14{,}285 \\ 13{,}270 \\ 4295 \end{bmatrix}$

34. $14{,}285 + 13{,}270 + 4295 = 31{,}850$
The total income from all three farms is \$31,850.

35. Any two matrices $\begin{bmatrix} a & b \\ c & d \end{bmatrix}$ and $\begin{bmatrix} e & f \\ g & h \end{bmatrix}$ where $bg = cf$, $a = d$, and $e = h$

36. $S = \begin{bmatrix} 72 & 49 \\ 68 & 63 \\ 90 & 56 \\ 86 & 62 \end{bmatrix}$, $E = \begin{bmatrix} 1.00 \\ 0.50 \end{bmatrix}$

37. $SE = \begin{bmatrix} 72 & 49 \\ 68 & 63 \\ 90 & 56 \\ 86 & 62 \end{bmatrix} \cdot \begin{bmatrix} 1.00 \\ 0.50 \end{bmatrix}$

$= \begin{bmatrix} 72(1.00) + 49(0.50) \\ 68(1.00) + 63(0.50) \\ 90(1.00) + 56(0.50) \\ 86(1.00) + 62(0.50) \end{bmatrix}$

$= \begin{bmatrix} 96.50 \\ 99.50 \\ 118.00 \\ 117.00 \end{bmatrix}$

38. The Juniors earned the most money since the amount in the third row is the greatest.

39. $96.50 + 99.50 + 118.00 + 117.00 = 431.00$
The school made \$431 from the fund-raiser.

40. Purchase price: $P = [54.00\ 48.00\ 60.00]$;

Number of shares: $N = \begin{bmatrix} 150 \\ 100 \\ 200 \end{bmatrix}$

$PN = [54.00\ 48.00\ 60.00] \cdot \begin{bmatrix} 150 \\ 100 \\ 200 \end{bmatrix}$

$= [54(150) + 48(100) + 60(200)]$
$= [24,900]$

Taini spent $24,900 for the stock.

41. Selling Price: $S = [55.20\ \ 58.60\ \ 61.10]$;

Number of shares: $N = \begin{bmatrix} 150 \\ 100 \\ 200 \end{bmatrix}$

$SN = [55.20\ \ 58.60\ \ 61.10] \cdot \begin{bmatrix} 150 \\ 100 \\ 200 \end{bmatrix}$

$= [55.20(150) + 58.60(100) + 61.10(200)]$
$= [26,360]$

Taini received $26,360 for selling the stock.

42. $SN - PN = [26,360] - [24,900]$
$\qquad\qquad = [1460]$

Taini made $1460.

43. $\begin{bmatrix} 3 & 5 \\ -1 & 7 \end{bmatrix} \cdot \begin{bmatrix} a & b \\ c & d \end{bmatrix} = \begin{bmatrix} 3a + 5c & 3b + 5d \\ -a + 7c & -b + 7d \end{bmatrix}$

Write the corresponding system of equations.
$3a + 5c = 3$
$3b + 5d = 5$
$-a + 7c = -1 \qquad$ or $\qquad a = 7c + 1$
$-b + 7d = 7 \qquad$ or $\qquad b = 7d - 7$

Substitute $7c + 1$ for a in the first equation and solve for c.
$\qquad\quad 3a + 5c = 3$
$\ 3(7c + 1) + 5c = 3$
$\quad 21c + 3 + 5c = 3$
$\qquad\qquad\ 26c = 0$
$\qquad\qquad\quad c = 0$

Substitute 0 for c in the third equation and solve for a.
$a = 7c + 1$
$\ \ = 7(0) + 1$
$\ \ = 1$

Substitute $7d - 7$ for b in the second equation and solve for d.
$\qquad\quad 3b + 5d = 5$
$\ 3(7d - 7) + 5d = 5$
$\quad 21d - 21 + 5d = 5$
$\qquad\qquad\ 26d = 26$
$\qquad\qquad\quad d = 1$

Substitute 1 for d in the fourth equation and solve for b.
$b = 7d - 7$
$\ \ = 7(1) - 7$
$\ \ = 0$

Thus, $a = d = 1$ and $b = c = 0$, or $\begin{bmatrix} a & b \\ c & d \end{bmatrix} = \begin{bmatrix} 1 & 0 \\ 0 & 1 \end{bmatrix}$.

If the matrix $\begin{bmatrix} 1 & 0 \\ 0 & 1 \end{bmatrix}$ is multiplied by any matrix containing two columns, the result is the original matrix.

44. Sports statistics are often listed in columns and matrices. In this case, you can find the total number of points scored by multiplying the point matrix, which doesn't change, by the record matrix, which changes for each season. Answers should include the following.
- $P \cdot R = [479]$
- Basketball and wrestling use different point values in scoring.

45. B; A 3×5 matrix times a 5×1 matrix is a 3×1 matrix.

46. A; Since the first matrix is a 1×3 matrix and the second matrix is a 3×2 matrix, the product is defined and is a 1×2 matrix. Thus, we can eliminate answer choices B, C, and D.

Page 174   Maintain Your Skills

47. $3\begin{bmatrix} 4 & -2 \\ -1 & 7 \end{bmatrix} = \begin{bmatrix} 3(4) & 3(-2) \\ 3(-1) & 3(7) \end{bmatrix}$

$\qquad\qquad\qquad = \begin{bmatrix} 12 & -6 \\ -3 & 21 \end{bmatrix}$

48. Impossible; the matrices have different dimensions.

49. $2\begin{bmatrix} 6 & 3 \\ -8 & -2 \end{bmatrix} - 4\begin{bmatrix} 8 & 1 \\ 3 & -4 \end{bmatrix}$

$= \begin{bmatrix} 12 & 6 \\ -16 & -4 \end{bmatrix} - \begin{bmatrix} 32 & 4 \\ 12 & -16 \end{bmatrix}$

$= \begin{bmatrix} 12 - 32 & 6 - 4 \\ -16 - 12 & 4 - (-16) \end{bmatrix}$

$= \begin{bmatrix} -20 & 2 \\ -28 & 12 \end{bmatrix}$

50. Write the corresponding system of equations.
$\ 3x + 2 = 23$
$\ 15 = -4y - 1$

Solve the first equation for x.
$3x + 2 = 23$
$\quad\ 3x = 21$
$\qquad x = 7$

Solve the second equation for y.
$\ 15 = -4y - 1$
$\ 16 = -4y$
$-4 = y$

The solution is $(7, -4)$.

51. Write the corresponding system of equations.

$x + 3y = -22$
$2x - y = 19$

Solve the first equation for x.

$x + 3y = -22$
$\quad x = -3y - 22$

Substitute $-3y - 22$ for x in the second equation.

$2x - y = 19$
$2(-3y - 22) - y = 19$
$-6y - 44 - y = 19$
$\quad\quad -7y = 63$
$\quad\quad\quad y = -9$

Substitute -9 for y in the second equation.

$2x - y = 19$
$2x - (-9) = 19$
$\quad 2x = 10$
$\quad\quad x = 5$

The solution is $(5, -9)$.

52. Write the corresponding system of equations.

$x + 3z = -19$
$-2x + y - z = -2$
$5y - 7z = 24$

Eliminate x in the first two equations.

$x \quad\quad + 3z = -19$
$-2x + y - z = -2$

Multiply by 2.
$\quad\quad 2x \quad\quad + 6z = -19$
$\underline{(+) - 2x + y - z = -2}$
$\quad\quad\quad\quad y + 5z = -21$

Use this equation and the third equation to eliminate y.

$y + 5z = -40$
$5y - 7z = 24$

Multiply by -5.
$\quad\quad -5y - 25z = 200$
$\underline{(+) 5y - 7z = 24}$
$\quad\quad\quad -32z = 224$
$\quad\quad\quad\quad z = -7$

Substitute -7 for z in the first equation.

$x + 3z = -19$
$x + 3(-7) = -19$
$x - 21 = -19$
$\quad\quad x = 2$

Substitute -7 for z in the third equation.

$5y - 7z = 24$
$5y - 7(-7) = 24$
$5y + 49 = 24$
$\quad 5y = -25$
$\quad\quad y = -5$

The solution is $(2, -5, -7)$.

53. Let f be the price of a roll of film.
Let b be the price of a camera battery.

$8f + 2b = 23$
$6f + 2b = 18$

Subtract the second equation from the first to eliminate b.

$8f + 2b = 23$
$\underline{(-) 6f + 2b = 18}$
$\quad 2f \quad\quad = 5$
$\quad\quad f = 2.5$

Substitute 2.5 for f in the first equation.

$8f + 2b = 23$
$8(2.5) + 2b = 23$
$\quad 20 + 2b = 23$
$\quad\quad 2b = 3$
$\quad\quad\quad b = 1.5$

A roll of film costs \$2.50, and a camera battery costs \$1.50.

54. x-intercept:

$y = 3 - 2x$
$0 = 3 - 2x$
$-3 = -2x$
$\frac{3}{2} = x$

y-intercept:

$y = 3 - 2x$
$y = 3 - 2(0)$
$y = 3$

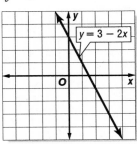

$y = 3 - 2x$

55. x-intercept:

$x - \frac{1}{2}y = 8$
$x - \frac{1}{2}(0) = 8$
$\quad\quad x = 8$

y-intercept:

$x - \frac{1}{2}y = 8$
$0 - \frac{1}{2}y = 8$
$-\frac{1}{2}y = 8$
$\quad y = -16$

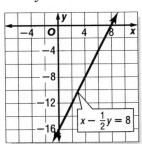

$x - \frac{1}{2}y = 8$

56. *x*-intercept:
$$5x - 2y = 10$$
$$5x - 2(0) = 10$$
$$5x = 10$$
$$x = 2$$

y-intercept:
$$5x - 2y = 10$$
$$5(0) - 2y = 10$$
$$-2y = 10$$
$$y = -5$$

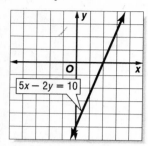

57.

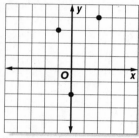

58.

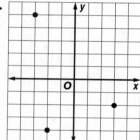

59.

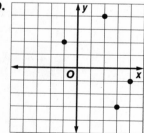

60.

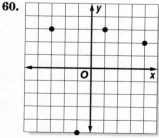

Page 174   Practice Quiz 1

1. Write the corresponding system of equations.
$$3x + 1 = 19$$
$$7y = 21$$
Solve the first equation for *x*.
$$3x + 1 = 19$$
$$3x = 18$$
$$x = 6$$
Solve the second equation for *y*.
$$7y = 21$$
$$y = 3$$
The solution is (6, 3).

2. Write the corresponding system of equations.
$$2x + y = 9$$
$$4x + 3y = 23$$
Eliminate *x* from the first and second equations.
$$2x + \ y = \ 9$$
$$4x - 3y = 23$$
Multiply by -2.
$$\begin{aligned} -4x - 2y &= -18 \\ (+) \ 4x - 3y &= \ \ 23 \\ \hline -5y &= \ \ \ 5 \\ y &= -1 \end{aligned}$$
Substitute -1 for *y* in the first equation.
$$2x + y = 9$$
$$2x - 1 = 9$$
$$2x = 10$$
$$x = 5$$
The solution is $(5, -1)$.

3. Write the corresponding system of equations.
$$2 = 2$$
$$x = 1$$
$$y = 3$$
$$5 = z$$
The solution is (1, 3, 5).

4. Monday: $M = \begin{bmatrix} 120 & 80 & 64 & 75 \\ 65 & 105 & 77 & 53 \end{bmatrix}$

Tuesday: $T = \begin{bmatrix} 112 & 79 & 56 & 74 \\ 69 & 95 & 82 & 50 \end{bmatrix}$

5. $M + T = \begin{bmatrix} 120 & 80 & 64 & 75 \\ 65 & 105 & 77 & 53 \end{bmatrix} + \begin{bmatrix} 112 & 79 & 56 & 74 \\ 69 & 95 & 82 & 50 \end{bmatrix}$

$= \begin{bmatrix} 120 + 112 & 80 + 79 & 64 + 56 & 75 + 74 \\ 65 + 69 & 105 + 95 & 77 + 82 & 53 + 50 \end{bmatrix}$

$= \begin{bmatrix} 232 & 159 & 120 & 149 \\ 134 & 200 & 159 & 103 \end{bmatrix}$

6. $\begin{bmatrix} 3 & 0 \\ 7 & 12 \end{bmatrix} - \begin{bmatrix} 6 & -5 \\ 4 & -1 \end{bmatrix} = \begin{bmatrix} 3 - 6 & 0 - (-5) \\ 7 - 4 & 12 - (-1) \end{bmatrix}$

$= \begin{bmatrix} -3 & 5 \\ 3 & 13 \end{bmatrix}$

7. $\dfrac{2}{3}\begin{bmatrix} 9 & 0 \\ 12 & 15 \end{bmatrix} + \begin{bmatrix} -2 & 3 \\ -7 & -7 \end{bmatrix}$

$= \begin{bmatrix} \frac{2}{3}(9) & \frac{2}{3}(0) \\ \frac{2}{3}(12) & \frac{2}{3}(15) \end{bmatrix} + \begin{bmatrix} -2 & 3 \\ -7 & -7 \end{bmatrix}$

$= \begin{bmatrix} 6 & 0 \\ 8 & 10 \end{bmatrix} + \begin{bmatrix} -2 & 3 \\ -7 & -7 \end{bmatrix}$

$= \begin{bmatrix} 6 + (-2) & 0 + 3 \\ 8 + (-7) & 10 + (-7) \end{bmatrix}$

$= \begin{bmatrix} 4 & 3 \\ 1 & 3 \end{bmatrix}$

8. $5\begin{bmatrix} -2 & 4 & 5 \\ 0 & -4 & 7 \end{bmatrix} = \begin{bmatrix} 5(-2) & 5(4) & 5(5) \\ 5(0) & 5(-4) & 5(7) \end{bmatrix}$

$= \begin{bmatrix} -10 & 20 & 25 \\ 0 & -20 & 35 \end{bmatrix}$

9. Not possible; the inner dimensions are not equal.

10. $\begin{bmatrix} 3 & -1 \\ 2 & 5 \end{bmatrix} \cdot \begin{bmatrix} 4 & -1 & -2 \\ -3 & 5 & 4 \end{bmatrix}$

$= \begin{bmatrix} 3(4) + (-1)(-3) & 3(-1) + (-1)5 & 3(-2) + (-1)4 \\ 2(4) + 5(-3) & 2(-1) + 5(5) & 2(-2) + 5(4) \end{bmatrix}$

$= \begin{bmatrix} 15 & -8 & -10 \\ -7 & 23 & 16 \end{bmatrix}$

4-4 Transformations with Matrices

Pages 178–179   Check for Understanding

1.

Transformation	Size	Shape	Isometry
reflection	same	same	yes
rotation	same	same	yes
translation	same	same	yes
dilation	changes	same	no

2. Each vertex of the original figure is translated 3 units to the left and 2 units down. Add -3 to each x-coordinate and -2 to each y-coordinate.

$\begin{bmatrix} -3 & -3 & -3 \\ -2 & -2 & -2 \end{bmatrix}$

3. To move up, add a positive number to each y-coordinate. To move to the left, add a negative number to each x-coordinate.

Sample answer: $\begin{bmatrix} -4 & -4 & -4 \\ 1 & 1 & 1 \end{bmatrix}$

4. To translate 3 units right, add 3 to each x-coordinate. To translate 1 unit down, add -1 to each y-coordinate.

$\begin{bmatrix} 3 & 3 & 3 \\ -1 & -1 & -1 \end{bmatrix}$

5. $\begin{bmatrix} 1 & 2 & -6 \\ 4 & -5 & -6 \end{bmatrix} + \begin{bmatrix} 3 & 3 & 3 \\ -1 & -1 & -1 \end{bmatrix} = \begin{bmatrix} 4 & 5 & -3 \\ 3 & -6 & -7 \end{bmatrix}$

The vertices are $A'(4, 3), B'(5, -6)$, and $C'(-3, -7)$.

6.

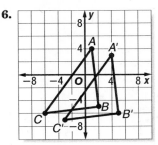

7. $\begin{bmatrix} 0 & 5 & 5 & 0 \\ 4 & 4 & 0 & 0 \end{bmatrix}$

8. $3\begin{bmatrix} 0 & 5 & 5 & 0 \\ 4 & 4 & 0 & 0 \end{bmatrix} = \begin{bmatrix} 0 & 15 & 15 & 0 \\ 12 & 12 & 0 & 0 \end{bmatrix}$

The coordinates are $A'(0, 12), B'(15, 12), C'(15, 0)$, and $D'(0, 0)$.

9. $\begin{bmatrix} 1 & 0 \\ 0 & -1 \end{bmatrix} \cdot \begin{bmatrix} 0 & 5 & 5 & 0 \\ 4 & 4 & 0 & 0 \end{bmatrix} = \begin{bmatrix} 0 & 5 & 5 & 0 \\ -4 & -4 & 0 & 0 \end{bmatrix}$

The coordinates are $A'(0, -4), B'(5, -4), C'(5, 0)$, and $D'(0, 0)$.

10. $\begin{bmatrix} -1 & 0 \\ 0 & -1 \end{bmatrix} \cdot \begin{bmatrix} 0 & 5 & 5 & 0 \\ 4 & 4 & 0 & 0 \end{bmatrix} = \begin{bmatrix} 0 & -5 & -5 & 0 \\ -4 & -4 & 0 & 0 \end{bmatrix}$

The coordinates are $A'(0, -4), B'(-5, -4)$, $C'(-5, 0)$, and $D'(0, 0)$.

11. B; $\begin{bmatrix} -4 \\ 3 \end{bmatrix} + \begin{bmatrix} 5 \\ -2 \end{bmatrix} = \begin{bmatrix} 1 \\ 1 \end{bmatrix}$

Pages 179–181   Practice and Apply

12. To translate 4 units left, add -4 to each x-coordinate. To translate 2 units up, add 2 to each y-coordinate.

$\begin{bmatrix} -4 & -4 & -4 \\ 2 & 2 & 2 \end{bmatrix}$

13. $\begin{bmatrix} 1 & 2 & -6 \\ 4 & -5 & -6 \end{bmatrix} + \begin{bmatrix} -4 & -4 & -4 \\ 2 & 2 & 2 \end{bmatrix} = \begin{bmatrix} -3 & -2 & -10 \\ 6 & -3 & -4 \end{bmatrix}$

The coordinates are $D'(-3, 6), E'(-2, -3)$, and $F'(-10, -4)$.

14.

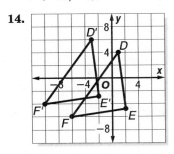

15. $\begin{bmatrix} 0 & 1.5 & -2.5 \\ 2 & -1.5 & 0 \end{bmatrix}$

16. $3\begin{bmatrix} 0 & 1.5 & -2.5 \\ 2 & -1.5 & 0 \end{bmatrix} = \begin{bmatrix} 0 & 4.5 & -7.5 \\ 6 & -4.5 & 0 \end{bmatrix}$

The coordinates are $A'(0, 6)$, $B'(4.5, -4.5)$, and $C'(-7.5, 0)$.

17.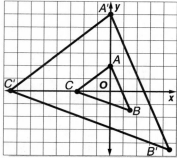

18. $\begin{bmatrix} 1 & 2 & 7 \\ -1 & -4 & -1 \end{bmatrix}$

19. $\begin{bmatrix} 0 & 1 \\ 1 & 0 \end{bmatrix} \cdot \begin{bmatrix} 1 & 2 & 7 \\ -1 & -4 & -1 \end{bmatrix} = \begin{bmatrix} -1 & -4 & -1 \\ 1 & 2 & 7 \end{bmatrix}$

The coordinates are $X'(-1, 1)$, $Y'(-4, 2)$, and $Z'(-1, 7)$.

20.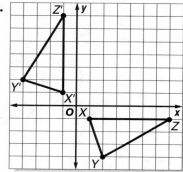

21. $\begin{bmatrix} 2 & 5 & 4 & 1 \\ 4 & 4 & 1 & 1 \end{bmatrix}$

22. $\begin{bmatrix} 0 & 1 \\ -1 & 0 \end{bmatrix} \cdot \begin{bmatrix} 2 & 5 & 4 & 1 \\ 4 & 4 & 1 & 1 \end{bmatrix} = \begin{bmatrix} 4 & 4 & 1 & 1 \\ -2 & -5 & -4 & -1 \end{bmatrix}$

The coordinates are $D'(4, -2)$, $E'(4, -5)$, $F'(1, -4)$, and $G'(1, -1)$.

23.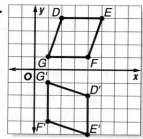

24. Vertex D has been translated 3 units right and 7 units down. Write the translation matrix.

$\begin{bmatrix} 3 & 3 & 3 \\ -7 & -7 & -7 \end{bmatrix}$

Add the translation matrix to the vertex matrix.

$\begin{bmatrix} -2 & 3 & 5 \\ 2 & 5 & -2 \end{bmatrix} + \begin{bmatrix} 3 & 3 & 3 \\ -7 & -7 & -7 \end{bmatrix} = \begin{bmatrix} 1 & 6 & 8 \\ -5 & -2 & -9 \end{bmatrix}$

The coordinates are $E'(6, -2)$ and $F'(8, -9)$.

25. Let (a, b), (c, d), and (e, f) represent the original vertices J, K, and L.

$\begin{bmatrix} 0 & -1 \\ 1 & 0 \end{bmatrix} \cdot \begin{bmatrix} a & c & e \\ b & d & f \end{bmatrix} = \begin{bmatrix} -3 & -2 & 1 \\ -5 & 7 & 4 \end{bmatrix}$

$\begin{bmatrix} -b & -d & -f \\ a & c & e \end{bmatrix} = \begin{bmatrix} -3 & -2 & 1 \\ -5 & 7 & 4 \end{bmatrix}$

Thus, $b = 3$, $d = 2$, $f = -1$, $a = -5$, $c = 7$, and $e = 4$. The coordinates are $J(-5, 3)$, $K(7, 2)$, and $L(4, -1)$.

26. The vertex matrix is $\begin{bmatrix} 2 & 4 & 2 & -3 \\ 3 & -3 & -5 & -2 \end{bmatrix}$.

$-1\begin{bmatrix} 2 & 4 & 2 & -3 \\ 3 & -3 & -5 & -2 \end{bmatrix} = \begin{bmatrix} -2 & -4 & -2 & 3 \\ -3 & 3 & 5 & 2 \end{bmatrix}$

27.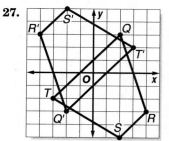

28. The graph represents a 180° rotation.

29. $\begin{bmatrix} -1 & 0 \\ 0 & 1 \end{bmatrix} \cdot \left(\begin{bmatrix} 1 & 0 \\ 0 & -1 \end{bmatrix} \cdot \begin{bmatrix} -4 & 4 & 4 & -4 \\ 4 & 4 & -4 & -4 \end{bmatrix} \right)$

$= \begin{bmatrix} -1 & 0 \\ 0 & 1 \end{bmatrix} \cdot \begin{bmatrix} -4 & 4 & 4 & -4 \\ -4 & -4 & 4 & 4 \end{bmatrix}$

$= \begin{bmatrix} 4 & -4 & -4 & 4 \\ -4 & -4 & 4 & 4 \end{bmatrix}$

30. $\begin{bmatrix} -1 & 0 \\ 0 & -1 \end{bmatrix} \cdot \begin{bmatrix} -4 & 4 & 4 & -4 \\ 4 & 4 & -4 & -4 \end{bmatrix} = \begin{bmatrix} 4 & -4 & -4 & 4 \\ -4 & -4 & 4 & 4 \end{bmatrix}$

31. $\begin{bmatrix} 0 & 1 \\ 1 & 0 \end{bmatrix} \cdot \begin{bmatrix} -4 & 4 & 4 & -4 \\ 4 & 4 & -4 & -4 \end{bmatrix} = \begin{bmatrix} 4 & 4 & -4 & -4 \\ -4 & 4 & 4 & -4 \end{bmatrix}$

32. The figures in Exercise 29 and Exercise 30 have the same coordinates, but the figure in Exercise 31 has different coordinates.

33. $0.75\begin{bmatrix} -2 & -6 & -8 & -4 \\ -2 & -2 & -5 & -5 \end{bmatrix}$

$= \begin{bmatrix} -1.5 & -4.5 & -6 & -3 \\ -1.5 & -1.5 & -3.75 & -3.75 \end{bmatrix}$

The new coordinates are $(-1.5, -1.5)$, $(-4.5, -1.5)$, $(-6, -3.75)$, and $(-3, -3.75)$.

34. $0.75\begin{bmatrix} -5 \\ -3.5 \end{bmatrix} = \begin{bmatrix} -3.75 \\ -2.625 \end{bmatrix}$

The new coordinates are $(-3.75, -2.625)$.

35. $\begin{bmatrix} 3 \\ 4 \end{bmatrix}$

36. $\begin{bmatrix} 3.5 \\ 2.25 \end{bmatrix} + \begin{bmatrix} 3 \\ 4 \end{bmatrix} = \begin{bmatrix} 6.5 \\ 6.25 \end{bmatrix}$

The coordinates are (6.5, 6.25).

37. $\begin{bmatrix} 0 & -1 \\ 1 & 0 \end{bmatrix} \cdot \begin{bmatrix} 7 \\ 8 \end{bmatrix} = \begin{bmatrix} -8 \\ 7 \end{bmatrix}$

$\begin{bmatrix} 0 & -1 \\ 1 & 0 \end{bmatrix} \cdot \begin{bmatrix} -8 \\ 7 \end{bmatrix} = \begin{bmatrix} -7 \\ -8 \end{bmatrix}$

$\begin{bmatrix} 0 & -1 \\ 1 & 0 \end{bmatrix} \cdot \begin{bmatrix} -7 \\ -8 \end{bmatrix} = \begin{bmatrix} 8 \\ -7 \end{bmatrix}$

The coordinates are $(-8, 7)$, $(-7, -8)$, and $(8, -7)$.

38. The object is reflected over the x-axis, then translated 6 units to the right.

39. Multiply the coordinates by $\begin{bmatrix} 1 & 0 \\ 0 & -1 \end{bmatrix}$, then add the result to $\begin{bmatrix} 6 \\ 0 \end{bmatrix}$.

40. No; since the translation does not change the y-coordinate, it does not matter whether you do the translation or the reflection over the x-axis first. However, if the translation did change the y-coordinate, then order would be important.

41. $\begin{bmatrix} 1 & 0 \\ 0 & -1 \end{bmatrix} \cdot \begin{bmatrix} 11 \\ 2 \end{bmatrix} + \begin{bmatrix} 6 \\ 0 \end{bmatrix} = \begin{bmatrix} 11 \\ -2 \end{bmatrix} + \begin{bmatrix} 6 \\ 0 \end{bmatrix}$

$= \begin{bmatrix} 17 \\ -2 \end{bmatrix}$

$\begin{bmatrix} 1 & 0 \\ 0 & -1 \end{bmatrix} \cdot \begin{bmatrix} 17 \\ -2 \end{bmatrix} + \begin{bmatrix} 6 \\ 0 \end{bmatrix} = \begin{bmatrix} 17 \\ 2 \end{bmatrix} + \begin{bmatrix} 6 \\ 0 \end{bmatrix}$

$= \begin{bmatrix} 23 \\ 2 \end{bmatrix}$

The coordinates are $(17, -2)$ and $(23, 2)$.

42. There is no single matrix to achieve this. However, you could reflect the object over the y-axis and then translate it 2(3) or 6 units to the right.

43. Transformations are used in computer graphics to create special effects. You can simulate the movement of an object, like in space, which you wouldn't be able to recreate otherwise. Answers should include the following.
- A figure with points (a, b), (c, d), (e, f), (g, h), and (i, j) could be written in a 2×5 matrix $\begin{bmatrix} a & c & e & g & i \\ b & d & f & h & j \end{bmatrix}$ and multiplied on the left by the 2×2 rotation matrix.
- The object would get smaller and appear to be moving away from you.

44. B; $\begin{bmatrix} 1 & 0 \\ 0 & -1 \end{bmatrix} \cdot \begin{bmatrix} -1 & 0 \\ 0 & 1 \end{bmatrix} = \begin{bmatrix} -1 & 0 \\ 0 & -1 \end{bmatrix}$

45. A; $3\begin{bmatrix} -4 & -4 & 3 \\ 2 & -3 & -2 \end{bmatrix} = \begin{bmatrix} -12 & -12 & 9 \\ 6 & -9 & -6 \end{bmatrix}$

46. 2×2

47. Undefined; the inner dimensions are not equal.

48. 2×5

49. $2\begin{bmatrix} 4 & 9 & -8 \\ 6 & -11 & -2 \\ 12 & -10 & 3 \end{bmatrix} + 3\begin{bmatrix} 1 & 2 & 3 \\ 2 & 3 & 4 \\ 3 & 4 & 5 \end{bmatrix}$

$= \begin{bmatrix} 8 & 18 & -16 \\ 12 & -22 & -4 \\ 24 & -20 & 6 \end{bmatrix} + \begin{bmatrix} 3 & 6 & 9 \\ 6 & 9 & 12 \\ 9 & 12 & 15 \end{bmatrix}$

$= \begin{bmatrix} 11 & 24 & -7 \\ 18 & -13 & 8 \\ 33 & -8 & 21 \end{bmatrix}$

50. $4\begin{bmatrix} 3 & 4 & -7 \\ 6 & -9 & -2 \\ -3 & 1 & 3 \end{bmatrix} - \begin{bmatrix} -8 & 6 & -4 \\ -7 & 10 & 1 \\ -2 & 1 & 5 \end{bmatrix}$

$= \begin{bmatrix} 12 & 16 & -28 \\ 24 & -36 & -8 \\ -12 & 4 & 12 \end{bmatrix} - \begin{bmatrix} -8 & 6 & -4 \\ -7 & 10 & 1 \\ -2 & 1 & 5 \end{bmatrix}$

$= \begin{bmatrix} 20 & 10 & -24 \\ 31 & -46 & -9 \\ -10 & 3 & 7 \end{bmatrix}$

51.

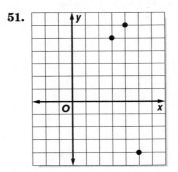

$D = \{3, 4, 5\}$, $R = \{-4, 5, 6\}$

Yes; the relation is a function.

52. $x = -5y + 2$

x	y
2	0
-3	1

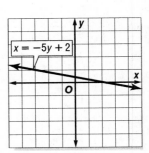

$D = \{\text{all real numbers}\}$, $R = \{\text{all real numbers}\}$

Yes; the relation is a function.

53. $x = y^2$

x	y
4	-2
1	-1
0	0
1	1
4	2

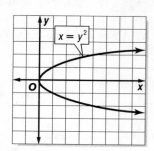

$D = \{x \mid x \geq 0\}$, $R = \{$all real numbers$\}$

No, the graph of the equation does not pass the vertical line test.

54. $|x| \geq 4$

55. $|x| < 2.8$

56. $|x - (-1)| > 2$ or $|x + 1| > 2$

57. $|x - 1| < 1$

58. Let m be the number of miles that Mr. Romero drives per day.

$$0.15m + 12.95 \leq 90$$
$$0.15m \leq 77.05$$
$$m \leq 513.6\overline{7}$$
$$m \leq 513\tfrac{2}{3}$$

Mr. Romero can drive at most $513\tfrac{2}{3}$ miles per day.

59. $\frac{x}{8} = \frac{3}{4}$
$4x = 8(3)$
$4x = 24$
$x = 6$

60. $\frac{4}{20} = \frac{1}{m}$
$\frac{1}{5} = \frac{1}{m}$
$m(1) = 5(1)$
$m = 5$

61. $\frac{2}{3} = \frac{a}{42}$
$42(2) = 3a$
$84 = 3a$
$28 = a$

62. $\frac{5}{6} = \frac{k}{4}$
$4(5) = 6k$
$20 = 6k$
$\frac{20}{6} = k$
$\frac{10}{3} = k$

63. $\frac{2}{y} = \frac{8}{9}$
$9(2) = 8y$
$18 = 8y$
$\frac{18}{8} = y$
$\frac{9}{4} = y$

64. $\frac{x}{5} = \frac{x + 1}{8}$
$8x = 5(x + 1)$
$8x = 5x + 5$
$3x = 5$
$x = \frac{5}{3}$

4-5 Determinants

Pages 185–186 Check for Understanding

1. Sample answer: $\begin{bmatrix} 2 & 1 \\ 8 & 4 \end{bmatrix}$; $\begin{vmatrix} 2 & 1 \\ 8 & 4 \end{vmatrix} = 2(4) - 1(8)$ or 0

2. Khalid; the value of the determinant is the difference of the products of the diagonals.

3. It is not a square matrix.

4. Sample answer: $\begin{bmatrix} 3 & 1 \\ 6 & 5 \end{bmatrix}$, $\begin{bmatrix} 4 & 3 \\ 1 & 3 \end{bmatrix}$; both have determinant 9.

5. Cross out the column and row that contains 6. The minor is the remaining 2×2 matrix, $\begin{bmatrix} 11 & 7 \\ 3 & 8 \end{bmatrix}$.

6. First calculate the determinant using expansion by minors.

$$\begin{vmatrix} -2 & 3 & 5 \\ 0 & -1 & 4 \\ 9 & 7 & 2 \end{vmatrix} = -2\begin{vmatrix} -1 & 4 \\ 7 & 2 \end{vmatrix} - 3\begin{vmatrix} 0 & 4 \\ 9 & 2 \end{vmatrix} + 5\begin{vmatrix} 0 & -1 \\ 9 & 7 \end{vmatrix}$$

$$= -2(-2 - 28) - 3(0 - 36) + 5(0 - (-9))$$
$$= -2(-30) - 3(-36) + 5(9)$$
$$= 60 + 108 + 45$$
$$= 213$$

Next calculate the determinant using diagonals.

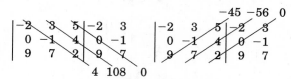

$4 + 108 + 0 - (-45) - (-56) - 0 = 213$

The two methods yield the same result.

7. $\begin{vmatrix} 7 & 8 \\ 3 & -2 \end{vmatrix} = 7(-2) - 8(3)$
$= -14 - 24$
$= -38$

8. $\begin{vmatrix} -3 & -6 \\ 4 & 8 \end{vmatrix} = -3(8) - (-6)(4)$
$= -24 + 24$
$= 0$

9. $\begin{vmatrix} 0 & 8 \\ 5 & 9 \end{vmatrix} = 0(9) - 8(5)$
$= 0 - 40$
$= -40$

10. $\begin{vmatrix} 0 & -4 & 0 \\ 3 & -2 & 5 \\ 2 & -1 & 1 \end{vmatrix} = 0\begin{vmatrix} -2 & 5 \\ -1 & 1 \end{vmatrix} - (-4)\begin{vmatrix} 3 & 5 \\ 2 & 1 \end{vmatrix} + 0\begin{vmatrix} 3 & -2 \\ 2 & -1 \end{vmatrix}$
$= 0 + 4(3 - 10) + 0$
$= 4(-7)$
$= -28$

11. $\begin{vmatrix} 2 & 3 & 4 \\ 6 & 5 & 7 \\ 1 & 2 & 8 \end{vmatrix} = 2\begin{vmatrix} 5 & 7 \\ 2 & 8 \end{vmatrix} - 3\begin{vmatrix} 6 & 7 \\ 1 & 8 \end{vmatrix} + 4\begin{vmatrix} 6 & 5 \\ 1 & 2 \end{vmatrix}$

$\qquad = 2(40 - 14) - 3(48 - 7) + 4(12 - 5)$

$\qquad = 2(26) - 3(41) + 4(7)$

$\qquad = 52 - 123 + 28$

$\qquad = -43$

12. $\begin{vmatrix} 1 & 6 & 4 \\ -2 & 3 & 1 \\ 1 & 6 & 4 \end{vmatrix}\begin{matrix} 1 & 6 \\ -2 & 3 \\ 1 & 6 \end{matrix} \qquad \begin{vmatrix} 1 & 6 & 4 \\ -2 & 3 & 1 \\ 1 & 6 & 4 \end{vmatrix}\begin{matrix} 1 & 6 \\ -2 & 3 \\ 1 & 6 \end{matrix}$

$\qquad 12 + 6 + (-48) - 12 - 6 - (-48) = 0$

13. $\begin{vmatrix} -1 & 4 & 0 \\ 3 & -2 & -5 \\ -3 & -1 & 2 \end{vmatrix}\begin{matrix} -1 & 4 \\ 3 & -2 \\ -3 & -1 \end{matrix} \qquad \begin{vmatrix} -1 & 4 & 0 \\ 3 & -2 & -5 \\ -3 & -1 & 2 \end{vmatrix}\begin{matrix} -1 & 4 \\ 3 & -2 \\ -3 & -1 \end{matrix}$

$\qquad 4 + 60 + 0 - 0 - (-5) - 24 = 45$

14. $A = \frac{1}{2}\begin{vmatrix} 5 & 4 & 1 \\ 3 & -4 & 1 \\ -3 & -2 & 1 \end{vmatrix}$

$\qquad = \frac{1}{2}\left[5\begin{vmatrix} -4 & 1 \\ -2 & 1 \end{vmatrix} - 4\begin{vmatrix} 3 & 1 \\ -3 & 1 \end{vmatrix} + 1\begin{vmatrix} 3 & -4 \\ -3 & -2 \end{vmatrix} \right]$

$\qquad = \frac{1}{2}[5(-4 + 2) - 4(3 + 3) + 1(-6 - 12)]$

$\qquad = \frac{1}{2}[-10 - 24 - 18]$

$\qquad = -26$

The area of the triangle is 26 units^2.

Pages 186–188 Practice and Apply

15. $\begin{vmatrix} 10 & 6 \\ 5 & 5 \end{vmatrix} = 10(5) - 6(5)$

$\qquad = 50 - 30$

$\qquad = 20$

16. $\begin{vmatrix} 8 & 5 \\ 6 & 1 \end{vmatrix} = 8(1) - 5(6)$

$\qquad = 8 - 30$

$\qquad = -22$

17. $\begin{vmatrix} -7 & 3 \\ -9 & 7 \end{vmatrix} = -7(-7) - 3(-9)$

$\qquad = -49 + 27$

$\qquad = -22$

18. $\begin{vmatrix} -2 & 4 \\ 3 & -6 \end{vmatrix} = -2(-6) - 4(3)$

$\qquad = 12 - 12$

$\qquad = 0$

19. $\begin{vmatrix} 2 & -7 \\ -5 & 3 \end{vmatrix} = 2(3) - (-7)(-5)$

$\qquad = 6 - 35$

$\qquad = -29$

20. $\begin{vmatrix} -6 & -2 \\ 8 & 5 \end{vmatrix} = -6(5) - (-2)(8)$

$\qquad = -30 + 16$

$\qquad = -14$

21. $\begin{vmatrix} -9 & 0 \\ -12 & -7 \end{vmatrix} = -9(-7) - 0(-12)$

$\qquad = 63 - 0$

$\qquad = 63$

22. $\begin{vmatrix} 6 & 14 \\ -3 & -8 \end{vmatrix} = 6(-8) - 14(-3)$

$\qquad = -48 + 42$

$\qquad = -6$

23. $\begin{vmatrix} 15 & 11 \\ 23 & 19 \end{vmatrix} = 15(19) - 11(23)$

$\qquad = 285 - 253$

$\qquad = 32$

24. $\begin{vmatrix} 21 & 43 \\ 16 & 31 \end{vmatrix} = 21(31) - 43(16)$

$\qquad = 651 - 688$

$\qquad = -37$

25. $\begin{vmatrix} 7 & 5.2 \\ -4 & 1.6 \end{vmatrix} = 7(1.6) - 5.2(-4)$

$\qquad = 11.2 + 20.8$

$\qquad = 32$

26. $\begin{vmatrix} -3.2 & -5.8 \\ 4.1 & 3.9 \end{vmatrix} = -3.2(3.9) - (-5.8)(4.1)$

$\qquad = -12.48 + 23.78$

$\qquad = 11.3$

27. $\begin{vmatrix} 3 & 1 & 2 \\ 0 & 6 & 4 \\ 2 & 5 & 1 \end{vmatrix} = 3\begin{vmatrix} 6 & 4 \\ 5 & 1 \end{vmatrix} - 1\begin{vmatrix} 0 & 4 \\ 2 & 1 \end{vmatrix} + 2\begin{vmatrix} 0 & 6 \\ 2 & 5 \end{vmatrix}$

$\qquad = 3(6 - 20) - 1(0 - 8) + 2(0 - 12)$

$\qquad = 3(-14) - 1(-8) + 2(-12)$

$\qquad = -42 + 8 - 24$

$\qquad = -58$

28. $\begin{vmatrix} 7 & 3 & -4 \\ -2 & 9 & 6 \\ 0 & 0 & 0 \end{vmatrix} = 0\begin{vmatrix} 3 & -4 \\ 9 & 6 \end{vmatrix} - 0\begin{vmatrix} 7 & -4 \\ -2 & 6 \end{vmatrix} + 0\begin{vmatrix} 7 & 3 \\ -2 & 9 \end{vmatrix}$

$\qquad = 0 + 0 + 0$

$\qquad = 0$

29. $\begin{vmatrix} -2 & 7 & -2 \\ 4 & 5 & 2 \\ 1 & 0 & -1 \end{vmatrix} = 1\begin{vmatrix} 7 & -2 \\ 5 & 2 \end{vmatrix} - 0\begin{vmatrix} -2 & -2 \\ 4 & 2 \end{vmatrix} + (-1)\begin{vmatrix} -2 & 7 \\ 4 & 5 \end{vmatrix}$

$\qquad = 1(14 + 10) - 0 - 1(-10 - 28)$

$\qquad = 24 + 38$

$\qquad = 62$

30. $\begin{vmatrix} -3 & 0 & 6 \\ 6 & 5 & -2 \\ 1 & 4 & 2 \end{vmatrix} = -3\begin{vmatrix} 5 & -2 \\ 4 & 2 \end{vmatrix} - 0\begin{vmatrix} 6 & -2 \\ 1 & 2 \end{vmatrix} + 6\begin{vmatrix} 6 & 5 \\ 1 & 4 \end{vmatrix}$

$\qquad = -3(10 + 8) - 0 + 6(24 - 5)$

$\qquad = -3(18) + 6(19)$

$\qquad = -54 + 114$

$\qquad = 60$

31. $\begin{vmatrix} 1 & 5 & -4 \\ -7 & 3 & 2 \\ 6 & 3 & -1 \end{vmatrix} = 1\begin{vmatrix} 3 & 2 \\ 3 & -1 \end{vmatrix} - 5\begin{vmatrix} -7 & 2 \\ 6 & -1 \end{vmatrix} + (-4)\begin{vmatrix} -7 & 3 \\ 6 & 3 \end{vmatrix}$

$= 1(-3 - 6) - 5(7 - 12) - 4(-21 - 18)$

$= 1(-9) - 5(-5) - 4(-39)$

$= -9 + 25 + 156$

$= 172$

32. $\begin{vmatrix} 3 & 7 & 6 \\ -1 & 6 & 2 \\ 8 & -3 & -5 \end{vmatrix} = 3\begin{vmatrix} 6 & 2 \\ -3 & -5 \end{vmatrix} - 7\begin{vmatrix} -1 & 2 \\ 8 & -5 \end{vmatrix} + 6\begin{vmatrix} -1 & 6 \\ 8 & -3 \end{vmatrix}$

$= 3(-30 + 6) - 7(5 - 16) + 6(3 - 48)$

$= 3(-24) - 7(-11) + 6(-45)$

$= -72 + 77 - 270$

$= -265$

33.

$$\begin{array}{ccc} & 72 & 35 & 12 \end{array}$$
$$\begin{vmatrix} 1 & 1 & 1 \\ 3 & 9 & 5 \\ 8 & 7 & 4 \end{vmatrix} \begin{array}{cc} 1 & 1 \\ 3 & 9 \\ 8 & 7 \end{array} \quad \begin{vmatrix} 1 & 1 & 1 \\ 3 & 9 & 5 \\ 8 & 7 & 4 \end{vmatrix} \begin{array}{cc} 1 & 1 \\ 3 & 9 \\ 8 & 7 \end{array}$$
$$\begin{array}{ccc} 36 & 40 & 21 \end{array}$$

$36 + 40 + 21 - 72 - 35 - 12 = -22$

34.

$$\begin{array}{ccc} & -70 & 72 & 90 \end{array}$$
$$\begin{vmatrix} 1 & 5 & 2 \\ -6 & -7 & 8 \\ 5 & 9 & -3 \end{vmatrix} \begin{array}{cc} 1 & 5 \\ -6 & -7 \\ 5 & 9 \end{array} \quad \begin{vmatrix} 1 & 5 & 2 \\ -6 & -7 & 8 \\ 5 & 9 & -3 \end{vmatrix} \begin{array}{cc} 1 & 5 \\ -6 & -7 \\ 5 & 9 \end{array}$$
$$\begin{array}{ccc} 21 & 200 & -108 \end{array}$$

$21 + 200 - 108 - (-70) - 72 - 90 = 21$

35.

$$\begin{array}{ccc} & 0 & -64 & -27 \end{array}$$
$$\begin{vmatrix} 8 & -9 & 0 \\ 1 & 5 & 4 \\ 6 & -2 & 3 \end{vmatrix} \begin{array}{cc} 8 & -9 \\ 1 & 5 \\ 6 & -2 \end{array} \quad \begin{vmatrix} 8 & -9 & 0 \\ 1 & 5 & 4 \\ 6 & -2 & 3 \end{vmatrix} \begin{array}{cc} 8 & -9 \\ 1 & 5 \\ 6 & -2 \end{array}$$
$$\begin{array}{ccc} 120 & -216 & 0 \end{array}$$

$120 - 216 + 0 - 0 - (-64) - (-27) = -5$

36.

$$\begin{array}{ccc} & 0 & 20 & 60 \end{array}$$
$$\begin{vmatrix} 4 & 10 & 7 \\ 3 & 3 & 1 \\ 0 & 5 & 2 \end{vmatrix} \begin{array}{cc} 4 & 10 \\ 3 & 3 \\ 0 & 5 \end{array} \quad \begin{vmatrix} 4 & 10 & 7 \\ 3 & 3 & 1 \\ 0 & 5 & 2 \end{vmatrix} \begin{array}{cc} 4 & 10 \\ 3 & 3 \\ 0 & 5 \end{array}$$
$$\begin{array}{ccc} 24 & 0 & 105 \end{array}$$

$24 + 0 + 105 - 0 - 20 - 60 = 49$

37.

$$\begin{array}{ccc} & 20 & 30 & -12 \end{array}$$
$$\begin{vmatrix} 2 & -3 & 4 \\ -2 & 1 & 5 \\ 5 & 3 & -2 \end{vmatrix} \begin{array}{cc} 2 & -3 \\ -2 & 1 \\ 5 & 3 \end{array} \quad \begin{vmatrix} 2 & -3 & 4 \\ -2 & 1 & 5 \\ 5 & 3 & -2 \end{vmatrix} \begin{array}{cc} 2 & -3 \\ -2 & 1 \\ 5 & 3 \end{array}$$
$$\begin{array}{ccc} -4 & -75 & -24 \end{array}$$

$-4 - 75 - 24 - 20 - 30 - (-12) = -141$

38.

$$\begin{array}{ccc} & 27 & 64 & 8 \end{array}$$
$$\begin{vmatrix} 4 & -2 & 3 \\ -2 & 3 & 4 \\ 3 & 4 & 2 \end{vmatrix} \begin{array}{cc} 4 & -2 \\ -2 & 3 \\ 3 & 4 \end{array} \quad \begin{vmatrix} 4 & -2 & 3 \\ -2 & 3 & 4 \\ 3 & 4 & 2 \end{vmatrix} \begin{array}{cc} 4 & -2 \\ -2 & 3 \\ 3 & 4 \end{array}$$
$$\begin{array}{ccc} 24 & -24 & -24 \end{array}$$

$24 - 24 - 24 - 27 - 64 - 8 = -123$

39. $\det \begin{bmatrix} 2 & x \\ 5 & -3 \end{bmatrix} = 24$

$2(-3) - x(5) = 24$

$-6 - 5x = 24$

$-5x = 30$

$x = -6$

40. $\det \begin{bmatrix} 4 & x & -2 \\ -x & -3 & 1 \\ -6 & 2 & 3 \end{bmatrix} = -3$

$4\begin{vmatrix} -3 & 1 \\ 2 & 3 \end{vmatrix} - x\begin{vmatrix} -x & 1 \\ -6 & 3 \end{vmatrix} + (-2)\begin{vmatrix} -x & -3 \\ -6 & 2 \end{vmatrix} = -3$

$4(-9 - 2) - x(-3x + 6) - 2(-2x - 18) = -3$

$-44 + 3x^2 - 6x + 4x + 36 = -3$

$3x^2 - 2x - 8 = -3$

$3x^2 - 2x - 5 = 0$

$(3x - 5)(x + 1) = 0$

$3x - 5 = 0 \quad \text{or} \quad x + 1 = 0$

$3x = 5 \qquad\qquad x = -1$

$x = \frac{5}{3}$

41. The polygon is comprised of two triangles. Find the area of each triangle. Then add.

First triangle:

$A = \frac{1}{2}\begin{vmatrix} 4 & 5 & 1 \\ 2 & 2 & 1 \\ -2 & 2 & 1 \end{vmatrix}$

$= \frac{1}{2}\left[4\begin{vmatrix} 2 & 1 \\ 2 & 1 \end{vmatrix} - 5\begin{vmatrix} 2 & 1 \\ -2 & 1 \end{vmatrix} + 1\begin{vmatrix} 2 & 2 \\ -2 & 2 \end{vmatrix}\right]$

$= \frac{1}{2}[4(2 - 2) - 5(2 + 2) + (4 + 4)]$

$= \frac{1}{2}(0 - 20 + 8)$

$= \frac{1}{2}(-12) \text{ or } -6$

$|A| = 6$

Second triangle:

$A = \frac{1}{2}\begin{vmatrix} 4 & 5 & 1 \\ 2 & 2 & 1 \\ 5 & -2 & 1 \end{vmatrix}$

$= \frac{1}{2}\left[4\begin{vmatrix} 2 & 1 \\ -2 & 1 \end{vmatrix} - 5\begin{vmatrix} 2 & 1 \\ 2 & 1 \end{vmatrix} + 1\begin{vmatrix} 2 & 2 \\ 5 & -2 \end{vmatrix}\right]$

$= \frac{1}{2}[4(2 + 2) - 5(2 - 5) + (-4 - 10)]$

$= \frac{1}{2}(16 + 15 - 14)$

$= \frac{1}{2}(17) \text{ or } 8.5$

$|A| = 8.5$

Thus, the area of the polygon is $6 + 8.5$ or 14.5 square units.

42. Write an expression for the area of the triangle.

$$A = \frac{1}{2}\begin{vmatrix} & \\ & \end{vmatrix}$$

$$= \frac{1}{2}\left[6\begin{vmatrix} & \\ & \end{vmatrix} - 5\begin{vmatrix} & \\ & \end{vmatrix} + 1\begin{vmatrix} & \\ & \end{vmatrix}\right]$$

$$= \frac{1}{2}[6(2 - 11) - 5(8 - x) + (88 - 2x)]$$

$$= \frac{1}{2}(-54 - 40 + 5x + 88 - 2x)$$

$$= \frac{1}{2}(3x - 6) \text{ or } 1.5x - 3$$

Thus, the area is $|1.5x - 3|$.

$$|1.5x - 3| = 15$$
$$1.5x - 3 = \pm15$$
$$1.5x - 3 = 15 \quad \text{or} \quad 1.5x - 3 = -15$$
$$1.5x = 18 \qquad\qquad 1.5x = -12$$
$$x = 12 \qquad\qquad\quad x = -8$$

The area is 15 square units when x is either -8 or 12.

43. Find the area of the triangle formed by the three vertices. Then multiply by 2 to find the area of the rectangle.

$$A = \frac{1}{2}\begin{vmatrix} -1 & 6 & 1 \\ 4 & 5 & 1 \\ -3 & -4 & 1 \end{vmatrix}$$

$$= \frac{1}{2}\left[(-1)\begin{vmatrix} 5 & 1 \\ -4 & 1 \end{vmatrix} - 6\begin{vmatrix} 4 & 1 \\ -3 & 1 \end{vmatrix} + 1\begin{vmatrix} 4 & 5 \\ -3 & -4 \end{vmatrix}\right]$$

$$= \frac{1}{2}[-1(5 + 4) - 6(4 + 3) + (-16 + 15)]$$

$$= \frac{1}{2}(-9 - 42 - 1)$$

$$= \frac{1}{2}(-52) \text{ or } -26$$

$$|A| = 26$$

Thus, the area of the floor is about 2 · 26 or 52 square feet.

44. Find the area of the triangle on the grid. Then convert the area to square miles.

$$A = \frac{1}{2}\begin{vmatrix} 0 & 0 & 1 \\ 7 & 5 & 1 \\ 2.5 & 10 & 1 \end{vmatrix}$$

$$= \frac{1}{2}\left[0\begin{vmatrix} 5 & 1 \\ 10 & 1 \end{vmatrix} - 0\begin{vmatrix} 7 & 1 \\ 2.5 & 1 \end{vmatrix} + 1\begin{vmatrix} 7 & 5 \\ 2.5 & 10 \end{vmatrix}\right]$$

$$= \frac{1}{2}[0 - 0 + (70 - 12.5)]$$

$$= \frac{1}{2}[57.5]$$

$$= 28.75$$

Since each square unit represents 100 square miles, the area of the territory is 28.75 · 100 or 2875 square miles.

45. Sample answer: $\begin{vmatrix} 1 & 1 & 1 \\ 1 & 1 & 1 \\ 1 & 1 & 1 \end{vmatrix}$

46. Multiply each member in the top row by its minor and position sign. In this case the minor is a 3×3 matrix. Evaluate the 3×3 matrix using expansion by minors again.

47. If you know the coordinates of the vertices of a triangle, you can use a determinant to find the area. This is convenient since you don't need to know any additional information such as the measure of the angles. Answers should include the following.
- You could place a coordinate grid over a map of the Bermuda Triangle with one vertex at the origin. By using the scale of the map, you could determine coordinates to represent the other two vertices and use a determinant to estimate the area.
- The determinant method is advantageous since you don't need to physically measure the lengths of each side or the measure of the angles between the vertices.

48. C; $\det A = 0\begin{vmatrix} 0 & 1 \\ 2 & 0 \end{vmatrix} - 3\begin{vmatrix} -4 & 1 \\ 3 & 0 \end{vmatrix} + (-2)\begin{vmatrix} -4 & 0 \\ 3 & 2 \end{vmatrix}$

$$= 0 - 3(0 - 3) - 2(-8 - 0)$$

$$= 0 + 9 + 16$$

$$= 25$$

49. C; $A = \frac{1}{2}\begin{vmatrix} 2 & 3 & 1 \\ 1 & -3 & 1 \\ -3 & 1 & 1 \end{vmatrix}$

$$= \frac{1}{2}\left[2\begin{vmatrix} -3 & 1 \\ 1 & 1 \end{vmatrix} - 3\begin{vmatrix} 1 & 1 \\ -3 & 1 \end{vmatrix} + 1\begin{vmatrix} 1 & -3 \\ -3 & 1 \end{vmatrix}\right]$$

$$= \frac{1}{2}[2(-3 - 1) - 3(1 + 3) + (1 - 9)]$$

$$= \frac{1}{2}(-8 - 12 - 8)$$

$$= \frac{1}{2}(-28)$$

$$= -14$$

The area is $|-14|$ or 14 square units.

50. KEYSTROKES: MATRX ▶ ▶ 1 2 ENTER 2 ENTER 3 ENTER (−) 6.5 ENTER 8 ENTER 3.75 ENTER 2nd [QUIT] MATRX ▶ 1 MATRX 1) ENTER

The value of the determinant is 63.25.

51. KEYSTROKES: MATRX ▶ ▶ 1 2 ENTER 2 ENTER 1.3 ENTER 7.2 ENTER 6.1 ENTER 5.4 ENTER 2nd [QUIT] MATRX ▶ 1 MATRX 1) ENTER

The value of the determinant is -36.9.

52. KEYSTROKES: MATRX ▶ ▶ 1 2 ENTER 2 ENTER 6.1 ENTER 4.8 ENTER 9.7 ENTER 3.5 ENTER 2nd [QUIT] MATRX ▶ 1 MATRX 1) ENTER

The value of the determinant is -25.21.

53. KEYSTROKES: MATRX ▶ ▶ 1 3 ENTER 3 ENTER
8 ENTER 6 ENTER (−) 5 ENTER 10
ENTER (−) 7 ENTER 3 ENTER 9
ENTER 14 ENTER (−) 6 ENTER
2nd [QUIT] MATRX ▶ 1
MATRX 1) ENTER

The value of the determinant is −493.

54. KEYSTROKES: MATRX ▶ ▶ 1 3 ENTER 3 ENTER
10 ENTER 20 ENTER 30 ENTER 40
ENTER 50 ENTER 60 ENTER 70
ENTER 80 ENTER 90 ENTER 2nd
[QUIT] MATRX ▶ 1 MATRX 1
) ENTER

The value of the determinant is 0.

55. KEYSTROKES: MATRX ▶ ▶ 1 3 ENTER 3 ENTER
10 ENTER 12 ENTER 4 ENTER (−) 3
ENTER 18 ENTER (−) 9 ENTER 16
ENTER (−) 2 ENTER (−) 1 ENTER
2nd [QUIT] MATRX ▶ 1
MATRX 1) ENTER

The value of the determinant is −3252.

Page 188   Maintain Your Skills

56. $\begin{bmatrix} -2 & 1 & 2 \\ 1 & 2 & -3 \end{bmatrix}$

57. $2.5 \begin{bmatrix} -2 & 1 & 2 \\ 1 & 2 & -3 \end{bmatrix} = \begin{bmatrix} -5 & 2.5 & 5 \\ 2.5 & 5 & -7.5 \end{bmatrix}$

The coordinates are $A'(-5, 2.5)$, $B'(2.5, 5)$, and $C'(5, -7.5)$.

58.

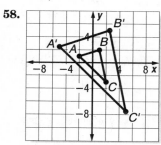

59. $[5 \ 2] \cdot \begin{bmatrix} -2 \\ 3 \end{bmatrix} = [5(-2) + 2(3)]$
$= [-4]$

60. $\begin{bmatrix} 2 & 4 \\ -2 & 3 \end{bmatrix} \cdot \begin{bmatrix} 3 & 9 \\ -1 & 2 \end{bmatrix}$

$= \begin{bmatrix} 2(3) + 4(-1) & 2(9) + 4(2) \\ -2(3) + 3(-1) & -2(9) + 3(2) \end{bmatrix}$

$= \begin{bmatrix} 6 - 4 & 18 + 8 \\ -6 - 3 & -18 + 6 \end{bmatrix}$

$= \begin{bmatrix} 2 & 26 \\ -9 & -12 \end{bmatrix}$

61. Undefined; the inner dimensions are not equal.

62. Undefined; the inner dimensions are not equal.

63. $[4 \ 2 \ 0] \cdot \begin{bmatrix} 3 & -2 \\ 1 & 0 \\ 5 & 6 \end{bmatrix}$

$= [4(3) + 2(1) + 0(5) \quad 4(-2) + 2(0) + 0(6)]$
$= [12 + 2 + 0 \quad -8 + 0 + 0]$
$= [14 \quad -8]$

64. $\begin{bmatrix} 7 & -5 & 4 \\ 6 & 1 & 3 \end{bmatrix} \cdot \begin{bmatrix} -1 & 3 \\ -2 & -8 \\ 1 & 2 \end{bmatrix}$

$= \begin{bmatrix} 7(-1) + (-5)(-2) + 4(1) & 7(3) + (-5)(-8) + 4(2) \\ 6(-1) + 1(-2) + 3(1) & 6(3) + 1(-8) + 3(2) \end{bmatrix}$

$= \begin{bmatrix} -7 + 10 + 4 & 21 + 40 + 8 \\ -6 - 2 + 3 & 18 - 8 + 6 \end{bmatrix}$

$= \begin{bmatrix} 7 & 69 \\ -5 & 16 \end{bmatrix}$

65. $f(m, y) = 5280m + 3y$
$f(26, 385) = 5280(26) + 3(385)$
$= 137{,}280 + 1155$
$= 138{,}435$

A marathon is 138,435 feet.

66. $y - y_1 = m(x - x_1)$
$y - 3 = 1(x - 5)$
$y = x - 2$

67. $y - y_1 = m(x - x_1)$
$y - (-8) = -\frac{4}{3}(x - 6)$
$y + 8 = -\frac{4}{3}x + 8$
$y = -\frac{4}{3}x$

68. First find the slope.
$m = \frac{y_2 - y_1}{x_2 - x_1}$
$= \frac{-3 - 7}{-2 - 3}$
$= \frac{-10}{-5}$
$= 2$

Now write the equation.
$y - y_1 = m(x - x_1)$
$y - 7 = 2(x - 3)$
$y - 7 = 2x - 6$
$y = 2x + 1$

69. First find the slope.
$$m = \frac{y_2 - y_1}{x_2 - x_1}$$
$$= \frac{10 - 5}{10 - 0}$$
$$= \frac{5}{10}$$
$$= \frac{1}{2}$$
Now write the equation.
$$y - y_1 = m(x - x_1)$$
$$y - 5 = \frac{1}{2}(x - 0)$$
$$y = \frac{1}{2}x + 5$$

70. First eliminate x.
$x + y = -3$
$3x + 4y = -12$
Multiply by -3.
$$\begin{array}{r} -3x - 3y = 9 \\ (+)\ 3x + 4y = -12 \\ \hline y = -3 \end{array}$$
Substitute -3 for y in the first equation.
$x + y = -3$
$x - 3 = -3$
$x = 0$
The solution is $(0, -3)$.

71. First eliminate y.
$$\begin{array}{r} x + y = 10 \\ (-)\ 2x + y = 11 \\ \hline -x = -1 \\ x = 1 \end{array}$$
Substitute 1 for x in the first equation.
$x + y = 10$
$1 + y = 10$
$y = 9$
The solution is $(1, 9)$.

72. First eliminate y.
$$\begin{array}{r} 2x + y = 5 \\ (-)\ 4x + y = 9 \\ \hline -2x = -4 \\ x = 2 \end{array}$$
Substitute 2 for x in the first equation.
$2x + y = 5$
$2(2) + y = 5$
$4 + y = 5$
$y = 1$
The solution is $(2, 1)$.

73. Solve the second equation for y.
$2x - y = -3$
$2x + 3 = y$
Substitute $2x + 3$ for y in the first equation.
$3x + 5y = 2$
$3x + 5(2x + 3) = 2$
$3x + 10x + 15 = 2$
$13x = -13$
$x = -1$

Substitute -1 for x in the second equation.
$2x - y = -3$
$2(-1) - y = -3$
$-2 + 3 = y$
$1 = y$
The solution is $(-1, 1)$.

74. First eliminate x.
$6x + 2y = 22$
$3x + 7y = 41$
Multiply by -2.
$$\begin{array}{r} 6x + 2y = 22 \\ (+)\ -6x - 14y = -82 \\ \hline -12y = -60 \\ y = 5 \end{array}$$
Substitute 5 for y in the first equation.
$6x + 2y = 22$
$6x + 2(5) = 22$
$6x + 10 = 22$
$6x = 12$
$x = 2$
The solution is $(2, 5)$.

75. First eliminate y.
$3x - 2y = -2$
$4x + 7y = 65$
Multiply by 7.
Multiply by 2.
$$\begin{array}{r} 21x - 14y = -14 \\ (+)\ 8x + 14y = 130 \\ \hline 29x = 116 \\ x = 4 \end{array}$$
Substitute 4 for x in the first equation.
$3x - 2y = -2$
$3(4) - 2y = -2$
$12 - 2y = -2$
$-2y = -14$
$y = 7$
The solution is $(4, 7)$.

4-6 Cramer's Rule

Page 192 Check for Understanding

1. The determinant of the coefficient matrix cannot be zero.

2. Sample answer:
$2x + y = 5$
$6x + 3y = 8$
Check the determinant of the coefficient matrix.
$$\begin{vmatrix} 2 & 1 \\ 6 & 3 \end{vmatrix} = 6 - 6 \text{ or } 0$$

3. $3x + 5y = -6$
$4x - 2y = 30$

4. $x = \dfrac{\begin{vmatrix} 1 & -4 \\ 13 & 3 \end{vmatrix}}{\begin{vmatrix} 1 & -4 \\ 2 & 3 \end{vmatrix}}$ $\qquad y = \dfrac{\begin{vmatrix} 1 & 1 \\ 2 & 13 \end{vmatrix}}{\begin{vmatrix} 1 & -4 \\ 2 & 3 \end{vmatrix}}$

$\quad = \dfrac{1(3) - (-4)(13)}{1(3) - (-4)(2)} \qquad = \dfrac{1(13) - 1(2)}{1(3) - (-4)(2)}$

$\quad = \dfrac{55}{11} \qquad\qquad\qquad = \dfrac{11}{11}$

$\quad = 5 \qquad\qquad\qquad\quad = 1$

The solution is $(5, 1)$.

5. First rewrite the system in standard form.

$0.2a - 0.3b = 0$

$0.4a - 0.2b = 0.2$

$$a = \frac{\begin{vmatrix} 0 & -0.3 \\ 0.2 & -0.2 \end{vmatrix}}{\begin{vmatrix} 0.2 & -0.3 \\ 0.4 & -0.2 \end{vmatrix}} \qquad b = \frac{\begin{vmatrix} 0.2 & 0 \\ 0.4 & 0.2 \end{vmatrix}}{\begin{vmatrix} 0.2 & -0.3 \\ 0.4 & -0.2 \end{vmatrix}}$$

$$= \frac{0(-0.2) - (-0.3)(0.2)}{(0.2)(-0.2) - (-0.3)(0.4)} \qquad = \frac{(0.2)(0.2) - 0(0.4)}{(0.2)(-0.2) - (-0.3)(0.4)}$$

$$= \frac{0.06}{0.08} \qquad = \frac{0.04}{0.08}$$

$$= 0.75 \qquad = 0.5$$

The solution is $(0.75, 0.5)$.

6. $r = \dfrac{\begin{vmatrix} \frac{7}{3} & -\frac{2}{3} \\ -10 & \frac{4}{5} \end{vmatrix}}{\begin{vmatrix} \frac{1}{2} & -\frac{2}{3} \\ \frac{3}{5} & \frac{4}{5} \end{vmatrix}}$ $\qquad s = \dfrac{\begin{vmatrix} \frac{1}{2} & \frac{7}{3} \\ \frac{3}{5} & -10 \end{vmatrix}}{\begin{vmatrix} \frac{1}{2} & -\frac{2}{3} \\ \frac{3}{5} & \frac{4}{5} \end{vmatrix}}$

$$= \frac{\left(\frac{7}{3}\right)\left(\frac{4}{5}\right) - \left(-\frac{2}{3}\right)(-10)}{\left(\frac{1}{2}\right)\left(\frac{4}{5}\right) - \left(-\frac{2}{3}\right)\left(\frac{3}{5}\right)} \qquad = \frac{\left(\frac{1}{2}\right)(-10) - \left(\frac{7}{3}\right)\left(\frac{3}{5}\right)}{\left(\frac{1}{2}\right)\left(\frac{4}{5}\right) - \left(-\frac{2}{3}\right)\left(\frac{3}{5}\right)}$$

$$= \frac{-4.8}{0.8} \qquad = \frac{-6.4}{0.8}$$

$$= -6 \qquad = -8$$

The solution is $(-6, -8)$.

7. You cannot use Cramer's Rule to solve this system of equations because the determinant of the coefficient matrix is 0.

$$\begin{vmatrix} 2 & -1 & 3 \\ 3 & 2 & -5 \\ 1 & -4 & 11 \end{vmatrix} = 0$$

8. $a = \dfrac{\begin{vmatrix} 2 & 9 & -2 \\ 1 & -3 & 4 \\ -5 & 3 & -6 \end{vmatrix}}{\begin{vmatrix} 1 & 9 & -2 \\ -1 & -3 & 4 \\ 2 & 3 & -6 \end{vmatrix}}$ $\quad b = \dfrac{\begin{vmatrix} 1 & 2 & -2 \\ -1 & 1 & 4 \\ 2 & -5 & -6 \end{vmatrix}}{\begin{vmatrix} 1 & 9 & -2 \\ -1 & -3 & 4 \\ 2 & 3 & -6 \end{vmatrix}}$ $\quad c = \dfrac{\begin{vmatrix} 1 & 9 & 2 \\ -1 & -3 & 1 \\ 2 & 3 & -5 \end{vmatrix}}{\begin{vmatrix} 1 & 9 & -2 \\ -1 & -3 & 4 \\ 2 & 3 & -6 \end{vmatrix}}$

$$= \frac{-90}{18} \qquad = \frac{12}{18} \qquad = \frac{-9}{18}$$

$$= -5 \qquad = \frac{2}{3} \qquad = -\frac{1}{2}$$

The solution is $\left(-5, \frac{2}{3}, -\frac{1}{2}\right)$.

9. $r = \dfrac{\begin{vmatrix} 10 & 4 & 3 \\ 15 & -2 & 1 \\ -1 & 2 & -3 \end{vmatrix}}{\begin{vmatrix} 1 & 4 & 3 \\ 2 & -2 & 1 \\ 1 & 2 & -3 \end{vmatrix}}$ $\quad s = \dfrac{\begin{vmatrix} 1 & 10 & 3 \\ 2 & 15 & 1 \\ 1 & -1 & -3 \end{vmatrix}}{\begin{vmatrix} 1 & 4 & 3 \\ 2 & -2 & 1 \\ 1 & 2 & -3 \end{vmatrix}}$ $\quad t = \dfrac{\begin{vmatrix} 1 & 4 & 10 \\ 2 & -2 & 15 \\ 1 & 2 & -1 \end{vmatrix}}{\begin{vmatrix} 1 & 4 & 3 \\ 2 & -2 & 1 \\ 1 & 2 & -3 \end{vmatrix}}$

$$= \frac{300}{50} \qquad = \frac{-25}{50} \qquad = \frac{100}{50}$$

$$= 6 \qquad = -\frac{1}{2} \qquad = 2$$

The solution is $\left(6, -\frac{1}{2}, 2\right)$.

10. $s + d = 4000$

$0.065s + 0.08d = 297.50$

11. Solve the system by using Cramer's Rule.

$$s = \frac{\begin{vmatrix} 4000 & 1 \\ 297.50 & 0.08 \end{vmatrix}}{\begin{vmatrix} 1 & 1 \\ 0.065 & 0.08 \end{vmatrix}} \qquad d = \frac{\begin{vmatrix} 1 & 4000 \\ 0.065 & 297.50 \end{vmatrix}}{\begin{vmatrix} 1 & 1 \\ 0.065 & 0.08 \end{vmatrix}}$$

$$= \frac{22.5}{0.015} \qquad = \frac{37.5}{0.015}$$

$$= 1500 \qquad = 2500$$

Jarrod should put $1500 in his savings account and $2500 in a certificate of deposit.

Pages 192–194　Practice and Apply

12. $x = \dfrac{\begin{vmatrix} 8 & 2 \\ 7 & -3 \end{vmatrix}}{\begin{vmatrix} 5 & 2 \\ 2 & -3 \end{vmatrix}}$ $\qquad y = \dfrac{\begin{vmatrix} 5 & 8 \\ 2 & 7 \end{vmatrix}}{\begin{vmatrix} 5 & 2 \\ 2 & -3 \end{vmatrix}}$

$$= \frac{8(-3) - 2(7)}{5(-3) - 2(2)} \qquad = \frac{5(7) - 8(2)}{5(-3) - 2(2)}$$

$$= \frac{-38}{-19} \qquad = \frac{19}{-19}$$

$$= 2 \qquad = -1$$

The solution is $(2, -1)$.

13. $m = \dfrac{\begin{vmatrix} 4 & 7 \\ -20 & -2 \end{vmatrix}}{\begin{vmatrix} 2 & 7 \\ 1 & -2 \end{vmatrix}}$ $\qquad n = \dfrac{\begin{vmatrix} 2 & 4 \\ 1 & -20 \end{vmatrix}}{\begin{vmatrix} 2 & 7 \\ 1 & -2 \end{vmatrix}}$

$$= \frac{4(-2) - 7(-20)}{2(-2) - 7(1)} \qquad = \frac{2(-20) - 4(1)}{2(-2) - 7(1)}$$

$$= \frac{132}{-11} \qquad = \frac{-44}{-11}$$

$$= -12 \qquad = 4$$

The solution is $(-12, 4)$.

14. $r = \dfrac{\begin{vmatrix} 1 & -1 \\ 19 & 2 \end{vmatrix}}{\begin{vmatrix} 2 & -1 \\ 3 & 2 \end{vmatrix}}$ $\qquad s = \dfrac{\begin{vmatrix} 2 & 1 \\ 3 & 19 \end{vmatrix}}{\begin{vmatrix} 2 & -1 \\ 3 & 2 \end{vmatrix}}$

$$= \frac{1(2) - (-1)(19)}{2(2) - (-1)(3)} \qquad = \frac{2(19) - 1(3)}{2(2) - (-1)(3)}$$

$$= \frac{21}{7} \qquad = \frac{35}{7}$$

$$= 3 \qquad = 5$$

The solution is $(3, 5)$.

15. $a = \dfrac{\begin{vmatrix} 33 & 5 \\ 51 & 7 \end{vmatrix}}{\begin{vmatrix} 3 & 5 \\ 5 & 7 \end{vmatrix}}$ $\qquad b = \dfrac{\begin{vmatrix} 3 & 33 \\ 5 & 51 \end{vmatrix}}{\begin{vmatrix} 3 & 5 \\ 5 & 7 \end{vmatrix}}$

$$= \frac{33(7) - 5(51)}{3(7) - 5(5)} \qquad = \frac{3(51) - 33(5)}{3(7) - 5(5)}$$

$$= \frac{-24}{-4} \qquad = \frac{-12}{-4}$$

$$= 6 \qquad = 3$$

The solution is $(6, 3)$.

16. Rewrite the system in standard form.

$2m - 4n = -1$

$-4m + 3n = -5$

$$m = \frac{\begin{vmatrix} -1 & -4 \\ -5 & 3 \end{vmatrix}}{\begin{vmatrix} 2 & -4 \\ -4 & 3 \end{vmatrix}} \qquad n = \frac{\begin{vmatrix} 2 & -1 \\ -4 & -5 \end{vmatrix}}{\begin{vmatrix} 2 & -4 \\ -4 & 3 \end{vmatrix}}$$

$$= \frac{-1(3) - (-4)(-5)}{2(3) - (-4)(-4)} \qquad = \frac{2(-5) - (-1)(-4)}{2(3) - (-4)(-4)}$$

$$= \frac{-23}{-10} \qquad = \frac{-14}{-10}$$

$$= 2.3 \qquad = 1.4$$

The solution is $(2.3, 1.4)$.

17. $x = \dfrac{\begin{vmatrix} 6 & 3 \\ -9 & -1 \end{vmatrix}}{\begin{vmatrix} 4 & 3 \\ 8 & -1 \end{vmatrix}}$ $\qquad y = \dfrac{\begin{vmatrix} 4 & 6 \\ 8 & -9 \end{vmatrix}}{\begin{vmatrix} 4 & 3 \\ 8 & -1 \end{vmatrix}}$

$\quad = \dfrac{6(-1) - 3(-9)}{4(-1) - 3(8)} \qquad = \dfrac{4(-9) - 6(8)}{4(-1) - 3(8)}$

$\quad = \dfrac{21}{-28} \qquad\qquad\quad = \dfrac{-84}{-28}$

$\quad = -0.75 \qquad\qquad\quad = 3$

The solution is $(-0.75, 3)$.

18. $r = \dfrac{\begin{vmatrix} -1 & -1 \\ -0.25 & 0.5 \end{vmatrix}}{\begin{vmatrix} 0.5 & -1 \\ 0.75 & 0.5 \end{vmatrix}}$ $\qquad s = \dfrac{\begin{vmatrix} 0.5 & -1 \\ 0.75 & -0.25 \end{vmatrix}}{\begin{vmatrix} 0.5 & -1 \\ 0.75 & 0.5 \end{vmatrix}}$

$\quad = \dfrac{-1(0.5) - (-1)(-0.25)}{0.5(0.5) - (-1)(0.75)} \quad = \dfrac{0.5(-0.25) - (-1)(0.75)}{0.5(0.5) - (-1)(0.75)}$

$\quad = \dfrac{-0.75}{1} \qquad\qquad\quad = \dfrac{0.625}{1}$

$\quad = -0.75 \qquad\qquad\quad = 0.625$

The solution is $(-0.75, 0.625)$.

19. $m = \dfrac{\begin{vmatrix} 0.5 & -0.7 \\ -7.4 & -0.6 \end{vmatrix}}{\begin{vmatrix} 1.5 & -0.7 \\ 2.2 & -0.6 \end{vmatrix}}$ $\qquad n = \dfrac{\begin{vmatrix} 1.5 & 0.5 \\ 2.2 & -7.4 \end{vmatrix}}{\begin{vmatrix} 1.5 & -0.7 \\ 2.2 & -0.6 \end{vmatrix}}$

$\quad = \dfrac{(0.5)(-0.6) - (-0.7)(-7.4)}{1.5(-0.6) - (-0.7)(2.2)} \quad = \dfrac{1.5(-7.4) - 0.5(2.2)}{1.5(-0.6) - (-0.7)(2.2)}$

$\quad = \dfrac{-5.48}{0.64} \qquad\qquad\quad = \dfrac{-12.2}{0.64}$

$\quad = -8.5625 \qquad\qquad\quad = -19.0625$

The solution is $(-8.5625, -19.0625)$.

20. $x = \dfrac{\begin{vmatrix} 4 & -2 \\ 1 & -\frac{2}{3} \end{vmatrix}}{\begin{vmatrix} 3 & -2 \\ \frac{1}{2} & -\frac{2}{3} \end{vmatrix}}$ $\qquad y = \dfrac{\begin{vmatrix} 3 & 4 \\ \frac{1}{2} & 1 \end{vmatrix}}{\begin{vmatrix} 3 & -2 \\ \frac{1}{2} & -\frac{2}{3} \end{vmatrix}}$

$\quad = \dfrac{4\left(-\frac{2}{3}\right) - (-2)(1)}{3\left(-\frac{2}{3}\right) - (-2)\left(\frac{1}{2}\right)} \quad = \dfrac{3(1) - 4\left(\frac{1}{2}\right)}{3\left(-\frac{2}{3}\right) - (-2)\left(\frac{1}{2}\right)}$

$\quad = \dfrac{-\frac{2}{3}}{-1} \qquad\qquad\quad = \dfrac{1}{-1}$

$\quad = \dfrac{2}{3} \qquad\qquad\qquad = -1$

The solution is $\left(\dfrac{2}{3}, -1\right)$.

21. $a = \dfrac{\begin{vmatrix} -16 & 3 \\ 1 & -\frac{7}{8} \end{vmatrix}}{\begin{vmatrix} 2 & 3 \\ \frac{3}{4} & -\frac{7}{8} \end{vmatrix}}$ $\qquad b = \dfrac{\begin{vmatrix} 2 & -16 \\ \frac{3}{4} & 10 \end{vmatrix}}{\begin{vmatrix} 2 & 3 \\ \frac{3}{4} & -\frac{7}{8} \end{vmatrix}}$

$\quad = \dfrac{-16\left(-\frac{7}{8}\right) - 3(10)}{2\left(-\frac{7}{8}\right) - 3\left(\frac{3}{4}\right)} \quad = \dfrac{2(10) - (-16)\left(\frac{3}{4}\right)}{2\left(-\frac{7}{8}\right) - 3\left(\frac{3}{4}\right)}$

$\quad = \dfrac{-16}{\frac{-16}{4}} \qquad\qquad\quad = \dfrac{32}{\frac{-16}{4}}$

$\quad = 4 \qquad\qquad\qquad = -8$

The solution is $(4, -8)$.

22. $r = \dfrac{\begin{vmatrix} 5 & \frac{2}{5} \\ -3 & -\frac{1}{2} \end{vmatrix}}{\begin{vmatrix} \frac{1}{3} & \frac{2}{5} \\ \frac{2}{3} & -\frac{1}{2} \end{vmatrix}}$ $\qquad s = \dfrac{\begin{vmatrix} \frac{1}{3} & 5 \\ \frac{2}{3} & -3 \end{vmatrix}}{\begin{vmatrix} \frac{1}{3} & \frac{2}{5} \\ \frac{2}{3} & -\frac{1}{2} \end{vmatrix}}$

$\quad = \dfrac{5\left(-\frac{1}{2}\right) - \frac{2}{5}(-3)}{\frac{1}{3}\left(-\frac{1}{2}\right) - \frac{2}{5}\left(\frac{2}{3}\right)} \quad = \dfrac{\frac{1}{3}(-3) - 5\left(\frac{2}{3}\right)}{\frac{1}{3}\left(-\frac{1}{2}\right) - \frac{2}{5}\left(\frac{2}{3}\right)}$

$\quad = \dfrac{-\frac{13}{10}}{-\frac{13}{30}} \qquad\qquad\quad = \dfrac{-\frac{13}{3}}{-\frac{13}{30}}$

$\quad = 3 \qquad\qquad\qquad = 10$

The solution is $(3, 10)$.

23. $x = \dfrac{\begin{vmatrix} \frac{11}{12} & \frac{1}{2} \\ \frac{1}{8} & -\frac{1}{4} \end{vmatrix}}{\begin{vmatrix} \frac{3}{4} & \frac{1}{2} \\ \frac{1}{2} & -\frac{1}{4} \end{vmatrix}}$ $\qquad y = \dfrac{\begin{vmatrix} \frac{3}{4} & \frac{11}{12} \\ \frac{1}{2} & \frac{1}{8} \end{vmatrix}}{\begin{vmatrix} \frac{3}{4} & \frac{1}{2} \\ \frac{1}{2} & -\frac{1}{4} \end{vmatrix}}$

$\quad = \dfrac{\left(\frac{11}{12}\right)\left(-\frac{1}{4}\right) - \left(\frac{1}{2}\right)\left(\frac{1}{8}\right)}{\left(\frac{3}{4}\right)\left(-\frac{1}{4}\right) - \left(\frac{1}{2}\right)\left(\frac{1}{2}\right)} \quad = \dfrac{\left(\frac{3}{4}\right)\left(\frac{1}{8}\right) - \left(\frac{11}{12}\right)\left(\frac{1}{2}\right)}{\left(\frac{3}{4}\right)\left(-\frac{1}{4}\right) - \left(\frac{1}{2}\right)\left(\frac{1}{2}\right)}$

$\quad = \dfrac{-\frac{14}{48}}{-\frac{7}{16}} \qquad\qquad\quad = \dfrac{-\frac{35}{96}}{-\frac{7}{16}}$

$\quad = \dfrac{2}{3} \qquad\qquad\qquad = \dfrac{5}{6}$

The solution is $\left(\dfrac{2}{3}, \dfrac{5}{6}\right)$.

24. The vertex of the angle is the point of intersection of the lines. To find the point, solve the system of equations.

$4x + y = -4$

$2x - 3y = -9$

$x = \dfrac{\begin{vmatrix} -4 & 1 \\ -9 & -3 \end{vmatrix}}{\begin{vmatrix} 4 & 1 \\ 2 & -3 \end{vmatrix}}$ $\qquad y = \dfrac{\begin{vmatrix} 4 & -4 \\ 2 & -9 \end{vmatrix}}{\begin{vmatrix} 4 & 1 \\ 2 & -3 \end{vmatrix}}$

$\quad = \dfrac{-4(-3) - 1(-9)}{4(-3) - 1(2)} \quad = \dfrac{4(-9) - (-4)(2)}{4(-3) - 1(2)}$

$\quad = \dfrac{21}{-14} \qquad\qquad\quad = \dfrac{-28}{-14}$

$\quad = -1.5 \qquad\qquad\quad = 2$

The coordinates of the vertex are $(-1.5, 2)$.

25. One vertex of the parallelogram is the point of intersection of the lines. To find this point, solve the system of equations.

$2.3x + 1.2y = 2.1$

$4.1x - 0.5y = 14.3$

$x = \dfrac{\begin{vmatrix} 2.1 & 1.2 \\ 14.3 & -0.5 \end{vmatrix}}{\begin{vmatrix} 2.3 & 1.2 \\ 4.1 & -0.5 \end{vmatrix}}$ $\qquad y = \dfrac{\begin{vmatrix} 2.3 & 2.1 \\ 4.1 & 14.3 \end{vmatrix}}{\begin{vmatrix} 2.3 & 1.2 \\ 4.1 & -0.5 \end{vmatrix}}$

$\quad = \dfrac{(2.1)(-0.5) - (1.2)(14.3)}{(2.3)(-0.5) - (1.2)(4.1)} \quad = \dfrac{(2.3)(14.3) - (2.1)(4.1)}{(2.3)(-0.5) - (1.2)(4.1)}$

$\quad = \dfrac{-18.21}{-6.07} \qquad\qquad\quad = \dfrac{24.28}{-6.07}$

$\quad = 3 \qquad\qquad\qquad = -4$

The coordinates of one vertex are $(3, -4)$.

26. $x = \dfrac{\begin{vmatrix} 6 & 1 & 1 \\ -15 & 1 & -4 \\ -10 & -3 & 1 \end{vmatrix}}{\begin{vmatrix} 1 & 1 & 1 \\ 2 & 1 & -4 \\ 5 & -3 & 1 \end{vmatrix}}$ $y = \dfrac{\begin{vmatrix} 1 & 6 & 1 \\ 2 & -15 & -4 \\ 5 & -10 & 1 \end{vmatrix}}{\begin{vmatrix} 1 & 1 & 1 \\ 2 & 1 & -4 \\ 5 & -3 & 1 \end{vmatrix}}$ $z = \dfrac{\begin{vmatrix} 1 & 1 & 6 \\ 2 & 1 & -15 \\ 5 & -3 & -10 \end{vmatrix}}{\begin{vmatrix} 1 & 1 & 1 \\ 2 & 1 & -4 \\ 5 & -3 & 1 \end{vmatrix}}$

$= \dfrac{44}{-44}$ $= \dfrac{-132}{-44}$ $= \dfrac{-176}{-44}$

$= -1$ $= 3$ $= 4$

The solution is $(-1, 3, 4)$.

27. $a = \dfrac{\begin{vmatrix} 7 & -2 & 1 \\ 4 & 2 & -2 \\ 14 & 6 & 4 \end{vmatrix}}{\begin{vmatrix} 1 & -2 & 1 \\ 6 & 2 & -2 \\ 4 & 6 & 4 \end{vmatrix}}$ $b = \dfrac{\begin{vmatrix} 1 & 7 & 1 \\ 6 & 4 & -2 \\ 4 & 14 & 4 \end{vmatrix}}{\begin{vmatrix} 1 & -2 & 1 \\ 6 & 2 & -2 \\ 4 & 6 & 4 \end{vmatrix}}$ $c = \dfrac{\begin{vmatrix} 1 & -2 & 7 \\ 6 & 2 & 4 \\ 4 & 6 & 14 \end{vmatrix}}{\begin{vmatrix} 1 & -2 & 1 \\ 6 & 2 & -2 \\ 4 & 6 & 4 \end{vmatrix}}$

$= \dfrac{224}{112}$ $= \dfrac{-112}{112}$ $= \dfrac{336}{112}$

$= 2$ $= -1$ $= 3$

The solution is $(2, -1, 3)$.

28. $r = \dfrac{\begin{vmatrix} -1 & -2 & -5 \\ 5 & 2 & -2 \\ -1 & 1 & 1 \end{vmatrix}}{\begin{vmatrix} 1 & -2 & -5 \\ 1 & 2 & -2 \\ 4 & 1 & 1 \end{vmatrix}}$ $s = \dfrac{\begin{vmatrix} 1 & -1 & -5 \\ 1 & 5 & -2 \\ 4 & -1 & 1 \end{vmatrix}}{\begin{vmatrix} 1 & -2 & -5 \\ 1 & 2 & -2 \\ 4 & 1 & 1 \end{vmatrix}}$ $t = \dfrac{\begin{vmatrix} 1 & -2 & -1 \\ 1 & 2 & 5 \\ 4 & 1 & -1 \end{vmatrix}}{\begin{vmatrix} 1 & -2 & -5 \\ 1 & 2 & -2 \\ 4 & 1 & 1 \end{vmatrix}}$

$= \dfrac{-33}{57}$ $= \dfrac{117}{57}$ $= \dfrac{-42}{57}$

$= -\dfrac{11}{19}$ $= \dfrac{39}{19}$ $= -\dfrac{14}{19}$

The solution is $\left(-\dfrac{11}{19}, \dfrac{39}{19}, -\dfrac{14}{19}\right)$.

29. $a = \dfrac{\begin{vmatrix} 23 & 0 & 1 \\ -22 & 7 & -2 \\ 34 & -1 & -1 \end{vmatrix}}{\begin{vmatrix} 3 & 0 & 1 \\ 4 & 7 & -2 \\ 8 & -1 & -1 \end{vmatrix}}$ $b = \dfrac{\begin{vmatrix} 3 & 23 & 1 \\ 4 & -22 & -2 \\ 8 & 34 & -1 \end{vmatrix}}{\begin{vmatrix} 3 & 0 & 1 \\ 4 & 7 & -2 \\ 8 & -1 & -1 \end{vmatrix}}$ $c = \dfrac{\begin{vmatrix} 3 & 0 & 23 \\ 4 & 7 & -22 \\ 8 & -1 & 34 \end{vmatrix}}{\begin{vmatrix} 3 & 0 & 1 \\ 4 & 7 & -2 \\ 8 & -1 & -1 \end{vmatrix}}$

$= \dfrac{-423}{-87}$ $= \dfrac{306}{-87}$ $= \dfrac{-732}{-87}$

$= \dfrac{141}{29}$ $= -\dfrac{102}{29}$ $= \dfrac{244}{29}$

The solution is $\left(\dfrac{141}{29}, -\dfrac{102}{29}, \dfrac{244}{29}\right)$.

30. $x = \dfrac{\begin{vmatrix} -32 & 2 & -3 \\ 54 & -3 & 1 \\ 78 & 2 & 8 \end{vmatrix}}{\begin{vmatrix} 4 & 2 & -3 \\ -1 & -3 & 1 \\ 0 & 2 & 8 \end{vmatrix}}$ $y = \dfrac{\begin{vmatrix} 4 & -32 & -3 \\ -1 & 54 & 1 \\ 0 & 78 & 8 \end{vmatrix}}{\begin{vmatrix} 4 & 2 & -3 \\ -1 & -3 & 1 \\ 0 & 2 & 8 \end{vmatrix}}$ $z = \dfrac{\begin{vmatrix} 4 & 2 & -32 \\ -1 & -3 & 54 \\ 0 & 2 & 78 \end{vmatrix}}{\begin{vmatrix} 4 & 2 & -3 \\ -1 & -3 & 1 \\ 0 & 2 & 8 \end{vmatrix}}$

$= \dfrac{-902}{-82}$ $= \dfrac{1394}{-82}$ $= \dfrac{-1148}{-82}$

$= 11$ $= -17$ $= 14$

The solution is $(11, -17, 14)$.

31. $r = \dfrac{\begin{vmatrix} 40 & 25 & 0 \\ -2 & 12 & 6 \\ -10 & -25 & 50 \end{vmatrix}}{\begin{vmatrix} 2 & 25 & 0 \\ 10 & 12 & 6 \\ 36 & -25 & 50 \end{vmatrix}}$ $s = \dfrac{\begin{vmatrix} 2 & 40 & 0 \\ 10 & -2 & 6 \\ 36 & -10 & 50 \end{vmatrix}}{\begin{vmatrix} 2 & 25 & 0 \\ 10 & 12 & 6 \\ 36 & -25 & 50 \end{vmatrix}}$ $t = \dfrac{\begin{vmatrix} 2 & 25 & 40 \\ 10 & 12 & -2 \\ 36 & -25 & -10 \end{vmatrix}}{\begin{vmatrix} 2 & 25 & 0 \\ 10 & 12 & 6 \\ 36 & -25 & 50 \end{vmatrix}}$

$= \dfrac{31{,}000}{-5600}$ $= \dfrac{-11{,}440}{-5600}$ $= \dfrac{-26{,}920}{-5600}$

$= -\dfrac{155}{28}$ $= \dfrac{143}{70}$ $= \dfrac{673}{140}$

The solution is $\left(-\dfrac{155}{28}, \dfrac{143}{70}, \dfrac{673}{140}\right)$.

32. Let r represent the number of times Marcus plays the race car simulator, and let s represent the number of times he plays the snowboard simulator.

$r + s = 8$

$7r + 5s = 50$

33. $r = \dfrac{\begin{vmatrix} 8 & 1 \\ 50 & 5 \end{vmatrix}}{\begin{vmatrix} 1 & 1 \\ 7 & 5 \end{vmatrix}}$ $s = \dfrac{\begin{vmatrix} 1 & 8 \\ 7 & 50 \end{vmatrix}}{\begin{vmatrix} 1 & 1 \\ 7 & 5 \end{vmatrix}}$

$= \dfrac{8(5) - 1(50)}{1(5) - 1(7)}$ $= \dfrac{1(50) - 8(7)}{1(5) - 1(7)}$

$= \dfrac{-10}{-2}$ $= \dfrac{-6}{-2}$

$= 5$ $= 3$

Marcus can play 5 games of the race car simulator and 3 games of the snowboard simulator.

34. Let s and c represent the cost per yard of the silk and cotton, respectively.

$8s + 13c = 604.79$

$5.5s + 14c = 542.30$

35. $s = \dfrac{\begin{vmatrix} 604.79 & 13 \\ 542.30 & 14 \end{vmatrix}}{\begin{vmatrix} 8 & 13 \\ 5.5 & 14 \end{vmatrix}}$ $c = \dfrac{\begin{vmatrix} 8 & 604.79 \\ 5.5 & 542.30 \end{vmatrix}}{\begin{vmatrix} 8 & 13 \\ 5.5 & 14 \end{vmatrix}}$

$= \dfrac{(604.79)(14) - 13(542.30)}{8(14) - 13(5.5)}$ $= \dfrac{8(542.30) - (604.79)(5.5)}{8(14) - 13(5.5)}$

$= \dfrac{1417.16}{40.5}$ $= \dfrac{1012.055}{40.5}$

≈ 34.99 ≈ 24.99

The silk costs \$34.99 per yard and the cotton costs \$24.99 per yard.

36. Let p, r, and c represent the pounds of peanuts, raisins, and carob-coated pretzels, respectively, that Santito buys.

$p + r + c = 5$

$p - 2r = 0$

$3.2p + 2.4r + 4c = 16.8$

37. $p = \dfrac{\begin{vmatrix} 5 & 1 & 1 \\ 0 & -2 & 0 \\ 16.8 & 2.4 & 4 \end{vmatrix}}{\begin{vmatrix} 1 & 1 & 1 \\ 1 & -2 & 0 \\ 3.2 & 2.4 & 4 \end{vmatrix}}$ $r = \dfrac{\begin{vmatrix} 5 & 1 & 1 \\ 1 & 0 & 0 \\ 3.2 & 16.8 & 4 \end{vmatrix}}{\begin{vmatrix} 1 & 1 & 1 \\ 1 & -2 & 0 \\ 3.2 & 2.4 & 4 \end{vmatrix}}$ $c = \dfrac{\begin{vmatrix} 1 & 1 & 5 \\ 1 & -2 & 0 \\ 3.2 & 2.4 & 16.8 \end{vmatrix}}{\begin{vmatrix} 1 & 1 & 1 \\ 1 & -2 & 0 \\ 3.2 & 2.4 & 4 \end{vmatrix}}$

$= \dfrac{-6.4}{-3.2}$ $= \dfrac{-3.2}{-3.2}$ $= \dfrac{-6.4}{-3.2}$

$= 2$ $= 1$ $= 2$

Santito can buy 2 lbs of peanuts, 1 lb of raisins, and 2 lbs of carob-coated pretzels.

38. If the determinant is zero, there is no unique solution to the system. There is either no solution or there are infinitely many solutions. Sample answer: $2x + y = 4$ and $4x + 2y = 8$ has a det = 0; there are infinitely many solutions of this system. $2x + y = 4$ and $4x + 2y = 10$ has a det = 0; there are no solutions of this system.

39. Cramer's Rule is a formula for the variables x and y where (x, y) is a solution for a system of equations. Answers should include the following.
- Cramer's Rule uses determinants composed of the coefficients and constants in a system of linear equations to solve the system.
- Cramer's Rule is convenient when coefficients are large or involve fractions or decimals. Finding the value of the determinant is sometimes easier than trying to find a greatest common factor if you are solving by using elimination or substituting complicated numbers.

40. B; $x = \dfrac{\begin{vmatrix} 28 & 8 \\ -55 & -7 \end{vmatrix}}{\begin{vmatrix} 3 & 8 \\ 5 & -7 \end{vmatrix}}$ $y = \dfrac{\begin{vmatrix} 3 & 28 \\ 5 & -55 \end{vmatrix}}{\begin{vmatrix} 3 & 8 \\ 5 & -7 \end{vmatrix}}$

$= \dfrac{28(-7) - 8(-55)}{3(-7) - 8(5)}$ $= \dfrac{3(-55) - 28(5)}{3(-7) - 8(5)}$

$= \dfrac{244}{-61}$ $= \dfrac{-305}{-61}$

$= -4$ $= 5$

The solution is $(-4, 5)$.

41. Solve the following equation to find the measure of $\angle ABC$.

$x + \left(\dfrac{2}{3}x - 5\right) = 180$

$\dfrac{5}{3}x - 5 = 180$

$\dfrac{5}{3}x = 185$

$x = 111$

Substitute 111 for x in the expression $\dfrac{2}{3}x - 5$ to find the measure of $\angle CBD$.

$\dfrac{2}{3}x - 5 = \dfrac{2}{3}(111) - 5$ or 69

Thus $\angle ABC$ measures 111°, and $\angle CBD$ measures 69.

Page 194   Maintain Your Skills

42. $\begin{vmatrix} 3 & 2 \\ -2 & 4 \end{vmatrix} = 3(4) - 2(-2)$

$= 12 + 4$

$= 16$

43. $\begin{vmatrix} 8 & 6 \\ 4 & 8 \end{vmatrix} = 8(8) - 6(4)$

$= 64 - 24$

$= 40$

44. $\begin{vmatrix} -5 & 2 \\ 4 & 9 \end{vmatrix} = -5(9) - 2(4)$

$= -45 - 8$

$= -53$

45. To translate the triangle 1 unit right and 3 units up, add 1 to each x-coordinate and add 3 to each y-coordinate.

$\begin{bmatrix} 1 & 1 & 1 \\ 3 & 3 & 3 \end{bmatrix}$

46. $\begin{bmatrix} 0 & -3 & -2 \\ 2 & -1 & -4 \end{bmatrix} + \begin{bmatrix} 1 & 1 & 1 \\ 3 & 3 & 3 \end{bmatrix} = \begin{bmatrix} 1 & -2 & -1 \\ 5 & 2 & -1 \end{bmatrix}$

The coordinates are $A'(1, 5)$, $B'(-2, 2)$, and $C'(-1, -1)$.

47.
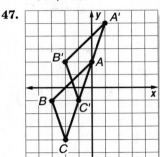

48.
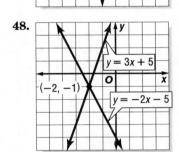

The graphs appear to intersect at $(-2, -1)$.

Check: $y = 3x + 5$ $y = -2x - 5$

$-1 \stackrel{?}{=} 3(-2) + 5$ $-1 \stackrel{?}{=} -2(-2) - 5$

$-1 = -1$ ✓ $-1 = -1$ ✓

The solution is $(-2, -1)$.

49.
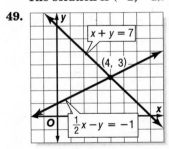

The graphs appear to intersect at $(4, 3)$.

Check: $x + y = 7$ $\dfrac{1}{2}x - y = -1$

$4 + 3 \stackrel{?}{=} 7$ $\dfrac{1}{2}(4) - 3 \stackrel{?}{=} -1$

$7 = 7$ ✓ $-1 = -1$ ✓

The solution is $(4, 3)$.

50.

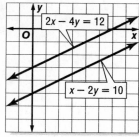

The lines are parallel; there is no solution.

51. $C = 10h + 35$

52. $[2 \quad 5] \cdot \begin{bmatrix} 3 & 1 \\ -2 & 6 \end{bmatrix} = [2(3) + 5(-2) \quad 2(1) + 5(6)]$

$= [-4 \quad 32]$

53. $\begin{bmatrix} 0 & 9 \\ 5 & 7 \end{bmatrix} \cdot \begin{bmatrix} 2 & -6 \\ 8 & 1 \end{bmatrix} = \begin{bmatrix} 0(2) + 9(8) & 0(-6) + 9(1) \\ 5(2) + 7(8) & 5(-6) + 7(1) \end{bmatrix}$

$= \begin{bmatrix} 72 & 9 \\ 66 & -23 \end{bmatrix}$

54. $\begin{bmatrix} 5 & -4 \\ 8 & 3 \end{bmatrix} \cdot \begin{bmatrix} 5 \\ 1 \end{bmatrix} = \begin{bmatrix} 5(5) + (-4)(1) \\ 8(5) + 3(1) \end{bmatrix}$

$= \begin{bmatrix} 21 \\ 43 \end{bmatrix}$

Page 194   Practice Quiz 2

1. $\begin{bmatrix} 1 & 4 & 1 & -2 \\ 2 & -1 & -4 & -1 \end{bmatrix}$

2. $\begin{bmatrix} -1 & 0 \\ 0 & 1 \end{bmatrix} \begin{bmatrix} 1 & 4 & 1 & -2 \\ 2 & -1 & -4 & -1 \end{bmatrix}$

$= \begin{bmatrix} -1(1) + 0(2) & -1(4) + 0(-1) & -1(1) + 0(-4) & -1(-2) + 0(-1) \\ 0(1) + 1(2) & 0(4) + 1(-1) & 0(1) + 1(-4) & 0(-2) + 1(-1) \end{bmatrix}$

$= \begin{bmatrix} -1 & -4 & -1 & 2 \\ 2 & -1 & -4 & -1 \end{bmatrix}$

The coordinates are $A'(-1, 2)$, $B'(-4, -1)$, $C'(-1, -4)$, and $D'(2, -1)$.

3.

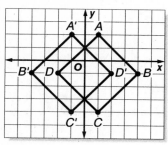

4. $\begin{vmatrix} 3 & -2 \\ 5 & 4 \end{vmatrix} = 3(4) - (-2)(5)$

$= 12 + 10$
$= 22$

5. $\begin{vmatrix} -8 & 3 \\ 6 & 5 \end{vmatrix} = -8(5) - 3(6)$

$= -40 - 18$
$= -58$

6. $\begin{vmatrix} 1 & 3 & -2 \\ 7 & 0 & 4 \\ -3 & 5 & -1 \end{vmatrix} = 1 \begin{vmatrix} 0 & 4 \\ 5 & -1 \end{vmatrix} - 3 \begin{vmatrix} 7 & 4 \\ -3 & -1 \end{vmatrix} + (-2) \begin{vmatrix} 7 & 0 \\ -3 & 5 \end{vmatrix}$

$= 1(0 - 20) - 3(-7 + 12) - 2(35 - 0)$
$= -20 - 15 - 70$
$= -105$

7. $\begin{vmatrix} 3 & 4 & 4 \\ 2 & 1 & 5 \\ 0 & -8 & 6 \end{vmatrix} = 0 \begin{vmatrix} 4 & 4 \\ 1 & 5 \end{vmatrix} - (-8) \begin{vmatrix} 3 & 4 \\ 2 & 5 \end{vmatrix} + 6 \begin{vmatrix} 3 & 4 \\ 2 & 1 \end{vmatrix}$

$= 0 + 8(15 - 8) + 6(3 - 8)$
$= 56 - 30$
$= 26$

8. $x = \dfrac{\begin{vmatrix} 7 & -2 \\ 6 & -1 \end{vmatrix}}{\begin{vmatrix} 3 & -2 \\ 4 & -1 \end{vmatrix}}$ $\qquad$ $y = \dfrac{\begin{vmatrix} 3 & 7 \\ 4 & 6 \end{vmatrix}}{\begin{vmatrix} 3 & -2 \\ 4 & -1 \end{vmatrix}}$

$= \dfrac{7(-1) - (-2)(6)}{3(-1) - (-2)(4)}$ $\qquad$ $= \dfrac{3(6) - 7(4)}{3(-1) - (-2)(4)}$

$= \dfrac{5}{5}$ $\qquad\qquad$ $= \dfrac{-10}{5}$

$= 1$ $\qquad\qquad\quad$ $= -2$

The solution is $(1, -2)$.

9. $r = \dfrac{\begin{vmatrix} 3 & 5 \\ 22 & -2 \end{vmatrix}}{\begin{vmatrix} 7 & 5 \\ 3 & -2 \end{vmatrix}}$ $\qquad$ $s = \dfrac{\begin{vmatrix} 7 & 3 \\ 3 & 22 \end{vmatrix}}{\begin{vmatrix} 7 & 5 \\ 3 & -2 \end{vmatrix}}$

$= \dfrac{3(-2) - 5(22)}{7(-2) - 5(3)}$ $\qquad$ $= \dfrac{7(22) - 3(3)}{7(-2) - 5(3)}$

$= \dfrac{-116}{-29}$ $\qquad\qquad$ $= \dfrac{145}{-29}$

$= 4$ $\qquad\qquad\quad$ $= -5$

The solution is $(4, -5)$.

10. $a = \dfrac{\begin{vmatrix} -5 & -5 & 2 \\ 9 & 1 & 3 \\ 1 & 0 & -1 \end{vmatrix}}{\begin{vmatrix} 3 & -5 & 2 \\ 4 & 1 & 3 \\ 2 & 0 & -1 \end{vmatrix}}$ $b = \dfrac{\begin{vmatrix} 3 & -5 & 2 \\ 4 & 9 & 3 \\ 2 & 1 & -1 \end{vmatrix}}{\begin{vmatrix} 3 & -5 & 2 \\ 4 & 1 & 3 \\ 2 & 0 & -1 \end{vmatrix}}$ $c = \dfrac{\begin{vmatrix} 3 & -5 & -5 \\ 4 & 1 & 9 \\ 2 & 0 & 1 \end{vmatrix}}{\begin{vmatrix} 3 & -5 & 2 \\ 4 & 1 & 3 \\ 2 & 0 & -1 \end{vmatrix}}$

$= \dfrac{-57}{-57}$ $\qquad$ $= \dfrac{-114}{-57}$ $\qquad$ $= \dfrac{-57}{-57}$

$= 1$ $\qquad\qquad$ $= 2$ $\qquad\qquad$ $= 1$

The solution is $(1, 2, 1)$.

4-7   Identity and Inverse Matrices

Pages 198–199   Check for Understanding

1. $\begin{bmatrix} 1 & 0 & 0 & 0 \\ 0 & 1 & 0 & 0 \\ 0 & 0 & 1 & 0 \\ 0 & 0 & 0 & 1 \end{bmatrix}$

2. Exchange the values for a and d in the first diagonal in the matrix. Multiply the values for b and c by -1 in the second diagonal in the matrix. Find the determinant of the original matrix. Multiply the negative reciprocal of the determinant by the matrix with the above mentioned changes.

3. Sample answer: $\begin{bmatrix} 3 & 3 \\ 3 & 3 \end{bmatrix}$ does not have an inverse because its determinant is 0.

4. $A \cdot B = \begin{bmatrix} 2 & -1 \\ 1 & -3 \end{bmatrix} \cdot \begin{bmatrix} \frac{1}{2} & 0 \\ 0 & -\frac{1}{3} \end{bmatrix}$

$= \begin{bmatrix} 1+0 & 0+\frac{1}{3} \\ \frac{1}{2}+0 & 0+1 \end{bmatrix}$

$= \begin{bmatrix} 1 & \frac{1}{3} \\ \frac{1}{2} & 1 \end{bmatrix}$

No; the matrices are not inverses, since $A \cdot B \neq I$.

5. $X \cdot Y = \begin{bmatrix} 3 & 1 \\ 5 & 2 \end{bmatrix} \cdot \begin{bmatrix} 2 & -1 \\ -5 & 3 \end{bmatrix}$

$= \begin{bmatrix} 6-5 & -3+3 \\ 10-10 & -5+6 \end{bmatrix}$

$= \begin{bmatrix} 1 & 0 \\ 0 & 1 \end{bmatrix}$

$Y \cdot X = \begin{bmatrix} 2 & -1 \\ -5 & 3 \end{bmatrix} \cdot \begin{bmatrix} 3 & 1 \\ 5 & 2 \end{bmatrix}$

$= \begin{bmatrix} 6-5 & 2-2 \\ -15+15 & -5+6 \end{bmatrix}$

$= \begin{bmatrix} 1 & 0 \\ 0 & 1 \end{bmatrix}$

Yes; the matrices are inverses, since both $X \cdot Y = I$ and $Y \cdot X = I$.

6. Find the value of the determinant.

$\begin{vmatrix} 8 & -5 \\ -3 & 2 \end{vmatrix} = 16 - 15$

$= 1$

Since the determinant is non-zero, the inverse exists.

$\frac{1}{ad-bc} \begin{bmatrix} d & -b \\ -c & a \end{bmatrix} = \frac{1}{8(2)-(-5)(-3)} \begin{bmatrix} 2 & -(-5) \\ -(-3) & 8 \end{bmatrix}$

$= \frac{1}{1} \begin{bmatrix} 2 & 5 \\ 3 & 8 \end{bmatrix}$

$= \begin{bmatrix} 2 & 5 \\ 3 & 8 \end{bmatrix}$

7. Find the value of the determinant.

$\begin{vmatrix} 4 & -8 \\ -1 & 2 \end{vmatrix} = 8 - 8$

$= 0$

Since the determinant is 0, the inverse does not exist.

8. Find the value of the determinant.

$\begin{vmatrix} -5 & 1 \\ 7 & 4 \end{vmatrix} = -20 - 7$

$= -27$

Since the determinant is non-zero, the inverse exists.

$\frac{1}{ad-bc} \begin{bmatrix} d & -b \\ -c & a \end{bmatrix} = \frac{1}{(-5)(4)-1(7)} \begin{bmatrix} 4 & -1 \\ -7 & -5 \end{bmatrix}$

$= -\frac{1}{27} \begin{bmatrix} 4 & -1 \\ -7 & -5 \end{bmatrix}$ or $\begin{bmatrix} -\frac{4}{27} & \frac{1}{27} \\ \frac{7}{27} & \frac{5}{27} \end{bmatrix}$

9. See students' work.

Pages 199–201   Practice and Apply

10. $P \cdot Q = \begin{bmatrix} 0 & 1 \\ 1 & 1 \end{bmatrix} \cdot \begin{bmatrix} -1 & 1 \\ 1 & 0 \end{bmatrix}$

$= \begin{bmatrix} 0+1 & 0+0 \\ -1+1 & 1+0 \end{bmatrix}$

$= \begin{bmatrix} 1 & 0 \\ 0 & 1 \end{bmatrix}$

$Q \cdot P = \begin{bmatrix} -1 & 1 \\ 1 & 0 \end{bmatrix} \cdot \begin{bmatrix} 0 & 1 \\ 1 & 1 \end{bmatrix}$

$= \begin{bmatrix} 0+1 & -1+1 \\ 0+0 & 1+0 \end{bmatrix}$

$= \begin{bmatrix} 1 & 0 \\ 0 & 1 \end{bmatrix}$

Yes; the matrices are inverses, since both $P \cdot Q = I$ and $Q \cdot P = I$.

11. $R \cdot S = \begin{bmatrix} 2 & 2 \\ 3 & 4 \end{bmatrix} \cdot \begin{bmatrix} 2 & -1 \\ -\frac{3}{2} & 1 \end{bmatrix}$

$= \begin{bmatrix} 4-3 & -2+2 \\ 6-6 & -3+4 \end{bmatrix}$

$= \begin{bmatrix} 1 & 0 \\ 0 & 1 \end{bmatrix}$

$S \cdot R = \begin{bmatrix} 2 & -1 \\ -\frac{3}{2} & 1 \end{bmatrix} \cdot \begin{bmatrix} 2 & 2 \\ 3 & 4 \end{bmatrix}$

$= \begin{bmatrix} 4-3 & 4-4 \\ -3+3 & -3+4 \end{bmatrix}$

$= \begin{bmatrix} 1 & 0 \\ 0 & 1 \end{bmatrix}$

Yes; the matrices are inverses, since both $R \cdot S = I$ and $S \cdot R = I$.

12. $A \cdot B = \begin{bmatrix} 6 & 2 \\ 5 & 2 \end{bmatrix} \cdot \begin{bmatrix} 2 & 1 \\ -\frac{5}{2} & -3 \end{bmatrix}$

$= \begin{bmatrix} 6-5 & 6-6 \\ 5-5 & 5-6 \end{bmatrix}$

$= \begin{bmatrix} 1 & 0 \\ 0 & -1 \end{bmatrix}$

No; the matrices are not inverses, since $A \cdot B \neq I$.

13. $X \cdot Y = \begin{bmatrix} \frac{1}{3} & -\frac{2}{3} \\ \frac{2}{3} & -\frac{1}{3} \end{bmatrix} \cdot \begin{bmatrix} 1 & 2 \\ 2 & 1 \end{bmatrix}$

$= \begin{bmatrix} \frac{1}{3} - \frac{4}{3} & \frac{2}{3} - \frac{2}{3} \\ \frac{2}{3} - \frac{2}{3} & \frac{4}{3} - \frac{1}{3} \end{bmatrix}$

$= \begin{bmatrix} -1 & 0 \\ 0 & 1 \end{bmatrix}$

No; the matrices are not inverses, since $X \cdot Y \neq I$.

14. $C \cdot D = \begin{bmatrix} 1 & 5 \\ 1 & -2 \end{bmatrix} \cdot \begin{bmatrix} \frac{2}{7} & \frac{5}{7} \\ \frac{1}{7} & -\frac{1}{7} \end{bmatrix}$

$= \begin{bmatrix} \frac{2}{7} + \frac{5}{7} & \frac{5}{7} - \frac{5}{7} \\ \frac{2}{7} - \frac{2}{7} & \frac{5}{7} + \frac{2}{7} \end{bmatrix}$

$= \begin{bmatrix} 1 & 0 \\ 0 & 1 \end{bmatrix}$

$D \cdot C = \begin{bmatrix} \frac{2}{7} & \frac{5}{7} \\ \frac{1}{7} & -\frac{1}{7} \end{bmatrix} \cdot \begin{bmatrix} 1 & 5 \\ 1 & -2 \end{bmatrix}$

$= \begin{bmatrix} \frac{2}{7} + \frac{5}{7} & \frac{10}{7} - \frac{10}{7} \\ \frac{1}{7} - \frac{1}{7} & \frac{5}{7} + \frac{2}{7} \end{bmatrix}$

$= \begin{bmatrix} 1 & 0 \\ 0 & 1 \end{bmatrix}$

Yes; the matrices are inverses, since both $C \cdot D = I$ and $D \cdot C = I$.

15. $J \cdot K = \begin{bmatrix} 1 & 2 & 3 \\ 2 & 3 & 1 \\ 1 & 1 & 2 \end{bmatrix} \cdot \begin{bmatrix} -\frac{5}{4} & \frac{1}{4} & \frac{7}{4} \\ \frac{3}{4} & \frac{1}{4} & -\frac{5}{4} \\ \frac{1}{4} & -\frac{1}{4} & \frac{1}{4} \end{bmatrix}$

$= \begin{bmatrix} -\frac{5}{4} + \frac{6}{4} + \frac{3}{4} & \frac{1}{4} + \frac{2}{4} - \frac{3}{4} & \frac{7}{4} - \frac{10}{4} + \frac{3}{4} \\ -\frac{10}{4} + \frac{9}{4} + \frac{1}{4} & \frac{2}{4} + \frac{3}{4} - \frac{1}{4} & \frac{14}{4} - \frac{15}{4} + \frac{1}{4} \\ -\frac{5}{4} + \frac{3}{4} + \frac{2}{4} & \frac{1}{4} + \frac{1}{4} - \frac{2}{4} & \frac{7}{4} - \frac{5}{4} + \frac{2}{4} \end{bmatrix}$

$= \begin{bmatrix} 1 & 0 & 0 \\ 0 & 1 & 0 \\ 0 & 0 & 1 \end{bmatrix}$

$K \cdot J = \begin{bmatrix} -\frac{5}{4} & \frac{1}{4} & \frac{7}{4} \\ \frac{3}{4} & \frac{1}{4} & -\frac{5}{4} \\ \frac{1}{4} & -\frac{1}{4} & \frac{1}{4} \end{bmatrix} \cdot \begin{bmatrix} 1 & 2 & 3 \\ 2 & 3 & 1 \\ 1 & 1 & 2 \end{bmatrix}$

$= \begin{bmatrix} -\frac{5}{4} + \frac{2}{4} + \frac{7}{4} & -\frac{10}{4} + \frac{3}{4} + \frac{7}{4} & -\frac{15}{4} + \frac{1}{4} + \frac{14}{4} \\ \frac{3}{4} + \frac{2}{5} - \frac{5}{4} & \frac{6}{4} + \frac{3}{4} - \frac{5}{4} & \frac{9}{4} + \frac{1}{4} - \frac{10}{4} \\ \frac{1}{4} - \frac{2}{4} + \frac{1}{4} & \frac{2}{4} - \frac{3}{4} + \frac{1}{4} & \frac{3}{4} - \frac{1}{4} + \frac{2}{4} \end{bmatrix}$

$= \begin{bmatrix} 1 & 0 & 0 \\ 0 & 1 & 0 \\ 0 & 0 & 1 \end{bmatrix}$

Yes; the matrices are inverses, since both $J \cdot K = I$ and $K \cdot J = I$.

16. True

17. True

18. True

19. False

20. Find the determinant.

$\begin{vmatrix} 5 & 0 \\ 0 & 1 \end{vmatrix} = 5 - 0$ or 5

Since the determinant does not equal 0, the inverse exists.

$\frac{1}{ad - bc} \begin{bmatrix} d & -b \\ -c & a \end{bmatrix} = \frac{1}{5(1) - 0(0)} \begin{bmatrix} 1 & 0 \\ 0 & 5 \end{bmatrix}$

$= \frac{1}{5} \begin{bmatrix} 1 & 0 \\ 0 & 5 \end{bmatrix}$ or $\begin{bmatrix} \frac{1}{5} & 0 \\ 0 & 1 \end{bmatrix}$

21. Find the determinant.

$\begin{vmatrix} 6 & 3 \\ 8 & 4 \end{vmatrix} = 24 - 24$ or 0

Since the determinant is 0, the inverse does not exist.

22. Find the determinant.

$\begin{vmatrix} 1 & 2 \\ 2 & 1 \end{vmatrix} = 1 - 4$ or -3

Since the determinant does not equal 0, the inverse exists.

$\frac{1}{ad - bc} \begin{bmatrix} d & -b \\ -c & a \end{bmatrix} = \frac{1}{1(1) - 2(2)} \begin{bmatrix} 1 & -2 \\ -2 & 1 \end{bmatrix}$

$= -\frac{1}{3} \begin{bmatrix} 1 & -2 \\ -2 & 1 \end{bmatrix}$ or $\begin{bmatrix} -\frac{1}{3} & \frac{2}{3} \\ \frac{2}{3} & -\frac{1}{3} \end{bmatrix}$

23. Find the determinant.

$\begin{vmatrix} 3 & 1 \\ -4 & 1 \end{vmatrix} = 3 - (-4)$ or 7

Since the determinant does not equal 0, the inverse exists.

$\frac{1}{ad - bc} \begin{bmatrix} d & -b \\ -c & a \end{bmatrix} = \frac{1}{3(1) - 1(-4)} \begin{bmatrix} 1 & -1 \\ -(-4) & 3 \end{bmatrix}$

$= \frac{1}{7} \begin{bmatrix} 1 & -1 \\ 4 & 3 \end{bmatrix}$ or $\begin{bmatrix} \frac{1}{7} & -\frac{1}{7} \\ \frac{4}{7} & \frac{3}{7} \end{bmatrix}$

24. Find the determinant.

$\begin{vmatrix} -3 & -2 \\ 6 & 4 \end{vmatrix} = -12 - (-12)$ or 0

Since the determinant is 0, the inverse does not exist.

25. Find the determinant.

$\begin{vmatrix} -3 & 7 \\ 2 & -6 \end{vmatrix} = 18 - 14$ or 4

Since the determinant does not equal 0, the inverse exists.

$\frac{1}{ad - bc} \begin{bmatrix} d & -b \\ -c & a \end{bmatrix} = \frac{1}{(-3)(-6) - (7)(2)} \begin{bmatrix} -6 & -7 \\ -2 & -3 \end{bmatrix}$

$= \frac{1}{4} \begin{bmatrix} -6 & -7 \\ -2 & -3 \end{bmatrix}$ or $\begin{bmatrix} -\frac{3}{2} & -\frac{7}{4} \\ -\frac{1}{2} & -\frac{3}{4} \end{bmatrix}$

26. Find the determinant.
$\begin{vmatrix} 4 & -3 \\ 2 & 7 \end{vmatrix} = 28 - (-6)$ or 34

Since the determinant does not equal 0, the inverse exists.

$\frac{1}{ad-bc}\begin{bmatrix} d & -b \\ -c & a \end{bmatrix} = \frac{1}{4(7)-(-3)(2)}\begin{bmatrix} 7 & -(-3) \\ -2 & 4 \end{bmatrix}$

$= \frac{1}{34}\begin{bmatrix} 7 & 3 \\ -2 & 4 \end{bmatrix}$ or $\begin{bmatrix} \frac{7}{34} & \frac{3}{34} \\ -\frac{1}{17} & \frac{2}{17} \end{bmatrix}$

27. Find the determinant.
$\begin{vmatrix} -2 & 0 \\ 5 & 6 \end{vmatrix} = -12 - 0$ or -12

Since the determinant is not equal to 0, the inverse exists.

$\frac{1}{ad-bc}\begin{bmatrix} d & -b \\ -c & a \end{bmatrix} = \frac{1}{-2(6)-0(5)}\begin{bmatrix} 6 & 0 \\ -5 & -2 \end{bmatrix}$

$= -\frac{1}{12}\begin{bmatrix} 6 & 0 \\ -5 & -2 \end{bmatrix}$ or $\begin{bmatrix} -\frac{1}{2} & 0 \\ \frac{5}{12} & \frac{1}{6} \end{bmatrix}$

28. Find the determinant.
$\begin{vmatrix} -4 & 6 \\ 6 & -9 \end{vmatrix} = 36 - 36$ or 0

Since the determinant is 0, the inverse does not exist.

29. Find the determinant.
$\begin{vmatrix} 2 & -5 \\ 6 & 1 \end{vmatrix} = 2 - (-30)$ or 32

Since the determinant is not equal to 0, the inverse exists.

$\frac{1}{ad-bc}\begin{bmatrix} d & -b \\ -c & a \end{bmatrix} = \frac{1}{2(1)-(-5)6}\begin{bmatrix} 1 & -(-5) \\ -6 & 2 \end{bmatrix}$

$= \frac{1}{32}\begin{bmatrix} 1 & 5 \\ -6 & 2 \end{bmatrix}$ or $\begin{bmatrix} \frac{1}{32} & \frac{5}{32} \\ -\frac{3}{16} & \frac{1}{16} \end{bmatrix}$

30. Find the determinant.
$\begin{vmatrix} \frac{1}{2} & -\frac{3}{4} \\ \frac{1}{6} & \frac{1}{4} \end{vmatrix} = \frac{1}{8} - \left(-\frac{3}{24}\right)$ or $\frac{1}{4}$

Since the determinant is not equal to 0, the inverse exists.

$\frac{1}{ad-bc}\begin{bmatrix} d & -b \\ -c & a \end{bmatrix} = \frac{1}{\left(\frac{1}{2}\right)\left(\frac{1}{4}\right)-\left(-\frac{3}{4}\right)\left(\frac{1}{6}\right)}\begin{bmatrix} \frac{1}{4} & -\left(-\frac{3}{4}\right) \\ -\frac{1}{6} & \frac{1}{2} \end{bmatrix}$

$= \frac{1}{\frac{1}{4}}\begin{bmatrix} \frac{1}{4} & \frac{3}{4} \\ -\frac{1}{6} & \frac{1}{2} \end{bmatrix}$

$= 4\begin{bmatrix} \frac{1}{4} & \frac{3}{4} \\ -\frac{1}{6} & \frac{1}{2} \end{bmatrix}$ or $\begin{bmatrix} 1 & 3 \\ -\frac{2}{3} & 2 \end{bmatrix}$

31. Find the determinant.
$\begin{vmatrix} \frac{3}{10} & \frac{5}{8} \\ \frac{1}{5} & \frac{3}{4} \end{vmatrix} = \frac{9}{40} - \frac{5}{40}$ or $\frac{1}{10}$

Since the determinant is not equal to 0, the inverse exists.

$\frac{1}{ad-bc}\begin{bmatrix} d & -b \\ -c & a \end{bmatrix} = \frac{1}{\left(\frac{3}{10}\right)\left(\frac{3}{4}\right)-\left(\frac{5}{8}\right)\left(\frac{1}{5}\right)}\begin{bmatrix} \frac{3}{4} & -\frac{5}{8} \\ -\frac{1}{5} & \frac{3}{10} \end{bmatrix}$

$= \frac{1}{\frac{1}{10}}\begin{bmatrix} \frac{3}{4} & -\frac{5}{8} \\ -\frac{1}{5} & \frac{3}{10} \end{bmatrix}$

$= 10\begin{bmatrix} \frac{3}{4} & -\frac{5}{8} \\ -\frac{1}{5} & \frac{3}{10} \end{bmatrix}$ or $\begin{bmatrix} \frac{15}{2} & -\frac{25}{4} \\ -2 & 3 \end{bmatrix}$

32a. No; they are not inverses, since their product is not the identity matrix.
$\begin{bmatrix} 1 & 0 \\ 0 & -1 \end{bmatrix} \cdot \begin{bmatrix} -1 & 0 \\ 0 & 1 \end{bmatrix}$

$= \begin{bmatrix} 1(-1)+0(0) & 1(0)+0(1) \\ 0(-1)+(-1)(0) & 0(0)+(-1)(1) \end{bmatrix}$

$= \begin{bmatrix} -1 & 0 \\ 0 & -1 \end{bmatrix}$

32b. The answer makes sense because a reflection over the x-axis followed by a reflection over the y-axis does not result in the original figure.

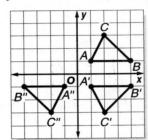

33a. Yes; they are inverses, since the products of the matrices in both orders yield the identity matrix.
$\begin{bmatrix} 0 & -1 \\ 1 & 0 \end{bmatrix} \cdot \begin{bmatrix} 0 & 1 \\ -1 & 0 \end{bmatrix}$

$= \begin{bmatrix} 0(0)+(-1)(-1) & 0(1)+(-1)(0) \\ 1(0)+(0)(-1) & 1(1)+(0)(0) \end{bmatrix}$

$= \begin{bmatrix} 1 & 0 \\ 0 & 1 \end{bmatrix}$

$\begin{bmatrix} 0 & 1 \\ -1 & 0 \end{bmatrix} \cdot \begin{bmatrix} 0 & -1 \\ 1 & 0 \end{bmatrix}$

$= \begin{bmatrix} 0(0)+(1)(1) & 0(-1)+(1)(0) \\ -1(0)+(0)(1) & -1(-1)+(0)(0) \end{bmatrix}$

$= \begin{bmatrix} 1 & 0 \\ 0 & 1 \end{bmatrix}$

33b. The answer makes sense because a 270° rotation followed by a 270° rotation is a 90° rotation, which means that the figure is back to its original position.

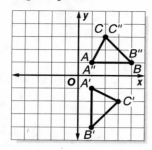

34. $A = \begin{bmatrix} 0 & -2 & 2 & 4 \\ 0 & 2 & 6 & 4 \end{bmatrix}$

35. $\begin{bmatrix} 2 & 0 \\ 0 & 2 \end{bmatrix} \cdot \begin{bmatrix} 0 & -2 & 2 & 4 \\ 0 & 2 & 6 & 4 \end{bmatrix} = \begin{bmatrix} 0 & -4 & 4 & 8 \\ 0 & 4 & 12 & 8 \end{bmatrix}$

36. The transformation is a dilation by a scale factor of 2.

37. B^{-1} should be a dilation by a scale factor of $\frac{1}{2}$.

38. $B^{-1} = \frac{1}{ad - bc} \begin{bmatrix} d & -b \\ -c & a \end{bmatrix}$

$= \frac{1}{2(2) - 0(0)} \begin{bmatrix} 2 & 0 \\ 0 & 2 \end{bmatrix}$

$= \frac{1}{4} \begin{bmatrix} 2 & 0 \\ 0 & 2 \end{bmatrix}$ or $\begin{bmatrix} \frac{1}{2} & 0 \\ 0 & \frac{1}{2} \end{bmatrix}$

$B^{-1}(BA) = \begin{bmatrix} \frac{1}{2} & 0 \\ 0 & \frac{1}{2} \end{bmatrix} \cdot \begin{bmatrix} 0 & -4 & 4 & 8 \\ 0 & 4 & 12 & 8 \end{bmatrix}$

$= \begin{bmatrix} 0 & -2 & 2 & 4 \\ 0 & 2 & 6 & 8 \end{bmatrix}$ or A

39. First find the inverse matrix of C.

$C^{-1} = \frac{1}{2(1) - (-1)(-1)} \begin{bmatrix} 1 & -1 \\ -1 & 2 \end{bmatrix}$

$= \frac{1}{1} \begin{bmatrix} 1 & -1 \\ -1 & 2 \end{bmatrix}$ or $\begin{bmatrix} 1 & -1 \\ -1 & 2 \end{bmatrix}$

Next decode the message by multiplying by C^{-1}.

$\begin{bmatrix} 50 & 36 \\ 51 & 29 \\ 18 & 18 \\ 26 & 13 \\ 33 & 26 \\ 44 & 22 \\ 48 & 33 \\ 59 & 34 \\ 61 & 35 \\ 4 & 2 \end{bmatrix} \cdot \begin{bmatrix} 1 & -1 \\ -1 & 2 \end{bmatrix} = \begin{bmatrix} 50 - 36 & -50 + 72 \\ 51 - 29 & -51 + 58 \\ 18 - 18 & -18 + 36 \\ 26 - 13 & -26 + 26 \\ 33 - 26 & -33 + 52 \\ 44 - 22 & -44 + 44 \\ 48 - 33 & -48 + 66 \\ 59 - 34 & -59 + 68 \\ 61 - 35 & -61 + 70 \\ 4 - 2 & -4 + 4 \end{bmatrix}$

$= \begin{bmatrix} 14 & 22 \\ 22 & 7 \\ 0 & 18 \\ 13 & 0 \\ 7 & 19 \\ 22 & 0 \\ 15 & 18 \\ 25 & 9 \\ 26 & 9 \\ 2 & 0 \end{bmatrix}$

14 | 22 | 22 | 7 | 0 | 18 | 13 | 0 | 7 | 19 | 22 | 0 | 15 | 18 | 25 | 9 | 26 | 9 | 2 | 0
M E E T – I N – T H E – L I B R A R Y –

40. Decode the message by multiplying by C^{-1}.

$\begin{bmatrix} 59 & 33 \\ 8 & 8 \\ 39 & 21 \\ 7 & 7 \\ 56 & 37 \\ 25 & 16 \\ 4 & 2 \end{bmatrix} \cdot \begin{bmatrix} 1 & -1 \\ -1 & 2 \end{bmatrix} = \begin{bmatrix} 59 - 33 & -59 + 66 \\ 8 - 8 & -8 + 16 \\ 39 - 21 & -39 + 42 \\ 7 - 7 & -7 + 14 \\ 56 - 37 & -56 + 74 \\ 25 - 16 & -25 + 32 \\ 4 - 2 & -4 + 4 \end{bmatrix}$

$= \begin{bmatrix} 26 & 7 \\ 0 & 8 \\ 18 & 3 \\ 0 & 7 \\ 19 & 18 \\ 9 & 7 \\ 2 & 0 \end{bmatrix}$

26 | 7 | 0 | 8 | 18 | 3 | 0 | 7 | 19 | 18 | 9 | 7 | 2 | 0
A T – S I X – T H I R T Y –

41. Decode the message by multiplying by C^{-1}.

$\begin{bmatrix} 59 & 34 \\ 49 & 31 \\ 40 & 20 \\ 16 & 14 \\ 21 & 15 \\ 25 & 25 \\ 36 & 24 \\ 32 & 16 \end{bmatrix} \cdot \begin{bmatrix} 1 & -1 \\ -1 & 2 \end{bmatrix} = \begin{bmatrix} 59 - 34 & -59 + 68 \\ 49 - 31 & -49 + 62 \\ 40 - 20 & -40 + 40 \\ 16 - 14 & -16 + 28 \\ 21 - 15 & -21 + 30 \\ 25 - 25 & -25 + 50 \\ 36 - 24 & -36 + 48 \\ 32 - 16 & -32 + 32 \end{bmatrix}$

$= \begin{bmatrix} 25 & 9 \\ 18 & 13 \\ 20 & 0 \\ 2 & 12 \\ 6 & 9 \\ 0 & 25 \\ 12 & 12 \\ 16 & 0 \end{bmatrix}$

25 | 9 | 18 | 13 | 20 | 0 | 2 | 12 | 6 | 9 | 0 | 25 | 12 | 12 | 16 | 0
B R I N G – Y O U R – B O O K –

42. See students' work.

43. Consider matrices where $a = \pm1$, $d = \pm1$, and $b = c = 0$.

$$A \cdot A = \begin{bmatrix} \pm1 & 0 \\ 0 & \pm1 \end{bmatrix} \begin{bmatrix} \pm1 & 0 \\ 0 & \pm1 \end{bmatrix}$$

$$= \begin{bmatrix} (\pm1)^2 + 0^2 & (\pm1)(0) + (0)(\pm1) \\ 0(\pm1) + (\pm1)(0) & 0^2 + (\pm1)^2 \end{bmatrix}$$

$$= \begin{bmatrix} 1 & 0 \\ 0 & 1 \end{bmatrix}$$

Thus, $A = A^{-1}$ when $a = \pm1$, $d = \pm1$, and $b = c = 0$.

44. A matrix can be used to code a message. The key to the message is the inverse of the matrix. Answers should include the following.

- The inverse matrix undoes the work of the matrix. So if you multiply a numeric message by a matrix it changes the message. When you multiply the changed message by the inverse matrix, the result is the original numeric message.

- You must consider the dimensions of the coding matrix so that you can write the numeric message in a matrix with dimensions that can be multiplied by the coding matrix.

45. A; Use the formula for the inverse.

$$\frac{1}{ad - bc} \begin{bmatrix} d & -b \\ -c & a \end{bmatrix} = \frac{1}{4(2) - 10(1)} \begin{bmatrix} 2 & -1 \\ -10 & 4 \end{bmatrix}$$

$$= -\frac{1}{2} \begin{bmatrix} 2 & -1 \\ -10 & 4 \end{bmatrix} \text{ or } \begin{bmatrix} -1 & \frac{1}{2} \\ 5 & -2 \end{bmatrix}$$

46. D; $\begin{vmatrix} -10 & -5 \\ 8 & 4 \end{vmatrix} = -40 - (-40)$ or 0

The determinant of $\begin{vmatrix} -10 & -5 \\ 8 & 4 \end{vmatrix}$ is 0, therefore it does not have an inverse.

47. Enter the matrix into A and then use the following KEYSTROKES: MATRX 1 x^{-1} ENTER.

The inverse is $\begin{bmatrix} -5 & -9 \\ -6 & -11 \end{bmatrix}$.

48. Enter the matrix into A and then use the following KEYSTROKES: MATRX 1 x^{-1} ENTER. The error indicates the matrix has no inverse.

49. Enter the matrix into A and then use the following KEYSTROKES: MATRX 1 x^{-1} ENTER MATH 1 ENTER.

The inverse is $\begin{bmatrix} \frac{3}{5} & -\frac{1}{5} \\ \frac{1}{5} & -\frac{2}{5} \end{bmatrix}$.

50. Enter the matrix into A and then use the following KEYSTROKES: MATRX 1 x^{-1} ENTER MATH 1 ENTER.

The inverse is $\begin{bmatrix} \frac{3}{5} & \frac{2}{5} \\ \frac{7}{2} & \frac{5}{2} \end{bmatrix}$ or $\begin{bmatrix} \frac{3}{5} & \frac{2}{5} \\ 3\frac{1}{2} & 2\frac{1}{2} \end{bmatrix}$.

51. Enter the matrix into A and then use the following KEYSTROKES: MATRX 1 x^{-1} ENTER MATH 1 ENTER.

The inverse is $\begin{bmatrix} -1 & 1 & \frac{1}{3} \\ -\frac{1}{3} & \frac{2}{3} & 0 \\ \frac{7}{3} & -\frac{8}{3} & -\frac{1}{3} \end{bmatrix}$.

52. Enter the matrix into A and then use the following KEYSTROKES: MATRX 1 x^{-1} ENTER MATH 1 ENTER.

The inverse is $\begin{bmatrix} \frac{5}{16} & -\frac{1}{8} & -\frac{1}{16} \\ -\frac{1}{4} & 0 & \frac{1}{4} \\ \frac{5}{32} & \frac{3}{16} & -\frac{1}{32} \end{bmatrix}$.

Page 201   Maintain Your Skills

53. $x = \dfrac{\begin{vmatrix} -2 & 2 \\ 14 & -3 \end{vmatrix}}{\begin{vmatrix} 3 & 2 \\ 1 & -3 \end{vmatrix}}$ $y = \dfrac{\begin{vmatrix} 3 & -2 \\ 1 & 14 \end{vmatrix}}{\begin{vmatrix} 3 & 2 \\ 1 & -3 \end{vmatrix}}$

$\quad = \dfrac{6 - 28}{-9 - 2}$ $= \dfrac{42 - (-2)}{-9 - 2}$

$\quad = \dfrac{-22}{-11}$ or 2 $= \dfrac{44}{-11}$ or -4

The solution is $(2, -4)$.

54. $x = \dfrac{\begin{vmatrix} 35 & 5 \\ -28 & -4 \end{vmatrix}}{\begin{vmatrix} 2 & 5 \\ 7 & -4 \end{vmatrix}}$ $y = \dfrac{\begin{vmatrix} 2 & 35 \\ 7 & -28 \end{vmatrix}}{\begin{vmatrix} 2 & 5 \\ 7 & -4 \end{vmatrix}}$

$\quad = \dfrac{-140 - (-140)}{-8 - 35}$ $= \dfrac{-56 - 245}{-8 - 35}$

$\quad = 0$ $= \dfrac{-301}{-43}$ or 7

The solution is $(0, 7)$.

55. $x = \dfrac{\begin{vmatrix} -23 & 0 & -3 \\ -9 & -5 & 1 \\ 3 & 1 & -1 \end{vmatrix}}{\begin{vmatrix} 4 & 0 & -3 \\ -2 & -5 & 1 \\ 0 & 1 & -1 \end{vmatrix}}$ $y = \dfrac{\begin{vmatrix} 4 & -23 & -3 \\ -2 & -9 & 1 \\ 0 & 3 & -1 \end{vmatrix}}{\begin{vmatrix} 4 & 0 & -3 \\ -2 & -5 & 1 \\ 0 & 1 & -1 \end{vmatrix}}$ $z = \dfrac{\begin{vmatrix} 4 & 0 & -23 \\ -2 & -5 & -9 \\ 0 & 1 & 3 \end{vmatrix}}{\begin{vmatrix} 4 & 0 & -3 \\ -2 & -5 & 1 \\ 0 & 1 & -1 \end{vmatrix}}$

$\quad = \dfrac{-110}{22}$ $= \dfrac{88}{22}$ $= \dfrac{22}{22}$

$\quad = -5$ $= 4$ $= 1$

The solution is $(-5, 4, 1)$.

56. $\begin{vmatrix} 2 & 8 & -6 \\ 4 & 5 & 2 \\ -3 & -6 & -1 \end{vmatrix}$

$= 2 \begin{vmatrix} 5 & 2 \\ -6 & -1 \end{vmatrix} - 8 \begin{vmatrix} 4 & 2 \\ -3 & -1 \end{vmatrix} + (-6) \begin{vmatrix} 4 & 5 \\ -3 & -6 \end{vmatrix}$

$= 2(-5 - (-12)) - 8(-4 - (-6)) - 6(-24 - (-15))$

$= 14 - 16 + 54$

$= 52$

57. $\begin{vmatrix} -3 & -3 & 1 \\ -9 & -2 & 3 \\ 5 & -2 & -1 \end{vmatrix}$

$$= -3\begin{vmatrix} -2 & 3 \\ -2 & -1 \end{vmatrix} - (-3)\begin{vmatrix} -9 & 3 \\ 5 & -1 \end{vmatrix} + 1\begin{vmatrix} -9 & -2 \\ 5 & -2 \end{vmatrix}$$
$$= -3(2 - (-6)) + 3(9 - 15) + (18 - (-10))$$
$$= -24 - 18 + 28$$
$$= -14$$

58. $\begin{vmatrix} 5 & -7 & 3 \\ -1 & 2 & -9 \\ 5 & -7 & 3 \end{vmatrix}$

$$= 5\begin{vmatrix} 2 & -9 \\ -7 & 3 \end{vmatrix} - (-7)\begin{vmatrix} -1 & -9 \\ 5 & 3 \end{vmatrix} + 3\begin{vmatrix} -1 & 2 \\ 5 & -7 \end{vmatrix}$$
$$= 5(6 - 63) + 7(-3 - (-45)) + 3(7 - 10)$$
$$= -285 + 294 - 9$$
$$= 0$$

59. $m = \dfrac{y_2 - y_1}{x_2 - x_1}$
$$= \dfrac{9 - 5}{6 - 2}$$
$$= \dfrac{4}{4}$$
$$= 1$$

60. $m = \dfrac{y_2 - y_1}{x_2 - x_1}$
$$= \dfrac{9 - 0}{-2 - 1}$$
$$= \dfrac{9}{-3}$$
$$= -3$$

61. $m = \dfrac{y_2 - y_1}{x_2 - x_1}$
$$= \dfrac{-6 - 4}{-3 - (-5)}$$
$$= \dfrac{-10}{2}$$
$$= -5$$

62. $m = \dfrac{y_2 - y_1}{x_2 - x_1}$
$$= \dfrac{1 - 2}{-5 - (-2)}$$
$$= \dfrac{-1}{-3}$$
$$= \dfrac{1}{3}$$

63. $m = \dfrac{y_2 - y_1}{x_2 - x_1}$
$$= \dfrac{-2 - 3}{-2 - 0}$$
$$= \dfrac{-5}{-2}$$
$$= \dfrac{5}{2}$$

64. $m = \dfrac{y_2 - y_1}{x_2 - x_1}$
$$= \dfrac{6 - 9}{0 - (-8)}$$
$$= \dfrac{-3}{8}$$
$$= -\dfrac{3}{8}$$

65. $f(x) = 1.15x$
$$f(6.8) = 1.15(6.8)$$
$$= 7.82$$

The water pressure at the deepest point in the trench is 7.82 tons/in^2.

66. $3(2^3 + 1) = 3(8 + 1)$
$$= 3(9)$$
$$= 27$$

67. $7 - 5 \div 2 + 1 = 7 - 2\frac{1}{2} + 1$
$$= 4\frac{1}{2} + 1$$
$$= 5\frac{1}{2}$$

68. $\dfrac{9 - 4 \cdot 3}{6} = \dfrac{9 - 12}{6}$
$$= \dfrac{-3}{6}$$
$$= -\dfrac{1}{2}$$

69. $[40 - (7 + 9)] \div 8 = [40 - 16] \div 8$
$$= 24 \div 8$$
$$= 3$$

70. $[(-2 + 8)6 + 1]8 = [6 \cdot 6 + 1]8$
$$= [36 + 1]8$$
$$= 37 \cdot 8$$
$$= 296$$

71. $(4 - 1)(8 + 2)^2 = (3)(10)^2$
$$= (3)(100)$$
$$= 300$$

72. $3k + 8 = 5$
$$3k = -3$$
$$k = -1$$

73. $12 = -5h + 2$
$$10 = -5h$$
$$-2 = h$$

74. $7z - 4 = 5z + 8$
$$7z = 5z + 12$$
$$2z = 12$$
$$z = 6$$

75. $\dfrac{x}{2} + 5 = 7$
$$\dfrac{x}{2} = 2$$
$$x = 4$$

76. $\dfrac{3 + n}{6} = -4$
$$3 + n = -24$$
$$n = -27$$

77. $6 = \dfrac{s - 8}{-7}$
$$-42 = s - 8$$
$$-34 = s$$
$$s = -34$$

4-8   Using Matrices to Solve Systems of Equations

Page 205   Graphing Calculator Investigation

1. $\begin{bmatrix} 3 & -2 & 1 \\ 2 & 3 & -1 \\ 5 & -1 & 4 \end{bmatrix} \cdot \begin{bmatrix} x \\ y \\ z \end{bmatrix} = \begin{bmatrix} 0 \\ 17 \\ -7 \end{bmatrix}$

2. Enter the coefficient matrix and the constant matrix in A and B, respectively. Then use the following keystrokes to solve the equation.

KEYSTROKES: $\boxed{\text{MATRX}}$ 1 $\boxed{x^{-1}}$ $\boxed{\text{X}}$ $\boxed{\text{MATRX}}$ 2
$\boxed{\text{ENTER}}$

The result is $\begin{bmatrix} 3 \\ 2 \\ -5 \end{bmatrix}$.

3. The solution is $(3, 2, -5)$.

Page 205   Check for Understanding

1. $2r - 3s = 4$
$r + 4s = -2$

2. Sample answer: $x + 3y = 8$ and $2x + 6y = 16$

3. Tommy; a 2×1 matrix cannot be multiplied by a 2×2 matrix.

4. $\begin{bmatrix} 1 & -1 \\ 1 & 3 \end{bmatrix} \cdot \begin{bmatrix} x \\ y \end{bmatrix} = \begin{bmatrix} -3 \\ 5 \end{bmatrix}$

5. $\begin{bmatrix} 2 & 3 \\ -4 & -7 \end{bmatrix} \cdot \begin{bmatrix} g \\ h \end{bmatrix} = \begin{bmatrix} 8 \\ -5 \end{bmatrix}$

6. $\begin{bmatrix} 3 & -5 & 2 \\ 4 & 7 & 1 \\ 2 & 0 & -1 \end{bmatrix} \cdot \begin{bmatrix} a \\ b \\ c \end{bmatrix} = \begin{bmatrix} 9 \\ 3 \\ 12 \end{bmatrix}$

7. Find the inverse of the coefficient matrix.
$A^{-1} = \dfrac{1}{-6 - 4} \begin{bmatrix} -2 & -1 \\ -4 & 3 \end{bmatrix}$

$= -\dfrac{1}{10} \begin{bmatrix} -2 & -1 \\ -4 & 3 \end{bmatrix}$

Multiply each side of the matrix equation by A^{-1}.
$-\dfrac{1}{10} \begin{bmatrix} -2 & -1 \\ -4 & 3 \end{bmatrix} \cdot \begin{bmatrix} 3 & 1 \\ 4 & -2 \end{bmatrix} \cdot \begin{bmatrix} x \\ y \end{bmatrix} = -\dfrac{1}{10} \begin{bmatrix} -2 & -1 \\ -4 & 3 \end{bmatrix} \cdot \begin{bmatrix} 13 \\ 24 \end{bmatrix}$

$\begin{bmatrix} 1 & 0 \\ 0 & 1 \end{bmatrix} \cdot \begin{bmatrix} x \\ y \end{bmatrix} = -\dfrac{1}{10} \begin{bmatrix} -50 \\ 20 \end{bmatrix}$

$\begin{bmatrix} x \\ y \end{bmatrix} = \begin{bmatrix} 5 \\ -2 \end{bmatrix}$

The solution is $(5, -2)$.

8. Find the inverse of the coefficient matrix.
$A^{-1} = \dfrac{1}{24 - (-2)} \begin{bmatrix} 3 & 1 \\ -2 & 8 \end{bmatrix}$

$= \dfrac{1}{26} \begin{bmatrix} 3 & 1 \\ -2 & 8 \end{bmatrix}$

Multiply each side of the matrix equation by A^{-1}.
$\dfrac{1}{26} \begin{bmatrix} 3 & 1 \\ -2 & 8 \end{bmatrix} \cdot \begin{bmatrix} 8 & -1 \\ 2 & 3 \end{bmatrix} \cdot \begin{bmatrix} a \\ b \end{bmatrix} = \dfrac{1}{26} \begin{bmatrix} 3 & 1 \\ -2 & 8 \end{bmatrix} \cdot \begin{bmatrix} 16 \\ -9 \end{bmatrix}$

$\begin{bmatrix} 1 & 0 \\ 0 & 1 \end{bmatrix} \cdot \begin{bmatrix} a \\ b \end{bmatrix} = \dfrac{1}{26} \begin{bmatrix} 39 \\ -104 \end{bmatrix}$

$\begin{bmatrix} a \\ b \end{bmatrix} = \begin{bmatrix} 1.5 \\ -4 \end{bmatrix}$

The solution is $(1.5, -4)$.

9. Write the matrix equation for the system.
$\begin{bmatrix} 5 & -3 \\ 8 & 5 \end{bmatrix} \cdot \begin{bmatrix} x \\ y \end{bmatrix} = \begin{bmatrix} -30 \\ 1 \end{bmatrix}$

Find the inverse of the coefficient matrix.
$A^{-1} = \dfrac{1}{25 - (-24)} \begin{bmatrix} 5 & 3 \\ -8 & 5 \end{bmatrix}$

$= \dfrac{1}{49} \begin{bmatrix} 5 & 3 \\ -8 & 5 \end{bmatrix}$

Multiply each side of the matrix equation by A^{-1}.
$\dfrac{1}{49} \begin{bmatrix} 5 & 3 \\ -8 & 5 \end{bmatrix} \cdot \begin{bmatrix} 5 & -3 \\ 8 & 5 \end{bmatrix} \cdot \begin{bmatrix} x \\ y \end{bmatrix} = \dfrac{1}{49} \begin{bmatrix} 5 & 3 \\ -8 & 5 \end{bmatrix} \cdot \begin{bmatrix} -30 \\ 1 \end{bmatrix}$

$\begin{bmatrix} 1 & 0 \\ 0 & 1 \end{bmatrix} \cdot \begin{bmatrix} x \\ y \end{bmatrix} = \dfrac{1}{49} \begin{bmatrix} -147 \\ 245 \end{bmatrix}$

$\begin{bmatrix} x \\ y \end{bmatrix} = \begin{bmatrix} -3 \\ 5 \end{bmatrix}$

The solution is $(-3, 5)$.

10. Write the matrix equation for the system.
$\begin{bmatrix} 5 & 4 \\ 4 & -3 \end{bmatrix} \cdot \begin{bmatrix} s \\ t \end{bmatrix} = \begin{bmatrix} 12 \\ -1.25 \end{bmatrix}$

Find the inverse of the coefficient matrix.
$A^{-1} = \dfrac{1}{-15 - 16} \begin{bmatrix} -3 & -4 \\ -4 & 5 \end{bmatrix}$

$= -\dfrac{1}{31} \begin{bmatrix} -3 & -4 \\ -4 & 5 \end{bmatrix}$

Multiply each side of the matrix equation by A^{-1}.
$-\dfrac{1}{31} \begin{bmatrix} -3 & -4 \\ -4 & 5 \end{bmatrix} \cdot \begin{bmatrix} 5 & 4 \\ 4 & -3 \end{bmatrix} \cdot \begin{bmatrix} s \\ t \end{bmatrix} = -\dfrac{1}{31} \begin{bmatrix} -3 & -4 \\ -4 & 5 \end{bmatrix} \cdot \begin{bmatrix} 12 \\ -1.25 \end{bmatrix}$

$\begin{bmatrix} 1 & 0 \\ 0 & 1 \end{bmatrix} \cdot \begin{bmatrix} s \\ t \end{bmatrix} = -\dfrac{1}{31} \begin{bmatrix} -31 \\ -54.25 \end{bmatrix}$

$\begin{bmatrix} s \\ t \end{bmatrix} = \begin{bmatrix} 1 \\ 1.75 \end{bmatrix}$

The solution is $(1, 1.75)$.

11. Find the inverse of the coefficient matrix.
$A^{-1} = \dfrac{1}{132 - 144} \begin{bmatrix} 22 & -12 \\ -12 & 6 \end{bmatrix}$

$= -\dfrac{1}{12} \begin{bmatrix} 22 & -12 \\ -12 & 6 \end{bmatrix}$

Multiply both sides of the matrix equation by A^{-1}.
$-\dfrac{1}{12} \begin{bmatrix} 22 & -12 \\ -12 & 6 \end{bmatrix} \cdot \begin{bmatrix} 6 & 12 \\ 12 & 22 \end{bmatrix} \cdot \begin{bmatrix} c \\ h \end{bmatrix} = -\dfrac{1}{12} \begin{bmatrix} 22 & -12 \\ -12 & 6 \end{bmatrix} \cdot \begin{bmatrix} 84 \\ 166 \end{bmatrix}$

$\begin{bmatrix} 1 & 0 \\ 0 & 1 \end{bmatrix} \cdot \begin{bmatrix} c \\ h \end{bmatrix} = -\dfrac{1}{12} \begin{bmatrix} -144 \\ -12 \end{bmatrix}$

$\begin{bmatrix} c \\ h \end{bmatrix} = \begin{bmatrix} 12 \\ 1 \end{bmatrix}$

Hydrogen weighs 1 amu, and carbon weighs 12 amu.

Pages 206–207   Practice and Apply

12. $\begin{bmatrix} 3 & -1 \\ 1 & 2 \end{bmatrix} \cdot \begin{bmatrix} x \\ y \end{bmatrix} = \begin{bmatrix} 0 \\ -21 \end{bmatrix}$

13. $\begin{bmatrix} 4 & -7 \\ 3 & 5 \end{bmatrix} \cdot \begin{bmatrix} x \\ y \end{bmatrix} = \begin{bmatrix} 2 \\ 9 \end{bmatrix}$

14. $\begin{bmatrix} 5 & -6 \\ 3 & 2 \end{bmatrix} \cdot \begin{bmatrix} a \\ b \end{bmatrix} = \begin{bmatrix} -47 \\ -17 \end{bmatrix}$

15. $\begin{bmatrix} 3 & -7 \\ 6 & 5 \end{bmatrix} \cdot \begin{bmatrix} m \\ n \end{bmatrix} = \begin{bmatrix} -43 \\ -10 \end{bmatrix}$

16. $\begin{bmatrix} 2 & 3 & -5 \\ 7 & 0 & 3 \\ 3 & -6 & 1 \end{bmatrix} \cdot \begin{bmatrix} a \\ b \\ c \end{bmatrix} = \begin{bmatrix} 1 \\ 7 \\ -5 \end{bmatrix}$

17. $\begin{bmatrix} 3 & -5 & 2 \\ 1 & -7 & 3 \\ 4 & 0 & -3 \end{bmatrix} \cdot \begin{bmatrix} x \\ y \\ z \end{bmatrix} = \begin{bmatrix} 9 \\ 11 \\ -1 \end{bmatrix}$

18. $\begin{bmatrix} 1 & -1 & 0 \\ -2 & -5 & -6 \\ 9 & 10 & -1 \end{bmatrix} \cdot \begin{bmatrix} x \\ y \\ z \end{bmatrix} = \begin{bmatrix} 8 \\ -27 \\ 54 \end{bmatrix}$

19. $\begin{bmatrix} 3 & -5 & 6 \\ 11 & -12 & 16 \\ -5 & 8 & -3 \end{bmatrix} \cdot \begin{bmatrix} r \\ s \\ t \end{bmatrix} = \begin{bmatrix} 21 \\ 15 \\ -7 \end{bmatrix}$

20. Find the inverse of the coefficient matrix.

$A^{-1} = \dfrac{1}{35 - (-6)} \begin{bmatrix} 5 & 3 \\ -2 & 7 \end{bmatrix}$

$= \dfrac{1}{41} \begin{bmatrix} 5 & 3 \\ -2 & 7 \end{bmatrix}$

Multiply both sides of the matrix equation by A^{-1}.

$\dfrac{1}{41} \begin{bmatrix} 5 & 3 \\ -2 & 7 \end{bmatrix} \cdot \begin{bmatrix} 7 & -3 \\ 2 & 5 \end{bmatrix} \cdot \begin{bmatrix} m \\ n \end{bmatrix} = \dfrac{1}{41} \begin{bmatrix} 5 & 3 \\ -2 & 7 \end{bmatrix} \cdot \begin{bmatrix} 41 \\ 0 \end{bmatrix}$

$\begin{bmatrix} 1 & 0 \\ 0 & 1 \end{bmatrix} \cdot \begin{bmatrix} m \\ n \end{bmatrix} = \dfrac{1}{41} \begin{bmatrix} 205 \\ -82 \end{bmatrix}$

$\begin{bmatrix} m \\ n \end{bmatrix} = \begin{bmatrix} 5 \\ -2 \end{bmatrix}$

The solution is $(5, -2)$.

21. Find the inverse of the coefficient matrix.

$A^{-1} = \dfrac{1}{-3 - 2} \begin{bmatrix} -1 & -1 \\ -2 & 3 \end{bmatrix}$

$= -\dfrac{1}{5} \begin{bmatrix} -1 & -1 \\ -2 & 3 \end{bmatrix}$

Multiply both sides of the matrix equation by A^{-1}.

$-\dfrac{1}{5} \begin{bmatrix} -1 & -1 \\ -2 & 3 \end{bmatrix} \cdot \begin{bmatrix} 3 & 1 \\ 2 & -1 \end{bmatrix} \cdot \begin{bmatrix} a \\ b \end{bmatrix} = -\dfrac{1}{5} \begin{bmatrix} -1 & -1 \\ -2 & 3 \end{bmatrix} \cdot \begin{bmatrix} 13 \\ 2 \end{bmatrix}$

$\begin{bmatrix} 1 & 0 \\ 0 & 1 \end{bmatrix} \cdot \begin{bmatrix} a \\ b \end{bmatrix} = -\dfrac{1}{5} \begin{bmatrix} -15 \\ -20 \end{bmatrix}$

$\begin{bmatrix} a \\ b \end{bmatrix} = \begin{bmatrix} 3 \\ 4 \end{bmatrix}$

The solution is $(3, 4)$.

22. Find the inverse of the coefficient matrix.

$A^{-1} = \dfrac{1}{8 - (-15)} \begin{bmatrix} 2 & 3 \\ -5 & 4 \end{bmatrix}$

$= \dfrac{1}{23} \begin{bmatrix} 2 & 3 \\ -5 & 4 \end{bmatrix}$

Multiply both sides of the matrix equation by A^{-1}.

$\dfrac{1}{23} \begin{bmatrix} 2 & 3 \\ -5 & 4 \end{bmatrix} \cdot \begin{bmatrix} 4 & -3 \\ 5 & 2 \end{bmatrix} \cdot \begin{bmatrix} a \\ b \end{bmatrix} = \dfrac{1}{23} \begin{bmatrix} 2 & 3 \\ -5 & 4 \end{bmatrix} \cdot \begin{bmatrix} -17 \\ -4 \end{bmatrix}$

$\begin{bmatrix} 1 & 0 \\ 0 & 1 \end{bmatrix} \cdot \begin{bmatrix} a \\ b \end{bmatrix} = \dfrac{1}{23} \begin{bmatrix} -46 \\ 69 \end{bmatrix}$

$\begin{bmatrix} a \\ b \end{bmatrix} = \begin{bmatrix} -2 \\ 3 \end{bmatrix}$

The solution is $(-2, 3)$.

23. Find the inverse of the coefficient matrix.

$A^{-1} = \dfrac{1}{-56 - 3} \begin{bmatrix} -8 & -1 \\ -3 & 7 \end{bmatrix}$

$= -\dfrac{1}{59} \begin{bmatrix} -8 & -1 \\ -3 & 7 \end{bmatrix}$

Multiply both sides of the matrix equation by A^{-1}.

$-\dfrac{1}{59} \begin{bmatrix} -8 & -1 \\ -3 & 7 \end{bmatrix} \cdot \begin{bmatrix} 7 & 1 \\ 3 & -8 \end{bmatrix} \cdot \begin{bmatrix} x \\ y \end{bmatrix} = -\dfrac{1}{59} \begin{bmatrix} -8 & -1 \\ -3 & 7 \end{bmatrix} \cdot \begin{bmatrix} 43 \\ 10 \end{bmatrix}$

$\begin{bmatrix} 1 & 0 \\ 0 & 1 \end{bmatrix} \cdot \begin{bmatrix} x \\ y \end{bmatrix} = -\dfrac{1}{59} \begin{bmatrix} -354 \\ -59 \end{bmatrix}$

$\begin{bmatrix} x \\ y \end{bmatrix} = \begin{bmatrix} 6 \\ 1 \end{bmatrix}$

The solution is $(6, 1)$.

24. Find the inverse of the coefficient matrix.

$A^{-1} = \dfrac{1}{10 - (-54)} \begin{bmatrix} 5 & 9 \\ -6 & 2 \end{bmatrix}$

$= \dfrac{1}{64} \begin{bmatrix} 5 & 9 \\ -6 & 2 \end{bmatrix}$

Multiply both sides of the matrix equation by A^{-1}.

$\dfrac{1}{64} \begin{bmatrix} 5 & 9 \\ -6 & 2 \end{bmatrix} \cdot \begin{bmatrix} 2 & -9 \\ 6 & 5 \end{bmatrix} \cdot \begin{bmatrix} c \\ d \end{bmatrix} = \dfrac{1}{64} \begin{bmatrix} 5 & 9 \\ -6 & 2 \end{bmatrix} \cdot \begin{bmatrix} 28 \\ -12 \end{bmatrix}$

$\begin{bmatrix} 1 & 0 \\ 0 & 1 \end{bmatrix} \cdot \begin{bmatrix} c \\ d \end{bmatrix} = \dfrac{1}{64} \begin{bmatrix} 32 \\ -192 \end{bmatrix}$

$\begin{bmatrix} c \\ d \end{bmatrix} = \begin{bmatrix} \frac{1}{2} \\ -3 \end{bmatrix}$

The solution is $\left(\frac{1}{2}, -3\right)$.

25. Find the inverse of the coefficient matrix.

$A^{-1} = \dfrac{1}{12 - 15} \begin{bmatrix} 2 & -5 \\ -3 & 6 \end{bmatrix}$

$= -\dfrac{1}{3} \begin{bmatrix} 2 & -5 \\ -3 & 6 \end{bmatrix}$

Multiply both sides of the matrix equation by A^{-1}.

$-\dfrac{1}{3} \begin{bmatrix} 2 & -5 \\ -3 & 6 \end{bmatrix} \cdot \begin{bmatrix} 6 & 5 \\ 3 & 2 \end{bmatrix} \cdot \begin{bmatrix} a \\ b \end{bmatrix} = -\dfrac{1}{3} \begin{bmatrix} 2 & -5 \\ -3 & 6 \end{bmatrix} \cdot \begin{bmatrix} 18 \\ 7 \end{bmatrix}$

$\begin{bmatrix} 1 & 0 \\ 0 & 1 \end{bmatrix} \cdot \begin{bmatrix} a \\ b \end{bmatrix} = -\dfrac{1}{3} \begin{bmatrix} 1 \\ -12 \end{bmatrix}$

$\begin{bmatrix} a \\ b \end{bmatrix} = \begin{bmatrix} -\frac{1}{3} \\ 4 \end{bmatrix}$

The solution is $\left(-\frac{1}{3}, 4\right)$.

26. Write the matrix equation for the system.

$$\begin{bmatrix} 6 & 1 \\ 3 & 2 \end{bmatrix} \cdot \begin{bmatrix} r \\ s \end{bmatrix} = \begin{bmatrix} 9 \\ 0 \end{bmatrix}$$

Find the inverse of the coefficient matrix.

$$A^{-1} = \frac{1}{12-3}\begin{bmatrix} 2 & -1 \\ -3 & 6 \end{bmatrix}$$

$$= \frac{1}{9}\begin{bmatrix} 2 & -1 \\ -3 & 6 \end{bmatrix}$$

Multiply both sides of the matrix equation by A^{-1}.

$$\frac{1}{9}\begin{bmatrix} 2 & -1 \\ -3 & 6 \end{bmatrix} \cdot \begin{bmatrix} 6 & 1 \\ 3 & 2 \end{bmatrix} \cdot \begin{bmatrix} r \\ s \end{bmatrix} = \frac{1}{9}\begin{bmatrix} 2 & -1 \\ -3 & 6 \end{bmatrix} \cdot \begin{bmatrix} 9 \\ 0 \end{bmatrix}$$

$$\begin{bmatrix} 1 & 0 \\ 0 & 1 \end{bmatrix} \cdot \begin{bmatrix} r \\ s \end{bmatrix} = \frac{1}{9}\begin{bmatrix} 18 \\ -27 \end{bmatrix}$$

$$\begin{bmatrix} r \\ s \end{bmatrix} = \begin{bmatrix} 2 \\ -3 \end{bmatrix}$$

The solution is $(2, -3)$.

27. Write the matrix equation for the system.

$$\begin{bmatrix} 5 & 9 \\ 2 & -1 \end{bmatrix} \cdot \begin{bmatrix} a \\ b \end{bmatrix} = \begin{bmatrix} -28 \\ -2 \end{bmatrix}$$

Find the inverse of the coefficient matrix.

$$A^{-1} = \frac{1}{-5-18}\begin{bmatrix} -1 & -9 \\ -2 & 5 \end{bmatrix}$$

$$= -\frac{1}{23}\begin{bmatrix} -1 & -9 \\ -2 & 5 \end{bmatrix}$$

Multiply both sides of the matrix equation by A^{-1}.

$$-\frac{1}{23}\begin{bmatrix} -1 & -9 \\ -2 & 5 \end{bmatrix} \cdot \begin{bmatrix} 5 & 9 \\ 2 & -1 \end{bmatrix} \cdot \begin{bmatrix} a \\ b \end{bmatrix} = -\frac{1}{23}\begin{bmatrix} -1 & -9 \\ -2 & 5 \end{bmatrix} \cdot \begin{bmatrix} -28 \\ -2 \end{bmatrix}$$

$$\begin{bmatrix} 1 & 0 \\ 0 & 1 \end{bmatrix} \cdot \begin{bmatrix} a \\ b \end{bmatrix} = -\frac{1}{23}\begin{bmatrix} 46 \\ 46 \end{bmatrix}$$

$$\begin{bmatrix} a \\ b \end{bmatrix} = \begin{bmatrix} -2 \\ -2 \end{bmatrix}$$

The solution is $(-2, -2)$.

28. Write the matrix equation for the system.

$$\begin{bmatrix} 1 & -2 \\ 1 & 5 \end{bmatrix} \cdot \begin{bmatrix} p \\ q \end{bmatrix} = \begin{bmatrix} 1 \\ 22 \end{bmatrix}$$

Find the inverse of the coefficient matrix.

$$A^{-1} = \frac{1}{5-(-2)}\begin{bmatrix} 5 & 2 \\ -1 & 1 \end{bmatrix}$$

$$= \frac{1}{7}\begin{bmatrix} 5 & 2 \\ -1 & 1 \end{bmatrix}$$

Multiply both sides of the matrix equation by A^{-1}.

$$\frac{1}{7}\begin{bmatrix} 5 & 2 \\ -1 & 1 \end{bmatrix} \cdot \begin{bmatrix} 1 & -2 \\ 1 & 5 \end{bmatrix} \cdot \begin{bmatrix} p \\ q \end{bmatrix} = \frac{1}{7}\begin{bmatrix} 5 & 2 \\ -1 & 1 \end{bmatrix} \cdot \begin{bmatrix} 1 \\ 22 \end{bmatrix}$$

$$\begin{bmatrix} 1 & 0 \\ 0 & 1 \end{bmatrix} \cdot \begin{bmatrix} p \\ q \end{bmatrix} = \frac{1}{7}\begin{bmatrix} 49 \\ 21 \end{bmatrix}$$

$$\begin{bmatrix} p \\ q \end{bmatrix} = \begin{bmatrix} 7 \\ 3 \end{bmatrix}$$

The solution is $(7, 3)$.

29. Write the matrix equation for the system.

$$\begin{bmatrix} 4 & -7 \\ 3 & 2 \end{bmatrix} \cdot \begin{bmatrix} m \\ n \end{bmatrix} = \begin{bmatrix} -63 \\ 18 \end{bmatrix}$$

Find the inverse of the coefficient matrix.

$$A^{-1} = \frac{1}{8-(-21)}\begin{bmatrix} 2 & 7 \\ -3 & 4 \end{bmatrix}$$

$$= \frac{1}{29}\begin{bmatrix} 2 & 7 \\ -3 & 4 \end{bmatrix}$$

Multiply both sides of the matrix equation by A^{-1}.

$$\frac{1}{29}\begin{bmatrix} 2 & 7 \\ -3 & 4 \end{bmatrix} \cdot \begin{bmatrix} 4 & -7 \\ 3 & 2 \end{bmatrix} \cdot \begin{bmatrix} m \\ n \end{bmatrix} = \frac{1}{29}\begin{bmatrix} 2 & 7 \\ -3 & 4 \end{bmatrix} \cdot \begin{bmatrix} -63 \\ 18 \end{bmatrix}$$

$$\begin{bmatrix} 1 & 0 \\ 0 & 1 \end{bmatrix} \cdot \begin{bmatrix} m \\ n \end{bmatrix} = \frac{1}{29}\begin{bmatrix} 0 \\ 261 \end{bmatrix}$$

$$\begin{bmatrix} m \\ n \end{bmatrix} = \begin{bmatrix} 0 \\ 9 \end{bmatrix}$$

The solution is $(0, 9)$.

30. Write the matrix equation for the system.

$$\begin{bmatrix} 1 & 2 \\ 3 & 2 \end{bmatrix} \cdot \begin{bmatrix} x \\ y \end{bmatrix} = \begin{bmatrix} 8 \\ 6 \end{bmatrix}$$

Find the inverse of the coefficient matrix.

$$A^{-1} = \frac{1}{2-6}\begin{bmatrix} 2 & -2 \\ -3 & 1 \end{bmatrix}$$

$$= -\frac{1}{4}\begin{bmatrix} 2 & -2 \\ -3 & 1 \end{bmatrix}$$

Multiply both sides of the matrix equation by A^{-1}.

$$-\frac{1}{4}\begin{bmatrix} 2 & -2 \\ -3 & 1 \end{bmatrix} \cdot \begin{bmatrix} 1 & 2 \\ 3 & 2 \end{bmatrix} \cdot \begin{bmatrix} x \\ y \end{bmatrix} = -\frac{1}{4}\begin{bmatrix} 2 & -2 \\ -3 & 1 \end{bmatrix} \cdot \begin{bmatrix} 8 \\ 6 \end{bmatrix}$$

$$\begin{bmatrix} 1 & 0 \\ 0 & 1 \end{bmatrix} \cdot \begin{bmatrix} x \\ y \end{bmatrix} = -\frac{1}{4}\begin{bmatrix} 4 \\ -18 \end{bmatrix}$$

$$\begin{bmatrix} x \\ y \end{bmatrix} = \begin{bmatrix} -1 \\ \frac{9}{2} \end{bmatrix}$$

The solution is $\left(-1, \frac{9}{2}\right)$.

31. Write the matrix equation for the system.

$$\begin{bmatrix} 4 & -3 \\ 2 & 9 \end{bmatrix} \cdot \begin{bmatrix} x \\ y \end{bmatrix} = \begin{bmatrix} 5 \\ 6 \end{bmatrix}$$

Find the inverse of the coefficient matrix.

$$A^{-1} = \frac{1}{36-(-6)}\begin{bmatrix} 9 & 3 \\ -2 & 4 \end{bmatrix}$$

$$= \frac{1}{42}\begin{bmatrix} 9 & 3 \\ -2 & 4 \end{bmatrix}$$

Multiply both sides of the matrix equation by A^{-1}.

$$\frac{1}{42}\begin{bmatrix} 9 & 3 \\ -2 & 4 \end{bmatrix} \cdot \begin{bmatrix} 4 & -3 \\ 2 & 9 \end{bmatrix} \cdot \begin{bmatrix} x \\ y \end{bmatrix} = \frac{1}{42}\begin{bmatrix} 9 & 3 \\ -2 & 4 \end{bmatrix} \cdot \begin{bmatrix} 5 \\ 6 \end{bmatrix}$$

$$\begin{bmatrix} 1 & 0 \\ 0 & 1 \end{bmatrix} \cdot \begin{bmatrix} x \\ y \end{bmatrix} = \frac{1}{42}\begin{bmatrix} 63 \\ 14 \end{bmatrix}$$

$$\begin{bmatrix} x \\ y \end{bmatrix} = \begin{bmatrix} \frac{3}{2} \\ \frac{1}{3} \end{bmatrix}$$

The solution is $\left(\frac{3}{2}, \frac{1}{3}\right)$.

32. Let a represent the number of hours that Hai-Ling spends training in an airplane, and let s represent the number of hours he spends training in a simulator.

$105a + 45s = 3870$

$a - s = 4$

Write the matrix equation for the system.

$$\begin{bmatrix} 105 & 45 \\ 1 & -1 \end{bmatrix} \cdot \begin{bmatrix} a \\ s \end{bmatrix} = \begin{bmatrix} 3870 \\ 4 \end{bmatrix}$$

Find the inverse of the coefficient matrix.

$$A^{-1} = \frac{1}{-105 - 45} \begin{bmatrix} -1 & -45 \\ -1 & 105 \end{bmatrix}$$

$$= -\frac{1}{150} \begin{bmatrix} -1 & -45 \\ -1 & 105 \end{bmatrix}$$

Multiply both sides of the matrix equation by A^{-1}.

$$-\frac{1}{150}\begin{bmatrix} -1 & -45 \\ -1 & 105 \end{bmatrix} \cdot \begin{bmatrix} 105 & 45 \\ 1 & -1 \end{bmatrix} \cdot \begin{bmatrix} a \\ s \end{bmatrix} = -\frac{1}{150}\begin{bmatrix} -1 & -45 \\ -1 & 105 \end{bmatrix} \cdot \begin{bmatrix} 3870 \\ 4 \end{bmatrix}$$

$$\begin{bmatrix} 1 & 0 \\ 0 & 1 \end{bmatrix} \cdot \begin{bmatrix} a \\ s \end{bmatrix} = -\frac{1}{150}\begin{bmatrix} -4050 \\ -3450 \end{bmatrix}$$

$$\begin{bmatrix} a \\ s \end{bmatrix} = \begin{bmatrix} 27 \\ 23 \end{bmatrix}$$

Hai-Ling can spend 27 hours training in an airplane and 23 hours training in a simulator.

33. Use the points (1995, 19.3) and (2001, 17.9) to write an equation for public schools.

$$m = \frac{y_2 - y_1}{x_2 - x_1}$$

$$= \frac{17.9 - 19.3}{2001 - 1995}$$

$$= \frac{-1.4}{6} \text{ or } -\frac{7}{30}.$$

Use the point-slope form.

$$y - y_1 = m(x - x_1)$$

$$y - 19.3 = -\frac{7}{30}(x - 1995)$$

$$y - 19.3 = -\frac{7}{30}x + 465.5$$

$$\frac{7}{30}x + y = 484.8$$

Use the points (1995, 16.6) and (2001, 16.3) to write an equation for private schools.

$$m = \frac{y_2 - y_1}{x_2 - x_1}$$

$$= \frac{16.3 - 16.6}{2001 - 1995}$$

$$= \frac{-0.3}{6} \text{ or } -\frac{1}{20}.$$

Use the point-slope form.

$$y - y_1 = m(x - x_1)$$

$$y - 16.6 = -\frac{1}{20}(x - 1995)$$

$$y - 16.6 = -\frac{1}{20}x + 99.75$$

$$\frac{1}{20}x + y = 116.35$$

Write the matrix equation for the system.

$$\begin{bmatrix} \frac{7}{30} & 1 \\ \frac{1}{20} & 1 \end{bmatrix} \cdot \begin{bmatrix} x \\ y \end{bmatrix} = \begin{bmatrix} 484.8 \\ 116.35 \end{bmatrix}$$

Find the inverse of the coefficient matrix.

$$A^{-1} = \frac{1}{\frac{7}{30} - \frac{1}{20}} \begin{bmatrix} 1 & -1 \\ -\frac{1}{20} & \frac{7}{30} \end{bmatrix} \text{ or } \frac{60}{11}\begin{bmatrix} 1 & -1 \\ -\frac{1}{20} & \frac{7}{30} \end{bmatrix}$$

Multiply each side of the matrix equation by A^{-1}.

$$\frac{60}{11}\begin{bmatrix} 1 & -1 \\ -\frac{1}{20} & \frac{7}{30} \end{bmatrix} \cdot \begin{bmatrix} \frac{7}{30} & 1 \\ \frac{1}{20} & 1 \end{bmatrix} \cdot \begin{bmatrix} x \\ y \end{bmatrix} = \frac{60}{11}\begin{bmatrix} 1 & -1 \\ -\frac{1}{20} & \frac{7}{30} \end{bmatrix} \cdot \begin{bmatrix} 484.8 \\ 116.35 \end{bmatrix}$$

$$\begin{bmatrix} 1 & 0 \\ 0 & 1 \end{bmatrix} \cdot \begin{bmatrix} x \\ y \end{bmatrix} \approx \frac{60}{11}\begin{bmatrix} 368.45 \\ 2.91 \end{bmatrix}$$

$$\begin{bmatrix} x \\ y \end{bmatrix} \approx \begin{bmatrix} 2010 \\ 15.9 \end{bmatrix}$$

The ratios should be the same in 2010.

34. Let x and y represent the volume in ml of the 60% and the 40% acid solutions, respectively.

$x + y = 200$

$0.60x + 0.40y = 0.48(200) \rightarrow 0.6x + 0.4y = 96$

Write the matrix equation for this system.

$$\begin{bmatrix} 1 & 1 \\ 0.6 & 0.4 \end{bmatrix} \cdot \begin{bmatrix} x \\ y \end{bmatrix} = \begin{bmatrix} 200 \\ 96 \end{bmatrix}$$

Find the inverse of the coefficient matrix.

$$A^{-1} = \frac{1}{0.4 - 0.6} \begin{bmatrix} 0.4 & -1 \\ -0.6 & 1 \end{bmatrix}$$

$$= -5\begin{bmatrix} 0.4 & -1 \\ -0.6 & 1 \end{bmatrix}$$

Multiply both sides of the matrix equation by A^{-1}.

$$-5\begin{bmatrix} 0.4 & -1 \\ -0.6 & 1 \end{bmatrix} \cdot \begin{bmatrix} 1 & 1 \\ 0.6 & 0.4 \end{bmatrix} \cdot \begin{bmatrix} x \\ y \end{bmatrix} = -5\begin{bmatrix} 0.4 & -1 \\ -0.6 & 1 \end{bmatrix} \cdot \begin{bmatrix} 200 \\ 96 \end{bmatrix}$$

$$\begin{bmatrix} 1 & 0 \\ 0 & 1 \end{bmatrix} \cdot \begin{bmatrix} x \\ y \end{bmatrix} = -5\begin{bmatrix} -16 \\ -24 \end{bmatrix}$$

$$\begin{bmatrix} x \\ y \end{bmatrix} = \begin{bmatrix} 80 \\ 120 \end{bmatrix}$$

Cara should mix 80 ml of the 60% solution with 120 ml of the 40% solution.

35. The solution set is the empty set or infinite solutions.

36. The food and territory that two species of birds require form a system of equations. Any independent system of equations can be solved using a matrix equation. Answers should include the following.

- Let a represent the number of nesting pairs of Species A and be b represent the number of nesting pairs of Species B. Then, $140a + 120b = 20,000$ and $500a + 400b = 69,000$.

- $$\begin{bmatrix} a \\ b \end{bmatrix} = -\frac{1}{4000}\begin{bmatrix} 400 & -120 \\ -500 & 140 \end{bmatrix} \cdot \begin{bmatrix} 20,000 \\ 69,000 \end{bmatrix};$$
  $a = 70$ and $b = 85$, so the area can support 70 pairs of Species A and 85 pairs of Species B.

37. D; $\begin{bmatrix} 6 & 8 \\ 10 & -12 \end{bmatrix} \cdot \begin{bmatrix} a \\ b \end{bmatrix} = \begin{bmatrix} 5 \\ 2 \end{bmatrix}$

Find the inverse of the coefficient matrix.

$A^{-1} = \dfrac{1}{-72 - 80} \begin{bmatrix} -12 & -8 \\ -10 & 6 \end{bmatrix}$

$\quad = -\dfrac{1}{152} \begin{bmatrix} -12 & -8 \\ -10 & 6 \end{bmatrix}$

Multiply both sides of the matrix equation by A^{-1}.

$-\dfrac{1}{152}\begin{bmatrix} -12 & -8 \\ -10 & 6 \end{bmatrix} \cdot \begin{bmatrix} 6 & 8 \\ 10 & -12 \end{bmatrix} \cdot \begin{bmatrix} a \\ b \end{bmatrix} = -\dfrac{1}{152}\begin{bmatrix} -12 & -8 \\ -10 & 6 \end{bmatrix} \cdot \begin{bmatrix} 5 \\ 2 \end{bmatrix}$

$\begin{bmatrix} 1 & 0 \\ 0 & 1 \end{bmatrix} \cdot \begin{bmatrix} a \\ b \end{bmatrix} = -\dfrac{1}{152}\begin{bmatrix} -76 \\ -38 \end{bmatrix}$

$\begin{bmatrix} a \\ b \end{bmatrix} = \begin{bmatrix} \frac{1}{2} \\ \frac{1}{4} \end{bmatrix}$

38. Let s, m, and l represent the numbers of small, medium, and large cones sold, respectively.

$$\begin{array}{ll} s + m + l = 52 & s + m + l = 52 \\ m = s + 7 & \rightarrow \quad -s + m = 7 \\ 0.89s + 1.19m + 1.39l = 58.98 & 0.89s + 1.19m + 1.39l = 58.98 \end{array}$$

Use Cramer's rule.

$$s = \dfrac{\begin{vmatrix} 52 & 1 & 1 \\ 7 & 1 & 0 \\ 58.98 & 1.19 & 1.39 \end{vmatrix}}{\begin{vmatrix} 1 & 1 & 1 \\ -1 & 1 & 0 \\ 0.89 & 1.19 & 1.39 \end{vmatrix}} \qquad m = \dfrac{\begin{vmatrix} 1 & 52 & 1 \\ -1 & 7 & 0 \\ 0.89 & 58.98 & 1.39 \end{vmatrix}}{\begin{vmatrix} 1 & 1 & 1 \\ -1 & 1 & 0 \\ 0.89 & 1.19 & 1.39 \end{vmatrix}} \qquad l = \dfrac{\begin{vmatrix} 1 & 1 & 52 \\ -1 & 1 & 7 \\ 0.89 & 1.19 & 58.98 \end{vmatrix}}{\begin{vmatrix} 1 & 1 & 1 \\ -1 & 1 & 0 \\ 0.89 & 1.19 & 1.39 \end{vmatrix}}$$

$\quad = \dfrac{11.9}{0.7} \qquad\qquad = \dfrac{16.8}{0.7} \qquad\qquad = \dfrac{7.7}{0.7}$

$\quad = 17 \qquad\qquad\quad = 24 \qquad\qquad\quad = 11$

Scott sold 17 small, 24 medium, and 11 large cones.

39. Write the matrix equation for the system.

$\begin{bmatrix} 2 & -1 & 4 \\ 1 & 5 & -2 \\ 3 & -2 & 6 \end{bmatrix} \cdot \begin{bmatrix} a \\ b \\ c \end{bmatrix} = \begin{bmatrix} 6 \\ -6 \\ 8 \end{bmatrix}$

After you enter the coefficient matrix in A, and the constant matrix in B, enter the following to find $A^{-1} \cdot B$.

KEYSTROKES: $\boxed{\text{MATRX}}$ 1 $\boxed{x^{-1}}$ $\boxed{X}$ $\boxed{\text{MATRX}}$ 2

The solution is $(-6, 2, 5)$.

40. Write the matrix equation for the system.

$\begin{bmatrix} 3 & -5 & 2 \\ 2 & 3 & -1 \\ 4 & 3 & 3 \end{bmatrix} \cdot \begin{bmatrix} x \\ y \\ z \end{bmatrix} = \begin{bmatrix} 22 \\ -9 \\ 1 \end{bmatrix}$

After you enter the coefficient matrix in A, and the constant matrix in B, enter the following to find $A^{-1} \cdot B$.

KEYSTROKES: $\boxed{\text{MATRX}}$ 1 $\boxed{x^{-1}}$ $\boxed{X}$ $\boxed{\text{MATRX}}$ 2

The solution is $(1, -3, 2)$.

41. Write the matrix equation for the system.

$\begin{bmatrix} 2 & 1 & 1 \\ -1 & -1 & 2 \\ -3 & 2 & 3 \end{bmatrix} \cdot \begin{bmatrix} q \\ r \\ s \end{bmatrix} = \begin{bmatrix} 2 \\ 7 \\ 7 \end{bmatrix}$

After you enter the coefficient matrix in A, and the constant matrix in B, enter the following to find $A^{-1} \cdot B$.

KEYSTROKES: $\boxed{\text{MATRX}}$ 1 $\boxed{x^{-1}}$ $\boxed{X}$ $\boxed{\text{MATRX}}$ 2

The solution is $(0, -1, 3)$.

Page 207 Maintain Your Skills

42. $\dfrac{1}{ad - bc}\begin{bmatrix} d & -b \\ -c & a \end{bmatrix} = \dfrac{1}{12 - 8}\begin{bmatrix} 3 & -4 \\ -2 & 4 \end{bmatrix}$

$\qquad\qquad = \dfrac{1}{4}\begin{bmatrix} 3 & -4 \\ -2 & 4 \end{bmatrix}$ or $\begin{bmatrix} \frac{3}{4} & -1 \\ -\frac{1}{2} & 1 \end{bmatrix}$

43. $\dfrac{1}{ad - bc}\begin{bmatrix} d & -b \\ -c & a \end{bmatrix} = \dfrac{1}{36 - 35}\begin{bmatrix} 4 & -5 \\ -7 & 9 \end{bmatrix}$

$\qquad\qquad = \dfrac{1}{1}\begin{bmatrix} 4 & -5 \\ -7 & 9 \end{bmatrix}$ or $\begin{bmatrix} 4 & -5 \\ -7 & 9 \end{bmatrix}$

44. $\begin{vmatrix} -3 & -6 \\ 5 & 10 \end{vmatrix} = -3(10) - (-6)(5)$ or 0

Since the determinant is 0, no inverse exists.

45. $x = \dfrac{\begin{vmatrix} 10 & 7 \\ 20 & -4 \end{vmatrix}}{\begin{vmatrix} 6 & 7 \\ 3 & -4 \end{vmatrix}} \qquad\qquad y = \dfrac{\begin{vmatrix} 6 & 10 \\ 3 & 20 \end{vmatrix}}{\begin{vmatrix} 6 & 7 \\ 3 & -4 \end{vmatrix}}$

$\quad = \dfrac{10(-4) - 7(20)}{6(-4) - 7(3)} \qquad = \dfrac{6(20) - 10(3)}{6(-4) - 7(3)}$

$\quad = \dfrac{-180}{-45} \qquad\qquad\quad = \dfrac{90}{-45}$

$\quad = 4 \qquad\qquad\qquad = -2$

The solution is $(4, -2)$.

46. $a = \dfrac{\begin{vmatrix} -10.15 & 7 \\ 69.944 & -6 \end{vmatrix}}{\begin{vmatrix} 6 & 7 \\ 9.2 & -6 \end{vmatrix}} \qquad b = \dfrac{\begin{vmatrix} 6 & -10.15 \\ 9.2 & 69.944 \end{vmatrix}}{\begin{vmatrix} 6 & 7 \\ 9.2 & -6 \end{vmatrix}}$

$\quad = \dfrac{(-10.15)(-6) - 7(69.944)}{6(-6) - 7(9.2)} \qquad = \dfrac{6(69.944) - (-10.15)(9.2)}{6(-6) - 7(9.2)}$

$\quad = \dfrac{-428.708}{-100.4} \qquad\qquad\qquad = \dfrac{513.044}{-100.4}$

$\quad = 4.27 \qquad\qquad\qquad\qquad = -5.11$

The solution is $(4.27, -5.11)$.

47. $x = \dfrac{\begin{vmatrix} \frac{7}{3} & -\frac{2}{3} \\ -50 & 4 \end{vmatrix}}{\begin{vmatrix} \frac{1}{2} & -\frac{2}{3} \\ 3 & 4 \end{vmatrix}} \qquad\qquad y = \dfrac{\begin{vmatrix} \frac{1}{2} & -\frac{7}{3} \\ 3 & -50 \end{vmatrix}}{\begin{vmatrix} \frac{1}{2} & -\frac{2}{3} \\ 3 & 4 \end{vmatrix}}$

$\quad = \dfrac{\left(\frac{7}{3}\right)(4) - \left(-\frac{2}{3}\right)(-50)}{\left(\frac{1}{2}\right)(4) - \left(-\frac{2}{3}\right)(3)} \qquad = \dfrac{\left(\frac{1}{2}\right)(-50) - \left(\frac{7}{3}\right)(3)}{\left(\frac{1}{2}\right)(4) - \left(-\frac{2}{3}\right)(3)}$

$\quad = \dfrac{-24}{4} \qquad\qquad\qquad\quad = \dfrac{-32}{4}$

$\quad = -6 \qquad\qquad\qquad\quad = -8$

The solution is $(-6, -8)$.

48. Use the points $(0, 0)$ and $(3.5, 20)$ to write the equation.

$$m = \frac{y_2 - y_1}{x_2 - x_1}$$
$$= \frac{20 - 0}{3.5 - 0}$$
$$= \frac{40}{7}$$

Use the point-slope form.

$$y - y_1 = m(x - x_1)$$
$$y - 0 = \frac{40}{7}(x - 0)$$
$$y = \frac{40}{7}x$$

Substitute 20 for x.

$$y = \frac{40}{7}x$$
$$= \frac{40}{7}(20)$$
$$\approx 114.3$$

Recycling a 20-foot stack of newspaper saves approximately 114.3 feet of loblolly pine.

49. $|x - 3| = 7$

$$x - 3 = 7 \quad \text{or} \quad x - 3 = -7$$
$$x = 10 \qquad\qquad x = -4$$

Check: $|x - 3| = 7$ $\qquad$ $|x - 3| = 7$
$\qquad$ $|10 - 3| \stackrel{?}{=} 7$ $\qquad$ $|-4 - 3| \stackrel{?}{=} 7$
$\qquad\qquad$ $|7| \stackrel{?}{=} 7$ $\qquad\qquad$ $|-7| \stackrel{?}{=} 7$
$\qquad\qquad\qquad$ $7 = 7 \checkmark$ $\qquad\qquad\qquad$ $7 = 7 \checkmark$

The solution set is $\{-4, 10\}$

50. $-4|d + 2| = -12$
$\qquad$ $|d + 2| = 3$
$\qquad\qquad$ $d + 2 = 3 \quad \text{or} \quad d + 2 = -3$
$\qquad\qquad\qquad$ $d = 1 \qquad\qquad\qquad d = -5$

Check:
$-4|d + 2| = -12$ $\qquad$ $-4|d + 2| = -12$
$-4|1 + 2| \stackrel{?}{=} -12$ $\qquad$ $-4|-5 + 2| \stackrel{?}{=} -12$
$\qquad$ $-4|3| \stackrel{?}{=} -12$ $\qquad\qquad$ $-4|-3| \stackrel{?}{=} -12$
$\qquad$ $-4(3) \stackrel{?}{=} -12$ $\qquad\qquad$ $-4(3) \stackrel{?}{=} -12$
$\qquad\qquad$ $-12 = -12 \checkmark$ $\qquad\qquad$ $-12 = -12 \checkmark$

The solution set is $\{-5, 1\}$.

51. $5|k - 4| = k + 8$
$5(k - 4) = k + 8 \quad \text{or} \quad 5(k - 4) = -(k + 8)$
$5k - 20 = k + 8 \qquad\qquad 5k - 20 = -k - 8$
$\qquad$ $4k = 28 \qquad\qquad\qquad\qquad 6k = 12$
$\qquad\quad$ $k = 7 \qquad\qquad\qquad\qquad\quad k = 2$

Check: $5|k - 4| = k + 8$ $\qquad$ $5|k - 4| = k + 8$
$\qquad$ $5|7 - 4| \stackrel{?}{=} 7 + 8$ $\qquad$ $5|2 - 4| \stackrel{?}{=} 2 + 8$
$\qquad\qquad$ $5|3| \stackrel{?}{=} 15$ $\qquad\qquad$ $5|-2| \stackrel{?}{=} 10$
$\qquad\qquad$ $5(3) \stackrel{?}{=} 15$ $\qquad\qquad$ $5(2) \stackrel{?}{=} 10$
$\qquad\qquad\qquad$ $15 = 15 \checkmark$ $\qquad\qquad$ $10 = 10 \checkmark$

The solution set is $\{2, 7\}$.

Page 208 **Graphing Calculator Investigation (Follow-Up of Lesson 4-8)**

1. Write the augmented matrix and enter it into matrix A.

KEYSTROKES: MATRX ▶ ALPHA

B MATRX 1) ENTER

$$\begin{bmatrix} 1 & -3 & | & 5 \\ 2 & 1 & | & 1 \end{bmatrix} \longrightarrow \begin{bmatrix} 1 & 0 & | & 1.14 \\ 0 & 1 & | & -1.29 \end{bmatrix}$$

The solution is about $(1.14, -1.29)$.

2. Write the augmented matrix and enter it into matrix A.

KEYSTROKES: MATRX ▶ ALPHA

B MATRX 1) ENTER

$$\begin{bmatrix} 15 & 11 & | & 36 \\ 4 & -3 & | & -26 \end{bmatrix} \longrightarrow \begin{bmatrix} 1 & 0 & | & -2 \\ 0 & 1 & | & 6 \end{bmatrix}$$

The solution is about $(-2, 6)$.

3. Write the augmented matrix and enter it into matrix A.

KEYSTROKES: MATRX ▶ ALPHA

B MATRX 1) ENTER

$$\begin{bmatrix} 2 & 1 & | & 5 \\ 2 & -3 & | & 1 \end{bmatrix} \longrightarrow \begin{bmatrix} 1 & 0 & | & 2 \\ 0 & 1 & | & 1 \end{bmatrix}$$

The solution is $(2, 1)$.

4. Write the augmented matrix and enter it into matrix A.

KEYSTROKES: MATRX ▶ ALPHA

B MATRX 1) ENTER

$$\begin{bmatrix} 3 & -1 & | & 0 \\ 2 & -3 & | & 1 \end{bmatrix} \longrightarrow \begin{bmatrix} 1 & 0 & | & -0.14 \\ 0 & 1 & | & -0.43 \end{bmatrix}$$

The solution is about $(-0.14, -0.43)$.

5. Write the augmented matrix and enter it into matrix A.

KEYSTROKES: MATRX ▶ ALPHA

B MATRX 1) ENTER

$$\begin{bmatrix} 3 & -2 & 1 & | & -2 \\ 1 & -1 & 3 & | & 5 \\ -1 & 1 & 1 & | & -1 \end{bmatrix} \longrightarrow \begin{bmatrix} 1 & 0 & 0 & | & -7 \\ 0 & 1 & 0 & | & -9 \\ 0 & 0 & 1 & | & 1 \end{bmatrix}$$

The solution is $(-7, -9, 1)$.

6. Write the augmented matrix and enter it into matrix A.

KEYSTROKES: MATRX ▶ ALPHA

B MATRX 1) ENTER

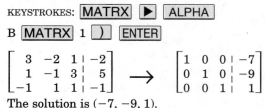

$$\begin{bmatrix} 1 & -1 & 1 & | & 2 \\ 1 & 0 & -1 & | & 1 \\ 0 & 1 & 2 & | & 0 \end{bmatrix} \longrightarrow \begin{bmatrix} 1 & 0 & 0 & | & 1.25 \\ 0 & 1 & 0 & | & -0.5 \\ 0 & 0 & 1 & | & 0.25 \end{bmatrix}$$

The solution is $(1.25, -0.5, 0.25)$.

Chapter 4 Study Guide and Review

Page 209　Vocabulary and Concept Check

1. identity matrix
2. isometry
3. Scalar multiplication
4. rotation
5. determinant
6. matrix equation
7. dimensions
8. translation
9. equal matrices
10. dilation

Pages 209–214　Lesson-by-Lesson Review

11. Write the corresponding system of equations.

$2y - x = 3$
$x = 4y - 1$

Substitute $4y - 1$ for x in the first equation.

$2y - x = 3$
$2y - (4y - 1) = 3$
$2y - 4y + 1 = 3$
$-2y = 2$
$y = -1$

Substitute -1 for y in the second equation.

$x = 4y - 1$
$= 4(-1) - 1$
$= -4 - 1$
$= -5$

The solution is $(-5, -1)$.

12. Write the corresponding system of equations.

$7x = 5 + 2y$
$x + y = 11$

Solve the second equation for x.

$x + y = 11$
$x = 11 - y$

Substitute $11 - y$ for x in the first equation.

$7x = 5 + 2y$
$7(11 - y) = 5 + 2y$
$77 - 7y = 5 + 2y$
$72 = 9y$
$8 = y$

Substitute 8 for y in the second equation.

$x + y = 11$
$x + 8 = 11$
$x = 3$

The solution is $(3, 8)$.

13. Write the corresponding system of equations.

$3x + y = -3$
$x - 3y = -1$

Solve the second equation for x.

$x - 3y = -3$
$x = 3y - 1$

Substitute $3y - 1$ for x in the first equation.

$3x + y = -3$
$3(3y - 1) + y = -3$
$9y - 3 + y = -3$
$10y = 0$
$y = 0$

Substitute 0 for y in the second equation.

$x - 3y = -1$
$x - 3(0) = -1$
$x = -1$

The solution is $(-1, 0)$.

14. Write the corresponding system of equations.

$2x - y = 2$
$6x - y = 22$

Solve the first equation for y.

$2x - y = 2$
$-y = -2x + 2$
$y = 2x - 2$

Substitute $2x - 2$ for y in the second equation.

$6x - y = 22$
$6x - (2x - 2) = 22$
$6x - 2x + 2 = 22$
$4x = 20$
$x = 5$

Substitute 5 for x in the first equation.

$2x - y = 2$
$2(5) - y = 2$
$10 - y = 2$
$8 = y$

The solution is $(5, 8)$.

15. $\begin{bmatrix} -4 & 3 \\ -5 & 2 \end{bmatrix} + \begin{bmatrix} 1 & -3 \\ 3 & -8 \end{bmatrix} = \begin{bmatrix} -4+1 & 3+(-3) \\ -5+3 & 2+(-8) \end{bmatrix}$

$= \begin{bmatrix} -3 & 0 \\ -2 & -6 \end{bmatrix}$

16. $\begin{bmatrix} 0.2 & 1.3 & -0.4 \end{bmatrix} - \begin{bmatrix} 2 & 1.7 & 2.6 \end{bmatrix}$
$= \begin{bmatrix} 0.2 - 2 & 1.3 - 1.7 & -0.4 - 2.6 \end{bmatrix}$
$= \begin{bmatrix} -1.8 & -0.4 & -3 \end{bmatrix}$

17. $\begin{bmatrix} 1 & -5 \\ -2 & 3 \end{bmatrix} + \frac{3}{4} \begin{bmatrix} 0 & 4 \\ -16 & 8 \end{bmatrix}$

$= \begin{bmatrix} 1 & -5 \\ -2 & 3 \end{bmatrix} + \begin{bmatrix} \frac{3}{4}(0) & \frac{3}{4}(4) \\ \frac{3}{4}(-16) & \frac{3}{4}(8) \end{bmatrix}$

$= \begin{bmatrix} 1 & -5 \\ -2 & 3 \end{bmatrix} + \begin{bmatrix} 0 & 3 \\ -12 & 6 \end{bmatrix}$

$= \begin{bmatrix} 1+0 & -5+3 \\ -2+(-12) & 3+6 \end{bmatrix}$

$= \begin{bmatrix} 1 & -2 \\ -14 & 9 \end{bmatrix}$

18. $\begin{bmatrix} 1 & 0 & -3 \\ 4 & -5 & 2 \end{bmatrix} - 2 \begin{bmatrix} -2 & 3 & 5 \\ -3 & -1 & 2 \end{bmatrix}$

$= \begin{bmatrix} 1 & 0 & -3 \\ 4 & -5 & 2 \end{bmatrix} - \begin{bmatrix} 2(-2) & 2(3) & 2(5) \\ 2(-3) & 2(-1) & 2(2) \end{bmatrix}$

$= \begin{bmatrix} 1 & 0 & -3 \\ 4 & -5 & 2 \end{bmatrix} - \begin{bmatrix} -4 & 6 & 10 \\ -6 & -2 & 4 \end{bmatrix}$

$= \begin{bmatrix} 1-(-4) & 0-6 & -3-10 \\ 4-(-6) & -5-(-2) & 2-4 \end{bmatrix}$

$= \begin{bmatrix} 5 & -6 & -13 \\ 10 & -3 & -2 \end{bmatrix}$

19. $\begin{bmatrix} 2 & 7 \end{bmatrix} \cdot \begin{bmatrix} 5 \\ -4 \end{bmatrix} = \begin{bmatrix} 2(5) + 7(-4) \end{bmatrix}$

$= \begin{bmatrix} -18 \end{bmatrix}$

20. $\begin{bmatrix} 8 & -3 \\ 6 & 1 \end{bmatrix} \cdot \begin{bmatrix} 2 & -3 \\ 1 & -5 \end{bmatrix}$

$= \begin{bmatrix} 8(2) + (-3)(1) & 8(-3) + (-3)(-5) \\ 6(2) + 1(1) & 6(-3) + 1(-5) \end{bmatrix}$

$= \begin{bmatrix} 13 & -9 \\ 13 & -23 \end{bmatrix}$

21. Not possible; the inner dimensions are not the same.

22. $\begin{bmatrix} 3 & 0 & -1 \\ 4 & -2 & 3 \end{bmatrix} \cdot \begin{bmatrix} 7 & 1 \\ 6 & -3 \\ 2 & 1 \end{bmatrix}$

$= \begin{bmatrix} 3(7) + 0(6) + (-1)(2) & 3(1) + 0(-3) + (-1)(1) \\ 4(7) + (-2)(6) + (3)(2) & 4(1) + (-2)(-3) + (3)(1) \end{bmatrix}$

$= \begin{bmatrix} 19 & 2 \\ 22 & 13 \end{bmatrix}$

23. $\begin{bmatrix} -3 & 4 & -1 \\ 5 & 3 & -2 \end{bmatrix} \cdot \begin{bmatrix} 4 & 4 & 4 \\ -5 & -5 & -5 \end{bmatrix} = \begin{bmatrix} 1 & 8 & 3 \\ 0 & -2 & -7 \end{bmatrix}$

The coordinates are $A'(1, 0)$, $B'(8, -2)$, and $C'(3, -7)$.

24. $2\begin{bmatrix} -3 & 4 & -1 \\ 5 & 3 & -2 \end{bmatrix} = \begin{bmatrix} -6 & 8 & -2 \\ 10 & 6 & -4 \end{bmatrix}$

The coordinates are $A'(-6, 10)$, $B'(8, 6)$, and $C'(-2, -4)$.

25. $\begin{bmatrix} -1 & 0 \\ 0 & 1 \end{bmatrix} \cdot \begin{bmatrix} -3 & 4 & -1 \\ 5 & 3 & -2 \end{bmatrix} = \begin{bmatrix} 3 & -4 & 1 \\ 5 & 3 & -2 \end{bmatrix}$

The coordinates are $A'(3, 5)$, $B'(-4, 3)$, and $C'(1, -2)$.

26. $\begin{bmatrix} -1 & 0 \\ 0 & -1 \end{bmatrix} \cdot \begin{bmatrix} -3 & 4 & -1 \\ 5 & 3 & -2 \end{bmatrix} = \begin{bmatrix} 3 & -4 & 1 \\ -5 & -3 & 2 \end{bmatrix}$

The coordinates are $A'(3, -5)$, $B'(-4, -3)$, and $C'(1, 2)$.

27. $\begin{vmatrix} 4 & 11 \\ -7 & 8 \end{vmatrix} = 4(8) - 11(-7)$

$= 32 + 77$

$= 109$

28. $\begin{vmatrix} 6 & -7 \\ 5 & 3 \end{vmatrix} = 6(3) - (-7)(5)$

$= 18 + 35$

$= 53$

29. $\begin{vmatrix} 12 & 8 \\ 9 & 6 \end{vmatrix} = 12(6) - 8(9)$

$= 72 - 72$

$= 0$

30. $\begin{vmatrix} 2 & -3 & 1 \\ 0 & 7 & 8 \\ 2 & 1 & 3 \end{vmatrix} = 2\begin{vmatrix} 7 & 8 \\ 1 & 3 \end{vmatrix} - (-3)\begin{vmatrix} 0 & 8 \\ 2 & 3 \end{vmatrix} + 1\begin{vmatrix} 0 & 7 \\ 2 & 1 \end{vmatrix}$

$= 2(21 - 8) + 3(0 - 16) + 1(0 - 14)$

$= 26 - 48 - 14$

$= -36$

31. $\begin{vmatrix} 7 & -4 & 5 \\ 1 & 3 & -6 \\ 5 & -1 & -2 \end{vmatrix} = 7\begin{vmatrix} 3 & -6 \\ -1 & -2 \end{vmatrix} - (-4)\begin{vmatrix} 1 & -6 \\ 5 & -2 \end{vmatrix} + 5\begin{vmatrix} 1 & 3 \\ 5 & -1 \end{vmatrix}$

$= 7(-6 - 6) + 4(-2 - (-30)) + 5(-1 - 15)$

$= -84 + 112 - 80$

$= -52$

32. $\begin{bmatrix} 6 & 3 & -2 \\ -4 & 2 & 5 \\ -3 & -1 & 0 \end{bmatrix}$

$= 6\begin{vmatrix} 2 & 5 \\ -1 & 0 \end{vmatrix} - 3\begin{vmatrix} -4 & 5 \\ -3 & 0 \end{vmatrix} + (-2)\begin{vmatrix} -4 & 2 \\ -3 & -1 \end{vmatrix}$

$= 6(0 - (-5)) - 3(0 - (-15)) - 2(4 - (-6))$

$= 30 - 45 - 20$

$= -35$

33. $a = \dfrac{\begin{vmatrix} 1 & -1 \\ 12 & 2 \end{vmatrix}}{\begin{vmatrix} 9 & -1 \\ 3 & 2 \end{vmatrix}}$ $\qquad b = \dfrac{\begin{vmatrix} 9 & 1 \\ 3 & 12 \end{vmatrix}}{\begin{vmatrix} 9 & -1 \\ 3 & 2 \end{vmatrix}}$

$= \dfrac{2 + 12}{18 + 3}$ $\qquad\qquad = \dfrac{108 - 3}{18 + 3}$

$= \dfrac{14}{21}$ $\qquad\qquad\quad = \dfrac{105}{21}$

$= \dfrac{2}{3}$ $\qquad\qquad\quad = 5$

The solution is $\left(\dfrac{2}{3}, 5\right)$.

34. $x = \dfrac{\begin{vmatrix} 14 & 5 \\ 4 & 6 \end{vmatrix}}{\begin{vmatrix} 1 & 5 \\ -2 & 6 \end{vmatrix}}$ $\qquad y = \dfrac{\begin{vmatrix} 1 & 14 \\ -2 & 4 \end{vmatrix}}{\begin{vmatrix} 1 & 5 \\ -2 & 6 \end{vmatrix}}$

$= \dfrac{84 - 20}{6 + 10}$ $\qquad\quad = \dfrac{4 + 28}{6 + 10}$

$= \dfrac{64}{16}$ $\qquad\qquad = \dfrac{32}{16}$

$= 4$ $\qquad\qquad\quad = 2$

The solution is $(4, 2)$.

35. $x = \dfrac{\begin{vmatrix} -15 & 4 \\ 19 & -7 \end{vmatrix}}{\begin{vmatrix} 3 & 4 \\ 2 & -7 \end{vmatrix}}$ $\qquad y = \dfrac{\begin{vmatrix} 3 & -15 \\ 2 & 19 \end{vmatrix}}{\begin{vmatrix} 3 & 4 \\ 2 & -7 \end{vmatrix}}$

$= \dfrac{105 - 76}{-21 - 8}$ $\qquad = \dfrac{57 + 30}{-21 - 8}$

$= \dfrac{29}{-29}$ $\qquad\qquad = \dfrac{87}{-29}$

$= -1$ $\qquad\qquad\quad = -3$

The solution is $(-1, -3)$.

36. $a = \dfrac{\begin{vmatrix} 2 & 5 \\ -1 & -4 \end{vmatrix}}{\begin{vmatrix} 8 & 5 \\ -6 & -4 \end{vmatrix}}$ $\qquad b = \dfrac{\begin{vmatrix} 8 & 2 \\ -6 & -1 \end{vmatrix}}{\begin{vmatrix} 8 & 5 \\ -6 & -4 \end{vmatrix}}$

$= \dfrac{-8 + 5}{-32 + 30}$ $\qquad = \dfrac{-8 + 12}{-32 + 30}$

$= \dfrac{-3}{-2}$ $\qquad\qquad = \dfrac{4}{-2}$

$= \dfrac{3}{2}$ $\qquad\qquad\quad = -2$

The solution is $\left(\dfrac{3}{2}, -2\right)$.

37. $x = \dfrac{\begin{vmatrix} 13 & 0 & -7 \\ 14 & 8 & 2 \\ 6 & 0 & 1 \end{vmatrix}}{\begin{vmatrix} 6 & 0 & -7 \\ 0 & 8 & 2 \\ 7 & 0 & 1 \end{vmatrix}}$ $\quad y = \dfrac{\begin{vmatrix} 6 & 13 & -7 \\ 0 & 14 & 2 \\ 7 & 6 & 1 \end{vmatrix}}{\begin{vmatrix} 6 & 0 & -7 \\ 0 & 8 & 2 \\ 7 & 0 & 1 \end{vmatrix}}$ $\quad z = \dfrac{\begin{vmatrix} 6 & 0 & 13 \\ 0 & 8 & 14 \\ 7 & 0 & 6 \end{vmatrix}}{\begin{vmatrix} 6 & 0 & -7 \\ 0 & 8 & 2 \\ 7 & 0 & 1 \end{vmatrix}}$

$= \dfrac{440}{440}$ $\qquad\quad = \dfrac{880}{440}$ $\qquad\quad = \dfrac{-440}{440}$

$= 1$ $\qquad\qquad = 2$ $\qquad\qquad = -1$

The solution is $(1, 2, -1)$.

38. $a = \dfrac{\begin{vmatrix} -20 & -1 & -3 \\ 6 & 2 & 1 \\ -6 & 1 & -1 \end{vmatrix}}{\begin{vmatrix} 2 & -1 & -3 \\ 4 & 2 & 1 \\ 2 & 1 & -1 \end{vmatrix}}$ $b = \dfrac{\begin{vmatrix} 2 & -20 & -3 \\ 4 & 6 & 1 \\ 2 & -6 & -1 \end{vmatrix}}{\begin{vmatrix} 2 & -1 & -3 \\ 4 & 2 & 1 \\ 2 & 1 & -1 \end{vmatrix}}$ $c = \dfrac{\begin{vmatrix} 2 & -1 & -20 \\ 4 & 2 & 6 \\ 2 & 1 & -6 \end{vmatrix}}{\begin{vmatrix} 2 & -1 & -3 \\ 4 & 2 & 1 \\ 2 & 1 & -1 \end{vmatrix}}$

$\quad = \dfrac{6}{-12} \qquad\qquad = \dfrac{-12}{-12} \qquad\qquad = \dfrac{-72}{-72}$

$\quad = -\dfrac{1}{2} \qquad\qquad\ = 1 \qquad\qquad\quad = 6$

The solution is $\left(-\dfrac{1}{2},\, 1,\, 6\right)$.

39. Find the value of the determinant.

$\begin{bmatrix} 3 & 2 \\ 4 & -2 \end{bmatrix} = -6 - 8$ or -14

Use the formula for the inverse matrix.

$A^{-1} = -\dfrac{1}{14}\begin{bmatrix} -2 & -2 \\ -4 & 3 \end{bmatrix}$

40. Find the value of the determinant.

$\begin{vmatrix} 8 & 6 \\ 9 & 7 \end{vmatrix} = 56 - 54$ or 2

Use the formula for the inverse matrix.

$A^{-1} = \dfrac{1}{2}\begin{bmatrix} 7 & -6 \\ -9 & 8 \end{bmatrix}$

41. Find the value of the determinant.

$\begin{vmatrix} 2 & 4 \\ -3 & 6 \end{vmatrix} = 12 - (-12)$ or 24

Use the formula for the inverse matrix.

$A^{-1} = \dfrac{1}{24}\begin{bmatrix} 6 & -4 \\ 3 & 2 \end{bmatrix}$

42. Find the value of the determinant.

$\begin{vmatrix} 6 & -2 \\ 3 & -1 \end{vmatrix} = -6 - (-6)$ or 0

Since the determinant is 0, no inverse exists.

43. Find the value of the determinant.

$\begin{vmatrix} 0 & 2 \\ 5 & -4 \end{vmatrix} = 0 - 10$ or -10

Use the formula for the inverse matrix.

$A^{-1} = -\dfrac{1}{10}\begin{bmatrix} -4 & -2 \\ -5 & 0 \end{bmatrix}$

44. Since the matrix is not a square matrix, no inverse exists.

45. Find the inverse of the coefficient matrix.

$A^{-1} = \dfrac{1}{15 - (-2)}\begin{bmatrix} 3 & 2 \\ -1 & 5 \end{bmatrix}$ or $\dfrac{1}{17}\begin{bmatrix} 3 & 2 \\ -1 & 5 \end{bmatrix}$

Multiply each side of the matrix equation by A^{-1}.

$\dfrac{1}{17}\begin{bmatrix} 3 & 2 \\ -1 & 5 \end{bmatrix} \cdot \begin{bmatrix} 5 & -2 \\ 1 & 3 \end{bmatrix} \cdot \begin{bmatrix} x \\ y \end{bmatrix} = \dfrac{1}{17}\begin{bmatrix} 3 & 2 \\ -1 & 5 \end{bmatrix} \cdot \begin{bmatrix} 16 \\ 10 \end{bmatrix}$

$\begin{bmatrix} 1 & 0 \\ 0 & 1 \end{bmatrix} \cdot \begin{bmatrix} x \\ y \end{bmatrix} = \dfrac{1}{17}\begin{bmatrix} 68 \\ 34 \end{bmatrix}$

$\begin{bmatrix} x \\ y \end{bmatrix} = \begin{bmatrix} 4 \\ 2 \end{bmatrix}$

The solution is $(4, 2)$.

46. Find the inverse of the coefficient matrix.

$A^{-1} = \dfrac{1}{-8 - 3}\begin{bmatrix} -2 & -1 \\ -3 & 4 \end{bmatrix}$ or $-\dfrac{1}{11}\begin{bmatrix} -2 & -1 \\ -3 & 4 \end{bmatrix}$

Multiply each side of the matrix equation by A^{-1}.

$-\dfrac{1}{11}\begin{bmatrix} -2 & -1 \\ -3 & 4 \end{bmatrix} \cdot \begin{bmatrix} 4 & 1 \\ 3 & -2 \end{bmatrix} \cdot \begin{bmatrix} a \\ b \end{bmatrix} = -\dfrac{1}{11}\begin{bmatrix} -2 & -1 \\ -3 & 4 \end{bmatrix} \cdot \begin{bmatrix} 9 \\ 4 \end{bmatrix}$

$\begin{bmatrix} 1 & 0 \\ 0 & 1 \end{bmatrix} \cdot \begin{bmatrix} a \\ b \end{bmatrix} = -\dfrac{1}{11}\begin{bmatrix} -22 \\ -11 \end{bmatrix}$

$\begin{bmatrix} a \\ b \end{bmatrix} = \begin{bmatrix} 2 \\ 1 \end{bmatrix}$

The solution is $(2, 1)$.

47. Write the matrix equation for the system.

$\begin{bmatrix} 3 & 1 \\ 4 & -2 \end{bmatrix} \cdot \begin{bmatrix} x \\ y \end{bmatrix} = \begin{bmatrix} -8 \\ -14 \end{bmatrix}$

Find the inverse of the coefficient matrix.

$A^{-1} = \dfrac{1}{-6 - 4}\begin{bmatrix} -2 & -1 \\ -4 & 3 \end{bmatrix}$ or $-\dfrac{1}{10}\begin{bmatrix} -2 & -1 \\ -4 & 3 \end{bmatrix}$

Multiply each side of the matrix equation by A^{-1}.

$-\dfrac{1}{10}\begin{bmatrix} -2 & -1 \\ -4 & 3 \end{bmatrix} \cdot \begin{bmatrix} 3 & 1 \\ 4 & -2 \end{bmatrix} \cdot \begin{bmatrix} x \\ y \end{bmatrix} = -\dfrac{1}{10}\begin{bmatrix} -2 & -1 \\ -4 & 3 \end{bmatrix} \cdot \begin{bmatrix} -8 \\ -14 \end{bmatrix}$

$\begin{bmatrix} 1 & 0 \\ 0 & 1 \end{bmatrix} \cdot \begin{bmatrix} x \\ y \end{bmatrix} = -\dfrac{1}{10}\begin{bmatrix} 30 \\ -10 \end{bmatrix}$

$\begin{bmatrix} x \\ y \end{bmatrix} = \begin{bmatrix} -3 \\ 1 \end{bmatrix}$

The solution is $(-3, 1)$.

48. Write the matrix equation for the system.

$\begin{bmatrix} 3 & -5 \\ 4 & 3 \end{bmatrix} \cdot \begin{bmatrix} x \\ y \end{bmatrix} = \begin{bmatrix} -13 \\ 2 \end{bmatrix}$

Find the inverse of the coefficient matrix.

$A^{-1} = \dfrac{1}{9 - (-20)}\begin{bmatrix} 3 & 5 \\ -4 & 3 \end{bmatrix}$ or $\dfrac{1}{29}\begin{bmatrix} 3 & 5 \\ -4 & 3 \end{bmatrix}$

Multiply each side of the matrix equation by A^{-1}.

$\dfrac{1}{29}\begin{bmatrix} 3 & 5 \\ -4 & 3 \end{bmatrix} \cdot \begin{bmatrix} 3 & -5 \\ 4 & 3 \end{bmatrix} \cdot \begin{bmatrix} x \\ y \end{bmatrix} = \dfrac{1}{29}\begin{bmatrix} 3 & 5 \\ -4 & 3 \end{bmatrix} \cdot \begin{bmatrix} -13 \\ 2 \end{bmatrix}$

$\begin{bmatrix} 1 & 0 \\ 0 & 1 \end{bmatrix} \cdot \begin{bmatrix} x \\ y \end{bmatrix} = \dfrac{1}{29}\begin{bmatrix} -29 \\ 58 \end{bmatrix}$

$\begin{bmatrix} x \\ y \end{bmatrix} = \begin{bmatrix} -1 \\ 2 \end{bmatrix}$

The solution is $(-1, 2)$.

Chapter 4 Practice Test

Page 215

1. b

2. c

3. a

4. Write the corresponding system of equations.

$3x + 1 = 10$

$2y = 4 + y$

Solve the first equation for x.

$3x + 1 = 10$

$3x = 9$

$x = 3$

Solve the second equation for y.

$2y = 4 + y$

$y = 4$

The solution is $(3, 4)$.

5. Write the corresponding system of equations.

$2x = -16$

$y + 1 = -7$

$13 = 13$

$-2 = z - 8$

Solve the first equation for x.

$2x = -16$

$x = -8$

Solve the second equation for y.

$y + 1 = -7$

$y = -8$

Solve the fourth equation for z.

$-2 = z - 8$

$6 = z$

The solution is $(-8, -8, 6)$.

6. $\begin{bmatrix} 2 & -4 & 1 \\ 3 & 8 & -2 \end{bmatrix} - 2\begin{bmatrix} 1 & 2 & -4 \\ -2 & 3 & 7 \end{bmatrix}$

$= \begin{bmatrix} 2 & -4 & 1 \\ 3 & 8 & -2 \end{bmatrix} - \begin{bmatrix} 2(1) & 2(2) & 2(-4) \\ 2(-2) & 2(3) & 2(7) \end{bmatrix}$

$= \begin{bmatrix} 2 & -4 & 1 \\ 3 & 8 & -2 \end{bmatrix} - \begin{bmatrix} 2 & 4 & -8 \\ -4 & 6 & 14 \end{bmatrix}$

$= \begin{bmatrix} 2 - 2 & -4 - 4 & 1 - (-8) \\ 3 - (-4) & 8 - 6 & -2 - 14 \end{bmatrix}$

$= \begin{bmatrix} 0 & -8 & 9 \\ 7 & 2 & -16 \end{bmatrix}$

7. $\begin{bmatrix} 1 & 6 & 7 \\ 1 & -3 & -4 \end{bmatrix} \cdot \begin{bmatrix} -4 & 3 \\ -1 & -2 \\ 2 & 5 \end{bmatrix}$

$= \begin{bmatrix} 1(-4) + 6(-1) + 7(2) & 1(3) + 6(-2) + 7(5) \\ 1(-4) + (-3)(-1) + (-4)(2) & 1(3) + (-3)(-2) + (-4)(5) \end{bmatrix}$

$= \begin{bmatrix} 4 & 26 \\ -9 & -11 \end{bmatrix}$

8. $\begin{vmatrix} -1 & 4 \\ -6 & 3 \end{vmatrix} = -1(3) - 4(-6)$

$= 21$

9. $\begin{vmatrix} 5 & -3 & 2 \\ -6 & 1 & 3 \\ -1 & 4 & -7 \end{vmatrix}$

$= 5\begin{vmatrix} 1 & 3 \\ 4 & -7 \end{vmatrix} - (-3)\begin{vmatrix} -6 & 3 \\ -1 & -7 \end{vmatrix} + 2\begin{vmatrix} -6 & 1 \\ -1 & 4 \end{vmatrix}$

$= 5(-7 - 12) + 3(42 - (-3)) + 2(-24 - (-1))$

$= -95 + 135 - 46$

$= -6$

10. Find the determinant.

$\begin{vmatrix} -2 & 5 \\ 3 & 1 \end{vmatrix} = -2 - 15$ or -17

Use the formula for the inverse matrix.

$A^{-1} = -\frac{1}{17}\begin{bmatrix} 1 & -5 \\ -3 & -2 \end{bmatrix}$

11. Find the determinant.

$\begin{vmatrix} -6 & -3 \\ 8 & 4 \end{vmatrix} = -24 - (-24)$ or 0

Since the determinant is 0, no inverse exists.

12. Find the determinant.

$\begin{vmatrix} 5 & -2 \\ 6 & 3 \end{vmatrix} = 15 - (-12)$ or 27

Use the formula for the inverse matrix.

$A^{-1} = \frac{1}{27}\begin{bmatrix} 3 & 2 \\ -6 & 5 \end{bmatrix}$

13. Find the inverse of the coefficient matrix.

$A^{-1} = \frac{1}{-6 - 16}\begin{bmatrix} -6 & -8 \\ -2 & 1 \end{bmatrix}$ or $-\frac{1}{22}\begin{bmatrix} -6 & -8 \\ -2 & 1 \end{bmatrix}$

Multiply each side of the matrix equation by A^{-1}.

$-\frac{1}{22}\begin{bmatrix} -6 & -8 \\ -2 & 1 \end{bmatrix} \cdot \begin{bmatrix} 1 & 8 \\ 2 & -6 \end{bmatrix} \cdot \begin{bmatrix} x \\ y \end{bmatrix} = -\frac{1}{22}\begin{bmatrix} -6 & -8 \\ -2 & 1 \end{bmatrix} \cdot \begin{bmatrix} -3 \\ -17 \end{bmatrix}$

$\begin{bmatrix} x \\ y \end{bmatrix} = -\frac{1}{22}\begin{bmatrix} 154 \\ -11 \end{bmatrix}$

$\begin{bmatrix} x \\ y \end{bmatrix} = \begin{bmatrix} -7 \\ \frac{1}{2} \end{bmatrix}$

The solution is $\left(-7, \frac{1}{2}\right)$.

14. Find the inverse of the coefficient matrix.

$A^{-1} = \frac{1}{15 - (-63)}\begin{bmatrix} 3 & -7 \\ 9 & 5 \end{bmatrix}$ or $\frac{1}{78}\begin{bmatrix} 3 & -7 \\ 9 & 5 \end{bmatrix}$

Multiply each side of the matrix equation by A^{-1}.

$\frac{1}{78}\begin{bmatrix} 3 & -7 \\ 9 & 5 \end{bmatrix} \cdot \begin{bmatrix} 5 & 7 \\ -9 & 3 \end{bmatrix} \cdot \begin{bmatrix} m \\ n \end{bmatrix} = \frac{1}{78}\begin{bmatrix} 3 & -7 \\ 9 & 5 \end{bmatrix} \cdot \begin{bmatrix} 41 \\ -105 \end{bmatrix}$

$\begin{bmatrix} 1 & 0 \\ 0 & 1 \end{bmatrix} \cdot \begin{bmatrix} m \\ n \end{bmatrix} = \frac{1}{78}\begin{bmatrix} 858 \\ -156 \end{bmatrix}$

$\begin{bmatrix} m \\ n \end{bmatrix} = \begin{bmatrix} 11 \\ -2 \end{bmatrix}$

The solution is $(11, -2)$.

15. Write the matrix equation for the system.

$\begin{bmatrix} 5 & 2 \\ 2 & 9 \end{bmatrix} \cdot \begin{bmatrix} a \\ b \end{bmatrix} = \begin{bmatrix} -49 \\ 5 \end{bmatrix}$

Find the inverse of the coefficient matrix.

$A^{-1} = \frac{1}{45 - 4}\begin{bmatrix} 9 & -2 \\ -2 & 5 \end{bmatrix}$ or $\frac{1}{41}\begin{bmatrix} 9 & -2 \\ -2 & 5 \end{bmatrix}$

Multiply each side of the matrix equation by A^{-1}.

$\frac{1}{41}\begin{bmatrix} 9 & -2 \\ -2 & 5 \end{bmatrix} \cdot \begin{bmatrix} 5 & 2 \\ 2 & 9 \end{bmatrix} \cdot \begin{bmatrix} a \\ b \end{bmatrix} = \frac{1}{41}\begin{bmatrix} 9 & -2 \\ -2 & 5 \end{bmatrix} \cdot \begin{bmatrix} -49 \\ 5 \end{bmatrix}$

$\begin{bmatrix} 1 & 0 \\ 0 & 1 \end{bmatrix} \cdot \begin{bmatrix} a \\ b \end{bmatrix} = \frac{1}{41}\begin{bmatrix} -451 \\ 123 \end{bmatrix}$

$\begin{bmatrix} a \\ b \end{bmatrix} = \begin{bmatrix} -11 \\ 3 \end{bmatrix}$

The solution is $(-11, 3)$.

16. Area $\triangle ABC = \frac{1}{2}\begin{vmatrix} 6 & 3 & 1 \\ 1 & 5 & 1 \\ -1 & 4 & 1 \end{vmatrix}$

$= \frac{1}{2}\left[6\begin{vmatrix} 5 & 1 \\ 4 & 1 \end{vmatrix} - 3\begin{vmatrix} 1 & 1 \\ -1 & 1 \end{vmatrix} + 1\begin{vmatrix} 1 & 5 \\ -1 & 4 \end{vmatrix}\right]$

$= \frac{1}{2}[6(5-4) - 3(1-(-1)) + 1(4-(-5))]$

$= \frac{1}{2}[6 - 6 + 9]$

$= 4.5$

The area of $\triangle ABC$ is 4.5 units^2.

17. The x-coordinate of B has been increased by 2 and the y-coordinate decreased by 4.

$\begin{bmatrix} 6 & 1 & -1 \\ 3 & 5 & 4 \end{bmatrix} + \begin{bmatrix} 2 & 2 & 2 \\ -4 & -4 & -4 \end{bmatrix} = \begin{bmatrix} 8 & 3 & 1 \\ -1 & 1 & 0 \end{bmatrix}$

The coordinates are $A'(8, -1)$ and $C'(1, 0)$.

18. $5\begin{bmatrix} 6 & 1 & -1 \\ 3 & 5 & 4 \end{bmatrix} = \begin{bmatrix} 30 & 5 & -5 \\ 15 & 25 & 20 \end{bmatrix}$

The coordinates are $A'(30, 15)$, $B'(5, 25)$, and $C'(-5, 20)$.

19. Let p and c represent the pounds of peanuts and caramels, respectively, used to prepare the assorted chocolates.

$p - c = 5$

$7p + 6.5c = 575$

Write the matrix equation for this system.

$\begin{bmatrix} 1 & -1 \\ 7 & 6.5 \end{bmatrix} \cdot \begin{bmatrix} p \\ c \end{bmatrix} = \begin{bmatrix} 5 \\ 575 \end{bmatrix}$

Find the inverse of the coefficient matrix.

$A^{-1} = \frac{1}{6.5 - (-7)}\begin{bmatrix} 6.5 & 1 \\ -7 & 1 \end{bmatrix}$ or $\frac{1}{13.5}\begin{bmatrix} 6.5 & 1 \\ -7 & 1 \end{bmatrix}$

Multiply each side of the matrix equation by A^{-1}.

$\frac{1}{13.5}\begin{bmatrix} 6.5 & 1 \\ -7 & 1 \end{bmatrix} \cdot \begin{bmatrix} 1 & -1 \\ 7 & 6.5 \end{bmatrix} \cdot \begin{bmatrix} p \\ c \end{bmatrix} = \frac{1}{13.5}\begin{bmatrix} 6.5 & 1 \\ -7 & 1 \end{bmatrix} \cdot \begin{bmatrix} 5 \\ 575 \end{bmatrix}$

$\begin{bmatrix} 1 & 0 \\ 0 & 1 \end{bmatrix} \cdot \begin{bmatrix} p \\ c \end{bmatrix} = \frac{1}{13.5}\begin{bmatrix} 607.5 \\ 540 \end{bmatrix}$

$\begin{bmatrix} p \\ c \end{bmatrix} = \begin{bmatrix} 45 \\ 40 \end{bmatrix}$

45 lbs of peanuts and 40 lbs of caramels were used to make the boxes.

20. B; Write the equations obtained by setting the elements of the second row equal.

$7x - 2 = y$

$2x + 3 = 37$

Solve the second equation for x.

$2x + 3 = 37$

$2x = 34$

$x = 17$

Substitute 17 for x in the first equation.

$7x - 2 = y$

$7(17) - 2 = y$

$119 - 2 = y$

$117 = y$

Chapter 4 Standardized Test Practice

Pages 216–217

1. C; Let a represent the average of the other four numbers.

$6(12) + 4a = 10(18)$

$72 + 4a = 180$

$4a = 108$

$a = 27$

2. B; Using the formula $d = rt$, the distance traveled by the car is $65 \cdot 2$ or 130 miles. The distance traveled by the truck is $60 \cdot 1.5$ or 90 miles. The difference is $130 - 90$ or 40 miles.

3. B; Use the Pythagorean Theorem.

$8^2 + 6^2 = (5a)^2$

$64 + 36 = 25a^2$

$100 = 25a^2$

$4 = a^2$

$\pm 2 = a$

Since a must be nonnegative, $a = 2$.

4. A; Use the equation for the circumference of a circle to solve for the radius r.

$2\pi r = C$

$2\pi r = \frac{4\pi}{3}$

$\frac{2\pi r}{2\pi} = \frac{4\pi}{3 \cdot 2\pi}$

$r = \frac{2}{3}$

Substitute $\frac{2}{3}$ for r in the equation for the area of a circle.

$A = \pi r^2$

$= \pi\left(\frac{2}{3}\right)^2$

$= \frac{4}{9}\pi$

Half the area is $\frac{2}{9}\pi$.

5. D; Vertical lines have undefined slope.

6. B; The minor arc BC is $\frac{1}{4}$ the circumference of the circle.

$C = 2\pi r$

$\frac{1}{4}C = \frac{2\pi r}{4}$

$\frac{1}{4}C = \frac{\pi(10)}{2}$

$\frac{1}{4}C = 5\pi$

7. A; Suppose $x = 4$ and $y = 6$. Then $\frac{x}{y} = \frac{4}{6}$ or $\frac{2}{3}$.

Since $\frac{2}{3} > \frac{1}{2}$, this eliminates answer choices B and C. Now suppose $x = 4$ and $y = 9$. Then $\frac{x}{y} = \frac{4}{9}$.

Since $\frac{4}{9} < \frac{3}{5}$, this eliminates answer choice D. Only answer choice A remains.

8. C; Solve the second equation for y.

$\frac{2}{3}x - y = 5$

$\frac{2}{3}x - 5 = y$

Substitute $\frac{2}{3}x - 5$ for y in the first equation.

$x + 3y = 12$

$x + 3\left(\frac{2}{3}x - 5\right) = 12$

$x + 2x - 15 = 12$

$3x = 27$

$x = 9$

9. C; Substitute $2x - 3$ for y in the first equation.

$7x - 3y = 13$

$7x - 3(2x - 3) = 13$

$7x - 6x + 9 = 13$

$x = 4$

Substitute 4 for x in the second equation.

$y = 2x - 3$

$y = 2(4) - 3$

$y = 5$

The solution is $(4, 5)$.

10. C; $\begin{bmatrix} -1 & 0 \\ 5 & -2 \end{bmatrix} - \begin{bmatrix} -1 & 0 \\ 5 & 2 \end{bmatrix}$

$= \begin{bmatrix} -1 - (-1) & 0 - 0 \\ 5 - 5 & -2 - 2 \end{bmatrix}$ or $\begin{bmatrix} 0 & 0 \\ 0 & -4 \end{bmatrix}$

11. Let b represent the price in dollars of the Model X computer before the price reduction. A 3% reduction can be calculated by multiplying b by 0.97.

$0.97b = 2489$

$\frac{0.97b}{0.97} = \frac{2489}{0.97}$

$b = 2565.98$

The computer costs about \$2566 before the price was reduced.

12. The area of $\triangle PQS$ is $\frac{1}{2}(4)(4)$ or 8 square units.

The area of $\triangle PUT$ is $\frac{1}{2}(2)(2)$ or 2 square units.

Thus, the area of the shaded region is $8 - 2$ or 6 square units.

13. $V = \ell \cdot w \cdot h$

$= 3 \cdot 3 \cdot 6$

$= 54$

The volume is 54 cubic units.

14. Since the average of the three numbers is 60, their sum is $3 \cdot 60$ or 180. The least that two of the numbers can be are 1 and 2, so the greatest the third number can be is 177.

15. The sum of the lengths of any two sides of a triangle must be greater than the length of the third side. If one of the sides had length 1, the lengths would be 1, 6, and 8, but $1 + 6 < 8$, so this is not possible. However, if the side had length 2, the lengths would be 2, 6, and 7, and $2 + 6 > 7$. The shortest possible length is 2.

16. $320 \quad 80 \quad 20 \quad 5 \quad \frac{5}{4} \quad \frac{5}{16}$

$\quad \times \frac{1}{4} \quad \times \frac{1}{4} \quad \times \frac{1}{4} \quad \times \frac{1}{4} \quad \times \frac{1}{4}$

The sixth term is $\frac{5}{16}$.

17. Let m and n represent the numbers.

$m + n = 5$

$m - n = 2$

Add the equations to eliminate n.

$\begin{array}{r} m + n = 5 \\ (+)\ m - n = 2 \\ \hline 2m \quad\ = 7 \\ m = \frac{7}{2} \text{ or } 3.5 \end{array}$

Substitute 3.5 for m in the first equation.

$m + n = 5$

$3.5 + n = 5$

$n = 1.5$

The numbers are 3.5 and 1.5. Their product is $3.5 \cdot 1.5$ or 5.25.

18. D; When $x = 0$, y can be any real number.

19. B; The greatest number which is the sum of two equal even integers is $8 + 8$ or 16. The greatest number that is the sum of two equal odd integers is $9 + 9$ or 18.

20. C; In Column A, $V = 4^3$ or 64 cubic inches. In Column B, $8V = 8 \cdot 2^3$ or 64 cubic inches.

21. D; P could be $(0, 4)$ or $(4, 0)$.

22. C; Subtract the equations.

$\begin{array}{r} r + s + t = 30 \\ (-)\ r + s - t = \ 8 \\ \hline 2t = 22 \\ t = 11 \end{array}$

Chapter 5 Polynomials

1. $2 - 7 = 2 + (-7)$
2. $-6 - 11 = -6 + (-11)$
3. $x - y = x + (-y)$
4. $8 - 2x = 8 + (-2x)$
5. $2xy - 6yz = 2xy + (-6yz)$
6. $6a^2b - 12b^2c = 6a^2b + (-12b^2c)$
7. $-2(4x^3 + x - 3) = -2(4x^3) - 2(+x) - 2(-3)$
   $= -8x^3 - 2x + 6$
8. $-1(x + 2) = -1(x) - 1(+2)$
   $= -x - 2$
9. $-1(x - 3) = -1(x) - 1(-3)$
   $= -x + 3$
10. $-3(2x^4 - 5x^2 - 2) = -3(2x^4) - 3(-5x^2) - 3(-2)$
    $= -6x^4 + 15x^2 + 6$
11. $-\frac{1}{2}(3a + 2) = -\frac{1}{2}(3a) - \frac{1}{2}(2)$
    $= -\frac{3}{2}a - 1$
12. $-\frac{2}{3}(2 + 6z) = -\frac{2}{3}(2) - \frac{2}{3}(6z)$
    $= -\frac{4}{3} - 4z$
13. $2.6 + 3.7 = 6.3$;
    6.3 belongs to the reals and rationals.
14. $18 \div (-3) = -6$;
    -6 belongs to the reals, rationals, and integers.
15. $2^3 + 3^2 = 2 \cdot 2 \cdot 2 + 3 \cdot 3$
    $= 8 + 9$
    $= 17$;
    17 belongs to the reals, rationals, integers, whole numbers, and natural numbers.
16. $\sqrt{4 + 1} = \sqrt{5}$;
    $\sqrt{5}$ belongs to the reals and irrationals.
17. $\frac{18 + 14}{8} = \frac{32}{8}$
    $= 4$;
    4 belongs to the reals, rationals, integers, whole numbers, and natural numbers.
18. $3\sqrt{4} = 3\sqrt{2^2}$
    $= 3(2)$
    $= 6$;
    6 belongs to the reals, rationals, integers, whole numbers, and natural numbers.

5-1 Monomials

1. Sample answer: $(2x^2)^3 = 8x^6$
   since $(2x^2)^3 = 2x^2 \cdot 2x^2 \cdot 2x^2$
   $= 2x \cdot x \cdot 2x \cdot x \cdot 2x \cdot x$
   $= 8x^6$
2. Sometimes; in general $x^y \cdot x^z = x^{y+z}$. So,
   $x^y \cdot x^z = x^{yz}$ when $y + z = yz$, such as when $y = 2$ and $z = 2$.

3. Alejandra; when Kyle used the power of Product Property in his first step, he forgot to put an exponent of -2 on a. Also, in his second step, $(-2)^{-2}$ should be $\frac{1}{4}$, not 4.
4. $x^2 \cdot x^8 = x^{2+8}$
   $= x^{10}$
5. $(2b)^4 = 2^4 \cdot b^4$
   $= 16b^4$
6. $(n^3)^3(n^{-3})^3 = n^{3(3)} \cdot n^{-3(3)}$
   $= n^9 \cdot n^{-9}$
   $= n^{9-9}$
   $= n^0$
   $= 1$
7. $\frac{30y^4}{-5y^2} = \frac{30}{-5} \cdot y^{4-2}$
   $= -6y^2$
8. $\frac{-2a^3b^6}{18a^2b^2} = -\frac{2}{18} \cdot a^{3-2} \cdot b^{6-2}$
   $= -\frac{1}{9}a^1 \cdot b^4$
   $= -\frac{ab^4}{9}$
9. $\frac{81p^6q^5}{(3p^2q)^2} = \frac{81p^6q^5}{3^2 \cdot (p^2)^2 \cdot (q^2)}$
   $= \frac{81p^6q^5}{9 \cdot p^4 \cdot q^2}$
   $= \frac{81}{9} \cdot p^{6-4} \cdot q^{5-2}$
   $= 9p^2q^3$
10. $\left(\frac{1}{w^4z^2}\right)^3 = \frac{1^3}{(w^4)^3 \cdot (z^2)^3}$
    $= \frac{1}{w^{12}z^6}$
11. $\left(\frac{cd}{3}\right)^{-2} = \left(\frac{3}{cd}\right)^2$
    $= \frac{3^2}{c^2d^2}$
    $= \frac{9}{c^2d^2}$
12. $\left(\frac{-6x^6}{3x^3}\right)^{-2} = \left(\frac{3x^3}{-6x^6}\right)^2$
    $= \left(\frac{1}{-2x^{6-3}}\right)^2$
    $= \left(\frac{1}{-2x^3}\right)^2$
    $= \frac{1^2}{(-2)^2x^{3(2)}}$
    $= \frac{1}{4x^6}$
13. $421,000 = 4.21 \times 100,000$
    $= 4.21 \times 10^5$
14. $0.000862 = 8.62 \times 0.0001$
    $= 8.62 \times \frac{1}{10^4}$
    $= 8.62 \times 10^{-4}$
15. $(3.42 \times 10^8)(1.1 \times 10^{-5})$
    $= (3.42 \times 1.1) \times (10^8 \times 10^{-5})$
    $= (3.762) \times (10^{8-5})$
    $= 3.762 \times 10^3$
16. $\frac{8 \times 10^{-1}}{16 \times 10^{-2}} = \frac{8}{16} \times 10^{-1-(-2)}$
    $= \frac{1}{2} \times 10^1$
    $= \frac{10}{2} \times 10^0$
    $= 5 \times 10^0$

17. $t = \dfrac{d}{r}$

$t = \dfrac{3.84 \times 10^8}{3.00 \times 10^8}$

$= \dfrac{3.84}{3.00} \times 10^{8-8}$

≈ 1.28

It would take about 1.28 seconds.

Pages 226–228   Practice and Apply

18. $a^2 \cdot a^6 = a^{2+6}$
$= a^8$

19. $b^{-3} \cdot b^7 = b^{-3+7}$
$= b^4$

20. $(n^4)^4 = n^{4(4)}$
$= n^{16}$

21. $(z^2)^5 = z^{2(5)}$
$= z^{10}$

22. $(2x)^4 = 2^4 \cdot x^4$
$= 16x^4$

23. $(-2c)^3 = (-2)^3 \cdot c^3$
$= -8c^3$

24. $\dfrac{a^2 n^6}{an^5} = a^{2-1} \cdot n^{6-5}$
$= an$

25. $\dfrac{-y^5 z^7}{y^2 z^5} = -y^{5-2} \cdot z^{7-5}$
$= -y^3 z^2$

26. $(7x^3 y^{-5})(4xy^3) = (7 \cdot 4)x^{3+1} \cdot y^{-5+3}$
$= 28x^4 y^{-2}$
$= \dfrac{28x^4}{y^2}$

27. $(-3b^3 c)(7b^2 c^2) = (-3 \cdot 7)b^{3+2} \cdot c^{1+2}$
$= -21b^5 c^3$

28. $(a^3 b^3)(ab)^{-2} = (a^3 b^3)(a^{-2} b^{-2})$
$= a^{3-2} \cdot b^{3-2}$
$= ab$

29. $(-2r^2 s)^3(3rs^2) = (-2)^3(r^2)^3(s^3)(3rs^2)$
$= (-8 \cdot 3) \cdot r^6 \cdot s^3 \cdot r \cdot s^2$
$= -24r^7 \cdot s^5$

30. $2x^2(6y^3)(2x^2 y) = (2 \cdot 6 \cdot 2) \cdot x^{2+2} \cdot y^{3+1}$
$= 24x^4 y^4$

31. $3a(5a^2 b)(6ab^3) = (3 \cdot 5 \cdot 6) \cdot a^{1+2+1} \cdot b^{1+3}$
$= 90a^4 b^4$

32. $\dfrac{-5x^3 y^3 z^4}{20x^3 y^7 z^4} = \dfrac{-5}{20} \cdot x^{3-3} \cdot y^{3-7} \cdot z^{4-4}$
$= -\dfrac{1}{4} \cdot x^0 \cdot y^{-4} \cdot z^0$
$= -\dfrac{1}{4y^4}$

33. $\dfrac{3a^5 b^3 c^3}{9a^3 b^7 c} = \dfrac{3}{9} \cdot a^{5-3} \cdot b^{3-7} \cdot c^{3-1}$
$= \dfrac{1}{3}a^2 \cdot b^{-4} \cdot c^2$
$= \dfrac{a^2 c^2}{3b^4}$

34. $\dfrac{2c^3 d(3c^2 d^5)}{30c^4 d^2} = \dfrac{2 \cdot 3 \cdot c^{3+2} \cdot d^{1+5}}{30c^4 d^2}$
$= \dfrac{6c^5 d^6}{30c^4 d^2}$
$= \dfrac{6}{30} \cdot c^{5-4} \cdot d^{6-2}$
$= \dfrac{cd^4}{5}$

35. $\dfrac{-12m^4 n^8(m^3 n^2)}{36m^3 n} = \dfrac{-12 \cdot m^{4+3} \cdot n^{8+2}}{36m^3 n}$
$= \dfrac{-12m^7 n^{10}}{36m^3 n}$
$= \dfrac{-12}{36} \cdot m^{7-3} \cdot n^{10-1}$
$= -\dfrac{m^4 n^9}{3}$

36. $\left(\dfrac{8a^3 b^2}{16a^2 b^3}\right)^4 = \left(\dfrac{8}{16} \cdot a^{3-2} \cdot b^{2-3}\right)^4$
$= \left(\dfrac{1}{2} \cdot a \cdot b^{-1}\right)^4$
$= \dfrac{1}{2^4} \cdot a^4 \cdot b^{-4}$
$= \dfrac{a^4}{16b^4}$

37. $\left(\dfrac{6x^2 y^4}{3x^4 y^3}\right)^3 = \left(\dfrac{6}{3} \cdot x^{2-4} \cdot y^{4-3}\right)^3$
$= (2 \cdot x^{-2} \cdot y)^3$
$= (2^3 \cdot x^{-6} \cdot y^3)$
$= \dfrac{8y^3}{x^6}$

38. $\left(\dfrac{x}{y^{-1}}\right)^{-2} = (x \cdot y)^{-2}$
$= \left(\dfrac{1}{xy}\right)^2$
$= \dfrac{1}{x^2 y^2}$

39. $\left(\dfrac{v}{w^{-2}}\right)^{-3} = (vw^2)^{-3}$
$= \left(\dfrac{1}{vw^2}\right)^3$
$= \dfrac{1}{v^3 w^6}$

40. $\dfrac{30a^{-2} b^{-6}}{60a^{-6} b^{-8}} = \dfrac{30}{60}a^{-2-(-6)} \cdot b^{-6-(-8)}$
$= \dfrac{1}{2}a^4 \cdot b^2$
$= \dfrac{a^4 b^2}{2}$

41. $\dfrac{12x^{-3} y^{-2} z^{-8}}{30x^{-6} y^{-4} z^{-1}} = \dfrac{12}{30} \cdot x^{-3-(-6)} \cdot y^{-2-(-4)} \cdot z^{-8-(-1)}$
$= \dfrac{2}{5} \cdot x^3 \cdot y^2 \cdot z^{-7}$
$= \dfrac{2x^3 y^2}{5z^7}$

42. $2^{r+5} = 2^{2r-1}$
$r + 5 = 2r - 1$
$r + 5 - r = 2r - 1 - r$
$5 = r - 1$
$5 + 1 = r - 1 + 1$
$6 = r$

43. $y^{28} = y^{3r} \cdot y^7$
$y^{28} = y^{3r+7}$
$28 = 3r + 7$
$21 = 3r$
$\dfrac{21}{3} = \dfrac{3r}{3}$
$7 = r$ or $r = 7$

44. $462.3 = 4.623 \times 100$
$= 4.623 \times 10^2$

45. $43,200 = 4.32 \times 10,000$
$= 4.32 \times 10^4$

46. $0.0001843 = 1.843 \times 0.0001$
$= 1.843 \times 10^{-4}$

47. $0.006810 = 6.81 \times 0.001$
$= 6.81 \times 10^{-3}$

48. $502,020,000 = 5.0202 \times 100,000,000$
$= 5.0202 \times 10^8$

49. $675,400,000 = 6.754 \times 100,000,000$
$= 6.754 \times 10^8$

50. $(4.15 \times 10^3)(3.0 \times 10^6) = (4.15 \times 3.0)(10^3 \times 10^6)$
$$= (12.45)(10^9)$$
$$= (1.245 \times 10)(10^9)$$
$$= 1.245 \times 10^{10}$$

51. $(3.01 \times 10^{-2})(2 \times 10^{-3}) = (3.01 \times 2)(10^{-2} \times 10^{-3})$
$$= 6.02 \times 10^{-5}$$

52. $\dfrac{6.3 \times 10^5}{1.4 \times 10^3} = \dfrac{6.3}{1.4} \times \dfrac{10^5}{10^3}$
$$= 4.5 \times 10^2$$

53. $\dfrac{9.3 \times 10^7}{1.5 \times 10^{-3}} = \dfrac{9.3}{1.5} \times \dfrac{10^7}{10^{-3}}$
$$= 6.2 \times 10^{10}$$

54. $(6.5 \times 10^4)^2 = (6.5)^2 \times (10^4)^2$
$$= 42.25 \times 10^8$$
$$= 4.225 \times 10 \times 10^8$$
$$= 4.225 \times 10^9$$

55. $(4.1 \times 10^{-4})^2 = (4.1)^2 \times (10^{-4})^2$
$$= 16.81 \times 10^{-8}$$
$$= 1.681 \times 10 \times 10^{-8}$$
$$= 1.681 \times 10^{-7}$$

56. $6{,}080{,}000{,}000 = 6.08 \times 1{,}000{,}000{,}000$
$$= 6.08 \times 10^9$$

57. $0.0000002 = 2 \times 0.0000001 \text{ m}$
$$= 2 \times 10^{-7} \text{ m}$$

58. $(500)(3.34 \times 10^{22}) = (500 \times 3.34) \times 10^{22}$
$$= 1670 \times 10^{22}$$
$$= 1.67 \times 1000 \times 10^{22}$$
$$= 1.67 \times 10^{25}$$

59. mass of Sun $= 1.99 \times 10^{30} \text{ kg}$
mass of Earth $= 5.976 \times 10^{24} \text{ kg}$
$\dfrac{\text{mass of Sun}}{\text{mass of Earth}} = \dfrac{1.99 \times 10^{30}}{5.976 \times 10^{24}} \approx 330{,}000$

The Sun is about 330,000 times larger than the Earth.

60. Write the numbers so they have the same base, 10.
$100^{10} = (10^2)^{10}$
$$= 10^{20}$$
$10^{100} > 10^{20}$
So, $10^{100} > 100^{10}$.

61. definition of an exponent

62.
$$\overbrace{(ab)^m = ab \cdot ab \cdot \ldots \cdot ab}^{m \text{ factors}} = \overbrace{a \cdot a \cdot \ldots \cdot a}^{m \text{ factors}} \cdot \overbrace{b \cdot b \cdot \ldots \cdot b}^{m \text{ factors}} = a^m b^m$$

63. Economics often involves large amounts of money. Answers should include the following.

• The national debt in 2000 was five trillion, six hundred seventy-four billion, two hundred million or 5.6742×10^{12} dollars. The population was two hundred eighty-one million or 2.81×10^8.

• Divide the national debt by the population.
$\dfrac{5.6742 \times 10^{12}}{2.81 \times 10^8} \approx \$2.0193 \times 10^4$ or about \$20,193 per person.

64. D; $\dfrac{(2x^2)^3}{12x^4} = \dfrac{2^3 \cdot (x^2)^3}{12x^4}$
$$= \dfrac{8}{12} \cdot \dfrac{x^6}{x^4}$$
$$= \dfrac{2x^2}{3}$$

65. B; $7.3 \times 10^5 = 7.3 \times 100{,}000$
$$= 730{,}000$$

Page 228 Maintain Your Skills

66. $2x + 3y = 8$
$x - 2y = -3$
$\begin{bmatrix} 2 & 3 \\ 1 & -2 \end{bmatrix}\begin{bmatrix} x \\ y \end{bmatrix} = \begin{bmatrix} 8 \\ -3 \end{bmatrix}$

$A = \begin{bmatrix} 2 & 3 \\ 1 & -2 \end{bmatrix}$

$A^{-1} = \dfrac{1}{-4-3}\begin{bmatrix} -2 & -3 \\ -1 & 2 \end{bmatrix}$
$$= -\dfrac{1}{7}\begin{bmatrix} -2 & -3 \\ -1 & 2 \end{bmatrix}$$

$-\dfrac{1}{7}\begin{bmatrix} -2 & -3 \\ -1 & 2 \end{bmatrix}\begin{bmatrix} 2 & 3 \\ 1 & -2 \end{bmatrix}\begin{bmatrix} x \\ y \end{bmatrix} = -\dfrac{1}{7}\begin{bmatrix} -2 & -3 \\ -1 & 2 \end{bmatrix}\begin{bmatrix} 8 \\ -3 \end{bmatrix}$

$\begin{bmatrix} 1 & 0 \\ 0 & 1 \end{bmatrix}\begin{bmatrix} x \\ y \end{bmatrix} = -\dfrac{1}{7}\begin{bmatrix} -7 \\ -14 \end{bmatrix}$

$\begin{bmatrix} x \\ y \end{bmatrix} = \begin{bmatrix} 1 \\ 2 \end{bmatrix}$

$x = 1, y = 2$
The solution is $(1, 2)$.

67. $x + 4y = 9$
$3x + 2y = -3$
$\begin{bmatrix} 1 & 4 \\ 3 & 2 \end{bmatrix}\begin{bmatrix} x \\ y \end{bmatrix} = \begin{bmatrix} 9 \\ -3 \end{bmatrix}$

$A = \begin{bmatrix} 1 & 4 \\ 3 & 2 \end{bmatrix}$

$A^{-1} = \dfrac{1}{2-12}\begin{bmatrix} 2 & -4 \\ -3 & 1 \end{bmatrix}$

$A^{-1} = -\dfrac{1}{10}\begin{bmatrix} 2 & -4 \\ -3 & 1 \end{bmatrix}$

$-\dfrac{1}{10}\begin{bmatrix} 2 & -4 \\ -3 & 1 \end{bmatrix}\begin{bmatrix} 1 & 4 \\ 3 & 2 \end{bmatrix}\begin{bmatrix} x \\ y \end{bmatrix} = -\dfrac{1}{10}\begin{bmatrix} 2 & -4 \\ -3 & 1 \end{bmatrix}\begin{bmatrix} 9 \\ -3 \end{bmatrix}$

$\begin{bmatrix} 1 & 0 \\ 0 & 1 \end{bmatrix}\begin{bmatrix} x \\ y \end{bmatrix} = -\dfrac{1}{10}\begin{bmatrix} 30 \\ -30 \end{bmatrix}$

$\begin{bmatrix} x \\ y \end{bmatrix} = \begin{bmatrix} -3 \\ 3 \end{bmatrix}$

$x = -3, y = 3$
The solution is $(-3, 3)$.

68. $A = \begin{bmatrix} 2 & 5 \\ -1 & -2 \end{bmatrix}$

$A^{-1} = \dfrac{1}{2(-2) - 5(-1)}\begin{bmatrix} -2 & -5 \\ 1 & 2 \end{bmatrix}$
$$= \dfrac{1}{-4+5}\begin{bmatrix} -2 & -5 \\ 1 & 2 \end{bmatrix}$$
$$= \begin{bmatrix} -2 & -5 \\ 1 & 2 \end{bmatrix}$$

69. $A = \begin{bmatrix} 4 & 3 \\ 2 & 1 \end{bmatrix}$

$A^{-1} = \dfrac{1}{4-6}\begin{bmatrix} 1 & -3 \\ -2 & 4 \end{bmatrix}$
$$= -\dfrac{1}{2}\begin{bmatrix} 1 & -3 \\ -2 & 4 \end{bmatrix}$$
$$= \begin{bmatrix} -\dfrac{1}{2} & \dfrac{3}{2} \\ 1 & -2 \end{bmatrix}$$

70. $\begin{vmatrix} 3 & 0 \\ 2 & -2 \end{vmatrix} = 3(-2) - 0(2)$

$\qquad = -6 - 0$

$\qquad = -6$

71. $\begin{vmatrix} 1 & 0 & -3 \\ 2 & -1 & 4 \\ -3 & 0 & 2 \end{vmatrix} = 1\begin{vmatrix} -1 & 4 \\ 0 & 2 \end{vmatrix} - 0\begin{vmatrix} 2 & 4 \\ -3 & 2 \end{vmatrix} - 3\begin{vmatrix} 2 & -1 \\ -3 & 0 \end{vmatrix}$

$\qquad = 1(-2 - 0) - 0(4 + 12) - 3(0 - 3)$

$\qquad = -2 + 9$

$\qquad = 7$

72. $x + y = 5$

$x + y + z = 4$

$2x - y + 2z = -1$

Eliminate x and y by adding negative 1 times the first equation to the second equation.

$\qquad -x - y \qquad = -5$

$(+) \quad x + y + z = \quad 4$

$\overline{\qquad\qquad\quad z = -1}$

Replace $z = -1$ in the last two equations.

$x + y - 1 = 4$

$2x - y + 2(-1) = -1$

$\qquad x + y = 5$

$\qquad 2x - y = 1$

Add these two equations to eliminate y.

$\qquad x + y = 5$

$(+)\ 2x - y = 1$

$\overline{\quad 3x \qquad = 6}$

$\qquad x = 2$

Replace $x = 2$ in the first equation.

$2 + y = 5$

$\qquad y = 3$

The solution of the system is $(2, 3, -1)$.

73. $a + b + c = 6$

$2a - b + 3c = 16$

$a + 3b - 2c = -6$

Eliminate b by adding the first two equations.

$\quad a + b + \ c = \ 6$

$\ 2a - b + 3c = 16$

$\overline{\ 3a \qquad + 4c = 22 \quad (1)}$

Multiply the second equation by 3 and then add it to the third equation to eliminate b.

$\qquad 6a - 3b + 9c = 48$

$(+)\quad a + 3b - 2c = -6$

$\overline{\qquad 7a \qquad + 7c = 42}$

$\qquad\quad 7(a + c) = 42$

$\qquad\qquad a + c = 6 \qquad (2)$

Multiply equation (2) by -4 and add the result to equation (1) to eliminate c.

$\qquad -4a - 4c = -24$

$(+)\ \ 3a + 4c = \quad 22$

$\overline{\qquad -a \qquad = \quad -2}$

$\qquad\qquad a = 2$

Substitute 2 for a in equation (2).

$2 + c = 6$

$\qquad c = 4$

Substitute 4 for c in the first equation.

$2 + b + 4 = 6$

$\qquad b + 6 = 6$

$\qquad\qquad b = 0$

The solution of the system is $(2, 0, 4)$.

74.

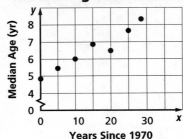

Median Age of Vehicles

75. Sample answer: using $(0, 4.9)$ and $(28, 8.3)$:

slope $= \frac{8.3 - 4.9}{28 - 0} \approx 0.12,$

y-intercept $= 4.9$; $y = 0.12x + 4.9$

76. Sample answer: Let $x = 2010 - 1970 = 40$.

$y = 0.12(40) + 4.9 = 9.7$

The prediction is 9.7 years.

77. $\qquad 2x + 11 = 25$

$2x + 11 - 11 = 25 - 11$

$\qquad\qquad 2x = 14$

$\qquad\qquad \frac{2x}{2} = \frac{14}{2}$

$\qquad\qquad x = 7$

78. $\qquad -12 - 5x = 3$

$-12 - 5x + 12 = 3 + 12$

$\qquad\qquad -5x = 15$

$\qquad\qquad \frac{-5x}{-5} = \frac{15}{-5}$

$\qquad\qquad\qquad x = -3$

79. $2(x + y) = 2x + 2y$

80. $3(x - z) = 3x - 3z$

81. $4(x + 2) = 4x + 8$

82. $-2(3x - 5) = -2(3x) - 2(-5)$

$\qquad\qquad = -6x + 10$

83. $-5(x - 2y) = -5(x) - 5(-2y)$

$\qquad\qquad = -5x + 10y$

84. $-3(-y + 5) = -3(-y) - 3(5)$

$\qquad\qquad = 3y - 15$

5-2 **Polynomials**

Page 231 **Check for Understanding**

1. Sample answer: $x^5 + x^4 + x^3$

2. The degree of the polynomial is 4, since the degree of the monomial $3x^4$ is the greatest degree.

3.

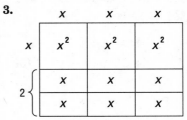

4. $2a + 5b$

The expression is a polynomial because each term is a monomial. The degree of the polynomial is 1 since the degree of each monomial is 1.

5. $\frac{1}{3}x^3 - 9y$

The expression is a polynomial because each term is a monomial. The degree of the first term is 3 and the degree of the second term is 1. The degree of the polynomial is 3.

6. $\frac{mw^2 - 3}{nz^3 + 1}$

The expression is not a polynomial because it is not the sum of monomials.

7. $(2a + 3b) + (8a - 5b) = 2a + 3b + 8a - 5b$
$\qquad\qquad\qquad\qquad\quad = (2a + 8a) + (3b - 5b)$
$\qquad\qquad\qquad\qquad\quad = 10a - 2b$

8. $(x^2 - 4x + 3) - (4x^2 + 3x - 5)$
$\quad = x^2 - 4x + 3 - 4x^2 - 3x + 5$
$\quad = (x^2 - 4x^2) + (-4x - 3x) + (3 + 5)$
$\quad = -3x^2 - 7x + 8$

9. $2x(3y + 9) = 2x(3y) + 2x(9)$
$\qquad\qquad\quad = 6xy + 18x$

10. $2p^2q(5pq - 3p^3q^2 + 4pq^4)$
$\quad = 2p^2q(5pq) + 2p^2q(-3p^3q^2) + 2p^2q(4pq^4)$
$\quad = 10p^3q^2 - 6p^5q^3 + 8p^3q^5$

11. $(y - 10)(y + 7) = y^2 + 7y - 10y - 70$
$\qquad\qquad\qquad\quad = y^2 - 3y - 70$

12. $(x + 6)(x + 3) = x^2 + 3x + 6x + 18$
$\qquad\qquad\qquad\quad = x^2 + 9x + 18$

13. $(2z - 1)(2z + 1) = (2z)(2z) + 2z - 2z - 1$
$\qquad\qquad\qquad\qquad = 4z^2 - 1$

14. $(2m - 3n)^2$
$\quad = (2m - 3n)(2m - 3n)$
$\quad = (2m)(2m) + 2m(-3n) - 3n(2m) + (-3n)(-3n)$
$\quad = 4m^2 - 6mn - 6mn + 9n^2$
$\quad = 4m^2 - 12mn + 9n^2$

15. $A = \frac{5x(3x + 5)}{2}$ ft^2
$\qquad = \frac{15x^2 + 25x}{2}$ ft^2
$\qquad = \frac{15}{2}x^2 + \frac{25}{2}x$ ft^2
$\qquad = 7.5x^2 + 12.5x$ ft^2

Pages 231–232 Practice and Apply

16. $3z^2 - 5z + 11$

The expression is a polynomial because each term is a monomial. The degree of the first term is 2, the second term is 1, and the third term is 0. The degree of the polynomial is 2.

17. $x^3 - 9$

The expression is a polynomial because each term is a monomial. The degree of the first term is 3 and the second term is 0. The degree of the polynomial is 3.

18. $\frac{6xy}{z} - \frac{3c}{d}$

The expression is not a polynomial because it is not the sum of monomials.

19. $\sqrt{m - 5}$

The expression is not a polynomial because $\sqrt{m - 5}$ is not a monomial.

20. $5x^2y^4 + x\sqrt{3}$

The expression is a polynomial because each term is a monomial. The degree of the first term is $2 + 4 = 6$ and the degree of the second term is 1. The degree of the polynomial is 6.

21. $\frac{4}{3}y^2 + \frac{5}{6}y^7$

The expression is a polynomial because each term is a monomial. The degree of the first term is 2 and the second term is 7. The degree of the polynomial is 7.

22. $(3x^2 - x + 2) + (x^2 + 4x - 9)$
$\quad = 3x^2 - x + 2 + x^2 + 4x - 9$
$\quad = (3x^2 + x^2) + (-x + 4x) + (2 - 9)$
$\quad = 4x^2 + 3x - 7$

23. $(5y + 3y^2) + (-8y - 6y^2)$
$\quad = 5y + 3y^2 - 8y - 6y^2$
$\quad = (3y^2 - 6y^2) + (5y - 8y)$
$\quad = -3y^2 - 3y$

24. $(9r^2 + 6r + 16) - (8r^2 + 7r + 10)$
$\quad = 9r^2 + 6r + 16 - 8r^2 - 7r - 10$
$\quad = (9r^2 - 8r^2) + (6r - 7r) + (16 - 10)$
$\quad = r^2 - r + 6$

25. $(7m^2 + 5m - 9) + (3m^2 - 6)$
$\quad = 7m^2 + 5m - 9 + 3m^2 - 6$
$\quad = (7m^2 + 3m^2) + 5m + (-9 - 6)$
$\quad = 10m^2 + 5m - 15$

26. $(4x^2 - 3y^2 + 5xy) - (8xy + 3y^2)$
$\quad = 4x^2 - 3y^2 + 5xy - 8xy - 3y^2$
$\quad = 4x^2 + (-3y^2 - 3y^2) + (5xy - 8xy)$
$\quad = 4x^2 - 6y^2 - 3xy$

27. $(10x^2 - 3xy + 4y^2) - (3x^2 + 5xy)$
$\quad = 10x^2 - 3xy + 4y^2 - 3x^2 - 5xy$
$\quad = (10x^2 - 3x^2) + 4y^2 + (-3xy - 5xy)$
$\quad = 7x^2 + 4y^2 - 8xy$

28. $4b(cb - zd) = 4b(cb) + 4b(-zd)$
$\qquad\qquad\qquad = 4b^2c - 4bdz$

29. $4a(3a^2 + b) = 4a(3a^2) + 4a(b)$
$\qquad\qquad\qquad = 12a^3 + 4ab$

30. $-5ab^2(-3a^2b + 6a^3b - 3a^4b^4)$
$\quad = -5ab^2(-3a^2b) - 5ab^2(6a^3b) - 5ab^2(-3a^4b^4)$
$\quad = 15a^3b^3 - 30a^4b^3 + 15a^5b^6$

31. $2xy(3xy^3 - 4xy + 2y^4)$
$\quad = 2xy(3xy^3) + 2xy(-4xy) + 2xy(2y^4)$
$\quad = 6x^2y^4 - 8x^2y^2 + 4xy^5$

32. $\frac{3}{4}x^2(8x + 12y - 16xy^2)$
$\quad = \frac{3}{4}x^2(8x) + \frac{3}{4}x^2(12y) + \frac{3}{4}x^2(-16xy^2)$
$\quad = 6x^3 + 9x^2y - 12x^3y^2$

33. $\frac{1}{2}a^3(4a - 6b + 8ab^4)$
$\quad = \frac{1}{2}a^3(4a) + \frac{1}{2}a^3(-6b) + \frac{1}{2}a^3(8ab^4)$
$\quad = 2a^4 - 3a^3b + 4a^4b^4$

34. If $x =$ amount in savings account, then
$850 - x =$ amount in money market account.
$0.037x + 0.055(850 - x)$
$\quad = 0.037x + 46.75 - 0.055x$
$\quad = 46.75 - 0.018x$

35. Profit = Revenue − Cost
$\qquad\quad = 10x - (0.001x^2 + 5x + 500)$
$\qquad\quad = -0.001x^2 + 5x - 500$

36. Profit $= -0.001(1850) + 5(1850) - 500$
$\qquad = -0.001(3,422,500) + 9250 - 500$
$\qquad = -3422.5 + 9250 - 500$
$\qquad = 5327.5$
The profit is \$5327.50.

37. $(p + 6)(p - 4) = p^2 - 4p + 6p - 24$
$\qquad\qquad\qquad = p^2 + 2p - 24$

38. $(a + 6)(a + 3) = a^2 + 3a + 6a + 18$
$\qquad\qquad\qquad = a^2 + 9a + 18$

39. $(b + 5)(b - 5) = b^2 - 5b + 5b - 25$
$\qquad\qquad\qquad = b^2 - 25$

40. $(6 - z)(6 + z) = 36 + 6z - 6z - z^2$
$\qquad\qquad\qquad = 36 - z^2$

41. $(3x + 8)(2x + 6) = (3x)(2x) + 3x(6) + 8(2x) + 8(6)$
$\qquad\qquad\qquad\quad = 6x^2 + 18x + 16x + 48$
$\qquad\qquad\qquad\quad = 6x^2 + 34x + 48$

42. $(4y - 6)(2y + 7) = (4y)(2y) + 4y(7) - 6(2y) - 6(7)$
$\qquad\qquad\qquad\quad = 8y^2 + 28y - 12y - 42$
$\qquad\qquad\qquad\quad = 8y^2 + 16y - 42$

43. $(a^3 - b)(a^3 + b) = a^6 + a^3b - a^3b - b^2$
$\qquad\qquad\qquad\quad = a^6 - b^2$

44. $(m^2 - 5)(2m^2 + 3) = 2m^4 + 3m^2 - 10m^2 - 15$
$\qquad\qquad\qquad\qquad = 2m^4 - 7m^2 - 15$

45. $(x - 3y)^2 = (x - 3y)(x - 3y)$
$\qquad\qquad\quad = x^2 - 3xy - 3xy + 9y^2$
$\qquad\qquad\quad = x^2 - 6xy + 9y^2$

46. $(1 + 4c)^2 = (1 + 4c)(1 + 4c)$
$\qquad\qquad\quad = 1 + 4c + 4c + 16c^2$
$\qquad\qquad\quad = 1 + 8c + 16c^2$

47. $d^{-3}(d^5 - 2d^3 + d^{-1}) = d^2 - 2d^0 + d^{-4}$
$\qquad\qquad\qquad\qquad\quad = d^2 - 2 + \dfrac{1}{d^4}$

48. $x^{-3}y^2(yx^4 + y^{-1}x^3 + y^{-2}x^2)$
$\qquad = x^1y^3 + x^0y^1 + x^{-1}y^0$
$\qquad = xy^3 + y + \dfrac{1}{x}$

49. $(3b - c)^3$
$\qquad = (3b - c)(3b - c)(3b - c)$
$\qquad = (9b^2 - 3bc - 3bc + c^2)(3b - c)$
$\qquad = (9b^2 - 6bc + c^2)(3b - c)$
$\qquad = 27b^3 - 9b^2c - 18b^2c + 6bc^2 + 3bc^2 - c^3$
$\qquad = 27b^3 - 27b^2c + 9bc^2 - c^3$

50. $(x^2 + xy + y^2)(x - y)$
$\qquad = x^3 - x^2y + x^2y - xy^2 + xy^2 - y^3$
$\qquad = x^3 - y^3$

51. $(c^2 - 6cd - 2d^2) + (7c^2 - cd + 8d^2) - (-c^2 + 5cd - d^2)$
$\qquad = c^2 - 6cd - 2d^2 + 7c^2 - cd + 8d^2 + c^2 - 5cd + d^2$
$\qquad = (c^2 + 7c^2 + c^2) + (-6cd - cd - 5cd) + (-2d^2 + 8d^2 + d^2)$
$\qquad = 9c^2 - 12cd + 7d^2$

52. $(6x - 5)(-3x + 2) = -18x^2 + 12x + 15x - 10$
$\qquad\qquad\qquad\qquad = -18x^2 + 27x - 10$

53. $(R + W)^2 = (R + W)(R + W)$
$\qquad\qquad\quad = R^2 + RW + WR + W^2$
$\qquad\qquad\quad = R^2 + 2RW + W^2$

54. degree: 14
verification: $(x^8 + 1)(x^6 + 1) = x^{14} + x^8 + x^6 + 1$

55. The expression for how much an amount of money will grow to is a polynomial in terms of the interest rate. Answers should include the following.
- If an amount A grows by r percent for n years, the amount will be $A(1 + r)^n$ after n years. When this expression is expanded, a polynomial results.
- $13,872(1 + r)^3$, $13,872r^3 + 41,616r^2 + 41,616r + 13,872$
- Evaluate one of the expressions when $r = 0.04$. For example, $13,872(1 + r)^3 = 13,872(1.04)^3$ or \$15,604.11 to the nearest cent. The value given in the table is \$15,604 rounded to the nearest dollar.

56. D; $1 + x + x^3$, degree: 3
The monomial with the greatest degree is x^3.

57. B; $(x + y) - (y + z) - (x + z) = x + y - y - z - x - z$
$\qquad\qquad\qquad\qquad\qquad\qquad = -2z$

Page 232　Maintain Your Skills

58. $(-4d^2)^3 = (-4)^3(d^2)^3$
$\qquad\qquad = -64d^6$

59. $5rt^2(2rt)^2 = 5rt^2(4r^2t^2)$
$\qquad\qquad\quad = 20r^3t^4$

60. $\dfrac{x^2yz^4}{xy^3z^2} = xy^{-2}z^2$
$\qquad\quad = \dfrac{xz^2}{y^2}$

61. $\left(\dfrac{3ab^2}{6a^2b}\right)^2 = \left(\dfrac{b}{2a}\right)^2$
$\qquad\qquad = \dfrac{b^2}{4a^2}$

62. $4x - y = 0$
$2x + 3y = 14$

$\begin{bmatrix} 4 & -1 \\ 2 & 3 \end{bmatrix}\begin{bmatrix} x \\ y \end{bmatrix} = \begin{bmatrix} 0 \\ 14 \end{bmatrix}$

$A^{-1} = \dfrac{1}{12 + 2}\begin{bmatrix} 3 & 1 \\ -2 & 4 \end{bmatrix}$

$\qquad = \dfrac{1}{14}\begin{bmatrix} 3 & 1 \\ -2 & 4 \end{bmatrix}$

$\dfrac{1}{14}\begin{bmatrix} 3 & 1 \\ -2 & 4 \end{bmatrix}\begin{bmatrix} 4 & -1 \\ 2 & 3 \end{bmatrix}\begin{bmatrix} x \\ y \end{bmatrix} = \dfrac{1}{14}\begin{bmatrix} 3 & 1 \\ -2 & 4 \end{bmatrix}\begin{bmatrix} 0 \\ 14 \end{bmatrix}$

$\begin{bmatrix} 1 & 0 \\ 0 & 1 \end{bmatrix}\begin{bmatrix} x \\ y \end{bmatrix} = \begin{bmatrix} 1 \\ 4 \end{bmatrix}$

$\begin{bmatrix} x \\ y \end{bmatrix} = \begin{bmatrix} 1 \\ 4 \end{bmatrix}$

$x = 1, y = 4$
The solution is $(1, 4)$.

63. $y \le -\frac{1}{3}x + 2$

Graph the boundary line $y = -\frac{1}{3}x + 2$ with a solid line since the inequality symbol $\le$ is used.
Test the point $(0, 0)$.

$$0 \le -\frac{1}{3}(0) + 2$$

$0 \le 2$ True

Shade the region that includes $(0, 0)$.

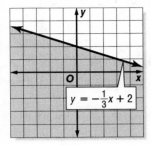

64. $x + y > -2$

Graph the boundary line $x + y = -2$ with a dashed line since the inequality symbol $>$ is used.
Test the point $(0, 0)$.

$$0 + 0 > -2$$

$0 > -2$ True

Shade the region that includes $(0, 0)$.

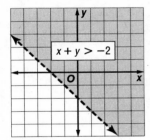

65. $2x + y < 1$

Graph the boundary line $2x + y = 1$ with a dashed line since the inequality symbol $<$ is used.
Test the point $(0, 0)$.

$$2(0) + 0 < 1$$

$0 < 1$ True

Shade the region that includes $(0, 0)$.

66. $\frac{x^3}{x} = x^{3-1}$

$\quad = x^2$

67. $\frac{4y^5}{2y^2} = \frac{4}{2} \cdot \frac{y^5}{y^2}$

$\quad = 2y^{5-2}$

$\quad = 2y^3$

68. $\frac{x^2 y^3}{xy} = x^{2-1} \cdot y^{3-1}$

$\quad = xy^2$

69. $\frac{9a^3 b}{3ab} = \frac{9}{3} \cdot \frac{a^3}{a} \cdot \frac{b}{b}$

$\quad = 3 \cdot a^{3-1} \cdot b^{1-1}$

$\quad = 3a^2$

5-3   Dividing Polynomials

Page 236   Check for Understanding

1. Sample answer: $(x^2 + x + 5) \div (x + 1)$

$$\begin{array}{r} x \\ x + 1 \overline{)x^2 + x + 5} \\ (-)\ \underline{x^2 + x} \\ +5 \end{array}$$

2. The divisor contains an x^2 term.

3. Jorge; Shelly is subtracting in the columns instead of adding

4. $\dfrac{6xy^2 - 3xy + 2x^2 y}{xy}$

$\quad = \dfrac{6xy^2}{xy} - \dfrac{3xy}{xy} + \dfrac{2x^2 y}{xy}$

$\quad = 6x^{1-1}y^{2-1} - 3x^{1-1}y^{1-1} + 2x^{2-1}y^{1-1}$

$\quad = 6y - 3 + 2x$

5. $(5ab^2 - 4ab + 7a^2 b) \cdot (ab)^{-1}$

$\quad = \dfrac{5ab^2 - 4ab + 7a^2 b}{ab}$

$\quad = \dfrac{5ab^2}{ab} - \dfrac{4ab}{ab} + \dfrac{7a^2 b}{ab}$

$\quad = 5a^{1-1}b^{2-1} - 4a^{1-1}b^{1-1} + 7a^{2-1}b^{1-1}$

$\quad = 5b - 4 + 7a$

6.

$$\begin{array}{r} x - 12 \\ x + 2 \overline{)x^2 - 10x - 24} \\ (-)\ \underline{x^2 + 2x} \\ -12x - 24 \\ (-)\ \underline{-12x - 24} \\ 0 \end{array}$$

$(x^2 - 10x - 24) \div (x + 2) = x - 12$

7.

$$\begin{array}{r} 3a^3 - 9a^2 + 7a - 6 \\ a + 1 \overline{)3a^4 - 6a^3 - 2a^2 + a - 6} \\ (-)\ \underline{3a^4 + 3a^3} \\ -9a^3 - 2a^2 \\ (-)\ \underline{-9a^3 - 9a^2} \\ 7a^2 + a \\ (-)\ \underline{7a^2 + 7a} \\ -6a - 6 \\ (-)\ \underline{-6a - 6} \\ 0 \end{array}$$

$(3a^4 - 6a^3 - 2a^2 + a - 6) \div (a + 1)$
$\quad = 3a^3 - a^2 + 7a - 6$

8.

$$\begin{array}{c|cccccc} 2 & 1 & 0 & 0 & -3 & 0 & -20 \\ & & 2 & 4 & 8 & 10 & 20 \\ \hline & 1 & 2 & 4 & 5 & 10 & 0 \end{array}$$

$(z^5 - 3z^2 - 20) \div (z - 2) = z^4 + 2z^3 + 4z^2 + 5z + 10$

9.

$$\begin{array}{r} x^2 - xy + y^2 \\ x + y \overline{)x^3 + 0x^2 y + 0xy^2 + y^3} \\ (-)\ \underline{x^3 + x^2 y} \\ -x^2 y + 0xy^2 \\ (-)\ \underline{-x^2 y - xy^2} \\ xy^2 + y^3 \\ (-)\ \underline{xy^2 + y^3} \\ 0 \end{array}$$

$(x^3 + y^3) \div (x + y) = x^2 - xy + y^2$

10.

$$
\begin{array}{r|rrrr}
-2 & 1 & 13 & -12 & -8 \\
& & -2 & -22 & 68 \\
\hline
& 1 & 11 & -34 & 60 \\
\end{array}
$$

$$(x^3 + 13x^2 - 12x - 8) \div (x + 2)$$
$$= x^2 + 11x - 34 + \frac{60}{x + 2}$$

11. $(b^4 - 2b^3 + b^2 - 3b + 2)(b - 2)^{-1}$

$$= \frac{b^4 - 2b^3 + b^2 - 3b + 2}{b - 2}$$

$$
\begin{array}{r}
b^3 \qquad\quad + b - 1 \\
b - 2\overline{)b^4 - 2b^3 + b^2 - 3b + 2} \\
\underline{(-)\ b^4 - 2b^3} \qquad\qquad\qquad \\
b^2 - 3b \qquad\quad \\
\underline{(-)\ b^2 - 2b} \qquad\quad \\
-b + 2 \\
\underline{(-)\ -b + 2} \\
0
\end{array}
$$

$$(b^4 - 2b^3 + b^2 - 3b + 2)(b - 2)^{-1} = b^3 + b - 1$$

12. $(12y^2 + 36y + 15) \div (6y + 3)$

$$= \frac{12y^2 + 36y + 15}{6y + 3}$$

$$= \frac{(12y^2 + 36y + 15) \div 6}{}$$

$$= \frac{2y^2 + 6y + \frac{5}{2}}{}$$

$$
\begin{array}{r|rrr}
-\frac{1}{2} & 2 & 6 & \frac{5}{2} \\
& & -1 & -\frac{5}{2} \\
\hline
& 2 & 5 & 0 \\
\end{array}
$$

$$(12y^2 + 36y + 15) \div (6y + 3) = 2y + 5$$

13. $\dfrac{9b^2 + 9b - 10}{3b - 2} = \dfrac{(9b^2 + 9b - 10) \div 3}{(3b - 2) \div 3}$

$$= \frac{3b^2 + 3b - \frac{10}{3}}{b - \frac{2}{3}}$$

$$
\begin{array}{r|rrr}
\frac{2}{3} & 3 & 3 & -\frac{10}{3} \\
& & 2 & \frac{10}{3} \\
\hline
& 3 & 5 & 0 \\
\end{array}
$$

$$\frac{9b^2 + 9b - 10}{3b - 2} = 3b + 5$$

14. B; $(x^2 - 4x + 6)(x - 3)^{-1} = \dfrac{x^2 - 4x + 6}{x - 3}$

$$
\begin{array}{r|rrr}
3 & 1 & -4 & 6 \\
& & 3 & -3 \\
\hline
& 1 & -1 & 3 \\
\end{array}
$$

$$(x^2 - 4x + 6)(x - 3)^{-1} = x - 1 + \frac{3}{x - 3}$$

Pages 236–238   Practice and Apply

15. $\dfrac{9a^3b^2 - 18a^2b^3}{3a^2b} = \dfrac{9a^3b^2}{3a^2b} - \dfrac{18a^2b^3}{3a^2b}$

$$= \frac{9}{3} \cdot a^{3 - 2} \cdot b^{2 - 1} - \frac{18}{3}a^{2 - 2} \cdot b^{3 - 1}$$

$$= 3ab - 6b^2$$

16. $\dfrac{5xy^2 - 6y^3 + 3x^2y^3}{xy}$

$$= \frac{5xy^2}{xy} - \frac{6y^3}{xy} + \frac{3x^2y^3}{xy}$$

$$= 5 \cdot x^{1 - 1} \cdot y^{2 - 1} - 6 \cdot x^{-1}y^{3 - 1} + 3 \cdot x^{2 - 1} \cdot y^{3 - 1}$$

$$= 5x^0y - 6x^{-1}y^2 + 3xy^2$$

$$= 5y - \frac{6y^2}{x} + 3xy^2$$

17. $(28c^3d - 42cd^2 + 56cd^3) \div (14cd)$

$$= \frac{28c^3d}{14cd} - \frac{42cd^2}{14cd} + \frac{56cd^3}{14cd}$$

$$= \frac{28}{14} \cdot c^{3 - 1} \cdot d^{1 - 1} - \frac{42}{14}c^{1 - 1} \cdot d^{2 - 1} + \frac{56}{14} \cdot c^{1 - 1} \cdot d^{3 - 1}$$

$$= 2c^2 - 3d + 4d^2$$

18. $(12mn^3 + 9m^2n^2 - 15m^2n) \div (3mn)$

$$= \frac{12mn^3}{3mn} + \frac{9m^2n^2}{3mn} - \frac{15m^2n}{3mn}$$

$$= \frac{12}{3} \cdot m^{1 - 1} \cdot n^{3 - 1} + \frac{9}{3} \cdot m^{2 - 1} \cdot n^{2 - 1} - \frac{15}{3} \cdot m^{2 - 1} \cdot n^{1 - 1}$$

$$= 4n^2 + 3mn - 5m$$

19. $(2y^3z + 4y^2z^2 - 8y^4z^5)(yz)^{-1}$

$$= \frac{2y^3z + 4y^2z^2 - 8y^4z^5}{yz}$$

$$= \frac{2y^3z}{yz} + \frac{4y^2z^2}{yz} - \frac{8y^4z^5}{yz}$$

$$= 2 \cdot y^{3 - 1} \cdot z^{1 - 1} + 4 \cdot y^{2 - 1} \cdot z^{2 - 1} - 8 \cdot y^{4 - 1} \cdot z^{5 - 1}$$

$$= 2y^2 + 4yz - 8y^3z^4$$

20. $(a^3b^2 - a^2b + 2a)(-ab)^{-1}$

$$= \frac{a^3b^2 - a^2b + 2a}{-ab}$$

$$= \frac{a^3b^2}{-ab} - \frac{a^2b}{-ab} + \frac{2a}{-ab}$$

$$= -a^{3 - 1} \cdot b^{2 - 1} + a^{2 - 1} \cdot b^{1 - 1} - 2a^{1 - 1} \cdot b^{-1}$$

$$= -a^2b + a - \frac{2}{b}$$

21.

$$
\begin{array}{r|rrrr}
2 & 1 & 8 & -20 & 0 \\
& & 2 & 20 & 0 \\
\hline
& 1 & 10 & 0 & 0 \\
\end{array}
$$

$$(b^3 + 8b^2 - 20b) \div (b - 2) = b^2 + 10b$$

22.

$$
\begin{array}{r|rrr}
-3 & 1 & -12 & -45 \\
& & -3 & 45 \\
\hline
& 1 & -15 & 0 \\
\end{array}
$$

$$(x^2 - 12x - 45) \div (x + 3) = x - 15$$

23.

$$
\begin{array}{r|rrrr}
-4 & 1 & 2 & -5 & 12 \\
& & -4 & 8 & -12 \\
\hline
& 1 & -2 & 3 & 0 \\
\end{array}
$$

$$(n^3 + 2n^2 - 5n + 12) \div (n + 4) = n^2 - 2n + 3$$

24.

$$
\begin{array}{r}
2c^2 + c + 5 \\
c - 2\overline{)2c^3 - 3c^2 + 3c - 4} \\
\underline{(-)\ 2c^3 - 4c^2} \qquad\qquad\quad \\
c^2 + 3c \qquad\quad \\
\underline{(-)\ c^2 - 2c} \qquad\quad \\
5c - 4 \\
\underline{(-)\ 5c - 10} \\
6
\end{array}
$$

$$(2c^3 - 3c^2 + 3c - 4) \div (c - 2)$$
$$= 2c^2 + c + 5 + \frac{6}{c - 2}$$

25.

$$
\begin{array}{r}
x^3 - 5x^2 + 11x - 22 \\
x+2\overline{)x^4 - 3x^3 + x^2 + 0x - 5} \\
\underline{(-)\ x^4 + 2x^3} \\
-5x^3 + x^2 \\
\underline{(-)\ -5x^3 - 10x^2} \\
11x^2 + 0x \\
\underline{(-)\ 11x^2 + 22x} \\
-22x - 5 \\
\underline{(-)\ -22x - 44} \\
39
\end{array}
$$

$(x^4 - 3x^3 + x^2 - 5) \div (x + 2)$

$= x^3 - 5x^2 + 11x - 22 + \dfrac{39}{x+2}$

26.

$$
\begin{array}{r|rrrrrr}
2 & 6 & 0 & 0 & -18 & 0 & -120 \\
  &   & 12 & 24 & 48 & 60 & 120 \\
\hline
  & 6 & 12 & 24 & 30 & 60 & 0
\end{array}
$$

$(6w^5 - 18w^2 - 120) \div (w - 2)$

$= 6w^4 + 12w^3 + 24w^2 + 30w + 60$

27.

$$
\begin{array}{r}
x^2 \\
x-4\overline{)x^3 - 4x^2} \\
\underline{(-)\ x^3 - 4x^2} \\
0
\end{array}
$$

$(x^3 - 4x^2) \div (x - 4) = x^2$

28.

$$
\begin{array}{r}
x^2 + 3x + 9 \\
x-3\overline{)x^3 + 0x^2 + 0x - 27} \\
\underline{(-)\ x^3 - 3x^2} \\
3x^2 + 0x \\
\underline{(-)\ 3x^2 - 9x} \\
9x - 27 \\
\underline{(-)\ 9x - 27} \\
0
\end{array}
$$

$(x^3 - 27) \div (x - 3) = x^2 + 3x + 9$

29.

$$
\begin{array}{r}
y^2 - y - 1 \\
y+4\overline{)y^3 + 3y^2 - 5y - 4} \\
\underline{(-)\ y^3 + 4y^2} \\
-y^2 - 5y \\
\underline{(-)\ -y^2 - 4y} \\
-y - 4 \\
\underline{(-)\ -y - 4} \\
0
\end{array}
$$

$\dfrac{y^3 + 3y^2 - 5y - 4}{y+4} = y^2 - y - 1$

30.

$$
\begin{array}{r}
m^2 \qquad - 7 \\
m+3\overline{)m^3 + 3m^2 - 7m - 21} \\
\underline{(-)\ m^3 + 3m^2} \\
-7m - 21 \\
\underline{(-)\ -7m - 21} \\
0
\end{array}
$$

$\dfrac{m^3 + 3m^2 - 7m - 21}{\ } = m^2 - 7$

31.

$$
\begin{array}{r}
a^3 - 6a^2 - 7a + 7 \\
a+1\overline{)a^4 - 5a^3 - 13a^2 + 0a + 10} \\
\underline{(-)\ a^4 + a^3} \\
-6a^3 - 13a^2 \\
\underline{(-)\ -6a^3 - 6a^2} \\
-7a^2 + 0a \\
\underline{(-)\ -7a^2 - 7a} \\
7a + 10 \\
\underline{(-)\ 7a + 7} \\
3
\end{array}
$$

$\dfrac{a^4 - 5a^3 - 13a^2 + 10}{\ } = a^3 - 6a^2 - 7a + 7 + \dfrac{3}{a+1}$

32.

$$
\begin{array}{r}
2m^3 + m^2 + 3m - 1 \\
m-3\overline{)2m^4 - 5m^3 + 0m^2 - 10m + 8} \\
\underline{(-)\ 2m^4 - 6m^3} \\
m^3 + 0m^2 \\
\underline{(-)\ m^3 - 3m^2} \\
3m^2 - 10m \\
\underline{(-)\ 3m^2 - 9m} \\
-m + 8 \\
\underline{(-)\ -m + 3} \\
5
\end{array}
$$

$\dfrac{2m^4 - 5m^3 - 10m + 8}{m-3} = 2m^3 + m^2 + 3m - 1 + \dfrac{5}{m-3}$

33.

$$
\begin{array}{r}
x^4 - 3x^3 + 2x^2 - 6x + 19 \\
x+3\overline{)x^5 + 0x^4 - 7x^3 + 0x^2 + x + 1} \\
\underline{(-)\ x^5 + 3x^4} \\
-3x^4 - 7x^3 \\
\underline{(-)\ -3x^4 - 9x^3} \\
2x^3 + 0x^2 \\
\underline{(-)\ 2x^3 + 6x^2} \\
-6x^2 + x \\
\underline{(-)\ -6x^2 - 18x} \\
19x + 1 \\
\underline{(-)\ 19x + 57} \\
-56
\end{array}
$$

$\dfrac{x^5 - 7x^3 + x + 1}{x+3} = x^4 - 3x^3 + 2x^2 - 6x + 19 - \dfrac{56}{x+3}$

34.

$$
\begin{array}{r}
3c^4 - c^3 + 2c^2 - 4c + 9 \\
c+2\overline{)3c^5 + 5c^4 + 0c^3 + 0c^2 + c + 5} \\
\underline{(-)\ 3c^5 + 6c^4} \\
-c^4 + 0c^3 \\
\underline{(-)\ -c^4 - 2c^3} \\
2c^3 + 0c^2 \\
\underline{(-)\ 2c^3 + 4c^2} \\
-4c^2 + c \\
\underline{(-)\ -4c^2 - 8c} \\
9c + 5 \\
\underline{(-)\ 9c + 18} \\
-13
\end{array}
$$

$\dfrac{3c^5 + 5c^4 + c + 5}{\ } = 3c^4 - c^3 + 2c^2 - 4c + 9 - \dfrac{13}{c+2}$

35.

$$
\begin{array}{r|rrr}
-3 & 1 & 8 & 15 \\
   &   & -3 & -15 \\
\hline
   & 1 & 5 & 0
\end{array}
$$

$(g^2 + 8g + 15)(g + 3)^{-1} = \dfrac{g^2 + 8g + 15}{g+3}$

$= g + 5$

36.

$$
\begin{array}{r}
2b^2 - b - 1 \\
b+1\overline{)2b^3 + b^2 - 2b + 3} \\
\underline{(-)\ 2b^3 + 2b^2} \\
-b^2 - 2b \\
\underline{(-)\ -b^2 - b} \\
-b + 3 \\
\underline{(-)\ -b - 1} \\
4
\end{array}
$$

$$(2b^3 + b^2 - 2b + 3)(b+1)^{-1}$$

$$= \frac{2b^3 + b^2 - 2b + 3}{b+1}$$

$$= 2b^2 - b - 1 + \frac{4}{b+1}$$

37.

$$
\begin{array}{r|rrrrr}
2 & 1 & 0 & 0 & -3 & 0 & -20 \\
  &   & 2 & 4 & 8 & 10 & 20 \\
\hline
  & 1 & 2 & 4 & 5 & 10 & 0
\end{array}
$$

$$(t^5 - 3t^2 - 20)(t-2)^{-1} = \frac{t^5 - 3t^2 - 20}{t-2}$$

$$= t^4 + 2t^3 + 4t^2 + 5t + 10$$

38.

$$
\begin{array}{r|rrrrrr}
-2 & 1 & 0 & 0 & 0 & 0 & 32 \\
   &   & -2 & 4 & -8 & 16 & -32 \\
\hline
   & 1 & -2 & 4 & -8 & 16 & 0
\end{array}
$$

$$(y^5 + 32)(y+2)^{-1} = \frac{y^5 + 32}{y+2}$$

$$= y^4 - 2y^3 + 4y^2 - 8y + 16$$

39.

$$
\begin{array}{r}
3t^2 - 2t + 3 \\
2t+3\overline{)6t^3 + 5t^2 + 0t + 9} \\
\underline{(-)\ 6t^3 + 9t^2} \\
-4t^2 + 0t \\
\underline{(-)\ -4t^2 - 6t} \\
6t + 9 \\
\underline{(-)\ 6t + 9} \\
0
\end{array}
$$

$$(6t^3 + 5t^2 + 9) \div (2t+3) = 3t^2 - 2t + 3$$

40.

$$
\begin{array}{r}
h^2 - 4h + 17 \\
2h+3\overline{)2h^3 - 5h^2 + 22h + 0} \\
\underline{(-)\ 2h^3 + 3h^2} \\
-8h^2 + 22h \\
\underline{(-)\ -8h^2 - 12h} \\
34h + 0 \\
\underline{(-)\ 34h + 51} \\
-51
\end{array}
$$

$$(2h^3 - 5h^2 + 22h) \div (2h+3)$$

$$= h^2 - 4h + 17 - \frac{51}{2h+3}$$

41.

$$
\begin{array}{r}
3d^2 + 2d + 3 \\
3d-2\overline{)9d^3 + 0d^2 + 5d - 8} \\
\underline{(-)\ 9d^3 - 6d^2} \\
6d^2 + 5d \\
\underline{(-)\ 6d^2 - 4d} \\
9d - 8 \\
\underline{(-)\ 9d - 6} \\
-2
\end{array}
$$

$$\frac{9d^3 + 5d - 8}{3d-2} = 3d^2 + 2d + 3 - \frac{2}{3d-2}$$

42.

$$\frac{4x^3 + 5x^2 - 3x - 1}{4} = \frac{(4x^3 + 5x^2 - 3x - 1) \div 4}{}$$

$$= \frac{x^3 + \frac{5}{4}x^2 - \frac{3}{4}x - \frac{1}{4}}{}$$

$$
\begin{array}{r|rrrr}
-\frac{1}{4} & 1 & \frac{5}{4} & -\frac{3}{4} & -\frac{1}{4} \\
   &   & -\frac{1}{4} & -\frac{1}{4} & \frac{1}{4} \\
\hline
   & 1 & 1 & -1 & 0
\end{array}
$$

$$\frac{4x^3 + 5x^2 - 3x - 1}{} = x^2 + x - 1$$

43.

$$
\begin{array}{r}
x^3 \qquad - x \\
2x+3\overline{)2x^4 + 3x^3 - 2x^2 - 3x - 6} \\
\underline{(-)\ 2x^4 + 3x^3} \\
-2x^2 - 3x \\
\underline{(-)\ -2x^2 - 3x} \\
-6
\end{array}
$$

$$\frac{2x^4 + 3x^3 - 2x^2 - 3x - 6}{} = x^3 - x - \frac{6}{2x+3}$$

44.

$$
\begin{array}{r}
2x^3 + x^2 \qquad - 1 \\
3x+1\overline{)6x^4 + 5x^3 + x^2 - 3x + 1} \\
\underline{(-)\ 6x^4 + 2x^3} \\
3x^3 + x^2 \\
\underline{(-)\ 3x^3 + x^2} \\
-3x + 1 \\
\underline{(-)\ -3x - 1} \\
2
\end{array}
$$

$$\frac{6x^4 + 5x^3 + x^2 - 3x + 1}{} = 2x^3 + x^2 - 1 + \frac{2}{3x+1}$$

45.

$$
\begin{array}{r}
x - 3 \\
x^2+1\overline{)x^3 - 3x^2 + x - 3} \\
\underline{(-)\ x^3 \qquad + x} \\
-3x^2 \qquad - 3 \\
\underline{(-)\ -3x^2 \qquad - 3} \\
0
\end{array}
$$

$$\frac{x^3 - 3x^2 + x - 3}{x^2 + 1} = x - 3$$

46.

$$
\begin{array}{r}
x^2 \qquad - 1 \\
x^2+2\overline{)x^4 + x^2 - 3x + 5} \\
\underline{(-)\ x^4 + 2x^2} \\
-x^2 + 3x + 5 \\
\underline{(-)\ -x^2 \qquad - 2} \\
-3x + 7
\end{array}
$$

$$\frac{x^4 + x^2 - 3x + 5}{x^2 + 2} = x^2 - 1 + \frac{-3x + 7}{x^2 + 2}$$

47.

$$
\begin{array}{r}
x + 2 \\
x^2+x+1\overline{)x^3 + 3x^2 + 3x + 2} \\
\underline{(-)\ x^3 + x^2 + x} \\
2x^2 + 2x + 2 \\
\underline{(-)\ 2x^2 + 2x + 2} \\
0
\end{array}
$$

$$\frac{x^3 + 3x^2 + 3x + 2}{} = x + 2$$

48.

$$
\begin{array}{r}
x - 3 \\
x^2-x+2\overline{)x^3 - 4x^2 + 5x - 6} \\
\underline{(-)\ x^3 - x^2 + 2x} \\
-3x^2 + 3x - 6 \\
\underline{(-)\ -3x^2 + 3x - 6} \\
0
\end{array}
$$

$$\frac{x^3 - 4x^2 + 5x - 6}{} = x - 3$$

49.

$$\begin{array}{r|rrrr} 1 & 1 & -2 & 4 & -3 \\ & & 1 & -1 & 3 \\ \hline & 1 & -1 & 3 & | \; 0 \end{array}$$

$(x^3 - 2x^2 + 4x - 3) \div (x - 1) = x^2 - x + 3$

50.

$$\begin{array}{r|rrrr} -2 & 2 & 1 & -5 & 2 \\ & & -4 & 6 & -2 \\ \hline & 2 & -3 & 1 & | \; 0 \end{array}$$

$(2y^3 + y^2 - 5y + 2) \div (y + 2) = 2y^2 - 3y + 1$

51. $\dfrac{0.03x^2 + 4x + 1000}{x} = \dfrac{0.03x^2}{x} + \dfrac{4x}{x} + \dfrac{1000}{x}$

$\qquad\qquad = \$\left(0.03x + 4 + \dfrac{1000}{x}\right)$

52. Let x be the number. Multiplying by 3 results in $3x$. The sum of the number 8, and the result of the multiplication is $(x + 8 + 3x)$ or $(4x + 8)$. Dividing by the sum of the number and 2 gives $\dfrac{4x + 8}{x + 2}$ or 4. The end result is always 4.

53.

$$\begin{array}{r} 170 \\ t^2 + 1 \overline{)170t^2} \\ (-)\;170t^2 + 170 \\ \hline -170 \end{array}$$

$n = \dfrac{170t^2}{t^2 + 1} = 170 - \dfrac{170}{t^2 + 1}$

54. Number of people who will become ill during first week $= \dfrac{170(1)}{(1)^2 + 1}$

$\qquad = \dfrac{170}{2}$

$\qquad = 85$

During the first week, 85 people are estimated to become ill.

55. distance at $t = 2$ from starting point
$\qquad = 2^3 + 2^4 + 6(2)$
$\qquad = 8 + 4 + 12$
$\qquad = 24$ ft
distance at $t = x$ from starting point
$\qquad = (x^3 + x^2 + 6x)$ ft
(Distance travelled between the time $t = 2$ and $t = x$)
$\qquad = $ (distance at $t = x$) $-$ (distance at $t = 2$)
$\qquad = (x^3 + x^2 + 6x) - 24$
$\qquad = (x^3 + x^2 + 6x - 24)$ ft

56. elapsed time between $t = 2$ and $t = x$ is $x - 2$ seconds

57. Average speed $= \dfrac{\text{distance}}{\text{time}}$

Average speed $= \dfrac{x^3 + x^2 + 6x - 24}{x - 2}$

$$\begin{array}{r|rrrr} 2 & 1 & 1 & 6 & -24 \\ & & 2 & 6 & 24 \\ \hline & 1 & 3 & 12 & | \; 0 \end{array}$$

The average speed is $(x^2 + 3x + 12)$ ft/s.

58. Sample answer: $r^3 - 9r^2 + 27r - 28$ and $r - 3$
dividend polynomial
$\qquad = (r^2 - 6r + 9)(r - 3) - 1$
$\qquad = r^3 - 3r^2 - 6r^2 + 18r + 9r - 27 - 1$
$\qquad = r^3 - 9r^2 + 27r - 28$
divisor polynomial $= r - 3$

59. Division of polynomials can be used to solve for unknown quantities in geometric formulas that apply to manufacturing situations. Answers should include the following.
- $8x$ in. by $4x + s$ in.
- The area of a rectangle is equal to the length times the width. That is, $A = \ell w$.
- Substitute $32x^2 + x$ for A, $8x$ for ℓ, and $4x + s$ for w. Solving for s involves dividing $32x^2 + x$ by $8x$.

$\qquad\quad A = \ell w$
$\qquad 32x^2 + x = 8x(4x + s)$
$\qquad \dfrac{32x^2 + x}{8x} = 4x + s$
$\qquad\quad 4x + \dfrac{1}{8} = 4x + s$
$\qquad\qquad\;\; \dfrac{1}{8} = s$

The seam is $\dfrac{1}{8}$ inch.

60. A; $\qquad$ number of women $= x$
$\qquad\qquad\qquad$ number of men $= 3$
total number of employees $= x + 3$

$\dfrac{\text{total number of employees}}{\text{number of women}} = \dfrac{x + 3}{x}$

$\qquad\qquad\qquad\qquad\quad = \dfrac{x}{x} + \dfrac{3}{x}$

$\qquad\qquad\qquad\qquad\quad = 1 + \dfrac{3}{x}$

61. D; If $c - b = 2a$ is true, add corresponding sides of

$$\begin{array}{r} a + b = c \\ c - b = 2a \\ \hline a + b + c - b = c + 2a \\ a = 2a \\ \dfrac{a}{a} = \dfrac{2a}{a} \\ 1 = 2 \end{array}$$

The conclusion is false. Therefore, $c - b = 2a$ is false.

Page 238 Maintain Your Skills

62. $(2x^2 - 3x + 5) - (3x^2 + x - 9)$
$\qquad = 2x^2 - 3x + 5 - 3x^2 - x + 9$
$\qquad = (2x^2 - 3x^2) + (-3x - x) + (5 + 9)$
$\qquad = -x^2 - 4x + 14$

63. $y^2z(y^2z^3 - yz^2 + 3)$
$\qquad = y^2z(y^2z^3) + y^2z(-yz^2) + y^2z(3)$
$\qquad = y^4z^4 - y^3z^3 + 3y^2z$

64. $(y + 5)(y - 3) = y^2 - 3y + 5y - 15$
$\qquad\qquad\qquad\quad = y^2 + 2y - 15$

65. $(a - b)^2 = (a - b)(a - b)$
$\qquad\qquad = a^2 - ab - ab + b^2$
$\qquad\qquad = a^2 - 2ab + b^2$

66. $\dfrac{1.5 \times 10^{11}}{3 \times 10^8} = \dfrac{1.5}{3} \times 10^{11-8}$
$\qquad\qquad = 0.5 \times 10^3$
$\qquad\qquad = 5 \times 10^2$

It takes sunlight 5×10^2 seconds to reach Earth, or $\dfrac{5 \times 10^2 \text{ s}}{60 \text{ s/min}} = 8$ min 20 s.

67. Given points: $A(1, 1)$ and $B(3, -1)$

$m = \frac{y_2 - y_1}{x_2 - x_1}$

$m = \frac{1 - (-1)}{1 - 3} = \frac{2}{-2} = -1$

$y = mx + b$

$1 = (-1)(1) + b$

$1 = -1 + b$

$2 = b$

$y = (-1)x + 2$

$y = -x + 2$

68. Given points: $A(2, 0)$ and $B(-4, -4)$

$m = \frac{y_2 - y_1}{x_2 - x_1}$

$m = \frac{0 - (-4)}{2 - (-4)} = \frac{4}{6} = \frac{2}{3}$

Replace $m = \frac{2}{3}$ and $A(2, 0)$ in $y = mx + b$.

$0 = \frac{2}{3}(2) + b$

$0 = \frac{4}{3} + b$

$-\frac{4}{3} = b$

Therefore, $y = \frac{2}{3}x - \frac{4}{3}$.

69. $18 = 2 \cdot 3 \cdot 3$

$\quad = 2 \cdot 3^2$

$27 = 3 \cdot 3 \cdot 3$

$\quad = 3^3$

Greatest common factor of 18 and 27 = 3^2 or 9

70. $24 = 2 \cdot 2 \cdot 2 \cdot 3$

$\quad = 2^3 \cdot 3$

$84 = 2 \cdot 2 \cdot 3 \cdot 7$

$\quad = 2^2 \cdot 3 \cdot 7$

Greatest common factor of 18 and 27 = $2^2 \cdot 3$ or 12

71. $16 = 2 \cdot 2 \cdot 2 \cdot 2$

$\quad = 2^4$

$28 = 2 \cdot 2 \cdot 7$

$\quad = 2^2 \cdot 7$

Greatest common factor of 16 and 28 = 2^2 or 4

72. $12 = 2 \cdot 2 \cdot 3$

$\quad = 2^2 \cdot 3$

$27 = 3 \cdot 3 \cdot 3$

$\quad = 3^3$

$48 = 2 \cdot 2 \cdot 2 \cdot 2 \cdot 3$

$\quad = 2^4 \cdot 3$

Greatest common factor of 12, 27 and 48 = 3

73. $12 = 2 \cdot 2 \cdot 3$

$\quad = 2^2 \cdot 3$

$30 = 2 \cdot 3 \cdot 5$

$54 = 2 \cdot 3 \cdot 3 \cdot 3$

$\quad = 2 \cdot 3^3$

Greatest common factor of 12, 30 and 54 = $2 \cdot 3$ or 6

74. $15 = 3 \cdot 5$

$30 = 2 \cdot 3 \cdot 5$

$65 = 5 \cdot 13$

Greatest common factor of 15, 30, and 65 = 5

Page 238   Practice Quiz 1

1. $653,000,000 = 6.53 \times 100,000,000$

$\qquad\qquad\quad = 6.53 \times 10^8$

2. $0.0072 = 7.2 \times 0.001$

$\qquad\quad = 7.2 \times 10^{-3}$

3. $(-3x^2y)^3(2x)^2 = (-3)^3(x^2)^3(y)^3(2)^2(x^2)$

$\qquad\qquad\qquad = (-27)(x^6)(y^3)(4)(x^2)$

$\qquad\qquad\qquad = (-27)(4)(x^{6 + 2})y^3$

$\qquad\qquad\qquad = -108x^8y^3$

4. $\frac{a^6b^{-2}c}{a^3b^2c^4} = a^{6 - 3} \cdot b^{-2 - 2} \cdot c^{1 - 4}$

$\qquad\quad = a^3 \cdot b^{-4} \cdot c^{-3}$

$\qquad\quad = \frac{a^3}{b^4c^3}$

5. $\left(\frac{x^2z}{xz^4}\right)^2 = (x^{2 - 1} \cdot z^{1 - 4})^2$

$\qquad\quad = (x \cdot z^{-3})^2$

$\qquad\quad = x^2 \cdot z^{-3 \cdot 2}$

$\qquad\quad = x^2 \cdot z^{-6}$

$\qquad\quad = \frac{x^2}{z^6}$

6. $(9x + 2y) - (7x - 3y) = 9x + 2y - 7x + 3y$

$\qquad\qquad\qquad\qquad = (9x - 7x) + (2y + 3y)$

$\qquad\qquad\qquad\qquad = 2x + 5y$

7. $(t + 2)(3t - 4) = 3t^2 - 4t + 6t - 8$

$\qquad\qquad\qquad = 3t^2 + 2t - 8$

8. $(n + 2)(n^2 - 3n + 1)$

$\quad = n^3 - 3n^2 + n + 2n^2 - 6n + 2$

$\quad = n^3 - n^2 - 5n + 2$

9.

$$
\begin{array}{r}
m^2 \qquad\quad - 3 \\
m - 4 \overline{)\, m^3 - 4m^2 - 3m - 7} \\
\underline{(-)\ m^3 - 4m^2} \qquad\qquad\quad \\
-3m - 7 \\
\underline{(-)\ -3m + 12} \\
-19
\end{array}
$$

$\frac{m^3 - 4m^2 - 3m - 7}{m - 4} = m^2 - 3 - \frac{19}{m - 4}$

10. $\frac{2d^3 - d^2 - 9d + 9}{2d - 3} = \frac{(2d^3 - d^2 - 9d + 9) \div 2}{(2d - 3) \div 2}$

$\qquad\qquad\qquad\qquad = \frac{d^3 - \frac{1}{2}d^2 - \frac{9}{2}d + \frac{9}{2}}{d - \frac{3}{2}}$

$$
\begin{array}{c|cccc}
\frac{3}{2} & 1 & -\frac{1}{2} & -\frac{9}{2} & \frac{9}{2} \\
& & \frac{3}{2} & \frac{3}{2} & -\frac{9}{2} \\
\hline
& 1 & 1 & -3 & 0
\end{array}
$$

$\frac{2d^3 - d^2 - 9d + 9}{2d - 3} = d^2 + d - 3$

5-4 | Factoring Polynomials

Page 240   Algebra Activity

1. The coefficient of x is 1 and of $6x$ is 6.

sum: $1 + 6 = 7$

product: $1 \cdot 6 = 6$

2. They are the same. Each is 7.

3. The coefficient of $2x^2$ is 2 and the constant term is 3.

product: $2 \cdot 3 = 6$

It is the same.

4. Find two numbers with a product of $3 \cdot 2$ or 6 and a sum of 7. Use those numbers to rewrite the trinomial. Then factor.

Page 241   Graphing Calculator Investigation

1. No; when graphing the functions $y = x^2 + 5x - 6$ and $y = (x - 3)(x - 2)$, two different graphs appear.

$$
\begin{aligned}
x^2 + 5x - 6 &= x^2 + 6x - x - 6 \\
&= (x^2 + 6x) - (x + 6) \\
&= x(x + 6) - 1(x + 6) \\
&= (x + 6)(x - 1)
\end{aligned}
$$

2. No; in some cases, the graphs might be so close in shape that they seem to coincide but do not.

Page 242   Check for Understanding

1. Sample answer:
$$
\begin{aligned}
x^2 + 2x + 1 &= x^2 + x + x + 1 \\
&= (x^2 + x) + (x + 1) \\
&= x(x + 1) + 1(x + 1) \\
&= (x + 1)(x + 1) \\
&= (x + 1)^2
\end{aligned}
$$

2. Sample answer: If $a = 1$ and $b = 1$, then $a^2 + b^2 = 2$ but $(a + b)^2 = 4$.

3. $\dfrac{x - 2}{x^2 + x - 6} = \dfrac{(x - 2)}{(x + 3)(x - 2)} = \dfrac{x}{x + 3}$

It is sometimes true, when $x - 2 \neq 0$.

4.
$$
\begin{aligned}
-12x^2 - 6x &= -2 \cdot 2 \cdot 3 \cdot x \cdot x - 2 \cdot 3 \cdot x \\
&= (-6x \cdot 2x) + (-6x \cdot 1) \\
&= -6x(2x + 1)
\end{aligned}
$$

5.
$$
\begin{aligned}
a^2 + 5a + ab &= a \cdot a + 5 \cdot a + a \cdot b \\
&= a(a + 5 + b)
\end{aligned}
$$

6.
$$
\begin{aligned}
21 - 7y + 3x - xy &= (21 - 7y) + (3x - xy) \\
&= 7(3 - y) + x(3 - y) \\
&= (3 - y)(7 + x)
\end{aligned}
$$

7.
$$
\begin{aligned}
y^2 - 6y + 8 &= y^2 - 2y - 4y + 8 \\
&= y(y - 2) - 4(y - 2) \\
&= (y - 2)(y - 4)
\end{aligned}
$$

8.
$$
\begin{aligned}
z^2 - 4z - 12 &= z^2 - 6z + 2z - 12 \\
&= z(z - 6) + 2(z - 6) \\
&= (z - 6)(z + 2)
\end{aligned}
$$

9.
$$
\begin{aligned}
3b^2 - 48 &= 3(b^2 - 16) \\
&= 3(b^2 - 4^2) \\
&= 3(b - 4)(b + 4)
\end{aligned}
$$

10.
$$
\begin{aligned}
16w^2 - 169 &= (4w)^2 - (13)^2 \\
&= (4w - 13)(4w + 13)
\end{aligned}
$$

11.
$$
\begin{aligned}
h^3 + 8000 &= h^3 + (20)^3 \\
&= (h + 20)(h^2 - 20h + 400)
\end{aligned}
$$

12.
$$
\begin{aligned}
\frac{x^2 - 2x - 8}{x^2 - 5x - 14} &= \frac{(x - 4)(x + 2)}{(x - 7)(x + 2)} \\
&= \frac{x - 4}{x - 7}
\end{aligned}
$$

13.
$$
\begin{aligned}
\frac{2y^2 + 8y}{y^2 - 16} &= \frac{2y(y + 4)}{y^2 - 4^2} \\
&= \frac{2y(y + 4)}{(y - 4)(y + 4)} \\
&= \frac{2y}{y - 4}
\end{aligned}
$$

14. width of $ABCD = \dfrac{3x^2 + 9xy + 6y^2}{3x + 6y}$

$$
\begin{aligned}
&= \frac{3x^2 + 3xy + 6xy + 6y^2}{} \\
&= \frac{(3x^2 + 3xy) + (6xy + 6y^2)}{} \\
&= \frac{3x(x + y) + 6y(x + y)}{} \\
&= \frac{(x + y)(3x + 6y)}{3x + 6y} \\
&= x + y
\end{aligned}
$$

The width is $(x + y)$ cm.

Pages 242–244   Practice and Apply

15.
$$
\begin{aligned}
2xy^3 - 10x &= (2 \cdot x \cdot y \cdot y \cdot y) - (2 \cdot 5 \cdot x) \\
&= (2x \cdot y^3) - (2x \cdot 5) \\
&= 2x(y^3 - 5)
\end{aligned}
$$

16. $6a^2b^2 + 18ab^3$
$$
\begin{aligned}
&= (2 \cdot 3 \cdot a \cdot a \cdot b \cdot b) + (2 \cdot 3 \cdot 3 \cdot a \cdot b \cdot b \cdot b) \\
&= (6ab^2 \cdot a) + (6ab^2 \cdot 3b) \\
&= 6ab^2(a + 3b)
\end{aligned}
$$

17. $12cd^3 - 8c^2d^2 + 10c^5d^3$
$$
\begin{aligned}
&= (2 \cdot 2 \cdot 3 \cdot c \cdot d \cdot d \cdot d) - (2 \cdot 2 \cdot 2 \cdot c \cdot c \cdot d \cdot d) + (2 \cdot 5 \cdot c \cdot c \cdot c \cdot c \cdot c \cdot d \cdot d \cdot d) \\
&= (2cd^2 \cdot 6d) - (2cd^2 \cdot 4c) + (2cd^2 \cdot 5c^4d) \\
&= 2cd^2(6d - 4c + 5c^4d)
\end{aligned}
$$

18. $3a^2bx + 15cx^2y + 25ad^3y$
$$
= (3 \cdot a \cdot a \cdot b \cdot x) + (3 \cdot 5 \cdot c \cdot x \cdot x \cdot y) + (5 \cdot 5 \cdot a \cdot d \cdot d \cdot d \cdot y)
$$

The polynomial is prime.

19.
$$
\begin{aligned}
8yz - 6z - 12y + 9 &= (8yz - 6z) + (-12y + 9) \\
&= 2z(4y - 3) - 3(4y - 3) \\
&= (4y - 3)(2z - 3)
\end{aligned}
$$

20.
$$
\begin{aligned}
3ax - 15a + x - 5 &= (3ax - 15a) + (x - 5) \\
&= 3a(x - 5) + 1(x - 5) \\
&= (x - 5)(3a + 1)
\end{aligned}
$$

21.
$$
\begin{aligned}
x^2 + 7x + 6 &= x^2 + 6x + x + 6 \\
&= (x^2 + 6x) + (x + 6) \\
&= x(x + 6) + 1(x + 6) \\
&= (x + 6)(x + 1)
\end{aligned}
$$

22.
$$
\begin{aligned}
y^2 - 5y + 4 &= y^2 - y - 4y + 4 \\
&= (y^2 - y) + (-4y + 4) \\
&= y(y - 1) - 4(y - 1) \\
&= (y - 1)(y - 4)
\end{aligned}
$$

23.
$$
\begin{aligned}
2a^2 + 3a + 1 &= 2a^2 + 2a + a + 1 \\
&= (2a^2 + 2a) + (a + 1) \\
&= 2a(a + 1) + 1(a + 1) \\
&= (a + 1)(2a + 1)
\end{aligned}
$$

24.
$$
\begin{aligned}
2b^2 + 13b - 7 &= 2b^2 + 14b - b - 7 \\
&= (2b^2 + 14b) + (-b - 7) \\
&= 2b(b + 7) - 1(b + 7) \\
&= (b + 7)(2b - 1)
\end{aligned}
$$

25.
$$
\begin{aligned}
6c^2 + 13c + 6 &= 6c^2 + 4c + 9c + 6 \\
&= (6c^2 + 4c) + (9c + 6) \\
&= 2c(3c + 2) + 3(3c + 2) \\
&= (3c + 2)(2c + 3)
\end{aligned}
$$

26.
$$
\begin{aligned}
12m^2 - m - 6 &= 12m^2 - 9m + 8m - 6 \\
&= (12m^2 - 9m) + (8m - 6) \\
&= 3m(4m - 3) + 2(4m - 3) \\
&= (4m - 3)(3m + 2)
\end{aligned}
$$

27. $3n^2 + 21n - 24 = 3(n^2 + 7n - 8)$
$$= 3[(n^2 + 8n) + (-n - 8)]$$
$$= 3[n(n + 8) - 1(n + 8)]$$
$$= 3(n - 1)(n + 8)$$

28. $3z^2 + 24z + 45 = 3(z^2 + 8z + 15)$
$$= 3[(z^2 + 5z) + (3z + 15)]$$
$$= 3[z(z + 5) + 3(z + 5)]$$
$$= 3(z + 3)(z + 5)$$

29. $x^2 + 12x + 36 = x^2 + 2 \cdot 6 \cdot x + 6^2$
$$= (x + 6)^2$$

30. $x^2 - 6x + 9 = x^2 - 2 \cdot 3 \cdot x + 3^2$
$$= (x - 3)^2$$

31. $16a^2 + 25b^2$ prime

32. $3m^2 - 3n^2 = 3(m^2 - n^2)$
$$= 3(m - n)(m + n)$$

33. $y^4 - z^2 = (y^2)^2 - z^2$
$$= (y^2 - z)(y^2 + z)$$

34. $3x^2 - 27y^2 = 3(x^2 - 9y^2)$
$$= 3[x^2 - (3y)^2]$$
$$= 3(x - 3y)(x + 3y)$$

35. $z^3 + 125 = z^3 + 5^3$
$$= (z + 5)(z^2 - 5z + 5^2)$$
$$= (z + 5)(z - 5z + 25)$$

36. $t^3 - 8 = t^3 - 2^3$
$$= (t - 2)(t^2 + 2t + 2^2)$$
$$= (t - 2)(t^2 + 2t + 4)$$

37. $p^4 - 1 = (p^2)^2 - 1^2$
$$= (p^2 - 1)(p^2 + 1)$$
$$= (p^2 - 1^2)(p^2 + 1)$$
$$= (p - 1)(p + 1)(p^2 + 1)$$

38. $x^4 - 81 = (x^2)^2 - (3^2)^2$
$$= (x^2 - 3^2)(x^2 + 3^2)$$
$$= (x - 3)(x + 3)(x^2 + 9)$$

39. $7ac^2 + 2bc^2 - 7ad^2 - 2bd^2$
$$= (7ac^2 - 7ad^2) + (2bc^2 - 2bd^2)$$
$$= 7a(c^2 - d^2) + 2b(c^2 - d^2)$$
$$= (c^2 - d^2)(7a + 2b)$$
$$= (c - d)(c + d)(7a + 2b)$$

40. $8x^2 + 8xy + 8xz + 3x + 3y + 3z$
$$= (8x^2 + 8xy + 8xz) + (3x + 3y + 3z)$$
$$= 8x(x + y + z) + 3(x + y + z)$$
$$= (x + y + z)(8x + 3)$$

41. $5a^2x + 4aby + 3acz - 5abx - 4b^2y - 3bcz$
$$= (5a^2x + 4aby + 3acz) + (-5abx - 4b^2y - 3bcz)$$
$$= a(5ax + 4by + 3cz) - b(5ax + 4by + 3cz)$$
$$= (5ax + 4by + 3cz)(a - b)$$

42. $3a^3 + 2a^2 - 5a + 9a^2b + 6ab - 15b$
$$= (3a^3 + 2a^2 - 5a) + (9a^2b + 6ab - 15b)$$
$$= a(3a^2 + 2a - 5) + 3b(3a^2 + 2a - 5)$$
$$= (3a^2 + 2a - 5)(a + 3b)$$
$$= (3a^2 + 5a - 3a - 5)(a + 3b)$$
$$= [(3a^2 + 5a) + (-3a - 5)](a + 3b)$$
$$= [a(3a + 5) - 1(3a + 5)](a + 3b)$$
$$= (3a + 5)(a - 1)(a + 3b)$$

43. $3x^2 + x - 2 = 3x^2 + 3x - 2x - 2$
$$= (3x^2 + 3x) + (-2x - 2)$$
$$= 3x(x + 1) - 2(x + 1)$$
$$= (x + 1)(3x - 2)$$

44. $2y^2 + 9y + 4 = 2y^2 + 8y + y + 4$
$$= (2y^2 + 8y) + (y + 4)$$
$$= 2y(y + 4) + 1(y + 4)$$
$$= (y + 4)(2y + 1)$$

45. $4x^2 + 140x + 1200 = (4x^2 + 80x) + (60x + 1200)$
$$= 2x(2x + 40) + 30(2x + 40)$$
$$= (2x + 30)(2x + 40)$$
Length + 2(width of boardwalk) = $2x + 40$
Width + 2(width of boardwalk) = $2x + 30$
Therefore, length = $2x + 40 - 2x$
$$= 40 \text{ ft}$$
width = $2x + 30 - 2x$
$$= 30 \text{ ft}$$

46. $\dfrac{x^2 + 4x + 3}{x^2 - x - 12} = \dfrac{(x + 1)(x + 3)}{(x - 4)(x + 3)}$
$$= \dfrac{x + 1}{x - 4}$$

47. $\dfrac{x^2 + 4x - 5}{x^2 - 7x + 6} = \dfrac{(x + 5)(x - 1)}{(x - 6)(x - 1)}$
$$= \dfrac{x + 5}{x - 6}$$

48. $\dfrac{x^2 - 25}{x^2 + 3x - 10} = \dfrac{(x - 5)(x + 5)}{(x - 2)(x + 5)}$
$$= \dfrac{x - 5}{x - 2}$$

49. $\dfrac{x^2 - 6x + 8}{x^3 - 8} = \dfrac{(x - 2)(x - 4)}{}$
$$= \dfrac{x - 4}{x^2 + 2x + 4}$$

50. $\dfrac{x^2}{(x^2 - x)(x - 1)^{-1}} = \dfrac{x^2(x - 1)}{(x^2 - x)}$
$$= \dfrac{x^2(x - 1)}{x(x - 1)}$$
$$= x$$

51. $\dfrac{x + 1}{(x^2 + 3x + 2)(x + 2)^{-2}} = \dfrac{(x + 1)(x + 2)^2}{x^2 + 3x + 2}$
$$= \dfrac{(x + 1)(x + 2)^2}{(x + 1)(x + 2)}$$
$$= x + 2$$

52. time elapsed after 1 second = 1 s
time elapsed after x seconds = x s
time between 1 and x seconds of the drop
$$= (x - 1) \text{ s}$$

53. average speed = $\dfrac{\text{distance}}{\text{time}}$
$$= \dfrac{16x^2 - 16}{x - 1}$$
$$= \dfrac{16(x^2 - 1^2)}{x - 1}$$
$$= \dfrac{16(x - 1)(x + 1)}{(x - 1)}$$
$$= 16(x + 1)$$
The average speed is $16x + 16$ ft/s.

54. Area of right triangle = $\dfrac{\text{product of lengths of legs}}{2}$
or
product of length of legs = 2(Area of right triangle)
or
Length of a leg = $\dfrac{2(\text{Area of right triangle})}{\text{length of the other leg}}$
Length of a leg = $\dfrac{2\left(\frac{1}{2}x^2 - 7x + 24\right)}{x - 6}$
$$= \dfrac{x^2 - 14x + 48}{x - 6}$$
$$= \dfrac{(x - 8)(x - 6)}{x - 6}$$
$$= x - 8$$
The length of the other leg is $x - 8$ cm.

55. $64p^{2n} + 16p^n + 1 = 8^2 \cdot (p^n)^2 + 2 \cdot 1 \cdot 8p^n + 1^2$
$= (8p^n)^2 + 2 \cdot 1 \cdot (8p^n) + 1^2$
$= (8p^n + 1)^2$

56. Factoring can be used to find possible dimensions of a geometric figure, given the area. Answers should include the following.

• Since the area of the rectangle is the product of its length and its width, the length and width are factors of the area. One set of possible dimensions is $4x - 2$ by $x + 3$.

• The complete factorization of the area is $2(2x - 1)(x + 3)$, so the factor of 2 could be placed with either $2x - 1$ or $x + 3$ when assigning the dimensions.

57. B; $2x - 15 + x^2 = x^2 + 5x - 3x - 15$
$= (x^2 + 5x) + (-3x - 15)$
$= x(x + 5) -3(x + 5)$
$= (x + 5)(x - 3)$

58. C; $x^3 - x^2 - 2x = x(x^2 - x - 2)$
$= x[(x^2 - 2x) + (x - 2)]$
$= x[x(x - 2) + 1(x - 2)]$
$= x(x - 2)(x + 1)$

59. Yes; $3x^2 + 5x + 2 = 3x^2 + 3x + 2x + 2$
$= (3x^2 + 3x) + (2x + 2)$
$= 3x(x + 1) + 2(x + 1)$
$= (x + 1)(3x + 2)$

60. No; $x^3 + 8 = x^3 + 2^3$
$= (x + 2)(x^2 - 2x + 2^2)$
$= (x + 2)(x^2 - 2x + 4)$

61. No; $2x^2 - 5x - 3 = 2x^2 - 6x + x - 3$
$= (2x^2 - 6x) + (x - 3)$
$= 2x(x - 3) + 1(x - 3)$
$= (x - 3)(2x + 1)$

62. Yes; $3x^2 - 48 = 3(x^2 - 16)$
$= 3(x^2 - 4^2)$
$= 3(x + 4)(x - 4)$

Page 244　Maintain Your Skills

63.

$$\begin{array}{r|rrrr} -2 & 1 & 0 & -3 & 2 \\ & & -2 & 4 & -2 \\ \hline & 1 & -2 & 1 & \,\vline\ 0 \end{array}$$

$(t^3 - 3t + 2) \div (t + 2) = t^2 - 2t + 1$

64.

$$\begin{array}{r|rrr} -1 & 1 & 4 & 3 \\ & & -1 & -3 \\ \hline & 1 & 3 & \,\vline\ 0 \end{array}$$

$(y^2 + 4y + 3)(y + 1)^{-1} = \dfrac{y^2 + 4y + 3}{y + 1}$
$= y + 3$

65.

$$\require{enclose}\begin{array}{r} x^2 + 2 \\ x - 3 \enclose{longdiv}{x^3 - 3x^2 + 2x - 6} \\ \underline{(-)\ x^3 - 3x^2 } \\ 2x - 6 \\ \underline{(-)\ 2x - 6} \\ 0 \end{array}$$

$\dfrac{x^3 - 3x^2 + 2x - 6}{x - 3} = x^2 + 2$

66.

$$\require{enclose}\begin{array}{r} x^3 + x^2 - 2x + 2 \\ 3x - 2 \enclose{longdiv}{3x^4 + x^3 - 8x^2 + 10x - 3} \\ \underline{(-)\ 3x^4 - 2x^3 } \\ 3x^3 - 8x^2 \\ \underline{(-)\ 3x^3 - 2x^2 } \\ -6x^2 + 10x \\ \underline{(-)\ -6x^2 + 4x } \\ 6x - 3 \\ \underline{(-)\ 6x - 4} \\ 1 \end{array}$$

$\dfrac{3x^4 + x^3 - 8x^2 + 10x - 3}{3x - 2} = x^3 + x^2 - 2x + 2 + \dfrac{1}{3x - 2}$

67. $(3x^2 - 2xy + y^2) + (x^2 + 5xy - 4y^2)$
$= 3x^2 - 2xy + y^2 + x^2 + 5xy - 4y^2$
$= (3x^2 + x^2) + (-2xy + 5xy) + (y^2 - 4y^2)$
$= 4x^2 + 3xy - 3y^2$

68. $(2x + 4)(7x - 1)$
$= (2x)(7x) + (2x)(-1) + 4(7x) + 4(-1)$
$= 14x^2 - 2x + 28x - 4$
$= 14x^2 + 26x - 4$

69. $[3 \quad -1] \cdot \begin{bmatrix} 0 \\ 2 \end{bmatrix} = [3 \cdot 0 + (-1) \cdot 2]$
$= [0 - 2]$
$= [-2]$

70. $\begin{bmatrix} 1 & -4 \\ 2 & 2 \end{bmatrix} \cdot \begin{bmatrix} 0 & 3 \\ 9 & -1 \end{bmatrix}$
$= \begin{bmatrix} 1 \cdot 0 + (-4) \cdot 9 & 1 \cdot 3 + (-4)(-1) \\ 2 \cdot 0 + 2 \cdot 9 & 2 \cdot 3 + 2(-1) \end{bmatrix}$
$= \begin{bmatrix} 0 - 36 & 3 + 4 \\ 0 + 18 & 6 - 2 \end{bmatrix}$
$= \begin{bmatrix} -36 & 7 \\ 18 & 4 \end{bmatrix}$

71. measure of a length $= x$
measure of a length $= y$
$\begin{cases} 2(x + y) = 86 \\ 2y = x + 2 \end{cases}$
$\begin{cases} \dfrac{2(x + y)}{2} = \dfrac{86}{2} \\ 2y - x = 2 \end{cases}$
$\begin{array}{r} x + y = 43 \\ \underline{-x + 2y = 2} \\ 3y = 45 \end{array}$
$\dfrac{3y}{3} = \dfrac{45}{3}$
$y = 15$
measure of width $= 15$ in.
$x + 15 = 43$
$x + 15 - 15 = 43 - 15$
$x = 28$
measure of length $= 28$ in.

72. Yes; no vertical line intersects the graph in more than one point.

73. No; a vertical line can intersect the graph in more than one point.

74. $(3 + 8)5 = 3(5) + 8(5)$
Distributive Property

75. $1 + (7 + 4) = (1 + 7) + 4$
Associative Property of Addition

76. 4.63
rational since decimal terminates

77. π

irrational since the decimal form of π neither terminates nor repeats.

78. $\frac{16}{3} = 5.333...$

rational, since the decimal form repeats

79. $8.333...$

rational, since the decimal repeats

80. $7.323223222...$

irrational since the decimal neither repeats nor terminates

81. $9.7\overline{1} = 9.7111...$

rational, since the decimal repeats

5-5 | Roots of Real Numbers

Pages 247–248 Check for Understanding

1. Sample answer: 64
$$\sqrt{64} = \sqrt{8^2}$$
$$= 8$$
$$\sqrt[3]{64} = \sqrt{4^3}$$
$$= 4$$

2. If all of the powers in the results of an even root have even exponents, the result is nonnegative without taking the absolute value.

3. Sometimes; it is true when $x > 0$

4. $\sqrt{77} \approx 8.775$

5. $-\sqrt[3]{19} \approx -2.668$

6. $\sqrt[4]{48} \approx 2.632$

7. $\sqrt[3]{64} = \sqrt[3]{4^3}$
$$= 4$$

8. $\sqrt{(-2)^2} = \sqrt{4}$
$$= 2$$

9. $\sqrt[5]{-243} = \sqrt[5]{(-3)^5}$
$$= -3$$

10. $\sqrt[4]{-4096} =$ not a real number

11. $\sqrt[3]{x^3} = x$

12. $\sqrt[4]{y^4} = |y|$

13. $\sqrt{36a^2b^4} = \sqrt{6^2a^2(b^2)^2}$
$$= \sqrt{(6ab^2)^2}$$
$$= 6|a|b^2$$

14. $\sqrt{(4x + 3y)^2} = |4x + 3y|$

15. $D = 1.23\sqrt{h}$
$$D = 1.23\sqrt{6}$$
$$\approx (1.23)(2.45)$$
$$\approx 3.01$$
The horizon is about 3.01 miles away.

Pages 248–249 Practice and Apply

16. $\sqrt{129} \approx 11.358$

17. $-\sqrt{147} \approx -12.124$

18. $\sqrt{0.87} \approx 0.933$

19. $\sqrt{4.27} \approx 2.066$

20. $\sqrt[3]{59} \approx 3.893$

21. $\sqrt[3]{-480} \approx -7.830$

22. $\sqrt[4]{602} \approx 4.953$

23. $\sqrt[5]{891} \approx 3.890$

24. $\sqrt[6]{4123} \approx 4.004$

25. $\sqrt[7]{46,815} \approx 4.647$

26. $\sqrt[6]{(723)^3} \approx 26.889$

27. $\sqrt[4]{(3500)^2} \approx 59.161$

28. $\sqrt{225} = \sqrt{15^2}$
$$= 15$$

29. $\pm\sqrt{169} = \pm\sqrt{(13)^2}$
$$= \pm 13$$

30. $\sqrt{-(-7)^2} = \sqrt{-49}$
not a real number

31. $\sqrt{(-18)^2} = \sqrt{324}$
$$= \sqrt{18^2}$$
$$= 18$$

32. $\sqrt[3]{-27} = \sqrt[3]{(-3)^3}$
$$= -3$$

33. $\sqrt[7]{-128} = \sqrt{(-2)^7}$
$$= -2$$

34. $\sqrt{\frac{1}{16}} = \sqrt{\left(\frac{1}{4}\right)^2}$
$$= \frac{1}{4}$$

35. $\sqrt[3]{\frac{1}{125}} = \sqrt[3]{\left(\frac{1}{5}\right)^3}$
$$= \frac{1}{5}$$

36. $\sqrt{0.25} = \sqrt{(0.5)^2}$
$$= 0.5$$

37. $\sqrt[3]{-0.064} = \sqrt[3]{(-0.4)^3}$
$$= -0.4$$

38. $\sqrt[4]{z^8} = \sqrt[4]{(z^2)^4}$
$$= z^2$$

39. $-\sqrt[6]{x^6} = -|x|$

40. $\sqrt{49m^6} = \sqrt{(7m^3)^2}$
$$= 7|m^3|$$

41. $\sqrt{64a^8} = \sqrt{(8a^4)^2}$
$$= 8a^4$$

42. $\sqrt[3]{27r^3} = \sqrt{(3r)^3}$
$$= 3r$$

43. $\sqrt[3]{-c^6} = \sqrt[3]{(-c^2)^3}$
$$= -c^2$$

44. $\sqrt{(5g)^4} = \sqrt{[(5g)^2]^2}$
$$= (5g)^2$$
$$= 25g^2$$

45. $\sqrt[3]{(2z)^6} = \sqrt[3]{[(2z)^2]^3}$
$$= (2z)^2$$
$$= 4z^2$$

46. $\sqrt{25x^4y^6} = \sqrt{(5x^2y^3)^2}$
$$= 5x^2|y^3|$$

47. $\sqrt{36x^4z^4} = \sqrt{(6x^2z^2)^2}$
$$= 6x^2z^2$$

48. $\sqrt{169x^8y^4} = \sqrt{(13x^4y^2)^2}$
$$= 13x^4y^2$$

49. $\sqrt{9p^{12}q^6} = \sqrt{(3p^6q^3)^2}$
$$= 3p^6|q^3|$$

50. $\sqrt[3]{8a^3b^3} = \sqrt[3]{(2ab)^3}$
$$= 2ab$$

51. $\sqrt[3]{-27c^9d^{12}} = \sqrt[3]{(-3c^3d^4)^3}$
$= -3c^3d^4$

52. $\sqrt{(4x-y)^2} = |4x - y|$

53. $\sqrt[3]{(p + q)^3} = p + q$

54. $-\sqrt{x^2 + 4x + 4} = -\sqrt{(x + 2)^2}$
$= -|x + 2|$

55. $\sqrt{z^2 + 8z + 16} = \sqrt{(z + 4)^2}$
$= |z + 4|$

56. $\sqrt{4a^2 + 4a + 1} = \sqrt{(2a + 1)^2}$
$= |2a + 1|$

57. $\sqrt{-9x^2 - 12x - 4} = \sqrt{-(9x^2 + 12x + 4)}$
$= \sqrt{-(3x + 2)^2}$
not a real number

58. $\sqrt[5]{32} = \sqrt[5]{2^5}$
$= 2$

59. $\sqrt[3]{-125} = \sqrt[3]{(-5)^3}$
$= -5$

60. Using Pythagorean Relationship
distance $= \sqrt{(90)^2 + (90)^2}$
$= \sqrt{8100 + 8100}$
$= \sqrt{16,200}$
≈ 127.28
The catcher has to throw a ball about 127.28 feet.

61. $L = 0.46\sqrt[3]{M}$
$L = 0.46\sqrt[3]{25}$
$L \approx (0.46)(2.92)$
≈ 1.35
The length is about 1.35 m.

62. $v = \sqrt{\dfrac{2GM}{R}}$
$v = \sqrt{\dfrac{2(6.67 \times 10^{-11})(5.98 \times 10^{24})}{6.37 \times 10^6}}$
$= \sqrt{\dfrac{79.77 \times 10^{13}}{6.37 \times 10^6}}$
$= \sqrt{12.52 \times 10^7}$
$\approx 11,200$
The escape velocity for Earth is about 11,200 m/s.

63. $\sqrt{x^2 + y^2} = x + y$ when $x = 0$ and $y \geq 0$ or $y = 0$ and $x \geq 0$

64. The speed and length of a wave are related by an expression containing a square root. Answers should include the following.
- about 1.90 knots, about 300 knots, and 4.24 knots.
- As the value of ℓ increases, the value of s increases.

65. B; $\sqrt{7.32} \approx 2.70555$

66. D; $BC = 9$
$2BC = BD$
$BD = 2(9)$
$= 18$

Page 249   Maintain Your Skills

67. $7xy^3 - 14x^2y^5 + 28x^3y^2$
$= (7 \cdot x \cdot y \cdot y \cdot y) - (2 \cdot 7 \cdot x \cdot x \cdot y \cdot y \cdot y \cdot y \cdot y) + (2 \cdot 2 \cdot 7 \cdot x \cdot x \cdot x \cdot y \cdot y)$
$= (7xy^2 \cdot y) - (7xy^2 \cdot 2xy^3) + (7xy^2 \cdot 4x^2)$
$= 7xy^2 (y - 2xy^3 + 4x^2)$

68. $ab - 5a + 3b - 15 = (ab - 5a) + (3b - 15)$
$= a(b - 5) + 3(b - 5)$
$= (b - 5)(a + 3)$

69. $2x^2 + 15x + 25 = 2x^2 + 10x + 5x + 25$
$= (2x^2 + 10x) + (5x + 25)$
$= 2x(x + 5) + 5(x + 5)$
$= (x + 5)(2x + 5)$

70. $c^3 - 216 = c^3 - 6^3$
$= (c - 6)(c^2 + 6c + 6^2)$
$= (c - 6)(c^2 + 6c + 36)$

71.

$$
\begin{array}{r}
4x^2 + x + 5 \\
x - 2\overline{)4x^3 - 7x^2 + 3x - 2} \\
\underline{(-)\ 4x^3 - 8x^2} \\
x^2 + 3x \\
\underline{(-)\ x^2 - 2x} \\
5x - 2 \\
\underline{(-)\ 5x - 10} \\
8
\end{array}
$$

$(4x^3 - 7x^2 + 3x - 2) \div (x - 2) = 4x^2 + x + 5 + \dfrac{8}{x - 2}$

72.

$$
\begin{array}{r|rrrrr}
-5 & 1 & 4 & -4 & 5 & 0 \\
 & & -5 & 5 & -5 & 0 \\
\hline
 & 1 & -1 & 1 & 0 & 0
\end{array}
$$

$\dfrac{x^4 + 4x^3 - 4x^2 + 5x}{} = x^3 - x^2 + x$

73. $2\begin{bmatrix} 405 & 1166 \\ 709 & 1252 \end{bmatrix} = \begin{bmatrix} 810 & 2320 \\ 1418 & 2504 \end{bmatrix}$

74. $a + 4b = 6$
$3a + 2b = -2$
Eliminate b by adding -2 times the second equation to the first equation.
$$
\begin{array}{r}
a + 4b = 6 \\
\underline{(+)\ -6a - 4b = 4} \\
-5a = 10
\end{array}
$$
$-5a = 10$
$\dfrac{-5a}{-5} = \dfrac{10}{-5}$
$a = -2$
Substitute -2 for a in the first equation.
$-2 + 4b = 6$
$4b = 8$
$b = 2$
The solution is $(-2, 2)$

75. $10x - y = 13$
$3x - 4y = 15$
Eliminate y by adding -4 times the first equation to the second equation.
$$
\begin{array}{r}
-40x + 4y = -52 \\
\underline{(+)\ 3x - 4y = 15} \\
-37x = -37
\end{array}
$$
$\dfrac{-37x}{-37} = \dfrac{-37}{-37}$
$x = 1$
Substitute 1 for x in the first equation.
$10(1) - y = 13$
$10 - y = 13$
$y = -3$
The solution is $(1, -3)$.

76. $3c - 7d = -1$
$2c - 6d = -6$
Eliminate c by adding 2 times the first equation to -3 times the second equation.
$$6c - 14d = -2$$
$$\underline{-6c + 18d = 18}$$
$$4d = 16$$
$$\frac{4d}{4} = \frac{16}{4}$$
$$d = 4$$
Substitute 4 for d in the first equation.
$$3c - 7(4) = -1$$
$$3c - 28 = -1$$
$$3c = 27$$
$$c = 9$$
The solution is $(9, 4)$.

77. $(x + 3)(x + 8) = x^2 + 8x + 3x + 24$
$$= x^2 + 11x + 24$$

78. $(y - 2)(y + 5) = y^2 + 5y - 2y - 10$
$$= y^2 + 3y - 10$$

79. $(a + 2)(a - 9) = a^2 - 9a + 2a - 18$
$$= a^2 - 7a - 18$$

80. $(a + b)(a + 2b) = a^2 + 2ab + ab + 2b^2$
$$= a^2 + 3ab + 2b^2$$

81. $(x - 3y)(x + 3y) = x^2 - (3y)^2$
$$= x^2 - 9y^2$$

82. $(2w + z)(3w - 5z)$
$$= (2w)(3w) + (2w)(-5z) + z(3w) + z(-5z)$$
$$= 6w^2 - 10wz + 3wz - 5z^2$$
$$= 6w^2 - 7wz - 5z^2$$

5-6 Radical Expressions

Page 252 Algebra Activity

1. No; $\sqrt{2} + \sqrt{2}$ units is the length of the hypotenuse of an isosceles right triangle whose legs have length 2 units. Therefore, $\sqrt{2} + \sqrt{2} > 2$.

2. See students' work.

Page 254 Check for Understanding

1. Sometimes; $\frac{1}{\sqrt[n]{a}} = \sqrt[n]{a}$ only when $a = 1$.

2. Sample answer: $\sqrt{2} + \sqrt{3} + \sqrt{2}$

3. The product of two conjugates yields a difference of two squares. Each square produces a rational number and the difference of two rational numbers is a rational number.

4. $5\sqrt{63} = 5 \cdot \sqrt{3^2 \cdot 7}$
$$= 5 \cdot \sqrt{3^2} \cdot \sqrt{7}$$
$$= 5 \cdot 3 \cdot \sqrt{7}$$
$$= 15\sqrt{7}$$

5. $\sqrt[4]{16x^5y^4} = \sqrt[4]{2^4 \cdot x^4 \cdot x \cdot y^4}$
$$= \sqrt[4]{2^4} \cdot \sqrt[4]{x^4} \cdot \sqrt[4]{x} \cdot \sqrt[4]{y^4}$$
$$= 2xy\sqrt[4]{x}$$

6. $\sqrt{\frac{7}{8y}} = \frac{\sqrt{7}}{\sqrt{8y}}$
$$= \frac{\sqrt{7}}{\sqrt{2^2 \cdot 2y}}$$
$$= \frac{\sqrt{7}}{\sqrt{2^2} \cdot \sqrt{2y}}$$
$$= \frac{\sqrt{7}}{2\sqrt{2y}}$$
$$= \frac{\sqrt{7}}{2 \cdot \sqrt{2y}} \cdot \frac{\sqrt{2y}}{\sqrt{2y}}$$
$$= \frac{\sqrt{7} \cdot \sqrt{2y}}{2 \cdot 2y}$$
$$= \frac{\sqrt{14y}}{4y}$$

7. $(-2\sqrt{15})(4\sqrt{21}) = (-2)(4)\sqrt{(15)(21)}$
$$= -8 \cdot \sqrt{5 \cdot 3 \cdot 3 \cdot 7}$$
$$= -8 \cdot \sqrt{3^2 \cdot 35}$$
$$= -8 \cdot \sqrt{3^2} \cdot \sqrt{35}$$
$$= -8 \cdot 3 \cdot \sqrt{35}$$
$$= -24\sqrt{35}$$

8. $\frac{\sqrt[3]{625}}{\sqrt[3]{25}} = \sqrt[3]{\frac{625}{25}}$
$$= \sqrt[3]{25}$$

9. $\sqrt{2ab^2} \cdot \sqrt{6a^3b^2} = \sqrt{2ab^2 \cdot 6a^3b^2}$
$$= \sqrt{2^2 \cdot 3 \cdot (a^2)^2 \cdot (b^2)^2}$$
$$= \sqrt{2^2} \cdot \sqrt{3} \cdot \sqrt{(a^2)^2} \cdot \sqrt{(b^2)^2}$$
$$= 2a^2b^2\sqrt{3}$$

10. $\sqrt{3} - 2\sqrt[4]{3} + 4\sqrt{3} + 5\sqrt[4]{3}$
$$= (-2\sqrt[4]{3} + 5\sqrt[4]{3}) + (\sqrt{3} + 4\sqrt{3})$$
$$= 3\sqrt[4]{3} + 5\sqrt{3}$$

11. $3\sqrt[3]{128} + 5\sqrt[3]{16} = 3\sqrt[3]{4^3 \cdot 2} + 5\sqrt[3]{2^3 \cdot 2}$
$$= 3\sqrt[3]{4^3} \cdot \sqrt[3]{2} + 5\sqrt[3]{2^3} \cdot \sqrt[3]{2}$$
$$= 3 \cdot 4 \cdot \sqrt[3]{2} + 5 \cdot 2 \cdot \sqrt[3]{2}$$
$$= 12\sqrt[3]{2} + 10\sqrt[3]{2}$$
$$= 22\sqrt[3]{2}$$

12. $(3 - \sqrt{5})(1 + \sqrt{3})$
$$= 3 \cdot 1 + 3 \cdot \sqrt{3} - \sqrt{5} \cdot 1 - \sqrt{5} \cdot \sqrt{3}$$
$$= 3 + 3\sqrt{3} - \sqrt{5} - \sqrt{15}$$

13. $\frac{1 + \sqrt{5}}{3 - \sqrt{5}} = \frac{(1 + \sqrt{5})(3 + \sqrt{5})}{(3 - \sqrt{5})(3 + \sqrt{5})}$
$$= \frac{3 + \sqrt{5} + 3\sqrt{5} + (\sqrt{5})^2}{3^2 - (\sqrt{5})^2}$$
$$= \frac{3 + 4\sqrt{5} + 5}{9 - 5}$$
$$= \frac{8 + 4\sqrt{5}}{4}$$
$$= \frac{4(2 + \sqrt{5})}{4}$$
$$= 2 + \sqrt{5}$$

14. $s = 2\sqrt{5\ell}$
$$s = \sqrt{2(5)(120)}$$
$$= 2 \cdot \sqrt{10^2 \cdot 6}$$
$$= 2 \cdot \sqrt{10^2} \cdot \sqrt{6}$$
$$= 2 \cdot 10 \cdot \sqrt{6}$$
$$= 20\sqrt{6}$$
$$\approx 49$$
The car was traveling about 49 mph.

Pages 254–255 Practice and Apply

15. $243 = \sqrt{9^2 \cdot 3}$
$$= \sqrt{9^2} \cdot \sqrt{3}$$
$$= 9\sqrt{3}$$

16. $\sqrt{72} = \sqrt{6^2 \cdot 2}$
$= \sqrt{6^2} \cdot \sqrt{2}$
$= 6\sqrt{2}$

17. $\sqrt[3]{54} = \sqrt[3]{3^3 \cdot 2}$
$= \sqrt[3]{3^3} \cdot \sqrt[3]{2}$
$= 3\sqrt[3]{2}$

18. $\sqrt[4]{96} = \sqrt[4]{2^4 \cdot 6}$
$= \sqrt[4]{2^4} \cdot \sqrt[4]{6}$
$= 2\sqrt[4]{6}$

19. $\sqrt{50x^4} = \sqrt{5^2 \cdot 2 \cdot (x^2)^2}$
$= \sqrt{5^2} \cdot \sqrt{2} \cdot \sqrt{(x^2)^2}$
$= 5x^2\sqrt{2}$

20. $\sqrt[3]{16y^3} = \sqrt[3]{2^3 \cdot 2 \cdot y^3}$
$= \sqrt[3]{2^3} \cdot \sqrt[3]{2} \cdot \sqrt[3]{y^3}$
$= 2y\sqrt[3]{2}$

21. $\sqrt{18x^2y^3} = \sqrt{3^2 \cdot 2 \cdot x^2 \cdot y^2 \cdot y}$
$= \sqrt{3^2} \cdot \sqrt{2} \cdot \sqrt{x^2} \cdot \sqrt{y^2} \cdot \sqrt{y}$
$= 3\,|x|\,y\sqrt{2y}$

22. $\sqrt{40a^3b^4} = \sqrt{2^2 \cdot 10 \cdot a^2 \cdot a \cdot (b^2)^2}$
$= \sqrt{2^2} \cdot \sqrt{10} \cdot \sqrt{a^2} \cdot \sqrt{a} \cdot \sqrt{(b^2)^2}$
$= 2ab^2\sqrt{10a}$

23. $3\sqrt[3]{56y^6z^3} = 3\sqrt[3]{2^3 \cdot 7 \cdot (y^2)^3 \cdot z^3}$
$= 3 \cdot \sqrt[3]{2^3} \cdot \sqrt[3]{7} \cdot \sqrt[3]{(y^2)^3} \cdot \sqrt[3]{z^3}$
$= 3 \cdot 2y^2z\sqrt[3]{7}$
$= 6y^2z\sqrt[3]{7}$

24. $2\sqrt[3]{24m^4n^5}$
$= 2\sqrt[3]{2^3 \cdot 3 \cdot m^3 \cdot m \cdot n^3 \cdot n^2}$
$= 2\sqrt[3]{2^3} \cdot \sqrt[3]{3} \cdot \sqrt[3]{m^3} \cdot \sqrt[3]{m} \cdot \sqrt[3]{n^3} \cdot \sqrt[3]{n^2}$
$= 2 \cdot 2 \cdot mn\sqrt[3]{3mn^2}$
$= 4mn\sqrt[3]{3mn^2}$

25. $\sqrt[4]{\frac{1}{81}c^5d^4} = \sqrt[4]{\left(\frac{1}{3}\right)^4 \cdot c^4 \cdot c \cdot d^4}$
$= \sqrt[4]{\left(\frac{1}{3}\right)^4} \cdot \sqrt[4]{c^4} \cdot \sqrt[4]{c} \cdot \sqrt[4]{d^4}$
$= \frac{1}{3}c\,|d|\,\sqrt[4]{c}$

26. $\sqrt[5]{\frac{1}{32}w^6z^7} = \sqrt[5]{\left(\frac{1}{2}\right)^5 \cdot w^5 \cdot w \cdot z^5 \cdot z^2}$
$= \sqrt[5]{\left(\frac{1}{2}\right)^5} \cdot \sqrt[5]{w^5} \cdot \sqrt[5]{w} \cdot \sqrt[5]{z^5} \cdot \sqrt[5]{z^2}$
$= \frac{1}{2}wz\sqrt[5]{wz^2}$

27. $\sqrt[3]{\frac{3}{4}} = \frac{\sqrt[3]{3}}{\sqrt[3]{4}}$
$= \frac{\sqrt[3]{3}}{\sqrt[3]{4}} \cdot \frac{\sqrt[3]{2}}{\sqrt[3]{2}}$
$= \frac{\sqrt[3]{3 \cdot 2}}{\sqrt[3]{4 \cdot 2}}$
$= \frac{\sqrt[3]{6}}{\sqrt[3]{8}}$
$= \frac{\sqrt[3]{6}}{2}$

28. $\sqrt[4]{\frac{2}{3}} = \frac{\sqrt[4]{2}}{\sqrt[4]{3}}$
$= \frac{\sqrt[4]{2}}{\sqrt[4]{3}} \cdot \frac{\sqrt[4]{27}}{\sqrt[4]{27}}$
$= \frac{\sqrt[4]{2 \cdot 27}}{\sqrt[4]{3 \cdot 27}}$
$= \frac{\sqrt[4]{54}}{\sqrt[4]{81}}$
$= \frac{\sqrt[4]{54}}{3}$

29. $\sqrt{\frac{a^4}{b^3}} = \frac{\sqrt{a^4}}{\sqrt{b^3}}$
$= \frac{\sqrt{(a^2)^2}}{\sqrt{b^2 \cdot b}}$
$= \frac{a^2}{\sqrt{b^2} \cdot \sqrt{b}}$
$= \frac{a^2}{b\sqrt{b}}$
$= \frac{a^2}{b\sqrt{b}} \cdot \frac{\sqrt{b}}{\sqrt{b}}$
$= \frac{a^2\sqrt{b}}{b^2}$

30. $\sqrt{\frac{4r^8}{t^9}} = \frac{\sqrt{4r^8}}{\sqrt{t^9}}$
$= \frac{\sqrt{2^2 \cdot (r^4)^2}}{\sqrt{(t^4)^2 \cdot t}}$
$= \frac{\sqrt{2^2} \cdot \sqrt{(r^4)^2}}{\sqrt{(t^4)^2} \cdot \sqrt{t}}$
$= \frac{2r^4}{t^4\sqrt{t}}$
$= \frac{2r^4}{t^4\sqrt{t}} \cdot \frac{\sqrt{t}}{\sqrt{t}}$
$= \frac{2r^4\sqrt{t}}{t^5}$

31. $(3\sqrt{12})(2\sqrt{21}) = 3 \cdot 2\sqrt{12 \cdot 21}$
$= 3 \cdot 2 \cdot \sqrt{2^2 \cdot 3^2 \cdot 7}$
$= 3 \cdot 2 \cdot \sqrt{2^2} \cdot \sqrt{3^2} \cdot \sqrt{7}$
$= 6 \cdot 2 \cdot 3 \cdot \sqrt{7}$
$= 36\sqrt{7}$

32. $(-3\sqrt{24})(5\sqrt{20}) = -3 \cdot 5 \cdot \sqrt{24 \cdot 20}$
$= -3 \cdot 5 \cdot \sqrt{4^2 \cdot 30}$
$= -3 \cdot 5 \cdot \sqrt{4^2} \cdot \sqrt{30}$
$= -3 \cdot 5 \cdot 4 \cdot \sqrt{30}$
$= -60\sqrt{30}$

33. $\frac{\sqrt{39}}{\sqrt{26}} = \sqrt{\frac{39}{26}}$
$= \sqrt{\frac{3}{2}}$
$= \frac{\sqrt{3}}{\sqrt{2}}$
$= \frac{\sqrt{3}}{\sqrt{2}} \cdot \frac{\sqrt{2}}{\sqrt{2}}$
$= \frac{\sqrt{6}}{2}$

34. $\frac{\sqrt{14}}{\sqrt{35}} = \sqrt{\frac{14}{35}}$
$= \sqrt{\frac{2}{5}}$
$= \frac{\sqrt{2}}{\sqrt{5}}$
$= \frac{\sqrt{2}}{\sqrt{5}} \cdot \frac{\sqrt{5}}{\sqrt{5}}$
$= \frac{\sqrt{10}}{5}$

35. $\sqrt{12} + \sqrt{48} - \sqrt{27}$
$= \sqrt{2^2 \cdot 3} + \sqrt{4^2 \cdot 3} - \sqrt{3^2 \cdot 3}$
$= \sqrt{2^2} \cdot \sqrt{3} + \sqrt{4^2} \cdot \sqrt{3} - \sqrt{3^2} \cdot \sqrt{3}$
$= 2\sqrt{3} + 4\sqrt{3} - 3\sqrt{3}$
$= 3\sqrt{3}$

36. $\sqrt{98} - \sqrt{72} + \sqrt{32}$
$= \sqrt{7^2 \cdot 2} - \sqrt{6^2 \cdot 2} + \sqrt{4^2 \cdot 2}$
$= \sqrt{7^2} \cdot \sqrt{2} - \sqrt{6^2} \cdot \sqrt{2} + \sqrt{4^2} \cdot \sqrt{2}$
$= 7\sqrt{2} - 6\sqrt{2} + 4\sqrt{2}$
$= 5\sqrt{2}$

37. $\sqrt{3} + \sqrt{72} - \sqrt{128} + \sqrt{108}$
$= \sqrt{3} + \sqrt{6^2 \cdot 2} - \sqrt{8^2 \cdot 2} + \sqrt{6^2 \cdot 3}$
$= \sqrt{3} + 6\sqrt{2} - 8\sqrt{2} + 6\sqrt{3}$
$= 7\sqrt{3} - 2\sqrt{2}$

38. $5\sqrt{20} + \sqrt{24} - \sqrt{180} + 7\sqrt{54}$
$= 5\sqrt{2^2 \cdot 5} + \sqrt{2^2 \cdot 6} - \sqrt{6^2 \cdot 5} + 7 \cdot \sqrt{3^2 \cdot 6}$
$= 5 \cdot \sqrt{2^2} \cdot \sqrt{5} + \sqrt{2^2} \cdot \sqrt{6} - \sqrt{6^2} \cdot \sqrt{5} + 7 \cdot \sqrt{3^2} \cdot \sqrt{6}$
$= 5 \cdot 2 \cdot \sqrt{5} + 2 \cdot \sqrt{6} - 6 \cdot \sqrt{5} + 7 \cdot 3 \cdot \sqrt{6}$
$= 10\sqrt{5} + 2\sqrt{6} - 6\sqrt{5} + 21\sqrt{6}$
$= 4\sqrt{5} + 23\sqrt{6}$

39. $(5 + \sqrt{6})(5 - \sqrt{2})$
$= 5^2 - 5 \cdot \sqrt{2} + 5 \cdot \sqrt{6} - \sqrt{6} \cdot \sqrt{2}$
$= 25 - 5\sqrt{2} + 5\sqrt{6} - \sqrt{12}$
$= 25 - 5\sqrt{2} + 5\sqrt{6} - \sqrt{2^2 \cdot 3}$
$= 25 - 5\sqrt{2} + 5\sqrt{6} - 2\sqrt{3}$

40. $(3 + \sqrt{7})(2 + \sqrt{6})$
$= 3 \cdot 2 + 3\sqrt{6} + 2\sqrt{7} + \sqrt{7} \cdot \sqrt{6}$
$= 6 + 3\sqrt{6} + 2\sqrt{7} + \sqrt{7 \cdot 6}$
$= 6 + 3\sqrt{6} + 2\sqrt{7} + \sqrt{42}$

41. $(\sqrt{11} - \sqrt{2})^2 = (\sqrt{11})^2 - 2(\sqrt{11})(\sqrt{2}) + (\sqrt{2})^2$
$= 11 - 2\sqrt{11 \cdot 2} + 2$
$= 13 - 2\sqrt{22}$

42. $(\sqrt{3} - \sqrt{5})^2 = (\sqrt{3})^2 - 2(\sqrt{3})(\sqrt{5}) + (\sqrt{5})^2$
$= 3 - 2\sqrt{3 \cdot 5} + 5$
$= 8 - 2\sqrt{15}$

43. $\dfrac{7}{4 - \sqrt{3}} = \dfrac{7(4 + \sqrt{3})}{(4 - \sqrt{3})(4 + \sqrt{3})}$
$= \dfrac{28 + 7\sqrt{3}}{(4^2) - (\sqrt{3})^2}$
$= \dfrac{28 + 7\sqrt{3}}{16 - 3}$
$= \dfrac{28 + 7\sqrt{3}}{13}$

44. $\dfrac{\sqrt{6}}{5 + \sqrt{3}} = \dfrac{\sqrt{6}(5 - \sqrt{3})}{(5 + \sqrt{3})(5 - \sqrt{3})}$
$= \dfrac{5\sqrt{6} - \sqrt{6} \cdot \sqrt{3}}{5^2 - (\sqrt{3})^2}$
$= \dfrac{5\sqrt{6} - \sqrt{6 \cdot 3}}{5^2 - (\sqrt{3})^2}$
$= \dfrac{5\sqrt{6} - \sqrt{3^2 \cdot 2}}{25 - 3}$
$= \dfrac{5\sqrt{6} - 3\sqrt{2}}{22}$

45. $\dfrac{-2 - \sqrt{3}}{1 + \sqrt{3}} = \dfrac{(-2 - \sqrt{3})(1 - \sqrt{3})}{(1 + \sqrt{3})(1 - \sqrt{3})}$
$= \dfrac{-2 + 2\sqrt{3} - \sqrt{3} + (\sqrt{3})^2}{1^2 - (\sqrt{3})^2}$
$= \dfrac{-2 + \sqrt{3} + 3}{1 - 3}$
$= \dfrac{1 + \sqrt{3}}{-2}$
$= \dfrac{-1 - \sqrt{3}}{2}$

46. $\dfrac{2 + \sqrt{2}}{5 - \sqrt{2}} = \dfrac{(2 + \sqrt{2})(5 + \sqrt{2})}{(5 - \sqrt{2})(5 + \sqrt{2})}$
$= \dfrac{2 \cdot 5 + 2\sqrt{2} + 5\sqrt{2} + (\sqrt{2})^2}{5^2 - (\sqrt{2})^2}$
$= \dfrac{10 + 7\sqrt{2} + 2}{25 - 2}$
$= \dfrac{12 + 7\sqrt{2}}{23}$

47. $\dfrac{x + 1}{\sqrt{x^2 - 1}} = \dfrac{(x + 1)\sqrt{(x^2 - 1)}}{(\sqrt{x^2 - 1})(\sqrt{x^2 - 1})}$
$= \dfrac{(x + 1)\sqrt{x^2 - 1}}{(\sqrt{x^2 - 1})^2}$
$= \dfrac{(x + 1)\sqrt{x^2 - 1}}{x^2 - 1}$
$= \dfrac{(x + 1)\sqrt{x^2 - 1}}{(x + 1)(x - 1)}$
$= \dfrac{\sqrt{x^2 - 1}}{x - 1}$

48. $\dfrac{x - 1}{\sqrt{x} - 1} = \dfrac{(x - 1)(\sqrt{x} + 1)}{(\sqrt{x} - 1)(\sqrt{x} + 1)}$
$= \dfrac{(x - 1)(\sqrt{x} + 1)}{(\sqrt{x})^2 - 1^2}$
$= \dfrac{(x - 1)(\sqrt{x} + 1)}{(x - 1)}$
$= \sqrt{x} + 1$

49. Perimeter $= 2(3 + 6\sqrt{2}) + 2\sqrt{8}$
$= 2 \cdot 3 + 2 \cdot 6 \cdot \sqrt{2} + 2\sqrt{2^2 \cdot 2}$
$= 6 + 12\sqrt{2} + 2 \cdot 2\sqrt{2}$
$= 6 + 16\sqrt{2}$ yd
Area $= \sqrt{8}(3 + 6\sqrt{2})$
$= 3\sqrt{8} + 6(\sqrt{2})(\sqrt{8})$
$= 3\sqrt{2^2 \cdot 2} + 6\sqrt{2 \cdot 8}$
$= 3 \cdot 2\sqrt{2} + 6\sqrt{4^2}$
$= 6\sqrt{2} + 6 \cdot 4$
$= (24 + 6\sqrt{2})$ yd^2

50. The square root of a difference is not the difference of the square roots.

51. $v_0 = \sqrt{v^2 - 64h}$
$v_0 = \sqrt{(120)^2 - 64(225)}$
$= \sqrt{14{,}400 - 14{,}400}$
$= \sqrt{0}$
$= 0$ ft/s

52. $d = v\sqrt{\dfrac{h}{4.9}}$
$= v\sqrt{\dfrac{(h)(4.9)}{(4.9)(4.9)}}$
$= v\dfrac{\sqrt{4.9h}}{4.9}$

53. $d = v\sqrt{\dfrac{h}{4.9}}$
$d = (45)\sqrt{\dfrac{0.8}{4.9}}$
$= 45\sqrt{\dfrac{8}{49}}$
$= \dfrac{45 \cdot \sqrt{2^2 \cdot 2}}{\sqrt{7^2}}$
$= \dfrac{45 \cdot \sqrt{2^2} \cdot \sqrt{2}}{7}$
$= \dfrac{45 \cdot 2 \cdot \sqrt{2}}{7}$
$= \dfrac{90\sqrt{2}}{7}$
≈ 18.18
The ball will travel about 18.18 m.

54. $v = \sqrt{\dfrac{F_c r}{100}}$

$v = \sqrt{\dfrac{(2000)(320)}{100}}$

$= \sqrt{20 \cdot 320}$

$= \sqrt{80^2}$

$= 80$ ft/s

≈ 55 mph

The maximum velocity is 80 ft/s or about 55 mph.

55. x and y are nonnegative.

56. The formula for the time it takes an object to fall a certain distance can be written in various forms involving radicals. Answers should include the following.

- By the Quotient Property of Radicals, $t = \dfrac{\sqrt{2d}}{\sqrt{g}}$.

  Multiply by $\dfrac{\sqrt{g}}{\sqrt{g}}$ to rationalize the denominator.

  The result is $h = \dfrac{\sqrt{2dg}}{g}$

- $t = \sqrt{\dfrac{2d}{g}}$

  $t = \sqrt{\dfrac{2(25-5)}{32}}$

  $= \sqrt{\dfrac{20}{16}}$

  ≈ 1.12 s

57. B; $\sqrt{180} = \sqrt{6^2 \cdot 5}$

$= \sqrt{6^2} \cdot \sqrt{5}$

$= 6\sqrt{5}$

58. D; Let x be the length of the third side. By Pythagorean Relationship.

$x^2 = (\sqrt{2})^2 + (\sqrt{6})^2$

$x^2 = 2 + 6$

$x^2 = 8$

$x = \sqrt{8} \leftarrow$ A

$x = \sqrt{4 \cdot 2} \leftarrow$ B

$x = 2\sqrt{2} \leftarrow$ C

Page 256 Maintain Your Skills

59. $\sqrt{144z^8} = \sqrt{(12)^2 \cdot (z^4)^2}$

$= \sqrt{12^2} \cdot \sqrt{(z^4)^2}$

$= 12z^4$

60. $\sqrt[3]{216a^3b^9} = \sqrt[3]{6^3 \cdot a^3 \cdot (b^3)^3}$

$= \sqrt[3]{6^3} \cdot \sqrt[3]{a^3} \cdot \sqrt[3]{(b^3)^3}$

$= 6ab^3$

61. $\sqrt{(y+2)^2} = |y+2|$

62. $\dfrac{x^2 + 5x - 14}{x^2 - 6x + 8} = \dfrac{(x-2)(x+7)}{(x-2)(x-4)}$

$= \dfrac{x+7}{x-4}$

63. $\dfrac{x^2 - 3x - 4}{x^2 - 16} = \dfrac{(x-4)(x+1)}{(x-4)(x+4)}$

$= \dfrac{x+1}{x+4}$

64. $\begin{bmatrix} 3 & -4 \\ 2 & 8 \\ 0 & 1 \end{bmatrix} + \begin{bmatrix} -5 & 0 \\ 7 & 7 \\ 3 & -6 \end{bmatrix} = \begin{bmatrix} 3-5 & -4+0 \\ 2+7 & 8+7 \\ 0+3 & 1-6 \end{bmatrix}$

$= \begin{bmatrix} -2 & -4 \\ 9 & 15 \\ 3 & -5 \end{bmatrix}$

65. $\begin{bmatrix} 3 & 3 \\ 0 & -2 \end{bmatrix} - \begin{bmatrix} 2 & -1 \\ 5 & 2 \end{bmatrix} = \begin{bmatrix} 3-2 & 3-(-1) \\ 0-5 & -2-2 \end{bmatrix}$

$= \begin{bmatrix} 1 & 4 \\ -5 & -4 \end{bmatrix}$

66. $f(x, y) = 2x + 3y$

$(2, 4), (-1, 3), (-3, -3),$ and $(2, -5)$

(x, y)	$2x + 3y$	$f(x, y)$
$(2, 4)$	$2(2) + 3(4)$	16
$(-1, 3)$	$2(-1) + 3(3)$	7
$(-3, -3)$	$2(-3) + 3(-3)$	-15
$(2, -5)$	$2(2) + 3(-5)$	-11

max at $f(x, y) = 16$

min at $f(x, y) = -15$

67. Consistent because it has at least one solution and independent because it has exactly one solution

68. $c(x) = 3 + 0.15x$

$c(8) = 3 + (0.15)(8)$

$= 3 + 1.2$

$= 4.2$

The charge is $4.20.

69. $2x + 7 = -3$

$2x + 7 - 7 = -3 - 7$

$2x = -10$

$\dfrac{2x}{2} = \dfrac{-10}{2}$

$x = -5$

The solution is -5.

70. $-5x + 6 = -4$

$-5x + 6 - 6 = -4 - 6$

$-5x = -10$

$\dfrac{-5x}{-5} = \dfrac{-10}{-5}$

$x = 2$

The solution is 2.

71. $|x - 1| = 3$

$x - 1 = 3$ or $x - 1 = -3$

$x - 1 + 1 = 3 + 1$ $x - 1 + 1 = -3 + 1$

$x = 4$ $x = -2$

The solution set is $\{-2, 4\}$.

72. $|3x + 2| = 5$

$3x + 2 = 5$ or $3x + 2 = -5$

$3x + 2 - 2 = 5 - 2$ $3x + 2 - 2 = -5 - 2$

$3x = 3$ $3x = -7$

$\dfrac{3x}{3} = \dfrac{3}{3}$ $\dfrac{3x}{3} = \dfrac{-7}{3}$

$x = 1$ $x = -\dfrac{7}{3}$

The solution set is $\left\{-\dfrac{7}{3}, 1\right\}$.

73. $2x - 4 > 8$

$2x - 4 + 4 > 8 + 4$

$2x > 12$

$\dfrac{2x}{2} > \dfrac{12}{2}$

$x > 6$

The solution set is $\{x \mid x > 6\}$.

74.
$$-x - 3 \le 4$$
$$-x - 3 + 3 \le 4 + 3$$
$$-x \le 7$$
$$\frac{-x}{-1} \ge \frac{7}{-1}$$
$$x \ge -7$$
The solution set is $\{x \mid x \ge -7\}$.

75. $2\left(\frac{1}{8}\right) = \frac{2}{8}$
$$= \frac{1}{4}$$

76. $3\left(\frac{1}{6}\right) = \frac{3}{6}$
$$= \frac{1}{2}$$

77. $\frac{1}{2} + \frac{1}{3} = \frac{3}{6} + \frac{2}{6}$
$$= \frac{3 + 2}{6}$$
$$= \frac{5}{6}$$

78. $\frac{1}{3} + \frac{3}{4} = \frac{1 \cdot 4 + 3 \cdot 3}{12}$
$$= \frac{4 + 9}{12}$$
$$= \frac{13}{12}$$

79. $\frac{1}{8} + \frac{5}{12} = \frac{1 \cdot 3 + 5 \cdot 2}{24}$
$$= \frac{3 + 10}{24}$$
$$= \frac{13}{24}$$

80. $\frac{5}{6} - \frac{1}{5} = \frac{5 \cdot 5 - 1 \cdot 6}{30}$
$$= \frac{25 - 6}{30}$$
$$= \frac{19}{30}$$

81. $\frac{5}{8} - \frac{1}{4} = \frac{5 \cdot 1 - 1 \cdot 2}{8}$
$$= \frac{5 - 2}{8}$$
$$= \frac{3}{8}$$

82. $\frac{1}{4} - \frac{2}{3} = \frac{1 \cdot 3 - 2 \cdot 4}{12}$
$$= \frac{3 - 8}{12}$$
$$= -\frac{5}{12}$$

Page 256 Practice Quiz 2

1. $3x^3y + x^2y^2 + x^2y$
$$= x^2y \cdot 3x + x^2y \cdot y + x^2y \cdot 1$$
$$= x^2y(3x + y + 1)$$

2. $3x^2 - 2x - 2$ is prime

3. $ax^2 + 6ax + 9a = a \cdot x^2 + a \cdot 6x + a \cdot 9$
$$= a(x^2 + 6x + 9)$$
$$= a(x + 3)^2$$

4. $8r^3 - 64s^6 = 8 \cdot r^3 - 8 \cdot 8s^6$
$$= 8(r^3 - 8s^6)$$
$$= 8[r^3 - (2s^2)^3]$$
$$= 8(r - 2s^2)[r^2 + r(2s^2) + (2s^2)^2]$$
$$= 8(r - 2s^2)(r^2 + 2rs^2 + 4s^4)$$

5. $\sqrt{36x^2y^6} = \sqrt{6^2 \cdot x^2 \cdot (y^3)^2}$
$$= \sqrt{6^2} \cdot \sqrt{x^2} \cdot \sqrt{(y^3)^2}$$
$$= 6|x| \, |y^3|$$

6. $\sqrt[3]{-64a^6b^9} = \sqrt[3]{(-4)^3 \cdot (a^2)^3 \cdot (b^3)^3}$
$$= \sqrt[3]{(-4)^3} \cdot \sqrt[3]{(a^2)^3} \cdot \sqrt[3]{(b^3)^3}$$
$$= -4a^2b^3$$

7. $\sqrt{4n^2 + 12n + 9} = \sqrt{(2n)^2 + 12n + 3^2}$
$$= \sqrt{(2n + 3)^2}$$
$$= |2n + 3|$$

8. $\sqrt{\frac{x^4}{y^3}} = \frac{\sqrt{x^4}}{\sqrt{y^3}}$
$$= \frac{\sqrt{(x^2)^2}}{\sqrt{y^2 \cdot y}}$$
$$= \frac{x^2}{\sqrt{y^2} \cdot \sqrt{y}}$$
$$= \frac{x^2}{y\sqrt{y}}$$
$$= \frac{x^2 \cdot \sqrt{y}}{y\sqrt{y} \cdot \sqrt{y}}$$
$$= \frac{x^2\sqrt{y}}{y^2}$$

9. $(3 + \sqrt{7})(2 - \sqrt{7}) = 3 \cdot 2 - 3\sqrt{7} + 2\sqrt{7} - (\sqrt{7})^2$
$$= 6 - \sqrt{7} - 7$$
$$= -1 - \sqrt{7}$$

10. $\frac{5 + \sqrt{2}}{2 + \sqrt{2}} = \frac{(5 + \sqrt{2})(2 - \sqrt{2})}{(2 + \sqrt{2})(2 - \sqrt{2})}$
$$= \frac{5 \cdot 2 - 5\sqrt{2} + 2\sqrt{2} - (\sqrt{2})^2}{2^2 - (\sqrt{2})^2}$$
$$= \frac{10 - 3\sqrt{2} - 2}{4 - 2}$$
$$= \frac{8 - 3\sqrt{2}}{2}$$

5-7 Rational Exponents

Pages 260–261 Check for Understanding

1. Sample answer: 64

2. In radical form, the expression would be $\sqrt{-16}$, which is not a real number because the index is even and the radicand is negative.

3. In exponential form $\sqrt[n]{b^m}$ is equal to $\left(b^m\right)^{\frac{1}{n}}$. By the Power of a Power Property, $\left(b^m\right)^{\frac{1}{n}} = b^{\frac{m}{n}}$. But, $b^{\frac{m}{n}}$ is also equal to $\left(b^{\frac{1}{n}}\right)^m$ by the Power of a Power Property. This last expression is equal to $(\sqrt[n]{b})^m$. Thus, $\sqrt[n]{b^m} = (\sqrt[n]{b})^m$.

4. $7^{\frac{1}{3}} = \sqrt[3]{7}$

5. $x^{\frac{2}{3}} = \sqrt[3]{x^2}$ or $(\sqrt[3]{x})^2$

6. $\sqrt[4]{26} = 26^{\frac{1}{4}}$

7. $\sqrt[3]{6x^5y^7} = (6x^5y^7)^{\frac{1}{3}}$
$$= 6^{\frac{1}{3}} x^{\frac{5}{3}} y^{\frac{7}{3}}$$

8. $125^{\frac{1}{3}} = (5^3)^{\frac{1}{3}}$
$$= 5^{\frac{3}{3}}$$
$$= 5$$

9. $81^{-\frac{1}{4}} = (3^4)^{-\frac{1}{4}}$
$$= 3^{-\frac{4}{4}}$$
$$= 3^{-1}$$
$$= \frac{1}{3}$$

10. $27^{\frac{2}{3}} = (3^3)^{\frac{2}{3}}$
$$= 3^{3 \cdot \frac{2}{3}}$$
$$= 3^2$$
$$= 9$$

11. $\dfrac{54}{9^{\frac{3}{2}}} = \dfrac{54}{(3^2)^{\frac{3}{2}}}$

$= \dfrac{54}{3^3}$

$= \dfrac{54}{27}$

$= 2$

12. $a^{\frac{2}{3}} \cdot a^{\frac{1}{4}} = a^{\frac{2}{3} + \frac{1}{4}}$

$= a^{\frac{11}{12}}$

13. $\dfrac{x^{\frac{5}{6}}}{x^{\frac{1}{6}}} = x^{\frac{5}{6} - \frac{1}{6}}$

$= x^{\frac{2}{3}}$

14. $\dfrac{1}{2z^{\frac{1}{3}}} = \dfrac{1}{2z^{\frac{1}{3}}} \cdot \dfrac{z^{\frac{2}{3}}}{z^{\frac{2}{3}}}$

$= \dfrac{z^{\frac{2}{3}}}{2z^{\frac{1}{3} + \frac{2}{3}}}$

$= \dfrac{z^{\frac{2}{3}}}{2z}$

15. $\dfrac{a^2}{b^{\frac{1}{3}}} \cdot \dfrac{b}{a^{\frac{1}{2}}} = a^{2 - \frac{1}{2}} \cdot b^{1 - \frac{1}{3}}$

$= a^{\frac{3}{2}} b^{\frac{2}{3}}$

16. $(mn^2)^{-\frac{1}{3}} = \dfrac{1}{(mn^2)^{\frac{1}{3}}}$

$= \dfrac{1}{m^{\frac{1}{3}} n^{\frac{2}{3}}}$

$= \dfrac{1}{m^{\frac{1}{3}} n^{\frac{2}{3}}} \cdot \dfrac{m^{\frac{2}{3}} n^{\frac{1}{3}}}{m^{\frac{2}{3}} n^{\frac{1}{3}}}$

$= \dfrac{m^{\frac{2}{3}} \cdot n^{\frac{1}{3}}}{mn}$

17. $z(x - 2y)^{-\frac{1}{2}} = \dfrac{z}{(x - 2y)^{\frac{1}{2}}}$

$= \dfrac{z}{(x - 2y)^{\frac{1}{2}}} \cdot \dfrac{(x - 2y)^{\frac{1}{2}}}{(x - 2y)^{\frac{1}{2}}}$

$= \dfrac{z(x - 2y)^{\frac{1}{2}}}{x - 2y}$

18. $\sqrt[6]{27x^3} = \sqrt[6]{3^3 x^3}$

$= \sqrt[6]{(3x)^3}$

$= (3x)^{\frac{3}{6}}$

$= (3x)^{\frac{1}{2}}$

$= \sqrt{3x}$

19. $\dfrac{\sqrt[4]{27}}{\sqrt{3}} = \sqrt[4]{\dfrac{27}{3}}$

$= \sqrt[4]{9}$

$= \sqrt[4]{3^2}$

$= 3^{\frac{2}{4}}$

$= 3^{\frac{1}{2}}$

$= \sqrt{3}$

20. $C = c(1 + r)^n$

$C = 4.99(1 + 0.05)^{\frac{6}{12}}$

$= 4.99(1 + 0.05)^{\frac{1}{2}}$

$= (4.99)(1.025)$

$= 5.11$

The price would be \$5.11.

Pages 261–262   Practice and Apply

21. $6^{\frac{1}{5}} = \sqrt[5]{6}$

22. $4^{\frac{1}{3}} = \sqrt[3]{4}$

23. $c^{\frac{2}{5}} = \sqrt[5]{c^2}$ or $(\sqrt[5]{c})^2$

24. $(x^2)^{\frac{4}{3}} = \sqrt[3]{(x^2)^4}$

$= \sqrt[3]{x^8}$

$= \sqrt[3]{(x^2)^3 \cdot x^2}$

$= \sqrt[3]{(x^2)^3} \cdot \sqrt[3]{x^2}$

$= x^2 \sqrt[3]{x^2}$

25. $\sqrt{23} = 23^{\frac{1}{2}}$

26. $\sqrt[3]{62} = 62^{\frac{1}{3}}$

27. $\sqrt[4]{16z^2} = \sqrt[4]{2^4 z^2}$

$= (2^4 z^2)^{\frac{1}{4}}$

$= 2^{\frac{4}{4}} z^{\frac{2}{4}}$

$= 2z^{\frac{1}{2}}$

28. $\sqrt[3]{5x^2 y} = (5x^2 y)^{\frac{1}{3}}$

$= 5^{\frac{1}{3}} x^{\frac{2}{3}} y^{\frac{1}{3}}$

29. $16^{\frac{1}{4}} = (2^4)^{\frac{1}{4}}$

$= 2^{\frac{4}{4}}$

$= 2$

30. $216^{\frac{1}{3}} = (6^3)^{\frac{1}{3}}$

$= 6^{\frac{3}{3}}$

$= 6$

31. $25^{-\frac{1}{2}} = (5^2)^{-\frac{1}{2}}$

$= 5^{-\frac{2}{2}}$

$= 5^{-1}$

$= \dfrac{1}{5}$

32. $81^{-\frac{3}{4}} = (3^4)^{-\frac{3}{4}}$

$= 3^{-\frac{12}{4}}$

$= 3^{-3}$

$= \dfrac{1}{3^3}$

$= \dfrac{1}{27}$

33. $(-27)^{-\frac{2}{3}} = [(-3)^3]^{-\frac{2}{3}}$

$= (-3)^{-\frac{6}{3}}$

$= (-3)^{-2}$

$= \dfrac{1}{(-3)^2}$

$= \dfrac{1}{9}$

34. $(-32)^{-\frac{3}{5}} = [(-2)^5]^{-\frac{3}{5}}$

$= (-2)^{-\frac{15}{5}}$

$= (-2)^{-3}$

$= \dfrac{1}{(-2)^3}$

$= \dfrac{1}{-8}$

$= -\dfrac{1}{8}$

35. $81^{-\frac{1}{2}} \cdot 81^{\frac{3}{2}} = 81^{-\frac{1}{2} + \frac{3}{2}}$

$= 81^{\frac{2}{2}}$

$= 81$

36. $8^{\frac{3}{2}} \cdot 8^{\frac{5}{2}} = 8^{\frac{3}{2} + \frac{5}{2}}$

$= 8^{\frac{8}{2}}$

$= 8^4$

$= 4096$

37. $\left(\dfrac{8}{27}\right)^{\frac{1}{3}} = \left[\left(\dfrac{2}{3}\right)^3\right]^{\frac{1}{3}}$

$= \left(\dfrac{2}{3}\right)^{\frac{3}{3}}$

$= \dfrac{2}{3}$

38. $\left(\dfrac{1}{243}\right)^{-\frac{3}{5}} = \left(\dfrac{1}{3^5}\right)^{-\frac{3}{5}}$

$= (3^{-5})^{-\frac{3}{5}}$

$= 3^{\frac{15}{5}}$

$= 3^3$

$= 27$

39. $\dfrac{16^{\frac{1}{2}}}{9^{\frac{1}{2}}} = \dfrac{(4^2)^{\frac{1}{2}}}{(3^2)^{\frac{1}{2}}}$

$= \dfrac{4^{\frac{2}{2}}}{3^{\frac{2}{2}}}$

$= \dfrac{4}{3}$

40. $\dfrac{8^{\frac{1}{3}}}{64^{\frac{1}{3}}} = \dfrac{(2^3)^{\frac{1}{3}}}{(4^3)^{\frac{1}{3}}}$

$= \dfrac{2^{\frac{3}{3}}}{4^{\frac{3}{3}}}$

$= \dfrac{2}{4}$

$= \dfrac{1}{2}$

41. $y^{\frac{5}{3}} \cdot y^{\frac{7}{3}} = y^{\frac{5}{3}+\frac{7}{3}}$

$= y^{\frac{12}{3}}$

$= y^4$

42. $x^{\frac{3}{4}} \cdot x^{\frac{9}{4}} = x^{\frac{3+9}{4}}$

$= x^{\frac{12}{4}}$

$= x^3$

43. $\left(b^{\frac{1}{3}}\right)^{\frac{3}{5}} = b^{\frac{3}{15}}$

$= b^{\frac{1}{5}}$

44. $\left(a^{-\frac{2}{3}}\right)^{-\frac{1}{6}} = a^{\frac{2}{18}}$

$= a^{\frac{1}{9}}$

45. $w^{-\frac{4}{5}} = \dfrac{1}{w^{\frac{4}{5}}}$

$= \dfrac{1}{w^{\frac{4}{5}}} \cdot \dfrac{w^{\frac{1}{5}}}{w^{\frac{1}{5}}}$

$= \dfrac{w^{\frac{1}{5}}}{w^{\frac{5}{5}}}$

$= \dfrac{w^{\frac{1}{5}}}{w}$

46. $x^{-\frac{1}{6}} = \dfrac{1}{x^{\frac{1}{6}}}$

$= \dfrac{1}{x^{\frac{1}{6}}} \cdot \dfrac{x^{\frac{5}{6}}}{x^{\frac{5}{6}}}$

$= \dfrac{x^{\frac{5}{6}}}{x^{\frac{6}{6}}}$

$= \dfrac{x^{\frac{5}{6}}}{x}$

47. $\dfrac{t^{\frac{3}{4}}}{t^{\frac{1}{2}}} = t^{\frac{3}{4}-\frac{1}{2}}$

$= t^{\frac{3}{4}-\frac{2}{4}}$

$= t^{\frac{1}{4}}$

48. $\dfrac{r^{\frac{2}{3}}}{r^{\frac{1}{6}}} = r^{\frac{2}{3}-\frac{1}{6}}$

$= r^{\frac{3}{6}}$

$= r^{\frac{1}{2}}$

49. $\dfrac{a^{-\frac{1}{2}}}{6a^{\frac{1}{3}} \cdot a^{-\frac{1}{4}}} = \dfrac{1}{6} \cdot a^{-\frac{1}{2}} \cdot a^{-\frac{1}{3}} \cdot a^{\frac{1}{4}}$

$= \dfrac{1}{6} a^{-\frac{1}{2} - \frac{1}{3} + \frac{1}{4}}$

$= \dfrac{1}{6} a^{-\frac{7}{12}}$

$= \dfrac{1}{6 a^{\frac{7}{12}}}$

$= \dfrac{1}{6 a^{\frac{7}{12}}} \cdot \dfrac{a^{\frac{5}{12}}}{a^{\frac{5}{12}}}$

$= \dfrac{a^{\frac{5}{12}}}{6 a^{\frac{12}{12}}}$

$= \dfrac{a^{\frac{5}{12}}}{6a}$

50. $\dfrac{2c^{\frac{1}{8}}}{c^{-\frac{1}{16}} \cdot c^{\frac{1}{4}}} = 2c^{\frac{1}{8}} \cdot c^{\frac{1}{16}} \cdot c^{-\frac{1}{4}}$

$= 2c^{\frac{1}{8} + \frac{1}{16} - \frac{1}{4}}$

$= 2c^{-\frac{1}{16}}$

$= \dfrac{2}{c^{\frac{1}{16}}}$

$= \dfrac{2}{c^{\frac{1}{16}}} \cdot \dfrac{c^{\frac{15}{16}}}{c^{\frac{15}{16}}}$

$= \dfrac{2c^{\frac{15}{16}}}{c^{\frac{16}{16}}}$

$= \dfrac{2c^{\frac{15}{16}}}{c}$

51. $\dfrac{y^{\frac{3}{2}}}{y^{\frac{1}{2}} + 2} = \dfrac{y^{\frac{3}{2}}\left(y^{\frac{1}{2}} - 2\right)}{\left(y^{\frac{1}{2}} + 2\right)\left(y^{\frac{1}{2}} - 2\right)}$

$= \dfrac{y^{\frac{3}{2}}\left(y^{\frac{1}{2}} - 2\right)}{\left(y^{\frac{1}{2}}\right)^2 - 2^2}$

$= \dfrac{y^{\frac{3}{2}} \cdot y^{\frac{1}{2}} - 2y^{\frac{3}{2}}}{y^{\frac{2}{2}} - 4}$

$= \dfrac{y^{\frac{3}{2} + \frac{1}{2}} - 2y^{\frac{3}{2}}}{y - 4}$

$= \dfrac{y^2 - 2y^{\frac{3}{2}}}{y - 4}$

52. $\dfrac{x^{\frac{1}{2}} + 2}{x^{\frac{1}{2}} - 1} = \dfrac{\left(x^{\frac{1}{2}} + 2\right)\left(x^{\frac{1}{2}} + 1\right)}{\left(x^{\frac{1}{2}} - 1\right)\left(x^{\frac{1}{2}} + 1\right)}$

$= \dfrac{\left(x^{\frac{1}{2}}\right)^2 + x^{\frac{1}{2}} \cdot 1 + 2 \cdot x^{\frac{1}{2}} + 2 \cdot 1}{\left(x^{\frac{1}{2}}\right)^2 - 1^2}$

$= \dfrac{x^{\frac{2}{2}} + 3x^{\frac{1}{2}} + 2}{x^{\frac{2}{2}} - 1}$

$= \dfrac{x + 3x^{\frac{1}{2}} + 2}{x - 1}$

53. $\sqrt[4]{25} = \sqrt[4]{5^2}$

$= 5^{\frac{2}{4}}$

$= 5^{\frac{1}{2}}$

$= \sqrt{5}$

54. $\sqrt[6]{27} = \sqrt[6]{3^3}$

$= (3^3)^{\frac{1}{6}}$

$= 3^{\frac{1}{2}}$

$= \sqrt{3}$

55. $\sqrt{17} \cdot \sqrt[3]{17^2} = 17^{\frac{1}{2}} \cdot 17^{\frac{2}{3}}$

$= 17^{\frac{1}{2} + \frac{2}{3}}$

$= 17^{\frac{7}{6}}$

$= 17^{\frac{6}{6} + \frac{1}{6}}$

$= 17^{\frac{6}{6}} \cdot 17^{\frac{1}{6}}$

$= 17\sqrt[6]{17}$

56. $\sqrt[3]{5} \cdot \sqrt{5^3} = 5^{\frac{1}{3}} \cdot 5^{\frac{3}{2}}$
$$= 5^{\frac{1}{3} + \frac{3}{2}}$$
$$= 5^{\frac{11}{6}}$$
$$= 5^{\frac{6}{6} + \frac{5}{6}}$$
$$= 5^{\frac{6}{6}} \cdot 5^{\frac{5}{6}}$$
$$= 5\sqrt[6]{5^5}$$

57. $\sqrt[8]{25x^4y^4} = \sqrt[8]{5^2(x^2)^2(y^2)^2}$
$$= \sqrt[8]{(5x^2y^2)^2}$$
$$= [(5x^2y^2)^2]^{\frac{1}{8}}$$
$$= (5x^2y^2)^{\frac{1}{4}}$$
$$= \sqrt[4]{5x^2y^2}$$

58. $\sqrt[6]{81a^4b^8} = \sqrt[6]{3^4 \cdot a^4 \cdot (b^2)^4}$
$$= \sqrt[6]{(3ab^2)^4}$$
$$= [(3ab^2)^4]^{\frac{1}{6}}$$
$$= (3ab^2)^{\frac{2}{3}}$$
$$= \sqrt[3]{(3ab^2)^2}$$
$$= \sqrt[3]{9a^2b^4}$$
$$= \sqrt[3]{9a^2b^3 \cdot b}$$
$$= b\sqrt[3]{9a^2b}$$

59. $\dfrac{xy}{\sqrt{z}} = \dfrac{xy\sqrt{z}}{\sqrt{z} \cdot \sqrt{z}}$
$$= \dfrac{xy\sqrt{z}}{(\sqrt{z})^2}$$
$$= \dfrac{xy\sqrt{z}}{z}$$

60. $\dfrac{ab}{\sqrt[3]{c}} = \dfrac{ab}{\sqrt[3]{c}} \cdot \dfrac{\sqrt[3]{c^2}}{\sqrt[3]{c^2}}$
$$= \dfrac{ab\sqrt[3]{c^2}}{\sqrt[3]{c^{1+2}}}$$
$$= \dfrac{ab\sqrt[3]{c^2}}{\sqrt[3]{c^3}}$$
$$= \dfrac{ab\sqrt[3]{c^2}}{c}$$

61. $\sqrt[3]{\sqrt{8}} = (\sqrt{8})^{\frac{1}{3}}$
$$= \left[(8)^{\frac{1}{2}}\right]^{\frac{1}{3}}$$
$$= (8)^{\frac{1}{2} \cdot \frac{1}{3}}$$
$$= (2^3)^{\frac{1}{6}}$$
$$= 2^{\frac{3}{6}}$$
$$= 2^{\frac{1}{2}}$$
$$= \sqrt{2}$$

62. $\sqrt{\sqrt[3]{36}} = (\sqrt[3]{36})^{\frac{1}{2}}$
$$= \left[(6^2)^{\frac{1}{3}}\right]^{\frac{1}{2}}$$
$$= 6^{2 \cdot \frac{1}{3} \cdot \frac{1}{2}}$$
$$= 6^{\frac{1}{3}}$$
$$= \sqrt[3]{6}$$

63. $\dfrac{8^{\frac{1}{6}} - 9^{\frac{1}{4}}}{\sqrt{3} + \sqrt{2}} = \dfrac{[(2^3)^{\frac{1}{6}} - (3^2)^{\frac{1}{4}}](\sqrt{3} - \sqrt{2})}{(\sqrt{3} + \sqrt{2})(\sqrt{3} - \sqrt{2})}$
$$= \dfrac{\left(2^{\frac{3}{6}} - 3^{\frac{2}{4}}\right)(\sqrt{3} - \sqrt{2})}{(\sqrt{3})^2 - (\sqrt{2})^2}$$
$$= \dfrac{\left(2^{\frac{1}{2}} - 3^{\frac{1}{2}}\right)\left(3^{\frac{1}{2}} - 2^{\frac{1}{2}}\right)}{3 - 2}$$
$$= \dfrac{2^{\frac{1}{2}} \cdot 3^{\frac{1}{2}} - 2^{\frac{1}{2}} \cdot 2^{\frac{1}{2}} - 3^{\frac{1}{2}} \cdot 3^{\frac{1}{2}} + 3^{\frac{1}{2}} \cdot 2^{\frac{1}{2}}}{1}$$
$$= (2 \cdot 3)^{\frac{1}{2}} - 2^{\frac{1}{2} + \frac{1}{2}} + 3^{\frac{1}{2} + \frac{1}{2}} + (3 \cdot 2)^{\frac{1}{2}}$$
$$= 6^{\frac{1}{2}} - 2 - 3 + 6^{\frac{1}{2}}$$
$$= 2\sqrt{6} - 5$$

64. $\dfrac{x^{\frac{5}{3}} - x^{\frac{1}{3}}z^{\frac{4}{3}}}{x^{\frac{2}{3}} + z^{\frac{2}{3}}}$

$$= \dfrac{\left(x^{\frac{5}{3}} - x^{\frac{1}{3}}z^{\frac{4}{3}}\right)\left[\left(x^{\frac{2}{3}}\right)^2 - x^{\frac{2}{3}} \cdot z^{\frac{2}{3}} + \left(z^{\frac{2}{3}}\right)^2\right]}{\left(x^{\frac{2}{3}} + z^{\frac{2}{3}}\right)\left[\left(x^{\frac{2}{3}}\right)^2 - x^{\frac{2}{3}} \cdot z^{\frac{2}{3}} + \left(z^{\frac{2}{3}}\right)^2\right]}$$

$$= \dfrac{\left(x^{\frac{5}{3}} - x^{\frac{1}{3}}z^{\frac{4}{3}}\right)\left(x^{\frac{4}{3}} - x^{\frac{2}{3}} \cdot z^{\frac{2}{3}} + z^{\frac{4}{3}}\right)}{\left(x^{\frac{2}{3}}\right)^3 + \left(z^{\frac{2}{3}}\right)^3}$$

$$= \dfrac{x^{\frac{5}{3}} \cdot x^{\frac{4}{3}} - x^{\frac{5}{3}} \cdot x^{\frac{2}{3}} \cdot z^{\frac{2}{3}} + x^{\frac{5}{3}} \cdot z^{\frac{4}{3}} - x^{\frac{1}{3}} \cdot z^{\frac{4}{3}} \cdot x^{\frac{4}{3}} + x^{\frac{1}{3}} \cdot z^{\frac{4}{3}} \cdot x^{\frac{2}{3}} \cdot z^{\frac{2}{3}} - x^{\frac{1}{3}} \cdot z^{\frac{4}{3}} \cdot z^{\frac{4}{3}}}{x^{\frac{6}{3}} + z^{\frac{6}{3}}}$$

$$= \dfrac{x^3 - x^{\frac{7}{3}}z^{\frac{2}{3}} + x^{\frac{5}{3}} \cdot z^{\frac{4}{3}} - x^{\frac{5}{3}} \cdot z^{\frac{4}{3}} + xz^2 - x^{\frac{1}{3}}z^{\frac{8}{3}}}{x^2 + z^2}$$

$$= \dfrac{x^3 - x^{\frac{7}{3}}z^{\frac{2}{3}} + xz^2 - x^{\frac{1}{3}}z^{\frac{8}{3}}}{x^2 + z^2}$$

$$= \dfrac{x^2\left(x - x^{\frac{1}{3}}z^{\frac{2}{3}}\right) + z^2\left(x - x^{\frac{1}{3}}z^{\frac{2}{3}}\right)}{(x^2 + z^2)}$$

$$= \dfrac{\left(x - x^{\frac{1}{3}}z^{\frac{2}{3}}\right)(x^2 + z^2)}{(x^2 + z^2)}$$

$$= x - x^{\frac{1}{3}}z^{\frac{2}{3}}$$

65. $32^{\frac{1}{2}} + 3^{\frac{1}{2}} - 8^{\frac{1}{2}} = (2^4 \cdot 2^1)^{\frac{1}{2}} + 3^{\frac{1}{2}} - (2^2 \cdot 2)^{\frac{1}{2}}$
$$= \left(2^{\frac{4}{2}}\right)\left(2^{\frac{1}{2}}\right) + 3^{\frac{1}{2}} - \left(2^{\frac{2}{2}}\right)\left(2^{\frac{1}{2}}\right)$$
$$= 4 \cdot 2^{\frac{1}{2}} + 3^{\frac{1}{2}} - 2 \cdot 2^{\frac{1}{2}}$$
$$= 2 \cdot 2^{\frac{1}{2}} + 3^{\frac{1}{2}}$$
$$= 2^{\frac{3}{2}} + 3^{\frac{1}{2}}$$

66. $81^{\frac{1}{3}} - 24^{\frac{1}{3}} + 3^{\frac{1}{3}} = (3^3 \cdot 3)^{\frac{1}{3}} - (2^3 \cdot 3)^{\frac{1}{3}} + 3^{\frac{1}{3}}$
$$= 3^{\frac{3}{3}} \cdot 3^{\frac{1}{3}} - 2^{\frac{3}{3}} \cdot 3^{\frac{1}{3}} + 3^{\frac{1}{3}}$$
$$= 3 \cdot 3^{\frac{1}{3}} - 2 \cdot 3^{\frac{1}{3}} + 3^{\frac{1}{3}}$$
$$= 2 \cdot 3^{\frac{1}{3}}$$

67. $f_n = 440 \cdot 2^{\frac{n}{12}}$
$$f_{12} = (440)\left(2^{\frac{12}{12}}\right)$$
$$= (440)(2)$$
$$= 880$$
The frequency should be set at 880 vibrations per second.

68. $f_n = 440 \cdot 2^{\frac{n}{12}}$
$$f_8 = 440 \cdot 2^{-\frac{9}{12}}$$
$$= 440 \cdot 2^{-\frac{3}{4}}$$
$$\approx 262$$
The frequency is about 262 vibrations per second.

69. $N = 100 \cdot 2^{\frac{t}{2}}$
$$N = 100 \cdot 2^{\frac{3.5}{2}}$$
$$N \approx 336$$
There will be about 336 bacteria after $3\frac{1}{2}$ hours.

70. Rewrite the equation so that the bases are the same on each side.
$$9x = 3^{x + \frac{1}{2}}$$
$$(3^2)^x = 3^{x + \frac{1}{2}}$$
$$3^{2x} = 3^{x + \frac{1}{2}}$$

Since the bases are the same and this is an equation, the exponents must be equal. Solve $2x = x + \frac{1}{2}$. The result is $x = \frac{1}{2}$.

71. The equation that determines the size of the region around a planet where the planet's gravity is stronger than the sun's can be written in terms of a fractional exponent. Answers should include the following.

- The radical form of the equation is $r = D\sqrt[5]{\left(\dfrac{M_p}{M_s}\right)^2}$ or $r = D\sqrt[5]{\dfrac{M_p^2}{M_s^2}}$. Multiply the fraction under the radical by $\dfrac{M_s^3}{M_s^3}$.

$$r = D\sqrt[5]{\dfrac{M_p^2}{M_s^2} \cdot \dfrac{M_s^3}{M_s^3}}$$
$$= D\sqrt[5]{\dfrac{M_p^2 M_s^3}{M_s^5}}$$
$$= D\dfrac{\sqrt[5]{M_p^2 M_s^3}}{\sqrt[5]{M_s^5}}$$
$$= \dfrac{D\sqrt[5]{M_p^2 M_s^3}}{M_s}$$

The simplified radical form is $r = \dfrac{D\sqrt[5]{M_p^2 M_s^3}}{M_s}$.

- If M_p and M_s are constant, then r increases as D increases because r is a linear function of D with positive slope.

72. C; $4^{\frac{1}{2}} + \left(\dfrac{1}{2}\right)^4 = (2^2)^{\frac{1}{2}} + \left(\dfrac{1}{2}\right)^4$
$$= 2^{\frac{2}{2}} + \left(\dfrac{1}{2^4}\right)$$
$$= 2 + \dfrac{1}{16}$$
$$= 2\dfrac{1}{16}$$

73. C; $4x + 2y = 5$
$x - y = 1$
Add the first equation to -1 times the second equation.

$$\begin{array}{r} 4x + 2y = 5 \\ (+) - x + y = -1 \\ \hline 3x + 3y = 4 \end{array}$$

Page 262 Maintain Your Skills

74. $\sqrt{4x^3y^2} = \sqrt{2^2 \cdot x^2 \cdot x \cdot y^2}$
$= \sqrt{z^2} \cdot \sqrt{x^2} \cdot \sqrt{x} \cdot \sqrt{y^2}$
$= 2x|y|\sqrt{x}$

75. $(2\sqrt{6})(3\sqrt{12}) = 3 \cdot 2 \cdot \sqrt{6 \cdot 12}$
$= 6 \cdot \sqrt{6^2 \cdot 2}$
$= 6 \cdot \sqrt{6^2} \cdot \sqrt{2}$
$= 6 \cdot 6 \cdot \sqrt{2}$
$= 36\sqrt{2}$

76. $\sqrt{32} + \sqrt{18} - \sqrt{50}$
$= \sqrt{4^2 \cdot 2} + \sqrt{3^2 \cdot 2} + \sqrt{5^2 \cdot 2}$
$= \sqrt{4^2} \cdot \sqrt{2} + \sqrt{3^2} \cdot \sqrt{2} + \sqrt{5^2} \cdot \sqrt{2}$
$= 4\sqrt{2} + 3\sqrt{2} - 5\sqrt{2}$
$= 2\sqrt{2}$

77. $\sqrt[4]{(-8)^4} = \sqrt[4]{4096}$
$= \sqrt[4]{8^4}$
$= 8$

78. $4\sqrt{(x-5)^2} = 4|x-5|$

79. $\sqrt{\dfrac{9}{36}x^4} = \sqrt{\left(\dfrac{3}{6}\right)^2 (x^2)^2}$
$= \left[\left(\dfrac{3}{6}\right)^2 (x^2)^2\right]^{\frac{1}{2}}$
$= \left(\dfrac{3}{6}\right)^{\frac{2}{2}} (x^2)^{\frac{2}{2}}$
$= \dfrac{3}{6}x^{\frac{4}{2}}$
$= \dfrac{1}{2}x^2$

80. Number of seconds in 2 hours $= 2 \times 60 \times 60$
$ = 7200$

$\dfrac{7200}{5} = 1440$

Humans blink their eyes 1440 times in two hours.

81. $(\sqrt{x-2})^2 = \left[(x-2)^{\frac{1}{2}}\right]^2$
$= (x-2)^{\frac{2}{2}}$
$= x - 2$

82. $(\sqrt[3]{2x-3})^3 = \left[(2x-3)^{\frac{1}{3}}\right]^3$
$= (2x-3)^{\frac{3}{3}}$
$= 2x - 3$

83. $(\sqrt{x}+1)^2 = (\sqrt{x})^2 + 2(\sqrt{x})(1) + 1^2$
$= x^2 + 2\sqrt{x} + 1$

84. $(2\sqrt{x}-3)^2 = (2\sqrt{x})^2 - (2\sqrt{x})(3) + 3^2$
$= 4x - 12\sqrt{x} + 9$

5-8 Radical Equations and Inequalities

Pages 265–266 Check for Understanding

1. Since x is not under the radical, the equation is a linear equation, not a radical equation. The solution is $x = \dfrac{\sqrt{3}-1}{2}$.

2. The trinomial is a perfect square in terms of $\sqrt{x}$. $x - 6\sqrt{x} + 9 = (\sqrt{x}-3)^2$, so the equation can be written as $(\sqrt{x}-3)^2 = 0$. Take the square root of each side to get $\sqrt{x} - 3 = 0$. Use the Addition Property of Equality to add 3 to each side, then square each side to get $x = 9$.

3. Sample answer: $\sqrt{x} + \sqrt{x+3} = 3$

4. $\sqrt{4x+1} = 3$
$(\sqrt{4x+1})^2 = 3^2$
$4x + 1 = 9$
$4x = 8$
$x = 2$

5. $4 - (7-y)^{\frac{1}{2}} = 0$
$4 = (7-y)^{\frac{1}{2}}$
$4^2 = \left[(7-y)^{\frac{1}{2}}\right]^2$
$16 = 7 - y$
$y = -9$

6. $1 + \sqrt{x+2} = 0$
$\sqrt{x+2} = -1$
Since the square root of a real number is not negative, there is no solution.

7. $\sqrt{z - 6} - 3 = 0$
$\sqrt{z - 6} = 3$
$(\sqrt{z - 6})^2 = 3^2$
$z - 6 = 9$
$z = 15$

8. $\frac{1}{6}(12a)^{\frac{1}{3}} = 1$
$(12a)^{\frac{1}{3}} = 6$
$\left[(12a)^{\frac{1}{3}}\right]^3 = 6^3$
$12a = 216$
$a = 18$

9. $\sqrt[3]{x - 4} = 3$
$(\sqrt[3]{x - 4})^3 = 3^3$
$x - 4 = 27$
$x = 31$

10. $\sqrt{2x + 3} - 4 \leq 5$
$\sqrt{2x + 3} \leq 9$
$(\sqrt{2x + 3})^2 \leq 9^2$
$2x + 3 \leq 81$
$2x \leq 78$
$x \leq 39$

Also, the radicand of a square root must be greater than or equal to zero.
$2x + 3 \geq 0$
$2x \geq -3$
$x \geq -\frac{3}{2}$

The solution is $-\frac{3}{2} \leq x \leq 39$.

11. $\sqrt{b + 12} - \sqrt{b} > 2$

The radicand of a square root must be greater than or equal to zero.
So, $b + 12 \geq 0$ or $b \geq -12$ and $b \geq 0$.
Now solve the equation.
$\sqrt{b + 12} - \sqrt{b} + \sqrt{b} > 2 + \sqrt{b}$
$\sqrt{b + 12} > 2 + \sqrt{b}$
$(\sqrt{b + 12})^2 > (2 + \sqrt{b})^2$
$b + 12 > 4 + 4\sqrt{b} + b$
$8 > 4\sqrt{b}$
$2 > \sqrt{b}$
$2^2 > (\sqrt{b})^2$
$4 > b$

The solution is $0 \leq b < 4$.

12. $S = \pi r \sqrt{r^2 + h^2}$
$225 = (3.14)(5)\sqrt{5^2 + h^2}$
$\frac{225}{(3.14)(5)} = \sqrt{25 + h^2}$
$(14.33)^2 = (\sqrt{25 + h^2})^2$
$205.35 = 25 + h^2$
$180.35 = h^2$
$\sqrt{180.35} = \sqrt{h^2}$
$h \approx 13.42$
The height of the cone is about 13.42 cm.

Pages 266–267 Practice and Apply

13. $\sqrt{x} = 4$
$(\sqrt{x})^2 = 4^2$
$x = 16$

14. $\sqrt{y} - 7 = 0$
$\sqrt{y} = 7$
$(\sqrt{y})^2 = 7^2$
$y = 49$

15. $a^{\frac{1}{2}} + 9 = 0$
$a^{\frac{1}{2}} = -9$
The square root of a real number cannot be negative, so there is no solution.

16. $2 + 4z^{\frac{1}{2}} = 0$
$4z^{\frac{1}{2}} = -2$
$z^{\frac{1}{2}} = -\frac{1}{2}$

The square root of a real number cannot be negative, so there is no solution.

17. $\sqrt[3]{c - 1} = 2$
$(\sqrt[3]{c - 1})^3 = 2^3$
$c - 1 = 8$
$c = 9$

18. $\sqrt[3]{5m + 2} = 3$
$(\sqrt[3]{5m + 2})^3 = 3^3$
$5m + 2 = 27$
$5m = 25$
$m = 5$

19. $7 + \sqrt{4x + 8} = 9$
$\sqrt{4x + 8} = 2$
$(\sqrt{4x + 8})^2 = 2^2$
$4x + 8 = 4$
$4x = -4$
$x = -1$

20. $5 + \sqrt{4y - 5} = 12$
$\sqrt{4y - 5} = 7$
$(\sqrt{4y - 5})^2 = 7^2$
$4y - 5 = 49$
$4y = 54$
$y = \frac{27}{2}$

21. $(6n - 5)^{\frac{1}{3}} + 3 = -2$
$(6n - 5)^{\frac{1}{3}} = -5$
$\left[(6n - 5)^{\frac{1}{3}}\right]^3 = (-5)^3$
$6n - 5 = -125$
$6n = -120$
$n = -20$

22. $(5x + 7)^{\frac{1}{5}} + 3 = 5$
$(5x + 7)^{\frac{1}{5}} = 2$
$\left[(5x + 7)^{\frac{1}{5}}\right]^5 = 2^5$
$5x + 7 = 32$
$5x = 25$
$x = 5$

23. $\sqrt{x - 5} = \sqrt{2x - 4}$
$(\sqrt{x - 5})^2 = (\sqrt{2x - 4})^2$
$x - 5 = 2x - 4$
$-1 = x$

Replacing the answer $x = -1$ results in a negative number in each radicand.
So, $x = -1$ is not acceptable and there is no solution.

225

24. $\sqrt{2t-7} = \sqrt{t+2}$
$(\sqrt{2t-7})^2 = (\sqrt{t+2})^2$
$2t-7 = t+2$
$t-7 = 2$
$t = 9$

25. $1 + \sqrt{7x-3} > 3$
The radicand of a square root must be greater than or equal to zero.
$7x - 3 \geq 0$
$7x \geq 3$
$x \geq \frac{3}{7}$
Now solve the equation.
$1 + \sqrt{7x-3} - 1 > 3 - 1$
$\sqrt{7x-3} > 2$
$(\sqrt{7x-3})^2 > 2^2$
$7x - 3 > 4$
$7x > 7$
$x > 1$
A check shows the solution is $x > 1$.

26. $\sqrt{3x+6} + 2 \leq 5$
The radicand of a square root must be greater than or equal to zero.
$3x + 6 \geq 0$
$3x \geq -6$
$x \geq -2$
Now solve the equation.
$\sqrt{3x+6} + 2 - 2 \leq 5 - 2$
$\sqrt{3x+6} \leq 3$
$(\sqrt{3x+6})^2 \leq 3^2$
$3x + 6 \leq 9$
$3x \leq 3$
$x \leq 1$
A check shows the solution is $-2 \leq x \leq 1$.

27. $-2 + \sqrt{9-5x} \geq 6$
The radicand of a square root must be greater than or equal to zero.
$9 - 5x \geq 0$
$9 \geq 5x$
$\frac{9}{5} \geq x$
Now solve the equation.
$-2 + \sqrt{9-5x} + 2 \geq 6 + 2$
$\sqrt{9-5x} \geq 8$
$(\sqrt{9-5x})^2 \geq 8^2$
$9 - 5x \geq 64$
$-5x \geq 55$
$x \leq -11$
A check shows the solution is $x \leq -11$.

28. $6 - \sqrt{2y+1} < 3$
The radicand of a square root must be greater than or equal to zero.
$2y + 1 \geq 0$
$2y \geq -1$
$y \geq -\frac{1}{2}$
Now solve the equation.
$6 - \sqrt{2y+1} - 6 < 3 - 6$
$-\sqrt{2y+1} < -3$
$(-\sqrt{2y+1})^2 > (-3)^2$
$2y + 1 > 9$
$2y > 8$
$y > 4$
A check shows the solution is $y > 4$.

29. $\sqrt{x-6} - \sqrt{x} = 3$
$\sqrt{x-6} = 3 + \sqrt{x}$
$(\sqrt{x-6})^2 = (3 + \sqrt{x})^2$
$x - 6 = 9 + 6\sqrt{x} + x$
$-15 = 6\sqrt{x}$
$-\frac{5}{2} = \sqrt{x}$
The square root of a real number cannot be negative, so there is no solution.

30. $\sqrt{y+21} - 1 = \sqrt{y+12}$
$(\sqrt{y+21} - 1)^2 = (\sqrt{y+12})^2$
$y + 21 - 2\sqrt{y+21} + 1 = y + 12$
$-2\sqrt{y+21} = -10$
$\sqrt{y+21} = -5$
$(\sqrt{y+21})^2 = (-5)^2$
$y + 21 = 25$
$y = 4$

31. $\sqrt{b+1} = \sqrt{b+6} - 1$
$(\sqrt{b+1})^2 = (\sqrt{b+6} - 1)^2$
$b + 1 = b + 6 - 2\sqrt{b+6} + 1$
$b + 1 = b + 7 - 2\sqrt{b+6}$
$-6 = -2\sqrt{b+6}$
$3 = \sqrt{b+6}$
$3^2 = (\sqrt{b+6})^2$
$9 = b + 6$
$3 = b$

32. $\sqrt{4z+1} = 3 + \sqrt{4z-2}$
$(\sqrt{4z+1})^2 = (3 + \sqrt{4z-2})^2$
$4z + 1 = 3^2 + 6\sqrt{4z-2} + (\sqrt{4z-2})^2$
$4z + 1 = 9 + 6\sqrt{4z-2} + 4z - 2$
$-1 = \sqrt{4z-2}$
The square root of a real number cannot be negative, so there is no solution.

33. $\sqrt{2} - \sqrt{x+6} \leq -\sqrt{x}$
The radicand of a square root must be greater than or equal to zero.
$x + 6 \geq 0$
$x \geq -6$
and
$x \geq 0$
Now solve the equation.
$(\sqrt{2} - \sqrt{x+6})^2 \geq (-\sqrt{x})^2$
$2 - 2\sqrt{2} \cdot \sqrt{x+6} + x + 6 \geq x$
$8 - 2\sqrt{2(x+6)} + x \geq x$
$-2\sqrt{2(x+6)} \geq -8$
$\sqrt{2(x+6)} \leq 4$
$(\sqrt{2(x+6)})^2 \leq 4^2$
$2(x+6) \leq 16$
$x + 6 \leq 8$
$x \leq 2$
A check shows the solution is $0 \leq x \leq 2$.

34. $\sqrt{a+9} - \sqrt{a} > \sqrt{3}$

The radicand of a square root must be greater than or equal to zero.

$a + 9 \geq 0$

$\quad a \geq -9$

and

$\quad a \geq 0$

Now solve the equation.

$\sqrt{a+9} - \sqrt{a} + \sqrt{a} > \sqrt{3} + \sqrt{a}$

$\qquad \sqrt{a+9} > \sqrt{3} + \sqrt{a}$

$\qquad (\sqrt{a+9})^2 > (\sqrt{3} + \sqrt{a})^2$

$\qquad a + 9 > 3 + 2\sqrt{3a} + a$

$\qquad\qquad 6 > 2\sqrt{3a}$

$\qquad\qquad 3 > \sqrt{3a}$

$\qquad\qquad 3^2 > (\sqrt{3a})^2$

$\qquad\qquad 9 > 3a$

$\qquad\qquad 3 > a$

A check shows the solution is $0 \leq a < 3$.

35. $\sqrt{b-5} - \sqrt{b+7} \leq 4$

The radicand of a square root must be greater than or equal to zero.

$b - 5 \geq 0$

$\quad b \geq 5$

$b + 7 \geq 0$

$\quad b \geq -7$

Now solve the equation.

$\sqrt{b+5} \leq 4 + \sqrt{b+7}$

$(\sqrt{b+5})^2 \leq (4 + \sqrt{b+7})^2$

$\quad b + 5 \leq 16 + b + 7 + 8\sqrt{b+7}$

$\quad -18 \leq 8\sqrt{b+7}$

$\quad -\frac{9}{4} \leq \sqrt{b+7}$

$\left(-\frac{9}{4}\right)^2 \leq (\sqrt{b+7})^2$

$\quad \frac{81}{16} \leq b + 7$

$\frac{81}{16} - 7 \leq b$

$\frac{81}{16} - \frac{112}{16} \leq b$

$\quad -\frac{31}{16} \leq b$

A check shows the solution is $b \geq 5$.

36. $\sqrt{c+5} + \sqrt{c+10} > 2.5$

The radicand of a square root must be greater than or equal to zero.

$c + 5 \geq 0$

$\quad c \geq -5$

$c + 10 \geq 0$

$\quad c \geq -10$

Now solve the equation.

$\sqrt{c+5} > 2.5 - \sqrt{c+10}$

$(\sqrt{c+5})^2 > (2.5 - \sqrt{c+10})^2$

$\quad c + 5 > (2.5)^2 - 5\sqrt{c+10} + c + 10$

$\quad c + 5 > 16.25 - 5\sqrt{c+10} + c$

$\quad -11.25 > -5\sqrt{c+10}$

$\quad 2.25 < \sqrt{c+10}$

$\quad (2.25)^2 < c + 10$

$\quad \frac{81}{16} < c + 10$

A check shows the solution is $-\frac{79}{16} < c$.

37. $2 - \sqrt{x+6} = -1$

$\quad -\sqrt{x+6} = -3$

$\quad (-\sqrt{x+6})^2 = (-3)^2$

$\quad x + 6 = 9$

$\quad x = 3$

38. $\sqrt{2x+4} - 4 = 2$

$\quad \sqrt{2x+4} = 6$

$\quad (\sqrt{2x+4})^2 = 6^2$

$\quad 2x + 4 = 36$

$\quad 2x = 32$

$\quad x = 16$

39. $d = \sqrt{\frac{sl}{576w}}$

$\quad 5 = \sqrt{\frac{s \cdot 25}{576 \cdot 2}}$

$\quad 5^2 = \left(\sqrt{\frac{s \cdot 25}{576 \cdot 2}}\right)^2$

$\quad 25 = \frac{25s}{1152}$

$\quad s = 1152$

The load can be 1152 lb.

40. $r = \sqrt[3]{\frac{GMt^2}{4\pi^2}}$

$\quad r^3 = \left(\sqrt[3]{\frac{GMt^2}{4\pi^2}}\right)^3$

$\quad r^3 = \frac{GMt^2}{4\pi^2}$

$\quad \frac{4\pi^2}{GM} \cdot r^3 = \frac{4\pi^2}{GM} \cdot \frac{GMt^2}{4\pi^2}$

$\quad \frac{4\pi^2 r^3}{GM} = t^2$

$\quad t = \sqrt{\frac{4\pi^2 r^3}{GM}}$

41. $\quad \frac{\sqrt{50-h}}{4} = t$

$\quad \frac{\sqrt{50-h}}{4} = 1$

$\quad \sqrt{50-h} = 4$

$\quad (\sqrt{50-h})^2 = 4^2$

$\quad 50 - h = 16$

$\quad -h = -34$

$\quad h = 34$

The object will be 34 ft above the ground after 1 second.

42. $\quad p = \frac{\sqrt[3]{m}}{h}$

$\quad 2.5 = \frac{\sqrt[3]{m}}{1.8}$

$\quad 2.5 \cdot 1.8 = \sqrt[3]{m}$

$\quad (2.5 \cdot 1.8)^3 = (\sqrt[3]{m})^2$

$\quad m = 91.125 \text{ kg}$

$91.125 - 70 = 21.125 \text{ kg}$

The person could weigh 91.125 kg, so he or she could gain 21.125 kg.

43. Since $\sqrt{x+2} \geq 0$ and $\sqrt{2x-3} \geq 0$, the left side of the equation is nonnegative. Therefore, the left side of the equation cannot equal -1. Thus, the equation has no solution.

44. If a company's cost and number of units manufactured are related by an equation involving radicals or rational exponents, then the production level associated with a given cost can be found by solving a radical equation. Answers should include the following.

- $C = 10\sqrt[3]{n^2} + 1500$

- $\begin{aligned} 10{,}000 &= 10n^{\frac{2}{3}} + 1500 &&\quad C = 10{,}000 \\ 8500 &= 10n^{\frac{2}{3}} &&\quad \textit{Subtract 1500 from} \\ &&&\quad \textit{each side.} \\ 850 &= n^{\frac{2}{3}} &&\quad \textit{Divide each side} \\ &&&\quad \textit{by 10.} \\ 850^{\frac{3}{2}} &= n &&\quad \textit{Raise each side to} \\ &&&\quad \textit{the } \tfrac{3}{2} \textit{ power.} \\ 24{,}781.55 &\approx n &&\quad \textit{Use a calculator.} \end{aligned}$

Round down so that the cost does not exceed $10,000. The company can make at most 24,781 chips.

45. D; $\begin{aligned} \sqrt{x+5} + 1 &= 4 \\ \sqrt{x+5} &= 3 \\ (\sqrt{x+5})^2 &= 3^2 \\ x + 5 &= 9 \\ x &= 4 \end{aligned}$

46. C; $x_C = 8$
$\begin{aligned} (y_C)^2 &= 10^2 - 8^2 \\ &= 100 - 64 \\ &= 36 \\ y^2{}_C &= 36 \\ y_C &= 6 \\ m_{(AC)} &= \frac{6-0}{8-0} \\ m_{(AC)} &= \frac{3}{4} \end{aligned}$

Equation of AC: $y - 0 = \frac{3}{4}(x - 0)$
$$y = \frac{3}{4}x$$

Only point (4, 3) fits this equation.

Page 267 Maintain Your Skills

47. $\sqrt[7]{5^3} = (5^3)^{\frac{1}{7}} = 5^{\frac{3}{7}}$

48. $\sqrt{x+7} = (x+7)^{\frac{1}{2}}$

49. $\begin{aligned} (\sqrt[3]{x^2+1})^2 &= \left[(x^2+1)^{\frac{1}{3}}\right]^2 \\ &= (x^2+1)^{\frac{2}{3}} \end{aligned}$

50. $\begin{aligned} \sqrt{72x^6y^3} &= \sqrt{6^2 \cdot 2 \cdot (x^3)^2 \cdot y^2 \cdot y} \\ &= \sqrt{6^2} \cdot \sqrt{2} \cdot \sqrt{(x^3)^2} \cdot \sqrt{y^2} \cdot \sqrt{y} \\ &= 6x^3|y|\sqrt{2y} \end{aligned}$

51. $\begin{aligned} \frac{1}{\sqrt[3]{10}} &= \frac{1}{\sqrt[3]{10}} \cdot \frac{\sqrt[3]{100}}{\sqrt[3]{100}} \\ &= \frac{\sqrt[3]{100}}{\sqrt[3]{1000}} \\ &= \frac{\sqrt[3]{100}}{\sqrt[3]{10^3}} \\ &= \frac{\sqrt[3]{100}}{10} \end{aligned}$

52. $\begin{aligned} (5 - \sqrt{3})^2 &= (5 - \sqrt{3})(5 - \sqrt{3}) \\ &= 5.5 - 5\sqrt{3} - 5\sqrt{3} + \sqrt{3} \cdot \sqrt{3} \\ &= 25 - 10\sqrt{3} + \sqrt{3^2} \\ &= 25 - 10\sqrt{3} + 3 \\ &= 28 - 10\sqrt{3} \end{aligned}$

53. Let x = number of drums of $30-cleaner,
y = number of drums of $20-cleaner.
$x + y = 7$
$30x + 20y = 160$

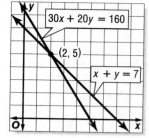

The graphs intersect at point (2, 5), so (2, 5) is the solution to the system. The company ordered 2 drums of $30-cleaner and 5 drums of $20-cleaner.

54. $\begin{aligned} (5 + 2x) + (-1 - x) &= 5 + 2x - 1 - x \\ &= (2x - x) + (5 - 1) \\ &= x + 4 \end{aligned}$

55. $\begin{aligned} (-3 - 2y) + (4 + y) &= -3 - 2y + 4 + y \\ &= (-2y + y) + (-3 + 4) \\ &= 1 - y \end{aligned}$

56. $\begin{aligned} (4 + x) - (2 - 3x) &= 4 + x - 2 + 3x \\ &= (x + 3x) + (4 - 2) \\ &= 4x + 2 \end{aligned}$

57. $\begin{aligned} (-7 - 3x) - (4 - 3x) &= -7 - 3x - 4 + 3x \\ &= (-3x + 3x) + (-7 - 4) \\ &= -11 \end{aligned}$

58. $\begin{aligned} (1 + z)(4 + 2z) &= 4 + 2z + 4z + 2z^2 \\ &= 2z^2 + 6z + 4 \end{aligned}$

59. $\begin{aligned} (-3 - 4x)(1 + 2x) &= -3 - 6x - 4x - 8x^2 \\ &= -8x^2 - 10x - 3 \end{aligned}$

Page 269 Graphing Calculator Investigation
(Follow-Up of Lesson 5-8)

1. $\sqrt{x + 4} = 3$
Graph $y_1 = \sqrt{x + 4}$ and $y_2 = 3$.

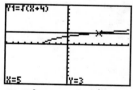

$[-10, 10]$ scl: 1 by $[-10, 10]$ scl: 1

The x-coordinate of the intersection is 5. The solution is 5.

2. $\sqrt{3x - 5} = 1$
Graph $y_1 = \sqrt{3x - 5}$ and $y_2 = 1$.

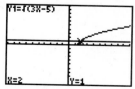

$[-10, 10]$ scl: 1 by $[-10, 10]$ scl: 1

The x-coordinate of the intersection is 2. The solution is 2.

3. $\sqrt{x + 5} = \sqrt{3x + 4}$

Graph $y_1 = \sqrt{x + 5}$ and $y_2 = \sqrt{3x + 4}$.

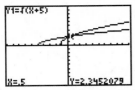

$[-10, 10]$ scl: 1 by $[-10, 10]$ scl: 1

The x-coordinate of the intersection is 0.5.
The solution is 0.5.

4. $\sqrt{x + 3} + \sqrt{x - 2} = 4$

Graph $y_1 = \sqrt{x + 3} + \sqrt{x - 2}$ and $y_2 = 4$.

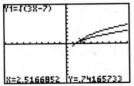

$[-10, 10]$ scl: 1 by $[-10, 10]$ scl: 1

The x-coordinate of the intersection is about 3.89.
The solution is about 3.89.

5. $\sqrt{3x - 7} = \sqrt{2x - 2} - 1$

Graph $y_1 = \sqrt{3x - 7}$ and $y_2 = \sqrt{2x - 2} - 1$.

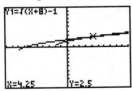

$[-10, 10]$ scl: 1 by $[-10, 10]$ scl: 1

The x-coordinate of the intersection is about 2.52.
The solution is about 2.52.

6. $\sqrt{x + 8} - 1 = \sqrt{x + 2}$

Graph $y_1 = \sqrt{x + 8} - 1$ and $y_2 = \sqrt{x + 2}$.

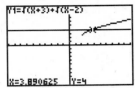

$[-10, 10]$ scl: 1 by $[-10, 10]$ scl: 1

The x-coordinate of the intersection is 4.25.
The solution is 4.25.

7. $\sqrt{x - 3} \geq 2$

Graph $y_1 = \sqrt{x - 3}$ and $y_2 = 2$.

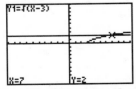

$[-10, 10]$ scl: 1 by $[-10, 10]$ scl: 1

The first curve is above the second curve for
points to the right of $x = 7$.
The solution is $x \geq 7$.

8. $\sqrt{x + 3} > 2\sqrt{x}$

Graph $y_1 = \sqrt{x + 3}$ and $y_2 = 2\sqrt{x}$.

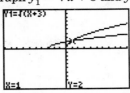

$[-10, 10]$ scl: 1 by $[-10, 10]$ scl: 1

The first curve is above the second curve for
points to the left of $x = 1$.
The solution is $0 \leq x < 1$, since $x \geq 0$ in $\sqrt{x}$ of the
second equation.

9. $\sqrt{x} + \sqrt{x - 1} < 4$

Graph $y_1 = \sqrt{x} + \sqrt{x - 1}$ and $y_2 = 4$.

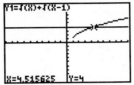

$[-10, 10]$ scl: 1 by $[-10, 10]$ scl: 1

The first curve is above the second curve for
points to the left of $x \approx 4.52$.
The solution is about $1 \leq x < 4.52$, since $x \geq 1$ in
$\sqrt{x - 1}$ of the first equation.

10. Rewrite the inequality so that one side is 0. Then
graph the other side and find the x values for
which the graph is above or below the x-axis,
according to the inequality symbol. Use the zero
feature to approximate the x-coordinate of the
point at which the graph crosses the x-axis.

5-9 Complex Numbers

Page 272 Algebra Activity

1. $(-3 + 2i) + (4 - i)$

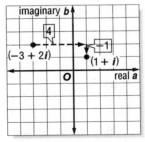

2. Rewrite the difference as a sum,
$(-3 + 2i) - (4 - i) = (-3 + 2i) + (-4 + i)$. Then
apply the method discussed in this activity.

3. $|2 + 5i| = \sqrt{2^2 + 5^2}$
$= \sqrt{4 + 25}$
$= \sqrt{29}$

4. $|a + bi| = \sqrt{a^2 + b^2}$

1a. True; every real number is a complex number, i.e., $1 = 1 + 0i$

1b. True; every imaginary number is a complex number, i.e., $i = 0 + i$

2. It satisfies all of them.

3. Sample answer: $1 + 3i$ and $1 - 3i$

4. $\sqrt{-36} = \sqrt{-1 \cdot 6^2}$
$= \sqrt{-1} \cdot \sqrt{6^2}$
$= i \cdot 6$
$= 6i$

5. $\sqrt{-50x^2y^2} = \sqrt{-1 \cdot 5^2 \cdot 2 \cdot x^2 \cdot y^2}$
$= \sqrt{-1} \cdot \sqrt{5^2} \cdot \sqrt{2} \cdot \sqrt{x^2} \cdot \sqrt{y^2}$
$= i \cdot 5 \cdot |x| \cdot |y| \cdot \sqrt{2}$
$= 5i\,|xy|\sqrt{2}$

6. $(6i)(-2i) = -12(i)^2$
$= -12(-1)$
$= 12$

7. $5\sqrt{-24} \cdot 3\sqrt{-18} = 5i\sqrt{24} \cdot 3i\sqrt{18}$
$= 15(i)^2\sqrt{24 \cdot 18}$
$= 15(-1)(12)\sqrt{3}$
$= -180\sqrt{3}$

8. $i^{29} = i^{28} \cdot i$
$= (i^2)^{14} \cdot i$
$= (-1)^{14} \cdot i$
$= 1 \cdot i$
$= i$

9. $(8 + 6i) - (2 + 3i) = (8 - 2) + (6 - 3)i$
$= 6 + 3i$

10. $(3 - 5i)(4 + 6i) = 12 + 18i - 20i - 30i^2$
$= 12 - 2i - 30(-1)$
$= 12 - 2i + 30$
$= 42 - 2i$

11. $\dfrac{3 + i}{1 + 4i} = \dfrac{3 + i}{1 + 4i} \cdot \dfrac{1 - 4i}{1 - 4i}$
$= \dfrac{3 - 12i + i - 4(i)^2}{1^2 - (4i)^2}$
$= \dfrac{3 - 11i - 4(-1)}{1 - 16(-1)}$
$= \dfrac{3 - 11i + 4}{1 + 16}$
$= \dfrac{7 - 11i}{17}$
$= \dfrac{7}{17} - \dfrac{11}{17}i$

12. $2x^2 + 18 = 0$
$2x^2 = -18$
$x^2 = -9$
$x = \pm\sqrt{-9}$
$= \pm 3i$

13. $4x^2 + 32 = 0$
$4x^2 = -32$
$x^2 = -8$
$x = \pm\sqrt{-8}$
$= \pm\sqrt{4 \cdot (-2)}$
$= \pm 2i\sqrt{2}$

14. $-5x^2 - 25 = 0$
$-5x^2 = 25$
$x^2 = -5$
$x = \pm\sqrt{-5}$
$x = \pm i\sqrt{5}$

15. $2m + (3n + 1)i = 6 - 8i$
$2m = 6$
$m = 3$
$3n + 1 = -8$
$3n = -9$
$n = -3$

16. $(2n - 5) + (-m - 2)i = 3 - 7i$
$2n - 5 = 3$
$2n = 8$
$n = 4$
$-m - 2 = -7$
$-m = -5$
$m = 5$

17. $(4 - j) + (6 + 4j) = (4 + 6) + (-1 + 4)j$
$= 10 + 3j$

18. $\sqrt{-144} = \sqrt{-1 \cdot 12^2}$
$= \sqrt{-1} \cdot \sqrt{12^2}$
$= 12i$

19. $\sqrt{-81} = \sqrt{-1 \cdot 9^2}$
$= \sqrt{-1} \cdot \sqrt{9^2}$
$= 9i$

20. $\sqrt{-64x^4} = \sqrt{-1 \cdot 8^2(x^2)^2}$
$= \sqrt{-1} \cdot \sqrt{8^2} \cdot \sqrt{(x^2)^2}$
$= 8x^2i$

21. $\sqrt{-100a^4b^2} = \sqrt{-1 \cdot 10^2 \cdot (a^2)^2 \cdot b^2}$
$= \sqrt{-1} \cdot \sqrt{10^2} \cdot \sqrt{(a^2)^2} \cdot \sqrt{b^2}$
$= 10a^2\,|b|\,i$

22. $\sqrt{-13} \cdot \sqrt{-26} = i\sqrt{13} \cdot i\sqrt{26}$
$= i^2 \cdot \sqrt{13 \cdot 26}$
$= -1 \cdot \sqrt{13^2 \cdot 2}$
$= -13\sqrt{2}$

23. $\sqrt{-6} \cdot \sqrt{-24} = i\sqrt{6} \cdot i\sqrt{24}$
$= i^2\sqrt{144}$
$= -1 \cdot 12$
$= -12$

24. $(-2i)(-6i)(4i) = (-2) \cdot (-6) \cdot (4)(i^2)(i)$
$= 48(-1)(i)$
$= -48i$

25. $3i(-5i)^2 = 3i(-5)^2(i)^2$
$= 3i(25)(-1)$
$= -75i$

26. $i^{13} = i^{12} \cdot i$
$= (i^2)^6 \cdot i$
$= (-1)^6 \cdot i$
$= i$

27. $i^{24} = (i^2)^{12}$
$= (-1)^{12}$
$= 1$

28. $i^{38} = (i^2)^{19}$
$= (-1)^{19}$
$= -1$

29. $i^{63} = i^{62} \cdot i$
$= (i^2)^{31} \cdot i$
$= (-1)^{31} \cdot i$
$= (-1) \cdot i$
$= -i$

30. $(5 - 2i) + (4 + 4i) = (5 + 4) + (-2 + 4)i$
$$= 9 + 2i$$

31. $(3 - 5i) + (3 + 5i) = (3 + 3) + (-5 + 5)i$
$$= 6 + 0i$$
$$= 6$$

32. $(3 - 4i) - (1 - 4i) = (3 - 1) + (-4 + 4)i$
$$= 2 + 0i$$
$$= 2$$

33. $(7 - 4i) - (3 + i) = (7 - 3) + (-4 - 1)i$
$$= 4 - 5i$$

34. $(3 + 4i)(3 - 4i) = 3^2 - (4i)^2$
$$= 9 - 16(i)^2$$
$$= 9 - 16(-1)$$
$$= 9 + 16$$
$$= 25$$

35. $(1 - 4i)(2 + i) = (2 + 4) + (-8 + 1)i$
$$= 6 - 7i$$

36. $(6 - 2i)(1 + i) = 6 + 6i - 2i - 2i^2$
$$= 6 + 4i - 2(-1)$$
$$= 6 + 4i + 2$$
$$= 8 + 4i$$

37. $(-3 - i)(2 - 2i) = -6 + 6i - 2i + 2(i^2)$
$$= -6 + 4i + 2(-1)$$
$$= -6 + 4i - 2$$
$$= -8 + 4i$$

38. $\dfrac{4i}{3 + i} = \dfrac{4i(3 - i)}{(3 + i)(3 - i)}$
$$= \dfrac{12i - 4i^2}{3^2 - i^2}$$
$$= \dfrac{12i - 4(-1)}{9 - (-1)}$$
$$= \dfrac{12i + 4}{9 + 1}$$
$$= \dfrac{2(6i + 2)}{10}$$
$$= \dfrac{6i + 2}{5}$$
$$= \dfrac{2}{5} + \dfrac{6}{5}i$$

39. $\dfrac{4}{5 + 3i} = \dfrac{4(5 - 3i)}{(5 + 3i)(5 - 3i)}$
$$= \dfrac{4(5 - 3i)}{5^2 - 3^2 \cdot i^2}$$
$$= \dfrac{4(5 - 3i)}{25 - 9(-1)}$$
$$= \dfrac{4(5 - 3i)}{34}$$
$$= \dfrac{2(5 - 3i)}{17}$$
$$= \dfrac{10 - 6i}{17}$$
$$= \dfrac{10}{17} - \dfrac{6}{17}i$$

40. $\dfrac{10 + i}{4 - i} = \dfrac{(10 + i)(4 + i)}{(4 - i)(4 + i)}$
$$= \dfrac{40 + 10i + 4i + i^2}{4^2 - i^2}$$
$$= \dfrac{40 + 14i - 1}{16 + 1}$$
$$= \dfrac{39 + 14i}{17}$$
$$= \dfrac{39}{17} + \dfrac{14}{17}i$$

41. $\dfrac{2 - i}{3 - 4i} = \dfrac{(2 - i)(3 + 4i)}{(3 - 4i)(3 + 4i)}$
$$= \dfrac{6 + 8i - 3i - 4i^2}{3^2 - 4^2 i^2}$$
$$= \dfrac{6 + 5i - 4(-1)}{9 - 16(-1)}$$
$$= \dfrac{6 + 5i + 4}{9 + 16}$$
$$= \dfrac{5(2 + i)}{25}$$
$$= \dfrac{2 + i}{5}$$
$$= \dfrac{2}{5} + \dfrac{1}{5}i$$

42. $(-5 + 2i)(6 - i)(4 + 3i)$
$$= (-5 + 2i)(24 + 18i - 4i - 3i^2)$$
$$= (-5 + 2i)(24 + 14i + 3)$$
$$= (-5 + 2i)(27 + 14i)$$
$$= -135 - 70i + 54i + 28i^2$$
$$= -135 - 16i - 28$$
$$= -163 - 16i$$

43. $(2 + i)(1 + 2i)(3 - 4i)$
$$= (2 + i)(3 - 4i + 6i - 8i^2)$$
$$= (2 + i)(3 + 2i + 8)$$
$$= (2 + i)(11 + 2i)$$
$$= 22 + 4i + 11i + 2i^2$$
$$= 22 + 15i - 2$$
$$= 20 + 15i$$

44. $\dfrac{5 - i\sqrt{3}}{5 + i\sqrt{3}} = \dfrac{(5 - i\sqrt{3})(5 - i\sqrt{3})}{(5 + i\sqrt{3})(5 - i\sqrt{3})}$
$$= \dfrac{5^2 - 10i\sqrt{3} + (i\sqrt{3})^2}{5^2 - (i\sqrt{3})^2}$$
$$= \dfrac{25 - 10i\sqrt{3} - 3}{25 + 3}$$
$$= \dfrac{22 - 10i\sqrt{3}}{28}$$
$$= \dfrac{22}{28} - \dfrac{10\sqrt{3}}{28}i$$
$$= \dfrac{11}{14} - \dfrac{5\sqrt{3}}{14}i$$

45. $\dfrac{1 - i\sqrt{2}}{1 + i\sqrt{2}} = \dfrac{(1 - i\sqrt{2})(1 - i\sqrt{2})}{(1 + i\sqrt{2})(1 - i\sqrt{2})}$
$$= \dfrac{1^2 - 2\sqrt{2}i + (i\sqrt{2})^2}{1^2 - (i\sqrt{2})^2}$$
$$= \dfrac{1 - 2\sqrt{2}i - 2}{1 + 2}$$
$$= \dfrac{-1 - 2\sqrt{2}i}{3}$$
$$= -\dfrac{1}{3} - \dfrac{2\sqrt{3}}{3}i$$

46. $(ix^2 - (2 + 3i)x + 2) + [4x^2 + (5 + 2i)x - 4i]$
$$= ix^2 - 2x - 3ix + 2 + 4x^2 + 5x + 2xi - 4i$$
$$= (ix^2 + 4x^2) + (3x - ix) + 2 - 4i$$
$$= (i + 4)x^2 + (3 - i)x + 2 - 4i$$
or $(4x^2 + 3x + 2) + (x^2 - x - 4)i$

47. $[(3 + i)x^2 - ix + 4 + i] - [(-2 + 3i)x^2 + (1 - 2i)x - 3]$
$$= 3x^2 + x^2 i - xi + 4 + i + 2x^2 - 3x^2 i - x + 2xi + 3$$
$$= (5x^2 - x + 7) + (-2x^2 + x + 1)i$$
$$= 5x^2 - 2ix^2 - x + ix + 7 + i$$
$$= (5 - 2i)x^2 + (-1 + i)x + 7 + i$$

48. $5x^2 + 5 = 0$
$$5x^2 = -5$$
$$x^2 = -1$$
$$x = \pm\sqrt{-1}$$
$$x = \pm i$$

49. $4x^2 + 64 = 0$

$\quad\quad 4x^2 = -64$

$\quad\quad\quad x^2 = -16$

$\quad\quad\quad\quad x = \pm\sqrt{-16}$

$\quad\quad\quad\quad x = \pm 4i$

50. $2x^2 + 12 = 0$

$\quad\quad 2x^2 = -12$

$\quad\quad\quad x^2 = -6$

$\quad\quad\quad\quad x = \pm\sqrt{-6}$

$\quad\quad\quad\quad x = \pm i\sqrt{6}$

51. $6x^2 + 72 = 0$

$\quad\quad 6x^2 = -72$

$\quad\quad\quad x^2 = -12$

$\quad\quad\quad\quad x = \pm\sqrt{-4.3}$

$\quad\quad\quad\quad x = \pm 2i\sqrt{3}$

52. $-3x^2 - 9 = 0$

$\quad\quad -3x^2 = 9$

$\quad\quad\quad x^2 = -3$

$\quad\quad\quad\quad x = \pm\sqrt{-3}$

$\quad\quad\quad\quad x = \pm i\sqrt{3}$

53. $-2x^2 - 80 = 0$

$\quad\quad -2x^2 = 80$

$\quad\quad\quad x^2 = -40$

$\quad\quad\quad\quad x = \pm\sqrt{-40}$

$\quad\quad\quad\quad x = \pm 2i\sqrt{10}$

54. $\frac{2}{3}x^2 + 30 = 0$

$\quad\quad \frac{2}{3}x^2 = -30$

$\quad\quad\quad x^2 = -45$

$\quad\quad\quad\quad x = \pm\sqrt{-45}$

$\quad\quad\quad\quad x = \pm 3i\sqrt{5}$

55. $\frac{4}{5}x^2 + 1 = 0$

$\quad\quad \frac{4}{5}x^2 = -1$

$\quad\quad\quad x^2 = -\frac{5}{4}$

$\quad\quad\quad\quad x = \pm\sqrt{\frac{-5}{4}}$

$\quad\quad\quad\quad x = \pm\frac{\sqrt{5}}{2}i$

56. $8 + 15i = 2m + 3ni$

$\quad\quad 2m = 8$

$\quad\quad\quad m = 4$

$\quad\quad 3n = 15$

$\quad\quad\quad n = 5$

57. $(m + 1) + 3ni = 5 - 9i$

$\quad\quad m + 1 = 5$

$\quad\quad\quad\quad m = 4$

$\quad\quad\quad 3n = -9$

$\quad\quad\quad\quad n = -3$

58. $(2m + 5) + (1 - n)i = -2 + 4i$

$\quad\quad 2m + 5 = -2$

$\quad\quad\quad 2m = -7$

$\quad\quad\quad\quad m = -\frac{7}{2}$

$\quad\quad 1 - n = 4$

$\quad\quad\quad\quad n = -3$

59. $(4 + n) + (3m - 7)i = 8 - 2i$

$\quad\quad 4 + n = 8$

$\quad\quad\quad\quad n = 4$

$\quad\quad 3m - 7 = -2$

$\quad\quad\quad 3m = 5$

$\quad\quad\quad\quad m = \frac{5}{3}$

60. $(m + 2n) + (2m - n)i = 5 + 5i$

$\quad\quad m + 2n = 5$

$\quad\quad 2m - n = 5$

Add the first equation to 2 times the second equation.

$\quad m + 2n = 5$

$\quad \underline{4m - 2n = 10}$

$\quad 5m = 15$

$\quad m = 3$

Substitute 3 for m in the first equation.

$\quad 3 + 2n = 5$

$\quad\quad 2n = 2$

$\quad\quad n = 1$

61. $(2m - 3n)i + (m + 4n) = 13 + 7i$

$\quad\quad 2m - 3n = 7$

$\quad\quad m + 4n = 13$

Add the first equation to -2 times the second equation.

$\quad 2m - 3n = 7$

$\quad \underline{-2m - 8n = -26}$

$\quad -11n = -19$

$\quad\quad\quad\quad n = \frac{19}{11}$

Substitute $\frac{19}{11}$ for n in the first equation.

$\quad 2m - 3\left(\frac{19}{11}\right) = 7$

$\quad 2m - \frac{57}{11} = 7$

$\quad\quad 2m = \frac{134}{11}$

$\quad\quad m = \frac{67}{11}$

62. $(3 + 4j) + (2 - 6j) = (3 + 2) + (4 - 6)j$

$\quad\quad\quad\quad\quad\quad\quad\quad = 5 - 2j$

The total impedance is $5 - 2j$ ohms.

63. $(2 + 5j)(4 - j) = 8 - 2j + 20j - 5j^2$

$\quad\quad\quad\quad\quad\quad\quad = 8 + 18j + 5$

$\quad\quad\quad\quad\quad\quad\quad = 13 + 18j$

The voltage is $13 + 18j$ volts.

64. $\frac{14 - 8j}{2 - 3j} = \frac{(14 - 8j)(2 + 3j)}{(2 - 3j)(2 + 3j)}$

$\quad\quad\quad\quad = \frac{28 + 42j - 16j - 24j^2}{2^2 - (3j)^2}$

$\quad\quad\quad\quad = \frac{28 + 26j + 24}{4 + 9}$

$\quad\quad\quad\quad = \frac{52 + 26j}{13}$

$\quad\quad\quad\quad = \frac{13(4 + 2j)}{13}$

$\quad\quad\quad\quad = 4 + 2j$

The current is $4 + 2j$ amps.

65. Case 1: $i > 0$
Multiply each side by i to get $i^2 > 0 \cdot i$ or $-1 > 0$. This is a contradiction.
Case 2: $i < 0$
Since you are assuming i is negative in this case, you must change the inequality symbol when you multiply each side by i. The result is again $i^2 > 0 \cdot i$ or $-1 > 0$, a contradiction.
Since both possible cases result in contradictions, the order relation "$<$" cannot be applied to the complex numbers.

66. Some polynomial equations have complex solutions. Answers should include the following.
- a and c must have the same sign.
- $\pm i$

67. C; $i^2 = -1$
$$\begin{aligned} i^{71} &= i^{70} \cdot i \\ &= (i^2)^{35} \cdot i \\ &= (-1)^{35} \cdot i \\ &= -i \end{aligned}$$

68. C; Let x be the length of a side of the square. Then,
$$\begin{aligned} x^2 &= 16 \\ x &= \sqrt{16} \\ x &= 4 \end{aligned}$$
$$\begin{aligned} \text{Radius of circle} &= \frac{x}{2} \\ &= \frac{\pi}{2} \\ &= 2 \end{aligned}$$
$$\begin{aligned} \text{Area of circle} &= 2 \cdot 2 \cdot \pi \\ &= 4\pi \text{ units} \end{aligned}$$

69. $i^6 = (i^2)^3$
$\quad = (-1)^3$
$\quad = -1$
$i^7 = i^6 \cdot i$
$\quad = (-1)i$
$\quad = -i$
$i^8 = (i^2)^4$
$\quad = (-1)^4$
$\quad = 1$
$i^9 = i^8 \cdot i$
$\quad = (1)i$
$\quad = i$
$i^{10} = (i^2)^5$
$\quad = (-1)^5$
$\quad = -1$
$i^{11} = i^{10} \cdot i$
$\quad = (-1)i$
$\quad = -i$
$i^{12} = (i^2)^6$
$\quad = (-1)^6$
$\quad = 1$
$i^{13} = i^{12} \cdot i$
$\quad = 1 \cdot i$
$\quad = i$
$i^{14} = (i^2)^7$
$\quad = (-1)^7$
$\quad = -1$

70. Examine the remainder when the exponent is divided by 4. If the remainder is 0, the result is 1. If the remainder is 1, the result is i. If the remainder is 2, the result is -1. And if the remainder is 3, the result is $-i$.

Page 275   Maintain Your Skills

71. $\begin{aligned} \sqrt{2x + 1} &= 5 \\ (\sqrt{2x + 1})^2 &= 5^2 \\ 2x + 1 &= 25 \\ 2x &= 24 \\ x &= 12 \end{aligned}$

72. $\begin{aligned} \sqrt[3]{x - 3} + 1 &= 3 \\ \sqrt[3]{x - 3} &= 2 \\ (\sqrt[3]{x - 3})^3 &= 2^3 \\ x - 3 &= 8 \\ x &= 11 \end{aligned}$

73. $\begin{aligned} \sqrt{x + 5} + \sqrt{x} &= 5 \\ \sqrt{x + 5} &= 5 - \sqrt{x} \\ (\sqrt{x + 5})^2 &= (5 - \sqrt{x})^2 \\ x + 5 &= 25 - 10\sqrt{x} + x \\ -20 &= -10\sqrt{x} \\ 2 &= \sqrt{x} \\ 2^2 &= (\sqrt{x})^2 \\ 4 &= x \end{aligned}$

74. $\begin{aligned} x^{-\frac{1}{5}} \cdot x^{\frac{2}{3}} &= x^{-\frac{1}{5} - \frac{2}{3}} \\ &= x^{\frac{7}{15}} \end{aligned}$

75. $\begin{aligned} \left(y^{-\frac{1}{2}}\right)^{-\frac{2}{3}} &= y^{\left(-\frac{1}{2}\right)\left(-\frac{2}{3}\right)} \\ &= y^{\frac{1}{3}} \end{aligned}$

76. $\begin{aligned} a^{-\frac{3}{4}} &= \frac{1}{a^{\frac{3}{4}}} \\ &= \frac{1}{a^{\frac{3}{4}}} \cdot \frac{a^{\frac{1}{4}}}{a^{\frac{1}{4}}} \\ &= \frac{a^{\frac{1}{4}}}{a^{\frac{4}{4}}} \\ &= \frac{a^{\frac{1}{4}}}{a} \end{aligned}$

77. $A(2, 3), B(1, -2), C(-2, 1)$
$\begin{bmatrix} 2 & 1 & -2 \\ 3 & -2 & 1 \end{bmatrix}$

78. Reflection matrix over the x-axis.
$\begin{bmatrix} 1 & 0 \\ 0 & -1 \end{bmatrix}$

79. $(x, y) \rightarrow (x, -y)$
$\begin{bmatrix} 2 & 1 & -2 \\ -3 & 2 & -1 \end{bmatrix}$

80.
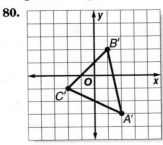

81. x = cost of a sofa
y = cost of a love seat
z = cost of a coffee table
$x + y + z = 2050$
$\qquad x = 2y$
$\quad x + z = 1450$
Add the first equation to -1 times the second equation.

$$
\begin{array}{r}
x + y + z = 2050 \\
(+)\ -x + 2y = 0 \\
\hline
3y + z = 2050 \quad (4)
\end{array}
$$

Add the third equation to -1 times the second equation.

$$
\begin{array}{r}
-x + 2y = 0 \\
(+)\ \ x + z = 1450 \\
\hline
2y + z = 1450 \quad (5)
\end{array}
$$

Add -1 times (5) to (4).

$$
\begin{array}{r}
3y - z = 2050 \\
(+)\ -2y - z = -1450 \\
\hline
y = 600
\end{array}
$$

Substitute 600 for y in the second equation.
$x = 2(600)$
$x = 1200$
Substitute 1200 for x in the third equation.
$1200 + z = 1450$
$\qquad z = 250$
The sofa costs $1200, the love seat costs $600, and the coffee table costs $250.

82. Graph $y = x + 1$ as a dashed boundary line, and $y = -2x - 2$ as a dashed boundary line.
Test point: $(0, 0)$
$0 < 0 + 1$ true
$0 > -2(0) - 2$ true
Shade the area including $(0, 0)$.

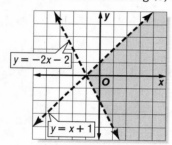

83. Graph $x + y = 1$ and $x - 2y = 4$ are solid boundary lines.
Test point: $(2, 1)$
$\quad 2 + 1 \geq 1$ true
$2 - 2(1) \leq 4$ true
Shade the area including the point $(2, 1)$.

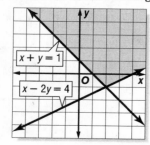

84. $m = \frac{y_2 - y_1}{x_2 - x_1}$
$(-2, 1), (8, 2)$
$m = \frac{2 - 1}{8 - (-2)}$
$ = \frac{1}{8 + 2}$
$ = \frac{1}{10}$

85. $m = \frac{y_2 - y_1}{x_2 - x_1}$
$(4, -3), (5, -3)$
$m = \frac{-3 - (-3)}{5 - 4}$
$ = \frac{-3 + 3}{1}$
$ = \frac{0}{1}$
$ = 0$

Chapter 5   Study Guide and Review

Page 276   Vocabulary and Concept Check
1. scientific notation
2. synthetic division
3. FOIL method
4. monomial
5. extraneous solution
6. Complex conjugates
7. square root
8. trinomial
9. principal root
10. imaginary unit

Pages 276–280   Lesson-by-Lesson Review
11. $f^{-7} \cdot f^4 = f^{-7 + 4}$
$\phantom{f^{-7} \cdot f^4} = f^{-3}$
$\phantom{f^{-7} \cdot f^4} = \frac{1}{f^3}$

12. $(3x^2)^3 = 3^3 \cdot (x^2)^3$
$ = 3^3(x^{2 \cdot 3})$
$ = 27x^6$

13. $(2y)(4xy^3) = 2 \cdot 4 \cdot xy^{1 + 3}$
$ = 8xy^4$

14. $\left(\frac{3}{5}c^2f\right)\left(\frac{4}{3}cd\right)^2 = \frac{3}{5}c^2f \cdot \frac{16}{9}c^2d^2$
$\phantom{\left(\frac{3}{5}c^2f\right)\left(\frac{4}{3}cd\right)^2} = \frac{3 \cdot 16}{5 \cdot 9} \cdot c^{2 + 2} \cdot f^1 \cdot d^2$
$\phantom{\left(\frac{3}{5}c^2f\right)\left(\frac{4}{3}cd\right)^2} = \frac{16}{15}c^4fd^2$

15. $(2000)(85,000) = (2 \times 10^3)(8.5 \times 10^4)$
$ = 2 \cdot 8.5 \times 10^{3 + 4}$
$ = 17 \times 10^7$
$ = 1.7 \times 10^8$

16. $(0.0014)^2 = (1.4 \times 10^{-3})^2$
$ = (1.4)^2 \times (10^{-3})^2$
$ = 1.96 \times 10^{-6}$

17. $\frac{5,400,000}{6000} = \frac{5.4 \times 10^6}{6 \times 10^3}$
$\phantom{\frac{5,400,000}{6000}} = \frac{5.4}{6} \times 10^{6 - 3}$
$\phantom{\frac{5,400,000}{6000}} = 0.9 \times 10^3$
$\phantom{\frac{5,400,000}{6000}} = 9 \times 10^2$

18. $(4c - 5) - (c + 11) + (-6c + 17)$
$= 4c - 5 - c - 11 - 6c + 17$
$= (4c - c - 6c) + (-5 - 11 + 17)$
$= -3c + 1$

19. $(11x^2 + 13x - 15) - (7x^2 - 9x + 19)$
$= 11x^2 + 13x - 15 - 7x^2 + 9x - 19$
$= (11x^2 - 7x^2) + (13x + 9x) + (-15 - 19)$
$= 4x^2 + 22x - 34$

20. $-6m^2(3mn + 13m - 5n)$
$= -6m^2(3mn) - 6m^2(13m) - 6m^2(-5n)$
$= -18m^3n - 78m^3 + 30m^2n$

21. $x^{-8}y^{10}(x^{11}y^{-9} + x^{10}y^{-6})$
$= x^{-8}y^{10}(x^{11}y^{-9}) + x^{-8}y^{10}(x^{10}y^{-6})$
$= x^3y + x^2y^4$

22. $(d - 5)(d + 3) = d^2 + 3d - 5d - 5 \cdot 3$
$= d^2 - 2d - 15$

23. $(2a^2 + 6)^2 = (2a^2)^2 + 2(2a^2)(6) + 6^2$
$= 4a^4 + 24a^2 + 36$

24. $(2b - 3c)^3$
$= (2b)^3 + 3(2b)^2(-3c) + 3(2b)(-3c)^2 + (-3c)^3$
$= 8b^3 - 36b^2c + 54bc^2 - 27c^3$

25.

$$
\begin{array}{r|rrrrr}
3 & 2 & -6 & 1 & -3 & -3 \\
  &   & 6 & 0 & 3 & 0 \\
\hline
  & 2 & 0 & 1 & 0 & -3 \\
\end{array}
$$

$(2x^4 - 6x^3 + x^2 - 3x - 3) \div (x - 3)$
$= 2x^3 + x - \dfrac{3}{x - 3}$

26.

$$
\begin{array}{r|rrrrr}
-1 & 10 & 5 & 4 & 0 & -9 \\
   &   & -10 & 5 & -9 & 9 \\
\hline
   & 10 & -5 & 9 & -9 & 0 \\
\end{array}
$$

$(10x^4 + 5x^3 + 4x^2 - 9) \div (x + 1)$
$= 10x^3 - 5x^2 + 9x - 9$

27.

$$
\begin{array}{r|rrr}
1 & 1 & -5 & +4 \\
  &   & 1 & -4 \\
\hline
  & 1 & 4 & 0 \\
\end{array}
$$

$(x^2 - 5x + 4) \div (x - 1) = x - 4$

28. $(5x^4 + 18x^3 + 10x^2 + 3x) \div (x^2 + 3x)$
$= x(5x^3 + 18x^2 + 10x + 3) \div x(x + 3)$
$= (5x^3 + 18x^2 + 10x + 3) \div (x + 3)$

$$
\begin{array}{r|rrrr}
-3 & 5 & 18 & 10 & 3 \\
   &   & -15 & -9 & -3 \\
\hline
   & 5 & 3 & 1 & 0 \\
\end{array}
$$

$(5x^4 + 18x^3 + 10x^2 + 3x) \div (x^2 + 3x)$
$= 5x^2 + 3x + 1$

29. $200x^2 - 50 = 50 \cdot 4x^2 + 50 \cdot (-1)$
$= 50(4x^2 - 1)$
$= 50(2x - 1)(2x + 1)$

30. $10a^3 - 20a^2 - 2a + 4$
$= 2(5a^3 - 10a^2 - a + 2)$
$= 2[(5a^3 - 10a^2) + (-a + 2)]$
$= 2[5a^2(a - 2) - 1(a - 2)]$
$= 2(a - 2)(5a^2 - 1)$

31. $5w^3 - 20w^2 + 3w - 12$
$= (5w^3 - 20w^2) + (3w - 12)$
$= 5w^2(w - 4) + 3(w - 4)$
$= (w - 4)(5w^2 + 3)$

32. $x^4 - 7x^3 + 12x^2$
$= x^2(x^2 - 7x + 12)$
$= x^2(x^2 - 4x - 3x + 12)$
$= x^2[x(x - 4) - 3(x - 4)]$
$= x^2(x - 3)(x - 4)$

33. $s^3 + 512 = s^3 + 8^3$
$= (s - 8)(s^2 + 8s + 8^2)$
$= (s - 8)(s^2 + 8s + 64)$

34. $x^2 - 7x + 5$ is prime

35. $\pm\sqrt{256} = \pm\sqrt{16^2}$
$= \pm 16$

36. $\sqrt[3]{-216} = \sqrt[3]{(-6)^3}$
$= -6$

37. $\sqrt{(-8)^2} = |-8|$
$= 8$

38. $\sqrt[5]{c^5d^{15}} = \sqrt[5]{c^5(d^3)^5}$
$= \sqrt[5]{(cd^3)^5}$
$= cd^3$

39. $\sqrt{(x^4 - 3)^2} = |x^4 - 3|$

40. $\sqrt[3]{(512 + x^2)^3} = 512 + x^2$

41. $\sqrt[4]{16m^8} = \sqrt[4]{2^4(m^2)^4}$
$= \sqrt[4]{(2m^2)^4}$
$= 2m^2$

42. $\sqrt{a^2 - 10a + 25} = \sqrt{(a - 5)^2}$
$= |a - 5|$

43. $\sqrt[6]{128} = \sqrt[6]{2^6 \cdot 2}$
$= \sqrt[6]{2^6} \cdot \sqrt[6]{2}$
$= 2\sqrt[6]{2}$

44. $\sqrt{5} + \sqrt{20} = \sqrt{5} + \sqrt{2^2 \cdot 5}$
$= \sqrt{5} + \sqrt{2^2} \cdot \sqrt{5}$
$= \sqrt{5} + 2\sqrt{5}$
$= 3\sqrt{5}$

45. $5\sqrt{12} - 3\sqrt{75} = 5\sqrt{2^2 \cdot 3} - 3\sqrt{5^2 \cdot 3}$
$= 5 \cdot \sqrt{2^2} \cdot \sqrt{3} - 3 \cdot \sqrt{5^2} \cdot \sqrt{3}$
$= 5 \cdot 2\sqrt{3} - 3 \cdot 5\sqrt{3}$
$= 10\sqrt{3} - 15\sqrt{3}$
$= -5\sqrt{3}$

46. $6\sqrt[5]{11} - 8\sqrt[5]{11} = (6 - 8)\sqrt[5]{11}$
$= -2\sqrt[5]{11}$

47. $(\sqrt{8} + \sqrt{12})^2 = (\sqrt{8})^2 + 2(\sqrt{8})(\sqrt{12}) + (\sqrt{12})^2$
$= 8 + 2\sqrt{8 \cdot 12} + 12$
$= 20 + 2\sqrt{4^2 \cdot 6}$
$= 20 + 2 \cdot \sqrt{4^2} \cdot \sqrt{6}$
$= 20 + 2 \cdot 4 \cdot \sqrt{6}$
$= 20 + 8\sqrt{6}$

48. $\sqrt{8} \cdot \sqrt{15} \cdot \sqrt{21} = \sqrt{8 \cdot 15 \cdot 21}$
$= \sqrt{4 \cdot 2 \cdot 3 \cdot 5 \cdot 7 \cdot 3}$
$= \sqrt{2^2 \cdot 2 \cdot 3^2 \cdot 5 \cdot 7}$
$= \sqrt{2^2} \cdot \sqrt{3^2} \cdot \sqrt{2 \cdot 5 \cdot 7}$
$= 2 \cdot 3\sqrt{2 \cdot 5 \cdot 7}$
$= 6\sqrt{70}$

49. $\dfrac{\sqrt{243}}{\sqrt{3}} = \sqrt{\dfrac{243}{3}}$

$= \sqrt{81}$

$= \sqrt{9^2}$

$= 9$

50. $\dfrac{1}{3 + \sqrt{5}} = \dfrac{3 - \sqrt{5}}{(3 + \sqrt{5})(3 - \sqrt{5})}$

$= \dfrac{3 - \sqrt{5}}{3^2 - (\sqrt{5})^2}$

$= \dfrac{3 - \sqrt{5}}{9 - 5}$

$= \dfrac{3 - \sqrt{5}}{4}$

51. $\dfrac{\sqrt{10}}{4 + \sqrt{2}} = \dfrac{\sqrt{10}(4 - \sqrt{2})}{(4 + \sqrt{2})(4 - \sqrt{2})}$

$= \dfrac{4\sqrt{10} - (\sqrt{10})(\sqrt{2})}{4^2 - (\sqrt{2})^2}$

$= \dfrac{4\sqrt{10} - \sqrt{10 \cdot 2}}{16 - 2}$

$= \dfrac{4\sqrt{10} - \sqrt{2^2 \cdot 5}}{14}$

$= \dfrac{4\sqrt{10} - 2\sqrt{5}}{14}$

$= \dfrac{2(2\sqrt{10} - \sqrt{5})}{14}$

$= \dfrac{2\sqrt{10} - \sqrt{5}}{7}$

52. $27^{-\frac{2}{3}} = (3^3)^{-\frac{2}{3}}$

$= 3^{(3)\left(-\frac{2}{3}\right)}$

$= 3^{-2}$

$= \dfrac{1}{3^2}$

$= \dfrac{1}{9}$

53. $9^{\frac{1}{3}} \cdot 9^{\frac{5}{3}} = 9^{\frac{1}{3} + \frac{5}{3}}$

$= 9^2$

$= 81$

54. $\left(\dfrac{8}{27}\right)^{-\frac{2}{3}} = \left(\dfrac{2^3}{3^3}\right)^{-\frac{2}{3}}$

$= \left[\left(\dfrac{2}{3}\right)^3\right]^{-\frac{2}{3}}$

$= \left(\dfrac{2}{3}\right)^{3\left(-\frac{2}{3}\right)}$

$= \left(\dfrac{2}{3}\right)^{-2}$

$= \left(\dfrac{3}{2}\right)^2$

$= \dfrac{9}{4}$

55. $\dfrac{1}{y^{\frac{2}{5}}} = \dfrac{1}{y^{\frac{2}{5}}} \cdot \dfrac{y^{\frac{3}{5}}}{y^{\frac{3}{5}}}$

$= \dfrac{y^{\frac{3}{5}}}{y^{\frac{5}{5}}}$

$= \dfrac{y^{\frac{3}{5}}}{y}$

56. $\dfrac{xy}{\sqrt[3]{z}} = \dfrac{xy}{z^{\frac{1}{3}}}$

$= \dfrac{xyz^{\frac{2}{3}}}{z^{\frac{1}{3}} \cdot z^{\frac{2}{3}}}$

$= \dfrac{xyz^{\frac{2}{3}}}{z}$

57. $\dfrac{3x + 4x^2}{x^{-\frac{2}{3}}} = x^{\frac{2}{3}}(3x + 4x^2)$

$= 3x^{\frac{2}{3} + 1} + 4x^{\frac{2}{3} + 2}$

$= 3x^{\frac{5}{3}} + 4x^{\frac{8}{3}}$

58. $\sqrt{x} = 6$

$(\sqrt{x})^2 = 6^2$

$x = 36$

59. $y^{\frac{1}{3}} - 7 = 0$

$y^{\frac{1}{3}} = 7$

$\left(y^{\frac{1}{3}}\right)^3 = 7^3$

$y = 343$

60. $(x - 2)^{\frac{3}{2}} = -8$

$[(x - 2)^3]^{\frac{1}{2}} = -8$

$\sqrt{(x - 2)^3} = -8$

The square root of a real number cannot be negative. There is no solution.

61. $\sqrt{x + 5} - 3 = 0$

$\sqrt{x + 5} = 3$

$(\sqrt{x + 5})^2 = 3^2$

$x + 5 = 9$

$x = 4$

62. $\sqrt{3t - 5} - 3 = 4$

$\sqrt{3t - 5} = 7$

$(\sqrt{3t - 5})^2 = 7^2$

$3t - 5 = 49$

$3t = 54$

$t = 18$

63. $\sqrt{2x - 1} = 3$

$(\sqrt{2x - 1})^2 = 3^2$

$2x - 1 = 9$

$2x = 10$

$x = 5$

64. $\sqrt[4]{2x - 1} = 2$

$(\sqrt[4]{2x - 1})^4 = 2^4$

$2x - 1 = 16$

$2x = 17$

$x = 8.5$

65. $\sqrt{y + 5} = \sqrt{2y - 3}$

$(\sqrt{y + 5})^2 = (\sqrt{2y - 3})^2$

$y + 5 = 2y - 3$

$y = 8$

66. $\sqrt{y + 1} + \sqrt{y - 4} = 5$

$\sqrt{y + 1} = 5 - \sqrt{y - 4}$

$(\sqrt{y + 1})^2 = (5 - \sqrt{y - 4})^2$

$y + 1 = 5^2 - 2 \cdot 5\sqrt{y - 4} + (\sqrt{y - 4})^2$

$y + 1 = 25 - 10\sqrt{y - 4} + y - 4$

$-20 = -10\sqrt{y - 4}$

$2 = \sqrt{y - 4}$

$2^2 = (\sqrt{y - 4})^2$

$4 = y - 4$

$8 = y$

67. $\sqrt{-64m^{12}} = \sqrt{-1 \cdot 8^2 \cdot (m^6)^2}$

$= \sqrt{-1} \cdot \sqrt{8^2} \cdot \sqrt{(m^6)^2}$

$= 8m^6 i$

68. $(7 - 4i) - (-3 + 6i) = 7 - 4i + 3 - 6i$

$= (7 + 3) + (-4 - 6)i$

$= 10 - 10i$

69. $-6\sqrt{-9} \cdot 2\sqrt{-4} = -6i\sqrt{9} \cdot 2i\sqrt{4}$

$= (-6i)(2i)\sqrt{9 \cdot 4}$

$= -12i^2\sqrt{6^2}$

$= -12(-1)(6)$

$= 72$

70. $i^6 = (i^2)^3$
$= (-1)^3$
$= -1$

71. $(3 + 4i)(5 - 2i) = 15 - 6i + 20i - 8i^2$
$= 15 + 14i - 8(-1)$
$= 15 + 14i + 8$
$= 23 + 14i$

72. $(\sqrt{6} + i)(\sqrt{6} - i) = (\sqrt{6})^2 - i^2$
$= 6 - (-1)$
$= 6 + 1$
$= 7$

73. $\dfrac{1 + i}{1 - i} = \dfrac{(1 + i)(1 + i)}{(1 - i)(1 + i)}$
$= \dfrac{1^2 + 2 \cdot 1 \cdot i + i^2}{1^2 - i^2}$
$= \dfrac{1 + 2i - 1}{1 - (-1)}$
$= \dfrac{2i}{2}$
$= i$

74. $\dfrac{4 - 3i}{1 + 2i} = \dfrac{(4 - 3i)(1 - 2i)}{(1 + 2i)(1 - 2i)}$
$= \dfrac{4 - 8i - 3i + 6i^2}{1^2 - (2i)^2}$
$= \dfrac{4 - 11i + 6(-1)}{1 - 4(-1)}$
$= \dfrac{4 - 11i - 6}{1 + 4}$
$= \dfrac{-2 - 11i}{5}$
$= -\dfrac{2}{5} - \dfrac{11}{5}i$

75. $\dfrac{3 - 9i}{4 + 2i} = \dfrac{(3 - 9i)(4 - 2i)}{(4 + 2i)(4 - 2i)}$
$= \dfrac{12 - 6i - 36i + 18i^2}{4^2 - (2i)^2}$
$= \dfrac{12 - 42i + 18(-1)}{4^2 - 4(-1)}$
$= \dfrac{12 - 42i - 18}{16 + 4}$
$= \dfrac{-6 - 42i}{20}$
$= \dfrac{2(-3 - 21i)}{20}$
$= \dfrac{-3 - 21i}{10}$
$= -\dfrac{3}{10} - \dfrac{21}{10}i$

Chapter 5 Practice Test

Page 281

1. c; coefficient

2. a; degree

3. b; constant term

4. $(5b)^4(6c)^2 = 5^4 \cdot b^4 \cdot 6^2 \cdot c^2$
$= 625 \cdot b^4 \cdot 36 \cdot c^2$
$= 22{,}500b^4c^2$

5. $(13x - 1)(x + 3) = 13x^2 + 13x \cdot 3 - x - 1 \cdot 3$
$= 13x^2 + 39x - x - 3$
$= 13x^2 + 38x - 3$

6. $(2h - 6)^3$
$= (2h)^3 + 3(2h)^2(-6) + 3(2h)(-6)^2 + (-6)^3$
$= 8h^3 - 18(4h^2) + 6h(36) + (-216)$
$= 8h^3 - 72h^2 + 216h - 216$

7. $(3.16 \times 10^3)(24 \times 10^2)$
$= (3.16 \times 24) \times 10^3 \times 10^2$
$= 75.84 \times 10^5$
$= 7.584 \times 10 \times 10^5$
$= 7.584 \times 10^6$

8. $\dfrac{7{,}200{,}000 \cdot 0.0011}{0.018} = \dfrac{7.2 \times 10^6 \cdot 1.1 \times 10^{-3}}{1.8 \times 10^{-2}}$
$= \dfrac{7.2 \cdot 1.1}{1.8} \times 10^{6 - 3 - (-2)}$
$= 4.4 \times 10^5$

9.

$$
\begin{array}{r|rrrrr}
2 & 1 & -1 & -10 & 4 & 24 \\
  &   & 2 & 2 & -16 & -24 \\
\hline
  & 1 & 1 & -8 & -12 & \;0 \\
\end{array}
$$

$(x^4 - x^3 - 10x^2 + 4x + 24) \div (x - 2)$
$= x^3 + x^2 - 8x - 12$

10.

$$
\begin{array}{r|rrrr}
-2 & 2 & 9 & -2 & 7 \\
   &   & -4 & -10 & 24 \\
\hline
   & 2 & 5 & -12 & \;31 \\
\end{array}
$$

$(2x^3 + 9x^2 - 2x + 7) \div (x + 2)$
$= 2x^2 + 5x - 12 + \dfrac{31}{x + 2}$

11. $x^2 - 14x + 45 = x^2 - 5x - 9x + 45$
$= x(x - 5) - 9(x - 5)$
$= (x - 5)(x - 9)$

12. $2r^2 + 3pr - 2p^2 = 2r^2 + 4pr - pr - 2p^2$
$= (2r^2 + 4pr) + (-pr - 2p^2)$
$= 2r(r + 2p) - p(r + 2p)$
$= (r + 2p)(2r - p)$

13. $x^2 + 2\sqrt{3}x + 3 = x^2 + 2\sqrt{3} + (\sqrt{3})^2$
$= (x + \sqrt{3})^2$

14. $\sqrt{175} = \sqrt{5^2 \cdot 7}$
$= \sqrt{5^2} \cdot \sqrt{7}$
$= 5\sqrt{7}$

15. $(5 + \sqrt{3})(7 - 2\sqrt{3})$
$= 35 - 10\sqrt{3} + 7\sqrt{3} - 2(\sqrt{3})^2$
$= 35 - 3\sqrt{3} - 2 \cdot 3$
$= 35 - 3\sqrt{3} - 6$
$= 29 - 3\sqrt{3}$

16. $3\sqrt{6} + 5\sqrt{54} = 3\sqrt{6} + 5\sqrt{3^2 \cdot 6}$
$= 3\sqrt{6} + 5 \cdot \sqrt{3^2} \cdot \sqrt{6}$
$= 3\sqrt{6} + 5 \cdot 3\sqrt{6}$
$= 3\sqrt{6} + 15\sqrt{6}$
$= 18\sqrt{6}$

17. $\dfrac{9}{5 - \sqrt{3}} = \dfrac{9 \cdot (5 + \sqrt{3})}{(5 - \sqrt{3})(5 + \sqrt{3})}$
$= \dfrac{45 + 9\sqrt{3}}{5^2 - (\sqrt{3})^2}$
$= \dfrac{45 + 9\sqrt{3}}{25 - 3}$
$= \dfrac{45 + 9\sqrt{3}}{22}$

18. $\left(9^{\frac{1}{2}} \cdot 9^{\frac{2}{3}}\right)^{\frac{1}{6}} = 9^{\frac{1}{2} \cdot \frac{1}{6}} \cdot 9^{\frac{2}{3} \cdot \frac{1}{6}}$
$= (3^2)^{\frac{1}{12}} \cdot (3^2)^{\frac{1}{9}}$
$= 3^{\frac{2}{12}} \cdot 3^{\frac{2}{9}}$
$= 3^{\frac{1}{6}} \cdot 3^{\frac{2}{9}}$
$= 3^{\frac{1}{6} + \frac{2}{9}}$
$= 3^{\frac{7}{18}}$

19. $11^{\frac{1}{2}} \cdot 11^{\frac{7}{3}} \cdot 11^{\frac{1}{6}} = 11^{\frac{1}{2} + \frac{7}{3} + \frac{1}{6}}$

$\qquad\qquad\qquad\quad = 11^{\frac{18}{6}}$

$\qquad\qquad\qquad\quad = 11^3$

$\qquad\qquad\qquad\quad = 1331$

20. $\sqrt[6]{256s^{11}t^{18}} = \sqrt[6]{2^6 \cdot 4 \cdot s^6 \cdot s^5 \cdot (t^3)^6}$

$\qquad\qquad\quad = \sqrt[6]{2^6} \cdot \sqrt[6]{4} \cdot \sqrt[6]{s^6} \cdot \sqrt[6]{s^5} \cdot \sqrt[6]{(t^3)^6}$

$\qquad\qquad\quad = 2s\,|t^3|\,\sqrt[6]{4s^5}$

21. $v^{-\frac{7}{11}} = \dfrac{1}{v^{\frac{7}{11}}}$

$\qquad\quad = \dfrac{1}{v^{\frac{7}{11}}} \cdot \dfrac{v^{\frac{4}{11}}}{v^{\frac{4}{11}}}$

$\qquad\quad = \dfrac{v^{\frac{4}{11}}}{v^{\frac{11}{11}}}$

$\qquad\quad = \dfrac{v^{\frac{4}{11}}}{v}$

22. $\dfrac{b^{\frac{1}{2}}}{b^{\frac{3}{2}} - b^{\frac{1}{2}}} = \dfrac{b^{\frac{1}{2}}\left(b^{\frac{3}{2}} + b^{\frac{1}{2}}\right)}{\left(b^{\frac{3}{2}} - b^{\frac{1}{2}}\right)\left(b^{\frac{3}{2}} + b^{\frac{1}{2}}\right)}$

$\qquad\qquad = \dfrac{b^{\frac{1}{2}} \cdot b^{\frac{3}{2}} + b^{\frac{1}{2}} \cdot b^{\frac{1}{2}}}{\left(b^{\frac{3}{2}}\right)^2 - \left(b^{\frac{1}{2}}\right)^2}$

$\qquad\qquad = \dfrac{b^{\frac{1}{2} + \frac{3}{2}} + b^{\frac{1}{2} + \frac{1}{2}}}{b^{\frac{3}{2} \cdot 2} - b^{\frac{1}{2} \cdot 2}}$

$\qquad\qquad = \dfrac{b^2 + b}{b^3 - b}$

$\qquad\qquad = \dfrac{b(b + 1)}{b(b - 1)(b + 1)}$

$\qquad\qquad = \dfrac{1}{b - 1}$

23. $\sqrt{b + 15} = \sqrt{3b + 1}$

$\qquad \left(\sqrt{b + 15}\right)^2 = \left(\sqrt{3b + 1}\right)^2$

$\qquad\quad b + 15 = 3b + 1$

$\qquad\qquad\quad 14 = 2b$

$\qquad\qquad\quad\; 7 = b$

24. $\sqrt{2x} = \sqrt{x - 4}$

$\qquad \left(\sqrt{2x}\right)^2 = \left(\sqrt{x - 4}\right)^2$

$\qquad\quad 2x = x - 4$

$\qquad\quad\; x = -4$

But, $x = -4$ is an extraneous solution, so there is no solution.

25. $\sqrt[4]{y + 2} + 9 = 14$

$\qquad\quad \sqrt[4]{y + 2} = 5$

$\qquad \left(\sqrt[4]{y + 2}\right)^4 = 5^4$

$\qquad\quad y + 2 = 625$

$\qquad\qquad\; y = 623$

26. $\sqrt[3]{2w - 1} + 11 = 18$

$\qquad\quad \sqrt[3]{2w - 1} = 7$

$\qquad \left(\sqrt[3]{2w-1}\right)^3 = 7^3$

$\qquad\quad 2w - 1 = 343$

$\qquad\qquad 2w = 344$

$\qquad\qquad\; w = 172$

27. $\sqrt{4x + 28} = \sqrt{6x + 38}$

$\qquad \left(\sqrt{4x + 28}\right)^2 = \left(\sqrt{6x + 38}\right)^2$

$\qquad\quad 4x + 28 = 6x + 38$

$\qquad\qquad -10 = 2x$

$\qquad\qquad\;\; -5 = x$

28. $1 + \sqrt{x + 5} = \sqrt{x + 12}$

$\qquad \left(1 + \sqrt{x + 5}\right)^2 = \left(\sqrt{x + 12}\right)^2$

$1^2 + 2 \cdot 1 \cdot \sqrt{x + 5} + \left(\sqrt{x + 5}\right)^2 = x + 12$

$\qquad 1 + 2\sqrt{x+5} + x + 5 = x + 12$

$\qquad\qquad\quad 2\sqrt{x + 5} = 6$

$\qquad\qquad\qquad \sqrt{x + 5} = 3$

$\qquad\qquad\; \left(\sqrt{x + 5}\right)^2 = 3^2$

$\qquad\qquad\qquad\; x + 5 = 9$

$\qquad\qquad\qquad\qquad x = 4$

29. $(5 - 2i) - (8 - 11i) = 5 - 2i - 8 + 11i$

$\qquad\qquad\qquad\qquad = (5 - 8) + (-2 + 11)i$

$\qquad\qquad\qquad\qquad = -3 + 9i$

30. $(14 - 5i)^2 = 14^2 - 2 \cdot 14 \cdot 5i + (5i)^2$

$\qquad\qquad\quad = 196 - 140i + 25i^2$

$\qquad\qquad\quad = 196 - 140i + 25(-1)$

$\qquad\qquad\quad = 196 - 140i - 25$

$\qquad\qquad\quad = 171 - 140i$

31. $t = \sqrt{\dfrac{d}{16}}$

$\quad\; 11 = \sqrt{\dfrac{d}{16}}$

$\quad\; 11^2 = \left(\sqrt{\dfrac{d}{16}}\right)^2$

$\quad 121 = \dfrac{d}{16}$

$\qquad d = 1936$

The parachutist will fall 1936 ft during this time period.

32. $s = \frac{1}{2}(a + b + c)$

$\quad s = \frac{1}{2}(6 + 9 + 12)$

$\quad s = \frac{1}{2}(27)$

$\quad s = \frac{27}{2}$

$\quad A = \sqrt{s(s - a)(s - b)(s - c)}$

$\quad A = \sqrt{\dfrac{27}{2}\left(\dfrac{27}{2} - 6\right)\left(\dfrac{27}{2} - 9\right)\left(\dfrac{27}{2} - 12\right)}$

$\qquad = \sqrt{\dfrac{27}{2}\left(\dfrac{27 - 12}{2}\right)\left(\dfrac{27 - 18}{2}\right)\left(\dfrac{27 - 24}{2}\right)}$

$\qquad = \sqrt{\dfrac{27}{2} \cdot \dfrac{15}{2} \cdot \dfrac{9}{2} \cdot \dfrac{3}{2}}$

$\qquad = \sqrt{\dfrac{27 \cdot 15 \cdot 9 \cdot 3}{2 \cdot 2 \cdot 2 \cdot 2}}$

$\qquad = \sqrt{\dfrac{(3^3)^2 \cdot 15}{(2^2)^2}}$

$\qquad = \dfrac{\sqrt{(3^3)^2 \cdot \sqrt{15}}}{\sqrt{(2^2)^2}}$

$\qquad = \dfrac{3^3\sqrt{15}}{2^2}$

$\qquad = \dfrac{27\sqrt{15}}{4}$

The area is $\dfrac{27\sqrt{15}}{4}$ ft^2.

33. D; $2 + \left(x + \dfrac{1}{x}\right)^2 = 2 + x^2 + 2 \cdot x \cdot \dfrac{1}{x} + \left(\dfrac{1}{x}\right)^2$

$\qquad\qquad\qquad\quad = 2 + x^2 + 2 + \dfrac{1}{x^2}$

$\qquad\qquad\qquad\quad = x^2 + \dfrac{1}{x^2} + 4$

Chapter 5 Standardized Test Practice

Pages 282–283

1. B; $x^3 = 30$

$\sqrt[3]{x^3} = \sqrt[3]{30}$ $3^3 = 27$

    $x = 3.11$ $4^3 = 64$

 $3 < x < 4$ $27 < 30 < 64$

2. C; $12x + 7y = 19$

     $4x - y = 3$

Multiply the second equation by -1 and add the result to the first equation.

$12x + 7y = 19$

$\underline{-4x + y = -3}$

$8x + 8y = 16$

3. B; $\boxed{8} = 8 - 1$

           $= 7$

    $\boxed{13} = \frac{1}{2}(13 + 1)$

          $= \frac{1}{2} \cdot 14$

          $= 7$

$\boxed{8} \times \boxed{13} = 7 \times 7$

              $= 49$

4. D; $x \circledast y = xy - y$

    $x \circledast y = 0$

    $xy - y = 0$

        $xy = y$

        $\frac{xy}{y} = \frac{y}{y}$

         $x = 1$

5. D; $x = $ unknown number

        $x + \sqrt{x} = 3x$

 $x + \sqrt{x} - x = 3x - x$

          $\sqrt{x} = 2x$

     $(\sqrt{x})^2 = (2x)^2$

           $x = 4x^2$

     $x - x = 4x^2 - x$

   $4x^2 - x = 0$

  $x(4x - 1) = 0$

        $x = 0$ or $4x - 1 = 0$

                                  $x = \frac{1}{4}$

6. C; $AC = 2AD$

         $AC = 2(8)$

            $= 16$

 $(AC)^2 = (AD)^2 + (CD)^2$

    $16^2 = 8^2 + (CD)^2$

    $256 = 64 + (CD)^2$

$256 - 64 = 64 + (CD)^2 - 64$

    $192 = (CD)^2$

 $\sqrt{192} = \sqrt{(CD)^2}$

     $CD = \sqrt{8^2 \cdot 3}$

          $= \sqrt{8^2} \cdot \sqrt{3}$

          $= 8\sqrt{3}$

     $CD = 8\sqrt{3}$ units

7. D; Let $x = $ first of the two consecutive integers.

$x + 1 = $ the second of the two consecutive integers.

   $x + (x + 1) = s$

       $2x + 1 = s$

       $2x + 2 = s + 1$

   $2(x + 1) = s + 1$

   $\frac{2(x + 1)}{2} = \frac{s + 1}{2}$

      $x + 1 = \frac{s + 1}{2}$

8. C; $x = $ scores by Latha

     $y = $ scores by Renee

     $z = $ scores by Cindy

$x + y + z = 30$

        $x = 3y$

  $x + z = 4y$

Add the first equation to -1 times the second equation.

      $x + y + z = 30$

$(+) \underline{-x + 3y = 0}$

           $4y + z = 30$ (4)

Multiply the second equation by -1 and add to the third equation.

     $-x + 3y = 0$

$(+) \underline{x - 4y + z = 0}$

          $-y + z = 0$ (5)

Add (4) to -1 times (5).

    $4y + z = 30$

$(+) \underline{y - z = 0}$

   $5y = 30$

    $y = 6$

Substitute 6 for y in the second equation.

$x = 3(6)$

$x = 18$

9. D; $s = t + 1$

        $s^2 = (t + 1)^2$

        $s^2 = t^2 + 2t + 1$

 $s^2 - t^2 = t^2 + 2t + 1 - t^2$

 $s^2 - t^2 = 2t + 1$

          $= (t + 1) + t$

          $= s + t$

10. $3 \clubsuit 4 = 3 + \frac{1}{4}$

        $= \frac{12 + 1}{4}$

        $= \frac{13}{4}$ or 3.25

11. $3x^2 = 27$

     $\frac{3x^2}{3} = \frac{27}{3}$

      $x^2 = 9$

  $(x^2)^2 = 9^2$

      $x^4 = 81$

 $3 \cdot x^4 = 3 \cdot 81$

   $3x^4 = 243$

12. $x° + y° + z° = 180°$

  $25° + y° + 50° = 180°$

       $75° + y° = 180°$

 $75° + y° - 75° = 180° - 75$

            $y° = 105°$

             $y = 105$

13. Factors of 70: 2, 5, 7, 14, 35
Factors of 27: 3, 9
$\dfrac{\boxed{70}}{\boxed{27}} = \dfrac{7}{3}$

14. $3x + 2y = 36$
$\dfrac{5y}{3x} = 5$

Solve the second equation for y.

$3x \cdot \dfrac{5y}{3x} = 3x \cdot 5$

$5y = 15x$

$\dfrac{5y}{5} = \dfrac{15y}{5}$

$y = 3x$

Substitute $3x$ for y in the first equation.

$3x + 2(3x) = 36$

$3x + 6x = 36$

$9x = 36$

$\dfrac{9x}{9} = \dfrac{36}{9}$

$x = 4$

15. Draw a diameter of the circle from one corner diagonally to the other corner of the square.
diameter $= 2r$
length of side of square $= 2\sqrt{2}$
$(\text{diameter})^2 = (\text{side})^2 + (\text{side})^2$
$(2r)^2 = (2\sqrt{2})^2 + (2\sqrt{2})^2$
$4r^2 = 4 \cdot 2 + 4 \cdot 2$
$4r^2 = 8 + 8$
$4r^2 = 16$
$\dfrac{4r^2}{4} = \dfrac{16}{4}$
$r^2 = 4$
$\sqrt{r^2} = \sqrt{4}$
$r = 2$
Area of the circle $= \pi r^2$
$\pi k = \pi \cdot 2^2$
$\pi k = 4\pi$
$\dfrac{\pi k}{\pi} = \dfrac{4\pi}{\pi}$
$k = 4$

16. $\boxed{n} = \dfrac{\sqrt{n}}{2}$

$4 = \dfrac{\sqrt{n}}{2}$

$2 \cdot 4 = 2 \cdot \dfrac{\sqrt{n}}{2}$

$8 = \sqrt{n}$

$8^2 = (\sqrt{n})^2$

$64 = n$

17. $\dfrac{a + b + c}{3} = 2b$

$\dfrac{0 + b + c}{3} = 2b$

$\dfrac{b + c}{3} = 2b$

$3 \cdot \dfrac{b + c}{3} = 3 \cdot 2b$

$b + c = 6b$

$b + c - b = 6b - b$

$c = 5b$

$\dfrac{c}{b} = \dfrac{5b}{b}$

$\dfrac{c}{b} = 5$

18. A; Let $x = \dfrac{s + t}{s}$

Since x is a positive number. Then $x > \dfrac{1}{x}$.

$\dfrac{1}{x} = \dfrac{s}{s + t}$

So, $\dfrac{s + t}{s} > \dfrac{s}{s + t}$.

19. A; Let x be the original price.
Then $x - (20\%)x = 108$.

$x - 0.20x = 108$

$0.80x = 108$

$\dfrac{0.8x}{0.8} = \dfrac{108}{0.8}$

$x = 135$

The original price was \$135.

20. B; Area of the rectangle $= w \cdot 3w$
$= 3w^2$

Area of the circle $= \pi r^2$
$= \pi(w)^2$
$\approx 3.14w^2$

21. D; $k^n = 64$
$k^n = 2^6$
$k = 2$ and $n = 6$
or
$k^n = 4^3$
$k = 4$ and $n = 3$

22. C; $m + p = 4(m + p) - mp$
$8 + 3 = 4(8 + 3) - 8 \cdot 3$
$= 4 \cdot 11 - 24$
$= 44 - 24$
$= 20$
$3 + 8 = 4(3 + 8) - 3 \cdot 8$
$= 4 \cdot 11 - 24$
$= 44 - 24$
$= 20$

Chapter 6 Quadratic Functions and Inequalities

Page 285 Getting Started

1.

x	y
-3	-3
-2	-1
-1	1
0	3

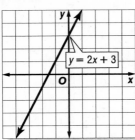

$y = 2x + 3$

2.

x	y
-5	0
-2	-3
0	-5
1	-6

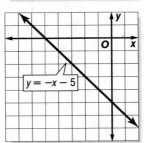

$y = -x - 5$

3.

x	y
-2	8
-1	5
0	4
1	5
2	8

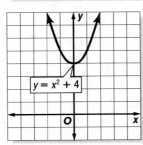

$y = x^2 + 4$

4.

x	y
-3	-2
-2	1
-1	2
0	1
1	-2

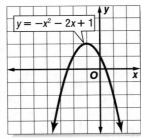

$y = -x^2 - 2x + 1$

5. $(x - 4)(7x + 12) = x(7x + 12) - 4(7x + 12)$
$$= x(7x) + x(12) - 4(7x) - 4(12)$$
$$= 7x^2 + 12x - 28x - 48$$
$$= 7x^2 - 16x - 48$$

6. $(x + 5)^2 = (x + 5)(x + 5)$
$$= x(x + 5) + 5(x + 5)$$
$$= x(x) + x(5) + 5(x) + 5(5)$$
$$= x^2 + 5x + 5x + 25$$
$$= x^2 + 10x + 25$$

7. $(3x - 1)^2 = (3x - 1)(3x - 1)$
$$= 3x(3x - 1) - 1(3x - 1)$$
$$= 3x(3x) + 3x(-1) - 1(3x) - 1(-1)$$
$$= 9x^2 - 3x - 3x + 1$$
$$= 9x^2 - 6x + 1$$

8. $(3x - 4)(2x - 9) = 3x(2x - 9) - 4(2x - 9)$
$$= 3x(2x) + 3x(-9) - 4(2x) - 4(-9)$$
$$= 6x^2 - 27x - 8x + 36$$
$$= 6x^2 - 35x + 36$$

9. $x^2 + 11x + 30 = x^2 + 5x + 6x + 30$
$$= (x^2 + 5x) + (6x + 30)$$
$$= x(x + 5) + 6(x + 5)$$
$$= (x + 6)(x + 5)$$

10. $x^2 - 13x + 36 = x^2 - 9x - 4x + 36$
$$= (x^2 - 9x) + (-4x + 36)$$
$$= x(x - 9) - 4(x - 9)$$
$$= (x - 4)(x - 9)$$

11. $x^2 - x - 56 = x^2 - 8x + 7x - 56$
$$= (x^2 - 8x) + (7x - 56)$$
$$= x(x - 8) + 7(x - 8)$$
$$= (x + 7)(x - 8)$$

12. $x^2 - 5x - 14 = x^2 - 7x + 2x - 14$
$$= (x^2 - 7x) + (2x - 14)$$
$$= x(x - 7) + 2(x - 7)$$
$$= (x + 2)(x - 7)$$

13. Since there are no factors of 2 whose sum is 1, $x^2 + x + 2$ is prime.

14. $x^2 + 10x + 25 = x^2 + 5x + 5x + 25$
$$= (x^2 + 5x) + (5x + 25)$$
$$= x(x + 5) + 5(x + 5)$$
$$= (x + 5)(x + 5)$$
$$= (x + 5)^2$$

15. $x^2 - 22x + 121 = x^2 - 11x - 11x + 121$
$$= (x^2 - 11x) + (-11x + 121)$$
$$= x(x - 11) - 11(x - 11)$$
$$= (x - 11)(x - 11)$$
$$= (x - 11)^2$$

16. $x^2 - 9 = x^2 - 3x + 3x - 9$
$$= (x^2 - 3x) + (3x - 9)$$
$$= x(x - 3) + 3(x - 3)$$
$$= (x + 3)(x - 3)$$

17. $\sqrt{225} = \sqrt{3^2 \cdot 5^2}$
$$= \sqrt{3^2} \cdot \sqrt{5^2}$$
$$= 3 \cdot 5$$
$$= 15$$

18. $\sqrt{48} = \sqrt{2^2 \cdot 2^2 \cdot 3}$
$$= \sqrt{2^2} \cdot \sqrt{2^2} \cdot \sqrt{3}$$
$$= 2 \cdot 2 \cdot \sqrt{3}$$
$$= 4\sqrt{3}$$

19. $\sqrt{180} = \sqrt{2^2 \cdot 3^2 \cdot 5}$
$$= \sqrt{2^2} \cdot \sqrt{3^2} \cdot \sqrt{5}$$
$$= 2 \cdot 3 \cdot \sqrt{5}$$
$$= 6\sqrt{5}$$

20. $\sqrt{68} = \sqrt{2^2 \cdot 17}$
$$= \sqrt{2^2} \cdot \sqrt{17}$$
$$= 2 \cdot \sqrt{17}$$
$$= 2\sqrt{17}$$

21. $\sqrt{-25} = \sqrt{-1 \cdot 5^2}$
$$= \sqrt{-1} \cdot \sqrt{5^2}$$
$$= i \cdot 5$$
$$= 5i$$

22. $\sqrt{-32} = \sqrt{-1 \cdot 2^2 \cdot 2^2 \cdot 2}$
$$= \sqrt{-1} \cdot \sqrt{2^2} \cdot \sqrt{2^2} \cdot \sqrt{2}$$
$$= i \cdot 2 \cdot 2 \cdot \sqrt{2}$$
$$= 4i\sqrt{2}$$

23. $\sqrt{-270} = \sqrt{-1 \cdot 3^2 \cdot 30}$
$= \sqrt{-1} \cdot \sqrt{3^2} \cdot \sqrt{30}$
$= i \cdot 3 \cdot \sqrt{30}$
$= 3i\sqrt{30}$

24. $\sqrt{-15} = \sqrt{-1 \cdot 15}$
$= \sqrt{-1} \cdot \sqrt{15}$
$= i \cdot \sqrt{15}$
$= i\sqrt{15}$

6-1 Graphing Quadratic Functions

Pages 290–291 Check for Understanding

1. Sample answer: $f(x) = 3x^2 + 5x - 6$;
$3x^2$ is the quadratic term, $5x$ is the linear term, and -6 is the constant term.

2a. The point that contains the minimum is (2, 1). Therefore, the vertex is (2, 1), and the axis of symmetry is $x = 2$.

2b. The point that contains the maximum is $(-3, -2)$. Therefore, the vertex is $(-3, -2)$, and the axis of symmetry is $x = -3$.

3a. For this function, $a = 3$. Since $a > 0$, the graph opens up and the function has a minimum value.

3b. For this function, $a = -2$. Since $a < 0$, the graph opens down and the function has a maximum value.

3c. For this function, $a = -5$. Since $a < 0$, the graph opens down and the function has a maximum value.

3d. For this function, $a = 6$. Since $a > 0$, the graph opens up and the function has a minimum value.

4a. $f(x) = -4x^2 \rightarrow f(x) = -4x^2 + 0x + 0$
So, $a = -4$, $b = 0$, and $c = 0$.
Since $c = 0$, the y-intercept is 0.
Axis of symmetry:
$x = -\frac{b}{2a}$
$x = -\frac{0}{2(-4)}$
$x = 0$
The equation of the axis of symmetry is $x = 0$.
Therefore, the x-coordinate of the vertex is 0.

4b.

x	$-4x^2$	$f(x)$	$(x, f(x))$
-1	$-4(-1)^2$	-4	$(-1, -4)$
0	$-4(0)^2$	0	$(0, 0)$
1	$-4(1)^2$	-4	$(1, -4)$

4c.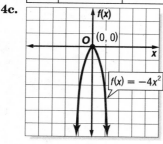

5a. $f(x) = x^2 + 2x \rightarrow f(x) = 1x^2 + 2x + 0$
So, $a = 1$, $b = 2$, and $c = 0$.
Since $c = 0$, the y-intercept is 0.
Axis of symmetry:
$x = -\frac{b}{2a}$
$x = -\frac{2}{2(1)}$
$x = -1$
The equation of the axis of symmetry is $x = -1$.
Therefore, the x-coordinate of the vertex is -1.

5b.

x	$x^2 + 2x$	$f(x)$	$(x, f(x))$
-3	$(-3)^2 + 2(-3)$	3	$(-3, 3)$
-2	$(-2)^2 + 2(-2)$	0	$(-2, 0)$
-1	$(-1)^2 + 2(-1)$	-1	$(-1, -1)$
0	$(0)^2 + 2(0)$	0	$(0, 0)$
1	$(1)^2 + 2(1)$	3	$(1, 3)$

5c.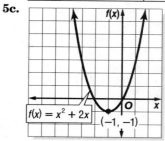

6a. $f(x) = -x^2 + 4x - 1$
Since $c = -1$, the y-intercept is -1.
Axis of symmetry:
$x = -\frac{b}{2a}$
$x = -\frac{4}{2(-1)}$
$x = 2$
The equation of the axis of symmetry is $x = 2$.
Therefore, the x-coordinate of the vertex is 2.

6b.

x	$-x^2 + 4x - 1$	$f(x)$	$(x, f(x))$
0	$-(0)^2 + 4(0) - 1$	-1	$(0, -1)$
1	$-(1)^2 + 4(1) - 1$	2	$(1, 2)$
2	$-(2)^2 + 4(2) - 1$	3	$(2, 3)$
3	$-(3)^2 + 4(3) - 1$	2	$(3, 2)$
4	$-(4)^2 + 4(4) - 1$	-1	$(4, -1)$

6c.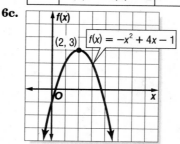

7a. $f(x) = x^2 + 8x + 3$
Since $c = 3$, the y-intercept is 3.
Axis of symmetry:
$x = -\frac{b}{2a}$
$x = -\frac{8}{2(1)}$
$x = -4$
The equation of the axis of symmetry is $x = -4$.
Therefore, the x-coordinate of the vertex is -4.

7b.

x	$x^2 + 8x + 3$	$f(x)$	$(x, f(x))$
-6	$(-6)^2 + 8(-6) + 3$	-9	$(-6, -9)$
-5	$(-5)^2 + 8(-5) + 3$	-12	$(-5, -12)$
-4	$(-4)^2 + 8(-4) + 3$	-13	$(-4, -13)$
-3	$(-3)^2 + 8(-3) + 3$	-12	$(-3, -12)$
-2	$(-2)^2 + 8(-2) + 3$	-9	$(-2, -9)$

7c.

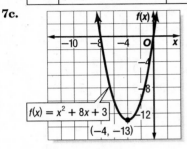

8a. $f(x) = 2x^2 - 4x + 1$
Since $c = 1$, the y-intercept is 1.
Axis of symmetry:
$x = -\frac{b}{2a}$
$x = -\frac{-4}{2(2)}$
$x = 1$
The equation of the axis of symmetry is $x = 1$.
Therefore, the x-coordinate of the vertex is 1.

8b.

x	$2x^2 - 4x + 1$	$f(x)$	$(x, f(x))$
-1	$2(-1)^2 - 4(-1) + 1$	7	$(-1, 7)$
0	$2(0)^2 - 4(0) + 1$	1	$(0, 1)$
1	$2(1)^2 - 4(1) + 1$	-1	$(1, -1)$
2	$2(2)^2 - 4(2) + 1$	1	$(2, 1)$
3	$2(3)^2 - 4(3) + 1$	7	$(3, 7)$

8c.

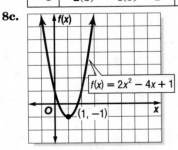

9a. $f(x) = 3x^2 + 10x \rightarrow f(x) = 3x^2 + 10x + 0$
So, $a = 3$, $b = 10$, and $c = 0$.
Since $c = 0$, the y-intercept is 0.
Axis of symmetry:
$x = -\frac{b}{2a}$
$x = -\frac{10}{2(3)}$
$x = -\frac{5}{3}$

The equation of the axis of symmetry is
$x = -\frac{5}{3}$.

Therefore, the x-coordinate of the vertex is $-\frac{5}{3}$.

9b.

x	$3x^2 + 10x$	$f(x)$	$(x, f(x))$
-3	$3(-3)^2 + 10(-3)$	-3	$(-3, -3)$
-2	$3(-2)^2 + 10(-2)$	-8	$(-2, -8)$
$-\frac{5}{3}$	$3\left(-\frac{5}{3}\right)^2 + 10\left(-\frac{5}{3}\right)$	$-\frac{25}{3}$	$\left(-\frac{5}{3}, -\frac{25}{3}\right)$
-1	$3(-1)^2 + 10(-1)$	-7	$(-1, -7)$
0	$3(0)^2 + 10(0)$	0	$(0, 0)$

9c.

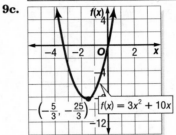

10. For this function, $a = -1$, $b = 0$, and $c = 7$.
Since $a < 0$, the graph opens down and has a maximum value. The x-coordinate of the vertex is
$-\frac{0}{2(-1)}$ or 0.
$f(x) = -x^2 + 7$
$f(0) = -(0)^2 + 7$
$\quad\; = 7$

Therefore, the maximum value of the function is 7.

11. For this function, $a = 1$, $b = -1$, and $c = -6$.
Since $a > 0$, the graph opens up and has a minimum value. The x-coordinate of the vertex is
$-\frac{-1}{2(1)}$ or $\frac{1}{2}$.
$f(x) = x^2 - x - 6$
$f\left(\frac{1}{2}\right) = \left(\frac{1}{2}\right)^2 - \left(\frac{1}{2}\right) - 6$
$\quad\;\; = -\frac{25}{4}$

Therefore, the minimum value of the function is $-\frac{25}{4}$.

12. For this function, $a = 4$, $b = 12$, and $c = 9$. Since $a > 0$, the graph opens up and has a minimum value. The x-coordinate of the vertex is $-\frac{12}{2(4)}$ or $-\frac{3}{2}$.

$$f(x) = 4x^2 + 12x + 9$$
$$f\left(-\frac{3}{2}\right) = 4\left(-\frac{3}{2}\right)^2 + 12\left(-\frac{3}{2}\right) + 9$$
$$= 0$$

Therefore, the minimum value of the function is 0.

13. Let x = the number of $0.25 price increases. Then $7.50 + 0.25x$ = the subscription rate and $50,000 - 1250x$ = the number of subscribers. Let $I(x)$ = income as a function of x.

The income	is	the number of subscribers	multi-plied by	the subscription rate.

$$I(x) = (50,000 - 1250x) \cdot (7.50 + 0.25x)$$
$$= 50,000(7.50) + 50,000(0.25x)$$
$$\quad - 1250x(7.50) - 1250x(0.25x)$$
$$= 375,000 + 12,500x - 9375x - 312.5x^2$$
$$= 375,000 + 3125x - 312.5x^2$$
$$= -312.5x^2 + 3125x + 375,000$$

$I(x)$ is a quadratic function with $a = -312.5$, $b = 3125$, and $c = 375,000$. Since $a < 0$, the function has a maximum value at the vertex of the graph. Use the formula to find the x-coordinate of the vertex.

$$x\text{-coordinate of the vertex} = -\frac{b}{2a}$$
$$= -\frac{3125}{2(-312.5)}$$
$$= 5$$

This means the newspaper should make 5 price increases of $0.25 to maximize their income. Thus, the subscription rate should be $7.50 + 0.25(5)$ or $8.75.

Pages 291–293　Practice and Apply

14a. $f(x) = 2x^2 \rightarrow f(x) = 2x^2 + 0x + 0$
So, $a = 2$, $b = 0$, and $c = 0$.
Since $c = 0$, the y-intercept is 0.
Axis of symmetry:
$$x = -\frac{b}{2a}$$
$$x = -\frac{0}{2(2)}$$
$$x = 0$$
The equation of the axis of symmetry is $x = 0$.
Therefore, the x-coordinate of the vertex is 0.

14b.

x	$2x^2$	$f(x)$	$(x, f(x))$
-2	$2(-2)^2$	8	$(-2, 8)$
-1	$2(-1)^2$	2	$(-1, 2)$
0	$2(0)^2$	0	$(0, 0)$
1	$2(1)^2$	2	$(1, 2)$
2	$2(2)^2$	8	$(2, 8)$

14c.

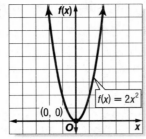

15a. $f(x) = -5x^2 \rightarrow f(x) = -5x^2 + 0x + 0$
So, $a = -5$, $b = 0$, and $c = 0$.
Since $c = 0$, the y-intercept is 0.
Axis of symmetry:
$$x = -\frac{b}{2a}$$
$$x = -\frac{0}{2(-5)}$$
$$x = 0$$
The equation of the axis of symmetry is $x = 0$.
Therefore, the x-coordinate of the vertex is 0.

15b.

x	$-5x^2$	$f(x)$	$(x, f(x))$
-2	$-5(-2)^2$	-20	$(-2, -20)$
-1	$-5(-1)^2$	-5	$(-1, -5)$
0	$-5(0)^2$	0	$(0, 0)$
1	$-5(1)^2$	-5	$(1, -5)$
2	$-5(2)^2$	-20	$(2, -20)$

15c.

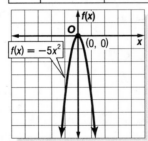

16a. $f(x) = x^2 + 4 \rightarrow f(x) = 1x^2 + 0x + 4$
So, $a = 1$, $b = 0$, and $c = 4$.
Since $c = 4$, the y-intercept is 4.
Axis of symmetry:
$$x = -\frac{b}{2a}$$
$$x = -\frac{0}{2(1)}$$
$$x = 0$$
The equation of the axis of symmetry is $x = 0$.
Therefore, the x-coordinate of the vertex is 0.

16b.

x	$x^2 + 4$	$f(x)$	$(x, f(x))$
-2	$(-2)^2 + 4$	8	$(-2, 8)$
-1	$(-1)^2 + 4$	5	$(-1, 5)$
0	$(0)^2 + 4$	4	$(0, 4)$
1	$(1)^2 + 4$	5	$(1, 5)$
2	$(2)^2 + 4$	8	$(2, 8)$

16c.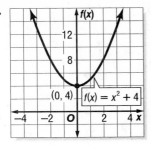

17a. $f(x) = x^2 - 9 \rightarrow f(x) = 1x^2 + 0x - 9$
So, $a = 1$, $b = 0$, and $c = -9$.
Since $c = -9$, the y-intercept is -9.
Axis of symmetry:
$x = -\frac{b}{2a}$
$x = -\frac{0}{2(1)}$
$x = 0$
The equation of the axis of symmetry is $x = 0$.
Therefore, the x-coordinate of the vertex is 0.

17b.

x	$x^2 - 9$	$f(x)$	$(x, f(x))$
-2	$(-2)^2 - 9$	-5	$(-2, -5)$
-1	$(-1)^2 - 9$	-8	$(-1, -8)$
0	$(0)^2 - 9$	-9	$(0, -9)$
1	$(1)^2 - 9)$	-8	$(1, -8)$
2	$(2)^2 - 9$	-5	$(2, -5)$

17c.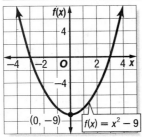

18a. $f(x) = 2x^2 - 4 \rightarrow f(x) = 2x^2 + 0x - 4$
So, $a = 2$, $b = 0$, and $c = -4$.
Since $c = -4$, the y-intercept is -4.
Axis of symmetry:
$x = -\frac{b}{2a}$
$x = -\frac{0}{2(2)}$
$x = 0$
The equation of the axis of symmetry is $x = 0$.
Therefore, the x-coordinate of the vertex is 0.

18b.

x	$2x^2 - 4$	$f(x)$	$(x, f(x))$
-2	$2(-2)^2 - 4$	4	$(-2, 4)$
-1	$2(-1)^2 - 4$	-2	$(-1, -2)$
0	$2(0)^2 - 4$	-4	$(0, -4)$
1	$2(1)^2 - 4$	-2	$(1, -2)$
2	$2(2)^2 - 4$	4	$(2, 4)$

18c.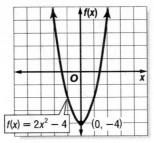

19a. $f(x) = 3x^2 + 1 \rightarrow f(x) = 3x^2 + 0x + 1$
So, $a = 3$, $b = 0$, and $c = 1$.
Since $c = 1$, the y-intercept is 1.
Axis of symmetry:
$x = -\frac{b}{2a}$
$x = -\frac{0}{2(3)}$
$x = 0$
The equation for the axis of symmetry is $x = 0$.
Therefore, the x-coordinate of the vertex is 0.

19b.

x	$3x^2 + 1$	$f(x)$	$(x, f(x))$
-2	$3(-2)^2 + 1$	13	$(-2, 13)$
-1	$3(-1)^2 + 1$	4	$(-1, 4)$
0	$3(0)^2 + 1$	1	$(0, 1)$
1	$3(1)^2 + 1$	4	$(1, 4)$
2	$3(2)^2 + 1$	13	$(2, 13)$

19c.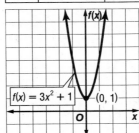

20a. $f(x) = x^2 - 4x + 4$
Since $c = 4$, the y-intercept is 4.
Axis of symmetry:
$x = -\frac{b}{2a}$
$x = -\frac{-4}{2(1)}$
$x = 2$
The equation for the axis of symmetry is $x = 2$.
Therefore, the x-coordinate of the vertex is 2.

20b.

x	$x^2 - 4x + 4$	$f(x)$	$(x, f(x))$
0	$(0)^2 - 4(0) + 4$	4	$(0, 4)$
1	$(1)^2 - 4(1) + 4$	1	$(1, 1)$
2	$(2)^2 - 4(2) + 4$	0	$(2, 0)$
3	$(3)^2 - 4(3) + 4$	1	$(3, 1)$
4	$(4)^2 - 4(4) + 4$	4	$(4, 4)$

20c.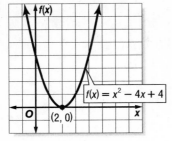

21a. $f(x) = x^2 - 9x + 9$

Since $c = 9$, the y-intercept is 9.

Axis of symmetry:

$x = -\frac{b}{2a}$

$x = -\frac{-9}{2(1)}$

$x = \frac{9}{2}$

The equation for the axis of symmetry is $x = \frac{9}{2}$.

Therefore, the x-coordinate of the vertex is $\frac{9}{2}$.

21b.

x	$x^2 - 9x + 9$	$f(x)$	$(x, f(x))$
3	$(3)^2 - 9(3) + 9$	-9	$(3, -9)$
4	$(4)^2 - 9(4) + 9$	-11	$(4, -11)$
$\frac{9}{2}$	$\left(\frac{9}{2}\right)^2 - 9\left(\frac{9}{2}\right) + 9$	$-\frac{45}{4}$	$\left(\frac{9}{2}, -\frac{45}{4}\right)$
5	$(5)^2 - 9(5) + 9$	-11	$(5, -11)$
6	$(6)^2 - 9(6) + 9$	-9	$(6, -9)$

21c.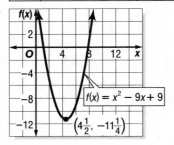

22a. $f(x) = x^2 - 4x - 5$

Since $c = -5$, the y-intercept is -5.

Axis of symmetry:

$x = -\frac{b}{2a}$

$x = -\frac{-4}{2(1)}$

$x = 2$

The equation for the axis of symmetry is $x = 2$.

Therefore, the x-coordinate of the vertex is 2.

22b.

x	$x^2 - 4x - 5$	$f(x)$	$(x, f(x))$
0	$(0)^2 - 4(0) - 5$	-5	$(0, -5)$
1	$(1)^2 - 4(1) - 5$	-8	$(1, -8)$
2	$(2)^2 - 4(2) - 5$	-9	$(2, -9)$
3	$(3)^2 - 4(3) - 5$	-8	$(3, -8)$
4	$(4)^2 - 4(4) - 5$	-5	$(4, -5)$

22c.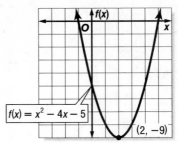

23a. $f(x) = x^2 + 12x + 36$

Since $c = 36$, the y-intercept is 36.

Axis of symmetry:

$x = -\frac{b}{2a}$

$x = -\frac{12}{2(1)}$

$x = -6$

The equation for the axis of symmetry is $x = -6$.

Therefore, the x-coordinate of the vertex is -6.

23b.

x	$x^2 + 12x + 36$	$f(x)$	$(x, f(x))$
-8	$(-8)^2 + 12(-8) + 36$	4	$(-8, 4)$
-7	$(-7)^2 + 12(-7) + 36$	1	$(-7, 1)$
-6	$(-6)^2 + 12(-6) + 36$	0	$(-6, 0)$
-5	$(-5)^2 + 12(-5) + 36$	1	$(-5, 1)$
-4	$(-4)^2 + 12(-4) + 36$	4	$(-4, 4)$

23c.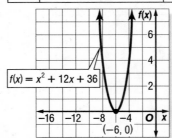

24a. $f(x) = 3x^2 + 6x - 1$

Since $c = -1$, the y-intercept is -1.

Axis of symmetry:

$x = -\frac{b}{2a}$

$x = -\frac{6}{2(3)}$

$x = -1$

The equation for the axis of symmetry is $x = -1$.

Therefore, the x-coordinate of the vertex is -1.

24b.

x	$3x^2 + 6x - 1$	$f(x)$	$(x, f(x))$
-3	$3(-3)^2 + 6(-3) - 1$	8	$(-3, 8)$
-2	$3(-2)^2 + 6(-2) - 1$	-1	$(-2, -1)$
-1	$3(-1)^2 + 6(-1) - 1$	-4	$(-1, -4)$
0	$3(0) + 6(0) - 1$	-1	$(0, -1)$
1	$3(1) + 6(1) - 1$	8	$(1, 8)$

24c.

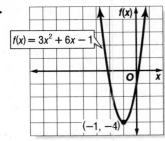

$f(x) = 3x^2 + 6x - 1$

$(-1, -4)$

25a. $f(x) = -2x^2 + 8x - 3$
So, $a = -2$, $b = 8$, and $c = -3$.
Since $c = -3$, the y-intercept is -3.
Axis of symmetry:
$x = -\dfrac{b}{2a}$
$x = -\dfrac{8}{2(-2)}$
$x = 2$
The equation for the axis of symmetry is $x = 2$.
Therefore, the x-coordinate of the vertex is 2.

25b.

x	$-2x^2 + 8x - 3$	$f(x)$	$(x, f(x))$
0	$-2(0)^2 + 8(0) - 3$	-3	$(0, -3)$
1	$-2(1)^2 + 8(1) - 3$	3	$(1, 3)$
2	$-2(2)^2 + 8(2) - 3$	5	$(2, 5)$
3	$-2(3)^2 + 8(3) - 3$	3	$(3, 3)$
4	$-2(4)^2 + 8(4) - 3$	-3	$(4, -3)$

25c.

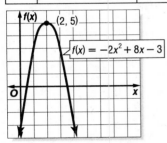

$(2, 5)$

$f(x) = -2x^2 + 8x - 3$

26a. $f(x) = -3x^2 - 4x \rightarrow f(x) = -3x^2 - 4x + 0$
So, $a = -3$, $b = -4$, and $c = 0$.
Since $c = 0$, the y-intercept is 0.
Axis of symmetry:
$x = -\dfrac{b}{2a}$
$x = -\dfrac{-4}{2(-3)}$
$x = -\dfrac{2}{3}$
The equation for the axis of symmetry is $x = -\dfrac{2}{3}$.
Therefore, the x-coordinate of the vertex is $-\dfrac{2}{3}$.

26b.

x	$-3x^2 - 4x$	$f(x)$	$(x, f(x))$
-2	$-3(-2)^2 - 4(-2)$	-4	$(-2, -4)$
-1	$-3(-1)^2 - 4(-1)$	1	$(-1, 1)$
$-\dfrac{2}{3}$	$-3\left(-\dfrac{2}{3}\right)^2 - 4\left(-\dfrac{2}{3}\right)$	$\dfrac{4}{3}$	$\left(-\dfrac{2}{3}, \dfrac{4}{3}\right)$
0	$-3(0)^2 - 4(0)$	0	$(0, 0)$
1	$-3(1)^2 - 4(1)$	-7	$(1, -7)$

26c.

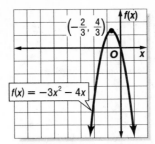

$\left(-\dfrac{2}{3}, \dfrac{4}{3}\right)$

$f(x) = -3x^2 - 4x$

27a. $f(x) = 2x^2 + 5x \rightarrow f(x) = 2x^2 + 5x + 0$
So, $a = 2$, $b = 5$, and $c = 0$.
Since $c = 0$, the y-intercept is 0.
Axis of symmetry:
$x = -\dfrac{b}{2a}$
$x = -\dfrac{5}{2(2)}$
$x = -\dfrac{5}{4}$
The equation for the axis of symmetry is $x = -\dfrac{5}{4}$.
Therefore, the x-coordinate of the vertex is $-\dfrac{5}{4}$.

27b.

x	$2x^2 + 5x$	$f(x)$	$(x, f(x))$
-3	$2(-3)^2 + 5(-3)$	3	$(-3, 3)$
-2	$2(-2)^2 + 5(-2)$	-2	$(-2, -2)$
$-\dfrac{5}{4}$	$2\left(-\dfrac{5}{4}\right)^2 + 5\left(-\dfrac{5}{4}\right)$	$-\dfrac{25}{8}$	$\left(-\dfrac{5}{4}, -\dfrac{25}{8}\right)$
-1	$2(-1) + 5(-1)$	-3	$(-1, -3)$
0	$2(0) + 5(0)$	0	$(0, 0)$

27c.

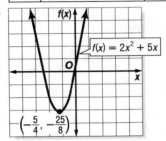

$f(x) = 2x^2 + 5x$

$\left(-\dfrac{5}{4}, -\dfrac{25}{8}\right)$

28a. $f(x) = 0.5x^2 - 1 \rightarrow f(x) = 0.5x^2 + 0x - 1$
So, $a = 0.5$, $b = 0$, and $c = -1$.
Since $c = -1$, the y-intercept is -1.
Axis of symmetry:
$x = -\dfrac{b}{2a}$
$x = -\dfrac{0}{2(0.5)}$
$x = 0$
The equation for the axis of symmetry is $x = 0$.
Therefore, the x-coordinate of the vertex is 0.

28b.

x	$0.5x^2 - 1$	$f(x)$	$(x, f(x))$
-2	$0.5(-2)^2 - 1$	1	$(-2, 1)$
-1	$0.5(-1)^2 - 1$	-0.5	$(-1, -0.5)$
0	$0.5(0)^2 - 1$	-1	$(0, -1)$
1	$0.5(1)^2 - 1$	-0.5	$(1, -0.5)$
2	$0.5(2)^2 - 1$	1	$(2, 1)$

28c.

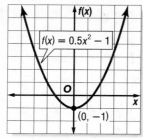

$f(x) = 0.5x^2 - 1$

$(0, -1)$

29a. $f(x) = -0.25x^2 - 3x \rightarrow f(x) = -0.25x^2 - 3x + 0$
So, $a = -0.25$, $b = -3$, and $c = 0$.
Since $c = 0$, the y-intercept is 0.
Axis of symmetry:

$x = -\frac{b}{2a}$

$x = -\frac{-3}{2(-0.25)}$

$x = -6$

The equation for the axis of symmetry is $x = -6$.
Therefore, the x-coordinate of the vertex is -6.

29b.

x	$-0.25x^2 - 3x$	$f(x)$	$(x, f(x))$
-8	$-0.25(-8)^2 - 3(-8)$	8	$(-8, 8)$
-7	$-0.25(-7)^2 - 3(-7)$	8.75	$(-7, 8.75)$
-6	$-0.25(-6)^2 - 3(-6)$	9	$(-6, 9)$
-5	$-0.25(-5)^2 - 3(-5)$	8.75	$(-5, 8.75)$
-4	$-0.25(-4)^2 - 3(-4)$	8	$(-4, 8)$

29c.

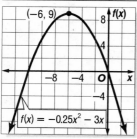

$(-6, 9)$

$f(x) = -0.25x^2 - 3x$

30a. $f(x) = \frac{1}{2}x^2 + 3x + \frac{9}{2}$

Since $c = \frac{9}{2}$, the y-intercept is $\frac{9}{2}$.

Axis of symmetry:

$x = -\frac{b}{2a}$

$x = -\frac{3}{2\left(\frac{1}{2}\right)}$

$x = -3$

The equation for the axis of symmetry is $x = -3$.
Therefore, the x-coordinate of the vertex is -3.

30b.

x	$\frac{1}{2}x^2 + 3x + \frac{9}{2}$	$f(x)$	$(x, f(x))$
-5	$\frac{1}{2}(-5)^2 + 3(-5) + \frac{9}{2}$	2	$(-5, 2)$
-4	$\frac{1}{2}(-4)^2 + 3(-4) + \frac{9}{2}$	$\frac{1}{2}$	$\left(-4, \frac{1}{2}\right)$
-3	$\frac{1}{2}(-3)^2 + 3(-3) + \frac{9}{2}$	0	$(-3, 0)$
-2	$\frac{1}{2}(-2)^2 + 3(-2) + \frac{9}{2}$	$\frac{1}{2}$	$\left(-2, \frac{1}{2}\right)$
-1	$\frac{1}{2}(-1)^2 + 3(-1) + \frac{9}{2}$	2	$(-1, 2)$

30c.

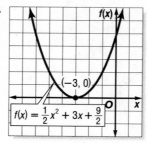

$(-3, 0)$

$f(x) = \frac{1}{2}x^2 + 3x + \frac{9}{2}$

31a. $f(x) = x^2 - \frac{2}{3}x - \frac{8}{9}$

Since $c = -\frac{8}{9}$, the y-intercept is $-\frac{8}{9}$.

Axis of symmetry:

$x = -\frac{b}{2a}$

$x = -\frac{-\frac{2}{3}}{2(1)}$

$x = \frac{1}{3}$

The equation for the axis of symmetry is $x = \frac{1}{3}$.

Therefore, the x-coordinate of the vertex is $\frac{1}{3}$.

31b.

x	$x^2 - \frac{2}{3}x - \frac{8}{9}$	$f(x)$	$(x, f(x))$
-1	$(-1)^2 - \frac{2}{3}(-1) - \frac{8}{9}$	$\frac{7}{9}$	$\left(-1, \frac{7}{9}\right)$
0	$(0)^2 - \frac{2}{3}(0) - \frac{8}{9}$	$-\frac{8}{9}$	$\left(0, -\frac{8}{9}\right)$
$\frac{1}{3}$	$\left(\frac{1}{3}\right)^2 - \frac{2}{3}\left(\frac{1}{3}\right) - \frac{8}{9}$	-1	$\left(\frac{1}{3}, -1\right)$
1	$(1)^2 - \frac{2}{3}(1) - \frac{8}{9}$	$-\frac{5}{9}$	$\left(1, -\frac{5}{9}\right)$
2	$(2)^2 - \frac{2}{3}(2) - \frac{8}{9}$	$\frac{16}{9}$	$\left(2, \frac{16}{9}\right)$

31c.

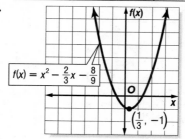

$f(x) = x^2 - \frac{2}{3}x - \frac{8}{9}$

$\left(\frac{1}{3}, -1\right)$

32. For this function, $a = 3$, $b = 0$, and $c = 0$. Since $a > 0$, the graph opens up and has a minimum value. The x-coordinate of the vertex is $-\frac{0}{2(3)}$ or 0.

$f(x) = 3x^2$
$f(0) = 3(0)^2$
$\quad = 0$

Therefore, the minimum value of the function is 0.

33. For this function, $a = -1$, $b = 0$, and $c = -9$. Since $a < 0$, the graph opens down and has a maximum value. The x-coordinate of the vertex is $-\frac{0}{2(-1)}$ or 0.

$f(x) = -x^2 - 9$
$f(0) = -(0)^2 - 9$
$\quad = -9$

Therefore, the maximum value of the function is -9.

34. For this function, $a = 1$, $b = -8$, and $c = 2$. Since $a > 0$, the graph opens up and has a minimum value. The x-coordinate of the vertex is $-\frac{-8}{2(1)}$ or 4.

$$f(x) = x^2 - 8x + 2$$
$$f(4) = (4)^2 - 8(4) + 2$$
$$= -14$$

Therefore, the minimum value of the function is -14.

35. For this function, $a = 1$, $b = 6$, and $c = -2$. Since $a > 0$, the graph opens up and has a minimum value. The x-coordinate of the vertex is $-\frac{6}{2(1)}$ or -3.

$$f(x) = x^2 + 6x - 2$$
$$f(-3) = (-3)^2 + 6(-3) - 2$$
$$= -11$$

Therefore, the minimum value of the function is -11.

36. $f(x) = 4x - x^2 + 1 \rightarrow f(x) = -x^2 + 4x + 1$
For this function, $a = -1$, $b = 4$, and $c = 1$. Since $a < 0$, the graph opens down and has a maximum value. The x-coordinate of the vertex is $-\frac{4}{2(-1)}$ or 2.

$$f(x) = -x^2 + 4x + 1$$
$$f(2) = -(2)^2 + 4(2) + 1$$
$$= 5$$

Therefore, the maximum value of the function is 5.

37. $f(x) = 3 - x^2 - 6x \rightarrow f(x) = -x^2 - 6x + 3$
For this function, $a = -1$, $b = -6$, and $c = 3$. Since $a < 0$, the graph opens down and has a maximum value. The x-coordinate of the vertex is $-\frac{-6}{2(-1)}$ or -3.

$$f(x) = -x^2 - 6x + 3$$
$$f(-3) = -(-3)^2 - 6(-3) + 3$$
$$= 12$$

Therefore, the maximum value of the function is 12.

38. $f(x) = 2x + 2x^2 + 5 \rightarrow f(x) = 2x^2 + 2x + 5$
For this function, $a = 2$, $b = 2$, and $c = 5$. Since $a > 0$, the graph opens up and has a minimum value. The x-coordinate of the vertex is $-\frac{2}{2(2)}$ or $-\frac{1}{2}$.

$$f(x) = 2x^2 + 2x + 5$$
$$f\left(-\frac{1}{2}\right) = 2\left(-\frac{1}{2}\right)^2 + 2\left(-\frac{1}{2}\right) + 5$$
$$= \frac{9}{2}$$

Therefore, the minimum value of the function is $\frac{9}{2}$.

39. $f(x) = x - 2x^2 - 1 \rightarrow f(x) = -2x^2 + x - 1$
For this function, $a = -2$, $b = 1$, and $c = -1$. Since $a < 0$, the graph opens down and has a maximum value. The x-coordinate of the vertex is $-\frac{1}{2(-2)}$ or $\frac{1}{4}$.

$$f(x) = -2x^2 + x - 1$$
$$f\left(\frac{1}{4}\right) = -2\left(\frac{1}{4}\right)^2 + \left(\frac{1}{4}\right) - 1$$
$$= -\frac{7}{8}$$

Therefore, the maximum value of the function is $-\frac{7}{8}$.

40. $f(x) = -7 - 3x^2 + 12x \rightarrow f(x) = -3x^2 + 12x - 7$
For this function, $a = -3$, $b = 12$, and $c = -7$. Since $a < 0$, the graph opens down and has a maximum value. The x-coordinate of the vertex is $-\frac{12}{2(-3)}$ or 2.

$$f(x) = -3x^2 + 12x - 7$$
$$f(2) = -3(2)^2 + 12(2) - 7$$
$$= 5$$

Therefore, the maximum value of the function is 5.

41. $f(x) = -20x + 5x^2 + 9 \rightarrow f(x) = 5x^2 - 20x + 9$
For this function, $a = 5$, $b = -20$, and $c = 9$. Since $a > 0$, the graph opens up and has a minimum value. The x-coordinate of the vertex is $-\frac{-20}{2(5)}$ or 2.

$$f(x) = 5x^2 - 20x + 9$$
$$f(2) = 5(2)^2 - 20(2) + 9$$
$$= -11$$

Therefore, the minimum value of the function is -11.

42. For this function, $a = -\frac{1}{2}$, $b = -2$, and $c = 3$. Since $a < 0$, the graph opens down and has a maximum value. The x-coordinate of the vertex is $-\frac{-2}{2\left(-\frac{1}{2}\right)}$ or -2.

$$f(x) = -\frac{1}{2}x^2 - 2x + 3$$
$$f(-2) = -\frac{1}{2}(-2)^2 - 2(-2) + 3$$
$$= 5$$

Therefore, the maximum value of the function is 5.

43. For this function, $a = \frac{3}{4}$, $b = -5$, and $c = -2$. Since $a > 0$, the graph opens up and has a minimum value. The x-coordinate of the vertex is $-\frac{-5}{2\left(\frac{3}{4}\right)}$ or $\frac{10}{3}$.

$$f(x) = \frac{3}{4}x^2 - 5x - 2$$
$$f\left(\frac{10}{3}\right) = \frac{3}{4}\left(\frac{10}{3}\right)^2 - 5\left(\frac{10}{3}\right) - 2$$
$$= -\frac{31}{3}$$

Therefore, the minimum value of the function is $-\frac{31}{3}$.

44. $h(x)$ is a quadratic function with $a = -0.025$, $b = 2$, and $c = 0$.

$$x = -\frac{b}{2a}$$

$$x = -\frac{2}{2(-0.025)}$$

$$x = 40$$

The equation of the axis of symmetry is $x = 40$. Therefore, the x-coordinate of the vertex is 40.

$$h(x) = -0.025x^2 + 2x$$

$$h(40) = -0.025(40)^2 + 2(40)$$

$$= 40$$

Therefore, the vertex of the graph is (40, 40).

45. The maximum height of the arch is 40 meters.

46. $h(t)$ is a quadratic function with $a = -16$, $b = 80$, and $c = 200$. Since $a < 0$, the function has a maximum value at the vertex of the graph.

$$t\text{-coordinate of the vertex} = -\frac{b}{2a}$$

$$= -\frac{80}{2(-16)}$$

$$= 2.5$$

$$h(t) = -16t^2 + 80t + 200$$

$$h(2.5) = -16(2.5)^2 + 80(2.5) + 200$$

$$= 300$$

This means the maximum height is 300 feet at 2.5 seconds after firing.

47. The y-intercept is the initial height of the object.

48. Let x = the width of the kennel.
Then $120 - 2x$ = the length of the kennel.

49. Let x = the width of the kennel.
Then $120 - 2x$ = the length of the kennel.

Area	is	width	multiplied by	length.
$A(x)$	$=$	x	$\cdot$	$(120 - 2x)$

$$= x(120) + x(-2x)$$

$$= 120x - 2x^2$$

$$= -2x^2 + 120x$$

$A(x)$ is a quadratic function with $a = -2$, $b = 120$, and $c = 0$. Since $a < 0$, the function has a maximum value at the vertex of the graph.

$$x\text{-coordinate of the vertex} = -\frac{b}{2a}$$

$$= -\frac{120}{2(-2)}$$

$$= 30$$

This means the kennel should have a width of 30 feet and a length of $120 - 2(30)$ or 60 feet to have the greatest area.

50. $A(x) = -2x^2 + 120x$

$$A(30) = -2(30)^2 + 120(30)$$

$$= 1800$$

The maximum area of the kennel is 1800 square feet.

51. Let x = the number of \$1 increases.
Then $8 + x$ = the fare per passenger and $300 - 20x$ = the number of passengers.

The income	is	the number of passengers	multiplied by	the fare per passenger.
$I(x)$	$=$	$(300 - 20x)$	$\cdot$	$(8 + x)$

$$= 300(8) + 300(x) - 20x(8) - 20x(x)$$

$$= 2400 + 300x - 160x - 20x^2$$

$$= 2400 + 140x - 20x^2$$

$$= -20x^2 + 140x + 2400$$

$I(x)$ is a quadratic function with $a = -20$, $b = 140$, and $c = 2400$. Since $a < 0$, the function has a maximum value at the vertex of the graph.

$$x\text{-coordinate of the vertex} = -\frac{b}{2a}$$

$$= -\frac{140}{2(-20)}$$

$$= 3.5$$

This means the company should make 3.5 increases to maximize their income. Thus, the fare should be $8 + 3.5$ or \$11.50.

52. $I(x) = -20x^2 + 140x + 2400$

$$I(3.5) = -20(3.5)^2 + 140(3.5) + 2400$$

$$= 2645$$

The maximum income the company can expect is \$2645.

53. Let x = the length of the rectangle.
Then $8 - \frac{4}{5}x$ = the height of the rectangle.

Area	is	length	multiplied by	height.
$A(x)$	$=$	x	$\cdot$	$\left(8 - \frac{4}{5}x\right)$

$$= x(8) + x\left(-\frac{4}{5}x\right)$$

$$= 8x - \frac{4}{5}x^2$$

$$= -\frac{4}{5}x^2 + 8x$$

$A(x)$ is a quadratic function with $a = -\frac{4}{5}$, $b = 8$, and $c = 0$. Since $a < 0$, the function has a maximum value at the vertex of the graph.

$$x\text{-coordinate of the vertex} = -\frac{b}{2a}$$

$$= -\frac{8}{2\left(-\frac{4}{5}\right)}$$

$$= 5$$

This means the maximum area occurs with length 5 inches and height $8 - \frac{4}{5}(5)$ or 4 inches.

54. C; The x-coordinate of the vertex of $y = ax^2 + c$ is $-\frac{0}{2a}$ or 0, so the y-coordinate of the vertex, the minimum of the function is $a(0)^2 + c$ or c.
For $y = 8.6x^2 - 12.5$, $a = 8.6$, $b = 0$, and $c = -12.5$.
Therefore the minimum value is -12.5.

55. If a quadratic function can be used to model ticket price versus profit, then by finding the x-coordinate of the vertex of the parabola you can determine the price per ticket that should be charged to achieve maximum profit. Answers should include the following.

- If the price of a ticket is too low, then you won't make enough money to cover your costs, but if the ticket price is too high fewer people will buy them.
- You can locate the vertex of the parabola on the graph of the function. It occurs when $x = 40$. Algebraically this is found by calculating $x = -\frac{b}{2a}$ which, for this case, is $x = -\frac{4000}{2(-50)}$ or 40. Thus the ticket price should be set at \$40 each to achieve maximum profit.

56. C; For $y = 6x^2 + 9$, $a = 6$, $b = 0$, and $c = 9$.

$$x = -\frac{b}{2a}$$
$$x = -\frac{0}{2(6)}$$
$$x = 0$$

The equation of the axis of symmetry is $x = 0$, which is the y-axis.

57. C; The smooth curve passing through the points $(1, 6)$, $(2, 3)$, $(3, 2)$, $(4, 3)$, and $(5, 6)$ forms a parabola. Therefore, these coordinate pairs represent a quadratic relationship.

58. Graph $f(x) = 3x^2 - 7x + 2$ so that the vertex of the parabola is visible.
Select 3: minimum from the CALC menu.
Using the arrow keys, locate a left bound and press ENTER.

Locate a right bound and press ENTER twice.

The cursor appears on the minimum value of the function, and the coordinates are $(1.17, -2.08)$.

59. Graph $f(x) = -5x^2 + 8x$ so that the vertex of the parabola is visible.
Select 4: maximum from the CALC menu.
Using the arrow keys, locate a left bound and press ENTER.

Locate a right bound and press ENTER twice.

The cursor appears on the maximum value of the function, and the coordinates are $(0.80, 3.20)$.

60. Graph $f(x) = 2x^2 - 3x + 2$ so that the vertex of the parabola is visible.
Select 3: minimum from the CALC menu.
Using the arrow keys, locate a left bound and press ENTER.

Locate a right bound and press ENTER twice.

The cursor appears on the minimum value of the function, and the coordinates are $(0.75, 0.88)$.

61. Graph $f(x) = -6x^2 + 9x$ so that the vertex of the parabola is visible.
Select 4: maximum from the CALC menu.
Using the arrow keys, locate a left bound and press ENTER.

Locate a right bound and press ENTER twice.

The cursor appears on the maximum value of the function, and the coordinates are $(0.75, 3.38)$.

62. Graph $f(x) = 7x^2 + 4x + 1$ so that the vertex of the parabola is visible.
Select 3: minimum from the CALC menu.
Using the arrow keys, locate a left bound and press ENTER.

Locate a right bound and press ENTER twice.

The cursor appears on the minimum value of the function, and the coordinates are $(-0.29, 0.43)$.

63. Graph $f(x) = -4x^2 + 5x$ so that the vertex of the parabola is visible.
Select 4: maximum from the CALC menu.
Using the arrow keys, locate a left bound and press ENTER.

Locate a right bound and press ENTER twice.

The cursor appears on the maximum value of the function, and the coordinates are $(0.62, 1.56)$.

Page 293　Maintain Your Skills

64. $i^{14} = (i^2)^7$
$$= (-1)^7$$
$$= -1$$

65. $(4 - 3i) - (5 - 6i) = (4 - 5) + [-3 - (-6)]i$
$$= -1 + 3i$$

66. $(7 + 2i)(1 - i) = 7(1) + 7(-i) + 2i(1) + 2i(-i)$
$$= 7 - 7i + 2i - 2i^2$$
$$= 7 - 5i - 2(-1)$$
$$= 9 - 5i$$

67. $5 - \sqrt{b + 2} = 0$
$$5 = \sqrt{b + 2}$$
$$5^2 = (\sqrt{b + 2})^2$$
$$25 = b + 2$$
$$23 = b$$
Check $5 - \sqrt{b + 2} = 0$
$$5 - \sqrt{23 + 2} \stackrel{?}{=} 0$$
$$0 = 0 \checkmark$$
The solution is 23.

68. $\sqrt[3]{x + 5} + 6 = 4$
$$\sqrt[3]{x + 5} = -2$$
$$(\sqrt[3]{x + 5})^3 = (-2)^3$$
$$x + 5 = -8$$
$$x = -13$$
Check $\sqrt[3]{x + 5} + 6 = 4$
$$\sqrt[3]{-13 + 5} + 6 \stackrel{?}{=} 4$$
$$\sqrt[3]{-8} + 6 \stackrel{?}{=} 4$$
$$4 = 4 \checkmark$$
The solution is -13.

69. $\sqrt{n + 12} - \sqrt{n} = 2$

$$\sqrt{n + 12} = 2 + \sqrt{n}$$
$$(\sqrt{n + 12})^2 = (2 + \sqrt{n})^2$$
$$n + 12 = 4 + 4\sqrt{n} + n$$
$$8 = 4\sqrt{n}$$
$$2 = \sqrt{n}$$
$$(2)^2 = (\sqrt{n})^2$$
$$4 = n$$

Check $\sqrt{n + 12} - \sqrt{n} = 2$
$$\sqrt{4 + 12} - \sqrt{4} \stackrel{?}{=} 2$$
$$2 = 2 \checkmark$$

The solution is 4.

70. $[4 \quad 1 \quad -3] + [6 \quad -5 \quad 8]$
$$= [4 + 6 \quad 1 + (-5) \quad -3 + 8]$$
$$= [10 \quad -4 \quad 5]$$

71. $[2 \quad -5 \quad 7] - [-3 \quad 8 \quad -1]$
$$= [2 - (-3) \quad -5 - 8 \quad 7 - (-1)]$$
$$= [5 \quad -13 \quad 8]$$

72. $4\begin{bmatrix} -7 & 5 & -11 \\ 2 & -4 & 9 \end{bmatrix} = \begin{bmatrix} 4(-7) & 4(5) & 4(-11) \\ 4(2) & 4(-4) & 4(9) \end{bmatrix}$

$$= \begin{bmatrix} -28 & 20 & -44 \\ 8 & -16 & 36 \end{bmatrix}$$

73. $-2\begin{bmatrix} -3 & 0 & 12 \\ -7 & \frac{1}{3} & 4 \end{bmatrix} = \begin{bmatrix} -2(-3) & -2(0) & -2(12) \\ -2(-7) & -2\left(\frac{1}{3}\right) & -2(4) \end{bmatrix}$

$$= \begin{bmatrix} 6 & 0 & -24 \\ 14 & -\frac{2}{3} & -8 \end{bmatrix}$$

74. $y = -3x$

$y - x = 4 \rightarrow y = x + 4$

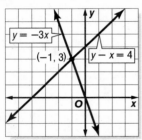

The graphs intersect at $(-1, 3)$. Since there is one solution, this system is *consistent and independent*.

75. $f(x) = x^2 + 2x - 3$

$$f(2) = (2)^2 + 2(2) - 3$$
$$= 4 + 4 - 3$$
$$= 5$$

76. $f(x) = -x^2 - 4x + 5$

$$f(-3) = -(-3)^2 - 4(-3) + 5$$
$$= -9 + 12 + 5$$
$$= 8$$

77. $f(x) = 3x^2 + 7x$

$$f(-2) = 3(-2)^2 + 7(-2)$$
$$= 12 - 14$$
$$= -2$$

78. $f(x) = \frac{2}{3}x^2 + 2x - 1$

$$f(-3) = \frac{2}{3}(-3)^2 + 2(-3) - 1$$
$$= 6 - 6 - 1$$
$$= -1$$

| 6-2 | **Solving Quadratic Equations by Graphing** |

Page 297 Check for Understanding

1a. The solution is the value that satisfies an equation.

1b. A root is a solution of an equation.

1c. A zero is the x value of a function that makes the function equal to 0.

1d. An x-intercept is the point at which a graph crosses the x-axis. The solutions, or roots, of a quadratic equation are the zeros of the related quadratic function. You can find the zeros of a quadratic function by finding the x-intercepts of its graph.

2. Sample answer: $f(x) = 3x^2 + 2x - 1$; $3x^2 + 2x - 1 = 0$

3. The x-intercepts of the related function are the solutions to the equation. You can estimate the solutions by stating the consecutive integers between which the x-intercepts are located.

4. From the graph, we can see that the zeros of the function are -4 and 1. Therefore, the solutions of the equation are -4 and 1.

5. From the graph, we can see that the zeros of the function are -2 and 1. Therefore, the solutions of the equation are -2 and 1.

6. The graph has only one x-intercept, -4. Thus, the equation's only solution is -4.

7. Graph the related quadratic function $f(x) = -x^2 - 7x$.

x	-5	-4	-3.5	-3	-2
$f(x)$	10	12	12.25	12	10

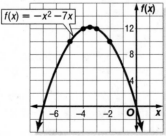

From the graph, we can see that the zeros of the function are -7 and 0. Therefore, the solutions of the equation are -7 and 0.

8. Graph the related quadratic function
$f(x) = x^2 - 2x - 24$.

x	-1	0	1	2	3
$f(x)$	-21	-24	-25	-24	-21

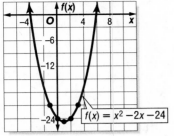

From the graph, we can see that the zeros of the function are -4 and 6. Therefore, the solutions of the equation are -4 and 6.

9. $x^2 + 3x = 28 \rightarrow x^2 + 3x - 28 = 0$
Graph the related quadratic function
$f(x) = x^2 + 3x - 28$.

x	-6	-4	-1.5	0	2
$f(x)$	-10	-24	-30.25	-28	-18

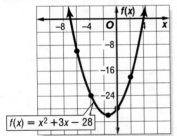

From the graph, we can see that the zeros of the function are -7 and 4. Therefore, the solutions of the equation are -7 and 4.

10. Graph the related quadratic function
$f(x) = x^2 + 10x + 25$.

x	-7	-6	-5	-4	-3
$f(x)$	4	1	0	1	4

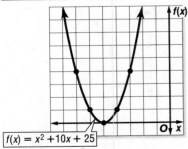

The graph has only one x-intercept, -5. Thus, the equation's only solution is -5.

11. Graph the related quadratic function
$f(x) = 4x^2 - 7x - 15$.

x	-1	0	1	2	3
$f(x)$	-4	-15	-18	-13	0

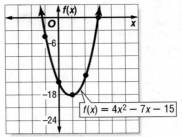

The x-intercepts are 3 and between -2 and -1. So one solution is 3, and the other is between -2 and -1.

12. Graph the related quadratic function
$f(x) = 2x^2 - 2x - 3$.

x	-1	0	0.5	1	2
$f(x)$	1	-3	-3.5	-3	1

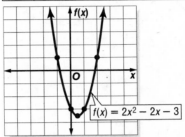

The x-intercepts of the graph are between -1 and 0 and between 1 and 2. So, one solution is between -1 and 0, and the other is between 1 and 2.

13. Let $x =$ one of the numbers. Then $5 - x =$ the other number.
Since the product of the two numbers is -14, you know that $x(5 - x) = -14$.
$$x(5 - x) = -14$$
$$5x - x^2 = -14$$
$$-x^2 + 5x + 14 = 0$$
You can solve $-x^2 + 5x + 14 = 0$ by graphing the related function $f(x) = -x^2 + 5x + 14$.

x	1	2	2.5	3	4
$f(x)$	18	20	20.25	20	18

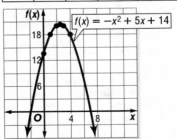

The graph has x-intercepts at -2 and 7. This means the original equation has solutions -2 and 7.
If $x = -2$, then $5 - x = 5 - (-2)$ or 7.
If $x = 7$, then $5 - x = 5 - 7$ or -2.
Thus, the two real numbers are -2 and 7.

14. From the graph, we can see that the zeros of the function are 0 and 6. Therefore, the solutions of the equation are 0 and 6.

15. The graph has only one x-intercept, 3. Thus, the equation's only solution is 3.

16. The x-intercepts of the graph are -2 and between 1 and 2. So, one solution is -2, and the other is between 1 and 2.

17. The graph has only one x-intercept, 0. Thus, the equation's only solution is 0.

18. The x-intercepts of the graph are 3 and between -1 and 0. So, one solution is 3, and the other is between -1 and 0.

19. The graph has no x-intercepts. This means that the equation has no real solutions.

20. Graph the related quadratic function $f(x) = x^2 - 3x$.

x	0	1	1.5	2	3
$f(x)$	0	-2	-2.25	-2	0

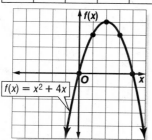

From the graph, we can see that the zeros of the function are 0 and 3. Therefore, the solutions of the equation are 0 and 3.

21. Graph the related function $f(x) = -x^2 + 4x$.

x	0	1	2	3	4
$f(x)$	0	3	4	3	0

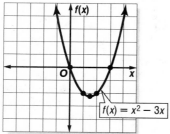

From the graph, we can see that the zeros of the function are 0 and 4. Therefore, the solutions of the equation are 0 and 4.

22. Graph the related function $f(x) = x^2 + 4x - 4$.

x	-4	-3	-2	-1	0
$f(x)$	-4	-7	-8	-7	-4

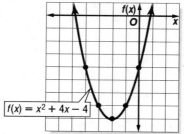

The x-intercepts of the graph are between -5 and -4 and between 0 and 1. So, one solution is between -5 and -4, and the other is between 0 and 1.

23. Graph the related function $f(x) = x^2 - 2x - 1$.

x	-1	0	1	2	3
$f(x)$	2	-1	-2	-1	2

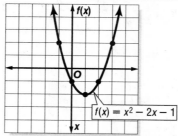

The x-intercepts of the graph are between -1 and 0 and between 2 and 3. So, one solution is between -1 and 0, and the other is between 2 and 3.

24. $-x^2 + x = -20 \rightarrow -x^2 + x + 20 = 0$
Graph the related function $f(x) = -x^2 + x + 20$.

x	-1	0	0.5	1	2
$f(x)$	18	20	20.25	20	18

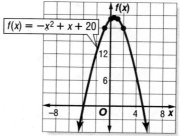

From the graph, we can see that the zeros of the function are -4 and 5. Therefore, the solutions of the equation are -4 and 5.

25. $x^2 - 9x = -18 \rightarrow x^2 - 9x + 18 = 0$
Graph the related function $f(x) = x^2 - 9x + 18$.

x	3	4	4.5	5	6
$f(x)$	0	−2	−2.25	−2	0

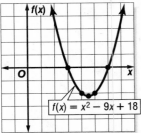

From the graph, we can see that the zeros of the function are 3 and 6. Therefore, the solutions of the equation are 3 and 6.

26. Graph the related function $f(x) = x^2 + 14x + 49$.

x	−9	−8	−7	−6	−5
$f(x)$	4	1	0	1	4

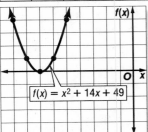

The graph has only one x-intercept, −7. Thus, the equation's only solution is −7.

27. $-12x + x^2 = -36 \rightarrow x^2 - 12x + 36 = 0$
Graph the related function $f(x) = x^2 - 12x + 36$.

x	4	5	6	7	8
$f(x)$	4	1	0	1	4

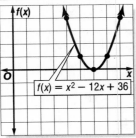

The graph has only one x-intercept, 6. Thus, the equation's only solution is 6.

28. $2x^2 - 3x = 9 \rightarrow 2x^2 - 3x - 9 = 0$
Graph the related function $f(x) = 2x^2 - 3x - 9$.

x	−1	0	1	2	3
$f(x)$	−4	−9	−10	−7	0

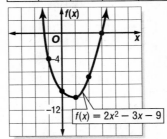

The x-intercepts of the graph are 3 and between −2 and −1. So, one solution is 3, and the other is between −2 and −1.

29. $4x^2 - 8x = 5 \rightarrow 4x^2 - 8x - 5 = 0$
Graph the related function $f(x) = 4x^2 - 8x - 5$.

x	−1	0	1	2	3
$f(x)$	7	−5	−9	−5	7

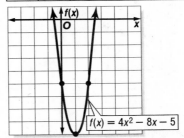

The x-intercepts of the graph are between −1 and 0 and between 2 and 3. So, one solution is between −1 and 0, and the other is between 2 and 3.

30. $2x^2 = -5x + 12 \rightarrow 2x^2 + 5x - 12 = 0$
Graph the related function $f(x) = 2x^2 + 5x - 12$.

x	−3	−2	−1	0	1
$f(x)$	−9	−14	−15	−12	−5

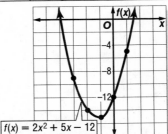

The x-intercepts of the graph are −4 and between 1 and 2. So, one solution is −4, and the other is between 1 and 2.

31. $2x^2 = x + 15 \rightarrow 2x^2 - x - 15 = 0$
Graph the related function $f(x) = 2x^2 - x - 15$.

x	-2	-1	0	1	2
$f(x)$	-5	-12	-15	-14	-9

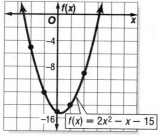

The x-intercepts of the graph are 3 and between -3 and -2. So, one solution is 3, and the other is between -3 and -2.

32. Graph the related function $f(x) = x^2 + 3x - 2$.

x	-3	-2	-1.5	-1	0
$f(x)$	-2	-4	-4.25	-4	-2

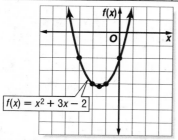

The x-intercepts of the graph are between -4 and -3 and between 0 and 1. So, one solution is between -4 and -3, and the other is between 0 and 1.

33. Graph the related function $f(x) = x^2 - 4x + 2$.

x	0	1	2	3	4
$f(x)$	2	-1	-2	-1	2

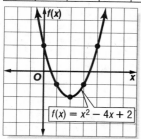

The x-intercepts of the graph are between 0 and 1 and between 3 and 4. So, one solution is between 0 and 1, and the other is between 3 and 4.

34. Graph the related function $f(x) = -2x^2 + 3x + 3$.

x	-1	0	1	2	3
$f(x)$	-2	3	4	1	-6

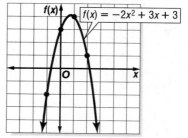

The x-intercepts of the graph are between -1 and 0 and between 2 and 3. So, one solution is between -1 and 0, and the other is between 2 and 3.

35. Graph the related function $f(x) = 0.5x^2 - 3$.

x	-2	-1	0	1	2
$f(x)$	-1	-2.5	-3	-2.5	-1

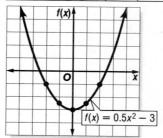

The x-intercepts of the graph are between -3 and -2 and between 2 and 3. So, one solution is between -3 and -2, and the other is between 2 and 3.

36. Graph the related function $f(x) = x^2 + 2x + 5$.

x	-3	-2	-1	0	1
$f(x)$	8	5	4	5	8

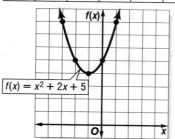

The graph has no x-intercepts. This means that the original equation has no real solution.

37. Graph the related function $f(x) = -x^2 + 4x - 6$.

x	0	1	2	3	4
$f(x)$	−6	−3	−2	−3	−6

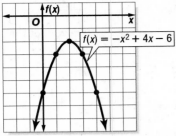

The graph has no x-intercepts. This means that the original equation has no real solution.

38. Let $x =$ one of the numbers. Then $-17 - x =$ the other number.

Since the product of the two numbers is 72, you know that $x(-17 - x) = 72$.

$$x(-17 - x) = 72$$
$$-17x - x^2 = 72$$
$$-x^2 - 17x - 72 = 0$$

You can solve $-x^2 - 17x - 72 = 0$ by graphing the related function $f(x) = -x^2 - 17x - 72$.

x	−10	−9	−8.5	−8	−7
$f(x)$	−2	0	0.25	0	−2

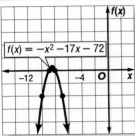

The graph has x-intercepts at -9 and -8. This means the original equation has solutions -9 and -8.
If $x = -9$, then $-17 - x = -17 - (-9)$ or -8.
If $x = -8$, then $-17 - x = -17 - (-8)$ or -9.
Thus, the two real numbers are -9 and -8.

39. Let $x =$ one of the numbers. Then $7 - x =$ the other number.

Since the product of the two numbers is 14, you know that $x(7 - x) = 14$.

$$x(7 - x) = 14$$
$$7x - x^2 = 14$$
$$-x^2 + 7x - 14 = 0$$

You can solve $-x^2 + 7x - 14 = 0$ by graphing the related function $f(x) = -x^2 + 7x - 14$.

x	2	3	3.5	4	5
$f(x)$	−4	−2	−1.75	−2	−4

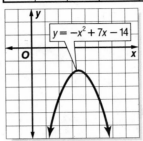

The graph has no x-intercepts. This means that the original equation has no real solutions. Thus, it is not possible for two numbers to have a sum of 7 and a product of 14.

40. Let $x =$ one of the numbers. Then $-9 - x =$ the other number.

Since the product of the two numbers is 24, you know that $x(-9 - x) = 24$.

$$x(-9 - x) = 24$$
$$-9x - x^2 = 24$$
$$-x^2 - 9x - 24 = 0$$

You can solve $-x^2 - 9x - 24 = 0$ by graphing the related function $f(x) = -x^2 - 9x - 24$.

x	−6	−5	−4.5	−4	−3
$f(x)$	−6	−4	−3.75	−4	−6

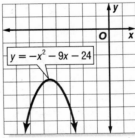

The graph has no x-intercepts. This means that the original equation has no real solutions. Thus, it is not possible for two numbers to have a sum of -9 and a product of 24.

41. Let x = one of the numbers. Then $12 - x$ = the other number.

Since the product of the two numbers is -28, you know that $x(12 - x) = -28$.

$$x(12 - x) = -28$$
$$12x - x^2 = -28$$
$$-x^2 + 12x + 28 = 0$$

You can solve $-x^2 + 12x + 28 = 0$ by graphing the related function $f(x) = -x^2 + 12x + 28$.

x	-2	2	6	10	14
$f(x)$	0	48	64	48	0

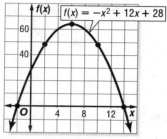

The graph has x-intercepts at -2 and 14. This means the original equation has solutions -2 and 14.

If $x = -2$, then $12 - x = 12 - (-2)$ or 14.
If $x = 14$, then $12 - x = 12 - 14$ or -2.
Thus, the two real numbers are -2 and 14.

42. We need to find t when $v_0 = 64$ and $h(t) = 0$.
Solve $0 = 64t - 16t^2$.

$$0 = 64t - 16t^2$$
$$0 = -16t^2 + 64t$$

Graph the related function $y = -16t^2 + 64t$ using a graphing calculator. Use the ZERO feature, [2nd] [CALC], to find the positive zero of the function.

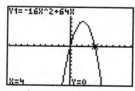

$[-10, 10]$ scl: 1 by $[-100, 100]$ scl: 10

The positive zero of the function is 4.
The arrow will hit the ground in 4 seconds.

43. We need to find t when $v_0 = 48$ and $h(t) = 0$.
Solve $0 = 48t - 16t^2$.

$$0 = 48t - 16t^2$$
$$0 = -16t^2 + 48t$$

Graph the related function $y = -16t^2 + 48t$ using a graphing calculator. Use the ZERO feature, [2nd] [CALC], to find the positive zero of the function.

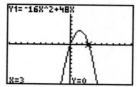

$[-10, 10]$ scl: 1 by $[-100, 100]$ scl: 10

The positive zero of the function is 3.
The ball will hit the ground in 3 seconds.

44. We need to find t when $v_0 = 190$ and $h(t) = 0$.
Solve $0 = 190t - 16t^2$.

$$0 = 190t - 16t^2$$
$$0 = -16t^2 + 190t$$

Graph the related function $y = -16t^2 + 190t$ using a graphing calculator. Use the ZERO feature, [2nd] [CALC], to find the positive zero of the function.

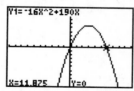

$[-20, 20]$ scl: 2 by $[-1000, 1000]$ scl: 100

The positive zero of the function is about 11.9.
The flare will hit the water in about 12 seconds.

45. We need to find s when $d = 50$.

Solve $\frac{s^2}{24} = 50$.

$$\frac{s^2}{24} = 50$$
$$0 = -\frac{s^2}{24} + 50$$

Graph the related function $y = -\frac{s^2}{24} + 50$ using a graphing calculator. Use the ZERO feature, [2nd] [CALC], to find the positive zero of the function.

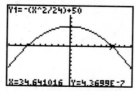

$[-50, 50]$ scl: 5 by $[-100, 100]$ scl: 10

The positive zero of the function is about 34.6.
The car was traveling about 35 miles per hour.

46. We need to find t when $h_0 = 1050$ and $h(t) = 0$.
Solve $0 = -16t^2 + 1050$.
Graph the related function $y = -16t^2 + 1050$ using a graphing calculator. Use the ZERO feature, $\boxed{\text{2nd}}$ [CALC], to find the positive zero of the function.

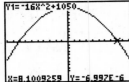

[−10, 10] scl: 1 by [−1200, 1200] scl: 100

The positive zero of the function is about 8.1. The object will reach the ground in about 8 seconds.

47. $f(x)$ must have a zero between -4 and -2. The value of the function changes from negative to positive, therefore the value of the function is zero between these two numbers.

48. Answers should include the following.

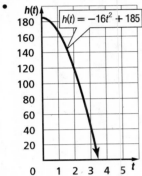

- Locate the positive x-intercept at about 3.4. This represents the time when the height of the ride is 0. Thus, if the ride were allowed to fall to the ground, it would take about 3.4 seconds.

49. A; If 4 is a root, then 4 is a solution of the equation, $x^2 + kx - 12 = 0$. Substitute 4 for x and solve for k.

$$x^2 + kx - 12 = 0$$
$$(4)^2 + k(4) - 12 = 0$$
$$16 + 4k - 12 = 0$$
$$4k = -4$$
$$k = -1$$

50. B; For this equation, $a = 1$, $b = 5$, and $c = 6$.

$$x = -\frac{b}{2a}$$
$$x = -\frac{5}{2(1)}$$
$$x = -\frac{5}{2}$$

The x-coordinate of the vertex is $-\frac{5}{2}$.

51. Graph $y = |x + 1|$.

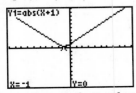

[−10, 10] scl: 1 by [−10, 10] scl: 1

The only x-intercept is -1. Thus, the equation's only solution is -1.

52. Graph $y = |x| - 3$.

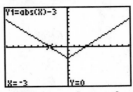

[−10, 10] scl: 1 by [−10, 10] scl: 1

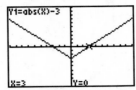

[−10, 10] scl: 1 by [−10, 10] scl: 1

The x-intercepts of the graph are -3 and 3. Thus, the solutions of the equation are -3 and 3.

53. Graph $y = |x - 4| - 1$.

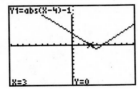

[−10, 10] scl: 1 by [−10, 10] scl: 1

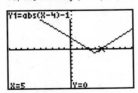

[−10, 10] scl: 1 by [−10, 10] scl: 1

The x-intercepts of the graph are 3 and 5. Thus, the solutions of the equations are 3 and 5.

54. Graph $y = -|x + 4| + 5$.

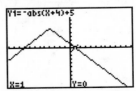

[−12, 12] scl: 1 by [−10, 10] scl: 1

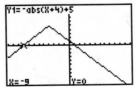

[−12, 12] scl: 1 by [−10, 10] scl: 1

The x-intercepts of the graph are -9 and 1. Thus, the solutions of the equations are -9 and 1.

55. Graph $y = 2|3x| - 8$.

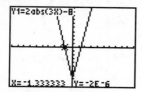

[−10, 10] scl: 1 by [−10, 10] scl: 1

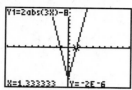

[−10, 10] scl: 1 by [−10, 10] scl: 1

The x-intercepts of the graph are about -1.33 and about 1.33. Thus, the solutions of the equation are -1.33 and 1.33.

56. Graph $y = |2x + 3| + 1$.

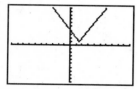

[−10, 10] scl: 1 by [−10, 10] scl: 1

The graph has no x-intercept. This means that the original equation has no real solution.

Page 299   Maintain Your Skills

57. $f(x) = x^2 - 6x + 4$

Since $c = 4$, the y-intercept is 4.
Axis of symmetry:
$$x = -\frac{b}{2a}$$
$$x = -\frac{-6}{2(1)}$$
$$x = 3$$
The equation of the axis of symmetry is $x = 3$.
Therefore, the x-coordinate of the vertex is 3.

x	$x^2 - 6x + 4$	$f(x)$	$(x, f(x))$
1	$(1)^2 - 6(1) + 4$	-1	$(1, -1)$
2	$(2)^2 - 6(2) + 4$	-4	$(2, -4)$
3	$(3)^2 - 6(3) + 4$	-5	$(3, -5)$
4	$(4)^2 - 6(4) + 4$	-4	$(4, -4)$
5	$(5)^2 - 6(5) + 4$	-1	$(5, -1)$

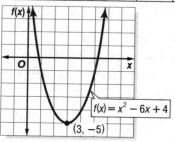

58. $f(x) = -4x^2 + 8x - 1$

Since $c = -1$, the y-intercept is -1.
Axis of symmetry:
$$x = -\frac{b}{2a}$$
$$x = -\frac{8}{2(-4)}$$
$$x = 1$$
The equation of the axis of symmetry is $x = 1$.
Therefore, the x-coordinate of the vertex is 1.

x	$-4x^2 + 8x - 1$	$f(x)$	$(x, f(x))$
-1	$-4(-1)^2 + 8(-1) - 1$	-13	$(-1, -13)$
0	$-4(0)^2 + 8(0) - 1$	-1	$(0, -1)$
1	$-4(1)^2 + 8(1) - 1$	3	$(1, 3)$
2	$-4(2)^2 + 8(2) - 1$	-1	$(2, -1)$
3	$-4(3)^2 + 8(3) - 1$	-13	$(3, -13)$

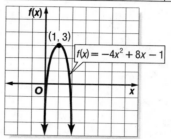

59. $f(x) = \frac{1}{4}x^2 + 3x + 4$

Since $c = 4$, the y-intercept is 4.
Axis of symmetry:
$$x = -\frac{b}{2a}$$
$$x = -\frac{3}{2\left(\frac{1}{4}\right)}$$
$$x = -6$$
The equation of the axis of symmetry is $x = -6$.
Therefore, the x-coordinate of the vertex is -6.

x	$\frac{1}{4}x^2 + 3x + 4$	$f(x)$	$(x, f(x))$
-8	$\frac{1}{4}(-8)^2 + 3(-8) + 4$	-4	$(-8, -4)$
-7	$\frac{1}{4}(-7)^2 + 3(-7) + 4$	-4.75	$(-7, -4.75)$
-6	$\frac{1}{4}(-6)^2 + 3(-6) + 4$	-5	$(-6, -5)$
-5	$\frac{1}{4}(-5)^2 + 3(-5) + 4$	-4.75	$(-5, -4.75)$
-4	$\frac{1}{4}(-4)^2 + 3(-4) + 4$	-4	$(-4, -4)$

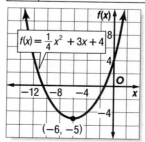

60. $\dfrac{2i}{3+i} = \dfrac{2i}{3+i} \cdot \dfrac{3-i}{3-i}$

$\qquad = \dfrac{6i - 2i^2}{9 - i^2}$

$\qquad = \dfrac{6i + 2}{10}$

$\qquad = \dfrac{1}{5} + \dfrac{3}{5}i$

61. $\dfrac{4}{5-i} = \dfrac{4}{5-i} \cdot \dfrac{5+i}{5+i}$

$\qquad = \dfrac{20 + 4i}{25 - i^2}$

$\qquad = \dfrac{20 + 4i}{26}$

$\qquad = \dfrac{10}{13} + \dfrac{2}{13}i$

62. $\dfrac{1+i}{3-2i} = \dfrac{1+i}{3-2i} \cdot \dfrac{3+2i}{3+2i}$

$\qquad = \dfrac{3 + 5i + 2i^2}{9 - 4i^2}$

$\qquad = \dfrac{1 + 5i}{13}$

$\qquad = \dfrac{1}{13} + \dfrac{5}{13}i$

63. $\begin{vmatrix} 6 & 4 \\ -3 & 2 \end{vmatrix} = 6(2) - (-3)(4)$

$\qquad = 12 - (-12)$

$\qquad = 24$

64. $\begin{vmatrix} 2 & -1 & -6 \\ 5 & 0 & 3 \\ -3 & 2 & 11 \end{vmatrix}$

$= 2\begin{vmatrix} 0 & 3 \\ 2 & 11 \end{vmatrix} - (-1)\begin{vmatrix} 5 & 3 \\ -3 & 11 \end{vmatrix} + (-6)\begin{vmatrix} 5 & 0 \\ -3 & 2 \end{vmatrix}$

$= 2(0 - 6) + 1(55 - (-9)) - 6(10 - 0)$

$= 2(-6) + 1(64) - 6(10)$

$= -12 + 64 - 60$

$= -8$

65. $\begin{vmatrix} 6 & 5 & -2 \\ -3 & 0 & 6 \\ 1 & 4 & 2 \end{vmatrix} = 6\begin{vmatrix} 0 & 6 \\ 4 & 2 \end{vmatrix} - 5\begin{vmatrix} -3 & 6 \\ 1 & 2 \end{vmatrix} + (-2)\begin{vmatrix} -3 & 0 \\ 1 & 4 \end{vmatrix}$

$\qquad = 6(0 - 24) - 5(-6 - 6) - 2(-12 - 0)$

$\qquad = 6(-24) - 5(-12) - 2(-12)$

$\qquad = -144 + 60 + 24$

$\qquad = -60$

66. Let x = the number of adults.

Let y = the number of students.

Since the number of people cannot be negative, x and y must be nonnegative numbers.

$x \geq 0$ and $y \geq 0$

The theater seats 300 people.

$x + y \leq 300$

Every two adults must bring at least one student.

$x \leq 2y$

Graph the system of inequalities.

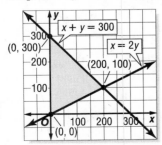

From the graph, the vertices of the feasible region are at $(0, 0)$, $(0, 300)$, and $(200, 100)$.

The function that describes the ticket sales is $f(x, y) = 2x + y$.

(x, y)	$2x + y$	$f(x, y)$
$(0, 0)$	$2(0) + 0$	0
$(0, 300)$	$2(0) + 300$	300
$(200, 100)$	$2(200) + 100$	500

The maximum value for the function is 500 at $(200, 100)$. This means the maximum amount of money that can be raised is \$500 when 200 adult tickets are sold, and 100 student tickets are sold.

67. $x^2 + 5x = x(x + 5)$

68. $x^2 - 100 = (x + 10)(x - 10)$

69. $x^2 - 11x + 28 = x^2 - 4x - 7x + 28$

$\qquad = (x^2 - 4x) + (-7x + 28)$

$\qquad = x(x - 4) - 7(x - 4)$

$\qquad = (x - 7)(x - 4)$

70. $x^2 - 18x + 81 = x^2 - 9x - 9x + 81$

$\qquad = (x^2 - 9x) + (-9x + 81)$

$\qquad = x(x - 9) - 9(x - 9)$

$\qquad = (x - 9)(x - 9)$

$\qquad = (x - 9)^2$

71. $3x^2 + 8x + 4 = 3x^2 + 6x + 2x + 4$

$\qquad = (3x^2 + 6x) + (2x + 4)$

$\qquad = 3x(x + 2) + 2(x + 2)$

$\qquad = (3x + 2)(x + 2)$

72. $6x^2 - 14x - 12 = 2(3x^2 - 7x - 6)$

$\qquad = 2(3x^2 - 9x + 2x - 6)$

$\qquad = 2[(3x^2 - 9x) + (2x - 6)]$

$\qquad = 2[3x(x - 3) + 2(x - 3)]$

$\qquad = 2(3x + 2)(x - 3)$

Page 300   Graphing Calculator Investigation (Follow-Up of Lesson 6-2)

1. Enter the speeds in L1 and the distances in L2. The linear regression equation is $y = 4.343x - 89.669$. Graph a scatter plot and the regression equation.

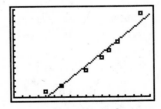

[0, 85] scl: 5 by [0, 300] scl: 20

The quadratic regression equation is $y = 0.044x^2 - 0.003x + 0.218$. Copy the equation to the Y= list and graph.

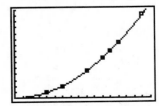

[0, 85] scl: 5 by [0, 300] scl: 20

The quadratic equation fits the data better.

2. Use the CALC menu with the linear regression equation.

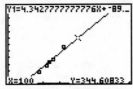

[0, 175] scl: 25 by [0, 600] scl: 50

At 100 miles per hour the braking distance is about 345 feet.

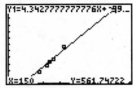

[0, 175] scl: 25 by [0, 600] scl: 50

At 150 miles per hour the braking distance is about 562 feet.

Use the CALC menu with the quadratic regression equation.

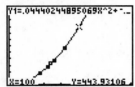

[0, 175] scl: 25 by [0, 1000] scl: 50

At 100 miles per hour the braking distance is about 440 feet.

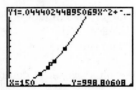

[0, 175] scl: 25 by [0, 1000] scl: 50

At 150 miles per hour the braking distance is about 990 feet.

3. The quadratic estimates are much greater.

4. Sample answer: Choosing a model that does not fit the data well may cause inaccurate predictions when the data are very large or small.

6-3 Solving Quadratic Equations by Factoring

Page 303   Check for Understanding

1. Sample answer: If the product of two factors is zero, then at least one of the factors must be zero.

2. Sample answer: roots 6 and -5; $x^2 - x - 30 = 0$

3. Kristin; The Zero Product Property applies only when one side of the equation is 0.

4. $x^2 - 11x = 0$
$x(x - 11) = 0$
$x = 0$ or $x - 11 = 0$
$\phantom{x = 0 \text{ or }} x = 11$
The solution set is {0, 11}.

5. $x^2 + 6x - 16 = 0$
$(x - 2)(x + 8) = 0$
$x - 2 = 0$ or $x + 8 = 0$
$x = 2 x = -8$
The solution set is $\{-8, 2\}$.

6. $x^2 = 49$
$x^2 - 49 = 0$
$(x - 7)(x + 7) = 0$
$x - 7 = 0$ or $x + 7 = 0$
$x = 7 x = -7$
The solution set is $\{-7, 7\}$.

7. $x^2 + 9 = 6x$
$x^2 - 6x + 9 = 0$
$(x - 3)(x - 3) = 0$
$x - 3 = 0$ or $x - 3 = 0$
$x = 3 x = 3$
The solution set is {3}.

8. $4x^2 - 13x = 12$
$4x^2 - 13x - 12 = 0$
$(x - 4)(4x + 3) = 0$
$x - 4 = 0$ or $4x + 3 = 0$
$x = 4 4x = -3$
$ x = -\dfrac{3}{4}$
The solution set is $\left\{-\dfrac{3}{4}, 4\right\}$.

9. $5x^2 - 5x - 60 = 0$
$(5x - 20)(x + 3) = 0$
$5x - 20 = 0$ or $x + 3 = 0$
$5x = 20 x = -3$
$x = 4$
The solution set is $\{-3, 4\}$.

10. $[x - (-4)](x - 7) = 0$
$(x + 4)(x - 7) = 0$
$x^2 - 3x - 28 = 0$
A quadratic equation with roots -4 and 7 and integral coefficients is $x^2 - 3x - 28 = 0$.

11. $\left(x - \dfrac{1}{2}\right)\left(x - \dfrac{4}{3}\right) = 0$
$x^2 - \dfrac{11}{6}x + \dfrac{2}{3} = 0$
$6x^2 - 11x + 4 = 0$

A quadratic equation with roots $\dfrac{1}{2}$ and $\dfrac{4}{3}$ and integral coefficients is $6x^2 - 11x + 4 = 0$.

12. $\left[x - \left(-\dfrac{3}{5}\right)\right]\left[x - \left(-\dfrac{1}{3}\right)\right] = 0$
$\left(x + \dfrac{3}{5}\right)\left(x + \dfrac{1}{3}\right) = 0$
$x^2 + \dfrac{14}{15}x + \dfrac{1}{5} = 0$
$15x^2 + 14x + 3 = 0$

A quadratic equation with roots $-\dfrac{3}{5}$ and $-\dfrac{1}{3}$ and integral coefficients is $15x^2 + 14x + 3 = 0$.

13. D; Solve this equation by factoring.
$$x^2 - 2x - 8 = 0$$
$$(x - 4)(x + 2) = 0$$
$$x - 4 = 0 \text{ or } x + 2 = 0$$
$$x = 4 \qquad x = -2$$
Add the two solutions.
$$4 + (-2) = 2$$

Pages 304–305 Practice and Apply

14. $x^2 + 5x - 24 = 0$
$(x - 3)(x + 8) = 0$
$x - 3 = 0 \text{ or } x + 8 = 0$
$\quad x = 3 \qquad x = -8$
The solution set is {-8, 3}.

15. $x^2 - 3x - 28 = 0$
$(x - 7)(x + 4) = 0$
$x - 7 = 0 \text{ or } x + 4 = 0$
$\quad x = 7 \qquad x = -4$
The solution set is {-4, 7}.

16. $\qquad x^2 = 25$
$\qquad x^2 - 25 = 0$
$(x - 5)(x + 5) = 0$
$x - 5 = 0 \text{ or } x + 5 = 0$
$\quad x = 5 \qquad x = -5$
The solution set is {-5, 5}.

17. $\qquad x^2 = 81$
$\qquad x^2 - 81 = 0$
$(x - 9)(x + 9) = 0$
$x - 9 = 0 \text{ or } x + 9 = 0$
$\quad x = 9 \qquad x = -9$
The solution set {-9, 9}

18. $\qquad x^2 + 3x = 18$
$\qquad x^2 + 3x - 18 = 0$
$(x - 3)(x + 6) = 0$
$x - 3 = 0 \text{ or } x + 6 = 0$
$\quad x = 3 \qquad x = -6$
The solution set is {-6, 3}.

19. $\qquad x^2 - 4x = 21$
$\qquad x^2 - 4x - 21 = 0$
$(x - 7)(x + 3) = 0$
$x - 7 = 0 \text{ or } x + 3 = 0$
$\quad x = 7 \qquad x = -3$
The solution set is {-3, 7}.

20. $\qquad 3x^2 = 5x$
$\qquad 3x^2 - 5x = 0$
$\qquad x(3x - 5) = 0$
$x = 0 \text{ or } 3x - 5 = 0$
$\qquad\qquad 3x = 5$
$\qquad\qquad x = \frac{5}{3}$
The solution set is $\left\{0, \frac{5}{3}\right\}$.

21. $\qquad 4x^2 = -3x$
$\qquad 4x^2 + 3x = 0$
$\qquad x(4x + 3) = 0$
$x = 0 \text{ or } 4x + 3 = 0$
$\qquad\qquad 4x = -3$
$\qquad\qquad x = -\frac{3}{4}$
The solution set is $\left\{-\frac{3}{4}, 0\right\}$.

22. $\qquad x^2 + 36 = 12x$
$\qquad x^2 - 12x + 36 = 0$
$(x - 6)(x - 6) = 0$
$x - 6 = 0 \text{ or } x - 6 = 0$
$\quad x = 6 \qquad x = 6$
The solution set is {6}.

23. $\qquad x^2 + 64 = 16x$
$\qquad x^2 - 16x + 64 = 0$
$(x - 8)(x - 8) = 0$
$x - 8 = 0 \text{ or } x - 8 = 0$
$\quad x = 8 \qquad x = 8$
The solution set is {8}.

24. $\qquad 4x^2 + 7x = 2$
$\qquad 4x^2 + 7x - 2 = 0$
$(4x - 1)(x + 2) = 0$
$4x - 1 = 0 \text{ or } x + 2 = 0$
$\quad 4x = 1 \qquad x = -2$
$\quad x = \frac{1}{4}$
The solution set is $\left\{-2, \frac{1}{4}\right\}$.

25. $\qquad 4x^2 - 17x = -4$
$\qquad 4x^2 - 17x + 4 = 0$
$(4x - 1)(x - 4) = 0$
$4x - 1 = 0 \text{ or } x - 4 = 0$
$\quad 4x = 1 \qquad x = 4$
$\quad x = \frac{1}{4}$
The solution set is $\left\{\frac{1}{4}, 4\right\}$.

26. $\qquad 4x^2 + 8x = -3$
$\qquad 4x^2 + 8x + 3 = 0$
$(2x + 1)(2x + 3) = 0$
$2x + 1 = 0 \text{ or } 2x + 3 = 0$
$\quad 2x = -1 \qquad 2x = -3$
$\quad x = -\frac{1}{2} \qquad x = -\frac{3}{2}$
The solution set is $\left\{-\frac{3}{2}, -\frac{1}{2}\right\}$.

27. $\qquad 6x^2 + 6 = -13x$
$\qquad 6x^2 + 13x + 6 = 0$
$(3x + 2)(2x + 3) = 0$
$3x + 2 = 0 \text{ or } 2x + 3 = 0$
$\quad 3x = -2 \qquad 2x = -3$
$\quad x = -\frac{2}{3} \qquad x = -\frac{3}{2}$
The solution set is $\left\{-\frac{3}{2}, -\frac{2}{3}\right\}$.

28. $\qquad 9x^2 + 30x = -16$
$\qquad 9x^2 + 30x + 16 = 0$
$(3x + 2)(3x + 8) = 0$
$3x + 2 = 0 \text{ or } 3x + 8 = 0$
$\quad 3x = -2 \qquad 3x = -8$
$\quad x = -\frac{2}{3} \qquad x = -\frac{8}{3}$
The solutions set is $\left\{-\frac{8}{3}, -\frac{2}{3}\right\}$.

29.
$$16x^2 - 48x = -27$$
$$16x^2 - 48x + 27 = 0$$
$$(4x - 9)(4x - 3) = 0$$
$$4x - 9 = 0 \text{ or } 4x - 3 = 0$$
$$4x = 9 \qquad 4x = 3$$
$$x = \frac{9}{4} \qquad x = \frac{3}{4}$$
The solution set is $\left\{\frac{3}{4}, \frac{9}{4}\right\}$.

30.
$$-2x^2 + 12x - 16 = 0$$
$$-2(x^2 - 6x + 8) = 0$$
$$x^2 - 6x + 8 = 0$$
$$(x - 4)(x - 2) = 0$$
$$x - 4 = 0 \text{ or } x - 2 = 0$$
$$x = 4 \qquad x = 2$$
The solution set is $\{2, 4\}$.

31.
$$-3x^2 - 6x + 9 = 0$$
$$-3(x^2 + 2x - 3) = 0$$
$$x^2 + 2x - 3 = 0$$
$$(x - 1)(x + 3) = 0$$
$$x - 1 = 0 \text{ or } x + 3 = 0$$
$$x = 1 \qquad x = -3$$
The solution set is $\{-3, 1\}$.

32.
$$x(x + 6)(x - 5) = 0$$
$$x = 0 \text{ or } x + 6 = 0 \text{ or } x - 5 = 0$$
$$x = -6 \qquad x = 5$$
The roots are 0, -6, and 5.

33.
$$x^3 = 9x$$
$$x^3 - 9x = 0$$
$$x(x^2 - 9) = 0$$
$$x(x - 3)(x + 3) = 0$$
$$x = 0 \text{ or } x - 3 = 0 \text{ or } x + 3 = 0$$
$$x = 3 \qquad x = -3$$
The solution set is $\{-3, 0, 3\}$.

34.
$$(x - 4)(x - 5) = 0$$
$$x^2 - 9x + 20 = 0$$

35.
$$[x - (-2)](x - 7) = 0$$
$$(x + 2)(x - 7) = 0$$
$$x^2 - 5x - 14 = 0$$

36.
$$(x - 4)[x - (-5)] = 0$$
$$(x - 4)(x + 5) = 0$$
$$x^2 + x - 20 = 0$$

37.
$$[x - (-6)][x - (-8)] = 0$$
$$(x + 6)(x + 8) = 0$$
$$x^2 + 14x + 48 = 0$$

38.
$$\left(x - \frac{1}{2}\right)(x - 3) = 0$$
$$x^2 - \frac{7}{2}x + \frac{3}{2} = 0$$
$$2x^2 - 7x + 3 = 0$$

39.
$$\left(x - \frac{1}{3}\right)(x - 5) = 0$$
$$x^2 - \frac{16}{3}x + \frac{5}{3} = 0$$
$$3x^2 - 16x + 5 = 0$$

40.
$$\left[x - \left(-\frac{2}{3}\right)\right]\left(x - \frac{3}{4}\right) = 0$$
$$\left(x + \frac{2}{3}\right)\left(x - \frac{3}{4}\right) = 0$$
$$x^2 - \frac{1}{12}x - \frac{1}{2} = 0$$
$$12x^2 - x - 6 = 0$$

41.
$$\left[x - \left(-\frac{3}{2}\right)\right]\left[x - \left(-\frac{4}{5}\right)\right] = 0$$
$$\left(x + \frac{3}{2}\right)\left(x + \frac{4}{5}\right) = 0$$
$$x^2 + \frac{23}{10}x + \frac{6}{5} = 0$$
$$10x^2 + 23x + 12 = 0$$

42. Substitute 26 for h in the equation and solve for t.
$$h = -16t^2 + 4t + 26$$
$$26 = -16t^2 + 4t + 26$$
$$0 = -16t^2 + 4t$$
$$0 = -4t(4t - 1)$$
$$-4t = 0 \text{ or } 4t - 1 = 0$$
$$t = 0 \qquad 4t = 1$$
$$t = \frac{1}{4}$$
She will be at the height of 26 feet in $\frac{1}{4}$ second.

43. Let $n =$ an even integer. Then $n + 2 =$ the next consecutive even integer.
$$n(n + 2) = 224$$
$$n^2 + 2n = 224$$
$$n^2 + 2n - 224 = 0$$
$$(n - 14)(n + 16) = 0$$
$$n - 14 = 0 \text{ or } n + 16 = 0$$
$$n = 14 \qquad n = -16$$
Therefore, the two integers are 14 and $14 + 2 = 16$, or -16 and $-16 + 2 = -14$.

44. The area of the photograph is $8 \cdot 12$ or 96 cm^2.
Let $x =$ the amount of increase.
$$2(96) = (8 + x)(12 + x)$$
$$192 = 96 + 20x + x^2$$
$$0 = x^2 + 20x - 96$$
$$0 = (x - 4)(x + 24)$$
$$x - 4 = 0 \text{ or } x + 24 = 0$$
$$x = 4 \qquad x = -24$$
Since the dimensions are increased, 4 is the only solution. The dimensions of the new photograph are $8 + 4$ or 12 cm by $12 + 4$ or 16 cm.

45. Substitute 16 for L in the equation.
$$B = \frac{L}{16}(D^2 - 8D + 16)$$
$$B = \frac{16}{16}(D^2 - 8D + 16)$$
$$B = D^2 - 8D + 16$$

46. Substitute 0 for B in the equation and solve for D.
$$B = D^2 - 8D + 16$$
$$0 = D^2 - 8D + 16$$
$$0 = (D - 4)(D - 4)$$
$$D - 4 = 0 \text{ or } D - 4 = 0$$
$$D = 4 \qquad D = 4$$
The root is 4. The logs must have a diameter greater than 4 inches for the rule to produce positive board feet values.

47. Write the related function in the form
$y = ax^2 + bx + c$.
$y = (x - p)(x - q)$
$y = x^2 - px - gx + pq$
$y = x^2 - (p + q)x + pq$
Now use $a = 1$, $b = -(p + q)$, and $c = pq$ to find the axis of symmetry.
$$x = -\frac{b}{2a}$$
$$x = -\frac{-(p + q)}{2(1)}$$
$$x = \frac{p + q}{2}$$

The axis of symmetry is the average of the x-intercepts. Therefore the axis of symmetry is located halfway between the x-intercepts.

48. Substitute -3 for x and solve for k.
$$2x^2 + kx - 21 = 0$$
$$2(-3)^2 + k(-3) - 21 = 0$$
$$18 - 3k - 21 = 0$$
$$-3k = 3$$
$$k = -1$$

49. Substitute $\frac{1}{2}$ for x and solve for k.
$$2x^2 + 11x = -k$$
$$2\left(\frac{1}{2}\right)^2 + 11\left(\frac{1}{2}\right) = -k$$
$$\frac{1}{2} + \frac{11}{2} = -k$$
$$6 = -k$$
$$-6 = k$$

50. Answers should include the following.
- Subtract 24 from each side of $x^2 + 5x = 24$ so that the equation becomes $x^2 + 5x - 24 = 0$. Factor the left side as $(x - 3)(x + 8)$. Set each factor equal to zero. Solve each equation for x. The solutions to the equation are 3 and -8. Since length cannot be negative, the width of the rectangle is 3 inches, and the length is $3 + 5$ or 8 inches.
- To use the Zero Product Property, one side of the equation must equal zero.

51. D; $6x^2 - 5x + 1 = 0$
$$(3x - 1)(2x - 1) = 0$$
$$3x - 1 = 0 \quad \text{or} \quad 2x - 1 = 0$$
$$3x = 1 \qquad\qquad 2x = 1$$
$$x = \frac{1}{3} \qquad\qquad x = \frac{1}{2}$$

52. B; $(x - 6)[x - (-3)] = 0$
$$(x - 6)(x + 3) = 0$$
$$x^2 - 3x - 18 = 0$$
$$a = 1, b = -3, c = -18$$
$$x = -\frac{b}{2a}$$
$$x = -\frac{-3}{2(1)}$$
$$x = \frac{3}{2}$$

Page 305　Maintain Your Skills

53. Graph the related function $f(x) = -x^2 - 4x + 5$.

x	-4	-3	-2	-1	0
$f(x)$	5	8	9	8	5

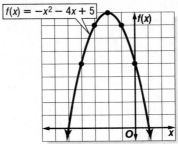

From the graph, we can see that the zeros of the function are -5 and 1.

54. Graph the related function $f(x) = 4x^2 + 4x + 1$.

x	-2	-1	-0.5	0	1
$f(x)$	9	1	0	1	9

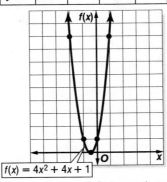

The graph has only one x-intercept, -0.5.

55. Graph the related function $f(x) = 3x^2 - 10x - 4$.

x	0	1	2	3	4
$f(x)$	-4	-11	-12	-7	4

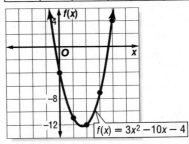

The x-intercepts of the graph are between -1 and 0 and between 3 and 4.

56. For this function, $a = 3$, $b = -12$, and $c = -7$. Since $a > 0$, the graph opens up and the function has a minimum value.

The x-coordinate of the vertex is $\frac{-(-12)}{2(3)}$ or 2.

Find the y-coordinate of the vertex by evaluating the function for $x = 2$.
$$f(x) = 3x^2 - 12x - 7$$
$$f(2) = 3(2)^2 - 12(2) - 7$$
$$= -19$$

Therefore, the minimum value of the function is -19.

57. $\sqrt{3}(\sqrt{6} - 2) = \sqrt{3}(\sqrt{6}) + \sqrt{3}(-2)$
$$= \sqrt{3 \cdot 6} - 2\sqrt{3}$$
$$= \sqrt{3^2 \cdot 2} - 2\sqrt{3}$$
$$= 3\sqrt{2} - 2\sqrt{3}$$

58. $\sqrt{108} - \sqrt{48} + (\sqrt{3})^3$
$= \sqrt{2^2 \cdot 3^2 \cdot 3} - \sqrt{2^2 \cdot 2^2 \cdot 3} + (\sqrt{3})^2 \cdot \sqrt{3}$
$= \sqrt{2^2} \cdot \sqrt{3^2} \cdot \sqrt{3} - \sqrt{2^2} \cdot \sqrt{2^2} \cdot \sqrt{3} + 3 \cdot \sqrt{3}$
$= 2 \cdot 3 \cdot \sqrt{3} - 2 \cdot 2 \cdot \sqrt{3} + 3 \cdot \sqrt{3}$
$= 6\sqrt{3} - 4\sqrt{3} + 3\sqrt{3}$
$= 5\sqrt{3}$

59. $(5 + \sqrt{8})^2 = (5 + \sqrt{8})(5 + \sqrt{8})$
$= 5(5 + \sqrt{8}) + \sqrt{8}(5 + \sqrt{8})$
$= 5(5) + 5 \cdot \sqrt{8} + \sqrt{8} \cdot 5 + \sqrt{8} \cdot \sqrt{8}$
$= 25 + 5\sqrt{8} + 5\sqrt{8} + \sqrt{8^2}$
$= 25 + 5\sqrt{8} + 5\sqrt{8} + 8$
$= 33 + 10\sqrt{8}$
$= 33 + 10\sqrt{2^2 \cdot 2}$
$= 33 + 10\sqrt{2^2} \cdot \sqrt{2}$
$= 33 + 10 \cdot 2 \cdot \sqrt{2}$
$= 33 + 20\sqrt{2}$

60. Multiply the first equation by 2 and the second equation by 3. Then subtract the equations to eliminate the b variables.

$4a - 3b = -4 \qquad \quad 8a - 6b = -8$
$3a - 2b = -4 \qquad \underline{(-)\ 9a - 6b = -12}$
$\qquad\qquad\qquad\qquad -a \qquad\quad = \quad 4$
$\qquad\qquad\qquad\qquad\qquad a = -4$

Replace a with -4 and solve for b.

$4a - 3b = -4$
$4(-4) - 3b = -4$
$-16 - 3b = -4$
$-3b = 12$
$b = -4$

The solution is $(-4, -4)$.

61. Add the equations to eliminate the s variable.

$2r + s = 1$
$\underline{(+)\ r - s = 8}$
$3r \qquad = 9$
$\qquad r = 3$

Replace r with 3 and solve for s.

$2r + s = 1$
$2(3) + s = 1$
$6 + s = 1$
$s = -5$

The solution is $(3, -5)$.

62. Subtract the equations to eliminate the x variable.

$3x - 2y = -3$
$\underline{(-)\ 3x +\ \ y =\ \ 3}$
$\qquad\qquad -3y = -6$
$\qquad\qquad\ \ y = 2$

Replace y with 2 and solve for x.

$3x - 2y = -3$
$3x - 2(2) = -3$
$3x - 4 = -3$
$3x = 1$
$x = \frac{1}{3}$

The solution is $\left(\frac{1}{3}, 2\right)$.

63. $\sqrt{8} = \sqrt{2^2 \cdot 2}$
$= \sqrt{2^2} \cdot \sqrt{2}$
$= 2 \cdot \sqrt{2}$
$= 2\sqrt{2}$

64. $\sqrt{20} = \sqrt{2^2 \cdot 5}$
$= \sqrt{2^2} \cdot \sqrt{5}$
$= 2 \cdot \sqrt{5}$
$= 2\sqrt{5}$

65. $\sqrt{27} = \sqrt{3^2 \cdot 3}$
$= \sqrt{3^2} \cdot \sqrt{3}$
$= 3 \cdot \sqrt{3}$
$= 3\sqrt{3}$

66. $\sqrt{-50} = \sqrt{-1 \cdot 5^2 \cdot 2}$
$= \sqrt{-1} \cdot \sqrt{5^2} \cdot \sqrt{2}$
$= i \cdot 5 \cdot \sqrt{2}$
$= 5i\sqrt{2}$

67. $\sqrt{-12} = \sqrt{-1}$
$= \sqrt{-1} \cdot \sqrt{2^2} \cdot \sqrt{3}$
$= i \cdot 2 \cdot \sqrt{3}$
$= 2i\sqrt{3}$

68. $\sqrt{-48} = \sqrt{-1 \cdot 2^2 \cdot 2^2 \cdot 3}$
$= \sqrt{-1} \cdot \sqrt{2^2} \cdot \sqrt{2^2} \cdot \sqrt{3}$
$= i \cdot 2 \cdot 2 \cdot \sqrt{3}$
$= 4i\sqrt{3}$

Page 305   Practice Quiz 1

1. $f(x) = 3x^2 - 12x + 4$
So, $a = 3$, $b = -12$, and $c = 4$.
Since $c = 4$, the y-intercept is 4.
Axis of symmetry:
$x = -\frac{b}{2a}$
$x = -\frac{-12}{2(3)}$
$x = 2$
The equation for the axis of symmetry is $x = 2$.
Therefore, the x-coordinate of the vertex is 2.

x	$3x^2 - 12x + 4$	$f(x)$	$(x, f(x))$
0	$3(0)^2 - 12(0) + 4$	4	$(0, 4)$
1	$3(1)^2 - 12(1) + 4$	-5	$(1, -5)$
2	$3(2)^2 - 12(2) + 4$	-8	$(2, -8)$
3	$3(3)^2 - 12(3) + 4$	-5	$(3, -5)$
4	$3(4)^2 - 12(4) + 4$	4	$(4, 4)$

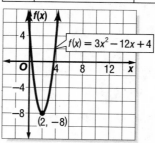

2. $f(x) = 3 - x^2 + 5x \rightarrow f(x) = -x^2 + 5x + 3$

For this function, $a = -1$, $b = 5$, and $c = 3$.

Since $a < 0$, the graph opens down and has a maximum value. The x-coordinate of the vertex is $-\frac{5}{2(-1)}$ or $\frac{5}{2}$.

$f(x) = -x^2 + 5x + 3$

$f\left(\frac{5}{2}\right) = -\left(\frac{5}{2}\right)^2 + 5\left(\frac{5}{2}\right) + 3$

$\qquad = \frac{37}{4}$

Therefore, the maximum value of the function is $\frac{37}{4}$ or $9\frac{1}{4}$.

3. Graph the related function $f(x) = 2x^2 - 11x + 12$.

x	1	2	3	4	5
$f(x)$	3	-2	-3	0	7

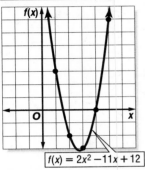

$f(x) = 2x^2 - 11x + 12$

The x-intercepts of the graph are 4 and between 1 and 2.

4. $2x^2 - 5x - 3 = 0$

$(2x - 1)(x + 3) = 0$

$2x - 1 = 0$ or $x + 3 = 0$

$\quad 2x = 1 \qquad\quad x = -3$

$\quad\ \ x = \frac{1}{2}$

5. $[x - (-4)]\left(x - \frac{1}{3}\right) = 0$

$\quad (x + 4)\left(x - \frac{1}{3}\right) = 0$

$\quad\ x^2 + \frac{11}{3}x - \frac{4}{3} = 0$

$\quad\ 3x^2 + 11x - 4 = 0$

Page 308 Algebra Activity

1. Represent $x^2 + 2x - 4 = 0$ on an equation mat.

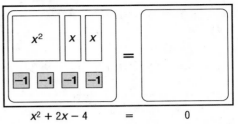

$x^2 + 2x - 4 \qquad = \qquad 0$

Add 4 to each side of the mat. Remove the zero pairs.

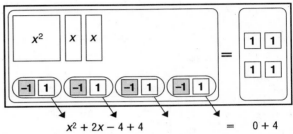

$x^2 + 2x - 4 + 4 \qquad\qquad = \qquad 0 + 4$

Begin to arrange the x^2 and x tiles into a square.

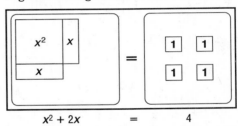

$x^2 + 2x \qquad\qquad = \qquad 4$

To complete the square, add 1 yellow 1 tile to each side. The completed equation is $x^2 + 2x + 1 = 5$ or $(x + 1)^2 = 5$.

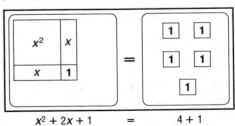

$x^2 + 2x + 1 \qquad = \qquad 4 + 1$

$(x + 1)^2 = 5$

2. Represent $x^2 + 4x + 1 = 0$ on an equation mat.

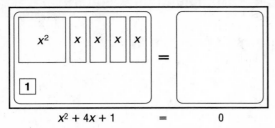

$$x^2 + 4x + 1 \quad = \quad 0$$

Add -1 to each side of the mat. Remove the zero pair

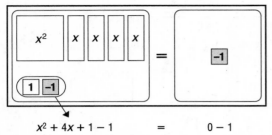

$$x^2 + 4x + 1 - 1 \quad = \quad 0 - 1$$

Begin to arrange the x^2 and x tiles into a square.

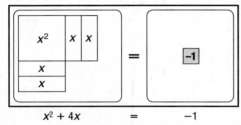

$$x^2 + 4x \quad = \quad -1$$

To complete the square, add 4 yellow 1 tiles to each side. The completed equation is
$x^2 + 4x + 4 = 3$ or $(x + 2)^2 = 3$.

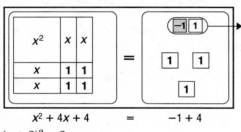

$$x^2 + 4x + 4 \quad = \quad -1 + 4$$
$$(x + 2)^2 = 3$$

3. Represent $x^2 - 6x = -5$ on an equation mat.

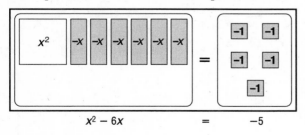

$$x^2 - 6x \quad = \quad -5$$

Begin to arrange the x^2 and x tiles into a square.

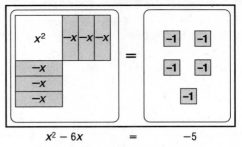

$$x^2 - 6x \quad = \quad -5$$

To complete the square, add 9 yellow 1 tiles to each side. The completed equation is
$x^2 - 6x + 9 = 4$ or $(x - 3)^2 = 4$.

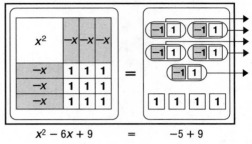

$$x^2 - 6x + 9 \quad = \quad -5 + 9$$
$$(x - 3)^2 = 4$$

4. Represent $x^2 - 2x = -1$ on an equation mat.

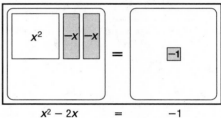

$$x^2 - 2x \quad = \quad -1$$

Begin to arrange the x^2 and x tiles into a square.

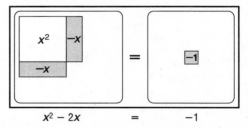

$$x^2 - 2x \quad = \quad -1$$

To complete the square, add 1 yellow 1 tile to each side. The completed equation is $x^2 - 2x + 1 = 0$ or
$(x - 1)^2 = 0$.

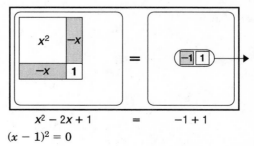

$$x^2 - 2x + 1 \quad = \quad -1 + 1$$
$$(x - 1)^2 = 0$$

1. Completing the square allows you to rewrite one side of a quadratic equation in the form of a perfect square. Once in this form, the equation is solved by using the Square Root Property.

2. Never; the value of c that makes $ax^2 + bx + c$ a perfect square trinomial is the square of $\frac{b}{2\sqrt{a}}$ and the square of a number can never be negative.

3. Tia; before completing the square, you must first check to see that the coefficient of the quadratic term is 1. If it is not, you must first divide the equation by that coefficient.

4. $x^2 + 14x + 49 = 9$
$(x + 7)^2 = 9$
$x + 7 = \pm\sqrt{9}$
$x + 7 = \pm 3$
$x = -7 \pm 3$
$x = -7 + 3$ or $x = -7 - 3$
$x = -4$ $\quad\quad x = -10$
The solution set is $\{-10, -4\}$.

5. $9x^2 - 24x + 16 = 2$
$(3x - 4)^2 = 2$
$3x - 4 = \pm\sqrt{2}$
$3x = 4 \pm \sqrt{2}$
$x = \frac{4 \pm \sqrt{2}}{3}$
$x = \frac{4 + \sqrt{2}}{3}$ or $x = \frac{4 - \sqrt{2}}{3}$

The exact solutions are $\frac{4 - \sqrt{2}}{3}$ and $\frac{4 + \sqrt{2}}{3}$. The approximate solutions are 0.9 and 1.8.

6. **Step 1** Find one half of -12. $\quad\quad \frac{-12}{2} = -6$

Step 2 Square the result of Step 1. $\quad (-6)^2 = 36$
Step 3 Add the result of Step 2 to $x^2 - 12x$. $\quad\quad x^2 - 12x + 36$
The trinomial $x^2 - 12x + 36$ can be written as $(x - 6)^2$.

7. **Step 1** Find one half of -3. $\quad\quad \frac{-3}{2} = -\frac{3}{2}$

Step 2 Square the result of Step 1. $\quad \left(-\frac{3}{2}\right)^2 = \frac{9}{4}$

Step 3 Add the result of Step 2 to $x^2 - 3x$. $\quad\quad x^2 - 3x + \frac{9}{4}$
The trinomial $x^2 - 3x + \frac{9}{4}$ can be written as $\left(x - \frac{3}{2}\right)^2$.

8. $x^2 + 3x - 18 = 0$
$x^2 + 3x = 18$
$x^2 + 3x + \frac{9}{4} = 18 + \frac{9}{4}$
$\left(x + \frac{3}{2}\right)^2 = \frac{81}{4}$
$x + \frac{3}{2} = \pm\frac{9}{2}$
$x = -\frac{3}{2} \pm \frac{9}{2}$
$x = -\frac{3}{2} + \frac{9}{2}$ or $x = -\frac{3}{2} - \frac{9}{2}$
$x = 3$ $\quad\quad x = -6$
The solution set is $\{-6, 3\}$.

9. $x^2 - 8x + 11 = 0$
$x^2 - 8x = -11$
$x^2 - 8x + 16 = -11 + 16$
$(x - 4)^2 = 5$
$x - 4 = \pm\sqrt{5}$
$x = 4 \pm \sqrt{5}$
The solution set is $\{4 + \sqrt{5}, 4 - \sqrt{5}\}$.

10. $x^2 + 2x + 6 = 0$
$x^2 + 2x = -6$
$x^2 + 2x + 1 = -6 + 1$
$(x + 1)^2 = -5$
$x + 1 = \pm\sqrt{-5}$
$x + 1 = \pm i\sqrt{5}$
$x = -1 \pm i\sqrt{5}$
The solution set is $\{-1 + i\sqrt{5}, -1 - i\sqrt{5}\}$.

11. $2x^2 - 3x - 3 = 0$
$x^2 - \frac{3}{2}x - \frac{3}{2} = 0$
$x^2 - \frac{3}{2}x = \frac{3}{2}$
$x^2 - \frac{3}{2}x + \frac{9}{16} = \frac{3}{2} + \frac{9}{16}$
$\left(x - \frac{3}{4}\right)^2 = \frac{33}{16}$
$x - \frac{3}{4} = \pm\frac{\sqrt{33}}{4}$
$x = \frac{3}{4} \pm \frac{\sqrt{33}}{4}$

The solution set is $\left\{\frac{3}{4} + \frac{\sqrt{33}}{4}, \frac{3}{4} - \frac{\sqrt{33}}{4}\right\}$.

12. The acceleration due to gravity is greater on Jupiter than on Earth. Therefore, the object should reach the ground first on Jupiter.

13. Substitute 9.8 for g, 100 for h_0, and 0 for h and solve for t.
$h = -\frac{1}{2}gt^2 + h_0$
$0 = -\frac{1}{2}(9.8)t^2 + 100$
$0 = -4.9t^2 + 100$
$4.9t^2 = 100$
$t^2 = \frac{100}{4.9}$
$t = \pm\sqrt{\frac{100}{4.9}}$
$t = \sqrt{\frac{100}{4.9}}$ or $t = -\sqrt{\frac{100}{4.9}}$
$t \approx 4.5$ $\quad\quad t \approx -4.5$
So, on Earth the object will reach the ground about 4.5 seconds after it is dropped.
Substitute 23.1 for g, 100 for h_0, and 0 for h and solve for t.
$h = -\frac{1}{2}gt^2 + h_0$
$0 = -\frac{1}{2}(23.1)t^2 + 100$
$0 = -11.55t^2 + 100$
$11.55t^2 = 100$
$t^2 = \frac{100}{11.55}$
$t = \pm\sqrt{\frac{100}{11.55}}$
$t = \sqrt{\frac{100}{11.55}}$ or $t = -\sqrt{\frac{100}{11.55}}$
$t \approx 2.9$ $\quad\quad t \approx -2.9$
So, on Jupiter the object will reach the ground about 2.9 seconds after it is dropped.

14. $x^2 + 4x + 4 = 25$
$(x + 2)^2 = 25$
$x + 2 = \pm\sqrt{25}$
$x + 2 = \pm 5$
$x = -2 \pm 5$
$x = -2 + 5$ or $x = -2 - 5$
$x = 3 \qquad\qquad x = -7$
The solution set is $\{-7, 3\}$.

15. $x^2 - 10x + 25 = 49$
$(x - 5)^2 = 49$
$x - 5 = \pm\sqrt{49}$
$x - 5 = \pm 7$
$x = 5 \pm 7$
$x = 5 + 7$ or $x = 5 - 7$
$x = 12 \qquad\quad x = -2$
The solution set is $\{-2, 12\}$.

16. $x^2 + 8x + 16 = 7$
$(x + 4)^2 = 7$
$x + 4 = \pm\sqrt{7}$
$x = -4 \pm \sqrt{7}$
$x = -4 + \sqrt{7}$ or $x = -4 - \sqrt{7}$
$x \approx -1.4 \qquad\qquad x \approx -6.6$
The exact solutions are $-4 - \sqrt{7}$ and $-4 + \sqrt{7}$.
The approximate solutions are -6.6 and -1.4.

17. $x^2 - 6x + 9 = 8$
$(x - 3)^2 = 8$
$x - 3 = \pm\sqrt{8}$
$x - 3 = \pm 2\sqrt{2}$
$x = 3 \pm 2\sqrt{2}$
$x = 3 + 2\sqrt{2}$ or $x = 3 - 2\sqrt{2}$
$x \approx 5.8 \qquad\qquad x \approx 0.2$
The exact solutions are $3 - 2\sqrt{2}$ and $3 + 2\sqrt{2}$.
The approximate solutions are 0.2 and 5.8.

18. $4x^2 - 28x + 49 = 5$
$(2x - 7)^2 = 5$
$2x - 7 = \pm\sqrt{5}$
$2x = 7 \pm \sqrt{5}$
$x = \dfrac{7 \pm \sqrt{5}}{2}$
$x = \dfrac{7 + \sqrt{5}}{2}$ or $x = \dfrac{7 - \sqrt{5}}{2}$.
$x \approx 4.6 \qquad\qquad x \approx 2.4$
The exact solutions are $\dfrac{7 - \sqrt{5}}{2}$ and $\dfrac{7 + \sqrt{5}}{2}$.
The approximate solutions are 2.4 and 4.6.

19. $9x^2 + 30x + 25 = 11$
$(3x + 5)^2 = 11$
$3x + 5 = \pm\sqrt{11}$
$3x = -5 \pm \sqrt{11}$
$x = \dfrac{-5 \pm \sqrt{11}}{3}$
$x = \dfrac{-5 + \sqrt{11}}{3}$ or $x = \dfrac{-5 - \sqrt{11}}{3}$
$x \approx -0.6 \qquad\qquad x \approx -2.8$
The exact solutions are $\dfrac{-5 - \sqrt{11}}{3}$ and $\dfrac{-5 + \sqrt{11}}{3}$.
The approximate solutions are -2.8 and -0.6.

20. $x^2 + x + \dfrac{1}{4} = \dfrac{9}{16}$
$\left(x + \dfrac{1}{2}\right)^2 = \dfrac{9}{16}$
$x + \dfrac{1}{2} = \pm\sqrt{\dfrac{9}{16}}$
$x + \dfrac{1}{2} = \pm\dfrac{3}{4}$
$x = -\dfrac{1}{2} \pm \dfrac{3}{4}$
$x = -\dfrac{1}{2} + \dfrac{3}{4}$ or $x = -\dfrac{1}{2} - \dfrac{3}{4}$
$x = \dfrac{1}{4} \qquad\qquad x = -\dfrac{5}{4}$
The solution set is $\left\{-\dfrac{5}{4}, \dfrac{1}{4}\right\}$.

21. $x^2 + 1.4x + 0.49 = 0.81$
$(x + 0.7)^2 = 0.81$
$x + 0.7 = \pm\sqrt{0.81}$
$x + 0.7 = \pm 0.9$
$x = -0.7 \pm 0.9$
$x = -0.7 + 0.9$ or $x = -0.7 - 0.9$
$x = 0.2 \qquad\qquad x = -1.6$
The solution set is $\{-1.6, 0.2\}$.

22. Substitute 100 for A in the equation and solve for d.
$A = 0.16d^2$
$100 = 0.16d^2$
$625 = d^2$
$\pm\sqrt{625} = d$
$\pm 25 = d$
So, the area will be 100 square feet at a distance of 25 feet.

23. Substitute 10 for d in the equation and solve for t.
$d = -1.5t^2 + 120$
$10 = -1.5t^2 + 120$
$-110 = -1.5t^2$
$\dfrac{220}{3} = t^2$
$\pm\sqrt{\dfrac{220}{3}} = t$
$t = \sqrt{\dfrac{220}{3}}$ or $t = -\sqrt{\dfrac{220}{3}}$
$t \approx 8.56 \qquad t \approx -8.56$
So, about 8.56 seconds have passed when the shed is 10 meters from the target.

24. Step 1 Find one half of 16. $\qquad \dfrac{16}{2} = 8$

Step 2 Square the result of Step 1. $\qquad 8^2 = 64$
Step 3 Add the result of Step 2 to $x^2 + 16x$. $\qquad x^2 + 16x + 64$
The trinomial $x^2 + 16x + 64$ can be written as $(x + 8)^2$.

25. Step 1 Find one half of -18. $\qquad \dfrac{-18}{2} = -9$

Step 2 Square the result of Step 1. $\qquad (-9)^2 = 81$
Step 3 Add the result of Step 2 to $x^2 - 18x$. $\qquad x^2 - 18x + 81$
The trinomial $x^2 - 18x + 81$ can be written as $(x - 9)^2$.

26. Step 1 Find one half of -15. $\qquad \dfrac{-15}{2} = -\dfrac{15}{2}$

Step 2 Square the result of Step 1. $\quad \left(-\dfrac{15}{2}\right)^2 = \dfrac{225}{4}$

Step 3 Add the result of Step 2 to

$x^2 - 15x$. $\qquad\qquad\qquad\qquad x^2 - 15x + \dfrac{225}{4}$

The trinomial $x^2 - 15x + \dfrac{225}{4}$ can be written as $\left(x - \dfrac{15}{2}\right)^2$.

27. Step 1 Find one half of 7. $\qquad \dfrac{7}{2} = \dfrac{7}{2}$

Step 2 Square the result of Step 1. $\quad \left(\dfrac{7}{2}\right)^2 = \dfrac{49}{4}$

Step 3 Add the result of Step 2 to

$x^2 + 7x$. $\qquad\qquad\qquad\qquad x^2 + 7x + \dfrac{49}{4}$

The trinomial $x^2 + 7x + \dfrac{49}{4}$ can be written as $\left(x + \dfrac{7}{2}\right)^2$.

28. Step 1 Find one half of 0.6. $\qquad \dfrac{0.6}{2} = 0.3$

Step 2 Square the result of Step 1. $\quad 0.3^2 = 0.09$

Step 3 Add the result of Step 2 to

$x^2 + 0.6x$. $\qquad\qquad\qquad\qquad x^2 + 0.6x + 0.09$

The trinomial $x^2 + 0.6x + 0.09$ can be written as $(x + 0.3)^2$.

29. Step 1 Find one half of -2.4. $\qquad \dfrac{-2.4}{2} = -1.2$

Step 2 Square the result of Step 1. $(-1.2)^2 = 1.44$

Step 3 Add the result of Step 2 to

$x^2 - 2.4x$. $\qquad\qquad\qquad\qquad x^2 - 2.4x + 1.44$

The trinomial $x^2 - 2.4x + 1.44$ can be written as $(x - 1.2)^2$.

30. Step 1 Find one half of $-\dfrac{8}{3}$. $\qquad \dfrac{-\frac{8}{3}}{2} = -\dfrac{4}{3}$

Step 2 Square the result of Step 1. $\quad \left(-\dfrac{4}{3}\right)^2 = \dfrac{16}{9}$

Step 3 Add the result of Step 2 to

$x^2 - \dfrac{8}{3}x$. $\qquad\qquad\qquad\qquad x^2 - \dfrac{8}{3}x + \dfrac{16}{9}$

The trinomial $x^2 - \dfrac{8}{3}x + \dfrac{16}{9}$ can be written

as $\left(x - \dfrac{4}{3}\right)^2$.

31. Step 1 Find one half of $\dfrac{5}{2}$. $\qquad \dfrac{\frac{5}{2}}{2} = \dfrac{5}{4}$

Step 2 Square the result of Step 1. $\quad \left(\dfrac{5}{4}\right)^2 = \dfrac{25}{16}$

Step 3 Add the result of Step 2 to

$x^2 + \dfrac{5}{2}x$. $\qquad\qquad\qquad\qquad x^2 + \dfrac{5}{2}x + \dfrac{25}{16}$

The trinomial $x^2 + \dfrac{5}{2}x + \dfrac{25}{16}$ can be written as $\left(x + \dfrac{5}{4}\right)^2$.

32. $x^2 - 8x + 15 = 0$
$$x^2 - 8x = -15$$
$$x^2 - 8x + 16 = -15 + 16$$
$$(x - 4)^2 = 1$$
$$x - 4 = \pm 1$$
$$x = 4 \pm 1$$
$x = 4 + 1 \text{ or } x = 4 - 1$
$x = 5 \qquad\quad x = 3$
The solution set is $\{3, 5\}$.

33. $x^2 + 2x - 120 = 0$
$$x^2 + 2x = 120$$
$$x^2 + 2x + 1 = 120 + 1$$
$$(x + 1)^2 = 121$$
$$x + 1 = \pm 11$$
$$x = -1 \pm 11$$
$x = -1 + 11 \text{ or } x = -1 - 11$
$x = 10 \qquad\qquad x = -12$
The solution set is $\{-12, 10\}$.

34. $x^2 + 2x - 6 = 0$
$$x^2 + 2x = 6$$
$$x^2 + 2x + 1 = 6 + 1$$
$$(x + 1)^2 = 7$$
$$x + 1 = \pm\sqrt{7}$$
$$x = -1 \pm \sqrt{7}$$
The solution set is $\{-1 - \sqrt{7}, -1 + \sqrt{7}\}$.

35. $x^2 - 4x + 1 = 0$
$$x^2 - 4x = -1$$
$$x^2 - 4x + 4 = -1 + 4$$
$$(x - 2)^2 = 3$$
$$x - 2 = \pm\sqrt{3}$$
$$x = 2 \pm \sqrt{3}$$
The solution set is $\{2 - \sqrt{3}, 2 + \sqrt{3}\}$.

36. $x^2 - 4x + 5 = 0$
$$x^2 - 4x = -5$$
$$x^2 - 4x + 4 = -5 + 4$$
$$(x - 2)^2 = -1$$
$$x - 2 = \pm\sqrt{-1}$$
$$x - 2 = \pm i$$
$$x = 2 \pm i$$
The solution set is $\{2 - i, 2 + i\}$.

37. $x^2 + 6x + 13 = 0$
$$x^2 + 6x = -13$$
$$x^2 + 6x + 9 = -13 + 9$$
$$(x + 3)^2 = -4$$
$$x + 3 = \pm\sqrt{-4}$$
$$x + 3 = \pm 2i$$
$$x = -3 \pm 2i$$
The solution set is $\{-3 - 2i, -3 + 2i\}$.

38. $2x^2 + 3x - 5 = 0$
$$x^2 + \dfrac{3}{2}x - \dfrac{5}{2} = 0$$
$$x^2 + \dfrac{3}{2}x = \dfrac{5}{2}$$
$$x^2 + \dfrac{3}{2}x + \dfrac{9}{16} = \dfrac{5}{2} + \dfrac{9}{16}$$
$$\left(x + \dfrac{3}{4}\right)^2 = \dfrac{49}{16}$$
$$x + \dfrac{3}{4} = \pm\dfrac{7}{4}$$
$$x = -\dfrac{3}{4} \pm \dfrac{7}{4}$$
$x = -\dfrac{3}{4} + \dfrac{7}{4} \text{ or } x = -\dfrac{3}{4} - \dfrac{7}{4}$
$x = 1 \qquad\qquad x = -\dfrac{5}{2}$
The solution set is $\left\{-\dfrac{5}{2}, 1\right\}$.

39. $2x^2 - 3x + 1 = 0$

$x^2 - \frac{3}{2}x + \frac{1}{2} = 0$

$x^2 - \frac{3}{2}x = -\frac{1}{2}$

$x^2 - \frac{3}{2}x + \frac{9}{16} = -\frac{1}{2} + \frac{9}{16}$

$\left(x - \frac{3}{4}\right)^2 = \frac{1}{16}$

$x - \frac{3}{4} = \pm\frac{1}{4}$

$x = \frac{3}{4} \pm \frac{1}{4}$

$x = \frac{3}{4} + \frac{1}{4}$ or $x = \frac{3}{4} - \frac{1}{4}$

$x = 1$ $\qquad x = \frac{1}{2}$

The solution set is $\left\{\frac{1}{2}, 1\right\}$.

40. $3x^2 - 5x + 1 = 0$

$x^2 - \frac{5}{3}x + \frac{1}{3} = 0$

$x^2 - \frac{5}{3}x = -\frac{1}{3}$

$x^2 - \frac{5}{3}x + \frac{25}{36} = -\frac{1}{3} + \frac{25}{36}$

$\left(x - \frac{5}{6}\right)^2 = \frac{13}{36}$

$x - \frac{5}{6} = \pm\sqrt{\frac{13}{36}}$

$x - \frac{5}{6} = \pm\frac{\sqrt{13}}{6}$

$x = \frac{5}{6} \pm \frac{\sqrt{13}}{6}$

The solution set is $\left\{\frac{5}{6} - \frac{\sqrt{13}}{6}, \frac{5}{6} + \frac{\sqrt{13}}{6}\right\}$.

41. $3x^2 - 4x - 2 = 0$

$x^2 - \frac{4}{3}x - \frac{2}{3} = 0$

$x^2 - \frac{4}{3}x = \frac{2}{3}$

$x^2 - \frac{4}{3}x + \frac{4}{9} = \frac{2}{3} + \frac{4}{9}$

$\left(x - \frac{2}{3}\right)^2 = \frac{10}{9}$

$x - \frac{2}{3} = \pm\sqrt{\frac{10}{9}}$

$x - \frac{2}{3} = \pm\frac{\sqrt{10}}{3}$

$x = \frac{2}{3} \pm \frac{\sqrt{10}}{3}$

The solution set is $\left\{\frac{2}{3} - \frac{\sqrt{10}}{3}, \frac{2}{3} + \frac{\sqrt{10}}{3}\right\}$.

42. $2x^2 - 7x + 12 = 0$

$x^2 - \frac{7}{2}x + 6 = 0$

$x^2 - \frac{7}{2}x = -6$

$x^2 - \frac{7}{2}x + \frac{49}{16} = -6 + \frac{49}{16}$

$\left(x - \frac{7}{4}\right)^2 = -\frac{47}{16}$

$x - \frac{7}{4} = \pm\sqrt{-\frac{47}{16}}$

$x - \frac{7}{4} = \pm i\frac{\sqrt{47}}{4}$

$x = \frac{7}{4} \pm i\frac{\sqrt{47}}{4}$

The solution set is $\left\{\frac{7}{4} - i\frac{\sqrt{47}}{4}, \frac{7}{4} + i\frac{\sqrt{47}}{4}\right\}$.

43. $3x^2 + 5x + 4 = 0$

$x^2 + \frac{5}{3}x + \frac{4}{3} = 0$

$x^2 + \frac{5}{3}x = -\frac{4}{3}$

$x^2 + \frac{5}{3}x + \frac{25}{36} = -\frac{4}{3} + \frac{25}{36}$

$\left(x + \frac{5}{6}\right)^2 = -\frac{23}{36}$

$x + \frac{5}{6} = \pm\sqrt{-\frac{23}{36}}$

$x + \frac{5}{6} = \pm i\frac{\sqrt{23}}{6}$

$x = -\frac{5}{6} \pm i\frac{\sqrt{23}}{6}$

The solution set is $\left\{-\frac{5}{6} - i\frac{\sqrt{23}}{6}, -\frac{5}{6} + i\frac{\sqrt{23}}{6}\right\}$.

44. $\qquad x^2 + 1.4x = 1.2$

$x^2 + 1.4x + 0.49 = 1.2 + 0.49$

$(x + 0.7)^2 = 1.69$

$x + 0.7 = \pm 1.3$

$x = -0.7 \pm 1.3$

$x = -0.7 + 1.3$ or $x = -0.7 - 1.3$

$x = 0.6$ $\qquad x = -2$

The solution set is $\{-2, 0.6\}$.

45. $\qquad x^2 - 4.7x = -2.8$

$x^2 - 4.7x + 5.5225 = -2.8 + 5.5225$

$(x - 2.35)^2 = 2.7225$

$x - 2.35 = \pm 1.65$

$x = 2.35 \pm 1.65$

$x = 2.35 + 1.65$ or $x = 2.35 - 1.65$

$x = 4$ $\qquad x = 0.7$

The solution set is $\{0.7, 4\}$.

46. $x^2 - \frac{2}{3}x - \frac{26}{9} = 0$

$x^2 - \frac{2}{3}x = \frac{26}{9}$

$x^2 - \frac{2}{3}x + \frac{1}{9} = \frac{26}{9} + \frac{1}{9}$

$\left(x - \frac{1}{3}\right)^2 = 3$

$x - \frac{1}{3} = \pm\sqrt{3}$

$x = \frac{1}{3} \pm \sqrt{3}$

The solution set is $\left\{\frac{1}{3} - \sqrt{3}, \frac{1}{3} + \sqrt{3}\right\}$.

47. $x^2 - \frac{3}{2}x - \frac{23}{16} = 0$

$x^2 - \frac{3}{2}x = \frac{23}{16}$

$x^2 - \frac{3}{2}x + \frac{9}{16} = \frac{23}{16} + \frac{9}{16}$

$\left(x - \frac{3}{4}\right)^2 = 2$

$x - \frac{3}{4} = \pm\sqrt{2}$

$x = \frac{3}{4} \pm \sqrt{2}$

The solution set is $\left\{\frac{3}{4} - \sqrt{2}, \frac{3}{4} + \sqrt{2}\right\}$.

48. Let x = the side length of the picture. Then $x + 4$ = the side length of the frame.

The area of the picture	is	one-third	of	the total area of the picture and frame.
x^2	$=$	$\frac{1}{3}$	$\cdot$	$(x + 4)^2$

$$x^2 = \frac{1}{3}(x + 4)^2$$
$$x^2 = \frac{1}{3}(x^2 + 8x + 16)$$
$$3x^2 = x^2 + 8x + 16$$
$$2x^2 - 8x - 16 = 0$$
$$x^2 - 4x - 8 = 0$$
$$x^2 - 4x = 8$$
$$x^2 - 4x + 4 = 8 + 4$$
$$(x - 2)^2 = 12$$
$$x - 2 = \pm\sqrt{12}$$
$$x = 2 \pm \sqrt{12}$$
$$x = 2 + \sqrt{12} \text{ or } x = 2 - \sqrt{12}$$
$$x \approx 5.5 \qquad x \approx -1.5$$

So, the side length of the picture is about 5.5. The dimensions are $5\frac{1}{2}$ inches by $5\frac{1}{2}$ inches.

49. For rectangle $ABCD$, the length of the longer side is x, and the length of the shorter side is 1.

Therefore, the ratio is $x{:}1$ or $\frac{x}{1}$. For rectangle $EBCF$, the length of the longer side is 1, and the length of the shorter side is $x - 1$. Therefore, the ratio is $1{:}(x - 1)$ or $\frac{1}{x - 1}$.

50.
$$\frac{x}{1} = \frac{1}{x - 1}$$
$$x(x - 1) = 1(1)$$
$$x^2 - x = 1$$
$$x^2 - x + \frac{1}{4} = 1 + \frac{1}{4}$$
$$\left(x - \frac{1}{2}\right)^2 = \frac{5}{4}$$
$$x - \frac{1}{2} = \pm\sqrt{\frac{5}{4}}$$
$$x - \frac{1}{2} = \pm\frac{\sqrt{5}}{2}$$
$$x = \frac{1}{2} \pm \frac{\sqrt{5}}{2}$$

Since the golden ratio is positive, the golden ratio is $\frac{1 + \sqrt{5}}{2}$.

51. Sample answer: The golden rectangle is found in much of ancient Greek architecture, such as the Parthenon, as well as in modern architecture, such as in the windows of the United Nations buildings. Many songs have their climax at a point occurring 61.8% of the way through the piece, with 0.618 being about the reciprocal of the golden ratio. The reciprocal of the golden ratio is also used in the design of some violins.

52. Solve the equation for x.
$$x^2 + bx + \left(\frac{b}{2}\right)^2 = n$$
$$\left(x + \frac{b}{2}\right)^2 = n$$
$$x + \frac{b}{2} = \pm\sqrt{n}$$
$$x = -\frac{b}{2} \pm \frac{\sqrt{n}}{2}$$

52a. There will be one real root if the two solutions are equal.
$$-\frac{b}{2} + \frac{\sqrt{n}}{2} = -\frac{b}{2} - \frac{\sqrt{n}}{2}$$
$$\frac{\sqrt{n}}{2} = -\frac{\sqrt{n}}{2}$$
$$\sqrt{n} = -\sqrt{n}$$
$$2\sqrt{n} = 0$$
$$\sqrt{n} = 0$$
$$n = 0$$

52b. There will be two real roots if $\sqrt{n}$ is a real nonzero number. $\sqrt{n}$ is a real nonzero number when $n > 0$.

52c. There will be two imaginary roots if $\sqrt{n}$ is an imaginary number. $\sqrt{n}$ is an imaginary number when $n < 0$.

53. 164 feet of fencing to enclose the region as shown can be written as $6\ell + 4w = 164$. The total area to be enclosed is 576 square feet can be written as $3\ell \cdot w = 576$. Solve the second equation for ℓ.
$$3\ell w = 576$$
$$\ell = \frac{576}{3w}$$
$$\ell = \frac{192}{w}$$

Substitute $\frac{192}{w}$ for ℓ in the first equation.
$$6\ell + 4w = 164$$
$$6\left(\frac{192}{w}\right) + 4w = 164$$
$$\frac{1152}{w} + 4w = 164$$
$$1152 + 4w^2 = 164w$$
$$4w^2 - 164w + 1152 = 0$$
$$w^2 - 41w + 288 = 0$$
$$w^2 - 41w = -288$$
$$w^2 - 41w + 420.25 = -288 + 420.25$$
$$(w - 20.5)^2 = 132.25$$
$$w - 20.5 = \pm11.5$$
$$w = 20.5 \pm 11.5$$
$$w = 20.5 + 11.5 \text{ or } w = 20.5 - 11.5$$
$$w = 32 \qquad w = 9$$

Substitute 32 for w in one of the equations.
$$3\ell w = 576$$
$$3\ell(32) = 576$$
$$96\ell = 576$$
$$\ell = 6$$

Substitute 9 for w in one of the equations.
$$3\ell w = 576$$
$$3\ell(9) = 576$$
$$27\ell = 576$$
$$\ell = \frac{64}{3}$$

Therefore, the entire region is $3 \cdot 6$ or 18 ft by 32 ft, or $3 \cdot \frac{64}{3}$ or 64 ft by 9 ft.

54. To find the distance traveled by the accelerating race car in the given situation, you must solve the equation $t^2 + 22t + 121 = 246$ or $t^2 + 22t - 125 = 0$.

Answers should include the following.

- Since the expression $t^2 + 22t - 125$ is prime, the solutions of $t^2 + 22t + 121 = 246$ cannot be obtained by factoring.

- Rewrite $t^2 + 22t + 121$ as $(t + 11)^2$. Solve $(t + 11)^2 = 246$ by applying the Square Root Property. Then, subtract 11 from each side. Using a calculator, the two solutions are about 4.7 or -26.7. Since time cannot be negative, the driver takes about 4.7 seconds to reach the finish line.

55. D; Solve $x^2 - 2x - 2 = 0$.

$$x^2 - 2x - 2 = 0$$
$$x^2 - 2x = 2$$
$$x^2 - 2x + 1 = 2 + 1$$
$$(x - 1)^2 = 3$$
$$x - 1 = \pm\sqrt{3}$$
$$x = 1 \pm \sqrt{3}$$

The solution set is $\{1 - \sqrt{3}, 1 + \sqrt{3}\}$.
Find $\left|(1 - \sqrt{3})(1 + \sqrt{3})\right|$.

$$\left|(1 - \sqrt{3})(1 + \sqrt{3})\right|$$
$$= \left|1 \cdot 1 + 1 \cdot \sqrt{3} - \sqrt{3} \cdot 1 - \sqrt{3} \cdot \sqrt{3}\right|$$
$$= \left|1 + \sqrt{3} - \sqrt{3} - \sqrt{3^2}\right|$$
$$= \left|1 - 3\right|$$
$$= \left|-2\right|$$
$$= 2$$

56. D; The roots will be real and equal if $x^2 + 4x + c$ is a perfect square.

Step 1 Find one half of 4. $\quad \frac{4}{2} = 2$

Step 2 Square the result of Step 1. $\quad 2^2 = 4$

Step 3 Add the result of Step 2 to $x^2 + 4x$. $\quad x^2 + 4x + 4$

The roots will be real and equal if $c = 4$.

Page 312　Maintain Your Skills

57. $(x - 2)(x - 1) = 0$
$$x^2 - 3x + 2 = 0$$

58. $[x - (-3)](x - 9) = 0$
$$(x + 3)(x - 9) = 0$$
$$x^2 - 6x - 27 = 0$$

59. $(x - 6)\left(x - \frac{1}{3}\right) = 0$
$$x^2 - \frac{19}{3}x + 2 = 0$$
$$3x^2 - 19x + 6 = 0$$

60. $\left[x - \left(-\frac{1}{3}\right)\right]\left[x - \left(-\frac{3}{4}\right)\right] = 0$
$$\left(x + \frac{1}{3}\right)\left(x + \frac{3}{4}\right) = 0$$
$$x^2 + \frac{13}{12}x + \frac{1}{4} = 0$$
$$12x^2 + 13x + 3 = 0$$

61. $3x^2 = 4 - 8x \rightarrow 3x^2 + 8x - 4 = 0$
Graph the related function $f(x) = 3x^2 + 8x - 4$.

x	-3	-2	-1	0	1
$f(x)$	-1	-8	-9	-4	7

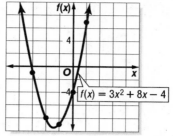

The x-intercepts of the graph are between -4 and -3 and between 0 and 1. So, one solution is between -4 and -3, and the other is between 0 and 1.

62. $x^2 + 48 = 14x \rightarrow x^2 - 14x + 48 = 0$
Graph the related function $f(x) = x^2 - 14x + 48$.

x	5	6	7	8	9
$f(x)$	3	0	-1	0	3

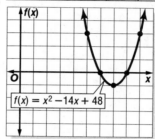

From the graph, we can see that the zeros of the function are 6 and 8. Therefore, the solutions of the equation are 6 and 8.

63. $2x^2 + 11x = -12 \rightarrow 2x^2 + 11x + 12 = 0$
Graph the related function $f(x) = 2x^2 + 11x + 12$.

x	-5	-4	-3	-2	-1
$f(x)$	7	0	-3	-2	3

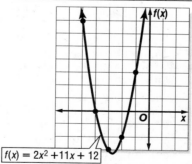

The x-intercepts of the graph are -4 and between -2 and -1.

64. $7\sqrt{5^3} = 5^{\frac{3}{7}}$

65. The matrix equation is $\begin{bmatrix} 5 & 3 \\ 7 & 5 \end{bmatrix} \cdot \begin{bmatrix} x \\ y \end{bmatrix} = \begin{bmatrix} -5 \\ -11 \end{bmatrix}$.

Find the inverse of the coefficient matrix.

$A^{-1} = \frac{1}{25-21}\begin{bmatrix} 5 & -3 \\ -7 & 5 \end{bmatrix}$ or $\frac{1}{4}\begin{bmatrix} 5 & -3 \\ -7 & 5 \end{bmatrix}$

Multiply each side of the matrix equation by the inverse matrix.

$\frac{1}{4}\begin{bmatrix} 5 & -3 \\ -7 & 5 \end{bmatrix} \cdot \begin{bmatrix} 5 & 3 \\ 7 & 5 \end{bmatrix} \cdot \begin{bmatrix} x \\ y \end{bmatrix} = \frac{1}{4}\begin{bmatrix} 5 & -3 \\ -7 & 5 \end{bmatrix} \cdot \begin{bmatrix} -5 \\ -11 \end{bmatrix}$

$\begin{bmatrix} 1 & 0 \\ 0 & 1 \end{bmatrix} \cdot \begin{bmatrix} x \\ y \end{bmatrix} = \frac{1}{4}\begin{bmatrix} 8 \\ -20 \end{bmatrix}$

$\begin{bmatrix} x \\ y \end{bmatrix} = \begin{bmatrix} 2 \\ -5 \end{bmatrix}$

The solution is $(2, -5)$.

66. The matrix equation is $\begin{bmatrix} 6 & 5 \\ 3 & -1 \end{bmatrix} \cdot \begin{bmatrix} x \\ y \end{bmatrix} = \begin{bmatrix} 8 \\ 7 \end{bmatrix}$.

Find the inverse of the coefficient matrix.

$A^{-1} = \frac{1}{-6-15}\begin{bmatrix} -1 & -5 \\ -3 & 6 \end{bmatrix}$ or $-\frac{1}{21}\begin{bmatrix} -1 & -5 \\ -3 & 6 \end{bmatrix}$

Multiply each side of the matrix equation by the inverse matrix.

$-\frac{1}{21}\begin{bmatrix} -1 & -5 \\ -3 & 6 \end{bmatrix} \cdot \begin{bmatrix} 6 & 5 \\ 3 & -1 \end{bmatrix} \cdot \begin{bmatrix} x \\ y \end{bmatrix} = -\frac{1}{21}\begin{bmatrix} -1 & -5 \\ -3 & 6 \end{bmatrix} \cdot \begin{bmatrix} 8 \\ 7 \end{bmatrix}$

$\begin{bmatrix} 1 & 0 \\ 0 & 1 \end{bmatrix} \cdot \begin{bmatrix} x \\ y \end{bmatrix} = -\frac{1}{21}\begin{bmatrix} -43 \\ 18 \end{bmatrix}$

$\begin{bmatrix} x \\ y \end{bmatrix} = \begin{bmatrix} \frac{43}{21} \\ -\frac{6}{7} \end{bmatrix}$

The solution is $\left(\frac{43}{21}, -\frac{6}{7}\right)$.

67. The greatest and least temperatures will be 2 units away from -257. Therefore, the equation is $|x - (-257)| = 2$.

68. Case 1:   or Case 2:

$x - (-257) = 2$	$x - (-257) = -2$
$x + 257 = 2$	$x + 257 = -2$
$x + 257 - 257 = -2 - 257$	$x + 257 - 257 = 2 - 257$
$x = -255$	$x = -259$

Check: $|x - (-257)| = 2$ Check: $|x - (-257)| = 2$

$|-255 - (-257)| \overset{?}{=} 2$ $|-259 - (-257)| \overset{?}{=} 2$

$|-255 + 257| \overset{?}{=} 2$ $|-2| \overset{?}{=} 2$

$|2| \overset{?}{=} 2$ $2 = 2$ ✓

$2 = 2$ ✓

The greatest temperature is $-255°C$, and the least temperature is $-259°C$.

69. $b^2 - 4ac = 7^2 - 4(1)(3)$
$= 49 - 4(1)(3)$
$= 49 - 4(3)$
$= 49 - 12$
$= 37$

70. $b^2 - 4ac = 2^2 - 4(1)(5)$
$= 4 - 4(1)(5)$
$= 4 - 4(5)$
$= 4 - 20$
$= -16$

71. $b^2 - 4ac = (-9)^2 - 4(2)(-5)$
$= 81 - 4(2)(-5)$
$= 81 - 8(-5)$
$= 81 - (-40)$
$= 121$

72. $b^2 - 4ac = (-12)^2 - 4(4)(9)$
$= 144 - 4(4)(9)$
$= 144 - 16(9)$
$= 144 - 144$
$= 0$

6-5   The Quadratic Formula and the Discriminant

Pages 317–318   Check for Understanding

1a. If the discriminant is positive, then the graph should intersect the x-axis twice.

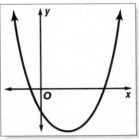

1b. If the discriminant is negative, then the graph should not intersect the x-axis.

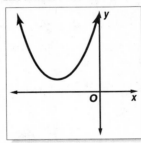

1c. If the discriminant is zero, then the graph should intersect the x-axis exactly once.

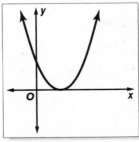

2. The square root of a negative number is a complex number.

3. $b^2 - 4ac$ must equal 0.

4a. $a = 8, b = 18, c = -5$
$b^2 - 4ac = (18)^2 - 4(8)(-5)$
$= 324 + 160$
$= 484$ or 22^2

4b. The discriminant is 484, which is a perfect square. Therefore, there are two rational roots.

4c. $x = \dfrac{-b \pm \sqrt{b^2 - 4ac}}{2a}$

$\quad x = \dfrac{-(18) \pm \sqrt{(18)^2 - 4(8)(-5)}}{2(8)}$

$\quad x = \dfrac{-18 \pm \sqrt{484}}{16}$

$\quad x = \dfrac{-18 \pm 22}{16}$

$\quad x = \dfrac{-18 + 22}{16}$ or $x = \dfrac{-18 - 22}{16}$

$\quad x = \dfrac{1}{4} \qquad\qquad x = -\dfrac{5}{2}$

5a. $a = 2, b = -4, c = 1$
$\quad b^2 - 4ac = (-4)^2 - 4(2)(1)$
$\qquad\qquad\quad = 16 - 8$
$\qquad\qquad\quad = 8$

5b. The discriminant is 8, which is not a perfect square. Therefore, there are two irrational roots.

5c. $x = \dfrac{-b \pm \sqrt{b^2 - 4ac}}{2a}$

$\quad x = \dfrac{-(-4) \pm \sqrt{(-4)^2 - 4(2)(1)}}{2(2)}$

$\quad x = \dfrac{4 \pm \sqrt{8}}{4}$

$\quad x = \dfrac{4 \pm 2\sqrt{2}}{4}$

$\quad x = \dfrac{2 \pm \sqrt{2}}{2}$

6a. $a = 4, b = 4, c = 1$
$\quad b^2 - 4ac = (4)^2 - 4(4)(1)$
$\qquad\qquad\quad = 16 - 16$
$\qquad\qquad\quad = 0$

6b. The discriminant is 0, so there is one rational root.

6c. $x = \dfrac{-b \pm \sqrt{b^2 - 4ac}}{2a}$

$\quad x = \dfrac{-(4) \pm \sqrt{(4)^2 - 4(4)(1)}}{2(4)}$

$\quad x = \dfrac{-4 \pm \sqrt{0}}{8}$

$\quad x = \dfrac{-4}{8}$

$\quad x = -\dfrac{1}{2}$

7a. $x^2 + 3x + 8 = 5$
$\quad x^2 + 3x + 3 = 0$
$\quad a = 1, b = 3, c = 3$
$\quad b^2 - 4ac = (3)^2 - 4(1)(3)$
$\qquad\qquad\quad = 9 - 12$
$\qquad\qquad\quad = -3$

7b. The discriminant is negative, so there are two complex roots.

7c. $x = \dfrac{-b \pm \sqrt{b^2 - 4ac}}{2a}$

$\quad x = \dfrac{-(3) \pm \sqrt{(3)^2 - 4(1)(3)}}{2(1)}$

$\quad x = \dfrac{-3 \pm \sqrt{-3}}{2}$

$\quad x = \dfrac{-3 \pm i\sqrt{3}}{2}$

8. $x^2 + 8x = 0$
$\quad x(x + 8) = 0$
$\quad x = 0$ or $x + 8 = 0$
$\qquad\qquad\qquad x = -8$

9. $x^2 + 5x + 6 = 0$
$\quad (x + 2)(x + 3) = 0$
$\quad x + 2 = 0$ or $x + 3 = 0$
$\qquad x = -2 \qquad\quad x = -3$

10. $x^2 - 2x - 2 = 0$
$\quad x^2 - 2x = 2$
$\quad x^2 - 2x + 1 = 2 + 1$
$\quad (x - 1)^2 = 3$
$\qquad x - 1 = \pm\sqrt{3}$
$\qquad\quad x = 1 \pm \sqrt{3}$

11. $4x^2 + 20x + 25 = -2$
$\quad 4x^2 + 20x + 27 = 0$
$\quad a = 4, b = 20, c = 27$
$\quad x = \dfrac{-b \pm \sqrt{b^2 - 4ac}}{2a}$

$\quad x = \dfrac{-(20) \pm \sqrt{(20)^2 - 4(4)(27)}}{2(4)}$

$\quad x = \dfrac{-20 \pm \sqrt{-32}}{8}$

$\quad x = \dfrac{-20 \pm 4i\sqrt{2}}{8}$

$\quad x = \dfrac{-5 \pm i\sqrt{2}}{2}$

12. Substitute 50 for $h(t)$ and solve for t.
$\qquad\qquad 50 = -16t^2 + 85t$
$\quad 16t^2 - 85t + 50 = 0$
$\quad a = 16, b = -85, c = 50$
$\quad x = \dfrac{-b \pm \sqrt{b^2 - 4ac}}{2a}$

$\quad x = \dfrac{-(-85) \pm \sqrt{(-85)^2 - 4(16)(50)}}{2(16)}$

$\quad x = \dfrac{85 \pm \sqrt{4025}}{32}$

$\quad x = \dfrac{85 \pm 5\sqrt{161}}{32}$

The approximate solutions are 0.7 and 4.6. Therefore, the object will be at a height of 50 feet at about 0.7 second and again at about 4.6 seconds.

13. Substitute 120 for $h(t)$ and solve for t.
$\qquad\qquad 120 = -16t^2 + 85t$
$\quad 16t^2 - 85t + 120 = 0$
$\quad a = 16, b = -85, c = 120$
$\quad b^2 - 4ac = (-85)^2 - 4(16)(120)$
$\qquad\qquad\quad = 7225 - 7680$
$\qquad\qquad\quad = -455$

No; the object will not reach a height of 120 feet. The discriminant of $120 = -16t^2 + 85t$ is -455, indicating that the equation has no real solutions.

Pages 318–319　Practice and Apply

14a. $b^2 - 4ac = (3)^2 - 4(1)(-3)$
$\qquad\qquad\quad = 9 + 12$
$\qquad\qquad\quad = 21$

14b. The discriminant is 21, which is not a perfect square. Therefore, there are two irrational roots.

14c. $x =$

$x =$

$x = \frac{-3 \pm \sqrt{21}}{2}$

15a. $b^2 - 4ac = (-16)^2 - 4(1)(4)$
$= 256 - 16$
$= 240$

15b. The discriminant is 240, which is not a perfect square. Therefore, there are two irrational roots.

15c. $x = \frac{-b \pm \sqrt{b^2 - 4ac}}{2a}$

$x = \frac{-(-16) \pm \sqrt{(-16)^2 - 4(1)(4)}}{2(1)}$

$x = \frac{16 \pm \sqrt{240}}{2}$

$x = 8 \pm 2\sqrt{15}$

16a. $b^2 - 4ac = (-2)^2 - 4(1)(5)$
$= 4 - 20$
$= -16$

16b. The discriminant is negative, so there are two complex roots.

16c. $x = \frac{-b \pm \sqrt{b^2 - 4ac}}{2a}$

$x = \frac{-(-2) \pm \sqrt{(-2)^2 - 4(1)(5)}}{2(1)}$

$x = \frac{2 \pm \sqrt{-16}}{2}$

$x = \frac{2 \pm 4i}{2}$

$x = 1 \pm 2i$

17a. $b^2 - 4ac = (-1)^2 - 4(1)(6)$
$= 1 - 24$
$= -23$

17b. The discriminant is negative, so there are two complex roots.

17c. $x = \frac{-b \pm \sqrt{b^2 - 4ac}}{2a}$

$x = \frac{-(-1) \pm \sqrt{(-1)^2 - 4(1)(6)}}{2(1)}$

$x = \frac{1 \pm \sqrt{-23}}{2}$

$x = \frac{1 \pm i\sqrt{23}}{2}$

18a. $b^2 - 4ac = (5)^2 - 4(-12)(2)$
$= 25 + 96$
$= 121$

18b. The discriminant is 121, which is a perfect square. Therefore, there are two rational roots.

18c. $x = \frac{-b \pm \sqrt{b^2 - 4ac}}{2a}$

$x = \frac{-(5) \pm \sqrt{(5)^2 - 4(-12)(2)}}{2(-12)}$

$x = \frac{-5 \pm \sqrt{121}}{-24}$

$x = \frac{-5 \pm 11}{-24}$

$x = \frac{-5 + 11}{-24}$ or $x = \frac{-5 - 11}{-24}$

$x = -\frac{1}{4}$ $x = \frac{2}{3}$

19a. $b^2 - 4ac = (-5)^2 - 4(-3)(2)$
$= 25 + 24$
$= 49$

19b. The discriminant is 49, which is a perfect square. Therefore, there are two rational roots.

19c. $x = \frac{-b \pm \sqrt{b^2 - 4ac}}{2a}$

$x = \frac{-(-5) \pm \sqrt{(-5)^2 - 4(-3)(2)}}{2(-3)}$

$x = \frac{5 \pm \sqrt{49}}{-6}$

$x = \frac{5 \pm 7}{-6}$

$x = \frac{5 + 7}{-6}$ or $x = \frac{5 - 7}{-6}$

$x = -2$ $x = \frac{1}{3}$

20a. $x^2 + 4x + 3 = 4$
$x^2 + 4x - 1 = 0$
$a = 1, b = 4, c = -1$
$b^2 - 4ac = 4^2 - 4(1)(-1)$
$= 16 + 4$
$= 20$

20b. The discriminant is 20, which is not a perfect square. Therefore, there are two irrational roots.

20c. $x = \frac{-b \pm \sqrt{b^2 - 4ac}}{2a}$

$x = \frac{-(4) \pm \sqrt{(4)^2 - 4(1)(-1)}}{2(1)}$

$x = \frac{-4 \pm \sqrt{20}}{2}$

$x = \frac{-4 \pm 2\sqrt{5}}{2}$

$x = -2 \pm \sqrt{5}$

21a. $2x - 5 = -x^2$
$x^2 + 2x - 5 = 0$
$a = 1, b = 2, c = -5$
$b^2 - 4ac = (2)^2 - 4(1)(-5)$
$= 4 + 20$
$= 24$

21b. The discriminant is 24, which is not a perfect square. Therefore, there are two irrational roots.

21c. $x = \frac{-b \pm \sqrt{b^2 - 4ac}}{2a}$

$x = \frac{-(2) \pm \sqrt{(2)^2 - 4(1)(-5)}}{2(1)}$

$x = \frac{-2 \pm \sqrt{24}}{2}$

$x = \frac{-2 \pm 2\sqrt{6}}{2}$

$x = -1 \pm \sqrt{6}$

22a. $9x^2 - 6x - 4 = -5$
$9x^2 - 6x + 1 = 0$
$a = 9, b = -6, c = 1$
$b^2 - 4ac = (-6)^2 - 4(9)(1)$
$= 36 - 36$
$= 0$

22b. The discriminant is 0, so there is one rational root.

22c. $x = \dfrac{-b \pm \sqrt{b^2 - 4ac}}{2a}$

$x = \dfrac{-(-6) \pm \sqrt{(-6)^2 - 4(9)(1)}}{2(9)}$

$x = \dfrac{6 \pm \sqrt{0}}{18}$

$x = \dfrac{6}{18}$

$x = \dfrac{1}{3}$

23a. $\qquad 25 + 4x^2 = -20x$

$4x^2 + 20x + 25 = 0$

$a = 4, b = 20, c = 25$

$b^2 - 4ac = (20)^2 - 4(4)(25)$

$= 400 - 400$

$= 0$

23b. The discriminant is 0, so there is one rational root.

23c. $x = \dfrac{-b \pm \sqrt{b^2 - 4ac}}{2a}$

$x = \dfrac{-(20) \pm \sqrt{(20)^2 - 4(4)(25)}}{2(4)}$

$x = \dfrac{-20 \pm \sqrt{0}}{8}$

$x = \dfrac{-20}{8}$

$x = -\dfrac{5}{2}$

24a. $\qquad 4x^2 + 7 = 9x$

$4x^2 - 9x + 7 = 0$

$a = 4, b = -9, c = 7$

$b^2 - 4ac = (-9)^2 - 4(4)(7)$

$= 81 - 112$

$= -31$

24b. The discriminant is negative, so there are two complex roots.

24c. $x = \dfrac{-b \pm \sqrt{b^2 - 4ac}}{2a}$

$x = \dfrac{-(-9) \pm \sqrt{(-9)^2 - 4(4)(7)}}{2(4)}$

$x = \dfrac{9 \pm \sqrt{-31}}{8}$

$x = \dfrac{9 \pm i\sqrt{31}}{8}$

25a. $\qquad 3x + 6 = -6x^2$

$6x^2 + 3x + 6 = 0$

$a = 6, b = 3, c = 6$

$b^2 - 4ac = (3)^2 - 4(6)(6)$

$= 9 - 144$

$= -135$

25b. The discriminant is negative, so there are two complex roots.

25c. $x = \dfrac{-b \pm \sqrt{b^2 - 4ac}}{2a}$

$x = \dfrac{-(3) \pm \sqrt{(3)^2 - 4(6)(6)}}{2(6)}$

$x = \dfrac{-3 \pm \sqrt{-135}}{12}$

$x = \dfrac{-3 \pm 3i\sqrt{15}}{12}$

$x = \dfrac{-1 \pm i\sqrt{15}}{4}$

26a. $b^2 - 4ac = \left(-\dfrac{1}{3}\right)^2 - 4\left(\dfrac{3}{4}\right)(-1)$

$= \dfrac{1}{9} + 3$

$= \dfrac{28}{9}$

26b. The discriminant is $\dfrac{28}{9}$, which is not a perfect square. Therefore, there are two irrational roots.

26c. $x = \dfrac{-b \pm \sqrt{b^2 - 4ac}}{2a}$

$x = \dfrac{-\left(-\dfrac{1}{3}\right) \pm \sqrt{\left(-\dfrac{1}{3}\right)^2 - 4\left(\dfrac{3}{4}\right)(-1)}}{2\left(\dfrac{3}{4}\right)}$

$x = \dfrac{\dfrac{1}{3} \pm \sqrt{\dfrac{28}{9}}}{\dfrac{3}{2}}$

$x = \dfrac{\dfrac{1}{3} \pm \dfrac{2}{3}\sqrt{7}}{\dfrac{3}{2}}$

$x = \dfrac{2 + 4\sqrt{7}}{9}$

27a. $b^2 - 4ac = (1)^2 - 4(0.4)(-0.3)$

$= 1 + 0.48$

$= 1.48$

27b. The discriminant is 1.48, which is not a perfect square. Therefore, there are two irrational roots.

27c. $x = \dfrac{-b \pm \sqrt{b^2 - 4ac}}{2a}$

$x = \dfrac{-(1) \pm \sqrt{(1)^2 - 4(0.4)(-0.3)}}{2(0.4)}$

$x = \dfrac{-1 \pm \sqrt{1.48}}{0.8}$

$x = \dfrac{-1 \pm 2\sqrt{0.37}}{0.8}$

28. $x^2 - 30x - 64 = 0$

$(x - 32)(x + 2) = 0$

$x - 32 = 0 \quad \text{or} \ x + 2 = 0$

$x = 32 \qquad \qquad x = -2$

29. $7x^2 + 3 = 0$

$7x^2 = -3$

$x^2 = -\dfrac{3}{7}$

$x = \pm\sqrt{-\dfrac{3}{7}}$

$x = \pm i\sqrt{\dfrac{3}{7}}$

$x = \pm i\dfrac{\sqrt{21}}{7}$

30. $x^2 - 4x + 7 = 0$

$x^2 - 4x = -7$

$x^2 - 4x + 4 = -7 + 4$

$(x - 2)^2 = -3$

$x - 2 = \pm\sqrt{-3}$

$x - 2 = \pm i\sqrt{3}$

$x = 2 \pm i\sqrt{3}$

31. $x = \dfrac{-b \pm \sqrt{b^2 - 4ac}}{2a}$

$x = \dfrac{-(6) \pm \sqrt{(6)^2 - 4(2)(-3)}}{2(2)}$

$x = \dfrac{-6 \pm \sqrt{60}}{4}$

$x = \dfrac{-6 \pm 2\sqrt{15}}{4}$

$x = \dfrac{-3 \pm \sqrt{15}}{2}$

32. $4x^2 - 8 = 0$
$4x^2 = 8$
$x^2 = 2$
$x = \pm\sqrt{2}$

33. $4x^2 + 81 = 36x$
$4x^2 - 36x + 81 = 0$
$(2x - 9)(2x - 9) = 0$
$2x - 9 = 0 \text{ or } 2x - 9 = 0$
$2x = 9 \qquad\qquad 2x = 9$
$x = \frac{9}{2} \qquad\qquad x = \frac{9}{2}$

34. $-4(x + 3)^2 = 28$
$(x + 3)^2 = -7$
$x + 3 = \pm\sqrt{-7}$
$x + 3 = \pm i\sqrt{7}$
$x = -3 \pm i\sqrt{7}$

35. $3x^2 - 10x = 7$
$3x^2 - 10x - 7 = 0$
$x = \frac{-b \pm \sqrt{b^2 - 4ac}}{2a}$
$x = \frac{-(-10) \pm \sqrt{(-10)^2 - 4(3)(-7)}}{2(3)}$
$x = \frac{10 \pm \sqrt{184}}{6}$
$x = \frac{10 \pm 2\sqrt{46}}{6}$
$x = \frac{5 \pm \sqrt{46}}{3}$

36. $x^2 + 9 = 8x$
$x^2 - 8x + 9 = 0$
$x = \frac{-b \pm \sqrt{b^2 - 4ac}}{2a}$
$x = \frac{-(-8) \pm \sqrt{(-8)^2 - 4(1)(9)}}{2(1)}$
$x = \frac{8 \pm \sqrt{28}}{2}$
$x = \frac{8 \pm 2\sqrt{7}}{2}$
$x = 4 \pm \sqrt{7}$

37. $10x^2 + 3x = 0$
$x(10x + 3) = 0$
$x = 0 \text{ or } 10x + 3 = 0$
$10x = -3$
$x = -\frac{3}{10}$

38. $2x^2 - 12x + 7 = 5$
$2x^2 - 12x + 2 = 0$
$x^2 - 6x + 1 = 0$
$x = \frac{-b \pm \sqrt{b^2 - 4ac}}{2a}$
$x = \frac{-(-6) \pm \sqrt{(-6)^2 - 4(1)(1)}}{2(1)}$
$x = \frac{6 \pm \sqrt{32}}{2}$
$x = \frac{6 \pm 4\sqrt{2}}{2}$
$x = 3 \pm 2\sqrt{2}$

39. $21 = (x - 2)^2 + 5$
$16 = (x - 2)^2$
$\pm\sqrt{16} = x - 2$
$\pm 4 = x - 2$
$2 \pm 4 = x$
$2 + 4 = x \text{ or } 2 - 4 = x$
$6 = x \qquad\qquad -2 = x$

40. $a = 0.00012, b = 0, c = 6$
$b^2 - 4ac = (0)^2 - 4(0.00012)(6)$
$= 0 - 0.00288$
$= -0.00288$

41. This means that the cables do not touch the floor of the bridge, since the graph does not intersect the x-axis and the roots are imaginary.

42. Since t is the number of years since 1975, and $2000 - 1975 = 25$, a reasonable domain would be $0 \le t \le 25$.
$a = 2.3, b = -12.4, c = 73.7$
The x-coordinate of the vertex is $-\frac{-12.4}{2(2.3)}$ or about 2.7 which is contained in the domain. Since a is positive the vertex yeilds a minimum. The minimum is about $A(2.7) = 56.987$. Since $A(0) = 73.7$ and $A(25) = 1201.2$, a reasonable range would be $73.7 \le A(t) \le 1201.2$.

43. Substitute 1000 for $A(t)$ and solve for t.
$A(t) = 2.3t^2 - 12.4t + 73.7$
$1000 = 2.3t^2 - 12.4t + 73.7$
$0 = 2.3t^2 - 12.4t - 926.3$
$a = 2.3, b = -12.4, c = -926.3$
$x = \frac{-b \pm \sqrt{b^2 - 4ac}}{2a}$
$x = \frac{-(-12.4) \pm \sqrt{(-12.4)^2 - 4(2.3)(-926.3)}}{2(2.3)}$
$x = \frac{12.4 \pm \sqrt{8675.72}}{4.6}$
$x = \frac{12.4 + \sqrt{8675.72}}{4.6} \text{ or } x = \frac{12.4 - \sqrt{8675.72}}{4.6}$
$x \approx 23 \qquad\qquad x \approx -18$
Therefore, 23 years after 1975 or in 1998 the average salary exceeded 1 million dollars.

44. Substitute 125 for d and solve for s.
$d = 0.05s^2 + 1.1s$
$125 = 0.05s^2 + 1.1s$
$0 = 0.05s^2 + 1.1s - 125$
$a = 0.05, b = 1.1, c = -125$
$x = \frac{-b \pm \sqrt{b^2 - 4ac}}{2a}$
$x = \frac{-(1.1) \pm \sqrt{(1.1)^2 - 4(0.05)(-125)}}{2(0.05)}$
$x = \frac{-1.1 \pm \sqrt{26.21}}{0.1}$
$x = \frac{-1.1 + \sqrt{26.21}}{0.1} \text{ or } x = \frac{-1.1 - \sqrt{26.21}}{0.1}$
$x \approx 40.2 \qquad\qquad x \approx -62.2$
Therefore, the fastest the car could have been traveling is about 40.2 miles per hour.

45. $a = 1, b = -k, c = 9$

45a. The equation has one real root if the discriminant equals zero.

$$b^2 - 4ac = 0$$
$$(-k)^2 - 4(1)(9) = 0$$
$$k^2 - 36 = 0$$
$$k^2 = 36$$
$$k = \pm\sqrt{36}$$
$$k = \pm 6$$

45b. The equation has two real roots if the discriminant is positive.

$$b^2 - 4ac > 0$$
$$(-k)^2 - 4(1)(9) > 0$$
$$k^2 - 36 > 0$$
$$k^2 > 36$$
$$|k| > \sqrt{36}$$
$$|k| > 6$$
$$k > 6 \text{ or } k < -6$$

45c. The equation has no real roots if the discriminant is negative.

$$b^2 - 4ac < 0$$
$$(-k)^2 - 4(1)(9) < 0$$
$$k^2 - 36 < 0$$
$$k^2 < 36$$
$$|k| < 36$$
$$|k| < 6$$
$$-6 < k < 6$$

46. The person's age can be substituted for A in the appropriate formula, depending upon their gender, and their average blood pressure calculated. See student's work.

- If a woman's blood pressure is given to be 118, then solve the equation $118 = 0.01A^2 + 0.05A + 107$ to find the value of A. Use the Quadratic Formula, substituting 0.01 for a, 0.05 for b, and -11 for c. This gives solutions of about -35.8 or 30.8. Since age cannot be negative, the only valid solution for A is 30.8.

47. D; $a = 2, b = -5, c = -9$

$$x = \frac{-b \pm \sqrt{b^2 - 4ac}}{2a}$$
$$x = \frac{-(-5) \pm \sqrt{(-5)^2 - 4(2)(-9)}}{2(2)}$$
$$x = \frac{5 \pm \sqrt{97}}{4}$$
$$x = \frac{5 + \sqrt{97}}{4} \text{ or } x = \frac{5 - \sqrt{97}}{4}$$
$$x \approx 3.71 \qquad x \approx -1.21$$

48. C; $a = 1, b = -3, c = 4$

$$b^2 - 4ac = (-3)^2 - 4(1)(4)$$
$$= 9 - 16$$
$$= -7$$

The discriminant is negative, so there are two complex roots.

49.
$$x^2 + 18x + 81 = 25$$
$$(x + 9)^2 = 25$$
$$x + 9 = \pm\sqrt{25}$$
$$x + 9 = \pm 5$$
$$x = -9 \pm 5$$
$$x = -9 + 5 \text{ or } x = -9 - 5$$
$$x = -4 \qquad x = -14$$
The solution set is $\{-14, -4\}$.

50.
$$x^2 - 8x + 16 = 7$$
$$(x - 4)^2 = 7$$
$$x - 4 = \pm\sqrt{7}$$
$$x = 4 \pm \sqrt{7}$$
$$x = 4 + \sqrt{7} \text{ or } x = 4 - \sqrt{7}$$
$$x \approx 6.6 \qquad x \approx 1.4$$
The exact solutions are $4 - \sqrt{7}$ and $4 + \sqrt{7}$.
The approximate solutions are 1.4 and 6.6.

51.
$$4x^2 - 4x + 1 = 8$$
$$(2x - 1)^2 = 8$$
$$2x - 1 = \pm\sqrt{8}$$
$$2x - 1 = \pm 2\sqrt{2}$$
$$2x = 1 \pm 2\sqrt{2}$$
$$x = \frac{1 \pm 2\sqrt{2}}{2}$$
$$x = \frac{1 + 2\sqrt{2}}{2} \text{ or } x = \frac{1 - 2\sqrt{2}}{2}$$
$$x \approx 1.9 \qquad x \approx -0.9$$
The exact solutions are $\frac{1 - 2\sqrt{2}}{2}$ and $\frac{1 + 2\sqrt{2}}{2}$.
The approximate solutions are -0.9 and 1.9.

52.
$$4x^2 + 8x = 0$$
$$4x(x + 2) = 0$$
$$4x = 0 \text{ or } x + 2 = 0$$
$$x = 0 \qquad x = -2$$
The solution set is $\{-2, 0\}$.

53.
$$x^2 - 5x = 14$$
$$x^2 - 5x - 14 = 0$$
$$(x - 7)(x + 2) = 0$$
$$x - 7 = 0 \text{ or } x + 2 = 0$$
$$x = 7 \qquad x = -2$$
The solution set is $\{-2, 7\}$.

54.
$$3x^2 + 10 = 17x$$
$$3x^2 - 17x + 10 = 0$$
$$(3x - 2)(x - 5) = 0$$
$$3x - 2 = 0 \text{ or } x - 5 = 0$$
$$3x = 2 \qquad x = 5$$
$$x = \frac{2}{3}$$
The solution set is $\left\{\frac{2}{3}, 5\right\}$.

55.
$$\sqrt{a^8 b^{20}} = \sqrt{(a^4 b^{10})^2}$$
$$= a^4 b^{10}$$

56.
$$\sqrt{100p^{12}q^2} = \sqrt{(10p^6|q|)^2}$$
$$= 10p^6|q|$$

57.
$$\sqrt[3]{64b^6 c^6} = \sqrt[3]{(4b^2 c^2)^3}$$
$$= 4b^2 c^2$$

58. $\dfrac{133{,}000 \text{ beats}}{1 \text{ minute}} \cdot \dfrac{60 \text{ minutes}}{1 \text{ hour}}$

$= \dfrac{133{,}000(60) \text{ beats}}{1 \text{ hour}}$

$= 7{,}980{,}000$ beats per hour

$= 7.98 \times 1{,}000{,}000$ beats per hour

$= 7.98 \times 10^6$ beats per hour

59. Graph all of the inequalities on the same coordinate plane and shade the region or regions that are common to all.

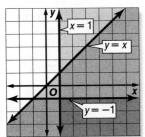

60. Graph all of the inequalities on the same coordinate plane and shade the region or regions that are common to all.

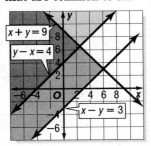

61. Since $x^2 - 5x - 10$ cannot be written in the form $a^2 - 2ab + b^2$, it is not a perfect square.

62. Since $x^2 - 14x + 49$ can be written in the form $a^2 - 2ab + b^2$, it is a perfect square.

$\begin{aligned} x^2 - 14x + 49 &= (x)^2 - 2(x)(7) + (7)^2 \\ &= (x - 7)^2 \end{aligned}$

63. Since $4x^2 + 12x + 9$ can be written in the form $a^2 + 2ab + b^2$, it is a perfect square.

$\begin{aligned} 4x^2 + 12x + 9 &= (2x)^2 + 2(2x)(3) + (3)^2 \\ &= (2x + 3)^2 \end{aligned}$

64. Since $25x^2 + 20x + 4$ can be written in the form $a^2 + 2ab + b^2$, it is a perfect square.

$\begin{aligned} 25x^2 + 20x + 4 &= (5x)^2 + 2(5x)(2) + (2)^2 \\ &= (5x + 2)^2 \end{aligned}$

65. Since $9x^2 - 12x + 16$ cannot be written in the form $a^2 - 2ab + b^2$, it is not a perfect square.

66. Since $36x^2 - 60x + 25$ can be written in the form $a^2 - 2ab + b^2$, it is a perfect square.

$\begin{aligned} 36x^2 - 60x + 25 &= (6x)^2 - 2(6x)(5) + (5)^2 \\ &= (6x - 5)^2 \end{aligned}$

Pages 320–321 Graphing Calculator Investigation (Preview of Lesson 6-6)

1. Changing the value of h moves the graph to the left and to the right. If $h > 0$, the graph translates to the right, and if $h < 0$, it translates to the left. In $y = x^2$, the vertex is at $(0, 0)$ and in $y = (x - 2)^2$, the vertex is at $(2, 0)$. The graph has been translated to the right.

2. Changing the value of k moves the graph up and down. If $k > 0$, the graph translates upward, and if $k < 0$, it translates downward. In $y = x^2$, the vertex is at $(0, 0)$ and in $y = x^2 - 3$, the vertex is at $(0, -3)$. The graph has been translated downward.

3. Using $-a$ instead of a reflects the graph over the x-axis. The graph of $y = x^2$ opens upward, while the graph of $y = -x^2$ opens downward.

4. Both graphs have the same shape, but the graph of $y = x^2 + 2.5$ is 2.5 units above the graph of $y = x^2$.

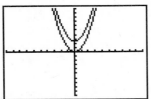

5. Both graphs have the same shape, but the graph of $y = -x^2$ opens downward while the graph of $y = x^2 - 9$ opens upward and is 9 units lower than the graph of $y = x^2$.

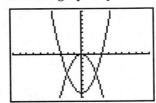

6. The graph of $y = 3x^2$ is narrower than the graph of $y = x^2$.

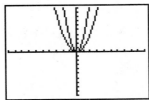

7. The graph of $y = -6x^2$ opens downward and is narrower than the graph of $y = x^2$.

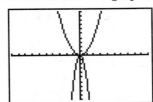

8. The graphs have the same shape, but the graph of $y = (x + 3)^2$ is 3 units to the left of the graph of $y = x^2$

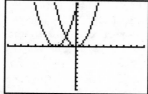

9. The graphs have the same shape and open downward, but the graph of $y = -\frac{1}{3}x^2 + 2$ is two units above the graph of $y = -\frac{1}{3}x^2$.

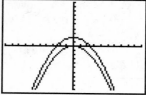

10. The graphs have the same shape, but the graph of $y = (x - 7)^2$ is 7 units to the right of the graph of $y = x^2$.

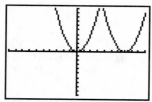

11. The graph of $y = 3(x + 4)^2 - 7$ is 4 units to the left, 7 units below, and narrower than the graph of $y = x^2$.

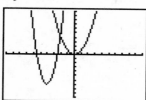

12. The graph of $y = -\frac{1}{4}x^2 + 1$ opens downward, is wider than and 1 unit above the graph of $y = x^2$.

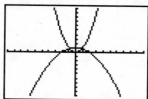

13. The graphs have the same shape, but the graph of $y = (x + 3)^2 + 5$ is 7 units above the graph of $y = (x + 3)^2 - 2$.

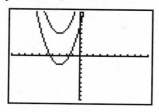

14. The graph of $y = 6(x + 2)^2 - 1$ is narrower than the graph of $y = 3(x + 2)^2 - 1$.

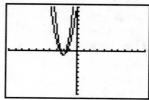

15. The graph of $y = \frac{1}{4}(x - 2)^2 - 1$ is wider than the graph of $y = 4(x - 2)^2 - 3$, and its vertex is 2 units above the vertex of $y = 4(x - 2)^2 - 3$.

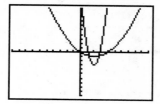

6-6 Analyzing Graphs of Quadratic Functions

Pages 325–326   Check for Understanding

1a. Add 2 units to k or to 3.
$y = 2(x + 1)^2 + (3 + 2)$
$y = 2(x + 1)^2 + 5$

1b. Subtract 3 units from k or from 3.
$y = 2(x + 1)^2 + (3 - 3)$
$y = 2(x + 1)^2$

1c. Add 2 units to h or to 1.
$y = 2[x + (1 + 2)]^2 + 3$
$y = 2(x + 3)^2 + 3$

1d. Subtract 3 units from h or from 1.
$y = 2[x + (1 - 3)]^2 + 3$
$y = 2(x - 2)^2 + 3$

1e. Add a positive number to a or to 2.
Sample answer: $y = (2 + 2)(x + 1)^2 + 3$
$y = 4(x + 1)^2 + 3$

1f. Subtract a number between 0 and 2 from a or from 2.
Sample answer: $y = (2 - 1)(x + 1)^2 + 3$
$y = (x + 1)^2 + 3$

1g. Multiply a or 2 by -1.
$y = -1 \cdot 2(x + 1)^2 + 3$
$y = -2(x + 1)^2 + 3$

2. Substitute the x-coordinate of the vertex for h and the y-coordinate of the vertex for k in the equation $y = a(x - h)^2 + k$. Then substitute the x-coordinate of the other point for x and the y-coordinate for y into this equation and solve for a. Replace a with this value in the equation you wrote with h and k.

3. Sample answer: $h = 2$ and $k = -1$. Pick a value for a. Let $a = 2$. Substitute these values into the vertex form of the equation.
$$y = a(x - h)^2 + k$$
$$y = 2(x - 2)^2 + (-1)$$
$$y = 2(x - 2)^2 - 1$$

4. Jenny; when completing the square is used to write a quadratic function in vertex form, the quantity added is then subtracted from the same side of the equation to maintain equality.

5. $y = 5(x + 3)^2 - 1$
$$y = 5[x - (-3)]^2 + (-1)$$
$$h = -3 \text{ and } k = -1.$$
The vertex is at $(-3, -1)$, and the axis of symmetry is $x = -3$. Since $a = 5$, the graph opens up.

6. $y = x^2 + 8x - 3$
$$y = (x^2 + 8x + 16) - 3 - 16$$
$$y = (x + 4)^2 - 19$$
$$y = [x - (-4)]^2 + (-19)$$
$$h = -4 \text{ and } k = -19.$$
The vertex is at $(-4, -19)$, and the axis of symmetry is $x = -4$. Since $a = 1$, the graph opens up.

7. $y = -3x^2 - 18x + 11$
$$y = -3(x^2 + 6x) + 11$$
$$y = -3(x^2 + 6x + 9) + 11 - (-3)(9)$$
$$y = -3(x + 3)^2 + 38$$
$$y = -3[x - (-3)]^2 + 38$$
$$h = -3 \text{ and } k = 38.$$
The vertex is at $(-3, 38)$, and the axis of symmetry is $x = -3$. Since $a = -3$, the graph opens down.

8. $y = 3(x + 3)^2$
$$y = 3[x - (-3)]^2 + 0$$
$$h = -3 \text{ and } k = 0.$$
The vertex is at $(-3, 0)$. Two points on the graph to the right of $x = -3$ are $(-2.5, 0.75)$ and $(-2, 3)$. Use symmetry to complete the graph.

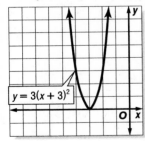

9. $y = \frac{1}{3}(x - 1)^2 + 3$
$$h = 1 \text{ and } k = 3.$$
The vertex is at $(1, 3)$. Two points on the graph to the right of $x = 1$ are $\left(2, 3\frac{1}{3}\right)$ and $\left(3, 4\frac{1}{3}\right)$. Use symmetry to complete the graph.

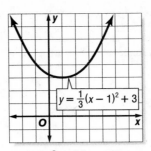

10. $y = -2x^2 + 16x - 31$
$$y = -2(x^2 - 8x) - 31$$
$$y = -2(x^2 - 8x + 16) - 31 - (-2)(16)$$
$$y = -2(x - 4)^2 + 1$$
$$h = 4 \text{ and } k = 1.$$
The vertex is at $(4, 1)$. Two points on the graph to the right of $x = 4$ are $(4.5, 0.5)$ and $(5, -1)$. Use symmetry to complete the graph.

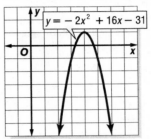

11. $h = 2$ and $k = 0$. Let $x = 1$ and $y = 4$. Substitute these values into the vertex form of the equation and solve for a.
$$y = a(x - h)^2 + k$$
$$4 = a(1 - 2)^2 + 0$$
$$4 = a$$
The equation of the parabola in vertex form is $y = 4(x - 2)^2$.

12. $h = -3$ and $k = 6$. Let $x = -5$ and $y = 2$. Substitute these values into the vertex form of the equation and solve for a.
$$y = a(x - h)^2 + k$$
$$2 = a[-5 - (-3)]^2 + 6$$
$$2 = a(4) + 6$$
$$-4 = 4a$$
$$-1 = a$$
The equation of the parabola in vertex form is $y = -(x + 3)^2 + 6$.

13. $h = -2$ and $k = -3$. Let $x = -4$ and $y = -5$. Substitute these values into the vertex form of the equation and solve for a.
$$y = a(x - h)^2 + k$$
$$-5 = a[-4 - (-2)]^2 + (-3)$$
$$-5 = a(4) - 3$$
$$-2 = 4a$$
$$-\frac{1}{2} = a$$
The equation of the parabola in vertex form is $y = -\frac{1}{2}(x + 2)^2 - 3$.

14. The vertex of the parabola is at $(1, 8)$, so $h = 1$ and $k = 8$. Since $(3, 0)$ is a solution of the equation, let $x = 3$ and $y = 0$. Substitute these values into the vertex form of the equation and solve for a.

$y = a(x - h)^2 + k$
$0 = a(3 - 1)^2 + 8$
$0 = a(4) + 8$
$-8 = 4a$
$-2 = a$

The equation of the parabola in vertex form is $y = -2(x - 1)^2 + 8$. Using $h(d)$ and d for y and x, the equation is $h(d) = -2(d - 1)^2 + 8$ or $h(d) = -2d^2 + 4d + 6$.

Pages 326–327   Practice and Apply

15. $y = -2(x + 3)^2$
$y = -2[x - (-3)]^2 + 0$
$h = -3$ and $k = 0$.
The vertex is at $(-3, 0)$, and the axis of symmetry is $x = -3$. Since $a = -2$, the graph opens down.

16. $y = \frac{1}{3}(x - 1)^2 + 2$
$h = 1$ and $k = 2$.
The vertex is at $(1, 2)$, and the axis of symmetry is $x = 1$. Since $a = \frac{1}{3}$, the graph opens up.

17. $y = 5x^2 - 6$
$y = 5(x - 0)^2 + (-6)$
$h = 0$ and $k = -6$.
The vertex is at $(0, -6)$, and the axis of symmetry is $x = 0$. Since $a = 5$, the graph opens up.

18. $y = -8x^2 + 3$
$y = -8(x - 0)^2 + 3$
$h = 0$ and $k = 3$.
The vertex is at $(0, 3)$, and the axis of symmetry is $x = 0$. Since $a = -8$, the graph opens down.

19. $y = -x^2 - 4x + 8$
$y = -(x^2 + 4x) + 8$
$y = -(x^2 + 4x + 4) + 8 - (-1)(4)$
$y = -(x + 2)^2 + 12$
$y = -[x - (-2)]^2 + 12$
$h = -2$ and $k = 12$.
The vertex is at $(-2, 12)$, and the axis of symmetry is $x = -2$. Since $a = -1$, the graph opens down.

20. $y = x^2 - 6x + 1$
$y = (x^2 - 6x + 9) + 1 - 9$
$y = (x - 3)^2 - 8$
$y = (x - 3)^2 + (-8)$
$h = 3$ and $k = -8$.
The vertex is at $(3, -8)$, and the axis of symmetry is $x = 3$. Since $a = 1$, the graph opens up.

21. $y = -3x^2 + 12x$
$y = -3(x^2 - 4x)$
$y = -3(x^2 - 4x + 4) - (-3)(4)$
$y = -3(x - 2)^2 + 12$
$h = 2$ and $k = 12$.
The vertex is at $(2, 12)$, and the axis of symmetry is $x = 2$. Since $a = -3$, the graph opens down.

22. $y = 4x^2 + 24x$
$y = 4(x^2 + 6x)$
$y = 4(x^2 + 6x + 9) - 4(9)$
$y = 4(x + 3)^2 - 36$
$y = 4[x - (-3)]^2 + (-36)$
$h = -3$ and $k = -36$.
The vertex is at $(-3, -36)$, and the axis of symmetry is $x = -3$. Since $a = 4$, the graph opens up.

23. $y = 4x^2 + 8x - 3$
$y = 4(x^2 + 2x) - 3$
$y = 4(x^2 + 2x + 1) - 3 - 4(1)$
$y = 4(x + 1)^2 - 7$
$y = 4[x - (-1)]^2 + (-7)$
$h = -1$ and $k = -7$.
The vertex is at $(-1, -7)$, and the axis of symmetry is $x = -1$. Since $a = 4$, the graph opens up.

24. $y = -2x^2 + 20x - 35$
$y = -2(x^2 - 10x) - 35$
$y = -2(x^2 - 10x + 25) - 35 - (-2)(25)$
$y = -2(x - 5)^2 + 15$
$h = 5$ and $k = 15$.
The vertex is at $(5, 15)$, and the axis of symmetry is $x = 5$. Since $a = -2$, the graph opens down.

25. $y = 3x^2 + 3x - 1$
$y = 3(x^2 + x) - 1$
$y = 3\left(x^2 + x + \frac{1}{4}\right) - 1 - 3\left(\frac{1}{4}\right)$
$y = 3\left(x + \frac{1}{2}\right)^2 - \frac{7}{4}$
$y = 3\left[x - \left(-\frac{1}{2}\right)\right]^2 + \left(-\frac{7}{4}\right)$
$h = -\frac{1}{2}$ and $k = -\frac{7}{4}$.
The vertex is at $\left(-\frac{1}{2}, -\frac{7}{4}\right)$, and the axis of symmetry is $x = -\frac{1}{2}$. Since $a = 3$, the graph opens up.

26. $y = 4x^2 - 12x - 11$
$y = 4(x^2 - 3x) - 11$
$y = 4\left(x^2 - 3x + \frac{9}{4}\right) - 11 - 4\left(\frac{9}{4}\right)$
$y = 4\left(x - \frac{3}{2}\right)^2 - 20$
$y = 4\left(x - \frac{3}{2}\right)^2 + (-20)$
$h = \frac{3}{2}$ and $k = -20$.
The vertex is at $\left(\frac{3}{2}, -20\right)$, and the axis of symmetry is $x = \frac{3}{2}$. Since $a = 4$, the graph opens up.

27. $y = 4(x + 3)^2 + 1$
$y = 4[x - (-3)]^2 + 1$
$h = -3$ and $k = 1$.
The vertex is at $(-3, 1)$. Two points on the graph to the right of $x = -3$ are $(-2.5, 2)$ and $(-2, 5)$. Use symmetry to complete the graph.

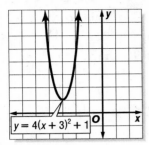

28. $y = -(x - 5)^2 - 3$
$y = -(x - 5)^2 + (-3)$
$h = 5$ and $k = -3$.
The vertex is at $(5, -3)$. Two points on the graph to the right of $x = 5$ are $(6, -4)$ and $(7, -7)$. Use symmetry to complete the graph.

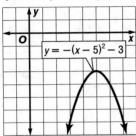

29. $y = \frac{1}{4}(x - 2)^2 + 4$

$h = 2$ and $k = 4$
The vertex is at $(2, 4)$. Two points on the graph to the right of $x = 2$ are $(3, 4.25)$ and $(4, 5)$. Use symmetry to complete the graph.

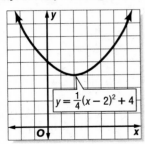

30. $y = \frac{1}{2}(x - 3)^2 - 5$

$y = \frac{1}{2}(x - 3)^2 + (-5)$

$h = 3$ and $k = -5$
The vertex is at $(3, -5)$. Two points on the graph to the right of $x = 3$ are $(4, -4.5)$ and $(5, -3)$. Use symmetry to complete the graph.

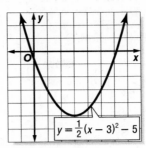

31. $y = x^2 + 6x + 2$
$y = (x^2 + 6x + 9) + 2 - 9$
$y = (x + 3)^2 - 7$
$y = [x - (-3)]^2 + (-7)$
$h = -3$ and $k = -7$.
The vertex is at $(-3, -7)$. Two points on the graph to the right of $x = -3$ are $(-4, -6)$ and $(-5, -3)$. Use symmetry to complete the graph.

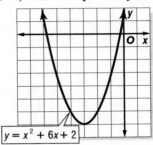

32. $y = x^2 - 8x + 18$
$y = (x^2 - 8x + 16) + 18 - 16$
$y = (x - 4)^2 + 2$
$h = 4$ and $k = 2$.
The vertex is at $(4, 2)$. Two points on the graph to the right of $x = 4$ are $(5, 3)$ and $(6, 6)$. Use symmetry to complete the graph.

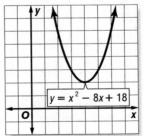

Chapter 6

33. $y = -4x^2 + 16x - 11$
$y = -4(x^2 - 4x) - 11$
$y = -4(x^2 - 4x + 4) - 11 - (-4)(4)$
$y = -4(x - 2)^2 + 5$
$h = 2$ and $k = 5$.
The vertex is at $(2, 5)$. Two points on the graph to the right of $x = 2$ are $(2.5, 4)$ and $(3, 1)$. Use symmetry to complete the graph.

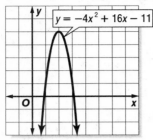

34. $y = -5x^2 - 40x - 80$
$y = -5(x^2 + 8x) - 80$
$y = -5(x^2 + 8x + 16) - 80 - (-5)(16)$
$y = -5(x + 4)^2$
$y = -5[x - (-4)]^2 + 0$
$h = -4$ and $k = 0$.
The vertex is at $(-4, 0)$. Two points on the graph to the right of $x = -4$ are $(-3.5, -1.25)$ and $(-3, -5)$. Use symmetry to complete the graph.

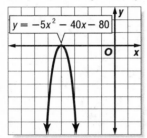

35. $y = -\frac{1}{2}x^2 + 5x - \frac{27}{2}$
$y = -\frac{1}{2}(x^2 - 10x) - \frac{27}{2}$
$y = -\frac{1}{2}(x^2 - 10x + 25) - \frac{27}{2} - \left(-\frac{1}{2}\right)(25)$
$y = -\frac{1}{2}(x - 5)^2 - 1$
$y = -\frac{1}{2}(x - 5)^2 + (-1)$
$h = 5$ and $k = -1$.
The vertex is at $(5, -1)$. Two points on the graph to the right of $x = 5$ are $(6, -1.5)$ and $(7, -3)$. Use symmetry to complete the graph.

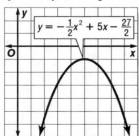

36. $y = \frac{1}{3}x^2 - 4x + 15$
$y = \frac{1}{3}(x^2 - 12x) + 15$
$y = \frac{1}{3}(x^2 - 12x + 36) + 15 - \left(\frac{1}{3}\right)(36)$
$y = \frac{1}{3}(x - 6)^2 + 3$
$h = 6$ and $k = 3$.
The vertex is at $(6, 3)$. Two points on the graph to the right of $x = 6$ are $\left(7, 3\frac{1}{3}\right)$ and $\left(8, 4\frac{1}{3}\right)$. Use symmetry to complete the graph.

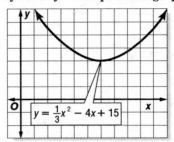

37. Sample answer: The graph of $y = 0.4(x + 3)^2 + 1$ is narrower than the graph of $y = 0.2(x + 3)^2 + 1$.

38. Sample anwer: The graphs have the same shape, but the graph of $y = 2(x - 4)^2 - 1$ is 1 unit to the left and 5 units below the graph of $y = 2(x - 5)^2 + 4$.

39. $h = 6$ and $k = 1$. Let $x = 5$ and $y = 10$. Substitute these values into the vertex form of the equation and solve for a.
$y = a(x - h)^2 + k$
$10 = a(5 - 6)^2 + 1$
$10 = a(1) + 1$
$9 = a$
The equation of the parabola in vertex form is $y = 9(x - 6)^2 + 1$.

40. $h = -4$ and $k = 3$. Let $x = -3$ and $y = 6$. Substitute these values into the vertex form of the equation and solve for a.
$y = a(x - h)^2 + k$
$6 = a[-3 - (-4]^2 + 3$
$6 = a(1) + 3$
$3 = a$
The equation of the parabola in vertex form is $y = 3(x + 4)^2 + 3$.

41. $h = 3$ and $k = 0$. Let $x = 6$ and $y = -6$. Substitute these values into the vertex form of the equation and solve for a.
$y = a(x - h)^2 + k$
$-6 = a(6 - 3)^2 + 0$
$-6 = a(9)$
$-6 = 9a$
$-\frac{2}{3} = a$
The equation of the parabola in vertex form is $y = -\frac{2}{3}(x - 3)^2$.

42. $h = 5$ and $k = 4$. Let $x = 3$ and $y = -8$. Substitute these values into the vertex form of the equation and solve for a.
$$y = a(x - h)^2 + k$$
$$-8 = a(3 - 5)^2 + 4$$
$$-8 = a(4) + 4$$
$$-12 = 4a$$
$$-3 = a$$
The equation of the parabola in vertex form is $y = -3(x - 5)^2 + 4$.

43. $h = 0$ and $k = 5$. Let $x = 3$ and $y = 8$. Substitute these values into the vertex form of the equation and solve for a.
$$y = a(x - h)^2 + k$$
$$8 = a(3 - 0)^2 + 5$$
$$8 = a(9) + 5$$
$$3 = 9a$$
$$\frac{1}{3} = a$$
The equation of the parabola in vertex form is $y = \frac{1}{3}x^2 + 5$.

44. $h = -3$ and $k = -2$. Let $x = -1$ and $y = 8$. Substitute these values into the vertex form of the equation and solve for a.
$$y = a(x - h)^2 + k$$
$$8 = a[-1 - (-3)]^2 + (-2)$$
$$8 = a(4) - 2$$
$$10 = 4a$$
$$\frac{5}{2} = a$$
The equation of the parabola in vertex form is $y = \frac{5}{2}(x + 3)^2 - 2$.

45. $h = 0$ and $k = 0$. Let $x = 2$ and $y = -8$. Substitute these values into the vertex form of the equation and solve for a.
$$y = a(x - h)^2 + k$$
$$-8 = a(2 - 0)^2 + 0$$
$$-8 = a(4)$$
$$-8 = 4a$$
$$-2 = a$$
The equation of the parabola in vertex form is $y = -2x^2$.

46. $h = -3$ and $k = -4$. Let $x = 0$ and $y = 8$. Substitute these values into the vertex form of the equation and solve for a.
$$y = a(x - h)^2 + k$$
$$8 = a[0 - (-3)]^2 + (-4)$$
$$8 = a(9) - 4$$
$$12 = 9a$$
$$\frac{4}{3} = a$$
The equation of the parabola in vertex form is $y = \frac{4}{3}(x + 3)^2 - 4$.

47. $h(t) = -9.09(t - 32.5)^2 + 34{,}000$
$h = 32.5$ and $k = 34{,}000$.
The vertex is at $(32.5, 34{,}000)$. Since $a = -9.09$, the graph opens down and has a maximum at the vertex. Thus, the maximum height is 34,000 feet which occurs 32.5 seconds after the aircraft begins its parabolic flight.

48. Substitute 0 for $d(t)$ and solve for t.
$$0 = -16t^2 + 8t + 30$$
$$a = -16, b = 8, \text{ and } c = 30.$$
$$x = \frac{-b \pm \sqrt{b^2 - 4ac}}{2a}$$
$$x = \frac{-(8) \pm \sqrt{(8)^2 - 4(-16)(30)}}{2(-16)}$$
$$x = \frac{-8 \pm \sqrt{1984}}{-32}$$
$$x = \frac{-8 + \sqrt{1984}}{-32} \text{ or } x = \frac{-8 - \sqrt{1984}}{-32}$$
$$x \approx -1.14 \qquad x \approx 1.64$$
The diver hits the water in about 1.6 seconds.

49. $d(t) = -16t^2 + 8t + 30$
$$d(t) = -16\left(t^2 - \frac{1}{2}t\right) + 30$$
$$d(t) = -16\left(t^2 - \frac{1}{2}t + \frac{1}{16}\right) + 30 - (-16)\left(\frac{1}{16}\right)$$
$$d(t) = -16\left(t - \frac{1}{4}\right)^2 + 31$$
$$h = \frac{1}{4} \text{ and } k = 31.$$
To move the graph 20 units up, add 20 to k or 31.
$$d(t) = -16\left(t - \frac{1}{4}\right)^2 + (31 + 20)$$
$$d(t) = -16\left(t - \frac{1}{4}\right)^2 + 51$$
The equation would be $d(t) = -16\left(t - \frac{1}{4}\right)^2 + 51$ or $d(t) = -16t^2 + 8t + 50$.

50. Substitute 0 for $d(t)$ and solve for t.
$$0 = -16t^2 + 8t + 50$$
$$a = -16, b = 8, \text{ and } c = 50.$$
$$x = \frac{-b \pm \sqrt{b^2 - 4ac}}{2a}$$
$$x = \frac{-8 \pm \sqrt{(8)^2 - 4(-16)(50)}}{2(-16)}$$
$$x = \frac{-8 \pm \sqrt{3264}}{-32}$$
$$x = \frac{-8 + \sqrt{3264}}{-32} \text{ or } x = \frac{-8 - \sqrt{3264}}{-32}$$
$$x \approx -1.54 \qquad x \approx 2.04$$
The diver hits the water in about 2.0 seconds.

51. Angle A; the graph of the equation for angle A is higher than the other two since 3.27 is greater than 2.39 or 1.53.

52. Angle B; the vertex of the equation for angle B is farther to the right than the other two since 3.57 is greater than 3.09 or 3.22.

53. $y = ax^2 + bx + c$
$$y = a\left(x^2 + \frac{b}{a}x\right) + c$$
$$y = a\left[x^2 + \frac{b}{a}x + \left(\frac{b}{2a}\right)^2\right] + c - a\left(\frac{b}{2a}\right)^2$$
$$y = a\left(x + \frac{b}{2a}\right)^2 + c - \frac{b^2}{4a}$$
The axis of symmetry is $x = h$ or $x = -\frac{b}{2a}$.

54. All quadratic equations are a transformation of the parent graph $y = x^2$. By identifying these transformations when a quadratic function is written in vertex form, you can redraw the graph of $y = x^2$. Answers should include the following.

- In the equation $y = a(x - h)^2 + k$, h translated the graph of $y = x^2$ h units to the right when h is positive and h units to the left when h is negative. The graph of $y = x^2$ is translated k units up when k is positive and k units down when k is negative. When a is positive, the graph opens upward and when a is negative, the graph opens downwards. If the absolute value of a is less than 1, the graph will be narrower than the graph of $y = x^2$, and if the absolute value of a is greater than 1, the graph will be wider than the graph of $y = x^2$.

- Sample answer: $y = 2(x + 2)^2 - 3$ is the graph of $y = x^2$ translated 2 units left and 3 units down. The graph opens upward, but is narrower than the graph of $y = x^2$.

55. D; Replace $f(x)$ with -4 and solve for x.
$$-4 = x^2 - 5x$$
$$0 = x^2 - 5x + 4$$
$$0 = (x - 4)(x - 1)$$
$$x - 4 = 0 \text{ or } x - 1 = 0$$
$$x = 4 \qquad x = 1$$

56. B; $y = 2(x - 6)^2 + 3$
$h = 6$ and $k = 3$.
The vertex is at $(6, 3)$.

Page 328   Maintain Your Skills

57. $a = 3, b = -6, c = 2$
$$b^2 - 4ac = (-6)^2 - 4(3)(2)$$
$$= 36 - 24$$
$$= 12$$

The discriminant is 12, which is not a perfect square. Therefore, there are two irrational roots.

58. $4x^2 + 7x = 11 \rightarrow 4x^2 + 7x - 11 = 0$
$a = 4, b = 7, c = -11$
$$b^2 - 4ac = (7)^2 - 4(4)(-11)$$
$$= 49 + 176$$
$$= 225$$

The discriminant is 225, which is a perfect square. Therefore, there are two rational roots.

59. $a = 2, b = -5, c = 6$
$$b^2 - 4ac = (-5)^2 - 4(2)(6)$$
$$= 25 - 48$$
$$= -23$$

The discriminant is negative, so there are two complex roots.

60. $x^2 + 10x + 17 = 0$
$$x^2 + 10x = -17$$
$$x^2 + 10x + 25 = -17 + 25$$
$$(x + 5)^2 = 8$$
$$x + 5 = \pm\sqrt{8}$$
$$x + 5 = \pm 2\sqrt{2}$$
$$x = -5 \pm 2\sqrt{2}$$
The solution set is $\{-5 - \sqrt{2}2, -5 + 2\sqrt{2}\}$.

61. $x^2 - 6x + 18 = 0$
$$x^2 - 6x = -18$$
$$x^2 - 6x + 9 = -18 + 9$$
$$(x - 3)^2 = -9$$
$$x - 3 = \pm\sqrt{-9}$$
$$x - 3 = \pm 3i$$
$$x = 3 \pm 3i$$
The solution set is $\{3 - 3i, 3 + 3i\}$.

62. $4x^2 + 8x = 9$
$$x^2 + 2x = \frac{9}{4}$$
$$x^2 + 2x + 1 = \frac{9}{4} + 1$$
$$(x + 1)^2 = \frac{13}{4}$$
$$x + 1 = \pm\sqrt{\frac{13}{4}}$$
$$x + 1 = \pm\frac{\sqrt{13}}{2}$$
$$x = -1 \pm \frac{\sqrt{13}}{2}$$
$$x = \frac{-2 \pm \sqrt{13}}{2}$$
The solution set is is $\left\{\frac{-2 + \sqrt{13}}{2}, \frac{-2 - \sqrt{13}}{2}\right\}$.

63.
$$\begin{array}{r} 2t^2 + 2t \\ t - 1)\overline{2t^3 + 0t^2 - 2t - 3} \\ \underline{(-)\ 2t^3 - 2t^2} \\ 2t^2 - 2t \\ \underline{(-)\ 2t^2 - 2t} \\ 0 - 3 \end{array}$$
The result is $2t^2 + 2t - \frac{3}{t - 1}$.

64.
$$\begin{array}{r} t^2 - 2t + 1 \\ t + 2)\overline{t^3 + 0t^2 - 3t + 2} \\ \underline{(-)\ t^3 + 2t^2} \\ -2t^2 - 3t \\ \underline{(-)\ -2t^2 - 4t} \\ t + 2 \\ \underline{(-)\ t + 2} \\ 0 \end{array}$$
The result is $t^2 - 2t + 1$.

65.
$$\begin{array}{r} n^3 - 3n^2 - 15n - 21 \\ n - 5)\overline{n^4 - 8n^3 + 0n^2 + 54n + 105} \\ \underline{(-)\ n^4 - 5n^3} \\ -3n^3 + 0n^2 \\ \underline{(-)\ -3n^3 + 15n^2} \\ -15n^2 + 54n \\ \underline{(-)\ -15n^2 + 75n} \\ -21n + 105 \\ \underline{(-)\ -21n + 105} \\ 0 \end{array}$$
The result is $n^3 - 3n^2 - 15n - 21$.

66.
$$\begin{array}{r} y^3 \qquad\quad + 1 \\ y + 3)\overline{y^4 + 3y^3 + 0y^2 + y - 1} \\ \underline{(-)\ y^4 + 3y^3} \\ y - 1 \\ \underline{(-)\ y + 3} \\ -4 \end{array}$$
The result is $y^3 + 1 - \frac{4}{y + 3}$.

67a. Find an equation of the line through (1994, 76,302) and (1997, 99,448). Find the slope.

$$m = \frac{y_2 - y_1}{x_2 - x_1}$$
$$= \frac{99{,}448 - 76{,}302}{1997 - 1994}$$
$$\approx 7715$$

$$y - y_1 = m(x - x_1)$$
$$y - 76{,}302 = 7715(x - 1994)$$
$$y - 76{,}302 = 7715x - 15{,}383{,}710$$
$$y = 7715x - 15{,}307{,}408$$

One prediction equation is
$y = 7715x - 15{,}307{,}408$.

67b. Use the prediction equation to find the value of y when $x = 2005$.

$$y = 7715x - 15{,}307{,}408$$
$$= 7715(2005) - 15{,}307{,}408$$
$$= 161{,}167$$

The model predicts that there will be about 161,167 students abroad in 2005.

68.
$$-2x^2 + 3 < 0$$
$$-2(5)^2 + 3 \overset{?}{<} 0$$
$$-50 + 3 \overset{?}{<} 0$$
$$-47 < 0 \checkmark$$

Yes, 5 satisfies the inequality.

69.
$$4x^2 + 2x - 3 \geq 0$$
$$4(-1)^2 + 2(-1) - 3 \overset{?}{\geq} 0$$
$$4 - 2 - 3 \overset{?}{\geq} 0$$
$$-1 \geq 0 \; \boldsymbol{\times}$$

No, -1 does not satisfy the inequality.

70.
$$4x^2 - 4x + 1 \leq 10$$
$$4(2)^2 - 4(2) + 1 \overset{?}{\leq} 10$$
$$16 - 8 + 1 \overset{?}{\leq} 10$$
$$9 \leq 10 \checkmark$$

Yes, 2 satisfies the inequality.

71.
$$6x^2 + 3x > 8$$
$$6(0)^2 + 3(0) \overset{?}{>} 8$$
$$0 + 0 \overset{?}{>} 8$$
$$0 > 8 \; \boldsymbol{\times}$$

No, 0 does not satisfy the inequality.

Page 328   Practice Quiz 2

1.
$$x^2 + 14x + 37 = 0$$
$$x^2 + 14x = -37$$
$$x^2 + 14x + 49 = -37 + 49$$
$$(x + 7)^2 = 12$$
$$x + 7 = \pm\sqrt{12}$$
$$x + 7 = \pm 2\sqrt{3}$$
$$x = -7 \pm 2\sqrt{3}$$

The solution set is $\{-7 - 2\sqrt{3},\ -7 + 2\sqrt{3}\}$.

2.
$$2x^2 - 2x + 5 = 0$$
$$x^2 - x + \frac{5}{2} = 0$$
$$x^2 - x = -\frac{5}{2}$$
$$x^2 - x + \frac{1}{4} = -\frac{5}{2} + \frac{1}{4}$$
$$\left(x - \frac{1}{2}\right)^2 = -\frac{9}{4}$$
$$x - \frac{1}{2} = \pm\sqrt{-\frac{9}{4}}$$
$$x - \frac{1}{2} = \pm\frac{3}{2}\boldsymbol{i}$$
$$x = \frac{1}{2} \pm \frac{3}{2}\boldsymbol{i}$$
$$x = \frac{1 \pm 3\boldsymbol{i}}{2}$$

The solution set is $\left\{\frac{1 + 3\boldsymbol{i}}{2}, \frac{1 - 3\boldsymbol{i}}{2}\right\}$.

3. $a = 5, b = -3, c = 1$
$$b^2 - 4ac = (-3)^2 - 4(5)(1)$$
$$= 9 - 20$$
$$= -11$$

The discriminant is negative, so there are two complex roots.

4. $a = 3, b = 4, c = -7$
$$b^2 - 4ac = (4)^2 - 4(3)(-7)$$
$$= 16 + 84$$
$$= 100$$

The discriminant is 100, which is a perfect square. Therefore there are two rational roots.

5.
$$x = \frac{-b \pm \sqrt{b^2 - 4ac}}{2a}$$
$$x = \frac{-(9) \pm \sqrt{(9)^2 - 4(1)(-11)}}{2(1)}$$
$$x = \frac{-9 \pm \sqrt{125}}{2}$$
$$x = \frac{-9 \pm 5\sqrt{5}}{2}$$

The exact solutions are $\frac{-9 - 5\sqrt{5}}{2}$ and $\frac{-9 + 5\sqrt{5}}{2}$.

The approximate solutions are -10.1 and 1.1.

6. $-3x^2 + 4x = 4 \rightarrow -3x^2 + 4x - 4 = 0$
$$x = \frac{-b \pm \sqrt{b^2 - 4ac}}{2a}$$
$$x = \frac{-(4) \pm \sqrt{(4)^2 - 4(-3)(-4)}}{2(-3)}$$
$$x = \frac{-4 \pm \sqrt{-32}}{-6}$$
$$x = \frac{-4 \pm 4\boldsymbol{i}\sqrt{2}}{-6}$$
$$x = \frac{2 \pm 2\boldsymbol{i}\sqrt{2}}{3}$$

The solutions are the complex numbers $\frac{2 + 2\boldsymbol{i}\sqrt{2}}{3}$ and $\frac{2 - 2\boldsymbol{i}\sqrt{2}}{3}$.

7. $h = 2$ and $k = -5$. Let $x = -1$ and $y = 1$.
Substitute these values into the vertex form of
the equation and solve for a.

$y = a(x - h)^2 + k$
$1 = a(-1 - 2)^2 + (-5)$
$1 = a(9) - 5$
$6 = 9a$
$\frac{2}{3} = a$

The equation of the parabola in vertex form is
$y = \frac{2}{3}(x - 2)^2 - 5$.

8. $y = x^2 + 8x + 18$
$y = (x^2 + 8x + 16) + 18 - 16$
$y = (x + 4)^2 + 2$
$y = [x - (-4)]^2 + 2$
$h = -4$ and $k = 2$.
The vertex is at $(-4, 2)$, and the axis of symmetry
is $x = -4$. Since $a = 1$, the graph opens up.

9. $y = -x^2 + 12x - 36$
$y = -(x^2 - 12x) - 36$
$y = -(x^2 - 12x + 36) - 36 - (-1)(36)$
$y = -(x - 6)^2$
$y = -(x - 6)^2 + 0$
$h = 6$ and $k = 0$.
The vertex is at $(6, 0)$, and the axis of symmetry is
$x = 6$. Since $a = -1$, the graph opens down.

10. $y = 2x^2 + 12x + 13$
$y = 2(x^2 + 6x) + 13$
$y = 2(x^2 + 6x + 9) + 13 - 2(9)$
$y = 2(x + 3)^2 - 5$
$y = 2[x - (-3)]^2 + (-5)$
$h = -3$ and $k = -5$.
The vertex is at $(-3, -5)$, and the axis of
symmetry is $x = -3$. Since $a = 2$, the graph
opens up.

| 6-7 | **Graphing and Solving Quadratic Inequalities** |

Pages 332–333   Check for Understanding

1. Test the point $(3, 0)$ in the inequalities.
$y \geq (x - 3)^2 - 1$
$0 \overset{?}{\geq} (3 - 3)^2 - 1$
$0 \overset{?}{\geq} 0 - 1$
$0 \geq -1$ ✓

$y \leq (x - 3)^2 - 1$
$0 \overset{?}{\leq} (3 - 3)^2 - 1$
$0 \overset{?}{\leq} 0 - 1$
$0 \leq -1$ ✗
So, $(3, 0)$ is a solution of $y \geq (x - 3)^2 - 1$.
Therefore, $y \geq (x - 3)^2 - 1$ describes the graph.

2. Sample answer: one number less than -3, one
number between -3 and 5, and one number
greater than 5.

3a. The x-intercepts of the graph are -1 and 5.
Therefore, the solutions of the equation are -1
and 5.

3b. The graph lies above the x-axis to the left of
$x = -1$ and to the right of $x = 5$. Therefore, the
solution set is $\{x \mid x \leq -1 \text{ or } x \geq 5\}$.

3c. The graph lies on and below the x-axis at
$x = -1$ and $x = 5$ and between these two values.
Therefore, the solution set is $\{x \mid -1 \leq x \leq 5\}$.

4. Graph the related quadratic equation
$y = x^2 - 10x + 25$. Since the inequality symbol
is $\geq$, the parabola should be solid.
Test $(5, 1)$.
$y \geq x^2 - 10x + 25$
$1 \overset{?}{\geq} (5)^2 - 10(5) + 25$
$1 \overset{?}{\geq} 25 - 50 + 25$
$1 \geq 0$ ✓
So, $(5, 1)$ is a solution of the inequality. Shade the
region inside the parabola.

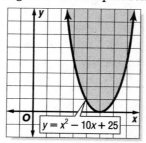

5. Graph the related quadratic equation $y = x^2 - 16$.
Since the inequality symbol is $<$, the parabola
should be dashed.
Test $(0, 0)$.
$y < x^2 - 16$
$0 \overset{?}{<} (0)^2 - 16$
$0 < -16$ ✗
So, $(0, 0)$ is not solution of the inequality. Shade
the region outside the parabola.

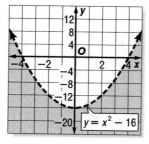

6. Graph the related quadratic equation
$y = -2x^2 - 4x + 3$. Since the inequality symbol
is >, the parabola should be dashed.
Test $(-1, 0)$.
$y > -2x^2 - 4x + 3$
$0 \overset{?}{>} -2(-1)^2 - 4(-1) + 3$
$0 \overset{?}{>} -2 + 4 + 3$
$0 > 5$ ✗
So, $(-1, 0)$ is not a solution of the inequality.
Shade the region outside the parabola.

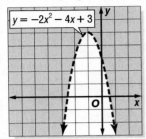

7. Graph the related quadratic equation
$y = -x^2 + 5x + 6$. Since the inequality symbol
is ≤, the parabola should be solid.
Test $(0, 0)$.
$y \leq -x^2 + 5x + 6$
$0 \overset{?}{\leq} -(0)^2 + 5(0) + 6$
$0 \overset{?}{\leq} 0 + 0 + 6$
$0 \leq 6$ ✓
So, $(0, 0)$ is a solution of the inequality. Shade the
region inside the parabola.

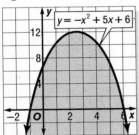

8. The graph lies below the x-axis to the left of $x = 1$
and to the right of $x = 5$. Therefore, the solution
set is $\{x \mid x < 1 \text{ or } x > 5\}$.

9. Solve the related quadratic equation
$x^2 - 6x - 7 = 0$.
$$x^2 - 6x - 7 = 0$$
$$(x + 1)(x - 7) = 0$$
$x + 1 = 0 \quad \text{or} \quad x - 7 = 0$
$\quad x = -1 \qquad\qquad x = 7$
Plot -1 and 7 on a number line. Use circles.

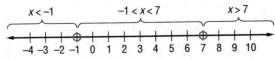

Test a value in each interval.

$x < -1$	$-1 < x < 7$	$x > 7$
Test $x = -2$.	Test $x = 0$.	Test $x = 8$.
$x^2 - 6x - 7 < 0$	$x^2 - 6x - 7 < 0$	$x^2 - 6x - 7 < 0$
$(-2)^2 - 6(-2) - 7 \overset{?}{<} 0$	$(0)^2 - 6(0) - 7 \overset{?}{<} 0$	$(8)^2 - 6(8) - 7 \overset{?}{<} 0$
$9 < 0$ ✗	$-7 < 0$ ✓	$9 < 0$ ✗

The solution set is $\{x \mid -1 < x < 7\}$.

10. Solve the related quadratic equation
$x^2 - x - 12 = 0$.
$$x^2 - x - 12 = 0$$
$$(x + 3)(x - 4) = 0$$
$x + 3 = 0 \quad \text{or} \quad x - 4 = 0$
$\quad x = -3 \qquad\qquad x = 4$
Plot -3 and 4 on a number line. Use circles.

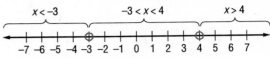

Test a value in each interval.

$x < -3$	$-3 < x < 4$	$x > 4$
Test $x = -4$.	Test $x = 0$.	Test $x = 5$.
$x^2 - x - 12 > 0$	$x^2 - x - 12 > 0$	$x^2 - x - 12 > 0$
$(-4)^2 - (-4) - 12 \overset{?}{>} 0$	$(0)^2 - (0) - 12 \overset{?}{>} 0$	$(5)^2 - (5) - 12 \overset{?}{>} 0$
$8 > 0$ ✓	$-12 > 0$ ✗	$8 > 0$ ✓

The solution set is $\{x \mid x < -3 \text{ or } x > 4\}$.

11. Solve the related quadratic equation
$x^2 = 10x - 25$.
$$x^2 = 10x - 25$$
$$x^2 - 10x + 25 = 0$$
$$(x - 5)(x - 5) = 0$$
$x - 5 = 0 \text{ or } x - 5 = 0$
$\quad x = 5 \qquad\qquad x = 5$
Plot 5 on a number line. Use a circle.

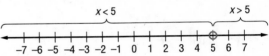

Test a value in each interval.

$x < 5$	$x > 5$
Test $x = 4$.	Test $x = 6$.
$x^2 < 10x - 25$	$x^2 < 10x - 25$
$(4)^2 \overset{?}{<} 10(4) - 25$	$(6)^2 \overset{?}{<} 10(6) - 25$
$16 < 15$ ✗	$36 < 35$ ✗

There is no solution. The solution set is $\varnothing$.

12. Solve the related quadratic equation $x^2 = 3$.
$x^2 = 3$
$x = \pm \sqrt{3}$
Plot $-\sqrt{3}$ and $\sqrt{3}$ on a number line. Use solid
dots.

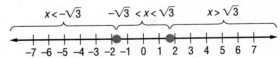

Test a value in each interval.

$x < -\sqrt{3}$	$-\sqrt{3} < x < \sqrt{3}$	$x > \sqrt{3}$
Test $x = -2$.	Test $x = 0$.	Test $x = 2$.
$x^2 \leq 3$	$x^2 \leq 3$	$x^2 \leq 3$
$(-2)^2 \overset{?}{\leq} 3$	$(0)^2 \overset{?}{\leq} 3$	$(2)^2 \overset{?}{\leq} 3$
$4 \leq 3$ ✗	$0 \leq 3$ ✓	$4 \leq 3$ ✗

The solution set is $\{x \mid -\sqrt{3} \leq x \leq \sqrt{3}\}$.

13. Replace $h(t)$ with 1.7 and solve for t.

$h(t) = -4.9t^2 + 30t + 1.4$

$1.7 = -4.9t^2 + 30t + 1.4$

$0 = -4.9t^2 + 30t - 0.3$

$a = -4.9, b = 30,$ and $c = -0.3.$

$t = \dfrac{-b \pm \sqrt{b^2 - 4ac}}{2a}$

$t = \dfrac{-(30) \pm \sqrt{(30)^2 - 4(-4.9)(-0.3)}}{2(-4.9)}$

$t = \dfrac{-30 \pm \sqrt{894.12}}{-9.8}$

$t = \dfrac{-30 + \sqrt{894.12}}{-9.8}$ or $t = \dfrac{-30 - \sqrt{894.12}}{-9.8}$

$t \approx 0.01 \qquad\qquad t \approx 6.11$

The ball is 1.7 meters above the ground at about 0.01 second after it was hit and again at about 6.11 seconds after it was hit. Assuming the ball was caught on its way down, the player has about 6.1 second to catch the ball.

Pages 333–335 Practice and Apply

14. Graph the related quadratic equation $y = x^2 + 3x - 18$. Since the inequality symbol is $\geq$, the parabola should be solid.

Test $(0, 0)$.

$y \geq x^2 + 3x - 18$

$0 \overset{?}{\geq} (0)^2 + 3(0) - 18$

$0 \overset{?}{\geq} 0 + 0 - 18$

$0 \geq -18$ ✓

So, $(0, 0)$ is a solution of the inequality. Shade the region inside the parabola.

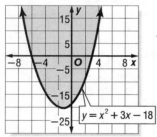

15. Graph the related quadratic equation $y = -x^2 + 7x + 8$. Since the inequality symbol is $<$, the parabola should be dashed.

Test $(0, 0)$.

$y < -x^2 + 7x + 8$

$0 \overset{?}{<} -(0)^2 + 7(0) + 8$

$0 \overset{?}{<} 0 + 0 + 8$

$0 < 8$ ✓

So, $(0, 0)$ is a solution of the inequality. Shade the region inside the parabola.

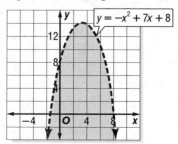

16. Graph the related quadratic equation $y = x^2 + 4x + 4$. Since the inequality symbol is $\leq$, the parabola should be solid.

Test $(-2, 1)$.

$y \leq x^2 + 4x + 4$

$1 \overset{?}{\leq} (-2)^2 + 4(-2) + 4$

$1 \overset{?}{\leq} 4 - 8 + 4$

$1 \leq 0$ ✗

So, $(-2, 1)$ is not a solution of the inequality. Shade the region outside the parabola.

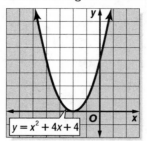

17. Graph the related quadratic equation $y = x^2 + 4x$. Since the inequality symbol is $\leq$, the parabola should be solid.

Test $(-2, 0)$.

$y \leq x^2 + 4x$

$0 \overset{?}{\leq} (-2)^2 + 4(-2)$

$0 \overset{?}{\leq} 4 - 8$

$0 \leq -4$ ✗

So, $(-2, 0)$ is not a solution of the inequality. Shade the region outside the parabola.

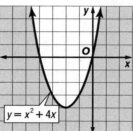

18. Graph the related quadratic equation $y = x^2 - 36$. Since the inequality symbol is $>$, the parabola should be dashed.

Test $(0, 0)$.

$y > x^2 - 36$

$0 \overset{?}{>} (0)^2 - 36$

$0 \overset{?}{>} 0 - 36$

$0 > -36$ ✓

So, $(0, 0)$ is a solution of the inequality. Shade the region inside the parabola.

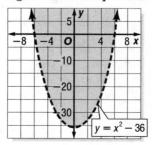

19. Graph the related quadratic equation $y = x^2 + 6x + 5$. Since the inequality symbol is $>$, the parabola should be dashed.
Test $(-3, 0)$.
$y > x^2 + 6x + 5$
$0 \overset{?}{>} (-3)^2 + 6(-3) + 5$
$0 \overset{?}{>} 9 - 18 + 5$
$0 > -4$ ✓
So, $(-3, 0)$ is a solution of the inequality. Shade the region inside the parabola.

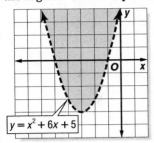

20. Graph the related quadratic equation $y = -x^2 - 3x + 10$. Since the inequality symbol is $\leq$, the parabola should be solid.
Test $(0, 0)$.
$y \leq -x^2 - 3x + 10$
$0 \overset{?}{\leq} -(0)^2 - 3(0) + 10$
$0 \overset{?}{\leq} 0 + 0 + 10$
$0 \leq 10$ ✓
So, $(0, 0)$ is a solution of the inequality. Shade the region inside the parabola.

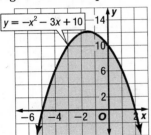

21. Graph the related quadratic equation $y = -x^2 - 7x + 10$. Since the inequality symbol is $\geq$, the parabola should be solid.
Test $(0, 0)$.
$y \geq -x^2 - 7x + 10$
$0 \overset{?}{\geq} -(0)^2 - 7(0) + 10$
$0 \overset{?}{\geq} 0 + 0 + 10$
$0 \geq 10$ ✗
So, $(0, 0)$ is not a solution of the inequality. Shade the region outside the parabola.

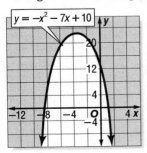

22. Graph the related quadratic equation $y = -x^2 + 10x - 23$. Since the inequality symbol is $>$, the parabola should be dashed.
Test $(5, 0)$.
$y > -x^2 + 10x - 23$
$0 \overset{?}{>} -(5)^2 + 10(5) - 23$
$0 \overset{?}{>} -25 + 50 - 23$
$0 > 2$ ✗
So, $(5, 0)$ is not a solution of the inequality. Shade the region outside the parabola.

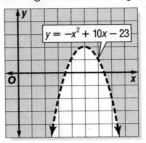

23. Graph the related quadratic equation $y = -x^2 + 13x - 36$. Since the inequality symbol is $<$, the parabola should be dashed.
Test $(6, 0)$.
$y < -x^2 + 13x - 36$
$0 \overset{?}{<} -(6)^2 + 13(6) - 36$
$0 \overset{?}{<} -36 + 78 - 36$
$0 < 6$ ✓
So, $(6, 0)$ is a solution of the inequality. Shade the region inside the parabola.

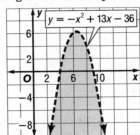

24. Graph the related quadratic equation $y = 2x^2 + 3x - 5$. Since the inequality symbol is $<$, the parabola should be dashed.
Test $(0, 0)$.
$y < 2x^2 + 3x - 5$
$0 \overset{?}{<} 2(0)^2 + 3(0) - 5$
$0 \overset{?}{<} 0 + 0 - 5$
$0 < -5$ ✗
So, $(0, 0)$ is not a solution of the inequality. Shade the region outside the parabola.

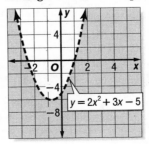

Chapter 6

25. Graph the related quadratic equation $y = 2x^2 + x - 3$. Since the inequality symbol is $\geq$, the parabola should be solid.

Test $(0, 0)$.

$y \geq 2x^2 + x - 3$

$0 \overset{?}{\geq} 2(0)^2 + 0 - 3$

$0 \overset{?}{\geq} 0 + 0 - 3$

$0 \geq -3$ ✓

So, $(0, 0)$ is a solution of the inequality. Shade the region inside the parabola.

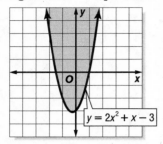

$y = 2x^2 + x - 3$

26. The graph lies on and above the x-axis at 5. Therefore, the solution set is $\{x \mid x = 5\}$.

27. The graph lies on and below the x-axis at $x = -2$ and $x = 6$ and between these two values. Therefore, the solution set is $\{x \mid -2 \leq x \leq 6\}$.

28. The graph lies above the x-axis to the left of $x = -3$ and to the right of $x = 3$. Therefore, the solution set is $\{x \mid x < -3 \text{ or } x > 3\}$.

29. The graph lies below the x-axis to the left of $x = -7$ and to the right of $x = -3$. Therefore, the solution set is $\{x \mid x < -7 \text{ or } x > -3\}$.

30. Solve the related quadratic equation $x^2 - 3x - 18 = 0$.

$x^2 - 3x - 18 = 0$

$(x + 3)(x - 6) = 0$

$x + 3 = 0 \quad \text{or } x - 6 = 0$

$\qquad x = -3 \qquad\quad x = 6$

Plot -3 and 6 on a number line. Use circles.

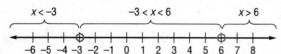

Test a value in each interval.

$x < -3$	$-3 < x < 6$	$x > 6$
Test $x = -4$.	Test $x = 0$.	Test $x = 7$.
$x^2 - 3x - 18 > 0$	$x^2 - 3x - 18 > 0$	$x^2 - 3x - 18 > 0$
$(-4)^2 - 3(-4) - 18 \overset{?}{>} 0$	$(0)^2 - 3(0) - 18 \overset{?}{>} 0$	$(7)^2 - 3(7) - 18 \overset{?}{>} 0$
$10 > 0$ ✓	$-18 > 0$ ✗	$10 > 0$ ✓

The solution set is $\{x \mid x < -3 \text{ or } x > 6\}$.

31. Solve the related quadratic equation $x^2 + 3x - 28 = 0$.

$x^2 + 3x - 28 = 0$

$(x + 7)(x - 4) = 0$

$x + 7 = 0 \quad \text{or } x - 4 = 0$

$\qquad x = -7 \qquad\quad x = 4$

Plot -7 and 4 on a number line. Use circles.

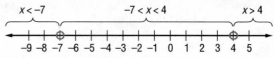

Test a value in each interval.

$x < -7$	$-7 < x < 4$	$x > 4$
Test $x = -8$.	Test $x = 0$.	Test $x = 5$.
$x^2 + 3x - 28 < 0$	$x^2 + 3x - 28 < 0$	$x^2 + 3x - 28 < 0$
$(-8)^2 + 3(-8) - 28 \overset{?}{<} 0$	$(0)^2 + 3(0) - 28 \overset{?}{<} 0$	$(5)^2 - 3(5) - 28 \overset{?}{<} 0$
$12 < 0$ ✗	$-28 < 0$ ✓	$12 < 0$ ✗

The solution set is $\{x \mid -7 < x < 4\}$.

32. Solve the related quadratic equation $x^2 - 4x = 5$.

$x^2 - 4x = 5$

$x^2 - 4x - 5 = 0$

$(x + 1)(x - 5) = 0$

$x + 1 = 0 \quad \text{or } x - 5 = 0$

$\qquad x = -1 \qquad\quad x = 5$

Plot -1 and 5 on a number line. Use solid dots.

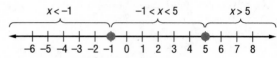

Test a value in each interval.

$x < -1$	$-1 < x < 5$	$x > 5$
Test $x = -2$.	Test $x = 0$.	Test $x = 6$.
$x^2 - 4x \leq 5$	$x^2 - 4x \leq 5$	$x^2 - 4x \leq 5$
$(-2)^2 - 4(-2) \overset{?}{\leq} 5$	$(0)^2 - 4(0) \overset{?}{\leq} 5$	$(6)^2 - 4(6) \overset{?}{\leq} 5$
$12 \leq 5$ ✗	$0 \leq 5$ ✓	$12 \leq 5$ ✗

The solution set is $\{x \mid -1 \leq x \leq 5\}$.

33. Solve the related quadratic equation $x^2 + 2x = 24$.

$x^2 + 2x = 24$

$x^2 + 2x - 24 = 0$

$(x + 6)(x - 4) = 0$

$x + 6 = 0 \quad \text{or } x - 4 = 0$

$\qquad x = -6 \qquad\quad x = 4$

Plot -6 and 4 on a number line. Use solid dots.

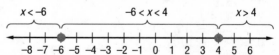

Test a value in each interval.

$x < -6$	$-6 < x < 4$	$x > 4$
Test $x = -7$.	Test $x = 0$.	Test $x = 5$.
$x^2 + 2x \geq 24$	$x^2 + 2x \geq 24$	$x^2 + 2x \geq 24$
$(-7)^2 + 2(-7) \overset{?}{\geq} 24$	$(0)^2 - 2(0) \overset{?}{\geq} 24$	$(5)^2 - 2(5) \overset{?}{\geq} 24$
$35 \geq 24$ ✓	$0 \geq 24$ ✗	$35 \geq 24$ ✓

The solution set is $\{x \mid x \leq -6 \text{ or } x \geq 4\}$.

34. Solve the related quadratic equation
$-x^2 - x + 12 = 0$.
$$-x^2 - x + 12 = 0$$
$$-(x^2 + x - 12) = 0$$
$$x^2 + x - 12 = 0$$
$$(x + 4)(x - 3) = 0$$
$$x + 4 = 0 \quad \text{or} \quad x - 3 = 0$$
$$x = -4 \qquad x = 3$$
Plot -4 and 3 on a number line. Use solid dots.

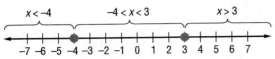

Test a value in each interval.

$x < -4$	$-4 < x < 3$	$x > 3$
Test $x = -5$.	Test $x = 0$.	Test $x = 4$.
$-x^2 - x + 12 \geq 0$	$-x^2 - x + 12 \geq 0$	$-x^2 - x + 12 \geq 0$
$-(-5)^2 - (-5) + 12 \overset{?}{\geq} 0$	$-(0)^2 - (0) + 12 \overset{?}{\geq} 0$	$-(4)^2 - (4) + 12 \overset{?}{\geq} 0$
$-8 \geq 0$ ✗	$12 \geq 0$ ✓	$-8 \geq 0$ ✗

The solution set is $\{x \mid -4 \leq x \leq 3\}$.

35. Solve the related quadratic equation
$-x^2 - 6x + 7 = 0$.
$$-x^2 - 6x + 7 = 0$$
$$-(x^2 + 6x - 7) = 0$$
$$x^2 + 6x - 7 = 0$$
$$(x + 7)(x - 1) = 0$$
$$x + 7 = 0 \quad \text{or} \quad x - 1 = 0$$
$$x = -7 \qquad x = 1$$
Plot -7 and 1 on a number line. Use solid dots.

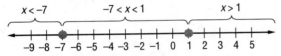

Test a value in each interval.

$x < -7$	$-7 < x < 1$	$x > 1$
Test $x = -8$.	Test $x = 0$.	Test $x = 2$.
$-x^2 - 6x + 7 \leq 0$	$-x^2 - 6x + 7 \leq 0$	$-x^2 - 6x + 7 \leq 0$
$-(-8)^2 - 6(-8) + 7 \overset{?}{\leq} 0$	$-(0)^2 - 6(0) + 7 \overset{?}{\leq} 0$	$-(2)^2 - 6(2) + 7 \overset{?}{\leq} 0$
$-9 \leq 0$ ✓	$7 \leq 0$ ✗	$-9 \leq 0$ ✓

The solution set is $\{x \mid x \leq -7 \text{ or } x \geq 1\}$.

36. Solve the related quadratic equation
$9x^2 - 6x + 1 = 0$.
$$9x^2 - 6x + 1 = 0$$
$$(3x - 1)(3x - 1) = 0$$
$$3x - 1 = 0 \quad \text{or} \quad 3x - 1 = 0$$
$$3x = 1 \qquad 3x = 1$$
$$x = \tfrac{1}{3} \qquad x = \tfrac{1}{3}$$
Plot $\tfrac{1}{3}$ on a number line. Use a solid dot.

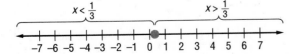

Test a value in each interval.

$x < \frac{1}{3}$	$x > \frac{1}{3}$
Test $x = 0$.	Test $x = 1$.
$9x^2 - 6x - 1 \leq 0$	$9x^2 - 6x + 1 \leq 0$
$9(0)^2 - 6(0) + 1 \overset{?}{\leq} 0$	$9(1)^2 - 6(1) + 1 \overset{?}{\leq} 0$
$1 \leq 0$ ✗	$4 \leq 0$ ✗

The solution set is $\left\{x \mid x = \tfrac{1}{3}\right\}$.

37. Solve the related quadratic equation
$4x^2 + 20x + 25 = 0$.
$$4x^2 + 20x + 25 = 0$$
$$(2x + 5)(2x + 5) = 0$$
$$2x + 5 = 0 \quad \text{or} \quad 2x + 5 = 0$$
$$2x = -5 \qquad 2x = -5$$
$$x = -\tfrac{5}{2} \qquad x = -\tfrac{5}{2}$$
Plot $-\tfrac{5}{2}$ on a number line. Use a solid dot.

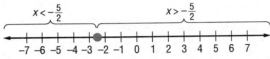

Test a value in each interval.

$x < -\frac{5}{2}$	$x > -\frac{5}{2}$
Test $x = -3$.	Test $x = -2$.
$4x^2 - 20x + 25 \geq 0$	$4x^2 - 20x + 25 \geq 0$
$4(-3)^2 + 20(-3) + 25 \overset{?}{\geq} 0$	$4(-2)^2 + 20(-2) + 25 \overset{?}{\geq} 0$
$1 \geq 0$ ✓	$1 \geq 0$ ✓

The solution set is all real numbers.

38. Solve the related quadratic equation
$x^2 + 12x = -36$.
$$x^2 + 12x = -36$$
$$x^2 + 12x + 36 = 0$$
$$(x + 6)(x + 6) = 0$$
$$x + 6 = 0 \quad \text{or} \quad x + 6 = 0$$
$$x = -6 \qquad x = -6$$
Plot -6 on a number line. Use a circle.

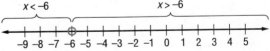

Test a value in each interval.

$x < -6$	$x > -6$
Test $x = -7$.	Test $x = -5$.
$x^2 + 12x < -36$	$x^2 + 12x < -36$
$(-7)^2 + 12(-7) \overset{?}{<} -36$	$(-5)^2 + 12(-5) \overset{?}{<} -36$
$-35 < -36$ ✗	$-35 < -36$ ✗

There is no solution. The solution set is $\varnothing$.

39. Solve the related quadratic equation
$-x^2 + 14x - 49 = 0$.
$$-x^2 + 14x - 49 = 0$$
$$-(x^2 - 14x + 49) = 0$$
$$x^2 - 14x + 49 = 0$$
$$(x - 7)(x - 7) = 0$$
$$x - 7 = 0 \text{ or } x - 7 = 0$$
$$x = 7 \qquad x = 7$$
Plot 7 on a number line. Use a solid dot.

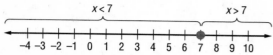

Test a value in each interval.

$x < 7$	$x > 7$
Test $x = 6$.	Test $x = 8$.
$-x^2 + 14x - 49 \geq 0$	$-x^2 + 14x - 49 \geq 0$
$-(6)^2 + 14(6) - 49 \overset{?}{\geq} 0$	$-(8)^2 + 14(8) - 49 \overset{?}{\geq} 0$
$-1 \geq 0$ ✗	$-1 \geq 0$ ✗

The solution set is $\{x \mid x = 7\}$.

40. Solve the related quadratic equation
$18x - x^2 = 81$.
$$18x - x^2 = 81$$
$$0 = x^2 - 18x + 81$$
$$0 = (x - 9)(x - 9)$$
$$x - 9 = 0 \text{ or } x - 9 = 0$$
$$x = 9 \qquad x = 9$$
Plot 9 on a number line. Use a solid dot.

Test a value in each interval.

$x < 9$	$x > 9$
Test $x = 8$.	Test $x = 10$.
$18x - x^2 \leq 81$	$18x - x^2 \leq 81$
$18(8) - (8)^2 \overset{?}{\leq} 81$	$18(10) - (10)^2 \overset{?}{\leq} 81$
$80 \leq 81$ ✓	$80 \leq 81$ ✓

The solution set is all real numbers.

41. Solve the related quadratic equation
$16x^2 + 9 = 24x$.
$$16x^2 + 9 = 24x$$
$$16x^2 - 24x + 9 = 0$$
$$(4x - 3)(4x - 3) = 0$$
$$4x - 3 = 0 \text{ or } 4x - 3 = 0$$
$$4x = 3 \qquad 4x = 3$$
$$x = \frac{3}{4} \qquad x = \frac{3}{4}$$
Plot $\frac{3}{4}$ on a number line. Use a circle.

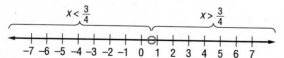

Test a value in each interval.

$x < \frac{3}{4}$	$x > \frac{3}{4}$
Test $x = 0$.	Test $x = 1$.
$16x^2 + 9 < 24x$	$16x^2 + 9 < 24x$
$16(0)^2 + 9 \overset{?}{<} 24(0)$	$16(1)^2 + 9 \overset{?}{<} 24(1)$
$9 < 0$ ✗	$25 < 24$ ✗

There is no solution. The solution set is $\varnothing$.

42. Solve the related equation
$(x - 1)(x + 4)(x - 3) = 0$.
$$(x - 1)(x + 4)(x - 3) = 0$$
$$x - 1 = 0 \text{ or } x + 4 = 0 \text{ or } x - 3 = 0$$
$$x = 1 \qquad x = -4 \qquad x = 3$$
Plot -4, 1, and 3 on a number line. Use circles.

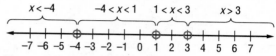

Test a value in each interval.

$x < -4$	$-4 < x < 1$
Test $x = -5$.	Test $x = 0$.
$(x - 1)(x + 4)(x - 3) > 0$	$(x - 1)(x + 4)(x - 3) > 0$
$(-5 - 1)(-5 + 4)(-5 - 3) \overset{?}{>} 0$	$(0 - 1)(0 + 4)(0 - 3) \overset{?}{>} 0$
$-48 > 0$ ✓	$12 > 0$ ✓

$1 < x < 3$	$x > 3$
Test $x = 2$.	Test $x = 4$.
$(x - 1)(x + 4)(x - 3) > 0$	$(x - 1)(x + 4)(x - 3) > 0$
$(2 - 1)(2 + 4)(2 - 3) \overset{?}{>} 0$	$(4 - 1)(4 + 4)(4 - 3) \overset{?}{>} 0$
$-6 > 0$ ✗	$24 > 0$ ✓

The solution set is $\{x \mid -4 < x < 1 \text{ or } x > 3\}$.

43. Let w = the width of the garden. Then
$34 - w$ = the length. Let $A(w)$ = area as a
function of w.

Area	equals	width	times	length.
$A(w)$	$=$	w	$\cdot$	$(34 - w)$

We want the values for w for which $A(w) \leq 240$.
$$A(w) \leq 240$$
$$w(34 - w) \leq 240$$
$$-w^2 + 34w - 240 \leq 0$$
Graph the related function $y = -w^2 + 34w - 240$.

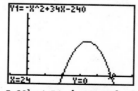

[−5, 30] scl: 5 by [−10, 100] scl: 10

The zeros of the function are at 10 and 24, and
the graph lies below the x-axis when $x < 10$ or
$x > 24$. Thus, the width could be 0 to 10 feet or 24
to 34 feet.

44a. $a = -8.1$, $b = 46.9$, and $c = -38.2$.

$$r = \frac{-b \pm \sqrt{b^2 - 4ac}}{2a}$$

$$r = \frac{-46.9 \pm \sqrt{(46.9)^2 - 4(-8.1)(-38.2)}}{2(-8.1)}$$

$$r = \frac{-46.9 \pm \sqrt{961.93}}{-16.2}$$

$$r = \frac{-46.9 + \sqrt{961.93}}{-16.2} \text{ or } r = \frac{-46.9 - \sqrt{961.93}}{-16.2}$$

$r \approx 0.98 \qquad\qquad r \approx 4.81$

The approximate solutions are 0.98 and 4.81. The owner will break even if he charges $0.98 or $4.81 per square foot.

44b. Solve the related equation
$-8.1r^2 + 46.9r - 38.2 = 0$.

$$r = \frac{-b \pm \sqrt{b^2 - 4ac}}{2a}$$

$$r = \frac{-46.9 \pm \sqrt{(46.9)^2 - 4(-8.1)(-38.2)}}{2(-8.1)}$$

$$r = \frac{-46.9 \pm \sqrt{961.93}}{-16.2}$$

$$r = \frac{-46.9 + \sqrt{961.93}}{-16.2} \text{ or } r = \frac{-46.9 - \sqrt{961.93}}{-16.2}$$

$r \approx 0.98 \qquad\qquad r \approx 4.81$

Sketch the graph of the parabola.

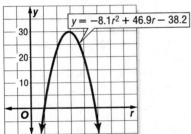

The graph lies above the x-axis between 0.98 and 4.81. Therefore, the solution set is $\{r \mid 0.98 < r < 4.81\}$. The owner will make a profit if the rent is between $0.98 and $4.81.

44c. Solve the related equation
$-8.1r^2 + 46.9r - 38.2 = 10$.
$-8.1r^2 + 46.9r - 38.2 = 10$
$-8.1r^2 + 46.9r - 48.2 = 0$

$$r = \frac{-b \pm \sqrt{b^2 - 4ac}}{2a}$$

$$r = \frac{-46.9 \pm \sqrt{(46.9)^2 - 4(-8.1)(-48.2)}}{2(-8.1)}$$

$$r = \frac{-46.9 \pm \sqrt{637.93}}{-16.2}$$

$$r = \frac{-46.9 + \sqrt{637.93}}{-16.2} \text{ or } r = \frac{-46.9 - \sqrt{637.93}}{-16.2}$$

$r \approx 1.34 \qquad\qquad r \approx 4.45$

Sketch the graph of the parabola.

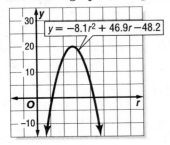

The graph lies above the x-axis between 1.34 and 4.45. Therefore, the solution set is $\{r \mid 1.34 < r < 4.45\}$. If rent is set between $1.34 and $4.45 per square foot, the profit will be greater than $10,000.

44d. Solve the related equation
$-8.1r^2 + 46.9r - 38.2 = 10$.
$-8.1r^2 + 46.9r - 38.2 = 10$
$-8.1r^2 + 46.9r - 48.2 = 0$

$$r = \frac{-b \pm \sqrt{b^2 - 4ac}}{2a}$$

$$r = \frac{-46.9 \pm \sqrt{(46.9)^2 - 4(-8.1)(-48.2)}}{2(-8.1)}$$

$$r = \frac{-46.9 \pm \sqrt{637.93}}{-16.2}$$

$$r = \frac{-46.9 + \sqrt{637.93}}{-16.2} \text{ or } r = \frac{-46.9 - \sqrt{637.93}}{-16.2}$$

$r \approx 1.34 \qquad\qquad r \approx 4.45$

Sketch the graph of the parabola.

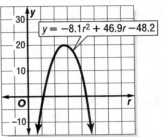

The graph lies above the x-axis to the left of 1.34 and to the right of 4.45. Therefore, the solution set is $\{r \mid r < 1.34 \text{ or } r > 4.45\}$. If rent is set between $0 and $1.34 or above $4.45 per square foot, the profit will be less than $10,000.

45. Let $w = $ the width of the rectangle. Then $w + 6 = $ the length of the rectangle. Let $A(w) = $ area as a function of w.

Area	equals	width	times	length.
$A(w)$	$=$	w	$\cdot$	$(w + 6)$

We want the values for w for which $A(w) > 216$.

$A(w) > 216$

$w(w + 6) > 216$

$w^2 + 6w - 216 > 0$

Graph the related function $y = w^2 + 6w - 216$.

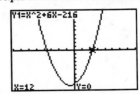

$[-40, 40]$ scl: 5 by $[-250, 250]$ scl: 25

The zeros of the function are at -18 and 12, and the graph lies above the x-axis when $x < -18$ or $x > 12$. Since the width cannot be negative. The width should be greater than 12 centimeters and the length should be greater than $12 + 6$ or 18 centimeters.

46. Let n = the number of passengers. Then $15 + 1.5(60 - n)$ = the price per passenger. Let $P(n)$ = profit as a function of n.

The profit	is	the number of passengers	multi-plied by	the price per passenger	minu s	the cost of the bus.
$P(n) =$		n	$\cdot$	$[15 + 1.5(60 - n)]$	$-$	525

$$P(n) = n[15 + 1.5(60 - n)] - 525$$
$$= n[15 + 90 - 1.5n] - 525$$
$$= n(105 - 1.5n) - 525$$
$$= 105n - 1.5n^2 - 525$$
$$= -1.5n^2 + 105n - 525$$

The equation is $P(n) = -1.5n^2 + 105n - 525$.

47. The function $P(n) = -1.5n^2 + 105n - 525$ describes the profit. You want to find the values of n for which $P(n) \geq 0$.
$$P(n) \geq 0$$
$$-1.5n^2 + 105n - 525 \geq 0$$
Graph the related function $y = -1.5n^2 + 105n - 525$.

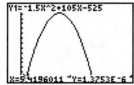

[−10, 100] scl: 5 by [−100, 1500] scl: 100

The zeros of the function are about 5.42 and 64.58, and the graph lies above the x-axis when $5.42 < x < 64.58$. Thus, the minimum number of passengers needed is 6.

48. $P(n)$ is a quadratic function with $a = -1.5$, $b = 105$, and $c = -525$. Since $a < 0$, the function has a maximum value at the vertex.

n-coordinate of the vertex $= -\dfrac{b}{2a}$
$$= -\dfrac{105}{2(-65)}$$
$$= 35$$

$$P(n) = -1.5n^2 + 105n - 525$$
$$P(35) = -1.5(35)^2 + 105(35) - 525$$
$$= 1312.5$$

Thus, the maximum profit is $1312.50, and this occurs with 35 passengers.

49. Graph the related quadratic equations, $y = -x^2 + 4$ and $y = x^2 - 4$.
Since the inequality symbols are $\leq$ and $\geq$, both parabolas should be solid.
Test $(0, 0)$.

$y \leq -x^2 + 4$ $y \geq x^2 - 4$
$0 \overset{?}{\leq} -(0)^2 + 4$ $0 \overset{?}{\geq} (0)^2 - 4$
$0 \leq 4$ ✓ $0 \geq -4$ ✓

Since $(0, 0)$ is a solution of both inequalities, shade the region inside both parabolas.

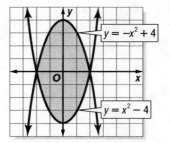

$y = -x^2 + 4$
$y = x^2 - 4$

50. Answers should include the following.
- $-16t^2 + 42t + 3.75 > 10$
- One method of solving this inequality is to graph the related function $h(t) = -16t^2 + 42t + 3.75 - 10$. The interval(s) at which the graph is above the x-axis represents the time when the trampolinist is above 10 feet. A second method of solving this inequality would be find the roots of the related quadratic equation $-16t^2 + 42t + 3.75 - 10 = 0$ and then test points in the three intervals determined by these roots to see if they satisfy the inequality. The interval(s) at which the inequality is satisfied represent the times when the trampolinist is above 10 feet.

51. C; Each square box in the grid has side length of 2. Thus, each square box represents $2(2)$ or 4 square units. There are 20 whole boxes and 16 partial boxes in the area under the curve. To get an estimate of the area multiply each whole box by 4, and each partial by 2.
$$20(4) + 16(2) = 112$$
Therefore, given the choices 29, 58, 116, and 232, we conclude there are 116 square units under the curve.

52. A; Solve $(x + 1)(x - 2) > 0$.
Solve the related quadratic equation $(x + 1)(x - 2) = 0$.
$$(x + 1)(x - 2) = 0$$
$$x + 1 = 0 \quad \text{or} \quad x - 2 = 0$$
$$x = -1 \qquad x = 2$$
Plot -1 and 2 on a number line. Use circles.

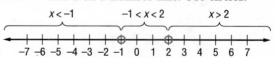

Test a value in each interval.

$x < -1$	$-1 < x < 2$	$x > 2$
Test $x = -2$.	Test $x = 0$.	Test $x = 3$.
$(x + 1)(x - 2) > 0$	$(x + 1)(x - 2) > 0$	$(x + 1)(x - 2) > 0$
$(-2 + 1)(-2 - 2) \overset{?}{>} 0$	$(0 + 1)(0 - 2) \overset{?}{>} 0$	$(3 + 1)(3 - 2) \overset{?}{>} 0$
$4 > 0$ ✓	$-2 > 0$ ✗	$4 > 0$ ✓

The solution set is $\{x \mid x < -1 \text{ or } x > 2\}$.

53. Graph $|x - 2| = 0$.

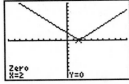

[−10, 10] scl: 1 by [−10, 10] scl: 1

The zero of the function is 2, and the graph lies above the x-axis when $x < 2$ or $x > 2$. Therefore, the solution set is $\{x \,|\, x < 2 \text{ or } x > 2\}$.

54. Graph $|x| - 7 = 0$.

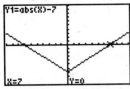

[−10, 10] scl: 1 by [−10, 10] scl: 1

The zeros of the function are −7 and 7, and the graph lies below the x-axis when $-7 < x < 7$. Therefore, the solution set is $\{x \,|\, -7 < x < 7\}$.

55. Graph $-|x + 3| + 6 = 0$.

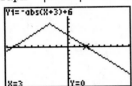

[−10, 10] scl: 1 by [−10, 10] scl: 1

The zeros of the function are −9 and 3, and the graph lies below the x-axis when $x < -9$ or $x > 3$. Therefore, the solution set is $\{x \,|\, x < -9 \text{ or } x > 3\}$.

56. Graph $2|x + 3| - 1 = 0$.

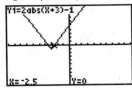

[−10, 10] scl: 1 by [−10, 10] scl: 1

The zeros of the function are −3.5 and −2.5, and the graph lies above the x-axis when $x < -3.5$ or $x > -2.5$. Therefore, the solution set is $\{x \,|\, x \leq -3.5 \text{ or } x \geq -2.5\}$.

57. Graph $|5x + 4| - 2 = 0$.

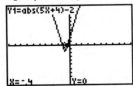

[−10, 10] scl: 1 by [−10, 10] scl: 1

The zeros of the function are −1.2 and −0.4, and the graph lies below the x-axis when $-1.2 < x < -0.4$. Therefore, the solution set is $\{x \,|\, -1.2 \leq x \leq -0.4\}$.

58. Graph $|4x - 1| + 3 = 0$.

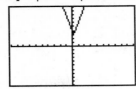

[−10, 10] scl: 1 by [−10, 10] scl: 1

There are no zeros of the function, and the graph never lies below the x-axis. Therefore, the solution set is $\varnothing$.

Page 335　Maintain Your Skills

59. $y = x^2 - 2x + 9$
$y = (x^2 - 2x + 1) + 9 - 1$
$y = (x - 1)^2 + 8$
$h = 1$ and $k = 8$.
The vertex is at (1, 8), and the axis of symmetry is $x = 1$. Since $a = 1$, the graph opens up.

60. $y = -2x^2 + 16x - 32$
$y = -2(x^2 - 8x) - 32$
$y = -2(x^2 - 8x + 16) - 32 - (-2)(16)$
$y = -2(x - 4)^2$
$y = -2(x - 4)^2 + 0$
$h = 4$ and $k = 0$.
The vertex is at (4, 0), and the axis of symmetry is $x = 4$. Since $a = -2$, the graph opens down.

61. $y = \frac{1}{2}x^2 + 6x + 18$
$y = \frac{1}{2}(x^2 + 12x) + 18$
$y = \frac{1}{2}(x^2 + 12x + 36) + 18 - \frac{1}{2}(36)$
$y = \frac{1}{2}(x + 6)^2$
$y = \frac{1}{2}[x - (-6)]^2 + 0$
$h = -6$ and $k = 0$.
The vertex is at (−6, 0), and the axis of symmetry is $x = -6$. Since $a = \frac{1}{2}$, the graph opens up.

62. $x^2 + 12x + 32 = 0$
$(x + 8)(x + 4) = 0$
$x + 8 = 0$　or $x + 4 = 0$
$\quad\quad x = -8$　　　$x = -4$
The solutions are −8 and −4.

63. $x^2 + 7 = -5x \rightarrow x^2 + 5x + 7 = 0$
$a = 1$, $b = 5$, and $c = 7$.
$x = \dfrac{-b \pm \sqrt{b^2 - 4ac}}{2a}$
$x = \dfrac{-(5) \pm \sqrt{(5)^2 - 4(1)(7)}}{2(1)}$
$x = \dfrac{-5 \pm \sqrt{-3}}{2}$
$x = \dfrac{-5 \pm i\sqrt{3}}{2}$

The solutions are the complex numbers $\dfrac{-5 + i\sqrt{3}}{2}$ and $\dfrac{-5 - i\sqrt{3}}{2}$.

64. $3x^2 + 6x - 2 = 3 \rightarrow 3x^2 + 6x - 5 = 0$
$a = 3$, $b = 6$, and $c = -5$.

$$x = \frac{-b \pm \sqrt{b^2 - 4ac}}{2a}$$

$$x = \frac{(-6) \pm \sqrt{(6)^2 - 4(3)(-5)}}{2(3)}$$

$$x = \frac{-6 \pm \sqrt{96}}{6}$$

$$x = \frac{-6 \pm 4\sqrt{6}}{6}$$

$$x = \frac{-3 \pm 2\sqrt{6}}{3}$$

The exact solutions are $\dfrac{-3 - 2\sqrt{6}}{3}$ and $\dfrac{-3 + 2\sqrt{6}}{3}$.

65. $(2a^2b - 3ab^2 + 5a - 6b) + (4a^2b^2 + 7ab^2 - b + 7a)$
$= 2a^2b - 3ab^2 + 5a - 6b + 4a^2b^2 + 7ab^2 - b + 7a$
$= 4a^2b^2 + 2a^2b + (-3ab^2 + 7ab^2) + (5a + 7a) + (-6b - b)$
$= 4a^2b^2 + 2a^2b + 4ab^2 + 12a - 7b$

66. $(x^3 - 3x^2y + 4xy^2 + y^3) - (7x^3 + x^2y - 9xy^2 + y^3)$
$= x^3 - 3x^2y + 4xy^2 + y^3 - 7x^3 - x^2y + 9xy^2 - y^3$
$= (x^3 - 7x^3) + (-3x^2y - x^2y) + (4xy^2 + 9xy^2) + (y^3 - y^3)$
$= -6x^3 - 4x^2y + 13xy^2$

67. $x^{-3}y^2(x^4y + x^3y^{-1} + x^2y^{-2})$
$= x^{-3}y^2(x^4y) + x^{-3}y^2(x^3y^{-1}) + x^{-3}y^2(x^2y^{-2})$
$= x^{-3+4}\,y^{2+1} + x^{-3+3}\,y^{2+(-1)} + x^{-3+2}\,y^{2+(-2)}$
$= x^1y^3 + x^0y^1 + x^{-1}y^0$
$= xy^3 + y + \frac{1}{x}$

68. $(5a - 3)(1 - 3a) = 5a(1 - 3a) - 3(1 - 3a)$
$= 5a(1) + 5a(-3a) - 3(1) - 3(-3a)$
$= 5a - 15a^2 - 3 + 9a$
$= -15a^2 + 14a - 3$

69. $\begin{bmatrix} -6 & 3 \\ 4 & 7 \end{bmatrix} \cdot \begin{bmatrix} 2 & -5 \\ -3 & 6 \end{bmatrix}$

$= \begin{bmatrix} -6(2) + 3(-3) & -6(-5) + 3(6) \\ 4(2) + 7(-3) & 4(-5) + 7(6) \end{bmatrix}$

$= \begin{bmatrix} -21 & 48 \\ -13 & 22 \end{bmatrix}$

70. $\begin{bmatrix} 2 & -6 & 3 \end{bmatrix} \cdot \begin{bmatrix} 3 & -3 \\ 9 & 0 \\ -2 & 4 \end{bmatrix}$

$= \begin{bmatrix} 2(3) + (-6)(9) + 3(-2) & 2(-3) + (-6)(0) + 3(4) \end{bmatrix}$
$= \begin{bmatrix} -54 & 6 \end{bmatrix}$

71. Let $x =$ a person's BAC

A person's BAC could differ from 0.08 by as much as 0.002.

$$\underbrace{|0.08 - x|}_{} \quad \underbrace{\leq}_{} \quad \underbrace{0.002}_{}$$

Rewrite the absolute value inequality as a compound inequality. Then solve for x.

$$-0.002 \leq 0.08 - x \leq 0.002$$
$$-0.002 - 0.08 \leq 0.08 - x - 0.08 \leq 0.002 - 0.08$$
$$-0.082 \leq -x \leq -0.078$$
$$0.0825 \geq x \geq 0.078$$

The solution set is $\{x \mid 0.078 \leq x \leq 0.082\}$. Thus, this device will register BACs that fall between 0.078 and 0.082, inclusive.

Chapter 6 Study Guide and Review

Page 336 Vocabulary and Concept Check
1. f; parabola
2. b; completing the square
3. a; axis of symmetry
4. h; quadratic function
5. i; roots
6. j; vertex form
7. c; discriminant
8. g; Quadratic Formula

Pages 336–340 Lesson-by-Lesson Review
9a. $f(x) = x^2 + 6x + 20 \rightarrow f(x) = 1x^2 + 6x + 20$
So, $a = 1$, $b = 6$, and $c = 20$.
Since $c = 20$, the y-intercept is 20.
Axis of symmetry:
$$x = -\frac{b}{2a}$$
$$x = -\frac{6}{2(1)}$$
$$x = -3$$
The equation of the axis of symmetry is $x = -3$.
Therefore, the x-coordinate of the vertex is -3.

9b.

x	$x^2 + 6x + 20$	$f(x)$	$(x, f(x))$
-5	$(-5)^2 + 6(-5) + 20$	15	$(-5, 15)$
-4	$(-4)^2 + 6(-4) + 20$	12	$(-4, 12)$
-3	$(-3)^2 + 6(-3) + 20$	11	$(-3, 11)$
-2	$(-2)^2 + 6(-2) + 20$	12	$(-2, 12)$
-1	$(-1)^2 + 6(-1) + 20$	15	$(-1, 15)$

9c.

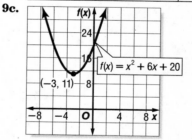

$f(x) = x^2 + 6x + 20$

10a. $f(x) = x^2 - 2x - 15 \rightarrow f(x) = 1x^2 - 2x - 15$
So, $a = 1$, $b = -2$, and $c = -15$.
Since $c = -15$, the y-intercept is -15.
Axis of symmetry:
$$x = -\frac{b}{2a}$$
$$x = -\frac{2}{2(1)}$$
$$x = 1$$
The equation of the axis of symmetry is $x = 1$.
Therefore, the x-coordinate of the vertex is 1.

10b.

x	$x^2 - 2x - 15$	$f(x)$	$(x, f(x))$
-1	$(-1)^2 - 2(-1) - 15$	-12	$(-1, -12)$
0	$(0)^2 - 2(0) - 15$	-15	$(0, -15)$
1	$(1)^2 - 2(1) - 15$	-16	$(1, -16)$
2	$(2)^2 - 2(2) - 15$	-15	$(2, -15)$
3	$(3)^2 - 2(3) - 15$	-12	$(3, -12)$

10c.

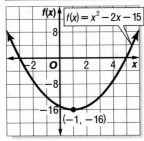

11a. $f(x) = x^2 - 8x + 7 \rightarrow f(x) = 1x^2 - 8x + 7$
So, $a = 1$, $b = -8$, and $c = 7$.
Since $c = 7$, the y-intercept is 7.
Axis of symmetry:
$x = -\frac{b}{2a}$
$x = -\frac{-8}{2(1)}$
$x = 4$
The equation of the axis of symmetry is $x = 4$.
Therefore, the x-coordinate of the vertex is 4.

11b.

x	$x^2 - 8x + 7$	$f(x)$	$(x, f(x))$
2	$(2)^2 - 8(2) + 7$	-5	$(2, -5)$
3	$(3)^2 - 8(3) + 7$	-8	$(3, -8)$
4	$(4)^2 - 8(4) + 7$	-9	$(4, -9)$
5	$(5)^2 - 8(5) + 7$	-8	$(5, -8)$
6	$(6)^2 - 8(6) + 7$	-5	$(6, -5)$

11c.

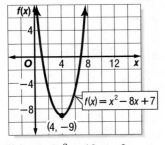

12a. $f(x) = -2x^2 + 12x - 9$
So, $a = -2$, $b = 12$, and $c = -9$.
Since $c = -9$, the y-intercept is -9.
Axis of symmetry:
$x = -\frac{b}{2a}$
$x = -\frac{12}{2(-2)}$
$x = 3$
The equation of the axis of symmetry is $x = 3$.
Therefore, the x-coordinate of the vertex is 3.

12b.

x	$-2x^2 + 12x - 9$	$f(x)$	$(x, f(x))$
1	$-2(1)^2 + 12(1) - 9$	1	$(1, 1)$
2	$-2(2)^2 + 12(2) - 9$	7	$(2, 7)$
3	$-2(3)^2 + 12(3) - 9$	9	$(3, 9)$
4	$-2(4)^2 + 12(4) - 9$	7	$(4, 7)$
5	$-2(5)^2 + 12(5) - 9$	1	$(5, 1)$

12c.

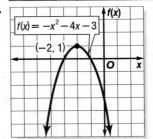

13a. $f(x) = -x^2 - 4x - 3 \rightarrow f(x) = -1x^2 - 4x - 3$
So, $a = -1$, $b = -4$, and $c = -3$.
Since $c = -3$, the y-intercept is -3.
Axis of symmetry:
$x = -\frac{b}{2a}$
$x = -\frac{-4}{2(-1)}$
$x = -2$
The equation of the axis of symmetry is $x = -2$.
Therefore, the x-coordinate of the vertex is -2.

13b.

x	$-x^2 - 4x - 3$	$f(x)$	$(x, f(x))$
-4	$-(-4)^2 - 4(-4) - 3$	-3	$(-4, -3)$
-3	$-(-3)^2 - 4(-3) - 3$	0	$(-3, 0)$
-2	$-(-2)^2 - 4(-2) - 3$	1	$(-2, 1)$
-1	$-(-1)^2 - 4(-1) - 3$	0	$(-1, 0)$
0	$-(0)^2 - 4(0) - 3$	-3	$(0, -3)$

13c.

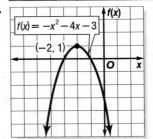

14a. $f(x) = 3x^2 + 9x + 6$
So, $a = 3$, $b = 9$, and $c = 6$.
Since $c = 6$, the y-intercept is 6.
Axis of symmetry:
$x = -\frac{b}{2a}$
$x = -\frac{9}{2(3)}$
$x = -\frac{3}{2}$
The equation of the axis of symmetry is $x = -\frac{3}{2}$.
Therefore, the x-coordinate of the vertex is $-\frac{3}{2}$.

14b.

x	$3x^2 + 9x + 6$	$f(x)$	$(x, f(x))$
-3	$3(-3)^2 + 9(-3) + 6$	6	$(-3, 6)$
-2	$3(-2)^2 + 9(-2) + 6$	0	$(-2, -0)$
$-\frac{3}{2}$	$3\left(-\frac{3}{2}\right)^2 + 9\left(-\frac{3}{2}\right) + 6$	$-\frac{3}{4}$	$\left(-\frac{3}{2}, -\frac{3}{4}\right)$
-1	$3(-1)^2 + 9(-1) + 6$	0	$(-1, 0)$
0	$3(0)^2 + 9(0) + 6$	6	$(0, 6)$

14c.

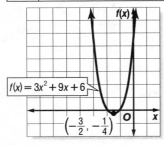

15. For this function, $a = 4$, $b = -3$, and $c = -5$. Since $a > 0$, the graph opens up and the function has a minimum value. The x-coordinate of the vertex is $-\frac{-3}{2(4)}$ or $\frac{3}{8}$.

$f(x) = 4x^2 - 3x - 5$

$f\left(\frac{3}{8}\right) = 4\left(\frac{3}{8}\right)^2 - 3\left(\frac{3}{8}\right) - 5$

$\qquad = -\frac{89}{16}$

Therefore, the minimum value of the function is $-\frac{89}{16}$.

16. For this function, $a = -3$, $b = 2$, and $c = -2$. Since $a < 0$, the graph opens down and the function has a maximum value. The x-coordinate of the vertex is $-\frac{2}{2(-3)}$ or $\frac{1}{3}$.

$f(x) = -3x^2 + 2x - 2$

$f\left(\frac{1}{3}\right) = -3\left(\frac{1}{3}\right)^2 + 2\left(\frac{1}{3}\right) - 2$

$\qquad = -\frac{5}{3}$

Therefore, the maximum value of the function is $-\frac{5}{3}$.

17. For this function, $a = -2$, $b = 0$, and $c = 7$. Since $a < 0$, the graph opens down and the function has a maximum value. The x-coordinate of the vertex is $-\frac{0}{2(-2)}$ or 0.

$f(x) = -2x^2 + 7$

$f(0) = -2(0)^2 + 7$

$\qquad = 7$

Therefore, the maximum value of the function is 7.

18. Graph the related quadratic function $f(x) = x^2 - 36$.

x	-4	-2	0	2	4
$f(x)$	-20	-32	-36	-32	-20

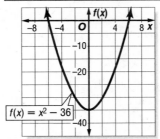

From the graph, we can see that the zeros of the function are -6 and 6. Therefore, the solutions of the equation are -6 and 6.

19. Graph the related quadratic function $f(x) = -x^2 - 3x + 10$.

x	-3	-2	-1.5	-1	0
$f(x)$	10	12	12.25	12	10

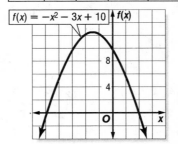

From the graph, we can see that the zeros of the function are -5 and 2. Therefore, the solutions of the equation are -5 and 2.

20. Graph the related quadratic function $f(x) = 2x^2 + x - 3$.

x	-2	-1	0	1	2
$f(x)$	3	-2	-3	0	7

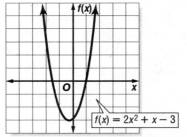

The x-intercepts of the graph are 1 and between -2 and -1. So, one solution is 1, and the other is between -2 and -1.

21. Graph the related quadratic function
$f(x) = -x^2 - 40x - 80$.

x	-30	-25	-20	-15	-10
$f(x)$	220	295	320	295	220

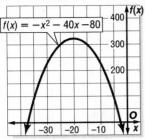

The x-intercepts of the graph are between -38 and -37 and between -3 and -2. So, one solution is between -38 and -37, and the other is between -3 and -2.

22. Graph the related quadratic function
$f(x) = -3x^2 - 6x - 2$.

x	-3	-2	-1	0	1
$f(x)$	-11	-2	1	-2	-11

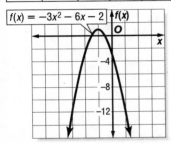

The x-intercepts of the graph are between -2 and -1 and between -1 and 0. So, one solution is between -2 and -1, and the other is between -1 and 0.

23. Graph the related quadratic function
$f(x) = \frac{1}{5}(x + 3)^2 - 5$.

x	-8	-6	-3	0	2
$f(x)$	0	-3.2	-5	-3.2	0

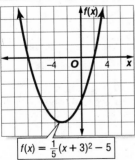

From the graph, we can see that the zeros of the function are -8 and 2. Therefore, the solutions of the equations are -8 and 2.

24. $x^2 - 4x - 32 = 0$
$(x - 8)(x + 4) = 0$
$x - 8 = 0$ or $x + 4 = 0$
$\qquad x = 8 \qquad\qquad x = -4$
The solution set is $\{-4, 8\}$.

25. $3x^2 + 6x + 3 = 0$
$3(x^2 + 2x + 1) = 0$
$\qquad x^2 + 2x + 1 = 0$
$\qquad (x + 1)(x + 1) = 0$
$x + 1 = 0$ or $x + 1 = 0$
$\qquad x = -1 \qquad\qquad x = -1$
The solution set is $\{-1\}$.

26. $\qquad 5y^2 = 80$
$\qquad 5y^2 - 80 = 0$
$\qquad 5(y^2 - 16) = 0$
$\qquad\qquad y^2 - 16 = 0$
$(y - 4)(y + 4) = 0$
$y - 4 = 0$ or $y + 4 = 0$
$\qquad y = 4 \qquad\qquad y = -4$
The solution set is $\{-4, 4\}$.

27. $2c^2 + 18c - 44 = 0$
$2(c^2 + 9c - 22) = 0$
$\qquad c^2 + 9c - 22 = 0$
$\qquad (c - 2)(c + 11) = 0$
$c - 2 = 0$ or $c + 11 = 0$
$\qquad c = 2 \qquad\qquad c = -11$
The solution set is $\{-11, 2\}$.

28. $\qquad 25x^2 - 30x = -9$
$\qquad 25x^2 - 30x + 9 = 0$
$\qquad (5x - 3)(5x - 3) = 0$
$5x - 3 = 0$ or $5x - 3 = 0$
$\qquad 5x = 3 \qquad\qquad 5x = 3$
$\qquad x = \frac{3}{5} \qquad\qquad x = \frac{3}{5}$
The solution set is $\left\{\frac{3}{5}\right\}$.

29. $\qquad 6x^2 + 7x = 3$
$\qquad 6x^2 + 7x - 3 = 0$
$(3x - 1)(2x + 3) = 0$
$3x - 1 = 0$ or $2x + 3 = 0$
$\qquad 3x = 1 \qquad\qquad 2x = -3$
$\qquad x = \frac{1}{3} \qquad\qquad x = -\frac{3}{2}$
The solution set is $\left\{-\frac{3}{2}, \frac{1}{3}\right\}$.

30. $[x - (-4)][x - (-25)] = 0$
$\qquad (x + 4)(x + 25) = 0$
$\qquad\qquad x^2 + 29x + 100 = 0$

31. $(x - 10)[x - (-7)] = 0$
$\qquad (x - 10)(x + 7) = 0$
$\qquad\qquad x^2 - 3x - 70 = 0$

32. $\left(x - \frac{1}{3}\right)(x - 2) = 0$
$\qquad x^2 - \frac{7}{3}x + \frac{2}{3} = 0$
$\qquad 3x^2 - 7x + 2 = 0$

33. Step 1 Find one half of 34. $\qquad \frac{34}{2} = 17$

Step 2 Square the result of Step 1. $\qquad 17^2 = 289$

Step 3 Add the result of Step 2 to $x^2 + 34x$. $\qquad x^2 + 34x + 289$

The trinomial $x^2 + 34x + 289$ can be written as $(x + 17)^2$.

34. Step 1 Find one half of -11. $\qquad \frac{-11}{2} = -\frac{11}{2}$

Step 2 Square the result of Step 1. $\quad \left(-\frac{11}{2}\right)^2 = \frac{121}{4}$

Step 3 Add the result of Step 2 to

$x^2 - 11x$. $\qquad\qquad\qquad x^2 - 11x + \frac{121}{4}$

The trinomial $x^2 - 11x + \frac{121}{4}$ can be written as $\left(x - \frac{11}{2}\right)^2$.

35. Step 1 Find one half of $\frac{7}{2}$. $\qquad \frac{\frac{7}{2}}{2} = \frac{7}{4}$

Step 2 Square the result of Step 1. $\quad \left(\frac{7}{4}\right) = \frac{49}{16}$

Step 3 Add the result of Step 2 to

$x^2 + \frac{7}{2}x$. $\qquad\qquad\qquad x^2 + \frac{7}{2}x + \frac{49}{16}$

The trinomial $x^2 + \frac{7}{2}x + \frac{49}{16}$ can be written as $\left(x + \frac{7}{4}\right)^2$.

36. $2x^2 - 7x - 15 = 0$

$\qquad x^2 - \frac{7}{2}x - \frac{15}{2} = 0$

$\qquad\qquad x^2 - \frac{7}{2}x = \frac{15}{2}$

$\quad x^2 - \frac{7}{2}x + \frac{49}{16} = \frac{15}{2} + \frac{49}{16}$

$\qquad\qquad \left(x - \frac{7}{4}\right)^2 = \frac{169}{16}$

$\qquad\qquad\qquad x - \frac{7}{4} = \pm\frac{13}{4}$

$\qquad\qquad\qquad\qquad x = \frac{7}{4} \pm \frac{13}{4}$

$x = \frac{7}{4} + \frac{13}{4} \ $ or $\ x = \frac{7}{4} - \frac{13}{4}$

$x = 5 \qquad\qquad\quad x = -\frac{3}{2}$

The solution set is $\left\{-\frac{3}{5}, 5\right\}$.

37. $2n^2 - 12n - 22 = 0$

$\qquad n^2 - 6n - 11 = 0$

$\qquad\qquad n^2 - 6n = 11$

$\qquad n^2 - 6n + 9 = 11 + 9$

$\qquad\qquad (n - 3)^2 = 20$

$\qquad\qquad\quad n - 3 = \pm\sqrt{20}$

$\qquad\qquad\quad n - 3 = \pm 2\sqrt{5}$

$\qquad\qquad\qquad n = 3 \pm 2\sqrt{5}$

The solution set is $\{3 - 2\sqrt{5}, 3 + 2\sqrt{5}\}$.

38. $2x^2 - 5x + 7 = 3$

$\qquad 2x^2 - 5x + 4 = 0$

$\qquad x^2 - \frac{5}{2}x + 2 = 0$

$\qquad\qquad x^2 - \frac{5}{2}x = -2$

$\quad x^2 - \frac{5}{2}x + \frac{25}{16} = -2 + \frac{25}{16}$

$\qquad\qquad \left(x - \frac{5}{4}\right)^2 = -\frac{7}{16}$

$\qquad\qquad\quad x - \frac{5}{4} = \pm\sqrt{-\frac{7}{16}}$

$\qquad\qquad\quad x - \frac{5}{4} = \pm i\frac{\sqrt{7}}{4}$

$\qquad\qquad\qquad x = \frac{5}{4} \pm i\frac{\sqrt{7}}{4}$

$\qquad\qquad\qquad x = \frac{5 \pm i\sqrt{7}}{4}$

The solution set is $\left\{\dfrac{5 + i\sqrt{7}}{4}, \ \dfrac{5 - i\sqrt{7}}{4}\right\}$.

39a. $a = 1, b = 2, c = 7$

$b^2 - 4ac = (2)^2 - 4(1)(7)$

$\qquad\qquad = 4 - 28$

$\qquad\qquad = -24$

39b. The discriminant is negative, so there are two complex roots.

39c. $x = \frac{-b \pm \sqrt{b^2 - 4ac}}{2a}$

$x = \frac{-(2) \pm \sqrt{(2)^2 - 4(1)(7)}}{2(1)}$

$x = \frac{-2 \pm \sqrt{-24}}{2}$

$x = \frac{-2 \pm 2i\sqrt{6}}{2}$

$x = -1 \pm i\sqrt{6}$

40a. $a = -2, b = 12, c = -5$

$b^2 - 4ac = (12)^2 - 4(-2)(-5)$

$\qquad\qquad = 144 - 40$

$\qquad\qquad = 104$

40b. The discriminant is 104, which is not a perfect square. Therefore, there are two irrational roots.

40c. $x = \frac{-b \pm \sqrt{b^2 - 4ac}}{2a}$

$x = \frac{-(12) \pm \sqrt{(12)^2 - 4(-2)(-5)}}{2(-2)}$

$x = \frac{-12 \pm \sqrt{104}}{-4}$

$x = \frac{-12 \pm 2\sqrt{26}}{-4}$

$x = \frac{6 \pm \sqrt{26}}{2}$

$x = 3 \pm \frac{\sqrt{26}}{2}$

The exact solutions are $\left\{3 + \dfrac{\sqrt{26}}{2}, 3 - \dfrac{\sqrt{26}}{2}\right\}$.

41a. $a = 3, b = 7, c = -2$

$b^2 - 4ac = (7)^2 - 4(3)(-2)$

$\qquad\qquad = 49 + 24$

$\qquad\qquad = 73$

41b. The discriminant is 73, which is not a perfect square. Therefore, there are two irrational roots.

41c. $x = \frac{-b \pm \sqrt{b^2 - 4ac}}{2a}$

$x = \frac{-(7) \pm \sqrt{(7)^2 - 4(3)(-2)}}{2(3)}$

$x = \frac{-7 \pm \sqrt{73}}{6}$

42. $y = -6(x + 2)^2 + 3$

$y = -6[x - (-2)]^2 + 3$

$h = -2$ and $k = 3$.

The vertex is at $(-2, 3)$, and the axis of symmetry is $x = -2$. Since $a = -6$, the graph opens down.

43. $y = 5x^2 + 35x + 58$
$y = 5(x^2 + 7x) + 58$
$y = 5\left(x^2 + 7x + \frac{49}{4}\right) + 58 - 5\left(\frac{49}{4}\right)$
$y = 5\left(x + \frac{7}{2}\right)^2 - \frac{13}{4}$
$y = 5\left[x - \left(-\frac{7}{2}\right)\right]^2 + \left(-\frac{13}{4}\right)$
$h = -\frac{7}{2}$ and $k = -\frac{13}{4}$.

The vertex is at $\left(-\frac{7}{2}, -\frac{13}{4}\right)$, and the axis of symmetry is $x = -\frac{7}{2}$. Since $a = 5$, the graph opens up.

44. $y = -\frac{1}{3}x^2 + 8x$
$y = -\frac{1}{3}(x^2 - 24x)$
$y = -\frac{1}{3}(x^2 - 24x + 144) - \left(-\frac{1}{3}\right)(144)$
$y = -\frac{1}{3}(x - 12)^2 + 48$
$h = 12$ and $k = 48$.

The vertex is at $(12, 48)$, and the axis of symmetry is $x = 12$. Since $a = -\frac{1}{3}$, the graph opens down.

45. Plot the vertex, $(2, -2)$.
Find and plot two points on one side of the axis of symmetry, such as $(3, -1)$ and $(4, 2)$.
Use symmetry to complete the graph.

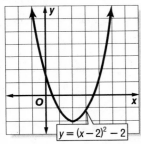

$y = (x - 2)^2 - 2$

46. Put the equation in vertex form.
$y = 2x^2 + 8x + 10$
$y = 2(x^2 + 4x) + 10$
$y = 2(x^2 + 4x + 4) + 10 - 2(4)$
$y = 2(x + 2)^2 + 2$
$y = 2[x - (-2)]^2 + 2$
Plot the vertex, $(-2, 2)$.
Find and plot two points on one side of the axis of symmetry, such as $(-1.5, 2.5)$ and $(-1, 4)$.
Use symmetry to complete the graph.

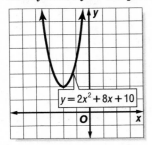

$y = 2x^2 + 8x + 10$

47. Put the equation in vertex form.
$y = -9x^2 - 18x - 6$
$y = -9(x^2 + 2x) - 6$
$y = -9(x^2 + 2x + 1) - 6 - (-9)(1)$
$y = -9(x + 1)^2 + 3$
$y = -9[x - (-1)]^2 + 3$
Plot the vertex, $(-1, 3)$.
Find and plot two points on one side of the axis of symmetry, such as $(-0.5, 0.75)$ and $(0, -6)$.
Use symmetry to complete the graph.

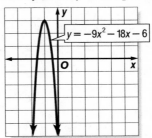

$y = -9x^2 - 18x - 6$

48. $h = 4$ and $k = 1$. Let $x = 2$ and $y = 13$.
Substitute these values into the vertex form of the equation and solve for a.
$y = a(x - h)^2 + k$
$13 = a(2 - 4)^2 + 1$
$13 = a(4) + 1$
$12 = 4a$
$3 = a$
The equation is $y = 3(x - 4)^2 + 1$.

49. $h = -2$ and $k = 3$. Let $x = -6$ and $y = 11$.
Substitute these values into the vertex form of the equation and solve for a.
$y = a(x - h)^2 + k$
$11 = a[-6 - (-2)]^2 + 3$
$11 = a(16) + 3$
$8 = 16a$
$\frac{1}{2} = a$
The equation is $y = \frac{1}{2}(x + 2)^2 + 3$.

50. $h = -3$ and $k = -5$. Let $x = 0$ and $y = -14$.
Substitute these values into the vertex form of the equation and solve for a.
$y = a(x - h)^2 + k$
$-14 = a[0 - (-3)]^2 + (-5)$
$-14 = a(9) - 5$
$-9 = 9a$
$-1 = a$
The equation is $y = -(x + 3)^2 - 5$.

51. Graph the related quadratic function $y = x^2 - 5x + 15$. Since the inequality symbol is $>$, the parabola should be dashed.
Test $(2, 10)$.

$y > x^2 - 5x + 15$
$10 \overset{?}{>} (2)^2 - 5(2) + 15$
$10 \overset{?}{>} 4 - 10 + 15$
$10 > 9$ ✓

So, $(2, 10)$ is a solution of the inequality. Shade the region inside the parabola.

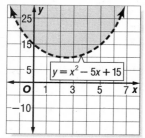

52. Graph the related quadratic function $y = 4x^2 - 36x + 17$. Since the inequality symbol is $\leq$, the parabola should be solid.
Test $(2, 0)$.

$y \leq 4x^2 - 36x + 17$
$0 \overset{?}{\leq} 4(2)^2 - 36(2) + 17$
$0 \overset{?}{\leq} 16 - 72 + 17$
$0 \leq -39$ ✗

So, $(2, 0)$ is not a solution of the inequality. Shade the region outside the parabola.

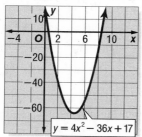

53. Graph the related quadratic function $y = -x^2 + 7x - 11$. Since the inequality symbol is $\geq$, the parabola should be solid.
Test $(3, 0)$.

$y \geq -x^2 + 7x - 11$
$0 \overset{?}{\geq} -(3)^2 + 7(3) - 11$
$0 \overset{?}{\geq} -9 + 21 - 11$
$0 \geq 1$ ✗

So, $(3, 0)$ is not a solution of the inequality. Shade the region outside the parabola.

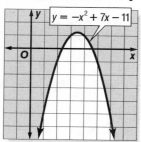

54. Solve the related quadratic equation $6x^2 + 5x = 4$.

$6x^2 + 5x = 4$
$6x^2 + 5x - 4 = 0$
$(2x - 1)(3x + 4) = 0$
$2x - 1 = 0$ or $3x + 4 = 0$
$2x = 1 \qquad\qquad 3x = -4$
$x = \frac{1}{2} \qquad\qquad x = -\frac{4}{3}$

Plot $-\frac{4}{3}$ and $\frac{1}{2}$ on a number line. Use circles.

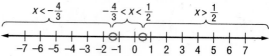

Test a value in each interval.

$x < -\frac{4}{3}$	$-\frac{4}{3} < x < \frac{1}{2}$	$x > \frac{1}{2}$
Test $x = -2$.	Test $x = 0$.	Test $x = 1$.
$6x^2 + 5x > 4$	$6x^2 + 5x > 4$	$6x^2 + 5x > 4$
$6(-2)^2 + 5(-2) \overset{?}{>} 4$	$6(0)^2 + 5(0) \overset{?}{>} 4$	$6(1)^2 + 5(1) \overset{?}{>} 4$
$14 > 4$ ✓	$0 > 4$ ✗	$11 > 4$ ✓

The solution set is $\left\{x \mid x < -\frac{4}{3} \text{ or } x > \frac{1}{2}\right\}$.

55. Solve the related quadratic equation $8x + x^2 = -16$.

$8x + x^2 = -16$
$x^2 + 8x + 16 = 0$
$(x + 4)(x + 4) = 0$
$x + 4 = 0$ or $x + 4 = 0$
$x = -4 \qquad\qquad x = -4$

Plot -4 on a number line. Use a solid dot.

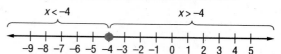

Test a value in each interval.

$x < -4$	$x > -4$
Test $x = -5$.	Test $x = -3$.
$8x + x^2 \geq -16$	$8x + x^2 \geq -16$
$8(-5) + (-5)^2 \overset{?}{\geq} -16$	$8(-3) + (-3)^2 \overset{?}{\geq} -16$
$-15 \geq -16$ ✓	$-15 \geq -16$ ✓

The solution set is $\{x \mid x \text{ is all real numbers}\}$.

56. Solve the related quadratic equation $2x^2 + 5x = 12$.
$$2x^2 + 5x = 12$$
$$2x^2 + 5x - 12 = 0$$
$$(2x - 3)(x + 4) = 0$$
$$2x - 3 = 0 \text{ or } x + 4 = 0$$
$$2x = 3 \qquad x = -4$$
$$x = \tfrac{3}{2}$$

Plot -4 and $\tfrac{3}{2}$ on a number line. Use circles.

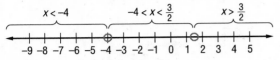

Test a value in each interval.

$x < -4$	$-4 < x < \dfrac{3}{2}$	$x > \dfrac{3}{2}$
Test $x = -5$.	Test $x = 0$.	Test $x = 2$.
$2x^2 + 5x < 12$	$2x^2 + 5x < 12$	$2x^2 + 5x < 12$
$2(-5)^2 + 5(-5) \overset{?}{<} 12$	$2(0)^2 + 5(0) \overset{?}{<} 12$	$2(2)^2 + 5(2) \overset{?}{<} 12$
$25 < 12$ ✗	$0 < 12$ ✓	$18 < 12$ ✗

The solution set is $\left\{x \,\middle|\, -4 < x < \tfrac{3}{2}\right\}$.

57. Solve the related quadratic equation $2x^2 - 5x = 3$.
$$2x^2 - 5x = 3$$
$$2x^2 - 5x - 3 = 0$$
$$(2x + 1)(x - 3) = 0$$
$$2x + 1 = 0 \text{ or } x - 3 = 0$$
$$2x = -1 \qquad x = 3$$
$$x = -\tfrac{1}{2}$$

Plot $-\tfrac{1}{2}$ and 3 on a number line. Use circles.

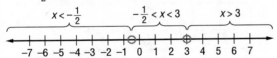

Test a value in each interval.

$x < -\dfrac{1}{2}$	$-\dfrac{1}{2} < x < 3$	$x > 3$
Test $x = -1$.	Test $x = 0$.	Test $x = 4$.
$2x^2 - 5x > 3$	$2x^2 - 5x > 3$	$2x^2 - 5x > 3$
$2(-1)^2 - 5(-1) \overset{?}{>} 3$	$2(0)^2 - 5(0) \overset{?}{>} 3$	$2(4)^2 - 5(4) \overset{?}{>} 3$
$7 > 3$ ✓	$0 > 3$ ✗	$12 > 3$ ✓

The solution set is $\left\{x \,\middle|\, x < -\tfrac{1}{2} \text{ or } x > 3\right\}$.

58. Solve the related quadratic equation $4x^2 - 9 = -4x$.
$$4x^2 - 9 = -4x$$
$$4x^2 + 4x - 9 = 0$$
$$x = \frac{-b \pm \sqrt{b^2 - 4ac}}{2a}$$
$$x = \frac{-4 \pm \sqrt{(4)^2 - 4(4)(-9)}}{2(4)}$$
$$x = \frac{-4 \pm \sqrt{160}}{8}$$
$$x = \frac{-4 \pm 4\sqrt{10}}{8}$$
$$x = \frac{-1 \pm \sqrt{10}}{2}$$

Plot $\dfrac{-1 - \sqrt{10}}{2}$ and $\dfrac{-1 + \sqrt{10}}{2}$ on a number line. Use solid dots.

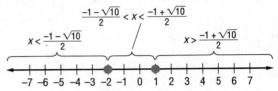

Test a value in each interval.

$x < \dfrac{-1 - \sqrt{10}}{2}$	$\dfrac{-1 - \sqrt{10}}{2} < x < \dfrac{-1 + \sqrt{10}}{2}$
Test $x = -3$.	Test $x = 0$.
$4x^2 - 9x \leq -4x$	$4x^2 - 9x \leq -4x$
$4(-3)^2 - 9 \overset{?}{\leq} 4(-3)$	$4(0)^2 - 9 \overset{?}{\leq} -4(0)$
$27 \leq 12$ ✗	$-9 \leq 0$ ✓

$x > \dfrac{-1 + \sqrt{10}}{2}$
Test $x = 2$.
$4x^2 - 9x \leq -4x$
$4(2)^2 - 9 \overset{?}{\leq} -4(2)$
$7 \leq -8$ ✗

The solution set is $\left\{x \,\middle|\, \dfrac{-1 - \sqrt{10}}{2} \leq x \leq \dfrac{-1 + \sqrt{10}}{2}\right\}$.

59. Solve the related quadratic equation $3x^2 - 5 = 6x$.

$$3x^2 - 5 = 6x$$
$$3x^2 - 6x - 5 = 0$$
$$x = \frac{-b \pm \sqrt{b^2 - 4ac}}{2a}$$
$$x = \frac{-(-6) \pm \sqrt{(-6)^2 - 4(3)(-5)}}{2(3)}$$
$$x = \frac{6 \pm \sqrt{96}}{6}$$
$$x = \frac{6 \pm 4\sqrt{6}}{6}$$
$$x = \frac{3 \pm 2\sqrt{6}}{3}$$

Plot $\frac{3 - 2\sqrt{6}}{3}$ and $\frac{3 + 2\sqrt{6}}{3}$ on a number line. Use circles.

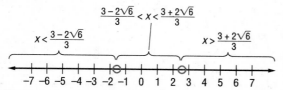

Test a value in each interval.

$x < \dfrac{3 - 2\sqrt{6}}{3}$	$\dfrac{3 - 2\sqrt{6}}{3} < x < \dfrac{3 + 2\sqrt{6}}{3}$
Test $x = -2$.	Test $x = 0$.
$3x^2 - 5 > 6x$	$3x^2 - 5 > 6x$
$3(-2)^2 - 5 \overset{?}{>} 6(-2)$	$3(0)^2 - 5 \overset{?}{>} 6(0)$
$7 > -12$ ✓	$-5 > 0$ ✗

$x > \dfrac{3 + 2\sqrt{6}}{3}$
Test $x = 3$.
$3x^2 - 5 > 6x$
$3(3)^2 - 5 \overset{?}{>} 6(3)$
$22 > 18$ ✓

The solution set is $\left\{ x \mid x < \dfrac{3 - 2\sqrt{6}}{3} \text{ or } x > \dfrac{3 + 2\sqrt{6}}{3} \right\}$.

Page 341   Chapter 6 Practice Test

1. minimum

2. Completing the square

3a. $f(x) = x^2 - 2x + 5 \rightarrow f(x) = 1x^2 - 2x + 5$
So, $a = 1$, $b = -2$, and $c = 5$.
Since $c = 5$, the y-intercept is 5.
Axis of symmetry:
$$x = -\frac{b}{2a}$$
$$x = -\frac{-2}{2(1)}$$
$$x = 1$$
The equation of the axis of symmetry is $x = 1$.
Therefore, the x-coordinate of the vertex is 1.

3b.

x	$x^2 - 2x + 5$	$f(x)$	$(x, f(x))$
-1	$(-1)^2 - 2(-1) + 5$	8	$(-1, 8)$
0	$(0)^2 - 2(0) + 5$	5	$(0, 5)$
1	$(1)^2 - 2(1) + 5$	4	$(1, 4)$
2	$(2)^2 - 2(2) + 5$	5	$(2, 5)$
3	$(3)^2 - 2(3) + 5$	8	$(3, 8)$

3c.

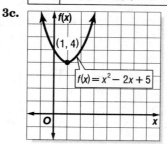

4a. $f(x) = -3x^2 + 8x \rightarrow f(x) = -3x^2 + 8x + 0$
So, $a = -3$, $b = 8$, and $c = 0$.
Since $c = 0$, the y-intercept is 0.
Axis of symmetry:
$$x = -\frac{b}{2a}$$
$$x = -\frac{8}{2(-3)}$$
$$x = \frac{4}{3}$$
The equation of the axis of symmetry is $x = \frac{4}{3}$.
Therefore, the x-coordinate of the vertex is $\frac{4}{3}$.

4b.

x	$-3x^2 + 8x$	$f(x)$	$(x, f(x))$
0	$-3(0)^2 + 8(0)$	0	$(0, 0)$
1	$-3(1)^2 + 8(1)$	5	$(1, 5)$
$\frac{4}{3}$	$-3\left(\frac{4}{3}\right)^2 + 8\left(\frac{4}{3}\right)$	$\frac{16}{3}$	$\left(\frac{4}{3}, \frac{16}{3}\right)$
2	$-3(2)^2 + 8(2)$	4	$(2, 4)$
3	$-3(3)^2 + 8(3)$	-3	$(3, -3)$

4c.

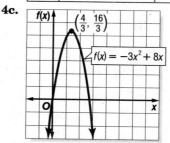

5a. $f(x) = -2x^2 - 7x - 1$
So, $a = -2$, $b = -7$, and $c = -1$.
Since $c = -1$, the y-intercept is -1.
Axis of symmetry:
$$x = -\frac{b}{2a}$$
$$x = -\frac{-7}{2(-2)}$$
$$x = -\frac{7}{4}$$
The equation of the axis of symmetry is $x = -\frac{7}{4}$.
Therefore, the x-coordinate of the vertex is $-\frac{7}{4}$.

5b.

x	$-2x^2 - 7x - 1$	$f(x)$	$(x, f(x))$
-3	$-2(-3)^2 - 7(-3) - 1$	2	$(-3, 2)$
-2	$-2(-2)^2 - 7(-3) - 1$	5	$(-2, 5)$
$-\frac{7}{4}$	$-2\left(-\frac{7}{4}\right)^2 - 7\left(-\frac{7}{4}\right) - 1$	$\frac{41}{8}$	$\left(-\frac{7}{4}, \frac{41}{8}\right)$
-1	$-2(-1)^2 - 7(-1) - 1$	4	$(-1, 4)$
0	$-2(0)^2 - 7(0) - 1$	-1	$(0, -1)$

5c.

6. For this function, $a = 1$, $b = 6$, and $c = 9$. Since $a > 0$, the graph opens up and the function has a minimum value. The x-coordinate of the vertex is $-\frac{6}{2(1)}$ or -3.
$$f(x) = x^2 + 6x + 9$$
$$f(-3) = (-3)^2 + 6(-3) + 9$$
$$= 0$$
Therefore, the minimum value of the function is 0.

7. For this function, $a = 3$, $b = -12$, and $c = -24$. Since $a > 0$, the graph opens up and the function has a minimum value. The x-coordinate of the vertex is $-\frac{-12}{2(3)}$ or 2.
$$f(x) = 3x^2 - 12x - 24$$
$$f(2) = 3(2)^2 - 12(2) - 24$$
$$= -36$$
Therefore, the minimum value of the function is -36.

8. For this function, $a = -1$, $b = 4$, and $c = 0$. Since $a < 0$, the graph opens down and the function has a maximum value. The x-coordinate of the vertex is $-\frac{4}{2(-1)}$ or 2.
$$f(x) = -x^2 + 4x$$
$$f(2) = -(2)^2 + 4(2)$$
$$= 4$$
Therefore, the maximum value of the function is 4.

9. $[x - (-4)](x - 5) = 0$
$(x + 4)(x - 5) = 0$
$x^2 - x - 20 = 0$

10. $x^2 + x - 42 = 0$
$(x - 6)(x + 7) = 0$
$x - 6 = 0$ or $x + 7 = 0$
$x = 6 \qquad x = -7$
The solution set is $\{-7, 6\}$.

11. $-1.6x^2 - 3.2x + 18 = 0$
$$x = \frac{-b \pm \sqrt{b^2 - 4ac}}{2a}$$
$$x = \frac{-(-3.2) \pm \sqrt{(-3.2)^2 - 4(-1.6)(18)}}{2(-1.6)}$$
$$x = \frac{3.2 \pm \sqrt{125.44}}{-3.2}$$
$$x = \frac{3.2 \pm 11.2}{-3.2}$$
$$x = \frac{3.2 + 11.2}{-3.2} \text{ or } x = \frac{3.2 - 11.2}{-3.2}$$
$$x = -4.5 \qquad x = 2.5$$
The solution set is $\{-4.5, 2.5\}$.

12. $15x^2 + 16x - 7 = 0$
$(5x + 7)(3x - 1) = 0$
$5x + 7 = 0$ or $3x - 1 = 0$
$5x = -7 \qquad 3x = 1$
$x = -\frac{7}{5} \qquad x = \frac{1}{3}$
The solution set is $\left\{-\frac{7}{5}, \frac{1}{3}\right\}$.

13. $x^2 + 8x - 48 = 0$
$(x - 4)(x + 12) = 0$
$x - 4 = 0$ or $x + 12 = 0$
$x = 4 \qquad x = -12$
The solution set is $\{-12, 4\}$.

14. $x^2 + 12x + 11 = 0$
$(x + 1)(x + 11) = 0$
$x + 1 = 0$ or $x + 11 = 0$
$x = -1 \qquad x = -11$
The solution set is $\{-11, -1\}$.

15. $x^2 - 9x - \frac{19}{4} = 0$
$$x^2 - 9x = \frac{19}{4}$$
$$x^2 - 9x + \frac{81}{4} = \frac{19}{4} + \frac{81}{4}$$
$$\left(x - \frac{9}{2}\right)^2 = \frac{100}{4}$$
$$x - \frac{9}{2} = \pm\frac{10}{2}$$
$$x = \frac{9}{2} \pm \frac{10}{2}$$
$$x = \frac{9}{2} + \frac{10}{2} \text{ or } x = \frac{9}{2} - \frac{10}{2}$$
$$x = \frac{19}{2} \qquad x = -\frac{1}{2}$$
The solution set is $\left\{-\frac{1}{2}, \frac{19}{2}\right\}$.

16. $3x^2 + 7x - 31 = 0$
$$x = \frac{-b \pm \sqrt{b^2 - 4ac}}{2a}$$
$$x = \frac{-7 \pm \sqrt{(7)^2 - 4(3)(-31)}}{2(3)}$$
$$x = \frac{-7 \pm \sqrt{421}}{6}$$
The solution set is $\left\{\frac{-7 - \sqrt{421}}{6}, \frac{-7 + \sqrt{421}}{6}\right\}$.

17. $10x^2 + 3x = 1$
$10x^2 + 3x - 1 = 0$
$(5x - 1)(2x + 1) = 0$
$5x - 1 = 0$ or $2x + 1 = 0$
$5x = 1 \qquad 2x = -1$
$x = \frac{1}{5} \qquad x = -\frac{1}{2}$
The solution set is $\left\{-\frac{1}{2}, \frac{1}{5}\right\}$.

18. $-11x^2 - 174x + 221 = 0$

$$x = \frac{-b \pm \sqrt{b^2 - 4ac}}{2a}$$

$$x = \frac{-(-174) \pm \sqrt{(-174)^2 - 4(-11)(221)}}{2(-11)}$$

$$x = \frac{174 \pm \sqrt{40,000}}{-22}$$

$$x = \frac{174 \pm 200}{-22}$$

$$x = \frac{174 + 200}{-22} \text{ or } x = \frac{174 - 200}{-22}$$

$$x = -17 \qquad x = \frac{13}{11}$$

The solution set is $\left\{-17, \frac{13}{11}\right\}$.

19. $-16t^2 - 28t + 250 = 0$

$$x = \frac{-b \pm \sqrt{b^2 - 4ac}}{2a}$$

$$x = \frac{-(-28) \pm \sqrt{(-28)^2 - 4(-16)(250)}}{2(-16)}$$

$$x = \frac{28 \pm \sqrt{16,784}}{-32}$$

$$x = \frac{28 \pm 4\sqrt{1049}}{-32}$$

$$x = \frac{7 \pm \sqrt{1049}}{-8}$$

$$x = \frac{7 + \sqrt{1049}}{-8} \text{ or } x = \frac{7 - \sqrt{1049}}{-8}$$

$$x \approx -4.92 \qquad x \approx 3.17$$

Since the time is positive, the marker will hit the target in about 3.17 seconds.

20. $y = (x + 2)^2 - 3$
$y = [x - (-2)]^2 + (-3)$
The vertex is at $(-2, -3)$, and the axis of symmetry is $x = -2$. Since $a = 1$, the graph opens up.

21. $y = x^2 + 10x + 27$
$y = (x^2 + 10x + 25) + 27 - 25$
$y = (x + 5)^2 + 2$
$y = [x - (-5)]^2 + 2$
The vertex is at $(-5, 2)$, and the axis of symmetry is at $x = -5$. Since $a = 1$, the graph opens up.

22. $y = -9x^2 + 54x - 8$
$y = -9(x^2 - 6x) - 8$
$y = -9(x^2 - 6x + 9) - 8 - (-9)(9)$
$y = -9(x - 3)^2 + 73$
The vertex is at $(3, 73)$, and the axis of symmetry is at $x = 3$. Since $a = -9$, the graph opens down.

23. Graph the related quadratic function $y = x^2 + 6x - 7$. Since the inequality symbol is $\leq$, the parabola should be solid.

Test $(0, 0)$.

$y \leq x^2 + 6x - 7$

$0 \overset{?}{\leq} (0)^2 + 6(0) - 7$

$0 \overset{?}{\leq} 0 + 0 - 7$

$0 \leq -7$ ✗

So, $(0, 0)$ is not a solution of the inequality. Shade the region outside the parabola.

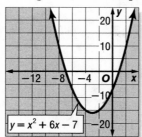

24. Graph the related quadratic function $y = -2x^2 + 9$.
Since the inequality symbol is $>$, the parabola should be dashed.

Test $(0, 0)$.

$y > -2x^2 + 9$

$0 \overset{?}{>} -2(0)^2 + 9$

$0 \overset{?}{>} 0 + 9$

$0 > 9$ ✗

So, $(0, 0)$ is not a solution of the inequality. Shade the region outside the parabola.

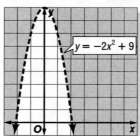

25. Graph the related quadratic function

$y = -\frac{1}{2}x^2 - 3x + 1$. Since the inequality symbol

is $\geq$, the parabola should be solid.

Test $(-1, 0)$.

$y \geq -\frac{1}{2}x^2 - 3x + 1$

$0 \overset{?}{\geq} -\frac{1}{2}(-1)^2 - 3(-1) + 1$

$0 \overset{?}{\geq} -\frac{1}{2} + 3 + 1$

$0 \geq \frac{7}{2}$ ✗

So, $(-1, 0)$ is not a solution of the inequality. Shade the region outside the parabola.

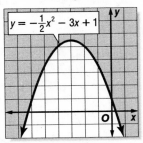

26. Solve the related quadratic equation $(x - 5)(x + 7) = 0$.

$(x - 5)(x + 7) = 0$

$x - 5 = 0$ or $x + 7 = 0$

$x = 5 \qquad x = -7$

Plot -7 and 5 on a number line. Use circles.

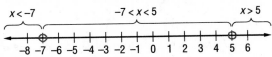

Test a value in each interval.

$x < -7$	$-7 < x < 5$	$x > 5$
Test $x = -8$.	Test $x = 0$.	Test $x = 6$.
$(x - 5)(x + 7) < 0$	$(x - 5)(x + 7) < 0$	$(x - 5)(x + 7) < 0$
$(-8 - 5)(-8 + 7) \overset{?}{<} 0$	$(0 - 5)(0 + 7) \overset{?}{<} 0$	$(6 - 5)(6 + 7) \overset{?}{<} 0$
$13 < 0$ ✗	$-35 < 0$ ✓	$13 < 0$ ✗

The solution set is $\{x \mid -7 < x < 5\}$.

27. Solve the related quadratic function $3x^2 = 16$.

$3x^2 = 16$

$x^2 = \frac{16}{3}$

$x = \pm\sqrt{\frac{16}{3}}$

$x = \pm\frac{4}{\sqrt{3}}$

$x = \pm\frac{4\sqrt{3}}{3}$

Plot $-\frac{4\sqrt{3}}{3}$ and $\frac{4\sqrt{3}}{3}$ on a number line. Use solid dots.

$x < -\frac{4\sqrt{3}}{3}$ $\qquad$ $-\frac{4\sqrt{3}}{3} < x < \frac{4\sqrt{3}}{3}$ $\qquad$ $x > \frac{4\sqrt{3}}{3}$

```
 ┌──────────┐ ┌───────────────┐ ┌──────────┐
←──┼──┼──┼──●──┼──┼──┼──┼──●──┼──┼──┼──┼──→
  -7 -6 -5 -4 -3 -2 -1  0  1  2  3  4  5  6  7
```

Test a value in each interval.

$x < -\frac{4\sqrt{3}}{3}$	$-\frac{4\sqrt{3}}{3} < x < \frac{4\sqrt{3}}{3}$	$x > \frac{4\sqrt{3}}{3}$
Test $x = -3$.	Test $x = 0$.	Test $x = 3$.
$3x^2 \geq 16$	$3x^2 \geq 16$	$3x^2 \geq 16$
$3(-3)^2 \overset{?}{\geq} 16$	$3(0)^2 \overset{?}{\geq} 16$	$3(3)^2 \overset{?}{\geq} 16$
$27 \geq 16$ ✓	$0 \geq 16$ ✗	$27 \geq 16$ ✓

The solution set is $\left\{x \mid x \leq -\frac{4\sqrt{3}}{3} \text{ or } x \geq \frac{4\sqrt{3}}{3}\right\}$.

28. Solve the related quadratic function $-5x^2 + x + 2 = 0$.

$-5x^2 + x + 2 = 0$

$x = \frac{-b \pm \sqrt{b^2 - 4ac}}{2a}$

$x = \frac{-1 \pm \sqrt{(1)^2 - 4(-5)(2)}}{2(-5)}$

$x = \frac{-1 \pm \sqrt{41}}{-10}$

$x = \frac{1 \pm \sqrt{41}}{10}$

Plot $\frac{1 - \sqrt{41}}{10}$ and $\frac{1 + \sqrt{41}}{10}$ on a number line. Use circles.

$x < \frac{1 - \sqrt{41}}{10}$ $\qquad$ $\frac{1 - \sqrt{41}}{10} < x < \frac{1 + \sqrt{41}}{10}$ $\qquad$ $x > \frac{1 + \sqrt{41}}{10}$

```
 ┌──────────┐      ┌──┐      ┌──────────┐
←──┼──┼──┼──┼──┼──┼──┼─○─○─┼──┼──┼──┼──┼──┼──→
  -7 -6 -5 -4 -3 -2 -1  0  1  2  3  4  5  6  7
```

Test a value in each interval.

$x < \frac{1 - \sqrt{41}}{10}$	$\frac{1 - \sqrt{41}}{10} < x < \frac{1 + \sqrt{41}}{10}$
Test $x = -1$.	Test $x = 0$.
$-5x^2 + x + 2 < 0$	$-5x^2 + x + 2 < 0$
$-5(-1)^2 + (-1) + 2 \overset{?}{<} 0$	$-5(0)^2 + (0) + 2 \overset{?}{<} 0$
$-4 < 0$ ✓	$2 < 0$ ✗

$x > \frac{1 + \sqrt{41}}{10}$
Test $x = 1$.
$-5x^2 + x + 2 < 0$
$-5(1)^2 + (1) + 2 \overset{?}{<} 0$
$-2 < 0$ ✓

The solution set is $\left\{x \mid x < \frac{1 - \sqrt{41}}{10} \text{ or } x > \frac{1 + \sqrt{41}}{10}\right\}$.

29. Let x = the amount of increase. Then $4 + x$ = the width of the pen and $6 + x$ = the length. The area of the old pen is $6 \cdot 4$ or 24.

Twice the old area	is	the width multiplied of the pen	by	the length of the pen.

$$2(24) \quad = \quad (4 + x) \quad \cdot \quad (6 + x)$$

$$2(24) = (4 + x)(6 + x)$$
$$48 = 24 + 10x + x^2$$
$$0 = x^2 + 10x - 24$$
$$0 = (x - 2)(x + 12)$$
$$0 = x - 2 \quad \text{or} \quad 0 = x + 12$$
$$2 = x \qquad -12 = x$$

Since the increase is positive, the solution is 2. Thus, the new pen is $6 + 2$ or 8 feet long and $4 + 2$ or 6 feet wide.

30. B; $x^2 + 8x - 48 = 0$
$$(x + 12)(x - 4) = 0$$
$$x + 12 = 0 \quad \text{or} \quad x - 4 = 0$$
$$x = -12 \qquad x = 4$$

The solutions are -12 and 4. Therefore, the sum of the solutions is $-12 + 4$ or -8.

Pages 342–343   Chapter 6 Standardized Test Practice

1. C; There are 30 students, and half or 15 are girls. If 4 girls do not ride the bus, then $15 - 4$ or 11 girls do ride the bus. If 24 students ride the bus, and 11 of the 24 are girls, then $24 - 11$ or 13 are boys.

2. D; The exterior angles of a triangle sum to $360°$.

3. C; $y - x = 0 \rightarrow y = x$

The line $y = x$ divides the coordinate plane into two regions, $y > x$ and $y < x$. Use $y > x$ and test each point in the inequality to determine in which region the point lies.

(x, y)	$y > x$	True or False
$(-4, -2)$	$-2 \overset{?}{>} -4$	true ✓
$(1, -3)$	$-3 \overset{?}{>} 1$	false
$(-1, 3)$	$3 \overset{?}{>} -1$	true ✓
$(3, 1)$	$1 \overset{?}{>} 3$	false
$(-2, 1)$	$1 \overset{?}{>} -2$	true ✓

The points $(-4, -2)$, $(-1, 3)$, and $(-2, 1)$ all lie in the region $y > x$.

4. B; $\dfrac{5k + 5}{5k} = \dfrac{5(k + 1)}{5k}$
$$= \dfrac{k + 1}{k}$$
$$= 1 + \dfrac{1}{k}$$

$1 + \dfrac{1}{k}$ is only an integer when $k = -1$ or 1.
$$\dfrac{5k + 5}{k + 1} = \dfrac{5(k + 1)}{k + 1}$$
$$= 5$$

5 is an integer for all values of k.
$$\dfrac{5k^2 + k}{5k} = \dfrac{k(5k + 1)}{5k}$$
$$= \dfrac{5k + 1}{5}$$
$$= k + \dfrac{1}{5}$$

$k + \dfrac{1}{5}$ is never an integer if k is an integer.

5. D; $x^2 - 7x - 8 = x^2 - 8x + x - 8$
$$= (x^2 - 8x) + (x - 8)$$
$$= x(x - 8) + (x - 8)$$
$$= (x + 1)(x - 8)$$

6. B; $\dfrac{\sqrt{16x^2 + 64x + 64}}{x + 2} = \dfrac{\sqrt{16(x^2 + 4x + 4)}}{x + 2}$
$$= \dfrac{4\sqrt{(x + 2)^2}}{x + 2}$$
$$= \dfrac{4(x + 2)}{x + 2}$$
$$= 4$$

7. D; For this equation $a = 4x^2$, $b = x$, and $c = -33$.
$$p = \dfrac{-b \pm \sqrt{b^2 - 4ac}}{2a}$$
$$p = \dfrac{-(x) \pm \sqrt{(x)^2 - 4(4x^2)(-33)}}{2(4x^2)}$$
$$p = \dfrac{-x \pm \sqrt{529x^2}}{8x^2}$$
$$p = \dfrac{-x \pm 23x}{8x^2}$$
$$p = \dfrac{-x + 23x}{8x^2} \quad \text{or} \quad p = \dfrac{-x - 23x}{8x^2}$$
$$p = \dfrac{22x}{8x^2} \qquad\qquad p = \dfrac{-24x}{8x^2}$$
$$p = \dfrac{11}{4x} \qquad\qquad p = -\dfrac{3}{x}$$

Since x and p are both greater than zero, the only solution is $\dfrac{11}{4x}$.

8. C; $\langle\overline{16}\rangle = 3\sqrt{16}$
$$= 3(4)$$
$$= 12$$

9. C; $x^2 - 3x - 18 = 0$
$$(x - 6)(x + 3) = 0$$
$$x - 6 = 0 \quad \text{or} \quad x + 3 = 0$$
$$x = 6 \qquad\qquad x = -3$$

The solutions are -3 and 6. Thus, the sum of the solutions is $-3 + 6$ or 3.

10. C; Substitute $-\dfrac{5}{2}$ for x and solve for k.
$$6x^2 + kx + 20 = 0$$
$$6\left(-\dfrac{5}{2}\right)^2 + k\left(-\dfrac{5}{2}\right) + 20 = 0$$
$$\dfrac{75}{2} - \dfrac{5}{2}k + 20 = 0$$
$$-\dfrac{5}{2}k + \dfrac{115}{2} = 0$$
$$-\dfrac{5}{2}k = -\dfrac{115}{2}$$
$$k = 23$$

11. Let x = the smallest of the three consecutives even integers. Then, $x + 2$ and $x + 4$ are the other two integers. Test values for x.

x	$3x(x + 2)(x + 4)$	n	Is n a three-digit number
2	$2(2 + 2)(2 + 4)$	48	no
4	$4(4 + 2)(4 + 4)$	192	yes ✓
6	$6(6 + 2)(6 + 4)$	480	yes ✓
8	$8(8 + 2)(8 + 4)$	960	yes ✓
10	$10(10 + 2)(10 + 4)$	1680	no
−14	$−14(−14 + 2)(−14 + 4)$	−1680	no
−12	$−12(−12 + 2)(−12 + 4)$	−960	yes ✓
−10	$−10(−10 + 2)(−10 + 4)$	−480	yes ✓
−8	$−8(−8 + 2)(−8 + 4)$	−192	yes ✓
−6	$−6(−6 + 2)(−6 + 4)$	−48	no

Thus, the possible values of n are 192, 480, 960, −192, −480, and −960.

12. If $x + y = 6$, then the only possible solutions are $(1, 5)$, $(2, 4)$, $(4, 2)$, and $(5, 1)$. Evaluate $3x + 5y$ at each point.

(x, y)	$3x + 5y$
$(1, 5)$	$3(1) + 5(5) = 28$
$(2, 4)$	$3(2) + 5(4) = 26$
$(4, 2)$	$3(4) + 5(2) = 22$
$(5, 1)$	$3(5) + 5(1) = 20$

Thus, the possible values are 20, 22, 26, and 28.

13. Find the area of a circle with radius 12 inches.
$A = \pi r^2$
$A = \pi (12)^2$
$A = 144\pi$
Find the area of a circle with radius 6 inches.
$A = \pi r^2$
$A = \pi (6)^2$
$A = 36\pi$
The decrease in area is $144\pi - 36\pi$ or 108π square inches.

What percent of 144π is 108π?
$\underbrace{\text{What percent}}_{x} \cdot \underbrace{144\pi}_{} = \underbrace{108\pi}_{}$

$x(144\pi) = 108\pi$
$x = \frac{108\pi}{144\pi}$
$x = 0.75$
The area was decreased by 75%.

14. $12k = 2^2 \cdot 3 \cdot k$
Since there are factors of 2 and 3 in $12k$ the smallest possible cube would be $2^3 \cdot 3^3$ or 216.
Solve $12k = 216$ for k.
$12k = 216$
$k = \frac{216}{12}$
$k = 18$
The least positive integer value of k is 18.

15. If $AB = BC$, then B is the midpoint of A and C. Thus, the y-coordinate of B is the mean of the y-coordinates of A and C.
$y = \frac{11 + 3}{2}$
$y = \frac{14}{2}$
$y = 7$

16. If O is the center of the circle, then the triangle is an isosceles triangle.
$x = \frac{180 - 110}{2}$
$x = \frac{70}{2}$
$x = 35$

17. $(75 \blacklozenge 90) - (76 \blacklozenge 89)$
$= [75 + (76 \blacklozenge 89) + 90] - (76 \blacklozenge 89)$
$= 75 + 90$
$= 165$

18. $\quad x^2 - y^2 = 42$
$(x + y)(x - y) = 42$
$\quad\quad 6(x - y) = 42$
$\quad\quad\quad x - y = 7$

19. $(x - 7)(x + 3) = 0$
$x - 7 = 0$ or $x + 3 = 0$
$\quad x = 7 \quad\quad\quad x = -3$
The sum of the roots is $-3 + 7$ or 4. The product of the roots is $-3(7)$ or -21. The sum exceeds the product by $4 - (-21)$ or 25.

20. If $x^2 = 36$, then $x = \pm 6$. If $y^2 = 9$, then $y = \pm 3$. For each possibility, evaluate $(x - y)^2$.

(x, y)	$(x - y)^2$
$(6, 3)$	$(6 - 3)^2 = 9$
$(6, -3)$	$[6 - (-3)]^2 = 81$
$(-6, 3)$	$(-6 - 3)^2 = 81$
$(-6, -3)$	$[-6 - (-3)]^2 = 9$

The greatest value is 81.

21. C; $\underbrace{s}_{s}$ $\underbrace{\text{increased by}}_{+}$ $\underbrace{300\%}_{3.00}$ $\underbrace{\text{of}}_{\cdot}$ $\underbrace{s}_{s}$
$s + 3.00(s) = s + 3s$
$\quad\quad\quad\quad = 4s$

22. D; From the triangle inequality $\overline{AC} < \overline{AB} + \overline{BC}$ and $\overline{AB} < \overline{AC} + \overline{BC}$.
$\overline{AC} < \overline{AB} + \overline{BC}$ and $\overline{AB} < \overline{AC} + \overline{BC}$
$\overline{AC} < 8 + 4$ $\quad\quad\quad\quad 8 < \overline{AC} + 4$
$\overline{AC} < 12$ $\quad\quad\quad\quad\quad 4 < \overline{AC}$
Thus, the length of side $\overline{AC}$ is a value between 4 and 12, and the relationship cannot be determined.

23. D; A 1 by 8 rectangle has area $1(8)$ or 8, and has perimeter $2(1) + 2(8) = 18$.
A 1 by 10 rectangle has area $1(10)$ or 10, and has perimeter $2(1) + 2(10) = 22$.
However, a 2 by 5 rectangle has area $2(5)$ or 10, and has perimeter $2(2) + 2(5) = 14$. Thus, the relationship cannot be determined.

24. C; $2^{350} - 2^{349} = 2^{349}(2 - 1)$
$$= 2^{349}(1)$$
$$= 2^{349}$$

25. A; $\quad t + 5 > 9$
$$t + 5 - 2 > 9 - 2$$
$$t + 3 > 7$$

26. B; $x^2 + 12x + 36 = 0$
$$(x + 6)^2 = 0$$
$$x + 6 = \pm \sqrt{0}$$
$$x + 6 = 0$$
$$x = -6$$

27. D; Let $p = 1$ and $q = 0$. Then, $|p| = |1|$ or 1, $|q| = |0|$ or 0, and $|p| > |q|$. Let $p = 0$ and $q = -1$. Then, $|p| = |0|$ or 0, $|q| = |-1| = 1$, and $|p| < |q|$. Thus, the relationship cannot be determined.

28. A; The angle opposite side x has measure of $180 - (71 + 54)$ or 55°. In a triangle, the side opposite the larger angle is longer. Therefore, the measure of side x is greater than the measure of side y.

Chapter 7 Polynomial Functions

1. One of the solutions is between 0 and 1, and the other one is between 4 and 5.

2. One of the solutions is 1 and the other one is between −2 and −1.

3. One of the solutions is between −5 and −4 and the other one is between 0 and 1.

4. $x^2 - 17x + 60 = 0$

$x = \dfrac{-b \pm \sqrt{b^2 - 4ac}}{2a}$

$x = \dfrac{-(-17) \pm \sqrt{(-17)^2 - 4(1)(60)}}{2(1)}$

$x = \dfrac{17 \pm \sqrt{289 - 240}}{2}$

$x = \dfrac{17 \pm \sqrt{49}}{2}$

$x = \dfrac{17 \pm 7}{2}$

$x = \dfrac{17 + 7}{2}$ or $x = \dfrac{17 - 7}{2}$

$x = 12 \qquad x = 5$

5. $14x^2 + 23x + 3 = 0$

$x = \dfrac{-b \pm \sqrt{b^2 - 4ac}}{2a}$

$x = \dfrac{-23 \pm \sqrt{(23)^2 - 4(14)(3)}}{2(14)}$

$x = \dfrac{-23 \pm \sqrt{529 - 168}}{28}$

$x = \dfrac{-23 \pm \sqrt{361}}{28}$

$x = \dfrac{-23 \pm 19}{28}$

$x = \dfrac{-23 + 19}{28}$ or $x = \dfrac{-23 - 19}{28}$

$x = \dfrac{-4}{28} \qquad x = \dfrac{-42}{28}$

$x = -\dfrac{1}{7} \qquad x = -\dfrac{3}{2}$

6. $2x^2 + 5x + 1 = 0$

$x = \dfrac{-b \pm \sqrt{b^2 - 4ac}}{2a}$

$x = \dfrac{-5 \pm \sqrt{(5)^2 - 4(2)(1)}}{2(1)}$

$x = \dfrac{-5 \pm \sqrt{25 - 8}}{2}$

$x = \dfrac{-5 \pm \sqrt{17}}{2}$

7. $x - r = x - 6$, so $r = 6$.

$3x^2 - 14x - 24$

$\downarrow \quad \downarrow \quad \downarrow$

$3 \quad -14 \quad -24$

$\begin{array}{r|rrr} 6 & 3 & -14 & -24 \\ & & 18 & 24 \\ \hline & 3 & 4 & 0 \end{array}$

The quotient is $3x + 4$.

8. $a - r = a + 7$, so $r = -7$.

$a^2 - 2a - 30$

$\downarrow \quad \downarrow \quad \downarrow$

$1 \quad -2 \quad -30$

$\begin{array}{r|rrr} -7 & 1 & -2 & -30 \\ & & -7 & +63 \\ \hline & 1 & -9 & 33 \end{array}$

The quotient is $a - 9 + \dfrac{33}{a + 7}$.

9. $f(x) = 4x - 7$

$f(-3) = 4(-3) - 7$

$ = -12 - 7$

$ = -19$

10. $g(x) = 2x^2 - 3x + 1$

$g(2a) = 2(2a)^2 - 3(2a) + 1$

$ = 2(4a^2) - 6a + 1$

$ = 8a^2 - 6a + 1$

11. $f(x) = 4x - 7$, $g(x) = 2x^2 - 3x + 1$

$f(4b^2) + g(b) = 4(4b^2) - 7 + 2b^2 - 3b + 1$

$ = 16b^2 - 7 + 2b^2 - 3b + 1$

$ = 18b^2 - 3b - 6$

7-1   Polynomial Functions

Page 350   Check for Understanding

1. By definition, the degree of a polynomial in one variable is the greatest exponent of its variable. If we rewrite $f(x) = 4$ as $f(x) = 4x^0$, we can see that it has degree 0. We can rewrite $f(x) = x + 5$ as $f(x) = x^1 + 5$. This form of $f(x)$ shows that the degree of a linear polynomial is 1.

2. Sample answer: Even-degree polynomial functions with positive leading coefficients have graphs in which $f(x) \to +\infty$ as $x \to +\infty$ and as $x \to -\infty$. Odd-degree polynomial functions with positive leading coefficients have graphs in which $f(x) \to +\infty$ as $x \to +\infty$ and $f(x) \to -\infty$ as $x \to -\infty$.

3. Sample answer:

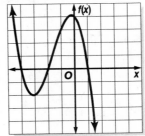

4. Sometimes; a polynomial function with 4 real roots may be a sixth degree polynomial function with 2 imaginary roots. A polynomial function that has 4 real roots is *at least* a fourth-degree polynomial.

5. degree: 6
leading coefficient: 5

6. degree: 5
leading coefficient: −3

7. $p(x) = -x^3 + x^2 - x$
$p(3) = -(3)^3 + (3)^2 - (3)$
$\quad = -27 + 9 - 3$
$\quad = -21$
$p(-1) = -(-1)^3 + (-1)^2 - (-1)$
$\quad = -(-1) + (1) - (-1)$
$\quad = 1 + 1 + 1$
$\quad = 3$

8. $p(x) = x^4 - 3x^3 + 2x^2 - 5x + 1$
$p(3) = (3)^4 - 3(3)^3 + 2(3)^2 - 5(3) + 1$
$\quad = 81 - 81 + 18 - 15 + 1$
$\quad = 4$
$p(-1) = (-1)^4 - 3(-1)^3 + 2(-1)^2 - 5(-1) + 1$
$\quad = 1 + 3 + 2 + 5 + 1$
$\quad = 12$

9. $p(x) = 2x^3 + 6x - 12$
$p(a^3) = 2(a^3)^3 + 6(a^3) - 12$
$\quad = 2(a^9) + 6a^3 - 12$
$\quad = 2a^9 + 6a^3 - 12$

10. $q(x) = 5x^2 + 4$
$5[q(2a)] = 5[5(2a)^2 + 4]$
$\quad = 5[5(4a^2) + 4]$
$\quad = 5(20a^2 + 4)$
$\quad = 100a^2 + 20$

11. $3p(a) - q(a + 1)$
$\quad = 3[2(a^3) + 6(a) - 12] - [5(a + 1)^2 + 4]$
$\quad = 3(2a^3 + 6a - 12) - 5(a^2 + 2a + 1) - 4$
$\quad = 6a^3 + 18a - 36 - 5a^2 - 10a - 5 - 4$
$\quad = 6a^3 - 5a^2 + 8a - 45$

12a. $f(x) \to -\infty$ as $x \to +\infty$, $f(x) \to +\infty$ as $x \to -\infty$
12b. The graph represents an odd-degree function.
12c. The function has 3 real zeros.
13a. $f(x) \to +\infty$ as $x \to \pm\infty$, $f(x) \to +\infty$ as $x \to -\infty$
13b. The graph represents an even-degree function.
13c. The function has no real zeros.
14a. $f(x) \to +\infty$ as $x \to +\infty$, $f(x) \to -\infty$ as $x \to -\infty$
14b. The graph represents an odd-degree function.
14c. The function has 1 real zero.
15. $L(t) = 10 + 0.3t + 0.4t^2 - 0.01t^3$
$L(30) = 10 + 0.3(30) + 0.4(30)^2 - 0.01(30)^3$
$\quad = 10 + 9 + 360 - 270$
$\quad = 109$ lumens

Pages 350–352   Practice and Apply

16. $7 - x$
degree: 1
leading coefficient: -1
17. $(a + 1)(a^2 - 4) = a^3 - 4a - a^2 - 4$
$\qquad\qquad\qquad = a^3 + a^2 - 4a + 4$
degree: 3
leading coefficient: 1
18. $a^2 + 2ab + b^2$
The polynomial contains two variables, a and b.
19. $6x^4 + 3x^2 + 4x - 8$
degree: 4
leading coefficient: 6

20. $7 + 3x^2 - 5x^3 + 6x^2 - 2x$
degree: 3
leading coefficient: -5
21. $c^2 + c - \frac{1}{c}$

This is not a polynomial because the term $\frac{1}{c}$ cannot be written in the form x^n, where n is a nonnegative integer.
22. $p(x) = 2 - x$
$p(4) = 2 - 4$
$\quad = -2$
$p(-2) = 2 - (-2)$
$\quad = 2 + 2$
$\quad = 4$
23. $p(x) = x^2 - 3x + 8$
$p(4) = (4)^2 - 3(4) + 8$
$\quad = 16 - 12 + 8$
$\quad = 12$
$p(-2) = (-2)^2 - 3(-2) + 8$
$\quad = 4 + 6 + 8$
$\quad = 18$
24. $p(x) = 2x^3 - x^2 + 5x - 7$
$p(4) = 2(4)^3 - (4)^2 + 5(4) - 7$
$\quad = 2(64) - 16 + 20 - 7$
$\quad = 128 - 16 + 20 - 7$
$\quad = 125$
$p(-2) = 2(-2)^3 - (-2)^2 + 5(-2) - 7$
$\quad = 2(-8) - 4 - 10 - 7$
$\quad = -16 - 4 - 10 - 7$
$\quad = -37$
25. $p(x) = x^5 - x^2$
$p(4) = (4)^5 - (4)^2$
$\quad = 1024 - 16$
$\quad = 1008$
$p(-2) = (-2)^5 - (-2)^2$
$\quad = -32 - 4$
$\quad = -36$
26. $p(x) = x^4 - 7x^3 + 8x - 6$
$p(4) = (4)^4 - 7(4)^3 + 8(4) - 6$
$\quad = 256 - 7(64) + 32 - 6$
$\quad = 256 - 448 + 32 - 6$
$\quad = -166$
$p(-2) = (-2)^4 - 7(-2)^3 + 8(-2) - 6$
$\quad = 16 - 7(-8) - 16 - 6$
$\quad = 16 + 56 - 16 - 6$
$\quad = 50$
27. $p(x) = 7x^2 - 9x + 10$
$p(4) = 7(4)^2 - 9(4) + 10$
$\quad = 7(16) - 36 + 10$
$\quad = 112 - 36 + 10$
$\quad = 86$
$p(-2) = 7(-2)^2 - 9(-2) + 10$
$\quad = 7(4) + 18 + 10$
$\quad = 28 + 18 + 10$
$\quad = 56$

28. $p(x) = \frac{1}{2}x^4 - 2x^2 + 4$

$p(4) = \frac{1}{2}(4)^4 - 2(4)^2 + 4$

$= \frac{1}{2}(256) - 2(16) + 4$

$= 128 - 32 + 4$

$= 100$

$p(-2) = \frac{1}{2}(-2)^4 - 2(-2)^2 + 4$

$= \frac{1}{2}(16) - 2(4) + 4$

$= 8 - 8 + 4$

$= 4$

29. $p(x) = \frac{1}{8}x^3 - \frac{1}{4}x^2 - \frac{1}{2}x + 5$

$p(4) = \frac{1}{8}(4)^3 - \frac{1}{4}(4)^2 - \frac{1}{2}(4) + 5$

$= \frac{1}{8}(64) - \frac{1}{4}(16) - 2 + 5$

$= 8 - 4 - 2 + 5$

$= 7$

$p(-2) = \frac{1}{8}(-2)^3 - \frac{1}{4}(-2)^2 - \frac{1}{2}(-2) + 5$

$= \frac{1}{8}(-8) - \frac{1}{4}(4) + 1 + 5$

$= -1 - 1 + 1 + 5$

$= 4$

30. $r(x) = x^3 + x + 1$

$r(3a) = (3a)^3 + (3a) + 1$

$= 27a^3 + 3a + 1$

31. $p(x) = 3x^2 - 2x + 5$

$4p(a) = 4[3(a)^2 - 2(a) + 5]$

$= 12a^2 - 8a + 20$

32. $p(a^2) = 3(a^2)^2 - 2(a^2) + 5$

$= 3a^4 - 2a^2 + 5$

33. $p(2a^3) = 3(2a^3)^2 - 2(2a^3) + 5$

$= 3(4a^6) - 4a^3 + 5$

$= 12a^6 - 4a^3 + 5$

34. $r(x + 1) = (x + 1)^3 + (x + 1) + 1$

$= x^3 + 3x^2 + 3x + 1 + x + 1 + 1$

$= x^3 + 3x^2 + 4x + 3$

35. $p(x^2 + 3) = 3(x^2 + 3)^2 - 2(x^2 + 3) + 5$

$= 3(x^4 + 6x^2 + 9) - 2x^2 - 6 + 5$

$= 3x^4 + 18x^2 + 27 - 2x^2 - 6 + 5$

$= 3x^4 + 16x^2 + 26$

36. $2[p(x + 4)] = 2[3(x + 4)^2 - 2(x + 4) + 5]$

$= 2[3(x^2 + 8x + 16) - 2x - 8 + 5]$

$= 2(3x^2 + 24x + 48 - 2x - 8 + 5)$

$= 2(3x^2 + 22x + 45)$

$= 6x^2 + 44x + 90$

37. $r(x + 1) - r(x^2)$

$= (x + 1)^3 + (x + 1) + 1 - [(x^2)^3 + (x^2) + 1]$

$= x^3 + 3x^2 + 3x + 1 + x + 1 + 1 - (x^6 + x^2 + 1)$

$= x^3 + 3x^2 + 4x + 3 - x^6 - x^2 - 1$

$= -x^6 + x^3 + 2x^2 + 4x + 2$

38. $3[p(x^2 - 1)] + 4p(x)$

$= 3[3(x^2 - 1)^2 - 2(x^2 - 1) + 5] + 4(3x^2 - 2x + 5)$

$= 3[3(x^4 - 2x^2 + 1) - 2x^2 + 2 + 5] + 12x^2 - 8x + 20$

$= 3(3x^4 - 6x^2 + 3) - 6x^2 + 6 + 15 + 12x^2 - 8x + 20$

$= 9x^4 - 18x^2 + 9 + 6x^2 - 8x + 41$

$= 9x^4 - 12x^2 - 8x + 50$

39a. $f(x) \to +\infty$ as $x \to +\infty$, $f(x) \to -\infty$ as $x \to -\infty$

39b. The graph represents an odd-degree polynomial.

39c. The polynomial has 3 real zeros.

40a. $f(x) \to +\infty$ as $x \to \pm\infty$, $f(x) \to +\infty$ as $x \to -\infty$

40b. The graph represents an even-degree polynomial.

40c. The polynomial has 4 real zeros.

41a. $f(x) \to -\infty$ as $x \to \pm\infty$, $f(x) \to -\infty$ as $x \to -\infty$

41b. The graph represents an even-degree polynomial.

41c. Since the graph does not intersect the x-axis, it has no real zeros.

42a. $f(x) \to +\infty$ as $x \to +\infty$, $f(x) \to -\infty$ as $x \to -\infty$

42b. The graph represents an odd-degree polynomial.

42c. The polynomial has 5 real zeros.

43a. $f(x) \to +\infty$ as $x \to +\infty$, $f(x) \to -\infty$ as $x \to -\infty$

43b. The graph represents an odd-degree polynomial.

43c. The polynomial has 1 real zero.

44a. $f(x) \to -\infty$ as $x \to \pm\infty$, $f(x) \to -\infty$ as $x \to -\infty$

44b. The graph represents an even-degree polynomial.

44c. The polynomial has 2 real zeros.

45. $P(s) = \frac{s^3}{1000}$

$P(18) = \frac{(18)^3}{1000}$

$= \frac{5832}{1000}$

$= 5.832$ units

46. even

47. $f(x) \to -\infty$ as $x \to \pm\infty$

48. Sample answer: Decrease; the graph appears to be turning at $x = 30$ indicating a relative maximum at that point. So attendance will decrease after 2000.

49.

$f(x) = ax(x - 4)(x + 1)$

$f(5) = 15$

$(a)(5)(5 - 4)(5 + 1) = 15$

$(a)(5)(1)(6) = 15$

$30a = 15$

$\frac{30a}{30} = \frac{15}{30}$

$a = \frac{1}{2}$

50. $f(x) = ax(x - 4)(x + 1) = 0$

$ax(x - 4)(x + 1) = 0$

$ax = 0$ or $x - 4 = 0$ or $x + 1 = 0$

$x = 4 \qquad x = -1$

Thus, $f(x) = 0$ when $x = -1, 0,$ or 4.

51. $f(x) = \frac{1}{2}x(x - 4)(x + 1)$

$= \frac{1}{2}x(x^2 - 3x - 4)$

$= \frac{1}{2}x^3 - \frac{3}{2}x^2 - 2x$

52.

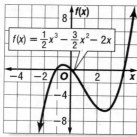

$f(x) = \frac{1}{2}x^3 - \frac{3}{2}x^2 - 2x$

53. degree: 4

54. $f(n) = \frac{1}{24}(n^4 - 6n^3 + 23n^2 - 18n + 24)$

$f(5) = \frac{1}{24}[(5)^4 - 6(5)^3 + 23(5)^2 - 18(5) + 24]$

$= \frac{1}{24}[625 - 6(125) + 23(25) - 90 + 24]$

$= \frac{1}{24}(625 - 750 + 575 - 90 + 24)$

$= \frac{384}{24}$

$= 16$ regions

55. $\quad \frac{1}{24}(n^4 - 6n^3 + 23n^2 - 18n + 24) = 99$

$24 \cdot \frac{1}{24}(n^4 - 6n^3 + 23n^2 - 18n + 24) = 99 \cdot 24$

$n^4 - 6n^3 + 23n^2 - 18n + 24 = 2376$

$n^4 - 6n^3 + 23n^2 - 18n + 24 - 2352 = 0$

Let $y = x^4 - 6x^3 + 23x^2 - 18x - 2352$. Graph the polynomial y. Its graph intersects the x-axis at $x = 8$, so connecting 8 points forms 99 regions.

56. Many relationships in nature can be modeled by polynomial functions, for example, the pattern in a honeycomb or the rings in a tree trunk. Answers should include the following.

- You can use the equation to find the number of hexagons in a honeycomb with 10 rings and the number of hexagons in a honeycomb with 9 rings. The difference is the number of the hexagons in the tenth ring.

- Other examples of patterns found in nature include pineapples, pinecones, and flower petals.

57. C

58. C; $\frac{1}{2}x^2 - 6x + 2 = 0$

$2\left(\frac{1}{2}x^2 - 6x + 2\right) = 0 \cdot 2$

$x^2 - 12x + 4 = 0$

$x = \frac{-b \pm \sqrt{b^2 - 4ac}}{2a}$

$x = \frac{-(-12) \pm \sqrt{(-12)^2 - 4(1)(4)}}{2(1)}$

$x = \frac{12 \pm \sqrt{144 - 16}}{2}$

$x \approx \frac{12 \pm 11.31}{2}$

$x \approx \frac{12 + 11.31}{2}$ or $x \approx \frac{12 - 11.31}{2}$

$x \approx 11.66 \qquad x \approx 0.34$

59. $x^2 - 8x + 12 = 0$

$(x - 2)(x - 6) = 0$

$x - 2 = 0$ or $x - 6 = 0$

$x = 2 \qquad x = 6$

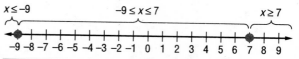

$x < 2$	$2 < x < 6$	$x < 6$
Test $x = 1$.	Test $x = 3$.	Test $x = 7$.
$x^2 - 8x + 12 < 0$	$x^2 - 8x + 12 < 0$	$x^2 - 8x + 12 < 0$
$(1)^2 - 8(1) + 12 \stackrel{?}{<} 0$	$(3)^2 - 8(3) + 12 \stackrel{?}{<} 0$	$(7)^2 - 8(7) + 12 \stackrel{?}{<} 0$
$5 < 0$ ✗	$-3 < 0$ ✓	$5 < 0$ ✗

The solution set is $\{x \mid 2 < x < 6\}$.

60. $x^2 + 2x - 86 = -23$

$x^2 + 2x - 63 = 0$

$(x + 9)(x - 7) = 0$

$x + 9 = 0$ or $x - 7 = 0$

$x = -9 \qquad x = 7$

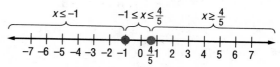

$x \le -9$	$-9 \le x \le 7$	$x \ge 7$
Test $x = -10$.	Test $x = 0$.	Test $x = 8$.
$x^2 - 2x - 63 \ge 0$	$x^2 - 2x - 63 \ge 0$	$x^2 - 2x - 63 \ge 0$
$(-10)^2 - 2(-10) - 63 \stackrel{?}{\ge} 0$	$(0)^2 - 2(0) - 63 \stackrel{?}{\ge} 0$	$(8)^2 - 2(8) - 63 \stackrel{?}{\ge} 0$
$17 \ge 0$ ✓	$-63 \ge 0$ ✗	$17 \ge 0$ ✓

The solution set is $\{x \mid x \le -9$ or $x \ge 7\}$.

61. $15x^2 + 3x - 12 = 0$

$3(5x^2 + x - 4) = 0$

$5x^2 + x - 4 = 0$

$(5x - 4)(x + 1) = 0$

$x + 1 = 0 \quad$ or $5x - 4 = 0$

$x = -1 \qquad\quad 5x = 4$

$x = \frac{4}{5}$

$x \le -1$	$-1 \le x \le \frac{4}{5}$	$x \ge \frac{4}{5}$
Test $x = -2$.	Test $x = 0$.	Test $x = 1$.
$15x^2 + 3x - 12 \le 0$	$15x^2 + 3x - 12 \le 0$	$15x^2 + 3x - 12 \le 0$
$15(-2)^2 + 3(-2) - 12 \stackrel{?}{\le} 0$	$15(0)^2 + 3(0) - 12 \stackrel{?}{\le} 0$	$15(1)^2 + 3(1) - 12 \stackrel{?}{\le} 0$
$42 \le 0$ ✗	$-12 \le 0$ ✓	$6 \le 0$ ✗

The solution set is $\left\{x \mid -1 \le x \le \frac{4}{5}\right\}$.

62. $y = -2(x - 2)^2 + 3$

vertex: $(2, 3)$

axis of symmetry: $x = 2$

two points on one side of $x = 2$: $(3, 1)$ and $\left(\frac{7}{2}, -\frac{3}{2}\right)$

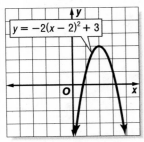

63. $y = \frac{1}{3}(x + 5)^2 - 1$

vertex: $(-5, -1)$

axis of symmetry: $x = -5$

two points on one side of $x = -5$: $\left(-1, \frac{13}{3}\right)$ and

$(-2, 2)$

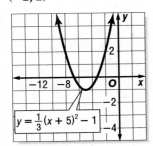

64. $y = \frac{1}{2}x^2 + x + \frac{3}{2}$

$\quad = \frac{1}{2}(x^2 + 2x) + \frac{3}{2}$

$\quad = \frac{1}{2}(x^2 + 2x + 1) + \frac{3}{2} - \frac{1}{2}(1)$

$\quad = \frac{1}{2}(x + 1)^2 + 1$

vertex: $(-1, 1)$

axis of symmetry: $x = -1$

two points on one side of $x = -1$: $\left(0, \frac{3}{2}\right)$ and $(1, 3)$

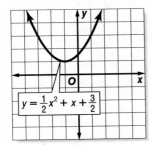

65. $x^2 - 8x - 2 = 0$

$\quad x^2 - 8x = 2$

$\quad x^2 - 8x + 16 = 2 + 16$

$\quad (x - 4)^2 = 18$

$\quad x - 4 = \pm\sqrt{18}$

$\quad x - 4 = \pm 3\sqrt{2}$

$\quad x = 4 \pm 3\sqrt{2}$

$\quad x = 4 + 3\sqrt{2} \text{ or } x = 4 - 3\sqrt{2}$

The solution set is $\{4 \pm 3\sqrt{2}\}$.

66. $x^2 + \frac{1}{3}x - \frac{35}{36} = 0$

$\quad x^2 + \frac{1}{3}x = \frac{35}{36}$

$\quad x^2 + \frac{1}{3}x + \frac{1}{36} = \frac{35}{36} + \frac{1}{36}$

$\quad \left(x + \frac{1}{6}\right)^2 = 1$

$\quad x + \frac{1}{6} = \pm 1$

$\quad x = -\frac{1}{6} \pm 1$

$\quad x = -\frac{1}{6} + 1 \text{ or } x = -\frac{1}{6} - 1$

$\quad x = \frac{5}{6} \qquad\qquad x = -\frac{7}{6}$

The solution set is $\left\{-\frac{7}{6}, \frac{5}{6}\right\}$.

67. salary after one year $= (23{,}450)(p) + 23{,}450$

$\qquad = (23{,}450)(p + 1)$

salary after two years

$\qquad = (23{,}450)(p + 1) + (23{,}450)(p + 1)p$

$\qquad = (23{,}450)(p + 1)(p + 1)$

$\qquad = (23{,}450)(p + 1)^2$

salary after three years

$\qquad = (23{,}450)(p + 1)^2 + (23{,}450)(p + 1)^2(p)$

$\qquad = (23{,}450)(p + 1)^2(p + 1)$

$\qquad = (23{,}450)(p + 1)^3$

68. $y = x^2 + 4$

x	$x^2 + 4$	y	(x, y)
0	$(0)^2 + 4$	4	$(0, 4)$
1	$(1)^2 + 4$	5	$(1, 5)$
2	$(2)^2 + 4$	8	$(2, 8)$
3	$(3)^2 + 4$	13	$(3, 13)$
4	$(4)^2 + 4$	20	$(4, 20)$

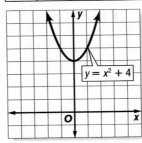

69. $y = -x^2 + 6x - 5$

x	$-x^2 + 6x - 5$	y	(x, y)
-2	$-(-2)^2 + 6(-2) - 5$	-21	$(-2, -21)$
-1	$-(-1)^2 + 6(-1) - 5$	-12	$(-1, -12)$
0	$-(0)^2 + 6(0) - 5$	-5	$(0, -5)$
1	$-(1)^2 + 6(1) - 5$	0	$(1, 0)$
2	$-(2)^2 + 6(2) - 5$	3	$(2, 3)$

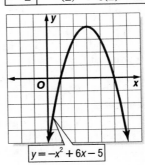

70. $y = \frac{1}{2}x^2 = 2x - 6$

x	$\frac{1}{2}x^2 + 2x - 6$	y	(x, y)
0	$\frac{1}{2}(0)^2 + 2(0) - 6$	-6	$(0, -6)$
1	$\frac{1}{2}(1)^2 + 2(1) - 6$	$-\frac{7}{2}$	$\left(1, -\frac{7}{2}\right)$
2	$\frac{1}{2}(2)^2 + 2(2) - 6$	0	$(2, 0)$
3	$\frac{1}{2}(3)^2 + 2(3) - 6$	$\frac{9}{2}$	$\left(3, \frac{9}{2}\right)$
4	$\frac{1}{2}(4)^2 + 2(4) - 6$	10	$(4, 10)$

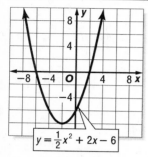

$y = \frac{1}{2}x^2 + 2x - 6$

7-2 Graphing Polynomial Functions

Page 356 Graphing Calculator Investigation

1. $f(x) = x^3 - 3x^2 + 4$

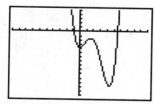

relative maximum at $x = 0$
relative minimum at $x = 2$

2. relative maximum at $(0, 4)$
relative minimum at $(2, 0)$

3. $f(x) = \frac{1}{2}x^4 - 4x^3 + 7x^2 - 8$

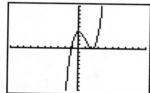

$[-10, 10]$ scl: 1 by $[-30, 10]$ scl: 2

Sample answer: The graph has two relative minimum points at $(0, -8)$ and $(4.4, -25.8)$, and one relative maximum point at $(1.6, -3.2)$.

Page 356 Check for Understanding

1. There must be at least one real zero between two points on a graph when one of the points lies below the x-axis and the other point lies above the x-axis.

2. The number of turning points is 4.

3. Sample answer:

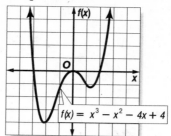

$f(x) = x^3 - x^2 - 4x + 4$

4. $f(x) = x^3 - x^2 - 4x + 4$

x	$f(x)$
-3	-20
-2	0
-1	6
0	4
1	0
2	0
3	10

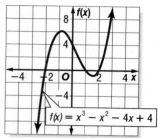

$f(x) = x^3 - x^2 - 4x + 4$

5. $f(x) = x^4 - 7x^2 + x + 5$

x	$f(x)$
-3	20
-2	-9
-1	-2
0	5
1	0
2	-5
3	26

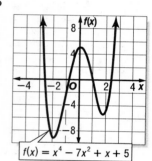

$f(x) = x^4 - 7x^2 + x + 5$

6. $f(x) = x^3 - x^2 + 1$

x	$f(x)$
-1	-1
0	1
1	1
2	5
3	19

The only zero is between -1 and 0.

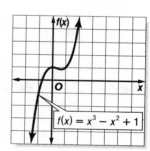

$f(x) = x^3 - x^2 + 1$

7. $f(x) = x^4 - 4x^2 + 2$

x	$f(x)$
-3	47
-2	2
-1	-1
0	2
1	-1
2	2
3	47

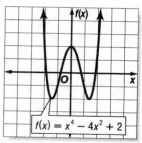

$f(x) = x^4 - 4x^2 + 2$

The real zeros are between -2 and -1, between -1 and 0, between 0 and 1, and between 1 and 2.

8. $f(x) = x^3 + 2x^2 - 3x - 5$
relative maximum at $x = -2$
relative minimum at $x = 0.5$

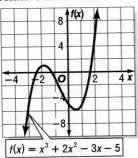

$f(x) = x^3 + 2x^2 - 3x - 5$

9. $f(x) = x^4 - 8x^2 + 10$
relative maximum at $x = 0$
relative minimum at $x = 2$ and at $x = -2$

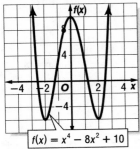

$f(x) = x^4 - 8x^2 + 10$

10.

$C(t) = -43.2t^2 + 1343t + 790$

Years Since 1985

11. There is no relative minimum, and the relative maximum is between $x = 15$ and $x = 16$. $f(x) \rightarrow -\infty$ as $x \rightarrow \pm\infty$.

12. The number of cable TV systems rose steadily from 1985 to 2000. Then the number began to decline.

Pages 356–358   Practice and Apply

13a. $f(x) = -x^3 - 4x^2$

x	$f(x)$
-5	25
-4	0
-3	-9
-2	-8
-1	-3
0	0
1	-5
2	-24

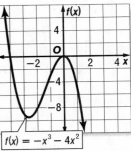

$f(x) = -x^3 - 4x^2$

13b. The real zeros are at -4 and 0.

13c. Sample answer:
Relative maximum is at $x = 0$.
Relative minimum is at $x = -3$.

14a. $f(x) = x^3 - 2x^2 + 6$

x	$f(x)$
-2	-10
-1	3
0	6
1	5
2	6
3	15
4	38

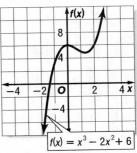

$f(x) = x^3 - 2x^2 + 6$

14b. The real zero is between -2 and -1.

14c. Sample answer:
Relative maximum is at $x = 0$.
Relative minimum is at $x = \frac{3}{2}$.

15a. $f(x) = x^3 - 3x^2 + 2$

x	$f(x)$
-2	-18
-1	-2
0	2
1	0
2	-2
3	2
4	18

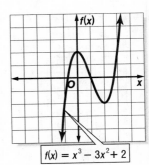

$f(x) = x^3 - 3x^2 + 2$

15b. The real zeros are between -1 and 0, and between 2 and 3.

15c. Sample answer:
Relative maximum is at $x = 0$.
Relative minimum is at $x = 2$.

16a. $f(x) = x^3 + 5x^2 - 9$

x	f(x)
−5	−9
−4	7
−3	9
−2	3
−1	−5
0	−9
1	−3
2	19

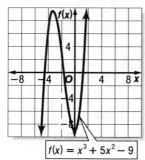

$f(x) = x^3 + 5x^2 - 9$

16b. The real zeros are between −5 and −4, between −2 and −1, and between 1 and 2.

16c. Sample answer:
Relative maximum is at $x = -3$.
Relative minimum is at $x = 0$.

17a. $f(x) = -3x^3 + 20x^2 - 36x + 16$

x	f(x)
−1	75
0	16
1	−3
2	0
3	7
4	0
5	−39

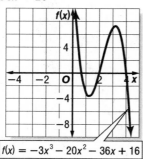

$f(x) = -3x^3 - 20x^2 - 36x + 16$

17b. The real zeros are at 2, at 4, and between 0 and 1.

17c. Sample answer:
Relative maximum is at $x = 3$.
Relative minimum is at $x = 1$.

18a. $f(x) = x^3 - 4x^2 + 2x - 1$

x	f(x)
−2	−29
−1	−8
0	−1
1	−2
2	−5
3	−4
4	7
5	34

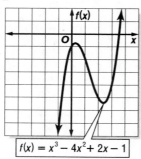

$f(x) = x^3 - 4x^2 + 2x - 1$

18b. The real zero is between 3 and 4.

18c. Sample answer:
Relative maximum is at $x = 0.5$.
Relative minimum is at $x = 2.5$.

19a. $f(x) = x^4 - 8$

x	f(x)
−3	73
−2	8
−1	−7
0	−8
1	−7
2	8
3	73

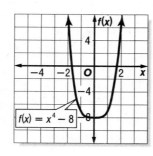

$f(x) = x^4 - 8$

19b. The real zeros are between −2 and −1, and between 1 and 2.

19c. Sample answer:
Relative minimum is at $x = 0$.
There are no relative maxima.

20a. $f(x) = x^4 - 10x^2 + 9$

x	f(x)
−3	0
−2	−15
−1	0
0	9
1	0
2	−15
3	0
4	105

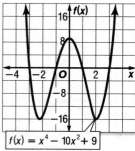

$f(x) = x^4 - 10x^2 + 9$

20b. The real zeros are between −3 and −1, and between 1 and 3.

20c. Sample answer:
Relative maximum is at $x = 0$.
Relative minima are at $x = -2$ and $x = 2$.

21a. $f(x) = -x^4 - 5x^2 - 2x - 1$

x	f(x)
−4	−169
−3	−31
−2	7
−1	5
0	−1
1	1
2	−1
3	−43

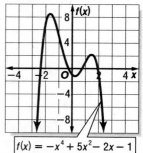

$f(x) = -x^4 + 5x^2 - 2x - 1$

21b. The real zeros are between −3 and −2, between −1 and 0, between 0 and 1, and between 1 and 2.

21c. Sample answer:
Relative maxima are at $x = -2$ and $x = 1.5$.
Relative minimum is at $x = 0$.

22a. $f(x) = -x^4 + x^3 + 8x^2 - 3$

x	f(x)
−3	−39
−2	5
−1	3
0	−3
1	5
2	21
3	15
4	−67

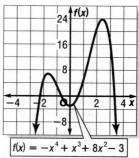

$f(x) = -x^4 + x^3 + 8x^2 - 3$

22b. The real zeros are between −3 and −2, between −1 and 0, between 0 and 1, and between 3 and 4.

22c. Sample answer:
Relative minimum is at $x = 0$.
Relative maxima are at $x = -1.5$ and $x = 2.5$.

23a. $f(x) = x^4 - 9x^3 + 25x^2 - 24x + 6$

x	$f(x)$
-1	65
0	6
1	-1
2	2
3	-3
4	-10
5	11

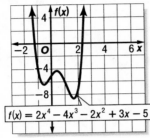

$f(x) = x^4 - 9x^3 + 25x^2 - 24x + 6$

23b. The real zeros are between 0 and 1, between 1 and 2, between 2 and 3, and between 4 and 5.

23c. Sample answer:
Relative maximum is at $x = 2$.
Relative minima are at $x = 0.5$ and $x = 4$.

24a. $f(x) = 2x^4 - 4x^3 - 2x^2 + 3x - 5$

x	$f(x)$
-2	45
-1	-4
0	-5
1	-6
2	-7
3	40

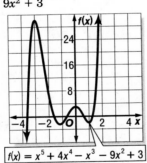

$f(x) = 2x^4 - 4x^3 - 2x^2 + 3x - 5$

24b. The real zeros are between -2 and -1, and between 2 and 3.

24c. Sample answer:
Relative maximum is at $x = 0.5$.
Relative minima are at $x = -0.5$ and $x = 1.5$.

25a. $f(x) = x^5 + 4x^4 - x^3 - 9x^2 + 3$

x	$f(x)$
-4	-77
-3	30
-2	7
-1	-2
0	3
1	-2
2	55

$f(x) = x^5 + 4x^4 - x^3 - 9x^2 + 3$

25b. The real zeros are between -4 and -3, between -2 and -1, between -1 and 0, between 0 and 1, and between 1 and 2.

25c. Sample answer:
Relative maxima are at $x = -3$ and $x = 0$.
Relative minima are at $x = -1$ and $x = 1$.

26a. $f(x) = x^5 - 6x^4 + 4x^3 + 17x^2 - 5x - 6$

x	$f(x)$
-2	-88
-1	5
0	-6
1	5
2	20
3	-3
4	-10
5	269

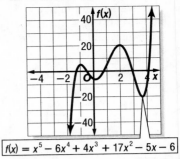

$f(x) = x^5 - 6x^4 + 4x^3 + 17x^2 - 5x - 6$

26b. The real zeros are between -2 and -1, between -1 and 0, between 0 and 1, between 2 and 3, and between 4 and 5.

26c. Sample answer:
Relative maxima are at $x = 2$ and $x = -1$.
Relative minima are at $x = 0$ and $x = 3.5$.

27. highest rate: 1982
lowest rate: 2000

28. The relative maxima occur between 1980 and 1985 and between 1990 and 1995. The relative minima occur between 1975 and 1980 and between 1985 and 1990.
As the number of years increases, the percent of the labor force that is unemployed decreases.

29. degree 5

30. Sample answer: Based on the past fluctuation of the graph, the unemployment rate is expected to increase.

31.

x	0	2	4	6	8	10	12	14	16	18	20
$B(x)$	25	34	40	45	50	54	59	64	68	71	71
$G(x)$	26	33	39	44	49	53	56	59	61	61	60

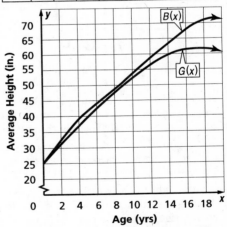

32. The growth rates for both girls and boys increase steadily until age 18 and then begin to level off, with boys averaging a height of 71 in. and girls a height of 60 in.

33. One of the real zeros is 0, and the other two are between -1 and 0, and between 5 and 6.

34. Since t represents time, only $t \geq 0$ is significant. Based on where the zeros of the function are located in the $t \geq 0$ region, a regular respiratory cycle lasts about 5.3 s.

Chapter 7

35. Looking at a graph of $V(t)$, the function has a relative maximum at $t \approx 3.4$. Since a cycle starts at $t = 0$, it takes about 3.4 s for the lungs to fill to their maximum volume of air.

36. Sample answer:

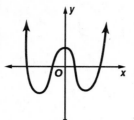

37. Sample answer:

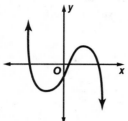

38. Sample answer:

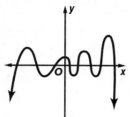

39. Sample answer:

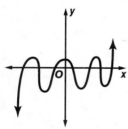

40. The turning points of a polynomial function that models a set of data can indicate fluctuations that may repeat. Answers should include the following.

- Polynomial equations best model data that contain turning points, rather than a constant increase or decrease like linear equations.
- To determine when the percentage of foreign-born citizens was at its highest, look for the relative maximum of the graph, which is at $t = 5$. The lowest percentage is found at $t = 75$, the relative minimum of the graph.

41. D; $f(x)$ is an odd-degree polynomial with a positive leading coefficient, so $f(x) \to +\infty$ as $x \to +\infty$, and $f(x) \to -\infty$ as $x \to -\infty$.

42. B; After graphing $f(x) = x^2 - 4x + 3$, use the [CALC] menu to find the relative minimium at $x = 2$.

43. After graphing $f(x) = x^3 + x^2 - 7x - 3$, find the maxima and minima using the [CALC] menu.

relative maximum: $x \approx -1.90$
relative minimum: $x \approx 1.23$

44. After graphing $f(x) = -x^3 + 6x^2 - 6x - 5$, find the maxima and minima using the [CALC] menu.

relative maximum: $x \approx 3.41$
relative minimum: $x \approx 0.59$

45. After graphing $f(x) = -x^4 + 3x^2 - 8$, find the maxima and minima using the [CALC] menu.

relative maximum: $x = 0$
relative minima: $x \approx -1.22$ and $x \approx 1.22$

46. After graphing $f(x) = 3x^4 - 7x^3 + 4x - 5$, find the maxima and minima using the [CALC] menu.

relative maximum: $x \approx 0.52$
relative minima: $x \approx -0.39$ and $x \approx 1.62$

Page 358   Maintain Your Skills

47. $r(2a) = 3(2a)^3 - (2a)^2 - 2$
$= 3(8a^3) - (4a^2) - 2$
$= 24a^3 - 4a^2 - 2$

48. $5p(c) = 5(2c^2 - 5c + 4)$
$= 10c^2 - 25c + 20$

49. $p(2a^2) = 2(2a^2)^2 - 5(2a^2) + 4$
$= 2(4a^4) - 10a^2 + 4$
$= 8a^4 - 10a^2 + 4$

50. $r(x - 1) = 3(x - 1)^3 - (x - 1)^2 - 2$
$= 3(x^3 - 3x^2 + 3x - 1) - (x^2 - 2x + 1) - 2$
$= 3x^3 - 9x^2 + 9x - 3 - x^2 + 2x - 1 - 2$
$= 3x^3 - 10x^2 + 11x - 6$

51. $p(x^2 + 4) = 2(x^2 + 4)^2 - 5(x^2 + 4) + 4$
$= 2(x^4 + 8x^2 + 16) - 5(x^2 + 4) + 4$
$= 2x^4 + 16x^2 + 32 - 5x^2 - 20 + 4$
$= 2x^4 + 11x^2 + 16$

52. $2[p(x^2 + 1)] - 3r(x - 1)$
$= 2[2(x^2 + 1)^2 - 5(x^2 + 1) + 4] - 3[3(x - 1)^3 - (x - 1)^2 - 2]$
$= 2[2(x^4 + 2x^2 + 1) - 5(x^2 + 1) + 4] - 3[3(x^3 - 3x^2 + 3x - 1) - (x^2 - 2x + 1) - 2]$
$= 2(2x^4 + 4x^2 + 2 - 5x^2 - 5 + 4) - 3(3x^3 - 9x^2 + 9x - 3 - x^2 + 2x - 1 - 2)$
$= 2(2x^4 - x^2 + 1) - 3(3x^3 - 10x^2 + 11x - 6)$
$= 4x^4 - 2x^2 + 2 - 9x^3 + 30x^2 - 33x + 18$
$= 4x^4 - 9x^3 + 28x^2 - 33x + 20$

53. $y > x^2 - 4x + 6$
Test a point inside the parabola, such as $(2, 3)$.
$3 \overset{?}{>} (2)^2 - 4(2) + 6$
$3 \overset{?}{>} 4 - 8 + 6$
$3 > 2$ ✓
So, $(2, 3)$ is a solution of the inequality. Shade the region inside the parabola.

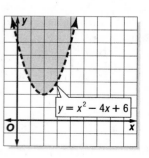

$y = x^2 - 4x + 6$

54. $y \leq -x^2 + 6x - 3$

Test a point inside the parabola, such as (3, 1).
$1 \overset{?}{\leq} -(3)^2 + 6(3) - 3$
$1 \overset{?}{\leq} -9 + 18 - 3$
$1 \leq 6$ ✓
So, (3, 1) is a solution of the inequality. Shade the region inside the parabola.

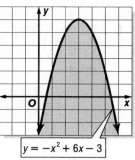

$y = -x^2 + 6x - 3$

55. $y < -x^2 - 2x$

Test a point inside the parabola, such as (1, 0).
$0 \overset{?}{<} (1)^2 - 2(1)$
$0 \overset{?}{<} 1 - 2$
$0 < -1$ ✗
So, (1, 0) is not a solution of the inequality. Shade the region outside the parabola.

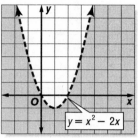

$y = x^2 - 2x$

56. $A = \begin{bmatrix} 3 & 6 \\ 2 & -1 \end{bmatrix}$

$A^{-1} = \frac{1}{-3 - 12} \begin{bmatrix} -1 & -6 \\ -2 & 3 \end{bmatrix}$

$\quad = \frac{1}{-15} \begin{bmatrix} -1 & -6 \\ -2 & 3 \end{bmatrix}$

Multiply each side of the matrix equation by the inverse matrix.

$-\frac{1}{15} \begin{bmatrix} -1 & -6 \\ -2 & 3 \end{bmatrix} \begin{bmatrix} 3 & 6 \\ 2 & -1 \end{bmatrix} \begin{bmatrix} a \\ b \end{bmatrix} = -\frac{1}{15} \begin{bmatrix} -1 & -6 \\ -2 & 3 \end{bmatrix} \begin{bmatrix} -3 \\ 18 \end{bmatrix}$

$\begin{bmatrix} 1 & 0 \\ 0 & 1 \end{bmatrix} \begin{bmatrix} a \\ b \end{bmatrix} = -\frac{1}{15} \begin{bmatrix} -105 \\ 60 \end{bmatrix}$

$\begin{bmatrix} a \\ b \end{bmatrix} = \begin{bmatrix} 7 \\ -4 \end{bmatrix}$

The solution is (7, −4).

57. $A = \begin{bmatrix} 5 & -7 \\ -3 & 4 \end{bmatrix}$

$A^{-1} = \frac{1}{20 - 21} \begin{bmatrix} 4 & 7 \\ 3 & 5 \end{bmatrix}$

$\quad = \begin{bmatrix} -4 & -7 \\ -3 & -5 \end{bmatrix}$

Multiply each side of the matrix equation by the inverse matrix.

$\begin{bmatrix} -4 & -7 \\ -3 & -5 \end{bmatrix} \begin{bmatrix} 5 & -7 \\ -3 & 4 \end{bmatrix} \begin{bmatrix} m \\ n \end{bmatrix} = \begin{bmatrix} -4 & -7 \\ -3 & -5 \end{bmatrix} \begin{bmatrix} -1 \\ 1 \end{bmatrix}$

$\begin{bmatrix} 1 & 0 \\ 0 & 1 \end{bmatrix} \begin{bmatrix} m \\ n \end{bmatrix} = \begin{bmatrix} -3 \\ -2 \end{bmatrix}$

$\begin{bmatrix} m \\ n \end{bmatrix} = \begin{bmatrix} -3 \\ -2 \end{bmatrix}$

The solution is (−3, −2).

58. $\begin{bmatrix} 3 & 2 \\ 1 & -7 \end{bmatrix} \begin{bmatrix} i \\ j \end{bmatrix} = \begin{bmatrix} 8 \\ 18 \end{bmatrix}$

$A^{-1} = \frac{1}{-21 - 2} \begin{bmatrix} -7 & -2 \\ -1 & 3 \end{bmatrix}$

$\quad = \frac{1}{-23} \begin{bmatrix} -7 & -2 \\ -1 & 3 \end{bmatrix}$

$-\frac{1}{23} \begin{bmatrix} -7 & -2 \\ -1 & 3 \end{bmatrix} \begin{bmatrix} 3 & 2 \\ 1 & -7 \end{bmatrix} \begin{bmatrix} i \\ j \end{bmatrix} = -\frac{1}{23} \begin{bmatrix} -7 & -2 \\ -1 & 3 \end{bmatrix} \begin{bmatrix} 8 \\ 18 \end{bmatrix}$

$\begin{bmatrix} 1 & 0 \\ 0 & 1 \end{bmatrix} \begin{bmatrix} i \\ j \end{bmatrix} = -\frac{1}{23} \begin{bmatrix} -92 \\ 46 \end{bmatrix}$

$\begin{bmatrix} i \\ j \end{bmatrix} = \begin{bmatrix} 4 \\ -2 \end{bmatrix}$

The solution is (4, −2).

59. $\begin{bmatrix} 5 & 2 \\ 10 & -4 \end{bmatrix} \begin{bmatrix} y \\ z \end{bmatrix} = \begin{bmatrix} 11 \\ -2 \end{bmatrix}$

$A^{-1} = \frac{1}{-20 - 20} \begin{bmatrix} -4 & -2 \\ -10 & 5 \end{bmatrix}$

$\quad = \frac{1}{-40} \begin{bmatrix} -4 & -2 \\ -10 & 5 \end{bmatrix}$

Multiply each side of the matrix equation by the inverse matrix.

$-\frac{1}{40} \begin{bmatrix} -4 & -2 \\ -10 & 5 \end{bmatrix} \begin{bmatrix} 5 & 2 \\ 10 & -4 \end{bmatrix} \begin{bmatrix} y \\ z \end{bmatrix} = -\frac{1}{40} \begin{bmatrix} -4 & -2 \\ -10 & 5 \end{bmatrix} \begin{bmatrix} 11 \\ -2 \end{bmatrix}$

$\begin{bmatrix} 1 & 0 \\ 0 & 1 \end{bmatrix} \begin{bmatrix} y \\ z \end{bmatrix} = -\frac{1}{40} \begin{bmatrix} -40 \\ -120 \end{bmatrix}$

$\begin{bmatrix} y \\ z \end{bmatrix} = \begin{bmatrix} 1 \\ 3 \end{bmatrix}$

The solution is (1, 3).

60. slope $= \frac{\text{rise}}{\text{run}}$

$\frac{1}{4} = \frac{x}{4}$

$4\left(\frac{1}{4}\right) = 4\left(\frac{x}{4}\right)$

$1 = x$

The ramp should be 1 foot tall.

61. $x^2 - x - 30 = x^2 - 6x + 5x - 30$
$\qquad\qquad\quad\ = x(x - 6) + 5(x - 6)$
$\qquad\qquad\quad\ = (x + 5)(x - 6)$

62. $2b^2 - 9b + 4 = 2b^2 - 8b - b + 4$
$\qquad\qquad\quad\ = 2b(b - 4) - (b - 4)$
$\qquad\qquad\quad\ = (2b - 1)(b - 4)$

63. $6a^2 + 17a + 5 = 6a^2 + 15a + 2a + 5$
$\qquad\qquad\qquad = 3a(2a + 5) + (2a + 5)$
$\qquad\qquad\qquad = (3a + 1)(2a + 5)$

64. $4m^2 - 9 = (2m)^2 - (3)^2$
$\qquad\qquad = (2m + 3)(2m - 3)$

65. $t^3 - 27 = (t - 3)(t^2 + 3t + 9)$

66. $r^4 - 1 = (r^2)^2 - (1)^2$
$\qquad\quad = (r^2 + 1)(r^2 - 1)$
$\qquad\quad = (r^2 + 1)(r + 1)(r - 1)$

1. scatter plot:

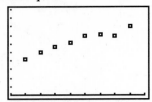

[1930, 2010] scl: 10 by [0, 200] scl: 20

LinReg:

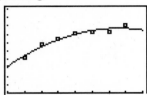

[1930, 2010] scl: 10 by [0, 200] scl: 20

QuadReg:

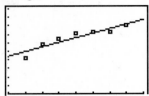

[1930, 2010] scl: 10 by [0, 200] scl: 20

CubicReg:

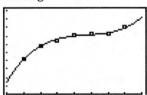

[1930, 2010] scl: 10 by [0, 200] scl: 20

2. On the graphing calculator, enter the years into List 1 and the minutes into List 2. Using a Cubic Regression line, we get $(9.4444444 \times 10^{-4})x^3 - 0.1057143x^2 + 4.21031746x + 83.1904762$.

3. Let $x = 70$.
$(9.4444444 \times 10^{-4})(70)^3 - 0.1057143(70)^2 + 4.21031746(70) + 83.1904762 \approx 184$
In 2010, you should expect to work about 184 minutes each day to pay one day's taxes.

7-3 Solving Equations Using Quadratic Techniques

Pages 362–363   Check for Understanding

1. Sample answer: $16x^4 - 12x^2 = 0$
   In quadradic form, this is written as $4[4(x^2)^2 - 3x^2] = 0$.

2. The solutions of a polynomial equation are the points at which the graph intersects the x-axis.

---

3. Factor out an x and write the equation in quadratic form so you have $x[(x^2)^2 - 2(x^2) + 1] = 0$. Factor the trinomial and solve for x using the Zero Product Property. The solutions are -1, 0, and 1.

4. This cannot be written in quadratic form since $y^3 \neq (y)^2$.

5. $84n^4 - 62n^2 = 84(n^2)^2 - 62(n^2)$

6. $x^3 + 9x^2 + 20x = 0$
   $x(x^2 + 9x + 20) = 0$
   $x(x + 5)(x + 4) = 0$
   $x = 0$ or $x + 4 = 0$ or $x + 5 = 0$
   $\qquad\qquad x = -4 \qquad\quad x = -5$
   The solutions are 0, -5, and -4.

7. $\qquad\qquad x^4 - 17x^2 + 16 = 0$
   $\qquad\qquad (x^2)^2 - 17(x^2) + 16 = 0$
   $\qquad\qquad (x^2 - 16)(x^2 - 1) = 0$
   $(x + 4)(x - 4)(x + 1)(x - 1) = 0$
   $x + 4 = 0$ or $x - 4 = 0$ or $x + 1 = 0$ or $x - 1 = 0$
   $\quad x = -4 \qquad\quad x = 4 \qquad\quad x = -1 \qquad\quad x = 1$
   The solutions are -4, -1, 4 and 1.

8. $\qquad\qquad x^3 - 216 = 0$
   $\qquad\qquad x^3 - 6^3 = 0$
   $(x - 6)(x^2 + 6x + 36) = 0$
   $x - 6 = 0$
   $\quad x = 6$
   $x^2 + 6x + 36 = 0$
   $x = \dfrac{-6 \pm \sqrt{(6)^2 - 4(1)(36)}}{2(1)}$
   $x = \dfrac{-6 \pm \sqrt{36 - 144}}{2}$
   $x = \dfrac{-6 \pm \sqrt{-108}}{2}$
   $x = \dfrac{-6 \pm 6i\sqrt{3}}{2}$
   $x = \dfrac{2(-3 \pm 3i\sqrt{3})}{2}$
   $x = -3 + 3i\sqrt{3}$ or $x = -3 - 3i\sqrt{3}$
   The solutions are 6, $(-3 + 3i\sqrt{3})$, and $(-3 - 3i\sqrt{3})$.

9. $\qquad\qquad x - 16x^{\frac{1}{2}} = -64$
   $\left(x^{\frac{1}{2}}\right)^2 - 16\left(x^{\frac{1}{2}}\right) + 64 = 0$
   $x^{\frac{1}{2}} = \dfrac{16 \pm \sqrt{(-16)^2 - 4(1)(64)}}{2(1)}$
   $x^{\frac{1}{2}} = \dfrac{16 \pm \sqrt{256 - 256}}{2}$
   $x^{\frac{1}{2}} = \dfrac{16 \pm 0}{2}$
   $x^{\frac{1}{2}} = 8$
   $x = 64$

10. $V = \ell \cdot w \cdot h$
    $V = x(7x - 6)(9x - 2)$
    $\qquad x(7x - 6)(9x - 2) = 28,000$
    $\quad x(63x^2 - 14x - 54x + 12) = 28,000$
    $63x^3 - 68x^2 + 12x - 28,000 = 0$
    A graph of the equation intersects the x-axis at $x = 8$. Thus, the pool is 8 feet deep.

Pages 363–364   Practice and Apply

11. $2(x^2)^2 + 6(x^2) - 10$

12. This cannot be written in quadradic form since $a^8 \neq (a^2)^2$.

13. $11(n^3)^2 + 44(n^3)$

14. $b(7b^4 - 4b^2 + 2) = b[7(b^2)^2 - 4(b^2) + 2]$

15. This cannot be written in quadradic form since $x^{\frac{1}{9}} \neq \left(x^{\frac{1}{3}}\right)^2$.

16. $6\left(x^{\frac{1}{5}}\right)^2 - 4\left(x^{\frac{1}{5}}\right) - 16$

17. $m^4 + 7m^3 + 12m^2 = 0$
$m^2(m^2 + 7m + 12) = 0$
$m^2(m + 3)(m + 4) = 0$
$m^2 = 0$ or $m + 3 = 0$ or $m + 4 = 0$
$m = 0 \qquad\quad m = -3 \qquad\quad m = -4$

18. $a^5 + 6a^4 + 5a^3 = 0$
$a^3(a^2 + 6a + 5) = 0$
$a^3(a + 1)(a + 5) = 0$
$a^3 = 0$ or $a + 1 = 0$ or $a + 5 = 0$
$a = 0 \qquad\quad a = -1 \qquad\quad a = -5$

19.
$$b^4 = 9$$
$$b^4 - 9 = 0$$
$$(b^2)^2 - 3^2 = 0$$
$$(b^2 - 3)(b^2 + 3) = 0$$
$$[b^2 - (\sqrt{3})^2](b^2 + 3) = 0$$
$$(b - \sqrt{3})(b + \sqrt{3})(b^2 + 3) = 0$$
$b - \sqrt{3} = 0$ or $b + \sqrt{3} = 0$ or $b^2 + 3 = 0$
$\quad b = \sqrt{3} \qquad\quad b = -\sqrt{3} \qquad\quad b = \pm i\sqrt{3}$

20.
$$t^5 - 256t = 0$$
$$t(t^4 - 256) = 0$$
$$t[(t^2)^2 - (16)^2] = 0$$
$$t(t^2 - 16)(t^2 + 16) = 0$$
$$t(t - 4)(t + 4)(t^2 + 16) = 0$$
$t = 0$ or $t - 4 = 0$ or $t + 4 = 0$ or $t^2 + 16 = 0$
$t = 0 \qquad t = 4 \qquad t = -4 \qquad t = \pm 4i$

21.
$$d^4 + 32 = 12d^2$$
$$(d^2)^2 - 12(d^2) + 32 = 0$$
$$(d^2 - 8)(d^2 - 4) = 0$$
$$[d^2 - (2\sqrt{2})^2](d^2 - 2^2) = 0$$
$$(d - 2\sqrt{2})(d + 2\sqrt{2})(d - 2)(d + 2) = 0$$
$d - 2\sqrt{2} = 0$ or $d + 2\sqrt{2} = 0$
$\quad d = 2\sqrt{2} \qquad\qquad d = -2\sqrt{2}$
or $d - 2 = 0 \qquad$ or $d + 2 = 0$
$\quad d = 2 \qquad\qquad\quad d = -2$

22.
$$x^4 + 18 = 11x^2$$
$$(x^2)^2 - 11(x^2) + 18 = 0$$
$$(x^2 - 9)(x^2 - 2) = 0$$
$$(x^2 - 3^2)(x^2 - (\sqrt{2})^2) = 0$$
$$(x - 3)(x + 3)(x - \sqrt{2})(x + \sqrt{2}) = 0$$
$x - 3 = 0$ or $x + 3 = 0$ or $x - \sqrt{2} = 0$ or $x + \sqrt{2} = 0$
$x = 3 \qquad x = -3 \qquad x = \sqrt{2} \qquad x = -\sqrt{2}$

23.
$$x^3 + 729 = 0$$
$$x^3 + 9^3 = 0$$
$$(x + 9)(x^2 - 9x + 81) = 0$$
$x + 9 = 0$ or $x^2 - 9x + 81 = 0$
$\quad x = -9 \qquad\qquad x = \dfrac{9 \pm \sqrt{9^2 - 4(81)}}{2}$
$$x = \dfrac{9 \pm \sqrt{-243}}{2}$$
$$x = \dfrac{9 \pm 9\sqrt{-3}}{2}$$
$$x = \dfrac{9 \pm 9i\sqrt{3}}{2}$$

24.
$$y^3 - 512 = 0$$
$$y^3 - 8^3 = 0$$
$$(y - 8)(y^2 + 8y + 64) = 0$$
$y - 8 = 0$ or $y^2 + 8y + 64 = 0$
$\quad y = 8 \qquad\qquad y = \dfrac{-8 \pm \sqrt{64 - 4(1)(64)}}{2}$
$$y = \dfrac{-8 \pm \sqrt{-192}}{2}$$
$$y = \dfrac{-8 \pm 8\sqrt{-3}}{2}$$
$$y = \dfrac{2(-4 \pm 4i\sqrt{3})}{2}$$
$$y = -4 \pm 4i\sqrt{3}$$

25.
$$x^{\frac{1}{2}} - 8x^{\frac{1}{4}} + 15 = 0$$
$$\left(x^{\frac{1}{4}}\right)^2 - 8\left(x^{\frac{1}{4}}\right) + 15 = 0$$
$$\left(x^{\frac{1}{4}} - 3\right)\left(x^{\frac{1}{4}} - 5\right) = 0$$
$x^{\frac{1}{4}} - 3 = 0$ or $x^{\frac{1}{4}} - 5 = 0$
$\quad x^{\frac{1}{4}} = 3 \qquad\qquad x^{\frac{1}{4}} = 5$
$\left(x^{\frac{1}{4}}\right)^4 = 3^4 \qquad \left(x^{\frac{1}{4}}\right)^4 = 5^4$
$\quad x = 81 \qquad\qquad x = 625$

26.
$$p^{\frac{2}{3}} + 11p^{\frac{1}{3}} + 28 = 0$$
$$\left(p^{\frac{1}{3}}\right)^2 + 11\left(p^{\frac{1}{3}}\right) + 28 = 0$$
$$\left(p^{\frac{1}{3}} + 4\right)\left(p^{\frac{1}{3}} + 7\right) = 0$$
$p^{\frac{1}{3}} + 4 = 0$ or $p^{\frac{1}{3}} + 7 = 0$
$\quad p^{\frac{1}{3}} = -4 \qquad\qquad p^{\frac{1}{3}} = -7$
$\left(p^{\frac{1}{3}}\right)^3 = (-4)^3 \qquad \left(p^{\frac{1}{3}}\right)^3 = (-7)^3$
$\quad p = -64 \qquad\qquad p = -343$

27.
$$y - 19\sqrt{y} = -60$$
$$(\sqrt{y})^2 - 19(\sqrt{y}) + 60 = 0$$
$$(\sqrt{y} - 4)(\sqrt{y} - 15) = 0$$
$\sqrt{y} - 4 = 0$ or $\sqrt{y} - 15 = 0$
$\quad \sqrt{y} = 4 \qquad\qquad \sqrt{y} = 15$
$(\sqrt{y})^2 = 4^2 \qquad (\sqrt{y})^2 = (15)^2$
$\quad y = 16 \qquad\qquad y = 225$

28.
$$z = 8\sqrt{z} + 240$$
$$(\sqrt{z})^2 - 8(\sqrt{z}) - 240 = 0$$
$$(\sqrt{z} + 12)(\sqrt{z} - 20) = 0$$
$\sqrt{z} + 12 = 0 \qquad$ or $\sqrt{z} - 20 = 0$
$\quad \sqrt{z} = -12 \qquad\qquad \sqrt{z} = 20$
not an acceptable $\qquad (\sqrt{z})^2 = (20)^2$
solution $\qquad\qquad\qquad z = 400$

29. $s^3 + 4s^2 - s - 4 = 0$
$s^2(s + 4) - (s + 4) = 0$
$(s + 4)(s^2 - 1) = 0$
$(s + 4)(s - 1)(s + 1) = 0$
$s + 4 = 0$ or $s - 1 = 0$ or $s + 1 = 0$
$\quad s = -4 \qquad\quad s = 1 \qquad\quad s = -1$

30. $h^3 - 8h^2 + 3h - 24 = 0$
$h^2(h - 8) + 3(h - 8) = 0$
$(h - 8)(h^2 + 3) = 0$
$h^2 + 3 = 0 \qquad\qquad$ or $h - 8 = 0$
$\quad h^2 = -3 \qquad\qquad\qquad h = 8$
$\quad h = \pm\sqrt{-3}$
$\quad h = i\sqrt{3}$ or $-i\sqrt{3}$

31. $V = \ell \cdot w \cdot h$

$h = w - 2$

$\ell = w + 4$

$V = w(w - 2)(w + 4)$

$V = 8(w + 4)$

$\qquad w(w - 2)(w + 4) = 8(w + 4)$

$\qquad w(w^2 + 2w - 8) = 8w + 32$

$\qquad w^3 + 2w^2 - 8w = 8w + 32$

$w^3 + 2w^2 - 8w - 8w - 32 = 0$

$\qquad w^3 + 2w^2 - 16w - 32 = 0$

$\qquad w^2(w + 2) - 16(w + 2) = 0$

$\qquad\qquad (w + 2)(w^2 - 16) = 0$

$\qquad (w + 2)(w - 4)(w + 4) = 0$

$w + 2 = 0 \quad$ or $w - 4 = 0$ or $w + 4 = 0$

$\quad w = -2 \qquad\quad w = 4 \qquad\quad w = -4$

The solutions -2 and -4 are not acceptable since this is a measurement problem. Thus, $w = 4$ cm.

$\ell = w + 4$

$\;\; = 4 + 4$

$\;\; = 8$ cm

$h = w - 2$

$\;\; = 4 - 2$

$\;\; = 2$ cm

32. area of total project $-$ area of glass = area of frame

$\qquad (x^2 - 3)^2 - x^2 = 27$

$x^4 - 6x^2 + 9 - x^2 = 27$

$\qquad x^4 - 7x^2 + 9 = 27$

33. $\qquad x^4 - 7x^2 + 9 = 27$

$\qquad\quad x^4 - 7x^2 - 18 = 0$

$\qquad\quad (x^2 - 9)(x^2 + 2) = 0$

$(x + 3)(x - 3)(x^2 + 2) = 0$

$x^2 + 2 \neq 0$

$x + 3 = 0 \quad$ or $x - 3 = 0$

$\quad x = -3 \qquad\quad x = 3$

$x = -3$ is not an acceptable solution since x is a measurement. Thus, $x = 3$, so the dimensions of the glass piece are 3 in. $\times$ 3 in.

34. $x = 3$

$x^2 - 3 = (3)^2 - 3$

$\qquad\quad = 9 - 3$

$\qquad\quad = 6$

Thus, the dimensions of the frame are 6 in. $\times$ 6 in.

35. $V(h) = 3h^4 + 11h^3 + 18h^2 + 44h + 24$

$\qquad = (3h^4 + 18h^2 + 24) + (11h^3 + 44h)$

$\qquad = 3(h^4 + 6h^2 + 8) + 11h(h^2 + 4)$

$\qquad = 3(h^2 + 4)(h^2 + 2) + 11h(h^2 + 4)$

$\qquad = (h^2 + 4)[3(h^2 + 2) + 11h]$

$\qquad = (h^2 + 4)(3h^2 + 6 + 11h)$

$\qquad = (h^2 + 4)(3h^2 + 9h + 2h + 6)$

$\qquad = (h^2 + 4)[3h(h + 3) + 2(h + 3)]$

$\qquad = (h^2 + 4)(h + 3)(3h + 2)$

new height: $h + 3$

new width: $3h + 2$

new length: $h^2 + 4$

36. The height increased by 3, the width increased by 2, and the length increased by 4.

37. Write the equation in quadratic form $u^2 - 9u = -8$ where $u = |a - 3|$. Then factor and use the Zero Product Property to solve for u.

Solution:

$\qquad u^2 - 9u = -8$

$\quad u^2 - 9u + 8 = 0$

$(u - 1)(u - 8) = 0$

$u - 1 = 0 \quad$ or $u - 8 = 0$

$\quad u = 1 \qquad\qquad u = 8$

Then

$|a - 3| = 1 \quad\; |a - 3| = 8$

$\; a - 3 = \pm 1 \quad\; a - 3 = \pm 8$

$a - 3 = 1 \quad$ or $a - 3 = -1$

$\quad a = 4 \qquad\qquad a = 2$

or $a - 3 = 8 \quad$ or $a - 3 = -8$

$\quad\; a = 11 \qquad\qquad a = -5$

38. Answers should include the following.

- Solve the cubic equation $4x^3 - 164x^2 + 1600x = 3600$ in order to determine the dimensions of the cut square if the desired volume is 3600 in³. Solutions are 10 in. and $\dfrac{31 \pm \sqrt{601}}{2}$ in.

- There can be more than one square cut to produce the same volume because the height of the box is not specified and 3600 has a variety of different factors.

39. D; $x^4 - 2x^2 - 3 = 0$

$(x^2)^2 - 2(x^2) - 3 = 0$

$(x^2 - 3)(x^2 + 1) = 0$

$x^2 - 3 = 0 \qquad$ or $x^2 + 1 = 0$

$\quad x^2 = 3 \qquad\qquad\quad x^2 = -1$

$\quad x = \pm\sqrt{3} \qquad\qquad x = \pm\sqrt{-1}$

$\qquad\qquad\qquad\qquad\qquad\; x = \pm i$

40. $\qquad\qquad 18x + 9\sqrt{2x} - 4 = 0$

$18(\sqrt{x})^2 + 9\sqrt{2}(\sqrt{x}) - 4 = 0$

$\sqrt{x} = \dfrac{-9\sqrt{2} \pm \sqrt{(9\sqrt{2})^2 - 4(18)(-4)}}{2(18)}$

$\sqrt{x} = \dfrac{-9\sqrt{2} \pm \sqrt{162 + 288}}{36}$

$\sqrt{x} = \dfrac{-9\sqrt{2} \pm 15\sqrt{2}}{36}$

$\sqrt{x} = \dfrac{3(-3\sqrt{2} \pm 5\sqrt{2})}{3(12)}$

$\sqrt{x} = \dfrac{-3\sqrt{2} \pm 5\sqrt{2}}{12}$

$\sqrt{x} = \dfrac{-3\sqrt{2} + 5\sqrt{2}}{12} \quad$ or $x = \dfrac{-3\sqrt{2} - 5\sqrt{2}}{12}$

$\sqrt{x} = \dfrac{2\sqrt{2}}{12} \qquad\qquad\qquad x = \dfrac{-8\sqrt{2}}{12}$

$\sqrt{x} = \dfrac{\sqrt{2}}{6} \qquad\qquad\qquad x = \dfrac{-2\sqrt{2}}{3}$

$(\sqrt{x})^2 = \left(\dfrac{\sqrt{2}}{6}\right)^2 \qquad\qquad$ not an acceptable solution

$\quad x = \dfrac{2}{36}$

$\quad x = \dfrac{1}{18}$

41. $f(x) = x^3 - 4x^2 + x + 5$

x	$f(x)$
-2	-21
-1	-1
0	5
1	3
2	-1
3	-1
4	9
5	35

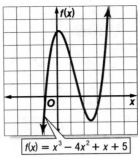

$$f(x) = x^3 - 4x^2 + x + 5$$

42. $f(x) = x^4 - 6x^3 + 10x^2 - x - 3$

x	$f(x)$
-1	15
0	-3
1	1
2	3
3	3
4	25

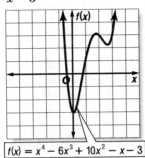

$$f(x) = x^4 - 6x^3 + 10x^2 - x - 3$$

43. $p(x) = x^2 - 5x + 3$

$$\begin{aligned} p(7) &= (7)^2 - 5(7) + 3 \\ &= 49 - 35 + 3 \\ &= 17 \end{aligned} \qquad \begin{aligned} p(-3) &= (-3)^2 - 5(-3) + 3 \\ &= 9 + 15 + 3 \\ &= 27 \end{aligned}$$

44. $p(x) = x^3 - 11x - 4$

$$\begin{aligned} p(7) &= (7)^3 - 11(7) - 4 \\ &= 343 - 77 - 4 \\ &= 262 \end{aligned}$$

$$\begin{aligned} p(-3) &= (-3)^3 - 11(-3) - 4 \\ &= -27 + 33 - 4 \\ &= 2 \end{aligned}$$

45. $p(x) = \frac{2}{3}x^4 - 3x^3$

$$\begin{aligned} p(7) &= \frac{2}{3}(7)^4 - 3(7)^3 \\ &= \frac{2}{3}(2401) - 3(343) \\ &= \frac{4802}{3} - \frac{3087}{3} \\ &= \frac{1715}{3} \end{aligned}$$

$$\begin{aligned} p(-3) &= \frac{2}{3}(-3)^4 - 3(-3)^3 \\ &= \frac{2}{3}(81) - 3(-27) \\ &= 54 + 81 \\ &= 135 \end{aligned}$$

46. $\begin{bmatrix} -2 & -3 & 3 \\ 1 & -3 & -1 \end{bmatrix}$

47. $\begin{bmatrix} 0 & -1 \\ 1 & 0 \end{bmatrix} \begin{bmatrix} -2 & -3 & 3 \\ 1 & -3 & -1 \end{bmatrix} = \begin{bmatrix} -1 & 3 & 1 \\ -2 & -3 & 3 \end{bmatrix}$

A$'(-1, -2)$, B$'(3, -3)$, and C$'(1, 3)$

48.

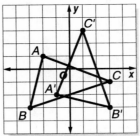

49.

$$\begin{array}{r} x^2 + 5x - 4 \\ x - 1 \overline{)\smash{x^3 + 4x^2 - 9x + 4}} \\ \underline{-(x^3 - x^2)} \\ 5x^2 - 9x + 4 \\ \underline{-(5x^2 - 5x)} \\ -4x + 4 \\ \underline{-(-4x + 4)} \\ 0 \end{array}$$

Quotient: $x^2 + 5x - 4$

50.

$$\begin{array}{r} 4x^2 - 16x + 27 \\ x + 2 \overline{)\smash{4x^3 - 8x^2 - 5x - 10}} \\ \underline{-(4x^3 + 8x^2)} \\ -16x^2 - 5x - 10 \\ \underline{-(-16x^2 - 32x)} \\ 27x - 10 \\ \underline{-(27x + 54)} \\ -64 \end{array}$$

Quotient: $4x^2 - 16x + 27 - \frac{64}{x+2}$

51.

$$\begin{array}{r} x^3 + 3x^2 - 2 \\ x - 3 \overline{)\smash{x^4 + 0x^3 - 9x^2 - 2x + 6}} \\ \underline{-(x^4 - 3x^3)} \\ 3x^3 - 9x^2 - 2x + 6 \\ \underline{-(3x^3 - 9x^2)} \\ -2x + 6 \\ \underline{-(-2x + 6)} \\ 0 \end{array}$$

Quotient: $x^3 - 3x^2 - 2$

52.

$$\begin{array}{r} x^3 + 2x^2 - 10x + 15 \\ x + 1 \overline{)\smash{x^4 + 3x^3 - 8x^2 + 5x - 6}} \\ \underline{-(x^4 + x^3)} \\ 2x^3 - 8x^2 + 5x - 6 \\ \underline{-(2x^3 + 2x^2)} \\ -10x^2 + 5x - 6 \\ \underline{-(-10x^2 - 10x)} \\ 15x - 6 \\ \underline{-(15x + 15)} \\ -21 \end{array}$$

Quotient: $x^3 + 2x^2 - 10x + 15 - \frac{21}{x+1}$

Page 364   Practice Quiz 1

1.
$$p(x) = 2x^3 - x$$
$$\begin{aligned} p(a - 1) &= 2(a - 1)^3 - (a - 1) \\ &= 2(a^3 - 3a^2 + 3a - 1) - (a - 1) \\ &= 2a^3 - 6a^2 + 6a - 2 - a + 1 \\ &= 2a^3 - 6a^2 + 5a - 1 \end{aligned}$$

2. $f(x) \to -\infty$ as $x \to +\infty$, $f(x) \to +\infty$ as $x \to -\infty$
The graph represents an odd-degree polynomial, and there are 3 real zeros.

3.

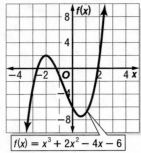

$$f(x) = x^3 + 2x^2 - 4x - 6$$

relative maximum at $x = -2$
relative minimum at $x = 0.5$

4. $18x^{\frac{1}{3}} + 36x^{\frac{2}{3}} + 5 = 36\left(x^{\frac{1}{3}}\right)^2 + 18\left(x^{\frac{1}{3}}\right) + 5$
$$= \left(6x^{\frac{1}{3}}\right)^2 + 3\left(6x^{\frac{1}{3}}\right) + 5$$
$$\text{or } 36(\sqrt[3]{x^3})^2 + 18(\sqrt[3]{x}) + 5$$

5.
$$a^4 = 6a^2 + 27$$
$$(a^2)^2 - 6(a^2) - 27 = 0$$
$$(a^2 - 9)(a^2 + 3) = 0$$
$$(a - 3)(a + 3)(a - i\sqrt{3})(a + i\sqrt{3}) = 0$$
$$a - 3 = 0 \text{ or } a + 3 = 0$$
$$a = 3 \qquad a = -3$$
$$\text{or } a - i\sqrt{3} = 0 \quad \text{or } a + i\sqrt{3} = 0$$
$$a = i\sqrt{3} \qquad\quad a = -i\sqrt{3}$$

7-4 The Remainder and Factor Theorems

Page 368 Check for Understanding

1. Sample answer:
$$f(x) = x^2 - 2x - 3$$

$$\begin{array}{r|rrr} 4 & 1 & -2 & -3 \\ & & 4 & 8 \\ \hline & 1 & 2 & 5 \end{array}$$

2. The degree of the depressed polynomial is 4.

3. dividend: $x^3 + 6x + 32$
divisor: $x + 2$
quotient: $x^2 - 2x + 10$
remainder: 12

4. By the Remainder theorem, $f(3)$ should be the remainder when you divide the polynomial by $x - 3$.

$$\begin{array}{r|rrrr} 3 & 1 & -2 & -1 & 1 \\ & & 3 & 3 & 6 \\ \hline & 1 & 1 & 2 & 7 \end{array}$$

$f(3) = 7$
$f(-4):$

$$\begin{array}{r|rrrr} -4 & 1 & -2 & -1 & 1 \\ & & -4 & 24 & -92 \\ \hline & 1 & -6 & 23 & -91 \end{array}$$

$f(-4) = -91$

---

5. $f(x): 5x^4 - 6x^2 + 2$

$$\begin{array}{r|rrrrr} 3 & 5 & 0 & -6 & 0 & 2 \\ & & 15 & 45 & 117 & 351 \\ \hline & 5 & 15 & 39 & 117 & 353 \end{array}$$

$f(3) = 353$
$f(-4):$

$$\begin{array}{r|rrrrr} -4 & 5 & 0 & -6 & 0 & 2 \\ & & -20 & 80 & -296 & 1184 \\ \hline & 5 & -20 & 74 & -296 & 1186 \end{array}$$

$f(-4) = 1186$

6.
$$\begin{array}{r|rrrr} -1 & 1 & -1 & -5 & -3 \\ & & -1 & 2 & 3 \\ \hline & 1 & -2 & -3 & 0 \end{array}$$

$x^3 - x^2 - 5x - 3 = (x + 1)(x^2 - 2x - 3)$
$$= (x + 1)(x - 3)(x + 1)$$

7.
$$\begin{array}{r|rrrr} 1 & 1 & 0 & -3 & 2 \\ & & 1 & 1 & -2 \\ \hline & 1 & 1 & -2 & 0 \end{array}$$

$x^3 - 3x + 2 = (x - 1)(x^2 + x - 2)$
$$= (x - 1)(x - 1)(x + 2)$$

8.
$$\begin{array}{r} 2x^2 - 7x - 4 \\ 3x - 2 \overline{)6x^3 - 25x^2 + 2x + 8} \\ \underline{-(6x^3 - 4x^2)} \\ -21x^2 + 2x + 8 \\ \underline{-(-21x^2 + 14x)} \\ -12x + 8 \\ \underline{-(-12x + 8)} \\ 0 \end{array}$$

$6x^3 - 25x^2 + 2x + 8 = (3x - 2)(2x^2 - 7x - 4)$
$$= (3x - 2)(2x + 1)(x - 4)$$

9.
$$\begin{array}{r|rrrrr} -2 & 1 & 2 & 0 & 8 & -16 \\ & & -2 & 0 & 0 & 16 \\ \hline & 1 & 0 & 0 & 8 & 0 \end{array}$$

$x^4 + 2x^3 + 8x - 16 = (x + 2)(x^3 - 8)$
$$= (x + 2)(x - 2)(x^2 + 2x + 4)$$

10.
$$\begin{array}{r|rrrr} 6 & -17 & 200 & -113 & 44 \\ & & -102 & 588 & 2850 \\ \hline & -17 & 98 & 475 & 2894 \end{array}$$

$2894 million = $2.894 billion

11. $S(6) = -17(6)^3 + 200(6)^2 - 113(6) + 44$
$$= -17(216) + 200(36) - 113(6) + 44$$
$$= -3672 + 7200 - 678 + 44$$
$$= \$2894 \text{ million}$$
$$= \$2.894 \text{ billion}$$

12. Sample answer: Use direct substitution, because it can be done quickly with a calculator.

13. $g(x) = x^2 - 8x + 6$

$$
\begin{array}{r|rrr}
3 & 1 & -8 & 6 \\
  &   & 3 & -15 \\
\hline
  & 1 & -5 & -9 \\
\end{array}
$$

$g(3) = -9$

$$
\begin{array}{r|rrr}
-4 & 1 & -8 & 6 \\
   &   & -4 & 48 \\
\hline
   & 1 & -12 & 54 \\
\end{array}
$$

$g(-4) = 54$

14. $g(x) = x^3 + 2x^2 - 3x + 1$

$$
\begin{array}{r|rrrr}
3 & 1 & 2 & -3 & 1 \\
  &   & 3 & 15 & 36 \\
\hline
  & 1 & 5 & 12 & 37 \\
\end{array}
$$

$g(3) = 37$

$$
\begin{array}{r|rrrr}
-4 & 1 & 2 & -3 & 1 \\
   &   & -4 & 8 & -20 \\
\hline
   & 1 & -2 & 5 & -19 \\
\end{array}
$$

$g(-4) = -19$

15. $g(x) = x^3 - 5x + 2$

$$
\begin{array}{r|rrrr}
3 & 1 & 0 & -5 & 2 \\
  &   & 3 & 9 & 12 \\
\hline
  & 1 & 3 & 4 & 14 \\
\end{array}
$$

$g(3) = 14$

$$
\begin{array}{r|rrrr}
-4 & 1 & 0 & -5 & 2 \\
   &   & -4 & 16 & -44 \\
\hline
   & 1 & -4 & 11 & -42 \\
\end{array}
$$

$g(-4) = -42$

16. $g(x) = x^4 - 6x - 8$

$$
\begin{array}{r|rrrrr}
3 & 1 & 0 & 0 & -6 & -8 \\
  &   & 3 & 9 & 27 & 63 \\
\hline
  & 1 & 3 & 9 & 21 & 55 \\
\end{array}
$$

$g(3) = 55$

$$
\begin{array}{r|rrrrr}
-4 & 1 & 0 & 0 & -6 & -8 \\
   &   & -4 & 16 & -64 & 280 \\
\hline
   & 1 & -4 & 16 & -70 & 272 \\
\end{array}
$$

$g(-4) = 272$

17. $g(x) = 2x^3 - 8x^2 - 2x + 5$

$$
\begin{array}{r|rrrr}
3 & 2 & -8 & -2 & 5 \\
  &   & 6 & -6 & -24 \\
\hline
  & 2 & -2 & -8 & -19 \\
\end{array}
$$

$g(3) = -19$

$$
\begin{array}{r|rrrr}
-4 & 2 & -8 & -2 & 5 \\
   &   & -8 & 64 & -248 \\
\hline
   & 2 & -16 & 62 & -243 \\
\end{array}
$$

$g(-4) = -243$

18. $g(x) = 3x^4 + x^3 - 2x^2 + x + 12$

$$
\begin{array}{r|rrrrr}
3 & 3 & 1 & -2 & 1 & 12 \\
  &   & 9 & 30 & 84 & 255 \\
\hline
  & 3 & 10 & 28 & 85 & 267 \\
\end{array}
$$

$g(3) = 267$

$$
\begin{array}{r|rrrrr}
-4 & 3 & 1 & -2 & 1 & 12 \\
   &   & -12 & 44 & -168 & 668 \\
\hline
   & 3 & -11 & 42 & -167 & 680 \\
\end{array}
$$

$g(-4) = 680$

19. $g(x) = x^5 + 8x^3 + 2x - 15$

$$
\begin{array}{r|rrrrrr}
3 & 1 & 0 & 8 & 0 & 2 & -15 \\
  &   & 3 & 9 & 51 & 153 & 465 \\
\hline
  & 1 & 3 & 17 & 51 & 155 & 450 \\
\end{array}
$$

$g(3) = 450$

$$
\begin{array}{r|rrrrrr}
-4 & 1 & 0 & 8 & 0 & 2 & -15 \\
   &   & -4 & 16 & -96 & 384 & -1544 \\
\hline
   & 1 & -4 & 24 & -96 & 386 & -1559 \\
\end{array}
$$

$g(-4) = -1559$

20. $g(x) = x^6 - 4x^4 + 3x^2 - 10$

$$
\begin{array}{r|rrrrrrr}
3 & 1 & 0 & -4 & 0 & 3 & 0 & -10 \\
  &   & 3 & 9 & 15 & 45 & 144 & 432 \\
\hline
  & 1 & 3 & 5 & 15 & 48 & 144 & 422 \\
\end{array}
$$

$g(3) = 422$

$$
\begin{array}{r|rrrrrrr}
-4 & 1 & 0 & -4 & 0 & 3 & 0 & -10 \\
   &   & -4 & 16 & -48 & 192 & -780 & 3120 \\
\hline
   & 1 & -4 & 12 & -48 & 195 & -780 & 3110 \\
\end{array}
$$

$g(-4) = 3110$

21.

$$
\begin{array}{r|rrrr}
1 & 1 & 2 & -1 & -2 \\
  &   & 1 & 3 & 2 \\
\hline
  & 1 & 3 & 2 & 0 \\
\end{array}
$$

$$
\begin{aligned}
x^3 + 2x^2 - x - 2 &= (x - 1)(x^2 + 3x + 2) \\
&= (x - 1)(x + 1)(x + 2)
\end{aligned}
$$

22.

$$
\begin{array}{r|rrrr}
-1 & 1 & -1 & -10 & -8 \\
   &   & -1 & 2 & 8 \\
\hline
   & 1 & -2 & -8 & 0 \\
\end{array}
$$

$$
\begin{aligned}
x^3 - x^2 - 10x - 8 &= (x + 1)(x^2 - 2x - 8) \\
&= (x + 1)(x - 4)(x + 2)
\end{aligned}
$$

23.

$$
\begin{array}{r|rrrr}
-4 & 1 & 1 & -16 & -16 \\
   &   & -4 & 12 & 16 \\
\hline
   & 1 & -3 & -4 & 0 \\
\end{array}
$$

$$
\begin{aligned}
x^3 + x^2 - 16x - 16 &= (x + 4)(x^2 - 3x - 4) \\
&= (x + 4)(x - 4)(x + 1)
\end{aligned}
$$

24.

$$
\begin{array}{r|rrrr}
2 & 1 & -6 & 11 & -6 \\
  &   & 2 & -8 & 6 \\
\hline
  & 1 & -4 & 3 & 0 \\
\end{array}
$$

$$
\begin{aligned}
x^3 - 6x^2 + 11x - 6 &= (x - 2)(x^2 - 4x + 3) \\
&= (x - 2)(x - 3)(x - 1)
\end{aligned}
$$

25.

$$\begin{array}{r|rrrr} 5 & 2 & -5 & -28 & 15 \\ & & 10 & 25 & -15 \\ \hline & 2 & 5 & -3 & \,|\,0 \end{array}$$

$2x^3 - 5x^2 - 28x + 15 = (x - 5)(2x^2 + 5x - 3)$
$\qquad\qquad\qquad\qquad = (x - 5)(x + 3)(2x - 1)$

26.

$$\begin{array}{r|rrrr} -3 & 3 & 10 & -1 & -12 \\ & & -9 & -3 & 12 \\ \hline & 3 & 1 & -4 & \,|\,0 \end{array}$$

$3x^3 + 10x^2 - x - 12 = (x + 3)(3x^2 + x - 4)$
$\qquad\qquad\qquad\qquad = (x + 3)(x - 1)(3x + 4)$

27.

$$\begin{array}{r} x^2 + 3x - 28 \\ 2x + 1\overline{)2x^3 + 7x^2 - 53x - 28} \\ \underline{-\,(2x^3 + x^2)} \\ 6x^2 - 53x - 28 \\ \underline{-\,(6x^2 + 3x)} \\ -56x - 28 \\ \underline{-\,(-56x - 28)} \\ 0 \end{array}$$

$2x^3 + 7x^2 - 53x - 28 = (2x + 1)(x^2 + 3x - 28)$
$\qquad\qquad\qquad\qquad\quad = (2x + 1)(x + 7)(x - 4)$

28.

$$\begin{array}{r} x^2 + 5x - 6 \\ 2x + 7\overline{)2x^3 + 17x^2 + 23x - 42} \\ \underline{-\,(2x^3 + 7x^2)} \\ 10x^2 + 23x - 42 \\ \underline{-\,(10x^2 + 35x)} \\ -12x - 42 \\ \underline{-(-12x - 42)} \\ 0 \end{array}$$

$2x^3 + 17x^2 + 23x - 42 = (2x + 7)(x^2 + 5x - 6)$
$\qquad\qquad\qquad\qquad\quad = (2x + 7)(x + 6)(x - 1)$

29.

$$\begin{array}{r|rrrrr} -1 & 1 & 2 & 2 & -2 & -3 \\ & & -1 & -1 & -1 & 3 \\ \hline & 1 & 1 & 1 & -3 & \,|\,0 \end{array}$$

$x^4 + 2x^3 + 2x^2 - 2x - 3 = (x + 1)(x^3 + x^2 + x - 3)$
$\qquad\qquad\qquad\qquad\qquad = (x + 1)(x - 1)(x^2 + 2x + 3)$

30.

$$\begin{array}{r|rrrrrr} 2 & 16 & -32 & 0 & 0 & -81 & 162 \\ & & 32 & 0 & 0 & 0 & -162 \\ \hline & 16 & 0 & 0 & 0 & -81 & \,|\,0 \end{array}$$

$16x^5 - 32x^4 - 81x + 162$
$\qquad = (x - 2)(16x^4 - 81)$
$\qquad = (x - 2)(4x^2 - 9)(4x^2 + 9)$
$\qquad = (x - 2)(2x - 3)(2x + 3)(4x^2 + 9)$

31. The graph shows that $x = -2$ and $x = 2$ are zeros of the function. Therefore, $x + 2$ and $x - 2$ or $(x + 2)(x - 2) = x^2 - 4$ are factors of the polynomial.

$$\begin{array}{r} x^2 + 1 \\ x^2 - 4\overline{)x^4 - 3x^2 - 4} \\ \underline{-\,(x^4 - 4x^2)} \\ x^2 - 4 \\ \underline{-\,(x^2 - 4)} \\ 0 \end{array}$$

Thus $x^4 - 3x^2 - 4 = (x + 2)(x - 2)(x^2 + 1)$.

32. $x^3 - 4x^2 - 29x - 24$

$$\begin{array}{r|rrrr} 8 & 1 & -4 & -29 & -24 \\ & & 8 & 32 & 24 \\ \hline & 1 & 4 & 3 & \,|\,0 \end{array}$$

$x^3 - 4x^2 - 29x - 24 = (x - 8)(x^2 + 4x + 3)$
$\qquad\qquad\qquad\qquad = (x - 8)(x + 1)(x + 3)$

33. $(x^2 - x + k) \div (x - 1)$
By the Remainder Theorem,
$(1)^2 - (1) + k = 3$
$\qquad 1 - 1 + k = 3$
$\qquad\qquad\quad k = 3$

34. $(x^2 + kx - 17) \div (x - 2)$
By the Remainder Theorem,
$(2)^2 + k(2) - 17 = 3$
$\quad 4 + 2k - 17 = 3$
$\qquad\quad 2k - 13 = 3$
$\qquad\qquad\quad 2k = 16$
$\qquad\qquad\quad\; k = 8$

35. $(x^2 + 5x + 7) \div (x + k)$
By the Remainder Theorem,
$(-k)^2 + 5(-k) + 7 = 3$
$\qquad k^2 - 5x + 7 = 3$
$\qquad k^2 - 5k + 4 = 0$
$\quad (k - 4)(k - 1) = 0$
$\quad k - 4 = 0 \quad \text{or } k - 1 = 0$
$\qquad k = 4 \qquad\qquad k = 1$

36. $(x^3 + 4x^2 + x + k) \div (x + 2)$
By the Remainder Theorem,
$(-2)^3 + 4(-2)^2 + (-2) + k = 3$
$\qquad -8 + 16 - 2 + k = 3$
$\qquad\qquad\quad 6 + k = 3$
$\qquad\qquad\qquad\quad k = -3$

37.

$$\begin{array}{r|rrrr} 5 & -14 & 69 & -140 & 100 \\ & & 5 & -45 & 120 & -100 \\ \hline & -9 & 24 & -20 & \,|\,0 \end{array}$$

38.

$$\begin{array}{r} x^3 - 9x^2 + 24x - 20 \\ x - 5\overline{)x^4 - 14x^3 + 69x^2 - 140x + 100} \\ \underline{-\,(x^4 - 5x^3)} \\ -9x^3 + 69x^2 - 140x + 100 \\ \underline{-\,(-9x^3 + 45x^2)} \\ 24x^2 - 140x + 100 \\ \underline{-\,(24x^2 - 120x)} \\ -20x + 100 \\ \underline{-\,(-20x + 100)} \\ 0 \end{array}$$

$(x^4 - 14x^3 + 69x^2 - 140x + 100)$
$\quad = (x - 5)(x^3 - 9x^2 + 24x - 20)$
$\quad = (x - 5)(x - 2)(x^2 - 7x + 10)$
$\quad = (x - 5)(x - 2)(x - 2)(x - 5)$

Since $x - 2$ is a factor of the polynomial, 2-ft lengths are extremely weak.

39. $f(1) = -0.5(1)^4 + 4(1)^3 - 12(1)^2 + 16(1)$
$= -0.5 + 4 - 12 + 16$
$= 7.5$ ft/s

$f(2) = -0.5(2)^4 + 4(2)^3 - 12(2)^2 + 16(2)$
$= -0.5(16) + 4(8) - 12(4) + 16(2)$
$= -8 + 32 - 48 + 32$
$= 8$ ft/s

$f(3) = -0.5(3)^4 + 4(3)^3 - 12(3)^2 + 16(3)$
$= -0.5(81) + 4(27) - 12(9) + 16(3)$
$= -40.5 + 108 - 108 + 48$
$= 7.5$ ft/s

40.

$$
\begin{array}{r|rrrrr}
4 & -0.5 & 4 & -12 & 16 & 0 \\
  &   & -2 & 8 & -16 & 0 \\
\hline
  & -0.5 & 2 & -4 & 0 & 0 \\
\end{array}
$$

Thus, the speed of the elevator is zero. In other words, it has stopped.

41. By the Remainder Theorem, the remainder when $f(x)$ is divided by $x - 1$ is equivalent to $f(1)$, or $a + b + c + d + e$. Since $a + b + c + d + e = 0$, the remainder when $f(x)$ is divided by $x - 1$ is 0. Therefore, $x - 1$ is a factor of $f(x)$.

42. $x = 1 + \dfrac{0.12}{12}$

$= 1.01$

$B(1.01) = 2000(1.01)^6 - 340[(1.01)^5 + (1.01)^4 + (1.01)^3 + (1.01)^2 + (1.01) + 1]$

$\approx 2000(1.0615202) - 340(6.1520151)$

$\approx 2123.0404 - 2091.685134$

$\approx \$31.36$

43. $x = 1 + \dfrac{0.096}{12}$

$= 1.008$

$B(1.008) = 2000(1.008)^6 - 340[(1.008)^5 + (1.008)^4 + (1.008)^3 + (1.008)^2 + (1.008) + 1]$

$\approx 2000(1.0489703) - 340(6.1212877)$

$\approx \$16.70$

44. The formula would be degree 5 instead of degree 6.

$B(x) = 2000x^5 - 340(x^4 + x^3 + x^2 + x + 1)$

45. $B(x) = 2000x^5 - 410(x^4 + x^3 + x^2 + x + 1)$

$x = 1 + \dfrac{0.108}{12}$

$= 1.009$

$B(1.009) = 2000(1.009)^5 - 410[(1.009)^4 + (1.009)^3 + (1.009)^2 + (1.009) + 1]$

$\approx 2000(1.0458173) - 410(5.0908137)$

$\approx 2091.6346 - 2087.233617$

$\approx \$4.40$

No, he will still owe $4.40.

46. Using the Remainder Theorem, you can evaluate a polynomial for a value a by dividing the polynomial by $(x - a)$ using synthetic division. Answers should include the following.

- It is easier to use the Remainder Theorem when you have polynomials of degree 2 and lower or when you have access to a calculator.
- The estimated number of international travelers to the U.S. in 2006 is 65.9 million.

47. D; $f(x) = x^2 + 7x + 12$
$= (x + 4)(x + 3)$

$x + 4 = 0$ or $x + 3 = 0$
$x = -4$ $x = -3$

48. Looking at the graph, the zeros of the function are $x = -2$, $x = 1$, and $x = 2$. Therefore, $(x - 2)$, $(x + 1)$, and $(x + 2)$ are factors of the polynomial function.
$(x - 2)(x + 2)(x + 1) = (x^2 - 4)(x + 1)$
$= x^3 + x^2 - 4x - 4$

$$
\begin{array}{r}
x^2 \qquad\quad + 1 \\
x^3 + x^2 - 4x - 4 \overline{)x^5 + x^4 - 3x^3 - 3x^2 - 4x - 4} \\
\underline{-(x^5 + x^4 - 4x^3 - 4x^2)} \\
x^3 + x^2 - 4x - 4 \\
\underline{-(x^3 + x^2 - 4x - 4)} \\
0
\end{array}
$$

Therefore, the other factor is $(x^2 + 1)$.

Page 370   Maintain Your Skills

49. $x^4 - 8x^2 + 4 = (x^2)^2 - 8(x^2) + 4$

50. $9d^6 + 5d^3 - 2 = 9(d^3)^2 + 5(d^3) - 2$

51. It is not possible to write this expression in quadradic form.

52.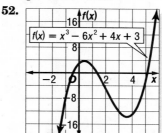

Sample answer: The relative maximum occurs at $x = 0.5$, and the relative minimum occurs at $x = 3.5$.

53.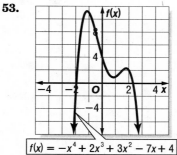

Sample answer: The relative maxima occur at $x = -1$ and $x = 1.5$, and the the relative minimum occurs at $x = 1$.

54. $F_c = m\left(\dfrac{4\pi^2 r}{T^2}\right)$

$T^2(F_c) = T^2\left[m\left(\dfrac{4\pi^2 r}{T^2}\right)\right]$

$T^2(F_c) = m(4\pi^2 r)$

$T^2 = \dfrac{4\pi^2 mr}{F_c}$

$T = \dfrac{2\pi\sqrt{mr}}{\sqrt{F_c}}$

$T = 2\pi\sqrt{\dfrac{mr}{F_c}}$

$T = \dfrac{2\pi\sqrt{mrF_c}}{F_c}$

55. $\begin{bmatrix} 7x \\ 12 \end{bmatrix} = \begin{bmatrix} 28 \\ -6y \end{bmatrix}$

$7x = 28$

$x = 4$

$12 = -6y$

$-2 = y$

Thus, the solution is $(4, -2)$.

56. $\begin{bmatrix} 5a + 2b \\ a - 7b \end{bmatrix} = \begin{bmatrix} -17 \\ 4 \end{bmatrix}$

$A = \begin{bmatrix} 5 & 2 \\ 1 & -7 \end{bmatrix}$

$A^{-1} = \frac{1}{-35 - 2} \begin{bmatrix} -7 & -2 \\ -1 & 5 \end{bmatrix}$

$\quad = \frac{1}{-37} \begin{bmatrix} -7 & -2 \\ -1 & 5 \end{bmatrix}$

$-\frac{1}{37} \begin{bmatrix} -7 & -2 \\ -1 & 5 \end{bmatrix} \begin{bmatrix} 5 & 2 \\ 1 & -7 \end{bmatrix} \begin{bmatrix} a \\ b \end{bmatrix} = -\frac{1}{37} \begin{bmatrix} -7 & -2 \\ -1 & 5 \end{bmatrix} \begin{bmatrix} -17 \\ 4 \end{bmatrix}$

$\begin{bmatrix} 1 & 0 \\ 0 & 1 \end{bmatrix} \begin{bmatrix} a \\ b \end{bmatrix} = \begin{bmatrix} -3 \\ -1 \end{bmatrix}$

$\begin{bmatrix} a \\ b \end{bmatrix} = \begin{bmatrix} -3 \\ -1 \end{bmatrix}$

Thus, the solution is $(-3, -1)$.

57. A

58. C

59. S

60. $x^2 + 7x + 8 = 0$

$x = \frac{-7 \pm \sqrt{(7)^2 - 4(1)(8)}}{2(1)}$

$x = \frac{-7 \pm \sqrt{17}}{2}$

$x = \frac{-7 + \sqrt{17}}{2}$ or $x = \frac{-7 - \sqrt{17}}{2}$

61. $3x^2 - 9x + 2 = 0$

$x = \frac{9 \pm \sqrt{(-9)^2 - 4(3)(2)}}{2(3)}$

$x = \frac{9 \pm \sqrt{57}}{6}$

$x = \frac{9 + \sqrt{57}}{6}$ or $x = \frac{9 - \sqrt{57}}{6}$

62. $2x^2 + 3x + 2 = 0$

$x = \frac{-3 \pm \sqrt{(3)^2 - 4(2)(2)}}{2(2)}$

$x = \frac{-3 \pm \sqrt{-7}}{4}$

$x = \frac{-3 \pm i\sqrt{7}}{4}$

$x = \frac{-3 + i\sqrt{7}}{4}$ or $x = \frac{-3 - i\sqrt{7}}{4}$

7-5 Roots and Zeros

Page 375   Check for Understanding

1. Sample answer: $p(x) = x^3 - 6x^2 + x + 1$; $p(x)$ has either 2 or 0 positive real zeros, 1 negative real zero, and 2 or 0 imaginary zeros.

2. An odd-degree function approaches positive infinity in one direction and negative infinity in the other direction, so the graph must cross the x-axis at least once, giving it at least one real root.

3. 6; By the Complex Conjugates Theorem $x = 5 - i$ and $x = 3 + 2i$ are also roots. Given these 6 roots, a polynomial equation with real coefficients must be of at least degree 6.

4. $\qquad x^2 + 4 = 0$

$(x - 2i)(x + 2i) = 0$

$x - 2i = 0$ or $x + 2i = 0$

$\quad x = 2i \qquad\qquad x = -2i$

2 imaginary roots

5. $x^3 + 4x^2 - 21x = 0$

$x(x^2 + 4x - 21) = 0$

$x(x + 7)(x - 3) = 0$

$x = 0$ or $x + 7 = 0$ or $x - 3 = 0$

$\qquad\qquad\qquad x = -7 \qquad\qquad x = 3$

3 real roots

6. $f(x) = 5x^3 + 8x^2 - 4x + 3$

$\qquad\qquad\quad$ no $\;$ yes $\;$ yes

$f(-x) = -5x^3 + 8x^2 + 4x + 3$

$\qquad\qquad\quad$ yes $\;$ no $\;$ no

0 or 2 positive real zeros(s)

1 negative real zero

0 or 2 imaginary zero(s)

7. $r(x) = x^5 - x^3 - x + 1$

$\qquad\qquad$ yes $\;$ no $\;$ yes

$r(-x) = -x^5 + x^3 + x + 1$

$\qquad\qquad$ yes $\;$ no $\;$ no

0 or 2 positive real zero(s)

1 negative real zero

2 or 4 imaginary zeros

8. $p(x) = x^3 + 2x^2 - 3x + 20$

$p(-x) = -x^3 + 2x^2 + 3x + 20$

Since $p(x)$ has 2 sign changes, the function has 2 or 0 positive real zeros. Since $p(-x)$ has 1 sign change, $p(x)$ has 1 negative real zero. Thus, $p(x)$ has either 3 real zeros, or 1 real zero and 2 imaginary zeros.

x	1	2	-3	20
-4	1	-2	5	0

$x^2 - 2x + 5 = 0$

$x = \frac{2 \pm \sqrt{(-2)^2 - 4(1)(5)}}{2(1)}$

$\quad = \frac{2 \pm \sqrt{-16}}{2}$

$\quad = \frac{2 \pm 4i}{2}$

$\quad = 1 \pm 2i$

Thus, the zeros of the function are -4 and $1 \pm 2i$.

9. $f(x) = x^3 - 4x^2 + 6x - 4$
$f(-x) = -x^3 - 4x^2 - 6x - 4$
Since $f(x)$ has 3 sign changes, the function has 3 or 1 positive real zeros. Since $f(-x)$ has no sign changes, $f(x)$ has no negative real zeros. Thus, $f(x)$ has either 3 real zeros, or 1 real zero and 2 imaginary zeros.

x	1	−4	6	−4
2	1	−2	2	0

$x^2 - 2x + 2 = 0$
$x = \dfrac{2 \pm \sqrt{(-2)^2 - 4(1)(2)}}{2(1)}$
$= \dfrac{2 \pm \sqrt{-4}}{2}$
$= \dfrac{2 \pm 2i}{2}$
$= 1 \pm i$
Thus, the zeros of the function are 2 and $1 \pm i$.

10. $v(x) = x^3 - 3x^2 + 4x - 12$
$v(-x) = -x^3 - 3x^2 - 4x - 12$
Since $v(x)$ has 3 sign changes, the function has 3 or 1 positive real zeros. Since $v(-x)$ has no sign changes, $v(x)$ has no negative zeros. Thus, $v(x)$ has either 3 real zeros, or 1 real zero and 2 imaginary zeros.

x	1	−3	4	−12
3	1	0	4	0

$x^2 + 4 = 0$
$x^2 = -4$
$x = \pm 2i$
Thus, the zeros of the function are 3 and $\pm 2i$.

11. $f(x) = x^3 - 3x^2 + 9x + 13$
$f(-x) = -x^3 - 3x^2 - 9x + 13$
Since $f(x)$ has 2 sign changes, the function has 2 or 0 positive real zeros. Since $f(-x)$ has 1 sign change, $f(x)$ has 1 negative real zero. Thus, $f(x)$ has either 3 real zeros, or 1 real zero and 2 imaginary zeros.

x	1	−3	9	13
−1	1	−4	13	0

$x^2 - 4x + 13 = 0$
$x = \dfrac{4 \pm \sqrt{(-4)^2 - 4(1)(13)}}{2(1)}$
$= \dfrac{4 \pm \sqrt{-36}}{2}$
$= \dfrac{4 \pm 6i}{2}$
$= 2 \pm 3i$
Thus, the zeros of the function are -1 and $2 \pm 3i$.

12. The zeros of $f(x)$ are $x = 2$, $x = 4i$, and by the Complex Conjugates Theorem, $x = -4i$. This means the factors of $f(x)$ are $x - 2$, $x - 4i$, and $x + 4i$, so
$f(x) = (x - 2)(x - 4i)(x + 4i)$
$= (x - 2)(x^2 + 16)$
$= x^3 - 2x^2 + 16x - 32$.

Pages 375–377   Practice and Apply

13. $3x + 8 = 0$
$3x + 8 - 8 = 0 - 8$
$3x = -8$
$\dfrac{3x}{3} = \dfrac{-8}{3}$
$x = -\dfrac{8}{3}$
The equation has one real root.

14. $2x^2 - 5x + 12 = 0$
$x = \dfrac{5 \pm \sqrt{(-5)^2 - 4(2)(12)}}{2(2)}$
$= \dfrac{5 \pm \sqrt{-71}}{4}$
$= \dfrac{5 \pm i\sqrt{71}}{4}$
The equation has two imaginary roots.

15. $x^3 + 9x = 0$
$x(x^2 + 9) = 0$
$x(x - 3i)(x + 3i) = 0$
$x = 0$ or $x - 3i = 0$ or $x + 3i = 0$
$\qquad\qquad x = 3i \qquad\quad x = -3i$
The equation has one real root and two imaginary roots.

16. $x^4 - 81 = 0$
$(x^2 + 9)(x^2 - 9) = 0$
$x^2 + 9 = 0$ or $x^2 - 9 = 0$
$\quad x^2 = -9 \qquad\qquad x^2 = 9$
$\quad x = -\sqrt{9} \qquad\qquad x = \sqrt{9}$
$\quad x = 3i$ or $-3i \qquad x = 3$ or -3
The equation has two real roots and two imaginary roots.

17. $x^4 - 16 = 0$
$(x^2 - 4)(x^2 + 4) = 0$
$(x - 2)(x + 2)(x + 2i)(x - 2i) = 0$
$x - 2 = 0$ or $x + 2 = 0$
$\quad x = 2 \qquad\quad x = -2$
or $x + 2i = 0$ or $x - 2i = 0$
$\qquad x = -2i \qquad\quad x = 2i$
The equation has two real and two imaginary roots.

18. $x^5 - 8x^3 + 16x = 0$
$x(x^4 - 8x^2 + 16) = 0$
$x(x^2 - 4)(x^2 - 4) = 0$
$x(x - 2)(x + 2)(x - 2)(x + 2) = 0$
$x = 0$ or $x - 2 = 0$ or $x + 2 = 0$
$\qquad\qquad x = 2 \qquad\quad x = -2$
or $x - 2 = 0$ or $x + 2 = 0$
$\quad x = 2 \qquad\quad x = -2$
The equation has five real roots.

19. $f(x) = x^3 - 6x + 1$
$\qquad\qquad\underbrace{\quad}\ \underbrace{\quad}$
$\qquad\qquad\;$ yes yes
$f(-x) = -x^3 + 6x + 1$
$\qquad\qquad\quad\underbrace{\quad}\ \underbrace{\quad}$
$\qquad\qquad\qquad$ yes no
Number of positive real zeros: 2 or 0
Number of negative real zeros: 1
Number of imaginary zeros: 2 or 0

20. $g(x) = 5x^3 + 8x^2 - 4x + 3$

             no   yes yes

$g(-x) = -5x^3 + 8x^2 + 4x + 3$

             yes   no no

Number of positive real zeros: 2 or 0
Number of negative real zeros: 1
Number of imaginary zeros: 2 or 0

21. $h(x) = 4x^3 - 6x^2 + 8x - 5$

             yes   yes yes

$h(-x) = -4x^3 - 6x^2 - 8x - 5$

             no   no no

Number of positive real zeros: 3 or 1
Number of negative real zeros: 0
Number of imaginary zeros: 2 or 0

22. $q(x) = x^4 + 5x^3 + 2x^2 - 7x - 9$

             no   no yes no

$q(-x) = x^4 - 5x^3 + 2x^2 + 7x - 9$

             yes   yes no yes

Number of positive real zeros: 1
Number of negative real zeros: 3 or 1
Number of imaginary zeros: 2 or 0

23. $p(x) = x^5 - 6x^4 - 3x^3 + 7x^2 - 8x + 1$

             yes   no yes yes yes

$p(-x) = -x^5 - 6x^4 + 3x^3 + 7x^2 + 8x + 1$

             no   yes no no no

Number of positive real zeros: 4, 2, or 0
Number of negative real zeros: 1
Number of imaginary zeros: 4, 2, or 0

24. $f(x) = x^{10} - x^8 + x^6 - x^4 + x^2 - 1$

             yes yes yes yes yes

$f(-x) = x^{10} - x^8 + x^6 - x^4 + x^2 - 1$

             yes yes yes yes yes

Number of positive real zeros: 5, 3, or 1
Number of negative real zeros: 5, 3, or 1
Number of imaginary zeros: 0, 2, 4, 6, or 8

25. $g(x) = x^3 + 6x^2 + 21x + 26$

$g(-x) = -x^3 + 6x^2 - 21x + 26$

Since $g(x)$ has no sign changes, there are no positive real zeros. Since $g(-x)$ has 3 sign changes, $g(x)$ has 3 or 1 negative real zeros. Thus, $g(x)$ has either 3 real zeros, or 1 real zero and 2 imaginary zeros.

x	1	6	21	26
-2	1	4	13	0

$x^2 + 4x + 13 = 0$

$x = \dfrac{-4 \pm \sqrt{(4)^2 - 4(1)(13)}}{2(1)}$

$\quad = \dfrac{-4 \pm \sqrt{-36}}{2}$

$\quad = \dfrac{-4 \pm 6i}{2}$

$\quad = -2 \pm 3i$

Thus, the zeros of the function are -2 and $-2 \pm 3i$.

26. $h(x) = x^3 - 6x^2 + 10x - 8$

$h(-x) = -x^3 - 6x^2 - 10x - 8$

Since $h(x)$ has 3 sign changes, the function has 3 or 1 positive real zeros. Since $h(-x)$ has no sign changes, $h(x)$ has no negative real zeros. Thus, $h(x)$ has either 3 real zeros, or 1 real zero and 2 imaginary zeros.

x	1	-6	10	-8
4	1	-2	2	0

$x^2 - 2x + 2 = 0$

$x = \dfrac{2 \pm \sqrt{(-2)^2 - 4(1)(2)}}{2(1)}$

$\quad = \dfrac{2 \pm \sqrt{-4}}{2}$

$\quad = \dfrac{2 \pm 2i}{2}$

$\quad = 1 \pm i$

Thus, the zeros of the function are 4 and $1 \pm i$.

27. $h(x) = 4x^4 + 17x^2 + 4$

$h(-x) = 4x^4 + 17x^2 + 4$

Since $h(x)$ has no sign changes, the function has no positive real zeros. Since $h(-x)$ has no sign changes, $h(x)$ has no negative real zeros. Thus, $h(x)$ has 4 imaginary zeros.

$4x^4 + 17x^2 + 4 = 0$

$4(x^2)^2 + 17(x^2) + 4 = 0$

$x^2 = \dfrac{-17 \pm \sqrt{(17)^2 - 4(4)(4)}}{2(4)}$

$x^2 = \dfrac{-17 \pm \sqrt{225}}{8}$

$x^2 = \dfrac{-17 \pm 15}{8}$

$x^2 = \dfrac{-17 + 15}{8}$ or $x^2 = \dfrac{-17 - 15}{8}$

$x^2 = -\dfrac{1}{4} \qquad\qquad x^2 = -4$

$x = \pm\dfrac{i}{2} \qquad\qquad x = \pm 2i$

Thus, the zeros of the function are $\pm\dfrac{i}{2}$ and $\pm 2i$.

28. $f(x) = x^3 - 7x^2 + 25x - 175$

$f(x) = -x^3 - 7x^2 - 25x - 175$

Since $f(x)$ has 3 sign changes, the function has 3 or 1 positive real zeros. Since $f(-x)$ has no sign changes, $f(x)$ has no negative real zeros. Thus, $f(x)$ has either 3 real zeros, or 1 real zero and 2 imaginary zeros.

x	1	-7	25	-175
7	1	0	25	0

$x^2 + 25 = 0$

$x^2 = -25$

$x = \pm 5i$

Thus, the zeros of the function are 7 and $\pm 5i$.

29. $g(x) = 2x^3 - x^2 + 28x + 51$

$g(-x) = -2x^3 - x^2 - 28x + 51$

Since $g(x)$ has 2 sign changes, the function has 2 or 0 positive real zeros. Since $g(-x)$ has 1 sign change, $g(x)$ has 1 negative real zero. Thus, $g(x)$ has either 3 real zeros, or 1 real zero and 2 imaginary zeros.

x	2	−1	28	51
$-\frac{3}{2}$	2	−4	54	0

$2x^2 - 4x + 54 = 0$

$2(x^2 - 2x + 27) = 0$

$x^2 - 2x + 27 = 0$

$x = \frac{2 \pm \sqrt{(-2)^2 - 4(1)(27)}}{2(1)}$

$= \frac{2 \pm \sqrt{-104}}{2}$

$= \frac{2 \pm 2i\sqrt{26}}{2}$

$= 1 \pm i\sqrt{26}$

Thus, the zeros of the function are $-\frac{3}{2}$ and $1 \pm i\sqrt{26}$.

30. $q(x) = 2x^3 - 17x^2 + 90x - 41$

$q(-x) = -2x^3 - 17x^2 - 90x - 41$

Since $q(x)$ has 3 sign changes, the function has 3 or 1 positive real zeros. Since $q(-x)$ has no sign changes, $q(x)$ has no negative real zeros. Thus, $q(x)$ has either 3 real zeros, or 1 real zero and 2 imaginary zeros.

x	2	−17	90	−41
$-\frac{1}{2}$	2	−16	82	0

$2x^2 - 16x + 82 = 0$

$2(x^2 - 8x + 41) = 0$

$x^2 - 8x + 41 = 0$

$x = \frac{8 \pm \sqrt{(-8)^2 - 4(1)(41)}}{2(1)}$

$= \frac{8 \pm \sqrt{-100}}{2}$

$= \frac{8 \pm 10i}{2}$

$= 4 \pm 5i$

Thus, the zeros of the function are $\frac{1}{2}$ and $4 \pm 5i$.

31. $f(x) = x^3 - 5x^2 - 7x + 51$

$f(-x) = -x^3 - 5x^2 + 7x + 51$

Since $f(x)$ has 2 sign changes, the function has 2 or 0 positive real zeros. Since $f(-x)$ has 1 sign change, $f(x)$ has 1 negative real zero. Thus, $f(x)$ has either 3 real zeros, or 1 real zero and 2 imaginary zeros.

x	1	−5	−7	51
−3	1	−8	17	0

$x^2 - 8x + 17 = 0$

$x = \frac{8 \pm \sqrt{(-8)^2 - 4(1)(17)}}{2(1)}$

$= \frac{8 \pm \sqrt{-4}}{2}$

$= \frac{8 \pm 2i}{2}$

$= 4 \pm i$

Thus, the zeros of the function are -3 and $4 \pm i$.

32. $p(x) = x^4 - 9x^3 + 24x^2 - 6x - 40$

$p(-x) = x^4 + 9x^3 + 24x^2 + 6x - 40$

Since $p(x)$ has 3 sign changes, the function has 3 or 1 positive real zeros. Since $p(-x)$ has 1 sign change, $p(x)$ has 1 negative real zero. Thus, $p(x)$ has either 4 real zeros, or 2 real zeros and 2 imaginary zeros.

x	1	−9	24	−6	−40
−1	1	−10	34	−40	0
4	1	−5	4	10	0

$(x + 1)(x - 4) = x^2 - 3x - 4$

$$
\begin{array}{r}
x^2 - 6x + 10 \\
x^2 - 3x - 4\overline{)x^4 - 9x^3 + 24x^2 - 6x - 40} \\
\underline{-(x^4 - 3x^3 - 4x^2)} \\
-6x^3 + 28x^2 - 6x - 40 \\
\underline{-(-6x^3 + 18x^2 + 24x)} \\
10x^2 - 30x - 40 \\
\underline{-(10x^2 - 30x - 40)} \\
0
\end{array}
$$

$x^2 - 6x + 10 = 0$

$x = \frac{6 \pm \sqrt{(-6)^2 - 4(1)(10)}}{2(1)}$

$= \frac{6 \pm \sqrt{-4}}{2}$

$= \frac{6 \pm 2i}{2}$

$= 3 \pm i$

Thus, the zeros of the function are -1, 4, and $3 \pm i$.

33. $r(x) = x^4 - 6x^3 + 12x^2 + 6x - 13$

$r(-x) = x^4 + 6x^3 + 12x^2 - 6x - 13$

Since $r(x)$ has 3 sign changes, the function has 3 or 1 positive real zeros. Since $r(-x)$ has 1 sign change, $r(x)$ has 1 negative real zero. Thus, $r(x)$ has either 4 real zeros, or 2 real zeros and 2 imaginary zeros.

x	1	−6	12	6	−13
−1	1	−7	19	−13	0
1	1	−5	7	13	0

$(x + 1)(x - 1) = x^2 - 1$

$$
\begin{array}{r}
x^2 - 6x + 13 \\
x^2 - 1\overline{)x^4 - 6x^3 + 12x^2 + 6x - 13} \\
\underline{-(x^4 + 0x^3 - x^2)} \\
-6x^3 + 13x^2 + 6x - 13 \\
\underline{-(-6x^3 + 0x^2 + 6x)} \\
13x^2 + 0x - 13 \\
\underline{-(13x^2 + 0x - 13)} \\
0
\end{array}
$$

$x^2 - 6x + 13 = 0$

$x = \frac{6 \pm \sqrt{(-6)^2 - 4(1)(13)}}{2(1)}$

$= \frac{6 \pm \sqrt{-16}}{2}$

$= \frac{6 \pm 4i}{2}$

$= 3 \pm 2i$

Thus, the zeros of the function are -1, 1, and $3 \pm 2i$.

34. $h(x) = x^4 - 15x^3 + 70x^2 - 70x - 156$
$h(-x) = x^4 + 15x^3 + 70x^2 + 70x - 156$
Since $h(x)$ has 3 sign changes, the function has 3 positive real zeros. Since $h(-x)$ has 1 sign change, $h(x)$ has 1 negative real zero. Thus, $h(x)$ has either 4 real zeros, or 2 real zeros and 2 imaginary zeros.

x	1	−15	70	−70	−156
−1	1	−16	86	−156	0
6	1	−9	16	26	0

$(x + 1)(x - 6) = x^2 - 5x - 6$

$$
\begin{array}{r}
x^2 - 10x + 26 \\
x^2 - 5x - 6 \overline{)x^4 - 15x^3 + 70x^2 - 70x - 156} \\
\underline{-(x^4 - 5x^3 - 6x^2)} \\
-10x^3 + 76x^2 - 70x - 156 \\
\underline{-(-10x^3 + 50x^2 + 60x)} \\
26x^2 - 130x - 156 \\
\underline{-(26x^2 - 130x - 156)} \\
0
\end{array}
$$

$x^2 - 10x + 26 = 0$

$x = \dfrac{10 \pm \sqrt{(-10)^2 - 4(1)(26)}}{2(1)}$

$= \dfrac{10 \pm \sqrt{-4}}{2}$

$= \dfrac{10 \pm 2i}{2}$

$= 5 \pm i$

Thus, the zeros of the function are −1, 6, and $5 \pm i$.

35. $f(x) = (x + 4)(x - 1)(x - 5)$
$= (x^2 + 3x - 4)(x - 5)$
$= x^3 - 5x^2 + 3x^2 - 15x - 4x + 20$
$= x^3 - 2x^2 - 19x + 20$

36. $f(x) = (x + 2)(x - 2)(x - 4)(x - 6)$
$= (x^2 - 4)(x^2 - 10x + 24)$
$= x^4 - 10x^3 + 24x^2 - 4x^2 + 40x - 96$
$= x^4 - 10x^3 + 20x^2 + 40x - 96$

37. $f(x) = (x - 4i)(x + 4i)(x - 3)(x + 3)$
$= (x^2 + 16)(x^2 - 9)$
$= x^4 + 7x^2 - 144$

38. $f(x) = (x - 2i)(x + 2i)(x - 3i)(x + 3i)(x - 1)$
$= (x^2 + 4)(x^2 + 9)(x - 1)$
$= (x^4 + 13x^2 + 36)(x - 1)$
$= x^5 + 13x^3 + 36x - x^4 - 13x^2 - 36$
$= x^5 - x^4 + 13x^3 - 13x^2 + 36x - 36$

39. $f(x) = (x - 9)(x - 1 - 2i)(x - 1 + 2i)$
$= (x - 9)[(x - 1)^2 - (2i)^2)]$
$= (x - 9)(x^2 - 2x + 1 + 4)$
$= (x - 9)(x^2 - 2x + 5)$
$= x^3 - 2x^2 + 5x - 9x^2 + 18x - 45$
$= x^3 - 11x^2 + 23x - 45$

40. $f(x) = (x - 6)(x - 2 - 2i)(x - 2 + 2i)$
$= (x - 6)[(x - 2)^2 - (2i)^2]$
$= (x - 6)(x^2 - 4x + 4 + 4)$
$= (x - 6)(x^2 - 4x + 8)$
$= x^3 - 4x^2 + 8x - 6x^2 + 24x - 48$
$= x^3 - 10x^2 + 32x - 48$

41a.
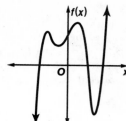

41b.
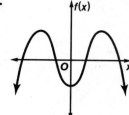

41c.
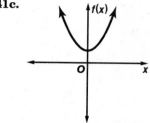

42.
$(3 - x)(4 - x)(5 - x) = 24$
$(x^2 - 7x + 12)(5 - x) = 24$
$5x^2 - 35x + 60 - x^3 + 7x^2 - 12x - 24 = 0$
$-x^3 + 12x^2 - 47x + 36 = 0$

43. $-x^3 + 12x^2 - 47x + 36 = 0$

$$
\begin{array}{r|rrrr}
1 & -1 & 12 & -47 & 36 \\
& & -1 & 11 & -36 \\
\hline
& -1 & 11 & -36 & 0
\end{array}
$$

1 is a solution of the equation.
1 foot should be added to each dimension.

44. $V(r) = \pi r^2(r + 17)$
$= \pi r^3 + 17\pi r^2$

45.
$\pi r^3 + 17\pi r^3 = 336\pi$
$r^3 + 17r^2 - 336 = 0$
$(r - 4)(r^2 + 21r + 84) = 0$
$r - 4 = 0$
$r = 4$
radius = 4 m   height = 4 + 17
$= 21$ m

46. $d(x) = -0.006x^4 - 0.15x^3 - 0.05x^2 + 1.8x$
$\underbrace{}_{\text{no}} \underbrace{}_{\text{no}} \underbrace{}_{\text{yes}}$

$d(-x) = -0.006x^4 + 0.15x^3 - 0.05x^2 - 1.8x$
$\underbrace{}_{\text{yes}} \underbrace{}_{\text{yes}} \underbrace{}_{\text{no}}$

Number of possible positive real zeros: 1
Number of possible negative real zeros: 2 or 0
Number of possible imaginary zeros: 2 or 0

47. $x = -24.1, x = -4, x = 0, x = 3.1$

$[-30, 10]$ scl: 5 by $[-20, 20]$ scl: 5

48. Nonnegative roots represent times when there is no concentration of dye registering on the monitor.

49. Sample answer: $f(x) = x^3 - 6x^2 + 5x + 12$ and $g(x) = 2x^3 - 12x^2 + 10x + 24$ each have zeros at $x = 4, x = -1,$ and $x = 3$.

50. One root is a double root.

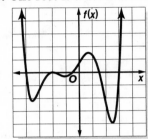

51. If the equation models the level of a medication in a patient's bloodstream, a doctor can use the roots of the equation to determine how often the patient should take the medication to maintain the necessary concentration in the body. Answers should include the following.

- A graph of this equation reveals that only the first positive real root of the equation, 5, has meaning for this situation, since the next positive real root occurs after the medication level in the bloodstream has dropped below 0 mg. Thus according to this model, after 5 hours there is no significant amount of medicine left in the bloodstream.

- The patient should not go more than 5 hours before taking their next dose of medication.

52. A;
$$x^4 - 1 = 0$$
$$(x^2 - 1)(x^2 + 1) = 0$$
$$(x - 1)(x + 1)(x - i)(x + i) = 0$$
$$x - 1 = 0 \text{ or } x + 1 = 0 \text{ or } x - i = 0 \text{ or } x + i = 0$$
$$x = 1 \qquad x = -1 \qquad x = i \qquad x = -i$$

53. C; $f(-x) = -x^5 - 2x^4 + 4x^3 + 4x^2 + 5x + 6$
no yes no no no

Page 377   Maintain Your Skills

54. $f(x) = x^3 - 5x^2 + 16x - 7$
$$f(-3) = (-3)^3 - 5(-3)^2 + 16(-3) - 7$$
$$= -27 - 45 - 48 - 7$$
$$= -127$$
$$f(4) = 4^3 - 5(4^2) + 16(4) - 7$$
$$= 64 - 80 + 64 - 7$$
$$= 41$$

55. $f(x) = x^4 + 11x^3 - 3x^2 + 2x - 5$
$$f(-3) = (-3)^4 + 11(-3)^3 - 3(-3)^2 + 2(-3) - 5$$
$$= 81 - 297 - 27 - 6 - 5$$
$$= -254$$
$$f(4) = (4)^4 + 11(4)^3 - 3(4)^2 + 2(4) - 5$$
$$= 256 + 704 - 48 + 8 - 5$$
$$= 915$$

56. $f(x) = 4x^3 - 168x^2 + 1728x$
$$= x(4x^2 - 168x + 1728)$$
$$= x(48 - 2x)(36 - 2x)$$
So, the width is 36 in.

57. $f(x) = x^2 - 8x + 3$
$$x = -\frac{b}{2a}$$
$$x = -\frac{-8}{2}$$
$$x = 4$$
$$f(4) = (4)^2 - 8(4) + 3$$
$$= 16 - 32 + 3$$
$$= -13$$
The minimum value of $f(x)$ is -13.

58. $f(x) = -3x^2 - 18x + 5$
$$x = -\frac{b}{2a}$$
$$x = -\frac{-18}{2(-3)}$$
$$x = -3$$
$$f(-3) = -3(-3)^2 - 18(-3) + 5$$
$$= -27 + 54 + 5$$
$$= 32$$
The maximum of $f(x)$ is 32.

59. $f(x) = -7 + 4x^2$
$$x = -\frac{0}{8}$$
$$x = 0$$
$$f(0) = -7 + 4(0)^2$$
$$= -7$$
The minimum of $f(x)$ is -7.

60. $15a^2b^2 - 5ab^2c^2$
$$15a^2b^2 - 5ab^2c^2 = 5ab^2(3a - c^2)$$

61. $12p^2 - 64p + 45$
$$12p^2 - 64p + 45 = 12p^2 - 54p - 10p + 45$$
$$= 6p(2p - q) - 5(2p - q)$$
$$= (2p - q)(6p - 5)$$

62. $4y^3 + 24y^2 + 36y$
$$4y^3 + 24y^2 + 36y = 4y(y^2 + 6y + 9)$$
$$= 4y(y + 3)^2$$

63. $A = \begin{bmatrix} -4 & 4 \\ 2 & -3 \\ 1 & 5 \end{bmatrix}$ and $D = \begin{bmatrix} 1 & -2 \\ 1 & -1 \\ -3 & 4 \end{bmatrix}$

$$A + D = \begin{bmatrix} -4 & 4 \\ 2 & -3 \\ 1 & 5 \end{bmatrix} + \begin{bmatrix} 1 & -2 \\ 1 & -1 \\ -3 & 4 \end{bmatrix}$$

$$= \begin{bmatrix} -3 & 2 \\ 3 & -4 \\ -2 & 9 \end{bmatrix}$$

64. $B = \begin{bmatrix} 7 & 0 \\ 4 & 1 \\ 6 & -2 \end{bmatrix}$ and $C = \begin{bmatrix} -4 & -5 \\ -3 & 1 \\ 2 & 3 \end{bmatrix}$

$$B - C = \begin{bmatrix} 7 & 0 \\ 4 & 1 \\ 6 & -2 \end{bmatrix} - \begin{bmatrix} -4 & -5 \\ -3 & 1 \\ 2 & 3 \end{bmatrix}$$

$$= \begin{bmatrix} 11 & 5 \\ 7 & 0 \\ 4 & -15 \end{bmatrix}$$

65. $3B - 2A = 3\begin{bmatrix} 7 & 0 \\ 4 & 1 \\ 6 & -2 \end{bmatrix} - 2\begin{bmatrix} -4 & 4 \\ 2 & -3 \\ 1 & 5 \end{bmatrix}$

$$= \begin{bmatrix} 21 & 0 \\ 12 & 3 \\ 18 & -6 \end{bmatrix} + \begin{bmatrix} 8 & -8 \\ -4 & 6 \\ -2 & -10 \end{bmatrix}$$

$$= \begin{bmatrix} 29 & -8 \\ 8 & 9 \\ 16 & -16 \end{bmatrix}$$

66. Let $A(0, -1)$ and $B(-3, 1)$.

$m = \dfrac{1 + 1}{-3 + 0}$

$\quad = \dfrac{2}{-3}$

$\quad = -\dfrac{2}{3}$

$y - 1 = -\dfrac{2}{3}(x + 3)$

$\quad\quad y = -\dfrac{2}{3}x - 2 + 1$

$\quad\quad y = -\dfrac{2}{3}x - 1$

$\quad\quad y \geq -\dfrac{2}{3}x - 1$

67. $a = \{1, 5\}, b = \{1, 2\}$

$\pm\dfrac{a}{b} = \left\{ \pm 1, \pm\dfrac{1}{2}, \pm 5, \pm\dfrac{5}{2} \right\}$

68. $a = \{1, 2\}, b = \{1, 2, 7, 14\}$

$\pm\dfrac{a}{b} = \left\{ \pm 1, \pm\dfrac{1}{2}, \pm\dfrac{1}{7}, \pm\dfrac{1}{14}, \pm 2, \pm\dfrac{2}{7} \right\}$

69. $a = \{1, 3\}, b = \{1, 3, 9\}$

$\pm\dfrac{a}{b} = \left\{ \pm\dfrac{1}{1}, \pm\dfrac{1}{3}, \pm\dfrac{1}{9}, \pm\dfrac{3}{1}, \pm\dfrac{3}{3}, \pm\dfrac{3}{9} \right\}$

$\quad\quad = \left\{ \pm 1, \pm\dfrac{1}{3}, \pm\dfrac{1}{9}, \pm 3 \right\}$

70. $a = \{1, 2, 4\}, b = \{1, 2, 4, 8, 16\}$

$\pm\dfrac{a}{b} = \left\{ \pm\dfrac{1}{1}, \pm\dfrac{1}{2}, \pm\dfrac{1}{4}, \pm\dfrac{1}{8}, \pm\dfrac{1}{16}, \pm\dfrac{2}{1}, \pm\dfrac{2}{2}, \pm\dfrac{2}{4}, \pm\dfrac{2}{8}, \right.$

$\quad\quad\quad \left. \pm\dfrac{2}{16}, \pm\dfrac{4}{1}, \pm\dfrac{4}{2}, \pm\dfrac{4}{4}, \pm\dfrac{4}{8}, \pm\dfrac{4}{16} \right\}$

$\quad\quad = \left\{ \pm 1, \pm\dfrac{1}{2}, \pm\dfrac{1}{4}, \pm\dfrac{1}{8}, \pm\dfrac{1}{16}, \pm 2, \pm 4 \right\}$

7-6   Rational Zero Theorem

Page 380   Check for Understanding

1. Sample answer: You limit the number of possible solutions.

2. Sample answer: $2x^2 - 8x + 3$

3. Luis is correct. Lauren found rational numbers in the form $\frac{q}{p}$, not $\frac{p}{q}$ as Luis did according to the Rational Zero Theorem.

4. $p(x) = x^4 - 10$
   p is a factor of -10.
   q is a factor of 1.
   The possible values of p are: $\pm 1, \pm 2, \pm 5, \pm 10$.
   The possible values of q are: ± 1.
   So, $\frac{p}{q} = \{\pm 1, \pm 2, \pm 5, \pm 10\}$.

5. $d(x) = 6x^3 + 6x^2 - 15x - 2$
   p is a factor of -2.
   q is a factor of 6.
   The possible values of p are: $\pm 1, \pm 2$.
   The possible values of q are: $\pm 1, \pm 2, \pm 3, \pm 6$.
   So, $\frac{p}{q} = \left\{ \pm 1, \pm 2, \pm\frac{1}{2}, \pm\frac{1}{3}, \pm\frac{1}{6}, \pm\frac{2}{3} \right\}$.

6. $p(x) = x^3 - 5x^2 - 22x + 56$
   The possible rational zeros are $\pm 1, \pm 2, \pm 4, \pm 7, \pm 8, \pm 14, \pm 28$, and ± 56.

$\frac{p}{q}$	1	-5	-22	56
-2	1	-7	-8	88
-4	1	-9	14	0
2	1	-3	-28	0
4	1	-1	-28	-48
7	1	2	-8	0

The Rational Zeros are -4, 2, and 7.

7. $f(x) = x^3 - x^2 - 34x - 56$
   The possible rational zeros are $\pm 1, \pm 2, \pm 4, \pm 7, \pm 8, \pm 14, \pm 28$, and ± 56.

$\frac{p}{q}$	1	-1	-34	-56
-4	1	-5	-14	0
-2	1	-3	-28	0
2	1	1	-32	-110
4	1	3	-22	-144
7	1	6	8	0

The Rational Zeros are -4, -2, and 7.

8. $t(x) = x^4 - 13x^2 + 36$
   The possible rational zeros are $\pm 1, \pm 2, \pm 3, \pm 4, \pm 9, \pm 12, \pm 18$, and ± 36.

$\frac{p}{q}$	1	0	-13	0	36
-3	1	-3	-4	12	0
-2	1	-2	-9	18	0
1	1	1	-13	-13	24
2	1	2	-9	-18	0
3	1	3	-4	-12	0

The Rational Zeros are -3, -2, 2, and 3.

9. $f(x) = 2x^3 - 7x^2 - 8x + 28$

The possible rational zeros are ± 1, $\pm\frac{1}{2}$, ± 2, $\pm\frac{7}{2}$, ± 4, ± 7, ± 14, and ± 28.

$\frac{p}{q}$	2	−7	−8	28
−2	2	−11	14	0
−3	2	−13	−30	−62
2	2	−3	−14	0
3	2	−1	−11	−5
$\frac{7}{2}$	2	0	−8	0

The Rational Zeros are -2, 2 and $\frac{7}{2}$.

10. $f(x) = 6x^3 + 5x^2 - 9x + 2$

The possible rational zeros are ± 1, $\pm\frac{1}{3}$, $\pm\frac{1}{2}$, $\pm\frac{1}{6}$, $\pm\frac{2}{3}$, and ± 2.

$\frac{p}{q}$	6	5	−9	2
−1	6	−1	−8	10
$\frac{2}{3}$	6	9	−3	0
1	6	11	2	4

So, $\frac{2}{3}$ is a rational zero. That is, $x - \frac{2}{3}$ is a factor of $f(x)$.

$$
\begin{array}{r}
6x^2 + 9x - 3 \\
x - \frac{2}{3} \overline{\smash{)}\,6x^3 + 5x^2 - 9x + 2} \\
-\,(6x^3 - 4x^2) \\
\hline
9x^2 - 9x \\
-\,(9x^2 - 6x) \\
\hline
-3x + 2 \\
-\,(-3x + 2) \\
\hline
0
\end{array}
$$

$6x^2 + 9x - 3 = 0$

$x = \dfrac{-9 \pm \sqrt{81 - 4(6)(-3)}}{12}$

$x = \dfrac{-9 \pm 3\sqrt{17}}{12}$

$x = \dfrac{-3 \pm \sqrt{17}}{4}$

The zeros of $f(x)$ are $\frac{2}{3}$, $\dfrac{-3 \pm \sqrt{17}}{4}$.

11.

$\ell(\ell + 1)(\ell + 3) = 1430$

$\ell(\ell^2 + 4\ell + 3) - 1430 = 0$

$\ell^3 + 4\ell^2 + 3\ell - 1430 = 0$

$\frac{p}{q}$	1	4	3	−1430
10	1	14	143	0
11	1	15	168	418
13	1	17	224	1482

So, $\ell = 10$. Therefore, the dimensions are 10 cm × 11 cm × 13 cm.

Pages 381–382 Practice and Apply

12. $f(x) = x^3 + 6x + 2$

The possible values of p are ± 1 and ± 2.

The possible values of q are ± 1.

Thus, the possible rational zeros of the function are ± 2 and ± 1.

13. $h(x) = x^3 + 8x + 6$

The possible values of p are ± 1, ± 2, ± 3 and ± 6.

The possible values of q are ± 1.

Thus, the possible rational zeros of the function are ± 1, ± 2, ± 3, and ± 6.

14. $f(x) = 3x^4 + 15$

The possible values of p are ± 1, ± 3, ± 5, and ± 15.

The possible values of q are ± 1 and ± 3.

Thus, the possible rational zeros of the function are ± 1, ± 3, ± 5, ± 15, $\pm\frac{1}{3}$, and $\pm\frac{5}{3}$.

15. $n(x) = x^5 + 6x^3 - 12x + 18$

The possible values of p are ± 1, ± 2, ± 3, ± 6, ± 9 and ± 18.

The possible values of q are ± 1.

Thus, the possible rational zeros of the function are ± 1, ± 2, ± 3, ± 6, ± 9, and ± 18.

16. $p(x) = 3x^3 - 5x^2 - 11x + 3$

The possible values of p are ± 1 and ± 3.

The possible values of q are ± 1 and ± 3.

Thus, the possible rational zeros of the function are ± 1, $\pm\frac{1}{3}$, and ± 3.

17. $h(x) = 9x^6 - 5x^3 + 27$

The possible values of p are ± 1, ± 3, ± 9 and ± 27.

The possible values of q are ± 1, ± 3, and ± 9.

Thus, the possible rational zeros of the function are ± 1, $\pm\frac{1}{3}$, $\pm\frac{1}{9}$, ± 3, ± 9, and ± 27.

18. $f(x) = x^3 + x^2 - 80x - 300$

The possible rational zeros are ± 1, ± 2, ± 3, ± 4, ± 5, ± 6, ± 10, ± 12, ± 15, ± 20, ± 25, ± 30, ± 50, ± 60, ± 75, ± 100, ± 150, and ± 300.

$\frac{p}{q}$	1	1	−80	−300
−6	1	−5	−50	0
−5	1	−4	−60	0
10	1	11	30	0

Rational zeros are -6, -5, and 10.

19. $p(x) = x^3 - 3x - 2$

The possible rational zeros are ± 2 and ± 1.

$\frac{p}{q}$	1	0	−3	−2
−1	1	−1	−2	0
1	1	1	−2	−4
2	1	2	1	0

Rational zeros are -1, and 2.

20. $h(x) = x^4 + x^2 - 2$

The possible rational zeros are ± 1 and ± 2.

$\frac{p}{q}$	1	0	1	0	−2
−1	1	−1	2	−2	0
1	1	1	2	2	0
2	1	2	3	6	10

Rational zeros are ± 1.

21. $g(x) = x^4 - 3x^3 - 53x^2 - 9x$
$= x(x^3 - 3x^2 - 53x - 9)$

The possible rational zeros are 0, and ± 1, ± 3, ± 9.

x	1	−3	−53	−9
−1	1	−4	−49	40
1	1	−2	−55	−64
9	1	6	1	0

Rational zeros are 0 and 9.

22. $f(x) = 2x^5 - x^4 - 2x + 1$

The possible rational zeros are ± 1 and $\pm \frac{1}{2}$.

x	2	−1	0	0	−2	1
−1	2	−3	3	−3	1	0
$\frac{1}{2}$	2	0	0	0	−2	0
1	2	1	1	1	−1	0

Rational zeros are -1, $\frac{1}{2}$, and 1.

23. $f(x) = x^5 - 6x^3 + 8x$
$= x(x^4 - 6x^2 + 8)$

The possible rational zeros are 0 and ± 1, ± 2, ± 4, ± 8.

x	1	0	−6	0	8
−2	1	−2	−2	4	0
1	1	1	−5	−5	3
2	1	2	−2	−4	0

Rational zeros are 0, 2, and -2.

24. $g(x) = x^4 - 3x^3 + x^2 - 3x$
$= x(x^3 - 3x^2 + x - 3)$

The possible rational zeros are 0 and ± 1, ± 3.

x	1	−3	1	−3
−3	1	−6	19	−60
3	1	0	1	0

Rational zeros are 0 and 3.

25. $p(x) = x^4 + 10x^3 + 33x^2 + 38x + 8$

The possible rational zeros are ± 1, ± 2, ± 4, and ± 8.

x	1	10	33	38	8
−2	1	8	17	4	0
−4	1	6	9	2	0

Rational zeros are -2 and -4.

26. $p(x) = x^3 + 3x^2 - 25x + 21$

The possible rational zeros are ± 1, ± 3, ± 7, and ± 21.

x	1	3	−25	21
−7	1	−4	3	0
1	1	4	−21	0
3	1	6	−7	0

Rational zeros are -7, 1, and 3.

27. $h(x) = 6x^3 + 11x^2 - 3x - 2$

The possible rational zeros are ± 1, ± 2, $\pm \frac{1}{2}$, $\pm \frac{1}{3}$, $\pm \frac{1}{6}$, and $\pm \frac{2}{3}$.

x	6	11	−3	−2
−2	6	−1	−1	0
$-\frac{1}{3}$	6	9	−6	0
$\frac{1}{2}$	6	14	4	0

Rational zeros are -2, $-\frac{1}{3}$, and $\frac{1}{2}$.

28. $h(x) = 10x^3 - 17x^2 - 7x + 2$

The possible rational zeros are ± 1, ± 2, $\pm \frac{1}{5}$, $\pm \frac{1}{10}$, and $\pm \frac{2}{5}$.

x	10	−17	−7	2
$-\frac{1}{2}$	10	−22	4	0
$\frac{1}{5}$	10	−15	−10	0
2	10	3	−1	0

Rational zeros are $-\frac{1}{2}$, $\frac{1}{5}$, and 2.

29. $g(x) = 48x^4 - 52x^3 + 13x - 3$

The possible rational zeros are ± 1, $\pm \frac{1}{2}$, $\pm \frac{1}{3}$, $\pm \frac{1}{4}$, $\pm \frac{1}{6}$, $\pm \frac{1}{8}$, $\pm \frac{1}{12}$, $\pm \frac{1}{16}$, $\pm \frac{1}{24}$, $\pm \frac{1}{48}$, ± 3, $\pm \frac{3}{2}$, $\pm \frac{3}{4}$, $\pm \frac{3}{8}$, and $\pm \frac{3}{16}$.

x	48	−52	0	13	−3
$-\frac{1}{2}$	48	−76	38	−6	0
$\frac{1}{3}$	48	−36	−12	9	0
$\frac{1}{2}$	48	−28	−14	6	0
$\frac{3}{4}$	48	−16	−12	4	0

Rational zeros are $-\frac{1}{2}$, $\frac{1}{3}$, $\frac{1}{2}$, and $\frac{3}{4}$.

30. $p(x) = 6x^4 + 22x^3 + 11x^2 - 38x - 40$

The possible rational zeros are ± 1, $\pm \frac{1}{2}$, $\pm \frac{1}{3}$, $\pm \frac{1}{6}$, ± 2, $\pm \frac{2}{3}$, ± 4, $\pm \frac{4}{3}$, ± 8, $\pm \frac{8}{3}$, ± 10, ± 5, $\pm \frac{5}{2}$, $\pm \frac{5}{6}$, $\pm \frac{10}{3}$, $\pm \frac{5}{3}$, ± 20, $\pm \frac{20}{3}$, ± 40, and $\pm \frac{40}{3}$.

x	6	22	11	−38	−4
−2	6	10	−9	−20	0
$\frac{4}{3}$	6	30	51	30	0

Rational zeros are -2 and $\frac{4}{3}$.

$p(x) = 6x^4 + 22x^3 + 11x^2 - 38x - 40$
$= 3(x + 2)\left(x - \frac{4}{3}\right)(2x^2 + 6x + 5)$

$2x^2 + 6x + 5 = 0$

$x = \frac{-3 \pm i}{2}$

The zeros of $p(x)$ are -2, $\frac{4}{3}$, and $\frac{-3 \pm i}{2}$.

31. $g(x) = 5x^4 - 29x^3 + 55x^2 - 28x$
$= x(5x^3 - 29x^2 + 55x - 28)$

The possible rational zeros are 0, ± 1, $\pm\frac{1}{5}$, ± 2, $\pm\frac{2}{5}$, ± 4, $\pm\frac{4}{5}$, ± 7, $\pm\frac{7}{5}$, ± 14, $\pm\frac{14}{5}$, ± 28, and $\pm\frac{28}{5}$.

x	5	-29	55	-28
$\frac{4}{5}$	5	-25	35	0

Rational zeros are 0 and $\frac{4}{5}$.

$y(x) = 5x\left(x - \frac{4}{5}\right)(x^2 - 5x + 7)$

$x = \frac{5 \pm i\sqrt{3}}{2}$

The zeros of $g(x)$ are 0, $\frac{4}{5}$, and $\frac{5 \pm i\sqrt{3}}{2}$.

32. $h(x) = 9x^5 - 94x^3 + 27x^2 + 40x - 12$

The possible rational zeros are ± 1, $\pm\frac{1}{3}$, $\pm\frac{1}{9}$, ± 2, $\pm\frac{2}{3}$, $\pm\frac{2}{9}$, ± 3, ± 4, $\pm\frac{4}{3}$, $\pm\frac{4}{9}$, ± 6, and ± 12.

x	9	0	-94	27	40	-12
$-\frac{2}{3}$	9	-6	-90	87	-18	0
$\frac{2}{3}$	9	6	-90	-33	18	0
3	9	27	-13	-12	4	0

Rational zeros are $-\frac{2}{3}$, $\frac{2}{3}$, and 3.

$h(x) = 9\left(x + \frac{2}{3}\right)\left(x - \frac{2}{3}\right)(x - 3)(x^2 + 3x - 1)$

$x = \frac{-3 \pm \sqrt{13}}{2}$

The zero of $h(x)$ are $\pm\frac{2}{3}$, 3, and $\frac{-3 \pm \sqrt{13}}{2}$.

33. $p(x) = x^5 - 2x^4 - 12x^3 - 12x^2 - 13x - 10$
The possible rational zeros are ± 1, ± 2, ± 5, and ± 10.

x	1	-2	-12	-12	-13	-10
-2	1	-4	-4	-4	-5	0
-1	1	-3	-9	-3	-10	0
5	1	3	3	3	2	0

The rational zeros are -2, -1, and 5.
$p(x) = (x + 2)(x + 1)(x - 5)(x^2 + 1)$
$x^2 + 1 = 0$
$x = \pm i$
The zeros of $p(x)$ are -2, -1, 5, and $\pm i$.

34. $V = \frac{1}{3}\pi r^2 h$

$h = 4 + r$

$V = \frac{1}{3}\pi r^2 (4 + r)$

$V = \frac{4}{3}\pi r^2 + \frac{1}{3}\pi r^3$

$V = \frac{1}{3}\pi r^3 + \frac{4}{3}\pi r^2$

35. $\frac{1}{3}\pi r^3 + \frac{4}{3}\pi r^2 = 8\pi$

$3\left(\frac{r^3}{3} + \frac{4r^2}{3}\right) = (3)(8)$

$r^3 + 4r^2 - 24 = 0$

Possible values of p are ± 1, ± 2, ± 3, ± 4, ± 6, ± 8, ± 12 and ± 24.
Possible values of q are ± 1.
Possible values of r are ± 1, ± 2, ± 3, ± 4, ± 6, ± 8, ± 12, and ± 24.
Only positive values are reasonable.

$\frac{p}{q}$	1	4	0	-24
1	1	5	5	-19
2	1	6	12	0

$V(r) = (r - 2)(r^2 + 6r + 12)$

$0 = r^2 + 6r + 12$

$r = \frac{-6 \pm \sqrt{36 - 4(12)}}{2}$

$= -3 \pm i\sqrt{3}$

The possible values of r are 2 and $-3 \pm i\sqrt{3}$. The value $r = 2$ is the only reasonable value.

36. The dimensions are $r = 2$ in. and $h = 2 + 4 = 6$ in.

37. $\ell = h + 4$
$w = 2h - 16$
$V = h(h + 4)(2h - 16)$
$= h(2h^2 - 16h + 8h - 64)$
$= 2h^3 - 8h^2 - 64h$

38. $2h^3 - 8h^2 - 64h = 55,296$

$2h^3 - 8h^2 - 64h - 55,296 = 0$
Possible values of h are ± 1, ± 2, ± 3, ± 4, ± 6, ± 8, ± 12, ± 16, ± 18, ± 24, ± 32, ± 36, ± 48, ...

h	2	-8	-64	$-55,296$
32	2	56	1728	0
36	2	66	2312	138,528

So, $h = 32$ in. Then $\ell = 32 + 4 = 36$ in. and $w = 2(32) - 16 = 48$ in.

39. $h = \ell - 9$

$B = \ell \cdot w = \ell \cdot \ell = \ell^2$

$V = \frac{1}{3}Bh$

$V = \frac{1}{3}\ell^2(\ell - 9)$

$V = \frac{1}{3}\ell^3 - 3\ell^2$

40. $\frac{1}{3}\ell^3 - 3\ell^2 = 6300$

41. $\frac{1}{3}\ell^3 - 3\ell^2 - 6300 = 0$

$\ell^3 - 9\ell^2 - 18,900 = 0$
The possible values of ℓ are ± 1, ± 2, ± 3, ± 4, ± 5, ± 6, ± 8, ± 10, ± 12, ± 15, ± 16, ± 18, ± 20, ± 24, ± 25, ± 30, ± 40, ± 45, ...

ℓ	1	-9	0	$-18,900$
20	1	11	220	$-14,500$
30	1	21	630	0

So, $\ell = 30$ in. then $w = 30$ in. and $h = 21$ in.

42. If k is a zero of $f(x)$, then
$$k^3 + 4k^2 + 9k^2 - 90 = 0$$
$$k^3 + 13k^2 - 90 = 0$$
The possible value of k are ± 1, ± 2, ± 3, ± 5, ± 6, ± 9, ± 10, ± 15, ± 18, ± 30, and ± 45.

k	1	4	0	-90
-3	1	1	-3	0
3	1	7	21	-27

$k = -3$
Substitute $k = -3$ in $f(x)$.
$f(x) = x^3 + 4x^2 - 27x - 90$.
Then $x + 3$ is a factor of $f(x)$.

$$
\begin{array}{r}
x^2 + x - 30 \\
x + 3 \overline{\smash{)}x^3 + 4x^2 - 27x - 90} \\
\underline{-(x^3 + 3x^2)} \\
x^2 - 27x \\
\underline{-(x^2 + 3x)} \\
-30x - 90 \\
\underline{-(-30x - 90)} \\
0
\end{array}
$$

$x^2 + x - 30 = 0$
$(x + 6)(x - 5) = 0$
$x + 6 = 0$ *or* $x - 5 = 0$
$x = -6 x = 5$
Therefore, the zeros of $f(x)$ are $x = -3$, $x = -6$, and $x = 5$.

43. The Rational Zero Theorem helps factor large numbers by eliminating some possible zeros because it is not practical to test all of them using synthetic substitution. Answers should include the following.

- The polynomial equation that represents the volume of the compartment is $V = w^3 + 3w^3 - 40w$.

- Reasonable measures of the width of the compartment are, in inches, 1, 2, 3, 4, 6, 7, 9, 12, 14, 18, 21, 22, 28, 33, 36, 42, 44, 63, 66, 77, and 84. The solution shows that $w = 14$ in., $\ell = 22$ in., and $d = 9$ in.

44. D; $f(1) = 12(1)^5 - 5(1)^3 + 2(1) - 9$
$$ = 12 - 5 + 2 - 9$$
$$ = 0$$

45. $f(x) = (x + 5)(x + 2)(x - 1)(x - 3)(x - 4)$
$ = (x^2 + 7x + 10)(x^2 - 4x + 3)(x - 4)$
$ = (x^4 + 3x^3 + 13x^2 - 28x^2 + 21x - 40x + 30)(x - 4)$
$ = (x^4 + 3x^3 - 15x^2 - 19x + 30)(x - 4)$
$ = x^5 + 3x^4 - 15x^3 - 19x^2 + 30x - 4x^4 - 12x^3 + 60x^2 + 76x - 120$
$ = x^5 - x^4 - 27x^3 + 41x^2 + 106x - 120$

46. $g(x) = x^3 + 4x^2 - 27x - 90$

$$
\begin{array}{r}
x^2 + x - 30 \\
x + 3 \overline{\smash{)}x^3 + 4x^2 - 27x - 90} \\
\underline{-(x^3 + 3x^2)} \\
x^2 - 27x \\
\underline{-(x^2 + 3x)} \\
-30x - 90 \\
\underline{-(-30x - 90)} \\
0
\end{array}
$$

$x^2 + x - 30 = 0$
$(x + 6)(x - 5) = 0$
$x + 6 = 0$ or $x - 5 = 0$
$x = -6 x = 5$
The zeros of $g(x)$ are -3, -6, and 5.

47. $h(x) = x^3 - 11x + 20$
If $2 + i$ is a zero of $h(x)$, $2 - i$ is also a zero.
$(x - 2 - i)(x - 2 + i) = x^2 - 4x + 4 + 1$
$$ = x^2 - 4x + 5$$

$$
\begin{array}{r}
x + 4 \\
x^2 - 4x + 5 \overline{\smash{)}x^3 - 11x + 20} \\
\underline{-(x^3 - 4x^2 + 5x)} \\
4x^2 - 16x + 20 \\
\underline{-(4x^2 - 16x + 20)} \\
0
\end{array}
$$

Thus, the zeros are -4, $2 + i$, and $2 - i$.

48. $f(x) = x^3 + 5x^2 + 9x + 45$
$x + 5$ is a factor of $f(x)$.

$$
\begin{array}{r}
x^2 + 9 \\
x + 5 \overline{\smash{)}x^3 + 5x^2 + 9x + 45} \\
\underline{-(x^3 + 5x^2)} \\
9x + 45 \\
\underline{-(9x + 45)} \\
0
\end{array}
$$

$x^2 + 9 = 0$
$(x - 3i)(x + 3i) = 0$
$x - 3i = 0$ or $x + 3i = 0$
$x = 3i x = -3i$
The zero of $f(x)$ are -5, $3i$, and $-3i$.

49. $g(x) = x^3 - 3x^2 - 41x + 203$
$(x + 7)$ is a factor of $f(x)$.

$$
\begin{array}{r}
x^2 - 10x + 29 \\
x + 7 \overline{\smash{)}x^3 - 3x^2 - 41x + 203} \\
\underline{-(x^3 + 7x^2)} \\
-10x^2 - 41x \\
\underline{-(-10x^2 - 70x)} \\
29x + 203 \\
\underline{-(29x + 203)} \\
0
\end{array}
$$

$x^2 - 10x + 29 = 0$
$x = \dfrac{10 \pm \sqrt{100 - 4(29)}}{2}$
$x = \dfrac{10 \pm 4i}{2}$
$x = 5 \pm 2i$
The zeros of $g(x)$ are -7 and $5 \pm 2i$.

50. $20x^3 - 29x^2 - 25x + 6; x - 2$

$$
\begin{array}{r}
20x^2 + 11x - 3 \\
x - 2\overline{)20x^2 - 29x^2 - 25x + 6} \\
\underline{-\,(20x^3 - 40x^2)} \\
11x^2 - 25x \\
\underline{-\,(-11x^2 - 22x)} \\
-3x + 6 \\
\underline{-\,(-3x + 6)} \\
0
\end{array}
$$

$$
\begin{aligned}
20x^2 + 11x - 3 &= 20x^2 + 11x - 3 \\
&= (4x + 3)(5x - 1)
\end{aligned}
$$

So, the other factors are $(4x + 3)$ and $(5x - 1)$.

51. $3x^4 - 21x^3 + 38x^2 - 14x + 24$

$$
\begin{array}{r}
3x^3 - 12x^2 + 2x - 8 \\
x - 3\overline{)3x^4 - 21x^3 + 38x^2 - 14x + 24} \\
\underline{-\,(3x^4 - 9x^3)} \\
-12x^3 + 38x^2 \\
\underline{-\,(-12x^3 + 36x^2)} \\
2x^2 - 14x \\
\underline{-\,(2x^2 - 6x)} \\
-8x + 24 \\
\underline{-\,(-8x + 24)} \\
0
\end{array}
$$

$$
\begin{aligned}
3x^3 - 12x^2 + 2x - 8 &= 3x^2(x - 4) + 2(x - 4) \\
&= (x - 4)(3x^2 + 2)
\end{aligned}
$$

So, the other factors are $3x^2 + 2$ and $x - 4$.

52. $\sqrt{245} = \sqrt{(49)(5)}$
$\qquad\qquad = 7\sqrt{5}$

53. $\pm\sqrt{18x^3y^2} = \pm\sqrt{(9)(2)(x^2y^2)(x)}$
$\qquad\qquad\qquad = \pm 3xy\sqrt{2x}$

54. $\sqrt{16x^2 - 40x + 25} = \sqrt{(4x - 5)^2}$
$\qquad\qquad\qquad\qquad = |4x - 5|$

55. Let ℓ = longer leg, s = shorter leg, and h = hypotenuse. Then $\ell + s + h = 24$, $3\ell - 2s = h + 2$, and $h - s = 0.5\ell$, so we have the system of equations

$\ell + s + h = 24$
$3\ell - 2s - h = 2$
$0.5\ell + s - h = 0$.

$$
\begin{array}{r}
\ell + s + h = 24 \\
\underline{(+)\ 3\ell - 2s - h = \ 2} \\
4\ell - s \qquad\quad = 26
\end{array}
$$

$$
\begin{array}{r}
3\ell - 2s - h = 2 \\
\underline{(-)\ 0.5\ell + s - h = 0} \\
2.5\ell - 3s \quad\ = 2
\end{array}
$$

$4\ell - s = 26$ Multiply by 3.
$2.5\ell - 3s = 2$

$$
\begin{array}{r}
-12\ell + 3s = -78 \\
\underline{(+)\ 2.5\ell - 3s = \quad 2} \\
9.5\ell \qquad\quad = -76 \\
\ell = 8
\end{array}
$$

$4\ell - s = 26$
$4(8) - s = 26$
$32 - s = 26$
$s = 6$

$\ell + s + h = 24$
$8 + 6 + h = 24$
$14 + h = 24$
$h = 10$

The lengths of all three sides of the triangle are 6 cm, 8 cm, and 10 cm.

56. $(x^2 - 7) + (x^3 + 3x^2 + 1) = x^3 + 4x^2 - 6$

57. $(8x^2 - 3x) - (4x^2 + 5x - 3)$
$\quad = 8x^2 - 3x - 4x^2 - 5x + 3$
$\quad = 4x^2 - 8x + 3$

58. $(x + 2)(x^2 + 3x - 5)$
$\quad = (x + 2)(x^2 + 3x - 5)$
$\quad = x^3 + 3x^2 - 5x + 2x^2 + 6x - 10$
$\quad = x^3 + 5x^2 + x - 10$

59. $(x^3 + 3x^2 - 3x + 1)(x - 5)^2$
$\quad = (x^3 + 3x^2 - 3x + 1)(x - 5)^2$
$\quad = (x^3 + 3x^2 - 3x + 1)(x^2 - 10x + 25)$
$\quad = x^5 + 3x^4 - 3x^3 + x^2 - 10x^4 - 30x^3 + 30x^2 - 10x + 25x^3 + 75x^2 - 75x + 25$
$\quad = x^5 - 7x^4 + 8x^3 + 106x^2 - 85x + 25$

60. $(x^2 - 2x - 30) \div (x + 7)$

$$
\begin{array}{r}
x - 9 \\
x + 7\overline{)x^2 - 2x - 30} \\
\underline{-\,(x^2 + 7x)} \\
-9x - 30 \\
\underline{-\,(-9x - 63)} \\
33
\end{array}
$$

$(x^2 - 2x - 30) \div (x + 7) = x - 9 + \dfrac{33}{x + 7}$

61. $(x^3 + 2x^2 - 3x + 1) \div (x + 1)$

$$
\begin{array}{r}
x^2 + x - 4 \\
x + 1\overline{)x^3 + 2x^2 - 3x + 1} \\
\underline{-\,(x^3 + x^2)} \\
x^2 - 3x \\
\underline{-\,(x^2 + x)} \\
-4x + 1 \\
\underline{-\,(-4x - 4)} \\
5
\end{array}
$$

$(x^3 + 2x^2 - 3x + 1) \div (x + 1) = x^2 + x - 4 + \dfrac{5}{x + 1}$

Page 382   Practice Quiz 2

1. $f(x) = 7x^5 - 25x^4 + 17x^3 - 32x^2 + 10x - 22$

$$
\begin{array}{r|rrrrrr}
-2 & 7 & -25 & 17 & -32 & 10 & -22 \\
   &   & -14 & 78 & -190 & 444 & -908 \\
\hline
   & 7 & -39 & 95 & -222 & 454 & -930
\end{array}
$$

$$
\begin{array}{r|rrrrrr}
3 & 7 & -25 & 17 & -32 & 10 & -22 \\
  &   & 21 & -12 & 15 & -51 & -123 \\
\hline
  & 7 & -4 & 5 & -17 & -41 & -145
\end{array}
$$

2. $f(x) = 3x^4 - 12x^3 - 21x^2 + 3x$

$$
\begin{array}{r|rrrrr}
-2 & 3 & -12 & -21 & 30 & 0 \\
   &   & -6 & 36 & -30 & 0 \\
\hline
   & 3 & -18 & 15 & 0 & 0
\end{array}
$$

$$
\begin{array}{r|rrrrr}
3 & 3 & -12 & -21 & 30 & 0 \\
  &   & 9 & -9 & -90 & -180 \\
\hline
  & 3 & -3 & -30 & -60 & -180
\end{array}
$$

3. $0 = (x + 2)(x + 1)(x - 3)(x - 4)$
$\quad = (x^2 - 2x - 8)(x^2 - 2x - 3)$
$\quad = x^4 - 4x^3 + 4x^2 - 11x^2 + 22x + 24$
$0 = x^4 - 4x^3 - 7x^2 + 22x + 24$

4. $f(x) = 5x^3 - 29x^2 + 55x - 28$

The possible values of p are ± 1, ± 2, ± 4, ± 7, ± 14, and ± 28.

The possible values of q are ± 1 and ± 5.

The possible values of $\frac{p}{q}$ are ± 1, $\pm \frac{1}{5}$, ± 2, $\pm \frac{2}{5}$, ± 4, $\pm \frac{4}{5}$, ± 7, $\pm \frac{7}{5}$, ± 14, $\pm \frac{14}{5}$, ± 28, and $\pm \frac{28}{5}$.

$\frac{p}{q}$	5	-29	55	-28
$-\frac{4}{5}$	5	-33	$\frac{407}{5}$	-1656
$\frac{4}{5}$	5	-25	35	0

The rational zero of $f(x)$ is $x = \frac{4}{5}$.

5. $g(x) = 4x^3 + 16x^2 - x - 24$

The possible values of p are ± 1, ± 2, ± 3, ± 4, ± 6, ± 8, ± 12, and ± 24.

The possible values of q are ± 1, ± 2, and ± 4.

The possible values of x are ± 1, $\pm \frac{1}{2}$, $\pm \frac{1}{4}$, ± 2, $\pm \frac{3}{1}$, $\pm \frac{3}{2}$, $\pm \frac{3}{4}$, $\ldots$

$\frac{p}{q}$	4	16	-1	-24
$-\frac{3}{2}$	4	10	-16	0
$\frac{3}{2}$	4	22	10	-9

The rational zero of $g(x)$ is $x = -\frac{3}{2}$.

7-7 Operations on Functions

Page 386 Check for Understanding

1. The statement is *sometimes* true.

Sample answer: If $f(x) = x - 2$ and $g(x) = x + 8$, then $f \circ g = x + 6$ and $g \circ f = x + 6$.

2. Sample answer: $g(x) = \{(-2, 1), (-1, 2), (4, 3)\}$
$f(x) = \{(1, 7), (2, 9), (3, 3)\}$

3. Danette; $[g \circ f](x) = g[f(x)]$ means to evaluate the f function first and then the g function. Marquan evaluated the functions in the wrong order.

4. $f(x) = 3x + 4$, $g(x) = 5 + x$

$(f + g)(x) = (3x + 4) + (5 + x)$
$\qquad = 4x + 9$

$(f - g)(x) = (3x + 4) - (5 + x)$
$\qquad = 3x + 4 - 5 - x$
$\qquad = 2x - 1$

$(f \cdot g)(x) = (3x + 4)(5 + x)$
$\qquad = 5x + 3x^2 + 20 + 4x$
$\qquad = 3x^2 + 19x + 20$

$\left(\frac{f}{g}\right)(x) = \frac{3x + 4}{5 + x}, x \neq -5$

5. $f(x) = x^2 + 3$, $g(x) = x - 4$

$(f + g)(x) = x^2 + 3 + x - 4$
$\qquad = x^2 + x - 1$

$(f - g)(x) = (x^2 + 3) - (x - 4)$
$\qquad = x^2 - x + 7$

$(f \cdot g)(x) = (x^2 + 3)(x - 4)$
$\qquad = x^3 + 4x^2 + 3x - 12$

$\left(\frac{f}{g}\right)(x) = \frac{x^2 + 3}{x - 4}, x \neq 4$

6. $f[g(-5)] = f(4)$ or 7
$f[g(7)] = f(12)$ undefined
$f[g(4)] = f(-1)$ or 9
Thus, $f \circ g = \{(-5, 7), (4, 9)\}$.
$g[f(-1)] = g(9)$ undefined
$g[f(4)] = g(7)$ or 12
Thus, $g \circ f = \{(4, 12)\}$.

7. $f[g(-1)] = f(10)$ undefined
$f[g(2)] = f(0)$ or -7
Thus, $f \circ g = \{(2, -7)\}$.
$g[f(0)] = g(-7)$ undefined
$g[f(1)] = g(2)$ or 0
$g[f(2)] = g(-1)$ or 10
Thus, $g \circ f = \{(1, 0), (2, 10)\}$.

8. $[g \circ h](x) = g[h(x)]$
$\qquad = g(3x - 4)$
$\qquad = 2(3x - 4)$
$\qquad = 6x - 8$

$[h \circ g](x) = h[g(x)]$
$\qquad = h(2x)$
$\qquad = 3(2x) - 4$
$\qquad = 6x - 4$

9. $[g \circ h](x) = g[h(x)]$
$\qquad = g(x^2 + 6)$
$\qquad = (x^2 + 6) + 5$
$\qquad = x^2 + 11$

$[h \circ g](x) = h[g(x)]$
$\qquad = h(x + 5)$
$\qquad = (x + 5)^2 + 6$
$\qquad = x^2 + 10x + 25 + 6$
$\qquad = x^2 + 10x + 31$

10. $f(x) = 3x$, $g(x) = x + 7$
$f[g(x)] = 3(x + 7)$
$\qquad = 3x + 21$
$f[g(3)] = 3(3) + 21$
$\qquad = 9 + 21$
$\qquad = 30$

11. $f(x) = 3x$, $g(x) = x + 7$
$g[h(x)] = x^2 + 7$
$g[h(-2)] = (-2)^2 + 7$
$\qquad = 11$

12. $f(x) = 3x$, $g(x) = x + 7$
$h[h(x)] = (x^2)^2$
$\qquad = x^4$
$h[h(1)] = (1)^4$
$\qquad = 1$

13. $p(x) = x - \frac{25}{100}x$
$\qquad = \frac{75x}{100}$
$\qquad = \frac{3}{4}x$
$c(x) = x - 5$

14. $32.49; c[p(x)] = \frac{3}{4}x - 5$

This model represents the price of the CD when the 25% discount is taken and then the coupon is subtracted.

15. $33.74; p[c(x)] = \frac{3}{4}(x - 5)$
$$= \frac{3}{4}x - \frac{15}{4}$$

This model represents the price of the CD when the coupon is subtracted and then the 25% discount is taken.

16. Discount first, then coupon;
Sample answer: 25% of 49.99 is greater than 25% of 44.99.

Pages 387–389　Practice and Apply

17. $f(x) = x + 9, g(x) = x - 9$
$(f + g)(x) = (x + 9) + (x - 9)$
$\qquad = 2x$
$(f - g)(x) = (x + 9) - (x - 9)$
$\qquad = x + 9 - x + 9$
$\qquad = 18$
$(f \cdot g)(x) = (x + 9)(x - 9)$
$\qquad = x^2 - 81$
$\left(\frac{f}{g}\right)(x) = \frac{x + 9}{x - 9}, x \neq 9$

18. $f(x) = 2x - 3, g(x) = x - 9$
$(f + g)(x) = (2x - 3) + (4x + 9)$
$\qquad = 6x + 6$
$(f - g)(x) = (2x - 3) - (4x + 9)$
$\qquad = 2x - 3 - 4x - 9$
$\qquad = -2x - 12$
$(f \cdot g)(x) = (2x - 3)(4x + 9)$
$\qquad = 8x^2 + 18x - 12x - 27$
$\qquad = 8x^2 + 6x - 27$
$\left(\frac{f}{g}\right)(x) = \frac{2x - 3}{4x + 9}, x \neq -\frac{9}{4}$

19. $f(x) = 2x^2, g(x) = 8 - x$
$(f + g)(x) = 2x^2 + 8 - x$
$\qquad = 2x^2 - x + 8$
$(f - g)(x) = 2x^2 - (8 - x)$
$\qquad = 2x^2 + x - 8$
$(f \cdot g)(x) = 2x^2(8 - x)$
$\qquad = 16x^2 - 2x^3$
$\left(\frac{f}{g}\right)(x) = \frac{2x^2}{8 - x}, x \neq 8$

20. $f(x) = x^2 + 6x + 9, g(x) = 2x + 6$
$(f + g)(x) = (x^2 + 6x + 9) + (2x + 6)$
$\qquad = x^2 + 8x + 15$
$(f - g)(x) = (x^2 + 6x + 9) - (2x + 6)$
$\qquad = x^2 + 6x + 9 - 2x - 6$
$\qquad = x^2 + 4x + 3$
$(f \cdot g)(x) = (x^2 + 6x + 9)(2x + 6)$
$\qquad = 2x^3 + 12x^2 + 18x + 6x^2 + 36x + 54$
$\qquad = 2x^3 + 18x^2 + 54x + 54$
$\left(\frac{f}{g}\right)(x) = \frac{x^2 + 6x + 9}{2x + 6} = \frac{x + 3}{2}, x \neq -3$

21. $f(x) = x^2 - 1, g(x) = \frac{x}{x + 1}$

$(f + g)(x) = x^2 - 1 + \frac{x}{x + 1}$
$\qquad = \frac{(x^2 - 1)(x + 1) + x}{x + 1}$

$\qquad = \frac{x^3 - x + x^2 - 1 + x}{x + 1}$
$\qquad = \frac{x^3 + x^2 - 1}{x + 1}, x \neq -1$
$(f - g)(x) = x^2 - 1 - \frac{x}{x + 1}$
$\qquad = \frac{(x^2 - 1)(x + 1) - x}{x + 1}$
$\qquad = \frac{x^3 - x + x^2 - 1 - x}{x + 1}$
$\qquad = \frac{x^3 + x^2 - 2x - 1}{x + 1}, x \neq -1$
$(f \cdot g)(x) = (x^2 - 1)\left(\frac{x}{x + 1}\right)$
$\qquad = \frac{(x - 1)(x + 1)(x)}{x + 1}$
$\qquad = (x - 1)x$
$\qquad = x^2 - x$
$\left(\frac{f}{g}\right)(x) = (x^2 - 1) \div \left(\frac{x}{x + 1}\right)$
$\qquad = (x^2 - 1)\left(\frac{x + 1}{x}\right)$
$\qquad = \frac{x^3 + x^2 - x - 1}{x}, x \neq 0$

22. $f(x) = x^2 - x - 6, g(x) = \frac{x - 3}{x + 2}$

$(f + g)(x) = (x^2 - x - 6) + \left(\frac{x - 3}{x + 2}\right)$
$\qquad = \frac{(x^2 - x - 6)(x + 2) + (x - 3)}{(x + 2)}$
$\qquad = \frac{x^3 - x^2 - 6x + 2x^2 - 2x - 12 + x - 3}{x + 2}$
$\qquad = \frac{x^3 + x^2 - 7x - 15}{x + 2}, x \neq -2$
$(f - g)(x) = x^2 - x - 6 - \frac{x - 3}{x + 2}$
$\qquad = \frac{(x^2 - x - 6)(x + 2) - (x - 3)}{x + 2}$
$\qquad = \frac{x^3 - x^2 - 6x + 2x^2 - 2x - 12 - x + 3}{x + 2}$
$\qquad = \frac{x^3 + x^2 - 9x - 9}{x + 2}, x \neq -2$
$(f \cdot g)(x) = (x^2 - x - 6)\left(\frac{x - 3}{x + 2}\right)$
$\qquad = (x - 3)(x + 2)\left(\frac{x - 3}{x + 2}\right)$
$\qquad = (x - 3)^2$
$\qquad = x^2 - 6x + 9, x \neq -2$
$\left(\frac{f}{g}\right)(x) = (x^2 - x - 6) \div \left(\frac{x - 3}{x + 2}\right)$
$\qquad = (x - 3)(x + 2)\left(\frac{x + 2}{x - 3}\right)$
$\qquad = (x + 2)^2$
$\qquad = x^2 + 4x + 4, x \neq -2, 3$

23. $f[g(1)] = f(0)$ or -3
$f[g(-3)] = f(1)$ or 1
$f[g(2)] = f(1)$ or 1
Thus, $f \circ g = \{(1, -3), (-3, 1), (2, 1)\}$.
$g[f(1)] = g(1)$ or 0
$g[f(0)] = g(-3)$ or 1
Thus, $g \circ f = \{(1, 0), (0, 1)\}$.

24. $f[g(2)] = f(5)$ or 4
$f[g(4)] = f(3)$ or 4
Thus, $f \circ g = \{(2, 4), (4, 4)\}$.
$g[f(1)] = g(2)$ or 5
$g[f(3)] = g(4)$ or 3
$g[f(5)] = g(4)$ or 3
Thus, $g \circ f = \{(1, 5), (3, 3), (5, 3)\}$.

25. $f[g(0)] = f(4)$ or 0

$f[g(8)] = f(6)$ or 3

$f[g(3)] = f(6)$ or 3

$f[g(-1)] = f(8)$ undefined

Thus, $f \circ g = \{(0, 0), (8, 3), (3, 3)\}$.

$g[f(3)] = g(8)$ or 6

$g[f(4)] = g(0)$ or 4

$g[f(6)] = g(3)$ or 6

$g[f(7)] = g(-1)$ or 8

Thus, $g \circ f = \{(3, 6), (4, 4), (6, 6), (7, 8)\}$.

26. $f[g(4)] = f(6)$ or 5

$f[g(2)] = f(4)$ or 5

$f[g(6)] = f(8)$ or 12

$f[g(8)] = f(10)$ or 12

Thus, $f \circ g = \{(4, 5), (2, 5), (6, 12), (8, 12)\}$.

$g[f(4)] = g(5)$ undefined

$g[f(6)] = g(5)$ undefined

$g[f(8)] = g(12)$ undefined

$g[f(10)] = g(12)$ undefined

Thus, $g \circ f$ does not exist.

27. $f[g(5)] = f(-4)$ or 1

$f[g(8)] = f(3)$ or 9

$f[g(2)] = f(-2)$ undefined

Thus, $f \circ g = \{(5, 1), (8, 9)\}$.

$g[f(2)] = g(5)$ or -4

$g[f(3)] = g(9)$ undefined

$g[f(-4)] = g(1)$ undefined

Thus, $g \circ f = \{(2, -4)\}$.

28. $f[g(2)] = f(-5)$ or 3

$f[g(1)] = f(0)$ undefined

$f[g(2)] = f(-9)$ or 2

$f[g(3)] = f(6)$ undefined

Thus, $f \circ g = \{(2, 3), (2, 2)\}$.

$g[f(7)] = g(0)$ undefined

$g[f(-5)] = g(3)$ or 6

$g[f(8)] = g(3)$ or 6

$g[f(-9)] = g(2)$ or -5 and -9

Thus, $g \circ f = \{(-5, 6), (8, 6), (-9, -5), (-9, -9)\}$.

29. $[g \circ h](x) = g[h(x)]$

$= g(2x - 1)$

$= 4(2x - 1)$

$= 8x - 4$

$[h \circ g](x) = h[g(x)]$

$= h(4x)$

$= 2(4x) - 1$

$= 8x - 1$

30. $[g \circ h](x) = g[h(x)]$

$= g(-3x + 1)$

$= -5(-3x + 1)$

$= -15x - 5$

$[h \circ g](x) = h[g(x)]$

$= g(-5x)$

$= -3(-5x) + 1$

$= 15x + 1$

31. $[g \circ h](x) = g[h(x)]$

$= g(x^2)$

$= x^2 + 2$

$[h \circ g](x) = h[g(x)]$

$= h(x + 2)$

$= (x + 2)^2$

$= x^2 + 4x + 4$

32. $[g \circ h](x) = g[h(x)]$

$= g(3x^2)$

$= 3x^2 - 4$

$[h \circ g](x) = h[g(x)]$

$= h(x - 4)$

$= 3(x - 4)^2$

$= 3(x^2 - 8x + 16)$

$= 3x^2 - 24x + 48$

33. $[g \circ h](x) = g[h(x)]$

$= g(x^3 + x^2 + x + 1)$

$= 2(x^3 + x^2 + x + 1)$

$= 2x^3 + 2x^2 + 2x + 2$

$[h \circ g](x) = h[g(x)]$

$= h(2x)$

$= (2x)^3 + (2x)^2 + 2x + 1$

$= 8x^3 + 4x^2 + 2x + 1$

34. $[g \circ h](x) = g[h(x)]$

$= g(2x^2 - 5x + 8)$

$= (2x^2 - 5x + 8) + 1$

$= 2x^2 - 5x + 9$

$[h \circ g](x) = h[g(x)]$

$= h(x + 1)$

$= 2(x + 1)^2 - 5(x + 1) + 8$

$= 2(x^2 + 2x + 1) - 5x - 5 + 8$

$= 2x^2 + 4x + 2 - 5x - 5 + 8$

$= 2x^2 - x + 5$

35. $f(x) = 4x, g(x) = 2x - 1$

$f[g(x)] = 4(2x - 1)$

$= 8x - 4$

$f[g(-1)] = 8(-1) - 4$

$= -12$

36. $g(x) = 2x - 1, h(x) = x^2 + 1$

$h[g(x)] = (2x - 1)^2 + 1$

$= 4x^2 - 4x + 1 + 1$

$= 4x^2 - 4x + 2$

$h[g(4)] = 4(4^2) - 4(4) + 2$

$= 4(16) - 16 + 2$

$= 64 - 16 + 2$

$= 50$

37. $g(x) = 2x - 1, f(x) = 4x$

$g[f(x)] = 2(4x) - 1$

$= 8x - 1$

$g[f(5)] = 8(5) - 1$

$= 40 - 1$

$= 39$

38. $f(x) = 4x, h(x) = x^2 + 1$

$f[h(x)] = 4(x^2 + 1)$

$= 4x^2 + 4$

$f[h(-4)] = 4(-4)^2 + 4$

$= 64 + 4$

$= 68$

39. $g(x) = x^2 + 1$

$g[g(x)] = 2(2x - 1) - 1$

$= 4x - 2 - 1$

$= 4x - 3$

$g[g(7)] = 4(7) - 3$

$= 25$

40. $f(x) = 4x$

$\quad f[f(x)] = 4(4x)$

$\qquad\quad = 16x$

$\quad f[f(-3)] = 16(-3)$

$\qquad\qquad = -48$

41. $f(x) = 4x$, $h(x) = x^2 + 1$

$\quad h[f(x)] = (4x)^2 + 1$

$\qquad\quad = 16x^2 + 1$

$\quad h\left[f\left(\frac{1}{4}\right)\right] = 16\left(\frac{1}{4}\right)^2 + 1$

$\qquad\qquad = 16\left(\frac{1}{16}\right) + 1$

$\qquad\qquad = 1 + 1$

$\qquad\qquad = 2$

42. $g(x) = 2x - 1$, $h(x) = x^2 + 1$

$\quad g[h(x)] = 2(x^2 + 1) - 1$

$\qquad\quad = 2x^2 + 2 - 1$

$\qquad\quad = 2x^2 + 1$

$\quad g\left[h\left(-\frac{1}{2}\right)\right] = 2\left(-\frac{1}{2}\right)^2 + 1$

$\qquad\qquad = 2\left(\frac{1}{4}\right) + 1$

$\qquad\qquad = \frac{1}{2} + 1$

$\qquad\qquad = 1\frac{1}{2}$

43. $f(x) = 4x$, $h(x) = x^2 + 1$

$\quad (f \circ h)(x) = 4(x^2 + 1)$

$\qquad\quad = 4x^2 + 4$

$\quad [g \circ (f \circ h)](x) = 2(4x^2 + 4) - 1$

$\qquad\qquad = 8x^2 + 7$

$\quad [g \circ (f \circ h)](3) = 8(3^2) + 7$

$\qquad\qquad = 72 + 7$

$\qquad\qquad = 79$

44. $g(x) = 2x - 1$, $h(x) = x^2 + 1$

$\quad (h \circ g)(x) = (2x - 1)^2 + 1$

$\qquad\quad = 4x^2 - 4x + 1 + 1$

$\qquad\quad = 4x^2 - 4x + 2$

$\quad [f \circ (h \circ g)](x) = 4(4x^2 - 4x + 2)$

$\qquad\qquad = 16x^2 - 16x + 8$

$\quad [f \circ (h \circ g)](3) = 16(3^2) - 16(3) + 8$

$\qquad\qquad = 16(9) - 16(3) + 8$

$\qquad\qquad = 144 - 48 + 8$

$\qquad\qquad = 104$

45. $f(x) = 4x$, $g(x) = 2x - 1$, $h(x) = x^2 + 1$

$\quad (g \circ f)(x) = 2(4x) - 1$

$\qquad\quad = 8x - 1$

$\quad [h \circ (g \circ f)](x) = (8x - 1)^2 + 1$

$\qquad\qquad = 64x^2 - 16x + 1 + 1$

$\qquad\qquad = 64x^2 - 16x + 2$

$\quad [h \circ (g \circ f)](2) = 64(2^2) - 16(2) + 2$

$\qquad\qquad = 256 - 32 + 2$

$\qquad\qquad = 226$

46. $g(x) = 2x - 1$, $h(x) = x^2 + 1$

$\quad (g \circ h)(x) = 2(x^2 + 1) - 1$

$\qquad\quad = 2x^2 + 1$

$\quad [f \circ (g \circ h)](x) = 4(2x^2 + 1)$

$\qquad\qquad = 8x^2 + 4$

$\quad [f \circ (g \circ h)](2) = 8(2^2) + 4$

$\qquad\qquad = 32 + 4$

$\qquad\qquad = 36$

47. $P(x) = b(x) - d(x)$

$\qquad = (-27x + 4103) - (23x + 2164)$

$\qquad = -50x + 1939$

48. $P(20) = -50(20) + 1939$

$\qquad = -1000 + 1939$

$\qquad = 939$

The net increase in population will be about 939,000.

49. $p(x) = x - \frac{30x}{100}$

$\qquad = \frac{100x - 30x}{100}$

$\qquad = 0.70x$

The price after the discount can be expressed as $p(x) = 0.70x$.

$s(x) = x + 0.0575x$

$s(x) = 1.0575x$

The price after the sales tax can be expressed as $s(x) = 1.0575x$.

50. The composition $s[p(x)]$ represents the price of the inline skates. The 30% would be taken off first, and then the sales tax would be calculated on this price.

51. $s[p(149)] = 1.0575[0.70(149)]$

$\qquad\quad \approx 110.30$

Liluye will pay about $110.30 for the inline skates.

52. $[K \circ C](F) = \frac{5}{9}(F - 32) + 273$

53. $K = \frac{5}{9}(212 - 32) + 273$

$\quad = \frac{5}{9}(180) + 273$

$\quad = 100 + 273$

$\quad = 373$ K

The boiling point of water is 373 K.

$K = \frac{5}{9}(212 - 212) + 273$

$\quad = 273$ K

The freezing point of water is 273 K.

54. $256°F - 158°F = 98°F$

$K = \frac{5}{9}(98 - 32) + 273$

$\quad = \frac{5}{9}(66) + 273$

$\quad = \frac{110}{3} + 273$

$\quad = 309.67$ K

55. $f(1) = \$700$

$\quad f(2) = f(2 - 1) + 0.016f(2 - 1) - 50$

$\qquad = 700 + 0.016(700) - 50$

$\qquad = \$661.20$

$\quad f(3) = f(3 - 1) + 0.016f(3 - 1) - 50$

$\qquad = 661.2 + (0.016)(661.2) - 50$

$\qquad = \$621.78$

$\quad f(4) = f(4 - 1) + 0.016f(4 - 1) - 50$

$\qquad = 621.78 + (0.016)(621.78) - 50$

$\qquad = \$581.73$

$\quad f(5) = f(5 - 1) + 0.016f(5 - 1) - 50$

$\qquad = 581.73 + (0.016)(581.73) - 50$

$\qquad = \$541.04$

56. $f(x + 1) = 3f(x) - 2, f(0) = 4$

$f(1) = 3f(0) - 2$
$f(1) = 3(4) - 2$
$\quad\quad = 10$

$f(2) = 3f(1) - 2$
$\quad\quad = 3(10) - 2$
$\quad\quad = 28$

$f(3) = 3f(2) - 2$
$f(3) = 3(28) - 2$
$\quad\quad = 82$

$f(4) = 3f(3) - 2$
$f(4) = 3(82) - 2$
$\quad\quad = 244$

57. Answers should include the following.
- Using the revenue and cost functions, a new function that represents the profit is $p(x) = r[c(x)]$.
- The benefit of combining two functions into one function is that there are fewer steps to compute and it is less confusing to the general population of people reading the formulas.

58. A; $g[h(x)] = \frac{2}{7}(7x - 5) + \frac{10}{7} + 3$

$\quad\quad\quad\quad = \frac{2}{7}(7x - 5) + \frac{31}{7}$

$\quad\quad\quad\quad = \frac{2}{7}[h(x)] + \frac{31}{7}$

$\quad g(x) = \frac{2x}{7} + \frac{31}{7}$

$\quad\quad\quad = \frac{2x + 31}{7}$

59. C; $(f - g)(x)$

$= (4x^4 + 5x^3 - 3x^2 - 14x + 31) - (7x^3 - 4x^2 + 5x - 42)$

$= 4x^4 + 5x^3 - 3x^2 - 14x + 31 - 7x^3 + 4x^2 - 5x + 42$

$= 4x^4 - 2x^3 + x^2 - 19x + 73$

Page 389   Maintain Your Skills

60. $r(x) = x^2 - 6x + 8$

Possible values of p are $\pm 1, \pm 2, \pm 4,$ and ± 8.
Possible values of q are ± 1.
Possible rational zeros of the function are $\pm 1, \pm 2, \pm 4,$ and ± 8.

61. $f(x) = 4x^3 - 2x^2 + 6$

Possible values of p are $\pm 1, \pm 2, \pm 3,$ and ± 6.
Possible values of q are $\pm 1, \pm 2,$ and ± 4.
Posible rational zeros of the function are $\pm 1, \pm \frac{1}{2},$ $\pm \frac{1}{4}, \pm 2, \pm 3, \pm \frac{3}{2}, \pm \frac{3}{4},$ and ± 6.

62. $g(x) = qx^2 - 1$

Possible values of p are ± 1.
Possible values of q are $\pm 1, \pm 3,$ and ± 9.
Possible rational zeros are $\pm 1, \pm \frac{1}{3},$ and $\pm \frac{1}{9}$.

63. $0 = (x - 5)(x - 3)(x + 4)$

$\quad = (x - 5)(x^2 + x - 12)$
$\quad = x^3 + x^2 - 12x - 5x^2 - 5x + 60$
$0 = x^3 - 4x^2 - 17x + 60$

64. $0 = (x + 3)(x + 2)(x - 8)$

$\quad = (x + 3)(x^2 - 6x - 16)$
$\quad = x^3 - 6x^2 - 16x + 3x^2 - 18x - 48$
$0 = x^3 - 3x^2 - 34x - 48$

65. $0 = (2)(3)(x - 1)\left(x - \frac{1}{2}\right)\left(x - \frac{2}{3}\right)$

$\quad = (x - 1)(2x - 1)(3x - 2)$
$\quad = (x - 1)(6x^2 - 4x - 3x + 2)$
$\quad = 6x^3 - 7x^2 + 2x - 6x^2 + 7x - 2$
$0 = 6x^3 - 13x^2 + 9x - 2$

66. $0 = (x - 6)(x - 2i)(x + 2i)$

$\quad = (x - 6)(x^2 + 4)$
$\quad = x^3 + 4x - 6x^2 - 24$
$0 = x^3 - 6x^2 + 4x - 24$

67. $0 = (x - 3)(x - 3 + 2i)(x - 3 - 2i)$

$\quad = (x - 3)(x^2 - 6x + 9 + 4)$
$\quad = x^3 - 6x^2 + 13x - 3x^2 + 18x - 39$
$0 = x^3 - 9x^2 + 31x - 39$

68. $0 = (x + 5)(x - 2)(x - 1 + i)(x - 1 - i)$

$\quad = (x^2 + 3x - 10)(x^2 - 2x + 1 + 1)$
$\quad = (x^2 + 3x - 10)(x^2 - 2x + 2)$
$\quad = x^4 - 2x^3 + 2x^2 + 3x^3 - 6x^2 + 6x - 10x^2 + 20x - 20$
$0 = x^4 + x^3 - 14x^2 + 26x - 20$

69. $(430 - 330j) = (35 - 40j)Z$

$Z = \frac{430 - 330j}{35 - 40j}$

$\quad = \frac{86 - 66j}{7 - 8j}$

$\quad = \frac{(86 - 66j)(7 + 8j)}{(7 - 8j)(7 + 8j)}$

$\quad = \frac{602 + 668j - 462j + 528}{49 + 64}$

$\quad = \frac{1130 + 226j}{113}$

$\quad = \frac{113(10 + 2j)}{113}$

$\quad = 10 + 2j$

70. $\begin{bmatrix} 8 & 6 \\ 7 & 5 \end{bmatrix}^{-1} = \frac{1}{40 - 42}\begin{bmatrix} 5 & -6 \\ -7 & 8 \end{bmatrix}$

$\quad\quad\quad\quad = -\frac{1}{2}\begin{bmatrix} 5 & -6 \\ -7 & 8 \end{bmatrix}$

71. $\begin{bmatrix} 1 & 2 \\ 1 & 3 \end{bmatrix}^{-1} = \frac{1}{3 - 2}\begin{bmatrix} 3 & -2 \\ -1 & 1 \end{bmatrix}$

$\quad\quad\quad\quad = \begin{bmatrix} 3 & -2 \\ -1 & 1 \end{bmatrix}$

72. $\begin{bmatrix} 8 & 4 \\ 6 & 3 \end{bmatrix}^{-1} = \frac{1}{24 - 24}\begin{bmatrix} 3 & -4 \\ -6 & 8 \end{bmatrix}$

The inverse does not exist.

73. $\begin{bmatrix} -4 & 2 \\ 3 & 1 \end{bmatrix}^{-1} = \frac{1}{4 - 6}\begin{bmatrix} -1 & -2 \\ -3 & -4 \end{bmatrix}$

$\quad\quad\quad\quad = \frac{1}{2}\begin{bmatrix} 1 & 2 \\ 3 & 4 \end{bmatrix}$

74. $\begin{bmatrix} 6 & -2 \\ 9 & -3 \end{bmatrix}^{-1} = \frac{1}{-18 + 18}\begin{bmatrix} -3 & 2 \\ -9 & -6 \end{bmatrix}$

The inverse does not exist.

75. $\begin{bmatrix} 2 & 2 \\ 3 & -5 \end{bmatrix}^{-1} = \frac{1}{-6 - 10}\begin{bmatrix} -5 & -2 \\ -3 & 2 \end{bmatrix}$

$\quad\quad\quad\quad = \frac{1}{16}\begin{bmatrix} 5 & 2 \\ 3 & -2 \end{bmatrix}$

76. $2x - 3y = 6$

$\quad 2x = 6 + 3y$

$\quad\quad x = \frac{6 + 3y}{2}$

77. $4x^2 - 5xy + 2 = 3$
$$-5xy = 3 - 4x^2 - 2$$
$$-5xy = 1 - 4x^2$$
$$y = -\frac{1 - 4x^2}{5x}$$

78. $3x + 7xy = -2$
$$x(3 + 7y) = -2$$
$$x = -\frac{2}{3 + 7y}$$

79. $I = prt$
$$\frac{I}{pr} = \frac{prt}{pr}$$
$$t = \frac{I}{pr}$$

80. $C = \frac{5}{9}(F - 32)$
$$\frac{9}{5} \cdot C = \frac{9}{5} \cdot \frac{5}{9}(F - 32)$$
$$\frac{9C}{5} = F - 32$$
$$F = \frac{9C}{5} + 32$$

81. $F = G\frac{Mm}{r^2}$
$$r^2F = GMm$$
$$\frac{r^2F}{GM} = \frac{GMm}{GM}$$
$$\frac{r^2F}{GM} = m$$

7-8 Inverse Functions and Relations

Page 392 Algebra Activity

1. $y = \frac{x + 3}{2}$

2. They are inverses.
$$f(x) = 2x - 3 \text{ and } g(x) = \frac{x + 3}{2}$$
$$f[g(x)] = 2\left(\frac{x + 3}{2}\right) - 3 = x$$
$$g[f(x)] = \frac{(2x - 3) + 3}{2} = x$$

3. No; the graph does not pass the vertical line test.

Page 393 Check for Understanding

1. $f(x) = 3x + 6$
$$y = 3x + 6$$
$$y - 6 = 3x$$
$$\frac{y - 6}{3} = x$$
$$\frac{x - 6}{3} = y$$
$$f^{-1}(x) = \frac{x - 6}{3}$$
$$f^{-1}(x) \neq g(x)$$
$f(x)$ and $g(x)$ are not inverses.

2. Switch x and y in the equation and solve for y.

3. Sample answer: $f(x) = 2x$
$$f^{-1}(x) = 0.5x$$
$$f[f^{-1}(x)] = f^{-1}[f(x)] = x$$

4. $f(x) = x^n$
$$y = x^n$$
$$x = y^n$$
$$y = \sqrt[n]{x}$$
$$f^{-1}(x) = \sqrt[n]{y}$$
$f(x) = x^n$ has an inverse if n is an odd whole number.

5. $\{(4, 2), (1, -3), (8, 2)\}$

6. $\{(3, 1), (-1, 1), (-3, 1), (1, 1)\}$

7. $f(x) = -x$
$$y = -x$$
$$x = -y$$
$$f^{-1}(x) = -x$$

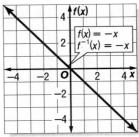

8. $g(x) = 3x + 1$
$$y = 3x + 1$$
$$x = 3y + 1$$
$$x - 1 = 3y$$
$$\frac{x - 1}{3} = y$$
$$g^{-1}(x) = \frac{x - 1}{3}$$
$$g^{-1}(x) = \frac{1}{3}x - \frac{1}{3}$$

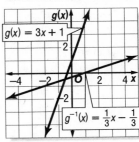

9. $y = \frac{1}{2}x + 5$
$$x = \frac{1}{2}y + 5$$
$$x - 5 = \frac{1}{2}y$$
$$2(x - 5) = y$$
$$y^{-1} = 2x - 10$$

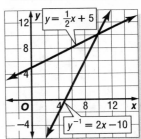

10. $f(x) = x + 7$
$$y = x + 7$$
$$x = y + 7$$
$$x - 7 = y$$
$$f^{-1}(x) = x - 7$$
$$g(x) = x - 7$$
Yes, $f(x)$ and $g(x)$ are inverse functions.

11. $g(x) = 3x - 2$
$$y = 3x - 2$$
$$x = 3y - 2$$
$$x + 2 = 3y$$
$$\frac{x + 2}{3} = y$$
$$g^{-1}(x) = \frac{x + 2}{3}$$
$$f(x) = \frac{x - 2}{3}$$
No, $g(x)$ and $f(x)$ are not inverse functions.

12. $\frac{9.8 \text{ m}}{\text{s}^2} \times \frac{100 \text{ cm}}{1 \text{ m}} \times \frac{1 \text{ in.}}{2.54 \text{ cm}} \times \frac{1 \text{ ft}}{12 \text{ in.}} = \frac{(9.8)(100)(1)(1) \text{ ft}}{(1)(2.54)(12) \text{ s}^2}$

$$= \frac{32.2 \text{ ft}}{\text{s}^2}$$

The value of the acceleration is 32.2 ft/s².

13. $\dfrac{50 \text{ ft}}{\text{s}^2} \times \dfrac{12 \text{ in.}}{1 \text{ ft}} \times \dfrac{2.54 \text{ cm}}{1 \text{ in.}} \times \dfrac{1 \text{ m}}{100 \text{ cm}} = \dfrac{15.24 \text{ m}}{\text{s}^2}$

An object is accelerating at 15.24 m/s².

Pages 393–394   Practice and Apply

14. $\{(6, 2), (5, 4), (-1, -3)\}$

15. $\{(8, 3), (-2, 4), (-3, 5)\}$

16. $\{(-4, 7), (5, 3), (4, -1), (5, 7)\}$

17. $\{(-2, -1), (-2, -3), (-4, -1), (6, 0)\}$

18. $(11, 6), (7, -2), (3, 0), (3, -5)\}$

19. $\{(8, 2), (5, -6), (2, 8), (-6, 5)\}$

20. $y = -3$
$x = -3$

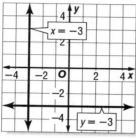

21. $g(x) = -2x$
$y = -2x$
$x = -2y$
$-\dfrac{1}{2}x = y$
$g^{-1}(x) = -\dfrac{1}{2}x$

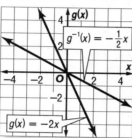

22. $f(x) = x - 5$
$y = x - 5$
$x = y - 5$
$x + 5 = y$
$f^{-1}(x) = x + 5$

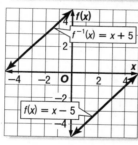

23. $g(x) = x + 4$
$y = x + 4$
$x = y + 4$
$x - 4 = y$
$g^{-1}(x) = x - 4$

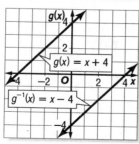

24. $f(x) = 3x + 3$
$y = 3x + 3$
$x = 3y + 3$
$x - 3 = 3y$
$\dfrac{x - 3}{3} = y$
$f^{-1}(x) = \dfrac{1}{3}x - 1$

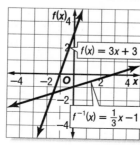

25. $y = -2x - 1$
$y = -2x - 1$
$x = -2y - 1$
$x + 1 = -2y$
$\dfrac{x + 1}{-2} = y$
$y^{-1} = -\dfrac{1}{2}x - \dfrac{1}{2}$

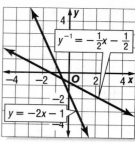

26. $y = \dfrac{1}{3}x$
$x = \dfrac{1}{3}y$
$3x = y$
$y^{-1} = 3x$

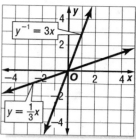

27. $f(x) = \dfrac{5}{8}x$
$y = \dfrac{5}{8}x$
$x = \dfrac{5}{8}y$
$8x = 5y$
$\dfrac{8}{5}x = y$
$f^{-1}(x) = \dfrac{8}{5}x$

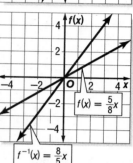

28. $f(x) = \dfrac{1}{3}x + 4$
$y = \dfrac{1}{3}x + 4$
$x = \dfrac{1}{3}y + 4$
$x - 4 = \dfrac{1}{3}y$
$3(x - 4) = y$
$f^{-1}(x) = 3x - 12$

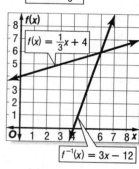

29. $f(x) = \dfrac{4}{5}x - 7$
$y = \dfrac{4}{5}x - 7$
$x = \dfrac{4}{5}y - 7$
$x + 7 = \dfrac{4}{5}y$
$5(x + 7) = 4y$
$\dfrac{5}{4}(x + 7) = y$
$f^{-1}(x) = \dfrac{5}{4}x + \dfrac{35}{4}$

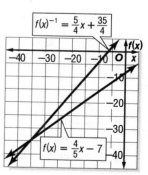

30.
$$g(x) = \frac{2x+3}{6}$$
$$y = \frac{2x+3}{6}$$
$$x = \frac{2y+3}{6}$$
$$6x = 2y + 3$$
$$6x - 3 = 2y$$
$$\frac{6x-3}{2} = y$$
$$g^{-1}(x) = 3x - \frac{3}{2}$$

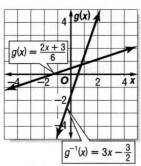

31.
$$f(x) = \frac{7x-4}{8}$$
$$y = \frac{7x-4}{8}$$
$$x = \frac{7y-4}{8}$$
$$8x = 7y - 4$$
$$8x + 4 = 7y$$
$$\frac{8x+4}{7} = y$$
$$f^{-1}(x) = \frac{8}{7}x + \frac{4}{7}$$

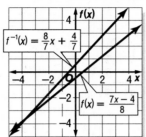

32. $f(x) = x - 5, g(x) = x + 5$
$$(f \circ g)(x) = (x + 5) - 5$$
$$= x + 5 - 5$$
$$= x$$
$$(g \circ f)(x) = (x - 5) + 5$$
$$= x - 5 + 5$$
$$= x$$
Yes, $f(x)$ and $g(x)$ are inverse functions.

33. $f(x) = 3x + 4, g(x) = 3x - 4$
$$(f \circ g)(x) = 3(3x - 4) + 4$$
$$= 9x - 36 + 4$$
$$= 9x - 32$$
No, $f(x)$ and $g(x)$ are not inverse functions.

34. $f(x) = 6x + 2, g(x) = x - \frac{1}{3}$
$$(f \circ g)(x) = 6\left(x - \frac{1}{3}\right) + 2$$
$$= 6x - 2 + 2$$
$$= 6x$$
No, $f(x)$ and $g(x)$ are not inverse functions.

35. $g(x) = 2x + 8, f(x) = \frac{1}{2}x - 4$
$$(g \circ f)(x) = 2\left(\frac{1}{2}x - 4\right) + 8$$
$$= x - 8 + 8$$
$$= x$$
$$(f \circ g)(x) = \frac{1}{2}(2x + 8) - 4$$
$$= x + 4 - 4$$
$$= x$$
Yes, $g(x)$ and $f(x)$ are inverse functions.

36. $h(x) = 5x - 7, g(x) = \frac{1}{5}(x + 7)$
$$(h \circ g)(x) = 5\left(\frac{1}{5}(x + 7)\right) - 7$$
$$= x + 7 - 7$$
$$= x$$
$$(g \circ h)(x) = \frac{1}{5}((5x - 7) - 7)$$
$$= \frac{1}{5}(5x)$$
$$= x$$
Yes, $h(x)$ and $g(x)$ are inverse functions.

37. $g(x) = 2x + 1, f(x) = \frac{x-1}{2}$
$$(g \circ f)(x) = 2\left(\frac{x-1}{2}\right) + 1$$
$$= x - 1 + 1$$
$$= x$$
$$(f \circ g)(x) = \frac{(2x + 1) - 1}{2}$$
$$= \frac{2x}{2}$$
$$= x$$
Yes, $g(x)$ and $f(x)$ are inverse functions.

38. If x is the chosen number and y is the final result, $y = \frac{4(x+7)-6}{2}$.

39.
$$x = \frac{4(y+7)-6}{2}$$
$$2x = 4(y + 7) - 6$$
$$2x + 6 = 4(y + 7)$$
$$\frac{2x+6}{4} = y + 7$$
$$\frac{x+3}{2} - 7 = y$$
$$\frac{1}{2}x + \frac{3}{2} - 7 = y$$

40.
$$y^{-1} = \frac{1}{2}(35) - \frac{11}{2}$$
$$= \frac{35 - 11}{2}$$
$$= \frac{24}{2}$$
$$= 12$$
Sophia's original number was 12.

41. $I(m) = (40)(8) + \frac{4}{100}(m)$
A function is $I(m) = 320 + 0.04m$.
$$500 = 320 + 0.04m$$
$$180 = 0.04m$$
$$m = \frac{180}{0.04}$$
$$m = 4500$$
Sales associates must sell $4500 in merchandise to earn $500.

42.
$$C(x) = \frac{5}{9}(x - 32)$$
$$y = \frac{5}{9}(x - 32)$$
$$x = \frac{5}{9}(y - 32)$$
$$\frac{9}{5}x = y - 32$$
$$\frac{9}{5}x + 32 = y$$
$$C^{-1}(x) = \frac{9}{5}x + 32$$
$$(C \circ C^{-1})(x) = \frac{5}{9}\left[\left(\frac{9}{5}x + 32\right) - 32\right]$$
$$= \frac{5}{9}\left(\frac{9}{5}x\right)$$
$$= x$$
$$(C^{-1} \circ C)(x) = \frac{9}{5}\left[\frac{5}{9}(x - 32)\right] + 32$$
$$= x - 32 + 32$$
$$= x$$

43. It can be used to convert Celsius to Fahrenheit.

44. Sample answer: $f(x) = x$ and $f^{-1}(x)$, or $f(x) = -x$ and $f^{-1}(x) = -x$

45. Inverses are used to convert between two units of measurement. Answers should include the following.

- Even if it is not necessary, it is helpful to know the imperial units when given the metric units because most measurements in the U.S. are given in imperial units so it is easier to understand the quantities using our system.
- To convert the speed of light from meters per second to miles per hour,

$$f(x) = \frac{3.0108 \text{ meters}}{1 \text{ second}} \cdot \frac{3600 \text{ seconds}}{1 \text{ hour}} \cdot \frac{1 \text{ mile}}{1600 \text{ meters}}$$

$$= 671{,}224{,}363 \text{ mi/h}.$$

46. A; $f\left(\dfrac{2x+5}{3}\right) = \dfrac{3\left(\frac{2x+5}{3}\right) - 5}{2}$

$$= \frac{2x + 5 - 5}{2}$$

$$= \frac{2x}{2}$$

$$= x$$

47. B; $y = x^3$

$\sqrt[3]{y} = x$

$f^{-1}(x) = \sqrt[3]{y}$

Page 394   Maintain Your Skills

48. $g(x) = 4x$, $h(x) = x + 5$

$[g \circ h](x) = 4(x + 5)$

$\qquad\qquad = 4x + 20$

$[h \circ g](x) = 4x + 5$

49. $g(x) = 3x + 2$, $h(x) = 2x - 4$

$[g \circ h](x) = 3(2x - 4) + 2$

$[g \circ h](x) = 6x - 12 + 2$

$\qquad\qquad = 6x - 10$

$[h \circ g](x) = 2(3x + 2) - 4$

$\qquad\qquad = 6x + 4 - 4$

$\qquad\qquad = 6x$

50. $g(x) = x + 4$, $h(x) = x^2 - 3x - 28$

$[g \circ h](x) = x^2 - 3x - 28 + 4$

$\qquad\qquad = x^2 - 3x - 24$

$[h \circ g](x) = (x + 4)^2 - 3(x + 4) - 28$

$\qquad\qquad = x^2 + 8x + 16 - 3x - 12 - 28$

$\qquad\qquad = x^2 + 5x - 24$

51. $f(x) = x^3 + 6x^2 - 13x - 42$

Possible values of p are ± 1, ± 2, ± 3, ± 6, ± 7, ± 14, ± 21, and ± 42.

Possible values of q are ± 1.

Possible rational zeros are ± 1, ± 2, ± 3, ± 6, ± 7, ± 14, ± 21, and ± 42.

$\dfrac{p}{q}$	1	6	−13	−42
−7	1	−1	−6	0
−2	1	4	−21	0
3	1	9	14	0

The rational zeros of $f(x)$ are -7, -2, and 3.

52. $h(x) = 24x^3 - 86x^2 + 57x + 20$

Possible values of p are ± 1, ± 2, ± 4, ± 5, ± 10, and ± 20.

Possible values of q are ± 1, ± 2, ± 3, ± 4, ± 6, ± 8, ± 12, and ± 24.

Possible rational zeros of $h(x)$ are ± 1, $\pm \frac{1}{2}$, $\pm \frac{1}{3}$, $\pm \frac{1}{4}$, $\pm \frac{1}{6}$, $\pm \frac{1}{8}$, $\pm \frac{1}{12}$, $\pm \frac{1}{24}$, ± 2, $\pm \frac{2}{3}$, ± 4, $\pm \frac{4}{3}$, ± 5, $\pm \frac{5}{2}$, $\pm \frac{5}{3}$, $\pm \frac{5}{4}$, $\pm \frac{5}{6}$, $\pm \frac{5}{8}$, $\pm \frac{5}{12}$, $\ldots$

$\dfrac{p}{q}$	24	−86	57	20
$-\dfrac{1}{4}$	24	−92	80	0
$\dfrac{4}{3}$	24	−54	−15	0
$\dfrac{5}{2}$	24	−26	−8	0

The rational zeros of $h(x)$ are $-\frac{1}{4}$, $\frac{4}{3}$, and $\frac{5}{2}$.

53. $16^{\frac{3}{2}} = (4^2)^{\frac{3}{2}}$

$\qquad\quad = (4)^{2 \cdot \frac{3}{2}}$

$\qquad\quad = 4^3$

$\qquad\quad = 64$

54. $64^{\frac{1}{3}} \cdot 64^{\frac{1}{2}} = 64^{\left(\frac{1}{3} + \frac{1}{2}\right)}$

$\qquad\qquad\quad = 64^{\frac{5}{6}}$

$\qquad\qquad\quad = (2^6)^{\frac{5}{6}}$

$\qquad\qquad\quad = 2^{6 \cdot \frac{5}{6}}$

$\qquad\qquad\quad = 2^5$

$\qquad\qquad\quad = 32$

55. $\dfrac{3^{\frac{4}{3}}}{81^{\frac{1}{12}}} = \left(3^{\frac{4}{3}}\right) \div (3^4)^{\frac{1}{12}}$

$\qquad\quad = \left(3^{\frac{4}{3}}\right) \div \left(3^{\frac{4}{12}}\right)$

$\qquad\quad = \left(3^{\frac{4}{3}}\right) \div \left(3^{\frac{1}{3}}\right)$

$\qquad\quad = 3^{\frac{4}{3} - \frac{1}{3}}$

$\qquad\quad = 3^{\frac{3}{3}}$

$\qquad\quad = 3$

56. $\sqrt{x} - 5 = -3$

$\qquad \sqrt{x} = 5 - 3$

$\qquad \sqrt{x} = 2$

$\qquad\quad x = 4$

57. $\sqrt{x + 4} = 11$

$\qquad x + 4 = 11^2$

$\qquad x + 4 = 121$

$\qquad\quad x = 121 - 4$

$\qquad\quad x = 117$

58. $12 - \sqrt{x} = -2$

$\qquad -\sqrt{x} = -12 - 2$

$\qquad -\sqrt{x} = -14$

$\qquad\quad x = 14^2$

$\qquad\quad x = 196$

59. $\sqrt{x - 5} = \sqrt{2x + 2}$

$\qquad x - 5 = 2x + 2$

$\qquad 2x - x = -5 - 2$

$\qquad\quad x = -7$

60. $\sqrt{x - 3} = \sqrt{2} - \sqrt{x}$
$$x - 3 = 2 + x - 2\sqrt{2x}$$
$$-5 = -2\sqrt{2x}$$
$$25 = 4(2x)$$
$$25 = 8x$$
$$\frac{25}{8} = x$$

61. $\quad 3 - \sqrt{x} = \sqrt{x - 6}$
$$9 + x - 6\sqrt{x} = x - 6$$
$$-6\sqrt{x} = -15$$
$$36x = 225$$
$$x = \frac{225}{36}$$
$$x = \frac{25}{4}$$

7-9 Square Root Functions and Inequalities

Page 396 Graphing Calculator Investigation

1.

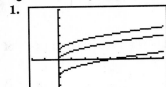

[−2, 8] scl: 1 by [−4, 6] scl: 1

$y = \sqrt{x}$ D: $x \geq 0$ R: $y \geq 0$
$y = \sqrt{x} + 1$ D: $x \geq 0$ R: $y \geq 1$
$y = \sqrt{x} - 2$ D: $x \geq 0$ R: $y \geq -2$

The graphs are the same except they are translated vertically.

2.

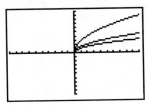

[−10, 10] scl: 1 by [−10, 10] scl: 1

$y = \sqrt{x}$ D: $x \geq 0$ R: $y \geq 0$
$y = \sqrt{2x}$ D: $x \geq 0$ R: $y \geq 0$
$y = \sqrt{8x}$ D: $x \geq 0$ R: $y \geq 0$

The graphs are the same except they get increasingly less steep.

3. To translate the graph $y = \sqrt{x}$ to the left three units, add 3 units to the x-term.
$$y = \sqrt{(x + 3)}$$
$$= \sqrt{x + 3}$$

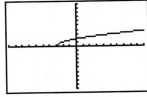

[−10, 10] scl: 1 by [−10, 10] scl: 1

Pages 397-398 Check for Understanding

1. In order for it to be a square root, only the nonnegative range can be considered.

2. The graph of $y = \sqrt{x} - 4$ has no x-intercept and its y-intercept is -4. The graph of $y = \sqrt{x - 4}$ has no y-intercept and its x-intercept is 4.

3. Sample answer: $y = \sqrt{2x - 4}$

4. $\sqrt{x} \geq 0$ $y = \sqrt{x} + 2$
$\quad x \geq 0$ $y \geq \sqrt{0} + 2$
              $y \geq 2$

x	y
0	2
1	3
2	3.4
3	3.7
4	4

D: $x \geq 0$, R: $y \geq 2$

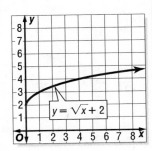

5. $\sqrt{4x} \geq 0$ $y = \sqrt{4x}$
$\quad 4x \geq 0$ $y \geq \sqrt{0}$
$\quad\ x \geq 0$ $y \geq 0$

x	y
0	0
1	2
2	2.8
3	3.5
4	4

D: $x \geq 0$, R: $y \geq 0$

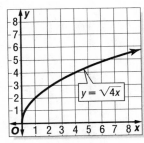

6. $\sqrt{x} \geq 0$ $y = 3 - \sqrt{x}$
$\quad x \geq 0$ $y \leq 3 - \sqrt{0}$
             $y \leq 3$

x	y
0	3
1	2
2	1.6
3	1.3
4	1

D: $x \geq 0$, R: $y \leq 3$

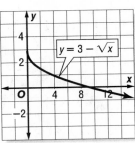

7. $\sqrt{x - 1} \geq 0$ $y = \sqrt{x - 1} + 3$
$\quad x - 1 \geq 0$ $y \geq \sqrt{0} + 3$
$\qquad\ x \geq 1$ $y \geq 3$

x	y
1	3
2	4
3	4.4
4	4.7

D: $x \geq 1$, R: $y \geq 3$

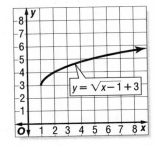

---

8. $y \leq \sqrt{x - 4} + 1$

The domain includes values for $x \geq 4$.

Test (5, 1).

$1 \leq \sqrt{5 - 4} + 1$

$1 \leq \sqrt{1} + 1$

$1 \leq 2$ true

Shade the region that does include (5, 1).

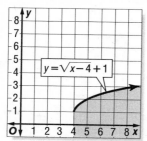

9. $y > \sqrt{2x + 4}$

The domain includes values for $x \geq -2$.

Test (0, 1).

$1 > \sqrt{2(0) + 4}$

$1 > \sqrt{4}$

$1 > 2$ false

Shade the region that does not include (0, 1).

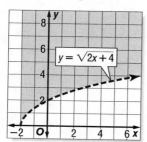

10. $y < 3 - \sqrt{5x + 1}$

The domain includes values for $x \geq -\frac{1}{5}$.

Test (3, 0).

$0 < 3 - \sqrt{5(3) + 1}$

$0 < 3 - \sqrt{16}$

$0 < 3 - 4$

$0 < -1$ false

Shade the region that does not include (3, 0).

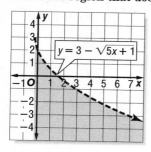

11. $y \geq \sqrt{x + 2} - 1$

The domain includes values for $x \geq -2$.

Test (2, 0).

$0 \geq \sqrt{2 + 2} - 1$

$0 \geq \sqrt{4} - 1$

$0 \geq 2 - 1$

$0 \geq 1$ false

Shade the region that does not include (2, 0).

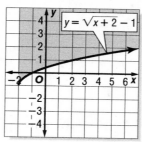

12. The velocity, v, as a function of the maximum height of the water is

$v = \sqrt{2gh}$.

$v^2 = 2gh$

$\frac{v^2}{2g} = h$

The maximum height of the water as a function of its velocity is $h = \frac{v^2}{2g}$.

13. $v = 75$

$h = \frac{(75)^2}{2(32)}$

$= \frac{5625}{64}$

$h \approx 87.9$

Yes; Sample answer: The advertised pump will reach a maximum height of 87.9 ft.

Pages 398-399   Practice and Apply

14.

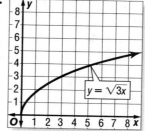

D: $x \geq 0$ R: $y \geq 0$

15.

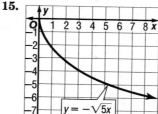

D: $x \geq 0$ R: $y \leq 0$

16.

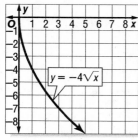

D: $x \geq 0$ R: $y \leq 0$

17.

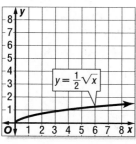

D: $x \geq 0$ R: $y \geq 0$

18.

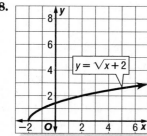

D: $x \geq -2$ R: $y \geq 0$

19.

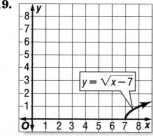

D: $x \geq 7$ R: $y \geq 0$

20.

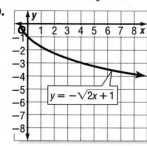

D: $x \geq -0.5$ R: $y \leq 0$

21.

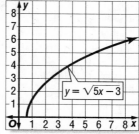

D: $x \geq 0.6$ R: $y \geq 0$

22.

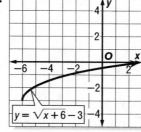

D: $x \geq -6$ R: $y \geq -3$

23.

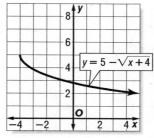

D: $x \geq -4$ R: $y \leq 5$

24.

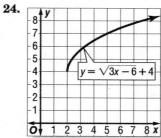

D: $x \geq 2$ R: $y \geq 4$

25.

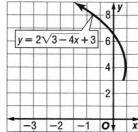

D: $x \leq 0.75$ R: $y \geq 3$

26.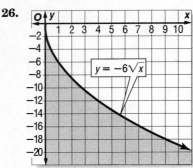

$y = -6\sqrt{x}$

27.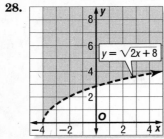

$y = \sqrt{x} + 5$

28.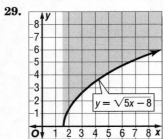

$y = \sqrt{2x + 8}$

29.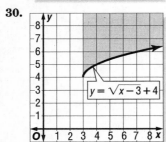

$y = \sqrt{5x - 8}$

30.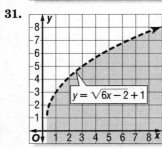

$y = \sqrt{x - 3} + 4$

31.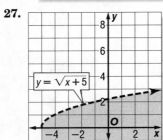

$y = \sqrt{6x - 2} + 1$

32. $90 = \sqrt{10^2 + 64h}$
$8100 = 100 + 64h$
$8000 = 64h$
$h = \frac{8000}{64}$
$h = 125$

The engineer should make the hill 125 feet high.

33. $r = \sqrt{\frac{(3960)^2(140)}{120}} - 3960$
$= \sqrt{18,295,200} - 3960$
$= 4277.29 - 3960$
$= 317.29$

The astronaut is 317.29 mi above the Earth's surface.

34.
$r = \sqrt{\frac{3960^2 W_E}{W_S}} - 3960$

$99 = \sqrt{\frac{(3960)^2(125)}{W_S}} - 3960$

$4059 = \sqrt{\frac{(3960)^2(125)}{W_S}}$

$16,475,481 = \frac{(3960)^2(125)}{W_S}$

$(16,475,481)W_S = (3960)^2(125)$

$W_S = \frac{(3960)^2(125)}{16,475,481}$

$W_S = 119$

The astronaut weighs 119 lb at 99 miles above the Earth's surface.

35. See students' work.

36. If a is negative, the graph is reflected over the x-axis. The larger the value of a, the less steep the graph. If h is positive, the origin is translated to the right, and if h is negative, the origin is translated to the left. When k is positive, the origin is translated up, and when k is negative, the origin is translated down.

37. Square root functions are used in bridge design because the engineers must determine what diameter of steel cable needs to be used to support a bridge based on its weight. Answers should include the following:
- Sample answer: when the weight to be supported is less than 8 tons
- $w = 8d^2$
  $= 8(9^2)$
  $= 8(81)$
  $= 648$ tons

38. C; $5x - 3 \geq 0$
$5x \geq 3$
$x \geq \frac{3}{5}$
$D = \left\{ x \mid x \geq \frac{3}{5} \right\}$

39. D; Based on the graph, the domain is $x \geq 1$ and this rules out I and II.

40. $f(x) = 3x, g(x) = \frac{1}{3}x$

$(f \circ g)(x) = 3\left(\frac{1}{3}x\right)$

$\qquad = x$

$(g \circ f)(x) = \frac{1}{3}(3x)$

$\qquad = x$

Yes, $f(x)$ and $g(x)$ are inverse functions.

41. $f(x) = 4x - 5, g(x) = \frac{1}{4}x - \frac{5}{16}$

$(f \circ g)(x) = 4\left(\frac{1}{4}x - \frac{5}{16}\right) - 5$

$\qquad = x - \frac{5}{4} - 5$

$\qquad = x - \frac{25}{4}$

$(g \circ f)(x) = \frac{1}{4}(4x - 5) - \frac{5}{16}$

$\qquad = x - \frac{5}{4} - \frac{5}{16}$

$\qquad = x - \frac{25}{16}$

No, $f(x)$ and $g(x)$ are not inverse functions.

42. $f(x) = \frac{3x + 2}{7}, g(x) = \frac{7x - 2}{3}$

$(f \circ g)(x) = \dfrac{3\left(\frac{7x - 2}{3}\right) + 2}{7}$

$\qquad = \dfrac{7x - 2 + 2}{7}$

$\qquad = \dfrac{7x}{7}$

$\qquad = x$

$(g \circ f)(x) = \dfrac{7\left(\frac{3x + 2}{7}\right) - 2}{3}$

$\qquad = \dfrac{3x + 2 - 2}{3}$

$\qquad = \dfrac{3x}{3}$

$\qquad = x$

Yes, $f(x)$ and $g(x)$ are inverse functions.

43. $f(x) = x + 5, g(x) = x - 3$

$(f + g)(x) = x + 5 + x - 3$

$\qquad = 2x + 2$

$(f - g)(x) = (x + 5) - (x - 3)$

$\qquad = x + 5 - x + 3$

$\qquad = 8$

$(f \cdot g)(x) = (x + 5)(x - 3)$

$\qquad = x^2 + 2x - 15$

$\left(\frac{f}{g}\right)(x) = \frac{x + 5}{x - 3}, x \neq 3$

44. $f(x) = 10x - 20, g(x) = x - 2$

$(f + g)(x) = 10x - 20 + x - 2$

$\qquad = 11x - 22$

$(f - g)(x) = (10x - 20) - (x - 2)$

$\qquad = 10x - 20 - x + 2$

$\qquad = 9x - 18$

$(f \cdot g)(x) = (10x - 20)(x - 2)$

$\qquad = 10x^2 - 20x - 20x + 40$

$\qquad = 10x^2 - 40x + 40$

$\left(\frac{f}{g}\right)(x) = \frac{10x - 20}{x - 2}$

$\qquad = \frac{10(x - 2)}{(x - 2)}, x \neq 2$

$\qquad = 10, x \neq 2$

45. $f(x) = 4x^2 - 9, g(x) = \frac{1}{2x + 3}$

$(f + g)(x) = 4x^2 - 9 + \frac{1}{2x + 3}$

$\qquad = \dfrac{(4x^2 - 9)(2x + 3) + 1}{(2x + 3)}, x \neq -\frac{3}{2}$

$\qquad = \dfrac{8x^3 + 12x^2 - 18x - 27 + 1}{2x + 3}, x \neq -\frac{3}{2}$

$\qquad = \dfrac{8x^3 + 12x^2 - 18x - 26}{2x + 3}, x \neq -\frac{3}{2}$

$(f - g)(x) = 4x - 9 - \frac{1}{2x + 3}$

$\qquad = \dfrac{(4x^2 - 9)(2x + 3) - 1}{2x + 3}, x \neq -\frac{3}{2}$

$\qquad = \dfrac{8x^3 + 12x^2 - 18x - 27 - 1}{2x + 3}, x \neq -\frac{3}{2}$

$\qquad = \dfrac{8x^3 + 12x^2 - 18x - 28}{2x + 3}, x \neq -\frac{3}{2}$

$(f \cdot g)(x) = (4x^2 - 9)\left(\frac{1}{2x + 3}\right)$

$\qquad = \dfrac{(2x - 3)(2x + 3)}{2x + 3}, x \neq -\frac{3}{2}$

$\qquad = 2x - 3, x \neq -\frac{3}{2}$

$\left(\frac{f}{g}\right)(x) = \dfrac{4x^2 - 9}{\frac{1}{2x + 3}}$

$\qquad = (4x^2 - 9) \div \frac{1}{2x + 3}$

$\qquad = (4x^2 - 9) \cdot (2x + 3), x \neq -\frac{3}{2}$

$\qquad = 8x^3 - 18x + 12x^2 - 27, x \neq -\frac{3}{2}$

$\qquad = 8x^3 + 12x^2 - 18x - 27, x \neq -\frac{3}{2}$

46. 4; If x is your number, you can write the expression $\frac{3x + x + 8}{x + 2}$, which equals 4 after dividing the numerator and denominator by the GCF, $x + 2$.

47. $(x + 2)(2x - 8) = 2x^2 - 8x + 4x - 16$

$\qquad = 2x^2 - 4x - 16$

48. $(3p + 5)(2p - 4) = 6p^2 - 12p + 10p - 20$

$\qquad = 6p^2 - 2p - 20$

49. $(a^2 + a + 1)(a - 1) = a^3 - a^2 + a^2 - a + a - 1$

$\qquad = a^3 - 1$

Chapter 7   Study Guide and Review

Page 400   Vocabulary and Concept Check

1. f; relative minimum

2. d; leading coefficient

3. a; Complex Conjugates Theorem

4. b; depressed polynomial

5. e; quadratic form

6. c; inverse functions

Pages 400–404   Lesson-by-Lesson Review

7. $p(x) = x - 2$

$p(-4) = -4 - 2$

$\qquad = -6$

$p(x + h) = (x + h) - 2$

$\qquad = x + h - 2$

8. $p(x) = -x + 4$
$p(-4) = -(-4) + 4$
$\quad\quad\;\; = 4 + 4$
$\quad\quad\;\; = 8$
$p(x + h) = -(x + h) + 4$
$\quad\quad\quad\; = -x - h + 4$

9. $p(x) = 6x + 3$
$p(-4) = 6(-4) + 3$
$\quad\quad\;\; = -24 + 3$
$\quad\quad\;\; = -21$
$p(x + h) = 6(x + h) + 3$
$\quad\quad\quad\; = 6x + 6h + 3$

10. $p(x) = x^2 + 5$
$p(-4) = (-4)^2 + 5$
$\quad\quad\;\; = 16 + 5$
$\quad\quad\;\; = 21$
$p(x + h) = (x + h)^2 + 5$
$\quad\quad\quad\; = x^2 + 2hx + h^2 + 5$

11. $p(x) = x^2 - x$
$p(-4) = (-4)^2 - (-4)$
$\quad\quad\;\; = 16 + 4$
$\quad\quad\;\; = 20$
$p(x + h) = (x + h)^2 - (x + h)$
$\quad\quad\quad\; = x^2 + 2hx + h^2 - x - h$

12. $p(x) = 2x^3 - 1$
$p(-4) = 2(-4)^3 - 1$
$\quad\quad\;\; = 2(-64) - 1$
$\quad\quad\;\; = -128 - 1$
$\quad\quad\;\; = -129$
$p(x + h) = 2(x + h)^3 - 1$
$\quad\quad\quad\; = 2(x^3 + 3hx^2 + 3h^2x + h^3) - 1$
$\quad\quad\quad\; = 2x^3 + 6hx^2 + 6h^2x + 2h^3 - 1$

13a. $h(x) = x^3 - 6x - 9$

x	$h(x)$
-2	-5
-1	-4
0	-9
1	-14
2	-13
3	0

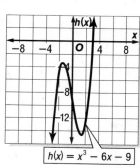

13b. There is a real zero at $x = 3$.

13c. Sample answer: relative maximum at $x = -1.4$, relative minimum at $x = 1.4$

14a. $f(x) = x^4 + 7x + 1$

x	$f(x)$
-2	3
-1	-5
0	1
1	9
2	31

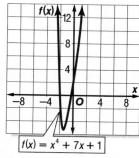

14b. There are real zeros between -2 and -1 and between -1 and 0.

14c. Sample answer: no relative maximum, relative minimum at $x = -1.2$

15a. $f(x) = x^5 + x^4 - 2x^3 + 1$

x	$f(x)$
-3	-107
-2	1
-1	3
0	1
1	1
2	33

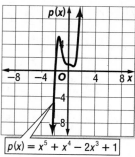

15b. There is a real zero between -3 and -2.

15c. Sample answer: relative maximum at $x = -1.6$, relative minimum at $x = 0.8$

16a. $g(x) = x^3 - x^2 + 1$

x	$g(x)$
-2	-11
-1	-1
0	1
1	1
2	5

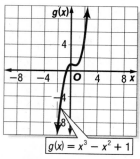

16b. There is a real zero between -1 and 0.

16c. Sample answer: relative maximum at $x = 0$, relative minimum at $x = 0.7$

17a. $r(x) = 4x^3 + x^2 - 11x + 3$

x	$r(x)$
-2	-3
-1	11
0	3
1	-3
2	17

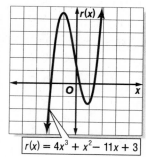

17b. There are real zeros between -2 and -1, between 0 and 1, and between 1 and 2.

17c. Sample answer: relative maximum at $x = -1$, relative minimum at $x = 0.9$

18a. $f(x) = x^3 + 4x^2 + x - 2$

x	$f(x)$
-4	-6
-3	4
-2	4
-2	0
0	-2
1	4

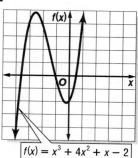

18b. There are real zeros between -4 and -3, at $x = -1$, and between 0 and 1.

18c. Sample answer: relative maximum at $x = -2.5$, relative minimum at $x = -0.1$

19. $3x^3 + 4x^2 - 15x = 0$

$x(3x^2 + 4x - 15) = 0$

$x = 0$ or $3x^2 + 4x - 15 = 0$

$x = \dfrac{-4 \pm \sqrt{16 + 180}}{6}$

$x = \dfrac{-4 \pm 14}{6}$

$x = \dfrac{-4 + 14}{6}$ or $x = \dfrac{-4 - 14}{6}$

$x = \dfrac{10}{6}$ $\qquad$ $x = -\dfrac{18}{6}$

$x = \dfrac{5}{3}$ $\qquad$ $x = -3$

20. $\qquad m^4 + 3m^3 = 40m^2$

$m^4 + 3m^3 - 40m^2 = 0$

$m^2(m^2 + 3m - 40) = 0$

$m^2(m + 8)(m - 5) = 0$

$m^2 = 0$ or $m + 8 = 0$ or $m - 5 = 0$

$m = 0$ $\qquad$ $m = -8$ $\qquad$ $m = 5$

21. $\qquad a^3 - 64 = 0$

$(a - 4)(a^2 + 4a + 16) = 0$

$a - 4 = 0$ or $a^2 + 4a + 16 = 0$

$a = 4$ $\qquad a = \dfrac{-4 \pm \sqrt{16 - 64}}{2}$

$\qquad\qquad\qquad a = \dfrac{-4 \pm 4i\sqrt{3}}{2}$

$\qquad\qquad\qquad a = \dfrac{2(-2 \pm 2i\sqrt{3})}{2}$

$\qquad\qquad\qquad a = -2 \pm 2i\sqrt{3}$

22. $r + 9\sqrt{r} = -8$

If $r \geq 0$, then the right hand side of the equation is always positive, $r + 9\sqrt{r} \geq 0$, and the left hand side of the equation is always negative, $-8 < 0$. Thus, no r exists that satisfies the equation. $\varnothing$

23. $\qquad x^4 - 8x^2 + 16 = 0$

$(x^2)^2 - 8(x^2) + 16 = 0$

$(x^2 - 4)^2 = 0$

$x^2 - 4 = 0$

$x^2 = 4$

$x = \pm 2$

24. $\qquad x^{\frac{2}{3}} - 9x^{\frac{1}{3}} + 20 = 0$

$\left(x^{\frac{1}{3}}\right)^2 - 9\left(x^{\frac{1}{3}}\right) + 20 = 0$

$\left(x^{\frac{1}{3}} - 4\right)\left(x^{\frac{1}{3}} - 5\right) = 0$

$x^{\frac{1}{3}} - 4 = 0$ or $x^{\frac{1}{3}} - 5 = 0$

$x^{\frac{1}{3}} = 4$ $\qquad$ $x^{\frac{1}{3}} = 5$

$x = 4^3$ $\qquad$ $x = 5^3$

$x = 64$ $\qquad$ $x = 125$

25. $f(x) = x^2 - 5$

$$\begin{array}{r|rrr} 3 & 1 & 0 & -5 \\ & & 3 & 9 \\ \hline & 1 & 3 & 4 \end{array}$$

So, $f(3) = 4$.

$$\begin{array}{r|rrr} -2 & 1 & 0 & -5 \\ & & -2 & 4 \\ \hline & 1 & -2 & -1 \end{array}$$

So, $f(-2) = -1$.

26. $f(x) = x^2 - 4x + 4$

$$\begin{array}{r|rrr} 3 & 1 & -4 & 4 \\ & & 3 & -3 \\ \hline & 1 & -1 & 1 \end{array}$$

So, $f(3) = 1$.

$$\begin{array}{r|rrr} -2 & 1 & -4 & 4 \\ & & -2 & 12 \\ \hline & 1 & -6 & 16 \end{array}$$

So, $f(-2) = 16$.

27. $f(x) = x^3 - 3x^2 + 4x + 8$

$$\begin{array}{r|rrrr} 3 & 1 & -3 & 4 & 8 \\ & & 3 & 0 & 12 \\ \hline & 1 & 0 & 4 & 20 \end{array}$$

So, $f(3) = 20$.

$$\begin{array}{r|rrrr} -2 & 1 & -3 & 4 & 8 \\ & & -2 & 10 & -28 \\ \hline & 1 & -5 & 14 & -20 \end{array}$$

So, $f(-2) = -20$.

28.

$$\begin{array}{r|rrrr} -1 & 1 & 5 & 8 & 4 \\ & & -1 & -4 & -4 \\ \hline & 1 & 4 & 4 & 0 \end{array}$$

$x^3 + 5x^2 + 8x + 4 = (x + 1)(x^2 + 4x + 4)$
$\qquad\qquad\qquad\qquad\ = (x + 1)(x + 2)(x + 2)$

29.

$$\begin{array}{r|rrrr} -2 & 1 & 4 & 7 & 6 \\ & & -2 & -4 & -6 \\ \hline & 1 & 2 & 3 & 0 \end{array}$$

$x^3 + 4x^2 + 7x + 6 = (x + 2)(x^2 + 2x + 3)$

30. $f(x) = 2x^4 - x^3 + 5x^2 + 3x - 9$

$\qquad\qquad$ yes $\quad$ yes $\quad$ no $\quad$ yes

$f(-x) = 2(-x)^4 - (-x)^3 + 5(-x)^2 + 3(-x) - 9$

$\qquad = 2x^4 + x^3 - 5x^2 - 3x - 9$

$\qquad\qquad$ no $\quad$ yes $\quad$ no $\quad$ no

The number of possible positive real zeros is 3 or 1.

The number of possible negative real zeros is 1.

The number of possible imaginary zeros is 0 or 2.

31. $f(x) = 7x^3 + 5x - 1$

$\qquad\qquad$ no $\quad$ yes

$f(-x) = -7x^3 - 5x - 1$

$\qquad\qquad$ no $\quad$ no

The number of possible positive real zeros is 1.

The number of possible negative real zeros is 0.

The number of possible imaginary zeros is 2.

32. $f(x) = -4x^4 - x^2 - x + 1$

$\underbrace{}_{\text{no}}\ \underbrace{}_{\text{no}}\ \underbrace{}_{\text{yes}}$

$f(-x) = -4(-x)^4 - (-x)^2 - (-x) + 1$

$\qquad = -4x^4 - x^2 + x + 1$

$\underbrace{}_{\text{no}}\ \underbrace{}_{\text{yes}}\ \underbrace{}_{\text{no}}$

The number of possible positive real zeros is 1.
The number of possible negative real zeros is 1.
The number of possible imaginary zeros is 2.

33. $f(x) = 3x^4 - x^3 + 8x^2 + x - 7$

$\underbrace{}_{\text{yes}}\ \underbrace{}_{\text{yes}}\ \underbrace{}_{\text{no}}\ \underbrace{}_{\text{yes}}$

$f(-x) = 3(-x)^4 - (-x)^3 + 8(-x)^2 + (-x) - 7$

$\qquad = 3x^4 + x^3 + 8x^2 - x - 7$

$\underbrace{}_{\text{no}}\ \underbrace{}_{\text{no}}\ \underbrace{}_{\text{yes}}\ \underbrace{}_{\text{no}}$

The number of possible positive real zeros is 3 or 1.
The number of possible negative real zeros is 1.
The number of possible imaginary zeros is 0 or 2.

34. $f(x) = x^4 + x^3 - 7x + 1$

$\underbrace{}_{\text{no}}\ \underbrace{}_{\text{yes}}\ \underbrace{}_{\text{yes}}$

$f(-x) = x^4 - x^3 + 7x + 1$

$\underbrace{}_{\text{yes}}\ \underbrace{}_{\text{yes}}\ \underbrace{}_{\text{no}}$

The number of possible positive real zeros is 2 or 0.
The number of possible negative real zeros is 2 or 0.
The number of possible imaginary zeros is 4, 2, or 0.

35. $f(x) = 2x^4 - 3x^3 - 2x^2 + 3$

$\underbrace{}_{\text{yes}}\ \underbrace{}_{\text{no}}\ \underbrace{}_{\text{yes}}$

$f(-x) = 2x^4 + 3x^3 - 2x^2 + 3$

$\underbrace{}_{\text{no}}\ \underbrace{}_{\text{yes}}\ \underbrace{}_{\text{yes}}$

The number of possible positive real zeros is 2 or 0.
The number of possible negative real zeros is 2 or 0.
The number of possible imaginary zeros is 4, 2, or 0.

36. $f(x) = 2x^3 - 13x^2 + 17x + 12$

Possible values of p are ± 1, ± 2, ± 3, ± 4, ± 6, and ± 12.

Possible values of q are ± 1, and ± 2.

Possible rational zeros are ± 1, $\pm\frac{1}{2}$, ± 2, $\pm\frac{3}{2}$, ± 3, ± 6, and ± 12.

$\frac{p}{q}$	2	-13	17	12
$-\frac{1}{2}$	2	-14	24	0
3	2	-7	-4	0
4	2	-5	-3	0

The zeros are $-\frac{1}{2}$, 3, and 4.

37. $f(x) = x^4 + 5x^3 + 15x^2 + 19x + 8$

Possible values of p are ± 1, ± 2, ± 4, and ± 8.
Possible values of q are ± 1.
Possible rational zeros are ± 1, ± 2, ± 4, and ± 8.

$\frac{p}{q}$	1	5	15	19	8
-1	1	4	11	8	0

$f(x) = 8(x - 1)^2(x^2 + 2x + 1)$
The zero is -1.

38. $f(x) = x^3 - 3x^2 - 10x + 24$

Possible values of p are ± 1, ± 2, ± 3, ± 4, ± 6, ± 8, ± 12, and ± 24.
Possible values of q are ± 1.
Possible rational zeros are ± 1, ± 2, ± 3, ± 4, ± 6, ± 8, ± 12, and ± 24.

$\frac{p}{q}$	1	-3	-10	24
-3	1	-6	8	0
2	1	-1	-12	0
4	1	1	-6	0

The zeros are -3, 2, and 4.

39. $f(x) = x^4 - 4x^3 - 7x^2 + 34x - 24$

Possible values of p are ± 1, ± 2, ± 3, ± 4, ± 6, ± 8, ± 12, and ± 24.
Possible values of q are ± 1.
Possible rational zeros are ± 1, ± 2, ± 3, ± 4, ± 6, ± 8, ± 12, and ± 24.

$\frac{p}{q}$	1	-4	-7	34	-24
-3	1	-7	14	-8	0
1	1	-3	-10	24	0
2	1	-2	-11	12	0
4	1	0	-7	6	0

The zeros are -3, 1, 2, and 4.

40. $f(x) = 2x^3 - 5x^2 - 28x + 15$

Possible values of p are ± 1, ± 3, ± 5, and ± 15.
Possible values of q are ± 1, and ± 2.

Possible rational zeros are ± 1, $\pm\frac{1}{2}$, ± 3, $\pm\frac{3}{2}$, ± 5, $\pm\frac{5}{2}$, ± 15, and $\pm\frac{15}{2}$.

$\frac{p}{q}$	2	-5	-28	15
-3	2	-11	5	0
$\frac{1}{2}$	2	-4	-30	0
5	2	5	-3	0

The zeros are -3, $\frac{1}{2}$, and 5.

41. $f(x) = 2x^4 - 9x^3 - 2x^2 + 21x - 10$

Possible values of p are ± 1, ± 2, ± 5, and ± 10.

Possible values of q are ± 1, and ± 2.

Possible rational zeros are ± 1, $\pm \frac{1}{2}$, ± 2, ± 5, $\pm \frac{5}{2}$, and ± 10.

$\frac{p}{q}$	2	-9	2	21	-10
$\frac{1}{2}$	2	-8	-2	20	0
2	2	-5	-8	5	0

The zeros are $\frac{1}{2}$ and 2.

42. $[g \circ h](x) = g[h(x)]$
$= g(2x - 1)$
$= 3(2x - 1) + 4$
$= 6x - 3 + 4$
$= 6x + 1$

$[h \circ g](x) = h[g(x)]$
$= h(3x + 4)$
$= 2(3x + 4) - 1$
$= 6x + 8 - 1$
$= 6x + 7$

43. $[g \circ h](x) = g[h(x)]$
$= g(x^2 + 2)$
$= (x^2 + 2) - 3$
$= x^2 - 1$

$[h \circ g](x) = h[g(x)]$
$= h(x - 3)$
$= (x - 3)^2 + 2$
$= x^2 - 6x + 9 + 2$
$= x^2 - 6x + 11$

44. $[g \circ h](x) = g[h(x)]$
$= g(x^2 + 1)$
$= -2(x^2 + 1) + 1$
$= -2x^2 - 2 + 1$
$= -2x^2 - 1$

$[h \circ g](x) = h[g(x)]$
$= h(-2x + 1)$
$= (-2x + 1)^2 + 1$
$= 4x^2 - 4x + 1 + 1$
$= 4x^2 - 4x + 2$

45. $[g \circ h](x) = g[h(x)]$
$= g(-5x)$
$= 3(-5x) - 5$
$= -15x - 5$

$[h \circ g](x) = h[g(x)]$
$= h(3x - 5)$
$= -5(3x - 5)$
$= -15x + 25$

46. $[g \circ h](x) = g[h(x)]$
$= g(x^3)$
$= x^3 - 2$

$[h \circ g](x) = h[g(x)]$
$= h(x - 2)$
$= (x - 2)^3$
$= x^3 - 6x^2 + 12x - 8$

47. $[g \circ h](x) = g[h(x)]$
$= g(x + 4)$
$= |x + 4|$

$[h \circ g](x) = h[g(x)]$
$= h(|x|)$
$= |x| + 4$

48. $f(x) = 3x - 4$
$y = 3x - 4$
$x = 3y - 4$
$x + 4 = 3y$
$\frac{x + 4}{3} = y$
$f^{-1}(x) = \frac{x + 4}{3}$

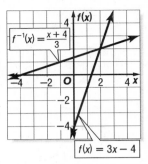

49. $f(x) = -2x - 3$
$y = -2x - 3$
$x = -2y - 3$
$x + 3 = -2y$
$\frac{-(x + 3)}{2} = y$
$f^{-1}(x) = \frac{-x - 3}{2}$

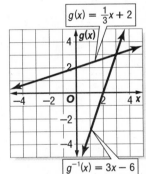

50. $g(x) = \frac{1}{3}x + 2$
$y = \frac{1}{3}x + 2$
$x = \frac{1}{3}y + 2$
$x - 2 = \frac{1}{3}y$
$3(x - 2) = y$
$g^{-1}(x) = 3x - 6$

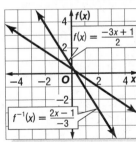

51. $f(x) = \frac{-3x + 1}{2}$
$y = \frac{-3x + 1}{2}$
$x = \frac{-3y + 1}{2}$
$2x = -3y + 1$
$2x - 1 = -3y$
$\frac{2x - 1}{-3} = y$
$f^{-1}(x) = \frac{2x - 1}{-3}$

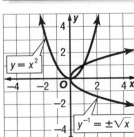

52. $y = x^2$
$x = y^2$
$\pm\sqrt{x} = y$
$y^{-1} = \pm\sqrt{x}$

53.
$$y = (2x + 3)^2$$
$$x = (2y + 3)^2$$
$$\pm\sqrt{x} = 2y + 3$$
$$\pm\sqrt{x} - 3 = 2y$$
$$\frac{\pm\sqrt{x} - 3}{2} = y$$
$$y^{-1} = \pm\frac{1}{2}\sqrt{x} - \frac{3}{2}$$

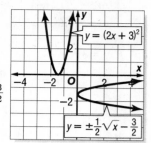

54. $x + 2 \geq 0$
D: $x \geq -2$
R: $y \geq 0$

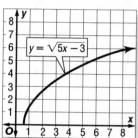

55. $5x - 3 \geq 0$
$5x \geq 3$
D: $x \geq \frac{3}{5}$
R: $y \geq 0$

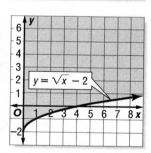

56. $x - 3 \geq 0$
D: $x \geq 3$
R: $y \geq 4$

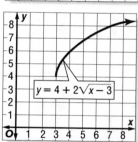

57. $y \geq \sqrt{x} - 2$

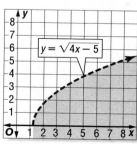

58. $y < \sqrt{4x - 5}$

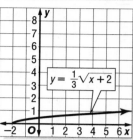

Chapter 7 Practice Test

Page 405

1. b; composition of functions

2. c; inverse functions

3. a; quadratic form

4a. $g(x) = x^3 + 6x^2 + 6x - 4$

x	g(x)
−5	−9
−4	4
−3	5
−2	0
−1	−5
0	−4
1	9

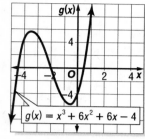

4b. The real zeros are between −5 and −4, at $x = -2$, and between 0 and 1.

4c. Sample answer: relative maximum at $x = -3.5$, relative mimimum at $x = -0.5$

5a. $h(x) = x^4 + 6x^3 + 8x^2 - x$

x	h(x)
−4	4
−3	−6
−2	2
−1	4
0	0
1	14

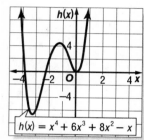

5b. The real zeros are between −4 and −3 and at $x = 0$.

5c. Sample answer: relative maximum at $x = -1.3$, relative mimimum at $x = 0$

6a. $f(x) = x^3 + 3x^2 - 2x + 1$

x	f(x)
−4	−7
−3	7
−2	9
−1	5
0	1
1	3

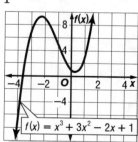

6b. The real zero is between −4 and −3.

6c. Sample answer: relative maximum at $x = -2.3$, relative mimimum at $x = 0.3$

7a. $g(x) = x^4 - 2x^3 - 6x^2 + 8x + 5$

x	$g(x)$
-3	62
-2	-3
-1	-6
0	5
1	6
2	-3
3	2

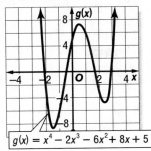

$g(x) = x^4 - 2x^3 - 6x^2 + 8x + 5$

7b. The real zeros are between -3 and -2, between -1 and 0, between 1 and 2, and between 2 and 3.

7c. Sample answer: relative maximum at $x = 0.6$, relative mimimum at $x = -1.5$ and $x = 2.4$

8.
$$p^3 + 8p^2 = 18p$$
$$p^3 + 8p^2 - 18p = 0$$
$$p(p^2 + 8p - 18) = 0$$
$$p = 0 \text{ or } p^2 + 8p - 18 = 0$$
$$p = \frac{-8 \pm \sqrt{64 + 72}}{2}$$
$$p = \frac{-8 \pm 2\sqrt{34}}{2}$$
$$p = \frac{2(-4 \pm \sqrt{34})}{2}$$
$$p = -4 \pm \sqrt{34}$$

9.
$$16x^4 - x^2 = 0$$
$$x^2(16x^2 - 1) = 0$$
$$x^2(4x - 1)(4x + 1) = 0$$
$$x^2 = 0 \text{ or } 4x - 1 = 0 \text{ or } 4x + 1 = 0$$
$$x = 0 \qquad 4x = 1 \qquad 4x = -1$$
$$x = \frac{1}{4} \qquad x = -\frac{1}{4}$$

10.
$$r^4 - 9r^2 + 18 = 0$$
$$(r^2)^2 - 9(r^2) + 18 = 0$$
$$(r^2 - 6)(r^2 - 3) = 0$$
$$(r - \sqrt{6})(r + \sqrt{6})(r - \sqrt{3})(r + \sqrt{3}) = 0$$
$$r - \sqrt{6} = 0 \quad \text{or } r + \sqrt{6} = 0$$
$$r = \sqrt{6} \qquad r = -\sqrt{6}$$
$$\text{or } r - \sqrt{3} = 0 \quad \text{or } r + \sqrt{3} = 0$$
$$r = \sqrt{3} \qquad r = -\sqrt{3}$$

11. $p^{\frac{3}{2}} - 8 = 0$
$$p^{\frac{3}{2}} = 8$$
$$p^{\frac{3}{2}} = 2^3$$
$$p^{\frac{1}{2}} = 2$$
$$p = 2^2$$
$$p = 4$$

12.

$$\begin{array}{r|rrrr} -1 & 1 & -1 & -5 & -3 \\ & & -1 & 2 & 3 \\ \hline & 1 & -2 & -3 & 0 \end{array}$$

$$x^3 - x^2 - 5x - 3 = (x + 1)(x^2 - 2x - 3)$$
$$= (x + 1)(x - 3)(x + 1)$$

13.

$$\begin{array}{r|rrrr} -2 & 1 & 0 & 8 & 24 \\ & & -2 & 4 & -24 \\ \hline & 1 & -2 & 12 & 0 \end{array}$$

$$x^3 + 8x + 24 = (x + 2)(x^2 - 2x + 12)$$

14. $f(x) = x^3 - x^2 - 14x + 24$

$$\underbrace{}_{\text{yes}} \underbrace{}_{\text{no}} \underbrace{}_{\text{yes}}$$

$$f(-x) = -x^3 - x^2 + 14x + 24$$

$$\underbrace{}_{\text{no}} \underbrace{}_{\text{yes}} \underbrace{}_{\text{no}}$$

The number of possible positive real zeros is 2 or 0.
The number of possible negative real zeros is 1.
The number of possible imaginary zeros is 0 or 2.

15. $f(x) = 2x^3 - x^2 + 16x - 5$

$$\underbrace{}_{\text{yes}} \underbrace{}_{\text{yes}} \underbrace{}_{\text{yes}}$$

$$f(-x) = -2x^3 - x^2 - 16x - 5$$

$$\underbrace{}_{\text{no}} \underbrace{}_{\text{no}} \underbrace{}_{\text{no}}$$

The number of possible positive real zeros is 3 or 1.
The number of possible negative real zeros is 0.
The number of possible imaginary zeros is 2 or 0.

16. $g(x) = x^3 - 3x^2 - 53x - 9$
Possible values of p are ± 1, ± 3, and ± 9.
Possible values of q are ± 1.
Possible rational zeros are ± 1, ± 3, and ± 9.

$\frac{p}{q}$	1	-3	-53	-9
9	1	6	1	0

The rational zero is 9.

17. $h(x) = x^4 - 2x^3 - 23x^2 + 2x - 24$
Possible values of p are ± 1, ± 2, ± 3, ± 4, ± 6, ± 8, ± 12, and ± 24.
Possible values of q are ± 1.
Possible rational zeros are ± 1, ± 2, ± 3, ± 4, ± 6, ± 8, ± 12, and ± 24.

$\frac{p}{q}$	1	2	-23	2	-24
-6	1	-4	1	-4	0
4	1	6	1	6	0

The rational zeros are -6 and 4.

18. $f(x) = 4x - 9$, $g(x) = \frac{x - 9}{4}$
$$[f \circ g](x) = 4\left(\frac{x - 9}{4}\right) - 9$$
$$= x - 9 - 9$$
$$= x - 18$$
No, $f(x)$ and $g(x)$ are not inverse functions.

19. $f(x) = \frac{1}{x + 2}$, $g(x) = \frac{1}{x} - 2$
$$[f \circ g](x) = \frac{1}{\left(\frac{1}{x} - 2\right) + 2}$$
$$= \frac{1}{\frac{1}{x}}$$
$$= x$$
$$[g \circ f](x) = \frac{1}{\frac{1}{x + 2}} - 2$$
$$= x + 2 - 2$$
$$= x$$
Yes, $f(x)$ and $g(x)$ are inverse functions.

20. $f(x) = 2x - 4$
$g(x) = x^2 + 3$
$$(f + g)(x) = 2x - 4 + x^2 + 3$$
$$= x^2 + 2x - 1$$

21. $(f - g)(x) = (2x - 4) - (x^2 + 3)$
$$= 2x - 4 - x^2 - 3$$
$$= -x^2 + 2x - 7$$

22. $(f \cdot g)(x) = (2x - 4)(x^2 + 3)$
$$= 2x^3 + 6x - 4x^2 - 12$$
$$= 2x^3 - 4x^2 + 6x - 12$$

23. $\left(\dfrac{f}{g}\right)(x) = \dfrac{2x - 4}{x^2 + 3}$

24a. $A = 1000(1 + r)^6 + 1000(1 + r)^5 +$
$1000(1 + r)^4 + 1200(1 + r)^3 +$
$12000(1 + r)^2 + 2000(1 + r)$

24b. $A = 1000(1 + 0.06)^6 + 1000(1 + 0.06)^5 +$
$1000(1 + 0.06)^4 + 1200(1 + 0.06)^3 +$
$1200(1 + 0.06)^2 + 2000(1 + 0.06)$
$$= \$8916.76$$

25. D; $(-2,-2)$: $-2 \not< \sqrt{-4}$
$(-1,-1)$: $-1 \not< \sqrt{-2}$
$(0, 0)$: $0 \not< \sqrt{0}$
None of the given points is in the graph of $y < \sqrt{2x}$.

Chapter 7 Standardized Test Practice

Pages 406-407

1. B; $\dfrac{2}{p} - \dfrac{4}{p^2} = -\dfrac{2}{p^3}$
$$p^3\left(\dfrac{2}{p} - \dfrac{4}{p^2}\right) = p^3\left(-\dfrac{2}{p^3}\right)$$
$$2p^2 - 4p = -2$$
$$2p^2 - 4p + 2 = 0$$
$$2(p^2 - 2p + 1) = 0$$
$$p^2 - 2p + 1 = 0$$
$$(p - 1)^2 = 0$$
$$p - 1 = 0$$
$$p = 1$$

2. A; $100 \cdot \dfrac{k \text{ gallons of liquid in the tank}}{n \text{ gallons of liquid available}} \% = \dfrac{100k}{n} \%$

3. D; $4 < s < 9$
To form a triangle, $4 + s > 9$.
So, $s = \{6, 7, 8\}$.
There are 3 possible triangles.

4. B; $\triangle ABC$ and $\triangle DEF$ are isosceles according to the figure.
$$AC^2 + CB^2 = AB^2$$
$$AC = CB$$
$$DF = FE$$
$$2AC^2 = 12^2$$
$$2AC^2 = 144$$
$$AC^2 = 72$$
$$AC = \sqrt{72}$$
$$AC = CB = 6\sqrt{2}$$
$$\dfrac{AC}{AB} = \dfrac{DF}{DE}$$
$$\dfrac{6\sqrt{2}}{12} = \dfrac{DF}{28}$$
$$DF = FE = 14\sqrt{2}$$
The perimeter of $\triangle DEF$ is
$DF + FE + DE = 14\sqrt{2} + 14\sqrt{2} + 28$
$$= 28 + 28\sqrt{2} \text{ square units}$$

5. A; $2 - 3x > -1$
$$-3x > -3$$
$$\dfrac{-3x}{-3} < \dfrac{-3}{-3}$$
$$x < 1$$
$$x + 5 > 0$$
$$x > -5$$
$$-5 < x < 1$$

6. B; $x_m = \dfrac{-5 - 1}{2}$
$$x_m = -3$$
$$y_m = \dfrac{-3 + 4}{2}$$
$$y_m = \dfrac{1}{2}$$
The midpoint $(x_m, y_m) = \left(-3, \dfrac{1}{2}\right)$.

7. D; $m = \dfrac{-k - k}{-n - n}$
$$= \dfrac{-2k}{-2n}$$
$$= \dfrac{k}{n}$$

8. B; $3x(x + 4) + 1 = 4x - 9$
$$3x^2 + 12x + 1 = 4x - 9$$
$$3x^2 + 8x + 10 = 0$$

9. D; $\sqrt[4]{t^3} \cdot \sqrt[8]{t^2} = t^{\frac{3}{4}} \cdot t^{\frac{2}{8}}$
$$= t^{\frac{3}{4}} \cdot t^{\frac{1}{4}}$$
$$= t^{\frac{4}{4}}$$
$$= t$$

10. C; $6x^2 - 19x + 10 = 0$
$$x = \dfrac{19 \pm \sqrt{361 - 240}}{12}$$
$$x = \dfrac{19 \pm 11}{12}$$
$$x = \dfrac{19 + 11}{12} \text{ or } x = \dfrac{19 - 11}{12}$$
$$x = \dfrac{30}{12} \qquad x = \dfrac{8}{12}$$
$$x = \dfrac{5}{2} \qquad x = \dfrac{2}{3}$$
$$x = 2\dfrac{1}{2}$$

11. D; $f(x) = 3x - 5$
$$g(x) = 2 + x^2$$
$$f[g(x)] = 3(2 + x^2) - 5$$
$$= 6 + 3x^2 - 5$$
$$f[g(2)] = 6 + 3(4) - 5$$
$$= 6 + 12 - 5$$
$$= 13$$

12. B; $f(2) = 2^3 - 7(2) + 6$
$$= 8 - 14 + 6$$
$$= 0$$

13. $N = \left\lfloor \dfrac{34}{3} \right\rfloor = 11$
$$n = \left\lceil \dfrac{34}{5} \right\rceil = 7$$
$$N - n = 11 - 7$$
$$= 4$$

14. x = weight of raisins in the mixture
y = weight of peanuts in the mixture

$\begin{cases} x + y = 20 \\ 2x + 3y = 2.75 \cdot 20 \end{cases}$

$\begin{cases} x + y = 20 \\ 2x + 3y = 55 \end{cases}$

$\begin{cases} -2x - 2y = -40 \\ 2x + 3y = 55 \end{cases}$

$y = 15$

15 pounds of peanuts are needed.

15. $\dfrac{x_1 + x_2 + x_3 + \ldots + x_{15}}{15} = 82$

$x_1 + x_2 + x_3 + \ldots + x_{15} = 1230$

$\dfrac{x_1 + x_2 + x_3 + x_4 + x_5 + x_6 + x_7}{7} = 78$

$\begin{cases} x_1 + x_2 + x_3 + \ldots + x_{15} = 1230 \\ x_1 + x_2 + x_3 + x_4 + x_5 + x_6 + x_7 = 546 \end{cases}$

$x_8 + x_9 + x_{10} + x_{11} + x_{12} + x_{13} + x_{14} + x_{15} = 684$

$\dfrac{x_8 + x_9 + x_{10} + x_{11} + x_{12} + x_{13} + x_{14} + x_{15}}{8} = 85.5$

16. $x = 10 \implies x' = 5$
$y = 10 \implies y' = 10$
$z = 10 \implies z' = 10 + 5 = 15$

5 marbles need to be transferred from jar x to jar z.

17. Area of $ABC = \dfrac{(BD)(AC)}{2}$

Area of $BCD = \dfrac{(BD)(CD)}{2}$

$(CD)^2 = (BC)^2 - (BD)^2$
$ = 25 - 9$
$ = 16$
$CD = 4$

$\dfrac{(BD)(CD)}{2} = \dfrac{40}{100} \cdot \dfrac{(BD)(AC)}{2}$

$CD = \dfrac{2AC}{5}$

$4 = \dfrac{2AC}{5}$

$AC = 10$

$AD = AC - CD$

$AD = 10 - 4 = 6$

18. To form a triangle,
$8 - 3 < x < 8 + 3$ and $5 < x < 11$.
The smallest x can be is 6.
$3 + 8 + 6 = 17$
The least possible perimeter is 17.

19. $w \clubsuit 6 = 2 \clubsuit w$
$3w - 6 = 3(2) - w$
$3w + w = 6 + 6$
$4w = 12$
$w = 3$

20. D; Column A $= \left(\dfrac{2.5}{100}\right)(10x)$
$ = 0.25x$

Column B $= 0.025x$
When $x < 0$, $0.25x < 0.025x$.
When $x > 0$, $0.25x > 0.025x$.
More information is needed about x.

21. B; $a + c = (180 - 160) + (180 - 120)$
$ = 20 + 60$
$ = 80°$
$b = 180 - 80$
$ = 100°$

22. B; Column A $= \dfrac{x}{0.4}$

Column B $= 3x$

$3x - \dfrac{x}{0.4} = 1.2x - x$
$\phantom{3x - \dfrac{x}{0.4}} = .2x$

$.2x > 0$ when $x > 0$

Thus, $3x > \dfrac{x}{0.4}$.

23. $y = x + z$
$180 = x + y + z$
$y = 90°$
$x + z = 90°$

This triangle is a right triangle and w is the hypotenuse.

$w^2 = s^2 + t^2$
$w = \sqrt{s^2 + t^2}$

24. C; Column A $= 2^8$

Column B $= 2^7 + 2^7$
$ = 2 \cdot 2^7$
$ = 2^8$

Chapter 8 Conic Sections

1. $x^2 + 10x + 24 = 0$
$$x^2 + 10x = -24$$
$$x^2 + 10x + 25 = -24 + 25$$
$$(x + 5)^2 = 1$$
$$x + 5 = \pm 1$$
$$x = -5 \pm 1$$
$x = -5 + 1$ or $x = -5 - 1$
$x = -4$ $x = -6$
The solution set is $\{-4, -6\}$.

2. $x^2 - 2x + 2 = 0$
$$x^2 - 2x = -2$$
$$x^2 - 2x + 1 = -2 + 1$$
$$(x - 1)^2 = -1$$
$$x - 1 = \pm\sqrt{-1}$$
$$x - 1 = \pm i$$
$$x = 1 \pm i$$
$x = 1 + i$ or $x = 1 - i$
The solution set is $\{1 + i, 1 - i\}$.

3. $2x^2 + 5x - 12 = 0$
$$x^2 + \frac{5}{2}x - 6 = 0$$
$$x^2 + \frac{5}{2}x = 6$$
$$x^2 + \frac{5}{2}x + \frac{25}{16} = 6 + \frac{25}{16}$$
$$\left(x + \frac{5}{4}\right)^2 = \frac{121}{16}$$
$$x + \frac{5}{4} = \pm\frac{11}{4}$$
$$x = -\frac{5}{4} \pm \frac{11}{4}$$
$x = -\frac{5}{4} + \frac{11}{4}$ or $x = -\frac{5}{4} - \frac{11}{4}$
$x = \frac{3}{2}$ $x = -4$
The solution set is $\left\{\frac{3}{2}, -4\right\}$.

4a. Since the vertices of the quadrilateral are $(-2, 1), (3, 1), (1, -2)$, and $(-4, -2)$, the vertex matrix is given by
$$\begin{bmatrix} -2 & 3 & 1 & -4 \\ 1 & 1 & -2 & -2 \end{bmatrix}.$$

4b. To translate the quadrilateral 4 units to the left, add -4 to each x-coordinate. To translate the quadrilateral 2 units up, add 2 to each y-coordinate. This can be done by adding the translation matrix
$$\begin{bmatrix} -4 & -4 & -4 & -4 \\ 2 & 2 & 2 & 2 \end{bmatrix}.$$

4c. The coordinates of the vertices of the translated figure are given by the sum of the vertex matrix and the translation matrix of the quadrilateral,
$$\begin{bmatrix} -2 & 3 & 1 & -4 \\ 1 & 1 & -2 & -2 \end{bmatrix} + \begin{bmatrix} -4 & -4 & -4 & -4 \\ 2 & 2 & 2 & 2 \end{bmatrix}$$
$$= \begin{bmatrix} -6 & -1 & -3 & -8 \\ 3 & 3 & 0 & 0 \end{bmatrix}.$$

5a. Since the vertices of the figure are $(-2, 2), (4, 0)$, and $(-1, -2)$, the vertex matrix is given by
$$\begin{bmatrix} -2 & 4 & -1 \\ 2 & 0 & -2 \end{bmatrix}.$$

5b. To translate the figure 5 units to the right, add 5 to each x-coordinate. To translate the figure 3 units down, add -3 to each y-coordinate. This can be done by adding the translation matrix
$$\begin{bmatrix} 5 & 5 & 5 \\ -3 & -3 & -3 \end{bmatrix}.$$

5c. The coordinates of the vertices of the translated figure are given by the sum of the vertex matrix and the translation matrix of the figure,
$$\begin{bmatrix} -2 & 4 & -1 \\ 2 & 0 & -2 \end{bmatrix} + \begin{bmatrix} 5 & 5 & 5 \\ -3 & -3 & -3 \end{bmatrix} = \begin{bmatrix} 3 & 9 & 4 \\ -1 & -3 & -5 \end{bmatrix}.$$

6. Since the inequality symbol is $<$, the graph of the related equation $y = x + 2$ is dashed. Graph the equation.
Test $(0, 0)$.
$y < x + 2$
$0 < 0 + 2$
$0 < 2$ true
Shade the region that includes $(0, 0)$.

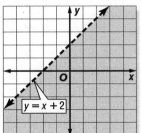

7. Since the inequality symbol is $\leq$, the graph of the related equation $x + y = 3$ is solid. Graph the equation.
Test $(0, 0)$.
$x + y \leq 3$
$0 + 0 \leq 3$
$0 \leq 3$ true
Shade the region that includes $(0, 0)$.

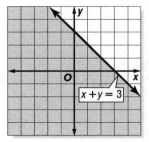

8. Since the inequality symbol is >, the graph of the related equation $2x - 3y = 6$ is dashed. Use the slope-intercept form, $y = \frac{2}{3}x - 2$. Graph the equation.

Test (0, 0).
$$2x - 3y > 6$$
$$2(0) - 3(0) > 6$$
$$0 - 0 > 6$$
$$0 > 6 \text{ false}$$

Shade the region that does not contain (0, 0).

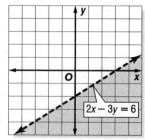

8-1 Midpoint and Distance Formulas

Page 414 Check for Understanding

1. Since the sum of the x-coordinates of the given points is negative, the x-coordinate of the midpoint is negative. Since the sum of the y-coordinates of the given points is positive, the y-coordinate of the midpoint is positive. Therefore, the midpoint is in Quadrant II.

2. All of the points on the perpendicular bisector of the segment are equidistant from the endpoints of the segment.

3. If $\sqrt{29}$ is the distance between two points given by (x_1, y_1) and (x_2, y_2), then by the Distance Formula,
$$\sqrt{29} = \sqrt{(x_2 - x_1)^2 + (y_2 - y_1)^2}.$$
$$29 = (x_2 - x_1)^2 + (y_2 - y_1)^2$$
Sample answer: Let $(x_1, y_1) = (0, 0)$.
$$29 = (x_2 - x_1)^2 + (y_2 - y_1)^2$$
$$29 = (x_2 - 0)^2 + (y_2 - 0)^2$$
$$29 = (x_2)^2 + (y_2)^2$$
One possible set of solutions for (x_2, y_2) is (5, 2).
Sample answer: (0, 0) and (5, 2).

4. $\left(\frac{x_1 + x_2}{2}, \frac{y_1 + y_2}{2}\right) = \left(\frac{-5 + 1}{2}, \frac{6 + 7}{2}\right)$
$$= \left(\frac{-4}{2}, \frac{13}{2}\right)$$
$$= \left(-2, \frac{13}{2}\right)$$

5. $\left(\frac{x_1 + x_2}{2}, \frac{y_1 + y_2}{2}\right) = \left(\frac{8 + (-3)}{2}, \frac{9 + (-4.5)}{2}\right)$
$$= \left(\frac{5}{2}, \frac{4.5}{2}\right)$$
$$= (2.5, 2.25)$$

6. $d = \sqrt{(x_2 - x_1)^2 + (y_2 - y_1)^2}$
$$= \sqrt{(10 - 2)^2 + [-10 - (-4)]^2}$$
$$= \sqrt{(8)^2 + (-6)^2}$$
$$= \sqrt{64 + 36} \quad \text{or} \quad 10$$
The distance between (2, −4) and (10, −10) is 10 units.

7. $d = \sqrt{(x_2 - x_1)^2 + (y_2 - y_1)^2}$
$$= \sqrt{(-4 - 7)^2 + (9 - 8)^2}$$
$$= \sqrt{(-11)^2 + (1)^2}$$
$$= \sqrt{121 + 1} \quad \text{or} \quad \sqrt{122}$$
The distance between (7, 8) and (−4, 9) is $\sqrt{122}$ units.

8. $d = \sqrt{(x_2 - x_1)^2 + (y_2 - y_1)^2}$
$$= \sqrt{(1.1 - 0.5)^2 + (2.9 - 1.4)^2}$$
$$= \sqrt{(0.6)^2 + (1.5)^2}$$
$$= \sqrt{0.36 + 2.25} \quad \text{or} \quad \sqrt{2.61}$$
The distance between (0.5, 1.44) and (1.1, 2.9) is $\sqrt{2.61}$ units.

9. D; Use the Distance Formula to find the distance from (2, −4) to each point.
Distance to (3, 1)
$$d = \sqrt{(3 - 2)^2 + [1 - (-4)]^2}$$
$$= \sqrt{(1)^2 + (5)^2}$$
$$= \sqrt{1 + 25} \quad \text{or} \quad \sqrt{26}$$
Distance to (−2, 0)
$$d = \sqrt{(-2 - 2)^2 + [0 - (-4)]^2}$$
$$= \sqrt{(-4)^2 + (4)^2}$$
$$= \sqrt{16 + 16} \quad \text{or} \quad 4\sqrt{2}$$
Distance to (1, 5)
$$d = \sqrt{(1 - 2)^2 + [5 - (-4)]^2}$$
$$= \sqrt{(-1)^2 + 9^2}$$
$$= \sqrt{1 + 81} \quad \text{or} \quad \sqrt{82}$$
Distance to (4, −2)
$$d = \sqrt{(4 - 2)^2 + [-2 - (-4)]^2}$$
$$= \sqrt{2^2 + 2^2}$$
$$= \sqrt{4 + 4} \quad \text{or} \quad 2\sqrt{2}$$
The shortest distance is $2\sqrt{2}$ units, so the closest point to (2, −4) is (4, −2).

Pages 414–416 Practice and Apply

10. $\left(\frac{x_1 + x_2}{2}, \frac{y_1 + y_2}{2}\right) = \left(\frac{8 + 16}{2}, \frac{3 + 7}{2}\right)$
$$= \left(\frac{24}{2}, \frac{10}{2}\right)$$
$$= (12, 5)$$

11. $\left(\frac{x_1 + x_2}{2}, \frac{y_1 + y_2}{2}\right) = \left(\frac{-5 + (-3)}{2}, \frac{3 + (-7)}{2}\right)$
$$= \left(\frac{-8}{2}, \frac{-4}{2}\right)$$
$$= (-4, -2)$$

12. $\left(\frac{x_1 + x_2}{2}, \frac{y_1 + y_2}{2}\right) = \left(\frac{6 + (-2)}{2}, \frac{-5 + (-7)}{2}\right)$
$$= \left(\frac{4}{2}, \frac{-12}{2}\right)$$
$$= (2, -6)$$

13. $\left(\dfrac{x_1 + x_2}{2}, \dfrac{y_1 + y_2}{2}\right) = \left(\dfrac{5 + 12}{2}, \dfrac{9 + 18}{2}\right)$

$= \left(\dfrac{17}{2}, \dfrac{27}{2}\right)$

14. $\left(\dfrac{x_1 + x_2}{2}, \dfrac{y_1 + y_2}{2}\right) = \left(\dfrac{0.45 + (-0.3)}{2}, \dfrac{7 + (-0.6)}{2}\right)$

$= \left(\dfrac{0.15}{2}, \dfrac{6.4}{2}\right)$

$= (0.075, 3.2)$

15. $\left(\dfrac{x_1 + x_2}{2}, \dfrac{y_1 + y_2}{2}\right) = \left(\dfrac{4.3 + 1.9}{2}, \dfrac{-2.1 + 7.5}{2}\right)$

$= \left(\dfrac{6.2}{2}, \dfrac{5.4}{2}\right)$

$= (3.1, 2.7)$

16. $\left(\dfrac{x_1 + x_2}{2}, \dfrac{y_1 + y_2}{2}\right) = \left(\dfrac{\frac{1}{2} + \frac{1}{3}}{2}, \dfrac{-\frac{2}{3} + \frac{1}{4}}{2}\right)$

$= \left(\dfrac{\frac{5}{6}}{2}, \dfrac{-\frac{5}{12}}{2}\right)$

$= \left(\dfrac{5}{12}, -\dfrac{5}{24}\right)$

17. $\left(\dfrac{x_1 + x_2}{2}, \dfrac{y_1 + y_2}{2}\right) = \left(\dfrac{\frac{1}{3} + \left(-\frac{1}{4}\right)}{2}, \dfrac{\frac{3}{4} + \frac{1}{2}}{2}\right)$

$= \left(\dfrac{\frac{1}{12}}{2}, \dfrac{\frac{5}{4}}{2}\right)$

$= \left(\dfrac{1}{24}, \dfrac{5}{8}\right)$

18. The vertices of triangle MNP are $M(3, 5)$, $N(-2, 8)$, and $P(7, -4)$.

Midpoint of the side with endpoints M and N:

$\left(\dfrac{x_1 + x_2}{2}, \dfrac{y_1 + y_2}{2}\right) = \left(\dfrac{3 + (-2)}{2}, \dfrac{5 + 8}{2}\right)$

$= \left(\dfrac{1}{2}, \dfrac{13}{2}\right)$

Midpoint of the side with endpoints N and P:

$\left(\dfrac{x_1 + x_2}{2}, \dfrac{y_1 + y_2}{2}\right) = \left(\dfrac{-2 + 7}{2}, \dfrac{8 + (-4)}{2}\right)$

$= \left(\dfrac{5}{2}, \dfrac{4}{2}\right)$

$= \left(\dfrac{5}{2}, 2\right)$

Midpoint of the side with endpoints P and M:

$\left(\dfrac{x_1 + x_2}{2}, \dfrac{y_1 + y_2}{2}\right) = \left(\dfrac{7 + 3}{2}, \dfrac{-4 + 5}{2}\right)$

$= \left(\dfrac{10}{2}, \dfrac{1}{2}\right)$

$= \left(5, \dfrac{1}{2}\right)$

The coordinates of the midpoint of each side of triangle MNP are $\left(\dfrac{1}{2}, \dfrac{13}{2}\right)$, $\left(\dfrac{5}{2}, 2\right)$, and $\left(5, \dfrac{1}{2}\right)$.

19. Circle Q has a diameter $\overline{AB}$. If the center of Q is at $(2, 3)$, then $(2, 3)$ lies on $\overline{AB}$, and is the midpoint of $\overline{AB}$, the segment joining A and B. Let B be (x_1, y_1). By the Midpoint Formula, solve for x_1 and y_1, the coordinates of B.

$\left(\dfrac{x_1 + x_2}{2}, \dfrac{y_1 + y_2}{2}\right) = $ midpoint of the segment joining (x_1, y_1) and (x_2, y_2)

$\left(\dfrac{x_1 + (-3)}{2}, \dfrac{y_1 + (-5)}{2}\right) = (2, 3)$

$\left(\dfrac{x_1 - 3}{2}, \dfrac{y_1 - 5}{2}\right) = (2, 3)$

$\dfrac{x_1 - 3}{2} = 2$ and $\dfrac{y_1 - 5}{2} = 3$

$x_1 - 3 = 4$ $\qquad$ $y_1 - 5 = 6$

$x_1 = 7$ $\qquad\qquad$ $y_1 = 11$

Therefore, if A is at $(-3, -5)$ and the center is at $(2, 3)$, the coordinates of B are $(7, 11)$.

20. The location of the gym can be represented by the ordered pair $(12, 15)$. The location of the deli can be represented by the ordered pair $(4, 5)$. The midpoint of the segment joining these two points will determine where John should look for an apartment.

$\left(\dfrac{x_1 + x_2}{2}, \dfrac{y_1 + y_2}{2}\right) = \left(\dfrac{12 + 4}{2}, \dfrac{15 + 5}{2}\right)$

$= \left(\dfrac{16}{2}, \dfrac{20}{2}\right)$

$= (8, 10)$

The ordered pair $(8, 10)$ represents the corner of 8th Street and 10th Avenue. So John should look for an apartment around 8th Street and 10th Avenue, since it is halfway between the gym and the deli.

21. Sample answer: Draw several line segments across a map of the U.S.: one from the northeast corner to the southwest corner, another from the southeast corner to the northwest corner, another across the middle of the U.S. from east to west, and so on. Find the midpoints of these segments. Locate a point to represent all of these midpoints. This point represents the approximate geographical center of the continental United States.

22. The geographical center of the continental United States is located near Lebanon, Kansas.

23. See students' work.

24. $d = \sqrt{[1 - (-4)]^2 + (-3 - 9)^2}$

$= \sqrt{5^2 + (-12)^2}$ or 13

The distance between $(-4, 9)$ and $(1, -3)$ is 13 units.

25. $d = \sqrt{(-6 - 1)^2 + [10 - (-14)]^2}$

$= \sqrt{(-7)^2 + 24^2}$ or 25

The distance between $(1, -14)$ and $(-6, 10)$ is 25 units.

26. $d = \sqrt{[-3 - (-4)]^2 + [-11 - (-10)]^2}$

$= \sqrt{1^2 + (-1)^2}$ or $\sqrt{2}$

The distance between $(-4, -10)$ and $(-3, -11)$ is $\sqrt{2}$ units.

27. $d = \sqrt{(12 - 9)^2 + [-14 - (-2)]^2}$

$= \sqrt{3^2 + (-12)^2}$ or $3\sqrt{17}$

The distance between $(9, -2)$ and $(12, -14)$ is $3\sqrt{17}$ units.

28. $d = \sqrt{(0.68 - 0.23)^2 + (-0.2 - 0.4)^2}$

$= \sqrt{0.45^2 + (-0.6)^2}$ or 0.75

The distance between $(0.23, 0.4)$ and $(0.68, -0.2)$ is 0.75 unit.

29. $d = \sqrt{(-4.5 - 2.3)^2 + [3.7 - (-1.2)]^2}$

$= \sqrt{(-6.8)^2 + 4.9^2}$ or $\sqrt{70.25}$

The distance between $(2.3, -1.2)$ and $(-4.5, 3.7)$ is $\sqrt{70.25}$ units.

30. $d = \sqrt{[5 - (-3)]^2 + \left[\frac{9}{11} - \left(-\frac{2}{11}\right)\right]^2}$

$\quad = \sqrt{8^2 + 1^2} \quad$ or $\quad \sqrt{65}$

The distance between $\left(-3, -\frac{2}{11}\right)$ and $\left(5, \frac{9}{11}\right)$ is $\sqrt{65}$ units.

31. $d = \sqrt{\left(\frac{3}{5} - 0\right)^2 + \left(-\frac{3}{5} - \frac{1}{5}\right)^2}$

$\quad = \sqrt{\frac{3}{5}^2 + \left(-\frac{4}{5}\right)^2} \quad$ or $\quad 1$

The distance between $\left(0, \frac{1}{5}\right)$ and $\left(\frac{3}{5}, -\frac{3}{5}\right)$ is 1 unit.

32. $d = \sqrt{(-3\sqrt{3} - 2\sqrt{3})^2 + [9 - (-5)]^2}$

$\quad = \sqrt{(-5\sqrt{3})^2 + 14^2} \quad$ or $\quad \sqrt{271}$

The distance between $(2\sqrt{3}, -5)$ and $(-3\sqrt{3}, 9)$ is $\sqrt{271}$ units.

33. $d = \sqrt{\left(-\frac{2\sqrt{3}}{3} - \frac{2\sqrt{3}}{3}\right)^2 + \left(\frac{\sqrt{5}}{2} - \frac{\sqrt{5}}{4}\right)^2}$

$\quad = \sqrt{\left(-\frac{4\sqrt{3}}{3}\right)^2 + \left(\frac{\sqrt{5}}{4}\right)^2} \quad$ or $\quad \frac{\sqrt{813}}{12}$

The distance between $\left(\frac{2\sqrt{3}}{3}, \frac{\sqrt{5}}{4}\right)$ and $\left(-\frac{2\sqrt{3}}{3}, \frac{\sqrt{5}}{2}\right)$ is $\frac{\sqrt{813}}{12}$ units.

34. The radius of the circle is given by the length of the segment joining the endpoints of the radius, $(2, 5)$ and $(-1, -4)$. Use the Distance Formula to find the radius.

$d = \sqrt{(-1 - 2)^2 + (-4 - 5)^2}$

$\quad = \sqrt{(-3)^2 + (-9)^2} \quad$ or $\quad \sqrt{90}$

The radius has a length of $\sqrt{90}$ units. The circumference of a circle is $2\pi r$ units, where r is the radius of the circle.

$C = 2\pi(\sqrt{90})$

$\quad = 2\sqrt{90}\pi$

$\quad = 6\sqrt{10}\pi$

The circumference is $6\sqrt{10}\pi$ units.

The area of a circle is πr^2 units^2, where r is the radius of the circle.

$A = \pi(\sqrt{90})^2$

$\quad = 90\pi$

The area of the circle is 90π units^2.

35. The perimeter of the triangle is the sum of the lengths of each of the three sides.

Distance from $(-3, -2)$ to $(4, 1)$

$d = \sqrt{[4 - (-3)]^2 + [1 - (-2)]^2}$

$\quad = \sqrt{7^2 + 3^2} \quad$ or $\quad \sqrt{58}$

Distance from $(4, 1)$ to $(-1, -4)$

$d = \sqrt{(-1 - 4)^2 + (-4 - 1)^2}$

$\quad = \sqrt{(-5)^2 + (-5)^2} \quad$ or $\quad 5\sqrt{2}$

Distance from $(-1, -4)$ to $(-3, -2)$

$d = \sqrt{[-3 - (-1)]^2 + [-2 - (-4)]^2}$

$\quad = \sqrt{(-2)^2 + 2^2} \quad$ or $\quad 2\sqrt{2}$

The perimeter of the triangle is $\sqrt{58} + 7\sqrt{2}$ units.

The area of the triangle is given by $\frac{1}{2}bh$, where b is the length of the base and h is the height of the triangle. The base of the triangle measures $2\sqrt{2}$ units, and the height of the triangle is $5\sqrt{2}$, where the endpoints of the base are $(-1, -4)$ and $(-3, -2)$, and the endpoints of the height of the triangle are $(4, 1)$ and $(-1, -4)$.

$A = \frac{1}{2}(2\sqrt{2})(5\sqrt{2}) \quad$ or $\quad 10$

The area of the triangle is 10 units^2.

36. The perimeter of the quadrilateral is the sum of the lengths of each of the four sides. Use the Distance Formula to find the length of sides $\overline{RS}, \overline{ST}, \overline{TV},$ and $\overline{VR}$.

Length of $\overline{RS}$

$d = \sqrt{[4 - (-4)]^2 + (5 - 6)^2}$

$\quad = \sqrt{8^2 + (-1)^2} \quad$ or $\quad \sqrt{65}$

Length of $\overline{ST}$

$d = \sqrt{(6 - 4)^2 + (3 - 5)^2}$

$\quad = \sqrt{2^2 + (-2)^2} \quad$ or $\quad 2\sqrt{2}$

Length of $\overline{TV}$

$d = \sqrt{(5 - 6)^2 + (-8 - 3)^2}$

$\quad = \sqrt{(-1)^2 + (-11)^2} \quad$ or $\quad \sqrt{122}$

Length of $\overline{VR}$

$d = \sqrt{(-4 - 5)^2 + [6 - (-8)]^2}$

$\quad = \sqrt{(-9)^2 + 14^2}$ or $\sqrt{277}$

The perimeter of quadrilateral $RSTV$ is $\sqrt{65} + 2\sqrt{2} + \sqrt{122} + \sqrt{277}$ units.

37. Use the Midpoint Formula to find the coordinates of the midpoint of the line segment that has endpoints at $T(-6, 5)$ and $A(8, -9)$.

$\left(\frac{x_1 + x_2}{2}, \frac{y_1 + y_2}{2}\right) = \left(\frac{-6 + 8}{2}, \frac{5 + (-9)}{2}\right)$

$\qquad\qquad\qquad\quad = \left(\frac{2}{2}, \frac{-4}{2}\right)$

$\qquad\qquad\qquad\quad = (1, -2)$

The length of median CM is the distance from $C(4, 9)$ to the midpoint $M(1, -2)$.

$d = \sqrt{(1 - 4)^2 + (-2 - 9)^2}$

$\quad = \sqrt{(-3)^2 + (-11)^2} \quad$ or $\quad \sqrt{130}$

The length of median $\overline{CM}$ is $\sqrt{130}$ units.

38. Birmingham is about 2 units above and 0.75 units to the left of Montgomery on the grid. Since each unit on the grid represents 40 miles, Birmingham is about 2(40), or 80, miles north and 0.75(40), or 30, miles west of Montgomery. Take these two lengths to be legs of a right triangle and use the Pythagorean Theorem to find the distance from Birmingham to Montgomery.

$c^2 = a^2 + b^2$

$c^2 = (80)^2 + (30)^2$

$c^2 = 7300$

$c = \sqrt{7300}$ or about 85

Birmingham is about 85 miles from Montgomery.

39. Huntsville is about 4 units above Montgomery on the grid. Since each unit on the grid represents 40 miles, Huntsville is about 4(40), or 160, miles north of Montgomery. Rate of travel is given by $\frac{d}{t}$, where d is the distance traveled and t is the time.

$$r = \frac{d}{t}$$
$$180 = \frac{160}{t}$$
$$180t = 160$$
$$t = \frac{8}{9} \quad \text{or} \quad \text{about } 0.9$$

If its average speed is 180 miles per hour, it would take a plane about 0.9 hour to fly from Huntsville to Montgomery.

40. Consider the grid as being the Cartesian plane with the origin at the lower lefthand corner. Represent the point at the top of the gingerbread shape as the point (1, 11), and the point at the bottom of the feet as the point (11, 1), where each square represents 1 foot. The height of the gingerbread shape is the distance from (1, 11) to (11, 1).

$$d = \sqrt{(11 - 1)^2 + (1 - 11)^2}$$
$$= \sqrt{10^2 + (-10)^2} \quad \text{or} \quad \text{about } 14$$

The gingerbread shape is about 14 inches tall.

41. The slope of the line through (x_1, y_1) and (x_2, y_2) is $\frac{y_2 - y_1}{x_2 - x_1}$ and the point-slope form of the equation of the line is $y - y_1 = \frac{y_2 - y_1}{x_2 - x_1}(x - x_1)$. Substitute $\left(\frac{x_1 + x_2}{2}, \frac{y_1 + y_2}{2}\right)$ into this equation.

The left side is $\frac{y_1 + y_2}{2} - y_1$ or $\frac{y_2 - y_1}{2}$. The right side is $\frac{y_2 - y_1}{x_2 - x_1}\left(\frac{x_1 + x_2}{2} - x_1\right) = \frac{y_2 - y_1}{x_2 - x_1}\left(\frac{x_2 - x_1}{2}\right)$ or $\frac{y_2 - y_1}{2}$.

Therefore, the point with coordinates $\left(\frac{x_1 + x_2}{2}, \frac{y_1 + y_2}{2}\right)$ lies on the line through (x_1, y_1) and (x_2, y_2).

The distance from $\left(\frac{x_1 + x_2}{2}, \frac{y_1 + y_2}{2}\right)$ to (x_1, y_1) is $\sqrt{\left(x_1 - \frac{x_1 + x_2}{2}\right)^2 + \left(y_1 - \frac{y_1 + y_2}{2}\right)^2}$ or $\sqrt{\left(\frac{x_1 - x_2}{2}\right)^2 + \left(\frac{y_1 - y_2}{2}\right)^2}$. The distance from $\left(\frac{x_1 + x_2}{2}, \frac{y_1 + y_2}{2}\right)$ to (x_2, y_2) is $\sqrt{\left(x_2 - \frac{x_1 + x_2}{2}\right)^2 + \left(y_2 - \frac{y_1 + y_2}{2}\right)^2} = \sqrt{\left(\frac{x_2 - x_1}{2}\right)^2 + \left(\frac{y_2 - y_1}{2}\right)^2}$ or $\sqrt{\left(\frac{x_1 - x_2}{2}\right)^2 + \left(\frac{y_1 - y_2}{2}\right)^2}$.

Therefore the point with coordinates $\left(\frac{x_1 + x_2}{2}, \frac{y_1 + y_2}{2}\right)$ is equidistant from (x_1, y_1) and (x_2, y_2).

42. The formulas can be used to decide from which location an emergency squad should be dispatched. Answers should include the following.

- Most maps have a superimposed grid. Think of the grid as a coordinate system and assign approximate coordinates to the two cities. Then use the Distance Formula to find the distance between the points with those coordinates.

- Suppose the bottom left of the grid is the origin. Then the coordinates of Lincoln are about (0.7, 0.2), the coordinates of Omaha are about (4.4, 3.9), and the coordinates of Fremont are about (1.7, 4.6). The distance from Omaha to Fremont is about $10\sqrt{(1.7 - 4.4)^2 + (4.6 - 3.9)^2}$ or about 28 miles. The distance from Lincoln to Fremont is about $10\sqrt{(1.7 - 0.7)^2 + (4.6 - 0.2)^2}$ or about 45 miles. Since Omaha is closer to Fremont than Lincoln, the helicopter should be dispatched from Omaha.

43. C; $d = \sqrt{(-4 - 4)^2 + [-8 - (-2)]^2}$
$= \sqrt{(-8)^2 + (-6)^2} \quad \text{or} \quad 10$

The distance between the points $A(4, -2)$ and $B(-4, -8)$ is 10 units.

44. B; Point $D(5, -1)$ is the midpoint of the segment that has endpoints $C(3, 2)$ and $E(x_2, y_2)$.

$$\left(\frac{3 + x_2}{2}, \frac{2 + y_2}{2}\right) = (5, -1)$$

$$\frac{3 + x_2}{2} = 5 \qquad \text{and} \qquad \frac{2 + y_2}{2} = -1$$
$$3 + x_2 = 10 \qquad\qquad\qquad 2 + y_2 = -2$$
$$x_2 = 7 \qquad\qquad\qquad\quad y_2 = -4$$

The coordinates of E are $(7, -4)$.

45. Since A' is the image when point A is reflected over the line with equation $y = x$, A' and A are equidistant from the line with equation $y = x$. The midpoint of $\overleftrightarrow{AA'}$ must be on the line with equation $y = x$.

46. $\overleftrightarrow{AA'}$ is perpendicular to the line with equation $y = x$, which has slope 1. Since they are perpendicular, the slopes must be opposite reciprocals of each other. The slope of $\overleftrightarrow{AA'}$ is -1.

Page 416   **Maintain Your Skills**

47.

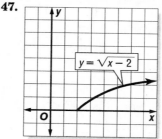

From the graph, the domain is $x \geq 2$, and the range is $y \geq 0$.

48.

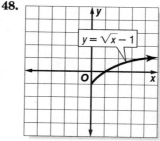

From the graph, the domain is $x \geq 0$, and the range is $y \geq -1$.

49.

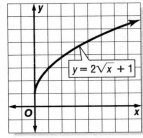

$y = 2\sqrt{x} + 1$

From the graph, the domain is $x \geq 0$, and the range is $y \geq 1$.

50. Check to see if the compositions of $f(x)$ and $g(x)$ are identity functions.

$$[f \circ g](x) = f[g(x)] \qquad [g \circ f](x) = g[f(x)]$$
$$= f(2x) \qquad\qquad = g(x - 2)$$
$$= (2x) - 2 \qquad\quad = 2(x - 2)$$
$$\qquad\qquad\qquad\qquad = 2x - 4$$

The functions are not inverses since neither $[f \circ g](x)$ nor $[g \circ f](x)$ equals x.

51. $(2 + 4i) + (-3 + 9i) = [2 + (-3)] + (4 + 9)i$
$$= -1 + 13i$$

52. $(4 - i) - (-2 + i) = [4 - (-2)] + (-1 - 1)i$
$$= 6 + (-2)i$$
$$= 6 - 2i$$

53. $(1 - 2i)(2 + i) = (1)(2) + (1)(i) + (-2i)(2) + (-2i)(i)$
$$= 2 + i - 4i + 2$$
$$= 4 - 3i$$

54. $y = x^2 + 6x + 9$
$$y = (x + 3)^2$$

55.
$$y = x^2 - 4x + 1$$
$$y - 1 = x^2 - 4x$$
$$y - 1 + 4 = x^2 - 4x + 4$$
$$y + 3 = (x - 2)^2$$
$$y = (x - 2)^2 - 3$$

56.
$$y = 2x^2 + 20x + 50$$
$$\tfrac{1}{2}y = x^2 + 10x + 25$$
$$\tfrac{1}{2}y = (x + 5)^2$$
$$y = 2(x + 5)^2$$

57.
$$y = 3x^2 - 6x + 5$$
$$\tfrac{1}{3}y = x^2 - 2x + \tfrac{5}{3}$$
$$\tfrac{1}{3}y - \tfrac{5}{3} = x^2 - 2x$$
$$\tfrac{1}{3}y - \tfrac{5}{3} + 1 = x^2 - 2x + 1$$
$$\tfrac{1}{3}y - \tfrac{2}{3} = (x - 1)^2$$
$$\tfrac{1}{3}y = (x - 1)^2 + \tfrac{2}{3}$$
$$y = 3(x - 1)^2 + 2$$

58.
$$y = -x^2 - 4x + 6$$
$$-y = x^2 + 4x - 6$$
$$-y + 6 = x^2 + 4x$$
$$-y + 6 + 4 = x^2 + 4x + 4$$
$$-y + 10 = (x + 2)^2$$
$$-y = (x + 2)^2 - 10$$
$$y = -(x + 2)^2 + 10$$

59.
$$y = -3x^2 - 18x - 10$$
$$-\tfrac{1}{3}y = x^2 + 6x + \tfrac{10}{3}$$
$$-\tfrac{1}{3}y - \tfrac{10}{3} = x^2 + 6x$$
$$-\tfrac{1}{3}y - \tfrac{10}{3} + 9 = x^2 + 6x + 9$$
$$-\tfrac{1}{3}y + \tfrac{17}{3} = (x + 3)^2$$
$$-\tfrac{1}{3}y = (x + 3)^2 - \tfrac{17}{3}$$
$$y = -3(x + 3)^2 + 17$$

Page 418 Algebra Activity
(Follow-Up of Lesson 8-1)

1. $d = \sqrt{(x_2 - x_1)^2 + (y_2 - y_1)^2 + (z_2 - z_1)^2}$
$$= \sqrt{(1 - 2)^2 + (2 - 4)^2 + (3 - 5)^2}$$
$$= \sqrt{(-1)^2 + (-2)^2 + (-2)^2}$$
$$= \sqrt{9} \ \text{ or } \ 3$$
The distance is 3 units.

2. $d = \sqrt{(x_2 - x_1)^2 + (y_2 - y_1)^2 + (z_2 - z_1)^2}$
$$= \sqrt{[4 - (-1)]^2 + [(-3) - 6]^2 + (0 - 2)^2}$$
$$= \sqrt{5^2 + (-9)^2 + (-2)^2}$$
$$= \sqrt{110}$$
The distance is $\sqrt{110}$ or about 10.49 units.

3. $d = \sqrt{(x_2 - x_1)^2 + (y_2 - y_1)^2 + (z_2 - z_1)^2}$
$$= \sqrt{[(-2) - (-2)]^2 + (6 - 1)^2 + [(-3) - 7]^2}$$
$$= \sqrt{0^2 + 5^2 + (-10)^2}$$
$$= \sqrt{125} \ \text{ or } \ 5\sqrt{5}$$
The distance is $5\sqrt{5}$ or about 11.18 units.

4. $d = \sqrt{(x_2 - x_1)^2 + (y_2 - y_1)^2 + (z_2 - z_1)^2}$
$$= \sqrt{[(-4) - 0]^2 + (1 - 7)^2 + [(3 - (-1)]^2}$$
$$= \sqrt{(-4)^2 + (-6)^2 + 4^2}$$
$$= \sqrt{68} \ \text{ or } \ 2\sqrt{17}$$
The distance is $2\sqrt{17}$ or about 8.25 units.

5. $\left(\frac{x_1 + x_2}{2}, \frac{y_1 + y_2}{2}, \frac{z_1 + z_2}{2}\right) = \left(\frac{2 + (-4)}{2}, \frac{6 + 8}{2}, \frac{-1 + 5}{2}\right)$
$$= \left(\frac{-2}{2}, \frac{14}{2}, \frac{4}{2}\right)$$
$$= (-1, 7, 2)$$
The midpoint has coordinates $(-1, 7, 2)$.

6. $\left(\frac{x_1 + x_2}{2}, \frac{y_1 + y_2}{2}, \frac{z_1 + z_2}{2}\right) = \left(\frac{4 + (-2)}{2}, \frac{(-3) + 7}{2}, \frac{2 + 6}{2}\right)$
$$= \left(\frac{2}{2}, \frac{4}{2}, \frac{8}{2}\right)$$
$$= (1, 2, 4)$$
The midpoint has coordinates $(1, 2, 4)$.

7. $\left(\frac{x_1 + x_2}{2}, \frac{y_1 + y_2}{2}, \frac{z_1 + z_2}{2}\right) = \left(\frac{1 + (-4)}{2}, \frac{3 + 2}{2}, \frac{7 + (-1)}{2}\right)$
$$= \left(\frac{-3}{2}, \frac{5}{2}, \frac{6}{2}\right)$$
$$= \left(-\frac{3}{2}, \frac{5}{2}, 3\right)$$
The midpoint has coordinates $\left(-\frac{3}{2}, \frac{5}{2}, 3\right)$.

8. $\left(\frac{x_1 + x_2}{2}, \frac{y_1 + y_2}{2}, \frac{z_1 + z_2}{2}\right)$
$$= \left(\frac{2.3 + (-2.7)}{2}, \frac{-1.7 + 3.1}{2}, \frac{0.6 + 1.8}{2}\right)$$
$$= \left(\frac{-0.4}{2}, \frac{1.4}{2}, \frac{2.4}{2}\right)$$
$$= (-0.2, 0.7, 1.2)$$
The midpoint has coordinates $(-0.2, 0.7, 1.2)$.

9. Let $(x_1, y_1, z_1) = (4, -2, 3)$. Find (x_2, y_2, z_2) so that $\left(\dfrac{4 + x_2}{2}, \dfrac{-2 + y_2}{2}, \dfrac{3 + z_2}{2}\right) = (3, 2, 5)$.

$$\dfrac{4 + x_2}{2} = 3 \qquad \dfrac{-2 + y_2}{2} = 2 \qquad \dfrac{3 + z_2}{2} = 5$$

$$4 + x_2 = 6 \qquad -2 + y_2 = 4 \qquad 3 + z_2 = 10$$

$$x_2 = 2 \qquad\quad y_2 = 6 \qquad\quad z_2 = 7$$

The coordinates of the other endpoint are $(2, 6, 7)$.

10.

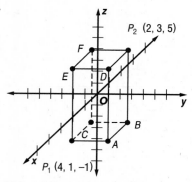

This solid has a rectangular base in the same plane as $P_1(4, 1, -1)$, so the remaining three points of the base have z-coordinates of -1. Since one of these points must lie directly below $P_2(2, 3, 5)$, its coordinates are $B(2, 3, -1)$. Since the x-coordinate and y-coordinate of P_1 and B differ by 2, the base of the solid is a square with a side length of 2 units. Therefore, the coordinates of the remaining two vertices of this base are $A(4, 3, -1)$ and $C(2, 1, -1)$. The other base of the solid must contain the point $P_2(2, 3, 5)$, so the remaining three vertices of this base have a z-coordinate of 5. Since each of these vertices must be directly above a vertex of the other, the remaining three vertices are $D(4, 3, 5)$, $E(4, 1, 5)$, and $F(2, 1, 5)$.

11. The distance between $(2, -4, 2)$ and $(3, 1, 5)$ is

$$d = \sqrt{(x_2 - x_1)^2 + (y_2 - y_1)^2 + (z_2 - z_1)^2}$$
$$= \sqrt{(3 - 2)^2 + [1 - (-4)]^2 + (5 - 2)^2}$$
$$= \sqrt{1^2 + 5^2 + 3^2}$$
$$= \sqrt{35}.$$

The distance between $(3, 1, 5)$ and $(6, -3, -1)$ is

$$d = \sqrt{(x_2 - x_1)^2 + (y_2 - y_1)^2 + (z_2 - z_1)^2}$$
$$= \sqrt{(6 - 3)^2 + (-3 - 1)^2 + (-1 - 5)^2}$$
$$= \sqrt{3^2 + (-4)^2 + (-6)^2}$$
$$= \sqrt{61}.$$

The distance between $(2, -4, 2)$ and $(6, -3, -1)$ is

$$d = \sqrt{(x_2 - x_1)^2 + (y_2 - y_1)^2 + (z_2 - z_1)^2}$$
$$= \sqrt{(6 - 2)^2 + [-3 - (-4)]^2 + (-1 - 2)^2}$$
$$= \sqrt{4^2 - 1^2 + (-3)^2}$$
$$= \sqrt{26}.$$

Since $(\sqrt{26})^2 + (\sqrt{35})^2 = (\sqrt{61})^2$, by the Pythagorean Theorem, the triangle is a right triangle.

12.

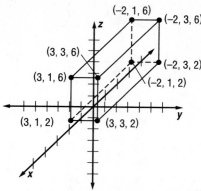

The length of the segment connecting $(3, 1, 2)$ and $(3, 3, 2)$ is the width of the solid.

$$w = \sqrt{(x_2 - x_1)^2 + (y_2 - y_1)^2 + (z_2 - z_1)^2}$$
$$= \sqrt{(3 - 3)^2 + (3 - 1)^2 + (2 - 2)^2}$$
$$= \sqrt{0^2 + 2^2 + 0^2}$$
$$= \sqrt{4} \text{ or } 2 \text{ units}$$

The length of the segment connecting $(3, 3, 2)$ and $(-2, 3, 2)$ is the length of the solid.

$$\ell = \sqrt{(x_2 - x_1)^2 + (y_2 - y_1)^2 + (z_2 - z_1)^2}$$
$$= \sqrt{(-2 - 3)^2 + (3 - 3)^2 + (2 - 2)^2}$$
$$= \sqrt{(-5)^2 + 0^2 + 0^2}$$
$$= \sqrt{25} \text{ or } 5 \text{ units}$$

The length of the segment connecting $(-2, 3, 2)$ and $(-2, 3, 6)$ is the height of the solid.

$$h = \sqrt{(x_2 - x_1)^2 + (y_2 - y_1)^2 + (z_2 - z_1)^2}$$
$$= \sqrt{[-2 - (-2)]^2 + (3 - 3)^2 + (6 - 2)^2}$$
$$= \sqrt{0^2 + 0^2 + 4^2}$$
$$= \sqrt{16} \text{ or } 4 \text{ units}$$

Since $w = 2$, $\ell = 5$, and $h = 4$, the volume of the solid is given by $V = \ell w h$.

$$V = \ell w h$$
$$= (5)(2)(4)$$
$$= 40$$

The volume of the solid is 40 units^3.

13. Since all four possible diagonals of a rectangle are congruent, find the length of any segment joining 2 opposite vertices. Sample answer: The distance between $(3, 1, 2)$ and $(-2, 3, 6)$ is

$$d = \sqrt{(x_2 - x_1)^2 + (y_2 - y_1)^2 + (z_2 - z_1)^2}$$
$$= \sqrt{(-2 - 3)^2 + (3 - 1)^2 + (6 - 2)^2}$$
$$= \sqrt{(-5)^2 + 2^2 + 4^2}$$
$$= \sqrt{45} \text{ or } 3\sqrt{5} \text{ units}.$$

The length of a diagonal of the solid is $3\sqrt{5}$ units.

14. The distance between the points with coordinates
$\left(\frac{x_1+x_2}{2}, \frac{y_1+y_2}{2}, \frac{z_1+z_2}{2}\right)$ and (x_1, y_1, z_1) is
$\sqrt{\left(x_1 - \frac{x_1+x_2}{2}\right)^2 + \left(y_1 - \frac{y_1+y_2}{2}\right)^2 + \left(z_1 - \frac{z_1+z_2}{2}\right)^2}$ or
$\sqrt{\left(\frac{x_1-x_2}{2}\right)^2 + \left(\frac{y_1-y_2}{2}\right)^2 + \left(\frac{z_1-z_2}{2}\right)^2}$ units.

The distance between the points with coordinates
$\left(\frac{x_1+x_2}{2}, \frac{y_1+y_2}{2}, \frac{z_1+z_2}{2}\right)$ and (x_2, y_2, z_2) is
$\sqrt{\left(x_2 - \frac{x_1+x_2}{2}\right)^2 + \left(y_2 - \frac{y_1+y_2}{2}\right)^2 + \left(z_2 - \frac{z_1+z_2}{2}\right)^2}$ or
$\sqrt{\left(\frac{x_2-x_1}{2}\right)^2 + \left(\frac{y_2-y_1}{2}\right)^2 + \left(\frac{z_2-z_1}{2}\right)^2}$ units.

Since $\sqrt{\left(\frac{x_2-x_1}{2}\right)^2 + \left(\frac{y_2-y_1}{2}\right)^2 + \left(\frac{z_2-z_1}{2}\right)^2}$
$= \sqrt{\left(\frac{x_1-x_2}{2}\right)^2 + \left(\frac{y_1-y_2}{2}\right)^2 + \left(\frac{z_1-z_2}{2}\right)^2}$, the distances are equal.

15. If the distance between $(2, 3, c)$ and $(-1, 0, 5)$ is $3\sqrt{6}$ units, use the Distance Formula to determine the value of c.

$$d = \sqrt{(x_2 - x_1)^2 + (y_2 - y_1)^2 + (z_2 - z_1)^2}$$
$$3\sqrt{6} = \sqrt{(-1 - 2)^2 + (0 - 3)^2 + (5 - c)^2}$$
$$3\sqrt{6} = \sqrt{(-3)^2 + (-3)^2 + (5 - c)^2}$$
$$3\sqrt{6} = \sqrt{18 + (5 - c)^2}$$
$$(3\sqrt{6})^2 = (\sqrt{18 + (5 - c)^2})^2$$
$$54 = 18 + (5 - c)^2$$
$$36 = (5 - c)^2$$
$$\sqrt{36} = \sqrt{(5 - c)^2}$$
$$\pm 6 = 5 - c$$
$$c \pm 6 = 5$$
$$c = 5 \pm 6$$

$c = 5 + 6$ or $c = 5 - 6$
$= 11$ $= -1$
Therefore, $c = 11$ or $c = -1$.

16. The length of the diameter is the distance between $(2, -3, 2)$ and $(-1, 1, -4)$.
$$d = \sqrt{(x_2 - x_1)^2 + (y_2 - y_1)^2 + (z_2 - z_1)^2}$$
$$= \sqrt{[2 - (-1)]^2 + (-3 - 1)^2 + [2 - (-4)]^2}$$
$$= \sqrt{3^2 + (-4)^2 + 6^2}$$
$$= \sqrt{61}$$

The length of the radius is half the length of the diameter.
$$r = \frac{1}{2}d$$
$$= \frac{1}{2}(\sqrt{61})$$
$$= \frac{\sqrt{61}}{2}$$

The length of the radius is $\frac{\sqrt{61}}{2}$ units.

17. The center of the sphere is the midpoint of the diameter whose endpoints are $(2, -3, 2)$ and $(-1, 1, -4)$.
$$\left(\frac{x_1+x_2}{2}, \frac{y_1+y_2}{2}, \frac{z_1+z_2}{2}\right) = \left(\frac{2+(-1)}{2}, \frac{-3+1}{2}, \frac{2+(-4)}{2}\right)$$
$$= \left(\frac{1}{2}, \frac{-2}{2}, \frac{-2}{2}\right)$$
$$= \left(\frac{1}{2}, -1, -1\right)$$

The coordinates of the center of the sphere are $\left(\frac{1}{2}, -1, -1\right)$.

8-2 Parabolas

Page 421 Algebra Activity
See students' work; as the distance between the directrix and the focus increases, the parabola becomes wider.

Page 423 Check for Understanding

1. The vertex of the parabola is located at $(3, -7)$.
The focus is located at $\left(3, -7 + \frac{1}{4(4)}\right)$ or $\left(3, -6\frac{15}{16}\right)$.
The axis of symmetry is $x = 3$, and the directrix is $y = -7 - \frac{1}{4(4)}$ or $y = -7\frac{1}{16}$.

2. Sample answer: $x = -y^2$

3. When Katie added 9 to complete the square, she forgot to also subtract 9 on the right side of the equation. The standard form is
$y = x^2 + 6x + 9 - 9 + 4$
$= (x + 3)^2 - 9 + 4$
$= (x + 3)^2 - 5$.

4. $y = 2x^2 - 12x + 6$
$y = 2(x^2 - 6x) + 6$
$y = 2(x^2 - 6x + \blacksquare) + 6 - 2(\blacksquare)$
$y = 2(x^2 - 6x + 9) + 6 - 2(9)$
$y = 2(x - 3)^2 - 12$

5. The equation $y = (x - 3)^2 - 4$ is of the form $y = a(x - h)^2 + k$, where $a = 1$, $h = 3$, and $k = -4$. The vertex is at $(3, -4)$, and the focus is at $\left(3, -4 + \frac{1}{4(1)}\right)$ or $\left(3, -3\frac{3}{4}\right)$. The axis of symmetry is $x = 3$, the directrix is $y = -4 - \frac{1}{4(1)}$ or $y = -4\frac{1}{4}$, and the parabola opens upward. The length of the latus rectum is $\left|\frac{1}{1}\right|$ or 1 unit.

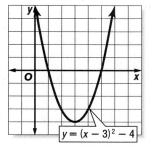

$y = (x - 3)^2 - 4$

6. The equation $y = 2(x + 7)^2 + 3$ is of the form $y = a(x - h)^2 + k$, where $a = 2$, $h = -7$, and $k = 3$. The vertex is at $(-7, 3)$, and the focus is at $\left(-7, 3 + \frac{1}{4(2)}\right)$ or $\left(-7, 3\frac{1}{8}\right)$. The axis of symmetry is $x = -7$, the directrix is $y = 3 - \frac{1}{4(2)}$ or $y = 2\frac{7}{8}$, and the parabola opens upward. The length of the latus rectum is $\left|\frac{1}{2}\right|$ or $\frac{1}{2}$ unit.

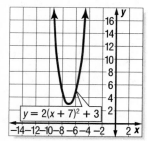

$y = 2(x + 7)^2 + 3$

7. $y = -3x^2 - 8x - 6$

$y = -3\left(x^2 + \frac{8}{3}x\right) - 6$

$y = -3\left(x^2 + \frac{8}{3}x + \blacksquare\right) - 6 - (-3)(\blacksquare)$

$y = -3\left(x^2 + \frac{8}{3}x + \frac{16}{9}\right) - 6 + 3\left(\frac{16}{9}\right)$

$y = -3\left(x + \frac{4}{3}\right)^2 - \frac{2}{3}$

The equation is of the form $y = a(x - h)^2 + k$, where $a = -3$, $h = -\frac{4}{3}$, and $k = -\frac{2}{3}$. The vertex is at $\left(-\frac{4}{3}, -\frac{2}{3}\right)$, and the focus is at $\left(-\frac{4}{3}, -\frac{2}{3} + \frac{1}{4(-3)}\right)$ or $\left(-\frac{4}{3}, -\frac{3}{4}\right)$. The axis of symmetry is $x = -\frac{4}{3}$, the directrix is $y = -\frac{2}{3} - \frac{1}{4(-3)}$ or $y = -\frac{7}{12}$, and the parabola opens downward. The length of the latus rectum is $\left|\frac{1}{-3}\right|$ or $\frac{1}{3}$ unit.

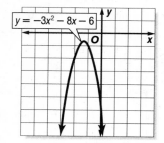

$y = -3x^2 - 8x - 6$

8. $x = \frac{2}{3}y^2 - 6y + 12$

$x = \frac{2}{3}(y^2 - 9y) + 12$

$x = \frac{2}{3}(y^2 - 9y + \blacksquare) + 12 - \frac{2}{3}(\blacksquare)$

$x = \frac{2}{3}\left(y^2 - 9y + \frac{81}{4}\right) + 12 - \frac{2}{3}\left(\frac{81}{4}\right)$

$x = \frac{2}{3}\left(y - \frac{9}{2}\right)^2 - \frac{3}{2}$

The equation is of the form $x = a(y - k)^2 + h$, where $a = \frac{2}{3}$, $k = \frac{9}{2}$, and $h = -\frac{3}{2}$. The vertex is at $\left(-\frac{3}{2}, \frac{9}{2}\right)$, and the focus is at $\left(-\frac{3}{2} + \frac{1}{4\left(\frac{2}{3}\right)}, \frac{9}{2}\right)$ or $\left(-\frac{9}{8}, \frac{9}{2}\right)$. The axis of symmetry is $y = \frac{9}{2}$, the directrix is $x = -\frac{3}{2} - \frac{1}{4\left(\frac{2}{3}\right)}$ or $x = -\frac{15}{8}$, and the parabola opens to the right. The length of the latus rectum is $\left|\frac{1}{\frac{2}{3}}\right|$ or $\frac{3}{2}$ units.

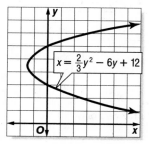

$x = \frac{2}{3}y^2 - 6y + 12$

9. The directrix is $y = 4$, so the equation of the parabola is of the form $y = a(x - h)^2 + k$. The focus is at $(3, 8)$, so $h = 3$, and $k + \frac{1}{4a} = 8$. The directrix is $y = 4$, so $k - \frac{1}{4a} = 4$ or $k = 4 + \frac{1}{4a}$. Use this k to find the value of a.

$k + \frac{1}{4a} = 8$

$\left(4 + \frac{1}{4a}\right) + \frac{1}{4a} = 8$

$4 + \frac{2}{4a} = 8$

$\frac{2}{4a} = 4$

$2 = 16a$

$\frac{1}{8} = a$

Now use $a = \frac{1}{8}$ to determine the value of k.

$k = 4 + \frac{1}{4\left(\frac{1}{8}\right)}$

$k = 4 + \frac{1}{\frac{1}{2}}$

$k = 4 + 2$

$k = 6$

An equation of the parabola is $y = \frac{1}{8}(x - 3)^2 + 6$.

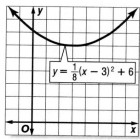

$y = \frac{1}{8}(x - 3)^2 + 6$

10. Since the vertex and the focus have the same y-coordinate, the equation of the parabola is of the form $x = a(y - k)^2 + h$, where $k = -1$. The x-coordinate of the vertex is 5, so $h = 5$. Use the x-coordinate of the vertex to determine the value of a.

$$5 + \frac{1}{4a} = 3$$
$$\frac{1}{4a} = -2$$
$$1 = -8a$$
$$-\frac{1}{8} = a$$

An equation of the parabola is $x = -\frac{1}{8}(y + 1)^2 + 5$.

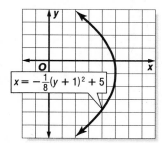

$x = -\frac{1}{8}(y + 1)^2 + 5$

11. Since the parabola opens to the right, the equation is of the form $x = a(y - k)^2 + h$. If the focus is at the origin, then $h + \frac{1}{4a} = 0$ and $k = 0$.

The microphone is at the focus, which is 6 in. to the right of the vertex, so the vertex is at $(-6, 0)$. Thus, $h = -6$ in the equation. Use h to determine the value of a.

$$-6 + \frac{1}{4a} = 0$$
$$\frac{1}{4a} = 6$$
$$1 = 24a$$
$$\frac{1}{24} = a$$

The equation of the parabola is

$$x = \frac{1}{24}(y - 0)^2 + (-6) \quad \text{or} \quad x = \frac{1}{24}y^2 - 6.$$

Pages 424–425 Practice and Apply

12. $y = x^2 - 6x + 11$
$y = (x^2 - 6x + \blacksquare) + 11 - \blacksquare$
$y = (x^2 - 6x + 9) + 11 - 9$
$y = (x - 3)^2 + 2$

13. $x = y^2 + 14y + 20$
$x = (y^2 + 14y + \blacksquare) + 20 - \blacksquare$
$x = (y^2 + 14y + 49) + 20 - 49$
$x = (y + 7)^2 - 29$

14. $y = \frac{1}{2}x^2 + 12x - 8$
$y = \frac{1}{2}(x^2 + 24x) - 8$
$y = \frac{1}{2}(x^2 + 24x + \blacksquare) - 8 - \frac{1}{2}(\blacksquare)$
$y = \frac{1}{2}(x^2 + 24x + 144) - 8 - \frac{1}{2}(144)$
$y = \frac{1}{2}(x + 12)^2 - 80$

15. $x = 3y^2 + 5y - 9$
$x = 3\left(y^2 + \frac{5}{3}y\right) - 9$
$x = 3\left(y^2 + \frac{5}{3}y + \blacksquare\right) - 9 - 3(\blacksquare)$
$x = 3\left(y^2 + \frac{5}{3}y + \frac{25}{36}\right) - 9 - 3\left(\frac{25}{36}\right)$
$x = 3\left(y + \frac{5}{6}\right)^2 - 11\frac{1}{12}$

16. $-6y = x^2$
$\quad y = -\frac{1}{6}x^2$

The equation is of the form $y = a(x - h)^2 + k$, where $a = -\frac{1}{6}$, $h = 0$, and $k = 0$. Thus, the vertex is at $(0, 0)$, and the focus is at $\left(0, 0 + \frac{1}{4\left(-\frac{1}{6}\right)}\right)$ or $\left(0, -\frac{3}{2}\right)$. The axis of symmetry is $x = 0$, the directrix is $y = 0 - \frac{1}{4\left(-\frac{1}{6}\right)}$ or $y = \frac{3}{2}$, and the parabola opens downward. The length of the latus rectum is $\left|\frac{1}{-\frac{1}{6}}\right|$ or 6 units.

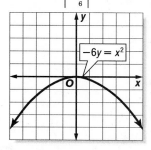

$-6y = x^2$

17. $y^2 = 2x$
$\frac{1}{2}y^2 = x$

The equation is of the form $x = a(y - k)^2 + h$, where $a = \frac{1}{2}$, $k = 0$, and $h = 0$. Thus, the vertex is at $(0, 0)$, and the focus is at $\left(0 + \frac{1}{4\left(\frac{1}{2}\right)}, 0\right)$ or $\left(\frac{1}{2}, 0\right)$. The axis of symmetry is $y = 0$, the directrix is $x = 0 - \frac{1}{4\left(\frac{1}{2}\right)}$ or $x = -\frac{1}{2}$, and the parabola opens to the right. The length of the latus rectum is $\left|\frac{1}{\frac{1}{2}}\right|$ or 2 units.

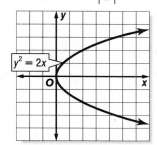

$y^2 = 2x$

377

18. $3(y - 3) = (x + 6)^2$

$\quad y - 3 = \frac{1}{3}(x + 6)^2$

$\quad\quad y = \frac{1}{3}(x + 6)^2 + 3$

The equation is of the form $y = a(x - h)^2 + k$, where $a = \frac{1}{3}$, $h = -6$, and $k = 3$. Thus, the vertex is at $(-6, 3)$, and the focus is at $\left(-6, 3 + \dfrac{1}{4\left(\frac{1}{3}\right)}\right)$ or $\left(-6, 3\frac{3}{4}\right)$. The axis of symmetry is $x = -6$, the directrix is $y = 3 - \dfrac{1}{4\left(\frac{1}{3}\right)}$ or $y = 2\frac{1}{4}$, and the parabola opens upward. The length of the latus rectum is $\left|\dfrac{1}{\frac{1}{3}}\right|$ or 3 units.

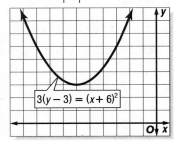

19. $-2(y - 4) = (x - 1)^2$

$\quad y - 4 = -\frac{1}{2}(x - 1)^2$

$\quad\quad y = -\frac{1}{2}(x - 1)^2 + 4$

The equation is of the form $y = a(x - h)^2 + k$, where $a = -\frac{1}{2}$, $h = 1$, and $k = 4$. Thus, the vertex is at $(1, 4)$, and the focus is at $\left(1, 4 + \dfrac{1}{4\left(-\frac{1}{2}\right)}\right)$ or $\left(1, 3\frac{1}{2}\right)$. The axis of symmetry is $x = 1$, the directrix is $y = 4 - \dfrac{1}{4\left(-\frac{1}{2}\right)}$ or $y = 4\frac{1}{2}$, and the parabola opens downward. The length of the latus rectum is $\left|\dfrac{1}{-\frac{1}{2}}\right|$ or 2 units.

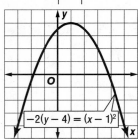

20. $4(x - 2) = (y + 3)^2$

$\quad x - 2 = \frac{1}{4}(y + 3)^2$

$\quad\quad x = \frac{1}{4}(y + 3)^2 + 2$

The equation is of the form $x = a(y - k)^2 + h$, where $a = \frac{1}{4}$, $k = -3$, and $h = 2$. Thus, the vertex is at $(2, -3)$, and the focus is at $\left(2 + \dfrac{1}{4\left(\frac{1}{4}\right)}, -3\right)$ or $(3, -3)$. The axis of symmetry $y = -3$, the directrix is $x = 2 - \dfrac{1}{4\left(\frac{1}{4}\right)}$ or $x = 1$, and the parabola opens to the right. The length of the latus rectum is $\left|\dfrac{1}{\frac{1}{4}}\right|$ or 4 units.

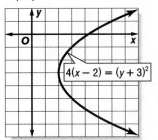

21. $\quad\quad (y - 8)^2 = -4(x - 4)$

$\quad -\frac{1}{4}(y - 8)^2 = x - 4$

$-\frac{1}{4}(y - 8)^2 + 4 = x$

The equation is of the form $x = a(y - k)^2 + h$, where $a = -\frac{1}{4}$, $k = 8$, and $h = 4$. Thus, the vertex is at $(4, 8)$, and the focus is at $\left(4 + \dfrac{1}{4\left(-\frac{1}{4}\right)}, 8\right)$ or $(3, 8)$. The axis of symmetry is $y = 8$, the directrix is $x = 4 - \dfrac{1}{4\left(-\frac{1}{4}\right)}$ or $x = 5$, and the parabola opens to the left. The length of the latus rectum is $\left|\dfrac{1}{-\frac{1}{4}}\right|$ or 4 units.

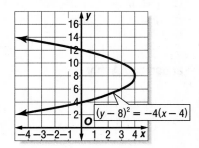

22. $y = x^2 - 12x + 20$
$y = (x^2 - 12x + \blacksquare) + 20 - \blacksquare$
$y = (x^2 - 12x + 36) + 20 - 36$
$y = (x - 6)^2 - 16$

The equation is of the form $y = a(x - h)^2 + k$, where $a = 1$, $h = 6$, and $k = -16$. Thus, the vertex is at $(6, -16)$, and the focus is at $\left(6, -16 + \frac{1}{4(1)}\right)$ or $\left(6, -15\frac{3}{4}\right)$. The axis of symmetry is $x = 6$, the directrix is $y = -16 - \frac{1}{4(1)}$ or $y = -16\frac{1}{4}$, and the parabola opens upward. The length of the latus rectum is $\left|\frac{1}{1}\right|$ or 1 unit.

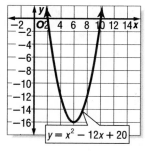

23. $x = y^2 - 14y + 25$
$x = (y^2 - 14y + \blacksquare) + 25 - \blacksquare$
$x = (y^2 - 14y + 49) + 25 - 49$
$x = (y - 7)^2 - 24$

The equation is of the form $x = a(y - k)^2 + h$, where $a = 1$, $k = 7$, and $h = -24$. Thus, the vertex is at $(-24, 7)$, and the focus is at $\left(-24 + \frac{1}{4(1)}, 7\right)$ or $\left(-23\frac{3}{4}, 7\right)$. The axis of symmetry is $y = 7$, the directrix is $x = -24 - \frac{1}{4(1)}$ or $x = -24\frac{1}{4}$, and the parabola opens to the right. The length of the latus rectum is $\left|\frac{1}{1}\right|$ or 1 unit.

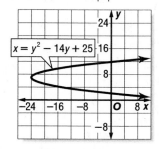

24. $x = 5y^2 + 25y + 60$
$x = 5(y^2 + 5y) + 60$
$x = 5(y^2 + 5y + \blacksquare) + 60 - 5(\blacksquare)$
$x = 5\left(y^2 + 5y + \frac{25}{4}\right) + 60 - 5\left(\frac{25}{4}\right)$
$x = 5\left(y + \frac{5}{2}\right)^2 + \frac{115}{4}$

The equation is of the form $x = a(y - k)^2 + h$, where $a = 5$, $k = -\frac{5}{2}$, and $h = \frac{115}{4}$. Thus, the vertex is at $\left(\frac{115}{4}, -\frac{5}{2}\right)$, and the focus is at $\left(\frac{115}{4} + \frac{1}{4(5)}, -\frac{5}{2}\right)$ or $\left(\frac{114}{5}, -\frac{5}{2}\right)$. The axis of symmetry is $y = -\frac{5}{2}$, the directrix is $x = \frac{115}{4} - \frac{1}{4(5)}$ or $x = \frac{287}{10}$, and the parabola opens to the right. The length of the latus rectum is $\left|\frac{1}{5}\right|$ or $\frac{1}{5}$ unit.

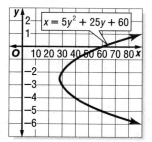

25. $y = 3x^2 - 24x + 50$
$y = 3(x^2 - 8x) + 50$
$y = 3(x^2 - 8x + \blacksquare) + 50 - 3(\blacksquare)$
$y = 3(x^2 - 8x + 16) + 50 - 3(16)$
$y = 3(x - 4)^2 + 2$

The equation is of the form $y = a(x - h)^2 + k$, where $a = 3$, $h = 4$, and $k = 2$. Thus, the vertex is at $(4, 2)$, and the focus is at $\left(4, 2 + \frac{1}{4(3)}\right)$ or $\left(4, 2\frac{1}{12}\right)$. The axis of symmetry is $x = 4$, the directrix is $y = 2 - \frac{1}{4(3)}$ or $y = 1\frac{11}{12}$, and the parabola opens upward. The length of the latus rectum is $\left|\frac{1}{3}\right|$ or $\frac{1}{3}$ unit.

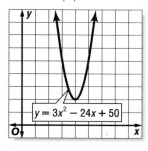

26. $y = -2x^2 + 5x - 10$

$y = -2\left(x^2 - \frac{5}{2}x\right) - 10$

$y = -2\left(x^2 - \frac{5}{2}x + \blacksquare\right) - 10 - (-2)(\blacksquare)$

$y = -2\left(x^2 - \frac{5}{2}x + \frac{25}{16}\right) - 10 + 2\left(\frac{25}{16}\right)$

$y = -2\left(x - \frac{5}{4}\right)^2 - \frac{55}{8}$

The equation is of the form $y = a(x - h)^2 + k$, where $a = -2$, $h = \frac{5}{4}$, and $k = -\frac{55}{8}$. Thus, the vertex is at $\left(\frac{5}{4}, -\frac{55}{8}\right)$, and the focus is at $\left(\frac{5}{4}, -\frac{55}{8} + \frac{1}{4(-2)}\right)$ or $\left(\frac{5}{4}, -7\right)$. The axis of symmetry is $x = \frac{5}{4}$, the directrix is $y = -\frac{55}{8} - \frac{1}{4(-2)}$ or $y = -\frac{27}{4}$, and the parabola opens downward. The length of the latus rectum is $\left|\frac{1}{-2}\right|$ or $\frac{1}{2}$ unit.

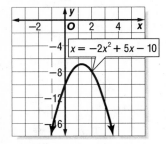

27. $x = -4y^2 + 6y + 2$

$x = -4\left(y^2 - \frac{3}{2}y\right) + 2$

$x = -4\left(y^2 - \frac{3}{2}y + \blacksquare\right) + 2 - (-4)(\blacksquare)$

$x = -4\left(y^2 - \frac{3}{2}y + \frac{9}{16}\right) + 2 + 4\left(\frac{9}{16}\right)$

$x = -4\left(y - \frac{3}{4}\right)^2 + \frac{17}{4}$

The equation is of the form $x = a(y - k)^2 + h$, where $a = -4$, $k = \frac{3}{4}$, and $h = \frac{17}{4}$. Thus, the vertex is at $\left(\frac{17}{4}, \frac{3}{4}\right)$, and the focus is at $\left(\frac{17}{4} + \frac{1}{4(-4)}, \frac{3}{4}\right)$ or $\left(\frac{67}{16}, \frac{3}{4}\right)$. The axis of symmetry is $y = \frac{3}{4}$, the directrix is $x = \frac{17}{4} - \frac{1}{4(-4)}$ or $x = \frac{69}{16}$, and the parabola opens downward. The length of the latus rectum is $\left|\frac{1}{-4}\right|$ or $\frac{1}{4}$ unit.

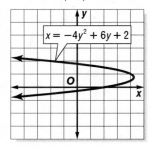

28. $y = \frac{1}{2}x^2 - 3x + \frac{19}{2}$

$y = \frac{1}{2}(x^2 - 6x) + \frac{19}{2}$

$y = \frac{1}{2}(x^2 - 6x + \blacksquare) + \frac{19}{2} - \frac{1}{2}(\blacksquare)$

$y = \frac{1}{2}(x^2 - 6x + 9) + \frac{19}{2} - \frac{1}{2}(9)$

$y = \frac{1}{2}(x - 3)^2 + 5$

This equation is of the form $y = a(x - h)^2 + k$, where $a = \frac{1}{2}$, $h = 3$, and $k = 5$. Thus, the vertex is at $(3, 5)$, and the focus is at $\left(3, 5 + \frac{1}{4\left(\frac{1}{2}\right)}\right)$ or $\left(3, 5\frac{1}{2}\right)$. The axis of symmetry is $x = 3$, the directrix is $y = 5 - \frac{1}{4\left(\frac{1}{2}\right)}$ or $y = 4\frac{1}{2}$, and the parabola opens upward. The length of the latus rectum is $\left|\frac{1}{\frac{1}{2}}\right|$ or 2 units.

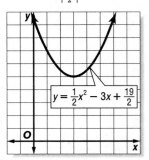

29. $x = -\frac{1}{3}y^2 - 12y + 15$

$x = -\frac{1}{3}(y^2 + 36y) + 15$

$x = -\frac{1}{3}(y^2 + 36y + \blacksquare) + 15 - \left(-\frac{1}{3}\right)(\blacksquare)$

$x = -\frac{1}{3}(y^2 + 36y + 324) + 15 + \frac{1}{3}(324)$

$x = -\frac{1}{3}(y + 18)^2 + 123$

The equation is of the form $x = a(y - k)^2 + h$, where $a = -\frac{1}{3}$, $k = -18$, and $h = 123$. Thus, the vertex is at $(123, -18)$, and the focus is at $\left(123 + \frac{1}{4\left(-\frac{1}{3}\right)}, -18\right)$ or $\left(122\frac{1}{4}, -18\right)$. The axis of symmetry is $y = -18$, the directrix is $x = 123 - \frac{1}{4\left(-\frac{1}{3}\right)}$ or $x = 123\frac{3}{4}$, and the parabola opens to the left. The length of the latus rectum is $\left|\frac{1}{-\frac{1}{3}}\right|$ or 3 units.

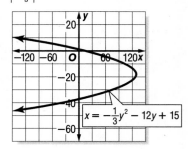

30.

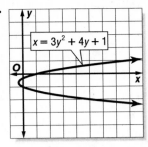

31. The x-intercept(s) occur where $y = 0$.
$x = 3(0)^2 + 4(0) + 1$
$x = 1$
The x-intercept is 1.

32. The y-intercept(s) occur where $x = 0$.
$0 = 3y^2 + 4y + 1$
$0 = (3y + 1)(y + 1)$
$3y + 1 = 0 \quad$ or $\quad y + 1 = 0$
$\quad 3y = -1 \qquad\qquad y = -1$
$\qquad y = -\frac{1}{3}$

The y-intercepts are at -1 and $-\frac{1}{3}$.

33. $x = 3y^2 + 4y + 1$
$x = 3\left(y^2 + \frac{4}{3}y\right) + 1$
$x = 3\left(y^2 + \frac{4}{3}y + \blacksquare\right) + 1 - 3(\blacksquare)$
$x = 3\left(y^2 + \frac{4}{3}y + \frac{4}{9}\right) + 1 - 3\left(\frac{4}{9}\right)$
$x = 3\left(y + \frac{2}{3}\right)^2 - \frac{1}{3}$

Since the equation is of the form
$x = a(y - k)^2 + h$, the axis of symmetry is of the form $y = k$ or $y = -\frac{2}{3}$.

34. The equation is of the form $x = a(y - k)^2 + h$, where $a = 3$, $k = -\frac{2}{3}$, and $h = -\frac{1}{3}$. Thus, the vertex is at $\left(-\frac{1}{3}, -\frac{2}{3}\right)$.

35. Assign the coordinates $(0, 0)$ to the vertex. Thus, the filament of the light bulb is represented by the focus of the parabola. The equation is of the form $y = a(x - h)^2 + k$, where $a = \frac{1}{3}$, $h = 0$, and $k = 0$. Thus, the focus is at $\left(0, 0 + \frac{1}{4\left(\frac{1}{3}\right)}\right)$ or $\left(0, \frac{3}{4}\right)$.

The distance between the vertex and the filament is the distance between the vertex and the focus.
$d = \sqrt{(0 - 0)^2 + \left(\frac{3}{4} - 0\right)^2}$
$\quad = \sqrt{\frac{9}{16}}$
$\quad = \frac{3}{4}$

The filament should be located 0.75 cm from the vertex.

36. Since the vertex and the focus have the same x-coordinate, the equation is of the form $y = a(x - h)^2 + k$. The vertex is at $(0, 1)$, so $h = 0$ and $k = 1$. The focus is at $(0, 5)$, so $k + \frac{1}{4a} = 5$. Use k to determine the value of a.

$1 + \frac{1}{4a} = 5$
$\quad \frac{1}{4a} = 4$
$\quad\quad 1 = 16a$
$\quad \frac{1}{16} = a$

Thus, an equation for the parabola is
$y = \frac{1}{16}(x - 0)^2 + 1$ or $y = \frac{1}{16}x^2 + 1$.

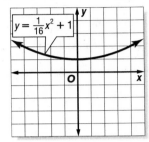

37. Since the vertex and the focus have the same y-coordinate, the equation is of the form $x = a(y - k)^2 + h$. The vertex is at $(8, 6)$, so $h = 8$ and $k = 6$. The focus is at $(2, 6)$, so $h + \frac{1}{4a} = 2$. Use h to determine the value of a.

$8 + \frac{1}{4a} = 2$
$\quad \frac{1}{4a} = -6$
$\quad\quad 1 = -24a$
$\quad -\frac{1}{24} = a$

Thus, an equation for the parabola is
$x = -\frac{1}{24}(y - 6)^2 + 8$.

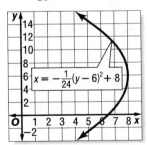

38. The directrix is $x = -8$, so the equation is of the form $x = a(y - k)^2 + h$. The focus is at $(-4, -2)$, so $k = -2$ and $h + \frac{1}{4a} = -4$ or $h = -4 - \frac{1}{4a}$. The directrix is $x = -8$, so $h - \frac{1}{4a} = -8$ or $h = -8 + \frac{1}{4a}$. Use h to determine the value of a.

$$-4 - \frac{1}{4a} = -8 + \frac{1}{4a}$$
$$-\frac{1}{4a} = -4 + \frac{1}{4a}$$
$$\frac{-2}{4a} = -4$$
$$-2 = -16a$$
$$\frac{1}{8} = a$$

Use a to find the value of h.

$$h = -4 - \frac{1}{4\left(\frac{1}{8}\right)} = -4 - 2 = -6$$

Thus, an equation for the parabola is

$$x = \frac{1}{8}(y + 2)^2 - 6.$$

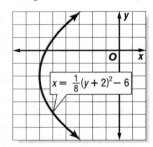

39. The directrix is $y = 3$, so the equation is of the form $y = a(x - h)^2 + k$. The vertex is at $(1, 7)$, so $h = 1$ and $k = 7$. The directrix is $y = 3$, so $k - \frac{1}{4a} = 3$. Use k to determine the value of a.

$$7 - \frac{1}{4a} = 3$$
$$-\frac{1}{4a} = -4$$
$$-1 = -16a$$
$$\frac{1}{16} = a$$

Thus, an equation for the parabola is

$$y = \frac{1}{16}(x - 1)^2 + 7.$$

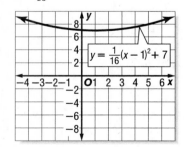

40. The axis of symmetry is $x = -7$, so the equation of the form $y = a(x - h)^2 + k$. The vertex is at $(-7, 4)$, so $h = -7$ and $k = 4$. The length of the latus rectum is 6, so $\left|\frac{1}{a}\right| = 6$, where $a < 0$.

$$-\frac{1}{a} = 6$$
$$-1 = 6a$$
$$-\frac{1}{6} = a$$

Thus, an equation for the parabola is

$$y = -\frac{1}{6}(x + 7)^2 + 4.$$

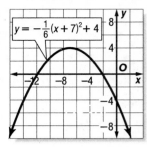

41. The axis of symmetry is $y = 3$, so the equation is of the form $x = a(y - k)^2 + h$. The vertex is at $(4, 3)$, so $h = 4$ and $k = 3$. The measure of the latus rectum is 4, so $\left|\frac{1}{a}\right| = 4$, and $a > 0$.

$$\frac{1}{a} = 4$$
$$1 = 4a$$
$$\frac{1}{4} = a$$

Thus, an equation of the parabola is

$$x = \frac{1}{4}(y - 3)^2 + 4.$$

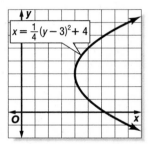

42. The parabola opens upward, so $a > 0$, and the equation is of the form $y = a(x - h)^2 + k$. The vertex is at $(0, -2)$, so $h = 0$ and $k = -2$. Thus, the equation becomes $y = a(x - 0)^2 - 2$ or $y = ax^2 - 2$. Now find a point with coordinates (x, y) on the parabola. The point $(3, 0)$ is on the parabola. Use the point to determine the value of a.

$$y = ax^2 - 2$$
$$0 = a(3)^2 - 2$$
$$2 = a(9)$$
$$\frac{2}{9} = a$$

Thus, an equation for the graph is $y = \frac{2}{9}x^2 - 2$.

43. The origin is at the surface of the water, beneath the vertex of the arch. The vertex is 325 ft above the origin. Thus, the vertex is at $(0, 325)$, so $h = 0$ and $k = 325$. The parabola opens downward, so $a < 0$, and the equation is of the form $y = a(x - h)^2 + k$. The equation becomes $y = a(x - 0)^2 + 325$ or $y = ax^2 + 325$. Now find a point with coordinates (x, y) on the parabola. The bridge has a length of 1675 ft. Since the parabola is symmetric about the origin, the leftmost point of the bridge is given by $\left(-\frac{1675}{2}, 0\right)$. Use this point to determine the value of a.

$$y = ax^2 + 325$$
$$0 = a\left(-\frac{1675}{2}\right)^2 + 325$$
$$-325 = a\left(\frac{2,805,625}{4}\right)$$
$$-0.00046 \approx a$$

Thus, an equation of the parabola that models the arch is $y = -0.00046x^2 + 325$.

44. The parabola opens downward, so $a < 0$, and the equation is of the form $y = a(x - h)^2 + k$. Assuming the ball was kicked at the origin, it hits the ground 100 feet from $(0, 0)$, or at $(100, 0)$. The vertex of the parabola is halfway between $(0, 0)$ and $(100, 0)$, and is 25 feet above ground level.

Thus, the vertex is at $\left(\frac{100}{2}, 25\right)$ or $(50, 25)$, so $h = 50$ and $k = 25$. The length of the latus rectum is the distance between $(0, 0)$ and $(100, 0)$, or 100 feet. Use this to determine the value of a.

$$\left|\frac{1}{a}\right| = 100$$
$$-\frac{1}{a} = 100$$
$$-1 = 100a$$
$$-\frac{1}{100} = a$$

Thus, an equation of the parabola is
$$y = -\frac{1}{100}(x - 50)^2 + 25.$$

45. The center of Earth is at the origin. The distance from the center of Earth to the vertex, that is, where the spacecraft reaches escape velocity, is given by the sum of the radius of Earth and the distance from the spacecraft to Earth. Thus, the vertex of the parabola is at $(0, 6400 + 150)$ or $(0, 6550)$. The parabola opens downward, so $a < 0$, and the equation is of the form $y = a(x - h)^2 + k$. The center of Earth is the focus of the parabola.

Thus, the focus is $(0, 0)$, so $h = 0$ and $k + \frac{1}{4a} = 0$.
The vertex is at $(0, 6550)$, so $h = 0$ and $k = 6550$.
Use k to determine the value of a.

$$k + \frac{1}{4a} = 0$$
$$6550 + \frac{1}{4a} = 0$$
$$\frac{1}{4a} = -6550$$
$$1 = -26,200a$$
$$-\frac{1}{26,200} = a$$

Thus, an equation that models the parabolic path of the spacecraft is $y = -\frac{1}{26,200}(x - 0)^2 + 6550$ or $y = -\frac{1}{26,200}x^2 + 6550$.

46. The equation is of the form $y = a(x - h)^2 + k$, where $a > 0$. Thus, the parabola opens upward. It is possible to find an equation of a different parabola with its vertex at $(4, 3)$ that passes through $(5, 4)$. The equation of the form $x = a(y - k)^2 + h$, where $a > 0$, is a parabola that opens to the right. The vertex is at $(4, 3)$, so $h = 4$ and $k = 3$. Thus, the equation is $x = a(y - 3)^2 + 4$. Use the point $(5, 4)$ on the parabola to determine the value of a.

$$x = a(y - 3)^2 + 4$$
$$5 = a(4 - 3)^2 + 4$$
$$1 = a(1)^2$$
$$1 = a$$

Thus, an equation for the parabola is
$$x = (y - 3)^2 + 4.$$

47. A parabolic reflector can be used to make a car headlight more effective.
Answers should include the following.
- Reflected rays are *focused* at that point.
- The light from an unreflected bulb would shine in all directions. With a parabolic reflector, most of the light can be directed forward toward the road.

48. B; A parabola opens downward if $a < 0$ in the equation of the form $y = a(x - h)^2 + k$. In the equation $y = 3x^2 - 2$, $a = 3$, so the parabola opens upward. In the equation $y = 2 - 3x^2$ or $y = -3x^2 + 2$, $a = -3$, so the parabola opens downward.

49. A; $y = x^2 - 10x + 8$
$$y = (x^2 - 10x + \blacksquare) + 8 - \blacksquare$$
$$y = (x^2 - 10x + 25) + 8 - 25$$
$$y = (x - 5)^2 - 17$$

The equation is of the form $y = a(x - h)^2 + k$, where $h = 5$ and $k = -17$. Thus, the vertex is at $(5, -17)$.

Page 425   Maintain Your Skills

50. $d = \sqrt{(-5 - 7)^2 + (8 - 3)^2}$
$$= \sqrt{(-12)^2 + 5^2}$$
$$= \sqrt{144 + 25} \quad \text{or} \quad 13 \text{ units}$$

51. $d = \sqrt{(-2 - 4)^2 + [7 - (-1)]^2}$
$$= \sqrt{(-6)^2 + 8^2}$$
$$= \sqrt{36 + 64} \quad \text{or} \quad 10 \text{ units}$$

52. $d = \sqrt{[0 - (-3)]^2 + (6 - 1)^2}$
$$= \sqrt{3^2 + 5^2}$$
$$= \sqrt{9 + 25} \quad \text{or} \quad \sqrt{34} \text{ units}$$

53. Graph the related equation $y = \sqrt{x + 1}$. The domain includes values for $x \geq -1$, so the graph includes $x = -1$ and the values of x to the right of $x = -1$. Select a point and test its ordered pair.

Test $(2, 1)$.
$y \leq \sqrt{x + 1}$
$1 \leq \sqrt{2 + 1}$
$1 \leq \sqrt{3}$ true

Shade the region that includes $(2, 1)$.

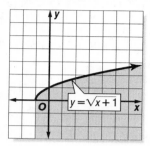

$y = \sqrt{x + 1}$

54. When he runs, Ty's heart rate is 120 beats/min. He runs 2 hrs/day for 2 weeks. The number of times his heart beats during the amount of time he exercises is given by $\frac{120 \text{ beats}}{1 \text{ min}} \cdot \frac{2 \text{ hrs}}{1 \text{ day}} \cdot \frac{2 \text{ weeks}}{1}$, where 2 hrs = 120 min, and 2 weeks = 14 days. Use substitution to find the number of times Ty's heart beats.

$\frac{120 \text{ beats}}{1 \text{ min}} \cdot \frac{2 \text{ hrs}}{1 \text{ day}} \cdot \frac{2 \text{ weeks}}{1} = \frac{120 \text{ beats}}{1 \text{ min}} \cdot \frac{120 \text{ min}}{1 \text{ day}} \cdot \frac{14 \text{ days}}{1}$
$= 201{,}600 \text{ beats}$
$= 2.016 \times 10^5 \text{ beats}$

55. $\sqrt{16} = \sqrt{4^2}$
$= 4$

56. $\sqrt{25} = \sqrt{5^2}$
$= 5$

57. $\sqrt{81} = \sqrt{9^2}$
$= 9$

58. $\sqrt{144} = \sqrt{12^2}$
$= 12$

59. $\sqrt{12} = \sqrt{4 \cdot 3}$
$= \sqrt{2^2 \cdot 3}$
$= \sqrt{2^2} \cdot \sqrt{3}$
$= 2\sqrt{3}$

60. $\sqrt{18} = \sqrt{9 \cdot 2}$
$= \sqrt{3^2 \cdot 2}$
$= \sqrt{3^2} \cdot \sqrt{2}$
$= 3\sqrt{2}$

61. $\sqrt{48} = \sqrt{16 \cdot 3}$
$= \sqrt{4^2 \cdot 3}$
$= \sqrt{4^2} \cdot \sqrt{3}$
$= 4\sqrt{3}$

62. $\sqrt{72} = \sqrt{36 \cdot 2}$
$= \sqrt{6^2 \cdot 2}$
$= \sqrt{6^2} \cdot \sqrt{2}$
$= 6\sqrt{2}$

8-3 | Circles

Pages 428–429 Check for Understanding

1. Answers should be of the form $(x - 6)^2 + (y + 2)^2 = r^2$ for some positive real number r. Sample answer: $(x - 6)^2 + (y + 2)^2 = 16$

2. $x^2 + y^2 + 6x - 2y - 54 = 0$
$x^2 + 6x + \blacksquare + y^2 - 2y + \blacksquare = 54 + \blacksquare + \blacksquare$
$x^2 + 6x + 9 + y^2 - 2y + 1 = 54 + 9 + 1$
$(x + 3)^2 + (y - 1)^2 = 64$
The graph of $(x + 3)^2 + (y - 1)^2 = 64$ is the graph of $x^2 + y^2 = 64$ translated left 3 units and up 1 unit.

3. The equation $(x - 4)^2 + y^2 = 36$ is of the form $(x - h)^2 + (y - k)^2 = r^2$, where $h = 4$, $k = 0$, and $r = 6$. Thus, 36 is the *square* of the radius. The radius is 6 units, so Lucy is correct.

4. The graph is a circle with center $(3, -1)$ and radius 3 units. The equation is of the form $(x - h)^2 + (y - k)^2 = r^2$, where $h = 3$, $k = -1$, and $r = 3$. Thus, an equation for the graph is $(x - 3)^2 + [y - (-1)]^2 = 3^2$ or $(x - 3)^2 + (y + 1)^2 = 9$.

5. An equation for the circle with center at $(-1, -5)$ and radius 2 units is $[x - (-1)]^2 + [y - (-5)]^2 = 2^2$ or $(x + 1)^2 + (y + 5)^2 = 4$.

6. The center of the circle is the midpoint of the diameter with endpoints $(-4, 1)$ and $(4, -5)$.
$(h, k) = \left(\frac{x_1 + x_2}{2}, \frac{y_1 + y_2}{2} \right)$
$= \left(\frac{-4 + 4}{2}, \frac{1 + (-5)}{2} \right)$
$= \left(\frac{0}{2}, \frac{-4}{2} \right)$
$= (0, -2)$

The center is at $(0, -2)$. The radius is the distance between the midpoint and one of the endpoints of the diameter.
$r = \sqrt{(x_2 - x_1)^2 + (y_2 - y_1)^2}$
$= \sqrt{(-4 - 0)^2 + [1 - (-2)]^2}$
$= \sqrt{(-4)^2 + 3^2}$
$= \sqrt{16 + 9}$ or 5

Thus, an equation for the circle is $(x - 0)^2 + [y - (-2)] = 5^2$ or $x^2 + (y + 2)^2 = 25$.

7. The center of the circle is at $(3, -7)$. Since the circle is tangent to the y-axis, the point with coordinates $(0, -7)$ is on the circle. Since the circle is tangent to the y-axis, a radius is the length of the horizontal segment connecting the y-axis and the center. This segment has length 3 units. Thus, an equation for the circle is $(x - 3)^2 + [y - (-7)] = 3^2$ or $(x - 3)^2 + (y + 7)^2 = 9$.

8. The circle with the given equation has its center at (4, 1) and its radius is 3 units.

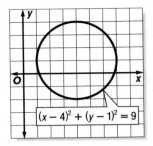

9. The circle with the given equation has its center at (0, 14) and its radius is $\sqrt{34}$ units.

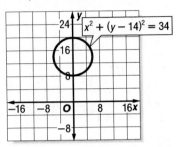

10. The circle with the given equation has its center at (4, 0) and its radius is $\frac{4}{5}$ unit.

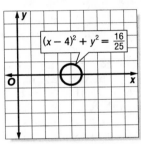

11. The circle with the given equation has its center at $\left(-\frac{2}{3}, \frac{1}{2}\right)$ and its radius is $\frac{2\sqrt{2}}{3}$ unit.

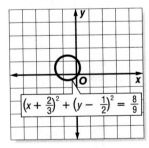

12.
$$x^2 + y^2 + 8x - 6y = 0$$
$$x^2 + 8x + \blacksquare + y^2 - 6y + \blacksquare = 0 + \blacksquare + \blacksquare$$
$$x^2 + 8x + 16 + y^2 - 6y + 9 = 0 + 16 + 9$$
$$(x + 4)^2 + (y - 3)^2 = 25$$

The center of the circle is (−4, 3), and the radius is 5 units.

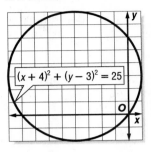

13.
$$x^2 + y^2 + 4x - 8 = 0$$
$$x^2 + 4x + \blacksquare + y^2 = 8 + \blacksquare$$
$$x^2 + 4x + 4 + y^2 = 8 + 4$$
$$(x + 2)^2 + y^2 = 12$$

The center of the circle is (−2, 0) and the radius is $2\sqrt{3}$ units.

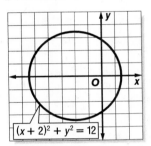

14. The center of Earth is the origin. The radius of the circle is given by the distance from the center of Earth to the satellite. This distance is the sum of the radius of Earth and the distance from the satellite to the equator, or 6400 km + 35,800 km. Thus, the radius of the circle is 42,200 km, and the center is (0, 0). The equation for the orbit of the satellite is $(x - 0)^2 + (y - 0)^2 = 42,200^2$ or $x^2 + y^2 = 42,200^2$.

15.

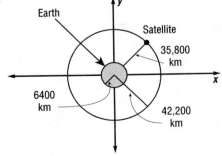

Pages 429–431   Practice and Apply

16. The graph is a circle with center at (−1, 1). The radius is 4. Thus, an equation for the graph is $[x - (-1)]^2 + (y - 1)^2 = 4^2$ or $(x + 1)^2 + (y - 1)^2 = 16$.

17. The graph is a circle with center at $(2, -1)$. The radius is 2. Thus, an equation for the graph is $(x - 2)^2 + [y - (-1)]^2 = 2^2$ or $(x - 2)^2 + (y + 1)^2 = 4$.

18. An equation for a circle with center at $(0, 3)$ and radius of 7 is $(x - 0)^2 + (y - 3)^2 = 7^2$ or $x^2 + (y - 3)^2 = 49$.

19. An equation for a circle with center at $(-8, 7)$ and radius $\frac{1}{2}$ is $[x - (-8)]^2 + (y - 7)^2 = \left(\frac{1}{2}\right)^2$ or $(x + 8)^2 + (y - 7)^2 = \frac{1}{4}$.

20. The center is the midpoint of the diameter with endpoints $(-5, 2)$ and $(3, 6)$.

$$(h, k) = \left(\frac{x_1 + x_2}{2}, \frac{y_1 + y_2}{2}\right)$$
$$= \left(\frac{-5 + 3}{2}, \frac{2 + 6}{2}\right)$$
$$= \left(\frac{-2}{2}, \frac{8}{2}\right)$$
$$= (-1, 4)$$

The radius is the distance from the center to one of the given points.

$$r = \sqrt{[3 - (-1)]^2 + (6 - 4)^2}$$
$$= \sqrt{4^2 + 2^2}$$
$$= \sqrt{16 + 4} \text{ or } \sqrt{20}$$

The radius of the circle is $\sqrt{20}$ units, so $r^2 = 20$. Thus, an equation of the circle is $[x - (-1)]^2 + (y - 4)^2 = 20$ or $(x + 1)^2 + (y - 4)^2 = 20$.

21. The center of the circle is the midpoint of the diameter with endpoints $(11, 18)$ and $(-13, -19)$.

$$(h, k) = \left(\frac{x_1 + x_2}{2}, \frac{y_1 + y_2}{2}\right)$$
$$= \left(\frac{11 + (-13)}{2}, \frac{18 + (-19)}{2}\right)$$
$$= \left(\frac{-2}{2}, \frac{-1}{2}\right)$$
$$= \left(-1, -\frac{1}{2}\right)$$

The radius is the distance from the center to one of the endpoints.

$$r = \sqrt{(x_2 - x_1)^2 + (y_2 - y_1)^2}$$
$$= \sqrt{[11 - (-1)]^2 + \left[18 - \left(-\frac{1}{2}\right)\right]^2}$$
$$= \sqrt{12^2 + \left(\frac{37}{2}\right)^2}$$
$$= \sqrt{144 + \frac{1369}{4}} \text{ or } \sqrt{\frac{1945}{4}}$$

The radius of the circle is $\sqrt{\frac{1945}{4}}$ units, so $r^2 = \frac{1945}{4}$.

Thus, an equation of the circle is $[x - (-1)]^2 + \left[y - \left(-\frac{1}{2}\right)\right]^2 = \frac{1945}{4}$ or $(x + 1)^2 + \left(y + \frac{1}{2}\right)^2 = \frac{1945}{4}$.

22. The center of the circle is at $(8, -9)$. The radius of the circle is the distance from the center to the given point.

$$r = \sqrt{(x_2 - x_1)^2 + (y_2 - y_1)^2}$$
$$= \sqrt{(21 - 8)^2 + [22 - (-9)]^2}$$
$$= \sqrt{13^2 + 31^2}$$
$$= \sqrt{169 + 961} \text{ or } \sqrt{1130}$$

The radius of the circle is $\sqrt{1130}$ units, so $r^2 = 1130$. Thus, an equation of the circle is $(x - 8)^2 + [y - (-9)]^2 = 1130$ or $(x - 8)^2 + (y + 9)^2 = 1130$.

23. The center of the circle is at $(-\sqrt{13}, 42)$. The radius of the circle is the distance from the center to the origin.

$$r = \sqrt{(x_2 - x_1)^2 + (y_2 - y_1)^2}$$
$$= \sqrt{[0 - (-\sqrt{13})]^2 + (0 - 42)^2}$$
$$= \sqrt{(\sqrt{13})^2 + (-42)^2}$$
$$= \sqrt{13 + 1764} \text{ or } \sqrt{1777}$$

The radius of the circle is $\sqrt{1777}$ units, so $r^2 = 1777$. Thus, an equation of the circle is $[x - (-\sqrt{13})]^2 + (y - 42)^2 = 1777$ or $(x + \sqrt{13})^2 + (y - 42)^2 = 1777$.

24. The center of the circle is at $(-8, -7)$. Since the circle is tangent to the y-axis, its radius is 8. Thus, an equation of the circle is $[x - (-8)]^2 + [y - (-7)]^2 = 8^2$ or $(x + 8)^2 + (y + 7)^2 = 64$.

25. The center of the circle is at $(4, 2)$. Since the circle is tangent to the x-axis, its radius is 2. Thus, an equation of the circle is $(x - 4)^2 + (y - 2)^2 = 4$.

26. Since the circle is tangent to $x = -3$ and $x = 5$, its center falls somewhere on the vertical line that is halfway between the two lines, that is, on the line $x = 1$. Thus, the radius of the circle is 4. Since the circle is also tangent to the x-axis, its center is 4 units above the x-axis, that is, where $y = 4$. So the center of the circle is at the point $(1, 4)$ where the lines $x = 1$ and $y = 4$ meet. Thus, an equation for the circle is $(x - 1)^2 + (y - 4)^2 = 16$.

27. Since the circle is tangent to $y = -1$ and $y = 9$, its center falls somewhere on the horizontal line that is halfway between the two lines, that is, on the line $y = 4$. Thus, the radius of the circle is 5. Since the circle is also tangent to the y-axis, its center is 5 units to the left of the y-axis in the second quadrant, that is, where $x = -5$. So the center of the circle is at the point $(-5, 4)$ where the lines $y = 4$ and $x = -5$ meet. Thus, an equation for the circle is $[x - (-5)]^2 + (y - 4)^2 = 25$ or $(x + 5)^2 + (y - 4)^2 = 25$.

28. The center of the pond is at the origin. Therefore, $h = 0$ and $k = 0$ in the equation $(x - h)^2 + (y - k)^2 = r^2$, so the equation becomes $x^2 + y^2 = r^2$. The largest circular pond that would fit within the walkways will not exceed the point, for example, (3, 3). The radius is the distance from the center to this point.

$$r = \sqrt{(x_2 - x_1)^2 + (y_2 - y_1)^2}$$
$$= \sqrt{(3 - 0)^2 + (3 - 0)^2}$$
$$= \sqrt{3^2 + 3^2}$$
$$= \sqrt{9 + 9} \quad \text{or} \quad \sqrt{18}$$

Thus, an equation for the largest circular pond is $(x - 0)^2 + (y - 0)^2 = \sqrt{18}^2$ or $x^2 + y^2 = 18$.

29. The origin of a coordinate plane is located at the center of Los Angeles. The location of the University of Southern California is 2.5 miles west and 2.8 miles south of downtown Los Angeles, which corresponds to the point $(-2.5, -2.8)$. The epicenter is about 40 miles from the university, so the radius of the circle is 40. Thus, an equation for the set of points that could be the epicenter of the earthquake is $[x - (-2.5)]^2 + [y - (-2.8)]^2 = 40^2$ or $(x + 2.5)^2 + (y + 2.8)^2 = 1600$.

30. The center of the circle is at $(0, -2)$, and its radius is 2 units.

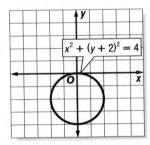

31. The center of the circle is at $(0, 0)$, and its radius is 12 units.

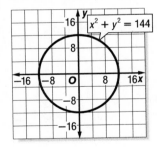

32. The center of the circle is at $(3, 1)$, and its radius is 5 units.

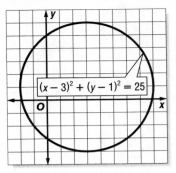

33. The center of the circle is at $(-3, -7)$, and its radius is 9 units.

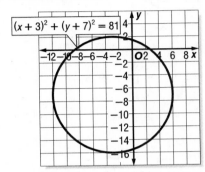

34. The center of the circle is at $(3, 0)$, and its radius is 4 units.

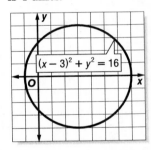

35. The center of the circle is at $(3, -7)$, and its radius is $5\sqrt{2}$ units.

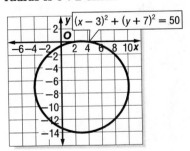

36.
$$(x + \sqrt{5})^2 + y^2 - 8y = 9$$
$$(x + \sqrt{5})^2 + y^2 - 8y + \blacksquare = 9 + \blacksquare$$
$$(x + \sqrt{5})^2 + y^2 - 8y + 16 = 9 + 16$$
$$(x + \sqrt{5})^2 + (y - 4)^2 = 25$$

The center of the circle is at $(-\sqrt{5}, 4)$, and its radius is 5 units.

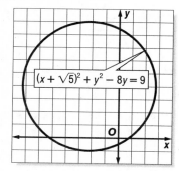

37.
$$x^2 + (y - \sqrt{3})^2 + 4x = 25$$
$$x^2 + 4x + \blacksquare + (y - \sqrt{3})^2 = 25 + \blacksquare$$
$$x^2 + 4x + 4 + (y - \sqrt{3})^2 = 25 + 4$$
$$(x + 2)^2 + (y - \sqrt{3})^2 = 29$$

The center of the circle is at $(-2, \sqrt{3})$, and the radius is $\sqrt{29}$ units.

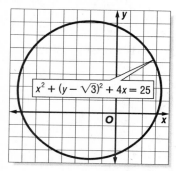

38.
$$x^2 + y^2 + 6y = -50 - 14x$$
$$x^2 + 14x + y^2 + 6y = -50$$
$$x^2 + 14x + \blacksquare + y^2 + 6y + \blacksquare = -50 + \blacksquare + \blacksquare$$
$$x^2 + 14x + 49 + y^2 + 6y + 9 = -50 + 49 + 9$$
$$(x + 7)^2 + (y + 3)^2 = 8$$

The center of the circle is at $(-7, -3)$, and its radius is $2\sqrt{2}$ units.

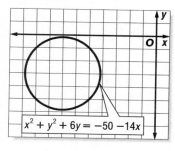

39. $x^2 + y^2 - 6y - 16 = 0$
$$x^2 + y^2 - 6y = 16$$
$$x^2 + y^2 - 6y + \blacksquare = 16 + \blacksquare$$
$$x^2 + y^2 - 6y + 9 = 16 + 9$$
$$x^2 + (y - 3)^2 = 25$$

The center of the circle is at $(0, 3)$, and its radius is 5 units.

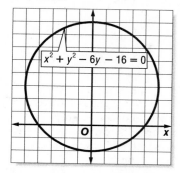

40. $x^2 + y^2 + 2x - 10 = 0$
$$x^2 + y^2 + 2x = 10$$
$$x^2 + 2x + \blacksquare + y^2 = 10 + \blacksquare$$
$$x^2 + 2x + 1 + y^2 = 10 + 1$$
$$(x + 1)^2 + y^2 = 11$$

The center of the circle is at $(-1, 0)$, and the radius is $\sqrt{11}$ units.

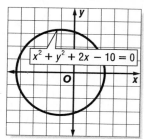

41.
$$x^2 + y^2 - 18x - 18y + 53 = 0$$
$$x^2 - 18x + \blacksquare + y^2 - 18y + \blacksquare = -53 + \blacksquare + \blacksquare$$
$$x^2 - 18x + 81 + y^2 - 18y + 81 = -53 + 81 + 81$$
$$(x - 9)^2 + (y - 9)^2 = 109$$

The center of the circle is at $(9, 9)$, and the radius is $\sqrt{109}$ units.

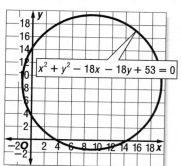

42.
$$x^2 + y^2 + 9x - 8y + 4 = 0$$
$$x^2 + y^2 + 9x - 8y = -4$$
$$x^2 + 9x + \blacksquare + y^2 - 8y + \blacksquare = -4 + \blacksquare + \blacksquare$$
$$x^2 + 9x + \frac{81}{4} + y^2 - 8y + 16 = -4 + \frac{81}{4} + 16$$
$$\left(x + \frac{9}{2}\right)^2 + (y - 4)^2 = \frac{129}{4}$$

The center of the circle is at $\left(-\frac{9}{2}, 4\right)$, and its radius is $\frac{\sqrt{129}}{2}$ units.

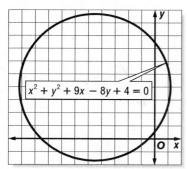

43.
$$x^2 + y^2 - 3x + 8y = 20$$
$$x^2 + 3x + \blacksquare + y^2 + 8y + \blacksquare = 20 + \blacksquare + \blacksquare$$
$$x^2 - 3x + \frac{9}{4} + y^2 + 8y + 16 = 20 + \frac{9}{4} + 16$$
$$\left(x - \frac{3}{2}\right)^2 + (y + 4)^2 = \frac{153}{4}$$

The center of the circle is at $\left(\frac{3}{2}, -4\right)$, and its radius is $\frac{3\sqrt{17}}{2}$ units.

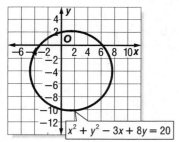

44.
$$x^2 - 12x + 84 = -y^2 + 16y$$
$$x^2 - 12x + y^2 - 16y = -84$$
$$x^2 - 12x + \blacksquare + y^2 - 16y + \blacksquare = -84 + \blacksquare + \blacksquare$$
$$x^2 - 12x + 36 + y^2 - 16y + 64 = -84 + 36 + 64$$
$$(x - 6)^2 + (y - 8)^2 = 16$$

The center of the circle is (6, 8), and its radius is 4 units.

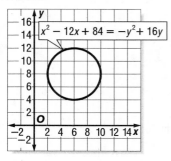

45.
$$x^2 + y^2 + 2x + 4y = 9$$
$$x^2 + 2x + \blacksquare + y^2 + 4y + \blacksquare = 9 + \blacksquare + \blacksquare$$
$$x^2 + 2x + 1 + y^2 + 4y + 4 = 9 + 1 + 4$$
$$(x + 1)^2 + (y + 2)^2 = 14$$

The center of the circle is at $(-1, -2)$, and its radius is $\sqrt{14}$ units.

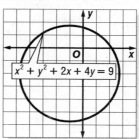

46.
$$3x^2 + 3y^2 + 12x - 6y + 9 = 0$$
$$x^2 + y^2 + 4x - 2y + 3 = 0$$
$$x^2 + 4x + \blacksquare + y^2 - 2y + \blacksquare = -3 + \blacksquare + \blacksquare$$
$$x^2 + 4x + 4 + y^2 - 2y + 1 = -3 + 4 + 1$$
$$(x + 2)^2 + (y - 1)^2 = 2$$

The center of the circle is at $(-2, 1)$, and its radius is $\sqrt{2}$ units.

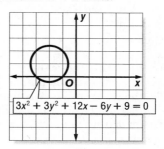

47.
$$4x^2 + 4y^2 + 36y + 5 = 0$$
$$x^2 + y^2 + 9y + \frac{5}{4} = 0$$
$$x^2 + y^2 + 9y + \blacksquare = -\frac{5}{4} + \blacksquare$$
$$x^2 + y^2 + 9y + \frac{81}{4} = -\frac{5}{4} + \frac{81}{4}$$
$$x^2 + \left(y + \frac{9}{2}\right)^2 = 19$$

The center of the circle is at $\left(0, -\frac{9}{2}\right)$, and its radius is $\sqrt{19}$ units.

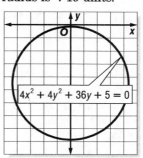

48. The radio signal can be heard as long as Doralina is within the 120 mile range of the radio station in Minot. This means that she must be within a circle with center at Minot and radius 120 miles. Minot can be represented by the point with coordinates $(-1, 3)$ on the coordinate plane. Since 1 unit = 30 miles, the center of the circle (at Minot) is given by the point $(-30, 90)$. Thus, the equation of the circle is $[x - (-30)]^2 + (y - 90)^2 = 120^2$ or $(x + 30)^2 + (y - 90)^2 = 120^2$. Driving west, Doralina will lose the signal when she leaves the circle, at the point where the circle intersects the x-axis. Since this is the x-intercept of the circle, use $y = 0$ to determine the value of x.

$$(x + 30)^2 + (y - 90)^2 = 120^2$$
$$(x + 30)^2 + (0 - 90)^2 = 120^2$$
$$(x + 30)^2 = 6300$$
$$x + 30 = \pm\sqrt{6300}$$
$$x = -30 \pm \sqrt{6300}$$
$$x \approx 49 \text{ or } -109$$

Since Doralina is traveling west on Interstate 94, the x-coordinate of the x-intercept where she will lose the radio signal is about -109. Thus, Doralina will lose the signal when she is about 109 miles west of Bismarck.

49. The circle has a radius of $\sqrt{5}$ units, so the equation is of the form $(x - h)^2 + (y - k)^2 = \sqrt{5}^2$ or $(x - h)^2 + (y - k)^2 = 5$, where the center is at (h, k). Since the circle has its center on the line with equation $y = 2x$, the center can be written as $(h, 2h)$. The circle passes through $(1, -3)$, or where $x = 1$ and $y = -3$. Use substitution to find the coordinates of the center.

$$(x - h)^2 + (y - k)^2 = 5$$
$$(1 - h)^2 + (-3 - 2h)^2 = 5$$
$$1 - 2h + h^2 + 9 + 12h + 4h^2 = 5$$
$$5h^2 + 10h + 10 = 5$$
$$h^2 + 2h + 2 = 1$$
$$h^2 + 2h + 1 = 0$$
$$(h + 1)^2 = 0$$
$$h + 1 = 0$$
$$h = -1$$

Thus, $h = -1$. Since the center is given by $(h, 2h)$, where $k = 2h$, use h to determine the value of k.
$$k = 2h$$
$$k = 2(-1)$$
$$k = -2$$

So the center is at $(-1, -2)$. The equation of the circle is $(x + 1)^2 + (y + 2)^2 = 5$.

50. A circle can be used to represent the limit at which planes can be detected by radar. Answers should include the following.

- Since the radar is at the origin, the center of the circle is at $(0, 0)$. The radius is the range of the radar, or 50 miles. Thus, the equation of the circle that determines the boundary of the region where planes can be detected is $(x - 0)^2 + (y - 0)^2 = 50^2$ or $x^2 + y^2 = 2500$.
- The region whose boundary is modeled by $x^2 + y^2 = 4900$ is larger, so there would be more planes to track.

51. A; $x^2 + y^2 + 8x + 8y + 28 = 0$
$$x^2 + 8x + \blacksquare + y^2 + 8y + \blacksquare = -28 + \blacksquare + \blacksquare$$
$$x^2 + 8x + 16 + y^2 + 8y + 16 = -28 + 16 + 16$$
$$(x + 4)^2 + (y + 4)^2 = 4$$

The equation is of the form $(x - h)^2 + (y - k)^2 = r^2$, where $r^2 = 4$. Thus, the radius r is 2.

52. D; $x^2 + y^2 - 10x + 6y + 27 = 0$
$$x^2 - 10x + \blacksquare + y^2 + 6y + \blacksquare = -27 + \blacksquare + \blacksquare$$
$$x^2 - 10x + 25 + y^2 + 6y + 9 = -27 + 25 + 9$$
$$(x - 5)^2 + (y + 3)^2 = 7$$

The center of the circle is at $(5, -3)$.

53. $(x + 3)^2 + y^2 = 16$
$$y^2 = 16 - (x + 3)^2$$
$$y = \pm\sqrt{16 - (x + 3)^2}$$

54. To graph the given equation, enter the functions $y = \sqrt{16 - (x + 3)^2}$ and $y = -\sqrt{16 - (x + 3)^2}$.

55.

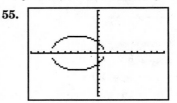

[−10, 10] scl:1 by [−10, 10] scl:1

56. $(x + 3)^2 + y^2 = 16$
$$(x + 3)^2 = 16 - y^2$$
$$x + 3 = \pm\sqrt{16 - y^2}$$
$$x = -3 \pm\sqrt{16 - y^2}$$

The equations with the $+$ symbol and $-$ symbol represent the right and left halves of the circle, respectively.

Page 431   Maintain Your Skills

57. The equation is of the form $x = a(y - k)^2 + h$, where $a = -3$, $k = 0$, and $h = 1$. The vertex is at $(1, 0)$, and the focus is at $\left(1 + \frac{1}{4(-3)}, 0\right)$ or $\left(\frac{11}{12}, 0\right)$. The axis of symmetry is $y = 0$, the directrix is $x = 1 - \frac{1}{4(-3)}$ or $x = 1\frac{1}{12}$, and the parabola opens to the left. The length of the latus rectum is $\left|\frac{1}{-3}\right|$ or $\frac{1}{3}$ unit.

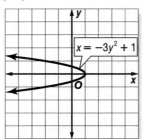

$x = -3y^2 + 1$

58. $y + 2 = -(x - 3)^2$
$\quad\quad y = -(x - 3)^2 - 2$

The equation is of the form $y = a(x - h)^2 + k$, where $a = -1$, $h = 3$, and $k = -2$. The vertex is at $(3, -2)$, and the focus is at $\left(3, -2 + \frac{1}{4(-1)}\right)$ or $\left(3, -2\frac{1}{4}\right)$. The axis of symmetry is $x = 3$, the directrix is $y = -2 - \frac{1}{4(-1)}$ or $y = -1\frac{3}{4}$, and the parabola opens downward. The length of the latus rectum is $\left|\frac{1}{-1}\right|$ or 1 unit.

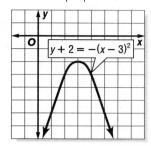

59. $\quad\quad y = x^2 + 4x$
$y + \blacksquare = x^2 + 4x + \blacksquare$
$y + 4 = x^2 + 4x + 4$
$y + 4 = (x + 2)^2$
$\quad\quad y = (x + 2)^2 - 4$

The equation is of the form $y = a(x - h)^2 + k$, where $a = 1$, $h = -2$, and $k = -4$. The vertex is at $(-2, -4)$, and the focus is at $\left(-2, -4 + \frac{1}{4(1)}\right)$ or $\left(-2, -3\frac{3}{4}\right)$. The axis of symmetry is $x = -2$, the directrix is $y = -4 - \frac{1}{4(1)}$ or $y = -4\frac{1}{4}$, and the parabola opens upward. The length of the latus rectum is $\left|\frac{1}{1}\right|$ or 1 unit.

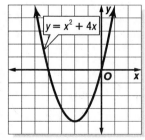

60. $\left(\frac{x_1 + x_2}{2}, \frac{y_1 + y_2}{2}\right) = \left(\frac{5 + 3}{2}, \frac{-7 + (-1)}{2}\right)$
$\quad\quad\quad\quad\quad\quad\quad = \left(\frac{8}{2}, \frac{-8}{2}\right)$
$\quad\quad\quad\quad\quad\quad\quad = (4, -4)$

61. $\left(\frac{x_1 + x_2}{2}, \frac{y_1 + y_2}{2}\right) = \left(\frac{2 + (-4)}{2}, \frac{-9 + 5}{2}\right)$
$\quad\quad\quad\quad\quad\quad\quad = \left(\frac{-2}{2}, \frac{-4}{2}\right)$
$\quad\quad\quad\quad\quad\quad\quad = (-1, -2)$

62. $\left(\frac{x_1 + x_2}{2}, \frac{y_1 + y_2}{2}\right) = \left(\frac{8 + (-5)}{2}, \frac{0 + 12}{2}\right)$
$\quad\quad\quad\quad\quad\quad\quad = \left(\frac{3}{2}, \frac{12}{2}\right)$
$\quad\quad\quad\quad\quad\quad\quad = \left(\frac{3}{2}, 6\right)$

63. Since $f(x)$ has degree 3, the function has three zeros. To determine the possible number and type of real zeros, examine the number of sign changes for $f(x)$ and $f(-x)$.

$$f(x) = \underbrace{x^3 + 5x^2}_{\text{no}} \underbrace{+ 2x}_{\text{no}} \underbrace{- 8}_{\text{yes}} \quad f(-x) = \underbrace{-x^3 + 5x^2}_{\text{yes}} \underbrace{- 2x}_{\text{yes}} \underbrace{- 8}_{\text{no}}$$

Since there is 1 sign change for the coefficients of $f(x)$, the function has 1 positive real zero. Since there are 2 sign changes for the coefficients of $f(-x)$, $f(x)$ has 2 or 0 negative real zeros. Thus, $f(x)$ has either 3 real zeros, or 1 real zero and 2 imaginary zeros.

To find these zeros, first list some possibilities and then eliminate those that are not zeros. Since $f(x)$ has 1 positive real zero and evaluating the function for 0 results in -8, begin by evaluating $f(x)$ for positive integral values.

Evaluating $f(x)$ for $x = 1$ shows that one zero occurs at $x = 1$. Factor the depressed polynomial of this zero, $x^2 + 6x + 8 = (x + 2)(x + 4)$. Thus, the function has roots $x = -2$ and $x = -4$. Therefore, the rational zeros for the function are -4, -2, and 1.

64. Since $g(x)$ has degree 3, the function has three zeros. To determine the possible number and type of real zeros, examine the number of sign changes for $g(x)$ and $g(-x)$.

$$g(x) = 2x^3 \underbrace{- 9x^2}_{\text{yes}} \underbrace{+ 7x}_{\text{yes}} \underbrace{+ 6}_{\text{no}}$$

$$g(-x) = -2x^3 \underbrace{- 9x^2}_{\text{no}} \underbrace{- 7x}_{\text{no}} \underbrace{+ 6}_{\text{yes}}$$

Since there are 2 sign changes for the coefficients of $g(x)$, the function has 2 or 0 positive real zeros. Since there is 1 sign change for the coefficients of $g(-x)$, $g(x)$ has exactly 1 negative real zero. Thus, $g(x)$ has either 3 real zeros, or 1 real zero and 2 imaginary zeros.

To find these zeros, first begin by evaluating $g(x)$ for positive integral values.

Evaluating $g(x)$ for $x = 2$ shows that one zero occurs at $x = 2$. Factor the depressed polynomial of this zero, $2x^2 - 5x - 3 = (2x + 1)(x - 3)$.
Find the roots of the depressed polynomial.

$2x^2 - 5x - 3 = 0$
$(2x + 1)(x - 3) = 0$
$2x + 1 = 0 \quad$ or $\quad x - 3 = 0$
$\quad\quad 2x = -1 \quad\quad\quad\quad\quad x = 3$
$\quad\quad\quad x = -\frac{1}{2}$

Therefore, the rational zeros for the function are $-\frac{1}{2}$, 2, and 3.

65. Let ℓ equal the length of the rectangle, and let w equal the width of the rectangle. The perimeter of the rectangle is 86 inches, so $\ell + \ell + w + w = 86$ or $2\ell + 2w = 86$. Twice the width exceeds the length by 2 inches, that is, $2w = \ell + 2$. Use substitution to find the dimensions of the rectangular picture.

$$2\ell + 2w = 86$$
$$2\ell + (\ell + 2) = 86$$
$$3\ell + 2 = 86$$
$$3\ell = 84$$
$$\ell = 28$$

The length of the rectangular picture is 28 inches. Use ℓ to find w.

$$2\ell + 2w = 86$$
$$2(28) + 2w = 86$$
$$56 + 2w = 86$$
$$2w = 30$$
$$w = 15$$

The width of the rectangular picture is 15 inches. Thus, the dimensions of the picture are 28 inches by 15 inches.

66.
$$c^2 = 13^2 - 5^2$$
$$c^2 = 169 - 25$$
$$c^2 = 144$$
$$c = \sqrt{144} \text{ or } 12$$

67.
$$c^2 = 10^2 - 8^2$$
$$c^2 = 100 - 64$$
$$c^2 = 36$$
$$c = \sqrt{36} \text{ or } 6$$

68.
$$(\sqrt{7})^2 = a^2 - 3^2$$
$$7 = a^2 - 9$$
$$16 = a^2$$
$$\sqrt{16} = a$$
$$4 = a$$

69.
$$24^2 = a^2 - 7^2$$
$$576 = a^2 - 49$$
$$625 = a^2$$
$$\sqrt{625} = a$$
$$25 = a$$

70.
$$4^2 = 6^2 - b^2$$
$$16 = 36 - b^2$$
$$b^2 + 16 = 36$$
$$b^2 = 20$$
$$b = \sqrt{20} \text{ or } 2\sqrt{5}$$

71.
$$(2\sqrt{14})^2 = 8^2 - b^2$$
$$56 = 64 - b^2$$
$$b^2 + 56 = 64$$
$$b^2 = 8$$
$$b = \sqrt{8} \text{ or } 2\sqrt{2}$$

Page 431 Practice Quiz 1

1. $\sqrt{(x_2 - x_1)^2 + (y_2 - y_1)^2}$
$$= \sqrt{(4 - 9)^2 + (-7 - 5)^2}$$
$$= \sqrt{(-5)^2 + (-12)^2}$$
$$= \sqrt{25 + 144}$$
$$= \sqrt{169} \text{ or } 13$$

The distance between $(9, 5)$ and $(4, -7)$ is 13 units.

2. $\sqrt{(x_2 - x_1)^2 + (y_2 - y_1)^2}$
$$= \sqrt{(10 - 0)^2 + [-3 - (-5)]^2}$$
$$= \sqrt{10^2 + 2^2}$$
$$= \sqrt{100 + 4}$$
$$= \sqrt{104} \text{ or } 2\sqrt{26}$$

The distance between $(0, -5)$ and $(10, -3)$ is $2\sqrt{26}$ units.

3. $y^2 = 6x$
$$\frac{1}{6}y^2 = x$$

The equation is of the form $x = a(y - k)^2 + h$, where $a = \frac{1}{6}$, $k = 0$, and $h = 0$. The vertex is at $(0, 0)$, and the focus is at $\left(0 + \frac{1}{4\left(\frac{1}{6}\right)}, 0\right)$ or $\left(1\frac{1}{2}, 0\right)$. The axis of symmetry is $y = 0$, the directrix is $x = 0 - \frac{1}{4\left(\frac{1}{6}\right)}$ or $x = -1\frac{1}{2}$, and the parabola opens to the right. The length of the latus rectum is $\left|\frac{1}{\frac{1}{6}}\right|$ or 6 units.

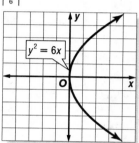

4.
$$y = x^2 + 8x + 20$$
$$y - 20 = x^2 + 8x$$
$$y - 20 + \blacksquare = x^2 + 8x + \blacksquare$$
$$y - 20 + 16 = x^2 + 8x + 16$$
$$y - 4 = (x + 4)^2$$
$$y = (x + 4)^2 + 4$$

The equation is of the form $y = a(x - h)^2 + k$, where $a = 1$, $h = -4$, and $k = 4$. The vertex is at $(-4, 4)$, and the focus is $\left(-4, 4 + \frac{1}{4(1)}\right)$ or $\left(-4, 4\frac{1}{4}\right)$. The axis of symmetry is $x = -4$, the directrix is $y = 4 - \frac{1}{4(1)}$ or $y = 3\frac{3}{4}$, and the parabola opens upward. The length of the latus rectum is $\left|\frac{1}{1}\right|$ or 1 unit.

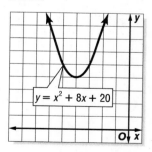

5. The equation is of the form
$(x - h)^2 + (y - k)^2 = r^2$, where $h = 0$, $k = 4$, and
$r = 7$. Therefore, the center is at $(0, 4)$, and the
radius is 7 units.

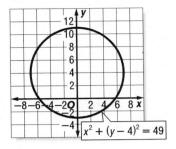

$x^2 + (y - 4)^2 = 49$

Page 432   Algebra Activity (Preview of Lesson 8-4)

1. See students' work.

2. See students' work; the ellipse is more circular.

3. See students' work.

4. See students' work.

5. See students' work.

6. The ellipse becomes more circular.

7. The ellipse becomes more elongated.

8. The ellipse becomes larger.

9. The ellipse is longer in the vertical direction than
in the horizontal direction.

10. The ellipse is a circle.

11. The sum of the distances is constant.

12. No; a rubber band might stretch so that the sum
of the distances to the thumbtacks would not be
constant.

8-4 | Ellipses

Page 437   Algebra Activity

See students' work.

Let $(d, 0)$ be the coordinates of the point located
on the positive x-axis. This point, the origin, and
the point of intersection in the first quadrant of
the circle and the ellipse form a right triangle.
The length of the hypotenuse is the radius of the
circle, which is half the length of the major axis of
the ellipse, or a. One leg of the triangle has length
d and the other has half the length of the minor
axis of the ellipse, or b. By the Pythagorean
Theorem, $a^2 = d^2 + b^2$ or $d^2 = a^2 - b^2$. Therefore,
d satisfies the equation relating a, b, and c for an
ellipse. Thus, one focus of the ellipse is at $(d, 0)$.
By symmetry, the other focus is at $(-d, 0)$, which
is the other point located by this method.

Pages 437–438   Check for Understanding

1. The axes of symmetry of the ellipse are $x = -1$
and $y = 2$.

2. The equation of a circle is $(x - h)^2 + (y - k)^2 = r^2$.
Divide each side by r^2 to get $\frac{(x - h)^2}{r^2} + \frac{(y - k)^2}{r^2} = 1$.
This is the equation of an ellipse with a and b
both equal to r. In other words, a circle is an
ellipse whose major and minor axes are equal.

3. The major axis is horizontal, so the equation is of
the form $\frac{(x - h)^2}{a^2} + \frac{(y - k)^2}{b^2} = 1$. The center is at
$(2, -5)$, so $h = 2$ and $k = -5$. Thus, equations
should be of the form $\frac{(x - 2)^2}{a^2} + \frac{(y + 5)^2}{b^2} = 1$, where a
and b are positive real numbers. Sample answer:
$\frac{(x - 2)^2}{4} + \frac{(y + 5)^2}{1} = 1$

4. The center of the ellipse is at the origin and its
major axis is horizontal, so the equation is of the
form $\frac{x^2}{a^2} + \frac{y^2}{b^2} = 1$. The length of the major axis of
an ellipse is $2a$ units. In this ellipse, the length of
the major axis is the distance between the points
at $(-6, 0)$ and $(6, 0)$. This distance is 12 units. Use
this length to determine the value of a.
$$2a = 12$$
$$a = 6$$
The foci are located at $(-4, 0)$ and $(4, 0)$, so $c = 4$.
Use the equation $c^2 = a^2 - b^2$, where $a = 6$ and
$c = 4$, to determine the value of b.
$$c^2 = a^2 - b^2$$
$$4^2 = 6^2 - b^2$$
$$16 = 36 - b^2$$
$$b^2 = 20$$
Thus, an equation for the ellipse is $\frac{x^2}{36} + \frac{y^2}{20} = 1$.

5. The major axis of the ellipse is vertical, so the
equation is of the form $\frac{(y - k)^2}{a^2} + \frac{(x - h)^2}{b^2} = 1$. The
center of the ellipse is the midpoint of the major
axis.
$$(h, k) = \left(\frac{x_1 + x_2}{2}, \frac{y_1 + y_2}{2} \right)$$
$$= \left(\frac{2 + 2}{2}, \frac{2 + (-10)}{2} \right)$$
$$= \left(\frac{4}{2}, \frac{-8}{2} \right)$$
$$= (2, -4)$$
The length of the major axis of an ellipse is $2a$
units. In this ellipse, the length of the major axis
is the distance between the points at $(2, 2)$ and
$(2, -10)$. This distance is 12 units. Use this length
to determine the value of a.
$$2a = 12$$
$$a = 6$$
The length of the minor axis of an ellipse is $2b$
units. In this ellipse, the length of the minor axis
is the distance between the points at $(0, -4)$ and
$(4, -4)$. This distance is 4 units. Use this length to
determine the value of b.
$$2b = 4$$
$$b = 2$$
Thus, an equation of the ellipse is
$\frac{[y - (-4)]^2}{6^2} + \frac{(x - 2)^2}{2^2} = 1$ or $\frac{(y + 4)^2}{36} + \frac{(x - 2)^2}{4} = 1$.

6. The major axis of the ellipse is vertical, so the equation is of the form $\frac{(y-k)^2}{a^2} + \frac{(x-h)^2}{b^2} = 1$. The center of the ellipse is the midpoint of the major axis. This point is at $(0, 0)$, so $h = 0$ and $k = 0$. The length of the major axis of an ellipse is $2a$ units. In this ellipse, the length of the major axis is the distance between the points at $(0, 10)$ and $(0, -10)$. This distance is 20 units. Use this length to determine the value of a.

$2a = 20$

$a = 10$

The foci are located at $(0, 8)$ and $(0, -8)$, so $c = 8$. Use the equation $c^2 = a^2 - b^2$, where $a = 10$ and $c = 8$, to determine the value of b.

$c^2 = a^2 - b^2$

$8^2 = 10^2 - b^2$

$64 = 100 - b^2$

$b^2 = 36$

Thus, an equation for the ellipse is

$\frac{(y-0)^2}{100} + \frac{(x-0)^2}{36} = 1$ or $\frac{y^2}{100} + \frac{x^2}{36} = 1$.

7. The equation is of the form $\frac{y^2}{a^2} + \frac{x^2}{b^2} = 1$. The center is at $(0, 0)$. Since $a^2 = 18$, $a = 3\sqrt{2}$. Since $b^2 = 9$, $b = 3$. The length of the major axis is $2(3\sqrt{2})$ or $6\sqrt{2}$ units. The length of the minor axis is $2(3)$ or 6 units. Use the equation $c^2 = a^2 - b^2$ to determine the value of c.

$c^2 = a^2 - b^2$

$c^2 = 18 - 9$

$c^2 = 9$

$c = 3$

The foci are at $(0, 3)$ and $(0, -3)$.

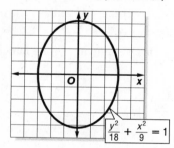

8. The equation is of the form $\frac{(x-h)^2}{a^2} + \frac{(y-k)^2}{b^2} = 1$. The center is at $(1, -2)$. Since $a^2 = 20$, $a = 2\sqrt{5}$. Since $b^2 = 4$, $b = 2$. The length of the major axis is $2(2\sqrt{5})$ or $4\sqrt{5}$ units. The length of the minor axis is $2(2)$ or 4 units. Use the equation $c^2 = a^2 - b^2$ to determine the value of c.

$c^2 = a^2 - b^2$

$c^2 = 20 - 4$

$c^2 = 16$

$c = 4$

The foci are at $(1 \pm 4, -2)$, or $(5, -2)$ and $(-3, -2)$.

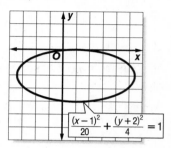

9. $4x^2 + 8y^2 = 32$

$\frac{4x^2}{32} + \frac{8y^2}{32} = 1$

$\frac{x^2}{8} + \frac{y^2}{4} = 1$

The equation is of the form $\frac{x^2}{a^2} + \frac{y^2}{b^2} = 1$. The center of this ellipse is at $(0, 0)$. Since $a^2 = 8$, $a = 2\sqrt{2}$. Since $b^2 = 4$, $b = 2$. The length of the major axis is $2(2\sqrt{2})$ or $4\sqrt{2}$ units. The length of the minor axis is $2(2)$ or 4 units. Use the equation $c^2 = a^2 - b^2$ to determine the value of c.

$c^2 = a^2 - b^2$

$c^2 = 8 - 4$

$c^2 = 4$

$c = 2$

The foci are at $(2, 0)$ and $(-2, 0)$.

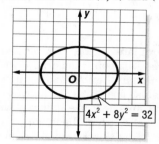

10. $x^2 + 25y^2 - 8x + 100y + 91 = 0$

$(x^2 - 8x + \blacksquare) + 25(y^2 + 4y + \blacksquare) = -91 + \blacksquare + 25(\blacksquare)$

$(x^2 - 8x + 16) + 25(y^2 + 4y + 4) = -91 + 16 + 25(4)$

$(x - 4)^2 + 25(y + 2)^2 = 25$

$\dfrac{(x - 4)^2}{25} + \dfrac{(y + 2)^2}{1} = 1$

The equation is of the form $\dfrac{(x - h)^2}{a^2} + \dfrac{(y - k)^2}{b^2} = 1$.

The center is $(4, -2)$. Since $a^2 = 25$, $a = 5$. Since $b^2 = 1$, $b = 1$. The length of the major axis is $2(5)$ or 10 units. The length of the minor axis is $2(1)$ or 2 units. Use the equation $c^2 = a^2 - b^2$ to determine the value of c.

$c^2 = a^2 - b^2$

$c^2 = 25 - 1$

$c^2 = 24$

$c = 2\sqrt{6}$

The foci are at $(4 \pm 2\sqrt{6}, -2)$, or $(4 + 2\sqrt{6}, -2)$ and $(4 - 2\sqrt{6}, -2)$.

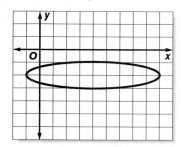

11. The orbit of Mercury can be represented by the equation of an ellipse. If the center of the orbit is the origin and the sun lies on the x-axis, then the points at which Mercury is closest and farthest from the Sun are the x-intercepts of the ellipse. These two points are the endpoints of the major axis. For an ellipse, the length of the major axis is $2a$. For this ellipse, the length of the major axis is the distance between the two x-intercepts. This distance is $43.8 + 29.0$ or 72.8 million miles. Use this to determine the value of a.

$2a = 72.8 \times 10^6$

$a = 36.4 \times 10^6$

In other words, the distance from the origin to one of the endpoints of the major axis is 36.4×10^6 or 36.4 million miles. Since $a = 36.4 \times 10^6$, $a^2 = 1.32 \times 10^{15}$. At its closest point, Mercury is 29.0 million miles from the Sun. Thus, the Sun is $36.4 - 29.0$ or 7.4 million miles from the center of the ellipse, so $c = 7.4 \times 10^6$. Use the equation $c^2 = a^2 - b^2$ to determine the value of b.

$c^2 = a^2 - b^2$

$(7.4 \times 10^6)^2 = (36.4 \times 10^6)^2 - b^2$

$5.48 \times 10^{13} \approx (1.32 \times 10^{15}) - b^2$

$b^2 \approx 1.27 \times 10^{15}$

Since the major axis is horizontal substitute 1.32×10^{15} for a^2 and 1.27×10^{15} for b^2 in the form $\dfrac{x^2}{a^2} + \dfrac{y^2}{b^2} = 1$. An equation for the ellipse is about

$\dfrac{x^2}{1.32 \times 10^{15}} + \dfrac{y^2}{1.27 \times 10^{15}} = 1$

12. The length of the major axis of an ellipse is $2a$ units. In this ellipse, the length of the major axis is the distance between the points at $(0, -8)$ and $(0, 8)$. This distance is 16 units. Use this length to determine the value of a.

$2a = 16$

$a = 8$

The foci are located at $(0, 5)$ and $(0, -5)$, so $c = 5$. Use the equation $c^2 = a^2 - b^2$ to determine the value of b.

$c^2 = a^2 - b^2$

$5^2 = 8^2 - b^2$

$25 = 64 - b^2$

$b^2 = 39$

Since the major axis is vertical, substitute 64 for a^2 and 39 for b^2 in the form $\dfrac{y^2}{a^2} + \dfrac{x^2}{b^2} = 1$. An equation for the ellipse is $\dfrac{y^2}{64} + \dfrac{x^2}{39} = 1$.

13. The length of the major axis of an ellipse is $2a$ units. In this ellipse, the length of the major axis is the distance between the points at $(-4, 0)$ and $(4, 0)$. This distance is 8 units. Use this length to determine the value of a.

$2a = 8$

$a = 4$

The foci are located at $(3, 0)$ and $(-3, 0)$, so $c = 3$. Use the equation $c^2 = a^2 - b^2$ to determine the value of b.

$c^2 = a^2 - b^2$

$3^2 = 4^2 - b^2$

$9 = 16 - b^2$

$b^2 = 7$

Since the major axis is horizontal, substitute 16 for a^2 and 7 for b^2 in the form $\dfrac{x^2}{a^2} + \dfrac{y^2}{b^2} = 1$. An equation for the ellipse is $\dfrac{x^2}{16} + \dfrac{y^2}{7} = 1$.

14. The center of the ellipse is at $(5, 4)$, so the equation is of the form $\dfrac{(x - h)^2}{a^2} + \dfrac{(y - k)^2}{b^2} = 1$, where $h = 5$ and $k = 4$. The length of the major axis of an ellipse is $2a$ units. In this ellipse, the length of the major axis is the distance between the points at $(-3, 4)$ and $(13, 4)$. This distance is 16 units. Use this length to determine the value of a.

$2a = 16$

$a = 8$

The foci are located at $(5 - \sqrt{55}, 4)$ and $(5 + \sqrt{55}, 4)$, so $c = \sqrt{55}$. Use the equation $c^2 = a^2 - b^2$ to determine the value of b.

$c^2 = a^2 - b^2$

$(\sqrt{55})^2 = 8^2 - b^2$

$55 = 64 - b^2$

$b^2 = 9$

Thus, an equation for the ellipse is $\dfrac{(x - 5)^2}{64} + \dfrac{(y - 4)^2}{9} = 1$.

15. The center of the ellipse is at $(-2, 0)$, so the equation is of the form $\frac{(y-k)^2}{a^2} + \frac{(x-h)^2}{b^2} = 1$, where $h = -2$ and $k = 0$. The length of the major axis of an ellipse is $2a$ units. In this ellipse, the length of the major axis is the distance between the points at $(-2, 4)$ and $(-2, -4)$. This distance is 8 units. Use this length to determine the value of a.

$2a = 8$

$a = 4$

The foci are located at $(-2, 2\sqrt{3})$ and $(-2, -2\sqrt{3})$, so $c = 2\sqrt{3}$. Use the equation $c^2 = a^2 - b^2$ to determine the value of b.

$c^2 = a^2 - b^2$

$(2\sqrt{3})^2 = 4^2 - b^2$

$12 = 16 - b^2$

$b^2 = 4$

Thus, an equation for the ellipse is

$\frac{(y-0)^2}{16} + \frac{[x-(-2)]^2}{4} = 1$ or $\frac{y^2}{16} + \frac{(x+2)^2}{4} = 1$.

16. The major axis of the ellipse is horizontal, so the equation is of the form $\frac{(x-h)^2}{a^2} + \frac{(y-k)^2}{b^2} = 1$. The center of the ellipse is the midpoint of the major axis, which has endpoints $(-11, 5)$ and $(7, 5)$. Use the endpoints to find the coordinates of the center.

$(h, k) = \left(\frac{x_1 + x_2}{2}, \frac{y_1 + y_2}{2} \right)$

$= \left(\frac{-11 + 7}{2}, \frac{5 + 5}{2} \right)$

$= \left(\frac{-4}{2}, \frac{10}{2} \right)$

$= (-2, 5)$

The center is at $(-2, 5)$, so $h = -2$ and $k = 5$. The length of the major axis of an ellipse is $2a$ units. In this ellipse, the length of the major axis is the distance between the points at $(-11, 5)$ and $(7, 5)$. This distance is 18 units. Use this length to determine the value of a.

$2a = 18$

$a = 9$

The length of the minor axis of an ellipse is $2b$ units. In this ellipse, the length of the minor axis is the distance between the points at $(-2, 9)$ and $(-2, 1)$. This distance is 8 units. Use this length to determine the value of b.

$2b = 8$

$b = 4$

Thus, an equation for the ellipse is

$\frac{[x-(-2)]^2}{9^2} + \frac{(y-5)^2}{4^2} = 1$ or $\frac{(x+2)^2}{81} + \frac{(y-5)^2}{16} = 1$.

17. The major axis of the ellipse is vertical, so the equation is of the form $\frac{(y-k)^2}{a^2} + \frac{(x-h)^2}{b^2} = 1$. The center of the ellipse is the midpoint of the major axis, which has endpoints $(2, 12)$ and $(2, -4)$. Use the endpoints to determine the coordinates of the center.

$(h, k) = \left(\frac{x_1 + x_2}{2}, \frac{y_1 + y_2}{2} \right)$

$= \left(\frac{2 + 2}{2}, \frac{12 + (-4)}{2} \right)$

$= \left(\frac{4}{2}, \frac{8}{2} \right)$

$= (2, 4)$

The center is at $(2, 4)$, so $h = 2$ and $k = 4$. The length of the major axis of an ellipse is $2a$ units. In this ellipse, the length of the major axis is the distance between the points at $(2, 12)$ and $(2, -4)$. This distance is 16 units. Use this length to determine the value of a.

$2a = 16$

$a = 8$

The length of the minor axis of an ellipse is $2b$ units. In this ellipse, the length of the minor axis is the distance between the points at $(4, 4)$ and $(0, 4)$. This distance is 4 units. Use this length to determine the value of b.

$2b = 4$

$b = 2$

Thus, an equation for the ellipse is

$\frac{(y-4)^2}{8^2} + \frac{(x-2)^2}{2^2} = 1$ or $\frac{(y-4)^2}{64} + \frac{(x-2)^2}{4} = 1$.

18. The major axis is vertical, so the equation is of the form $\frac{(y-k)^2}{a^2} + \frac{(x-h)^2}{b^2} = 1$. The center is at $(4, 2)$, so $h = 4$ and $k = 2$. The length of the major axis of an ellipse is $2a$ units. In this ellipse, the length of the major axis is 20 units, so $a = 10$. The length of the minor axis of an ellipse is $2b$ units. In this ellipse, the length of the minor axis is 6 units, so $b = 3$. Thus, an equation of the ellipse is

$\frac{(y-2)^2}{10^2} + \frac{(x-4)^2}{3^2} = 1$ or $\frac{(y-2)^2}{100} + \frac{(x-4)^2}{9} = 1$.

19. The major axis is horizontal, so the equation is of the form $\frac{(x-h)^2}{a^2} + \frac{(y-k)^2}{b^2} = 1$. The center is at $(5, 4)$, so $h = 5$ and $k = 4$. The length of the major axis of an ellipse is $2a$ units. In this ellipse, the length of the major axis is 16 units, so $a = 8$. The length of the minor axis of an ellipse is $2b$ units. In this ellipse, the length of the minor axis is 9 units, so $b = \frac{9}{2}$. Thus, an equation of the ellipse is

$\frac{(x-5)^2}{8^2} + \frac{(y-4)^2}{\left(\frac{9}{2}\right)^2} = 1$ or $\frac{(x-5)^2}{64} + \frac{(y-4)^2}{\frac{81}{4}} = 1$.

20. The major axis is horizontal, so the equation is of the form $\frac{(x-h)^2}{a^2} + \frac{(y-k)^2}{b^2} = 1$. The center of the ellipse is the midpoint of the major axis, which has endpoints $(10, 2)$ and $(-8, 2)$. Use the endpoints to find the coordinates of the center.

$$(h, k) = \left(\frac{x_1 + x_2}{2}, \frac{y_1 + y_2}{2} \right)$$
$$= \left(\frac{10 + (-8)}{2}, \frac{2 + 2}{2} \right)$$
$$= \left(\frac{2}{2}, \frac{4}{2} \right)$$
$$= (1, 2)$$

The center is $(1, 2)$, so $h = 1$ and $k = 2$. The length of the major axis of an ellipse is $2a$ units. In this ellipse, the length of the major axis is the distance between the points at $(10, 2)$ and $(-8, 2)$. This distance is 18 units. Use this length to determine the value of a.

$$2a = 18$$
$$a = 9$$

The foci are at $(6, 2)$ and $(-4, 2)$, so $c = 5$. Use the equation $c^2 = a^2 - b^2$ to determine the value of b.

$$c^2 = a^2 - b^2$$
$$5^2 = 9^2 - b^2$$
$$25 = 81 - b^2$$
$$b^2 = 56$$

Thus, an equation of the ellipse is
$$\frac{(x-1)^2}{81} + \frac{(y-2)^2}{56} = 1.$$

21. The minor axis is vertical, so the equation is of the form $\frac{(x-h)^2}{a^2} + \frac{(y-k)^2}{b^2} = 1$. The center of the ellipse is at $(0, 0)$, so $h = 0$ and $k = 0$. The length of the minor axis of an ellipse is $2b$ units. In this ellipse, the length of the minor axis is the distance between the points at $(0, 5)$ and $(0, -5)$. This distance is 10 units. Use this length to determine the value of b.

$$2b = 10$$
$$b = 5$$

The foci are at $(12, 0)$ and $(-12, 0)$, so $c = 12$. Use the equation $c^2 = a^2 - b^2$ to determine the value of a.

$$c^2 = a^2 - b^2$$
$$12^2 = a^2 - 5^2$$
$$144 = a^2 - 25$$
$$169 = a^2$$

Thus, an equation of the ellipse is
$$\frac{(x-0)^2}{169} + \frac{(y-0)^2}{5^2} = 1 \quad \text{or} \quad \frac{x^2}{169} + \frac{y^2}{25} = 1.$$

22. The origin is at the midpoint of the bottom edge of the window and the major axis of the ellipse is horizontal, so the equation is of the form $\frac{x^2}{a^2} + \frac{y^2}{b^2} = 1$. Since the length of the bottom edge of the window is 36 inches, the length of the major axis is 36. The length of the major axis of an ellipse is $2a$ units. Use this to determine the value of a.

$$2a = 36$$
$$a = 18$$

Since the window is the top half of an ellipse, the height of the window is half of the length of the minor axis. Thus, $b = 14$. Since $a = 18$, $a^2 = 324$. Since $b = 14$, $b^2 = 196$. An equation for the ellipse is $\frac{x^2}{324} + \frac{y^2}{196} = 1$.

23. The center of the orbit is the origin and the major axis is horizontal, so the equation for the orbit of Mars is of the form $\frac{x^2}{a^2} + \frac{y^2}{b^2} = 1$. The points at which Mars is the closest to and farthest from the Sun are the endpoints of the major axis. For an ellipse, the length of the major axis is $2a$ units. For this ellipse, the length of the major axis is the sum of the distance of Mars from the Sun at its closest and farthest point and the diameter of the Sun, or $155.0 \times 10^6 + 800,000 + 128.5 \times 10^6$ miles. Therefore, $2a = 284.3 \times 10^6$, or $a = 142.15 \times 10^6$. In other words, the distance from the origin to one of the endpoints of the major axis is 142.15×10^6 or 142.15 million miles. At its closest point, Mars is 128.5 million miles from the Sun. Therefore, the Sun is $142.15 \times 10^6 - 128.5 \times 10^6 - 400,000$ or 132.5×10^5 miles from the center of the orbit, so $c = 132.5 \times 10^5$. Use the equation $c^2 = a^2 - b^2$ to determine the value of b.

$$c^2 = a^2 - b^2$$
$$(132.5 \times 10^5)^2 = (142.15 \times 10^6)^2 - b^2$$
$$b^2 \approx 2.00 \times 10^{16}$$

Substitute the values for a^2 and b^2. An equation for the orbit of Mars is about
$$\frac{x^2}{2.02 \times 10^{16}} + \frac{y^2}{2.00 \times 10^{16}} = 1.$$

24. The center of the ellipse is at $(0, 0)$ and the major axis is vertical, so the equation is of the form $\frac{y^2}{a^2} + \frac{x^2}{b^2} = 1$. The length of the major axis of an ellipse is $2a$ units. In this ellipse, the length of the major axis is 1057 feet, so $a = 528.5$. The length of the minor axis of an ellipse is $2b$ units. In this ellipse, the length of the minor axis is 880 feet, so $b = 440$. Thus, an equation to model the ellipse is
$$\frac{y^2}{528.5^2} + \frac{x^2}{440^2} = 1 \quad \text{or} \quad \frac{y^2}{279,312.25} + \frac{x^2}{193,600} = 1.$$

25. $$10x^2 + 2y^2 = 40$$
$$\frac{10x^2}{40} + \frac{2y^2}{40} = 1$$
$$\frac{x^2}{4} + \frac{y^2}{20} = 1$$

26.
$$x^2 + 6y^2 - 2x + 12y - 23 = 0$$
$$(x^2 - 2x + \blacksquare) + 6(y^2 + 2y + \blacksquare) = 23 + \blacksquare + 6(\blacksquare)$$
$$(x^2 - 2x + 1) + 6(y^2 + 2y + 1) = 23 + 1 + 6(1)$$
$$(x - 1)^2 + 6(y + 1)^2 = 30$$
$$\frac{(x-1)^2}{30} + \frac{6(y+1)^2}{30} = 1$$
$$\frac{(x-1)^2}{30} + \frac{(y+1)^2}{5} = 1$$

27. The equation is of the form $\frac{y^2}{a^2} + \frac{x^2}{b^2} = 1$, where $a = \sqrt{10}$ and $b = \sqrt{5}$. The center is at $(0, 0)$. Use the equation $c^2 = a^2 - b^2$ to determine the value of c.

$c^2 = a^2 - b^2$
$c^2 = 10 - 5$
$c^2 = 5$
$c = \sqrt{5}$

Since $c = \sqrt{5}$, the foci are at $(0, \pm\sqrt{5})$. The length of the major axis is $2(\sqrt{10})$ or $2\sqrt{10}$ units. The length of the minor axis is $2(\sqrt{5})$ or $2\sqrt{5}$ units.

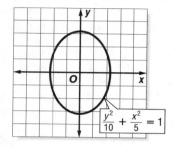

28. The equation is of the form $\frac{x^2}{a^2} + \frac{y^2}{b^2} = 1$, where $a = 5$ and $b = 3$. The center is at $(0, 0)$. Use the equation $c^2 = a^2 - b^2$ to determine the value of c.

$c^2 = a^2 - b^2$
$c^2 = 25 - 9$
$c^2 = 16$
$c = 4$

Since $c = 4$, the foci are at $(\pm 4, 0)$. The length of the major axis is $2(5)$ or 10 units. The length of the minor axis is $2(3)$ or 6 units.

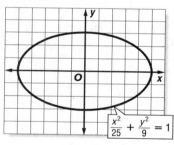

29. The equation is of the form $\frac{(x - h)^2}{a^2} + \frac{(y - k)^2}{b^2} = 1$, where $h = -8$, $k = 2$, $a = 12$, and $b = 9$. The center is at $(-8, 2)$. Use the equation $c^2 = a^2 - b^2$ to determine the value of c.

$c^2 = a^2 - b^2$
$c^2 = 144 - 81$
$c^2 = 63$
$c = 3\sqrt{7}$

Since $c = 3\sqrt{7}$, the foci are at $(-8 \pm 3\sqrt{7}, 2)$. The length of the major axis is $2(12)$ or 24 units. The length of the minor axis is $2(9)$ or 18 units.

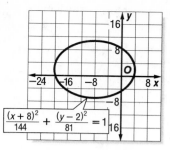

30. The equation is of the form $\frac{(y - k)^2}{a^2} + \frac{(x - h)^2}{b^2} = 1$, where $h = 5$, $k = -11$, $a = 12$, and $b = 11$. The center is at $(5, -11)$. Use the equation $c^2 = a^2 - b^2$ to determine the value of c.

$c^2 = a^2 - b^2$
$c^2 = 144 - 121$
$c^2 = 23$
$c = \sqrt{23}$

Since $c = \sqrt{23}$, the foci are at $(5, -11 \pm \sqrt{23})$. The length of the major axis is $2(12)$ or 24 units. The length of the minor axis is $2(11)$ or 22 units.

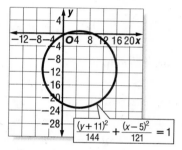

31. $3x^2 + 9y^2 = 27$

$\frac{3x^2}{27} + \frac{9y^2}{27} = 1$

$\frac{x^2}{9} + \frac{y^2}{3} = 1$

The equation is of the form $\frac{x^2}{a^2} + \frac{y^2}{b^2} = 1$, where $a = 3$ and $b = \sqrt{3}$. The center is at $(0, 0)$. Use the equation $c^2 = a^2 - b^2$ to determine the value of c.

$c^2 = a^2 - b^2$
$c^2 = 9 - 3$
$c^2 = 6$
$c = \sqrt{6}$

Since $c = \sqrt{6}$, the foci are at $(\pm\sqrt{6}, 0)$. The length of the major axis is $2(3)$ or 6 units. The length of the minor axis is $2(\sqrt{3})$ or $2\sqrt{3}$ units.

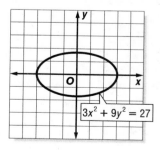

32. $27x^2 + 9y^2 = 81$

$$\frac{27x^2}{81} + \frac{9y^2}{81} = 1$$

$$\frac{x^2}{3} + \frac{y^2}{9} = 1$$

The equation is of the form $\frac{y^2}{a^2} + \frac{x^2}{b^2} = 1$, where $a = 3$ and $b = \sqrt{3}$. The center is at $(0, 0)$. Use the equation $c^2 = a^2 - b^2$ to determine the value of c.

$c^2 = a^2 - b^2$
$c^2 = 9 - 3$
$c^2 = 6$
$c = \sqrt{6}$

Since $c = \sqrt{6}$, the foci are at $(0, \pm\sqrt{6})$. The length of the major axis is $2(3)$ or 6 units. The length of the minor axis is $2(\sqrt{3})$ or $2\sqrt{3}$ units.

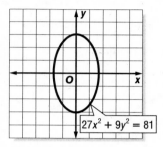

$27x^2 + 9y^2 = 81$

33. $16x^2 + 9y^2 = 144$

$$\frac{16x^2}{144} + \frac{9y^2}{144} = 1$$

$$\frac{x^2}{9} + \frac{y^2}{16} = 1$$

The equation is of the form $\frac{y^2}{a^2} + \frac{x^2}{b^2} = 1$, where $a = 4$ and $b = 3$. The center is at $(0, 0)$. Use the equation $c^2 = a^2 - b^2$ to determine the value of c.

$c^2 = a^2 - b^2$
$c^2 = 16 - 9$
$c^2 = 7$
$c = \sqrt{7}$

Since $c = \sqrt{7}$, the foci are at $(0, \pm\sqrt{7})$. The length of the major axis is $2(4)$ or 8 units. The length of the minor axis is $2(3)$ or 6 units.

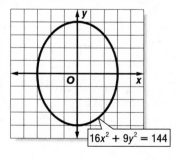

$16x^2 + 9y^2 = 144$

34. $36x^2 + 81y^2 = 2916$

$$\frac{36x^2}{2916} + \frac{81y^2}{2916} = 1$$

$$\frac{x^2}{81} + \frac{y^2}{36} = 1$$

The equation is of the form $\frac{x^2}{a^2} + \frac{y^2}{b^2} = 1$, where $a = 9$ and $b = 6$. The center is at $(0, 0)$. Use the equation $c^2 = a^2 - b^2$ to determine the value of c.

$c^2 = a^2 - b^2$
$c^2 = 81 - 36$
$c^2 = 45$
$c = 3\sqrt{5}$

Since $c = 3\sqrt{5}$, the foci are at $(\pm 3\sqrt{5}, 0)$. The length of the major axis is $2(9)$ or 18 units. The length of the minor axis is $2(6)$ or 12 units.

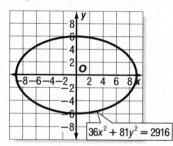

$36x^2 + 81y^2 = 2916$

35. $3x^2 + y^2 + 18x - 2y + 4 = 0$

$3(x^2 + 6x + \blacksquare) + (y^2 - 2y + \blacksquare) = -4 + 3(\blacksquare) + \blacksquare$

$3(x^2 + 6x + 9) + (y^2 - 2y + 1) = -4 + 3(9) + 1$

$3(x + 3)^2 + (y - 1)^2 = 24$

$$\frac{3(x + 3)^2}{24} + \frac{(y - 1)^2}{24} = 1$$

$$\frac{(x + 3)^2}{8} + \frac{(y - 1)^2}{24} = 1$$

The equation is of the form $\frac{(y - k)^2}{a^2} + \frac{(x - h)^2}{b^2} = 1$, where $h = -3$, $k = 1$, $a = 2\sqrt{6}$, and $b = 2\sqrt{2}$. The center is at $(-3, 1)$. Use the equation $c^2 = a^2 - b^2$ to determine the value of c.

$c^2 = a^2 - b^2$
$c^2 = 24 - 8$
$c^2 = 16$
$c = 4$

Since $c = 4$, the foci are at $(-3, 1 \pm 4)$, or $(-3, 5)$ and $(-3, -3)$. The length of the major axis is $2(2\sqrt{6})$ or $4\sqrt{6}$ units. The length of the minor axis is $2(2\sqrt{2})$ or $4\sqrt{2}$ units.

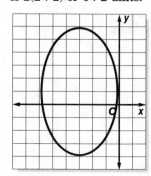

36. $x^2 + 5y^2 + 4x - 70y + 209 = 0$

$(x^2 + 4x + \blacksquare) + 5(y^2 - 14y + \blacksquare) = -209 + \blacksquare + 5(\blacksquare)$

$(x^2 + 4x + 4) + 5(y^2 - 14y + 49) = -209 + 4 + 5(49)$

$(x + 2)^2 + 5(y - 7)^2 = 40$

$$\frac{(x + 2)^2}{40} + \frac{5(y - 7)^2}{40} = 1$$

$$\frac{(x + 2)^2}{40} + \frac{(y - 7)^2}{8} = 1$$

The equation is of the form $\frac{(x - h)^2}{a^2} + \frac{(y - k)^2}{b^2} = 1$, where $h = -2$, $k = 7$, $a = 2\sqrt{10}$, and $b = 2\sqrt{2}$. The center is at $(-2, 7)$. Use the equation $c^2 = a^2 - b^2$ to determine the value of c.

$c^2 = a^2 - b^2$

$c^2 = 40 - 8$

$c^2 = 32$

$c = 4\sqrt{2}$

Since $c = 4\sqrt{2}$, the foci are at $(-2 \pm 4\sqrt{2}, 7)$. The length of the major axis is $2(2\sqrt{10})$ or $4\sqrt{10}$ units. The length of the minor axis is $2(2\sqrt{2})$ or $4\sqrt{2}$ units.

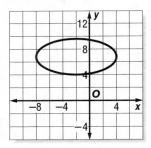

37. $7x^2 + 3y^2 - 28x - 12y = -19$

$7(x^2 - 4x + \blacksquare) + 3(y^2 - 4y + \blacksquare) = -19 + 7(\blacksquare) + 3(\blacksquare)$

$7(x^2 - 4x + 4) + 3(y^2 - 4y + 4) = -19 + 7(4) + 3(4)$

$7(x - 2)^2 + 3(y - 2)^2 = 21$

$$\frac{7(x - 2)^2}{21} + \frac{3(y - 2)^2}{21} = 1$$

$$\frac{(x - 2)^2}{3} + \frac{(y - 2)^2}{7} = 1$$

The equation is of the form $\frac{(y - k)^2}{a^2} + \frac{(x - h)}{b^2} = 1$, where $h = 2$, $k = 2$, $a = \sqrt{7}$, and $b = \sqrt{3}$. The center is at $(2, 2)$. Use the equation $c^2 = a^2 - b^2$ to determine the value of c.

$c^2 = a^2 - b^2$

$c^2 = 7 - 3$

$c^2 = 4$

$c = 2$

Since $c = 2$, the foci are at $(2, 2 \pm 2)$, or $(2, 4)$ and $(2, 0)$. The length of the major axis is $2(\sqrt{7})$ or $2\sqrt{7}$ units. The length of the minor axis is $2(\sqrt{3})$ or $2\sqrt{3}$ units.

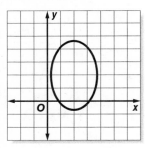

38. $16x^2 + 25y^2 + 32x - 150y = 159$

$16(x^2 + 2x + \blacksquare) + 25(y^2 - 6y + \blacksquare) = 159 + 16(\blacksquare) + 25(\blacksquare)$

$16(x^2 + 2x + 1) + 25(y^2 - 6y + 9) = 159 + 16(1) + 25(9)$

$16(x + 1)^2 + 25(y - 3)^2 = 400$

$$\frac{16(x + 1)^2}{400} + \frac{25(y - 3)^2}{400} = 1$$

$$\frac{(x + 1)^2}{25} + \frac{(y - 3)^2}{16} = 1$$

The equation is of the form $\frac{(x - h)^2}{a^2} + \frac{(y - k)^2}{b^2} = 1$, where $h = -1$, $k = 3$, $a = 5$, and $b = 4$. The center is at $(-1, 3)$. Use the equation $c^2 = a^2 - b^2$ to determine the value of c.

$c^2 = a^2 - b^2$

$c^2 = 25 - 16$

$c^2 = 9$

$c = 3$

Since $c = 3$, the foci are at $(-1 \pm 3, 3)$, or $(2, 3)$ and $(-4, 3)$. The length of the major axis is $2(5)$ or 10 units. The length of the minor axis is $2(4)$ or 8 units.

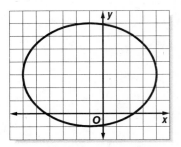

39. The foci are at $(\sqrt{3}, 0)$ and $(-\sqrt{3}, 0)$, so the major axis is horizontal, and the center of the ellipse (the midpoint of the segment with the foci as the endpoints) is $(0, 0)$. Thus, the equation is of the form $\frac{x^2}{a^2} + \frac{y^2}{b^2} = 1$. Since the foci are at $(\pm\sqrt{3}, 0)$, $c = \sqrt{3}$. The ellipse passes through the point $(0, 3)$, so the distance from one of the foci to $(0, 3)$ is a. Use the Distance Formula to determine the value of a.

$a = \sqrt{(x_2 - x_1)^2 + (y_2 - y_1)^2}$

$\quad = \sqrt{(\sqrt{3} - 0)^2 + (0 - 3)^2}$

$\quad = \sqrt{(\sqrt{3})^2 + (-3)^2}$

$\quad = \sqrt{3 + 9}$

$\quad = \sqrt{12}$

Since $a = \sqrt{12}$, $a^2 = 12$. Use the equation $c^2 = a^2 - b^2$ to find the value of b.

$c^2 = a^2 - b^2$

$3 = 12 - b^2$

$b^2 = 9$

Thus, an equation for the ellipse is $\frac{x^2}{12} + \frac{y^2}{9} = 1$.

40. Knowledge of the orbit of Earth can be used in predicting the seasons and in space exploration. Answers should include the following.

- Knowledge of the path of another planet would be needed if we wanted to send a spacecraft to that planet.
- The length of the major axis of an ellipse is $2a$ units. In this ellipse, the length of the major axis is $91.4 + 94.5$ or 185.9 million miles. Since $2a = 185.9 \times 10^6$, $a = 92.95 \times 10^6$, the distance from the center of Earth's orbit to the nearest or farthest point from the Sun. The distance from the center of Earth's orbit to the Sun is $92.95 - 91.4$ or 1.55 million miles.

41. C; The measure of $\angle ABE$ is $180° - 90° - 25°$ or $65°$. Similarly, the measure of $\angle CBD$ is $180° - 90° - 55°$ or $35°$. Since A, B, and C are collinear, the sum of the measures of $\angle ABE$, $\angle DBE$, and $\angle CBD$ is $180°$. Use substitution to find $m\angle DBE$, the measure of $\angle DBE$.

$$m\angle ABE + m\angle DBE + m\angle CBD = 180°$$
$$65° + m\angle DBE + 35° = 180°$$
$$m\angle DBE = 80°$$

The measure of $\angle DBE$ is $80°$.

42. B; $\sqrt{25 + 144} = \sqrt{169}$
$$= \sqrt{13^2}$$
$$= 13$$

43. The major axis of the ellipse is horizontal and the center of the orbit is the origin, so the equation is of the form $\frac{x^2}{a^2} + \frac{y^2}{b^2} = 1$. The length of the major axis of an ellipse is $2a$ units. In this ellipse, the length of the major axis is about 7.34 billion miles, so $a \approx 36.7 \times 10^8$. In an ellipse, $e = \frac{c}{a}$. For Pluto, $e \approx 0.25$. Use the equation to determine the value of c.

$$e = \frac{c}{a}$$
$$0.25 = \frac{c}{36.7 \times 10^8}$$
$$c = 917.5 \times 10^6$$

Use the equation $c^2 = a^2 - b^2$ to find the value of b.

$$c^2 = a^2 - b^2$$
$$(917.5 \times 10^6)^2 = (36.7 \times 10^8)^2 - b^2$$
$$b^2 \approx 1.26 \times 10^{19}$$

Thus, an equation to model the orbit of Pluto is

$$\frac{x^2}{(36.7 \times 10^8)^2} + \frac{y^2}{1.26 \times 10^{19}} \approx 1 \quad \text{or}$$
$$\text{about } \frac{x^2}{1.35 \times 10^{19}} + \frac{y^2}{1.26 \times 10^{19}} = 1.$$

44. An equation for the circle with center at $(3, -2)$ and radius 5 units is $(x - 3)^2 + [y - (-2)]^2 = 5^2$ or $(x - 3)^2 + (y + 2)^2 = 25$.

45. The center of the circle is the midpoint of the diameter.

$$(h, k) = \left(\frac{x_1 + x_2}{2}, \frac{y_1 + y_2}{2}\right)$$
$$= \left(\frac{5 + 3}{2}, \frac{-9 + 11}{2}\right)$$
$$= \left(\frac{8}{2}, \frac{2}{2}\right)$$
$$= (4, 1)$$

The radius of the circle is the distance from the center to any point on the circle.

$$r = \sqrt{(x_2 - x_1)^2 + (y_2 - y_1)^2}$$
$$= \sqrt{(3 - 4)^2 + (11 - 1)^2}$$
$$= \sqrt{(-1)^2 + 10^2}$$
$$= \sqrt{1 + 100}$$
$$= \sqrt{101}$$

Thus, an equation for the circle is $(x - 4)^2 + (y - 1)^2 = 101$.

46. The center of the circle is at $(-1, 0)$, so the equation is of the form $[x - (-1)]^2 + (y - 0)^2 = r^2$ or $(x + 1)^2 + y^2 = r^2$. The radius of the circle is the distance from the center to any point on the circle.

$$r = \sqrt{(x_2 - x_1)^2 + (y_2 - y_1)^2}$$
$$= \sqrt{[2 - (-1)]^2 + (-6 - 0)^2}$$
$$= \sqrt{3^2 + (-6)^2}$$
$$= \sqrt{9 + 36}$$
$$= \sqrt{45}$$

Thus, an equation for the circle is $(x + 1)^2 + y^2 = 45$.

47. The center of the circle is at $(4, -1)$, so the equation is of the form $(x - 4)^2 + [y - (-1)]^2 = r^2$ or $(x - 4)^2 + (y + 1)^2 = r^2$. Since the circle is tangent to the y-axis, the radius is 4 units. Thus, an equation for the circle is $(x - 4)^2 + (y + 1)^2 = 16$.

48. Since the vertex and focus have the same x-coordinate, the equation is of the form $y = a(x - h)^2 + k$. The vertex is at $(3, 1)$, so $h = 3$ and $k = 1$. The focus is at $\left(3, 1\frac{1}{2}\right)$, so $k + \frac{1}{4a} = 1\frac{1}{2}$.

Use k to determine the value of a.

$$k + \frac{1}{4a} = 1\frac{1}{2}$$
$$1 + \frac{1}{4a} = 1\frac{1}{2}$$
$$\frac{1}{4a} = \frac{1}{2}$$
$$1 = \frac{4a}{2}$$
$$1 = 2a$$
$$\frac{1}{2} = a$$

Thus, an equation of the parabola is

$$y = \frac{1}{2}(x - 3)^2 + 1.$$

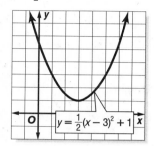

49.

Married Americans

50. Sample answer using $(0, 104.6)$ and $(10, 112.6)$:
$y = 0.8x + 104.6$

51. Sample answer: 128,600,000

52.

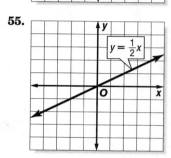

$y = 2x$

53.

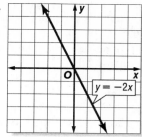

$y = -2x$

54.

$y = -\frac{1}{2}x$

55.

$y = \frac{1}{2}x$

56.

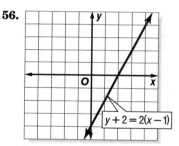

$y + 2 = 2(x - 1)$

57.

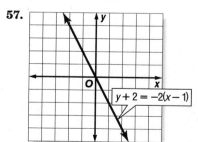

$y + 2 = -2(x - 1)$

Page 445   Check for Understanding

1. Sometimes; the hyperbolas represented by the equations $\frac{y^2}{9} - \frac{x^2}{7} = 1$ and $\frac{x^2}{9} - \frac{y^2}{4} = 1$ are symmetric about the x-axis, but the hyperbola represented by the equation $\frac{(x-4)^2}{9} - \frac{(y+1)^2}{4} = 1$ is not symmetric about the x-axis (See Examples 1, 3 and 4.)

2. As k increases, the branches of the hyperbola become wider.

3. Answers should be of the form $\frac{x^2}{a^2} - \frac{y^2}{b^2} = 1$, where $a^2 \le b^2$ for some real numbers a and b. Sample answer: $\frac{x^2}{4} - \frac{y^2}{9} = 1$

4. The center is the midpoint of the segment connecting the vertices, or $(0, 0)$. The value of a is the distance from the center to a vertex, or 2 units. The value of c is the distance from the center to a focus, or 5 units. Use the equation $c^2 = a^2 + b^2$ to determine the value of b.

$$c^2 = a^2 + b^2$$
$$5^2 = 2^2 + b^2$$
$$25 = 4 + b^2$$
$$21 = b^2$$

Since the transverse axis is vertical, the equation is of the form $\frac{y^2}{a^2} - \frac{x^2}{b^2} = 1$. Substitute the values for a^2 and b^2. An equation of the hyperbola is $\frac{y^2}{4} - \frac{x^2}{21} = 1$.

5. According to the coordinates of the foci, $c = 4$, and the transverse axis is horizontal. Therefore, the equation is of the form $\frac{x^2}{a^2} - \frac{y^2}{b^2} = 1$. Since $a = 1$, use the equation $c^2 = a^2 + b^2$ where $a = 1$ and $c = 4$ to determine the value of b for this hyperbola.

$$c^2 = a^2 + b^2$$
$$4^2 = 1^2 + b^2$$
$$16 = 1 + b^2$$
$$15 = b^2$$

Substitute the values for a^2 and b^2. An equation of the hyperbola is $\frac{x^2}{1} - \frac{y^2}{15} = 1$.

6. The equation is of the form $\frac{y^2}{a^2} - \frac{x^2}{b^2} = 1$, where $a = 3\sqrt{2}$ and $b = 2\sqrt{5}$. The vertices are at $(0, \pm 3\sqrt{2})$. Use the equation $c^2 = a^2 + b^2$ to determine the value of c.

$$c^2 = a^2 + b^2$$
$$c^2 = 18 + 20$$
$$c^2 = 38$$
$$c = \sqrt{38}$$

Since $c = \sqrt{38}$, the foci are at $(0, \pm\sqrt{38})$. The equations of the asymptotes are $y = \pm\frac{3\sqrt{2}}{2\sqrt{5}}x$ or $y = \pm\frac{3\sqrt{10}}{10}x$.

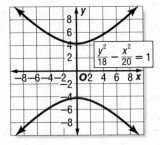

7. The equation is of the form $\frac{(y-k)^2}{a^2} - \frac{(x-h)^2}{b^2} = 1$, where $h = 1$, $k = -6$, $a = 2\sqrt{5}$, and $b = 5$. The coordinates of the vertices are $(h, k \pm a)$ or $(1, -6 \pm 2\sqrt{5})$. Use the equation $c^2 = a^2 + b^2$ to determine the value of c.

$$c^2 = a^2 + b^2$$
$$c^2 = 20 + 25$$
$$c^2 = 45$$
$$c = 3\sqrt{5}$$

Since $c = 3\sqrt{5}$, the foci are at $(h, k \pm c)$ or $(1, -6 \pm 3\sqrt{5})$. The equations of the asymptotes are $y - (-6) = \pm\frac{5}{2\sqrt{5}}(x - 1)$ or $y + 6 = \pm\frac{2\sqrt{5}}{5}(x - 1)$.

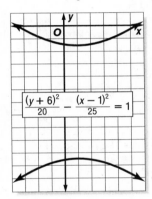

8. $x^2 - 36y^2 = 36$

$\frac{x^2}{36} - \frac{36y^2}{36} = 1$

$\frac{x^2}{36} - \frac{y^2}{1} = 1$

The equation is of the form $\frac{x^2}{a^2} - \frac{y^2}{b^2} = 1$, where $a = 6$ and $b = 1$. The vertices are at $(\pm6, 0)$. Use the equation $c^2 = a^2 + b^2$ to determine the value of c.

$c^2 = a^2 + b^2$

$c^2 = 36 + 1$

$c^2 = 37$

$c = \sqrt{37}$

Since $c = \sqrt{37}$, the foci are at $(\pm\sqrt{37}, 0)$. The equations of the asymptotes are $y = \pm\frac{1}{6}x$.

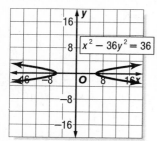

9. $5x^2 - 4y^2 - 40x - 16y - 36 = 0$

$5(x^2 - 8x + \blacksquare) - 4(y^2 + 4y + \blacksquare) = 36 + 5(\blacksquare) - 4(\blacksquare)$

$5(x^2 - 8x + 16) - 4(y^2 + 4y + 4) = 36 + 5(16) - 4(4)$

$5(x - 4)^2 - 4(y + 2)^2 = 100$

$\frac{5(x - 4)^2}{100} - \frac{4(y + 2)^2}{100} = 1$

$\frac{(x - 4)^2}{20} - \frac{(y + 2)^2}{25} = 1$

The equation is of the form $\frac{(x - h)^2}{a^2} - \frac{(y - k)^2}{b^2} = 1$, where $h = 4$, $k = -2$, $a = 2\sqrt{5}$, and $b = 5$. The coordinates of the vertices are $(h \pm a, k)$ or $(4 \pm 2\sqrt{5}, -2)$. Use the equation $c^2 = a^2 + b^2$ to determine the value of c.

$c^2 = a^2 + b^2$

$c^2 = 20 + 25$

$c^2 = 45$

$c = 3\sqrt{5}$

Since $c = 3\sqrt{5}$, the foci are located at $(h \pm c, k)$ or $(4 \pm 3\sqrt{5}, -2)$. The equations of the asymptotes are $y - (-2) = \pm\frac{5}{2\sqrt{5}}(x - 4)$ or $y + 2 = \pm\frac{\sqrt{5}}{2}(x - 4)$.

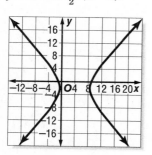

10. The equation is of the form $\frac{y^2}{a^2} - \frac{x^2}{b^2} = 1$, where $a = 15$ and $b = 20$. The coordinates of the vertices are $(0, \pm15)$. Use the equation $c^2 = a^2 + b^2$ to determine the value of c.

$c^2 = a^2 + b^2$

$c^2 = 225 + 400$

$c^2 = 625$

$c = 25$

Since $c = 25$, the foci are at $(0, \pm25)$. The equations of the asymptotes are $y = \pm\frac{15}{20}x$ or $y = \pm\frac{3}{4}x$.

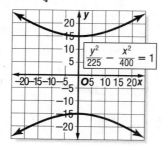

Pages 445–447 Practice and Apply

11. The center is the midpoint of the segment connecting the vertices, or $(0, 0)$. The value of a is the distance from the center to a vertex, or 2 units. The value of c is the distance from the center to a focus, or 4 units. Use the $c^2 = a^2 + b^2$ where $a = 2$ and $c = 4$ to determine the value of b for this hyperbola.

$c^2 = a^2 + b^2$

$4^2 = 2^2 + b^2$

$16 = 4 + b^2$

$12 = b^2$

Substitute the values for a^2 and b^2. An equation of the hyperbola is of the form $\frac{x^2}{a^2} - \frac{y^2}{b^2} = 1$ or $\frac{x^2}{4} - \frac{y^2}{12} = 1$.

12. The center is the midpoint of the segment connecting the vertices, or $(-2, 3)$. Therefore, $h = -2$ and $k = 3$. The transverse axis is vertical, so the equation is of the form $\frac{(y - 3)^2}{a^2} - \frac{[x - (-2)]^2}{b^2} = 1$ or $\frac{(y - 3)^2}{a^2} - \frac{(x + 2)^2}{b^2} = 1$. The value of a is the distance from the center to one of the vertices, or 1 unit, so $a^2 = 1$. The asymptotes have slope $\pm\frac{a}{b}$, or $\pm\frac{1}{2}$, so $b = 2$. Since $b = 2$, $b^2 = 4$. Substitute the values for a^2 and b^2. An equation of the hyperbola is $\frac{(y - 3)^2}{1} - \frac{(x + 2)^2}{4} = 1$.

13. The center is the midpoint of segment connecting the vertices, or $\left(0, -\frac{11}{2}\right)$, so $h = 0$ and $k = -\frac{11}{2}$. The transverse axis is vertical, so the equation is of the form $\dfrac{\left[y - \left(-\frac{11}{2}\right)\right]^2}{a^2} - \dfrac{(x - 0)^2}{b^2} = 1$ or

$\dfrac{\left(y + \frac{11}{2}\right)^2}{a^2} - \dfrac{x^2}{b^2} = 1$. The value of a is the distance from the center to a vertex, or $\frac{5}{2}$ units. The value of c is the distance from the center to a focus, or $\frac{7}{2}$ units. Use the equation $c^2 = a^2 + b^2$ to determine the value of b for this hyperbola.

$c^2 = a^2 + b^2$
$\left(\frac{7}{2}\right)^2 = \left(\frac{5}{2}\right)^2 + b^2$
$\frac{49}{4} = \frac{25}{4} + b^2$
$6 = b^2$

Substitute the values for a^2 and b^2. An equation of the hyperbola is $\dfrac{\left(y + \frac{11}{2}\right)^2}{\frac{25}{4}} - \dfrac{x^2}{6} = 1$.

14. The center is the midpoint of the segment connecting the vertices, or $(3, -5)$. Therefore, $h = 3$ and $k = -5$. The transverse axis is horizontal, so the equation is of the form $\dfrac{(x - 3)^2}{a^2} - \dfrac{[y - (-5)]^2}{b^2} = 1$ or $\dfrac{(x - 3)^2}{a^2} - \dfrac{(y + 5)^2}{b^2} = 1$. The value of a is the distance from the center to one of the vertices, or 2 units, so $a^2 = 4$. The asymptotes have slope $\pm\frac{b}{a}$, or $\pm\frac{3}{2}$, so $b = 3$. Since $b = 3$, $b^2 = 9$. Substitute the values for a^2 and b^2. An equation of the hyperbola is $\dfrac{(x - 3)^2}{4} - \dfrac{(y + 5)^2}{9} = 1$.

15. The center is the midpoint of the segment connecting the vertices, or $(0, 0)$. Since the vertices are at $(\pm 5, 0)$, $a = 5$, and the transverse axis is horizontal, the equation is of the form $\dfrac{x^2}{a^2} - \dfrac{y^2}{b^2} = 1$. The conjugate axis is a segment of length $2b$ units. Therefore, $2b = 12$, or $b = 6$. Since $a = 5$, $a^2 = 25$. Since $b = 6$, $b^2 = 36$. Substitute the values for a^2 and b^2. An equation of the hyperbola is $\dfrac{x^2}{25} - \dfrac{y^2}{36} = 1$.

16. The center is the midpoint of the segment connecting the vertices, or $(0, 0)$. Since the vertices are at $(0, \pm 4)$, $a = 4$, and the transverse axis is vertical, the equation is of the form $\dfrac{y^2}{a^2} - \dfrac{x^2}{b^2} = 1$. The conjugate axis is a segment of length $2b$ units. Therefore, $2b = 14$, or $b = 7$. Since $a = 4$, $a^2 = 16$. Since $b = 7$, $b^2 = 49$. Substitute the values for a^2 and b^2. An equation of the hyperbola is $\dfrac{y^2}{16} - \dfrac{x^2}{49} = 1$.

17. The center is the midpoint of the segment connecting the vertices, or $(2, -3)$. Therefore, $h = 2$ and $k = -3$. Since the transverse axis is horizontal, the equation is of the form $\dfrac{(x - 2)^2}{a^2} - \dfrac{[y - (-3)]^2}{b^2} = 1$ or $\dfrac{(x - 2)^2}{a^2} - \dfrac{(y + 3)^2}{b^2} = 1$. The value of a is the distance from the center to a vertex, or 7 units. Since $a = 7$, $a^2 = 49$. The value of c is the distance from the center to a focus, or $\sqrt{53}$ units. Use the equation $c^2 = a^2 + b^2$ to determine the value of b for the hyperbola.

$c^2 = a^2 + b^2$
$53 = 49 + b^2$
$4 = b^2$

Substitute the values for a^2 and b^2. An equation of the hyperbola is $\dfrac{(x - 2)^2}{49} - \dfrac{(y + 3)^2}{4} = 1$.

18. The center is the midpoint of the segment connecting the vertices, or $(-4, 5)$. Therefore, $h = -4$ and $k = 5$. Since the transverse axis is vertical, the equation is of the form $\dfrac{(y - 5)^2}{a^2} - \dfrac{[x - (-4)]^2}{b^2} = 1$ or $\dfrac{(y - 5)^2}{a^2} - \dfrac{(x + 4)^2}{b^2} = 1$. The value of a is the distance from the center to a vertex, or 4 units. Since $a = 4$, $a^2 = 16$. The value of c is the distance from the center to a focus, or $\sqrt{97}$ units. Since $c = \sqrt{97}$, $c^2 = 97$. Use the equation $c^2 = a^2 + b^2$ to determine the value of b for the hyperbola.

$c^2 = a^2 + b^2$
$97 = 16 + b^2$
$81 = b^2$

Substitute the values for a^2 and b^2. An equation of the hyperbola is $\dfrac{(y - 5)^2}{16} - \dfrac{(x + 4)^2}{81} = 1$.

19. An equation for a hyperbola centered at the origin with a horizontal transverse axis is of the form $\dfrac{x^2}{a^2} - \dfrac{y^2}{b^2} = 1$. The length of the transverse axis of a hyperbola is $2a$ units. In this hyperbola, the length of the transverse axis is 8 units. Therefore, $2a = 8$, or $a = 4$. The length of the conjugate axis of a hyperbola is $2b$ units. In this hyperbola, the length of the conjugate axis is 6 units. Therefore, $2b = 6$, or $b = 3$. Since $a = 4$, $a^2 = 16$. Since $b = 3$, $b^2 = 9$. Substitute the values for a^2 and b^2. An equation for the hyperbola is $\dfrac{x^2}{16} - \dfrac{y^2}{9} = 1$.

20. An equation for a hyperbola centered at the origin with a vertical transverse axis is of the form $\dfrac{y^2}{a^2} - \dfrac{x^2}{b^2} = 1$. The length of the transverse axis of a hyperbola is $2a$ units. In this hyperbola, the length of the transverse axis is 12 units. Therefore, $2a = 12$, or $a = 6$. The length of the conjugate axis of a hyperbola is $2b$ units. In this hyperbola, the length of the conjugate axis is 4 units. Therefore, $2b = 4$, or $b = 2$. Since $a = 6$, $a^2 = 36$. Since $b = 2$, $b^2 = 4$. Substitute the values for a^2 and b^2. An equation for the hyperbola is $\dfrac{y^2}{36} - \dfrac{x^2}{4} = 1$.

21. The equation is of the form $\frac{x^2}{a^2} - \frac{y^2}{b^2} = 1$, where $a = 9$ and $b = 7$. The vertices of the hyperbola are at $(\pm 9, 0)$. Use the equation $c^2 = a^2 + b^2$ to determine the value of c.

$c^2 = a^2 + b^2$
$c^2 = 81 + 49$
$c^2 = 130$
$c = \sqrt{130}$

Since $c = \sqrt{130}$, the foci are at $(\pm\sqrt{130}, 0)$. The equations of the asymptotes are $y = \pm\frac{7}{9}x$.

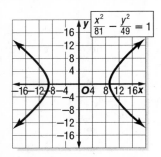

22. The equation is of the form $\frac{y^2}{a^2} - \frac{x^2}{b^2} = 1$, were $a = 6$ and $b = 2$. The vertices of the hyperbola are at $(0, \pm 6)$. Use the equation $c^2 = a^2 + b^2$ to determine the value of c.

$c^2 = a^2 + b^2$
$c^2 = 36 + 4$
$c^2 = 40$
$c = 2\sqrt{10}$

Since $c = 2\sqrt{10}$, the foci are at $(0, \pm 2\sqrt{10})$. The equations of the asymptotes are $y = \pm\frac{6}{2}x$ or $y = \pm 3x$.

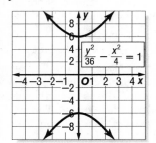

23. The equation is of the form $\frac{y^2}{a^2} - \frac{x^2}{b^2} = 1$, where $a = 4$ and $b = 5$. The vertices of the hyperbola are at $(0, \pm 4)$. Use the equation $c^2 = a^2 + b^2$ to determine the value of c.

$c^2 = a^2 + b^2$
$c^2 = 16 + 25$
$c^2 = 41$
$c = \sqrt{41}$

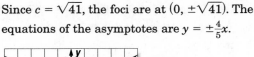

Since $c = \sqrt{41}$, the foci are at $(0, \pm\sqrt{41})$. The equations of the asymptotes are $y = \pm\frac{4}{5}x$.

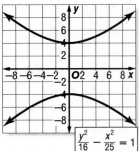

24. The equation is of the form $\frac{x^2}{a^2} - \frac{y^2}{b^2} = 1$, where $a = 3$ and $b = 5$. The vertices of the hyperbola are at $(\pm 3, 0)$. Use the equation $c^2 = a^2 + b^2$ to determine the value of c.

$c^2 = a^2 + b^2$
$c^2 = 9 + 25$
$c^2 = 34$
$c = \sqrt{34}$

Since $c = \sqrt{34}$, the foci are at $(\pm\sqrt{34}, 0)$. The equations of the asymptotes are $y = \pm\frac{5}{3}x$.

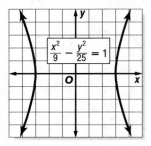

25. $x^2 - 2y^2 = 2$
$\frac{x^2}{2} - \frac{2y^2}{2} = 1$
$\frac{x^2}{2} - \frac{y^2}{1} = 1$

The equation is of the form $\frac{x^2}{a^2} - \frac{y^2}{b^2} = 1$, where $a = \sqrt{2}$ and $b = 1$. The vertices of the hyperbola are at $(\pm\sqrt{2}, 0)$.

Use the equation $c^2 = a^2 + b^2$ to determine the value of c.

$c^2 = a^2 + b^2$
$c^2 = 2 + 1$
$c^2 = 3$
$c = \sqrt{3}$

Since $c = \sqrt{3}$, the foci are at $(\pm\sqrt{3}, 0)$. The equations of the asymptotes are $y = \pm\frac{\sqrt{2}}{2}x$.

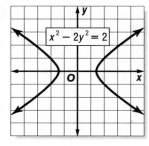

26. $x^2 - y^2 = 4$

$\dfrac{x^2}{4} - \dfrac{y^2}{4} = 1$

The equation is of the form $\dfrac{x^2}{a^2} + \dfrac{y^2}{b^2} = 1$, where $a = 2$ and $b = 2$. The vertices of the hyperbola are at $(\pm 2, 0)$. Use the equation $c^2 = a^2 + b^2$ to find the value of c.

$c^2 = a^2 + b^2$

$c^2 = 4 + 4$

$c^2 = 8$

$c = 2\sqrt{2}$

Since $c = 2\sqrt{2}$, the foci are at $(\pm 2\sqrt{2}, 0)$. The equations of the asymptotes are $y = \pm\dfrac{4}{4}x$ or $y = \pm x$.

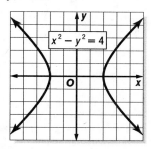

27. $\qquad y^2 = 36 + 4x^2$

$y^2 - 4x^2 = 36$

$\dfrac{y^2}{36} - \dfrac{4x^2}{36} = 1$

$\dfrac{y^2}{36} - \dfrac{x^2}{9} = 1$

The equation is of the form $\dfrac{y^2}{a^2} - \dfrac{x^2}{b^2} = 1$, where $a = 6$ and $b = 3$. The vertices the hyperbola are at $(0, \pm 6)$. Use the equation $c^2 = a^2 + b^2$ to determine the value of c.

$c^2 = a^2 + b^2$

$c^2 = 36 + 9$

$c^2 = 45$

$c = 3\sqrt{5}$

Since $c = 3\sqrt{5}$, the foci are at $(0, \pm 3\sqrt{5})$. The equations of the asymptotes are $y = \pm\dfrac{6}{3}x$ or $y = \pm 2x$.

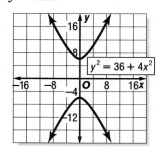

28. $\qquad 6y^2 = 2x^2 + 12$

$6y^2 - 2x^2 = 12$

$\dfrac{6y^2}{12} - \dfrac{2x^2}{12} = 1$

$\dfrac{y^2}{2} - \dfrac{x^2}{6} = 1$

The equation is of the form $\dfrac{y^2}{a^2} - \dfrac{x^2}{b^2} = 1$, where $a = \sqrt{2}$ and $b = \sqrt{6}$. The vertices of the hyperbola are at $(0, \pm\sqrt{2})$. Use the equation $c^2 = a^2 + b^2$ to determine the value of c.

$c^2 = a^2 + b^2$

$c^2 = 2 + 6$

$c^2 = 8$

$c = 2\sqrt{2}$

Since $c = 2\sqrt{2}$, the foci are at $(0, \pm 2\sqrt{2})$. The equations of the asymptotes are $y = \pm\dfrac{\sqrt{2}}{\sqrt{6}}x$ or $y = \pm\dfrac{\sqrt{3}}{3}x$.

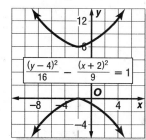

29. The equation is of the form $\dfrac{(y-k)^2}{a^2} - \dfrac{(x-h)^2}{b^2} = 1$, where $h = -2$, $k = 4$, $a = 4$, and $b = 3$. The center of the hyperbola is at $(-2, 4)$. The vertices are at $(-2, 4 \pm 4)$, or $(-2, 0)$ and $(-2, 8)$. Use the equation $c^2 = a^2 + b^2$ to determine the value of c.

$c^2 = a^2 + b^2$

$c^2 = 16 + 9$

$c^2 = 25$

$c = 5$

Since $c = 5$, the foci are at $(-2, 4 \pm 5)$, or $(-2, -1)$ and $(-2, 9)$. The equations of the asymptotes are $y - 4 = \pm\dfrac{4}{3}[x - (-2)]$ or $y - 4 = \pm\dfrac{4}{3}(x + 2)$.

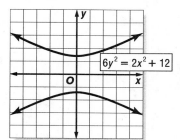

30. The equation is of the form $\frac{(y-k)^2}{a^2} - \frac{(x-h)^2}{b^2} = 1$, where $h = 2$, $k = 3$, $a = 5$, and $b = 4$. The center of the hyperbola is at $(2, 3)$. The vertices are at $(2, 3 \pm 5)$, or $(2, -2)$ and $(2, 8)$. Use the equation $c^2 = a^2 + b^2$ to determine the value of c.

$c^2 = a^2 + b^2$

$c^2 = 25 + 16$

$c^2 = 41$

$c = \sqrt{41}$

Since $c = \sqrt{41}$, the foci are at $(2, 3 \pm 41)$. The equations of the asymptotes are

$y - 3 = \pm\frac{5}{4}(x - 2)$.

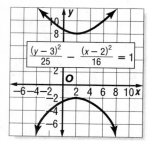

$\frac{(y-3)^2}{25} - \frac{(x-2)^2}{16} = 1$

31. The equation is of the form $\frac{(x-h)^2}{a^2} - \frac{(y-k)^2}{b^2} = 1$, where $h = -1$, $k = -3$, $a = 2$, and $b = 3$. The center of the hyperbola is at $(-1, -3)$. The vertices are at $(-1 \pm 2, -3)$, or $(-3, -3)$ and $(1, -3)$. Use the equation $c^2 = a^2 + b^2$ to determine the value of c.

$c^2 = a^2 + b^2$

$c^2 = 4 + 9$

$c^2 = 13$

$c = \sqrt{13}$

Since $c = \sqrt{13}$, the foci are at $(-1 \pm \sqrt{13}, -3)$. The equations of the asymptotes are

$y - (-3) = \pm\frac{3}{2}[x - (-1)]$ or $y + 3 = \pm\frac{3}{2}(x + 1)$.

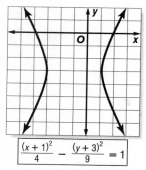

$\frac{(x+1)^2}{4} - \frac{(y+3)^2}{9} = 1$

32. The equation is of the form $\frac{(x-h)^2}{a^2} - \frac{(y-k)^2}{b^2} = 1$, where $h = -6$, $k = -3$, $a = 6$, and $b = 3$. The center of the hyperbola is at $(-6, -3)$. The vertices are at $(-6 \pm 6, -3)$, or $(-12, -3)$ and $(0, -3)$. Use the equation $c^2 = a^2 + b^2$ to determine the value of c.

$c^2 = a^2 + b^2$

$c^2 = 36 + 9$

$c^2 = \sqrt{45}$

$c = 3\sqrt{5}$

Since $c = 3\sqrt{5}$, the foci are at $(-6 \pm 3\sqrt{5}, -3)$. The equations of the asymptotes are

$y - (-3) = \pm\frac{3}{6}[x - (-6)]$ or $y + 3 = \pm\frac{1}{2}(x + 6)$.

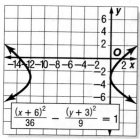

$\frac{(x+6)^2}{36} - \frac{(y+3)^2}{9} = 1$

33.

$y^2 - 3x^2 + 6y + 6x - 18 = 0$

$(y^2 + 6y + \blacksquare) - 3(x^2 - 2x + \blacksquare) = 18 + \blacksquare - 3(\blacksquare)$

$(y^2 + 6y + 9) - 3(x^2 - 2x + 1) = 18 + 9 - 3(1)$

$(y + 3)^2 - 3(x - 1)^2 = 24$

$\frac{(y+3)^2}{24} - \frac{3(x-1)^2}{24} = 1$

$\frac{(y+3)^2}{24} - \frac{(x-1)^2}{8} = 1$

The equation is of the form $\frac{(y-k)^2}{a^2} - \frac{(x-h)^2}{b^2} = 1$, where $h = 1$, $k = -3$, $a = 2\sqrt{6}$, and $b = 2\sqrt{2}$. The center of the hyperbola is at $(1, -3)$. The vertices are at $(1, -3 \pm 2\sqrt{6})$. Use the equation $c^2 = a^2 + b^2$ to determine the value of c.

$c^2 = a^2 + b^2$

$c^2 = 24 + 8$

$c^2 = 32$

$c = 4\sqrt{2}$

Since $c = 4\sqrt{2}$, the foci are at $(1, -3 \pm 4\sqrt{2})$. The equations of the asymptotes are

$y - (-3) = \pm\frac{2\sqrt{6}}{2\sqrt{2}}(x - 1)$ or $y + 3 = \pm\sqrt{3}(x - 1)$.

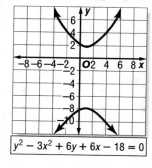

$y^2 - 3x^2 + 6y + 6x - 18 = 0$

34. $4x^2 - 25y^2 - 8x - 96 = 0$

$4(x^2 - 2x + \blacksquare) - 25y^2 = 96 + 4(\blacksquare)$

$4(x^2 - 2x + 1) - 25y^2 = 96 + 4(1)$

$4(x - 1)^2 - 25y^2 = 100$

$\dfrac{4(x - 1)^2}{100} - \dfrac{25y^2}{100} = 1$

$\dfrac{(x - 1)^2}{25} - \dfrac{y^2}{4} = 1$

The equation is of the form $\dfrac{(x - h)^2}{a^2} - \dfrac{(y - k)^2}{b^2} = 1$, where $h = 1$, $k = 0$, $a = 5$, and $b = 2$. The center of the hyperbola is at $(1, 0)$. The vertices are at $(1 \pm 5, 0)$, or $(-4, 0)$ and $(6, 0)$. Use the equation $c^2 = a^2 + b^2$ to determine the value of c.

$c^2 = a^2 + b^2$

$c^2 = 25 + 4$

$c^2 = 29$

$c = \sqrt{29}$

Since $c = \sqrt{29}$, the foci are at $(1 \pm \sqrt{29}, 0)$. The equations of the asymptotes are $y - 0 = \pm\dfrac{2}{5}(x - 1)$ or $y = \pm\dfrac{2}{5}(x - 1)$.

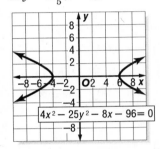

35. The center of the hyperbola is at the origin and the transverse axis is horizontal, so the equation of the hyperbola is of the form $\dfrac{x^2}{a^2} - \dfrac{y^2}{b^2} = 1$. The distance between the vertices of the hyperbola, $2a$ units, is given by the product of the amount of time between explosions and the speed of sound.

$2a = (6)(0.35)$

$2a = 2.1$

$a = 1.05$

Since $a = 1.05$, the distance between the center and one of the vertices is 1.05 units, and $a^2 = 1.1025$. The outpost and the primary station are 6 kilometers apart, so $2c = 6$, or $c = 3$. Since $c = 3$, $c^2 = 9$. Use the equation $c^2 = a^2 + b^2$ to find the value of b.

$c^2 = a^2 + b^2$

$9 = 1.1025 + b^2$

$b^2 = 7.8975$

Substitute the values for a^2 and b^2. An equation that describes all the possible locations of the explosion is $\dfrac{x^2}{1.1025} - \dfrac{y^2}{7.8975} = 1$.

36.

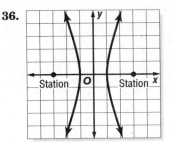

37. Assign the coordinates $(0, 0)$ to the point which is equidistant from the top and the bottom as well as from the sides of the column. If $(0, 0)$ represents the center of the column, then the point with coordinates $(0, 2)$ represents the center of the top of the pillar, since the height of the pillar is 4 units. Therefore, the width of the top of the pillar is twice the value of x when $y = 2$.

$\dfrac{x^2}{0.25} - \dfrac{y^2}{9} = 1$

$\dfrac{x^2}{0.25} - \dfrac{(2)^2}{9} = 1$

$\dfrac{x^2}{0.25} - \dfrac{4}{9} = 1$

$\dfrac{x^2}{0.25} = \dfrac{13}{9}$

$x^2 = \dfrac{13}{36}$

$x = \dfrac{\sqrt{13}}{6}$

Since $x = \dfrac{\sqrt{13}}{6}$, the distance from the y-axis to the edge of the top of the pillar is $\dfrac{\sqrt{13}}{6}$ units. Therefore, the width of the top of each pillar is $2\left(\dfrac{\sqrt{13}}{6}\right)$ or about 1.20 meters, or 120 centimeters. Likewise, the width of each pillar at the narrowest point in the middle is given by two times the value of x when $y = 0$.

$\dfrac{x^2}{0.25} - \dfrac{y^2}{9} = 1$

$\dfrac{x^2}{0.25} - \dfrac{(0)^2}{9} = 1$

$\dfrac{x^2}{0.25} = 1$

$x^2 = 0.25$

$x = 0.5$

Since $x = 0.5$, the width of each pillar at its narrowest point is $2(0.5)$ or 1 meter, or 100 centimeters.

38. The equation of a hyperbola with a horizontal transverse axis is of the form $\frac{(x-h)^2}{a^2} - \frac{(y-k)^2}{b^2} = 1$. The point at which the asymptotes intersect is the center of the hyperbola since $y - x = 1$, $y = 1 + x$. Use substitution of y in the equation $y + x = 5$ to determine the x-coordinate of the center.

$$y + x = 5$$
$$(1 + x) + x = 5$$
$$1 + 2x = 5$$
$$2x = 4$$
$$x = 2$$

Since $x = 2$, $y = 1 + 2$, or $y = 3$. Therefore, the center is at $(2, 3)$, so $h = 2$ and $k = 3$. The hyperbola contains the point $(4, 3)$, so the distance a from the center to the point at $(4, 3)$ is 2 units. Since $a = 2$, $a^2 = 4$. The equation of the asymptotes is of the form $y - k = \pm\frac{b}{a}(x - h)$. Use substitution to determine the value of b.

$$y - k = \pm\frac{b}{a}(x - h)$$
$$y - 3 = \pm\frac{b}{2}(x - 2)$$
$$2y - 6 = \pm b(x - 2)$$

Since $y = 1 + x$, substitute $1 + x$ for y in the equation and solve for b.

$$2(1 + x) - 6 = \pm b(x - 2)$$
$$2 + 2x - 6 = \pm b(x - 2)$$
$$2x - 4 = \pm b(x - 2)$$
$$\frac{2(x - 2)}{x - 2} = \pm b$$
$$a = \pm b$$

Since b represents a length, $b = 2$, so $b^2 = 4$. Substitute values for a^2 and b^2. An equation for the hyperbola is $\frac{(x-2)^2}{4} - \frac{(y-3)^2}{4} = 1$.

39. The equation is of the form $\frac{x^2}{a^2} - \frac{y^2}{b^2} = 1$, where $a = 1$ and $b = \sqrt{3}$. Use the equation $c^2 = a^2 + b^2$ to determine the value of c.

$$c^2 = a^2 + b^2$$
$$c^2 = 1 + 3$$
$$c^2 = 4$$
$$c = 2$$

Since $c = 2$, the foci are at $(-2, 0)$ and $(2, 0)$. The camera is placed so that the 2-foot diameter of the mirror is visible. Therefore, find the two points at which the diameter intersects the hyperbola, that is, where $y = 1$ and $y = -1$ in the equation.

$$\frac{x^2}{1} - \frac{y^2}{3} = 1 \qquad\qquad \frac{x^2}{1} - \frac{y^2}{3} = 1$$
$$\frac{x^2}{1} - \frac{(1)^2}{3} = 1 \qquad\qquad \frac{x^2}{1} - \frac{(-1)^2}{3} = 1$$
$$x^2 = \frac{4}{3} \qquad\qquad\qquad x^2 = \frac{4}{3}$$
$$x = \pm\frac{2\sqrt{3}}{3} \qquad\qquad\quad x = \pm\frac{2\sqrt{3}}{3}$$

Therefore, find equations of the lines through $(2, 0)$ and each edge of the mirror, that is $\left(\frac{2\sqrt{3}}{3}, 1\right)$ and $\left(\frac{2\sqrt{3}}{3}, -1\right)$, to determine where the lines intersect $x = -18$.

Find the slope of the line through $(2, 0)$ and $\left(\frac{2\sqrt{3}}{3}, 1\right)$.

$$m = \frac{1 - 0}{\frac{2\sqrt{3}}{3} - 2}$$
$$= \frac{-\sqrt{3} - 3}{4}$$

An equation of the line through $(2, 0)$ and $\left(\frac{2\sqrt{3}}{3}, 1\right)$ is $y - 0 = \left(\frac{-\sqrt{3} - 3}{4}\right)(x - 2)$ or $y = \left(\frac{-\sqrt{3} - 3}{4}\right)(x - 2)$. Substitute -18 for x in the equation to determine where the line intersects $x = -18$.

$$y = \left(\frac{-\sqrt{3} - 3}{4}\right)(x - 2)$$
$$y = \left(\frac{-\sqrt{3} - 3}{4}\right)(-18 - 2)$$
$$y = 5\sqrt{3} + 15$$

The line intersects $x = -18$ at $(-18, 5\sqrt{3} + 15)$. Now find the slope of the line through $(2, 0)$ and $\left(\frac{2\sqrt{3}}{3}, -1\right)$.

$$m = \frac{-1 - 0}{\frac{2\sqrt{3}}{3} - 2}$$
$$= \frac{\sqrt{3} + 3}{4}$$

An equation of the line through $(2, 0)$ and $\left(\frac{2\sqrt{3}}{3}, -1\right)$ is $y - 0 = \left(\frac{\sqrt{3} + 3}{4}\right)(x - 2)$ or $y = \left(\frac{\sqrt{3} + 3}{4}\right)(x - 2)$. Substitute -18 for x in the equation to determine where the line intersects $x = -18$.

$$y = \left(\frac{\sqrt{3} + 3}{4}\right)(x - 2)$$
$$y = \left(\frac{\sqrt{3} + 3}{4}\right)(-18 - 2)$$
$$y = -5\sqrt{3} - 15$$

The line intersects $x = -18$ at $(-18, -5\sqrt{3} - 15)$. The width of the room that is visible to the camera is the distance between $(-18, 5\sqrt{3} + 15)$ and $(-18, -5\sqrt{3} - 15)$.

$$d = \sqrt{(x_2 - x_1)^2 + (y_2 - y_1)^2}$$
$$= \sqrt{[-18 - (-18)]^2 + [-5\sqrt{3} - 15 - (5\sqrt{3} + 15)]^2}$$
$$= \sqrt{0^2 + (-5\sqrt{3} - 15 - 5\sqrt{3} - 15)^2}$$
$$= \sqrt{(-10\sqrt{3} - 30)^2}$$
$$= \sqrt{600\sqrt{3} + 1200}$$
$$= 10\sqrt{3} + 30 \text{ or about } 47.32$$

Therefore, about 47.32 feet of the back of the room is visible to the camera.

40. Hyperbolas and parabolas have different graphs and different reflective properties. Answers should include the following.

- Hyperbolas have two branches, two foci, and two vertices. Parabolas have only one branch, one focus, and one vertex. Hyperbolas have asymptotes, but parabolas do not.
- Hyperbolas reflect rays directed at one focus toward the other focus. Parabolas reflect parallel incoming rays toward the only focus.

41. C; Since the triangle is isosceles, its legs are congruent. Therefore, the length of each leg is 5 units. By the Pythagorean Theorem, if the hypotenuse of a right triangle has length c units and the lengths of its legs are a and b units, then $c^2 = a^2 + b^2$. In this triangle, $a = b$, since it is an isosceles triangle. Use substitution of the lengths to determine the value of c.

$$c^2 = a^2 + b^2$$
$$c^2 = 5^2 + 5^2$$
$$c^2 = 25 + 25$$
$$c^2 = 50$$
$$c = 5\sqrt{2}$$

Since $c = 5\sqrt{2}$, the length of the hypotenuse is $5\sqrt{2}$ units.

42. B; Both line segments $\overline{AB}$ and $\overline{AC}$ share one endpoint A and another endpoint that is 4 units from the origin on the x-axis. Therefore, the segments are symmetric about the y-axis, so their respective slopes are additive inverses of each other. Thus, the sum of the slopes of $\overline{AB}$ and $\overline{AC}$ is 0.

43.

x	y
-3	$-\frac{2}{3}$
-2	-1
-1	-2
0	$-$
1	2
2	1
3	$\frac{2}{3}$

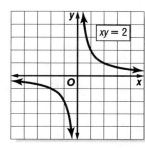

44. The points at which the graph of the equation intersect the line $y = x$ are the vertices of the graph. Use substitution to find the x-coordinates of the vertices.

$$xy = 2$$
$$x(x) = 2$$
$$x^2 = 2$$
$$x = \pm\sqrt{2}$$

The x-coordinates of the vertices are $\sqrt{2}$ and $-\sqrt{2}$. Since the vertices lie on the line $y = x$, the y-coordinates of the vertices are also $\sqrt{2}$ and $-\sqrt{2}$, respectively. Therefore, the coordinates of the vertices are $(\sqrt{2}, \sqrt{2})$ and $(-\sqrt{2}, -\sqrt{2})$.

45.

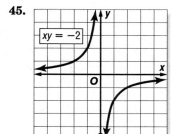

46. The graph of $xy = -2$ can be obtained by reflecting the graph of $xy = 2$ over the x-axis or over the y-axis. The graph of $xy = -2$ can also be obtained by rotating the graph of $xy = 2$ by 90°.

47. The major axis of the ellipse is horizontal, so the equation is of the form $\frac{(x-h)^2}{a^2} + \frac{(y-k)^2}{b^2} = 1$. The center is the midpoint of the major axis, or $(5, 2)$. Therefore, $h = 5$ and $k = 2$. The value of a is the distance from the center to one of the endpoints of the major axis, or 4 units. Therefore, $a = 4$, and $a^2 = 16$. The value of b is the distance from the center to one of the endpoints of the minor axis, or 1 unit. Therefore, $b = 1$, and $b^2 = 1$. Substitute the values for h, k, a^2, and b^2. An equation for the ellipse is $\frac{(x-5)^2}{16} + \frac{(y-2)^2}{1} = 1$.

48. The major axis is parallel to the y-axis, so the equation is of the form $\frac{(y-k)^2}{a^2} + \frac{(x-h)^2}{b^2} = 1$. The center is at $(-3, 1)$, so $h = -3$ and $k = 1$. The length of the major axis of an ellipse is $2a$ units, so $2a = 8$. Therefore, $a = 4$, and $a^2 = 16$. The length of the minor axis of an ellipse is $2b$ units, so $2b = 6$. Therefore, $b = 3$, and $b^2 = 9$. Substitute the values for h, k, a^2, and b^2. An equation for the ellipse is $\frac{(y-1)^2}{16} + \frac{(x+3)^2}{9} = 1$.

49. The center of the ellipse is the midpoint of the line segment connecting the foci, or $(1, 4)$. The major axis is horizontal, so the equation is of the form $\frac{(x-1)^2}{a^2} + \frac{(y-4)^2}{b^2} = 1$. The length of the major axis of an ellipse is $2a$ units, so $2a = 10$. Therefore, $a = 5$, and $a^2 = 25$. The foci are at $(5, 4)$ and $(-3, 4)$, so $c = 4$, and $c^2 = 16$. Use the equation $c^2 = a^2 - b^2$ to find the value of b.

$$c^2 = a^2 - b^2$$
$$16 = 25 - b^2$$
$$9 = b^2$$

Substitute the values for a^2 and b^2. An equation for the ellipse is $\frac{(x-1)^2}{25} + \frac{(y-4)^2}{9} = 1$.

50.
$$x^2 + y^2 - 10x + 2y + 22 = 0$$
$$(x^2 - 10x + \blacksquare) + (y^2 + 2y + \blacksquare) = -22 + \blacksquare + \blacksquare$$
$$(x^2 - 10x + 25) + (y^2 + 2y + 1) = -22 + 25 + 1$$
$$(x - 5)^2 + (y + 1)^2 = 4$$

The equation is of the form $(x - h)^2 + (y - k)^2 = r^2$, where $h = 5$, $k = -1$, and $r = 2$. Therefore, the center is at $(5, -1)$, and the radius is 2 units.

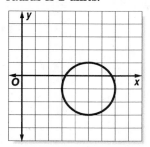

51.
$$x^2 + 6x + 8 = 0$$
$$(x + 2)(x + 4) = 0$$
$$x + 2 = 0 \quad \text{or} \quad x + 4 = 0$$
$$x = -2 \qquad\quad x = -4$$

The solutions are -2 and -4.

52.
$$2q^2 + 11q = 21$$
$$2q^2 + 11q - 21 = 0$$
$$(q + 7)(2q - 3) = 0$$

$q + 7 = 0$ or $2q - 3 = 0$
$q = -7$ $2q = 3$
                          $q = \frac{3}{2}$

The solutions are -7 and $\frac{3}{2}$.

53. $\begin{bmatrix} 2 & -1 \\ 0 & 5 \end{bmatrix} \cdot \begin{bmatrix} -3 & 2 \\ 1 & 4 \end{bmatrix}$

$= \begin{bmatrix} 2(-3) + (-1)(1) & 2(2) + (-1)(4) \\ 0(-3) + 5(1) & 0(2) + 5(4) \end{bmatrix}$

$= \begin{bmatrix} -6 + (-1) & 4 + (-4) \\ 0 + 5 & 0 + 20 \end{bmatrix}$

$= \begin{bmatrix} -7 & 0 \\ 5 & 20 \end{bmatrix}$

54. $[1\ -3] \cdot \begin{bmatrix} 4 & -2 & 1 \\ -3 & 2 & 0 \end{bmatrix}$

$= [1(4) + (-3)(-3) \quad 1(-2) + (-3)(2) \quad 1(1) + (-3)(0)]$
$= [4 + 9 \quad -2 + (-6) \quad 1 + 0]$
$= [13 \quad -8 \quad 1]$

55. Represent the number of pager subscribers in 1996 by the ordered pair (1996, 42). Likewise, represent the number of pager subscribers in 1999 by the ordered pair (1999, 58). The average rate of change of the number of pager subscribers from 1996 to 1999 is the slope of the line containing the two points.

$m = \frac{y_2 - y_1}{x_2 - x_1}$

$= \frac{58 - 42}{1999 - 1996}$

$= \frac{16}{3}$

≈ 5.31

Between 1996 and 1999, the number of pager subscribers increased at an average rate of about 5.31(100,000) or 5,330,000 subscribers per year.

56. $|2x + 1| = 9$
There are two cases.

   $a = b$ or $a = -b$
$2x + 1 = 9$ $2x + 1 = -9$
$2x = 8$ $2x = -10$
$x = 4$ $x = -5$
There are two solutions, -5 and 4.

57. $7x + 8y + 9y - 5x = 7x - 5x + 8y + 9y$
                        $= (7 - 5)x + (8 + 9)y$
                        $= 2x + 17y$

58. In the equation $2x^2 + 3xy - 5y^2 = 0, A = 2, B = 3,$ and $C = -5$.

59. In the equation $x^2 - 2xy + 9y^2 = 0, A = 1, B = -2,$ and $C = 9$.

60. In the equation $-3x^2 + xy + 2y^2 + 4x - 7y = 0,$ $A = -3, B = 1,$ and $C = 2$.

61. In the equation $5x^2 - 2y^2 + 5x - y = 0, A = 5,$ $B = 0,$ and $C = -2$.

62. In the equation $x^2 - 4x + 5y + 2 = 0, A = 1,$ $B = 0,$ and $C = 0$.

63. In the equation $xy - 2x - 3y + 6 = 0, A = 0,$ $B = 1,$ and $C = 0$.

Page 448   Practice Quiz 2

1. The major axis of the ellipse is vertical, so the equation is of the form $\frac{(y - k)^2}{a^2} + \frac{(x - h)^2}{b^2} = 1$. The center is the midpoint of the major axis, or (3, 1). The value of a is the distance between the center and one of the endpoints of the major axis, or 9 units. Since $a = 9, a^2 = 81$. The foci are at (3, 8) and (3, -6), so $c = 7$. Therefore, $c^2 = 49$. Use the equation $c^2 = a^2 - b^2$ to determine the value of b.
$$c^2 = a^2 - b^2$$
$$49 = 81 - b^2$$
$$b^2 = 32$$
Substitute the values for $h, k, a^2,$ and b^2. An equation of the ellipse is $\frac{(y - 1)^2}{81} + \frac{(x - 3)^2}{32} = 1$.

2. The equation is of the form $\frac{(x - h)^2}{a^2} + \frac{(y - k)^2}{b^2} = 1$, where $h = 4, k = -2, a = 3,$ and $b = 1$. The center is at (4, -2). Use the equation $c^2 = a^2 - b^2$ to determine the value of c.
$$c^2 = a^2 - b^2$$
$$c^2 = 3^2 - 1^2$$
$$c^2 = 9 - 1$$
$$c^2 = 8$$
$$c = 2\sqrt{2}$$
Since $c = 2\sqrt{2}$, the foci are at $(4 \pm 2\sqrt{2}, -2)$. The length of the major axis is 2(3) or 6 units. The length of the minor axis is 2(1) or 2 units.

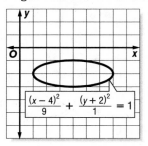

$\frac{(x - 4)^2}{9} + \frac{(y + 2)^2}{1} = 1$

3.
$$16x^2 + 5y^2 + 32x - 10y - 59 = 0$$
$$16(x^2 + 2x + \blacksquare) + 5(y^2 - 2y + \blacksquare) = 59 + 16(\blacksquare) + 5(\blacksquare)$$
$$16(x^2 + 2x + 1) + 5(y^2 - 2y + 1) = 59 + 16(1) + 5(1)$$
$$16(x + 1)^2 + 5(y - 1)^2 = 80$$
$$\frac{16(x + 1)^2}{80} + \frac{5(y - 1)^2}{80} = 1$$
$$\frac{(x + 1)^2}{5} + \frac{(y - 1)^2}{16} = 1$$

The equation is of the form $\frac{(y - k)^2}{a^2} + \frac{(x - h)^2}{b^2} = 1$, where $h = -1$, $k = 1$, $a = 4$, and $b = \sqrt{5}$. The center is at $(-1, 1)$. Use the equation $c^2 = a^2 - b^2$ to determine the value of c.
$$c^2 = a^2 - b^2$$
$$c^2 = 16 - 5$$
$$c^2 = 11$$
$$c = \sqrt{11}$$
Since $c = \sqrt{11}$, the foci are at $(-1, 1 \pm \sqrt{11})$. The length of the major axis is $2(4)$ or 8 units. The length of the minor axis is $2(\sqrt{5})$ or $2\sqrt{5}$ units.

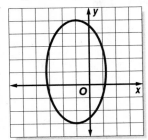

4. The transverse axis is horizontal and the center is at the origin, so the equation is of the form $\frac{x^2}{a^2} - \frac{y^2}{b^2} = 1$. The value of a is the distance from the center to a vertex, so $a = 3$. Since $a = 3$, $a^2 = 9$. The length of the conjugate axis of a hyperbola is $2b$ units, or $2b = 8$. Therefore, $b = 4$, and $b^2 = 16$.
Substitute the values for a^2 and b^2. An equation for the hyperbola is $\frac{x^2}{9} - \frac{y^2}{16} = 1$.

5. The transverse axis is horizontal, so the equation is of the form $\frac{(x - h)^2}{a^2} - \frac{(y - k)^2}{b^2} = 1$. The center is the
midpoint of the segment connecting the vertices, or $(2, 2)$. Thus, $h = 2$ and $k = 2$. The value of a is the distance between the center and a vertex, or 4 units. Since $a = 4$, $a^2 = 16$. The foci are at $(2 \pm \sqrt{21}, 2)$, so $c = \sqrt{21}$, or $c^2 = 21$. Use the equation $c^2 = a^2 + b^2$ to determine the value of b.
$$c^2 = a^2 + b^2$$
$$21 = 16 + b^2$$
$$5 = b^2$$
Substitute the values for h, k, a^2, and b^2. An equation for the hyperbola is $\frac{(x - 2)^2}{16} - \frac{(y - 2)^2}{5} = 1$.

Page 450 Check for Understanding

1. Answers should be of the form $2x^2 + Cy^2 + F = 0$, where $C = A$ and $F \leq 0$. Sample answer: $2x^2 + 2y^2 - 1 = 0$

2. The form of the general quadratic equation is $Ax^2 + Bxy + Cy^2 + Dx + Ey + F = 0$. Therefore, the equation for which $A = 2$, $B = 0$, $C = 0$, $D = -4$, $E = 7$, and $F = 1$ is $(2)x^2 + (0)xy + (0)y^2 + (-4)x + (7)y + (1) = 0$ or $2x^2 - 4x + 7y + 1 = 0$.

3.
$$x^2 + y^2 - 4x + 2y + 5 = 0$$
$$(x^2 - 4x + \blacksquare) + (y^2 + 2y + \blacksquare) = -5 + \blacksquare + \blacksquare$$
$$(x^2 - 4x + 4) + (y^2 + 2y + 1) = -5 + 4 + 1$$
$$(x - 2)^2 + (y + 1)^2 = 0$$
The standard form of the equation is $(x - 2)^2 + (y + 1)^2 = 0$. This is an equation of a circle centered at $(2, -1)$ with radius 0. In other words, $(2, -1)$ is the only point that satisfies the equation.

4.
$$y = x^2 + 3x + 1$$
$$y - 1 = x^2 + 3x$$
$$y - 1 + \blacksquare = x^2 + 3x + \blacksquare$$
$$y - 1 + \frac{9}{4} = x^2 + 3x + \frac{9}{4}$$
$$y + \frac{5}{4} = \left(x + \frac{3}{2}\right)^2$$
$$y = \left(x + \frac{3}{2}\right)^2 - \frac{5}{4}$$
The equation is of the form $y = a(x - h)^2 + k$, so the graph is a parabola with its vertex at $\left(-\frac{3}{2}, -\frac{5}{4}\right)$.

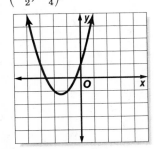

5.
$$y^2 - 2x^2 - 16 = 0$$
$$y^2 - 2x^2 = 16$$
$$\frac{y^2}{16} - \frac{2x^2}{16} = 1$$
$$\frac{y^2}{16} - \frac{x^2}{8} = 1$$
The equation is of the form $\frac{y^2}{a^2} - \frac{x^2}{b^2} = 1$, so the graph is a hyperbola.

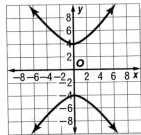

6.
$$x^2 + y^2 = x + 2$$
$$(x^2 - x + \blacksquare) + y^2 = 2 + \blacksquare$$
$$\left(x^2 - x + \frac{1}{4}\right) + y^2 = 2 + \frac{1}{4}$$
$$\left(x - \frac{1}{2}\right)^2 + y^2 = \frac{9}{4}$$

The equation is of the form $(x - h)^2 + (y - k)^2 = r^2$, so the graph is a circle with its center at $\left(\frac{1}{2}, 0\right)$ and a radius of $\frac{3}{2}$ units.

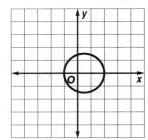

7.
$$x^2 + 4y^2 + 2x - 24y + 33 = 0$$
$$(x^2 + 2x + \blacksquare) + 4(y^2 - 6y + \blacksquare) = -33 + \blacksquare + 4(\blacksquare)$$
$$(x^2 + 2x + 1) + 4(y^2 - 6y + 9) = -33 + 1 + 4(9)$$
$$(x + 1)^2 - 4(y - 3)^2 = 4$$
$$\frac{(x + 1)^2}{4} - \frac{4(y - 3)^2}{4} = 1$$
$$\frac{(x + 1)^2}{4} - \frac{(y - 3)^2}{1} = 1$$

The equation is of the form $\frac{(x - h)^2}{a^2} - \frac{(y - k)^2}{b^2} = 1$, so the graph is an ellipse with its center at $(-1, 3)$.

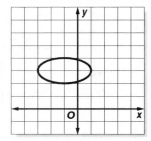

8. The equation is of the form $Ax^2 + Bxy + Cy^2 + Dx + Ey + F = 0$, where $A = 0$, $B = 0$, $C = 1$, $D = -1$, $E = -10$, and $F = 34$. Since $A = 0$ and $C \neq 0$, the graph of the equation is a parabola.

9. The equation is of the form $Ax^2 + Bxy + Cy^2 + Dx + Ey + F = 0$ where $A = 3$, $B = 0$, $C = 2$, $D = 12$, $E = -28$, and $F = 104$. Since A and C have the same sign and $A \neq C$, the graph of the equation is an ellipse.

10.
$$x^2 - 14x + 4 = 9y^2 - 36y$$
$$(x^2 - 14x + \blacksquare) - 9(y^2 - 4y + \blacksquare) = -4 + \blacksquare - 9(\blacksquare)$$
$$(x^2 - 14x + 49) - 9(y^2 - 4y + 4) = -4 + 49 - 9(4)$$
$$(x - 7)^2 - 9(y - 2)^2 = 9$$
$$\frac{(x - 7)^2}{9} - \frac{9(y - 2)^2}{9} = 1$$
$$\frac{(x - 7)^2}{9} - \frac{(y - 2)^2}{1} = 1$$

The equation is of the form $\frac{(x - h)^2}{a^2} - \frac{(y - k)^2}{b^2} = 1$, so the curve is a hyperbola with its center at $(7, 2)$.

11. $\frac{(x - 7)^2}{9} - \frac{(y - 2)^2}{1} = 1$

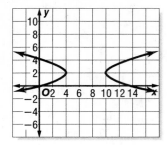

Pages 451–452   Practice and Apply
12. $6x^2 + 6y^2 = 162$
$$x^2 + y^2 = 27$$
The equation is of the form $(x - h)^2 + (y - k)^2 = r^2$, so the graph is a circle with its center at the origin and radius $\sqrt{27}$ units.

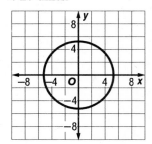

13. $4x^2 + 2y^2 = 8$
$$\frac{4x^2}{8} + \frac{2y^2}{8} = 1$$
$$\frac{x^2}{2} + \frac{y^2}{4} = 1$$
The equation is of the form $\frac{x^2}{a^2} + \frac{y^2}{b^2} = 1$, so the graph is a ellipse.

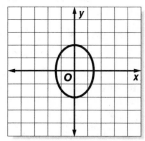

14. $x^2 = 8y$

$\frac{1}{8}x^2 = y$

The equation is of the form $y = a(x - h)^2 + k$, so the graph is a parabola.

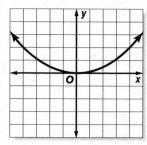

15. $4y^2 - x^2 + 4 = 0$

$4y^2 - x^2 = -4$

$\frac{4y^2}{-4} - \frac{x^2}{-4} = 1$

$\frac{x^2}{4} - \frac{y^2}{1} = 1$

The equation is of the form $\frac{x^2}{a^2} - \frac{y^2}{b^2} = 1$, so the graph is a hyperbola.

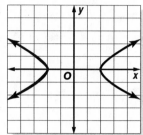

16. $(x - 1)^2 - 9(y - 4)^2 = 36$

$\frac{(x-1)^2}{36} - \frac{9(y-4)^2}{36} = 1$

$\frac{(x-1)^2}{36} - \frac{(y-4)^2}{4} = 1$

The equation is of the form $\frac{(x-h)^2}{a^2} - \frac{(y-k)^2}{b^2} = 1$, so the graph is a hyperbola.

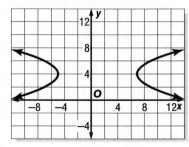

17. $y + 4 = (x - 2)^2$

$y = (x - 2)^2 - 4$

The equation is of the form $y = a(x - h)^2 + k$, so the graph is a parabola.

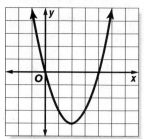

18. $(y - 4)^2 = 9(x - 4)$

$\frac{1}{9}(y - 4)^2 = x - 4$

$\frac{1}{9}(y - 4)^2 + 4 = x$

The equation is of the form $x = a(y - k)^2 + h$, so the graph is a parabola.

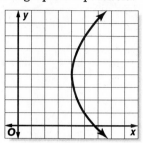

19. $x^2 + y^2 + 4x - 6y = -4$

$(x^2 + 4x + \blacksquare) + (y^2 - 6y + \blacksquare) = -4 + \blacksquare + \blacksquare$

$(x^2 + 4x + 4) + (y^2 - 6y + 9) = -4 + 4 + 9$

$(x + 2)^2 + (y - 3)^2 = 9$

The equation is of the form $(x - h)^2 + (y - k)^2 = r^2$, so the graph is a circle with its center at $(-2, 3)$ and radius 3 units.

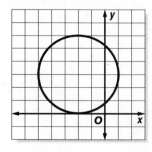

20. $x^2 + y^2 + 6y + 13 = 40$
$x^2 + y^2 + 6y = 27$
$x^2 + (y^2 + 6y + \blacksquare) = 27 + \blacksquare$
$x^2 + (y^2 + 6y + 9) = 27 + 9$
$x^2 + (y + 3)^2 = 36$

The equation is of the form $(x - h)^2 + (y - k)^2 = r^2$, so the graph is a circle with its center at $(0, -3)$ and radius 6 units.

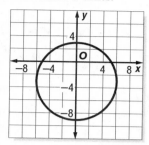

21. $x^2 - y^2 + 8x = 16$
$(x^2 + 8x + \blacksquare) - y^2 = 16 + \blacksquare$
$(x^2 + 8x + 16) - y^2 = 16 + 16$
$(x + 4)^2 - y^2 = 32$

$\dfrac{(x + 4)^2}{32} - \dfrac{y^2}{32} = 1$

The equation is of the form $\dfrac{(x - h)^2}{a^2} - \dfrac{(y - k)^2}{b^2} = 1$, so the graph is a hyperbola with its center at $(-4, 0)$.

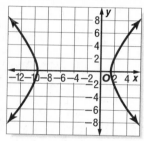

22. $x^2 + 2y^2 = 2x + 8$
$(x^2 - 2x + \blacksquare) + 2y^2 = 8 + \blacksquare$
$(x^2 - 2x + 1) + 2y^2 = 8 + 1$
$(x - 1)^2 + 2y^2 = 9$

$\dfrac{(x - 1)^2}{9} + \dfrac{y^2}{\frac{9}{2}} = 1$

The equation is of the form $\dfrac{(x - h)^2}{a^2} + \dfrac{(y + k)^2}{b^2} = 1$, so the graph is an ellipse with its center at $(1, 0)$.

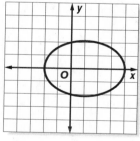

23. $x^2 - 8y + y^2 + 11 = 0$
$x^2 + (y^2 - 8y + \blacksquare) = -11 + \blacksquare$
$x^2 + (y^2 - 8y + 16) = -11 + 16$
$x^2 + (y - 4)^2 = 5$

The equation is of the form $(x - h)^2 + (y - k)^2 = r^2$, so the graph is a circle with its center at $(0, 4)$.

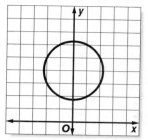

24. $9y^2 + 18y = 25x^2 + 216$
$9(y^2 + 2y + \blacksquare) - 25x^2 = 216 + 9(\blacksquare)$
$9(y^2 + 2y + 1) - 25x^2 = 216 + 9(1)$
$9(y + 1)^2 - 25x^2 = 225$

$\dfrac{9(y + 1)^2}{225} - \dfrac{25x^2}{225} = 1$

$\dfrac{(y + 1)^2}{25} - \dfrac{x^2}{9} = 1$

The equation is of the form $\dfrac{(y - k)^2}{a^2} - \dfrac{(x - h)^2}{b^2} = 1$, so the graph is a hyperbola with its center at $(0, -1)$.

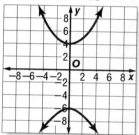

25. $3x^2 + 4y^2 + 8y = 8$
$3x^2 + 4(y^2 + 2y + \blacksquare) = 8 + 4(\blacksquare)$
$3x^2 + 4(y^2 + 2y + 1) = 8 + 4(1)$
$3x^2 + 4(y + 1)^2 = 12$

$\dfrac{3x^2}{12} + \dfrac{4(y + 1)^2}{12} = 1$

$\dfrac{x^2}{4} + \dfrac{(y + 1)^2}{3} = 1$

The equation is of the form $\dfrac{(x - h)^2}{a^2} + \dfrac{(y - k)^2}{b^2} = 1$, so the graph is an ellipse with its center at $(0, -1)$.

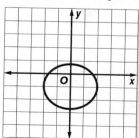

26.
$$x^2 + 4y^2 - 11 = 2(4y - x)$$
$$x^2 + 4y^2 - 11 = 8y - 2x$$
$$(x^2 + 2x + \blacksquare) + 4(y^2 - 2y + \blacksquare) = 11 + \blacksquare + 4(\blacksquare)$$
$$(x^2 + 2x + 1) + 4(y^2 - 2y + 1) = 11 + 1 + 4(1)$$
$$(x + 1)^2 + 4(y - 1)^2 = 16$$
$$\frac{(x + 1)^2}{16} + \frac{4(y - 1)^2}{16} = 1$$
$$\frac{(x + 1)^2}{16} + \frac{(y - 1)^2}{4} = 1$$

The equation is of the form $\frac{(x - h)^2}{a^2} + \frac{(y - k)^2}{b^2} = 1$, so the graph is an ellipse with its center at $(-1, 1)$.

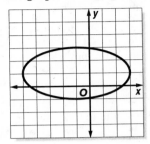

27.
$$y + x^2 = -(8x + 23)$$
$$y + x^2 = -8x - 23$$
$$y + 23 = -x^2 - 8x$$
$$y + 23 - \blacksquare = -(x^2 + 8x + \blacksquare)$$
$$y + 23 - 16 = -(x^2 + 8x + 16)$$
$$y + 7 = -(x + 4)^2$$
$$y = -(x + 4)^2 - 7$$

The equation is of the form $y = a(x - h)^2 + k$, so the graph is a parabola with its vertex at $(-4, -7)$.

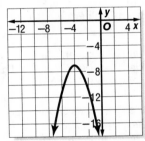

28.
$$6x^2 - 24x - 5y^2 - 10y - 11 = 0$$
$$6(x^2 - 4x + \blacksquare) - 5(y^2 + 2y + \blacksquare) = 11 + 6(\blacksquare) - 5(\blacksquare)$$
$$6(x^2 - 4x + 4) - 5(y^2 + 2y + 1) = 11 + 6(4) - 5(1)$$
$$6(x - 2)^2 - 5(y + 1)^2 = 30$$
$$\frac{6(x - 2)^2}{30} - \frac{5(y + 1)^2}{30} = 1$$
$$\frac{(x - 2)^2}{5} - \frac{(y + 1)^2}{6} = 1$$

The equation is of the form $\frac{(x - h)^2}{a^2} - \frac{(y - k)^2}{b^2} = 1$, so the graph is a hyperbola with its center at $(2, -1)$.

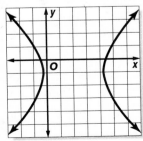

29.
$$25y^2 + 9x^2 - 50y - 54x = 119$$
$$25(y^2 - 2y + \blacksquare) + 9(x^2 - 6x + \blacksquare) = 119 + 25(\blacksquare) + 9(\blacksquare)$$
$$25(y^2 - 2y + 1) + 9(x^2 - 6x + 9) = 119 + 25(1) + 9(9)$$
$$25(y - 1)^2 + 9(x - 3)^2 = 225$$
$$\frac{25(y - 1)^2}{225} + \frac{9(x - 3)^2}{225} = 1$$
$$\frac{(y - 1)^2}{9} + \frac{(x - 3)^2}{25} = 1$$

The equation is of the form $\frac{(y - k)^2}{a^2} + \frac{(x - h)^2}{b^2} = 1$, so the graph is an ellipse with its center at $(3, 1)$.

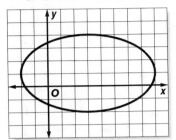

30. A comet with an orbit that is a parabola or a hyperbola will pass the Sun once, and then continue off into outer space.

31.
$$x^2 - 2y^2 - 2x - 5 = 0$$
$$(x^2 - 2x + \blacksquare) - 2y^2 = 5 + \blacksquare$$
$$(x^2 - 2x + 1) - 2y^2 = 5 + 1$$
$$(x - 1)^2 - 2y^2 = 6$$
$$\frac{(x - 1)^2}{6} - \frac{2y^2}{6} = 1$$
$$\frac{(x - 1)^2}{6} - \frac{y^2}{3} = 1$$

The equation is of the form $\frac{(x - h)^2}{a^2} - \frac{(y - k)^2}{b^2} = 1$, so the graph is a hyperbola.

32.

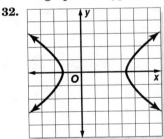

33. In the equation, $A = 1$ and $C = 1$. Since $A = C$, the graph is a circle.

34. In the equation, $A = 3$ and $C = -2$. Since A and C have opposite signs, the graph is a hyperbola.

35. In the equation, $A = 0$ and $C = 1$. Since $A = 0$ and $C \neq 0$, the graph is a parabola.

36. In the equation, $A = 7$ and $C = 4$. Since A and C have the same sign and $A \neq C$, the graph is an ellipse.

37. In the equation, $A = 5$ and $C = 1$. Since A and C have the same sign and $A \neq C$, the graph is an ellipse.

38. In the equation, $A = 2$ and $C = 2$. Since $A = C$, the graph is a circle.

39. In the equation, $A = 2$ and $C = 0$. Since $C = 0$ and $A \neq 0$, the graph is a parabola.

40. In the equation, $A = -1$ and $C = 1$. Since A and C have opposite signs, the graph is a hyperbola.

41. b; The flight of a baseball follows a path in the shape of a parabola. Since $A = 0.004$ and $C = 0$ in equation **b**, the graph is a parabola.

42. a; The oval opening in a picture frame is the shape of an ellipse. Since $A = 9$ and $C = 4$ in equation **a**, the graph is an ellipse.

43. c; The set of all points that are the same distance from one point is given by the equation of a circle. Since $A = 1$ and $C = 1$ in equation **c**, the graph is a circle.

44. $\frac{x^2}{a^2} - \frac{y^2}{b^2} = 0$

$$\frac{x^2}{a^2} = \frac{y^2}{b^2}$$

$$\sqrt{\frac{x^2}{a^2}} = \sqrt{\frac{y^2}{b^2}}$$

$$\pm\frac{x}{a} = \pm\frac{y}{b}$$

$$\pm\frac{b}{a}x = y$$

The equations $y = \pm\frac{b}{a}x$ are two intersecting lines.

45. The plane should be vertical and contain the axis of the double cone.

46. If you point a flashlight at a flat surface, you can make different conic sections by varying the angle at which you point the flashlight. Answers should include the following.

- Point the flashlight directly at a ceiling or wall. The light from the flashlight is in the shape of a cone and the ceiling or wall acts as a plane perpendicular to the axis of the cone.
- Hold the flashlight close to a wall and point it vertically toward the ceiling. A branch of a hyperbola will appear on the wall. In this case, the wall acts as a plane parallel to the axis of the cone.

47. D; the standard form of the equation $x^2 + y^2 - 2x - 3 = 0$ is $(x - 1)^2 + y^2 = 4$. This equation is of the form $(x - h)^2 + (y - k)^2 = r^2$, where $h = 1$, $k = 0$, and $r = 2$. Therefore, the graph is a circle with its center at $(1, 0)$, so this circle is not symmetric about the y-axis.

48. C; the graph shown is a hyperbola. In the equation $y^2 - x^2 = 1$, $A = -1$ and $C = 1$, so its graph is a hyperbola.

49. The equation relating a, b, and c for a noncircular ellipse is $c^2 = a^2 - b^2$, where $a^2 \geq b^2$, and a, b, and c are positive real numbers.

$$c^2 = a^2 - b^2$$

$$\frac{c^2}{a^2} = \frac{a^2 - b^2}{a^2}$$

$$\frac{c^2}{a^2} = 1 - \frac{b^2}{a^2}$$

$$\sqrt{\frac{c^2}{a^2}} = \sqrt{1 - \frac{b^2}{a^2}}$$

$$\frac{c}{a} = \sqrt{1 - \frac{b^2}{a^2}}$$

Since $e = \frac{c}{a}$, e cannot be less than or equal to 0, nor can it be greater than or equal to 1 because the value of $1 - \frac{b^2}{a^2}$ is always between 0 and 1. Therefore, $0 < e < 1$ for a noncircular ellipse.

The equation relating a, b, and c for a hyperbola is $c^2 = a^2 + b^2$, where $a \neq b$, and a, b, and c are positive real numbers.

$$c^2 = a^2 + b^2$$

$$\frac{c^2}{a^2} = \frac{a^2 + b^2}{a^2}$$

$$\frac{c^2}{a^2} = 1 + \frac{b^2}{a^2}$$

$$\sqrt{\frac{c^2}{a^2}} = \sqrt{1 + \frac{b^2}{a^2}}$$

$$\frac{c}{a} = \sqrt{1 + \frac{b^2}{a^2}}$$

Since $e = \frac{c}{a}$, e cannot have a value that is less than or equal to 1, since the square root of any number greater than 1 is a real number greater than 1. Therefore, $e > 1$ for a hyperbola.

Page 452   Maintain Your Skills

50. The vertices are at $(5, 10)$ and $(5, -2)$, so the transverse axis is vertical. Therefore, the equation is of the form $\frac{(y - k)^2}{a^2} - \frac{(x - h)^2}{b^2} = 1$. The center is the midpoint of the segment connecting the vertices, or $(5, 4)$, so $h = 5$ and $k = 4$. The value of a is the distance from the center to one of the vertices, or 6 units. Since $a = 6$, $a^2 = 36$. The conjugate axis is a segment of length $2b$ units, so $2b = 8$. Therefore $b = 4$, and $b^2 = 16$. Substitute the values for h, k, a^2, and b^2. An equation of the hyperbola is $\frac{(y - 4)^2}{36} - \frac{(x - 5)^2}{16} = 1$.

51. The vertices are at $(6, -6)$ and $(0, -6)$, so the transverse axis is horizontal. Therefore, the equation is of the form $\frac{(x - h)^2}{a^2} - \frac{(y - k)}{b^2} = 1$. The center is the midpoint of the segment connecting the vertices, or $(3, -6)$, so $h = 3$ and $k = -6$. The value of a is the distance from the center to one of the vertices, or 3 units. Since $a = 3$, $a^2 = 9$. The value of c is the distance from the center to a focus, or $\sqrt{13}$ units. Since $c = \sqrt{13}$, $c^2 = 13$. Use the equation $c^2 = a^2 + b^2$ to determine the value of b.

$$c^2 = a^2 + b^2$$
$$13 = 9 + b^2$$
$$4 = b^2$$

Substitute the values for a^2 and b^2. An equation of the hyperbola is $\frac{(x - 3)^2}{9} - \frac{[y - (-6)]^2}{4} = 1$ or $\frac{(x - 3)^2}{9} - \frac{(y + 6)^2}{4} = 1$.

52. $4x^2 + 9y^2 - 24x + 72y + 144 = 0$

$4(x^2 - 6x + \blacksquare) + 9(y^2 + 8y + \blacksquare) = -144 + 4(\blacksquare) + 9(\blacksquare)$

$4(x^2 - 6x + 9) + 9(y^2 + 8y + 16) = -144 + 4(9) + 9(16)$

$4(x - 3)^2 + 9(y + 4)^2 = 36$

$\dfrac{4(x - 3)^2}{36} + \dfrac{9(y + 4)^2}{36} = 1$

$\dfrac{(x - 3)^2}{9} + \dfrac{(y + 4)^2}{4} = 1$

The equation is of the form $\dfrac{(x - h)^2}{a^2} + \dfrac{(y - k)^2}{b^2} = 1$, where $h = 3$, $k = -4$, $a = 3$, and $b = 2$. The center is at $(3, -4)$. Use the equation $c^2 = a^2 - b^2$ to determine the value of c.

$c^2 = a^2 - b^2$

$c^2 = (3)^2 - (2)^2$

$c^2 = 9 - 4$

$c^2 = 5$

$c = \sqrt{5}$

Since $c = \sqrt{5}$, the foci are at $(3 \pm \sqrt{5}, -4)$. The length of the major axis is $2(3)$ or 6 units. The length of the minor axis is $2(2)$ or 4 units.

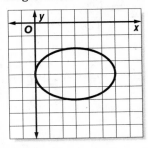

53. $(x^3)^4 = x^{3(4)}$

$= x^{12}$

54. $(m^5n^{-3})^2 \, m^2n^7 = (m^5)^2 \cdot (n^{-3})^2 \cdot m^2 \cdot n^7$

$= m^{5(2)}n^{-3(2)} \, m^2 \, n^7$

$= m^{10}n^{-6} \, m^2n^7$

$= m^{10+2} \, n^{-6+7}$

$= m^{12} \, n$

55. $\dfrac{x^2y^{-3}}{x^{-5}y} = \dfrac{x^{2 - (-5)}}{y^{1 - (-3)}}$

$= \dfrac{x^7}{y^4}$

56. Use the prediction equation to find the value of y when $x = 18$.

$y = 205 - 0.5x$

$y = 205 - 0.5(18)$

$y = 196$

The maximum heart rate for an 18-year-old is 196 beats per minute.

57. Substitute $x + 4$ for y in the second equation and solve for x.

$2x + y = 10$

$2x + (x + 4) = 10$

$3x = 6$

$x = 2$

Now substitute the value for x in either original equation and solve for y.

$y = x + 4$

$y = 2 + 4$

$y = 6$

The solution is $(2, 6)$.

58. Use addition to eliminate the y variable.

$ 4x + y = 14$

$\underline{(+) \; 4x - y = 10}$

$ 8x = 24$

$ x = 3$

Now find y by substituting 3 for x in either original equation.

$4x + y = 14$

$4(3) + y = 14$

$12 + y = 14$

$y = 2$

The solution is $(3, 2)$.

59. Use addition to eliminate the x variable.

$x + 5y = 10$ $\boxed{\text{Multiply by } -3}$ $\longrightarrow$ $ -3x - 15y = -30$

$3x - 2y = -4$ $\phantom{\boxed{\text{Multiply by } -3} \longrightarrow}$ $\underline{(+) \; 3x - 2y = -4}$

$\phantom{3x - 2y = -4 \boxed{\text{Multiply by } -3} \longrightarrow (+) \;} -17y = -34$

$\phantom{3x - 2y = -4 \boxed{\text{Multiply by } -3} \longrightarrow (+) \; -17} y = 2$

Now find x by substituting 2 for y in either original equation.

$x + 5y = 10$

$x + 5(2) = 10$

$x + 10 = 10$

$x = 0$

The solution is $(0, 2)$.

Page 454   Algebra Activity
(Follow-Up of Lesson 8-6)

1. Check students' work; The points on each graph are equidistant from the focus and the directrix.

2a. There are no intersecting circles whose sum is less than 10.

2b. The ellipses become more circular; the ellipses become more oblong.

3. Each branch of the hyperbola becomes more narrow and the vertices become farther apart; each branch of the hyperbola becomes wider and the vertices become closer.

8-7   Solving Quadratic Systems

Page 457   Graphing Calculator Investigation

1. The equation for a circle is of the form $(x - h)^2 + (y - k)^2 = r^2$, where the center is at (h, k) and the radius is r units. One circle has its center at $(0, 0)$ and a radius of 5 units. Therefore, an equation that represents the circle is $x^2 + y^2 = 25$. The second circle has its center at $(2, 0)$ and a radius of 5 units, so its equation is $(x - 2)^2 + y^2 = 25$.

2. $x^2 + y^2 = 25$
$y^2 = 25 - x^2$
$y = \pm\sqrt{25 - x^2}$
$(x - 2)^2 + y^2 = 25$
$y^2 = 25 - (x - 2)^2$
$y = \pm\sqrt{25 - (x - 2)^2}$

KEYSTROKES: $\boxed{Y=}$ $\boxed{2nd}$ [$\sqrt{\ }$] 25 $\boxed{-}$ $\boxed{X,T,\theta,n}$
$\boxed{x^2}$ $\boxed{)}$ $\boxed{ENTER}$ $\boxed{(-)}$ $\boxed{2nd}$ [$\sqrt{\ }$] 25
$\boxed{-}$ $\boxed{X,T,\theta,n}$ $\boxed{x^2}$ $\boxed{)}$ $\boxed{ENTER}$ $\boxed{2nd}$
[$\sqrt{\ }$] 25 $\boxed{-}$ $\boxed{(}$ $\boxed{X,T,\theta,n}$ $\boxed{-}$ 2
$\boxed{)}$ $\boxed{x^2}$ $\boxed{)}$ $\boxed{ENTER}$ $\boxed{(-)}$ $\boxed{2nd}$ [$\sqrt{\ }$]
25 $\boxed{-}$ $\boxed{(}$ $\boxed{X,T,\theta,n}$ $\boxed{-}$ 2 $\boxed{)}$ $\boxed{x^2}$
$\boxed{)}$ $\boxed{GRAPH}$ $\boxed{2nd}$ [CALC] 5
$\boxed{ENTER}$ $\boxed{\blacktriangledown}$ $\boxed{ENTER}$ $\boxed{ENTER}$
$x = 1$ $y = 4.90$

Indicates the point of intersection is at $(1, 4.90)$.
$\boxed{2nd}$ [CALC] 5 $\boxed{\blacktriangledown}$ $\boxed{ENTER}$ $\boxed{\blacktriangledown}$
$\boxed{ENTER}$ $\boxed{ENTER}$
$x = 1$ $y = -4.90$

Indicates the point of intersection is at $(1, -4.90)$.
Therefore, the solution is $(1, \pm4.90)$.

3. Use addition to eliminate the y variable.
$x^2 + y^2 = 25$ Multiply by -1. $\Rightarrow$ $-x^2 - y^2 = -25$
$(x - 2)^2 + y^2 = 25$ $\underline{(+)(x - 2)^2 + y^2 = 25}$
                                          $-x^2 + (x - 2)^2 = 0$
                                          $-x^2 + x^2 - 4x + 4 = 0$
                                          $-4x = -4$
                                          $x = 1$

Now find y by substituting 1 for x in either
original equation.
$x^2 + y^2 = 25$
$(1)^2 + y^2 = 25$
$y^2 = 24$
$y = \pm2\sqrt{6}$

Therefore, the solution is $(1, \pm2\sqrt{6})$.

4. No, you cannot always find an exact solution of a
system using a graphing calculator. A calculator
only gives decimal approximations. If the solution
involves irrational numbers or unfamiliar
fractions, you may not be able to recognize them.

5. $y = x + 2$ $x^2 + y^2 = 9$
$y^2 = 9 - x^2$
$y = \pm\sqrt{9 - x^2}$

KEYSTROKES: $\boxed{Y=}$ $\boxed{X,T,\theta,n}$ $\boxed{+}$ 2 $\boxed{ENTER}$ $\boxed{2nd}$
[$\sqrt{\ }$] 9 $\boxed{-}$ $\boxed{X,T,\theta,n}$ $\boxed{x^2}$ $\boxed{)}$
$\boxed{ENTER}$ $\boxed{(-)}$ $\boxed{2nd}$ [$\sqrt{\ }$] 9 $\boxed{-}$
$\boxed{X,T,\theta,n}$ $\boxed{x^2}$ $\boxed{)}$ $\boxed{GRAPH}$ $\boxed{2nd}$
[CALC] 5 $\boxed{ENTER}$ $\boxed{ENTER}$
$\boxed{ENTER}$
$x = 0.87$ $y = 2.87$

Indicates the point of intersection is at $(0.87, 2.87)$.
$\boxed{2nd}$ [CALC] 5 $\boxed{ENTER}$ $\boxed{\blacktriangledown}$
$\boxed{ENTER}$ $\boxed{ENTER}$
$x = -2.87$ $y = -0.87$

Indicates the point of intersection is at
$(-2.87, -0.87)$. Therefore, the solutions to the
system are $(0.87, 2.87)$ and $(-2.87, -0.87)$.

6. $3x^2 + y^2 = 11$ $y = x^2 + x + 1$
$y^2 = 11 - 3x^2$
$y = \pm\sqrt{11 - 3x^2}$

KEYSTROKES: $\boxed{X,T,\theta,n}$ $\boxed{x^2}$ $\boxed{+}$ $\boxed{X,T,\theta,n}$ $\boxed{+}$ 1
$\boxed{ENTER}$ $\boxed{Y=}$ $\boxed{2nd}$ [$\sqrt{\ }$] 11 $\boxed{-}$ 3
$\boxed{X,T,\theta,n}$ $\boxed{x^2}$ $\boxed{)}$ $\boxed{ENTER}$ $\boxed{(-)}$
$\boxed{2nd}$ [$\sqrt{\ }$] 11 $\boxed{-}$ 3 $\boxed{X,T,\theta,n}$ $\boxed{x^2}$
$\boxed{)}$ $\boxed{GRAPH}$ $\boxed{2nd}$ [CALC] 5
$\boxed{ENTER}$ $\boxed{ENTER}$ $\boxed{ENTER}$
$x = 0.96$ $y = 2.87$

Indicates the point of intersection is at
$(0.96, 2.87)$.

$\boxed{2nd}$ [CALC] 5 $\boxed{\blacktriangleleft}$ $\boxed{ENTER}$ $\boxed{ENTER}$
$\boxed{ENTER}$
$x = -1.57$ $y = 1.90$

Indicates the point of intersection is at
$(-1.57, 1.90)$. Therefore, the solutions of the
system are $(0.96, 2.87)$ and $(-1.57, 1.90)$.

Page 458 Check for Understanding

1a.

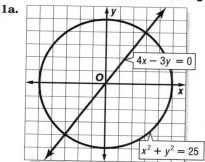

The solutions of the system are $(-3, -4)$ and
$(3, 4)$.

1b.

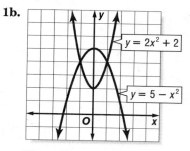

The solutions of the system are $(1, 4)$ and
$(-1, 4)$.

2. See students' work; The vertex of the parabola is on the ellipse. The parabola opens toward the interior of the ellipse and is narrow enough to intersect the ellipse in two other points. Thus, there are exactly three points of intersection.

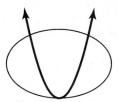

3. See students' work; Sample answer: $x^2 + y^2 = 40$, $y = x^2 + x$

4. Substitute 5 for y in the second equation and solve for x.
$$y^2 = x^2 + 9$$
$$(5)^2 = x^2 + 9$$
$$25 = x^2 + 9$$
$$16 = x^2$$
$$\pm 4 = x$$

The solutions are $(\pm 4, 5)$.

5. Solve the first equation for y.
$$y - x = 1$$
$$y = x + 1$$

Substitute $x + 1$ for y in the second equation and solve for x.
$$x^2 + y^2 = 25$$
$$x^2 + (x + 1)^2 = 25$$
$$x^2 + x^2 + 2x + 1 = 25$$
$$2x^2 + 2x = 24$$
$$x^2 + x = 12$$
$$x^2 + x - 12 = 0$$
$$(x - 3)(x + 4) = 0$$
$$x - 3 = 0 \quad \text{or} \quad x + 4 = 0$$
$$x = 3 \qquad x = -4$$

Now solve for y.
$$y - x = 1 \qquad y - x = 1$$
$$y - 3 = 1 \qquad y - (-4) = 1$$
$$y = 4 \qquad y = -3$$

The solutions are $(3, 4)$ and $(-4, -3)$.

6.
$$3x = 8y^2$$
$$-8y^2 + 3x = 0$$

Use elimination to solve the system.
$$-8y^2 \qquad + 3x \qquad = 0$$
$$(+)\ 8y^2 - 2x^2 \qquad = 16$$
$$\overline{\qquad -2x^2 + 3x \qquad = 16}$$
$$-2x^2 + 3x - 16 = 0$$

However, this equation does not hold true over the real numbers, so there is no solution of the system.

7. Use elimination to solve the system.
$$5x^2 + y^2 = \quad 30$$
$$(+)\ 9x^2 - y^2 = -16$$
$$\overline{\qquad 14x^2 = \quad 14}$$
$$x^2 = 1$$
$$x = \pm 1$$

Now solve for y.
$$9x^2 - y^2 = -16 \qquad\qquad 9x^2 - y^2 = -16$$
$$9(1)^2 - y^2 = -16 \qquad 9(-1)^2 - y^2 = -16$$
$$9 - y^2 = -16 \qquad\qquad 9 - y^2 = -16$$
$$y^2 = 25 \qquad\qquad\qquad y^2 = 25$$
$$y = \pm 5 \qquad\qquad\qquad y = \pm 5$$

The solutions are $(1, \pm 5)$ and $(-1, \pm 5)$.

8.

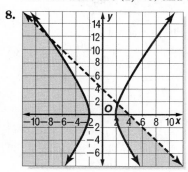

9.

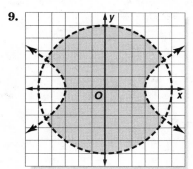

10. The epicenter is located at the point of intersection of the three circles that represent the range of the effects of the earthquake. Write a system of three equations that are circles with stations at the centers.

$$x^2 + y^2 = 50^2$$
$$x^2 + (y - 30)^2 = 40^2$$
$$(x - 35)^2 + (y - 18)^2 = 13^2$$

Solve the first equation for x^2.

$$x^2 + y^2 = 2500$$
$$x^2 = 2500 - y^2$$

Substitute $2500 - y^2$ for x^2 in the second equation and solve for y.

$$x^2 + (y - 30)^2 = 1600$$
$$2500 - y^2 + (y - 30)^2 = 1600$$
$$2500 - y^2 + y^2 - 60y + 900 = 1600$$
$$-60y = -1800$$
$$y = 30$$

Substitute 30 for y in the first equation and solve for x.

$$x^2 + y^2 = 2500$$
$$x^2 + (30)^2 = 2500$$
$$x^2 = 1600$$
$$x = 40$$

Verify that the point $(40, 30)$ lies on the third circle.

$$(40 - 35)^2 + (30 - 18)^2 \stackrel{?}{=} 13^2$$
$$5^2 + 12^2 \stackrel{?}{=} 169$$
$$25 + 144 \stackrel{?}{=} 169$$
$$169 = 169 \checkmark$$

The epicenter was located at $(40, 30)$.

Pages 458–460 Practice and Apply

11. Substitute $x + 2$ for y in the second equation and solve for x.

$$y = x^2$$
$$x + 2 = x^2$$
$$0 = x^2 - x - 2$$
$$0 = (x - 2)(x + 1)$$
$$x - 2 = 0 \quad \text{or} \quad x + 1 = 0$$
$$x = 2 \qquad\qquad x = -1$$

Now solve for y.

$$y = x + 2 \qquad y = x + 2$$
$$y = 2 + 2 \qquad y = -1 + 2$$
$$y = 4 \qquad\qquad y = 1$$

The solutions are $(2, 4)$ and $(-1, 1)$.

12. Substitute $x + 3$ for y in the second equation and solve for x.

$$y = 2x^2$$
$$x + 3 = 2x^2$$
$$0 = 2x^2 - x - 3$$
$$0 = (2x - 3)(x + 1)$$
$$2x - 3 = 0 \quad \text{or} \quad x + 1 = 0$$
$$2x = 3 \qquad\qquad x = -1$$
$$x = \frac{3}{2}$$

Now solve for y.

$$y = x + 3 \qquad y = x + 3$$
$$y = \frac{3}{2} + 3 \qquad y = -1 + 3$$
$$y = \frac{9}{2} \qquad\qquad y = 2$$

The solutions are $\left(\frac{3}{2}, \frac{9}{2}\right)$ and $(-1, 2)$.

13. Substitute $x + 2$ for y in the first equation and solve for x.

$$x^2 + y^2 = 36$$
$$x^2 + (x + 2)^2 = 36$$
$$x^2 + x^2 + 4x + 4 = 36$$
$$2x^2 + 4x = 32$$
$$x^2 + 2x = 16$$
$$x^2 + 2x - 16 = 0$$

Applying the quadratic formula,

$$x = \frac{-2 \pm \sqrt{4 - 4(1)(-16)}}{2}.$$
$$= \frac{-2 \pm \sqrt{68}}{2}$$
$$= \frac{-2 \pm 2\sqrt{17}}{2}$$
$$x = -1 \pm \sqrt{17}$$

Now solve for y.

$$y = x + 2 \qquad\qquad y = x + 2$$
$$y = -1 + \sqrt{17} + 2 \qquad y = -1 - \sqrt{17} + 2$$
$$y = 1 + \sqrt{17} \qquad\qquad y = 1 - \sqrt{17}$$

The solutions are $(-1 + \sqrt{17}, 1 + \sqrt{17})$ and $(-1 - \sqrt{17}, 1 - \sqrt{17})$.

14. Substitute $7 - x$ for y in the first equation and solve for x.

$$y^2 + x^2 = 9$$
$$(7 - x)^2 + x^2 = 9$$
$$x^2 - 14x + 49 + x^2 = 9$$
$$2x^2 - 14x = -40$$
$$x^2 - 7x = -20$$
$$x^2 - 7x + 20 = 0$$

There is no solution of this equation in the real numbers, so there is no solution of the system of equations.

15. Substitute x for y in the first equation and solve for x.

$$\frac{x^2}{30} + \frac{y^2}{6} = 1$$
$$\frac{x^2}{30} + \frac{x^2}{6} = 1$$
$$x^2 + 5x^2 = 30$$
$$6x^2 = 30$$
$$x^2 = 5$$
$$x = \pm\sqrt{5}$$

Since $x = y$, $y = \pm\sqrt{5}$. The solutions are $(\sqrt{5}, \sqrt{5})$ and $(-\sqrt{5}, -\sqrt{5})$.

16. Substitute x for y in the first equation and solve for x.

$$\frac{x^2}{36} - \frac{y^2}{4} = 1$$
$$\frac{x^2}{36} - \frac{x^2}{4} = 1$$
$$x^2 - 9x^2 = 1$$
$$-8x^2 = 1$$
$$x^2 = -\frac{1}{8}$$

There is no solution of this equation in the real numbers, so there is no solution of the system of equations.

17. Use elimination to solve the system.

$$4x \quad\quad + y^2 = \quad 20$$
$$\underline{(-)\quad\quad 4x^2 + y^2 = \quad 100}$$
$$4x - 4x^2 \quad\quad = -80$$
$$x - x^2 \quad = -20$$
$$0 = x^2 - x - 20$$
$$0 = (x - 5)(x + 4)$$

$$x - 5 = 0 \quad \text{or} \quad x + 4 = 0$$
$$x = 5 \quad\quad\quad x = -4$$

Now solve for y.

$4x + y^2 = 20$	$4x + y^2 = 20$
$4(5) + y^2 = 20$	$4(-4) + y^2 = 20$
$y^2 = 0$	$y^2 = 36$
$y = 0$	$y = \pm 6$

The solutions are $(5, 0)$ and $(-4, \pm 6)$.

18. Solve the first equation for y.

$$y + x^2 = 3$$
$$y = 3 - x^2$$

Substitute $3 - x^2$ for y in the second equation and solve for x.

$$x^2 + 4y^2 = 36$$
$$x^2 + 4(3 - x^2)^2 = 36$$
$$x^2 + 4(x^4 - 6x^2 + 9) = 36$$
$$x^2 + 4x^4 - 24x^2 + 36 = 36$$
$$4x^4 - 23x^2 = 0$$
$$x^2(4x^2 - 23) = 0$$

$$x^2 = 0 \quad \text{or} \quad 4x^2 - 23 = 0$$
$$x = 0 \quad\quad\quad 4x^2 = 23$$
$$x^2 = \frac{23}{4}$$
$$x = \pm\frac{\sqrt{23}}{2}$$

Now solve for y.

$y + x^2 = 3$	$y + x^2 = 3$
$y + (0)^2 = 3$	$y + \left(\pm\frac{\sqrt{23}}{2}\right)^2 = 3$
$y = 3$	$y + \frac{23}{4} = 3$
	$y = -\frac{11}{4}$

The solutions are $(0, 3)$ and $\left(\pm\frac{\sqrt{23}}{2}, -\frac{11}{4}\right)$.

19. Use elimination to solve the system.

$$x^2 \quad\quad + y^2 = 64$$
$$\underline{(-)\, x^2 + 64y^2 = 64}$$
$$-63y^2 = \quad 0$$
$$y^2 = 0$$
$$y = 0$$

Now solve for x.

$$x^2 + y^2 = 64$$
$$x^2 + (0)^2 = 64$$
$$x^2 = 64$$
$$x = \pm 8$$

The solutions are $(\pm 8, 0)$.

20. Use elimination to solve the system.

$$y^2 \quad + x^2 = 25$$
$$\underline{(-)\, y^2 + 9x^2 = 25}$$
$$-8x^2 = \quad 0$$
$$x^2 = 0$$
$$x = 0$$

Now solve for y.

$$y^2 + x^2 = 25$$
$$y^2 + (0)^2 = 25$$
$$y^2 = 25$$
$$y = \pm 5$$

The solutions are $(0, \pm 5)$.

21. Substitute $x^2 - 25$ for y^2 in the second equation and solve for x.

$$x^2 - y^2 = 7$$
$$x^2 - (x^2 - 25) = 7$$
$$x^2 - x^2 + 25 = 7$$
$$25 = 7$$

Since $25 \neq 7$, the system has no solution.

22. Substitute $x^2 - 7$ for y^2 in the second equation and solve for x.

$$x^2 + y^2 = 25$$
$$x^2 + x^2 - 7 = 25$$
$$2x^2 = 32$$
$$x^2 = 16$$
$$x = \pm 4$$

Now solve for y.

$y^2 = x^2 - 7$	$y^2 = x^2 - 7$
$y^2 = (4)^2 - 7$	$y^2 = (-4)^2 - 7$
$y^2 = 16 - 7$	$y^2 = 16 - 7$
$y^2 = 9$	$y^2 = 9$
$y = \pm 3$	$y = \pm 3$

The solutions are $(4, \pm 3)$ and $(-4, \pm 3)$.

23.
$$2x^2 - 8y^2 = -48y + 90$$
$$2x^2 - 8y^2 + 48y - 90 = 0$$

Use elimination to solve the system.

$$2x^2 + 8y^2 + 8x - 48y + 30 = 0$$
$$\underline{(+)\, 2x^2 - 8y^2 \quad\quad + 48y - 90 = 0}$$
$$4x^2 \quad\quad + 8x \quad\quad - 60 = 0$$
$$x^2 + 2x - 15 = 0$$
$$(x - 3)(x + 5) = 0$$

$$x - 3 = 0 \quad \text{or} \quad x + 5 = 0$$
$$x = 3 \quad\quad\quad x = -5$$

Now solve for y.

$2x^2 + 8y^2 + 8x - 48y + 30 = 0$	$2x^2 + 8y^2 + 8x - 48y + 30 = 0$
$2(3)^2 + 8y^2 + 8(3) - 48y + 30 = 0$	$2(-5)^2 + 8y^2 + 8(-5) - 48y + 30 = 0$
$8y^2 - 48y = -72$	$8y^2 - 48y = -40$
$y^2 - 6y = -9$	$y^2 - 6y = -5$
$y^2 - 6y + 9 = 0$	$y^2 - 6y + 5 = 0$
$(y - 3)^2 = 0$	$(y - 1)(y - 5) = 0$
$y - 3 = 0$	$y - 1 = 0 \text{ or } y - 5 = 0$
$y = 3$	$y = 1 \quad\quad y = 5$

The solutions are $(3, 3)$, $(-5, 1)$, and $(-5, 5)$.

24.
$$3x^2 + 20y^2 = 80y + 48$$
$$3x^2 + 20y^2 - 80y - 48 = 0$$

Use elimination to solve the system.

$$
\begin{array}{r}
3x^2 - 20y^2 - 12x + 80y - 96 = 0 \\
(+)\ 3x^2 + 20y^2 \qquad\quad - 80y - 48 = 0 \\
\hline
6x^2 \qquad\quad - 12x \qquad - 144 = 0
\end{array}
$$

$$x^2 - 2x - 24 = 0$$
$$(x - 6)(x + 4) = 0$$
$$x - 6 = 0 \quad\text{or}\quad x + 4 = 0$$
$$x = 6 \qquad\qquad x = -4$$

Now solve for y.

$$3x^2 - 20y^2 - 12x + 80y - 96 = 0 \qquad 3x^2 - 20y^2 - 12x + 80y - 96 = 0$$
$$3(6)^2 - 20y^2 - 12(6) + 80y - 96 = 0 \qquad 3(-4)^2 - 20y^2 - 12(-4) + 80y - 96 = 0$$
$$-20y^2 + 80y = 60 \qquad\qquad -20y^2 + 80y = 0$$
$$y^2 - 4y + 3 = 0 \qquad\qquad y^2 - 4y = 0$$
$$(y - 1)(y - 3) = 0 \qquad\qquad y(y - 4) = 0$$
$$y - 1 = 0 \text{ or } y - 3 = 0 \qquad\qquad y = 0 \text{ or } y - 4 = 0$$
$$y = 1 \qquad y = 3 \qquad\qquad y = 0 \qquad y = 4$$

The solutions are $(6, 1)$, $(6, 3)$, $(-4, 0)$, and $(-4, 4)$.

25. Substitute $2x + 1$ for y in the second equation and solve for x.

$$2x^2 + y^2 = 11$$
$$2x^2 + (2x + 1)^2 = 11$$
$$2x^2 + 4x^2 + 4x + 1 = 11$$
$$6x^2 + 4x = 10$$
$$3x^2 + 2x - 5 = 0$$
$$(3x + 5)(x - 1) = 0$$
$$3x + 5 = 0 \quad\text{or}\quad x - 1 = 0$$
$$3x = -5 \qquad\qquad x = 1$$
$$x = -\tfrac{5}{3}$$

Now solve for y.

$$y = 2x + 1 \qquad\qquad y = 2x + 1$$
$$y = 2\left(-\tfrac{5}{3}\right) + 1 \qquad y = 2(1) + 1$$
$$y = -\tfrac{10}{3} + 1 \qquad\qquad y = 2 + 1$$
$$y = -\tfrac{7}{3} \qquad\qquad y = 3$$

The graphs of the equations intersect at $\left(-\tfrac{5}{3}, -\tfrac{7}{3}\right)$ and $(1, 3)$.

26. $x^2 + y^2 = 25$
$$x^2 = 25 - y^2$$

Substitute $25 - y^2$ for x^2 in the second equation and solve for x.

$$2x^2 + 3y^2 = 66$$
$$2(25 - y^2) + 3y^2 = 66$$
$$50 - 2y^2 + 3y^2 = 66$$
$$y^2 = 16$$
$$y = \pm 4$$

Now solve for x.

$$x^2 + y^2 = 25 \qquad\qquad x^2 + y^2 = 25$$
$$x^2 + (4)^2 = 25 \qquad\qquad x^2 + (-4)^2 = 25$$
$$x^2 = 9 \qquad\qquad\qquad x^2 = 9$$
$$x = \pm 3 \qquad\qquad\qquad x = \pm 3$$

The points at $(3, \pm 4)$ and $(-3, \pm 4)$ lie on the graphs of both equations.

27. The rockets will be at the same height at the value of t where the graphs of the two equations intersect. Use elimination to solve the system of equations.

$$
\begin{array}{r}
y = -16t^2 + 150t + 5 \\
(-)\ y = -16t^2 + 160t \\
\hline
0 = \qquad\qquad -10t + 5
\end{array}
$$

$$10t = 5$$
$$2t = 1$$
$$t = 0.5$$

The rockets will be at the same height after 0.5 second.

28. Sample answer: $\dfrac{x^2}{36} + \dfrac{y^2}{16} = 1$, $\dfrac{x^2}{16} + \dfrac{(y - 2)^2}{4} = 1$, $\dfrac{x^2}{2} + \dfrac{y^2}{16} = 1$

29. The light from the source will hit the mirror at the point of intersection of the hyperbola and the line containing $(-10, 0)$ and the focus of the hyperbola. The equation is of the form $\dfrac{y^2}{a^2} - \dfrac{x^2}{b^2} = 1$, where $a^2 = 9$ and $b^2 = 16$. Use the equation $c^2 = a^2 + b^2$ to determine the value of c.

$$c^2 = a^2 + b^2$$
$$c^2 = 9 + 16$$
$$c^2 = 25$$
$$c = 5$$

Therefore, the other focus is at $(0, 5)$. Find the slope of the line through $(-10, 0)$ and $(0, 5)$.

$$m = \frac{y_2 - y_1}{x_2 - x_1}$$
$$= \frac{5 - 0}{0 - (-10)}$$
$$= \frac{1}{2}$$

The equation of the line in point-slope form is $y - 5 = \tfrac{1}{2}(x - 0)$ or $y = \tfrac{1}{2}x + 5$. Find the point of intersection of the line and the hyperbola by substituting $\tfrac{1}{2}x + 5$ for y in the equation of the hyperbola and solving for x.

$$\frac{y^2}{9} - \frac{x^2}{16} = 1$$
$$\frac{\left(\tfrac{1}{2}x + 5\right)^2}{9} - \frac{x^2}{16} = 1$$
$$16\left(\tfrac{1}{2}x + 5\right)^2 - 9x^2 = 144$$
$$16\left(\tfrac{1}{4}x^2 + 5x + 25\right) - 9x^2 = 144$$
$$4x^2 + 80x + 400 - 9x^2 = 144$$
$$-5x^2 + 80x + 256 = 0$$
$$x = \frac{24\sqrt{5} + 40}{5} \quad\text{or}\quad x = \frac{-24\sqrt{5} + 40}{5}$$

Now solve for y.

$$y = \tfrac{1}{2}x + 5 \qquad\qquad y = \tfrac{1}{2}x + 5$$
$$y = \tfrac{1}{2}\left(\frac{24\sqrt{5} + 40}{5}\right) + 5 \qquad y = \tfrac{1}{2}\left(\frac{-24\sqrt{5} + 40}{5}\right) + 5$$
$$y = \frac{12\sqrt{5} + 20}{5} + 5 \qquad\qquad y = \frac{-12\sqrt{5} + 20}{5} + 5$$
$$y = \frac{12\sqrt{5} + 45}{5} \qquad\qquad y = \frac{45 - 12\sqrt{5}}{5}$$

The point of intersection is $\left(\dfrac{40 - 24\sqrt{5}}{5}, \dfrac{45 - 12\sqrt{5}}{5}\right)$.

30. $x = y^2 + 20$
$x - 20 = y^2$

Substitute $x - 20$ for y^2 in the equation that models the orbit of Pluto, and solve for x.

$$\frac{x^2}{39.5^2} + \frac{y^2}{38.3^2} = 1$$

$$\frac{x^2}{1560.25} + \frac{y^2}{1466.89} = 1$$

$$\frac{x^2}{1560.25} + \frac{(x - 20)}{1466.89} = 1$$

$$1466.89x^2 + 1560.25(x - 20) = (1560.25)(1466.89)$$

$$1466.89x^2 + 1560.25x - 31,205 = 2,288,715.123$$

$$1466.89x^2 + 1560.25x - 2,319,920.123 = 0$$

The solutions of this equation are $x \approx 39.2$ and $x \approx -40.3$. Now solve for y.

$x = y^2 + 20$	$x = y^2 + 20$
$39.2 = y^2 + 20$	$-40.3 = y^2 + 20$
$19.2 = y^2$	$-60.3 = y^2$
$\pm\sqrt{19.2} = y$	no solution
$\pm 4.4 \approx y$	

Therefore, the intersections of the orbits are at about $(39.2, \pm 4.4)$

31. No, the comet may not necessarily hit Pluto. The comet and Pluto may not be at either point of intersection at the same time.

32.

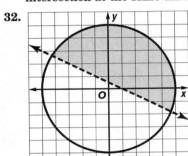

33.

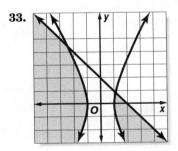

34.

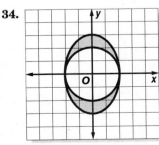

35.

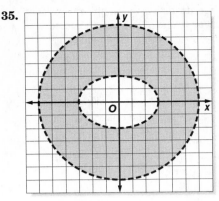

36.

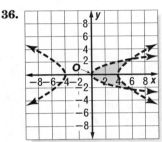

37.

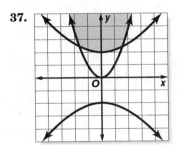

38. The system of equations will have no solutions when the graphs do not intersect. This situation occurs when $k < -3$, $-2 < k < 2$, or $k > 3$, that is, when the graph of the circle does not exceed the graph of the ellipse.

39. None; there is no value of k for which the given system has one solution. The graphs of the equations are a circle and an ellipse, which are symmetric about the x- and y-axes, and will always intersect in an even number of points.

40. The given system has two solutions when the radius of the circle touches but does not cross the vertices of the ellipse, that is, when $k = \pm 2$ or $k = \pm 3$ so the radius of the circle is 4 or 9.

41. None; there is no value of k for which the given system has three solutions. The graphs of the equations are a circle and an ellipse, which are symmetric about the x- and y-axes, and will always intersect in an even number of points.

42. The system of equations will have four solutions when the radius of the circle in between 4 and 9 units, that is, for $-3 < k < -2$ or $2 < k < 3$.

43. Systems of equations can be used to represent the locations and/or paths of objects on the screen. Answers should include the following.

- $y = 3x$, $x^2 + y^2 = 2500$
- The y-intercept of the graph of the equation $y = 3x$ is 0, so the path of the spaceship contains the origin.
- Substitute $3x$ for y in the equation $x^2 + y^2 = 2500$ and solve for x.

$$x^2 + y^2 = 2500$$
$$x^2 + (3x)^2 = 2500$$
$$x^2 + 9x^2 = 2500$$
$$10x^2 = 2500$$
$$x^2 = 250$$
$$x = \pm 5\sqrt{10}$$

Now solve for y.

$y = 3x$	$y = 3x$
$y = 3(5\sqrt{10})$	$y = 3(-5\sqrt{10})$
$y = 15\sqrt{10}$	$y = -15\sqrt{10}$

Assuming that the spaceship moves from the bottom of the screen toward the center, the spaceship will hit the force field at $(-5\sqrt{10}, -15\sqrt{10})$ or about $(-15.81, -47.43)$.

44. A; The expression $x^2 - 4x$ has the greatest value for $x = 0$. The value $4x$ is greater than x^2 for $x = 1$, $x = 2$, and $x = 3$, so the expression yields a negative value. For $x = 0$, $x^2 - 4x = 0$.

45. B; The three-digit numbers begin at 100 and end at 999, so there are 900 three-digit numbers, inclusive. Every third number is divisible by 3. Therefore, there are $\frac{900}{3}$ or 300 three-digit numbers that are divisible by 3.

46. Sample answer: $y = x^2$, $x = (y - 2)^2$

47. Sample answer: $x^2 + y^2 = 36$, $\frac{(x+2)^2}{16} - \frac{y^2}{4} = 1$

48. Sample answer: $x^2 + y^2 = 100$, $\frac{x^2}{16} + \frac{y^2}{4} = 1$

49. Sample answer: $x^2 + y^2 = 81$, $\frac{x^2}{4} + \frac{y^2}{100} = 1$

50. Sample answer: $\frac{x^2}{64} + \frac{y^2}{36} = 1$, $\frac{x^2}{64} - \frac{y^2}{36} = 1$

51. It is impossible to have two circles that intersect in three points. Two circles intersect in one point, two points, or infinitely many points.

Page 460 Maintain Your Skills

52.
$$x^2 + y^2 + 4x + 2y - 6 = 0$$
$$(x^2 + 4x + \blacksquare) + (y^2 + 2y + \blacksquare) = 6 + \blacksquare + \blacksquare$$
$$(x^2 + 4x + 4) + (y^2 + 2y + 1) = 6 + 4 + 1$$
$$(x + 2)^2 + (y + 1)^2 = 11$$

The equation is of the form $(x - h)^2 + (y - k) = r^2$, so the graph is a circle with its center at $(-2, -1)$ and radius $\sqrt{11}$ units.

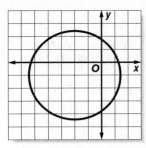

53.
$$9x^2 + 4y^2 - 24y = 0$$
$$9x^2 + 4(y^2 - 6y + \blacksquare) = 4(\blacksquare)$$
$$9x^2 + 4(y^2 - 6y + 9) = 4(9)$$
$$9x^2 + 4(y - 3)^2 = 36$$
$$\frac{9x^2}{36} + \frac{4(y - 3)^2}{36} = 1$$
$$\frac{x^2}{4} + \frac{(y - 3)^2}{9} = 1$$

The equation is of the form $\frac{(y - k)^2}{a^2} + \frac{(x - h)^2}{b^2} = 1$, so the graph is an ellipse with its center at $(0, 3)$.

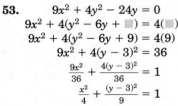

54. $6y^2 + 2x^2 = 24$
$$\frac{6y^2}{24} - \frac{2x^2}{24} = 1$$
$$\frac{y^2}{4} - \frac{x^2}{12} = 1$$

The equation is of the form $\frac{y^2}{a^2} - \frac{x^2}{b^2} = 1$, where $a = 2$ and $b = 2\sqrt{3}$. Therefore, the vertices are at $(0, 2)$ and $(0, -2)$. Use the equation $c^2 = a^2 + b^2$ to determine the value of c.
$$c^2 = a^2 + b^2$$
$$c^2 = 4 + 12$$
$$c^2 = 16$$
$$c = 4$$

Since $c = 4$, the foci are at $(0, 4)$ and $(0, -4)$. The equations of the asymptotes are $y = \pm \frac{2}{2\sqrt{3}}x$, or $y = \frac{\sqrt{3}}{3}x$ and $y = -\frac{\sqrt{3}}{3}x$.

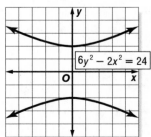

$6y^2 - 2x^2 = 24$

55. $x^2 + 7x = 0$
$x(x + 7) = 0$
$x = 0$ or $x + 7 = 0$
$x = -7$
The solutions are 0 and -7.

56. $x^2 - 3x = 0$
$x(x - 3) = 0$
$x = 0$ or $x - 3 = 0$
$x = 3$
The solutions are 0 and 3.

57. $21 = x^2 + 4x$
$0 = x^2 + 4x - 21$
$0 = (x - 3)(x + 7)$
$x - 3 = 0$ or $x + 7 = 0$
$x = 3$ $x = -7$
The solutions are -7 and 3.

58. $35 = -2x + x^2$
$0 = x^2 - 2x - 35$
$0 = (x + 5)(x - 7)$
$x + 5 = 0$ or $x - 7 = 0$
$x = -5$ $x = 7$
The solutions are -5 and 7.

59. $9x^2 + 24x = -16$
$9x^2 + 24x + 16 = 0$
$(3x + 4)^2 = 0$
$3x + 4 = 0$
$3x = -4$
$x = -\frac{4}{3}$
The solution is $-\frac{4}{3}$.

60. $8x^2 + 2x = 3$
$8x^2 + 2x - 3 = 0$
$(4x + 3)(2x - 1) = 0$
$4x + 3 = 0$ or $2x - 1 = 0$
$4x = -3$ $2x = 1$
$x = -\frac{3}{4}$ $x = \frac{1}{2}$
The solutions are $-\frac{3}{4}$ and $\frac{1}{2}$.

61a. $5x^2 = 2$
$5x^2 - 2 = 0$
$a = 5, b = 0, c = -2$
$b^2 - 4ac = (0)^2 - 4(5)(-2)$
$= 0 - (-40)$
$= 40$

61b. The discriminant is positive but *not* a perfect square, so there are two real, irrational roots.

61c. In the equation, $a = 5, b = 0$, and $c = -2$. Using the Quadratic Formula,
$x = \frac{-b \pm \sqrt{b^2 - 4ac}}{2a}$.
$x = \frac{-(0) \pm \sqrt{40}}{2(5)}$
$x = \pm \frac{2\sqrt{10}}{10}$
$x = \pm \frac{\sqrt{10}}{5}$
The solutions are $\frac{\sqrt{10}}{5}$ and $-\frac{\sqrt{10}}{5}$.

62a. $-3x^2 + 6x - 7 = 0$
$a = -3, b = 6, c = -7$
$b^2 - 4ac = (6)^2 - 4(-3)(-7)$
$= 36 - 84$
$= -48$

62b. The discriminant is negative, so there are two imaginary roots.

62c. In the equation, $a = -3, b = 6$, and $c = -7$. Using the Quadratic Formula,
$x = \frac{-b \pm \sqrt{b^2 - 4ac}}{2a}$.
$x = \frac{-(6) \pm \sqrt{-48}}{2(-3)}$
$x = \frac{-6 \pm i\sqrt{48}}{-6}$
$x = \frac{-6 \pm 4i\sqrt{3}}{-6}$
$x = \frac{1 \pm 2i\sqrt{3}}{3}$
The solutions are $1 + \frac{2i\sqrt{3}}{3}$ and $1 - \frac{2i\sqrt{3}}{3}$.

63. $(3 + 2i) - (1 - 7i) = (3 - 1) + [2 - (-7)]i$
$= 2 + 9i$

64. $(8 - i)(4 - 3i) = 8(4) + 8(-3i) - i(4) - i(-3i)$
$= 32 - 24i - 4i + 3i^2$
$= 32 - 28i - 3$
$= 29 - 28i$

65. $\frac{2 + 3i}{1 + 2i} = \frac{2 + 3i}{1 + 2i} \cdot \frac{1 - 2i}{1 - 2i}$
$= \frac{8 - i}{5}$
$= \frac{8}{5} - \frac{1}{5}i$

66. $\frac{1.67 \times 10^{-27}}{9.11 \times 10^{-31}} = \frac{1.67}{9.11} \cdot \left(10^{-27 - (-31)}\right)$
$= \frac{1.67}{9.11} \cdot 10^4$
≈ 1830

A proton is about 1830 times as massive as an electron.

67. $\begin{vmatrix} 2 & -3 \\ 2 & 0 \end{vmatrix} = (2)(0) - (-3)(2)$
$= 0 - (-6)$
$= 6$

68. $\begin{vmatrix} -4 & -2 \\ 5 & 3 \end{vmatrix} = (-4)(3) - (-2)(5)$
$= -12 - (-10)$
$= -2$

69. $\begin{vmatrix} 2 & 1 & -2 \\ 4 & 0 & 3 \\ -3 & 1 & 7 \end{vmatrix} = 2\begin{vmatrix} 0 & 3 \\ 1 & 7 \end{vmatrix} - 1\begin{vmatrix} 4 & 3 \\ -3 & 7 \end{vmatrix} + (-2)\begin{vmatrix} 4 & 0 \\ -3 & 1 \end{vmatrix}$
$= 2(0 - 3) - (28 - (-9)) - 2(4 - 0)$
$= 2(-3) - 37 - 2(4)$
$= -6 - 37 - 8$
$= -51$

70. Use elimination to solve the system.

$$\begin{array}{r} r + s + t = 15 \\ (-)\,r \quad\ \ + t = 12 \\ \hline s = 3 \end{array}$$

Substitute 3 for s in the third equation and solve for t.

$$s + t = 10$$
$$(3) + t = 10$$
$$t = 7$$

Substitute 7 for t in the second equation and solve for r.

$$r + t = 12$$
$$r + (7) = 12$$
$$r = 5$$

The solution to the system of equations is $(5, 3, 7)$.

71. The line passes through the points $(1, 1)$ and $(2, 4)$. Use these two points to find the slope of the line.

$$m = \frac{y_2 - y_1}{x_2 - x_1}$$
$$m = \frac{4 - 1}{2 - 1}$$
$$m = \frac{3}{1}$$
$$m = 3$$

The slope of the line is 3. Use the point $(1, 1)$ and slope-intercept form to find b, the y-intercept.

$$y = mx + b$$
$$1 = (3)(1) + b$$
$$1 = 3 + b$$
$$-2 = b$$

The y-intercept is -2. So the equation of the line in slope-intercept form is $y = 3x + (-2)$ or $y = 3x - 2$.

72. The line passes through the points $(-2, 2)$ and $(1, -3)$. Use these two points to find the slope of the line.

$$m = \frac{y_2 - y_1}{x_2 - x_1}$$
$$m = \frac{-3 - 2}{1 - (-2)}$$
$$m = \frac{-5}{3}$$

The slope of the line is $-\frac{5}{3}$. Use the point $(-2, 2)$ and slope-intercept form to find b, the y-intercept.

$$y = mx + b$$
$$2 = \left(-\frac{5}{3}\right)(-2) + b$$
$$2 = \frac{10}{3} + b$$
$$-\frac{4}{3} = b$$

The y-intercept is $-\frac{4}{3}$. So the equation of the line in slope intercept form is $y = -\frac{5}{3}x + \left(-\frac{4}{3}\right)$ or $y = -\frac{5}{3}x - \frac{4}{3}$.

Chapter 8 Study Guide and Review

Pages 461–466

1. true

2. true

3. true

4. False; a parabola is the set of all points that are the same distance from a given point called the focus and a given line called the directrix.

5. true

6. False; the conjugate axis of a hyperbola is a line segment perpendicular to the transverse axis.

7. true

8. False; a hyperbola is the set of all points in a plane such that the absolute value of the difference of the distances from any point on the hyperbola to two given points is constant.

9. False; the midpoint formula is given by $\left(\frac{x_1 + x_2}{2}, \frac{y_1 + y_2}{2}\right)$.

10. true

11.
$$\left(\frac{x_1 + x_2}{2}, \frac{y_1 + y_2}{2}\right) = \left(\frac{1 + 4}{2}, \frac{2 + 6}{2}\right)$$
$$= \left(\frac{5}{2}, \frac{8}{2}\right)$$
$$= \left(\frac{5}{2}, 4\right)$$

12.
$$\left(\frac{x_1 + x_2}{2}, \frac{y_1 + y_2}{2}\right) = \left(\frac{-8 + (-2)}{2}, \frac{0 + 3}{2}\right)$$
$$= \left(\frac{-10}{2}, \frac{3}{2}\right)$$
$$= \left(-5, \frac{3}{2}\right)$$

13.
$$\left(\frac{x_1 + x_2}{2}, \frac{y_1 + y_2}{2}\right) = \left(\frac{\frac{3}{5} + \frac{1}{4}}{2}, \frac{-\frac{7}{4} + \left(-\frac{2}{5}\right)}{2}\right)$$
$$= \left(\frac{\frac{17}{20}}{2}, \frac{-\frac{43}{20}}{2}\right)$$
$$= \left(\frac{17}{40}, -\frac{43}{40}\right)$$

14.
$$d = \sqrt{(x_2 - x_1)^2 + (y_2 - y_1)^2}$$
$$= \sqrt{[-2 - (-2)]^2 + (13 - 10)^2}$$
$$= \sqrt{0^2 + 3^2}$$
$$= \sqrt{9} \text{ or } 3$$

The distance between $(-2, 10)$ and $(-2, 13)$ is 3 units.

15.
$$d = \sqrt{(x_2 - x_1)^2 + (y_2 - y_1)^2}$$
$$= \sqrt{(-9 - 8)^2 + (4 - 5)^2}$$
$$= \sqrt{(-17)^2 + (-1)^2}$$
$$= \sqrt{289 + 1} \text{ or } \sqrt{290}$$

The distance between $(8, 5)$ and $(-9, 4)$ is $\sqrt{290}$ units.

16.
$$d = \sqrt{(x_2 - x_1)^2 + (y_2 - y_1)^2}$$
$$= \sqrt{(1 - 7)^2 + [2 - (-3)]^2}$$
$$= \sqrt{(-6)^2 + 5^2}$$
$$= \sqrt{36 + 25}$$
$$= \sqrt{61}$$

The distance between $(7, -3)$ and $(1, 2)$ is $\sqrt{61}$ units.

17. First, write the equation in the form
$y = a(x - h)^2 + k$.
$$(x - 1)^2 = 12(y - 1)$$
$$\frac{1}{12}(x - 1)^2 = y - 1$$
$$\frac{1}{12}(x - 1)^2 + 1 = y$$
Then use the following information to draw the graph.

vertex: $(1, 1)$

focus: $\left(1, 1 + \dfrac{1}{4\left(\frac{1}{12}\right)}\right)$ or $(1, 4)$

axis of symmetry: $x = 1$

directrix: $y = 1 - \dfrac{1}{4\left(\frac{1}{12}\right)}$ or $y = -2$

direction of opening: upward, since $a > 0$

length of latus rectum: $\left|\dfrac{1}{\frac{1}{12}}\right|$ or 12 units

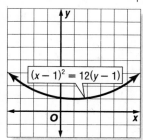

18. First, write the equation in the form
$y = a(x - h)^2 + k$.
$$y + 6 = 16(x - 3)^2$$
$$y = 16(x - 3)^2 - 6$$
Then use the following information to draw the graph.

vertex: $(3, -6)$

focus: $\left(3, -6 + \dfrac{1}{4(16)}\right)$ or $\left(3, -5\frac{63}{64}\right)$

axis of symmetry: $x = 3$

directrix: $y = -6 - \dfrac{1}{4(16)}$ or $y = -6\frac{1}{64}$

direction of opening: upward, since $a > 0$

length of latus rectum: $\left|\dfrac{1}{16}\right|$ or $\dfrac{1}{16}$ unit

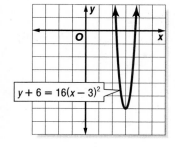

19. First, write the equation in the form
$y = a(x - h)^2 + k$.
$$x^2 - 8x + 8y + 32 = 0$$
$$(x^2 - 8x + \blacksquare) + 8y = -32 + \blacksquare$$
$$(x^2 - 8x + 16) + 8y = -32 + 16$$
$$(x - 4)^2 + 8y = -16$$
$$8y = -(x - 4)^2 - 16$$
$$y = -\frac{1}{8}(x - 4)^2 - 2$$
Then use the following information to draw the graph.

vertex: $(4, -2)$

focus: $\left(4, -2 + \dfrac{1}{4\left(-\frac{1}{8}\right)}\right)$ or $(4, -4)$

axis of symmetry: $x = 4$

directrix: $y = -2 - \dfrac{1}{4\left(-\frac{1}{8}\right)}$ or $y = 0$

direction of opening: downward, since $a < 0$

length of latus rectum: $\left|\dfrac{1}{-\frac{1}{8}}\right|$ or 8 units

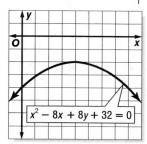

20. The equation is of the form $x = a(y - k)^2 + h$. Use the following information to draw the graph.

vertex: $(0, 0)$

focus: $\left(0 + \dfrac{1}{4(16)}, 0\right)$ or $\left(\dfrac{1}{64}, 0\right)$

axis of symmetry: $y = 0$

directrix: $x = 0 - \dfrac{1}{4(16)}$ or $x = -\dfrac{1}{64}$

direction of opening: right, since $a > 0$

length of latus rectum: $\left|\dfrac{1}{16}\right|$ or $\dfrac{1}{16}$ unit

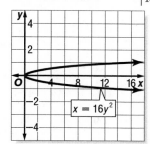

21. The vertex is at $(0, 1)$, so $h = 0$ and $k = 1$. The focus is at $(0, -1)$, so $k + \frac{1}{4a} = -1$. Use k to determine the value of a.

$$k + \frac{1}{4a} = -1$$
$$1 + \frac{1}{4a} = -1$$
$$\frac{1}{4a} = -2$$
$$1 = -8a$$
$$-\frac{1}{8} = a$$

An equation of the parabola is $y = -\frac{1}{8}(x - 0)^2 + 1$ or $y = -\frac{1}{8}x^2 + 1$.

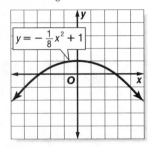

22. The center of the circle is at $(2, -3)$ and its radius is 5 units.

$$(x - h)^2 + (y - k)^2 = r^2$$
$$(x - 2)^2 + [y - (-3)]^2 = 5^2$$
$$(x - 2)^2 + (y + 3)^2 = 25$$

An equation for the circle is $(x - 2)^2 + (y + 3)^2 = 25$.

23. The center of the circle is at $(-4, 0)$ and its radius is $\frac{3}{4}$ unit.

$$(x - h)^2 + (y - k)^2 = r^2$$
$$[x - (-4)]^2 + (y - 0)^2 = \left(\frac{3}{4}\right)^2$$
$$(x + 4)^2 + y^2 = \frac{9}{16}$$

An equation for the circle is $(x + 4)^2 + y^2 = \frac{9}{16}$.

24. The center of the circle is the midpoint of the diameter.

$$(h, k) = \left(\frac{x_1 + x_2}{2}, \frac{y_1 + y_2}{2}\right)$$
$$= \left(\frac{9 + (-3)}{2}, \frac{4 + (-2)}{2}\right)$$
$$= \left(\frac{6}{2}, \frac{2}{2}\right)$$
$$= (3, 1)$$

The radius is the distance from the center to one of the points.

$$r = \sqrt{(x_2 - x_1)^2 + (y_2 - y_1)^2}$$
$$= \sqrt{(9 - 3)^2 + (4 - 1)^2}$$
$$= \sqrt{6^2 + 3^2}$$
$$= \sqrt{36 + 9}$$
$$= 3\sqrt{5}$$

The radius is $3\sqrt{5}$ units, so $r^2 = 45$. Substitute h, k, and r^2 into standard form of the equation of a circle. An equation of the circle is $(x - 3)^2 + (y - 1)^2 = 45$.

25. Since the circle is tangent to the x-axis, its radius is 2. Since $r = 2$, $r^2 = 4$. The center is at $(-1, 2)$, so $h = -1$ and $k = 2$. Substitute h, k, and r^2 into the standard form of the equation of a circle. An equation of the circle is $[x - (-1)]^2 + (y - 2)^2 = 4$ or $(x + 1)^2 + (y - 2)^2 = 4$.

26. The center of the circle is at $(0, 0)$ and the radius is $\sqrt{169}$ or 13 units.

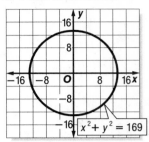

27. The center of the circle is at $(-5, 11)$ and the radius is $\sqrt{49}$ or 7 units.

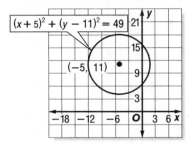

28.
$$x^2 + y^2 - 6x + 16y - 152 = 0$$
$$(x^2 - 6x + \blacksquare) + (y^2 + 16y + \blacksquare) = 152 + \blacksquare + \blacksquare$$
$$(x^2 - 6x + 9) + (y^2 + 16y + 64) = 152 + 9 + 64$$
$$(x - 3)^2 + (y + 8)^2 = 225$$

The center of the circle is at $(3, -8)$ and the radius is $\sqrt{225}$ or 15 units.

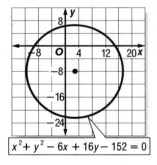

29.
$$x^2 + y^2 + 6x - 2y - 15 = 0$$
$$(x^2 + 6x + \blacksquare) + (y^2 - 2y + \blacksquare) = 15 + \blacksquare + \blacksquare$$
$$(x^2 + 6x + 9) + (y^2 - 2y + 1) = 15 + 9 + 1$$
$$(x + 3)^2 + (y - 1)^2 = 25$$

The center of the circle is at $(-3, 1)$ and the radius is $\sqrt{25}$ or 5 units.

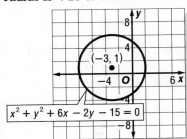

30. The center of the ellipse is the midpoint of the major axis.

$$(h, k) = \left(\frac{x_1 + x_2}{2}, \frac{y_1 + y_2}{2}\right)$$
$$= \left(\frac{4 + (-6)}{2}, \frac{1 + 1}{2}\right)$$
$$= \left(\frac{-2}{2}, \frac{2}{2}\right)$$
$$= (-1, 1)$$

The length of the major axis of an ellipse is $2a$ units. In this ellipse, the length of the major axis is the distance between the points at $(4, 1)$ and $(-6, 1)$. This distance is 10 units.

$$2a = 10$$
$$a = 5$$

The length of the minor axis of an ellipse is $2b$ units. In this ellipse, the length of the minor axis is the distance between the points at $(-1, 3)$ and $(-1, -1)$. This distance is 4 units.

$$2b = 4$$
$$b = 2$$

Since the major axis is horizontal, the equation is of the form $\frac{(x-h)^2}{a^2} + \frac{(y-k)^2}{b^2} = 1$. An equation of the ellipse is $\frac{[x-(-1)^2]}{5^2} + \frac{(y-1)^2}{2^2} = 1$ or $\frac{(x+1)^2}{25} + \frac{(y-1)^2}{4} = 1$.

31. The equation is of the form $\frac{y^2}{a^2} + \frac{x^2}{b^2} = 1$. The center of the ellipse is at $(0, 0)$. Since $a^2 = 25$, $a = 5$. Since $b^2 = 16$, $b = 4$. The length of the major axis is $2(5)$ or 10 units. The length of the minor axis is $2(4)$ or 8 units. Use the equation $c^2 = a^2 - b^2$ to determine the value of c.

$$c^2 = a^2 - b^2$$
$$c^2 = 25 - 16$$
$$c^2 = 9$$
$$c = 3$$

Since $c = 3$, the foci are at $(0, 3)$ and $(0, -3)$.

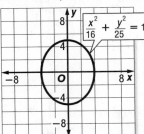

32. The equation is of the form $\frac{(x-h)^2}{a^2} + \frac{(y-k)^2}{b^2} = 1$. The center of the ellipse is at $(-2, 3)$. Since $a^2 = 16$, $a = 4$. Since $b^2 = 9$, $b = 3$. The length of the major axis is $2(4)$ or 8 units. The length of the minor axis is $2(3)$ or 6 units. Use the equation $c^2 = a^2 - b^2$ to determine the value of c.

$$c^2 = a^2 - b^2$$
$$c^2 = 16 - 9$$
$$c^2 = 7$$
$$c = \sqrt{7}$$

Since $c = \sqrt{7}$, the foci are at $(-2 \pm \sqrt{7}, 3)$, or $(-2 + \sqrt{7}, 3)$ and $(-2 - \sqrt{7}, 3)$.

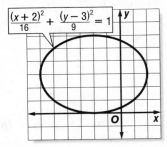

33.
$$x^2 + 4y^2 - 2x + 16y + 13 = 0$$
$$(x^2 - 2x + \blacksquare) + 4(y^2 + 4y + \blacksquare) = -13 + \blacksquare + 4\,(\blacksquare)$$
$$(x^2 - 2x + 1) + 4(y^2 + 4y + 4) = -13 + 1 + 4(4)$$
$$(x - 1)^2 + 4(y + 2)^2 = 4$$
$$\frac{(x-1)^2}{4} + \frac{4(y+2)^2}{4} = 1$$
$$\frac{(x-1)^2}{4} + \frac{(y+2)^2}{1} = 1$$

The equation is of the form $\frac{(x-h)^2}{a^2} + \frac{(y-k)^2}{b^2} = 1$.

The center is at $(1, -2)$. Since $a^2 = 4$, $a = 2$. Since $b^2 = 1$, $b = 1$. The length of the major axis is $2(2)$ or 4 units. The length of the minor axis is $2(1)$ or 2 units. Use the equation $c^2 = a^2 - b^2$ to determine the value of c.
$$c^2 = a^2 - b^2$$
$$c^2 = 4 - 1$$
$$c^2 = 3$$
$$c = \sqrt{3}$$

Since $c = \sqrt{3}$, the foci are at $(1 \pm \sqrt{3}, -2)$, or $(1 + \sqrt{3}, -2)$ and $(1 - \sqrt{3}, -2)$.

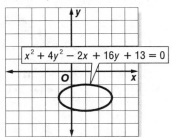

$x^2 + 4y^2 - 2x + 16y + 13 = 0$

34. The transverse axis of the hyperbola is vertical, so the equation is of the form $\frac{(y-k)^2}{a^2} - \frac{(x-h)^2}{b^2} = 1$.

The center of the hyperbola is the midpoint of the segment connecting the vertices.
$$(h, k) = \left(\frac{x_1 + x_2}{2}, \frac{y_1 + y_2}{2}\right)$$
$$= \left(\frac{2 + 2}{2}, \frac{5 + 1}{2}\right)$$
$$= \left(\frac{4}{2}, \frac{6}{2}\right)$$
$$= (2, 3)$$

The length of the transverse axis is $2a$ units. In this hyperbola, the length of the transverse axis is the distance between the vertices. This distance is 4 units.
$$2a = 4$$
$$a = 2$$

The length of the conjugate axis of a hyperbola is $2b$ units. In this hyperbola, the length of the conjugate axis is 6 units.
$$2b = 6$$
$$b = 3$$

Since $a = 2$, $a^2 = 4$. Since $b = 3$, $b^2 = 9$. Substitute the values for a^2 and b^2. An equation of the hyperbola is $\frac{(y-3)^2}{4} - \frac{(x-2)^2}{9} = 1$.

35. The center of this hyperbola is at the origin. According to the equation, $a^2 = 4$ and $b^2 = 9$, so $a = 2$ and $b = 3$. The coordinates of the vertices are $(0, 2)$ and $(0, -2)$. Use the equation $c^2 = a^2 + b^2$ to determine the value of c.
$$c^2 = a^2 + b^2$$
$$c^2 = 4 + 9$$
$$c^2 = 13$$
$$c = \sqrt{13}$$

Since $c = \sqrt{13}$, the foci are at $(0, \sqrt{13})$ and $(0, -\sqrt{13})$. The equations of the asymptotes are $y = \pm\frac{a}{b}x$ or $y = \pm\frac{2}{3}x$.

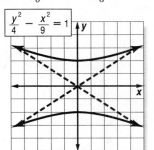

$\frac{y^2}{4} - \frac{x^2}{9} = 1$

36. The center of this hyperbola is at $(2, -1)$. According to the equation, $a^2 = 1$ and $b^2 = 9$, so $a = 1$ and $b = 3$. The coordinates of the vertices are $(2 \pm 1, -1)$, or $(3, -1)$ and $(1, -1)$. Use the equation $c^2 = a^2 + b^2$ to determine the value of c.
$$c^2 = a^2 + b^2$$
$$c^2 = 1 + 9$$
$$c^2 = 10$$
$$c = \sqrt{10}$$

Since $c = \sqrt{10}$, the foci are at $(2 \pm \sqrt{10}, -1)$. The equations of the asymptotes are $y - (-1) = \pm\frac{3}{1}(x - 2)$ or $y + 1 = \pm 3(x - 2)$.

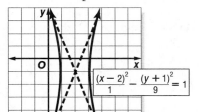

$\frac{(x-2)^2}{1} - \frac{(y+1)^2}{9} = 1$

37. $9y^2 - 16x^2 = 144$

$$\frac{9y^2}{144} - \frac{16x^2}{144} = 1$$

$$\frac{y^2}{16} - \frac{x^2}{9} = 1$$

The center of this hyperbola is at the origin. According to the equation, $a^2 = 16$ and $b^2 = 9$, so $a = 4$ and $b = 3$. The coordinates of the vertices are $(0, 4)$ and $(0, -4)$. Use the equation $c^2 = a^2 + b^2$ to determine the value of c.

$c^2 = a^2 + b^2$
$c^2 = 16 + 9$
$c^2 = 25$
$\ c = 5$

Since $c = 5$, the foci are at $(0, 5)$ and $(0, -5)$. The equations of the asymptotes are $y = \pm\frac{4}{3}x$.

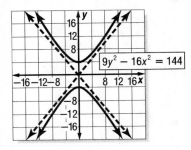

38. $16x^2 - 25y^2 - 64x - 336 = 0$

$16(x^2 - 4x + \blacksquare) - 25y^2 = 336 + 16(\blacksquare)$
$16(x^2 - 4x + 4) - 25y^2 = 336 + 16(4)$
$16(x - 2)^2 - 25y^2 = 400$

$$\frac{16(x - 2)^2}{400} - \frac{25y^2}{400} = 1$$

$$\frac{(x - 2)^2}{25} - \frac{y^2}{16} = 1$$

The center of this hyperbola is at $(2, 0)$. According to the equation, $a^2 = 25$ and $b^2 = 16$, so $a = 5$ and $b = 4$. The vertices are at $(2 \pm 5, 0)$, or $(-3, 0)$ and $(7, 0)$. Use the equation $c^2 = a^2 + b^2$ to determine the value of c.

$c^2 = a^2 + b^2$
$c^2 = 25 + 16$
$c^2 = 41$
$\ c = \sqrt{41}$

Since $c = \sqrt{41}$, the foci are at $(2 \pm \sqrt{41}, 0)$. The equations of the asymptotes are $y = \pm\frac{4}{5}(x - 2)$.

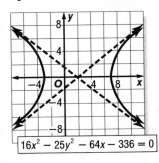

39. $\qquad x^2 + 4x - y = 0$
$\quad (x^2 + 4x + \blacksquare) - y = \blacksquare$
$\quad (x^2 + 4x + 4) - y = 4$
$\qquad\quad (x + 2)^2 - y = 4$
$\qquad\quad (x + 2)^2 - 4 = y$

The graph of the equation is a parabola.

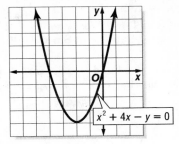

40. $9x^2 + 4y^2 = 36$

$$\frac{9x^2}{36} + \frac{4y^2}{36} = 1$$

$$\frac{x^2}{4} + \frac{y^2}{9} = 1$$

The graph of the equation is an ellipse.

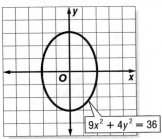

41. $-4x^2 + y^2 + 8x - 8 = 0$
$y^2 - 4(x^2 - 2x + \blacksquare) = 8 - 4(\blacksquare)$
$y^2 - 4(x^2 - 2x + 1) = 8 - 4(1)$
$\qquad y^2 - 4(x - 1)^2 = 4$

$$\frac{y^2}{4} - \frac{4(x - 1)^2}{4} = 1$$

$$\frac{y^2}{4} - \frac{(x - 1)^2}{1} = 1$$

The graph of the equation is a hyperbola.

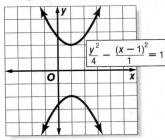

42. $\qquad\qquad x^2 + y^2 - 4x - 6y + 4 = 0$
$(x^2 - 4x + \blacksquare) + (y^2 - 6y + \blacksquare) = -4 + \blacksquare + \blacksquare$
$(x^2 - 4x + 4) + (y^2 - 6y + 9) = -4 + 4 + 9$
$\qquad\quad (x - 2)^2 + (y - 3)^2 = 9$

The graph of the equation is a circle.

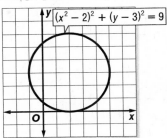

43. In this equation, $A = 7$ and $C = 9$. Since A and C are both positive and $A \neq C$, the graph is an ellipse.

44. In this equation, $A = 1$ and $C = 0$. Since $C = 0$ and $A \neq 0$, the graph is a parabola.

45. In this equation, $A = 1$ and $C = 1$. Since $A = C$, the graph is a circle.

46. In this equation, $A = -13$ and $C = 5$. Since A and C have opposite signs, the graph is a hyperbola.

47. Use substitution to solve the system. First, rewrite $4x + 3y = 0$ as $x = -\frac{3}{4}y$.

$$x^2 + y^2 - 18x + 24y + 200 = 0$$
$$\left(-\frac{3}{4}y\right)^2 + y^2 - 18\left(-\frac{3}{4}y\right) + 24y + 200 = 0$$
$$\frac{9}{16}y^2 + y^2 + \frac{27}{2}y + 24y + 200 = 0$$
$$\frac{25}{16}y^2 + \frac{75}{2}y + 200 = 0$$
$$y^2 + 24y + 128 = 0$$
$$(y + 8)(y + 16) = 0$$

$$y + 8 = 0 \qquad \text{or} \qquad y + 16 = 0$$
$$y = -8 \qquad\qquad\qquad y = -16$$

Now solve for x.

$$4x + 3y = 0 \qquad\qquad 4x + 3y = 0$$
$$4x + 3(-8) = 0 \qquad 4x + 3(-16) = 0$$
$$4x = 24 \qquad\qquad\qquad 4x = 48$$
$$x = 6 \qquad\qquad\qquad\quad x = 12$$

The solutions of the system are $(6, -8)$ and $(12, -16)$.

48. Use substitution to solve the system. First, rewrite $x^2 + 2y^2 = 4$ as $x^2 = 4 - 2y^2$.

$$4x^2 + y^2 = 16$$
$$4(4 - 2y^2) + y^2 = 16$$
$$16 - 8y^2 + y^2 = 16$$
$$-7y^2 = 0$$
$$y^2 = 0$$
$$y = 0$$

Now solve for x.
$$x^2 = 4 - 2y^2$$
$$x^2 = 4 - 2(0)^2$$
$$x^2 = 4$$
$$x = \pm 2$$

The solutions of the system are $(\pm 2, 0)$.

49.

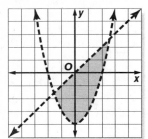

50.

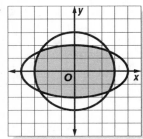

Page 467

1. b; parabola

2. c; hyperbola

3. a; ellipse

4. $\left(\frac{x_1 + x_2}{2}, \frac{y_1 + y_2}{2}\right) = \left(\frac{7 + (-5)}{2}, \frac{1 + 9}{2}\right)$
$= \left(\frac{2}{2}, \frac{10}{2}\right)$
$= (1, 5)$

5. $\left(\frac{x_1 + x_2}{2}, \frac{y_1 + y_2}{2}\right) = \left(\frac{\frac{3}{8} + \left(-\frac{8}{5}\right)}{2}, \frac{-1 + 2}{2}\right)$
$= \left(\frac{-\frac{49}{40}}{2}, \frac{1}{2}\right)$
$= \left(-\frac{49}{80}, \frac{1}{2}\right)$

6. $\left(\frac{x_1 + x_2}{2}, \frac{y_1 + y_2}{2}\right) = \left(\frac{-13 + (-1)}{2}, \frac{0 + (-8)}{2}\right)$
$= \left(\frac{-14}{2}, \frac{-8}{2}\right)$
$= (-7, -4)$

7. $d = \sqrt{(x_2 - x_1)^2 + (y_2 - y_1)^2}$
$= \sqrt{[3 - (-6)]^2 + (2 - 7)^2}$
$= \sqrt{9^2 + (-5)^2}$
$= \sqrt{81 + 25}$
$= \sqrt{106}$

The distance between $(-6, 7)$ and $(3, 2)$ is $\sqrt{106}$ units.

8. $d = \sqrt{(x_2 - x_1)^2 + (y_2 - y_1)^2}$
$= \sqrt{\left(-\frac{3}{4} - \frac{1}{2}\right)^2 + \left(-\frac{11}{4} - \frac{5}{2}\right)^2}$
$= \sqrt{\left(-\frac{5}{4}\right)^2 + \left(-\frac{21}{4}\right)^2}$
$= \sqrt{\frac{25}{16} + \frac{441}{16}}$
$= \frac{\sqrt{466}}{4}$

The distance between $\left(\frac{1}{2}, \frac{5}{2}\right)$ and $\left(-\frac{3}{4}, -\frac{11}{4}\right)$ is $\sqrt{\frac{466}{4}}$ units.

9. $d = \sqrt{(x_2 - x_1)^2 + (y_2 - y_1)^2}$
$= \sqrt{(8 - 8)^2 + [-9 - (-1)]^2}$
$= \sqrt{0^2 + (-8)^2}$
$= \sqrt{64}$
$= 8$

The distance between $(8, -1)$ and $(8, -9)$ is 8 units.

10. In the equation $x^2 + 4y^2 = 25$, $A = 1$ and $C = 4$. Since A and C have the same sign and $A \neq C$, the graph is an ellipse.

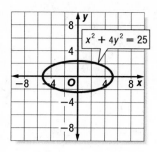

11. Since the equation is of the form $y = a(x - h)^2 + k$, the graph is a parabola.

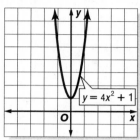

12. The equation is $x^2 = 36 - y^2$, or $x^2 + y^2 = 36$, which is of the form $(x - h)^2 + (y - k)^2 = r^2$. The graph is a circle.

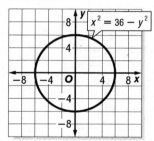

13.
$$(x + 4)^2 = 7(y + 5)$$
$$\frac{1}{7}(x + 4)^2 = y + 5$$
$$\frac{1}{7}(x + 4)^2 - 5 = y$$

The equation is of the form $y = a(x - h)^2 + k$, so the graph is a parabola.

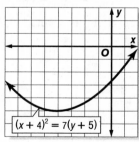

14. In the equation $4x^2 - 26y^2 + 10 = 0$, $A = 4$ and $C = -26$. Since A and C have opposite signs, the graph is a hyperbola.

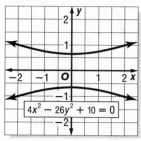

15. In the equation $25x^2 + 49y^2 = 1225$, $A = 25$ and $C = 49$. Since A and C have the same sign and $A \neq C$, the graph is an ellipse.

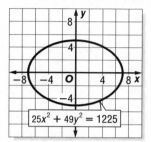

16.
$$-(y^2 - 24) = x^2 + 10x$$
$$-y^2 + 24 = x^2 + 10x$$
$$0 = x^2 + 10x + y^2 - 24$$

In the equation, $A = 1$ and $C = 1$. Since $A = C$, the graph is a circle.

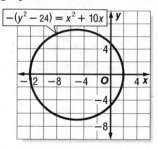

17. In the equation $5x^2 - y^2 = 49$, $A = 5$ and $C = -1$. Since A and C have opposite signs, the graph is a hyperbola.

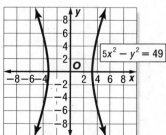

18. The equation is of the form $y = a(x - h)^2 + k$, the graph is a parabola.

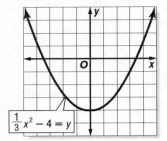

$\frac{1}{3}x^2 - 4 = y$

19. The equation is of the form $\frac{y^2}{a^2} - \frac{x^2}{b^2} = 1$, so the graph is a hyperbola.

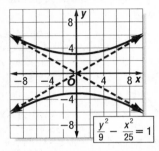

$\frac{y^2}{9} - \frac{x^2}{25} = 1$

20. Write an equation to model the opening of the tunnel, assuming that the origin represents the midpoint of the width of the tunnel. The major axis is vertical, the equation is of the form $\frac{y^2}{a^2} + \frac{x^2}{b^2} = 1$. The length of the major axis is $2(40)$ or 80 feet. Therefore, $a = 40$, so $a^2 = 1600$. The length of the minor axis is $2b$ units. Therefore, $2b = 60$, or $b = 30$, so $b^2 = 900$. An equation of the ellipse is $\frac{x^2}{900} + \frac{y^2}{1600} = 1$. The height of the arch 12 feet from the edge of the tunnel is the value of y when $x = \frac{1}{2}(60) - 12$ or 18.

$$\frac{x^2}{900} + \frac{y^2}{1600} = 1$$
$$\frac{18^2}{900} + \frac{y^2}{1600} = 1$$
$$\frac{y^2}{1600} = \frac{16}{25}$$
$$y^2 = 1024$$
$$y = 32$$

The height of the arch 12 feet from the edge is 32 feet.

21. Substitute $2 - x$ for y in the first equation and solve for x.

$$x^2 + y^2 = 100$$
$$x^2 + (2 - x)^2 = 100$$
$$x^2 + x^2 - 4x + 4 = 100$$
$$2x^2 - 4x + 4 = 100$$
$$x^2 - 2x + 2 = 50$$
$$x^2 - 2x - 48 = 0$$
$$(x + 6)(x - 8) = 0$$

$x + 6 = 0 \quad$ or $\quad x - 8 = 0$
$\quad\quad x = -6 \quad\quad\quad\quad\quad x = 8$

Now solve for y.

$y = 2 - x \quad\quad\quad\quad y = 2 - x$
$y = 2 - (-6) \quad\quad\quad y = 2 - (8)$
$y = 8 \quad\quad\quad\quad\quad\quad y = -6$

The solutions of the system are $(-6, 8)$ and $(8, -6)$.

22. $\quad x + y = 1$
$\quad\quad\quad x = 1 - y$

Substitute $1 - y$ for x in the first equation and solve for y.

$$x^2 + 2y^2 = 6$$
$$(1 - y)^2 + 2y^2 = 6$$
$$y^2 - 2y + 1 + 2y^2 = 6$$
$$3y^2 - 2y - 5 = 0$$
$$(3y - 5)(y + 1) = 0$$

$3y - 5 = 0 \quad$ or $\quad y + 1 = 0$
$\quad\quad 3y = 5 \quad\quad\quad\quad\quad y = -1$
$\quad\quad\quad y = \frac{5}{3}$

Now solve for x.

$x = 1 - y \quad\quad\quad\quad x = 1 - y$
$x = 1 - \left(\frac{5}{3}\right) \quad\quad x = 1 - (-1)$
$x = -\frac{2}{3} \quad\quad\quad\quad\quad x = 2$

The solutions of the system are $\left(-\frac{2}{3}, \frac{5}{3}\right)$ and $(2, -1)$.

23. Use elimination to solve the system.

$$\begin{array}{r} x^2 - y^2 - 12x + 12y \quad\quad = 36 \\ (+) \; x^2 + y^2 - 12x - 12y + 36 = \;\; 0 \\ \hline 2x^2 \quad\quad - 24x \quad\quad + 36 = 36 \end{array}$$

$$2x^2 - 24x = 0$$
$$x^2 - 12x = 0$$
$$x(x - 12) = 0$$

$x = 0 \quad$ or $\quad x - 12 = 0$
$\quad\quad\quad\quad\quad\quad\quad\quad x = 12$

Now solve for y.

$x^2 - y^2 - 12x + 12y = 36 \quad\quad x^2 - y^2 - 12x + 12y = 36$
$(0)^2 - y^2 - 12(0) + 12y = 36 \quad (12)^2 - y^2 - 12(12) + 12y = 36$
$-y^2 + 12y = 36 \quad\quad\quad\quad\quad\quad -y^2 + 12y = 36$
$-y^2 + 12y - 36 = 0 \quad\quad\quad\quad -y^2 + 12y - 36 = 0$
$-(y - 6)^2 = 0 \quad\quad\quad\quad\quad\quad -(y - 6)^2 = 0$
$y - 6 = 0 \quad\quad\quad\quad\quad\quad\quad y - 6 = 0$
$y = 6 \quad\quad\quad\quad\quad\quad\quad\quad\quad y = 6$

The solutions of the system are $(0, 6)$ and $(12, 6)$.

24.

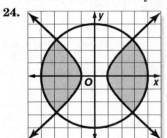

25. C; in the equation, $A = 1$ and $C = 2$. Since A and C have the same sign and $A \neq C$, the graph is an ellipse.

Standardized Test Practice

Pages 468–469

1. B

2. C; the population of Clayton in 2000 was $54,200 - 0.05(54,200)$ or $51,490$. In 2000, the population of Montrose was $47,500 - 0.05(47.500)$ or $45,125$. There were $51,490 - 45,125$ or 6365 more people in Clayton.

3. C; $0.04n = 0.40p$

$$\frac{0.04n}{0.40} = \frac{0.40p}{0.40}$$

$$\frac{1}{10}n = p$$

Since $p = \frac{1}{10}n$, $10p = 10\left(\frac{1}{10}n\right)$ or n. Therefore, n is 100% of $10p$.

4. A; $m(d) + p(2d + 1) = md + 2dp + p$
$$= d(m + 2p) + p$$

5. B; $\left(\frac{x_1 + x_2}{2}, \frac{y_1 + y_2}{2}\right) = \left(\frac{-5 + (-1)}{2}, \frac{-3 + 4}{2}\right)$
$$= \left(\frac{-6}{2}, \frac{1}{2}\right)$$
$$= \left(-3, \frac{1}{2}\right)$$

6. D; assign the point (x, y) to P.

$$(-2, 3) = \left(\frac{-7 + x}{2}, \frac{1 + y}{2}\right)$$

$$\frac{-7 + x}{2} = -2 \qquad \frac{1 + y}{2} = 3$$

$$-7 + x = -4 \qquad 1 + y = 6$$

$$x = 3 \qquad y = 5$$

The point P has coordinates $(3, 5)$.

7. D; the standard form of the equation $3x^2 + 4y = 8$ is $y = -\frac{3}{4}x + 2$, the equation whose graph is a parabola.

8. C; the standard form of the equation $x^2 + y^2 - 4x + 6y - 9 = 0$ is $(x - 2)^2 + (y + 3)^2 = 22$, so the center of the circle is at $(2, -3)$.

9. B; the points have coordinates $(-2, 4)$ and $(0, 5)$.

$$d = \sqrt{(x_2 - x_1)^2 + (y_2 - y_1)^2}$$
$$= \sqrt{[0 - (-2)]^2 + (5 - 4)^2}$$
$$= \sqrt{2^2 + 1^2}$$
$$= \sqrt{5}$$

The distance between the points is $\sqrt{5}$ units.

10. A; Since the average of the seven test scores is 53, the sum of the test scores is

$$7 \cdot 53 = 371$$

The sum of the three missing test scores is

$$371 - 40 - 52 - 64 - 64 = 151$$

Let x, y and z represent the missing scores. Since 40 is the lowest and 52 is the median,

$$40 \le x \le y \le 52 \quad \text{and} \quad z \ge 52$$

Since 64 is the mode

$$x \ne y$$
$$x \ne 40$$
$$y \ne 52$$
$$z \ne 52$$

To maximize the greatest test score means to minimize x and y. It follows that

$$x = 41$$
$$y = 42.$$

The greatest possible test score is

$$151 - 41 - 42 = 68.$$

11. Since p is a positive integer, it must be in the set $\{1, 2, 3, ...\}$. Make a table of values to determine the least of these values for which $2^{2p} + 3$ is not prime.

p	$2^{2p} + 3$	
1	$2^{2(1)} + 3 = 7$	prime
2	$2^{2(2)} + 3 = 19$	prime
3	$2^{2(3)} + 3 = 67$	prime
4	$2^{2(4)} + 3 = 259$	not prime, since $259 = 7(37)$

Thus, 4 is the least positive integer for which the expression is not prime.

12. Let c = the number of cars and let s = the number of SUVs.

$$\frac{c}{s} = \frac{4}{5} \qquad \frac{c - 6}{s} = \frac{1}{2}$$

$$5c = 4s \qquad 2(c - 6) = s$$
$$\qquad 2c - 12 = s$$

Since $s = 2c - 12$, substitute $2c - 12$ for s in the first equation.

$$5c = 4s$$
$$5c = 4(2c - 12)$$
$$5c = 8c - 48$$
$$-3c = -48$$
$$c = 16$$

Now solve for s.

$$s = 2c - 12$$
$$= 2(16) - 12$$
$$= 32 - 12$$
$$= 20$$

Since $s = 20$, there are 20 SUVs in the parking lot.

13. Since the area of one side of the box is 27 square units and each dimension must be greater than 1, the dimensions of this side must be 9×3 since the only integral factors of 27, other than 1 and 27, are 9 and 3. One of these dimensions is also a dimension of the other side whose area is 12 square units, the dimension of this side must be 3×4 since the only integral factors of 12, other than 1 and 12, are 2 and 6, and 3 and 4. Therefore, the dimensions of the box are $9 \times 3 \times 4$, so the volume of the box is $9(3)(4)$ or 108 cubic units.

14. $a * b = 2ab - (a + b)$

$$4 * x = 2(4)(x) - (4 + x)$$
$$= 8x - 4 - x$$
$$= 7x - 4$$

Since $4 * x = 10$, $7x - 4 = 10$. Solve for x.

$$7x - 4 = 10$$
$$7x = 14$$
$$x = 2$$

15. Since the slope of the line PQ is $\frac{1}{4}$ and the point P is at $(0, 3)$, the coordinates of Q are $(4, 4)$. Since $\overline{OP}$ and $\overline{OQ}$ are both perpendicular to $\overline{OR}$, the quadrilateral $\overline{OPQR}$ is a trapezoid with bases $\overline{OP}$ and $\overline{QR}$, and height $\overline{OR}$. Substitute $h = OR = 4$, $b_1 = OP = 3$, and $b_2 = QR = 4$ into the formula $A = \frac{1}{2}h(b_1 + b_2)$.

$$A = \frac{1}{2}h(b_1 + b_2)$$
$$= \frac{1}{2}(4)(3 + 4)$$
$$= \frac{1}{2}(4)(7)$$
$$= 14$$

The area of the quadrilateral is 14 square units.

16. Since the slope of ℓ is $\frac{5}{4}$, $\frac{y_1 - 0}{4 - 0} = \frac{5}{4}$ or $\frac{y_1}{4} = \frac{5}{4}$.

Therefore $y_1 = 5$. Since the slope of k is $\frac{3}{8}$, $\frac{y_2 - 0}{4 - 0} = \frac{3}{8}$ or $\frac{y_2}{4} = \frac{3}{8}$. Therefore, $y_2 = \frac{3}{2}$ or 1.5. The distance from A to B is the distance between $(4, 5)$ and $(4, 1.5)$. This distance is $5 - 1.5 = 3.5$ or $\frac{7}{2}$ units.

17.
$$(2x - 3)(4x + n) = ax^2 + bx - 15$$
$$8x^2 - 12x + 2nx - 3n = ax^2 + bx - 15$$
$$8x^2 + (2n - 12)x - 3n = ax^2 + bx - 15$$

Therefore, $a = 8$, $b = 2n - 12$, and $-3n = -15$. Solving the last equation for n gives $n = 5$. Substitute 5 for n in the second equation and solve for b.

$$b = 2n - 12$$
$$= 2(5) - 12$$
$$= -2$$

Therefore, $a + b = 8 + (-2)$ or 6.

18. B; the area of a circle is $2\pi r$ square units.

$$2\pi r = 16\pi$$
$$r = \frac{16\pi}{2\pi}$$
$$r = 8$$

The radius of each circle is 8 units. The perimeter of $\triangle RST$ is $6(8)$ or 48 units. The circumference of a circle is πr^2 units.

$$C = \pi r^2$$
$$= \pi(8)^2$$
$$= 64\pi \text{ or about } 201.1 \text{ units}$$

The circumference of the circle is greater than the perimeter of the triangle.

19. B; In class A suppose there are g_A girls. Then there are $g_A + 4$ boys and the ratio of girls to boys is $\frac{g_A}{g_A + 4}$. Since $g_A + 4 > g_A$, $\frac{g_A}{g_A + 4} < 1$.

In class B suppose there are g_B girls. Then there are $g_B - 4$ boys and the ratio of girls to boys is $\frac{g_B}{g_B - 4}$. Since $g_B - 4 < g_B$, $\frac{g_B}{g_B - 4} > 1$.

It follows that $\frac{g_A}{g_A + 4} < \frac{g_B}{g_B - 4}$.

20. A; the percent of students who do not live in Langton is $20 + 30 + 26$ or 76. The percent of students who do not live in Delton is $100 - 26$ or 74. Since 76 is greater than 74, the quantity in column A is greater.

21. D; if $n = 1$ and $k = 3$, then $nk = 3$, so $2 < nk < 10$. In this case, $n + k = 1 + 3$ or 4, so $nk < n + k$. If $n = 2$ and $k = 3$, then $nk = 6$, so $2 < nk < 10$. In this case, $n + k = 2 + 3$ or 5, so $nk > n + k$. Since in one case $nk < n + k$ and in another case $nk > n + k$, the relationship cannot be determined.

Chapter 9 Rational Expressions and Equations

1. $\frac{8}{5}x = \frac{4}{15}$

$\frac{5}{8}\left(\frac{8}{5}\right)x = \frac{5}{8}\left(\frac{4}{15}\right)$

$x = \frac{1}{6}$

2. $\frac{27}{14}t = \frac{6}{7}$

$\frac{14}{27}\left(\frac{27}{14}\right)t = \frac{14}{27}\left(\frac{6}{7}\right)$

$t = \frac{4}{9}$

3. $\frac{3}{10} = \frac{12}{25}a$

$\frac{25}{12}\left(\frac{3}{10}\right) = \frac{25}{12}\left(\frac{12}{25}\right)a$

$\frac{5}{8} = a$

4. $\frac{6}{7} = 9m$

$\frac{1}{9}\left(\frac{6}{7}\right) = \frac{1}{9}(9)m$

$\frac{2}{21} = m$

5. $\frac{9}{8}b = 18$

$\frac{8}{9}\left(\frac{9}{8}\right)b = \frac{8}{9}(18)$

$b = 16$

6. $\frac{6}{7}s = \frac{3}{4}$

$\frac{7}{6}\left(\frac{6}{7}\right)s = \frac{7}{6}\left(\frac{3}{4}\right)$

$s = \frac{7}{8}$

7. $\frac{1}{3}r = \frac{5}{6}$

$\frac{3}{1}\left(\frac{1}{3}\right)r = \frac{3}{1}\left(\frac{5}{6}\right)$

$r = \frac{5}{2}$ or $2\frac{1}{2}$

8. $\frac{2}{3}n = 7$

$\frac{3}{2}\left(\frac{2}{3}\right)n = \frac{3}{2}(7)$

$n = \frac{21}{2}$ or $10\frac{1}{2}$

9. $\frac{4}{5}r = \frac{5}{6}$

$\frac{5}{4}\left(\frac{4}{5}\right)r = \frac{5}{4}\left(\frac{5}{6}\right)$

$r = \frac{25}{24}$ or $1\frac{1}{24}$

10. The equations of the asymptotes are

$y - k = \pm\frac{b}{a}(x - h)$ or $y + 5 = \pm\frac{3}{2}(x - 3)$, which

simplifies to $y = \frac{3}{2}x - \frac{19}{2}$ and $y = -\frac{3}{2}x - \frac{1}{2}$. Graph

the asymptotes. Draw a 4-unit by 6-unit rectangle whose diagonals are the asymptotes. Then graph the hyperbola using the asymptotes as a guide.

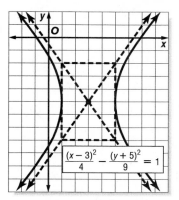

$$\frac{(x - 3)^2}{4} - \frac{(y + 5)^2}{9} = 1$$

11. The equations of the asymptotes are

$y - k = \pm\frac{a}{b}(x - h)$ or $y = \pm2(x + 4)$, which

simplifies to $y = 2x + 8$ and $y = -2x - 8$. Graph the asymptotes. Draw a 4-unit by 2-unit rectangle whose diagonals are the asymptotes. Then graph the hyperbola using the asymptotes as a guide.

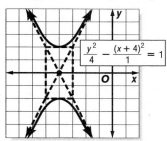

$$\frac{y^2}{4} - \frac{(x + 4)^2}{1} = 1$$

12. The equations of the asymptotes are

$y - k = \pm\frac{b}{a}(x - h)$ or $y - 3 = \pm\frac{5}{2}(x + 2)$, which

simplifies to $y = \frac{5}{2}x + 8$ and $y = -\frac{5}{2}x - 2$. Graph

the asymptotes. Draw a 4-unit by 10-unit rectangle whose diagonals are the asymptotes. Then graph the hyperbola using the asymptotes as a guide.

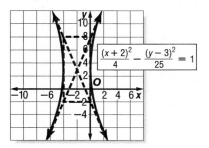

$$\frac{(x + 2)^2}{4} - \frac{(y - 3)^2}{25} = 1$$

13.
$$\frac{3}{4} = \frac{r}{16}$$
$$16\left(\frac{3}{4}\right) = 16\left(\frac{r}{16}\right)$$
$$12 = r$$

14.
$$\frac{8}{16} = \frac{5}{y}$$
$$y\left(\frac{8}{16}\right) = y\left(\frac{5}{y}\right)$$
$$\frac{8}{16}y = 5$$
$$\frac{16}{8}\left(\frac{8}{16}\right)y = \frac{16}{8}(5)$$
$$y = 10$$

15.
$$\frac{6}{8} = \frac{m}{20}$$
$$20\left(\frac{6}{8}\right) = 20\left(\frac{m}{20}\right)$$
$$15 = m$$

16.
$$\frac{t}{3} = \frac{5}{24}$$
$$3\left(\frac{t}{3}\right) = 3\left(\frac{5}{24}\right)$$
$$t = \frac{5}{8}$$

17.
$$\frac{5}{a} = \frac{6}{18}$$
$$a\left(\frac{5}{a}\right) = a\left(\frac{6}{18}\right)$$
$$5 = \frac{6}{18}a$$
$$\frac{18}{6}(5) = \frac{18}{6}\left(\frac{6}{18}\right)a$$
$$15 = a$$

18.
$$\frac{3}{4} = \frac{b}{6}$$
$$6\left(\frac{3}{4}\right) = 6\left(\frac{b}{6}\right)$$
$$\frac{9}{2} = b$$
$$\text{or } b = 4\frac{1}{2}$$

19.
$$\frac{v}{9} = \frac{12}{18}$$
$$9\left(\frac{v}{9}\right) = 9\left(\frac{12}{18}\right)$$
$$v = 6$$

20.
$$\frac{7}{p} = \frac{1}{4}$$
$$p\left(\frac{7}{p}\right) = p\left(\frac{1}{4}\right)$$
$$7 = \frac{1}{4}p$$
$$4(7) = 4\left(\frac{1}{4}\right)p$$
$$28 = p$$

21.
$$\frac{2}{5} = \frac{3}{z}$$
$$z\left(\frac{2}{5}\right) = z\left(\frac{3}{z}\right)$$
$$\frac{2}{5}z = 3$$
$$\frac{5}{2}\left(\frac{2}{5}\right)z = \frac{5}{2}(3)$$
$$z = \frac{15}{2} \text{ or } 7\frac{1}{2}$$

Page 476   Check for Understanding

1. Sample answer: $\frac{4}{6}, \frac{4(x+2)}{6(x+2)}$

2. To multiply rational numbers or rational expressions, you multiply the numerators and multiply the denominators. To divide rational numbers or rational expressions, you multiply by the reciprocal of the divisor. In either case, you can reduce your answer by dividing the numerator and the denominator of the results by any common factors.

3. Never; solving the equation using cross products leads to $15 = 10$, which is never true.

4. $\dfrac{45mn^3}{20n^7} = \dfrac{\overset{1}{\cancel{5}} \cdot 3 \cdot 3 \cdot m \cdot \overset{1}{\cancel{n}} \cdot \overset{1}{\cancel{n}} \cdot \overset{1}{\cancel{n}}}{\underset{1}{\cancel{5}} \cdot 2 \cdot 2 \cdot \underset{1}{\cancel{n}} \cdot \underset{1}{\cancel{n}} \cdot \underset{1}{\cancel{n}} \cdot n \cdot n \cdot n \cdot n}$

$= \dfrac{3 \cdot 3 \cdot m}{2 \cdot 2 \cdot n \cdot n \cdot n \cdot n}$

$= \dfrac{9m}{4n^4}$

5. $\dfrac{a+b}{a^2 - b^2} = \dfrac{\overset{1}{\cancel{a+b}}}{(a-b)(\underset{1}{\cancel{a+b}})}$

$= \dfrac{1}{a-b}$

6. $\dfrac{6y^3 - 9y^2}{2y^2 + 5y - 12} = \dfrac{3y^2(\overset{1}{\cancel{2y-3}})}{(y+4)(\underset{1}{\cancel{2y-3}})}$

$= \dfrac{3y^2}{y+4}$

7. $\dfrac{2a^2}{5b^2c} \cdot \dfrac{3bc^2}{8a^2} = \dfrac{\overset{1}{\cancel{2}} \cdot \overset{1}{\cancel{a}} \cdot \overset{1}{\cancel{a}} \cdot 3 \cdot \overset{1}{\cancel{b}} \cdot \overset{1}{\cancel{c}} \cdot c}{5 \cdot \underset{1}{\cancel{b}} \cdot b \cdot \underset{1}{\cancel{c}} \cdot \underset{1}{\cancel{2}} \cdot 2 \cdot 2 \cdot \underset{1}{\cancel{a}} \cdot \underset{1}{\cancel{a}}}$

$= \dfrac{3 \cdot c}{5 \cdot b \cdot 2 \cdot 2}$

$= \dfrac{3c}{20b}$

8. $\dfrac{35}{16x^2} \div \dfrac{21}{4x} = \dfrac{35}{16x^2} \cdot \dfrac{4x}{21}$

$= \dfrac{\overset{1}{\cancel{7}} \cdot 5 \cdot \overset{1}{\cancel{2}} \cdot \overset{1}{\cancel{2}} \cdot \overset{1}{\cancel{x}}}{\underset{1}{\cancel{2}} \cdot \underset{1}{\cancel{2}} \cdot 2 \cdot 2 \cdot \underset{1}{\cancel{x}} \cdot x \cdot \underset{1}{\cancel{7}} \cdot 3}$

$= \dfrac{5}{2 \cdot 2 \cdot x \cdot 3}$

$= \dfrac{5}{12x}$

9. $\dfrac{3t+6}{7t-7} \cdot \dfrac{14t-14}{5t+10} = \dfrac{3(t+2)}{7(\underset{1}{\cancel{t-1}})} \cdot \dfrac{14(\overset{1}{\cancel{t-1}})}{5(\underset{1}{\cancel{t+2}})}$

$= \dfrac{3 \cdot \overset{2}{\cancel{14}}}{\underset{1}{\cancel{7}} \cdot 5}$

$= \dfrac{6}{5}$

10. $\dfrac{12p^2 + 6p - 6}{4(p+1)^2} \div \dfrac{6p-3}{2p+10} = \dfrac{12p^2 + 6p - 6}{4(p+1)^2} \cdot \dfrac{2p+10}{6p-3}$

$= \dfrac{6(\overset{1}{\cancel{p+1}})(2p-1)}{4(\underset{1}{\cancel{p+1}})(p+1)} \cdot \dfrac{2(p+5)}{3(\underset{1}{\cancel{2p-1}})}$

$= \dfrac{\overset{2}{\cancel{6}} \cdot \overset{1}{\cancel{2}} \cdot (p+5)}{\underset{2}{\cancel{4}} \cdot (p+1) \cdot \underset{1}{\cancel{3}}}$

$= \dfrac{p+5}{p+1}$

11. $\dfrac{\frac{c^3d^3}{a}}{\frac{xc^2d}{ax^2}} = \dfrac{c^3d^3}{a} \div \dfrac{xc^2d}{ax^2}$

$= \dfrac{c^3d^3}{a} \cdot \dfrac{ax^2}{xc^2d}$

$= \dfrac{\overset{1}{\cancel{c}} \cdot \overset{1}{\cancel{c}} \cdot c \cdot \overset{1}{\cancel{d}} \cdot d \cdot d \cdot \overset{1}{\cancel{a}} \cdot \overset{1}{\cancel{x}} \cdot x}{\underset{1}{\cancel{a}} \cdot \underset{1}{\cancel{x}} \cdot \underset{1}{\cancel{c}} \cdot \underset{1}{\cancel{c}} \cdot \underset{1}{\cancel{d}}}$

$= c \cdot d \cdot d \cdot x$

$= cd^2x$

12. $\dfrac{\frac{2y}{y^2-4}}{\frac{3}{y^2-4y+4}} = \dfrac{2y}{y^2-4} \div \dfrac{3}{y^2-4y+4}$

$= \dfrac{2y}{y^2-4} \cdot \dfrac{y^2-4y+4}{3}$

$= \dfrac{2y}{(y \overset{1}{\cancel{-}} 2)(y+2)} \cdot \dfrac{(y \overset{1}{\cancel{-}} 2)(y-2)}{3}$

$= \dfrac{2y(y-2)}{3(y+2)}$

13. D; Since $y^2 - 4y - 12 = (y-6)(y+2)$, the denominator equals 0 when $y = 6$ or -2.

Pages 476–478 Practice and Apply

14. $\dfrac{30bc}{12b^2} = \dfrac{\overset{1}{\cancel{2}} \cdot \overset{1}{\cancel{3}} \cdot 5 \cdot \overset{1}{\cancel{b}} \cdot c}{2 \cdot \underset{1}{\cancel{2}} \cdot \underset{1}{\cancel{3}} \cdot \underset{1}{\cancel{b}} \cdot b}$

$= \dfrac{5c}{2b}$

15. $\dfrac{-3mn^4}{21m^2n^2} = \dfrac{-\overset{1}{\cancel{3}} \cdot \overset{1}{\cancel{m}} \cdot \overset{1}{\cancel{n}} \cdot \overset{1}{\cancel{n}} \cdot n \cdot n}{\underset{1}{\cancel{3}} \cdot 7 \cdot \underset{1}{\cancel{m}} \cdot m \cdot \underset{1}{\cancel{n}} \cdot \underset{1}{\cancel{n}}}$

$= \dfrac{-n \cdot n}{7 \cdot m}$

$= \dfrac{-n^2}{7m}$ or $-\dfrac{n^2}{7m}$

16. $\dfrac{(-3x^2y)^3}{9x^2y^2} = \dfrac{(-3x^2y)(-3x^2y)(-3x^2y)}{9x^2y^2}$

$= \dfrac{(-1)\,\overset{1}{\cancel{3}} \cdot \overset{1}{\cancel{x}} \cdot \overset{1}{\cancel{x}} \cdot \overset{1}{\cancel{y}}\,(-1)\,3 \cdot x \cdot x \cdot \overset{1}{\cancel{y}}\,(-1)\,3 \cdot x \cdot x \cdot y}{\underset{1}{\cancel{3}} \cdot 3 \cdot \underset{1}{\cancel{x}} \cdot \underset{1}{\cancel{x}} \cdot \underset{1}{\cancel{y}} \cdot \underset{1}{\cancel{y}}}$

$= \dfrac{(-1)(-1)\,x \cdot x\,(-1)3 \cdot x \cdot x \cdot y}{1}$

$= -3x^4y$

17. $\dfrac{(-2rs^2)^2}{12r^2s^3} = \dfrac{(-2rs^2)(-2rs^2)}{12r^2s^3}$

$= \dfrac{(-1)\,\overset{1}{\cancel{2}} \cdot \overset{1}{\cancel{r}} \cdot \overset{1}{\cancel{s}} \cdot \overset{1}{\cancel{s}}\,(-1)\,\overset{1}{\cancel{2}} \cdot \overset{1}{\cancel{r}} \cdot \overset{1}{\cancel{s}} \cdot s}{2 \cdot 2 \cdot 3 \cdot \underset{1}{\cancel{r}} \cdot \underset{1}{\cancel{r}} \cdot \underset{1}{\cancel{s}} \cdot \underset{1}{\cancel{s}} \cdot \underset{1}{\cancel{s}}}$

$= \dfrac{(-1)(-1)s}{3}$

$= \dfrac{s}{3}$

18. $\dfrac{5t-5}{t^2-1} = \dfrac{5(t \overset{1}{\cancel{-}} 1)}{(t \underset{1}{\cancel{-}} 1)(t+1)}$

$= \dfrac{5}{t+1}$

19. $\dfrac{c+5}{2c+10} = \dfrac{c \overset{1}{\cancel{+}} 5}{2(c \underset{1}{\cancel{+}} 5)}$

$= \dfrac{1}{2}$

20. $\dfrac{y^2+4y+4}{3y^2+5y-2} = \dfrac{(y \overset{1}{\cancel{+}} 2)(y+2)}{(y \underset{1}{\cancel{+}} 2)(3y-1)}$

$= \dfrac{y+2}{3y-1}$

21. $\dfrac{a^2+2a+1}{2a^2+3a+1} = \dfrac{(a \overset{1}{\cancel{+}} 1)(a+1)}{(a \underset{1}{\cancel{+}} 1)(2a+1)}$

$= \dfrac{a+1}{2a+1}$

22. $\dfrac{3xyz}{4xz} \cdot \dfrac{6x^2}{3y^2} = \dfrac{\overset{1}{\cancel{3}} \cdot \overset{1}{\cancel{x}} \cdot \overset{1}{\cancel{y}} \cdot \overset{1}{\cancel{z}} \cdot 2 \cdot 3 \cdot x \cdot x}{2 \cdot 2 \cdot \underset{1}{\cancel{x}} \cdot \underset{1}{\cancel{z}} \cdot 3 \cdot \underset{1}{\cancel{y}} \cdot y}$

$= \dfrac{3 \cdot x \cdot x}{2 \cdot y}$

$= \dfrac{3x^2}{2y}$

23. $\dfrac{-4ab}{21c} \cdot \dfrac{14c^2}{18a^2} = \dfrac{-\overset{1}{\cancel{2}} \cdot 2 \cdot \overset{1}{\cancel{a}} \cdot b \cdot 2 \cdot \overset{1}{\cancel{7}} \cdot \overset{1}{\cancel{c}} \cdot c}{3 \cdot \underset{1}{\cancel{7}} \cdot \underset{1}{\cancel{c}} \cdot \underset{1}{\cancel{2}} \cdot 3 \cdot 3 \cdot \underset{1}{\cancel{a}} \cdot a}$

$= \dfrac{-2 \cdot b \cdot 2 \cdot c}{3 \cdot 3 \cdot 3 \cdot a}$

$= \dfrac{-4bc}{27a}$ or $-\dfrac{4bc}{27a}$

24. $\dfrac{3}{5d} \div \left(\dfrac{-9}{15df}\right) = \dfrac{3}{5d} \cdot \left(\dfrac{15df}{-9}\right)$

$= \dfrac{\overset{1}{\cancel{3}} \cdot 3 \cdot 5 \cdot \overset{1}{\cancel{d}} \cdot f}{\underset{1}{\cancel{5}} \cdot \underset{1}{\cancel{d}}(-1)(\underset{1}{\cancel{3}} \cdot \underset{1}{\cancel{3}})}$

$= \dfrac{f}{-1}$

$= -f$

25. $\dfrac{p^3}{2q} \div \dfrac{-p}{4q} = \dfrac{p^3}{2q} \cdot \dfrac{4q}{-p}$

$= \dfrac{\overset{1}{\cancel{p}} \cdot p \cdot p \cdot \overset{1}{\cancel{2}} \cdot 2 \cdot \overset{1}{\cancel{q}}}{\underset{1}{\cancel{2}} \cdot \underset{1}{\cancel{q}}\,(-1)(\underset{1}{\cancel{p}})}$

$= \dfrac{p \cdot p \cdot 2}{-1}$

$= \dfrac{2p^2}{-1}$

$= -2p^2$

26. $\dfrac{2x^3y}{z^5} \div \left(\dfrac{4xy}{z^3}\right)^2 = \dfrac{2x^3y}{z^5} \div \dfrac{16x^2y^2}{z^6}$

$= \dfrac{2x^3y}{z^5} \cdot \dfrac{z^6}{16x^2y^2}$

$= \dfrac{\overset{1}{\cancel{2}} \cdot \overset{1}{\cancel{x}} \cdot \overset{1}{\cancel{x}} \cdot x \cdot \overset{1}{\cancel{y}} \cdot \overset{1}{\cancel{z}} \cdot \overset{1}{\cancel{z}} \cdot \overset{1}{\cancel{z}} \cdot \overset{1}{\cancel{z}} \cdot \overset{1}{\cancel{z}} \cdot z}{\underset{1}{\cancel{z}} \cdot \underset{1}{\cancel{z}} \cdot \underset{1}{\cancel{z}} \cdot \underset{1}{\cancel{z}} \cdot \underset{1}{\cancel{z}} \cdot 2 \cdot 2 \cdot 2 \cdot 2 \cdot \underset{1}{\cancel{x}} \cdot \underset{1}{\cancel{x}} \cdot \underset{1}{\cancel{y}} \cdot y}$

$= \dfrac{x \cdot z}{2 \cdot 2 \cdot 2 \cdot y}$

$= \dfrac{xz}{8y}$

27. $\dfrac{xy}{a^3} \div \left(\dfrac{xy}{ab}\right)^3 = \dfrac{xy}{a^3} \div \dfrac{x^3y^3}{a^3b^3}$

$= \dfrac{xy}{a^3} \cdot \dfrac{a^3b^3}{x^3y^3}$

$= \dfrac{\overset{1}{\cancel{x}} \cdot \overset{1}{\cancel{y}} \cdot \overset{1}{\cancel{a}} \cdot \overset{1}{\cancel{a}} \cdot \overset{1}{\cancel{a}} \cdot b \cdot b \cdot b}{\underset{1}{\cancel{a}} \cdot \underset{1}{\cancel{a}} \cdot \underset{1}{\cancel{a}} \cdot \underset{1}{\cancel{x}} \cdot x \cdot x \cdot \underset{1}{\cancel{y}} \cdot y \cdot y}$

$= \dfrac{b \cdot b \cdot b}{x \cdot x \cdot y \cdot y}$

$= \dfrac{b^3}{x^2y^2}$

28. $\dfrac{3t^2}{t+2} \cdot \dfrac{t+2}{t^2} = \dfrac{3 \cdot \overset{1}{\cancel{t}} \cdot \overset{1}{\cancel{t}}(t \overset{1}{\cancel{+}} 2)}{(t \underset{1}{\cancel{+}} 2)\underset{1}{\cancel{t}} \cdot \underset{1}{\cancel{t}}}$

$= \dfrac{3}{1}$ or 3

29. $\dfrac{4w+4}{3} \cdot \dfrac{1}{w+1} = \dfrac{4(w \overset{1}{\cancel{+}} 1)1}{3(w \underset{1}{\cancel{+}} 1)}$

$= \dfrac{4 \cdot 1}{3}$ or $\dfrac{4}{3}$

30. $\dfrac{4t^2-4}{9(t+1)^2} \cdot \dfrac{3t+3}{2t-2} = \dfrac{\overset{1}{\cancel{2}} \cdot 2(t \overset{1}{\cancel{-}} 1)(t \overset{1}{\cancel{+}} 1)\overset{1}{\cancel{3}}(t \overset{1}{\cancel{+}} 1)}{\underset{1}{\cancel{3}} \cdot 3(t \underset{1}{\cancel{+}} 1)(t \underset{1}{\cancel{+}} 1)\underset{1}{\cancel{2}}(t \underset{1}{\cancel{-}} 1)}$

$= \dfrac{2}{3}$

31. $\dfrac{3p-21}{p^2-49} \cdot \dfrac{p^2+7p}{3p} = \dfrac{\overset{1}{\cancel{3}}(p \overset{1}{\cancel{-}} 7)\overset{1}{\cancel{p}}(p \overset{1}{\cancel{+}} 7)}{(p \underset{1}{\cancel{-}} 7)(p \underset{1}{\cancel{+}} 7)\underset{1}{\cancel{3}} \cdot \underset{1}{\cancel{p}}}$

$= \dfrac{1}{1}$ or 1

32. $\dfrac{5x^2+10x-75}{4x^2-24x-28} \cdot \dfrac{2x^2-10x-28}{x^2+7x+10}$

$= \dfrac{5(x-3)(x \overset{1}{\cancel{+}} 5)\overset{1}{\cancel{2}}(x \overset{1}{\cancel{-}} 7)(x \overset{1}{\cancel{+}} 2)}{\underset{1}{\cancel{2}} \cdot 2(x \underset{1}{\cancel{-}} 7)(x+1)(x \underset{1}{\cancel{+}} 2)(x \underset{1}{\cancel{+}} 5)}$

$= \dfrac{5(x-3)}{2(x+1)}$

33. $\dfrac{w^2 - 11w + 24}{w^2 - 18w + 80} \cdot \dfrac{w^2 - 15w + 50}{w^2 - 9w + 20}$

$= \dfrac{(w - 8)(w - 3)(w - 10)(w - 5)}{(w - 10)(w - 8)(w - 5)(w - 4)}$

$= \dfrac{w - 3}{w - 4}$

34. $\dfrac{r^2 + 2r - 8}{r^2 + 4r + 3} \div \dfrac{r - 2}{3r + 3} = \dfrac{r^2 + 2r - 8}{r^2 + 4r + 3} \cdot \dfrac{3r + 3}{r - 2}$

$= \dfrac{(r - 2)(r + 4)\,3(r + 1)}{(r + 1)(r + 3)(r - 2)}$

$= \dfrac{3(r + 4)}{r + 3}$

35. $\dfrac{a^2 + 2a - 15}{a - 3} \div \dfrac{a^2 - 4}{2} = \dfrac{a^2 + 2a - 15}{a - 3} \cdot \dfrac{2}{a^2 - 4}$

$= \dfrac{(a - 3)(a + 5)2}{(a - 3)(a - 2)(a + 2)}$

$= \dfrac{2(a + 5)}{(a - 2)(a + 2)}$

36. $\dfrac{\frac{m^3}{3n}}{-\frac{m^4}{9n^2}} = \dfrac{m^3}{3n} \div \left(-\dfrac{m^4}{9n^2}\right)$

$= \dfrac{m^3}{3n} \cdot \left(-\dfrac{9n^2}{m^4}\right)$

$= -\dfrac{m \cdot m \cdot m \cdot 3 \cdot 3 \cdot n \cdot n}{3 \cdot n \cdot m \cdot m \cdot m \cdot m}$

$= -\dfrac{3n}{m}$

37. $\dfrac{\frac{p^3}{2q}}{\frac{-p^2}{4q}} = \dfrac{p^3}{2q} \div \dfrac{-p^2}{4q}$

$= \dfrac{p^3}{2q} \cdot \dfrac{4q}{-p^2}$

$= \dfrac{p \cdot p \cdot p \cdot 2 \cdot 2 \cdot q}{2 \cdot q \, (-1)\, p \cdot p}$

$= \dfrac{p \cdot 2}{-1}$

$= \dfrac{2p}{-1} \text{ or } -2p$

38. $\dfrac{\frac{m + n}{5}}{\frac{m^2 + n^2}{5}} = \dfrac{m + n}{5} \div \dfrac{m^2 + n^2}{5}$

$= \dfrac{m + n}{5} \cdot \dfrac{5}{m^2 + n^2}$

$= \dfrac{m + n}{m^2 + n^2}$

39. $\dfrac{\frac{x + y}{2x - y}}{\frac{x + y}{2x + y}} = \dfrac{x + y}{2x - y} \div \dfrac{x + y}{2x + y}$

$= \dfrac{x + y}{2x - y} \cdot \dfrac{2x + y}{x + y}$

$= \dfrac{2x + y}{2x - y}$

40. $\dfrac{\frac{6y^2 - 6}{8y^2 + 8y}}{\frac{3y - 3}{4y^2 + 4y}} = \dfrac{6y^2 - 6}{8y^2 + 8y} \div \dfrac{3y - 3}{4y^2 + 4y}$

$= \dfrac{6y^2 - 6}{8y^2 + 8y} \cdot \dfrac{4y^2 + 4y}{3y - 3}$

$= \dfrac{2 \cdot 3(y - 1)(y + 1)}{2 \cdot 2 \cdot y(y + 1)} \cdot \dfrac{2 \cdot 2 \cdot y(y + 1)}{3(y - 1)}$

$= \dfrac{y + 1}{1} \text{ or } y + 1$

41. $\dfrac{\frac{5x^2 - 5x - 30}{45 - 15x}}{\frac{6 + x - x^2}{4x - 12}} = \dfrac{5x^2 - 5x - 30}{45 - 15x} \div \dfrac{6 + x - x^2}{4x - 12}$

$= \dfrac{5x^2 - 5x - 30}{45 - 15x} \cdot \dfrac{4x - 12}{6 + x - x^2}$

$= \dfrac{5(x - 3)(x + 2)}{-(3.5)(x - 3)} \cdot \dfrac{2 \cdot 2(x - 3)}{-(x - 3)(x + 2)}$

$= \dfrac{2 \cdot 2}{-3(-1)} \text{ or } \dfrac{4}{3}$

42. Since $(d + 1)(d^2 - 4) = (d + 1)(d - 2)(d + 2)$, the denominator equals 0 when $d = -2, -1$, or 2.

43. Since $a^2 - b^2 = (a - b)(a + b)$, the denominator equals 0 when $a = -b$ or b.

44. $\dfrac{6827}{13,129}$

45. $\dfrac{6827 + m}{13,129 + a}$

46. Substitute the expression $6x^2 - 7x - 5$ for A and $3x - 5$ for b in the formula for the area of a parallelogram, $A = bh$, to determine the value of h.

$$A = bh$$
$$6x^2 - 7x - 5 = (3x - 5)h$$
$$\dfrac{6x^2 - 7x - 5}{3x - 5} = h$$
$$\dfrac{(2x + 1)(3x - 5)}{3x - 5} = h$$
$$2x + 1 = h$$

The height of the parallelogram is $2x + 1$ units.

47. Substitute the expression $3x^2 + 10x + 3$ for A and $3x + 1$ for h in the equation $A = b_1 h$ to determine b_1.

$$A = b_1 h$$
$$3x^2 + 10x + 3 = b_1(3x + 1)$$
$$\dfrac{3x^2 + 10x + 3}{3x + 1} = b_1$$
$$\dfrac{(x + 3)(3x + 1)}{3x + 1} = b_1$$
$$x + 3 = b_1$$

Substitute the expression $2x^2 - 13x + 20$ for A and $x - 4$ for h in the equation $A = b_2 h$ to determine b_2.

$$A = b_2 h$$
$$2x^2 - 13x + 20 = b_2(x - 4)$$
$$\dfrac{2x^2 - 13x + 20}{x - 4} = b_2$$
$$\dfrac{(x - 4)(2x - 5)}{x - 4} = b_2$$
$$2x - 5 = b_2$$

Since $b_1 = x + 3$ and $b_2 = 2x - 5$, the area of rectangle N is $(x + 3)(2x - 5)$ or $(2x^2 + x - 15)$ m^2.

48. $\dfrac{(a^2 - 5a + 6)^{-1}}{(a - 2)^{-2}} \div \dfrac{(a - 3)^{-1}}{(a - 2)^{-2}}$

$= \dfrac{(a - 2)^2}{a^2 - 5a + 6} \div \dfrac{(a - 2)^2}{a - 3}$

$= \dfrac{(a - 2)^2}{a^2 - 5a + 6} \cdot \dfrac{a - 3}{(a - 2)^2}$

$= \dfrac{(a - 2)(a - 2)}{(a - 3)(a - 2)} \cdot \dfrac{a - 3}{(a - 2)(a - 2)}$

$= \dfrac{1}{a - 2}$

49. A rational expression can be used to express the fraction of a nut mixture that is peanuts. Answers should include the following.

- The rational expression $\dfrac{8 + x}{13 + x}$ is in simplest form because the numerator and the denominator have no common factors.

- Sample answer: $\dfrac{8 + x}{13 + x + y}$ could be used to represent the fraction that is peanuts if x pounds of peanuts and y pounds of cashews were added to the original mixture.

50. C; Since $x^2 - x = x(x - 1)$, the denominator equals 0 when $x = 0$ or 1.

51. A; Since $\frac{a^2 + 3a - 10}{a - 2} = \frac{(a - 2)(a + 5)}{a - 2}$ or $a + 5$, and

$\frac{a^2 + a - 6}{a + 3} = \frac{(a - 2)(a + 3)}{a + 3}$ or $a - 2$, $a + 5 > a - 2$, so

$\frac{a^2 + 3a - 10}{a - 2} > \frac{a^2 + a - 6}{a + 3}$.

Page 478   Maintain Your Skills

52. Since $x^2 + y^2 - 19 = 2x$, $y^2 = -x^2 + 2x + 19$.
Substitute $-x^2 + 2x + 19$ for y^2 in the first equation and solve for x.

$$x^2 + 2y^2 = 33$$
$$x^2 + 2(-x^2 + 2x + 19) = 33$$
$$x^2 - 2x^2 + 4x + 38 = 33$$
$$0 = x^2 - 4x - 5$$
$$0 = (x + 1)(x - 5)$$

$x + 1 = 0$ or $x - 5 = 0$
$x = -1$ $x = 5$

Now solve for y.

$x^2 + 2y^2 = 33$	$x^2 + 2y^2 = 33$
$(-1)^2 + 2y^2 = 33$	$(5)^2 + 2y^2 = 33$
$2y^2 = 32$	$2y^2 = 8$
$y^2 = 16$	$y^2 = 4$
$y = \pm 4$	$y = \pm 2$

The solutions of the system are $(-1, \pm 4)$ and $(5, \pm 2)$.

53. Since $x^2 - y^2 = 9$, $x^2 = y^2 + 9$. Substitute $y^2 + 9$ for x^2 in the first equation and solve for y.

$$x^2 + 2y^2 = 33$$
$$(y^2 + 9) + 2y^2 = 33$$
$$3y^2 = 24$$
$$y^2 = 8$$
$$y = \pm 2\sqrt{2}$$

Now solve for x.

$x^2 - y^2 = 9$	$x^2 - y^2 = 9$
$x^2 - (2\sqrt{2})^2 = 9$	$x^2 - (-2\sqrt{2})^2 = 9$
$x^2 - 8 = 9$	$x^2 - 8 = 9$
$x^2 = 17$	$x^2 = 17$
$x = \pm\sqrt{17}$	$x = \pm\sqrt{17}$

The solutions of the system are $(\pm\sqrt{17}, \pm 2\sqrt{2})$.

54. $y^2 - 3x + 6y + 12 = 0$
$$y^2 + 6y + \blacksquare = 3x - 12 + \blacksquare$$
$$y^2 + 6y + 9 = 3x - 12 + 9$$
$$(y + 3)^2 = 3x - 3$$
$$(y + 3)^2 + 3 = 3x$$
$$\tfrac{1}{3}(y + 3)^2 + 1 = x$$

The graph of the equation is a parabola.

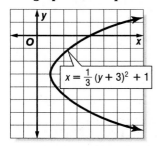

$x = \frac{1}{3}(y + 3)^2 + 1$

55.
$$x^2 - 14x + 4 = 9y^2 - 36y$$
$$x^2 - 14x - 9y^2 + 36y = -4$$
$$(x^2 - 14x + \blacksquare) - 9(y^2 - 4y + \blacksquare) = -4 + \blacksquare - 9(\blacksquare)$$
$$(x^2 - 14x + 49) - 9(y^2 - 4y + 4) = -4 + 49 - 9(4)$$
$$(x - 7)^2 - 9(y - 2)^2 = 9$$
$$\frac{(x - 7)^2}{9} - \frac{9(y - 2)^2}{9} = 1$$
$$\frac{(x - 7)^2}{9} - \frac{(y - 2)^2}{1} = 1$$

The graph of the equation is a hyperbola.

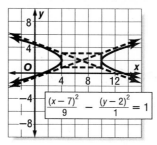

$\frac{(x - 7)^2}{9} - \frac{(y - 2)^2}{1} = 1$

56. The graph represents an even-degree function. The graph intersects the x-axis at two points, so the function has two real zeros.

57. The graph represents an odd-degree function. The graph intersects the x-axis at three points, so the function has three real zeros.

58. The graph represents an even-degree function. The graph does not intersect the x-axis, so the function has no real zeros.

59.
$$r^2 - 3r = 4$$
$$r^2 - 3r - 4 = 0$$
$$(r - 4)(r + 1) = 0$$

$r - 4 = 0$ or $r + 1 = 0$
$r = 4$ $r = -1$

The solution set is $\{-1, 4\}$.

60.
$$18u^2 - 3u = 1$$
$$18u^2 - 3u - 1 = 0$$
$$(3u - 1)(6u + 1) = 0$$

$3u - 1 = 0$ or $6u + 1 = 0$
$3u = 1$ $6u = -1$
$u = \frac{1}{3}$ $u = -\frac{1}{6}$

The solution set is $\left\{-\frac{1}{6}, \frac{1}{3}\right\}$.

61. $d^2 - 5d = 0$
$d(d - 5) = 0$

$d = 0$ or $d - 5 = 0$
               $d = 5$

The solution set is $\{0, 5\}$.

62. Use the formula $d = rt$, where d is the distance from Earth to the Sun, r is the speed of light, and t is the time it takes sunlight to reach Earth.

$$t = \frac{d}{r}$$
$$= \frac{1.496 \times 10^8 \text{ km}}{3 \times 10^5 \text{ km/s}}$$
$$= \frac{1.496}{3} \cdot \frac{10^8}{10^5 \text{ 1/s}}$$
$$\approx 0.499 \times 10^3 \text{ s}$$
$$= 4.99 \times 10^2 \text{ s}$$

It takes about 4.99×10^2 seconds or about 8 minutes and 19 seconds for light from the Sun to reach Earth.

63. $|2x + 7| + 5 = 0$

$\quad\quad |2x + 7| = -5$

This sentence is never true. So the solution set is $\varnothing$.

64. $5|3x - 4| = x + 1$

$\quad\quad |3x - 4| = \frac{1}{5}x + \frac{1}{5}$

Case 1: $a = b$ $\quad$ or $\quad$ Case 2: $a = -b$

$3x - 4 = \frac{1}{5}x + \frac{1}{5}$ $\quad\quad\quad$ $3x - 4 = -\left(\frac{1}{5}x + \frac{1}{5}\right)$

$\frac{14}{5}x - 4 = \frac{1}{5}$ $\quad\quad\quad\quad\quad$ $3x - 4 = -\frac{1}{5}x - \frac{1}{5}$

$\frac{14}{5}x = \frac{21}{5}$ $\quad\quad\quad\quad\quad\quad$ $\frac{16}{5}x - 4 = -\frac{1}{5}$

$x = \frac{3}{2}$ $\quad\quad\quad\quad\quad\quad\quad$ $\frac{16}{5}x = \frac{19}{5}$

$\quad\quad\quad\quad\quad\quad\quad\quad\quad\quad\quad\quad$ $x = \frac{19}{16}$

There appear to be two solutions, $\frac{3}{2}$ or $\frac{19}{16}$.

Check:

$5|3x - 4| = x + 1$ $\quad$ or $\quad$ $5|3x - 4| = x + 1$

$5\left|3\left(\frac{3}{2}\right) - 4\right| \stackrel{?}{=} \frac{3}{2} + 1$ $\quad\quad$ $5\left|3\left(\frac{19}{16}\right) - 4\right| \stackrel{?}{=} \frac{19}{16} + 1$

$5\left|\frac{1}{2}\right| \stackrel{?}{=} \frac{5}{2}$ $\quad\quad\quad\quad\quad$ $5\left|-\frac{7}{16}\right| \stackrel{?}{=} \frac{35}{16}$

$\frac{5}{2} = \frac{5}{2}$ ✓ $\quad\quad\quad\quad\quad\quad$ $\frac{35}{16} = \frac{35}{16}$ ✓

The solution set is $\left\{\frac{3}{2}, \frac{19}{16}\right\}$.

65. $\quad \frac{2}{3} + x = -\frac{4}{9}$

$\frac{2}{3} + x - \frac{2}{3} = -\frac{4}{9} - \frac{2}{3}$

$\quad\quad\quad x = -\frac{10}{9}$ or $-1\frac{1}{9}$

66. $\quad x + \frac{5}{8} = -\frac{5}{6}$

$x + \frac{5}{8} - \frac{5}{8} = -\frac{5}{6} - \frac{5}{8}$

$\quad\quad\quad x = -\frac{35}{24}$ or $-1\frac{11}{24}$

67. $\quad x - \frac{3}{5} = \frac{2}{3}$

$x - \frac{3}{5} + \frac{3}{5} = \frac{2}{3} + \frac{3}{5}$

$\quad\quad\quad x = \frac{19}{15}$ or $1\frac{4}{15}$

68. $\quad x + \frac{3}{16} = -\frac{1}{2}$

$x + \frac{3}{16} - \frac{3}{16} = -\frac{1}{2} - \frac{3}{16}$

$\quad\quad\quad x = -\frac{11}{16}$

69. $\quad x - \frac{1}{6} = -\frac{7}{9}$

$x - \frac{1}{6} + \frac{1}{6} = -\frac{7}{9} + \frac{1}{6}$

$\quad\quad\quad x = -\frac{11}{18}$

70. $\quad x - \frac{3}{8} = -\frac{5}{24}$

$x - \frac{3}{8} + \frac{3}{8} = -\frac{5}{24} + \frac{3}{8}$

$\quad\quad\quad x = \frac{1}{6}$

9-2 | ## Adding and Subtracting Rational Expressions

Pages 481–482 Check for Understanding

1. Catalina; you need a common denominator, not a common numerator, to subtract two rational expressions.

2. Sample answer: $d^2 - d, d + 1$

3a. Always; since a, b, and c are factors of abc, abc is always a common denominator of $\frac{1}{a} + \frac{1}{b} + \frac{1}{c}$.

3b. Sometimes; if a, b, and c have no common factors, then abc is the LCD of $\frac{1}{a} + \frac{1}{b} + \frac{1}{c}$.

3c. Sometimes; if a and b have no common factors and c is a factor of ab, then ab is the LCD of $\frac{1}{a} + \frac{1}{b} + \frac{1}{c}$.

3d. Sometimes; if a and c are factors of b, then b is the LCD of $\frac{1}{a} + \frac{1}{b} + \frac{1}{c}$.

3e. Always; since $\frac{1}{a} + \frac{1}{b} + \frac{1}{c} = \frac{bc}{abc} + \frac{ac}{abc} + \frac{ab}{abc}$, the sum is always $\frac{bc + ac + ab}{abc}$.

4. $12y^2 = 2^2 \cdot 3 \cdot y^2$

$\quad\; 6x^2 = 2 \cdot 3 \cdot x^2$

$\quad\; \text{LCM} = 2^2 \cdot 3 \cdot x^2 \cdot y^2$

$\quad\quad\quad\; = 12x^2y^2$

5. $16ab^3 = 2^4 \cdot a \cdot b^3$

$\quad\; 5b^2a^2 = 5 \cdot b^2 \cdot a^2$

$\quad\; 20ac = 2^2 \cdot 5 \cdot a \cdot c$

$\quad\; \text{LCM} = 2^4 \cdot 5 \cdot a^2 \cdot b^3 \cdot c$

$\quad\quad\quad\; = 80a^2b^3c$

6. $x^2 - 2x = x(x - 2)$

$\quad\; x^2 - 4 = (x - 2)(x + 2)$

$\quad\; \text{LCM} = x(x - 2)(x + 2)$

7. $\frac{2}{x^2y} - \frac{x}{y} = \frac{2}{x^2y} - \frac{x \cdot x^2}{y \cdot x^2}$

$\quad\quad\quad\quad = \frac{2}{x^2y} - \frac{x^3}{x^2y}$

$\quad\quad\quad\quad = \frac{2 - x^3}{x^2y}$

8. $\frac{7a}{15b^2} + \frac{b}{18ab} = \frac{7a \cdot 6a}{15b^2 \cdot 6a} + \frac{b \cdot 5b}{18ab \cdot 5b}$

$\quad\quad\quad\quad\quad = \frac{42a^2}{90ab^2} + \frac{5b^2}{90ab^2}$

$\quad\quad\quad\quad\quad = \frac{42a^2 + 5b^2}{90ab^2}$

9. $\frac{5}{3m} - \frac{2}{7m} - \frac{1}{2m} = \frac{5 \cdot 7 \cdot 2}{3m \cdot 7 \cdot 2} - \frac{2 \cdot 3 \cdot 2}{7m \cdot 3 \cdot 2} - \frac{1 \cdot 3 \cdot 7}{2m \cdot 3 \cdot 7}$

$\quad\quad\quad\quad\quad\quad = \frac{70}{42m} - \frac{12}{42m} - \frac{21}{42m}$

$\quad\quad\quad\quad\quad\quad = \frac{37}{42m}$

10. $\frac{6}{d^2 + 4d + 4} + \frac{5}{d + 2} = \frac{6}{(d + 2)^2} + \frac{5}{d + 2}$

$\quad\quad\quad\quad\quad\quad\quad = \frac{6}{(d + 2)^2} + \frac{5(d + 2)}{(d + 2)(d + 2)}$

$\quad\quad\quad\quad\quad\quad\quad = \frac{6}{(d + 2)^2} + \frac{5d + 10}{(d + 2)^2}$

$\quad\quad\quad\quad\quad\quad\quad = \frac{6 + 5d + 10}{(d + 2)^2}$

$\quad\quad\quad\quad\quad\quad\quad = \frac{5d + 16}{(d + 2)^2}$

11. $\dfrac{a}{a^2 - a - 20} + \dfrac{2}{a + 4} = \dfrac{a}{(a - 5)(a + 4)} + \dfrac{2}{a + 4}$

$\qquad\qquad = \dfrac{a}{(a - 5)(a + 4)} + \dfrac{2(a - 5)}{(a + 4)(a - 5)}$

$\qquad\qquad = \dfrac{a + 2(a - 5)}{(a - 5)(a + 4)}$

$\qquad\qquad = \dfrac{a + 2a - 10}{(a - 5)(a + 4)}$

$\qquad\qquad = \dfrac{3a - 10}{(a - 5)(a + 4)}$

12. $\dfrac{x + \frac{x}{3}}{x - \frac{x}{6}} = \dfrac{\frac{3x}{3} + \frac{x}{3}}{\frac{6x}{6} - \frac{x}{6}}$

$\qquad\quad = \dfrac{\frac{4x}{3}}{\frac{5x}{6}}$

$\qquad\quad = \dfrac{4x}{3} \div \dfrac{5x}{6}$

$\qquad\quad = \dfrac{4\overset{1}{x}}{\overset{1}{3}} \cdot \dfrac{\overset{2}{6}}{5\overset{1}{x}}$

$\qquad\quad = \dfrac{4 \cdot 2}{1 \cdot 5} \text{ or } \dfrac{8}{5}$

13. $\dfrac{4}{x^2 - 1} + \dfrac{3}{2x} + \dfrac{2}{x + 1} + \dfrac{3}{x}$

$\qquad = \dfrac{4}{(x - 1)(x + 1)} + \dfrac{3}{2x} + \dfrac{2}{x + 1} + \dfrac{3}{x}$

$\qquad = \dfrac{4 \cdot 2 \cdot x}{(x - 1)(x + 1)2 \cdot x} + \dfrac{3(x - 1)(x + 1)}{2x(x - 1)(x + 1)}$

$\qquad\quad + \dfrac{2 \cdot 2 \cdot x(x - 1)}{(x + 1)2 \cdot x(x - 1)} + \dfrac{3 \cdot 2(x - 1)(x + 1)}{x \cdot 2(x - 1)(x + 1)}$

$\qquad = \dfrac{8x}{2x(x - 1)(x + 1)} + \dfrac{3(x^2 - 1)}{2x(x - 1)(x + 1)}$

$\qquad\quad + \dfrac{4x(x - 1)}{2x(x - 1)(x + 1)} + \dfrac{6(x^2 - 1)}{2x(x - 1)(x + 1)}$

$\qquad = \dfrac{8x + 3(x^2 - 1) + 4x(x - 1) + 6(x^2 - 1)}{2x(x - 1)(x + 1)}$

$\qquad = \dfrac{8x + 3x^2 - 3 + 4x^2 - 4x + 6x^2 - 6}{2x(x - 1)(x + 1)}$

$\qquad = \dfrac{13x^2 + 4x - 9}{2x(x - 1)(x + 1)}$

The perimeter of the quadrilateral is
$\dfrac{13x^2 + 4x - 9}{2x(x - 1)(x + 1)}$ units.

Pages 482–484 Practice and Apply

14. $\quad 10s^2 = 2 \cdot 5 \cdot s^2$

$\qquad 35s^2t^2 = 5 \cdot 7 \cdot s^2 \cdot t^2$

$\qquad \text{LCM} = 2 \cdot 5 \cdot 7 \cdot s^2 \cdot t^2$

$\qquad\qquad = 70s^2t^2$

15. $\quad 36x^2y = 2^2 \cdot 3^2 \cdot x^2 \cdot y$

$\qquad 20xyz = 2^2 \cdot 5 \cdot x \cdot y \cdot z$

$\qquad \text{LCM} = 2^2 \cdot 3^2 \cdot 5 \cdot x^2 \cdot y \cdot z$

$\qquad\qquad = 180x^2yz$

16. $\quad 14a^3 = 2 \cdot 7 \cdot a^3$

$\qquad 15bc^3 = 3 \cdot 5 \cdot b \cdot c^3$

$\qquad 12b^3 = 2^2 \cdot 3 \cdot b^3$

$\qquad \text{LCM} = 2^2 \cdot 3 \cdot 5 \cdot 7 \cdot a^3 \cdot b^3 \cdot c^3$

$\qquad\qquad = 420a^3b^3c^3$

17. $9p^2q^3 = 3^2 \cdot p^2 \cdot q^3$

$\qquad 6pq^4 = 2 \cdot 3 \cdot p \cdot q^4$

$\qquad 4p^3 = 2^2 \cdot p^3$

$\qquad \text{LCM} = 2^2 \cdot 3^2 \cdot p^3 \cdot q^4$

$\qquad\qquad = 36p^3q^4$

18. $4w - 12 = 2^2(w - 3)$

$\qquad 2w - 6 = 2(w - 3)$

$\qquad \text{LCM} = 2^2(w - 3)$

$\qquad\qquad = 4(w - 3)$

19. $x^2 - y^2 = (x - y)(x + y)$

$\qquad x^3 + x^2y = x^2(x + y)$

$\qquad \text{LCM} = x^2(x - y)(x + y)$

20. $2t^2 + t - 3 = (t - 1)(2t + 3)$

$\qquad 2t^2 + 5t + 3 = (t + 1)(2t + 3)$

$\qquad \text{LCM} = (2t + 3)(t - 1)(t + 1)$

21. $n^2 - 7n + 12 = (n - 4)(n - 3)$

$\qquad n^2 - 2n - 8 = (n - 4)(n + 2)$

$\qquad \text{LCM} = (n - 4)(n - 3)(n + 2)$

22. $\dfrac{6}{ab} + \dfrac{8}{a} = \dfrac{6}{ab} + \dfrac{8 \cdot b}{a \cdot b}$

$\qquad\quad = \dfrac{6 + 8b}{ab}$

23. $\dfrac{5}{6v} + \dfrac{7}{4v} = \dfrac{5 \cdot 2}{6v \cdot 2} + \dfrac{7 \cdot 3}{4v \cdot 3}$

$\qquad\qquad = \dfrac{10}{12v} + \dfrac{21}{12v}$

$\qquad\qquad = \dfrac{31}{12v}$

24. $\dfrac{5}{r} + 7 = \dfrac{5}{r} + \dfrac{7 \cdot r}{r}$

$\qquad\quad = \dfrac{5 + 7r}{r}$

25. $\dfrac{2x}{3y} + 5 = \dfrac{2x}{3y} + \dfrac{5 \cdot 3y}{3y}$

$\qquad\qquad = \dfrac{2x}{3y} + \dfrac{15y}{3y}$

$\qquad\qquad = \dfrac{2x + 15y}{3y}$

26. $\dfrac{3x}{4y^2} - \dfrac{y}{6x} = \dfrac{3x \cdot 3x}{4y^2 \cdot 3x} - \dfrac{y \cdot 2y^2}{6x \cdot 2y^2}$

$\qquad\qquad = \dfrac{9x^2}{12xy^2} - \dfrac{2y^3}{12xy^2}$

$\qquad\qquad = \dfrac{9x^2 - 2y^3}{12xy^2}$

27. $\dfrac{5}{a^2b} - \dfrac{7a}{5b^2} = \dfrac{5 \cdot 5b}{a^2b \cdot 5b} - \dfrac{7a \cdot a^2}{5b^2 \cdot a^2}$

$\qquad\qquad = \dfrac{25b}{5a^2b^2} - \dfrac{7a^3}{5a^2 b^2}$

$\qquad\qquad = \dfrac{25b - 7a^3}{5a^2 b^2}$

28. $\dfrac{3}{4q} - \dfrac{2}{5q} - \dfrac{1}{2q} = \dfrac{3 \cdot 5}{4q \cdot 5} - \dfrac{2 \cdot 4}{5q \cdot 4} - \dfrac{1 \cdot 10}{2q \cdot 10}$

$\qquad\qquad = \dfrac{15}{20q} - \dfrac{8}{20q} - \dfrac{10}{20q}$

$\qquad\qquad = \dfrac{-3}{20q} \text{ or } \dfrac{-3}{20q}$

29. $\dfrac{11}{9} - \dfrac{7}{2w} - \dfrac{6}{5w} = \dfrac{11 \cdot 2 \cdot 5 \cdot w}{9 \cdot 2 \cdot 5 \cdot w} - \dfrac{7 \cdot 9 \cdot 5}{2w \cdot 9 \cdot 5} - \dfrac{6 \cdot 9 \cdot 2}{5w \cdot 9 \cdot 2}$

$\qquad\qquad = \dfrac{110w}{90w} - \dfrac{315}{90w} - \dfrac{108}{90w}$

$\qquad\qquad = \dfrac{110w - 315 - 108}{90w}$

$\qquad\qquad = \dfrac{110w - 423}{90w}$

30. $\dfrac{7}{y - 8} - \dfrac{6}{8 - y} = \dfrac{7}{y - 8} - \dfrac{6(-1)}{(8 - y)(-1)}$

$\qquad\qquad = \dfrac{7}{y - 8} - \dfrac{-6}{y - 8}$

$\qquad\qquad = \dfrac{7 - (-6)}{y - 8}$

$\qquad\qquad = \dfrac{13}{y - 8}$

31. $\dfrac{a}{a - 4} - \dfrac{3}{4 - a} = \dfrac{a}{a - 4} - \dfrac{3(-1)}{(4 - a)(-1)}$

$\qquad\qquad = \dfrac{a}{a - 4} - \dfrac{-3}{a - 4}$

$\qquad\qquad = \dfrac{a - (-3)}{a - 4}$

$\qquad\qquad = \dfrac{a + 3}{a - 4}$

32. $\dfrac{m}{m^2-4}+\dfrac{2}{3m+6}=\dfrac{m}{(m+2)(m-2)}+\dfrac{2}{3(m+2)}$

$\qquad = \dfrac{m\cdot 3}{(m+2)(m-2)3}+\dfrac{2(m-2)}{3(m+2)(m-2)}$

$\qquad = \dfrac{3m}{3(m+2)(m-2)}+\dfrac{2m-4}{3(m+2)(m-2)}$

$\qquad = \dfrac{3m+2m-4}{3(m+2)(m-2)}$

$\qquad = \dfrac{5m-4}{3(m+2)(m-2)}$

33. $\dfrac{y}{y+3}-\dfrac{6y}{y^2-9}=\dfrac{y}{y+3}-\dfrac{6y}{(y+3)(y-3)}$

$\qquad = \dfrac{y(y-3)}{(y+3)(y-3)}-\dfrac{6y}{(y+3)(y-3)}$

$\qquad = \dfrac{y(y-3)-6y}{(y+3)(y-3)}$

$\qquad = \dfrac{y^2-3y-6y}{(y+3)(y-3)}$

$\qquad = \dfrac{y^2-9y}{(y+3)(y-3)}$

$\qquad = \dfrac{y(y-9)}{(y+3)(y-3)}$

34. $\dfrac{5}{x^2-3x-28}+\dfrac{7}{2x-14}=\dfrac{5}{(x-7)(x+4)}+\dfrac{7}{2(x-7)}$

$\qquad = \dfrac{5(2)}{(x-7)(x+4)2}+\dfrac{7(x+4)}{2(x-7)(x+4)}$

$\qquad = \dfrac{10}{2(x-7)(x+4)}+\dfrac{7x+28}{2(x-7)(x+4)}$

$\qquad = \dfrac{10+7x+28}{2(x-7)(x+4)}$

$\qquad = \dfrac{7x+38}{2(x-7)(x+4)}$

35. $\dfrac{d-4}{d^2+2d-8}-\dfrac{d+2}{d^2-16}$

$\qquad = \dfrac{d-4}{(d+4)(d-2)}-\dfrac{d+2}{(d-4)(d+4)}$

$\qquad = \dfrac{(d-4)(d-4)}{(d+4)(d-2)(d-4)}-\dfrac{(d+2)(d-2)}{(d-4)(d+4)(d-2)}$

$\qquad = \dfrac{d^2-8d+16}{(d-4)(d+4)(d-2)}-\dfrac{d^2-4}{(d-4)(d+4)(d-2)}$

$\qquad = \dfrac{d^2-8d+16-(d^2-4)}{(d-4)(d+4)(d-2)}$

$\qquad = \dfrac{-8d+20}{(d-4)(d+4)(d-2)}$

36. $\dfrac{1}{h^2-9h+20}-\dfrac{5}{h^2-10h+25}$

$\qquad = \dfrac{1}{(h-4)(h-5)}-\dfrac{5}{(h-5)^2}$

$\qquad = \dfrac{1(h-5)}{(h-4)(h-5)(h-5)}-\dfrac{5(h-4)}{(h-5)^2(h-4)}$

$\qquad = \dfrac{h-5}{(h-4)(h-5)^2}-\dfrac{5h-20}{(h-4)(h-5)^2}$

$\qquad = \dfrac{h-5-(5h-20)}{(h-4)(h-5)^2}$

$\qquad = \dfrac{-4h+15}{(h-4)(h-5)^2}$

37. $\dfrac{x}{x^2+5x+6}-\dfrac{2}{x^2+4x+4}$

$\qquad = \dfrac{x}{(x+2)(x+3)}-\dfrac{2}{(x+2)^2}$

$\qquad = \dfrac{x(x+2)}{(x+2)(x+3)(x+2)}-\dfrac{2(x+3)}{(x+2)^2(x+3)}$

$\qquad = \dfrac{x^2+2x}{(x+2)^2(x+3)}-\dfrac{2x+6}{(x+2)^2(x+3)}$

$\qquad = \dfrac{x^2+2x-(2x+6)}{(x+2)^2(x+3)}$

$\qquad = \dfrac{x^2-6}{(x+2)^2(x+3)}$

38. $\dfrac{m^2+n^2}{m^2-n^2}+\dfrac{m}{n-m}+\dfrac{n}{m+n}$

$\qquad = \dfrac{m^2+n^2}{(m+n)(m-n)}+\dfrac{m}{n-m}+\dfrac{n}{m+n}$

$\qquad = \dfrac{m^2+n^2}{(m+n)(m-n)}+\dfrac{m(-1)(m+n)}{(n-m)(-1)(m+n)}+\dfrac{n(m-n)}{(m+n)(m-n)}$

$\qquad = \dfrac{m^2+n^2}{(m+n)(m-n)}+\dfrac{-m(m+n)}{(m+n)(m-n)}+\dfrac{mn-n^2}{(m+n)(m-n)}$

$\qquad = \dfrac{m^2+n^2-m(m+n)+mn-n^2}{(m+n)(m-n)}$

$\qquad = \dfrac{0}{(m+n)(m-n)}$

$\qquad = 0$

39. $\dfrac{y+1}{y-1}+\dfrac{y+2}{y-2}+\dfrac{y}{y^2-3y+2}$

$\qquad = \dfrac{y+1}{y-1}+\dfrac{y+2}{y-2}+\dfrac{y}{(y-1)(y-2)}$

$\qquad = \dfrac{(y+1)(y-2)}{(y-1)(y-2)}+\dfrac{(y+2)(y-1)}{(y-2)(y-1)}+\dfrac{y}{(y-1)(y-2)}$

$\qquad = \dfrac{y^2-y-2}{(y-1)(y-2)}+\dfrac{y^2+y-2}{(y-1)(y-2)}+\dfrac{y}{(y-1)(y-2)}$

$\qquad = \dfrac{y^2-y-2+y^2+y-2+y}{(y-1)(y-2)}$

$\qquad = \dfrac{2y^2+y-4}{(y-1)(y-2)}$

40. $\dfrac{\frac{1}{b+2}+\frac{1}{b-5}}{\frac{2b^2-b-3}{b^2-3b-10}}=\dfrac{\frac{b-5}{(b-5)(b+2)}+\frac{b+2}{(b-5)(b+2)}}{\frac{(b+1)(2b-3)}{(b-5)(b+2)}}$

$\qquad = \dfrac{\frac{b-5+b+2}{(b-5)(b+2)}}{\frac{(b+1)(2b-3)}{(b-5)(b+2)}}$

$\qquad = \dfrac{\frac{2b-3}{(b-5)(b+2)}}{\frac{(b+1)(2b-3)}{(b-5)(b+2)}}$

$\qquad = \dfrac{2b-3}{(b-5)(b+2)}\div\dfrac{(b+1)(2b-3)}{(b-5)(b+2)}$

$\qquad = \dfrac{2b-3}{(b-5)(b+2)}\div\dfrac{(b-5)(b+2)}{(b+1)(2b-3)}$

$\qquad = \dfrac{1}{b+1}$

41. $\dfrac{(x+y)\left(\frac{1}{x}-\frac{1}{y}\right)}{(x-y)\left(\frac{1}{x}+\frac{1}{y}\right)}=\dfrac{\frac{x+y}{x}-\frac{x+y}{y}}{\frac{x-y}{x}+\frac{x-y}{y}}$

$\qquad = \dfrac{\frac{(x+y)y}{xy}-\frac{(x+y)x}{yx}}{\frac{(x-y)y}{xy}+\frac{(x-y)x}{yx}}$

$\qquad = \dfrac{\frac{xy+y^2}{xy}-\frac{x^2+xy}{xy}}{\frac{xy-y^2}{xy}+\frac{x^2-xy}{xy}}$

$\qquad = \dfrac{\frac{xy+y^2-(x^2+xy)}{xy}}{\frac{xy-y^2+x^2-xy}{xy}}$

$\qquad = \dfrac{\frac{xy+y^2-x^2-xy}{xy}}{\frac{xy-y^2+x^2-xy}{xy}}$

$\qquad = \dfrac{\frac{y^2-x^2}{xy}}{\frac{-y^2+x^2}{xy}}$

$\qquad = \dfrac{y^2-x^2}{xy}\div\dfrac{-y^2+x^2}{xy}$

$\qquad = \dfrac{y^2-x^2}{xy}\cdot\dfrac{xy}{-y^2+x}\quad$ **or** -1

42. $\left(\dfrac{2s}{2s+1}-1\right)\div\left(1+\dfrac{2s}{1-2s}\right)$

$=\left(\dfrac{2s}{2s+1}-\dfrac{2s+1}{2s+1}\right)\div\left(\dfrac{1-2s}{1-2s}+\dfrac{2s}{1-2s}\right)$

$=\left(\dfrac{2s-(2s+1)}{2s+1}\right)\div\left(\dfrac{1-2s+2s}{1-2s}\right)$

$=\left(\dfrac{2s-2s-1}{2s+1}\right)\div\left(\dfrac{1}{1-2s}\right)$

$=\dfrac{-1}{2s+1}\div\dfrac{1}{1-2s}$

$=\dfrac{-1}{2s+1}\cdot\dfrac{1-2s}{1}$

$=\dfrac{(-1)(1-2s)}{2s+1}$

$=\dfrac{2s-1}{2s+1}$

43. $\left(3+\dfrac{5}{a+2}\right)\div\left(3-\dfrac{10}{a+7}\right)$

$=\left(\dfrac{3(a+2)}{a+2}+\dfrac{5}{a+2}\right)\div\left(\dfrac{3(a+7)}{a+7}-\dfrac{10}{a+7}\right)$

$=\left(\dfrac{3a+6}{a+2}+\dfrac{5}{a+2}\right)\div\left(\dfrac{3a+21}{a+7}-\dfrac{10}{a+7}\right)$

$=\dfrac{3a+11}{a+2}\div\dfrac{3a+11}{a+7}$

$=\dfrac{3a+\overset{1}{\cancel{11}}}{a+2}\cdot\dfrac{a+7}{3a+\underset{1}{\cancel{11}}}$

$=\dfrac{a+7}{a+2}$

44. $\dfrac{1}{R}=\dfrac{1}{R_1}+\dfrac{1}{R_2}$

$=\dfrac{1}{x}+\dfrac{1}{2x-4}$

$=\dfrac{1}{x}+\dfrac{1}{2(x-2)}$

$=\dfrac{2(x-2)}{x\cdot 2(x-2)}+\dfrac{x}{2(x-2)x}$

$=\dfrac{2x-4}{2x(x-2)}+\dfrac{x}{2x(x-2)}$

$=\dfrac{3x-4}{2x(x-2)}$

45. $\dfrac{1}{R}=\dfrac{1}{R_1}+\dfrac{1}{R_2}$

$=\dfrac{1}{30}+\dfrac{1}{20}$

$=\dfrac{2}{30(2)}+\dfrac{3}{20(3)}$

$=\dfrac{2}{60}+\dfrac{3}{60}$

$=\dfrac{5}{60}$ or $\dfrac{1}{12}$

Since $\dfrac{1}{R}=\dfrac{1}{12}$, the value of R is 12 ohms.

46. Use the equation $d=rt$, where d is the distance traveled at the faster rate, r is rate, and t is the time spent at that rate.

$t=\dfrac{d}{r}$

$=\dfrac{24\text{ mi}}{x\text{ mi/h}}$

$=\dfrac{24}{x}$ h

47. Use the equation $d=rt$, where d is the distance traveled at the slower rate, r is the rate, and t is the time spent at that rate.

$t=\dfrac{d}{r}$

$=\dfrac{24\text{mi}}{(x-4)\text{ mi/h}}$

$=\dfrac{24}{x-4}$ h

48. The amount of time Jalisa needed to complete the race is the sum of the amount of time spent at the faster pace and the amount of time spent at the slower pace.

$\dfrac{24}{x}+\dfrac{24}{x-4}=\dfrac{24(x-4)}{x(x-4)}+\dfrac{24x}{(x-4)x}$

$=\dfrac{24x-96}{x(x-4)}+\dfrac{24x}{x(x-4)}$

$=\dfrac{24x-96+24x}{x(x-4)}$

$=\dfrac{48x-96}{x(x-4)}$

$=\dfrac{48(x-2)}{x(x-4)}$ h

49. $H=\dfrac{m}{2L(d-L)^2}-\dfrac{m}{2L(d+L)^2}$

$=\dfrac{m(d+L)^2}{2L(d-L)^2(d+L)^2}-\dfrac{m(d-L)^2}{2L(d+L)^2(d-L)^2}$

$=\dfrac{m(d^2+2dL+L^2)}{2L(d-L)^2(d+L)^2}-\dfrac{m(d^2-2dL+L^2)}{2L(d-L)^2(d+L)^2}$

$=\dfrac{md^2+2mdL+mL^2}{2L(d-L)^2(d+L)^2}-\dfrac{md^2-2mdL+mL^2}{2L(d-L)^2(d+L)^2}$

$=\dfrac{md^2+2mdL+mL^2-(md^2-2mdL+mL^2)}{2L(d-L)^2(d+L)^2}$

$=\dfrac{md^2+2mdL+mL^2-md^2+2mdL-mL^2}{2L(d-L)^2(d+L)^2}$

$=\dfrac{\overset{1}{\cancel{2}}(2md\cancel{L})}{\underset{1\,1}{\cancel{2}\cancel{L}}(d-L)^2(d+L)^2}$

$=\dfrac{2md}{(d-L)^2(d+L)^2}$ or $\dfrac{2md}{(d^2-L^2)^2}$

50. Sample answer: $\dfrac{1}{x+1},\dfrac{1}{x-2}$

51. Subtraction of rational expressions can be used to determine the distance between the lens and the film if the focal length of the lens and the distance between the lens and the object are known. Answers should include the following.

- To subtract rational expressions, first find a common denominator. Then, write each fraction as an equivalent fraction with the common denominator. Subtract the numerators and place the difference over the common denominator. If possible, reduce the answer.

- $\dfrac{1}{q}=\dfrac{1}{10}-\dfrac{1}{60}$ could be used to determine the distance between the lens and the film if the focal length of the lens is 10 cm and the distance between the lens and the object is 60 cm.

52. B; $\dfrac{t^2-25}{3t-15}=\dfrac{(t-\overset{1}{\cancel{5}})(t+5)}{3(t-\underset{1}{\cancel{5}})}$

$=\dfrac{t+5}{3}$

53. C; $\dfrac{x-y}{5}+\dfrac{x+y}{4}=\dfrac{(x-y)4}{5(4)}+\dfrac{(x+y)5}{4(5)}$

$=\dfrac{4x-4y}{20}+\dfrac{5x+5y}{20}$

$=\dfrac{4x-4y+5x+5y}{20}$

$=\dfrac{9x+y}{20}$

54. $\dfrac{9x^2y^3}{(5xyz)^2} \div \dfrac{(3xy)^3}{20x^2y}$

$= \dfrac{9x^2y^3}{25x^2y^2z^2} \div \dfrac{27x^3y^3}{20x^2y}$

$= \dfrac{9x^2y^3}{25x^2y^2z^2} \cdot \dfrac{20x^2y}{27x^3y^3}$

$= \dfrac{\cancel{3}\cdot\cancel{3}\cdot\cancel{x}\cdot\cancel{x}\cdot\cancel{y}\cdot\cancel{y}\cdot\cancel{y}\cdot 2 \cdot 2 \cdot\cancel{5}\cdot\cancel{x}\cdot\cancel{x}\cdot\cancel{y}}{5\cdot 5\cdot\cancel{x}\cdot\cancel{x}\cdot\cancel{y}\cdot\cancel{y}\cdot z\cdot z\cdot\cancel{3}\cdot\cancel{3}\cdot 3\cdot\cancel{x}\cdot\cancel{x}\cdot x\cdot\cancel{y}\cdot\cancel{y}\cdot y}$

$= \dfrac{2 \cdot 2}{5 \cdot z \cdot z \cdot 3 \cdot x \cdot y}$

$= \dfrac{4}{15xyz^2}$

55. $\dfrac{5a^2 - 20}{2a + 2} \cdot \dfrac{4a}{10a - 20} = \dfrac{5(a-2)(a+2)}{2(a+1)} \cdot \dfrac{4a}{10(a-2)}$

$= \dfrac{\cancel{5}(a\cancel{-2})(a+2)\cdot\cancel{2}\cdot 2\cdot a}{2(a+1)\cdot\cancel{2}\cdot\cancel{5}(a\cancel{-2})}$

$= \dfrac{(a+2)a}{a+1}$

$= \dfrac{a(a+2)}{a+1}$

56. The graph of $9x^2 + y^2 < 81$ is the region inside the ellipse $9x^2 + y^2 = 81$. The graph of $x^2 + y^2 \geq 16$ is the circle $x^2 + y^2 = 16$ and the region outside it. The intersection of these regions represents the solution of the system of inequalities.

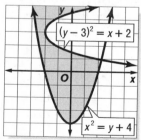

57. The graph of $(y-3)^2 \geq x + 2$ is the parabola $(y-3)^2 = x + 2$ and the region inside or to the right of it. The graph of $x^2 \leq y + 4$ is the parabola $x^2 = y + 4$ and the region inside or above it. The intersection of these regions represents the solution of the system of inequalities.

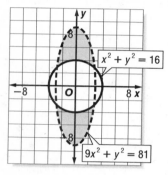

58. Let x be the amount by which each side of the garden is increased. Therefore, the dimensions of the larger garden are $25 + x + x$ or $25 + 2x$ feet by $50 + x + x$ or $50 + 2x$ feet. Use the equation $A = lw$ where A is the area of the larger rectangle or $1250 + 400 = 1650$ feet, $l = 50 + 2x$ and $w = 25 + 2x$ to determine the value of x.

$A = lw$

$1650 = (50 + 2x)(25 + 2x)$

$1650 = 1250 + 150x + 4x^2$

$400 = 150x + 4x^2$

$100 = x^2 + \dfrac{75}{2}x$

$100 + \dfrac{5625}{16} = x^2 + \dfrac{75}{2}x + \dfrac{5625}{16}$

$\dfrac{7225}{16} = \left(x + \dfrac{75}{4}\right)^2$

$\pm\dfrac{85}{4} = x + \dfrac{75}{4}$

$x = -\dfrac{75}{4} \pm \dfrac{85}{4}$

Each dimension should be increased by $\dfrac{5}{2}$ or 2.5 feet.

59. The equations of the asymptotes are $y = \pm\dfrac{b}{a}x$ or $y = \pm\dfrac{\sqrt{20}}{4}x$, which simplifies to $y = \pm\dfrac{\sqrt{5}}{2}x$. Graph the asymptotes. Draw an 8-unit by $4\sqrt{5}$-unit rectangle whose diagonals are the asymptotes. Then graph the hyperbola using the asymptotes as a guide.

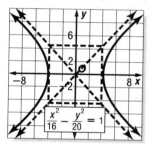

60. The equations of the asymptotes are $y = \pm\dfrac{a}{b}x$ or $y = \pm\dfrac{7}{5}x$. Graph the asymptotes. Draw a 10-unit by 14-unit rectangle whose diagonals are the asymptotes. Then graph the hyperbola using the asymptotes as a guide.

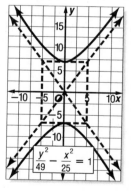

61. The equations of the asymptotes are

$y - k = \pm\frac{b}{a}(x - h)$ or $y - 5 = \pm\frac{5}{4}(x + 2)$, which

simplifies to $y = \frac{5}{4}x + \frac{15}{2}$ and $y = -\frac{5}{4}x + \frac{5}{2}$. Graph

the asymptotes. Draw an 8-unit by 10-unit rectangle whose diagonals are the asymptotes. Then graph the hyperbola using the asymptotes as a guide.

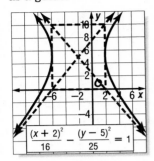

$$\frac{(x + 2)^2}{16} - \frac{(y - 5)^2}{25} = 1$$

Page 484 Practice Quiz 1

1. $\dfrac{t^2 - t - 6}{t^2 - 6t + 9} = \dfrac{(t - 3)(t + 2)}{(t - 3)(t - 3)}$

$\qquad = \dfrac{t + 2}{t - 3}$

2. $\dfrac{3ab^3}{8a^2b} \cdot \dfrac{4ac}{9b^4} = \dfrac{3 \cdot a \cdot b \cdot b \cdot b \cdot 2 \cdot 2 \cdot a \cdot c}{2 \cdot 2 \cdot 2 \cdot a \cdot a \cdot b \cdot 3 \cdot 3 \cdot b \cdot b \cdot b \cdot b}$

$\qquad = \dfrac{c}{2 \cdot 3 \cdot b \cdot b}$

$\qquad = \dfrac{c}{6b^2}$

3. $-\dfrac{4}{8x} \div \dfrac{16}{xy^2} = -\dfrac{4}{8x} \cdot \dfrac{xy^2}{16}$

$\qquad = -\dfrac{2 \cdot 2 \cdot x \cdot y \cdot y}{2 \cdot 2 \cdot 2 \cdot x \cdot 2 \cdot 2 \cdot 2 \cdot 2}$

$\qquad = -\dfrac{y \cdot y}{2 \cdot 2 \cdot 2 \cdot 2 \cdot 2}$

$\qquad = -\dfrac{y^2}{32}$

4. $\dfrac{48}{6a + 42} \cdot \dfrac{7a + 49}{16} = \dfrac{48}{6(a + 7)} \cdot \dfrac{7(a + 7)}{16}$

$\qquad = \dfrac{2 \cdot 2 \cdot 2 \cdot 2 \cdot 3 \cdot 7(a + 7)}{2 \cdot 3(a + 7) \cdot 2 \cdot 2 \cdot 2 \cdot 2}$

$\qquad = \dfrac{7}{2}$

5. $\dfrac{w^2 + 5w + 4}{6} \div \dfrac{w + 1}{18w + 24} = \dfrac{(w + 1)(w + 4)}{6} \div \dfrac{w + 1}{6(3w + 4)}$

$\qquad = \dfrac{(w + 1)(w + 4)}{6} \cdot \dfrac{6(3w + 4)}{w + 1}$

$\qquad = (w + 4)(3w + 4)$

6. $\dfrac{\frac{x^2 + x}{x + 1}}{\frac{x}{x - 1}} = \dfrac{\frac{x(x + 1)}{x + 1}}{\frac{x}{x - 1}}$

$\qquad = \dfrac{x(x + 1)}{x + 1} \div \dfrac{x}{x - 1}$

$\qquad = \dfrac{x(x + 1)}{x + 1} \cdot \dfrac{x - 1}{x}$

$\qquad = x - 1$

7. $\dfrac{4a + 2}{a + b} + \dfrac{1}{-b - a} = \dfrac{4a + 2}{a + b} + \dfrac{1(-1)}{(-b - a)(-1)}$

$\qquad = \dfrac{4a + 2}{a + b} + \dfrac{-1}{a + b}$

$\qquad = \dfrac{4a + 1}{a + b}$

8. $\dfrac{2x}{5ab^3} + \dfrac{4y}{3a^2b^2} = \dfrac{2x \cdot 3a}{5ab^3 \cdot 3a} + \dfrac{4y \cdot 5b}{3a^2b^2 \cdot 5b}$

$\qquad = \dfrac{6ax}{15a^2b^3} + \dfrac{20by}{15a^2b^3}$

$\qquad = \dfrac{6ax + 20by}{15a^2b^3}$

9. $\dfrac{5}{n + 6} - \dfrac{4}{n - 1} = \dfrac{5(n - 1)}{(n + 6)(n - 1)} - \dfrac{4(n + 6)}{(n - 1)(n + 6)}$

$\qquad = \dfrac{5n - 5}{(n + 6)(n - 1)} - \dfrac{4n + 24}{(n + 6)(n - 1)}$

$\qquad = \dfrac{5n - 5 - (4n + 24)}{(n + 6)(n - 1)}$

$\qquad = \dfrac{5n - 5 - 4n - 24}{(n + 6)(n - 1)}$

$\qquad = \dfrac{n - 29}{(n + 6)(n - 1)}$

10. $\dfrac{x - 5}{2x - 6} - \dfrac{x - 7}{4x - 12} = \dfrac{x - 5}{2(x - 3)} - \dfrac{x - 7}{4(x - 3)}$

$\qquad = \dfrac{(x - 5) \cdot 2}{2(x - 3) \cdot 2} - \dfrac{x - 7}{4(x - 3)}$

$\qquad = \dfrac{2x - 10}{4(x - 3)} - \dfrac{x - 7}{4(x - 3)}$

$\qquad = \dfrac{2x - 10 - (x - 7)}{4(x - 3)}$

$\qquad = \dfrac{2x - 10 - x + 7}{4(x - 3)}$

$\qquad = \dfrac{x - 3}{4(x - 3)}$

$\qquad = \dfrac{1}{4}$

Page 487 Algebra Activity

1.

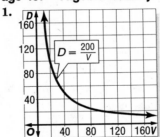

$$D = \frac{200}{V}$$

2. The asymptotes are $x = 0$ and $y = 0$.

9-3 Graphing Rational Equations

Page 488 Check for Understanding

1. Sample answer: $f(x) = \dfrac{1}{(x + 5)(x - 2)}$

2. Each of the graphs is a straight line passing through $(-5, 0)$ and $(0, 5)$. However, the graph of $f(x) = \dfrac{(x - 1)(x + 5)}{x - 1}$ has a hole at $(1, 6)$ and the graph of $g(x) = x + 5$ does not have a hole.

3. $x = 2$ and $y = 0$ are asymptotes of the graph. The y-intercept is 0.5 and there is no x-intercept because $y = 0$ is an asymptote.

4. $\dfrac{3}{x^2 - 4x + 4} = \dfrac{3}{(x - 2)^2}$

The function is undefined for $x = 2$. Since $\dfrac{3}{(x - 2)^2}$ is in simplest form, $x = 2$ is an asymptote.

5. $\dfrac{x - 1}{x^2 + 4x - 5} = \dfrac{x - 1}{(x - 1)(x + 5)}$

The function is undefined for $x = 1$ and $x = -5$.

Since $\dfrac{x - 1}{(x - 1)(x + 5)} = \dfrac{1}{x + 5}$, $x = -5$ is an asymptote, and $x = 1$ represents a hole in the graph.

449

6. The function is undefined for $x = -1$. Since $\frac{x}{x+1}$ is in simplest form, $x = -1$ is a vertical asymptote. Draw the asymptote. Make a table of values. Plot the points and draw the graph.

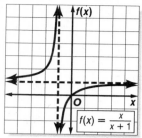

$$f(x) = \frac{x}{x+1}$$

7. The function is undefined for $x = 2$ and $x = -3$. Since $\frac{6}{(x-2)(x+3)}$ is in simplest form, $x = 2$ and $x = -3$ are asymptotes. Draw the asymptotes. Make a table of values. Plot the points and draw the graph.

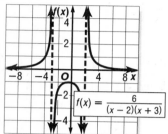

$$f(x) = \frac{6}{(x-2)(x+3)}$$

8. Notice that $\frac{x^2 - 25}{x - 5} = \frac{(x-5)(x+5)}{x-5}$ or $x + 5$.

Therefore, the graph of $f(x) = \frac{x^2 - 25}{x - 5}$ is the graph of $f(x) = x + 5$ with a hole at $x = 5$.

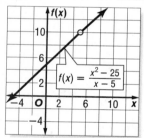

$$f(x) = \frac{x^2 - 25}{x - 5}$$

9. The function is undefined for $x = -1$. Since $\frac{x-5}{x+1}$ is in simplest form, $x = -1$ is an asymptote. Draw the asymptote. Make a table of values. Plot the points and draw the points and draw the graph.

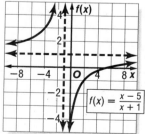

$$f(x) = \frac{x-5}{x+1}$$

10. The function is undefined for $x = 1$. Since $\frac{4}{(x-1)^2}$ is in simplest form, $x = 1$ is an asymptote. Draw the asymptote. Make a table of values. Plot the points and draw the graph.

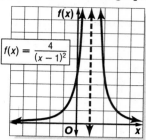

$$f(x) = \frac{4}{(x-1)^2}$$

11. Notice that $\frac{x+2}{x^2 - x - 6} = \frac{x+2}{(x-3)(x+2)}$. The function is undefined for $x = 3$ and $x = -2$. Since $\frac{x+2}{(x-3)(x+2)} = \frac{1}{x-3}$, $x = 3$ is an asymptote, and $x = -2$ represents a hole in the graph.

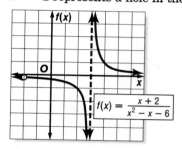

$$f(x) = \frac{x+2}{x^2 - x - 6}$$

12. $C = \frac{y}{y+12} \cdot D$

$= \frac{8}{8+12} \cdot 250$

$= 100$

The dosage is 100 mg.

13. The function is undefined for $y = -12$. Since $\frac{y}{y+12}$ is in simplest form, $y = -12$ is an asymptote. Graph the asymptote and the function. Notice that the horizontal asymptote is $C = 1$.

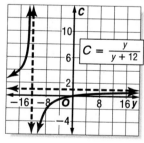

$$C = \frac{y}{y+12}$$

14. In the previous exercise, we determined that the asymptotes of the graph are $y = -12$ and $C = 1$. The y-intercept of the graph is the value of y when $C = 0$, or $y = 0$. The C-intercept of the graph is the value of C when $y = 0$, or $C = 0$.

15. In the problem context, the child's age and the child's dose are positive values. Therefore, only values of y greater than 0 and values of C between 0 and 1 are meaningful.

16. $\frac{2}{x^2 - 5x + 6} = \frac{2}{(x - 2)(x - 3)}$

The function is undefined for $x = 2$ and $x = 3$.

Since $\frac{2}{x^2 - 5x + 6}$ is in simplest form, $x = 2$ and

$x = 3$ are asymptotes of the function.

17. $\frac{4}{x^2 + 2x - 8} = \frac{4}{(x + 4)(x - 2)}$

The function is undefined for $x = -4$ and $x = 2$.

Since $\frac{4}{(x + 4)(x - 2)}$ is in simplest form, $x = -4$ and

$x = 2$ are asymptotes of the function.

18. $\frac{x + 3}{x^2 + 7x + 12} = \frac{x + 3}{(x + 3)(x + 4)}$

The function is undefined for $x = -3$ and $x = -4$.

Since $\frac{x + 3}{(x + 3)(x + 4)} = \frac{1}{x + 4}$, $x = -4$ is an asymptote,

and $x = -3$ represents a hole in the graph.

19. $\frac{x - 5}{x^2 - 4x - 5} = \frac{x - 5}{(x - 5)(x + 1)}$

The function is undefined for $x = 5$ and $x = -1$.

Since $\frac{x - 5}{(x - 5)(x + 1)} = \frac{1}{x + 1}$, $x = -1$ is an asymptote,

and $x = 5$ represents a hole in the graph.

20. $\frac{x^2 - 8x + 16}{x - 4} = \frac{(x - 4)^2}{x - 4}$

The function is undefined for $x = 4$. Since

$\frac{(x - 4)^2}{x - 4} = x - 4$, $x = 4$ represents a hole in the

graph.

21. $\frac{x^2 - 3x + 2}{x - 1} = \frac{(x - 2)(x - 1)}{x - 1}$

The function is undefined for $x = 1$. Since

$\frac{(x - 2)(x - 1)}{x - 1} = x - 2$, $x = 1$ represents a hole in the

graph.

22. The function is undefined for $x = 0$. Since $\frac{1}{x}$ is in

simplest form, $x = 0$ is an asymptote. Draw the
asymptote. Make a table of values. Plot the points
and draw the graph.

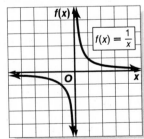

23. The function is undefined for $x = 0$. Since $\frac{3}{x}$ is in

simplest form, $x = 0$ is an asymptote. Draw the
asymptote. Make a table of values. Plot the points
and draw the graph.

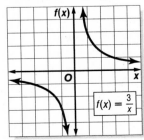

24. The function is undefined for $x = -2$. Since $\frac{1}{x + 2}$

is in simplest form, $x = -2$ is an asymptote. Draw
the asymptote: Make a table of values. Plot the
points and draw the graph.

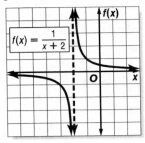

25. The function is undefined for $x = -1$. Since $\frac{-5}{x + 1}$

is in simplest form, $x = -1$ is an asymptote. Draw
the asymptote. Make a table of values. Plot the
points and draw the graph.

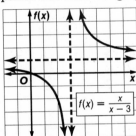

26. The function is undefined for $x = 3$. Since $\frac{x}{x - 3}$ is

in simplest form, $x = 3$ is an asymptote. Notice
that the horizontal asymptote is $y = 1$. Draw the
asymptotes. Make a table of values. Plot the
points and draw the graph.

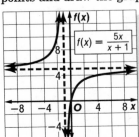

27. The function is undefined for $x = -1$. Since $\frac{5x}{x + 1}$ is

in simplest form, $x = -1$ is an asymptote. Notice
that the horizontal asymptote is $y = 5$. Draw the
asymptotes. Make a table of values. Plot the
points and draw the graph.

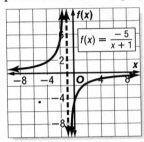

28. The function is undefined for $x = 2$. Since $\frac{-3}{(x-2)^2}$ is in simplest form, $x = 2$ is an asymptote. Draw the asymptote. Make a table of values. Plot the points and draw the graph.

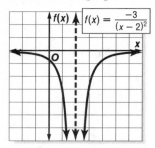

$$f(x) = \frac{-3}{(x-2)^2}$$

29. The function is undefined for $x = -3$. Since $\frac{1}{(x+3)^2}$ is in simplest form, $x = -3$ is an asymptote. Draw the asymptote. Make a table of values. Plot the points and draw the graph.

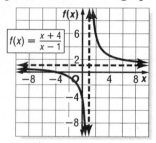

$$f(x) = \frac{1}{(x+3)^2}$$

30. The function is undefined for $x = 1$. Since $\frac{x+4}{x-1}$ is in simplest form, $x = 1$ is an asymptote. Notice that the horizontal asymptote is $y = 1$. Draw the asymptotes. Make a table of values. Plot the points and draw the graph.

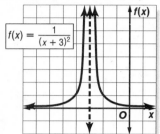

$$f(x) = \frac{x+4}{x-1}$$

31. The function is not defined for $x = 3$. Since $\frac{x-1}{x-3}$ is in simplest form, $x = 3$ is an asymptote. Notice that the horizontal asymptote is $y = 1$. Draw the asymptotes. Make a table of values. Plot the points and draw the graph.

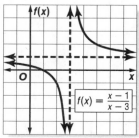

$$f(x) = \frac{x-1}{x-3}$$

32. Notice that $\frac{x^2 - 36}{x + 6} = \frac{(x+6)(x-6)}{x+6}$ or $x - 6$. Therefore, the graph of $f(x) = \frac{x^2 - 36}{x + 6}$ is the graph of $f(x) = x - 6$ with a hole at $x = -6$.

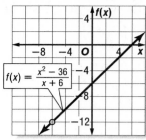

$$f(x) = \frac{x^2 - 36}{x + 6}$$

33. Notice that $\frac{x^2 - 1}{x - 1} = \frac{(x-1)(x+1)}{x-1}$ or $x + 1$. Therefore, the graph of $f(x) = \frac{x^2 - 1}{x - 1}$ is the graph of $f(x) = x + 1$ with a hole at $x = 1$.

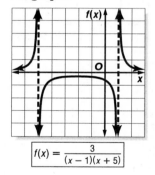

$$f(x) = \frac{x^2 - 1}{x - 1}$$

34. The function is undefined for $x = 1$ and $x = -5$. Since $\frac{3}{(x-1)(x+5)}$ is in simplest form, $x = 1$ and $x = -5$ are asymptotes. Draw the asymptotes. Make a table of values. Plot the points and draw the graph.

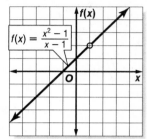

$$f(x) = \frac{3}{(x-1)(x+5)}$$

35. The function is undefined for $x = -2$ and $x = 3$. Since $\frac{-1}{(x+2)(x-3)}$ is in simplest form, $x = -2$ and $x = 3$ are asymptotes. Draw the asymptotes. Make a table of values. Plot the points and draw the graph.

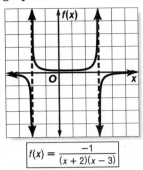

$$f(x) = \frac{-1}{(x+2)(x-3)}$$

36. Notice that $\frac{x}{x^2 - 1} = \frac{x}{(x-1)(x+1)}$. Therefore, the function is undefined for $x = 1$ and $x = -1$. Since $\frac{x}{x^2 - 1}$ is in simplest form, $x = 1$ and $x = -1$ are asymptotes. Draw the asymptotes. Make a table of values. Plot the points and draw the graph.

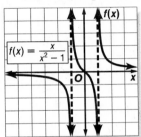

$$f(x) = \frac{x}{x^2 - 1}$$

37. Notice that $\frac{x-1}{x^2 - 4} = \frac{x-1}{(x-2)(x+2)}$. Therefore, the function is undefined for $x = 2$ and $x = -2$. Since $\frac{x-1}{x^2 - 4}$ is in simplest form, $x = 2$ and $x = -2$ are asymptotes. Draw the asymptotes. Make a table of values. Plot the points and draw the graph.

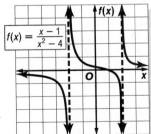

$$f(x) = \frac{x-1}{x^2 - 4}$$

38. The function is undefined for $x = 6$. Since $\frac{6}{(x-6)^2}$ is in simplest form, $x = 6$ is an asymptote. Draw the asymptote. Make a table of values. Plot the points and draw the graph.

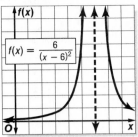

$$f(x) = \frac{6}{(x-6)^2}$$

39. The function is undefined for $x = -2$. Since $\frac{1}{(x+2)^2}$ is in simplest form, $x = -2$ is an asymptote. Draw the asymptote. Make a table of values. Plot the points and draw the graph.

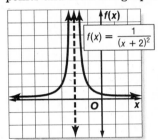

$$f(x) = \frac{1}{(x+2)^2}$$

40. $f(x) = \dfrac{a^3}{x^2 + a^2}$
$= \dfrac{(4)^3}{x^2 + (4)^2}$
$= \dfrac{64}{x^2 + 16}$

Make a table of values. Plot the points and draw the graph.

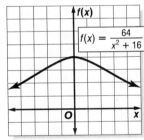

$$f(x) = \frac{64}{x^2 + 16}$$

41. From the previous exercise, we see that the graph is bell-shaped with a horizontal asymptote at $f(x) = 0$.

42. $f(x) = \dfrac{a^3}{x^2 + a^2}$
$= \dfrac{(-4)^3}{x^2 + (-4)^2}$
$= \dfrac{-64}{x^2 + 16}$

Since $\dfrac{-64}{x^2 + 16} = -\left(\dfrac{64}{x^2 + 16}\right)$, the graph of $f(x) = \dfrac{-64}{x^2 + 16}$ would be a reflection of the graph of $f(x) = \dfrac{64}{x^2 + 16}$ over the x-axis.

43. $V_f = \dfrac{(m_1 - m_2)v_i}{m_1 + m_2}$

$\quad = \dfrac{(m_1 - 7) \cdot 5}{m_1 + 7}$

The function is undefined for $m_1 = -7$. Since $\dfrac{(m_1 - 7) \cdot 5}{m_1 + 7}$ is in simplest form, $m_1 = -7$ is an asymptote. Graph the function.

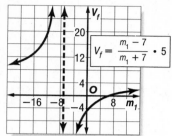

44. From the previous exercise, we know that the equation of the vertical asymptote is $m_1 = -7$. The m_1-intercept is the value of m_1 when $V_f = 0$, or 7. The V_f-intercept is the value of V_f when $m_1 = 0$, or -5.

45. $V_f = \dfrac{(m_1 - 7) \cdot 5}{m_1 + 7}$

$\quad = \dfrac{(5 - 7) \cdot 5}{5 + 7}$

$\quad = -\dfrac{5}{6}$

$\quad \approx -0.83$

The value of V_f when $m_1 = 5$ is about -0.83 m/s.

46. Student answers should be rational functions whose denominators have at least one factor of $x - 3$, and whose numerators and denominators have the same number of factors of $x + 2$; Sample answers: $f(x) = \dfrac{x + 2}{(x + 2)(x - 3)}$, $f(x) = \dfrac{2(x + 2)}{(x + 2)(x - 3)}$, $f(x) = \dfrac{5(x + 2)}{(x + 2)(x - 3)}$.

47. The function is not defined for $x = -10$. Since $\dfrac{6 + x}{10 + x}$ is in simplest form, $x = -10$ is an asymptote. Notice that the horizontal asymptote is $y = 1$. Draw the asymptotes. Make a table of values. Plot the points and draw the graph.

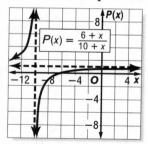

48. In the problem context, free-throw percentage and number of consecutive free throws are positive values. Therefore, the values of $P(x)$ and x are both greater than 0, so the part of the graph that is meaningful is the part in the first quadrant.

49. The y-intercept represents her original free-throw percentage of 60%.

50. From Exercise 47, we know that the equation of the horizontal asymptote is $y = 1$; This represents 100%, accuracy in making free throws, which she cannot achieve because she has already missed 4 free throws.

51. A rational function can be used to determine how much each person owes if the cost of the gift is known and the number of the people sharing the cost is s. Answers should include the following.

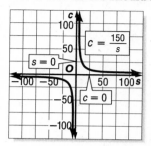

- Only the portion in the first quadrant is significant in the real world because there cannot be a negative number of people nor a negative amount of money owed for the gift.

52. A; The function graphed is undefined for $x = 0$ and $x = 2$.

53. B; Since $\dfrac{x^2 + 8}{2} = \dfrac{1}{2}x^2 + 4$, the graph of the function has a y-intercept of 4, so y must be greater than or equal to 4.

Page 490   Maintain Your Skills

54. $\dfrac{3m + 2}{m + n} + \dfrac{4}{2m + 2n} = \dfrac{3m + 2}{m + n} + \dfrac{4}{2(m + n)}$

$\quad = \dfrac{(3m + 2) \cdot 2}{(m + n) \cdot 2} + \dfrac{4}{2(m + n)}$

$\quad = \dfrac{6m + 4}{2(m + n)} + \dfrac{4}{2(m + n)}$

$\quad = \dfrac{6m + 8}{2(m + n)}$

$\quad = \dfrac{\overset{1}{\cancel{2}}(3m + 4)}{\underset{1}{\cancel{2}}(m + n)}$

$\quad = \dfrac{3m + 4}{m + n}$

55. $\dfrac{5}{x + 3} - \dfrac{2}{x - 2} = \dfrac{5(x - 2)}{(x + 3)(x - 2)} - \dfrac{2(x + 3)}{(x - 2)(x + 3)}$

$\quad = \dfrac{5x - 10}{(x + 3)(x - 2)} - \dfrac{2x + 6}{(x + 3)(x - 2)}$

$\quad = \dfrac{5x - 10 - (2x + 6)}{(x + 3)(x - 2)}$

$\quad = \dfrac{5x - 10 - 2x - 6}{(x + 3)(x - 2)}$

$\quad = \dfrac{3x - 16}{(x + 3)(x - 2)}$

56. $\dfrac{2w - 4}{w + 3} \div \dfrac{2w + 6}{5} = \dfrac{2(w - 2)}{w + 3} \div \dfrac{2(w + 3)}{5}$

$\quad = \dfrac{2(w - 2)}{w + 3} \cdot \dfrac{5}{2(w + 3)}$

$\quad = \dfrac{\overset{1}{\cancel{2}}(w - 2) \cdot 5}{(w + 3) \cdot \underset{1}{\cancel{2}}(w + 3)}$

$\quad = \dfrac{5(w - 2)}{(w + 3)^2}$

57. The center of the circle is at $(6, 2)$, and its radius is $\sqrt{25}$ or 5.

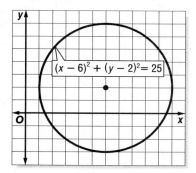

58.
$$x^2 + y^2 + 4x = 9$$
$$x^2 + 4x + \blacksquare + y^2 = 9 + \blacksquare$$
$$x^2 + 4x + 4 + y^2 = 9 + 4$$
$$(x + 2)^2 + y^2 = 13$$

The center of the circle is at $(-2, 0)$, and its radius is $\sqrt{13}$.

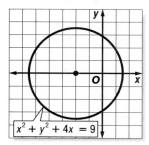

59. At the end of the first year, the value of the first painting Joyce bought was $20,000 + 0.14(20,000)$ or $22,800. After the second year, its value was $22,800 + 0.14(22,800)$ or $25,992. During the same year, the value of the second painting Joyce bought increased to $35,000 + 0.14(35,000)$ or $39,900. Therefore, the two paintings are now worth $25,992 + 39,900$ or $65,892.

60. $x^2 + 8x + 20 = 0$
$$x^2 + 8x = -20$$
$$x^2 + 8x + \blacksquare = -20 + \blacksquare$$
$$x^2 + 8x + 16 = -20 + 16$$
$$(x + 4)^2 = -4$$
$$x + 4 = \pm\sqrt{-4}$$
$$x + 4 = \pm i\sqrt{4}$$
$$x + 4 = \pm 2i$$
$$x = -4 \pm 2i$$

The solution set is $\{-4 + 2i, -4 - 2i\}$.

61. $x^2 + 2x - 120 = 0$
$$x^2 + 2x = 120$$
$$x^2 + 2x + \blacksquare = 120 + \blacksquare$$
$$x^2 + 2x + 1 = 120 + 1$$
$$(x + 1)^2 = 121$$
$$x + 1 = \pm 11$$
$$x = -1 \pm 11$$
$$x = -1 + 11 \quad \text{or} \quad x = -1 - 11$$
$$x = 10 \qquad\qquad x = -12$$

The solution set is $\{-12, 10\}$.

62. $x^2 + 7x - 17 = 0$
$$x^2 + 7x = 17$$
$$x^2 + 7x + \blacksquare = 17 + \blacksquare$$
$$x^2 + 7x + \frac{49}{4} = 17 + \frac{49}{4}$$
$$\left(x + \frac{7}{2}\right)^2 = \frac{117}{4}$$
$$x + \frac{7}{2} = \pm\frac{3\sqrt{13}}{2}$$
$$x = -\frac{7}{2} \pm \frac{3\sqrt{13}}{2} \quad \text{or} \quad -\frac{7 \pm 3\sqrt{13}}{2}$$

The solution set is $\left\{ -\frac{7 - 3\sqrt{13}}{2}, -\frac{7 + 3\sqrt{13}}{2} \right\}$.

63.
$$\frac{16}{v} = \frac{32}{9}$$
$$v\left(\frac{16}{v}\right) = v\left(\frac{32}{9}\right)$$
$$16 = \frac{32}{9}v$$
$$\frac{9}{32}(16) = \frac{9}{32}\left(\frac{32}{9}\right)v$$
$$4.5 = v$$

64.
$$\frac{7}{25} = \frac{a}{5}$$
$$5\left(\frac{7}{25}\right) = 5\left(\frac{a}{5}\right)$$
$$1.4 = a$$

65.
$$\frac{6}{15} = \frac{8}{s}$$
$$s\left(\frac{6}{15}\right) = s\left(\frac{8}{s}\right)$$
$$\frac{6}{15}s = 8$$
$$\frac{15}{6}\left(\frac{6}{15}\right)s = \frac{15}{6}(8)$$
$$s = 20$$

66.
$$\frac{b}{9} = \frac{40}{30}$$
$$9\left(\frac{b}{9}\right) = 9\left(\frac{40}{30}\right)$$
$$b = 12$$

Page 491   Graphing Calculator Investigation (Follow-Up of Lesson 9-3)

1. KEYSTROKES: $\boxed{y=}$ 1 $\boxed{\div}$ $\boxed{\text{X,T},\theta,n}$ $\boxed{\text{ZOOM}}$ 6

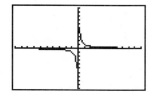

$[-10, 10]$ scl: 1 by $[-10, 10]$ scl: 1

By looking at the equation notice that the function is undefined for $x = 0$. The equation of the vertical asymptote is $x = 0$. As x grows larger and as x grows smaller, the y values approach 0. So, the equation of the horizontal asymptote is $y = 0$.

2. KEYSTROKES:

[−5, 5] scl: 1 by [−5, 5] scl: 1

By looking at the equation, notice that the function is undefined for $x = -2$. The equation of the vertical asymptote is $x = -2$. As x grows larger and as x grows smaller, the y values approach 1. So, the equation of the horizontal asymptote is $y = 1$.

3. KEYSTROKES:

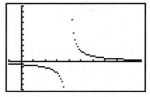

[−1, 10] scl: 1 by [−5, 10] scl: 1

By looking at the function, notice that the function is undefined for $x = 4$. The equation of the vertical asymptote is $x = 4$. As x grows larger and as x grows smaller, the y values approach 0. So, the equation of the horizontal asymptote is $y = 0$.

4. KEYSTROKES:

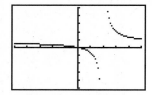

[−5, 5] scl: 1 by [−5, 5] scl: 1

By looking at the function, notice that the function is undefined for $x = 2$. The equation of the vertical asymptote is $x = 2$. As x grows larger and as x grows smaller, the y values approach $\frac{2}{3}$. So, the equation of the horizontal asymptote is $y = \frac{2}{3}$.

5. KEYSTROKES: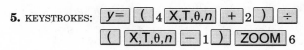

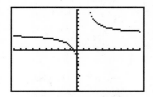

[−10, 10] scl: 1 by [−10, 10] scl: 1

By looking at the function, notice that the function is undefined for $x = 1$. The equation of the vertical asymptote is $x = 1$. As x grows larger and as x grows smaller, the y values approach 4. So, the equation of the horizontal asymptote is $y = 4$.

6. The function has a point discontinuity, so put the calculator in dot mode.

MODE ▼ ▼ ▼ ▼ ▶ ENTER

Graph the function.

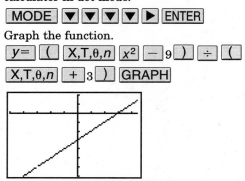

[−5, 4.4] scl: 1 by [−7, 2] scl: 1

This graph looks like a line with a break in continuity at $x = -3$. This is because the denominator equals 0 when $x = -3$. Therefore, the function is undefined when $x = -3$. The function has a point discontinuity at $x = -3$.

7. From the previous exercise, we know graph 6 has a point discontinuity.

8. Functions that have point discontinuity are rational functions where a value of the function is not defined, but the rational expression in simplest form is defined for that value.

9-4 **Direct, Joint, and Inverse Variation**

Page 495　Check for Understanding

1a. The graph represents an inverse variation.

1b. The graph represents a direct variation.

2. Both are examples of direct variation. For $y = 5x$, y increases as x increases. For $y = -5x$, y decreases as x increases.

3. Sample answers: wages and hours worked, total cost and number of pounds of apples; distances traveled and amount of gas remaining in the tank, distance of an object and the size it appears

4. The equation is of the form $xy = k$, where $k = 20$. Therefore, the equation represents an inverse variation; the constant of variation is 20.

5. Rewrite $\frac{y}{x} = -0.5$ as $y = -0.5x$. The equation is of the form $y = kx$, where $k = -0.5$. Therefore, the equation represents a direct variation; the constant of variation is -0.5.

6. The equation is of the form $y = kxz$, where $k = \frac{1}{2}$. Therefore, the equation represents a joint variation; the constant of variation is $\frac{1}{2}$.

7.
$$\frac{y_1}{x_1} = \frac{y_2}{x_2}$$
$$\frac{18}{15} = \frac{y_2}{20}$$
$$20(18) = 15(y_2)$$
$$360 = 15y_2$$
$$24 = y_2$$
When $x = 20$, the value of y is 24.

8.
$$\frac{y_1}{x_1 z_1} = \frac{y_2}{x_2 z_2}$$
$$\frac{-90}{-6(15)} = \frac{y_2}{9(-5)}$$
$$9(-5)(-90) = -6(15)(y_2)$$
$$4050 = -90y_2$$
$$-45 = y_2$$
When $x = 9$ and $z = -5$, the value of y is -45.

9.
$$\frac{x_1}{y_2} = \frac{x_2}{y_1}$$
$$\frac{12}{21} = \frac{x_2}{-14}$$
$$12(-14) = 21(x_2)$$
$$-168 = 21x_2$$
$$-8 = x_2$$
When $y = 21$, the value of x is -8.

10. Since the pressure in a person's ears varies directly with the depth at which he or she is swimming, an equation that represents the situation is of the form $\frac{y_1}{x_1} = \frac{y_2}{x_2}$, where y represents the pressure in the person's ears, and x represents the depth at which he or she is swimming.
$$\frac{y_1}{x_1} = \frac{y_2}{x_2}$$
$$\frac{P}{d} = \frac{4.3}{10}$$
$$\frac{P}{d} = 0.43$$
$$P = 0.43d$$
An equation of direct variation is $P = 0.43d$.

11. From the previous exercise, we know that an equation of direct variation that represents the given situation is $P = 0.43d$. Substitute 60 for d in the equation to determine the value of P.
$$P = 0.43d$$
$$P = 0.43(60)$$
$$P = 25.8$$
The pressure at 60 feet is 25.8 pounds per square inch.

12. We know from Exercise 10 that an equation of direct variation that represents the given situation is $P = 0.43d$. Substitute 65 for P in the equation to determine the value of d.
$$P = 0.43d$$
$$65 = 0.43d$$
$$151.16 \approx d$$
The amateur diver can safely swim to a depth of about 150 feet.

13. Answers may vary; Sample table:

Depth (ft)	Pressure (psi)
0	0
1	0.43
2	0.86
3	1.29
4	1.72

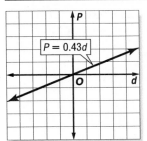

Pages 496–498   Practice and Apply

14. Rewrite $\frac{n}{m} = 1.5$ as $n = 1.5m$. The equation is of the form $y = kx$, where $k = 1.5$. Therefore, the equation represents a direct variation; the constant of variation is 1.5.

15. The equation is of the form $y = kxz$, where $k = 5$. Therefore, the equation represents a joint variation; the constant of variation is 5.

16. The equation is of the form $xy = k$, where $k = -18$. Therefore, the equation represents an inverse variation; the constant of variation is -18.

17. Rewrite $3 = \frac{a}{b}$ as $a = 3b$. The equation is of the form $y = kx$, where $k = 3$. Therefore, the equation represents a direct variation; the constant of variation is 3.

18. Rewrite $p = \frac{12}{q}$ as $pq = 12$. The equation is of the form $xy = k$, where $k = 12$. Therefore, the equation represents an inverse variation; the constant of variation is 12.

19. The equation is of the form $y = kx$, where $k = -7$. Therefore, the equation represents a direct variation; the constant of variation is -7.

20. The equation is of the form $y = kxz$, where $y = \frac{1}{3}$. Therefore, the equation represents a joint variation; the constant of variation is $\frac{1}{3}$.

21. Rewrite $\frac{2.5}{t} = s$ as $st = 2.5$. The equation is of the form $xy = k$, where $k = 2.5$. Therefore, the equation represents an inverse variation; the constant of variation is 2.5.

22. The equation is of the form $y = \frac{k}{x}$, where y is the variation in volume V, and x is the pressure P. Therefore, an equation for Boyle's Law is $V = \frac{k}{p}$.

23. The equation is of the form $y = kx$, where y is the volume V, and x is the temperature t. Therefore, an equation for Charles' Law is $V = kt$.

24. The formula for the circumference of a circle is $C = 2\pi r$, where C is the circumference, and r is the radius of the circle. The equation is of the form $y = kx$, where $k = 2\pi$. Therefore, the circumference of a circle varies directly with the radius, and the constant of variation is 2π.

25. The distance between the towns on the map is directly proportional to the distance between the towns in kilometers. Use the equation $\frac{y_1}{x_1} = \frac{y_2}{x_2}$, where x represents the distance on the map and y represents the distance in kilometers, to determine the distance between the towns if they are 7.9 centimeters apart on the map.

$$\frac{y_1}{x_1} = \frac{y_2}{x_2}$$
$$\frac{45}{3} = \frac{y_2}{7.9}$$
$$7.9(45) = 3(y_2)$$
$$355.5 = 3y_2$$
$$118.5 = y_2$$

The towns are 118.5 kilometers apart.

26.
$$\frac{y_1}{x_1} = \frac{y_2}{x_2}$$
$$\frac{15}{3} = \frac{y_2}{12}$$
$$12(15) = 3(y_2)$$
$$180 = 3y_2$$
$$60 = y_2$$

When $x = 12$, the value of y is 60.

27.
$$\frac{y_1}{x_1} = \frac{y_2}{x_2}$$
$$\frac{8}{6} = \frac{y_2}{15}$$
$$15(8) = 6(y_2)$$
$$120 = 6y_2$$
$$20 = y_2$$

When $x = 15$, the value of y is 20.

28.
$$\frac{y_1}{x_1 z_1} = \frac{y_2}{x_2 z_2}$$
$$\frac{192}{8(6)} = \frac{y_2}{2(27)}$$
$$2(27)(192) = 8(6)(y_2)$$
$$10,368 = 48y_2$$
$$216 = y_2$$

When $x = 2$ and $z = 27$, the value of y is 216.

29.
$$\frac{y_1}{x_1 z_1} = \frac{y_2}{x_2 z_2}$$
$$\frac{80}{5(8)} = \frac{y_2}{16(2)}$$
$$16(2)(80) = 5(8)(y_2)$$
$$2560 = 40y_2$$
$$64 = y_2$$

When $x = 16$ and $z = 2$, the value of y is 64.

30.
$$\frac{y_1}{x_2} = \frac{y_2}{x_1}$$
$$\frac{5}{2} = \frac{y_2}{10}$$
$$5(10) = 2(y_2)$$
$$50 = 2y_2$$
$$25 = y_2$$

When $x = 2$, the value of y is 25.

31.
$$\frac{y_1}{x_2} = \frac{y_2}{x_1}$$
$$\frac{16}{20} = \frac{y_2}{5}$$
$$16(5) = 20(y_2)$$
$$80 = 20y_2$$
$$4 = y_2$$

When $x = 20$, the value of y is 4.

32.
$$\frac{x_1}{y_2} = \frac{x_2}{y_1}$$
$$\frac{25}{40} = \frac{x_2}{2}$$
$$25(2) = 40(x_2)$$
$$50 = 40x_2$$
$$1.25 = x_2$$

When $y = 40$, the value of x is 1.25.

33.
$$\frac{y_1}{x_2} = \frac{y_2}{x_1}$$
$$\frac{4}{5} = \frac{y_2}{12}$$
$$4(12) = 5(y_2)$$
$$48 = 5y_2$$
$$9.6 = y_2$$

When $x = 5$, the value of y is 9.6.

34.
$$\frac{y_1}{x_1} = \frac{y_2}{x_2}$$
$$\frac{9}{-15} = \frac{y_2}{21}$$
$$9(21) = -15(y_2)$$
$$189 = -15y_2$$
$$-12.6 = y_2$$

When $x = 21$, the value of y is -12.6.

35.
$$\frac{y_1}{x_1} = \frac{y_2}{x_2}$$
$$\frac{0.5}{6} = \frac{y_2}{10}$$
$$0.5(10) = 6(y_2)$$
$$5 = 6y_2$$
$$0.83 \approx y_2$$

When $x = 10$, the value of y is about 0.83.

36.
$$\frac{y_1}{x_1 z_1} = \frac{y_2}{x_2 z_2}$$
$$\frac{45}{6(10)} = \frac{y_2}{\frac{1}{2}(6)}$$
$$\frac{1}{2}(6)(45) = 6(10)(y_2)$$
$$135 = 60y_2$$
$$2\frac{1}{4} = y_2$$

When $x = \frac{1}{2}$ and $z = 6$, the value of y is $2\frac{1}{4}$.

37.
$$\frac{y_1}{x_1 z_1} = \frac{y_2}{x_2 z_2}$$
$$\frac{\frac{1}{8}}{\frac{1}{2}(3)} = \frac{y_2}{6\left(\frac{1}{3}\right)}$$
$$6\left(\frac{1}{3}\right)\left(\frac{1}{8}\right) = \frac{1}{2}(3)(y_2)$$
$$\frac{1}{4} = \frac{3}{2}y_2$$
$$\frac{1}{6} = y_2$$

When $x = 6$ and $z = \frac{1}{3}$, the value of y is $\frac{1}{6}$.

38. Paul's average speed is inversely proportional to the time it takes him to drive between his house and work. Use the equation $\frac{x_1}{y_2} = \frac{x_2}{y_1}$, where x represents Paul's average speed and y represents the duration of his drive, to determine his average speed going home.
$$\frac{x_1}{y_2} = \frac{x_2}{y_1}$$
$$\frac{40}{20} = \frac{x_2}{15}$$
$$40(15) = 20(x_2)$$
$$600 = 20x_2$$
$$30 = x_2$$

Paul's average speed going home was 30 miles per hour.

39. The amount of water is directly proportional to the amount of snow. Use the equation $\frac{y_1}{x_1} = \frac{y_2}{x_2}$, where x represents the amount of snow and y represents the amount of water produced, to determine how much water 900 cubic centimeters of snow produces.
$$\frac{y_1}{x_1} = \frac{y_2}{x_2}$$
$$\frac{28}{250} = \frac{y_2}{900}$$
$$28(900) = 250(y_2)$$
$$25{,}200 = 250y_2$$
$$100.8 = y_2$$

900 cubic centimeters of snow produce 100.8 cubic centimeters of water.

40. See students' work.

41. The amount of meat m needed is the product of the number of pounds of meat required per Siberian tiger per day, the number of Siberian tigers s, and the number of days d. Therefore, an equation that represents the amount of meat needed is $m = 20sd$.

42. The equation in Exercise 41, $m = 20sd$, is of the form $y = kxz$. Therefore, it is a joint variation.

43. From Exercise 41, we know the amount of meat m needed to sustain s Siberian tigers for d days is given by the equation $m = 20sd$. Therefore, substitute 3 for s and the number of days in January, 31, for d in the equation to determine the value of m.
$$m = 20sd$$
$$m = 20(3)(31)$$
$$m = 1860$$
1860 pounds of meat are needed.

44. The average number of laughs ℓ is the product of the number of times the average American laughs per day, the number of household members m, and the number of days d. Therefore, an equation that represents the average number of laughs is $\ell = 15md$.

45. The equation in Exercise 44, $\ell = 15md$, is of the form $y = kxz$. Therefore, it is a joint variation.

46. See students' work.

47. Since sound intensity I varies inversely as the square of the distance from the sound source d, or d^2, an equation that represents this situation is $I = \frac{k}{d^2}$.

48.

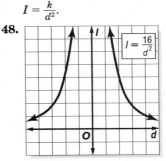

49. From Exercise 47, we know that the equation that represents sound intensity is $I = \frac{k}{d^2}$. If a person's distance from the speakers is d, then if he or she moves to a seat twice as far from the speakers, the new distance is $2d$. Therefore, the new sound intensity I is given by $\frac{k}{(2d)^2}$ or $\frac{k}{4d^2}$. Since $\frac{k}{4d^2} = \frac{1}{4} \cdot \frac{k}{d^2}$, the sound will be heard $\frac{1}{4}$ as intensely.

50.
$$C = \frac{kP_1P_2}{d^2}$$
$$204{,}000 = \frac{k(1{,}231{,}000)(1{,}499{,}000)}{(425)^2}$$
$$0.02 \approx k$$

The value of k is about 0.02. Therefore, the equation of variation is $C = \frac{0.02P_1P_2}{d^2}$.

51. From Exercise 50, we know that the value of k is about 0.02. Use substitution to determine the value of C.
$$C = \frac{kP_1P_2}{d^2}$$
$$C = \frac{(0.02)(1{,}231{,}000)(2{,}396{,}000)}{(680)^2}$$
$$C \approx 127{,}572$$

The average number of daily phone calls is about 127,572.

52. From Exercise 50, we know that the value of k is about 0.02. Use substitution to determine the value of d.
$$C = \frac{kP_1P_2}{d^2}$$
$$133{,}380 = \frac{(0.02)(1{,}607{,}000)(1{,}499{,}000)}{d^2}$$
$$d \approx 601$$

The distance between Indianapolis and Charlotte is about 601 miles.

53. No, this formula cannot be used to find the populations or the average number of phone calls between two adjoining cities. Since the cities are adjoining, the distance d between them is 0, so $d^2 = 0$. However, division by 0 is undefined, so the formula cannot be used in the given situation.

54. Sample answer: If the average student spends $2.50 for lunch in the school cafeteria, write an equation to represent the amount s students will spend for lunch in d days. How much will 30 students spend in a week? The amount a students will spend for lunch is the product of the cost of a lunch in the school cafeteria, the number of students s, and the number of days d. Therefore, an equation that represents the amount spent is $a = 2.50sd$. In one week, or 5 days, 30 students will spend $2.50(30)(5)$ or $375.

55. A direct variation can be used to determine the total cost when the cost per unit is known. Answers should include the following.

- Since the total cost T is the cost per unit u times the number of units n or $T = un$, the relationship is a direct variation. In this equation u is the constant of variation.
- Sample answer: The school store sells pencils for 20¢ each. John wants to buy 5 pencils. What is the total cost of the pencils? The total cost of the pencils is $(0.20)(5)$ or $1.00.

56. D; Set up a proportion that relates the values.

$$\frac{2a}{3b} = \frac{4}{5}$$
$$2a(5) = 3b(4)$$
$$5a(2) = 4b(3)$$
$$\frac{5a}{4b} = \frac{3}{2}$$

57. C; $b = \dfrac{k}{a^2}$

$$b = \frac{k}{(9a)^2}$$
$$b = \frac{k}{81a^2}$$
$$b = \frac{1}{81} \cdot \frac{k}{a^2}$$

If a is multiplied by 9, the value of b is multiplied by $\dfrac{1}{81}$.

Page 498   Maintain Your Skills

58. Notice that $\dfrac{x+1}{x^2-1} = \dfrac{x+1}{(x-1)(x+1)}$. The function is undefined for $x = 1$ and $x = -1$. Since $\dfrac{x+1}{(x-1)(x+1)} = \dfrac{1}{x-1}$, $x = 1$ is an asymptote, and $x = -1$ represents a hole in the graph.

59. Notice that $\dfrac{x+3}{x^2+x-12} = \dfrac{x+3}{(x-3)(x+4)}$. The function is undefined for $x = 3$ and $x = -4$. Since $\dfrac{x+3}{x^2+x-12}$ is in simplest form, $x = 3$ and $x = -4$ are asymptotes.

60. The function is undefined for $x = -3$. Since $\dfrac{x^2+4x+3}{x+3} = \dfrac{(x+1)(x+3)}{x+3}$ or $x + 1$, $x = -3$ represents a hole in the graph.

61.
$$\frac{3x}{x-y} + \frac{4x}{y-x} = \frac{3x(-1)}{(x-y)(-1)} + \frac{4x}{y-x}$$
$$= \frac{-3x}{y-x} + \frac{4x}{y-x}$$
$$= \frac{x}{y-x}$$

62.
$$\frac{t}{t+2} - \frac{2}{t^2-4} = \frac{t}{t+2} - \frac{2}{(t+2)(t-2)}$$
$$= \frac{t(t-2)}{(t+2)(t-2)} - \frac{2}{(t+2)(t-2)}$$
$$= \frac{t^2-2t}{(t+2)(t-2)} - \frac{2}{(t+2)(t-2)}$$
$$= \frac{t^2-2t-2}{(t+2)(t-2)}$$

63.
$$\frac{m - \frac{1}{m}}{1 + \frac{4}{m} - \frac{5}{m^2}} = \frac{\frac{m \cdot m}{m} - \frac{1}{m}}{\frac{m^2}{m^2} + \frac{4 \cdot m}{m \cdot m} - \frac{5}{m^2}}$$
$$= \frac{\frac{m^2-1}{m}}{\frac{m^2}{m^2} + \frac{4m}{m^2} - \frac{5}{m^2}}$$
$$= \frac{\frac{m^2-1}{m}}{\frac{m^2+4m-5}{m^2}}$$
$$= \frac{m^2-1}{m} \div \frac{m^2+4m-5}{m^2}$$
$$= \frac{m^2-1}{m} \cdot \frac{m^2}{m^2+4m-5}$$
$$= \frac{(m-1)(m+1)}{m} \cdot \frac{m \cdot m}{(m-1)(m+5)}$$
$$= \frac{m(m+1)}{m+5}$$

64. $93{,}000{,}000 = 9.3 \times 10{,}000{,}000$
$$= 9.3 \times 10^7$$

65. Since the equation is in the form $y = mx + b$, the slope m is 0.4, and the y-intercept b of the graph of the equation is 1.2.

66. Rewrite the equation in $y = mx + b$ form.
$$2y = 6x + 14$$
$$y = 3x + 7$$
The slope m is 3, and the y-intercept b is 7.

67. Rewrite the equation in $y = mx + b$ form.
$$3x + 5y = 15$$
$$5y = -3x + 15$$
$$y = -\frac{3}{5}x + 3$$
The slope m is $-\dfrac{3}{5}$, and the y-intercept b is 3.

68. C; Since the equation is of the form $f(x) = b$, the function is constant.

69. A; Since the equation is of the form $f(x) = |x|$, $g(x)$ is an absolute value function.

70. S; Since the equation is of the form $f(x) = [\![x]\!]$, $f(x)$ is a step function.

71. P; Since the function is written using two expressions, $f(x)$ is a piecewise function.

72. A; Since the equation is of the form $f(x) = |x|$, $h(x)$ is an absolute value function.

73. C; Since the equation is of the form $f(x) = b$, $g(x)$ is a constant function.

1. The function is undefined for $x = 4$. Since $\frac{x-1}{x-4}$ is in simplest form, $x = 4$ is a vertical asymptote. Notice that $y = 1$ is the horizontal asymptote. Draw the asymptotes. Make a table of values. Plot the points and draw the graph.

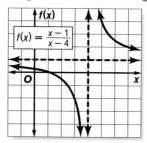

2. Notice that $\frac{-2}{x^2 - 6x + 9} = \frac{-2}{(x-3)^2}$. The function is undefined for $x = 3$. Since $\frac{-2}{(x-3)^2}$ is in simplest form, $x = 3$ is a vertical asymptote. Notice that $y = 0$ is the horizontal asymptote. Draw the asymptotes. Make a table of values. Plot the points and draw the graph.

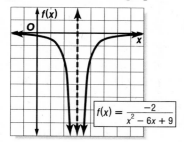

3. $\frac{x_1}{y_2} = \frac{x_2}{y_1}$

   $\frac{14}{2} = \frac{x_2}{7}$

   $14(7) = 2(x_2)$

   $98 = 2x_2$

   $49 = x_2$

   When $y = 2$, the value of x is 49.

4. $\frac{y_1}{x_1} = \frac{y_2}{x_2}$

   $\frac{1}{5} = \frac{y_2}{22}$

   $1(22) = 5(y_2)$

   $22 = 5y_2$

   $4.4 = y_2$

   When $x = 22$, the value of y is 4.4.

5. $\frac{y_1}{x_1 z_1} = \frac{y_2}{x_2 z_2}$

   $\frac{80}{25(4)} = \frac{y_2}{20(7)}$

   $20(7)(80) = 25(4)(y_2)$

   $11,200 = 100y_2$

   $112 = y_2$

   When $x = 20$ and $z = 7$, the value of y is 112.

9-5   Classes of Functions

Pages 501–502   Check for Understanding

1. Sample answer:

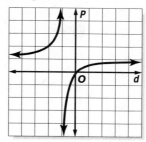

This graph is a rational function. It has an asymptote at $x = -1$. Therefore, it is not continuous.

2. Sample answer: The graphs of constant, direct variation, and identity functions are straight lines. For example, a constant function $y = 1$, a direct variation function $y = 2x$, and an identity function $y = x$ are functions whose graphs are straight lines.

3. The equation is a greatest integer function. The graph looks like a series of steps.

4. Since the graph looks like steps, the function is a greatest integer function.

5. Since the graph has more than one asymptote, and may or may not have any holes, the function is either an inverse variation or rational function.

6. Since the graph is a horizontal line that crosses the y-axis, the function is a constant function.

7. c; Since the graph has two asymptotes, $x = -2$ and $y = 1$, the function is a rational function; so the equation is of the form $y = \frac{p(x)}{q(x)}$, where $p(x)$ and $q(x)$ are polynomial functions.

8. b; Since the graph has a starting point and curves in one direction, the function is a square root function, so its equation includes an expression inside the radical sign.

9. The function is in the form $y = ax$, where $a = 1$. Therefore, it is either an identity or a direct variation function. The graph passes through the origin and has a slope of 1.

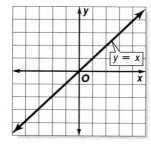

10. The function is in the form $y = ax^2 + bx + c$. Therefore, it is a quadratic function. The graph is a parabola. Determine some points on the graph, then graph the function.

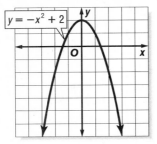

$y = -x^2 + 2$

11. Since the equation includes an expression inside absolute value symbols, it is an absolute value function. Therefore, the graph will be in the shape of a V. Determine some points on the graph, and graph the function.

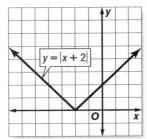

$y = |x + 2|$

12. The equation for the area of a circle is $A = \pi r^2$. Since the equation is in the form $y = ax^2 + bx + c$, it is a quadratic function. The graph is a parabola.

Pages 502–504 Practice and Apply

13. The graph is in the shape of a V, so it represents an absolute value function.

14. The graph has a starting point and curves in one direction. The graph represents a square root function.

15. The graph has a hole, so it represents a rational function.

16. The graph is a line that passes through the origin and is neither horizontal nor vertical. Therefore, the graph represents a direct variation function.

17. The graph is a parabola, so it represents a quadratic function.

18. The graph is a horizontal line. Therefore, the graph represents a constant function.

19. b; The graph is in the shape of a V, so the equation includes an expression inside absolute value symbols.

20. e; The graph is a parabola, so the equation is of the form $y = ax^2 + bx + c$, where $a \neq 0$.

21. g; The graph has two asymptotes, $x = 0$ and $y = 0$, so the equation is of the form $y = \dfrac{a}{x}$.

22. a; The graph looks like steps, so the equation includes an expression inside the greatest integer symbol.

23. The function is in the form $y = a$, where $a = -1.5$. Therefore, it is a constant function. The graph is a horizontal line that crosses the y-axis at -1.5.

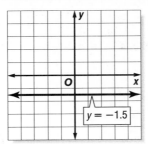

$y = -1.5$

24. The function is in the form $y = ax$, where $a = 2.5$. Therefore, it is a direct variation function. The graph passes through the origin and has a slope of 2.5.

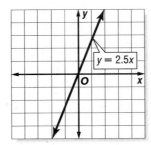

$y = 2.5x$

25. Since the equation includes an expression inside the radical sign, the function is a square root function. Therefore, the graph is a curve that starts at a point and continues in one direction. Determine some points on the graph, and graph the function.

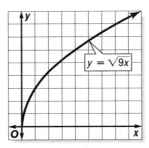

$y = \sqrt{9x}$

26. The function is in the form $y = \dfrac{a}{x}$, where $a = 4$.

Therefore, the graph represents either an inverse variation or a rational function. Its graph has two asymptotes, $x = 0$ and $y = 0$. Determine some points on the graph, and graph the function.

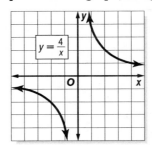

$y = \dfrac{4}{x}$

27. The function is in the form $y = \frac{p(x)}{q(x)}$, where $p(x)$ and $q(x)$ are polynomial functions. Therefore, the graph represents a rational function. Since $\frac{x^2 - 1}{x - 1} = \frac{(x - 1)(x + 1)}{x - 1}$ or $x + 1$, the graph of the function is the graph of the line $y = x + 1$, with a hole at $x = 1$.

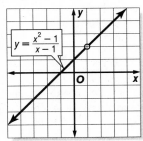

28. The equation includes an expression inside the greatest integer symbol, so the graph represents a greatest integer function. Its graph looks like steps. Determine some points on the graph, and graph the function.

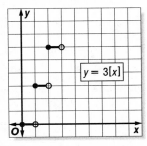

29. Since the equation includes an expression inside absolute value symbols, it is an absolute value function. Therefore, the graph will be in the shape of a V. Determine some points on the graph, and graph the function.

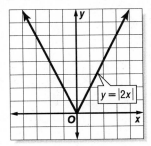

30. The function is in the form $y = ax^2 + bx + c$, where $a \neq 0$. Therefore, the graph represents a quadratic function. The graph is a parabola. Determine some points on the graph, and graph the function.

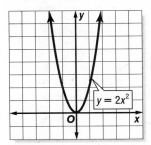

31. The number C of Calories burned is the product of the average number of Calories burned per minute and the number of minutes m. Therefore, an equation representing the situation is $C = 4.5m$.

32. From Exercise 31, we know that the equation is $C = 4.5m$. The equation is in the form $y = ax$, where $a = 4.5$. Therefore, it represents a direct variation function.

33. From Exercise 31, we know that the equation is $C = 4.5m$. The graph of the function is a line slanting to the right and passing through the origin.

34. The function is in the form $y = ax^2 + bx + c$, where $a \neq 0$. Therefore, it represents a quadratic function, so the shape of the Gateway Arch is similar to a parabola.

35.

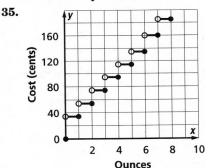

36. The graph is similar to the graph of the greatest integer function because both graphs look like a series of steps. In the graph of the postage rates, the solid dots are on the right and the circles are on the left. However, in the greatest integer function, the circles are on the right and the solid dots are on the left.

37a. Values of $f(x)$ vary by 2 as values of x vary by 2. Notice that all values of $f(x)$ are positive. Therefore, the table of values represents an absolute value function.

37b. Given the table of values, the equation is $y = x^2 - 1$, which is in the form $y = ax^2 + bx + c$. Therefore, the table of values represents a quadratic function.

37c. For a value of x, the function produces a value of $f(x)$ that is the least integer greater than or equal to x. Therefore, the table of values represents a greatest integer function.

37d. The function is undefined for negative values of x. Therefore, the table of values represents a square root function.

38. A graph of the function that relates a person's weight on Earth with his or her weight on a different planet can be used to determine a person's weight on the other planet by finding the point on the graph that corresponds with the weight on Earth and determining the value on the other planet's axis. Answers should include the following.

- The graph comparing weight on Earth and Mars represents a direct variation function because it is a straight line passing through the origin and is neither horizontal nor vertical.

- The equation $V = 0.9E$ compares a person's weight on Earth with his or her weight on Venus. The equation is in the form $y = ax$, where $a = 0.9$. Therefore, the graph is a line that passes through the origin and has a slope of 0.9.

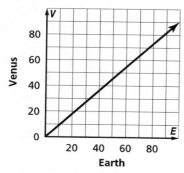

39. C; It appears that the graph has two asymptotes, $x = 0$ and $y = 0$, so it represents an inverse variation function. Therefore, the function is in the form $xy = a$.

40. D; $g(x) = \lceil x \rceil$

$$g\left(\frac{x}{2}\right) + 2 = \left\lceil \frac{x}{2} \right\rceil + 2$$

The graph of $g\left(\frac{x}{2}\right) + 2$ is the graph of $\left\lceil \frac{x}{2} \right\rceil + 2$.

41.
$$\frac{x_1}{y_1} = \frac{x_2}{y_2}$$
$$\frac{11}{\frac{1}{5}} = \frac{x_2}{\frac{2}{5}}$$
$$11\left(\frac{2}{5}\right) = \frac{1}{5}(x_2)$$
$$\frac{22}{5} = \frac{1}{5}x_2$$
$$22 = x_2$$
When $y = \frac{2}{5}$, the value of x is 22.

42. The function is undefined for $x = -2$. Since $\frac{3}{x+2}$ is in simplest form, $x = -2$ is a vertical asymptote. Draw the asymptote. Make a table of values. Plot the points and draw the graph.

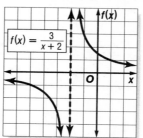

43. The function is undefined for $x = 1$ and $x = -3$. Since $\frac{8}{(x-1)(x+3)}$ is in simplest form, $x = 1$ and $x = -3$ are vertical asymptotes. Draw the asymptotes. Make a table of values. Plot the points and draw the graph.

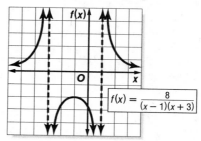

44. The function is undefined for $x = 4$. Notice that $\frac{x^2 - 5x + 4}{x - 4} = \frac{(x-4)(x-1)}{x-4}$ or $x - 1$. Therefore, the graph of $f(x) = \frac{x^2 - 5x + 4}{x - 4}$ is the graph of $f(x) = x - 1$ with a hole at $x = 4$.

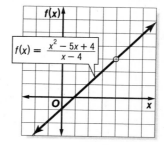

45. First, write the equation in the form
$y = a(x - h)^2 + k$.
$$\frac{1}{2}(y + 1) = (x - 8)^2$$
$$y + 1 = 2(x - 8)^2$$
$$y = 2(x - 8)^2 - 1$$
The vertex is at $(8, -1)$. The focus is at
$\left(8, -1 + \frac{1}{4(2)}\right)$ or $\left(8, -\frac{7}{8}\right)$. The equation of the axis
of symmetry is $x = 8$, and the equation of the
directrix is $y = -1 - \frac{1}{4(2)}$ or $y = -1\frac{1}{8}$. Since $a > 0$,
the parabola opens upward. The length of the
latus rectum is $\left|\frac{1}{2}\right|$ or $\frac{1}{2}$ unit.

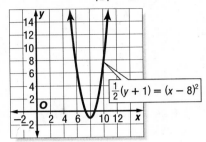

46. First, write the equation in the form
$x = a(y - k)^2 + h$.
$$x = \frac{1}{4}y^2 - \frac{1}{2}y - 3$$
$$x + 3 = \frac{1}{4}(y^2 - 2y)$$
$$x + 3 + \frac{1}{4}(\blacksquare) = \frac{1}{4}(y^2 - 2y + \blacksquare)$$
$$x + 3 + \frac{1}{4}(1) = \frac{1}{4}(y^2 - 2y + 1)$$
$$x + \frac{13}{4} = \frac{1}{4}(y - 1)^2$$
$$x = \frac{1}{4}(y - 1)^2 - \frac{13}{4}$$
The vertex is at $\left(-3\frac{1}{4}, 1\right)$. The focus is at
$\left(-\frac{13}{4} + \frac{1}{4\left(\frac{1}{4}\right)}, 1\right)$ or $\left(-2\frac{1}{4}, 1\right)$. The equation of the
axis of symmetry is $y = 1$, and the equation of the
directrix is $x = -\frac{13}{4} - \frac{1}{4\left(\frac{1}{4}\right)}$ or $x = -4\frac{1}{4}$. Since
$a > 0$, the parabola opens to the right. The length
of the latus rectum is $\left|\frac{1}{\frac{1}{4}}\right|$ or 4 units.

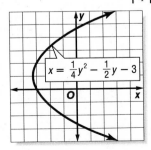

47. First, write the equation in the form
$x = a(y - k)^2 + h$.
$$3x - y^2 = 8y + 31$$
$$3x = y^2 + 8y + 31$$
$$3x = (y^2 + 8y + \blacksquare) + 31 - \blacksquare$$
$$3x = (y^2 + 8y + 16) + 31 - 16$$
$$3x = (y + 4)^2 + 15$$
$$x = \frac{1}{3}(y + 4)^2 + 5$$
The vertex is at $(5, -4)$. The focus is at
$\left(5 + \frac{1}{4\left(\frac{1}{3}\right)}, -4\right)$ or $\left(5\frac{3}{4}, -4\right)$. The equation of the
axis of symmetry is $y = -4$, and the equation of
the directrix is $x = 5 - \frac{1}{4\left(\frac{1}{3}\right)}$ or $x = 4\frac{1}{4}$.

Since $a > 0$, the parabola opens to the right. The
length of the latus rectum is $\left|\frac{1}{\frac{1}{3}}\right|$ or 3 units.

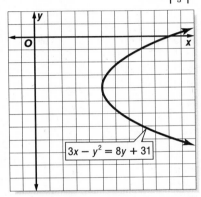

48. $\begin{bmatrix} 3 & -5 \\ 2 & 7 \end{bmatrix} \cdot \begin{bmatrix} 5 & 1 & -3 \\ 8 & -4 & 9 \end{bmatrix} = \begin{bmatrix} 15 - 40 & 3 + 20 & -9 - 45 \\ 10 + 56 & 2 - 28 & -6 + 63 \end{bmatrix}$

$= \begin{bmatrix} -25 & 23 & -54 \\ 66 & -26 & 57 \end{bmatrix}$

49. It is impossible to find the product because the
number of columns in the first matrix is not equal
to the number of rows in the second matrix.

50. Multiply the first equation by 3 and the second
equation by 5. Then add the equations to
eliminate the y variable.

$$\begin{array}{r} 9x + 15y = -12 \\ (+) \; 10x - 15y = 145 \\ \hline 19x = 133 \\ x = 7 \end{array}$$

Replace x with 7 and solve for y.

$$3x + 5y = -4$$
$$3(7) + 5y = -4$$
$$21 + 5y = -4$$
$$5y = -25$$
$$y = -5$$

The solution is $(7, -5)$.

51. In each equation, the coefficient of a is 3. Subtract the second equation from the first equation to eliminate the a variable.

$$3a - 2b = -3$$
$$(-)\ 3a + b = 3$$
$$\overline{-3b = -6}$$
$$b = 2$$

Replace b with 2 and solve for a.

$$3a + b = 3$$
$$3a + 2 = 3$$
$$3a = 1$$
$$a = \frac{1}{3}$$

The solution is $\left(\frac{1}{3}, 2\right)$.

52. Use substitution to solve the system of equations.

$$4s + t = 6$$
$$t = 6 - 4s$$

Substitute $6 - 4s$ for t in the first equation and solve for s.

$$3s - 2t = 10$$
$$3s - 2(6 - 4s) = 10$$
$$3s - 12 + 8s = 10$$
$$11s = 22$$
$$s = 2$$

Now, substitute 2 for s in either equation and solve for t.

$$4s + t = 6$$
$$4(2) + t = 6$$
$$8 + t = 6$$
$$t = -2$$

The solution is $(2, -2)$.

53.
$$m = \frac{y_2 - y_1}{x_2 - x_1}$$
$$\frac{-8}{3} = \frac{-6 - 2}{4 - r}$$
$$\frac{-8}{3} = \frac{-8}{4 - r}$$
$$-8(4 - r) = -8(3)$$
$$-32 + 8r = -24$$
$$8r = 8$$
$$r = 1$$

54.
$$m = \frac{y_2 - y_1}{x_2 - x_1}$$
$$\frac{1}{2} = \frac{4 - 6}{8 - r}$$
$$\frac{1}{2} = \frac{-2}{8 - r}$$
$$-4 = 8 - r$$
$$-12 = -r$$
$$12 = r$$

55. $[(-7 + 4) \times 5 - 2] \div 6 = [(-3) \times 5 - 2] \div 6$
$$= (-15 - 2) \div 6$$
$$= (-17) \div 6$$
$$= -\frac{17}{6}$$

56. $15ab^2c = 3 \cdot 5 \cdot a \cdot b^2 \cdot c$
$$6a^3 = 2 \cdot 3 \cdot a^3$$
$$4bc^2 = 2^2 \cdot b \cdot c^2$$
$$\text{LCM} = 2^2 \cdot 3 \cdot 5 \cdot a^3 \cdot b^2 \cdot c^2$$
$$= 60a^3b^2c^2$$

57. $9x^3 = 3^2 \cdot x^3$
$$5xy^2 = 5 \cdot x \cdot y^2$$
$$15x^2y^3 = 3 \cdot 5 \cdot x^2 \cdot y^3$$
$$\text{LCM} = 3^2 \cdot 5 \cdot x^3 \cdot y^3$$
$$= 45x^3y^3$$

58. $5d - 10 = 5(d - 2)$
$$3d - 6 = 3(d - 2)$$
$$\text{LCM} = 3 \cdot 5(d - 2)$$
$$= 15(d - 2)$$

59. $x^2 - y^2 = (x - y)(x + y)$
$$3x + 3y = 3(x + y)$$
$$\text{LCM} = 3(x - y)(x + y)$$

60. $a^2 - 2a - 3 = (a - 3)(a + 1)$
$$a^2 - a - 6 = (a - 3)(a + 2)$$
$$\text{LCM} = (a - 3)(a + 1)(a + 2)$$

61. $2t^2 - 9t - 5 = (t - 5)(2t + 1)$
$$t^2 + t - 30 = (t - 5)(t + 6)$$
$$\text{LCM} = (t - 5)(t + 6)(2t + 1)$$

9-6 ## Solving Rational Equations and Inequalities

Page 509 Check for Understanding

1. Sample answer: $\dfrac{1}{5} + \dfrac{2}{a + 2} = 1$

2. Multiply both sides of the equation by the LCD, or $2(x + 4)$, in order to solve the equation. The equation is undefined for $x = -4$, so $x = -4$ cannot be a solution.

3. Jeff is correct. The LCD for the denominators is $3a$. However, when Dustin multiplied by $3a$, he forgot to multiply the 2 by $3a$.

4.
$$\frac{2}{d} + \frac{1}{4} = \frac{11}{12}$$
$$12d\left(\frac{2}{d} + \frac{1}{4}\right) = 12d\left(\frac{11}{12}\right)$$
$$24 + 3d = 11d$$
$$24 = 8d$$
$$3 = d$$

Check: $\dfrac{2}{d} + \dfrac{1}{4} = \dfrac{11}{12}$
$$\frac{2}{3} + \frac{1}{4} \stackrel{?}{=} \frac{11}{12}$$
$$\frac{11}{12} = \frac{11}{12}\ \checkmark$$

The solution is 3.

5.
$$t + \frac{12}{t} - 8 = 0$$
$$t\left(t + \frac{12}{t} - 8\right) = t(0)$$
$$t^2 + 12 - 8t = 0$$
$$t^2 - 8t + 12 = 0$$
$$(t - 2)(t - 6) = 0$$

$$t - 2 = 0 \quad\quad \text{or} \quad\quad t - 6 = 0$$
$$t = 2 \quad\quad\quad\quad\quad\quad\quad t = 6$$

Check: $t + \dfrac{12}{t} - 8 = 0 \quad\quad t + \dfrac{12}{t} - 8 = 0$

$$2 + \frac{12}{2} - 8 \stackrel{?}{=} 0 \quad\quad 6 + \frac{12}{6} - 8 \stackrel{?}{=} 0$$
$$2 + 6 - 8 \stackrel{?}{=} 0 \quad\quad 6 + 2 - 8 \stackrel{?}{=} 0$$
$$0 = 0\ \checkmark \quad\quad\quad\quad\quad 0 = 0\ \checkmark$$

The solution is 2 or 6.

6.
$$\frac{1}{x-1} + \frac{2}{x} = 0$$
$$x(x-1)\left(\frac{1}{x-1} + \frac{2}{x}\right) = x(x-1)(0)$$
$$x(x-1)^{\overset{1}{}}\left(\frac{1}{x-1}\right) + x(x-1)\left(\frac{2}{x}\right) = 0$$
$$x + 2x - 2 = 0$$
$$3x = 2$$
$$x = \frac{2}{3}$$

Check: $\dfrac{1}{x-1} + \dfrac{2}{x} = 0$

$$\frac{1}{\left(\frac{2}{3}\right) - 1} + \frac{2}{\frac{2}{3}} \overset{?}{=} 0$$
$$-3 + 3 \overset{?}{=} 0$$
$$0 = 0 \checkmark$$

The solution is $\frac{2}{3}$.

7.
$$\frac{12}{v^2 - 16} - \frac{24}{v-4} = 3$$
$$(v^2 - 16)\left(\frac{12}{v^2-16} - \frac{24}{v-4}\right) = (v^2-16)(3)$$
$$(v^2 - 16)^{\overset{1}{}}\left(\frac{12}{v^2-16}\right) - (v^2 - 16)^{(v+4)}\left(\frac{24}{v-4}\right) = 3v^2 - 48$$
$$12 - (24v + 96) = 3v^2 - 48$$
$$12 - 24v - 96 = 3v^2 - 48$$
$$0 = 3v^2 + 24v + 36$$
$$0 = v^2 + 8v + 12$$
$$0 = (v+6)(v+2)$$

$v + 6 = 0$ or $v + 2 = 0$
$v = -6$ $v = -2$

Check: $\dfrac{12}{v^2-16} - \dfrac{24}{v-4} = 3$ $\dfrac{12}{v^2-16} - \dfrac{24}{v-4} = 3$

$$\frac{12}{(-6)^2-16} - \frac{24}{(-6)-4} \overset{?}{=} 3 \qquad \frac{12}{(-2)^2-16} - \frac{24}{(-2)-4} \overset{?}{=} 3$$
$$\frac{3}{5} - \left(-\frac{12}{5}\right) \overset{?}{=} 3 \qquad\qquad (-1) - (-4) \overset{?}{=} 3$$
$$3 = 3 \checkmark \qquad\qquad\qquad\qquad 3 = 3 \checkmark$$

The solution is -6 or -2.

8. Since values that make a denominator equal to 0 are excluded from the domain, the excluded value for this inequality is -2. Solve the related equation.
$$\frac{4}{c+2} = 1$$
$$4 = c + 2$$
$$2 = c$$

Now test a value in each region to determine if the values in the region satisfy the inequality.

Test $c = -3$.
$$\frac{4}{(-3)+2} \overset{?}{>} 1$$
$$\frac{4}{-1} \overset{?}{>} 1$$
$$-4 \not> 1$$
$c < 2$ is *not* a solution.

Test $c = 0$.
$$\frac{4}{(0)+2} \overset{?}{>} 1$$
$$\frac{4}{2} \overset{?}{>} 1$$
$$2 > 1 \checkmark$$
$-2 < c < 2$ is a solution.

Test $c = 3$.
$$\frac{4}{(3)+2} \overset{?}{>} 1$$

$$\frac{4}{5} \not> 1$$
$c > 2$ is *not* a solution.
The solution is $-2 < c < 2$.

9. Since values that make a denominator equal to 0 are excluded from the domain, the excluded value for this inequality is 0. Solve the related equation.
$$\frac{1}{3v} + \frac{1}{4v} = \frac{1}{2}$$
$$12v\left(\frac{1}{3v} + \frac{1}{4v}\right) = 12v\left(\frac{1}{2}\right)$$
$$4 + 3 = 6v$$
$$7 = 6v$$
$$1\frac{1}{7} = v$$

Now test a value in each region to determine if the values in the region satisfy the inequality.

Test $v = -1$.
$$\frac{1}{3(-1)} + \frac{1}{4(-1)} \overset{?}{<} \frac{1}{2}$$
$$-\frac{1}{3} - \frac{1}{4} \overset{?}{<} \frac{1}{2}$$
$$-\frac{7}{12} < \frac{1}{2} \checkmark$$
$v < 0$ is a solution.

Test $v = 1$.
$$\frac{1}{3(1)} + \frac{1}{4(1)} \overset{?}{<} \frac{1}{2}$$
$$\frac{1}{3} + \frac{1}{4} \overset{?}{<} \frac{1}{2}$$
$$\frac{7}{12} \not< \frac{1}{2}$$
$0 < v < 1\frac{1}{7}$ is *not* a solution.

Test $v = 2$.
$$\frac{1}{3(2)} + \frac{1}{4(2)} \overset{?}{<} \frac{1}{2}$$
$$\frac{1}{6} + \frac{1}{8} \overset{?}{<} \frac{1}{2}$$
$$\frac{7}{24} < \frac{1}{2} \checkmark$$
$v > 1\frac{1}{7}$ is a solution.

The solution is $v < 0$ or $v > 1\frac{1}{7}$.

10. In t hours, the first bricklayer can complete $\frac{1}{5}$ of the wall. Likewise, in t hours, the second bricklayer can complete $\frac{1}{4}$ of the wall. Together, they can complete the whole wall.
$$\frac{t}{5} + \frac{t}{4} = 1$$
$$20\left(\frac{t}{5} + \frac{t}{4}\right) = 20(1)$$
$$4t + 5t = 20$$
$$9t = 20$$
$$t = 2\frac{2}{9}$$
It will take $2\frac{2}{9}$ hours.

11.
$$\frac{y}{y+1} = \frac{2}{3}$$

$$3(y + 1)\left(\frac{y}{y+1}\right) = 3(y + 1)\left(\frac{2}{3}\right)$$

$$3y = 2y + 2$$

$$y = 2$$

Check: $\dfrac{y}{y+1} = \dfrac{2}{3}$

$$\frac{2}{2+1} \stackrel{?}{=} \frac{2}{3}$$

$$\frac{2}{3} = \frac{2}{3} \checkmark$$

The solution is 2.

12.
$$\frac{p}{p-2} = \frac{2}{5}$$

$$5(p - 2)\left(\frac{p}{p-2}\right) = 5(p - 2)\left(\frac{2}{5}\right)$$

$$5p = 2p - 4$$

$$3p = -4$$

$$p = -\frac{4}{3}$$

Check: $\dfrac{p}{p-2} = \dfrac{2}{5}$

$$\frac{-\frac{4}{3}}{\left(-\frac{4}{3}\right) - 2} \stackrel{?}{=} \frac{2}{5}$$

$$\frac{-\frac{4}{3}}{-\frac{10}{3}} \stackrel{?}{=} \frac{2}{5}$$

$$\frac{2}{5} = \frac{2}{5} \checkmark$$

The solution is $-\dfrac{4}{3}$.

13.
$$s + 5 = \frac{6}{s}$$

$$s(s + 5) = s\left(\frac{6}{s}\right)$$

$$s^2 + 5s = 6$$

$$s^2 + 5s - 6 = 0$$

$$(s + 6)(s - 1) = 0$$

$$s + 6 = 0 \quad \text{or} \quad s - 1 = 0$$

$$s = -6 \qquad\qquad s = 1$$

Check: $s + 5 = \dfrac{6}{s}$ $\qquad s + 5 = \dfrac{6}{s}$

$$-6 + 5 \stackrel{?}{=} \frac{6}{-6} \qquad 1 + 5 \stackrel{?}{=} \frac{6}{1}$$

$$-1 = -1 \checkmark \qquad\quad 6 = 6 \checkmark$$

The solutions are -6 and 1.

14.
$$a + 1 = \frac{6}{a}$$

$$a(a + 1) = a\left(\frac{6}{a}\right)$$

$$a^2 + a = 6$$

$$a^2 + a - 6 = 0$$

$$(a + 3)(a - 2) = 0$$

$$a + 3 = 0 \quad \text{or} \quad a - 2 = 0$$

$$a = -3 \qquad\qquad a = 2$$

Check: $a + 1 = \dfrac{6}{a}$ $\qquad a + 1 = \dfrac{6}{a}$

$$-3 + 1 \stackrel{?}{=} \frac{6}{-3} \qquad 2 + 1 \stackrel{?}{=} \frac{6}{2}$$

$$-2 = -2 \checkmark \qquad\quad 3 = 3 \checkmark$$

The solutions are -3 and 2.

15. Since values that make a denominator equal to 0 are excluded from the domain, -1 is excluded for this inequality. Solve the related equation.

$$\frac{7}{a+1} = 7$$

$$(a + 1)\left(\frac{7}{a+1}\right) = (a + 1)(7)$$

$$7 = 7a + 7$$

$$0 = 7a$$

$$0 = a$$

Test a sample value in each region to determine if the values in the region satisfy the inequality.

Test $a = -2$.

$$\frac{7}{a+1} > 7$$

$$\frac{7}{-2+1} \stackrel{?}{>} 7$$

$$-7 \not> 7$$

$a < -1$ is *not* a solution.

Test $a = -\frac{1}{2}$.

$$\frac{7}{a+1} > 7$$

$$\frac{7}{-\frac{1}{2}+1} \stackrel{?}{>} 7$$

$$14 > 7 \checkmark$$

$-1 < a < 0$ is a solution.

Test $a = 1$.

$$\frac{7}{a+1} > 7$$

$$\frac{7}{1+1} \stackrel{?}{>} 7$$

$$\frac{7}{2} \not> 7$$

$a > 0$ is *not* a solution.

The solution is $-1 < a < 0$.

16. Since values that make a denominator equal to 0 are excluded from the domain, -1 is excluded for this inequality. Solve the related equation.

$$\frac{10}{m+1} = 5$$

$$(m + 1)\left(\frac{10}{m + 1}\right) = (m + 1)(5)$$

$$10 = 5m + 5$$

$$5 = 5m$$

$$1 = m$$

Test a sample value in each region to determine if the values in the region satisfy the inequality.

Test $m = -2$.

$$\frac{10}{m + 1} > 5$$

$$\frac{10}{-2 + 1} \overset{?}{>} 5$$

$$-10 \not> 5$$

$m < -1$ is *not* a solution.

Test $m = 0$.

$$\frac{10}{m + 1} > 5$$

$$\frac{10}{0 + 1} \overset{?}{>} 5$$

$$10 > 5 \checkmark$$

$-1 < m < 1$ is a solution.

Test $m = 2$.

$$\frac{10}{m + 1} > 5$$

$$\frac{10}{2 + 1} \overset{?}{>} 5$$

$$\frac{10}{3} \not> 5$$

$m > 1$ is *not* a solution.

The solution is $-1 < m < 1$.

17.

$$\frac{9}{t - 3} = \frac{t - 4}{t - 3} + \frac{1}{4}$$

$$4(t - 3)\left(\frac{9}{t - 3}\right) = 4(t - 3)\left(\frac{t - 4}{t - 3} + \frac{1}{4}\right)$$

$$36 = 4(t - 3)\left(\frac{t - 4}{t - 3}\right) + 4(t - 3)\left(\frac{1}{4}\right)$$

$$36 = 4t - 16 + t - 3$$

$$55 = 5t$$

$$11 = t$$

Check:

$$\frac{9}{t - 3} = \frac{t - 4}{t - 3} + \frac{1}{4}$$

$$\frac{9}{11 - 3} \overset{?}{=} \frac{11 - 4}{11 - 3} + \frac{1}{4}$$

$$\frac{9}{8} \overset{?}{=} \frac{7}{8} + \frac{1}{4}$$

$$\frac{9}{8} = \frac{9}{8} \checkmark$$

The solution is 11.

18.

$$\frac{w}{w - 1} + w = \frac{4w - 3}{w - 1}$$

$$(w - 1)\left(\frac{w}{w - 1} + w\right) = (w - 1)\left(\frac{4w - 3}{w - 1}\right)$$

$$(w - 1)\left(\frac{w}{w - 1}\right) + (w - 1)(w) = 4w - 3$$

$$w + w^2 - w = 4w - 3$$

$$w^2 - 4w + 3 = 0$$

$$(w - 3)(w - 1) = 0$$

$$w - 3 = 0 \quad \text{or} \quad w - 1 = 0$$

$$w = 3 \qquad\qquad w = 1$$

Check:

$$\frac{w}{w - 1} + w = \frac{4w - 3}{w - 1}$$

$$\frac{3}{3 - 1} + 3 \overset{?}{=} \frac{4(3) - 3}{3 - 1}$$

$$\frac{3}{2} + 3 \overset{?}{=} \frac{9}{2}$$

$$\frac{9}{2} = \frac{9}{2} \checkmark$$

$$\frac{w}{w - 1} + w = \frac{4w - 3}{w - 1}$$

$$\frac{1}{1 - 1} + 1 \overset{?}{=} \frac{4(1) - 3}{1 - 1}$$

$$\frac{1}{0} + 1 \overset{?}{=} \frac{1}{0}$$

Since $w = 1$ results in a zero in the denominator, the only solution is 3.

19. Since values that make a denominator equal to 0 are excluded from the domain, 0 is excluded for this inequality. Solve the related equation.

$$5 + \frac{1}{t} = \frac{16}{t}$$

$$t\left(5 + \frac{1}{t}\right) = t\left(\frac{16}{t}\right)$$

$$5t + 1 = 16$$

$$5t = 15$$

$$t = 3$$

Test a sample value in each region to determine if the values in the region satisfy the inequality.

Test $t = -1$.

$$5 + \frac{1}{t} > \frac{16}{t}$$

$$5 + \frac{1}{-1} \overset{?}{>} \frac{16}{-1}$$

$$4 > -16 \checkmark$$

$t < 0$ is a solution.

Test $t = 1$.

$$5 + \frac{1}{t} > \frac{16}{t}$$

$$5 + \frac{1}{1} \overset{?}{>} \frac{16}{1}$$

$$6 \not> 16$$

$0 < t < 3$ is *not* a solution.

Test $t = 4$.

$$5 + \frac{1}{t} > \frac{16}{t}$$

$$5 + \frac{1}{4} \overset{?}{>} \frac{16}{4}$$

$$\frac{21}{4} > 4 \checkmark$$

$t > 3$ is a solution.

The solution is $t < 0$ or $t > 3$.

20. Since values that make a denominator equal to 0 are excluded from the domain, 0 is excluded for this inequality. Solve the related equation.

$$7 - \frac{2}{b} = \frac{5}{b}$$

$$b\left(7 - \frac{2}{b}\right) = b\left(\frac{5}{b}\right)$$

$$7b - 2 = 5$$

$$7b = 7$$

$$b = 1$$

Test a sample value in each region to determine if the values in the region satisfy the inequality.

Test $b = -1$.

$$7 - \frac{2}{b} < \frac{5}{b}$$

$$7 - \frac{2}{-1} \overset{?}{<} \frac{5}{-1}$$

$$9 \not< -5$$

$b < 0$ is *not* a solution.

Test $b = \frac{1}{2}$.

$$7 - \frac{2}{b} < \frac{5}{b}$$

$$7 - \frac{2}{\frac{1}{2}} \overset{?}{<} \frac{5}{\frac{1}{2}}$$

$$3 < 10$$

$0 < b < 1$ is a solution.

Test $b = 2$.

$$7 - \frac{2}{b} < \frac{5}{b}$$

$$7 - \frac{2}{2} \overset{?}{<} \frac{5}{2}$$

$$6 \not< \frac{5}{2}$$

$b > 1$ is *not* a solution.

The solution is $0 < b < 1$.

21. Since values that make a denominator equal to 0 are excluded from the domain, 0 is excluded for this inequality. Solve the related equation.

$$\frac{2}{3y} + \frac{5}{6y} = \frac{3}{4}$$

$$12y\left(\frac{2}{3y} + \frac{5}{6y}\right) = 12y\left(\frac{3}{4}\right)$$

$$12y\left(\frac{2}{3y}\right) + 12y\left(\frac{5}{6y}\right) = 9y$$

$$8 + 10 = 9y$$

$$18 = 9y$$

$$2 = y$$

Test a sample value in each region to determine if the values in the region satisfy the inequality.

Test $y = -1$.

$$\frac{2}{3y} + \frac{5}{6y} > \frac{3}{4}$$

$$\frac{2}{3(-1)} + \frac{5}{6(-1)} \overset{?}{>} \frac{3}{4}$$

$$-\frac{3}{2} \not> \frac{3}{4}$$

$y < 0$ is *not* a solution.

Test $y = 1$.

$$\frac{2}{3y} + \frac{5}{6y} > \frac{3}{4}$$

$$\frac{2}{3(1)} + \frac{5}{6(1)} \overset{?}{>} \frac{3}{4}$$

$$\frac{3}{2} > \frac{3}{4} \checkmark$$

$0 < y < 2$ is a solution.

Test $y = 3$.

$$\frac{2}{3y} + \frac{5}{6y} > \frac{3}{4}$$

$$\frac{2}{3(3)} + \frac{5}{6(3)} \overset{?}{>} \frac{3}{4}$$

$$\frac{1}{2} \not> \frac{3}{4}$$

$y > 2$ is *not* a solution.

The solution is $0 < y < 2$.

22. Since values that make a denominator equal to 0 are excluded from the domain, 0 is excluded for this inequality. Solve the related equation.

$$\frac{1}{2p} + \frac{3}{4p} = \frac{1}{2}$$

$$4p\left(\frac{1}{2p} + \frac{3}{4p}\right) = 4p\left(\frac{1}{2}\right)$$

$$4p\left(\frac{1}{2p}\right) + 4p\left(\frac{3}{4p}\right) = 2p$$

$$2 + 3 = 2p$$

$$5 = 2p$$

$$2\frac{1}{2} = p$$

Test a sample value in each region to determine if the values in the region satisfy the inequality.

Test $p = -1$.

$$\frac{1}{2p} + \frac{3}{4p} < \frac{1}{2}$$

$$\frac{1}{2(-1)} + \frac{3}{4(-1)} \overset{?}{<} \frac{1}{2}$$

$$-\frac{1}{2} + \left(-\frac{3}{4}\right) \overset{?}{<} \frac{1}{2}$$

$$-\frac{5}{4} < \frac{1}{2} \checkmark$$

$p < 0$ is a solution.

Test $p = 1$.

$$\frac{1}{2p} + \frac{3}{4p} < \frac{1}{2}$$

$$\frac{1}{2(1)} + \frac{3}{4(1)} \overset{?}{<} \frac{1}{2}$$

$$\frac{1}{2} + \frac{3}{4} \overset{?}{<} \frac{1}{2}$$

$$\frac{5}{4} \not< \frac{1}{2}$$

$0 < p < 2\frac{1}{2}$ is *not* a solution.

Test $p = 3$.

$$\frac{1}{2p} + \frac{3}{4p} < \frac{1}{2}$$

$$\frac{1}{2(3)} + \frac{3}{4(3)} \overset{?}{<} \frac{1}{2}$$

$$\frac{1}{6} + \frac{3}{12} \overset{?}{<} \frac{1}{2}$$

$$\frac{5}{12} < \frac{1}{2} \checkmark$$

$p > 2\frac{1}{2}$ is a solution.

The solution is $p < 0$ or $p > 2\frac{1}{2}$.

23.

$$\frac{b-4}{b-2} = \frac{b-2}{b+2} + \frac{1}{b-2}$$

$$(b-2)(b+2)\left(\frac{b-4}{b-2}\right) = (b-2)(b+2)\left(\frac{b-2}{b+2} + \frac{1}{b-2}\right)$$

$$(b+2)(b-4) = (b-2)(b+2)\left(\frac{b-2}{b+2}\right) + (b-2)(b+2)\left(\frac{1}{b-2}\right)$$

$$b^2 - 2b - 8 = (b-2)(b-2) + b + 2$$
$$b^2 - 2b - 8 = b^2 - 4b + 4 + b + 2$$
$$b = 14$$

Check: $\dfrac{b-4}{b-2} = \dfrac{b-2}{b+2} + \dfrac{1}{b-2}$

$$\frac{14-4}{14-2} \overset{?}{=} \frac{14-2}{14+2} + \frac{1}{14-2}$$
$$\frac{10}{12} \overset{?}{=} \frac{12}{16} + \frac{1}{12}$$
$$\frac{5}{6} = \frac{5}{6} \checkmark$$

The solution is 14.

24.

$$\frac{4n^2}{n^2-9} - \frac{2n}{n+3} = \frac{3}{n-3}$$

$$(n^2-9)\left(\frac{4n^2}{n^2-9} - \frac{2n}{n+3}\right) = (n^2-9)\left(\frac{3}{n-3}\right)$$

$$(n^2-9)\left(\frac{4n^2}{n^2-9}\right) - (n^2-9)\left(\frac{2n}{n+3}\right) = 3(n+3)$$

$$4n^2 - (2n^2 - 6n) = 3n + 9$$
$$4n^2 - 2n^2 + 6n = 3n + 9$$
$$2n^2 + 3n - 9 = 0$$

Use the Quadratic Equation to solve for n.

$$x = \frac{-b \pm \sqrt{b^2 - 4ac}}{2a}$$
$$n = \frac{-3 \pm \sqrt{3^2 - 4(2)(-9)}}{2(2)}$$
$$n = \frac{-3 \pm \sqrt{81}}{4}$$
$$n = \frac{-3 \pm 9}{4}$$
$$n = \frac{3}{2} \text{ or } -3$$

Check: $\dfrac{4n^2}{n^2-9} - \dfrac{2n}{n+3} = \dfrac{3}{n-3}$

$$\frac{4\left(\frac{3}{2}\right)^2}{\left(\frac{3}{2}\right)^2 - 9} - \frac{2\left(\frac{3}{2}\right)}{\frac{3}{2}+3} \overset{?}{=} \frac{3}{\frac{3}{2}-3}$$
$$-\frac{4}{3} - \frac{2}{3} \overset{?}{=} -2$$
$$-2 = -2 \checkmark$$

$$\frac{4n^2}{n^2-9} - \frac{2n}{n+3} = \frac{3}{n-3}$$
$$\frac{4(-3)^2}{(-3)^2 - 9} - \frac{2(-3)}{-3+3} \overset{?}{=} \frac{3}{-3-3}$$
$$\frac{36}{0} - \frac{-6}{0} \overset{?}{=} \frac{3}{-6}$$

Since $n = -3$ results in a zero in the denominator, the solution is $\frac{3}{2}$.

25.

$$\frac{1}{d+4} = \frac{2}{d^2 + 3d - 4} - \frac{1}{1-d}$$

$$(d-1)(d+4)\left(\frac{1}{d+4}\right) = (d-1)(d+4)\left(\frac{2}{d^2 + 3d - 4} - \frac{1}{1-d}\right)$$

$$d-1 = (d-1)(d+4)\left(\frac{2}{d^2 + 3d - 4}\right) - (d-1)(d+4)\left(\frac{1}{1-d}\right)$$

$$d - 1 = 2 - (-1)(d+4)$$
$$d - 1 = 2 + d + 4$$
$$0 = 7$$

This statement is never true, so there is no solution.

26.

$$\frac{2}{y+2} - \frac{y}{2-y} = \frac{y^2+4}{y^2-4}$$

$$(y^2-4)\left(\frac{2}{y+2} - \frac{y}{2-y}\right) = (y^2-4)\left(\frac{y^2+4}{y^2-4}\right)$$

$$(y^2-4)\left(\frac{2}{y+2}\right) - (y^2-4)\left(\frac{y}{2-y}\right) = y^2 + 4$$

$$2(y-2) - (-1)(y)(y+2) = y^2 + 4$$
$$2y - 4 + y^2 + 2y = y^2 + 4$$
$$4y = 8$$
$$y = 2$$

Check: $\dfrac{2}{y+2} - \dfrac{y}{2-y} = \dfrac{y^2+4}{y^2-4}$

$$\frac{2}{2+2} - \frac{2}{2-2} \overset{?}{=} \frac{2^2+4}{2^2-4}$$
$$\frac{2}{4} - \frac{2}{0} \overset{?}{=} \frac{8}{0}$$

Since $y = 2$ results in a 0 in the denominator, there is no solution.

27.

$$\frac{3}{b^2 + 5b + 6} + \frac{b-1}{b+2} = \frac{7}{b+3}$$

$$(b^2+5b+6)\left(\frac{3}{b^2+5b+5} + \frac{b-1}{b+2}\right) = (b^2+5b+6)\left(\frac{7}{b+3}\right)$$

$$(b^2+5b+6)\left(\frac{3}{b^2+5b+6}\right) + b^2+5b+6\left(\frac{b-1}{b+2}\right) = 7(b+2)$$

$$3 + (b+3)(b-1) = 7b + 14$$
$$3 + b^2 + 2b - 3 = 7b + 14$$
$$b^2 - 5b - 14 = 0$$
$$(b-7)(b+2) = 0$$

$b - 7 = 0 \qquad$ or $\qquad b + 2 = 0$

$b = 7 \qquad\qquad\qquad\qquad b = -2$

Check: $\dfrac{3}{b^2+5b+6} + \dfrac{b-1}{b+2} = \dfrac{7}{b+3}$

$$\frac{3}{7^2 + 5(7) + 6} + \frac{7-1}{7+2} \overset{?}{=} \frac{7}{7+3}$$
$$\frac{3}{90} + \frac{6}{9} \overset{?}{=} \frac{7}{10}$$
$$\frac{7}{10} = \frac{7}{10} \checkmark$$

$$\frac{3}{b^2+5b+6} + \frac{b-1}{b+2} = \frac{7}{b+3}$$
$$\frac{3}{(-2)^2 + 5(-2) + 6} + \frac{-2-1}{-2+2} \overset{?}{=} \frac{7}{-2+3}$$
$$\frac{3}{0} + \frac{-3}{0} \overset{?}{=} \frac{7}{1}$$

Since $b = -2$ results in a zero in the denominator, the solution is 7.

28.

$$\frac{1}{n-2} = \frac{2n+1}{n^2 + 2n - 8} + \frac{2}{n+4}$$

$$(n^2 + 2n - 8)\left(\frac{1}{n-2}\right) = (n^2 + 2n - 8)\left(\frac{2n+1}{n^2+2n-8} + \frac{2}{n+4}\right)$$

$$n + 4 = (n^2 + 2n - 8)\left(\frac{2n+1}{n^2+2n-8}\right) + (n^2 + 2n - 8)\left(\frac{2}{n+4}\right)$$

$$n + 4 = 2n + 1 + 2n - 4$$
$$7 = 3n$$
$$\frac{7}{3} = n$$

Check: $\frac{1}{n-2} = \frac{2n+1}{n^2+2n-8} + \frac{2}{n+4}$

$$\frac{1}{\frac{7}{3}-2} \overset{?}{=} \frac{2\left(\frac{7}{3}\right)+1}{\left(\frac{7}{3}\right)^2 + 2\left(\frac{7}{3}\right) - 8} + \frac{2}{\frac{7}{3}+4}$$

$$3 \overset{?}{=} \frac{51}{19} + \frac{6}{19}$$

$$3 = 3 \checkmark$$

The solution is $\frac{7}{3}$.

29.
$$\frac{2q}{2q+3} - \frac{2q}{2q-3} = 1$$

$$(2q+3)(2q-3)\left(\frac{2q}{2q+3} - \frac{2q}{2q-3}\right) = (2q+3)(2q-3)(1)$$

$$(2q+3)(2q-3)\left(\frac{2q}{2q+3}\right) - (2q+3)(2q-3)\left(\frac{2q}{2q-3}\right) = 4q^2 - 9$$

$$4q^2 - 6q - (4q^2 + 6q) = 4q^2 - 9$$

$$4q^2 - 6q - 4q^2 - 6q = 4q^2 - 9$$

$$0 = 4q^2 + 12q - 9$$

Use the Quadratic Formula to solve for q.

$$x = \frac{-b \pm \sqrt{b^2 - 4ac}}{2a}$$

$$q = \frac{-12 \pm \sqrt{12^2 - 4(4)(-9)}}{2(4)}$$

$$q = \frac{-12 \pm \sqrt{288}}{8}$$

$$q = \frac{-3 \pm 3\sqrt{2}}{2}$$

The solutions are $\frac{-3 + 3\sqrt{2}}{2}$ or $\frac{-3 - 3\sqrt{2}}{2}$.

30.
$$\frac{4}{z-2} - \frac{z+6}{z+1} = 1$$

$$(z-2)(z+1)\left(\frac{4}{z-2} - \frac{z+6}{z+1}\right) = (z-2)(z+1)(1)$$

$$(z-2)(z+1)\left(\frac{4}{z-2}\right) - (z-2)(z+1)\left(\frac{z+6}{z+1}\right) = z^2 - z - 2$$

$$4(z+1) - (z-2)(z+6) = z^2 - z - 2$$

$$4z + 4 - (z^2 + 4z - 12) = z^2 - z - 2$$

$$4z + 4 - z^2 - 4z + 12 = z^2 - z - 2$$

$$0 = 2z^2 - z - 18$$

Use the Quadratic Formula to solve for z.

$$x = \frac{-b \pm \sqrt{b^2 - 4ac}}{2a}$$

$$z = \frac{-(-1) \pm \sqrt{(-1)^2 - 4(2)(-18)}}{2(2)}$$

$$z = \frac{1 \pm \sqrt{145}}{4}$$

The solutions are $\frac{1 + \sqrt{145}}{4}$ or $\frac{1 - \sqrt{145}}{4}$.

31. Let x be the number.

$$\frac{x-8}{28+x} = \frac{2}{5}$$

$$5(28+x)\left(\frac{x-8}{28+x}\right) = 5(28+x)\left(\frac{2}{5}\right)$$

$$5x - 40 = 56 + 2x$$

$$3x = 96$$

$$x = 32$$

32. Let x be the number.

$$x + 8\left(\frac{1}{x}\right) = 6$$

$$x + \frac{8}{x} = 6$$

$$x\left(x + \frac{8}{x}\right) = x(6)$$

$$x^2 + 8 = 6x$$

$$x^2 - 6x + 8 = 0$$

$$(x-2)(x-4) = 0$$

$$x - 2 = 0 \quad \text{or} \quad x - 4 = 0$$

$$x = 2 \qquad\qquad x = 4$$

33. Let b be the number of members of the band. If there are c members of the chorale, then there are $c + 30$ members of the band, or $b = c + 30$. If each group had 10 more members, there would be $c + 30 + 10$ or $c + 40$ members of the band, and $c + 10$ members of the chorale; the ratio of their membership would be 3:2.

$$\frac{c+40}{c+10} = \frac{3}{2}$$

$$2(c+10)\left(\frac{c+40}{c+10}\right) = 2(c+10)\left(\frac{3}{2}\right)$$

$$2c + 80 = 3c + 30$$

$$50 = c$$

There are 50 members of the chorale. Therefore, there are 50 + 30 or 80 members of the band.

34.
$$\frac{1}{k} = \frac{1}{k_1} + \frac{1}{k_2}$$

$$\frac{1}{k} = \frac{1}{12} + \frac{1}{8}$$

$$24k\left(\frac{1}{k}\right) = 24k\left(\frac{1}{12} + \frac{1}{8}\right)$$

$$24 = 2k + 3k$$

$$24 = 5k$$

$$4.8 = k$$

The spring constant k is 4.8 centimeters per gram.

35. From the previous exercise, we know that the value of k is 4.8.

$$d = km$$

$$d = (4.8)(5)$$

$$d = 24$$

The springs will stretch 24 centimeters.

36. Let s represent Alfonso's normal bicycling speed with no wind. His rate when he was cycling with the wind was $s + 3$, and his rate on his return trip was $s - 3$.

$$\frac{s+3}{s-3} = \frac{36}{24}$$

$$24(s-3)\left(\frac{s+3}{s-3}\right) = 24(s-3)\left(\frac{36}{24}\right)$$

$$24s + 72 = 36s - 108$$

$$180 = 12s$$

$$15 = s$$

His normal bicycling speed with no wind is 15 kilometers per hour.

37.
$$f(x) = \frac{5(0.20) + x(0.80)}{5+x}$$

$$0.50 = \frac{1 + 0.80x}{5+x}$$

$$(5+x)(0.50) = (5+x)\left(\frac{1 + 0.80x}{5+x}\right)$$

$$2.50 + 0.50x = 1 + 0.80x$$

$$1.50 = 0.30x$$

$$5 = x$$

Since $x = 5$, 5 milliliters of 80% solution should be added.

38. If $\frac{1}{x}$ is the average of $\frac{1}{y}$ and $\frac{1}{z}$, then $\frac{1}{x} = \frac{1}{2}\left(\frac{1}{y} + \frac{1}{z}\right)$, or $\frac{1}{x} = \frac{1}{2y} + \frac{1}{2z}$. Use substitution to determine the value of y.

$$\frac{1}{x} = \frac{1}{2y} + \frac{1}{2z}$$
$$\frac{1}{8} = \frac{1}{2y} + \frac{1}{2(20)}$$
$$40y\left(\frac{1}{8}\right) = 40y\left(\frac{1}{2y} + \frac{1}{40}\right)$$
$$5y = 20 + y$$
$$4y = 20$$
$$y = 5$$

The value of y is 5.

39. If $\frac{1}{x}$ is the average of $\frac{1}{y}$ and $\frac{1}{z}$, then $\frac{1}{x} = \frac{1}{2}\left(\frac{1}{y} + \frac{1}{z}\right)$, or $\frac{1}{x} = \frac{1}{2y} + \frac{1}{2z}$. Use substitution to determine the value of x.

$$\frac{1}{x} = \frac{1}{2y} + \frac{1}{2z}$$
$$\frac{1}{x} = \frac{1}{2(5)} + \frac{1}{2(8)}$$
$$80x\left(\frac{1}{x}\right) = 80x\left(\frac{1}{10} + \frac{1}{16}\right)$$
$$80 = 8x + 5x$$
$$80 = 13x$$
$$6.15 \approx x$$

The value of x is about 6.15.

40.
$$\frac{1}{a} - \frac{1}{b} = c$$
$$ab\left(\frac{1}{a} - \frac{1}{b}\right) = ab(c)$$
$$b - a = abc$$
$$b = abc + a$$
$$b = a(bc + 1)$$
$$\frac{b}{bc + 1} = a$$

41. If something has a general fee and cost per unit, rational equations can be used to determine how many units a person must buy in order for the actual unit price to be a given number. Answers should include the following.

- To solve $\frac{500 + 5x}{x} = 6$, multiply each side of the equation by x to eliminate the rational expression. Then subtract $5x$ from each side. Therefore, $500 = x$. A person would need to use 500 minutes of long distance minutes to make the actual unit price 6¢.

- Since the cost is 5¢ per minute plus $5.00 per month, the actual cost per minute could never be 5¢ or less.

42. B;
$$T = \frac{4st}{s - t}$$
$$40 = \frac{4s(5)}{s - 5}$$
$$(s - 5)(40) = (s - 5)\left(\frac{20s}{s - 5}\right)$$
$$40s - 200 = 20s$$
$$20s = 200$$
$$s = 10$$

43. C; If T is the sum of Amanda's six test scores, then her average A is $\frac{T}{6}$. However, when she divided by 7, her average was 12 less than her actual average, or $A - 12$, so $\frac{T}{7} = A - 12$. Since $\frac{T}{6} = A$, by substitution, $\frac{T}{7} = \frac{T}{6} - 12$, or $\frac{T}{7} + 12 = \frac{T}{6}$.

Page 511   Maintain Your Skills

44. The function is in the form $y = ax^2 + bx + c$, where $a \neq 0$. Therefore, it is a quadratic function. The graph is a parabola. Determine some points on the graph, then graph the function.

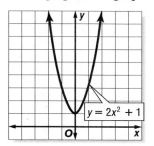

$y = 2x^2 + 1$

45. Since the equation includes an expression inside the radical sign, the function is a square root function. Therefore, the graph is a curve that starts at a point and continues in one direction. Determine some points on the graph, then graph the function.

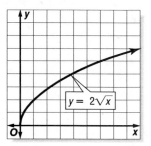

$y = 2\sqrt{x}$

46. The function is in the form $y = ax$, where $a = 0.8$. Therefore, it is a direct variation function. The graph passes through the origin and has a slope of 0.8.

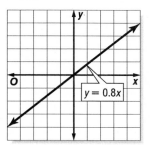

$y = 0.8x$

47.
$$\frac{y_1}{x_2} = \frac{y_2}{x_1}$$
$$\frac{24}{6} = \frac{y_2}{9}$$
$$24(9) = 6(y_2)$$
$$216 = 6y_2$$
$$36 = y_2$$
When $x = 6$, the value of y is 36.

48.
$$\frac{y_1}{x_1} = \frac{y_2}{x_2}$$
$$\frac{9}{4} = \frac{y_2}{15}$$
$$15(9) = 4(y_2)$$
$$135 = 4y_2$$
$$33.75 = y_2$$
When $x = 15$, the value of y is 33.75.

49.
$$d = \sqrt{(x_2 - x_1)^2 + (y_2 - y_1)^2}$$
$$= \sqrt{[9 - (5)]^2 + (-11 - 7)^2}$$
$$= \sqrt{14^2 + (-18)^2}$$
$$= \sqrt{196 + 324} \text{ or } 2\sqrt{130}$$
The distance between the points is $2\sqrt{130}$ units.

50.
$$d = \sqrt{(x_2 - x_1)^2 + (y_2 - y_1)^2}$$
$$= \sqrt{(7 - 3)^2 + (3 - 5)^2}$$
$$= \sqrt{4^2 + (-2)^2}$$
$$= \sqrt{16 + 4} \text{ or } 2\sqrt{5}$$
The distance between the points is $2\sqrt{5}$ units.

51.
$$d = \sqrt{(x_2 - x_1)^2 + (y_2 - y_1)^2}$$
$$= \sqrt{[-5 - (-1)]^2 + (-8 - 3)^2}$$
$$= \sqrt{(-4)^2 + (-11)^2}$$
$$= \sqrt{16 + 121} \text{ or } \sqrt{137}$$
The distance between the points is $\sqrt{137}$ units.

52. First solve the related equation
$(x + 11)(x - 3) = 0$.
$$(x + 11)(x - 3) = 0$$
$$x + 11 = 0 \quad \text{or} \quad x - 3 = 0$$
$$x = -11 \quad\quad x = 3$$
Test a value in each interval to see if it satisfies the original inequality.

Test $x = -12$.
$$(x + 11)(x - 3) > 0$$
$$(-12 + 11)(-12 - 3) \overset{?}{>} 0$$
$$15 > 0 \checkmark$$

Test $x = 0$.
$$(x + 11)(x - 3) > 0$$
$$(0 + 11)(0 - 3) \overset{?}{>} 0$$
$$-33 \not> 0$$

Test $x = 4$.
$$(x + 11)(x - 3) > 0$$
$$(4 + 11)(4 - 3) \overset{?}{>} 0$$
$$15 > 0 \checkmark$$

The solution set is $\{x \mid x < -11 \text{ or } x > 3\}$.

53. First solve the related equation $x^2 - 4x = 0$.
$$x^2 - 4x = 0$$
$$x(x - 4) = 0$$
$$x = 0 \quad \text{or} \quad x - 4 = 0$$
$$x = 4$$
Test a value in each interval to see if it satisfies the original inequality.

Test $x = -1$.
$$x^2 - 4x \leq 0$$
$$(-1)^2 - 4(-1) \overset{?}{\leq} 0$$
$$5 \not\leq 0$$

Test $x = 2$.
$$x^2 - 4x \leq 0$$
$$(2)^2 - 4(2) \overset{?}{\leq} 0$$
$$-4 \leq 0 \checkmark$$

Test $x = 5$.
$$x^2 - 4x \leq 0$$
$$(5)^2 - 4(5) \overset{?}{\leq} 0$$
$$(5)^2 - 4(5) \overset{?}{\leq} 0$$
$$5 \not\leq 0$$

The solution set is $\{x \mid 0 \leq x \leq 4\}$.

54. First solve the related equation $2b^2 - b = 6$.
$$2b^2 - b = 6$$
$$2b^2 - b - 6 = 0$$
$$(2b + 3)(b - 2) = 0$$
$$2b + 3 = 0 \quad \text{or} \quad b - 2 = 0$$
$$2b = -3 \quad\quad\quad b = 2$$
$$b = -\frac{3}{2}$$
Test a value in each interval to see if it satisfies the original inequality.

Test $b = -2$.
$$2b^2 - b < 6$$
$$2(-2)^2 - (-2) \overset{?}{<} 6$$
$$10 \not< 6$$

Test $b = 0$.
$$2b^2 - b < 6$$
$$2(0)^2 - 0 \overset{?}{<} 6$$
$$0 < 6 \checkmark$$

Test $b = 3$.
$$2b^2 - b < 6$$
$$2(3)^2 - 3 \overset{?}{<} 6$$
$$15 \not< 6$$

The solution set is $\left\{ b \mid -1\frac{1}{2} < b < 2 \right\}$.

1. First, rewrite as two functions, $y_1 = \frac{1}{x} + \frac{1}{2}$ and $y_2 = \frac{2}{x}$. Next, graph the two functions on a calculator.

KEYSTROKES: [y=] 1 [÷] [X,T,θ,n] [+] 1 [÷] 2
[▼] 2 [÷] [X,T,θ,n] [GRAPH]

Locate the point(s) of intersection.

KEYSTROKES: [2nd] [CALC] 5

Select one graph and press [ENTER]. Select the other graph, and press [ENTER] [ENTER]. The solution is 2.

2. First, rewrite as two functions, $y_1 = \frac{1}{x-4}$ and $y_2 = \frac{2}{x-2}$. Next, graph the two functions on a calculator.

KEYSTROKES: [y=] 1 [÷] [(] [X,T,θ,n] [−] 4 [)]
[▼] 2 [÷] [(] [X,T,θ,n] [−] 2 [)]
[GRAPH]

Locate the point(s) of intersection.

KEYSTROKES: [2nd] [CALC] 5

Select one graph and press [ENTER]. Select the other graph, and press [ENTER] [ENTER]. The solution is 6.

3. First, rewrite as two functions, $y_1 = \frac{4}{x}$ and $y_2 = \frac{6}{x_2}$. Next, graph the two functions on a calculator.

KEYSTROKES: [y=] 4 [÷] [X,T,θ,n] [▼] 6 [÷]
[X,T,θ,n] [x²] [GRAPH]

Locate the point(s) of intersection.

KEYSTROKES: [2nd] [CALC] 5

Select one graph and press [ENTER]. Select the other graph, and press [ENTER] [ENTER]. The solution is 1.5.

4. First, rewrite as two functions, $y_1 = \frac{1}{1-x}$ and $y_2 = 1 - \frac{x}{x-1}$. Next, graph the two functions on a calculator.

KEYSTROKES: [y=] 1 [÷] [(] 1 [−] [X,T,θ,n] [)]
[▼] 1 [−] [X,T,θ,n] [÷] [(]
[X,T,θ,n] [−] 1 [)] [GRAPH]

Notice that the graphs of the functions are the same. Both are undefined for $x = 1$. Therefore, the solution is all real numbers except 1.

5. First, rewrite as two functions, $y_1 = \frac{1}{x+4}$ and $y_2 = \frac{2}{x^2+3x-4} - \frac{1}{1-x}$. Next, graph the two functions on a calculator.

KEYSTROKES: [y=] 1 [÷] [(] [X,T,θ,n] [+] 4 [)]
[▼] 2 [÷] [(] [X,T,θ,n] [x²] [+] 3
[X,T,θ,n] [−] 4 [)] [−] 1 [÷] [(] 1
[−] [X,T,θ,n] [)] [GRAPH]

Locate the point(s) of intersection.

KEYSTROKES: [2nd] [CALC]5

Select one graph and press [ENTER]. Select the other graph, and press [ENTER] [ENTER]. However, the graphs do not intersect. Therefore, there is no real solution.

6. First, rewrite as two functions, $y_1 = \frac{1}{x-1} + \frac{1}{x+2}$ and $y_2 = \frac{1}{2}$. Next, graph the two functions on a calculator.

KEYSTROKES: [y=] 1 [÷] [(] [X,T,θ,n] [−] 1 [)]
[+] 1 [÷] [(] [X,T,θ,n] [+] 2 [)]
[▼] 1 [÷] 2 [GRAPH]

Locate the point(s) of intersection.

KEYSTROKES: [2nd] [CALC]5

Select one graph and press [ENTER]. Select the other graph, and press [ENTER] [ENTER]. The solutions are −1 and 4.

7. $\frac{3}{x} + \frac{7}{x} = 9$

$x\left(\frac{3}{x} + \frac{7}{x}\right) = x(9)$

$3 + 7 = 9x$

$10 = 9x$

$1\frac{1}{9} = x$

Check: $\frac{3}{x} + \frac{7}{x} = 9$

$\frac{3}{\left(1\frac{1}{9}\right)} + \frac{7}{\left(1\frac{1}{9}\right)} \stackrel{?}{=} 9$

$\frac{27}{10} + \frac{63}{10} \stackrel{?}{=} 9$

$9 = 9 \checkmark$

The solution is $1\frac{1}{9}$.

8. $\frac{1}{x-1} + \frac{2}{x} = 0$

$x(x-1)\left(\frac{1}{x-1} + \frac{2}{x}\right) = x(x-1)(0)$

$x(x-1)\left(\frac{1}{x-1}\right) + x(x-1)\left(\frac{2}{x}\right) = 0$

$x + 2x - 2 = 0$

$3x = 2$

$x = \frac{2}{3}$

Check: $\dfrac{1}{x-1} + \dfrac{2}{x} = 0$

$\dfrac{1}{\left(\frac{2}{3}\right)-1} + \dfrac{2}{\frac{2}{3}} \stackrel{?}{=} 0$

$-3 + 3 \stackrel{?}{=} 0$

$0 = 0 \checkmark$

The solution is $\dfrac{2}{3}$.

9. $1 + \dfrac{5}{x-1} = \dfrac{7}{6}$

$6(x-1)\left(1 + \dfrac{5}{x-1}\right) = \overset{1}{\cancel{6}}(x-1)\left(\dfrac{7}{\cancel{6}}\right)$

$6(x-1)(1) + 6(\cancel{x-1})^1\left(\dfrac{5}{\cancel{x-1}_1}\right) = 7(x-1)$

$6x - 6 + 30 = 7x - 7$

$6x + 24 = 7x - 7$

$31 = x$

Check: $1 + \dfrac{5}{x-1} = \dfrac{7}{6}$

$1 + \dfrac{5}{31-1} \stackrel{?}{=} \dfrac{7}{6}$

$1 + \dfrac{5}{30} \stackrel{?}{=} \dfrac{7}{6}$

$\dfrac{7}{6} = \dfrac{7}{6} \checkmark$

The solution is 31.

10. $\dfrac{1}{x^2-1} = \dfrac{2}{x^2+x-2}$

$(\cancel{x^2-1})^1(x+2)\left(\dfrac{1}{\cancel{x^2-1}_1}\right) = (\cancel{x^2-1})^1(x+2)\left(\dfrac{2}{\cancel{x^2+x-2}_1^{(x+1)}}\right)$

$x + 2 = 2x + 2$

$0 = x$

Check: $\dfrac{1}{x^2-1} = \dfrac{2}{x^2+x-2}$

$\dfrac{1}{0^2-1} = \dfrac{2}{0^2+0-2}$

$\dfrac{1}{-1} = \dfrac{2}{-2}$

$-1 = -1 \checkmark$

The solution is 0.

11. $\dfrac{6}{x^2+2x} - \dfrac{x+1}{x+2} = \dfrac{2}{x}$

$(x^2+2x)\left(\dfrac{6}{x^2+2x} - \dfrac{x+1}{x+2}\right) = (\cancel{x^2+2x})^{(x+2)}\left(\dfrac{2}{\cancel{x}}\right)$

$(\cancel{x^2+2x})^1\left(\dfrac{6}{\cancel{x^2+2x}_1}\right) - (\cancel{x^2+2x})^{(x)}\left(\dfrac{x+1}{\cancel{x+2}_1}\right) = 2(x+2)$

$6 - (x^2+x) = 2x + 4$

$6 - x^2 - x = 2x + 4$

$0 = x^2 + 3x - 2$

Use the Quadratic Formula to solve for x.

$x = \dfrac{-b \pm \sqrt{b^2-4ac}}{2a}$

$x = \dfrac{-3 \pm \sqrt{3^2 - 4(1)(-2)}}{2(1)}$

$x = \dfrac{-3 \pm \sqrt{17}}{2}$

$x \approx -3.56$ or 0.56

The solutions are $\dfrac{-3 \pm \sqrt{17}}{2}$, or about -3.56 and 0.56.

---

12. $\dfrac{3}{x^2+5x+6} + \dfrac{x-1}{x+2} = \dfrac{7}{x+3}$

$(x^2+5x+6)\left(\dfrac{3}{x^2+5x+6} + \dfrac{x-1}{x+2}\right) = (x^2+5x+6)\left(\dfrac{7}{x+3}\right)$

$(\cancel{x^2+5x+6})^1\left(\dfrac{3}{\cancel{x^2+5x+6}_1}\right) + (\cancel{x^2+5x+6})^{x+3}\left(\dfrac{x-1}{\cancel{x+2}_1}\right) = 7(x+2)$

$3 + (x+3)(x-1) = 7x + 14$

$3 + x^2 + 2x - 3 = 7x + 14$

$x^2 - 5x - 14 = 0$

$(x-7)(x+2) = 0$

$x - 7 = 0$ or $x + 2 = 0$

$x = 7$ $x = -2$

Check: $\dfrac{3}{x^2+5x+6} + \dfrac{x-1}{x+2} = \dfrac{7}{x+3}$

$\dfrac{3}{7^2+5(7)+6} + \dfrac{7-1}{7+2} \stackrel{?}{=} \dfrac{7}{7+3}$

$\dfrac{3}{90} + \dfrac{6}{9} \stackrel{?}{=} \dfrac{7}{10}$

$\dfrac{7}{10} = \dfrac{7}{10} \checkmark$

$\dfrac{3}{x^2+5x+6} + \dfrac{x-1}{x+2} = \dfrac{7}{x+3}$

$\dfrac{3}{(-2)^2+5(-2)+6} + \dfrac{-2-1}{-2+2} \stackrel{?}{=} \dfrac{7}{-2+3}$

$\dfrac{3}{0} + \dfrac{-3}{0} \stackrel{?}{=} \dfrac{7}{1}$

Since $x = -2$ results in a 0 in the denominator, the solution is 7.

Chapter 9 Study Guide and Review

Page 513   Vocabulary and Concept Check

1. False; since $\dfrac{x^2-1}{x+1} = \dfrac{(x+1)(x-1)}{x+1}$ or $x-1$, $y = \dfrac{x^2-1}{x+1}$ has a point discontinuity at $x = -1$.

2. True; since the equation is in the form $y = kx$ where $k = 3$, it is an example of a direct variation equation.

3. False; the equation $y = \dfrac{x^2}{x+1}$ is a rational equation.

4. False; the graph of $y = \dfrac{4}{x-4}$ has an asymptote at $x = 4$.

5. True; since the equation is in the form $b = \dfrac{k}{a}$ where $k = 2$, it is an inverse variation equation.

6. False; since the function is undefined for $x + 2 = 0$ or $x = -2$, the graph has a break in continuity at $x = -2$.

Pages 513–516   Lesson by Lesson Review

7. $\dfrac{-4ab}{21c} \cdot \dfrac{14c^2}{22a^2} = \dfrac{-\cancel{2}\cdot 2\cdot \cancel{a}\cdot b\cdot 2\cdot \cancel{7}\cdot \cancel{c}\cdot c}{3\cdot \cancel{7}\cdot \cancel{c}\cdot \cancel{2}\cdot 11\cdot \cancel{a}\cdot a}$

$= -\dfrac{2\cdot b\cdot 2\cdot c}{3\cdot 11\cdot a}$

$= -\dfrac{4bc}{33a}$

8. $\dfrac{a^2-b^2}{6b} \div \dfrac{a+b}{36b^2} = \dfrac{a^2-b^2}{6b} \cdot \dfrac{36b^2}{a+b}$

$= \dfrac{(\cancel{a+b})(a-b)}{\cancel{6b}_1} \cdot \dfrac{\overset{6}{\cancel{36}}\cdot 6\cdot \overset{b}{\cancel{b^2}}\cdot b}{\cancel{a+b}_1}$

$= \dfrac{(a-b)6\cdot b}{1}$

$= 6b(a-b)$

9. $\dfrac{y^2 - y - 12}{y + 2} \div \dfrac{y - 4}{y^2 - 4y - 12} = \dfrac{y^2 - y - 12}{y + 2} \cdot \dfrac{y^2 - 4y - 12}{y - 4}$

$\phantom{\dfrac{y^2 - y - 12}{y + 2}} = \dfrac{(y - 4)(y + 3)}{y + 2} \cdot \dfrac{(y - 6)(y + 2)}{y - 4}$

$\phantom{\dfrac{y^2 - y - 12}{y + 2}} = (y + 3)(y - 6)$

10. $\dfrac{\frac{x^2 + 7x + 10}{x + 2}}{\frac{x^2 + 2x - 15}{x + 2}} = \dfrac{x^2 + 7x + 10}{x + 2} \div \dfrac{x^2 + 2x - 15}{x + 2}$

$\phantom{\dfrac{x^2 + 7x + 10}{x + 2}} = \dfrac{x^2 + 7x + 10}{x + 2} \cdot \dfrac{x + 2}{x^2 + 2x - 15}$

$\phantom{\dfrac{x^2 + 7x + 10}{x + 2}} = \dfrac{(x + 2)(x + 5)}{x + 2} \cdot \dfrac{x + 2}{(x - 3)(x + 5)}$

$\phantom{\dfrac{x^2 + 7x + 10}{x + 2}} = \dfrac{x + 2}{x - 3}$

11. $\dfrac{\frac{1}{n^2 - 6n + 9}}{\frac{n + 3}{2n^2 - 18}} = \dfrac{1}{n^2 - 6n + 9} \div \dfrac{n + 3}{2n^2 - 18}$

$\phantom{\dfrac{1}{n^2 - 6n + 9}} = \dfrac{1}{n^2 - 6n + 9} \cdot \dfrac{2n^2 - 18}{n + 3}$

$\phantom{\dfrac{1}{n^2 - 6n + 9}} = \dfrac{1}{(n - 3)(n - 3)} \cdot \dfrac{2(n + 3)(n - 3)}{n + 3}$

$\phantom{\dfrac{1}{n^2 - 6n + 9}} = \dfrac{2}{n - 3}$

12. $\dfrac{x^2 + 3x - 10}{x^2 + 8x + 15} \cdot \dfrac{x^2 + 5x + 6}{x^2 + 4x + 4} = \dfrac{(x - 2)(x + 5)}{(x + 3)(x + 5)} \cdot \dfrac{(x + 2)(x + 3)}{(x + 2)(x + 2)}$

$\phantom{\dfrac{x^2 + 3x - 10}{x^2 + 8x + 15}} = \dfrac{x - 2}{x + 2}$

13. $\dfrac{x + 2}{x - 5} + 6 = \dfrac{x + 2}{x - 5} + \dfrac{6(x - 5)}{x - 5}$

$\phantom{\dfrac{x + 2}{x - 5} + 6} = \dfrac{x + 2}{x - 5} + \dfrac{6x - 30}{x - 5}$

$\phantom{\dfrac{x + 2}{x - 5} + 6} = \dfrac{x + 2 + 6x - 30}{x - 5}$

$\phantom{\dfrac{x + 2}{x - 5} + 6} = \dfrac{7x - 28}{x - 5}$

$\phantom{\dfrac{x + 2}{x - 5} + 6} = \dfrac{7(x - 4)}{x - 5}$

14. $\dfrac{x - 1}{x^2 - 1} + \dfrac{2}{5x + 5} = \dfrac{x - 1}{(x - 1)(x + 1)} + \dfrac{2}{5(x + 1)}$

$\phantom{\dfrac{x - 1}{x^2 - 1}} = \dfrac{(x - 1)(5)}{(x - 1)(x + 1)(5)} + \dfrac{2(x - 1)}{5(x + 1)(x - 1)}$

$\phantom{\dfrac{x - 1}{x^2 - 1}} = \dfrac{5x - 5}{5(x - 1)(x + 1)} + \dfrac{2x - 2}{5(x - 1)(x + 1)}$

$\phantom{\dfrac{x - 1}{x^2 - 1}} = \dfrac{5x - 5 + 2x - 2}{5(x - 1)(x + 1)}$

$\phantom{\dfrac{x - 1}{x^2 - 1}} = \dfrac{7x - 7}{5(x - 1)(x + 1)}$

$\phantom{\dfrac{x - 1}{x^2 - 1}} = \dfrac{7(x - 1)}{5(x - 1)(x + 1)}$

$\phantom{\dfrac{x - 1}{x^2 - 1}} = \dfrac{7}{5(x + 1)}$

15. $\dfrac{7}{y} - \dfrac{2}{3y} = \dfrac{7(3)}{y(3)} - \dfrac{2}{3y}$

$\phantom{\dfrac{7}{y} - \dfrac{2}{3y}} = \dfrac{21}{3y} - \dfrac{2}{3y}$

$\phantom{\dfrac{7}{y} - \dfrac{2}{3y}} = \dfrac{19}{3y}$

16. $\dfrac{7}{y - 2} - \dfrac{11}{2 - y} = \dfrac{7}{y - 2} - \dfrac{11(-1)}{(2 - y)(-1)}$

$\phantom{\dfrac{7}{y - 2}} = \dfrac{7}{y - 2} - \dfrac{-11}{y - 2}$

$\phantom{\dfrac{7}{y - 2}} = \dfrac{7 - (-11)}{y - 2}$

$\phantom{\dfrac{7}{y - 2}} = \dfrac{18}{y - 2}$

17. $\dfrac{3}{4b} - \dfrac{2}{5b} - \dfrac{1}{2b} = \dfrac{3(5)}{4b \cdot 5} - \dfrac{2(4)}{5b \cdot 4} - \dfrac{1(10)}{2b \cdot 10}$

$\phantom{\dfrac{3}{4b}} = \dfrac{15}{20b} - \dfrac{8}{20b} - \dfrac{10}{20b}$

$\phantom{\dfrac{3}{4b}} = \dfrac{15 - 8 - 10}{20b}$

$\phantom{\dfrac{3}{4b}} = -\dfrac{3}{20b}$

18. $\dfrac{m + 3}{m^2 - 6m + 9} - \dfrac{8m - 24}{9 - m^2}$

$= \dfrac{m + 3}{(m - 3)(m - 3)} - \dfrac{8m - 24}{-(m + 3)(m - 3)}$

$= \dfrac{(m + 3)(-1)(m + 3)}{(m - 3)(m - 3)(-1)(m + 3)} - \dfrac{(8m - 24)(m - 3)}{-(m + 3)(m - 3)(m - 3)}$

$= \dfrac{-(m^2 + 6m + 9)}{-(m + 3)(m - 3)^2} - \dfrac{8m^2 - 48m + 72}{-(m + 3)(m - 3)^2}$

$= \dfrac{-m^2 - 6m - 9 - (8m^2 - 48m + 72)}{-(m + 3)(m - 3)^2}$

$= \dfrac{-m^2 - 6m - 9 - 8m^2 + 48m - 72}{-(m + 3)(m - 3)^2}$

$= \dfrac{-9m^2 + 42m - 81}{-(m + 3)(m - 3)^2}$

$= \dfrac{-3(3m^2 - 14m + 27)}{-(m + 3)(m - 3)^2}$

$= \dfrac{3(3m^2 - 14m + 27)}{(m + 3)(m - 3)^2}$

19. The function is undefined for $x = 2$. Since $\dfrac{4}{x - 2}$ is in simplest form, $x = 2$ is a vertical asymptote. Draw the asymptote and sketch the graph.

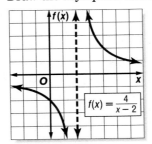

$f(x) = \dfrac{4}{x - 2}$

20. The function is undefined for $x = -3$. Since $\dfrac{x}{x + 3}$ is in simplest form, $x = -3$ is a vertical asymptote. Draw the asymptote and sketch the graph. Notice that the horizontal asymptote is $y = 1$.

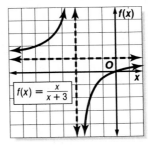

$f(x) = \dfrac{x}{x + 3}$

21. The function is undefined for $x = 0$. Since $\dfrac{2}{x}$ is in simplest form, $x = 0$ is a vertical asymptote. Draw the asymptote and sketch the graph.

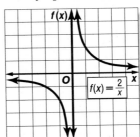

$f(x) = \dfrac{2}{x}$

22. The function is undefined for $x = -3$. Since $\frac{x-4}{x+3}$ is in simplest form, $x = -3$ is a vertical asymptote. Draw the asymptote and sketch the graph.

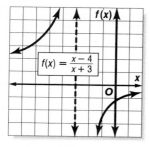

23. The graph is undefined for $x = -1$ and $x = 3$. Since $\frac{5}{(x+1)(x-3)}$ is in simplest form, $x = -1$ and $x = 3$ are vertical asymptotes. Draw the asymptotes and sketch the graph.

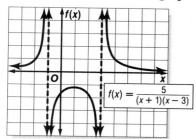

24. Notice that $\frac{x^2 + 2x + 1}{x+1} = \frac{(x+1)(x+1)}{x+1}$ or $x + 1$. Therefore, the graph of $f(x) = \frac{x^2 + 2x + 1}{x+1}$ is the graph of $f(x) = x + 1$ with a hole at $x = -1$.

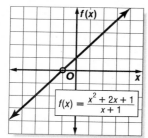

25.
$$\frac{x_1}{y_1} = \frac{x_2}{y_2}$$
$$\frac{7}{21} = \frac{x_2}{-5}$$
$$7(-5) = 21(x_2)$$
$$-35 = 21x_2$$
$$-1\tfrac{2}{3} = x_2$$
When $y = -5$, the value of x is $-1\tfrac{2}{3}$.

26.
$$\frac{y_1}{x_2} = \frac{y_2}{x_1}$$
$$\frac{9}{-0.6} = \frac{y_2}{2.5}$$
$$9(2.5) = -0.6(y_2)$$
$$22.5 = -0.6y_2$$
$$-37.5 = y_2$$
When $x = -0.6$, the value of y is -37.5.

27.
$$\frac{x_1}{y_2} = \frac{x_2}{y_1}$$
$$\frac{28}{63} = \frac{x_2}{18}$$
$$28(18) = 63(x_2)$$
$$504 = 63x_2$$
$$8 = x_2$$
When $y = 63$, the value of x is 8.

28.
$$\frac{x_1}{y_1} = \frac{x_2}{y_2}$$
$$\frac{28}{18} = \frac{x_2}{63}$$
$$28(63) = 18(x_2)$$
$$1764 = 18x_2$$
$$98 = x_2$$
When $y = 63$, the value of x is 98.

29.
$$\frac{y_1}{x_1 z_1} = \frac{y_2}{x_2 z_2}$$
$$\frac{16}{2(4)} = \frac{y_2}{5(8)}$$
$$5(8)(16) = 2(4)(y_2)$$
$$640 = 8y_2$$
$$80 = y_2$$
When $x = 5$ and $z = 8$, the value of y is 80.

30. The graph has a starting point and curves in one direction. The graph represents a square root function.

31. The graph is in the shape of a V. The graph represents an absolute value function.

32. The graph is a straight line that passes through the origin and is neither horizontal nor vertical. The graph represents a direct variation function.

33.
$$\frac{3}{y} + \frac{7}{y} = 9$$
$$y\left(\frac{3}{y} + \frac{7}{y}\right) = (y)(9)$$
$$3 + 7 = 9y$$
$$10 = 9y$$
$$1\tfrac{1}{9} = y$$
Check: $\dfrac{3}{y} + \dfrac{7}{y} = 9$
$$\frac{3}{\left(1\frac{1}{9}\right)} + \frac{7}{\left(1\frac{1}{9}\right)} \overset{?}{=} 9$$
$$\frac{27}{10} + \frac{63}{10} \overset{?}{=} 9$$
$$9 = 9 \checkmark$$
The solution is $1\tfrac{1}{9}$.

34.
$$1 + \frac{5}{y-1} = \frac{7}{6}$$
$$6(y-1)\left(1 + \frac{5}{y-1}\right) = \cancel{6}(y-1)\left(\frac{7}{\cancel{6}}\right)$$
$$6(y-1)(1) + 6(y \overset{1}{-} 1)\left(\frac{5}{y \underset{1}{-} 1}\right) = 7(y-1)$$
$$6y - 6 + 30 = 7y - 7$$
$$6y + 24 = 7y - 7$$
$$31 = y$$
Check: $1 + \dfrac{5}{y-1} = \dfrac{7}{6}$
$$1 + \frac{5}{31-1} \overset{?}{=} \frac{7}{6}$$
$$1 + \frac{5}{30} \overset{?}{=} \frac{7}{6}$$
$$\frac{7}{6} = \frac{7}{6} \checkmark$$
The solution is 31.

35.

$$\frac{3x+2}{4} = \frac{9}{4} - \frac{3-2x}{6}$$

$$12\left(\frac{3x+2}{4}\right) = 12\left(\frac{9}{4} - \frac{3-2x}{6}\right)$$

$$3(3x+2) = 27 - 2(3-2x)$$

$$9x + 6 = 27 - (6-4x)$$

$$9x + 6 = 27 - 6 + 4x$$

$$5x = 15$$

$$x = 3$$

Check: $\dfrac{3x+2}{4} = \dfrac{9}{4} - \dfrac{3-2x}{6}$

$$\frac{3(3)+2}{4} \overset{?}{=} \frac{9}{4} - \frac{3-2(3)}{6}$$

$$\frac{11}{4} \overset{?}{=} \frac{9}{4} - \frac{-3}{6}$$

$$\frac{11}{4} = \frac{11}{4} \checkmark$$

The solution is 3.

36.

$$\frac{1}{r^2-1} = \frac{2}{r^2+r-2}$$

$$(r^2-1)(r+2)\left(\frac{1}{r^2-1}\right) = (r^2-1)(r+2)\left(\frac{2}{r^2+r-2}\right)$$

$$r + 2 = 2r + 2$$

$$0 = r$$

Check: $\dfrac{1}{r^2-1} = \dfrac{2}{r^2+r-2}$

$$\frac{1}{0^2-1} \overset{?}{=} \frac{2}{0^2+0-2}$$

$$\frac{1}{-1} \overset{?}{=} \frac{2}{-2}$$

$$-1 = -1 \checkmark$$

The solution is 0.

37.

$$\frac{x}{x^2-1} + \frac{2}{x+1} = 1 + \frac{1}{2x-2}$$

$$2(x^2-1)\left(\frac{x}{x^2-1} + \frac{2}{x+1}\right) = 2(x^2-1)\left(1 + \frac{1}{2x-2}\right)$$

$$2(x^2-1)\left(\frac{x}{x^2-1}\right) + 2(x^2-1)\left(\frac{2}{x+1}\right) = 2(x^2-1)(1) + 2(x^2-1)\left(\frac{1}{2x-2}\right)$$

$$2x + 4x - 4 = 2x^2 - 2 + x + 1$$

$$0 = 2x^2 - 5x + 3$$

$$0 = (x-1)(2x-3)$$

$$x - 1 = 0 \quad \text{or} \quad 2x - 3 = 0$$

$$x = 1 \qquad\qquad\qquad 2x = 3$$

$$x = \frac{3}{2}$$

Check: $\dfrac{x}{x^2-1} + \dfrac{2}{x+1} = 1 + \dfrac{1}{2x-2}$

$$\frac{1}{1^2-1} + \frac{2}{1+1} \overset{?}{=} 1 + \frac{1}{2(1)-2}$$

$$\frac{1}{0} + \frac{2}{2} \overset{?}{=} 1 + \frac{1}{0}$$

$$\frac{x}{x^2-1} + \frac{2}{x+1} = 1 + \frac{1}{2x-2}$$

$$\frac{\frac{3}{2}}{\left(\frac{3}{2}\right)^2-1} + \frac{2}{\frac{3}{2}+1} \overset{?}{=} 1 + \frac{1}{2\left(\frac{3}{2}\right)-2}$$

$$\frac{6}{5} + \frac{4}{5} \overset{?}{=} 1 + \frac{1}{1}$$

$$2 = 2 \checkmark$$

Since $x = 1$ results in a 0 in the denominator, the solution is $\frac{3}{2}$ or $1\frac{1}{2}$.

38. Since values that make a denominator equal to 0 are excluded from the domain, 0 is excluded from this inequality. Solve the related equation,

$$\frac{1}{3b} - \frac{3}{4b} = \frac{1}{6}.$$

$$\frac{1}{3b} - \frac{3}{4b} = \frac{1}{6}$$

$$12b\left(\frac{1}{3b} - \frac{3}{4b}\right) = 12b\left(\frac{1}{6}\right)$$

$$4 - 9 = 2b$$

$$-5 = 2b$$

$$-2\frac{1}{2} = b$$

Test a sample value in each region to determine if the values in the region satisfy the inequality.

Test $b = -3$.

$$\frac{1}{3b} - \frac{3}{4b} > \frac{1}{6}$$

$$\frac{1}{3(-3)} - \frac{3}{4(-3)} \overset{?}{>} \frac{1}{6}$$

$$\frac{1}{-9} - \frac{3}{-12} \overset{?}{>} \frac{1}{6}$$

$$\frac{5}{36} \not> \frac{1}{6}$$

$b < -2\frac{1}{2}$ is *not* a solution.

Test $b = -1$.

$$\frac{1}{3b} - \frac{3}{4b} > \frac{1}{6}$$

$$\frac{1}{3(-1)} - \frac{3}{4(-1)} \overset{?}{>} \frac{1}{6}$$

$$\frac{1}{-3} - \frac{3}{-4} \overset{?}{>} \frac{1}{6}$$

$$\frac{5}{12} > \frac{1}{6} \checkmark$$

$-2\frac{1}{2} < b < 0$ is a solution.

Test $b = 1$.

$$\frac{1}{3b} - \frac{3}{4b} > \frac{1}{6}$$

$$\frac{1}{3(1)} - \frac{3}{4(1)} \overset{?}{>} \frac{1}{6}$$

$$\frac{1}{3} - \frac{3}{4} \overset{?}{>} \frac{1}{6}$$

$$-\frac{5}{12} \not> \frac{1}{6}$$

$b > 0$ is *not* a solution.

The solution is $-2\frac{1}{2} < b < 0$.

Chapter 9   Practice Test

Page 517

1. c; the equation is in the form $y = kxz$ where $k = 4$, so it is a joint variation equation.

2. b; the equation is in the form $y = kx$ where $k = 5$, so it is a direct variation equation.

3. a; the equation is in the form $y = \frac{k}{x}$ where $k = 7$, so it is an inverse variation equation.

4.

$$\frac{a^2-ab}{3a} \div \frac{a-b}{15b^2} = \frac{a^2-ab}{3a} \cdot \frac{15b^2}{a-b}$$

$$= \frac{a(a-b)}{3a} \cdot \frac{3 \cdot 5b^2}{a-b}$$

$$= 5b^2$$

5. $\dfrac{x^2 - y^2}{y^2} \cdot \dfrac{y^3}{y - x} = \dfrac{(\overset{1}{\cancel{x - y}})(x + y)}{\overset{1}{\cancel{y}} \cdot \overset{1}{\cancel{y}}} \cdot \dfrac{\overset{1}{\cancel{y}} \cdot \overset{1}{\cancel{y}} \cdot y}{\underset{1}{\cancel{y}} - \underset{1}{\cancel{x}}}$

$\qquad = \dfrac{(x + y) \cdot y}{-1}$

$\qquad = -y(x + y)$

6. $\dfrac{x^2 - 2x + 1}{y - 5} \div \dfrac{x - 1}{y^2 - 25} = \dfrac{x^2 - 2x + 1}{y - 5} \cdot \dfrac{y^2 - 25}{x - 1}$

$\qquad = \dfrac{(x \overset{1}{\cancel{- 1}})(x - 1)}{\overset{}{\cancel{y - 5}}} \cdot \dfrac{(\overset{1}{\cancel{y - 5}})(y + 5)}{\underset{1}{\cancel{x - 1}}}$

$\qquad = (x - 1)(y + 5)$

7. $\dfrac{\frac{x^2 - 1}{x^2 - 3x - 10}}{\frac{x^2 + 3x + 2}{x^2 - 12x + 35}} = \dfrac{x^2 - 1}{x^2 - 3x - 10} \div \dfrac{x^2 + 3x + 2}{x^2 - 12x + 35}$

$\qquad = \dfrac{x^2 - 1}{x^2 - 3x - 10} \cdot \dfrac{x^2 - 12x + 35}{x^2 + 3x + 2}$

$\qquad = \dfrac{(x - 1)(x \overset{1}{\cancel{+ 1}})}{(x \overset{1}{\cancel{- 5}})(x + 2)} \cdot \dfrac{(x - 7)(x \overset{1}{\cancel{- 5}})}{(x \underset{1}{\cancel{+ 1}})(x + 2)}$

$\qquad = \dfrac{(x - 1)(x - 7)}{(x + 2)^2}$

8. $\dfrac{x - 2}{x - 1} + \dfrac{6}{7x - 7} = \dfrac{x - 2}{x - 1} + \dfrac{6}{7(x - 1)}$

$\qquad = \dfrac{(x - 2)(7)}{(x - 1)(7)} + \dfrac{6}{7(x - 1)}$

$\qquad = \dfrac{7x - 14}{7(x - 1)} + \dfrac{6}{7(x - 1)}$

$\qquad = \dfrac{7x - 8}{7(x - 1)}$

9. $\dfrac{x}{x^2 - 9} + \dfrac{1}{2x + 6} = \dfrac{x}{(x - 3)(x + 3)} + \dfrac{1}{2(x + 3)}$

$\qquad = \dfrac{(x)(2)}{(x - 3)(x + 3)(2)} + \dfrac{1(x - 3)}{2(x + 3)(x - 3)}$

$\qquad = \dfrac{2x}{2(x - 3)(x + 3)} + \dfrac{x - 3}{2(x - 3)(x + 3)}$

$\qquad = \dfrac{3x - 3}{2(x - 3)(x + 3)}$

$\qquad = \dfrac{3(x - 1)}{2(x - 3)(x + 3)}$

10. The graph has two asymptotes, $x = 0$ and $y = 0$. Therefore, the graph represents an inverse variation function.

11. The graph looks like steps. Therefore, the graph represents a greatest integer function.

12. The function is undefined for $x = 3$. Since $\dfrac{-4}{x - 3}$ is in simplest form, $x = 3$ is a vertical asymptote. Draw the asymptote and sketch the graph.

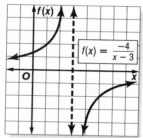

13. The function is undefined for $x = 2$ and $x = -1$. Since $\dfrac{2}{(x - 2)(x + 1)}$ is in simplest form, $x = 2$ and $x = -1$ are vertical asymptotes. Draw the asymptotes and sketch the graph.

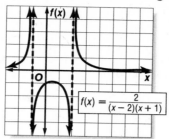

$f(x) = \dfrac{2}{(x - 2)(x + 1)}$

14. $\qquad \dfrac{2}{x - 1} = 4 - \dfrac{x}{x - 1}$

$\qquad (x \overset{1}{\cancel{- 1}})\left(\dfrac{2}{x \underset{1}{\cancel{- 1}}}\right) = (x - 1)\left(4 - \dfrac{x}{x - 1}\right)$

$\qquad 2 = (x - 1)(4) - (x \overset{1}{\cancel{- 1}})\left(\dfrac{x}{x \underset{1}{\cancel{- 1}}}\right)$

$\qquad 2 = 4x - 4 - x$

$\qquad 6 = 3x$

$\qquad 2 = x$

Check: $\dfrac{2}{x - 1} = 4 - \dfrac{x}{x - 1}$

$\qquad \dfrac{2}{2 - 1} \overset{?}{=} 4 - \dfrac{2}{2 - 1}$

$\qquad \dfrac{2}{1} \overset{?}{=} 4 - \dfrac{2}{1}$

$\qquad 2 = 2 ✓$

The solution is 2.

15. $\qquad \dfrac{9}{28} + \dfrac{3}{z + 2} = \dfrac{3}{4}$

$\qquad 28(z + 2)\left(\dfrac{9}{28} + \dfrac{3}{z + 2}\right) = \overset{7}{\cancel{28}}(z + 2)\left(\dfrac{3}{\underset{1}{\cancel{4}}}\right)$

$\qquad \overset{1}{\cancel{28}}(z + 2)\left(\dfrac{9}{\underset{1}{\cancel{28}}}\right) + 28(z \overset{1}{\cancel{+ 2}})\left(\dfrac{3}{z \underset{1}{\cancel{+ 2}}}\right) = 7(z + 2)(3)$

$\qquad 9z + 18 + 84 = 21(z + 2)$

$\qquad 9z + 102 = 21z + 42$

$\qquad 60 = 12z$

$\qquad 5 = z$

Check: $\dfrac{9}{28} + \dfrac{3}{z + 2} = \dfrac{3}{4}$

$\qquad \dfrac{9}{28} + \dfrac{3}{5 + 2} \overset{?}{=} \dfrac{3}{4}$

$\qquad \dfrac{9}{28} + \dfrac{3}{7} \overset{?}{=} \dfrac{3}{4}$

$\qquad \dfrac{3}{4} = \dfrac{3}{4} ✓$

The solution is 5.

16. Since values that make a denominator equal to 0 are excluded from the domain, 0 is excluded for this inequality. Solve the related equation.

$\qquad 5 + \dfrac{3}{t} = -\dfrac{2}{t}$

$\qquad t\left(5 + \dfrac{3}{t}\right) = t\left(-\dfrac{2}{t}\right)$

$\qquad 5t + 3 = -2$

$\qquad 5t = -5$

$\qquad t = -1$

Test a sample value in each region to determine if the values in the region satisfy the inequality.

Test $t = -2$.

$$5 + \frac{3}{t} > -\frac{2}{t}$$

$$5 + \frac{3}{-2} \overset{?}{>} -\frac{2}{-2}$$

$$5 + \left(-\frac{3}{2}\right) \overset{?}{>} 1$$

$$\frac{7}{2} > 1 \checkmark$$

$t < -1$ is a solution.

Test $t = -\frac{1}{2}$.

$$5 + \frac{3}{t} > -\frac{2}{t}$$

$$5 + \frac{3}{-\frac{1}{2}} \overset{?}{>} -\frac{2}{-\frac{1}{2}}$$

$$5 + (-6) \overset{?}{>} 4$$

$$-1 \not> 4$$

$1 < t < 0$ is *not* a solution.

Test $t = 1$.

$$5 + \frac{3}{t} > -\frac{2}{t}$$

$$5 + \frac{3}{1} \overset{?}{>} -\frac{2}{1}$$

$$5 + 3 \overset{?}{>} -2$$

$$8 > -2 \checkmark$$

$t > 0$ is a solution.

The solution is $t < -1$ or $t > 0$.

17.
$$x + \frac{12}{x} - 8 = 0$$

$$x\left(x + \frac{12}{x} - 8\right) = x(0)$$

$$x^2 + 12 - 8x = 0$$

$$x^2 - 8x + 12 = 0$$

$$(x - 6)(x - 2) = 0$$

$$x - 6 = 0 \quad \text{or} \quad x - 2 = 0$$

$$x = 6 \qquad\qquad x = 2$$

Check: $x + \frac{12}{x} - 8 = 0 \qquad x + \frac{12}{x} - 8 = 0$

$$6 + \frac{12}{6} - 8 \overset{?}{=} 0 \qquad 2 + \frac{12}{2} - 8 \overset{?}{=} 0$$

$$6 + 2 - 8 \overset{?}{=} 0 \qquad 2 + 6 - 8 \overset{?}{=} 0$$

$$0 = 0 \checkmark \qquad\qquad 0 = 0 \checkmark$$

The solutions are 2 and 6.

18.
$$\frac{5}{6} - \frac{2m}{2m + 3} = \frac{19}{6}$$

$$6(2m + 3)\left(\frac{5}{6} - \frac{2m}{2m + 3}\right) = 6(2m + 3)\left(\frac{19}{6}\right)$$

$$6(2m + 3)\left(\frac{5}{6}\right) - 6(2m + 3)\left(\frac{2m}{2m + 3}\right) = 19(2m + 3)$$

$$10m + 15 - 12m = 38m + 57$$

$$-42 = 40m$$

$$-1\frac{1}{20} = m$$

Check: $\frac{5}{6} - \frac{2m}{2m + 3} = \frac{19}{6}$

$$\frac{5}{6} - \frac{2\left(-1\frac{1}{20}\right)}{2\left(-1\frac{1}{20}\right) + 3} \overset{?}{=} \frac{19}{6}$$

$$\frac{5}{6} - \left(-\frac{7}{3}\right) \overset{?}{=} \frac{19}{6}$$

$$\frac{19}{6} = \frac{19}{6} \checkmark$$

The solution is $-1\frac{1}{20}$.

19.
$$\frac{x - 3}{2x} = \frac{x - 2}{2x + 1} - \frac{1}{2}$$

$$2x(2x + 1)\left(\frac{x - 3}{2x}\right) = 2x(2x + 1)\left(\frac{x - 2}{2x + 1} - \frac{1}{2}\right)$$

$$(2x + 1)(x - 3) = 2x(2x + 1)\left(\frac{x - 2}{2x + 1}\right) - 2x(2x + 1)\left(\frac{1}{2}\right)$$

$$2x^2 - 5x - 3 = 2x^2 - 4x - x(2x + 1)$$

$$2x^2 - 5x - 3 = 2x^2 - 4x - 2x^2 - x$$

$$2x^2 - 3 = 0$$

Use the Quadratic Formula to solve for x.

$$x = \frac{-b \pm \sqrt{b^2 - 4ac}}{2a}$$

$$x = \frac{-0 \pm \sqrt{0^2 - 4(2)(-3)}}{2(2)}$$

$$x = \frac{\pm\sqrt{24}}{4}$$

$$x = \pm\frac{\sqrt{6}}{2}$$

The solutions are $\frac{\sqrt{6}}{2}$ or $-\frac{\sqrt{6}}{2}$.

20.
$$\frac{x_1}{y_2} = \frac{x_2}{y_1}$$

$$\frac{-\frac{2}{3}}{-7} = \frac{x_2}{9}$$

$$9\left(-\frac{2}{3}\right) = -7(x_2)$$

$$-6 = -7x_2$$

$$\frac{6}{7} = x_2$$

When $y = -7$, the value of x is $\frac{6}{7}$.

21.
$$\frac{w_1}{g_1} = \frac{w_2}{g_2}$$

$$\frac{-3}{10} = \frac{w_2}{4}$$

$$-3(4) = 10(w_2)$$

$$-12 = 10w_2$$

$$-1\frac{1}{5} = w_2$$

When $g = 4$, the value of w is $-1\frac{1}{5}$.

22.
$$\frac{y_1}{x_1 z_1} = \frac{y_2}{x_2 z_2}$$

$$\frac{250}{10(5)} = \frac{2.5}{x_2(4.5)}$$

$$x_2(4.5)(250) = 10(5)(2.5)$$

$$1125x_2 = 125$$

$$x_2 = \frac{1}{9}$$

When $y = 2.5$ and $z = 4.5$, the value of x is $\frac{1}{9}$.

23. Let P represent the pressure and let V represent the volume. Use a proportion to find the pressure when the volume is 100 cubic inches.

$$\frac{P_1}{V_2} = \frac{P_2}{V_1}$$

$$\frac{30}{100} = \frac{P_2}{140}$$

$$140(30) = 100(P_2)$$

$$4200 = 100P_2$$

$$42 = P_2$$

The pressure is 42 pounds per square inch.

24a. Since the current I varies inversely with the resistance R, an equation relating I and R is of the form $I = \frac{k}{R}$. Notice that $IR = 6$. Therefore, an equation is $I = \frac{6}{R}$.

24b. From the previous exercise, we know that an equation relating the current and the resistance is $I = \frac{6}{R}$. Therefore, the constant of variation is 6.

25. D; Use substitution to find x.

$$r = \frac{1}{\frac{1}{2}q}$$
$$r = \frac{1}{\frac{1}{2}(14p)}$$
$$r = \frac{1}{7p}$$
$$r = \frac{1}{7\left(\frac{1}{n}\right)}$$
$$r = \frac{1}{\frac{7}{n}}$$
$$r = 1 \div \frac{7}{n}$$
$$r = 1 \cdot \frac{n}{7}$$
$$r = \frac{n}{7}$$
$$r = \frac{7m}{7}$$
$$r = m$$
$$r = \frac{1}{x}$$
$$x(r) = x\left(\frac{1}{x}\right)$$
$$xr = 1$$
$$x = \frac{1}{r}$$

Chapter 9 Standardized Test Practice

Pages 518–519

1. C; By the end of May, 0.40(5000) or 2000 bikes have been sold. Therefore, 5000 − 2000 or 3000 bikes remain unsold. By the end of June, 0.40(3000) or 1200 bikes have been sold. Therefore, a total of 3000 − 1200 or 1800 bikes remain unsold.

2. C; Since $m < C = 90°$ and $m < B = 45°$, $m < A = 45°$. Therefore, $AC = BC$. Use the Pythagorean Theorem to determine the length of $\overline{BC}$.

$$(AC)^2 + (BC)^2 = (AB)^2$$
$$(BC)^2 + (BC)^2 = 8^2$$
$$2(BC)^2 = 64$$
$$(BC)^2 = 32$$
$$BC = 4\sqrt{2}$$

3. D; The slope of $\overline{AB}$ is $\frac{10-4}{4-2}$ or 3. Since $3\left(-\frac{1}{3}\right) = -1$, $\overline{AB}$ and $\overline{AC}$ are perpendicular. Therefore, $m\angle B = 60°$, so the length of $\overline{BC}$ is twice the length of $\overline{AB}$. The length of $\overline{AB}$ is $\sqrt{(4-2)^2 + (10-4)^2}$ or $2\sqrt{10}$, so the length of $\overline{BC}$ is $2 \cdot 2\sqrt{10}$ or $4\sqrt{10}$.

4. B; $-|2 - 4k| = -14$
$$|2 - 4k| = 14$$
$2 - 4k = 14$ or $2 - 4k = -14$
$-4k = 12$ $-4k = -16$
$k = -3$ $k = 4$

5. B; The cost of one nail is given by $\frac{c}{n}$. Therefore, the cost of k nails can be expressed by $k \cdot \frac{c}{n}$ or $\frac{kc}{n}$.

6. D; $5w + 3 \le w - 9$
$$5w \le w - 12$$
$$4w \le -12$$
$$w \le -3$$

7. B; As the driver travels at 60 mph for 2 hours and then slows to 50 mph for 1 hour, the graph should begin as a straight line, then its slope should decrease to indicate the change in speed. When the driver stops for gas and lunch, the graph should be a horizontal line, since the driver is not traveling. The graph should then continue as a line with the same slope as the first part of the graph, as the driver is again traveling at 60 mph.

8. D; Since $x^3 - 2x^2 - 4n^2x + 8n^2 = (x + 2n)(x - 2n)(x - 2)$, the equation has roots where $x + 2n = 0$, $x - 2n = 0$, and $x - 2 = 0$. Therefore, it has roots of $-2n$, $2n$, and 2.

9. A; Find the value of x when $y = 5$.
$$y - x^2 = 2$$
$$5 - x^2 = 2$$
$$3 = x^2$$
$$\pm\sqrt{3} = x$$
Therefore, the point $(-\sqrt{3}, 5)$ is on the graph.

10. The center of the circle is at $(-5, 0)$. Therefore, the equation is of the form $[x - (-5)]^2 + (y - 0)^2 = r^2$ or $(x + 5)^2 + y^2 = r^2$. The radius r of the circle is the distance between the center of the circle and any one of the vertices of the square. The coordinates of the point at C are $(-2, 3)$. Therefore, QC is $\sqrt{(3 - 0)^2 + [-2 - (-5)]^2}$ or $\sqrt{18}$. Since $r = \sqrt{18}$, $r^2 = 18$. The equation of the circle is $(x + 5)^2 + y^2 = 18$.

11. If k is an integer between 20 and 40, then $k \in \{21, 22, 23, 24, 25, ..., 39\}$. Since k is not evenly divisible by 3 or 4, $k \in \{22, 23, 25, 26, 29, 31, 34, 35, 37, 38\}$. Both 26 and 38 have a remainder of 2 when divided by 3 and a remainder of 2 when divided by 4.

12. The area of a triangle is given by $\frac{1}{2}bh$. The length of the base of this triangle is $\sqrt{[-4 - (-4)]^2 + (10 - 2)^2}$ or 8. The area is 36 square units.
$$A = \frac{1}{2}bh$$
$$36 = \frac{1}{2}(8)(h)$$
$$36 = 4h$$
$$9 = h$$
The height of the triangle is 9 units. Therefore, possible values for b are $-4 + 9$ or 5, and $-4 - 9$ or -13.

13. $(x + 2)(x - 3) = 6$
$$x^2 - x - 6 = 6$$
$$x^2 - x - 12 = 0$$
$$(x + 3)(x - 4) = 0$$
$x + 3 = 0$ or $x - 4 = 0$
$x = -3$ $x = 4$

14. If the average of five consecutive even integers is 76, then the integers must be 72, 74, 76, 78, and 80. Therefore, the greatest of these integers must be 80.

15. Since the number of tents sold in May doubled in June, the number of tents sold increased by 100 percent.

16. $2^{n-4} = 64$
$2^{n-4} = 2^6$
$n - 4 = 6$
$n = 10$

17. $(x + y)^2 = x^2 + 2xy + y^2$
$= 2xy + x^2 + y^2$
$= 2(5) + 20$
$= 30$

18. $\dfrac{2}{a} - \dfrac{8}{a^2} = \dfrac{-8}{a^3}$
$a^3\left(\dfrac{2}{a} - \dfrac{8}{a^2}\right) = a^3\left(\dfrac{-8}{a^3}\right)$
$a^3\left(\dfrac{2}{a}\right) - a^3\left(\dfrac{8}{a^2}\right) = -8$
$2a^2 - 8a = -8$
$2a^2 - 8a + 8 = 0$
$a^2 - 4a + 4 = 0$
$(a - 2)^2 = 0$
$a - 2 = 0$
$a = 2$

19. $\sqrt[x]{80} = 2\sqrt[x]{5}$
$(\sqrt[x]{80})^x = (2\sqrt[x]{5})^x$
$80 = 2^x \cdot 5$
$16 = 2^x$
$2^4 = 2^x$
$4 = x$

20. The y-intercept of the graph is the value of y when $x = 0$
$3x + 2 = 4y - 6$
$3(0) + 2 = 4y - 6$
$2 = 4y - 6$
$8 = 4y$
$2 = y$

21. A; Since $105 = 3 \cdot 5 \cdot 7$, 105 has 3 distinct prime factors. Since $189 = 3 \cdot 3 \cdot 3 \cdot 7$ or $3^3 \cdot 7$, 189 has 2 distinct prime factors. Therefore, 105 has more distinct prime factors than 189.

22. D; the relationship between x and y cannot be determined without more information.

23. D; the relationship between t and $3t$ cannot be determined without more information.

24. A; The square of any x between 0 and 1 is always greater than the value of x^3.

25. B; The square root of any x between 0 and 1 is always greater than the value of x itself.

Chapter 10 Exponential and Logarithmic Relations

1. $x^5 \cdot x \cdot x^6 = x^{5+1+6}$
$\qquad = x^{12}$

2. $(3ab^4c^2)^3 = 3^3a^3b^{4\cdot3}c^{2\cdot3}$
$\qquad = 27a^3b^{12}c^6$

3. $\frac{-36x^7y^4z^3}{21x^4y^9z^4} = \frac{-12}{7}x^{7-4}y^{4-9}z^{3-4}$
$\qquad = \frac{-12}{7}x^3y^{-5}z^{-1}$
$\qquad = -\frac{12x^3}{7y^5z}$

4. $\left(\frac{4ab^2}{64b^3c}\right)^2 = \left(\frac{a}{16bc}\right)^2$
$\qquad = \frac{a^2}{256b^2c^2}$

5. $\quad a + 4 < -10$
$\quad a + 4 - 4 < -10 - 4$
$\qquad\qquad a < -14$

6. $-5n \leq 15$
$\quad \frac{-5n}{5} \leq \frac{15}{5}$
$\quad -n \leq 3$
$\quad n \geq -3$

7. $\quad 3y + 2 \geq -4$
$\quad 3y + 2 - 2 \geq -4 - 2$
$\qquad\quad 3y \geq -6$
$\qquad\quad \frac{3y}{3} \geq \frac{-6}{3}$
$\qquad\quad y \geq -2$

8. $\quad 15 - x > 9$
$\quad 15 - x - 15 > 9 - 15$
$\qquad\qquad -x > -6$
$\qquad\qquad x < 6$

9. $f(x) = -2x$
Replace $f(x)$ with y.
$y = -2x$
Interchange x and y.
$x = -2y$
Solve for y.
$\quad x = -2y$
$\quad \frac{x}{-2} = \frac{-2y}{-2}$
$\quad -\frac{1}{2}x = y$
Replace y with $f^{-1}(x)$.
$f^{-1}(x) = -\frac{1}{2}x$

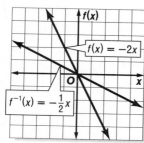

10. $f(x) = 3x - 2$
Replace $f(x)$ with y.
$y = 3x - 2$
Interchange x and y.
$x = 3y - 2$
Solve for y.
$\quad x = 3y - 2$
$\quad x + 2 = 3y - 2 + 2$
$\quad x + 2 = 3y$
$\quad \frac{x+2}{3} = \frac{3y}{3}$
$\quad \frac{x+2}{3} = y$
Replace y with $f^{-1}(x)$.
$f^{-1}(x) = \frac{x+2}{3}$

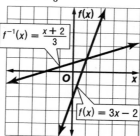

11. $f(x) = -x + 1$
Replace $f(x)$ with y.
$y = -x + 1$
Interchange x and y.
$x = -y + 1$
Solve for y.
$\quad x = -y + 1$
$\quad x - 1 = -y + 1 - 1$
$\quad x - 1 = -y$
$\quad \frac{x-1}{-1} = \frac{-y}{-1}$
$\quad -x + 1 = y$
Replace y with $f^{-1}(x)$.
$f^{-1}(x) = -x + 1$

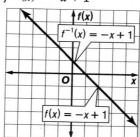

12. $f(x) = \frac{x-4}{3}$

Replace $f(x)$ with y.

$y = \frac{x-4}{3}$

Interchange x and y.

$x = \frac{y-4}{3}$

Solve for y.

$x = \frac{y-4}{3}$

$3(x) = 3\left(\frac{y-4}{3}\right)$

$3x = y - 4$

$3x + 4 = y - 4 + 4$

$3x + 4 = y$

Replace y with $f^{-1}(x)$.

$f^{-1}(x) = 3x + 4$

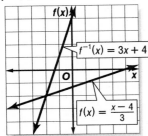

13. $g[h(x)] = g[3x + 4]$
$= (3x + 4) - 2$
$= 3x + 2$
$h[g(x)] = h[x - 2]$
$= 3(x - 2) + 4$
$= 3x - 6 + 4$
$= 3x - 2$

14. $g[h(x)] = g[2x - 7]$
$= 5(2x - 7)$
$= 10x - 35$
$h[g(x)] = h[5x]$
$= 2(5x) - 7$
$= 10x - 7$

15. $g[h(x)] = g[x - 4]$
$= (x - 4)^2$
$= x^2 - 8x + 16$
$h[g(x)] = h[x^2]$
$= x^2 - 4$

16. $g[h(x)] = g[4x + 1]$
$= -2(4x + 1) - 3$
$= -8x - 2 - 3$
$= -8x - 5$
$h[g(x)] = h[-2x - 3]$
$= 4(-2x - 3) + 1$
$= -8x - 12 + 1$
$= -8x - 11$

Page 522   Algebra Activity (Preview of Lesson 10-1)

1. $(0, 1), (1, 2), (2, 4), (3, 8), (4, 16), \ldots$

2. $(5, 32), (6, 64), (7, 128)$; The y value is found by raising 2 to the number of cuts each time.

3.

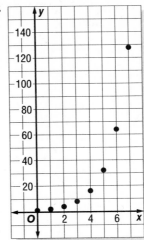

4. The points do not lie on a straight line. The slope increases as the x values increase.

5. $y = 2^x$

6. $y = 2^x$ $\qquad\qquad$ $y = 2^x$
$y = 2^8$ or 256 $\qquad$ $y = 2^9$ or 512
Yes, it gives the correct number of sheets.

7. Since there are 512 sheets, the thickness would be about 1 inch.

8. Sample answer: 1 million feet

9. Substitute $x = 36$, and then divide by 500 to find the number of inches, then by 12 to find the number of feet, and then by 5280 to find the number of miles. The stack would be about 2169 miles.

10-1 Exponential Functions

Page 524   Graphing Calculator Investigation

1. The shapes of the graphs are the same.

2. The asymptote for each graph is the x-axis and the y-intercept for each graph is 1.

3. The graphs are reflections of each other over the y-axis.

4a. As the value of x increases, the value of y for the graph of $y = 4^x$ increases faster than for the graph of $y = 3^x$, and the value of y for the graph of $y = 3^x$ increases faster than for the graph of $y = 2^x$. The graphs have the same domain, all real numbers, and range, $y > 0$. They have the same asymptote, the x-axis, and the same y-intercept, 1.

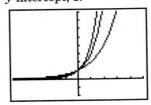

$[-5, 5]$ scl: 1 by $[-2, 8]$ scl: 1

4b. As the value of x increases, the value of y for the graph of $y = \left(\frac{1}{3}\right)^x$ decreases faster than for the graph of $y = \left(\frac{1}{2}\right)^x$, and the value of y for the graph of $y = \left(\frac{1}{4}\right)^x$ decreases faster than for the graph of $y = \left(\frac{1}{3}\right)^x$. The graphs have the same domain, all real numbers, and range, $y > 0$. They have the same asymptote, the x-axis, and the same y-intercept, 1.

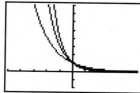

[−5, 5] scl: 1 by [−2, 8] scl: 1

4c. The graph of $y = -3(2)^x$ moves down and to the right more quickly than the graph of $y = -1(2)^x$. The graph of $y = 3(2)^x$ moves up and to the right more quickly than the graph of $y = 2^x$. All of the graphs have the same domain, all real numbers, and asymptote, the x-axis, but the range of $y = -3(2)^x$ and $y = -1(2)^x$ is $y < 0$, while the range of $y = 2^x$ and $y = 3(2)^x$ is $y > 0$. The y-intercept of $y = -3(2)^x$ is -3, of $y = -1(2)^x$ is -1, of $y = 2^x$ is 1, and of $y = 3(2)^x$ is 3.

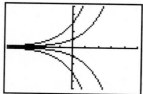

[−5, 5] scl: 1 by [−5, 5] scl: 1

5. The graphs are reflections of each other over the x-axis.

Pages 527–528   Check for Understanding

1. Sample answer: 0.8 or any value less than 1

2a. The function is quadratic, since the only variable, x, has an exponent of 2.

2b. The function is exponential, since 3 has a variable as an exponent.

2c. The function is linear, since all variables have exponent 1.

2d. The function is exponential, since 0.2 has a variable as an exponent.

3. The function $y = 5^x$ corresponds to graph **c**, since when $x = 0$, $y = 1$, and when $x = 1$, $y = 5$.

4. The function $y = 2(5)^x$ corresponds to graph **a**, since when $x = 0$, $y = 2$, and when $x = -1$, $y = \frac{2}{5}$.

5. The function $y = \left(\frac{1}{5}\right)^x$ corresponds to graph **b**, since when $x = 0$, $y = 1$, and when $x = -1$, $y = 5$.

6. $y = 3(4)^x$

x	$y = 3(4)^x$
−2	$\frac{3}{16}$
−1	$\frac{3}{4}$
0	3
1	12
2	48

D = {$x \mid x$ is all real numbers.}
R = {$y \mid y > 0$}

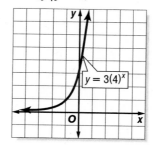

7. $y = 2\left(\frac{1}{3}\right)^x$

x	$y = 2\left(\frac{1}{3}\right)^x$
−2	18
−1	6
0	2
1	$\frac{2}{3}$
2	$\frac{2}{9}$

D = {$x \mid x$ is all real numbers.}
R = {$y \mid y > 0$}

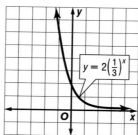

8. The function represents exponential growth, since the base, 7, is greater than 1.

9. The function represents exponential decay, since the base, 0.5, is between 0 and 1.

10. The function represents exponential growth, since the base, 5, is greater than 1.

11. Substitute $(0, 3)$ into the exponential function
$y = ab^x$.
$y = ab^x$
$3 = ab^0$
$3 = a$
Substitute $(-1, 6)$ into the intermediate function
$y = 3b^x$.
$y = 3b^x$
$6 = 3b^{-1}$
$2 = b^{-1}$
$\frac{1}{2} = b$
The equation is $y = 3\left(\frac{1}{2}\right)^x$.

12. Substitute $(0, -18)$ into the exponential function
$y = ab^x$.
$y = ab^x$
$-18 = ab^0$
$-18 = a$
Substitute $(-2, -2)$ into the intermediate
function $y = -18b^x$.
$y = -18b^x$
$-2 = -18b^{-2}$
$\frac{1}{9} = b^{-2}$
$9 = b^2$
$3 = b$
The equation is $y = -18(3)^x$.

13. $2^{\sqrt{7}} \cdot 2^{\sqrt{7}} = 2^{\sqrt{7}+\sqrt{7}}$
$= 2^{2\sqrt{7}}$
$= (2^2)^{\sqrt{7}}$
$= 4^{\sqrt{7}}$

14. $(a^\pi)^4 = a^{\pi \cdot 4}$
$= a^{4\pi}$

15. $81^{\sqrt{2}} \div 3^{\sqrt{2}} = \frac{81^{\sqrt{2}}}{3^{\sqrt{2}}}$
$= \frac{(3^4)^{\sqrt{2}}}{3^{\sqrt{2}}}$
$= \frac{3^{4\sqrt{2}}}{3^{\sqrt{2}}}$
$= 3^{4\sqrt{2}-\sqrt{2}}$
$= 3^{3\sqrt{2}}$
$= (3^3)^{\sqrt{2}}$
$= 27^{\sqrt{2}}$

16. $2^{n+4} = \frac{1}{32}$
$2^{n+4} = 2^{-5}$
$n + 4 = -5$
$n = -9$
Check: $2^{n+4} = \frac{1}{32}$
$2^{-9+4} \stackrel{?}{=} \frac{1}{32}$
$2^{-5} \stackrel{?}{=} \frac{1}{32}$
$\frac{1}{32} = \frac{1}{32}$ ✓

17. $5^{2x+3} \leq 125$
$5^{2x+3} \leq 5^3$
$2x + 3 \leq 3$
$2x \leq 0$
$x \leq 0$

Check: Test $x = -1$.
$5^{2x+3} \leq 125$
$5^{2(-1)+3} \stackrel{?}{\leq} 125$
$5^1 \stackrel{?}{\leq} 125$
$5 \leq 125$ ✓

18. $9^{2y-1} = 27^y$
$(3^2)^{2y-1} = (3^3)^y$
$3^{2(2y-1)} = 3^{3y}$
$2(2y - 1) = 3y$
$4y - 2 = 3y$
$y - 2 = 0$
$y = 2$
Check: $9^{2y-1} = 27^y$
$9^{2(2)-1} \stackrel{?}{=} 27^2$
$9^3 \stackrel{?}{=} 27^2$
$729 = 729$ ✓

19. Use the points $(0, 65{,}000)$ and $(2, 2{,}500{,}000)$.
Substitute $(0, 65{,}000)$ into $y = ab^x$.
$y = ab^x$
$65{,}000 = ab^0$
$65{,}000 = a$
Substitute $(2, 2{,}500{,}000)$ into $y = 65{,}000b^x$.
$y = 65{,}000b^x$
$2{,}500{,}000 = 65{,}000b^2$
$\frac{500}{13} = b^2$
$6.20 \approx b$
The function is $y = 65{,}000(6.20)^x$.

20. In 1872, $x = 7$.
$y = 65{,}000(6.20)^x$
$y = 65{,}000(6.20)^7$
$y \approx 22{,}890{,}495{,}000$
In 1872, the rabbit population was about
$22{,}890{,}495{,}000$.

Pages 528–530   Practice and Apply

21.

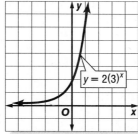
$y = 2(3)^x$

$D = \{x \,|\, x \text{ is all real numbers.}\}$
$R = \{y \,|\, y > 0\}$

22.

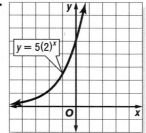
$y = 5(2)^x$

$D = \{x \,|\, x \text{ is all real numbers.}\}$
$R = \{y \,|\, y > 0\}$

23.

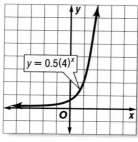

$y = 0.5(4)^x$

$D = \{x \mid x \text{ is all real numbers.}\}$
$R = \{y \mid y > 0\}$

24.

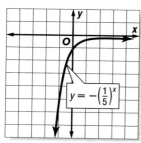

$y = 4\left(\frac{1}{3}\right)^x$

$D = \{x \mid x \text{ is all real numbers.}\}$
$R = \{y \mid y > 0\}$

25.

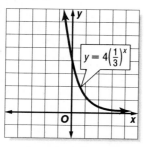

$y = -\left(\frac{1}{5}\right)^x$

$D = \{x \mid x \text{ is all real numbers.}\}$
$R = \{y \mid y < 0\}$

26.

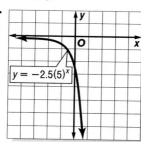

$y = -2.5(5)^x$

$D = \{x \mid x \text{ is all real numbers.}\}$
$R = \{y \mid y < 0\}$

27. The function represents exponential growth, since the base, 3.5, is greater than 1.

28. The function represents exponential growth, since the base, 4, is greater than 1.

29. The function represents exponential decay, since the base, $\frac{1}{3}$, is between 0 and 1.

30. The function represents exponential growth, since the base, $\frac{5}{2}$, is greater than 1.

31. The function represents exponential decay, since the base, 30^{-1} or $\frac{1}{30}$, is between 0 and 1.

32. The function represents exponential decay, since the base, 5^{-1} or $\frac{1}{5}$, is between 0 and 1.

33. Substitute $(0, -2)$ into the exponential equation $y = ab^x$.
$$y = ab^x$$
$$-2 = ab^0$$
$$-2 = a$$
Substitute $(-2, -32)$ into the intermediate function $y = -2b^x$.
$$y = -2b^x$$
$$-32 = -2b^{-2}$$
$$16 = b^{-2}$$
$$\frac{1}{16} = b^2$$
$$\frac{1}{4} = b$$
The equation is $y = -2\left(\frac{1}{4}\right)^x$.

34. Substitute $(0, 3)$ into the exponential equation $y = ab^x$.
$$y = ab^x$$
$$3 = ab^0$$
$$3 = a$$
Substitute $(1, 15)$ into the intermediate function $y = 3b^x$.
$$y = 3b^x$$
$$15 = 3b^1$$
$$5 = b$$
The equation is $y = 3(5)^x$.

35. Substitute $(0, 7)$ into the exponential equation $y = ab^x$.
$$y = ab^x$$
$$7 = ab^0$$
$$7 = a$$
Substitute $(2, 63)$ into the intermediate function $y = 7b^x$.
$$y = 7b^x$$
$$63 = 7b^2$$
$$9 = b^2$$
$$3 = b$$
The equation is $y = 7(3)^x$.

36. Substitute $(0, -5)$ into the exponential equation $y = ab^x$.
$$y = ab^x$$
$$-5 = ab^0$$
$$-5 = a$$
Substitute $(-3, -135)$ into the intermediate function $y = -5b^x$.
$$y = -5b^x$$
$$-135 = -5b^{-3}$$
$$27 = b^{-3}$$
$$\frac{1}{27} = b^3$$
$$\frac{1}{3} = b$$
The equation is $y = -5\left(\frac{1}{3}\right)^x$.

37. Substitute $(0, 0.2)$ into the exponential equation $y = ab^x$.

$$y = ab^x$$
$$0.02 = ab^0$$
$$0.02 = a$$

Substitute $(4, 51.2)$ into the intermediate function $y = 0.2b^x$.

$$y = 0.2b^x$$
$$51.2 = 0.2b^4$$
$$256 = b^4$$
$$4 = b$$

The equation is $y = 0.2(4)^x$.

38. Substitute $(0, -0.3)$ into the exponential equation $y = ab^x$.

$$y = ab^x$$
$$-0.3 = ab^0$$
$$-0.3 = a$$

Substitute $(5, -9.6)$ into the intermediate function $y = -0.3b^x$.

$$y = -0.3b^x$$
$$-9.6 = -0.3b^5$$
$$32 = b^5$$
$$2 = b$$

The equation is $y = -0.3(2)^x$.

39. $\left(5^{\sqrt{2}}\right)^{\sqrt{8}} = 5^{\sqrt{2} \cdot \sqrt{8}}$
$$= 5^{\sqrt{16}}$$
$$= 5^4 \text{ or } 625$$

40. $\left(x^{\sqrt{5}}\right)^{\sqrt{3}} = x^{\sqrt{5} \cdot \sqrt{3}}$
$$= x^{\sqrt{15}}$$

41. $7^{\sqrt{2}} \cdot 7^{3\sqrt{2}} = 7^{\sqrt{2} + 3\sqrt{2}}$
$$= 7^{4\sqrt{2}}$$

42. $y^{3\sqrt{3}} \div y^{\sqrt{3}} = y^{3\sqrt{3} - \sqrt{3}}$
$$= y^{2\sqrt{3}}$$

43. $n^2 n^{\pi} = n^{2 + \pi}$

44. $64^{\pi} \div 2^{\pi} = (2^6)^{\pi} \div 2^{\pi}$
$$= 2^{6\pi} \div 2^{\pi}$$
$$= 2^{6\pi - \pi}$$
$$= 2^{5\pi}$$

45. $3^{n - 2} = 27$
$$3^{n - 2} = 3^3$$
$$n - 2 = 3$$
$$n = 5$$

Check: $3^{n - 2} = 27$
$$3^{5 - 2} \stackrel{?}{=} 27$$
$$3^3 \stackrel{?}{=} 27$$
$$27 = 27 \checkmark$$

46. $2^{3x + 5} = 128$
$$2^{3x + 5} = 2^7$$
$$3x + 5 = 7$$
$$3x = 2$$
$$x = \frac{2}{3}$$

Check: $2^{3x + 5} = 128$
$$2^{3\left(\frac{2}{3}\right) + 5} \stackrel{?}{=} 128$$
$$2^7 \stackrel{?}{=} 128$$
$$128 = 128 \checkmark$$

47. $5^{n - 3} = \frac{1}{25}$
$$5^{n - 3} = 5^{-2}$$
$$n - 3 = -2$$
$$n = 1$$

Check: $5^{n - 3} = \frac{1}{25}$
$$5^{1 - 3} \stackrel{?}{=} \frac{1}{25}$$
$$5^{-2} \stackrel{?}{=} \frac{1}{25}$$
$$\frac{1}{25} = \frac{1}{25} \checkmark$$

48. $2^{2n} \leq \frac{1}{16}$
$$2^{2n} \leq 2^{-4}$$
$$2n \leq -4$$
$$n \leq -2$$

Check: Test $n = -3$.
$$2^{2n} \leq \frac{1}{16}$$
$$2^{2(-3)} \stackrel{?}{\leq} \frac{1}{16}$$
$$2^{-6} \stackrel{?}{\leq} \frac{1}{16}$$
$$\frac{1}{64} \stackrel{?}{\leq} \frac{1}{16} \checkmark$$

49. $\left(\frac{1}{9}\right)^m = 81^{m + 4}$
$$(3^{-2})^m = (3^4)^{m + 4}$$
$$3^{-2m} = 3^{4(m + 4)}$$
$$-2m = 4(m + 4)$$
$$-2m = 4m + 16$$
$$-6m = 16$$
$$m = -\frac{16}{6} \text{ or } -\frac{8}{3}$$

Check: $\left(\frac{1}{9}\right)^m = 81^{m + 4}$
$$\left(\frac{1}{9}\right)^{-\frac{8}{3}} \stackrel{?}{=} 81^{-\frac{8}{3} + 4}$$
$$9^{\frac{8}{3}} \stackrel{?}{=} 81^{\frac{4}{3}}$$
$$9^{\frac{8}{3}} \stackrel{?}{=} (9^2)^{\frac{4}{3}}$$
$$9^{\frac{8}{3}} = 9^{\frac{8}{3}} \checkmark$$

50. $\left(\frac{1}{7}\right)^{y - 3} = 343$
$$(7^{-1})^{y + 3} = 7^3$$
$$7^{-y + 3} = 7^3$$
$$-y + 3 = 3$$
$$-y = 0$$
$$y = 0$$

Check: $\left(\frac{1}{7}\right)^{y - 3} = 343$
$$\left(\frac{1}{7}\right)^{0 - 3} \stackrel{?}{=} 343$$
$$\left(\frac{1}{7}\right)^{-3} \stackrel{?}{=} 343$$
$$343 = 343 \checkmark$$

51. $16^n < 8^{n + 1}$
$$(2^4)^n < (2^3)^{n + 1}$$
$$2^{4n} < 2^{3(n + 1)}$$
$$4n < 3(n + 1)$$
$$4n < 3n + 3$$
$$n < 3$$

Check: Test $n = 2$.
$$16^n \stackrel{?}{<} 8^{n + 1}$$
$$16^2 \stackrel{?}{<} 8^{2 + 1}$$
$$16^2 \stackrel{?}{<} 8^3$$
$$256 < 512 \checkmark$$

52. $10^{x-1} = 100^{2x-3}$
$10^{x-1} = (10^2)^{2x-3}$
$10^{x-1} = 10^{2(2x-3)}$
$x - 1 = 2(2x - 3)$
$x - 1 = 4x - 6$
$-3x = -5$
$x = \frac{5}{3}$

Check: $10^{x-1} = 100^{2x-3}$
$10^{\frac{5}{3}-1} \stackrel{?}{=} 100^{2\left(\frac{5}{3}\right)-3}$
$10^{\frac{2}{3}} \stackrel{?}{=} 100^{\frac{1}{3}}$
$100^{\frac{1}{3}} = 100^{\frac{1}{3}}$ ✓

53. $36^{2p} = 216^{p-1}$
$(6^2)^{2p} = (6^3)^{p-1}$
$6^{2(2p)} = 6^{3(p-1)}$
$2(2p) = 3(p-1)$
$4p = 3p - 3$
$p = -3$

Check: $36^{2p} = 216^{p-1}$
$36^{2(-3)} \stackrel{?}{=} 216^{-3-1}$
$36^{-6} \stackrel{?}{=} 216^{-4}$
$(6^2)^{-6} \stackrel{?}{=} (6^3)^{-4}$
$6^{-12} = 6^{-12}$ ✓

54. $32^{5p+2} \geq 16^{5p}$
$(2^5)^{5p+2} \geq (2^4)^{5p}$
$2^{5(5p+2)} \geq 2^{4(5p)}$
$5(5p + 2) \geq 4(5p)$
$25p + 10 \geq 20p$
$5p + 10 \geq 0$
$5p \geq -10$
$p \geq -2$

Check: Test $p = -1$.
$32^{5p+2} \geq 16^{5p}$
$32^{5(-1)+2} \stackrel{?}{\geq} 16^{5(-1)}$
$32^{-3} \stackrel{?}{\geq} 16^{-5}$
$\frac{1}{32,768} \geq \frac{1}{1,048,576}$ ✓

55. $3^{5x} \cdot 81^{1-x} = 9^{x-3}$
$3^{5x} \cdot (3^4)^{1-x} = (3^2)^{x-3}$
$3^{5x} \cdot 3^{4(1-x)} = 3^{2(x-3)}$
$3^{5x+4(1-x)} = 3^{2(x-3)}$
$5x + 4(1-x) = 2(x-3)$
$5x + 4 - 4x = 2x - 6$
$x + 4 = 2x - 6$
$-x = -10$
$x = 10$

Check: $3^{5x} \cdot 81^{1-x} = 9^{x-3}$
$3^{5(10)} \cdot 81^{1-10} \stackrel{?}{=} 9^{10-3}$
$3^{50} \cdot 81^{-9} \stackrel{?}{=} 9^7$
$4,782,969 = 4,782,969$ ✓

56. $49^x = 7^{x^2-15}$
$(7^2)^x = 7^{x^2-15}$
$7^{2x} = 7^{x^2-15}$
$2x = x^2 - 15$
$x^2 - 2x - 15 = 0$
$(x-5)(x+3) = 0$

$x - 5 = 0 \qquad\qquad x + 3 = 0$
$x = 5 \qquad\qquad\quad x = -3$

Check: $49^x = 7^{x^2-15} \qquad 49^x = 7^{x^2-15}$
$49^5 \stackrel{?}{=} 7^{5^2-15} \qquad 49^{-3} \stackrel{?}{=} 7^{(-3)^2-15}$
$(7^2)^5 \stackrel{?}{=} 7^{10} \qquad (7^2)^{-3} \stackrel{?}{=} 7^{-6}$
$7^{10} = 7^{10}$ ✓ $\qquad\quad 7^{-6} = 7^{-6}$ ✓

57. Use the points $(0, 100)$ and $(2, 4000)$.
Substitute $(0, 100)$ into $y = ab^x$.
$y = ab^x$
$100 = ab^0$
$100 = a$
Substitute $(2, 4000)$ into $y = 100b^x$.
$y = 100b^x$
$4000 = 100b^2$
$40 = b^2$
$6.32 \approx b$
The function is $y = 100(6.32)^x$.

58. At 7 P.M., $x = 5$.
$y = 100(6.32)^x$
$y = 100(6.32)^5$
$y \approx 1,008,290$
At 7 P.M., there were about 1,008,290 bacteria.

59. Use the two points are $(0, 3.93)$ and $(1, 5.31)$.
Substitute $(0, 3.93)$ into $y = ab^x$.
$y = ab^x$
$3.93 = ab^0$
$3.93 = a$
Substitute $(1, 5.31)$ into $y = 3.93b^x$.
$y = 3.93b^x$
$5.31 = 3.93b^1$
$1.35 \approx b$
The function is $y = 3.93(1.35)^x$.

60. The years 1820, 1840, and 1860 correspond to $x = 3, 5,$ and 7, respectively.
$y = 3.93(1.35)^3$ or about 9.67
$y = 3.93(1.35)^5$ or about 17.62
$y = 3.93(1.35)^7$ or about 32.12
The estimated populations for 1820, 1840, and 1860 are 9.67 million, 17.62 million, and 32.12 million, respectively. These answers are in close agreement with the actual populations in these years.

61. No, the growth rate has slowed considerably.
In 2000, $x = 21$.
$y = 3.93(1.35)^{21}$
$y \approx 2144.87$
The actual population was 281.42 million. The population in 2000 was much smaller than the equation predicted it would be.

62. This is an exponential function. The base, $1 + \frac{r}{n}$, is fixed, but the exponent, nt, is variable since the time t can vary.

63. $A(t) = p\left(1 + \frac{r}{n}\right)^{nt}$
$A(t) = 1000\left(1 + \frac{0.04}{4}\right)^{4t}$
$A(t) = 1000(1.01)^{4t}$

64. After 20 years, $t = 20$.
$A(20) = 1000(1.01)^{80}$ or about 2216.72.
After 20 years, the account balance will be about $2216.72.

65. If computational speed multiplies by a factor of 4 every 3 years, after x three-year periods, it will have increased by a factor of 4^x. If the current speed is s, after x years it will operate at a speed $s \cdot 4^x$.

66. Solve $4800 = 600 \cdot 4^x$.

$$4800 = 600 \cdot 4^x$$
$$8 = 4^x$$
$$2^3 = (2^2)^x$$
$$2^3 = 2^{2x}$$
$$3 = 2x$$
$$1.5 = x$$

You will have to wait 1.5 three-year periods or 4.5 years.

67. Sometimes; true if $b > 1$, but false when $b < 1$.

68. The number of teams y that could compete in a tournament in which x rounds are played can be expressed as $y = 2^x$. The 2 teams that make it to the final round got there as a result of winning games played with 2 other teams, for a total of $2 \cdot 2 = 2^2$ or 4 games played in the previous round or semifinal round. Answers should include the following.
- Rewrite 128 as a power of 2, 2^7. Substitute 2^7 for y in the equation $y = 2^x$. Then, using the Property of Equality for Exponents, x must be 7. Therefore, 128 teams would need to play 7 rounds of tournament play.
- Sample answer: 52 would be an inappropriate number of teams to play in this type of tournament because 52 is not a power of 2.

69. A; $4^{x+2} = 48$

$$4^x \cdot 4^2 = 3 \cdot 4^2$$
$$4^x = 3$$

70. $A(t) = P\Big(1 + \dfrac{r}{n}\Big)^{nt}$

$$A(10) = 500\Big(1 + \dfrac{0.045}{2}\Big)^{2 \cdot 10}$$
$$\approx 780.25$$

There will be \$780.25 after 10 years.

71.

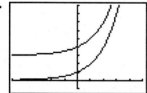

[−5, 5] scl: 1 by [−1, 9] scl: 1

The graphs have the same shape. The graph of $y = 2^x + 3$ is the graph of $y = 2^x$ translated three units up. The asymptote for the graph of $y = 2^x$ is the line $y = 0$ and for $y = 2^x + 3$ is the line $y = 3$. The graphs have the same domain, all real numbers, but the range of $y = 2^x$ is $y > 0$ and the range of $y = 2^x + 3$ is $y > 3$. The y-intercept of the graph of $y = 2^x$ is 1 and for the graph of $y = 2^x + 3$ is 4.

72.

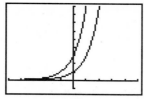

[−5, 5] scl: 1 by [−1, 9] scl: 1

The graphs have the same shape. The graph of $y = 3^{x+1}$ is the graph of $y = 3^x$ translated one unit to the left. The asymptote for the graph of $y = 3^x$ and for $y = 3^{x+1}$ is the line $y = 0$. The graphs have the same domain, all real numbers, and range, $y > 0$. The y-intercept of the graph of $y = 3^x$ is 1 and for the graph of $y = 3^{x+1}$ is 3.

73.

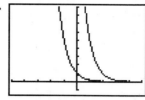

[−5, 5] scl: 1 by [−1, 9] scl: 1

The graphs have the same shape. The graph of $y = \Big(\dfrac{1}{5}\Big)^{x-2}$ is the graph of $y = \Big(\dfrac{1}{5}\Big)^x$ translated two units to the right. The asymptote for the graph of $y = \Big(\dfrac{1}{5}\Big)^x$ and for $y = \Big(\dfrac{1}{5}\Big)^{x-2}$ is the line $y = 0$. The graphs have the same domain, all real numbers, and range, $y > 0$. The y-intercept of the graph of $y = \Big(\dfrac{1}{5}\Big)^x$ is 1 and for the graph of $y = \Big(\dfrac{1}{5}\Big)^{x-2}$ is 25.

74.

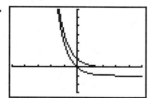

[−5, 5] scl: 1 by [−3, 7] scl: 1

The graphs have the same shape. The graph of $y = \Big(\dfrac{1}{4}\Big)^x - 1$ is the graph of $y = \Big(\dfrac{1}{4}\Big)^x$ translated one unit down. The asymptote for the graph of $y = \Big(\dfrac{1}{4}\Big)^x$ is the line $y = 0$ and for the graph of $y = \Big(\dfrac{1}{4}\Big)^x - 1$ is the line $y = -1$. The graphs have the same domain, all real numbers, but the range of $y = \Big(\dfrac{1}{4}\Big)^x$ is $y > 0$ and of $y = \Big(\dfrac{1}{4}\Big)^x - 1$ is $y > -1$. The y-intercept of the graph of $y = \Big(\dfrac{1}{4}\Big)^x$ is 1 and for the graph of $y = \Big(\dfrac{1}{4}\Big)^x - 1$ is 0.

75. For $h > 0$, the graph of $y = 2^x$ is translated $|h|$ units to the right. For $h < 0$, the graph of $y = 2^x$ is translated $|h|$ units to the left. For $k > 0$, the graph of $y = 2^x$ is translated k units up. For $k < 0$, the graph of $y = 2^x$ is translated k units down.

Exercises 76–79 For checks, see students' work.

76.
$$\frac{15}{p} + p = 16$$
$$15 + p^2 = 16p$$
$$p^2 - 16p + 15 = 0$$
$$(p - 1)(p - 15) = 0$$
$$(p - 1) = 0 \quad \text{or} \quad (p - 15) = 0$$
$$p = 1 \qquad\qquad p = 15$$

77.
$$\frac{s - 3}{s + 4} = \frac{6}{s - 16}$$
$$\frac{s - 3}{s + 4} = \frac{6}{(s + 4)(s - 4)}$$
$$\frac{s - 3}{s + 4} \cdot (s + 4)(s - 4) = \frac{6}{(s + 4)(s - 4)} \cdot (s + 4)(s - 4)$$
$$(s - 3)(s - 4) = 6$$
$$s^2 - 7s + 12 = 6$$
$$s^2 - 7s + 6 = 0$$
$$(s - 1)(s - 6) = 0$$
$$s - 1 = 0 \quad \text{or} \quad s - 6 = 0$$
$$s = 1 \qquad\qquad s = 6$$

78.
$$\frac{2a - 5}{a - 9} + \frac{a}{a + 9} = \frac{-6}{a^2 - 81}$$
$$(a - 9)(a + 9)\left(\frac{2a - 5}{a - 9} + \frac{a}{a + 9}\right) = (a - 9)(a + 9)\left(\frac{-6}{a^2 - 81}\right)$$
$$(a + 9)(2a - 5) + (a - 9)a = -6$$
$$2a^2 + 13a - 45 + a^2 - 9a = -6$$
$$3a^2 + 4a - 45 = -6$$
$$3a^2 + 4a - 39 = 0$$
$$(3a + 13)(a - 3) = 0$$
$$3a + 13 = 0 \qquad \text{or } a - 3 = 0$$
$$3a = -13 \qquad\qquad a = 3$$
$$a = -\frac{13}{3}$$

79. The excluded values are 0 and 6. Solve the related equation.
$$\frac{x - 2}{x} = \frac{x - 4}{x - 6}$$
$$(x - 2)(x - 6) = x(x - 4)$$
$$x^2 - 8x + 12 = x^2 - 4x$$
$$-4x = -12$$
$$x = 3$$

Divide the number line into regions at the excluded values and at the solution. Test a sample value in each to determine whether the inequality is satisfied in that region.

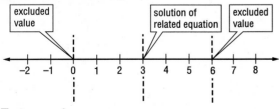

Test $x = -1$.
$$\frac{-1 - 2}{-1} \stackrel{?}{<} \frac{-1 - 4}{-1 - 6}$$
$$3 \not< \frac{5}{7}$$

Test $x = 1$.
$$\frac{1 - 2}{1} \stackrel{?}{<} \frac{1 - 4}{1 - 6}$$
$$-1 < \frac{3}{5}$$

Test $x = 4$.
$$\frac{4 - 2}{4} \stackrel{?}{<} \frac{4 - 4}{4 - 6}$$
$$\frac{1}{2} \not< 0$$

Test $x = 8$.
$$\frac{8 - 2}{8} \stackrel{?}{<} \frac{8 - 4}{8 - 6}$$
$$\frac{3}{4} < 2$$

The solution is $0 < x < 3$ or $x > 6$.

80. square root;

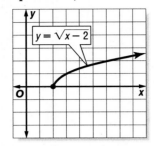

81. greatest integer;

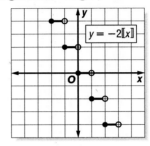

82. constant;

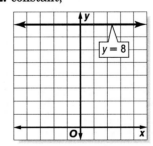

83. $\begin{vmatrix} 1 & 0 \\ 0 & 1 \end{vmatrix} = 1 - 0 = 1$

Since the determinant does not equal 0, the inverse exists.
$$\frac{1}{ad - bc}\begin{bmatrix} d & -b \\ -c & a \end{bmatrix} = \frac{1}{1}\begin{bmatrix} 1 & 0 \\ 0 & 1 \end{bmatrix}$$
$$= \begin{bmatrix} 1 & 0 \\ 0 & 1 \end{bmatrix}$$

84. $\begin{vmatrix} 2 & 4 \\ 5 & 10 \end{vmatrix} = 20 - 20 = 0$

Since the determinant equals 0, the inverse does not exist.

85. $\begin{vmatrix} -5 & 6 \\ -11 & 3 \end{vmatrix} = -15 - (-66) = 51$

Since the determinant does not equal 0, the inverse exists.

$\frac{1}{ad-bc} \begin{bmatrix} d & -b \\ -c & a \end{bmatrix} = \frac{1}{51} \begin{bmatrix} 3 & -6 \\ 11 & -5 \end{bmatrix}$

86. Let r represent the radius of the cell. The area of the cell is πr^2. The cell produces $0.01\pi r^2$ watts of energy.

$0.01\pi r^2 = 18$

$r^2 = \frac{1800}{\pi}$

$r \approx 23.94$

The radius is about 23.94 cm.

87. $g[h(x)] = g[2x - 1]$
$= (2x - 1) - 5$
$= 2x - 6$
$h[g(x)] = h[x - 5]$
$= 2(x - 5) - 1$
$= 2x - 10 - 1$
$= 2x - 11$

88. $g[h(x)] = g[x + 3]$
$= (x + 3)^2$
$= x^2 + 6x + 9$
$h[g(x)] = h[x^2]$
$= x^2 + 3$

89. $g[h(x)] = g[2x + 5]$
$= -(2x + 5) + 3$
$= -2x - 5 + 3$
$= -2x - 2$
$h[g(x)] = h[-x + 3]$
$= 2(-x + 3) + 5$
$= -2x + 6 + 5$
$= -2x + 11$

| 10-2 | **Logarithms and Logarithmic Functions** |

Page 535 **Check for Understanding**

1. Sample answer: $x = 5^y$ and $y = \log_5 x$

2. They are inverses.

3. Scott; the value of the logarithmic equation, 9, is the exponent of the equivalent exponential equation, and the base of the logarithmic expression, 3, is the base of the exponential equation. Thus, $x = 3^9$ or 19,683.

4. $5^4 = 625 \Rightarrow \log_5 625 = 4$

5. $7^{-2} = \frac{1}{49} \Rightarrow \log_7 \frac{1}{49} = -2$

6. $\log_3 81 = 4 \Rightarrow 3^4 = 81$

7. $\log_{36} 6 = \frac{1}{2} \Rightarrow 36^{\frac{1}{2}} = 6$

8. $\log_4 256 = x$
$4^x = 256$
$4^x = 4^4$
$x = 4$

9. $\log_2 \frac{1}{8} = x$
$2^x = \frac{1}{8}$
$2^x = 2^{-3}$
$x = -3$

10. $3^{\log_3 21} = 21$

11. $\log_5 5^{-1} = -1$

12. $\log_9 x = \frac{3}{2}$
$9^{\frac{3}{2}} = x$
$27 = x$
Check: $\log_9 27 \overset{?}{=} \frac{3}{2}$
$9^{\frac{3}{2}} \overset{?}{=} 27$
$27 = 27$ ✓

13. $\log_{\frac{1}{10}} x = -3$
$\left(\frac{1}{10}\right)^{-3} = x$
$1000 = x$
Check: $\log_{\frac{1}{10}} 1000 \overset{?}{=} -3$
$\left(\frac{1}{10}\right)^{-3} \overset{?}{=} 1000$
$1000 = 1000$ ✓

14. $\log_3(2x - 1) \leq 2$
$0 < 2x - 1 \leq 3^2$
$0 < 2x - 1 \leq 9$
$1 < 2x \leq 10$
$\frac{1}{2} < x \leq 5$
Check: Test $x = 2$.
$\log_3[2(2) - 1] \overset{?}{\leq} 2$
$\log_3 3 \overset{?}{\leq} 2$
$1 \leq 2$ ✓

15. $\log_5(3x - 1) = \log_5 2x^2$
$3x - 1 = 2x^2$
$2x^2 - 3x + 1 = 0$
$(2x - 1)(x - 1) = 0$
$2x - 1 = 0$ or $x - 1 = 0$
$2x = 1$ $\qquad x = 1$
$x = \frac{1}{2}$
Check: $\log_5\left[3\left(\frac{1}{2}\right) - 1\right] \overset{?}{=} \log_5 2\left(\frac{1}{2}\right)^2$
$\log_5[3(1) - 1] \overset{?}{=} \log_5 2(1)^2$
$\log_5 2 = \log_5 2$ ✓

16. $\log_2(3x - 5) > \log_2(x + 7)$
$3x - 5 > x + 7$
$2x > 12$
$x > 6$
Check: Test $x = 7$.
$\log_2(3 \cdot 7 - 5) \overset{?}{>} \log_2(7 + 7)$
$\log_2 16 > \log_2 14$ ✓

17. $\log_b 9 = 2$
$b^2 = 9$
$b = 3$
Check: $\log_3 9 \overset{?}{=} 2$
$3^2 \overset{?}{=} 9$
$9 = 9$ ✓

18. $130 = 10\log_{10} R$
$13 = \log_{10} R$
$R = 10^{13}$

19. $75 = 10 \log_{10} R$
$7.5 = \log_{10} R$
$R = 10^{7.5}$

20. The ratio of the intensity of the fireworks display to the intensity of the concert is $\frac{10^{13}}{10^{7.5}}$ or $10^{5.5}$.

The fireworks display is about $10^{5.5}$ or $316,228$ times more intense.

Pages 536–538 Practice and Apply

21. $8^3 = 512 \rightarrow \log_8 512 = 3$

22. $3^3 = 27 \rightarrow \log_3 27 = 3$

23. $5^{-3} = \frac{1}{125} \rightarrow \log_5 \frac{1}{125} = -3$

24. $\left(\frac{1}{3}\right)^{-2} = 9 \rightarrow \log_{\frac{1}{3}} 9 = -2$

25. $100^{\frac{1}{2}} = 10 \rightarrow \log_{100} 10 = \frac{1}{2}$

26. $2401^{\frac{1}{4}} = 7 \rightarrow \log_{2401} 7 = \frac{1}{4}$

27. $\log_5 125 = 3 \rightarrow 5^3 = 125$

28. $\log_{13} 169 = 2 \rightarrow 13^2 = 169$

29. $\log_4 \frac{1}{4} = -1 \rightarrow 4^{-1} = \frac{1}{4}$

30. $\log_{100} \frac{1}{10} = -\frac{1}{2} \rightarrow 100^{-\frac{1}{2}} = \frac{1}{10}$

31. $\log_8 4 = \frac{2}{3} \rightarrow 8^{\frac{2}{3}} = 4$

32. $\log_{\frac{1}{5}} 25 = -2 \rightarrow \left(\frac{1}{5}\right)^{-2} = 25$

33. $\log_2 16 = x$
$2^x = 16$
$2^x = 2^4$
$x = 4$

34. $\log_{12} 144 = x$
$12^x = 144$
$12^x = 12^2$
$x = 2$

35. $\log_{16} 4 = x$
$16^x = 4$
$(4^2)^x = 4$
$4^{2x} = 4^1$
$2x = 1$
$x = \frac{1}{2}$

36. $\log_9 243 = x$
$9^x = 243$
$(3^2)^x = 3^5$
$3^{2x} = 3^5$
$2x = 5$
$x = \frac{5}{2}$

37. $\log_2 \frac{1}{32} = x$
$2^x = \frac{1}{32}$
$2^x = 2^{-5}$
$x = -5$

38. $\log_3 \frac{1}{81} = x$
$3^x = \frac{1}{81}$
$3^x = 3^{-4}$
$x = -4$

39. $\log_5 5^7 = x$
$5^x = 5^7$
$x = 7$

40. $2^{\log_2 45} = 45$

41. $\log_{11} 11^{(n-5)} = n - 5$

42. $6^{\log_6 (3x + 2)} = 3x + 2$

43. $\log_{10} 0.001 = x$
$10^x = 0.001$
$10^x = \frac{1}{1000}$
$10^x = 10^{-3}$
$x = -3$

44. $\log_4 16^x = \log_4 (4^2)^x$
$= \log_4 4^{2x}$
$= 2x$

45. $L = 10 \log_{10} R$
$188 = 10 \log_{10} R$
$18.8 = \log_{10} R$
$R = 10^{18.8}$

46. $L = 10 \log_{10} R$
$106.7 = 10 \log_{10} R$
$10.67 = \log_{10} R$
$R = 10^{10.67}$

47. $\log_9 x = 2$
$x = 9^2$
$x = 81$
Check: $\log_9 81 \stackrel{?}{=} 2$
$9^2 \stackrel{?}{=} 81$
$81 = 81$ ✓

48. $\log_2 c > 8$
$c > 2^8$
$c > 256$
Check: Test $c = 512$.
$\log_2 512 \stackrel{?}{>} 8$
$9 > 8$ ✓

49. $\log_{64} y \leq \frac{1}{2}$
$0 < y \leq 64^{\frac{1}{2}}$
$0 < y \leq 8$
Check: Test $y = 4$.
$\log_{64} 4 \leq \frac{1}{2}$
$\frac{1}{3} \leq \frac{1}{2}$ ✓

50. $\log_{25} n = \frac{3}{2}$
$n = 25^{\frac{3}{2}}$
$n = 125$
Check: $\log_{25} 125 \stackrel{?}{=} \frac{3}{2}$
$\frac{3}{2} = \frac{3}{2}$ ✓

51. $\log_{\frac{1}{7}} x = -1$
$x = \left(\frac{1}{7}\right)^{-1}$
$x = 7$
Check: $\log_{\frac{1}{7}} 7 \stackrel{?}{=} -1$
$-1 = -1$ ✓

52. $\log_{\frac{1}{3}} p < 0$

$\quad\quad p > \left(\frac{1}{3}\right)^0$

$\quad\quad p > 1$

Check: Test $p = 3$.

$\quad\quad\quad \log_{\frac{1}{3}} 3 \overset{?}{<} 0$

$\quad\quad\quad\quad -1 < 0$ ✓

53. $\log_2(3x - 8) \geq 6$

$\quad\quad 3x - 8 \geq 2^6$

$\quad\quad 3x - 8 \geq 64$

$\quad\quad 3x \geq 72$

$\quad\quad x \geq 24$

Check: $\log_2(3 \cdot 24 - 8) \overset{?}{\geq} 6$

$\quad\quad\quad\quad \log_2 64 \overset{?}{\geq} 6$

$\quad\quad\quad\quad\quad 6 = 6$ ✓

54. $\log_{10}(x^2 + 1) = 1$

$\quad\quad x^2 + 1 = 10^1$

$\quad\quad x^2 - 9 = 0$

$\quad\quad x^2 = 9$

$\quad\quad x = \pm 3$

Check: $\log_{10}[(3)^2 + 1] \overset{?}{=} 1$

$\quad\quad\quad \log_{10}(9 + 1) \overset{?}{=} 1$

$\quad\quad\quad\quad \log_{10} 10 \overset{?}{=} 1$

$\quad\quad\quad\quad\quad 1 = 1$ ✓

$\quad\quad \log_{10}[(-3)^2 + 1] \overset{?}{=} 1$

$\quad\quad\quad\quad \log_{10}(9 + 1) \overset{?}{=} 1$

$\quad\quad\quad\quad\quad \log_{10} 10 \overset{?}{=} 1$

$\quad\quad\quad\quad\quad\quad 1 = 1$ ✓

55. $\log_b 64 = 3$

$\quad\quad b^3 = 64$

$\quad\quad b = 4$

Check: $\log_4 64 \overset{?}{=} 3$

$\quad\quad\quad\quad 3 = 3$ ✓

56. $\log_b 121 = 2$

$\quad\quad b^2 = 121$

$\quad\quad b = 11$

Check: $\log_{11} 121 \overset{?}{=} 2$

$\quad\quad\quad\quad 2 = 2$ ✓

57. $\log_5 5^{6n + 1} = 13$

$\quad\quad 6n + 1 = 13$

$\quad\quad 6n = 12$

$\quad\quad n = 2$

Check: $\log_5 5^{6(2) + 1} \overset{?}{=} 13$

$\quad\quad\quad \log_5 5^{12 + 1} \overset{?}{=} 13$

$\quad\quad\quad\quad \log_5 5^{13} \overset{?}{=} 13$

$\quad\quad\quad\quad\quad 13 = 13$ ✓

58. $\log_5 x = \frac{1}{2}$

$\quad\quad x = 5^{\frac{1}{2}}$

$\quad\quad x = \sqrt{5}$

Check: $\log_5 \sqrt{5} \overset{?}{=} \frac{1}{2}$

$\quad\quad\quad \log_5 5^{\frac{1}{2}} \overset{?}{=} \frac{1}{2}$

$\quad\quad\quad\quad \frac{1}{2} = \frac{1}{2}$ ✓

59. $\log_6(2x - 3) = \log_6(x + 2)$

$\quad\quad 2x - 3 = x + 2$

$\quad\quad x = 5$

Check: $\log_6[2(5) - 3] \overset{?}{=} \log_6(5 + 2)$

$\quad\quad\quad \log_6(10 - 3) \overset{?}{=} \log_6(7)$

$\quad\quad\quad\quad \log_6 7 = \log_6 7$ ✓

60. $\log_2(4y - 10) \geq \log_2(y - 1)$

$\quad\quad 4y - 10 \geq y - 1$

$\quad\quad 3y \geq 9$

$\quad\quad y \geq 3$

Check: Test $y = 4$.

$\quad\quad \log_2[4(4) - 10] \overset{?}{\geq} \log_2(4 - 1)$

$\quad\quad \log_2(16 - 10) \overset{?}{\geq} \log_2(4 - 1)$

$\quad\quad\quad \log_2 6 \overset{?}{\geq} \log_2 3$

$\quad\quad\quad\quad 6 \geq 3$ ✓

61. $\log_{10}(a^2 - 6) > \log_{10} a$

In order that $\log_{10}(a^2 - 6)$ be defined, a must satisfy $a < -\sqrt{6}$ or $a > \sqrt{6}$. In order that $\log_{10} a$ be defined, a must satisfy $a > 0$. Solutions can only occur where both expressions are defined, which is for $a > \sqrt{6}$.

$\quad \log_{10}(a^2 - 6) > \log_{10} a$

$\quad\quad\quad a^2 - 6 > a$

$\quad\quad a^2 - a - 6 > 0$

$\quad (a - 3)(a + 2) > 0$

Solving the related equation.

$(a + 2)(a - 3) = 0$

$a + 2 = 0 \quad$ or $\quad a - 3 = 0$

$\quad a = -2 \quad\quad\quad\quad a = 3$

The value $a = -2$ does not satisfy $a > \sqrt{6}$. The value $a = 3$ divides the numbers satisfying $a > \sqrt{6}$ into two regions. Test a value from each region.

Test $a = 2.5$.

$\log_{10}(2.5^2 - 6) \overset{?}{>} \log_{10} 2.5$

$\quad \log_{10} 0.25 \overset{?}{>} \log_{10} 2.5$

$\quad\quad\quad 0.25 \not> 2.5$

Test $a = 4$.

$\log_{10}(4^2 - 6) \overset{?}{>} \log_{10} 4$

$\quad \log_{10} 10 \overset{?}{>} \log_{10} 4$

$\quad\quad\quad 10 > 4$ ✓

The solutions are values of a satisfying $a > 3$.

62. $\log_7(x^2 + 36) = \log_7 100$

$\quad\quad x^2 + 36 = 100$

$\quad\quad x^2 = 64$

$\quad\quad x = \pm 8$

Check: $\log_7[(-8)^2 + 36] \overset{?}{=} \log_7 100$

$\quad\quad \log_7(8^2 + 36) \overset{?}{=} \log_7 100$

$\quad\quad\quad \log_7 100 = \log_7 100$ ✓

63. $\log_5 25 \overset{?}{=} 2 \log_5 5 \quad$ Original equation

$\quad 5^2 \overset{?}{=} 2 \log_5 5^1 \quad 25 = 5^2$ and $5 = 5^1$

$\quad 2 \overset{?}{=} 2(1) \quad\quad$ Inverse Property of Exponents and Logarithms

$\quad\quad 2 = 2$ ✓ $\quad\quad$ Simplify.

64. $\log_{16} 2 \cdot \log_2 16 \overset{?}{=} 1 \quad$ Original equation

$\quad \log_{16} 16^{\frac{1}{4}} \cdot \log_2 2^4 \overset{?}{=} 1 \quad 2 = 16^{\frac{1}{4}}$ and $16 = 2^4$

$\quad\quad\quad \frac{1}{4}(4) \overset{?}{=} 1 \quad\quad$ Inverse Property of Exponents and Logarithms

$\quad\quad\quad\quad 1 = 1$ ✓

65. $\log_7[\log_3(\log_2 8)] \overset{?}{=} 0$ Original equation

$\log_7[\log_3(\log_2 2^3)] \overset{?}{=} 0$ $8 = 2^3$

$\log_7(\log_3 3) \overset{?}{=} 0$ Inverse Property of Exponents and Logarithms

$\log_7(\log_3 3^1) \overset{?}{=} 0$ $3 = 3^1$

$\log_7 1 \overset{?}{=} 0$ Inverse Property of Exponents and Logarithms

$\log_7 7^0 \overset{?}{=} 0$ $1 = 7^0$

$0 = 0$ ✓   Inverse Property of Exponents and Logarithms

66a.

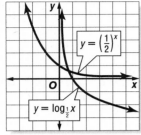

66b. The graphs are reflections of each other over the line $y = x$.

67a.

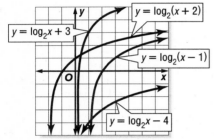

67b. The graph of $y = \log_2 x + 3$ is the graph of $y = \log_2 x$ translated 3 units up. The graph of $y = \log_2 x - 4$ is the graph of $y = \log_2 x$ translated 4 units down. The graph of $y = \log_2(x - 1)$ is the graph of $y = \log_2 x$ translated 1 unit to the right. The graph of $y = \log_2(x + 2)$ is the graph of $y = \log_2 x$ translated 2 units to the left.

68. First, let $M = 7$.

$7 = \log_{10} x$

$10^7 = x$

Now let $M = 4$.

$4 = \log_{10} x$

$10^4 = x$

Find the ratio of the amplitude.

$\frac{10^7}{10^4} = 10^3$

An earthquake of magnitude 7 has an amplitude 10^3 or 1000 times greater than an earthquake of magnitude 4.

69. First, let $M = 8.3$.

$8.3 = \log_{10} x$

$10^{8.3} = x$

Now let $M = 6.9$.

$6.9 = \log_{10} x$

$10^{6.9} = x$

Find the ratio of the amplitudes.

$\frac{10^{8.3}}{10^{6.9}} = 10^{1.4}$

The motion of the 1906 earthquake was $10^{1.4}$ or about 25 times greater than the motion of the 2001 earthquake.

70. Use the formula $L = 10 \log_{10} R$.

First let $L = 72$.

$72 = 10 \log_{10} R$

$7.2 = \log_{10} R$

$10^{7.2} = R$

Let $L = 55$.

$55 = 10 \log_{10} R$

$5.5 = \log_{10} R$

$10^{5.5} = R$

Find the ratio of the intensities.

$\frac{10^{7.2}}{10^{5.5}} = 10^{1.7}$

The noise level during the day is allowed to be $10^{1.7}$ or about 50 times greater than the noise allowed at night.

71. Let $\log_2 5 = x$. Note that $\log_2 4 = 2$, since $2^2 = 4$, and $\log_2 8 = 3$, since $2^3 = 8$.

By the Property of Inequality for Logarithmic Functions, $\log_2 4 < \log_2 5$ and $\log_2 5 < \log_2 8$. Therefore, $\log_2 5$ is between 2 and 3.

72. The exponential equation $1^y = x$ equivalent to $y = \log_1 x$ will always have a value of 1 no matter the value of y, since 1 raised to any power is 1. With a base of 1, therefore, the logarithmic equation cannot be a function.

73. A logarithmic scale illustrates that values next to each other vary by a factor of 10. Answers should include the following.

- Pin drop: 1×10^0; Whisper: 1×10^2; Normal conversation: 1×10^6; Kitchen noise: 1×10^{10}; Jet engine: 1×10^{12}

- On the scale shown above, the sound of a pin drop and the sound of normal conversation appear not to differ by much at all, when in fact they do differ in terms of the loudness we perceive. The first scale shows this difference more clearly.

74. B; Note that $(0, 2)$ is a point of the graph, so that the answer has to be either A or B. In equation A, $y = 2(3)^x$, when $x = -1$, $y = \frac{2}{3}$, while in equation B, $y = 2\left(\frac{1}{3}\right)^x$, when $x = -1$, $y = 6$.

75. D; From the figure, we write two equations.

$x + y + z = 180$

$w + z = 180$

Replace z with $3w$ and y with $\frac{2}{7}x$.

$x + \frac{2}{7}x + 3w = 180$

$w + 3w = 180$

Simplify.

$\frac{9}{7}x + 3w = 180$

$4w = 180$

From the latter, $w = 45$.

Substitute $w = 45$ into the former equation.

$\frac{9}{7}x + 3(45) = 180$

$\frac{9}{7}x + 135 = 180$

$\frac{9}{7}x = 45$

$x = 45 \cdot \frac{7}{9}$

$x = 35$

Page 538　Maintain Your Skills

76. $x^{\sqrt{6}} \cdot x^{\sqrt{6}} = x^{\sqrt{6}+\sqrt{6}}$

$= x^{2\sqrt{6}}$

77. $(b^{\sqrt{6}})^{\sqrt{24}} = b^{\sqrt{6}\cdot\sqrt{24}}$

$= b^{\sqrt{6\cdot24}}$

$= b^{\sqrt{12\cdot12}}$

$= b^{12}$

78.

$\frac{2x+1}{x} - \frac{x+1}{x-4} = \frac{-20}{x^2-4x}$

$x(x-4)\left(\frac{2x+1}{x} - \frac{x+1}{x-4}\right) = x(x-4)\left(\frac{-20}{x^2-4x}\right)$

$(x-4)(2x+1) - x(x+1) = -20$

$2x^2 - 7x - 4 - x^2 - x = -20$

$x^2 - 8x + 16 = 0$

$(x-4)(x-4) = 0$

$x - 4 = 0 \quad \text{or} \quad x - 4 = 0$

$x = 4 \qquad\qquad x = 4$

Check: $\frac{2\cdot4+1}{4} - \frac{4+1}{4-4} \overset{?}{=} \frac{-20}{4^2-4\cdot4}$

$\frac{9}{4} - \frac{5}{0} \overset{?}{=} \frac{-20}{0}$

Since $x = 4$ results in 0 in the denominator, there is no solution to this equation.

79.

$\frac{2a-5}{a-9} - \frac{a-3}{3a+2} = \frac{5}{3a^2-25a-18}$

$(a-9)(3a+2)\left(\frac{2a-5}{a-9} - \frac{a-3}{3a+2}\right) = (a-9)(3a+2)\left(\frac{5}{(a-9)(3a+2)}\right)$

$(3a+2)(2a-5) - (a-9)(a-3) = 5$

$6a^2 - 11a - 10 - (a^2 - 12a + 27) = 5$

$5a^2 + a - 37 = 5$

$5a^2 + a - 42 = 0$

$(5a-14)(a+3) = 0$

$5a - 14 = 0 \qquad \text{or } a + 3 = 0$

$5a = 14 \qquad\qquad a = -3$

$a = \frac{14}{5}$

Check: $\frac{2(-3)-5}{-3-9} - \frac{-3-3}{3(-3)+2} \overset{?}{=} \frac{5}{3(-3)^2-25(-3)-18}$

$\frac{-11}{-12} - \frac{-6}{-7} \overset{?}{=} \frac{5}{84}$

$\frac{5}{84} = \frac{5}{84} \checkmark$

$\frac{2\left(\frac{14}{5}\right)-5}{\frac{14}{5}-9} - \frac{\frac{14}{5}-3}{3\left(\frac{14}{5}\right)+2} \overset{?}{=} \frac{5}{3\left(\frac{14}{5}\right)^2-25\left(\frac{14}{5}\right)-18}$

$\frac{\frac{28}{5}-\frac{25}{5}}{\frac{14}{5}-\frac{45}{5}} - \frac{\frac{14}{5}-\frac{15}{5}}{\frac{42}{5}+\frac{10}{5}} \overset{?}{=} \frac{5}{\frac{588}{25}-\frac{1750}{25}-\frac{450}{25}}$

$\frac{3}{-31} - \frac{-1}{52} \overset{?}{=} \frac{-5}{1612}$

$\frac{125}{1612} = \frac{125}{1612} \checkmark$

80. $9y^2 = 49$

$y^2 = \frac{49}{9}$

$y = \pm\frac{7}{3}$

81. $2p^2 = 5p + 6$

$2p^2 - 5p - 6 = 0$

$p = \frac{-(-5) \pm \sqrt{(-5)^2 - 4(2)(-6)}}{2(2)}$

$= \frac{5 \pm \sqrt{73}}{4}$

82. $\frac{3}{2y} + \frac{4}{3y} - \frac{7}{5y} = \frac{3(3\cdot5) + 4(2\cdot5) - 7(2\cdot3)}{2\cdot3\cdot5y}$

$= \frac{43}{30y}$

83. $\frac{x-7}{x^2-9} - \frac{x-3}{x^2+10x+21}$

$= \frac{x-7}{(x+3)(x-3)} - \frac{x-3}{(x+3)(x+7)}$

$= \left(\frac{x+7}{x+7}\right)\left(\frac{x-7}{(x+3)(x-3)}\right) - \left(\frac{x-3}{x-3}\right)\left(\frac{x-3}{(x+3)(x+7)}\right)$

$= \frac{(x+7)(x-7) - (x-3)(x-3)}{(x+7)(x+3)(x-3)}$

$= \frac{x^2-49 - (x^2-6x+9)}{(x+7)(x+3)(x-3)}$

$= \frac{6x-58}{(x+7)(x+3)(x-3)}$

84. Let x be the amount Donna invests in the CD and y the amount she invests in a regular savings account.

$x + y = 4000$

$0.08 + 0.03y = 240$

$x = \dfrac{\begin{vmatrix} 4000 & 1 \\ 240 & 0.03 \end{vmatrix}}{\begin{vmatrix} 1 & 1 \\ 0.08 & 0.03 \end{vmatrix}}$

$= \frac{120 - 240}{0.03 - 0.08}$

$= \frac{-120}{-0.05}$

$= 2400$

$y = \dfrac{\begin{vmatrix} 1 & 4000 \\ 0.08 & 240 \end{vmatrix}}{\begin{vmatrix} 1 & 1 \\ 0.08 & 0.03 \end{vmatrix}}$

$= \frac{240 - 320}{0.03 - 0.08}$

$= \frac{-80}{-0.05}$

$= 1600$

Donna should put \$2400 into a CD and \$1600 into a savings account.

85. $x^4 \cdot x^6 = x^{4+6}$
$\qquad = x^{10}$

86. $(y^3)^8 = y^{3 \cdot 8}$
$\qquad = y^{24}$

87. $(2a^2b)^3 = 2^3 \cdot (a^2)^3 \cdot b^3$
$\qquad = 8a^6b^3$

88. $\frac{a^4n^7}{a^3n} = a^{4-3}n^{7-1}$
$\qquad = an^6$

89. $\frac{x^5yz^2}{x^2y^3z^5} = x^{5-2}y^{1-3}z^{2-5}$
$\qquad = x^3y^{-2}z^{-3}$
$\qquad = \frac{x^3}{y^2z^3}$

90. $\left(\frac{b^7}{a^4}\right)^0 = 1$

Page 538 Practice Quiz 1

1. $5(1.2)^x$ represents exponential growth since the base, 1.2, is greater than 1.

2. Substitute $(0, 2)$ into the exponential function $y = ab^x$.
$y = ab^x$
$2 = ab^0$
$2 = a$
Substitute $(2, 32)$ into the intermediate function $y = 2b^x$.
$y = 2b^x$
$32 = 2b^x$
$16 = b^2$
$4 = b$
The function is $y = 2(4)^x$.

3. $4^6 = 4096 \Rightarrow \log_4 4096 = 6$

4. $\log_9 27 = \frac{3}{2} \Rightarrow 9^{\frac{3}{2}} = 27$

5. $\log_8 16 = x$
$8^x = 16$
$(2^3)^x = 2^4$
$2^{3x} = 2^4$
$3x = 4$
$x = \frac{4}{3}$

6. $\log_4 4^{15} = 15$

7. $3^{4x} = 3^{3-x}$
$4x = 3 - x$
$5x = 3$
$x = \frac{3}{5}$
Check: $3^{4\left(\frac{3}{5}\right)} \overset{?}{=} 3^{3 - \frac{3}{5}}$
$\qquad 3^{\frac{12}{5}} \overset{?}{=} 3^{\frac{15}{5} - \frac{3}{5}}$
$\qquad 3^{\frac{12}{5}} = 3^{\frac{12}{5}} \checkmark$

8. $3^{2n} \le \frac{1}{9}$
$3^{2n} \le 3^{-2}$
$2n \le -2$
$n \le -1$
Check: Test $n = -2$.
$\qquad 3^{2(-2)} \overset{?}{\le} \frac{1}{9}$
$\qquad \frac{1}{3^4} \overset{?}{\le} \frac{1}{9}$
$\qquad \frac{1}{81} \le \frac{1}{9} \checkmark$

9. $\log_2(x + 6) > 5$
$x + 6 > 2^5$
$x + 6 > 32$
$x > 26$
Check: Test $x = 58$.
$\log_2(58 + 6) \overset{?}{>} 5$
$\log_2 64 \overset{?}{>} 5$
$6 > 5 \checkmark$

10. $\log_5(4x - 1) = \log_5(3x + 2)$
$4x - 1 = 3x + 2$
$x = 3$
Check: $\log_5(4(3) - 1) \overset{?}{=} \log_5(3(3) + 2)$
$\log_5(12 - 1) \overset{?}{=} \log_5(9 + 2)$
$\log_5 11 = \log_5 11$

Page 540 Graphing Calculator Investigation (Follow-Up of Lesson 10-2)

1.
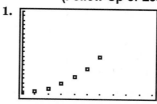
[0, 50] scl: 5 by [30, 400] scl: 20

2.
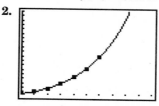
[0, 50] scl: 5 by [30, 400] scl: 20

3. $y = 29.99908551(1.065001351)^x$

4. This equation is a good fit because $r \approx 1$.

5. After 41 years, she will have approximately $397.

6. A quadratic equation might be a good model for this example because the shape is close to a portion of a parabola.

10-3 | Properties of Logarithms

Page 544 Check for Understanding

1. The properties of exponents are used to derive the properties of logarithms.

2. $2 \log_3 x + \log_3 5 = \log_3 x^2 + \log_3 5$
$\qquad = \log_3(x^2 \cdot 5)$
$\qquad = \log_3 5x^2$

3. Umeko; Clemente incorrectly applied the product and quotient properties of logarithms.
$\log_7 6 + \log_7 3 = \log_7(6 \cdot 3)$ or $\log_7 18$
Product Property of Logarithms
$\log_7 18 - \log_7 2 = \log_7(18 \div 2)$ or $\log_7 9$
Quotient Property of Logarithms

4. $\log_3 \frac{7}{2} = \log_3 7 - \log_3 2$
$\qquad = 1.7712 - 0.6310$
$\qquad = 1.1402$

5. $\log_3 18 = \log_3(3^2 \cdot 2)$
$= \log_3 3^2 + \log_3 2$
$= 2 \log_3 3 + \log_3 2$
$= 2(1) + 0.6310$
$= 2.6310$

6. $\log_3 \frac{2}{3} = \log_3 2 - \log_3 3$
$= 0.6310 - 1$
$= -0.3690$

7. $\log_3 42 - \log_3 n = \log_3 7$
$\log_3 \frac{42}{n} = \log_3 7$
$\frac{42}{n} = 7$
$42 = 7n$
$6 = n$
Check: $\log_3 42 - \log_3 6 \stackrel{?}{=} \log_3 7$
$\log_3 \frac{42}{6} \stackrel{?}{=} \log_3 7$
$\log_3 7 = \log_3 7$ ✓

8. $\log_2 3x + \log_2 5 = \log_2 30$
$\log_2(3x \cdot 5) = \log_2 30$
$15x = 30$
$x = 2$
Check: $\log_2(3 \cdot 2) + \log_2 5 \stackrel{?}{=} \log_2 30$
$\log_2 6 + \log_2 5 \stackrel{?}{=} \log_2 30$
$\log_2(6 \cdot 5) \stackrel{?}{=} \log_2 30$
$\log_2 30 = \log_2 30$ ✓

9. $2 \log_5 x = \log_5 9$
$\log_5 x^2 = \log_5 9$
$x^2 = 9$
$x = \pm 3$
Check: $2 \log_5 3 \stackrel{?}{=} \log_5 9$ $2 \log_5(-3) \stackrel{?}{=} \log_5 9$
$\log_5 3^2 \stackrel{?}{=} \log_5 9$ $\log_5(-3)$ is undefined.
$\log_5 9 = \log_5 9$ ✓
The solution is 3.

10. $\log_{10} a + \log_{10}(a + 21) = 2$
$\log_{10}[a(a + 21)] = 2$
$a(a + 21) = 10^2$
$a^2 + 21a = 100$
$a^2 + 21a - 100 = 0$
$(a + 25)(a - 4) = 0$
$a + 25 = 0$ or $a - 4 = 0$
$a = -25$ $a = 4$
Check: $\log_{10} 4 + \log_{10}(4 + 21) \stackrel{?}{=} 2$
$\log_{10} 4 + \log_{10} 25 \stackrel{?}{=} 2$
$\log_{10}(4 \cdot 25) \stackrel{?}{=} 2$
$\log_{10} 100 \stackrel{?}{=} 2$
$2 = 2$ ✓
$\log_{10}(-25) + \log_{10}(-25 + 21) \stackrel{?}{=} 2$
$\log_{10}(-25)$ is undefined.
The solution is $a = 4$.

11. $\text{pH} = 6.1 + \log_{10} B - \log_{10} C$
$\text{pH} = 6.1 + \log_{10}\left(\frac{B}{C}\right)$

12. $7.4 = 6.1 + \log_{10} B - \log_{10} C$
$1.3 = \log_{10}\left(\frac{B}{C}\right)$
$\frac{B}{C} = 10^{1.3}$
$\frac{B}{C} \approx 19.95$
The ratio is about 20:1.

Pages 544–546   Practice and Apply

13. $\log_5 9 = \log_5 3^2$
$= 2 \log_5 3$
$= 2 \cdot 0.6826$
$= 1.3652$

14. $\log_5 8 = \log_5 2^3$
$= 3 \log_5 2$
$= 3 \cdot 0.4307$
$= 1.2921$

15. $\log_5 \frac{2}{3} = \log_5 2 - \log_5 3$
$= 0.4307 - 0.6826$
$= -0.2519$

16. $\log_5 \frac{3}{2} = \log_5 3 - \log_5 2$
$= 0.6826 - 0.4307$
$= 0.2519$

17. $\log_5 50 = \log_5(5 \cdot 5 \cdot 2)$
$= \log_5 5^2 + \log_5 2$
$= 2 \log_5 5 + \log_5 2$
$= 2(1) + 0.4307$
$= 2.4307$

18. $\log_5 30 = \log_5(5 \cdot 2 \cdot 3)$
$= \log_5 5 + \log_5 2 + \log_5 3$
$= 1 + 0.4307 + 0.6826$
$= 2.1133$

19. $\log_5 0.5 = \log_5 \frac{1}{2}$
$= \log_5 1 - \log_5 2$
$= 0 - 0.4307$
$= -0.4307$

20. $\log_5 \frac{10}{9} = \log_5 10 - \log_5 9$
$= \log_5(2 \cdot 5) - \log_5 3^2$
$= \log_5 2 + \log_5 5 - 2 \log_5 3$
$= 0.4307 + 1 - 2 \cdot 0.6826$
$= 0.0655$

21. $\log_3 5 + \log_3 x = \log_3 10$
$\log_3(5 \cdot x) = \log_3 10$
$5x = 10$
$x = 2$
Check: $\log_3 5 + \log_3 2 \stackrel{?}{=} \log_3 10$
$\log_3(5 \cdot 2) \stackrel{?}{=} \log_3 10$
$\log_3 10 = \log_3 10$ ✓
The solution is 2.

22. $\log_4 a + \log_4 9 = \log_4 27$
$\log_4(a \cdot 9) = \log_4 27$
$9a = 27$
$a = 3$
Check: $\log_4 3 + \log_4 9 \stackrel{?}{=} \log_4 27$
$\log_4(3 \cdot 9) \stackrel{?}{=} \log_4 27$
$\log_4 27 = \log_4 27$ ✓
The solution is 3.

23. $\log_{10} 16 - \log_{10} 2t = \log_{10} 2$

$\log_{10} \frac{16}{2t} = \log_{10} 2$

$\frac{16}{2t} = 2$

$16 = 4t$

$4 = t$

Check: $\log_{10} 16 - \log_{10} 2(4) \stackrel{?}{=} \log_{10} 2$

$\log_{10} 16 - \log_{10} 8 \stackrel{?}{=} \log_{10} 2$

$\log_{10} \frac{16}{8} \stackrel{?}{=} \log_{10} 2$

$\log_{10} 2 = \log_{10} 2$ ✓

The solution is 4.

24. $\log_7 24 - \log_7(y + 5) = \log_7 8$

$\log_7 \frac{24}{y + 5} = \log_7 8$

$\frac{24}{y + 5} = 8$

$24 = 8(y + 5)$

$3 = y + 5$

$-2 = y$

Check: $\log_7 24 - \log_7(-2 + 5) \stackrel{?}{=} \log_7 8$

$\log_9 24 - \log_7 3 \stackrel{?}{=} \log_7 8$

$\log_7 \frac{24}{3} \stackrel{?}{=} \log_7 8$

$\log_7 8 = \log_7 8$ ✓

The solution is -2.

25. $\log_2 n = \frac{1}{4} \log_2 16 + \frac{1}{2} \log_2 49$

$\log_2 n = \log_2 16^{\frac{1}{4}} + \log^2 49^{\frac{1}{2}}$

$\log_2 n = \log_2 2 + \log_2 7$

$\log_2 n = \log_2(2 \cdot 7)$

$\log_2 n = \log_2 14$

$n = 14$

Check: $\log_2 14 \stackrel{?}{=} \frac{1}{4} \log_2 16 + \frac{1}{2} \log_2 49$

$\log_2 14 \stackrel{?}{=} \log_2 16^{\frac{1}{4}} + \log_2 49^{\frac{1}{2}}$

$\log_2 14 \stackrel{?}{=} \log_2 2 + \log_2 7$

$\log_2 14 = \log_2 14$ ✓

The solution is 14.

26. $2 \log_{10} 6 - \frac{1}{3} \log_{10} 27 = \log_{10} x$

$\log_{10} 6^2 - \log_{10} 27^{\frac{1}{3}} = \log_{10} x$

$\log_{10} 36 - \log_{10} 3 = \log_{10} x$

$\log_{10} \frac{36}{3} = \log_{10} x$

$12 = x$

Check: $2 \log_{10} 6 - \frac{1}{3} \log_{10} 27 \stackrel{?}{=} \log_{10} 12$

$\log_{10} 6^2 - \log_{10} 27^{\frac{1}{3}} \stackrel{?}{=} \log_{10} 12$

$\log_{10} 36 - \log_{10} 3 \stackrel{?}{=} \log_{10} 12$

$\log_{10} \frac{36}{3} \stackrel{?}{=} \log_{10} 12$

$\log_{10} 12 = \log_{10} 12$ ✓

The solution is 12.

27. $\log_{10} z + \log_{10}(z + 3) = 1$

$\log_{10}[z(z + 3)] = 1$

$z(z + 3) = 10^1$

$z^2 + 3z = 10$

$z^2 + 3z - 10 = 0$

$(z + 5)(z - 2) = 0$

$z + 5 = 0 \quad$ or $\quad z - 2 = 0$

$z = -5 \qquad\qquad z = 2$

Check: $\log_{10}(-5) + \log_{10}(-5 + 3) = 1$

$\log_{10}(-5)$ is undefined.

$\log_{10} 2 + \log_{10}(2 + 3) \stackrel{?}{=} 1$

$\log_{10} 2 + \log_{10} 5 \stackrel{?}{=} 1$

$\log_{10}(2 \cdot 5) \stackrel{?}{=} 1$

$\log_{10} 10 \stackrel{?}{=} 1$

$1 = 1$

The solution is 2.

28. $\log_6(a^2 + 2) + \log_6 2 = 2$

$\log_6[2(a^2 + 2)] = 2$

$2(a^2 + 2) = 6^2$

$2a^2 + 4 = 36$

$2a^2 = 32$

$a^2 = 16$

$a = \pm 4$

Check: $\log_6[(-4)^2 + 2] + \log_6 2 \stackrel{?}{=} 2$

$\log_6 18 + \log_6 2 \stackrel{?}{=} 2$

$\log_6(18 \cdot 2) \stackrel{?}{=} 2$

$\log_6 36 \stackrel{?}{=} 2$

$2 = 2$ ✓

$\log_6[(4)^2 + 2] + \log_6 2 \stackrel{?}{=} 2$

$\log_6 18 + \log_6 2 \stackrel{?}{=} 2$

$\log_6(18 \cdot 2) \stackrel{?}{=} 2$

$\log_6 36 \stackrel{?}{=} 2$

$2 = 2$ ✓

The solutions are 4 and -4.

29. $\log_2(12b - 21) - \log_2(b^2 - 3) = 2$

$\log_2 \frac{12b - 21}{b^2 - 3} = 2$

$\frac{12b - 21}{b^2 - 3} = 2^2$

$\frac{12b - 21}{b^2 - 3} = 4$

$12b - 21 = 4(b^2 - 3)$

$12b - 21 = 4b^2 - 12$

$4b^2 - 12b + 9 = 0$

$(2b - 3)^2 = 0$

$2b - 3 = 0$

$2b = 3$

$b = \frac{3}{2}$

Check: $\log_2\left[\left(\frac{3}{2}\right)^2 - 3\right] = \log_2\left(\frac{9}{4} - 3\right)$

$= \log_2\left(-\frac{3}{4}\right)$

$\log_2\left(-\frac{3}{4}\right)$ is undefined.

There is no solution.

30. $\log_2(y + 2) - \log_2(y - 2) = 1$

$\log_2 \frac{y + 2}{y - 2} = 1$

$\frac{y + 2}{y - 2} = 2^1$

$\frac{y + 2}{y - 2} = 2$

$y + 2 = 2(y - 2)$

$y + 2 = 2y - 4$

$6 = y$

Check: $\log_2(6 + 2) - \log_2(6 - 2) \stackrel{?}{=} 1$

$\log_2 8 - \log_2 4 \stackrel{?}{=} 1$

$\log_2 \frac{8}{4} \stackrel{?}{=} 1$

$\log_2 2 \stackrel{?}{=} 1$

$1 = 1$ ✓

The solution is 6.

31. $\log_3 0.1 + 2 \log_3 x = \log_3 2 + \log_3 5$

$\log_3 0.1 + \log_3 x^2 = \log_3(2 \cdot 5)$

$\log_3(0.1 \cdot x^2) = \log_3 10$

$0.1x^2 = 10$

$x^2 = 100$

$x = \pm 10$

Check: $\log_3 0.1 + 2 \log_3(-10) \overset{?}{=} \log_3 2 + \log_3 5$

$\log_3 0.1 + \log_3(-10)^2 \overset{?}{=} \log_3(2 \cdot 5)$

$\log_3 0.1 + \log_3 100 \overset{?}{=} \log_3 10$

$\log_3(0.1 \cdot 100) \overset{?}{=} \log_3 10$

$\log_3 10 = \log_3 10$ ✓

$\log_3 0.1 + 2 \log_3 10 \overset{?}{=} \log_3 2 + \log_3 5$

$\log_3 0.1 + \log_3 10^2 \overset{?}{=} \log_3(2 \cdot 5)$

$\log_3 0.1 + \log_3 100 \overset{?}{=} \log_3 10$

$\log_3(0.1 \cdot 100) \overset{?}{=} \log_3 10$

$\log_3 10 = \log_3 10$ ✓

The solution is 10.

32. $\log_5 64 - \log_5 \frac{8}{3} + \log_5 2 = \log_5 4p$

$\log_5 \frac{64 \cdot 2}{\frac{8}{3}} = \log_5 4p$

$\log_5 \frac{64 \cdot 2 \cdot 3}{8} = \log_5 4p$

$\log_5 48 = \log_5 4p$

$48 = 4p$

$12 = p$

Check: $\log_5 64 - \log_5 \frac{8}{3} + \log_5 2 \overset{?}{=} \log_5(4 \cdot 12)$

$\log_5 \frac{64 \cdot 2}{\frac{8}{3}} \overset{?}{=} \log_5 48$

$\log_5 48 = \log_5 48$ ✓

The solution is 12.

33. $\log_a 4n - 2 \log_a x = \log_a x$

$\log_a 4n = 3 \log_a x$

$\log_a 4n = \log_a x^3$

$4n = x^3$

$n = \frac{x^3}{4}$

34. $\log_b 8 + 3 \log_b n = 3 \log_b(x - 1)$

$\log_b 8 + \log_b n^3 = \log_b(x - 1)^3$

$\log_b(8 \cdot n^3) = \log_b(x - 1)^3$

$8n^3 = (x - 1)^3$

$2n = x - 1$

$n = \frac{1}{2}(x - 1)$

35. False; $\log_2(2^2 + 2^3) = \log_2 12$,

$\log_2 2^2 + \log_2 2^3 = 2 + 3$ or 5, and $\log_2 12 \neq 5$, since $2^5 \neq 12$.

36. True; $n \log_b x + m \log_b x \overset{?}{=} (n + m) \log_b x$

$\log_b x^n + \log_b x^m \overset{?}{=} (n + m) \log_b x$ Power Property of Logarithms

$\log_b(x^n \cdot x^m) \overset{?}{=} (n + m) \log_b x$ Product Property of Logarithms

$\log_b(x^{n + m}) \overset{?}{=} (n + m) \log_b x$ Product of Powers Property

$(n + m) \log_b x = (n + m) \log_b x$ ✓   Power Property of Logarithms

37. Let x be the amplitude of the San Francisco earthquake. Then $100x$ is the amplitude of the Alaskan earthquake.

$\log_{10} 100x - \log_{10} x = \log_{10} \frac{100x}{x}$

$= \log_{10} 100$

$= 2$

The difference is 2.

38. $E = 1.4(\log_{10} C_2 - \log_{10} C_1)$

$E = 1.4 \log_{10} \frac{C_2}{C_1}$

39. Let $C_1 = x$ and $C_2 = 2x$.

$E = 1.4 \log_{10} \frac{C_2}{C_1}$

$E = 1.4 \log_{10} \frac{2x}{x}$

$= 1.4 \log_{10} 2$

≈ 0.4214

About 0.4214 kilocalorie per gram are needed.

40. Let $C_1 = x$ and $C_2 = 4x$.

$E = 1.4 \log_{10} \frac{c_2}{c_1}$

$E = 1.4 \log_{10} \frac{4x}{x}$

$= 1.4 \log_{10} 4$

$\approx 1.4 \cdot 0.3010$

≈ 0.8429

About 0.8429 kilocalorie per gram are needed.

41. $10 \log_{10} 2R - 10 \log_{10} R = 10(\log_{10} 2R - \log_{10} R)$

$= 10 \log_{10} \frac{2R}{R}$

$= 10 \log_{10} 2$

$\approx 10 \cdot 0.3010$

≈ 3.010

The increase will be about 3 decibels.

42. $10 \log_{10} R - 10 \log_{10} \frac{R}{2}$

$= 10\left(\log_{10} R - \log_{10} \frac{R}{2}\right)$

$= 10 \log_{10} \frac{R}{\frac{R}{2}}$

$= 10 \log_{10} 2$

$\approx 10 \cdot 0.3010$

≈ 3.010

The decrease will be about 3 decibels.

43. About 95 decibels; $L = 10 \log_{10} R$, where L is the loudness of the sound in decibels and R is the relative intensity of the sound. Since the crowd increases by a factor of 3, we assume that the intensity also increases by a factor of 3. Thus, we need to find the loudness of $3R$.

$L = 10 \log_{10} 3R$

$L = 10(\log_{10} 3 + \log_{10} R)$

$L = 10 \log_{10} 3 + 10 \log_{10} R$

$L \approx 10(0.4771) + 90$

$L \approx 4.771 + 90$ or about 95 decibels

44. If L is the measured brightness of Sirius then $100L$ is the measured brightness of the moon.

$$\left(6 - 2.5 \log_{10} \frac{L}{L_0}\right) - \left(6 - 2.5 \log_{10} \frac{100L}{L_0}\right)$$

$$= 6 - 2.5 \log_{10} \frac{L}{L_0} - 6 + 2.5 \log_{10} \frac{100L}{L_0}$$

$$= 2.5 \log_{10} \frac{100L}{L_0} - 2.5 \log_{10} \frac{L}{L_0}$$

$$= 2.5\left(\log_{10} \frac{100L}{L_0} - \log_{10} \frac{L}{L_0}\right)$$

$$= 2.5 \log_{10} \frac{\frac{100L}{L_0}}{\frac{L}{L_0}}$$

$$= 2.5 \log_{10} 100$$

$$= 2.5 \cdot 2$$

$$= 5$$

45. If L is the measured brightness of Neptune then $1000L$ is the measured brightness of Saturn.

$$\left(6 - 2.5 \log_{10} \frac{L}{L_0}\right) - \left(6 - 2.5 \log_{10} \frac{1000L}{L_0}\right)$$

$$= 6 - 2.5 \log_{10} \frac{L}{L_0} - 6 + 2.5 \log_{10} \frac{1000L}{L_0}$$

$$= 2.5 \log_{10} \frac{1000L}{L_0} - 2.5 \log_{10} \frac{L}{L_0}$$

$$= 2.5\left(\log_{10} \frac{1000L}{L_0} - \log_{10} \frac{L}{L_0}\right)$$

$$= 2.5 \log_{10} \frac{\frac{1000L}{L_0}}{\frac{L}{L_0}}$$

$$= 2.5 \log_{10} 1000$$

$$= 2.5 \cdot 3$$

$$= 7.5$$

46. about 22; See students' work.

47. Let $b^x = m$ and $b^y = n$. Then $\log_b m = x$ and $\log_b n = y$.

$$\frac{b^x}{b^y} = \frac{m}{n}$$

$b^{x-y} = \dfrac{m}{n}$ Quotient Property

$\log_b b^{x-y} = \log_b \dfrac{m}{n}$ Property of Equality for Logarithmic Equations

$x - y = \log_b \dfrac{m}{n}$ Inverse Property of Exponents and Logarithms

$\log_b m - \log_b n = \log_b \dfrac{m}{n}$ Replace x with $\log_b m$ and y with $\log_b n$.

48. Since logarithms are exponents, the properties of logarithms are similar to the properties of exponents. The Product Property states that to multiply two powers that have the same base, add the exponents. Similarly, the logarithm of a product is the sum of the logarithms of its factors. The Quotient Property states that to divide two powers that have the same base, subtract their exponents. Similarly, the logarithm of a quotient is the difference of the logarithms of the numerator and the denominator. The Power Property states that to find the power of a power, multiply the exponents. Similarly, the logarithm of a power is the product of the logarithm and the exponent. Answers should include the following.

- Quotient Property:

$\log_2\left(\dfrac{32}{8}\right) = \log_2\left(\dfrac{2^5}{2^3}\right)$ Replace 32 with 2^5 and 8 with 2^3.

$= \log_2 2^{(5-3)}$ Quotient of Powers

$= 5 - 3$ or 2 Inverse Property of Exponents and Logarithms.

$\log_2 32 - \log_2 8 = \log_2 2^5 - \log_2 2^3$

Replace 32 with 2^5 and 8 with 2^3.

$= 5 - 3$ or 2

Inverse property of exponents and logarithms.

So, $\log_2\left(\dfrac{32}{8}\right) = \log_2 32 - \log_2 8.$

- Power Property:

$\log_3 9^4 = \log_3 (3^2)^4$ Replace 9 with 3^2.

$= \log_3 3^{(2 \cdot 4)}$ Power of a Power

$= 2 \cdot 4$ or 8 Inverse Property of Exponents and Logarithms

$4 \log_3 9 = (\log_3 9) \cdot 4$ Commutative Property($\times 6$)

$= (\log_3 3^2) \cdot 4$ Replace 9 with 3^2.

$= 2 \cdot 4$ or 8 Inverse Property of Exponents and Logarithms

So, $\log_3 9^4 = 4 \log_3 9.$

- The Product of Powers Property and Product Property of Logarithms both involve the addition of exponents, since logarithms are exponents.

49. A; $2 \log_5 12 - \log_5 8 - 2 \log_5 3$

$= \log_5 12^2 - \log_5 8 - \log_5 3^2$

$= \log_5 144 - \log_5 8 - \log_5 9$

$= \log_5 \dfrac{144}{8} - \log_5 9$

$= \log_5 18 - \log_5 9$

$= \log_5 \dfrac{18}{9}$ or $\log_5 2$

50. Let $b^x = m$, then $\log_b m = x$.

$(b^x)^p = m^p$

$b^{xp} = m^p$ Product of Powers

$\log_b b^{xp} = \log_b m^p$ Property of Equality for Logarithmic Equations

$xp = \log_b m^p$ Inverse Property of Exponents and Logarithms

$p \log_b m = \log_b m^p$ Replace x with $\log_b m$.

Page 546   Maintain Your Skills

51. $\log_3 81 = \log_3 3^4$

$= 4$

52. $\log_9 \dfrac{1}{729} = \log_9 \dfrac{1}{9^3}$

$= \log_9 9^{-3}$

$= -3$

53. $\log_7 7^{2x} = 2x$

54. $3^{5n+3} = 3^{33}$
$5n + 3 = 33$
$5n = 30$
$n = 6$
Check: $3^{5(6)+3} \stackrel{?}{=} 3^{33}$
$3^{30+3} \stackrel{?}{=} 3^{33}$
$3^{33} = 3^{33}$ ✓

55. $7^a = 49^{-4}$
$7^a = (7^2)^{-4}$
$7^a = 7^{-8}$
$a = -8$
Check: $7^{-8} \stackrel{?}{=} 49^{-4}$
$\frac{1}{5,764,801} = \frac{1}{5,764,801}$ ✓

56. $3^{d+4} > 9^d$
$3^{d+4} > (3^2)^d$
$3^{d+4} > 3^{2d}$
$d + 4 > 2d$
$4 > d$
$d < 4$
Check: Test $d = 3$.
$3^{3+4} \stackrel{?}{>} 9^3$
$3^7 \stackrel{?}{>} 9^3$
$3^7 \stackrel{?}{>} 9^3$
$2187 > 729$

57. odd degree; The graph crosses the x-axis at three points, so it has 3 zeros.

58. even degree; The graph crosses the x-axis at four points, so it has 4 zeros.

59. $\frac{39a^3b^4}{13a^4b^3} = \frac{3a^3b^4}{a^4b^3}$
$= \frac{3b^4}{ab^3}$
$= \frac{3b}{a}$

60. $\frac{k+3}{5k\ell} \cdot \frac{10k\ell}{k+3} = \frac{10k\ell}{5k\ell}$
$= 2$

61. $\frac{5y-15z}{42x^2} \div \frac{y-3z}{14x} = \frac{5(y-3z)}{42x^2} \cdot \frac{14x}{y-3z}$
$= \frac{5}{42x^2} \cdot 14x$
$= \frac{5}{3x}$

62. Substituting $d = 150$ into $t = \frac{1}{4}\sqrt{d}$.
$t = \frac{1}{4}\sqrt{150}$
$= 3.06$
It would take about 3.06 seconds.

63. $\log_3 x = \log_3(2x - 1)$
$x = 2x - 1$
$-x = -1$
$x = 1$
Check: $\log_3 1 \stackrel{?}{=} \log_3(2 \cdot 1 - 1)$
$\log_3 1 = \log_3 1$ ✓

64. $\log_{10} 2^x = \log_{10} 32$
$2^x = 32$
$2^x = 2^5$
$x = 5$
Check: $\log_{10} 2^5 \stackrel{?}{=} \log_{10} 32$
$\log_{10} 32 = \log_{10} 32$ ✓

65. $\log_2 3x > \log_2 5$
$3x > 5$
$x > \frac{5}{3}$

Check: Test $x = 2$.
$\log_2 3(2) \stackrel{?}{>} \log_2 5$
$\log_2 6 \stackrel{?}{>} \log_2 5$
$6 > 5$ ✓

66. $\log_5(4x + 3) < \log_5 11$
$0 < 4x + 3 < 11$
$-3 < 4x < 8$
$\frac{-3}{4} < x < \frac{8}{4}$
$-\frac{3}{4} < x < 2$
Check: Test $x = 0$.
$\log_5(4 \cdot 0 + 3) \stackrel{?}{<} \log_5 11$
$\log_5 3 \stackrel{?}{<} \log_5 11$
$3 < 11$ ✓

10-4 Common Logarithms

Page 549 Check for Understanding

1. base 10; common logarithms

2. Sample answer: $5^x = 2$
$\log 5^x = \log 2$
$x \log 5 = \log 2$
$x = \frac{\log 2}{\log 5}$
$x \approx 0.4307$

3. A calculator is not programmed to find base 2 logarithms. To find $\log_2 7$ on a calculator, you have to first convert the expression to a common logarithm, which is the only type of logarithm a calculator is programmed to compute.

4. $\log 4 \approx 0.6021$

5. $\log 23 \approx 1.3617$

6. $\log 0.5 \approx -0.3010$

7. $9^x = 45$
$\log 9^x = \log 45$
$x \log 9 = \log 45$
$x = \frac{\log 45}{\log 9}$
$x \approx 1.7325$

8. $4^{5n} > 30$
$\log 4^{5n} > \log 30$
$5n \log 4 > \log 30$
$n > \frac{\log 30}{5 \log 4}$
$n > 0.4907$
$\{n \mid n > 0.4907\}$

9. $3.1^{a-3} = 9.42$
$\log 3.1^{a-3} = \log 9.42$
$(a - 3) \log 3.1 = \log 9.42$
$a \log 3.1 - 3 \log 3.1 = \log 9.42$
$a \log 3.1 = \log 9.42 + 3 \log 3.1$
$a = \frac{\log 9.42 + 3 \log 3.1}{\log 3.1}$
$a \approx 4.9824$

10. $11^{x^2} = 25.4$

$\log 11^{x^2} = \log 25.4$

$x^2 \log 11 = \log 25.4$

$x^2 = \frac{\log 25.4}{\log 11}$

≈ 1.3490

$x \approx \pm 1.1615$

11. $7^{t-2} = 5^t$

$\log 7^{t-2} = \log 5^t$

$(t - 2) \log 7 = t \log 5$

$t \log 7 - 2 \log 7 = t \log 5$

$t \log 7 - t \log 5 = 2 \log 7$

$t(\log 7 - \log 5) = 2 \log 7$

$t = \frac{2 \log 7}{\log 7 - \log 5}$

$t \approx 11.5665$

12. $4^{p-1} \leq 3^p$

$\log 4^{p-1} \leq \log 3^p$

$(p - 1) \log 4 \leq p \log 3$

$p \log 4 - \log 4 \leq p \log 3$

$p \log 4 - p \log 3 \leq \log 4$

$p(\log 4 - \log 3) \leq \log 4$

$p \leq \frac{\log 4}{\log 4 - \log 3}$

$p \leq 4.8188$

$\{p \mid p \leq 4.8188\}$

13. $\log_7 5 = \frac{\log_{10} 5}{\log_{10} 7}$

≈ 0.8271

14. $\log_3 42 = \frac{\log_{10} 42}{\log_{10} 3}$

≈ 3.4022

15. $\log_2 9 = \frac{\log_{10} 9}{\log_{10} 2}$

≈ 3.1699

16. Use the formula pH $= -\log[\text{H}+]$. Since Sandra must avoid foods with a pH less than 4.5,

$-\log[\text{H}+] \geq 4.5$

$\log[\text{H}+] \leq -4.5$

$[\text{H}+] \leq 10^{-4.5}$

$[\text{H}+] \leq 0.00003$

Sandra must eat foods with hydrogen ion concentration of at most 0.00003 mole per liter.

Page 549–551   Practice and Apply

17. $\log 5 \approx 0.6990$

18. $\log 12 \approx 1.0792$

19. $\log 7.2 \approx 0.8573$

20. $\log 2.3 \approx 0.3617$

21. $\log 0.8 \approx -0.0969$

22. $\log 0.03 \approx -1.5229$

23. pH $= -\log(1 \times 10^{-11})$

$= -(\log 1 + \log 10^{-11})$

$= -(\log 1 - 11 \log 10)$

$= 0 + 11$

$= 11$

24. pH $= -\log(6.3 \times 10^{-3})$

$= -(\log 6.3 + \log 10^{-3})$

$= -(\log 6.3 - 3 \log 10)$

$\approx -0.7993 + 3$

≈ 2.2

25. pH $= -\log(7.9 \times 10^{-3})$

$= -(\log 7.9 + \log 10^{-3})$

$= -(\log 7.9 - 3 \log 10)$

$\approx -0.8976 + 3$

≈ 2.1

26. pH $= -\log(3.16 \times 10^{-4})$

$= -(\log 3.16 + \log 10^{-4})$

$= -(\log 3.16 - 4 \log 10)$

$\approx -0.4997 + 4$

≈ 3.5

27. $6^x \geq 42$

$\log 6^x \geq \log 42$

$x \log 6 \geq \log 42$

$x \geq \frac{\log 42}{\log 6}$

$x \geq 2.0860$

$\{x \mid x \geq 2.0860\}$

28. $5^x = 52$

$\log 5^x = \log 52$

$x \log 5 = \log 52$

$x = \frac{\log 52}{\log 5}$

≈ 2.4550

29. $8^{2a} < 124$

$\log 8^{2a} < \log 124$

$2a \log 8 < \log 124$

$a < \frac{\log 124}{2 \log 8}$

$a < 1.590$

$\{a \mid a < 1.1590\}$

30. $4^{3p} = 10$

$\log 4^{3p} = \log 10$

$3p \log 4 = 1$

$p = \frac{1}{3 \log 4}$

$p \approx 0.5537$

31. $3^{n+2} = 14.5$

$\log 3^{n+2} = \log 14.5$

$(n + 2) \log 3 = \log 14.5$

$n \log 3 + 2 \log 3 = \log 14.5$

$n = \frac{\log 14.5 - 2 \log 3}{\log 3}$

≈ 0.4341

32. $9^{z-4} = 6.28$

$\log 9^{z-4} = \log 6.28$

$(z - 4) \log 9 = \log 6.28$

$z \log 9 - 4 \log 9 = \log 6.28$

$z = \frac{4 \log 9 + \log 6.28}{\log 9}$

≈ 4.8362

33. $8.2^{n-3} = 42.5$

$\log 8.2^{n-3} = \log 42.5$

$(n - 3) \log 8.2 = \log 42.5$

$n \log 8.2 - 3 \log 8.2 = \log 42.5$

$n = \frac{3 \log 8.2 + \log 42.5}{\log 8.2}$

≈ 4.7820

34. $2.1^{t-5} = 9.32$

$2.1^{t-5} = \log 9.32$

$(t - 5) \log 2.1 = \log 9.32$

$t \log 2.1 - 5 \log 2.1 = \log 9.32$

$t = \frac{5 \log 2.1 + \log 9.32}{\log 2.1}$

≈ 8.0086

35.
$$20^{x^2} = 70$$
$$\log 20^{x^2} = \log 70$$
$$x^2 \log 20 = \log 70$$
$$x^2 = \frac{\log 70}{\log 20}$$
$$\approx 1.4182$$
$$x \approx \pm 1.1909$$

36.
$$2^{x^2 - 3} = 15$$
$$\log_2 2^{x^2 - 3} = \log 15$$
$$(x^2 - 3) \log 2 = \log 15$$
$$x^2 \log 2 - 3 \log 2 = \log 15$$
$$x^2 = \frac{3 \log 2 + \log 15}{\log 2}$$
$$\approx 6.9069$$
$$x \approx \pm 2.6281$$

37.
$$8^{2n} > 52^{4n + 3}$$
$$\log 8^{2n} > \log 52^{4n + 3}$$
$$2n \log 8 > (4n + 3) \log 52$$
$$2n \log 8 > 4n \log 52 + 3 \log 52$$
$$2n \log 8 - 4n \log 52 > 3 \log 52$$
$$n(2 \log 8 - 4 \log 52) > 3 \log 52$$
$$n > \frac{3 \log 52}{2 \log 8 - 4 \log 52}$$
$$n > -1.0178$$
$$\{n \,|\, n > -1.0178\}$$

38.
$$2^{2x + 3} = 3^{3x}$$
$$\log 2^{2x + 3} = \log 3^{3x}$$
$$(2x + 3) \log 2 = 3x \log 3$$
$$2x \log 2 + 3 \log 2 = 3x \log 3$$
$$3x \log 3 - 2x \log 2 = 3 \log 2$$
$$x(3 \log 3 - 2 \log 2) = 3 \log 2$$
$$x = \frac{3 \log 2}{3 \log 3 - 2 \log 2}$$
$$x \approx 1.0890$$

39.
$$16^{d - 4} = 3^{3 - d}$$
$$\log 16^{d - 4} = \log 3^{3 - d}$$
$$(d - 4) \log 16 = (3 - d) \log 3$$
$$d \log 16 - 4 \log 16 = 3 \log 3 - d \log 3$$
$$d \log 16 + d \log 3 = 3 \log 3 + 4 \log 16$$
$$d(\log 16 + \log 3) = 3 \log 3 + 4 \log 16$$
$$d = \frac{3 \log 3 + 4 \log 16}{\log 16 + \log 3}$$
$$d \approx 3.7162$$

40.
$$7^{p + 2} \leq 13^{5 - p}$$
$$\log 7^{p + 2} \leq \log 13^{5 - p}$$
$$(p + 2) \log 7 \leq (5 - p) \log 13$$
$$p \log 7 + 2 \log 7 \leq 5 \log 13 - p \log 13$$
$$p \log 7 + p \log 13 \leq 5 \log 13 - 2 \log 7$$
$$p(\log 7 + \log 13) \leq 5 \log 13 - 2 \log 7$$
$$p \leq \frac{5 \log 13 - 2 \log 7}{\log 7 + \log 13}$$
$$p \leq 1.9803$$
$$\{p \,|\, p \leq 1.9803\}$$

41.
$$5^{5y - 2} = 2^{2y + 1}$$
$$\log 5^{5y - 2} = \log 2^{2y + 1}$$
$$(5y - 2) \log 5 = (2y + 1) \log 2$$
$$5y \log 5 - 2 \log 5 = 2y \log 2 + \log 2$$
$$5y \log 5 - 2y \log 2 = 2 \log 5 + \log 2$$
$$y(5 \log 5 - 2 \log 2) = 2 \log 5 + \log 2$$
$$y = \frac{2 \log 5 + \log 2}{5 \log 5 - 2 \log 2}$$
$$y \approx 0.5873$$

42.
$$8^{2x - 5} = 5^{x + 1}$$
$$\log 8^{2x - 5} = \log 5^{x + 1}$$
$$(2x - 5) \log 8 = (x + 1) \log 5$$
$$2x \log 8 - 5 \log 8 = x \log 5 + \log 5$$
$$2x \log 8 - x \log 5 = 5 \log 8 + \log 5$$
$$x(2 \log 8 - \log 5) = 5 \log 8 + \log 5$$
$$x = \frac{5 \log 8 + \log 5}{2 \log 8 - \log 5}$$
$$x \approx 4.7095$$

43.
$$2^n = \sqrt{3^{n - 2}}$$
$$(2^n)^2 = (\sqrt{3^{n - 2}})^2$$
$$(2^n)^2 = (\sqrt{3^{n - 2}})^2$$
$$2^{2n} = 3^{n - 2}$$
$$\log 2^{2n} = \log 3^{n - 2}$$
$$2n \log 2 = (n - 2) \log 3$$
$$2n \log 2 = n \log 3 - 2 \log 3$$
$$2n \log 2 - n \log 3 = -2 \log 3$$
$$n(2 \log 2 - \log 3) = -2 \log 3$$
$$n = \frac{2 \log 3}{\log 3 - 2 \log 2}$$
$$n \approx -7.6377$$

44.
$$4^x = \sqrt{5^{x + 2}}$$
$$(4^x)^2 = (5^{x + 2})^2$$
$$4^{2x} = 5^{x + 2}$$
$$\log 4^{2x} = \log 5^{x + 2}$$
$$2x \log 4 = (x + 2) \log 5$$
$$2x \log 4 = x \log 5 + 2 \log 5$$
$$2x \log 4 - x \log 5 = 2 \log 5$$
$$x(2 \log 4 - \log 5) = 2 \log 5$$
$$x = \frac{2 \log 5}{2 \log 4 - \log 5}$$
$$\approx 2.7674$$

45. $\log_2 13 = \frac{\log_{10} 13}{\log_{10} 2}$
$$\approx 3.7004$$

46. $\log_5 20 = \frac{\log_{10} 20}{\log_{10} 5}$
$$\approx 1.8614$$

47. $\log_7 3 = \frac{\log_{10} 3}{\log_{10} 7}$
$$\approx 0.5646$$

48. $\log_3 8 = \frac{\log_{10} 8}{\log_{10} 3}$
$$\approx 1.8928$$

49. $\log_4 (1.6)^2 = 2 \log_4 1.6$
$$= \frac{2 \log_{10} 1.6}{\log_{10} 4}$$
$$\approx 0.6781$$

50. $\log_6 \sqrt{5} = \log_6 5^{\frac{1}{2}}$
$$= \frac{1}{2} \log_6 5$$
$$= \frac{0.5 \log_{10} 5}{\log_{10} 6}$$
$$= 0.4491$$

51. $\text{pH} = 6.0$
$6.0 = -\log[\text{H}+]$
$-6.0 = \log[\text{H}+]$
$10^{-6.0} = [\text{H}+]$
$0.000001 = [\text{H}+]$

$\text{pH} = 9.0$
$9.0 = -\log[\text{H}+]$
$-9.0 = \log[\text{H}+]$
$10^{-9.0} = [\text{H}+]$
$0.000000001 = [\text{H}+]$

The water's hydrogen ion concentration is between 0.000000001 and 0.000001 mole per liter.

52. Substituting $M = 6.3$ into the formula for Richter magnitude $M = \log_{10} x$,
$6.3 = \log_{10} x$
$x = 10^{6.3}$
$x = 1{,}995{,}262.$
Substituting 50 times this value into the formula,
$M = \log_{10}(50 \cdot 1{,}995{,}262)$
$\quad = \log_{10} 50 + \log_{10} 1{,}995{,}262$
$\quad \approx 8.$

53. Sirius, since its apparent magnitude of -1.44 is less than that of Vega's at 0.03.

54. Substituting for Sirius the values $d = 2.64$ and $m = -1.44$ into the formula
$M = m + 5 - d \log d$,
$M = -1.44 + 5 - 5 \log 2.64$
$M \approx 1.45.$
Substituting for Vega the values $d = 7.76$ and $m = 0.03$ into the formula $M = m + 5 - d \log d$,
$M = 0.03 + 5 - 5 \log 7.76$
$M \approx 0.58.$

55. Vega has a lower absolute magnitude and is therefore the brighter star.

56a. $\log_2 8 = \log_2 2^3$
$\quad = 3 \log_2 2$
$\quad = 3$
$\log_8 2 = \log_8 8^{\frac{1}{3}}$
$\quad = \frac{1}{3} \log_8 8$
$\quad = \frac{1}{3}$

56b. $\log_9 27 = \log_9(3 \cdot 9)$
$\quad = \log_9 3 + \log_9 9$
$\quad = \log_9 9^{\frac{1}{2}} + \log_9 9$
$\quad = \frac{1}{2} \log_9 9 + \log_9 9$
$\quad = \frac{1}{2} + 1$
$\quad = \frac{3}{2}$
$\log_{27} 9 = \log_{27} \frac{27}{3}$
$\quad = \log_{27} 27 - \log_{27} 3$
$\quad = \log_{27} 27 - \log_{27} 27^{\frac{1}{3}}$
$\quad = \log_{27} 27 - \frac{1}{3} \log_{27} 27$
$\quad = 1 - \frac{1}{3}$
$\quad = \frac{2}{3}$

56c. conjecture: $\log_a b = \frac{1}{\log_b a}$;
proof:

$\log_a b \stackrel{?}{=} \frac{1}{\log_b a}$	Original statement
$\frac{\log_b b}{\log_b a} \stackrel{?}{=} \frac{1}{\log_b a}$	Change of Base Formula
$\frac{1}{\log_b a} = \frac{1}{\log_b a}$ ✓	Inverse Property of Exponents and Logarithms

57. Substitute into the formula $A = P\left(1 + \frac{r}{n}\right)^{nt}$ the values $A = 125, P = 100, r = 0.06$ and $n = 4$.
$125 = 100\left(1 + \frac{0.06}{4}\right)$
$1.25 = 1.015^{4t}$
$\log 1.25 = \log 1.015^{4t}$
$\log 1.25 = 4t \log 1.015$
$\frac{\log 1.25}{4 \log 1.015} = t$
$3.75 \approx t$
about 3.75 years or 3 years and 9 months

58. Substitute into the formula $A = P\left(1 + \frac{r}{n}\right)^{nt}$ the values $A = 200, P = 100, r = 0.06$ and $n = 4$.
$200 = 100\left(1 + \frac{0.06}{4}\right)^{4t}$
$2 = 1.015^{4t}$
$\log 2 = \log 1.015^{4t}$
$\log 2 = 4t \log 1.015$
$\frac{\log 2}{4 \log 1.015} = t$
$11.64 \approx t$
about 11.64 years or 11 years and 7.5 months

59. Comparisons between substances of different acidities are more easily distinguished on a logarithmic scale. Answers should include the following.
- Sample answer:
  Tomatoes: 6.3×10^{-5} mole per liter
  Milk: 3.98×10^{-7} mole per liter
  Eggs: 1.58×10^{-8} mole per liter
- Those measurements correspond to pH measurements of 5 and 4, indicating a weak acid and a stronger acid. On the logarithmic scale we can see the difference in these acids, whereas on a normal scale, these hydrogen ion concentrations would appear nearly the same. For someone who has to watch the acidity of the foods they eat, this could be the difference between an enjoyable meal and heartburn.

60. A; $\log 10^3 \stackrel{?}{>} \log 10^2$
$3 \log 10 \stackrel{?}{>} 2 \log 10$
$3 > 2$

61. C; $2^4 = 3^x$
$16 = 3^x$
$\log 16 = \log 3^x$
$\log 16 = x \log 3$
$\frac{\log 16}{\log 3} = x$
$2.5237 \approx x$

62. $\log_7 16 = \log_7 2^4$
$= 4 \log_7 2$
$\approx 4 \cdot 0.3562$ or 1.4248

63. $\log_7 27 = \log_7 3^3$
$= 3 \log_7 3$
$\approx 3 \cdot 0.5646$ or 1.6938

64. $\log_7 36 = \log_7(4 \cdot 9)$
$= \log_7(2^2 \cdot 3^2)$
$= \log_7 2^2 + \log_7 3^2$
$= 2 \log_7 2 + 2 \log_7 3$
$\approx 2 \cdot 0.352 + 2 \cdot 0.5646$ or 1.8416

65. $\log_4 r = 3$
$r = 4^3$
$r = 64$

66. $\log_8 z \le -2$
$0 < z \le 8^{-2}$
$0 < z \le \frac{1}{64}$
$\left[z \middle| 0 < z \le \frac{1}{64} \right]$

67. $\log_3(4x - 5) = 5$
$4x - 5 = 3^5$
$4x - 5 = 243$
$4x = 248$
$x = 62$

68.
$$\begin{array}{r|rrrr} -2 & 1 & 0 & 6 & -2 \\ & & -2 & 4 & -20 \\ \hline & 1 & -2 & 10 & -22 \end{array}$$
$f(-2) = -22$

69. $3d^2 + 2d - 8 = (3d - 4)(d + 2)$

70. $42pq - 35p + 18q - 15 = (7p + 3)(6q - 5)$

71. $13xyz + 3x^2z + 4k$
This expression is prime since no factor of the third term can be a factor of the first term.

72. $\log_2 3 = x$
The base is 2 and the exponent is x, so the equivalent exponential is $2^x = 3$.

73. $\log_3 x = 2$
The base is 3 and the exponent is 2, so the equivalent exponential is $3^2 = x$.

74. $\log_5 125 = 3$
The base is 5 and the exponent is 3, so the equivalent exponential equation is $5^3 = 125$.

75. $5^x = 45$
The base is 5 and the exponential is x, so the equivalent logarithmic equation is $\log_5 45 = x$.

76. $7^3 = x$
The base is 7 and the exponent is 3, so the equivalent logarithmic equation is $\log_7 x = 3$.

77. $b^y = x$
The base is b and the exponent is y, so the equivalent logarithmic equation is $\log_b x = y$.

Page 553   Graphing Calculator Investigation (Follow-Up of Lesson 10-4)

1. Graph $y = 3.5^{x+2}$ as Y1 and $y = 1.75^{x+3}$ as Y2. The graphs intersect where x is about -1.2. The solution is -1.2.

2. Graph $y = -3^{x+4}$ as Y1 and $y = -0.5^{2x+3}$ as Y2. The graphs intersect where x is about -2.6. The solution is -2.6.

3. Graph $y = 6^{2-x} - 4 = -0.25^{x-2.5}$ as Y1 and $y = -0.25^{x-2.5}$ as Y2. The graphs intersect where x is about 1.8. The solution is 1.8.

4. Graph $y = 3^x - 4$ as Y1 and $y = 5^{\frac{x}{2}}$ as Y2. The graphs intersect where x is 2. The solution is 2.

5. Graph $y = \log_2 3x$ as Y1 and $y = \log_3(2x + 2)$ as Y2. The graphs intersect where x is about 0.7. The solution is 0.7.

6. Graph $y \le 2^{x-2}$ and $y \ge 0.5^{x-3}$. The regions overlap for $x \ge 2.5$. The solution is $\{x \mid x \ge 2.5\}$.

7. Graph $y \le \log_3(3x - 5)$ and $y \ge \log_3(x + 7)$. The regions overlap for $x \ge 6$. The solution set is $\{x \mid x \ge 6\}$.

8. Graph $y \ge 5^{x+3}$ and $y \le 2^{x+4}$. The regions overlap for $x < -2.24$. The solution set is $\{x \mid x < -2.24\}$.

9. Graph $y \ge \log_2 2x$ and $y \le \log_4(x + 3)$. The regions overlap for $0 < x \le 1$. The solution set is $\{x \mid x \; 0 < x \le 1\}$.

10-5   Base e and Natural Logarithms

Page 557   Check for Understanding

1. The number e is the base of natural logarithms.

2. Sample answer: $e^x = 8$

3. Elsu; Colby tried to write each side as a power of 10. Since the base of the natural logarithmic function is e, he should have written each side as a power of e; $10^{\ln 4x} \ne 4x$.

4. KEYSTROKES: $\boxed{\text{2nd}}$ $[e^x]$ 6 $\boxed{\text{ENTER}}$
$e^6 \approx 403.4288$

5. KEYSTROKES: $\boxed{\text{2nd}}$ $[e^x]$ -3.4 $\boxed{\text{ENTER}}$
≈ 0.0334

6. KEYSTROKES: $\boxed{\text{LN}}$ 1.2 $\boxed{\text{ENTER}}$
$\ln 1.2 \approx 0.1823$

7. KEYSTROKES: $\boxed{\text{LN}}$ 0.1 $\boxed{\text{ENTER}}$
$\ln 0.1 \approx -2.3026$

8. $e^x = 4 \to \log_e 4 = x$
$\ln 4 = x$

9. $\ln 1 = 0 \to \log_e 1 = 0$
$e^0 = 1$

10. $e^{\ln 3} = 3$

11. $\ln e^{5x} = 5x$

12. $e^x > 30$
$\ln e^x > \ln 30$
$x > \ln 30$
$x > 3.4012$

13. $2e^x - 5 = 1$
$2e^x = 6$
$e^x = 3$
$x = \ln 3$
$x \approx 1.0986$

14. $3 + e^{-2x} = 8$

$\quad e^{-2x} = 5$

$\quad \ln e^{-2x} = \ln 5$

$\quad -2x = \ln 5$

$\quad x = \frac{\ln 5}{-2}$

$\quad x \approx -0.8047$

15. $\ln x < 6$

$\quad 0 < x < e^6$

$\quad 0 < x < 403.4288$

16. $2 \ln 3x + 1 = 5$

$\quad 2 \ln 3x = 4$

$\quad \ln 3x = 2$

$\quad e^{\ln 3x} = e^2$

$\quad 3x = e^2$

$\quad x = \frac{e^2}{3}$

$\quad x \approx 2.4630$

17. $\ln x^2 = 9$

$\quad e^{\ln x^2} = e^9$

$\quad x^2 = e^9$

$\quad x \approx \pm\sqrt{e^9}$ or ± 90.0171

18. $\quad P = 101.3 e^{-\frac{h}{26,200}}$

$\quad \frac{P}{101.3} = e^{-\frac{h}{26,200}}$

$\quad \ln \frac{P}{101.3} = \ln e^{-\frac{h}{26,200}}$

$\quad \ln \frac{P}{101.3} = -\frac{h}{26,200}$

$\quad h = -26,200 \ln \frac{P}{101.3}$

19. $h = -26,200 \ln \frac{P}{101.3}$

$\quad h = -26,200 \ln \frac{57}{101.3}$

$\quad \approx 15,065.9208$

The height is about 15,066 ft.

Pages 557–559   Practice and Apply

20. $e^4 \approx 54.5982$

21. $e^5 \approx 148.4132$

22. $e^{-1.2} \approx 0.3012$

23. $e^{0.5} \approx 1.6487$

24. $\ln 3 \approx 1.0986$

25. $\ln 10 \approx 2.3026$

26. $\ln 5.42 \approx 1.6901$

27. $\ln 0.03 \approx -3.5066$

28. $A = Pe^{rt}$

$\quad A = 150 e^{0.045 \cdot 5}$

$\quad A = 150 e^{0.2}$

$\quad A \approx 183.21$

You will have \$183.21.

29. $\ln \frac{I_0}{I} = 0.014d$

$\quad \ln \frac{I_0}{\frac{I_0}{2}} = 0.014d$

$\quad \ln 2 = 0.014d$

$\quad d = \frac{\ln 2}{0.014}$

$\quad d \approx 49.5$

At a depth of about 49.5 cm underwater, the intensity of light is half the intensity of light in the atomosphere.

30. $e^{-x} = 5 \rightarrow -x = \log_e 5$

$\quad -x = \ln 5$

31. $e^2 = 6x \rightarrow 2 = \log_e 6x$

$\quad 2 = \ln 6x$

32. $\ln e = 1 \rightarrow \log_e e = 1$

$\quad e^1 = e$

33. $\ln 5.2 = x \rightarrow \log_e 5.2 = x$

$\quad e^x = 5.2$

34. $e^{\ln 0.2} = 0.2$

35. $e^{\ln y} = y$

36. $\ln e^{-4x} = -4x$

37. $\ln e^{45} = 45$

38. $3e^x + 1 = 5$

$\quad 3e^x = 4$

$\quad e^x = \frac{4}{3}$

$\quad \ln e^x = \ln \frac{4}{3}$

$\quad x = \ln \frac{4}{3}$

$\quad x \approx 0.2877$

39. $2e^x - 1 = 0$

$\quad 2e^x = 1$

$\quad e^x = \frac{1}{2}$

$\quad \ln e^x = \ln 0.5$

$\quad x = \ln 0.5$

$\quad x \approx -0.6931$

40. $\quad e^x < 4.5$

$\quad \ln e^x < \ln 4.5$

$\quad x < \ln 4.5$

$\quad x < 1.5041$

41. $\quad e^x > 1.6$

$\quad \ln e^x > \ln 1.6$

$\quad x > \ln 1.6$

$\quad x > 0.4700$

42. $-3e^{4x} + 11 = 2$

$\quad -3e^{4x} = -9$

$\quad e^{4x} = 3$

$\quad \ln e^{4x} = \ln 3$

$\quad 4x = \ln 3$

$\quad x = \frac{\ln 3}{4}$

$\quad x \approx 0.2747$

43. $8 + 3e^{3x} = 26$

$\quad 3e^{3x} = 18$

$\quad e^{3x} = 6$

$\quad \ln e^{3x} = \ln 6$

$\quad 3x = \ln 6$

$\quad x = \frac{\ln 6}{3}$

$\quad x \approx 0.5973$

44. $\quad e^{5x} \geq 25$

$\quad \ln e^{5x} \geq \ln 25$

$\quad 5x \geq \ln 25$

$\quad x \geq \frac{\ln 25}{5}$

$\quad x \geq 0.6438$

45. $e^{-2x} \leq 7$

$\ln e^{-2x} \leq \ln 7$

$-2x \leq \ln 7$

$x \geq -\frac{\ln 7}{2}$

$x \geq -0.9730$

46. $\ln 2x = 4$

$e^{\ln 2x} = e^4$

$2x = e^4$

$x = \frac{e^4}{2}$

$x \approx 27.2991$

47. $\ln 3x = 5$

$e^{\ln 3x} = e^5$

$3x = e^5$

$x = \frac{e^5}{3}$

$x \approx 49.4711$

48. $\ln(x + 1) = 1$

$e^{\ln(x+1)} = e^1$

$x + 1 = e$

$x = e - 1$

$x \approx 1.7183$

49. $\ln(x - 7) = 2$

$e^{\ln(x-7)} = e^2$

$x - 7 = e^2$

$x = e^2 + 7$

$x \approx 14.3891$

50. $\ln x + \ln 3x = 12$

$\ln(x \cdot 3x) = 12$

$\ln 3x^2 = 12$

$e^{\ln 3x^2} = e^{12}$

$3x^2 = e^{12}$

$x^2 = \frac{e^{12}}{3}$

$x = \pm\sqrt{\frac{e^{12}}{3}}$

$x \approx \pm 232.9197$

Since $\ln(-232.9197)$ is undefined, the only solution is about 232.9197.

51. $\ln 4x + \ln x = 9$

$\ln(4x \cdot x) = 9$

$\ln 4x^2 = 9$

$e^{\ln 4x^2} = e^9$

$4x^2 = e^9$

$x^2 = \frac{e^9}{4}$

$x = \pm\sqrt{\frac{e^9}{4}}$

$x = \pm 45.0086$

Since $\ln(-45.0086)$ is undefined, the only solution is 45.0086.

52. $\ln(x^2 + 12) = \ln x + \ln 8$

$\ln(x^2 + 12) = \ln(x \cdot 8)$

$\ln(x^2 + 12) = \ln 8x$

$x^2 + 12 = 8x$

$x^2 - 8x + 12 = 0$

$(x - 6)(x - 2) = 0$

$x - 6 = 0 \quad \text{or} \quad x - 2 = 0$

$x = 6 \qquad\qquad x = 2$

53. $\ln x + \ln(x + 4) = \ln 5$

$\ln[x(x + 4)] = \ln 5$

$x(x + 4) = 5$

$x^2 + 4x = 5$

$x^2 + 4x - 5 = 0$

$(x + 5)(x - 1) = 0$

$x + 5 = 0 \quad \text{or} \quad x - 1 = 0$

$x = -5 \qquad\qquad x = 1$

Since $\ln(-5)$ is undefined, the only solution is 1.

54. $A = Pe^{rt}$

$200 = 100e^{0.035t}$

$2 = e^{0.035t}$

$\ln 2 = \ln e^{0.035t}$

$\ln 2 = 0.035t$

$t = \frac{\ln 2}{0.035}$

$t \approx 19.8$

It will take about 19.8 years.

55. $A = Pe^{rt}$

$2P = Pe^{\frac{r}{100}t}$

$2 = e^{\frac{r}{100}t}$

$\ln 2 = \ln e^{\frac{r}{100}t}$

$\ln 2 = \frac{r}{100}t$

$t = \frac{100 \ln 2}{r}$

56. The numerator in the equation found in Exercise 55, or $100 \ln 2$, is approximately 70.

$100 \ln 2 \approx 69.31$

≈ 70

57. $3P = Pe^{\frac{rt}{100}}$

$3 = e^{\frac{rt}{100}}$

$\ln 3 = \ln e^{\frac{rt}{100}}$

$\ln 3 = \frac{rt}{100}$

$t = \frac{100 \ln 3}{r}$

$t \approx \frac{110}{r}$

58. $P = 6e^{0.02t}$

$P = 6e^{0.02 \cdot 10}$

$P \approx 7.3284$

In 2010, the population will be about 7.33 billion.

59. $P = 6e^{0.02t}$

$18 = 6e^{0.02t}$

$3 = e^{0.02t}$

$\ln 3 = \ln e^{0.02t}$

$\ln 3 = 0.02t$

$t = \frac{\ln 3}{0.02}$

$t \approx 54.9306$

The population will remain at 18 billion or less for about 55 more years.

60. $H = \frac{P}{1 + (P - S)e^{-0.35t}}$

$H = \frac{1600}{1 + (1600 - 2)e^{-0.35 \cdot 10}}$

$H = \frac{1600}{1 + 1598e^{-3.5}}$

$H \approx 32.48$

After 10 minutes, about 32 students will have heard the rumor.

61.

$$P = \frac{P}{1 + (p - s)e^{-0.35t}}$$

$$800 = \frac{1600}{1 + (1600 - 2)e^{-0.35t}}$$

$$1 = \frac{2}{1 + 1598e^{-0.35t}}$$

$$1 + 1598e^{-0.35t} = 2$$

$$1598e^{-0.35t} = 1$$

$$e^{-0.35t} = \frac{1}{1598}$$

$$e^{0.35t} = 1598$$

$$\ln e^{0.35t} = \ln 1598$$

$$0.35t = \ln 1598$$

$$t = \frac{\ln 1598}{0.35}$$

$$t \approx 21.0757$$

Half of the students will have heard the rumor after about 21 minutes.

62. always;

$$\frac{\log x}{\log y} \overset{?}{=} \frac{\ln x}{\ln y} \qquad \text{Original statement}$$

$$\frac{\log x}{\log y} \overset{?}{=} \frac{\frac{\log x}{\log e}}{\frac{\log y}{\log e}} \qquad \text{Change of Base Formula}$$

$$\frac{\log x}{\log y} \overset{?}{=} \frac{\log x}{\log e} \cdot \frac{\log e}{\log y} \qquad \text{Multiply } \frac{\log x}{\log e} \text{ by the reciprocal of } \frac{\log y}{\log e}.$$

$$\frac{\log x}{\log y} = \frac{\log x}{\log y} \qquad \text{Simplify.}$$

63. The number e is used in the formula for continuously compounded interest, $A = Pe^{rt}$. Although no banks actually pay interest compounded continually, the equation is so accurate in computing the amount of money for quarterly compounding, or daily compounding, that it is often used for this purpose. Answers should include the following.

- If you know the annual interest rate r and the principal P, the value of the account after t years is calculated by multiplying P times e raised to the r times t power. Use a calculator to find the value of e^{rt}.
- If you know the value A you wish the account to achieve, the principal P, and the annual interest rate r, the time t needed to achieve this value is found by first taking the natural of A minus the natural logarithm of P. Then, divide this quantity by r.

64. B; $e^{x^2} = \frac{1}{(\sqrt{2})^x}$

For the four value values given, the two sides of the equation are the closest in value when $x = -0.35$.

65.

$$P(t) = 40e^{0.02t}$$

$$100 = 40e^{0.02t}$$

$$2.5 = e^{0.02t}$$

$$\ln 2.5 = \ln e^{0.02t}$$

$$\ln 2.5 = 0.02t$$

$$t = \frac{\ln 2.5}{0.02}$$

$$t \approx 45.81$$

The population will be 100 million in 1900 + 46 or 1946.

$$P(t) = 40e^{0.02t}$$

$$200 = 40e^{0.02t}$$

$$5 = e^{0.02t}$$

$$\ln 5 = \ln e^{0.02t}$$

$$\ln 5 = 0.02t$$

$$t = \frac{\ln 5}{0.02}$$

$$t \approx 80.47$$

The population will be 200 million in 1900 + 81 or 1981.

$$P(t) = 40e^{0.02t}$$

$$400 = 40e^{0.02t}$$

$$10 = e^{0.02t}$$

$$\ln 10 = \ln e^{0.02t}$$

$$\ln 10 = 0.02t$$

$$t = \frac{\ln 10}{0.02}$$

$$t \approx 115.13$$

The population will be 400 million in 1900 + 115 or 2015. It takes between 34 and 35 years for the population to double.

Page 559   Maintain Your Skills

66. $\log_4 68 = \frac{\log 68}{\log 4}$

≈ 3.0437

67. $\log_6 0.047 = \frac{\log 0.047}{\log 6}$

≈ -1.7065

68. $\log_{50} 23 = \frac{\log 23}{\log 50}$

≈ 0.8015

69.
$$\log_3(a + 3) + \log_3(a - 3) = \log_3 16$$
$$\log_3[(a + 3)(a - 3)] = \log_3 16$$
$$(a + 3)(a - 3) = 16$$
$$a^2 - 9 = 16$$
$$a^2 = 25$$
$$a = \pm 5$$

Check: $\log_3(-5 - 3)$ is undefined.
$$\log_3(5 + 3) + \log_3(5 - 3) \overset{?}{=} \log_3 16$$
$$\log_3 8 + \log_3 2 \overset{?}{=} \log_3 16$$
$$\log_3(8 \cdot 2) \overset{?}{=} \log_3 16$$
$$\log_3 16 = \log_3 16 \checkmark$$

The only solution is 5.

70.
$$\log_{11} 2 + 2\log_{11} x = \log_{11} 32$$
$$\log_{11} 2 + \log_{11} x^2 = \log_{11} 32$$
$$\log_{11} 2x^2 = \log_{11} 32$$
$$2x^2 = 32$$
$$x^2 = 16$$
$$x = \pm 4$$

Check: $\log_{11}(-4) \overset{?}{=}$ is undefined.
$$\log_{11} 2 + 2\log_{11} 4 \overset{?}{=} \log_{11} 32$$
$$\log_{11} 2 + \log_{11} 4^2 \overset{?}{=} \log_{11} 32$$
$$\log_{11}(2 \cdot 16) \overset{?}{=} \log_{11} 32$$
$$\log_{11} 32 = \log_{11} 32 \checkmark$$

The only solution is 4.

71. $mn = 4$ is an example of inverse variation. The constant of variation is 4.

72. $\frac{a}{b} = c$ is an example of joint variation, since it may also be written $a = bc$, where a varies as the product of b and c. The constant of variation is 1.

73. $y = -7x$ is an example of direct variation. The constant of variation is -7.

74. Since the parabola opens to the right, its equation is $x = a(y - k)^2 + h$. Since the focus is 5 inches from the vertex and the focus is at the origin, the coordinates of the vertex are $(-5, 0)$, which are also (h, k), so $h = -5$ and $k = 0$. Since the the length of the latus rectum is 20, $\frac{1}{a} = 20$ and $a = \frac{1}{20}$.

$$x = a(y - k)^2 + h$$
$$x = \frac{1}{20}(y - 0)^2 + (-5)$$
$$x = \frac{1}{20}y^2 - 5$$

75.
$$2^x = 10$$
$$\log 2^x = \log 10$$
$$x \log 2 = 1$$
$$x = \frac{1}{\log 2}$$
$$x \approx 3.32$$

76.
$$5^x = 12$$
$$\log 5^x = \log 12$$
$$x \log 5 = \log 12$$
$$x = \frac{\log 12}{\log 5}$$
$$x \approx 1.54$$

77.
$$6^x = 13$$
$$\log 6^x = \log 13$$
$$x \log 6 = \log 13$$
$$x = \frac{\log 13}{\log 6}$$
$$x \approx 1.43$$

78.
$$2(1 + 0.1)^x = 50$$
$$2(1.1)^x = 50$$
$$1.1^x = 25$$
$$\log 1.1^x = \log 25$$
$$x \log 1.1 = \log 25$$
$$x = \frac{\log 25}{\log 1.1}$$
$$x \approx 33.77$$

79.
$$10(1 + 0.25)^x = 200$$
$$10(1.25)^x = 200$$
$$1.25^x = 20$$
$$\log 1.25^x = \log 20$$
$$x \log 1.25 = \log 20$$
$$x = \frac{\log 20}{\log 1.25}$$
$$x \approx 13.43$$

80.
$$400(1 - 0.2)^x = 50$$
$$400(0.8)^x = 50$$
$$0.8^x = 0.125$$
$$\log 0.8^x = \log 0.125$$
$$x \log 0.8 = \log 0.125$$
$$x = \frac{\log 0.125}{\log 0.8}$$
$$x \approx 9.32$$

Page 559   Practice Quiz 2

1. $\log_4 5 = \frac{\log 5}{\log 4}$
≈ 1.1610

2. $\ln 3x = 2 \rightarrow e^2 = 3x$

3.
$$\log_2(9x + 5) = 2 + \log_2(x^2 - 1)$$
$$\log_2(9x + 5) - \log_2(x^2 - 1) = 2$$
$$\log_2 \frac{9x + 5}{x^2 - 1} = 2$$
$$\frac{9x + 5}{x^2 - 1} = 2^2$$
$$9x + 5 = 4(x^2 - 1)$$
$$9x + 5 = 4x^2 - 4$$
$$4x^2 - 4 - 9x - 5 = 0$$
$$4x^2 - 9x - 9 = 0$$
$$(4x + 3)(x - 3) = 0$$
$$x = -\frac{3}{4}, 3$$

However, $\log_2\left[9\left(-\frac{3}{4}\right) + 5\right] = \log_2\left(-\frac{27}{4} + 5\right)$
$$= \log_2\left(-\frac{7}{4}\right)$$

is undefined, so $-\frac{3}{4}$ is an extraneous solution. The only solution is 3.

4.
$$2^{x - 3} > 5$$
$$\log 2^{x - 3} > \log 5$$
$$(x - 3) \log 2 > \log 5$$
$$x \log 2 - 3 \log 2 > \log 5$$
$$x \log 2 > 3 \log 2 + \log 5$$
$$x > \frac{3 \log 2 + \log 5}{\log 2}$$
$$x > 5.3219$$

5.
$$2e^x - 1 = 7$$
$$2e^x = 8$$
$$e^x = 4$$
$$\ln e^x = \ln 4$$
$$x = \ln 4$$
$$x \approx 1.3863$$

10-6 Exponential Growth and Decay

Page 563   Check for Understanding

1. $y = a(1 + r)^t$, where $r > 0$ represents exponential growth and $r < 0$ represents exponential decay

2. Take the common logarithm of each side, use the Power Property to write $\log(1 + r)^t$ as $t \log(1 + r)$, and then divide each side by the quantity $\log(1 + r)$.

3. Sample answer: amount of caffeine in a person's body, assuming she drinks the same amount of coffee each day.

4. Decay; the value of k in the exponent is $-\frac{1}{250}$, a negative number.

5. Use the formula $P = 50e^{-\frac{t}{250}}$.
$$P = 50e^{-\frac{t}{250}}$$
$$P = 50e^{-\frac{100}{250}}$$
$$P = 50e^{-0.4}$$
$$P \approx 33.5$$

After 100 days, the power available will be about 33.5 watts.

6. Use the formula $P = 50e^{-\frac{t}{250}}$.

$$P = 50e^{-\frac{t}{250}}$$
$$10 = 50e^{-\frac{t}{250}}$$
$$0.2 = e^{-\frac{t}{250}}$$
$$\ln 0.2 = \ln e^{-\frac{t}{250}}$$
$$\ln 0.2 = \frac{-t}{250}$$
$$402 \approx t$$
$$-250 \ln 0.2 = t$$
$$402 \approx t$$

The statellite can continue to operate for about 402 days.

7. Use the formula $y = ae^{kt}$.

$$y = ae^{kt}$$
$$259{,}000 = 212{,}000e^{k \cdot 8}$$
$$1.2217 \approx e^{8k}$$
$$\ln e^{8k} \approx \ln 1.2217$$
$$8k \approx \ln 1.2217$$
$$k \approx \frac{\ln 1.2217}{8}$$
$$\approx 0.025$$

Thus, the exponential growth equation is $y = 212{,}000e^{0.025t}$.

8. $y = 212{,}000e^{0.025(20)}$
$y = 212{,}000e^{0.5}$
$y \approx 349{,}529$

In 2010, the population will be about 349,529 people.

9. C; Use the formula $y = a(1 - r)^t$.

$$y = a(1 - r)^t$$
$$y = 95(1 - 0.025)^{15}$$
$$y \approx 65$$

After 15 uses, the bar of soap weighs about 65 grams.

Pages 563–564 Practice and Apply

10. Use the formula $y = a(1 - r)^t$.

$$y = a(1 - r)^t$$
$$y = 2500(1 - 0.2)^2$$
$$y = 1600$$

In 5 years, the value of the computer will be $1600.

11. Use the formula $y = a(1 + r)^t$.

$$y = a(1 + r)^t$$
$$y = 85{,}000(1 + 0.05)^5$$
$$\approx 108{,}483.93$$

In 5 years, the condo will be worth at most $108,483.93.

12. Use the formula $y = ae^{-0.0856t}$.

$$y = ae^{-0.0856t}$$
$$\frac{a}{2} = ae^{-0.0856t}$$
$$0.5 = e^{-0.0856t}$$
$$\ln 0.5 = \ln e^{-0.0856t}$$
$$\ln 0.5 = -0.0856t$$
$$\frac{\ln 0.5}{0.0856} = t$$
$$-8.0975 \approx t$$

The half-life of this substance is about 8.1 days.

13. Use the formula $y = ae^{-0.00012t}$.

$$y = ae^{-0.00012t}$$
$$\frac{a}{12} = ae^{-0.00012t}$$
$$\frac{1}{12} = e^{-0.00012t}$$
$$\ln \frac{1}{12} = \ln e^{-0.00012t}$$
$$\ln \frac{1}{12} = -0.00012t$$
$$\frac{\ln \frac{1}{12}}{-0.00012} = t$$
$$20{,}708 \approx t$$

The bone is only about 21,000 years old, and dinosaurs died out 63,000,000 years ago. Thus, the bone is not a dinosaur bone.

14. Use the formula $y = ae^{-0.00012t}$.

$$y = ae^{-0.00012t}$$
$$0.005a = ae^{-0.00012t}$$
$$0.005 = e^{-0.00012t}$$
$$\ln 0.005 = \ln e^{-0.00012t}$$
$$\ln 0.005 = -0.00012t$$
$$\frac{\ln 0.005}{-0.00012} = t$$
$$44{,}153 \approx t$$

The person died more than 44,000 years ago.

15. Use the formula $y = ae^{kt}$.

$$y = ae^{kt}$$
$$2a = ae^{20k}$$
$$2 = e^{20k}$$
$$\ln 2 = \ln e^{20k}$$
$$\ln 2 = 20k$$
$$\frac{\ln 2}{20} = k$$
$$0.0347 \approx k$$

16. The exponential growth equation is $y = ae^{0.0347t}$.

17. Use the formula $y = a(1 + r)^t$.

$$y = a(1 + r)^t$$
$$y = 5717(1 + 0.032)^{25}$$
$$y \approx 12{,}565$$

In the year 2010, the GDP will be about $12,565 billion.

18. Use the formula $y = a(1 + r)^t$.

$$y = a(1 + r)^t$$
$$20{,}000 = 5717(1 + 0.032)^t$$
$$3.4983 = 1.032^t$$
$$\log 3.4983 = \log 1.032^t$$
$$\log 3.4983 = t \log 1.032$$
$$\frac{\log 3.4983}{\log 1.032} = t$$
$$40 \approx t$$

In 2025, about 40 years after 1985, the GDP will reach $20 trillion.

19. Use the formula $y_w = a(1 + r)^t$.

$y_w = a(1 + r)^t$
$y_w = 62.5(1 + 0.0038)^t$
$\quad = 62.5(1.0038)^t$

Next, use the formula $y_m = a(1 + r)^t$.

$y_m = a(1 + r)^t$
$y_m = 76.5(1 + 0.003)^t$
$\quad = 76.5(1.003)^t$

Equating the two formulas,

$62.5(1.0038)^t = 76.5(1.003)^t$

$\dfrac{1.0038^t}{1.003^t} = 1.224$

$\log\left(\dfrac{1.0038}{1.003}\right)^t = \log 1.224$

$\log 1.0007976^t \approx \log 1.224$

$t \log 1.0007976 \approx \log 1.224$

$\dfrac{\log 1.224}{\log 1.0007976} \approx t$

$254 \approx t.$

In 2182, about 254 years after 1928, the women's winning high jump will be higher than the men's.

20. Use the formula $y = a(1 + r)^t$.

$y = a(1 + r)^t$
$191,000 = 120,000(1 + r)^{10}$
$1.5917 \approx (1 + r)^{10}$
$\log 1.5917 \approx \log(1 + r)^{10}$
$\log 1.5917 \approx 10 \log(1 + r)$
$\dfrac{\log 1.5917}{10} \approx \log(1 + r)$
$0.02019 \approx \log(1 + r)$
$10^{0.02019} \approx 1 + r$
$0.0476 \approx r$

The yearly rate of appreciation is about 4.8 percent.

21. A 20-gram sample of radium will never be completly gone. Theoretically, the amount left always be half of the amount.

22. Answers should include the following.
- Find the absolute value of the difference between the price of the car for two consecutive years. Then divide this difference by the price of the car for the earlier year.
- Find 1 minus the rate of decrease in the value of the car as a decimal. Raise this value to the number of years it has been since the car was purchased, and then multiply by the original value of the car.

23. Use the formula $y = a(1 - r)^t$.

$y = a(1 - r)^t$
$1000 = 2000(1 - 0.035)^t$
$0.5 = 0.965^t$
$\log 0.5 = \log 0.965^t$
$\log 0.5 = t \log 0.965$
$\dfrac{\log 0.5}{\log 0.965} = t$
$19.456 \approx t$

After about 19.5 years, the statue will weight less than 1000 pounds.

24. D; The graph in the figure is half the graph of a hyperbola with vertex at the origin; the standard equation of such a hyperbola is $xy = c$.

25. $e^3 = y$

The base is e and the exponent 3. The equivalent logarithmic equation is $\ln y = 3$.

26. $e^{4n - 2} = 29$

The base is e and the exponent $4n - 2$. The equivalent logarithmic equation is $\log 29 = 4n - 2$.

27. $\ln 4 + 2 \ln x = 8$

Simplifying, $\ln 4 + \ln x^2 = 8$ or $\ln 4x^2 = 8$. The base is e and the exponent 8. The equivalent exponential equation is $4x^2 = e^8$.

28. $\quad 16^x = 70$

$\log 16^x = \log 70$
$x \log 16 = \log 70$
$\quad\quad x = \dfrac{\log 70}{\log 16}$
$\quad\quad\quad \approx 1.5323$

29. $\quad 2^{3p} > 1000$

$\log 2^{3p} > \log 1000$
$3p \log 2 > 3$
$p \log 2 > 1$
$\quad\quad p > \dfrac{1}{\log 2}$
$\quad\quad p > 3.3219$

30. $\log_b 81 = 2$

$b^2 = 81$
$b = \pm 9$

A negative base is undefined so $b = 9$.

31. Each of the six managers receives one-sixth of the half of the 8% of the annual profit to be distributed among the managers. This amount is $\frac{1}{6}\left[\frac{1}{2}(0.08p)\right]$ or $\frac{0.5(0.08p)}{6}$. Each of the four nonsales managers will <u>also</u> each receive one-fourth of the other half of the 8% of the annual profit. This amount is $\frac{1}{4}\left[\frac{1}{2}(0.08p)\right]$ or $\frac{0.5(0.8p)}{4}$. Each of the nonsales managers will therefore receive $\frac{0.5(0.08p)}{6} + \frac{0.5(0.08p)}{4}$.

32. $\dfrac{0.5(0.08p)}{6} + \dfrac{0.5(0.08p)}{4} = \dfrac{0.08p}{2 \cdot 6} + \dfrac{0.08p}{2 \cdot 4}$

$\quad\quad\quad\quad\quad\quad\quad = \dfrac{0.08p}{12} + \dfrac{0.08p}{8}$

$\quad\quad\quad\quad\quad\quad\quad = 0.08p\left(\dfrac{1}{12} + \dfrac{1}{8}\right)$

$\quad\quad\quad\quad\quad\quad\quad = 0.08p\left(\dfrac{2 + 3}{24}\right)$

$\quad\quad\quad\quad\quad\quad\quad = \dfrac{p}{60}$

33. Each sales manager will receive

$\dfrac{0.5(0.08p)}{6} = \left(\dfrac{8}{2 \cdot 6 \cdot 100}\right)p$

$\quad\quad\quad\quad = \dfrac{p}{150}.$

34. Consider the formula $Ax^2 + Bxy + Cy^2 + Dx + Ey + F = 0$. Since $A = -3$ and $C = 4$, the equation is a hyperbola.

35. $A = 7$ and $C = 6$; therefore, the equation is an ellipse.

36. $A = 0$ and $C = 1$; therefore, the equation is a parabola.

37. $A = 1$ and $C = 1$; therefore, the equation is a circle.

38. 206 million $= 2.06 \times 10^8$

39. 80 million $= 8 \times 10^7$

40. $\frac{80}{206} = 0.3888$ or about 38.8%

Chapter 10 Study Guide and Review

Page 566   Vocabulary and Concept Check

1. True; if $24^{2y + 3} = 24^{y - 4}$, then $2y + 3 = y + 4$ by the Property of Equality for Exponential Functions.

2. False; the number of bacteria in a petri dish over time is an example of exponential growth.

3. False; the common logarithm is the inverse of the exponential function with base 10.

4. False; the Property of Inequality for Logarithms shows that $\ln 9 < \ln 81$.

5. True; if a savings account yields 2% interest per year, then 2% is the rate of growth.

6. True; radioactive half-life is an example of exponential decay.

7. False; the inverse of an exponential function is a logarithmic function.

8. False; the Product Property of Logarithms is illustrated by $\log_4 2x = \log_4 2 + \log_4 x$.

9. False, the function $f(x) = 2(5)^x$ is an example of an exponential function.

Pages 566–570   Lesson-by-Lesson Review

10. The function represents exponential decay since the base, 0.7, is between 0 and 1.

11. The function represents exponential growth since the base, 4, is greater than 1.

12. Substitute $(0, -2)$ into the exponential function $y = ab^x$.
$$y = ab^x$$
$$-2 = ab^0$$
$$-2 = a$$
Then substitute $(3, -54)$ into the equation $y = -2b^x$.
$$y = -2b^x$$
$$-54 = -2b^x$$
$$27 = b^3$$
$$3 = b$$
The equation is $y = -2(3)^x$.

13. Substitute $(0, 7)$ into the exponential function $y = ab^x$.
$$y = ab^x$$
$$7 = ab^0$$
$$7 = a$$
Then substitute $(1, 1.4)$ into the equation $y = 7b^x$.
$$y = 7b^x$$
$$1.4 = 7b^1$$
$$0.2 = b$$
The equation is $y = 7(0.2)^x$ or $y = 7\left(\frac{1}{5}\right)^x$.

14. $9^x = \frac{1}{81}$
$$9^x = \frac{1}{9^2}$$
$$9^x = 9^{-2}$$
$$x = -2$$

15. $2^{6x} = 4^{5x + 2}$
$$2^{6x} = (2^2)^{5x + 2}$$
$$2^{6x} = 2^{2(5x + 2)}$$
$$6x = 2(5x + 2)$$
$$6x = 10x + 4$$
$$-4x = 4$$
$$x = -1$$

16. $49^{3p + 1} = 7^{2p - 5}$
$$(7^2)^{3p + 1} = 7^{2p - 5}$$
$$7^{2(3p + 1)} = 7^{2p - 5}$$
$$2(3p + 1) = 2p - 5$$
$$6p + 2 = 2p - 5$$
$$4p = -7$$
$$p = \frac{-7}{4} \text{ or } -\frac{7}{4}$$

17. $9^{x^2} \leq 27^{x^2 - 2}$
$$(3^2)^{x^2} \leq (3^3)^{x^2 - 2}$$
$$3^{2x^2} \leq 3^{3(x^2 - 2)}$$
$$2x^2 \leq 3(x^2 - 2)$$
$$2x^2 \leq 3x^2 - 6$$
$$6 \leq x^2$$
Solve the related equation.
$$x^2 = 6$$
$$x = \pm\sqrt{6}$$
Test values less than $-\sqrt{6}$, between $-\sqrt{6}$ and $\sqrt{6}$, and greater than $\sqrt{6}$.

Test $x = -3$.   Test $x = 0$.   Test $x = 3$.

$9^{x^2} \leq 27^{x^2 - 2}$ 　　 $9^{x^2} \leq 27^{x^2 - 2}$ 　　 $9 \leq 27^{x^2 - 2}$

$9^{(-3)2} \overset{?}{\leq} 27^{(-3)2 - 2}$ 　 $9^{(0)2} \overset{?}{\leq} 27^{02} - 2$ 　 $9^{(3)2} \overset{?}{\leq} 27^{(3)2 - 2}$

$\quad 9^9 \leq 27^7 \checkmark$ 　　　 $1 \leq \frac{1}{27^2}$ 　　　 $9^9 \leq 27^7 \checkmark$

18. $7^3 = 343 \Rightarrow \log_7 343 = 3$

19. $5^{-2} = \frac{1}{25} \Rightarrow \log_5 \frac{1}{25} = -2$

20. $4^{\frac{3}{2}} = 8 \Rightarrow \log_4 8 = \frac{3}{2}$

21. $\log_4 64 = 3 \Rightarrow 4^3 = 64$

22. $\log_8 2 = \frac{1}{3} \Rightarrow 8^{\frac{1}{3}} = 2$

23. $\log_6 \frac{1}{36} = -2 \Rightarrow 6^{-2} = \frac{1}{36}$

24. $4^{\log_4 9} = 9$

25. $\log_7 7^{-5} = -5$

26. $\log_{81} 3 = x$
$$81^x = 3$$
$$(3^4)^x = 3$$
$$3^{4x} = 3^1$$
$$4x = 1$$
$$x = \frac{1}{4}$$

27. $\log_{13} 169 = x$
$$13^x = 169$$
$$13^x = 13^2$$
$$x = 2$$

28. $\log_4 x = \frac{1}{2}$
$$4^{\frac{1}{2}} = x$$
$$x = \pm 2$$
Since $\log_4(-2)$ is undefined, the only solution is 2.

29. $\log_{81} 729 = x$
$81^x = 729$
$(3^4)^x = 3^6$
$3^{4x} = 3^6$
$4x = 6$
$x = \frac{3}{2}$

30. $\log_b 9 = 2$
$b^2 = 9$
$b = \pm 3$
Since the base cannot be negative, the only solution is 3.

31. $\log_8(3y - 1) < \log_8(y + 5)$
$3y - 1 < y + 5$
$2y < 6$
$y < 3$
But since $\log_8(3y - 1)$ is undefined for $y \leq \frac{1}{3}$, the solution is $\frac{1}{3} < y < 3$.

32. $\log_5 12 < \log_5(5x - 3)$
$12 < 5x - 3$
$15 < 5x$
$3 < x$

33. $\log_8(x^2 + x) = \log_8 12$
$x^2 + x = 12$
$x^2 + x - 12 = 0$
$(x + 4)(x - 3) = 0$
$x + 4 = 0 \quad$ or $\quad x - 3 = 0$
$x = -4 \qquad\qquad x = 3$

34. $\log_9 28 = \log_9(7 \cdot 4)$
$= \log_9 7 + \log_9 4$
$= 0.8856 + 0.6309$
$= 1.5165$

35. $\log_9 49 = \log_9 7^2$
$= 2 \log_9 7$
$= 2(0.8856)$
$= 1.7712$

36. $\log_9 144 = \log_9(9 \cdot 16)$
$= \log_9 9 + \log_9 16$
$= 1 + \log_9 4^2$
$= 1 + 2 \log_9 4$
$= 1 + 2(0.6309)$
$= 2.2618$

37. $\log_2 y = \frac{1}{3} \log_2 27$
$\log_2 y = \log_2 27^{\frac{1}{3}}$
$\log_2 y = \log_2 3$
$y = 3$

38. $\log_5 7 + \frac{1}{2} \log_5 4 = \log_5 x$
$\log_5 7 + \log_5 4^{\frac{1}{2}} = \log_5 x$
$\log_5(7 \cdot 2) = \log_5 x$
$x = 14$

39. $2 \log_2 x - \log_2(x + 3) = 2$
$\log_2 x^2 - \log_2(x + 3) = 2$
$\log_2 \frac{x^2}{x + 3} = 2$
$2^2 = \frac{x^2}{x + 3}$
$4(x + 3) = x^2$
$4x + 12 = x^2$
$x^2 - 4x - 12 = 0$
$(x - 6)(x + 2) = 0$
$x - 6 = 0 \quad$ or $\quad x + 2 = 0$
$x = 6 \qquad\qquad x = -2$
Since $\log_2(-2)$ is undefined, the only solution is 6.

40. $\log_3 x - \log_3 4 = \log_3 12$
$\log_3 \frac{x}{4} = \log_3 12$
$\frac{x}{4} = 12$
$x = 48$

41. $\log_6 48 - \log_6 \frac{16}{5} + \log_6 5 = \log_6 5x$
$\log_6 \left(\frac{48}{\left(\frac{16}{5}\right)}\right) + \log_6 5 = \log_6 5x$
$\log_6 15 + \log_6 5 = \log_6 5x$
$\log_6(15 \cdot 5) = \log_5 5x$
$75 = 5x$
$x = 15$

42. $\log_7 m = \frac{1}{3} \log_7 64 + \frac{1}{2} \log_7 121$
$\log_7 m = \log_7 64^{\frac{1}{3}} + \log_7 121^{\frac{1}{2}}$
$\log_7 m = \log_7 4 + \log_7 11$
$\log_7 m = \log_7(4 \cdot 11)$
$\log_7 m = \log_7 44$
$m = 44$

43. $2^x = 53$
$\log 2^x = \log 53$
$x \log 2 = \log 53$
$x = \frac{\log 53}{\log 2}$
$x \approx 5.7279$

44. $2.3^{x^2} = 66.6$
$\log 2.3^{x^2} = \log 66.6$
$x^2 \log 2.3 = \log 66.6$
$x^2 = \frac{\log 66.6}{\log 2.3}$
$x = \pm\sqrt{\frac{\log 66.6}{\log 2.3}}$
$x \approx \pm 2.2452$

45. $3^{4x - 7} < 4^{2x + 3}$
$\log 3^{4x - 7} < \log 4^{2x + 3}$
$(4x - 7) \log 3 < (2x + 3) \log 4$
$4x \log 3 - 7 \log 3 < 2x \log 4 + 3 \log 4$
$4x \log 3 - 2x \log 4 < 3 \log 4 + 7 \log 3$
$x(4 \log 3 - 2 \log 4) < 3 \log 4 + 7 \log 3$
$x < \frac{3 \log 4 + 7 \log 3}{4 \log 3 - 2 \log 4}$
$x < 7.3059$

46.
$$6^{3y} = 8^{y-1}$$
$$\log 6^{3y} = \log 8^{y-1}$$
$$3y \log 6 = (y - 1) \log 8$$
$$3y \log 6 = y \log 8 - \log 8$$
$$3y \log 6 - y \log 8 = -\log 8$$
$$y(3 \log 6 - \log 8) = -\log 8$$
$$y = \frac{-\log 8}{3 \log 6 - \log 8}$$
$$y = \frac{\log 8}{\log 8 - 3 \log 6}$$
$$y \approx -0.6309$$

47.
$$12^{x-5} \geq 9.32$$
$$\log 12^{x-5} \geq \log 9.32$$
$$(x - 5) \log 12 \geq \log 9.32$$
$$x \log 12 - 5 \log 12 \geq \log 9.32$$
$$x \log 12 \geq \log 9.32 + 5 \log 12$$
$$x \geq \frac{\log 9.32 + 5 \log 12}{\log 12}$$
$$x \geq 5.8983$$

48.
$$2.1^{x-5} = 9.32$$
$$\log 2.1^{x-5} = \log 9.32$$
$$(x - 5) \log 2.1 = \log 9.32$$
$$x \log 2.1 - 5 \log 2.1 = \log 9.32$$
$$x \log 2.1 = 5 \log 2.1 + \log 9.32$$
$$x = \frac{5 \log 2.1 + \log 9.32}{\log 2.1}$$
$$x \approx 8.0086$$

49. $\log_4 11 = \dfrac{\log 11}{\log 4}$
$$\approx 1.7297$$

50. $\log_2 15 = \dfrac{\log 15}{\log 2}$
$$\approx 3.9069$$

51. $\log_{20} 1000 = \dfrac{\log 1000}{\log 20}$
$$\approx 2.3059$$

52. $e^x = 6 \Rightarrow \log_e 6 = x$
$$\ln 6 = x$$

53. $\ln 7.4 = x \Rightarrow \log_e 7.4 = x$
$$e^x = 7.4$$

54. $e^{\ln 12} = 12$

55. $\ln e^{7x} = 7x$

56. $2e^x - 4 = 1$
$$2e^x = 5$$
$$e^x = \frac{5}{2}$$
$$\ln e^x = \ln 2.5$$
$$x = \ln 2.5$$
$$x \approx 0.9163$$

57.
$$e^x > 3.2$$
$$\ln e^x > \ln 3.2$$
$$x > \ln 3.2$$
$$x > 1.1632$$

58. $-4e^{2x} + 15 = 7$
$$-4e^{2x} = -8$$
$$e^{2x} = 2$$
$$\ln e^{2x} = \ln 2$$
$$2x = \ln 2$$
$$x = \frac{\ln 2}{2}$$
$$x = 0.3466$$

59. $\ln 3x \leq 5$
$$0 < 3x \leq e^5$$
$$0 < x \leq \frac{e^5}{3}$$
$$0 < x \leq 49.4711$$

60. $\ln(x - 10) = 0.5$
$$x - 10 = e^{0.5}$$
$$x = e^{0.5} + 10$$
$$x = 11.6487$$

61. $\ln x + \ln 4x = 10$
$$\ln(x \cdot 4x) = 10$$
$$\ln 4x^2 = 10$$
$$4x^2 = e^{10}$$
$$x^2 = \frac{e^{10}}{4}$$
$$x = \pm\sqrt{\frac{e^{10}}{4}}$$
$$x = \pm 74.2066$$
Since $\ln(-74.2066)$ is undefined, the only solution is 74.2066.

62. $y = a(1 - r)^t$
$$y = 250(1 - 0.25)^3$$
$$y = 250(0.75)^3$$
$$\approx \$105.47$$
In 3 years, the fax machine will be worth about $105.47.

63.
$$y = ae^{kt}$$
$$738 = 9e^{0.872t}$$
$$82 = e^{0.872t}$$
$$\ln 82 = \ln e^{0.872t}$$
$$\ln 82 = 0.872t$$
$$t = \frac{\ln 82}{0.872}$$
$$= 5.05$$
It will take about 5.05 days.

64.
$$y = ae^{-kt}$$
$$0.5a = ae^{-k \cdot 1800}$$
$$0.5 = e^{-1800k}$$
$$\ln 0.5 = \ln e^{-1800k}$$
$$\ln 0.5 = -1800k$$
$$k = \frac{\ln 0.5}{-1800}$$
$$= 0.000385$$

65.
$$y = a(1 + r)^t$$
$$64{,}800 = 45{,}600(1 + r)^{10}$$
$$\frac{27}{19} = (1 + r)^{10}$$
$$1.03576 \approx 1 + r$$
$$0.03576 \approx r$$
The annual rate is about 36%.

Chapter 10 Practice Test

Page 571

1. Since the base, 4, is positive, the function is an exponential growth function.

2. The logarithm of a quotient is the difference of the logarithms of the numerator and the denominator.

3. The base of a natural logarithm is e.

4. $3^7 = 2187 \Rightarrow \log_3 2187 = 7$

5. $\log_8 16 = \frac{4}{3} \Rightarrow 8^{\frac{4}{3}} = 16$

6. Substitute $(0, 0.4)$ into $y = ab^x$.

$y = ab^x$

$0.4 = ab^0$

$0.4 = a$

Substitute $(2, 6.4)$ into $y = 0.46^x$.

$y = 0.4b^x$

$6.4 = 0.4b^2$

$16 = b^2$

$4 = b$

The equation is $y = 0.4(4)^x$.

7. $\log_3 5 = \frac{\log 5}{\log 3}$

8. $\log_2 \frac{1}{32} = x$

$2^x = \frac{1}{32}$

$2^x = 2^{-5}$

$x = -5$

9. $\log_4 21 = \log_4(3 \cdot 7)$

$= \log_4 3 + \log_4 7$

$= 1.4037 + 0.7925$

$= 2.1962$

10. $\log_4 \frac{7}{12} = \log_4 7 - \log_4 12$

$= \log_4 7 - \log_4(3 \cdot 4)$

$= \log_4 7 - (\log_4 3 + \log_4 4)$

$= 1.4037 - (0.7925 + 1)$

$= -0.3888$

11. $\left(3^{\sqrt{8}}\right)^{\sqrt{2}} = 3^{\sqrt{8} \cdot \sqrt{2}}$

$= 3^{\sqrt{8 \cdot 2}}$

$= 3^{\sqrt{16}}$

$= 3^4$

$= 81$

12. $81^{\sqrt{5}} \div 3^{\sqrt{5}} = (3^4)^{\sqrt{5}} \div 3^{\sqrt{5}}$

$= 3^{4\sqrt{5}} \div 3^{\sqrt{5}}$

$= \frac{3^{4\sqrt{5}}}{3^{\sqrt{5}}}$

$= 3^{4\sqrt{5} - \sqrt{5}}$

$= 3^{3\sqrt{5}}$

13. $2^{x-3} = \frac{1}{16}$

$2^{x-3} = \frac{1}{2^4}$

$2^{x-3} = 2^{-4}$

$x - 3 = -4$

$x = -1$

14. $27^{2p+1} = 3^{4p-1}$

$(3^3)^{2p+1} = 3^{4p-1}$

$3^{3(2p+1)} = 3^{4p-1}$

$3(2p + 1) = 4p - 1$

$6p + 3 = 4p - 1$

$2p = -4$

$p = -2$

15. $\log_2 x < 7$

$0 < x < 2^7$

$0 < x < 128$

16. $\log_m 144 = -2$

$m^{-2} = 144$

$m^2 = \frac{1}{144}$

$m = \pm \frac{1}{12}$

Since the base cannot be negative, the only solution is $\frac{1}{12}$.

17. $\log_3 x - 2 \log_3 2 = 3 \log_3 3$

$\log_3 x = 3 \log_3 3 + 2 \log_3 2$

$\log_3 x = \log_3 3^3 + \log_3 2^2$

$\log_3 x = \log_3 27 + \log_3 4$

$\log_3 x = \log_3(27 \cdot 4)$

$x = 27 \cdot 4$

$x = 108$

18. $\log_9(x + 4) + \log_9(x - 4) = 1$

$\log_9[(x + 4)(x - 4)] = 1$

$(x + 4)(x - 4) = 9^1$

$x^2 - 16 = 9$

$x^2 = 25$

$x = \pm 5$

Since $\log_9(-5 - 4) = \log_9(-9)$ is undefined, the only solution is 5.

19. $\log_5(8y - 7) = \log_5(y^2 + 5)$

$8y - 7 = y^2 + 5$

$y^2 - 8y + 12 = 0$

$(y - 6)(y - 2) = 0$

$y - 6 = 0 \quad \text{or} \quad y - 2 = 0$

$y = 6 \qquad\qquad y = 2$

20. $\log_3 3^{(4x-1)} = 15$

$4x - 1 = 15$

$4x = 16$

$x = 4$

21. $\qquad 7.6^{x-1} = 431$

$\log 7.6^{x-1} = \log 431$

$(x - 1) \log 7.6 = \log 431$

$x \log 7.6 - \log 7.6 = \log 431$

$x \log 7.6 = \log 431 + \log 7.6$

$x = \frac{\log 431 + \log 7.6}{\log 7.6}$

$x \approx 3.9910$

22. $\log_2 5 + \frac{1}{3} \log_2 27 = \log_2 x$

$\log_2 5 + \log_2 27^{\frac{1}{3}} = \log_2 x$

$\log_2 5 + \log_2 3 = \log_2 x$

$\log_2(5 \cdot 3) = \log_2 x$

$\log_2 15 = \log_2 x$

$15 = x$

23. $\qquad 3^x = 5^{x-1}$

$\log 3^x = \log 5^{x-1}$

$x \log 3 = (x - 1) \log 5$

$x \log 3 = x \log 5 - \log 5$

$x \log 3 - x \log 5 = -\log 5$

$x(\log 3 - \log 5) = -\log 5$

$x = \frac{-\log 5}{\log 3 - \log 5}$

$x = \frac{\log 5}{\log 5 - \log 3}$

$x \approx 3.1507$

24.
$$4^{2x-3} = 9^{x+3}$$
$$\log 4^{2x-3} = \log 9^{x+3}$$
$$(2x-3)\log 4 = (x+3)\log 9$$
$$2x \log 4 - 3 \log 4 = x \log 9 + 3 \log 9$$
$$2x \log 4 - x \log 9 = 3 \log 9 + 3 \log 4$$
$$x(2 \log 4 - \log 9) = 3(\log 9 + \log 4)$$
$$x = \frac{3(\log 9 + \log 4)}{2 \log 4 - \log 9}$$
$$x \approx 18.6848$$

25.
$$e^{3y} > 6$$
$$\ln e^{3y} > \ln 6$$
$$3y > \ln 6$$
$$y > \frac{\ln 6}{3}$$
$$y > 0.5973$$

26.
$$2e^{3x} + 5 = 11$$
$$2e^{3x} = 6$$
$$e^{3x} = 3$$
$$\ln e^{3x} = \ln 3$$
$$3x = \ln 3$$
$$x = \frac{\ln 3}{3}$$
$$x \approx 0.3662$$

27.
$$\ln 3x - \ln 15 = 2$$
$$\ln \frac{3x}{15} = 2$$
$$\ln \frac{x}{5} = 2$$
$$\frac{x}{5} = e^2$$
$$x = 5e^2$$
$$x \approx 36.9453$$

28.
$$y = a(1+r)^t$$
$$y = 25(1 + 0.0325)^{15}$$
$$y = 25(1.0325)^{15}$$
$$y \approx 40.39$$
The coin will be worth about $40.39.

29.
$$y = a(1+r)^t$$
$$50 = 25(1 + 0.0325)^t$$
$$2 = 1.0325^t$$
$$\log 2 = \log 1.0325^t$$
$$\log 2 = t \log 1.0325$$
$$t = \frac{\log 2}{\log 1.0325}$$
$$t \approx 21.6723$$
The coin will double in value in about 22 years.

30. B; In Column A, the value of the account is

determined using the formula $y = a\left(1 + \frac{r}{n}\right)^{nt}$.
$$y = a\left(1 + \frac{r}{n}\right)^{nt}$$
$$y = 100\left(1 + \frac{0.03}{4}\right)^{4 \cdot 5}$$
$$y = 100(1.0075)^{20}$$
$$y \approx 116.12$$

In Column B this value is determined using the formula $y = ae^{kt}$.
$$y = ae^{kt}$$
$$y = 100e^{0.03 \cdot 5}$$
$$y = 100e^{0.15}$$
$$y \approx 116.18$$

Chapter 10 Standardized Test Practice

Pages 572–573

1. B; The shaded region is a fourth of a circle with radius 8 units.
$$\text{Area} = \frac{1}{4}(\pi r^2)$$
$$= \frac{1}{4}(\pi \cdot 8^2)$$
$$= 16\pi$$

2. D; Let y be the measure of the third angle of the right triangle. Since alternate interior angles have equal measures, $150 = 130 + y$. Thus, $y = 20$.
The sum of the angles of a triangle is 180°.
$$x + y + 90 = 180$$
$$x + 20 + 90 = 180$$
$$x = 70$$

3. D; The increase from 1998 to 2000 was $15 - 10$ or 5. The percent increase was $\frac{5}{10} = 0.5$ or 50%.

4. B; Let $y = 0$.
$$y = 2x + 5$$
$$0 = 2x + 5$$
$$-5 = 2x$$
$$-\frac{5}{2} = x$$

5. D; $\frac{(xy)^2 z^0}{y^2 x^3} = \frac{x^2 \cdot y^2 \cdot 1}{y^2 \cdot x^3}$
$$= x^{2-3}$$
$$= x^{-1}$$
$$= \frac{1}{x}$$

6. A; $\frac{v^2 - 36}{6 - v} = 10$
$$v^2 - 36 = 10(6 - v)$$
$$v^2 - 36 = 60 - 10v$$
$$v^2 + 10v - 96 = 0$$
$$(v + 16)(v - 6) = 0$$
$$v + 16 = 0 \qquad \text{or } v - 6 = 0$$
$$v = -16 \qquad\qquad v = 6$$
Since 6 makes the denominator equal to 0, the only solution is -16.

7. A; $\frac{1}{3}\sqrt{45} = \frac{1}{3}\sqrt{9 \cdot 5}$
$$= \frac{1}{3}\sqrt{9} \cdot \sqrt{5}$$
$$= \frac{1}{3} \cdot 3 \cdot \sqrt{5}$$
$$= \sqrt{5}$$

8. B; Solve the related equation.
$$x^2 = 3x + 18$$
$$x^2 - 3x - 18 = 0$$
$$(x - 6)(x + 3) = 0$$
$$x - 6 = 0 \quad \text{or} \quad x + 3 = 0$$
$$x = 6 \qquad \qquad x = -3$$

The solutions divide the real numbers into three regions. Test a value from each region.

Test $x = -4$.   Test $x = 0$.
$$x^2 < 3x + 14 \qquad x^2 < 3x + 14$$
$$(-4)^2 \overset{?}{<} 3(-12) + 14 \qquad 0^2 \overset{?}{<} 3(0) + 14$$
$$16 \not< -22 \qquad 0 < 14 \checkmark$$

Test $x = 7$.
$$x^2 < 3x + 14$$
$$7^2 \overset{?}{<} 3(7) + 14$$
$$49 \not< 35$$

Thus, $-3 < x < 6$.

9. B; $f(x) = 2x^3 - 18x$
$$0 = 2x^3 - 18x$$
$$0 = 2x(x^2 - 9)$$
$$2x = 0 \quad \text{or} \quad x^2 - 9 = 0$$
$$x = 0 \qquad \qquad x^2 = 9$$
$$x = \pm 3$$

10. D; $\dfrac{17.5(10^{-2})}{500(10^{-4})} = \dfrac{17.5}{500(10^{-2})}$
$$= \dfrac{17.5}{5 \cdot 10^2 \cdot 10^{-2}}$$
$$= \dfrac{17.5}{5}$$
$$= 3.5$$
$$= 0.035(10^2)$$

11. The thickness of the tank is equal to one-half of the difference between the diameter of the outer circle and the diameter of the inner circle.
$$\tfrac{1}{2}(62.46 - 53.32) = \tfrac{1}{2}(9.14)$$
$$= 4.57$$

The thickness is 4.57 cm.

12. Let x represent the number.
$$x + 0.8x = 45$$
$$1.8x = 45$$
$$x = \dfrac{45}{1.8}$$
$$x = 25$$

13. 95% of the 200 families, or $0.95 \cdot 200 = 190$ families, have at least one TV and 60% of those, or $0.60 \cdot 190 = 114$, have more than two TVs. 50 families have exactly two TVs, so there are $190 - 114 - 50 = 26$ families with exactly one TV.

14. $AB = BC = 12$ so ABC is an isosceles triangle. Angle B is $30 + 15 + 15 = 60$, so ABC is an equilateral triangle and $AC = AB = BC = 12$. Since $A = C$, ABE and BDC are similar triangles, so $AE = DC$. Letting $AE = x$, we find $x + 8 + x = 12$, or $x = 2$. The measure of AE is 12.

15. $a - b + ab = 4 - 2 + 4(2)$
$$= 10$$
The value of $4 \leftrightarrow 2$ is 10.

16.
$$6(m + k) = 26 + 4(m + k)$$
$$6(m + k) - 4(m + k) = 26$$
$$2(m + k) = 26$$
$$m + k = 13$$

17. The least possible value of y is at the vertex of the parabola, or (h, k). In standard form the equation is $y = -x^2 + 1$, so that the vertex is at $(0, 1)$, and the greatest possible value of $y = 1$. The greatest possible value of y is at $x = -3$ or $y = 10$. The difference is $10 - 1 = 9$.

18. $f(x) = (x - \pi)(x - 3)(x - e)$
The roots of $f(x)$ are π, 3 and e.
$$\pi \approx 3.14$$
$$e \approx 2.72$$
so $e < 3 < \pi$.
The difference between the greatest and least roots is $\pi - e$ or about 0.42.

19. D; Consider these examples.
When $x = \tfrac{1}{2}$ and $y = -1$, $x + y = xy$.
When $x = -1$ and $y = \tfrac{1}{4}$, $x + y < xy$.
When $x = 1$ and $y = -\tfrac{1}{4}$, $x + y > xy$.

20. C; Since $z = x + y$, and $x + y + z = 180°$, so $z + z = 180°$ or $z = 90°$.
Then the triangle is a right triangle and the side opposite z is the hypotenuse. By the Pythagorean Theorem, the quantities are equal.

21. A; The circumference of a circle is πd, where d is the diameter of the circle.
$$\pi d = 8\pi$$
$$d = 8$$
$\overline{AC}$ is one diameter of the circle, so $AC = 8$.
$\overline{AC}$ is also the hypotenuse of triangles ADC and ABC.
Now the sum of any two sides of a triangle is greater than the third side.
Thus, $AC < AD + DC$ and $AC < AB + BC$.
$$AC + AC < AD + DC + AB + BC$$
$$16 < \text{perimeter of } ABCD$$

22. A; $x - y + z = 5$
$$x + y + z = 9$$
Simplify by adding the two equations.
$$2x + 2z = 14$$
Then divide by 2.
$$x + z = 7$$

23. B; Since $nx \neq 0$, neither x nor n is 0 and $-2nx \neq 0$.
$$x^2 + n^2 > 0$$
$$x^2 + n^2 - 2nx > -2nx$$
$$x^2 - 2nx + n^2 > -2nx$$
$$(x - n)^2 > -2nx$$

Chapter 11 Sequences and Series

1. $36 = 12 + 4x$
$\quad\;\; 24 = 4x$
$\qquad 6 = x$

2. $-40 = 10 + 5x$
$\quad\; -50 = 5x$
$\quad\; -10 = x$

3. $12 - 3x = 27$
$\qquad -3x = 15$
$\qquad\;\; x = -5$

4. $\quad 162 = 2x^4$
$\qquad\; 81 = x^4$
$\pm\sqrt[4]{81} = x$
$\quad\; \pm 3 = x$

5. $\quad \dfrac{1}{8} = 4x^5$
$\dfrac{1}{4}\left(\dfrac{1}{8}\right) = \dfrac{1}{4}(4x^5)$
$\quad\; \dfrac{1}{32} = x^5$
$\sqrt[5]{\dfrac{1}{32}} = x$
$\quad \dfrac{1}{2} = x$

6. $3x^3 + 4 = -20$
$\qquad 3x^3 = -24$
$\qquad\;\; x^3 = -8$
$\qquad\;\; x = \sqrt[3]{-8}$
$\qquad\;\; x = -2$

7.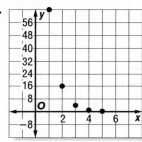

8.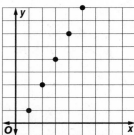

9.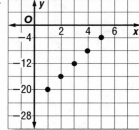

10.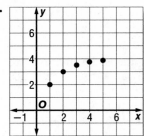

11. $x + (y - 1)z = 3 + (8 - 1)(2)$
$\qquad\qquad\quad = 3 + 7(2)$
$\qquad\qquad\quad = 3 + 14$
$\qquad\qquad\quad = 17$

12. $\dfrac{x}{2}(y + z) = \dfrac{10}{2}(3 + 25)$
$\qquad\qquad = \dfrac{10}{2}(28)$
$\qquad\qquad = 5(28)$
$\qquad\qquad = 140$

13. $a \cdot b^{c-1} = 2\left(\dfrac{1}{2}\right)^{7-1}$
$\qquad\qquad = 2\left(\dfrac{1}{2}\right)^{6}$
$\qquad\qquad = 2\left(\dfrac{1}{64}\right)$
$\qquad\qquad = \dfrac{1}{32}$

14. $\dfrac{a(1 - bc)^2}{1 - b} = \dfrac{-2(1 - 3 \cdot 5)^2}{1 - 3}$
$\qquad\qquad\quad = \dfrac{-2(1 - 15)^2}{-2}$
$\qquad\qquad\quad = \dfrac{-2(-14)^2}{-2}$
$\qquad\qquad\quad = \dfrac{-2(196)}{-2}$
$\qquad\qquad\quad = \dfrac{-392}{-2}$
$\qquad\qquad\quad = 196$

15. $\dfrac{a}{1 - b} = \dfrac{\frac{1}{2}}{1 - \frac{1}{6}}$
$\qquad\quad = \dfrac{\frac{1}{2}}{\frac{5}{6}}$
$\qquad\quad = \dfrac{1}{2} \cdot \dfrac{6}{5}$
$\qquad\quad = \dfrac{3}{5}$

16. $\dfrac{n(n + 1)}{2} = \dfrac{10(10 + 1)}{2}$
$\qquad\qquad = \dfrac{10(11)}{2}$
$\qquad\qquad = \dfrac{110}{2}$
$\qquad\qquad = 55$

11-1 Arithmetic Sequences

Page 580 Algebra Activity

1.

2. Since the volume of each cube is 1 cm^3, the volumes of the figures are 1 cm^3, 3 cm^3, 5 cm^3, and 7 cm^3.

3. $1 \underset{+2}{\frown} 3 \underset{+2}{\frown} 5 \underset{+2}{\frown} 7$

Use the nth term formula.
$V_n = V_1 + (n - 1)d$
$V_n = 1 + (n - 1)(2)$
$V_n = 1 + 2n - 2$
$V_n = 2n - 1$

4. $V_n = 2n - 1$
$V_{12} = 2(12) - 1$
$V_{12} = 24 - 1$
$V_{12} = 23$
The volume of the twelfth figure would be 23 cm^3.

Pages 580–581 Check for Understanding

1. $4 \underset{+1}{\frown} 5 \underset{+2}{\frown} 7 \underset{+3}{\frown} 10 \underset{+4}{\frown} 14$

The sequence is not arithmetic because the differences between the terms are not constant.

2. $-3 \underset{+7}{\frown} 4 \underset{+7}{\frown} 11 \underset{+7}{\frown} 18$

Use the nth term formula.
$a_n = a_1 + (n - 1)d$
$a_{15} = -3 + (15 - 1)(7)$
$a_{15} = -3 + 14(7)$
$a_{15} = -3 + 98$
$a_{15} = 95$

3. Sample answer: 1, −4, −9, −14, …
$1 \underset{+(-5)}{\frown} -4 \underset{+(-5)}{\frown} -9 \underset{+(-5)}{\frown} -14$

4. Find the common difference.
$d = 16 - 12$ or 4
Add 4 until the next four terms are found.
$20 \underset{+4}{\frown} 24 \underset{+4}{\frown} 28 \underset{+4}{\frown} 32 \underset{+4}{\frown} 36$

The next four terms are 24, 28, 32, and 36.

5. Find the common difference.
$d = 1 - 3$ or -2
Add −2 until the next four terms are found.
$-1 \underset{+(-2)}{\frown} -3 \underset{+(-2)}{\frown} -5 \underset{+(-2)}{\frown} -7 \underset{+(-2)}{\frown} -9$

The next four terms are −3, −5, −7, and −9.

6. Add 3 until the first five terms are found.
$5 \underset{+3}{\frown} 8 \underset{+3}{\frown} 11 \underset{+3}{\frown} 14 \underset{+3}{\frown} 17$

The first five terms are 5, 8, 11, 14, and 17.

7. Add −2 until the first five terms are found.
$14 \underset{+(-2)}{\frown} 12 \underset{+(-2)}{\frown} 10 \underset{+(-2)}{\frown} 8 \underset{+(-2)}{\frown} 6$

The first five terms are 14, 12, 10, 8, and 6.

8. Find the common difference.
$d = -12 - (-17)$ or 5
Use the nth term formula.
$a_n = a_1 + (n - 1)d$
$a_{13} = -17 + (13 - 1)(5)$
$a_{13} = -17 + 12(5)$
$a_{13} = -17 + 60$ or 43

9. $a_n = a_1 + (n - 1)d$
$a_{24} = 3 + (24 - 1)(-5)$
$a_{24} = 3 + 23(-5)$
$a_{24} = 3 + (-115)$ or -112

10. $a_n = a_1 + (n - 1)d$
$a_{13} = -5 + (13 - 1)(7)$
$a_{13} = -5 + 12(7)$
$a_{13} = -5 + 84$ or 79

11. Find the common difference.
$d = 3 - (-2)$ or 5
Use the nth term formula.
$a_n = a_1 + (n - 1)d$
$68 = -2 + (n - 1)(5)$
$68 = -2 + 5n - 5$
$68 = -7 + 5n$
$75 = 5n$
$15 = n$
68 is the 15th term of the sequence.

12. Find the common difference.
$d = -15 - (-26)$ or 11
Use the nth term formula.
$a_n = a_1 + (n - 1)d$
$a_n = -26 + (n - 1)(11)$
$a_n = -26 + 11n - 11$
$a_n = 11n - 37$

13. Use the nth term formula to find the common difference.
$a_n = a_1 + (n - 1)d$
$92 = 44 + (5 - 1)d$
$92 = 44 + 4d$
$48 = 4d$
$12 = d$
Now use the value of d to find the three arithmetic means.
$44 \underset{+12}{\frown} 56 \underset{+12}{\frown} 68 \underset{+12}{\frown} 80$

The arithmetic means are 56, 68, and 80.

14. Use the nth term formula. The first term is 5000, and the common difference is 500.
$a_n = a_1 + (n - 1)d$
$a_{15} = 5000 + (15 - 1)(500)$
$a_{15} = 5000 + 14(500)$
$a_{15} = 5000 + 7000$ or 12,000
The jackpot will be $12,000.

15. Find the common difference.

$d = 16 - 9$ or 7

Add 7 until the next four terms are found.

$$23 \underset{+7}{\frown} 30 \underset{+7}{\frown} 37 \underset{+7}{\frown} 44 \underset{+7}{\frown} 51$$

The next four terms are 30, 37, 44, and 51.

16. Find the common difference.

$d = 24 - 31$ or -7

Add -7 until the next four terms are found.

$$17 \underset{+(-7)}{\frown} 10 \underset{+(-7)}{\frown} 3 \underset{+(-7)}{\frown} -4 \underset{+(-7)}{\frown} -11$$

The next four terms are 10, 3, -4, and -11.

17. Find the common difference.

$d = -2 - (-6)$ or 4

Add 4 until the next four terms are found.

$$2 \underset{+4}{\frown} 6 \underset{+4}{\frown} 10 \underset{+4}{\frown} 14 \underset{+4}{\frown} 18$$

The next four terms are 6, 10, 14, and 18.

18. Find the common difference.

$d = -5 - (-8)$ or 3

Add 3 until the next four terms are found.

$$-2 \underset{+3}{\frown} 1 \underset{+3}{\frown} 4 \underset{+3}{\frown} 7 \underset{+3}{\frown} 10$$

The next four terms are 1, 4, 7, and 10.

19. Find the common difference.

$d = 1 - \frac{1}{3}$ or $\frac{2}{3}$

Add $\frac{2}{3}$ until the next four terms are found.

$$\frac{5}{3} \underset{+\frac{2}{3}}{\frown} \frac{7}{3} \underset{+\frac{2}{3}}{\frown} 3 \underset{+\frac{2}{3}}{\frown} \frac{11}{3} \underset{+\frac{2}{3}}{\frown} \frac{13}{3}$$

The next four terms are $\frac{7}{3}$, 3, $\frac{11}{3}$, and $\frac{13}{3}$.

20. Find the common difference.

$d = \frac{16}{5} - \frac{18}{5}$ or $-\frac{2}{5}$

Add $-\frac{2}{5}$ until the next four terms are found.

$$\frac{14}{5} \underset{+\left(-\frac{2}{5}\right)}{\frown} \frac{12}{5} \underset{+\left(-\frac{2}{5}\right)}{\frown} 2 \underset{+\left(-\frac{2}{5}\right)}{\frown} \frac{8}{5} \underset{+\left(-\frac{2}{5}\right)}{\frown} \frac{6}{5}$$

The next four terms are $\frac{12}{5}$, 2, $\frac{8}{5}$, and $\frac{6}{5}$.

21. Find the common difference.

$d = 6.3 - 6.7$ or -0.4

Add -0.4 until the next four terms are found.

$$5.9 \underset{+(-0.4)}{\frown} 5.5 \underset{+(-0.4)}{\frown} 5.1 \underset{+(-0.4)}{\frown} 4.7 \underset{+(-0.4)}{\frown} 4.3$$

The next four terms are 5.5, 5.1, 4.7, and 4.3.

22. Find the common difference.

$d = 3.8 - 1.3$ or 2.5

Add 2.5 until the next four terms are found.

$$6.3 \underset{+2.5}{\frown} 8.8 \underset{+2.5}{\frown} 11.3 \underset{+2.5}{\frown} 13.8 \underset{+2.5}{\frown} 16.3$$

The next four terms are 8.8, 11.3, 13.8, and 16.3.

23. Add 13 until the first five terms are found.

$$2 \underset{+13}{\frown} 15 \underset{+13}{\frown} 28 \underset{+13}{\frown} 41 \underset{+13}{\frown} 54$$

The first five terms are 2, 15, 28, 41, and 54.

24. Add 5 until the first five terms are found.

$$41 \underset{+5}{\frown} 46 \underset{+5}{\frown} 51 \underset{+5}{\frown} 56 \underset{+5}{\frown} 61$$

The first five terms are 41, 46, 51, 56, and 61.

25. Add -4 until the first five terms are found.

$$6 \underset{+(-4)}{\frown} 2 \underset{+(-4)}{\frown} -2 \underset{+(-4)}{\frown} -6 \underset{+(-4)}{\frown} -10$$

The first five terms are 6, 2, -2, -6, and -10.

26. Add -3 until the first five terms are found.

$$12 \underset{+(-3)}{\frown} 9 \underset{+(-3)}{\frown} 6 \underset{+(-3)}{\frown} 3 \underset{+(-3)}{\frown} 0$$

The first five terms are 12, 9, 6, 3, and 0.

27. Add $-\frac{1}{3}$ until the first five terms are found.

$$\frac{4}{3} \underset{+\left(-\frac{1}{3}\right)}{\frown} 1 \underset{+\left(-\frac{1}{3}\right)}{\frown} \frac{2}{3} \underset{+\left(-\frac{1}{3}\right)}{\frown} \frac{1}{3} \underset{+\left(-\frac{1}{3}\right)}{\frown} 0$$

The first five terms are $\frac{4}{3}$, 1, $\frac{2}{3}$, $\frac{1}{3}$, and 0.

28. Add $\frac{3}{8}$ until the first five terms are found.

$$\frac{5}{8} \underset{+\frac{3}{8}}{\frown} 1 \underset{+\frac{3}{8}}{\frown} \frac{11}{8} \underset{+\frac{3}{8}}{\frown} \frac{7}{4} \underset{+\frac{3}{8}}{\frown} \frac{17}{8}$$

The first five terms are $\frac{5}{8}$, 1, $\frac{11}{8}$, $\frac{7}{4}$, and $\frac{17}{8}$.

29. $a_n = 4 + 3n$

$a_8 = 4 + 3(8)$

$a_8 = 4 + 24$ or 28

30. $a_n = 1 - 5n$

$a_{10} = 1 - 5(10)$

$a_{10} = 1 - 50$ or -49

31. $a_n = a_1 + (n - 1)d$

$a_{14} = 3 + (14 - 1)(7)$

$a_{14} = 3 + 13(7)$

$a_{14} = 3 + 91$ or 94

32. $a_n = a_1 + (n - 1)d$

$a_{20} = -4 + (20 - 1)(-9)$

$a_{20} = -4 + 19(-9)$

$a_{20} = -4 + (-171)$ or -175

33. $a_n = a_1 + (n - 1)d$

$a_{101} = 35 + (101 - 1)(3)$

$a_{101} = 35 + 100(3)$

$a_{101} = 35 + 300$ or 335

34. $a_n = a_1 + (n - 1)d$

$a_{81} = 20 + (81 - 1)(4)$

$a_{81} = 20 + 80(4)$

$a_{81} = 20 + 320$ or 340

35. $a_n = a_1 + (n - 1)d$

$a_{12} = 5 + (12 - 1)\left(\frac{1}{3}\right)$

$a_{12} = 5 + 11\left(\frac{1}{3}\right)$

$a_{12} = 5 + \frac{11}{3}$ or $\frac{26}{3}$

36. $a_n = a_1 + (n - 1)d$

$a_{11} = \frac{5}{2} + (11 - 1)\left(-\frac{3}{2}\right)$

$a_{11} = \frac{5}{2} + 10\left(-\frac{3}{2}\right)$

$a_{11} = \frac{5}{2} + \left(-\frac{30}{2}\right)$ or $-\frac{25}{2}$

37. Find the common difference.
$d = -13 - (-17)$ or 4
Use the nth term formula.
$a_n = a_1 + (n - 1)d$
$a_{12} = -17 + (12 - 1)(4)$
$a_{12} = -17 + 11(4)$
$a_{12} = -17 + 44$ or 27

38. Find the common difference.
$d = 3 - 8$ or -5
Use the nth term formula.
$a_n = a_1 + (n - 1)d$
$a_{12} = 8 + (12 - 1)(-5)$
$a_{12} = 8 + 11(-5)$
$a_{12} = 8 + (-55)$ or -47

39. Find the common difference.
$d = 118 - 121$ or -3
Use the nth term formula.
$a_n = a_1 + (n - 1)d$
$a_{21} = 121 + (21 - 1)(-3)$
$a_{21} = 121 + 20(-3)$
$a_{21} = 121 + (-60)$ or 61

40. Find the common difference.
$d = 9 - 5$ or 4
Use the nth term formula.
$a_n = a_1 + (n - 1)d$
$a_{43} = 5 + (43 - 1)(4)$
$a_{43} = 5 + 42(4)$
$a_{43} = 5 + 168$ or 173

41. Use the nth term formula with $a_1 = 0.75$, $d = 0.75$, and $n = 50$.
$a_n = a_1 + (n - 1)d$
$a_{50} = 0.75 + (50 - 1)(0.75)$
$a_{50} = 0.75 + 49(0.75)$
$a_{50} = 0.75 + 36.75$ or 37.5
The continents will drift 37.5 inches in 30 years.

42. Find the common difference.
$d = 48 - 16$ or 32
Use the nth term formula.
$a_n = a_1 + (n - 1)d$
$a_{10} = 16 + (10 - 1)(32)$
$a_{10} = 16 + 9(32)$
$a_{10} = 16 + 288$ or 304
An object will fall 304 feet in the tenth second.

43. Find the common difference.
$d = 2 - (-4)$ or 6
Use the nth term formula.
$a_n = a_1 + (n - 1)d$
$170 = -4 + (n - 1)(6)$
$170 = -4 + 6n - 6$
$170 = -10 + 6n$
$180 = 6n$
$30 = n$
170 is the 30th term of the sequence.

44. Find the common difference.
$d = 5 - (-2)$ or 7
Use the nth term formula.
$a_n = a_1 + (n - 1)d$
$124 = -2 + (n - 1)(7)$
$124 = -2 + 7n - 7$
$124 = -9 + 7n$
$133 = 7n$
$19 = n$
124 is the 19th term of the sequence.

45. Find the common difference.
$d = 2 - 2\frac{1}{5}$ or $-\frac{1}{5}$
Use the nth term formula.
$a_n = a_1 + (n - 1)d$
$-14 = 2\frac{1}{5} + (n - 1)\left(-\frac{1}{5}\right)$
$-14 = 2\frac{1}{5} - \frac{1}{5}n + \frac{1}{5}$
$-14 = 2\frac{2}{5} - \frac{1}{5}n$
$-16\frac{2}{5} = -\frac{1}{5}n$
$82 = n$
-14 is the 82nd term of the sequence.

46. Find the common difference.
$d = 16 - 7$ or 9
Use the nth term formula.
$a_n = a_1 + (n - 1)d$
$a_n = 7 + (n - 1)(9)$
$a_n = 7 + 9n - 9$
$a_n = 9n - 2$

47. Find the common difference.
$d = 11 - 18$ or -7
Use the nth term formula.
$a_n = a_1 + (n - 1)d$
$a_n = 18 + (n - 1)(-7)$
$a_n = 18 - 7n + 7$
$a_n = -7n + 25$

48. Find the common difference.
$d = -5 - (-3)$ or -2
Use the nth term formula.
$a_n = a_1 + (n - 1)d$
$a_n = -3 + (n - 1)(-2)$
$a_n = -3 - 2n + 2$
$a_n = -2n - 1$

49. The next three numbers are 13, 17, and 21.

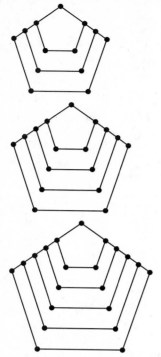

50. Find the common difference.
$d = 5 - 1$ or 4
Use the nth term formula.
$p_n = p_1 + (n - 1)d$
$p_n = 1 + (n - 1)(4)$
$p_n = 1 + 4n - 4$
$p_n = 4n - 3$

51. Yes; it corresponds to $n = 100$.
$p_n = 4n - 3$
$397 = 4n - 3$
$400 = 4n$
$100 = n$

52. Use the nth term formula to find the common difference.
$a_n = a_1 + (n - 1)d$
$115 = 55 + (5 - 1)d$
$115 = 55 + 4d$
$60 = 4d$
$15 = d$
Now use the value of d to find the three arithmetic means.
$55 \underset{+15}{\longrightarrow} 70 \underset{+15}{\longrightarrow} 85 \underset{+15}{\longrightarrow} 100$

The arithmetic means are 70, 85, and 100.

53. Use the nth term formula to find the common difference.
$a_n = a_1 + (n - 1)d$
$-8 = 10 + (4 - 1)d$
$-8 = 10 + 3d$
$-18 = 3d$
$-6 = d$
Now use the value of d to find the two arithmetic means.
$10 \underset{+(-6)}{\longrightarrow} 4 \underset{+(-6)}{\longrightarrow} -2$

The arithmetic means are 4 and -2.

54. Use the nth term formula to find the common difference.
$a_n = a_1 + (n - 1)d$
$7 = -8 + (6 - 1)d$
$7 = -8 + 5d$
$15 = 5d$
$3 = d$
Now use the value of d to find the four arithmetic means.
$-8 \underset{+3}{\longrightarrow} -5 \underset{+3}{\longrightarrow} -2 \underset{+3}{\longrightarrow} 1 \underset{+3}{\longrightarrow} 4$

The arithmetic means are -5, -2, 1, and 4.

55. Use the nth term formula to find the common difference.
$a_n = a_1 + (n - 1)d$
$27 = 3 + (7 - 1)d$
$27 = 3 + 6d$
$24 = 6d$
$4 = d$
Now use the value of d to find the four arithmetic means.
$3 \underset{+4}{\longrightarrow} 7 \underset{+4}{\longrightarrow} 11 \underset{+4}{\longrightarrow} 15 \underset{+4}{\longrightarrow} 19 \underset{+4}{\longrightarrow} 23$

The arithmetic means are 7, 11, 15, 19, and 23.

56. The common difference is $y - x$, and z is the 3rd term of the sequence.
$a_n = a_1 + (n - 1)d$
$z = x + (3 - 1)(y - x)$
$z = x + 2(y - x)$
$z = x + 2y - 2x$
$z = 2y - x$

57. Arithmetic sequences can be used to model the numbers of shingles in the rows on a section of roof. Answers should include the following.
• One additional shingle is needed in each successive row.
• One method is to successively add 1 to the terms of the sequence: $a_8 = 9 + 1$ or 10, $a_9 = 10 + 1$ or 11, $a_{10} = 11 + 1$ or 12, $a_{11} = 12 + 1$ or 13, $a_{12} = 13 + 1$ or 14, $a_{13} = 14 + 1$ or 15, $a_{14} = 15 + 1$ or 16, $a_{15} = 16 + 1$ or 17. Another method is to use the formula for the nth term: $a_{15} = 3 + (15 - 1)1$ or 17.

58. B; The common difference is $11 - 8$ or 3. Add 3 to 20. The next term is 23.

59. B; The common difference is $7 - 8\frac{1}{3}$ or $-1\frac{1}{3}$.
Subtract $-1\frac{1}{3}$ from $8\frac{1}{3}$ to find the term preceding $8\frac{1}{3}$. The first term is $8\frac{1}{3} - \left(-1\frac{1}{3}\right)$ or $9\frac{2}{3}$.

60.
$$y = a(1 - r)^t$$
$$600 = 3000(1 - r)^3$$
$$0.2 = (1 - r)^3$$
$$\sqrt[3]{0.2} = 1 - r$$
$$r + \sqrt[3]{0.2} = 1$$
$$r = 1 - \sqrt[3]{0.2}$$
$$r \approx 0.415$$

The average annual rate of depreciation is about 41.5%.

61. $3e^x - 2 = 0$
$$3e^x = 2$$
$$e^x = \frac{2}{3}$$
$$\ln e^x = \ln \frac{2}{3}$$
$$x = \ln \frac{2}{3} \text{ or about } -0.4055$$

62. $e^{3x} = 4$
$$\ln e^{3x} = \ln 4$$
$$3x = \ln 4$$
$$x = \frac{\ln 4}{3} \text{ or about } 0.4621$$

63. $\ln(x + 2) = 5$
$$e^{\ln(x + 2)} = e^5$$
$$x + 2 = e^5$$
$$x = e^5 - 2 \text{ or about } 146.4132$$

64.
$$\frac{y_1}{x_1} = \frac{y_2}{x_2}$$
$$\frac{5}{2} = \frac{y_2}{6}$$
$$5(6) = 2(y_2)$$
$$30 = 2y_2$$
$$15 = y_2$$
When $x = 6$, the value of y is 15.

65. Replace n with 1.
$$3n - 1 = 3(1) - 1$$
$$= 3 - 1$$
$$= 2$$
Replace n with 2.
$$3n - 1 = 3(2) - 1$$
$$= 6 - 1$$
$$= 5$$
Replace n with 3.
$$3n - 1 = 3(3) - 1$$
$$= 9 - 1$$
$$= 8$$
Replace n with 4.
$$3n - 1 = 3(4) - 1$$
$$= 12 - 1$$
$$= 11$$

66. Replace j with 1.
$$6 - j = 6 - 1$$
$$= 5$$
Replace j with 2.
$$6 - j = 6 - 2$$
$$= 4$$
Replace j with 3.
$$6 - j = 6 - 3$$
$$= 3$$
Replace j with 4.
$$6 - j = 6 - 4$$
$$= 2$$

67. Replace m with 1.
$$4m + 7 = 4(1) + 7$$
$$= 4 + 7$$
$$= 11$$
Replace m with 2.
$$4m + 7 = 4(2) + 7$$
$$= 8 + 7$$
$$= 15$$
Replace m with 3.
$$4m + 7 = 4(3) + 7$$
$$= 12 + 7$$
$$= 19$$
Replace m with 4.
$$4m + 7 = 4(4) + 7$$
$$= 16 + 7$$
$$= 23$$
Replace m with 5.
$$4m + 7 = 4(5) + 7$$
$$= 20 + 7$$
$$= 27$$

11-2 Arithmetic Series

Page 585   Graphing Calculator Investigation

1. The index of summation is always replaced by specific values, so the letter that is used does not affect the value of the sum.

2. Evaluate $\sum_{n=1}^{8} (2n - 1)$.

KEYSTROKES: [2nd] [LIST] [▶] [▶] 5 [2nd] [LIST] [▶] 5 2 [X,T,θ,n] [−] 1 [,] [X,T,θ,n] [,] 1 [,] 8 [,] 1 [)] [)] [ENTER]

The sum of the series is 64.

Evaluate $\sum_{j=5}^{12} (2j - 9)$.

KEYSTROKES: [2nd] [LIST] [▶] [▶] 5 [2nd] [LIST] [▶] 5 2 [X,T,θ,n] [−] 9 [,] [X,T,θ,n] [,] 5 [,] 12 [,] 1 [)] [)] [ENTER]

The sum of the series is 64.
They represent the same series. Any series can be written in many ways using sigma notation.

Page 586   Check for Understanding

1. In a series, the terms are added. In a sequence, they are not.

2. Sample answer: $0 + 1 + 2 + 3 + 4$
$$S_5 = 0 + 1 + 2 + 3 + 4 \text{ or } 10$$

3. Sample answer: $\sum_{n=1}^{4} (3n + 4)$

$$\sum_{n=1}^{4} (3n + 4)$$
$$= [3(1) + 4] + [3(2) + 4] + [3(3) + 4] + [3(4) + 4]$$
$$= 7 + 10 + 13 + 16$$

4. $S_n = \frac{n}{2}(a_1 + a_n)$

$S_{25} = \frac{25}{2}(4 + 100)$

$S_{25} = \frac{25}{2}(104)$

$S_{25} = 1300$

5. $S_n = \frac{n}{2}[2a_1 + (n - 1)d]$

$S_{20} = \frac{20}{2}[2(40) + (20 - 1)(-3)]$

$S_{20} = 10(23)$

$S_{20} = 230$

6. First find n.

$a_n = a_1 + (n - 1)d$

$52 = 132 + (n - 1)(-4)$

$52 = 132 - 4n + 4$

$52 = 136 - 4n$

$-84 = -4n$

$21 = n$

Now find the sum.

$S_n = \frac{n}{2}(a_1 + a_n)$

$S_{21} = \frac{21}{2}(132 + 52)$

$S_{21} = \frac{21}{2}(184)$

$S_{21} = 1932$

7. First find a_1.

$a_n = a_1 + (n - 1)d$

$72 = a_1 + (16 - 1)(5)$

$72 = a_1 + 15(5)$

$72 = a_1 + 75$

$-3 = a_1$

Now find the sum.

$S_n = \frac{n}{2}(a_1 + a_n)$

$S_{16} = \frac{16}{2}(-3 + 72)$

$S_{16} = 8(69)$

$S_{16} = 552$

8. The common difference is $11 - 5$ or 6. Find n.

$a_n = a_1 + (n - 1)d$

$95 = 5 + (n - 1)(6)$

$95 = 5 + 6n - 6$

$95 = -1 + 6n$

$96 = 6n$

$16 = n$

Now find the sum.

$S_n = \frac{n}{2}(a_1 + a_n)$

$S_{16} = \frac{16}{2}(5 + 95)$

$S_{16} = 8(100)$

$S_{16} = 800$

9. The common difference is $35 - 38$ or -3. Find n.

$a_n = a_1 + (n - 1)d$

$2 = 38 + (n - 1)(-3)$

$2 = 38 - 3n + 3$

$2 = 41 - 3n$

$-39 = -3n$

$13 = n$

Now find the sum.

$S_n = \frac{n}{2}(a_1 + a_n)$

$S_{13} = \frac{13}{2}(38 + 2)$

$S_{13} = \frac{13}{2}(40)$

$S_{13} = 260$

10. There are 7 terms, $a_1 = 2(1) + 1$ or 3, and $a_7 = 2(7) + 1$ or 15.

$S_n = \frac{n}{2}(a_1 + a_n)$

$S_7 = \frac{7}{2}(3 + 15)$

$S_7 = \frac{7}{2}(18)$

$S_7 = 63$

11. There are 5 terms, $a_1 = 3(3) + 4$ or 13, and $a_5 = 3(7) + 4$ or 25.

$S_n = \frac{n}{2}(a_1 + a_n)$

$S_5 = \frac{5}{2}(13 + 25)$

$S_5 = \frac{5}{2}(38)$

$S_5 = 95$

12. First find n.

$S_n = \frac{n}{2}(a_1 + a_n)$

$726 = \frac{n}{2}(11 + 110)$

$726 = \frac{n}{2}(121)$

$1452 = 121n$

$12 = n$

Now find d.

$a_n = a_1 + (n - 1)d$

$110 = 11 + (12 - 1)d$

$99 = 11d$

$9 = d$

Now find a_2 and a_3.

$a_2 = 11 + 9$ or 20

$a_3 = 20 + 9$ or 29

The first three terms are 11, 20, and 29.

13. First find a_1.

$S_n = \frac{n}{2}(a_1 + a_n)$

$120 = \frac{8}{2}(a_1 + 36)$

$120 = 4(a_1 + 36)$

$30 = a_1 + 36$

$-6 = a_1$

Now find d.

$a_n = a_1 + (n - 1)d$

$36 = -6 + (8 - 1)d$

$42 = 7d$

$6 = d$

Now find a_2 and a_3.

$a_2 = -6 + 6$ or 0

$a_3 = 0 + 6$ or 6

The first three terms are -6, 0, and 6.

14. $a_1 = 1$, $a_n = 7$, and $n = 7$

$S_n = \frac{n}{2}(a_1 + a_n)$

$S_7 = \frac{7}{2}(1 + 7)$

$S_7 = \frac{7}{2}(8)$

$S_7 = 28$

There are 28 candle lightings during the festival.

Pages 586–587   Practice and Apply

15. $S_n = \frac{n}{2}(a_1 + a_n)$

$S_8 = \frac{8}{2}(7 + 79)$

$S_8 = 4(86)$

$S_8 = 344$

16. $S_n = \frac{n}{2}(a_1 + a_n)$

$S_{26} = \frac{26}{2}(58 + (-7))$

$S_{26} = 13(51)$

$S_{26} = 663$

17. $S_n = \frac{n}{2}(a_1 + a_n)$

$S_{19} = \frac{19}{2}(43 + 115)$

$S_{19} = \frac{19}{2}(158)$

$S_{19} = 1501$

18. $S_n = \frac{n}{2}(a_1 + a_n)$

$S_{21} = \frac{21}{2}(76 + 176)$

$S_{21} = \frac{21}{2}(252)$

$S_{21} = 2646$

19. $S_n = \frac{n}{2}[2a_1 + (n - 1)d]$

$S_9 = \frac{9}{2}[2(7) + (9 - 1)(-2)]$

$S_9 = \frac{9}{2}(-2)$

$S_9 = -9$

20. $S_n = \frac{n}{2}[2a_1 + (n - 1)d]$

$S_8 = \frac{8}{2}[2(3) + (8 - 1)(-4)]$

$S_8 = 4(-22)$

$S_8 = -88$

21. $S_n = \frac{n}{2}[2a_1 + (n - 1)d]$

$S_{13} = \frac{13}{2}\left[2(5) + (13 - 1)\left(\frac{1}{2}\right)\right]$

$S_{13} = \frac{13}{2}(16)$

$S_{13} = 104$

22. $S_n = \frac{n}{2}[2a_1 + (n - 1)d]$

$S_{13} = \frac{13}{2}\left[2(12) + (13 - 1)\left(\frac{1}{3}\right)\right]$

$S_{13} = \frac{13}{2}(28)$

$S_{13} = 182$

23. First find a_1.

$a_n = a_1 + (n - 1)d$

$-64 = a_1 + (21 - 1)(-3)$

$-64 = a_1 + 20(-3)$

$-64 = a_1 - 60$

$-4 = a_1$

Now find the sum.

$S_n = \frac{n}{2}(a_1 + a_n)$

$S_{21} = \frac{21}{2}(-4 + (-64))$

$S_{21} = \frac{21}{2}(-68)$

$S_{21} = -714$

24. First find a_1.

$a_n = a_1 + (n - 1)d$

$72 = a_1 + (18 - 1)(7)$

$72 = a_1 + 17(7)$

$72 = a_1 + 119$

$-47 = a_1$

Now find the sum.

$S_n = \frac{n}{2}(a_1 + a_n)$

$S_{18} = \frac{18}{2}(-47 + 72)$

$S_{18} = 9(25)$

$S_{18} = 225$

25. First find a_1.

$a_n = a_1 + (n - 1)d$

$\frac{23}{10} = a_1 + (10 - 1)\left(\frac{1}{5}\right)$

$\frac{23}{10} = a_1 + 9\left(\frac{1}{5}\right)$

$\frac{23}{10} = a_1 + \frac{9}{5}$

$\frac{5}{10} = a_1$

$\frac{1}{2} = a_1$

Now find the sum.

$S_n = \frac{n}{2}(a_1 + a_n)$

$S_{10} = \frac{10}{2}\left(\frac{1}{2} + \frac{23}{10}\right)$

$S_{10} = 5\left(\frac{28}{10}\right)$

$S_{10} = 14$

26. First find a_1.

$a_n = a_1 + (n - 1)d$

$-\frac{53}{12} = a_1 + (20 - 1)\left(-\frac{1}{4}\right)$

$-\frac{53}{12} = a_1 + 19\left(-\frac{1}{4}\right)$

$-\frac{53}{12} = a_1 - \frac{19}{4}$

$\frac{4}{12} = a_1$

$\frac{1}{3} = a_1$

Now find the sum.

$S_n = \frac{n}{2}(a_1 + a_n)$

$S_{20} = \frac{20}{2}\left[\frac{1}{3} + \left(-\frac{53}{12}\right)\right]$

$S_{20} = 10\left(-\frac{49}{12}\right)$

$S_{20} = -\frac{245}{6}$

27. Let $a_1 = 1$, $d = 2$, and $S_n = 100$. Find n.

$$S_n = \frac{n}{2}[2a_1 + (n-1)d]$$

$$100 = \frac{n}{2}[2(1) + (n-1)(2)]$$

$$100 = \frac{n}{2}(2 + 2n - 2)$$

$$100 = \frac{n}{2}(2n)$$

$$100 = n^2$$

$$\pm\sqrt{100} = n$$

$$\pm 10 = n$$

Thus, $n = 10$. She can make 10 rows.

28. Let $a_1 = 4000$, $d = 1000$, and $S_n = 60{,}000$. Find n.

$$S_n = \frac{n}{2}[2a_1 + (n-1)d]$$

$$60{,}000 = \frac{n}{2}[2(4000) + (n-1)(1000)]$$

$$60{,}000 = \frac{n}{2}(8000 + 1000n - 1000)$$

$$60{,}000 = \frac{n}{2}(7000 + 1000n)$$

$$60{,}000 = 3500n + 500n^2$$

$$0 = 500n^2 + 3500n - 60{,}000$$

$$0 = n^2 + 7n - 120$$

$$0 = (n + 15)(n - 8)$$

$$n + 15 = 0 \quad \text{or} \quad n - 8 = 0$$

$$n = -15 \qquad\qquad n = 8$$

Ignore the negative value. Thus, $n = 8$.
The company can be late a maximum of 8 days.

29. The common difference is $13 - 6$ or 7. Find n.

$$a_n = a_1 + (n-1)d$$

$$97 = 6 + (n-1)(7)$$

$$97 = 6 + 7n - 7$$

$$97 = 7n - 1$$

$$98 = 7n$$

$$14 = n$$

Now find the sum.

$$S_n = \frac{n}{2}(a_1 + a_n)$$

$$S_{14} = \frac{14}{2}(6 + 97)$$

$$S_{14} = 7(103)$$

$$S_{14} = 721$$

30. The common difference is $14 - 7$ or 7. Find n.

$$a_n = a_1 + (n-1)d$$

$$98 = 7 + (n-1)(7)$$

$$98 = 7 + 7n - 7$$

$$98 = 7n$$

$$14 = n$$

Now find the sum.

$$S_n = \frac{n}{2}(a_1 + a_n)$$

$$S_{14} = \frac{14}{2}(7 + 98)$$

$$S_{14} = 7(105)$$

$$S_{14} = 735$$

31. The common difference is $30 - 34$ or -4. Find n.

$$a_n = a_1 + (n-1)d$$

$$2 = 34 + (n-1)(-4)$$

$$2 = 34 - 4n + 4$$

$$2 = 38 - 4n$$

$$-36 = -4n$$

$$9 = n$$

Now find the sum.

$$S_n = \frac{n}{2}(a_1 + a_n)$$

$$S_9 = \frac{9}{2}(34 + 2)$$

$$S_9 = \frac{9}{2}(36)$$

$$S_9 = 162$$

32. The common difference is $10 - 16$ or -6. Find n.

$$a_n = a_1 + (n-1)d$$

$$-50 = 16 + (n-1)(-6)$$

$$-50 = 16 - 6n + 6$$

$$-50 = 22 - 6n$$

$$-72 = -6n$$

$$12 = n$$

Now find the sum.

$$S_n = \frac{n}{2}(a_1 + a_n)$$

$$S_{12} = \frac{12}{2}(16 + (-50))$$

$$S_{12} = 6(-34)$$

$$S_{12} = -204$$

33. There are 6 terms, $a_1 = 2(1) + 11$ or 13, and $a_6 = 2(6) + 11$ or 23.

$$S_n = \frac{n}{2}(a_1 + a_n)$$

$$S_6 = \frac{6}{2}(13 + 23)$$

$$S_6 = 3(36)$$

$$S_6 = 108$$

34. There are 5 terms, $a_1 = 2 - 3(1)$ or -1, and $a_5 = 2 - 3(5)$ or -13.

$$S_n = \frac{n}{2}(a_1 + a_n)$$

$$S_5 = \frac{5}{2}(-1 + (-13))$$

$$S_5 = \frac{5}{2}(-14)$$

$$S_5 = -35$$

35. There are 5 terms, $a_1 = 42 - 9(7)$ or -21, and $a_5 = 42 - 9(11)$ or -57.

$$S_n = \frac{n}{2}(a_1 + a_n)$$

$$S_5 = \frac{5}{2}(-21 + (-57))$$

$$S_5 = \frac{5}{2}(-78)$$

$$S_5 = -195$$

36. There are 5 terms, $a_1 = 5(19) - 3$ or 92, and $a_5 = 5(23) - 3$ or 112.

$$S_n = \frac{n}{2}(a_1 + a_n)$$

$$S_5 = \frac{5}{2}(92 + 112)$$

$$S_5 = \frac{5}{2}(204)$$

$$S_5 = 510$$

37. There are 300 terms, $a_1 = 7(1) - 3$ or 4, and $a_{300} = 7(300) - 3$ or 2097.

$$S_n = \frac{n}{2}(a_1 + a_n)$$

$$S_{300} = \frac{300}{2}(4 + 2097)$$

$$S_{300} = 150(2101)$$

$$S_{300} = 315{,}150$$

38. There are 150 terms, $a_1 = 11 + 2(1)$ or 13, and $a_{150} = 11 + 2(150)$ or 311.

$$S_n = \frac{n}{2}(a_1 + a_n)$$
$$S_{150} = \frac{150}{2}(13 + 311)$$
$$S_{150} = 75(324)$$
$$S_{150} = 24{,}300$$

39. There are 1000 terms, $a_1 = 2$, and $d = 2$.

$$S_n = \frac{n}{2}[2a_1 + (n - 1)d]$$
$$S_{1000} = \frac{1000}{2}[2(2) + (1000 - 1)(2)]$$
$$S_{1000} = 500(2002)$$
$$S_{1000} = 1{,}001{,}000$$

40. $a_1 = 3$ $a_n = 999$, and $d = 3$. Find n.
$$a_n = a_1 + (n - 1)d$$
$$999 = 3 + (n - 1)(3)$$
$$999 = 3 + 3n - 3$$
$$999 = 3n$$
$$333 = n$$

Find the sum.
$$S_n = \frac{n}{2}(a_1 + a_n)$$
$$S_{333} = \frac{333}{2}(3 + 999)$$
$$S_{333} = \frac{333}{2}(1002)$$
$$S_{333} = 166{,}833$$

41. First find n.
$$S_n = \frac{n}{2}(a_1 + a_n)$$
$$2247 = \frac{n}{2}(17 + 197)$$
$$2247 = \frac{n}{2}(214)$$
$$2247 = 107n$$
$$21 = n$$

Now find d.
$$a_n = a_1 + (n - 1)d$$
$$197 = 17 + (21 - 1)d$$
$$180 = 20d$$
$$9 = d$$

Now find a_2 and a_3.
$a_2 = 17 + 9$ or 26
$a_3 = 26 + 9$ or 35
The first three terms are 17, 26, and 35.

42. First find n.
$$S_n = \frac{n}{2}(a_1 + a_n)$$
$$18{,}423 = \frac{n}{2}(-13 + 427)$$
$$18{,}423 = \frac{n}{2}(414)$$
$$18{,}423 = 207n$$
$$89 = n$$

Now find d.
$$a_n = a_1 + (n - 1)d$$
$$427 = -13 + (89 - 1)d$$
$$440 = 88d$$
$$5 = d$$

Now find a_2 and a_3.
$a_2 = -13 + 5 = -8$
$a_3 = -8 + 5 = -3$
The first three terms are -13, -8, and -3.

43. First find a_1.
$$S_n = \frac{n}{2}(a_1 + a_n)$$
$$1023 = \frac{31}{2}(a_1 + 78)$$
$$1023 = \frac{31}{2}a_1 + 1209$$
$$-186 = \frac{31}{2}a_1$$
$$-12 = a_1$$

Now find d.
$$a_n = a_1 + (n - 1)d$$
$$78 = -12 + (31 - 1)d$$
$$90 = 30d$$
$$3 = d$$

Now find a_2 and a_3.
$a_2 = -12 + 3$ or -9
$a_3 = -9 + 3$ or -6
The first three terms are -12, -9, and -6.

44. First find a_1.
$$S_n = \frac{n}{2}(a_1 + a_n)$$
$$1102 = \frac{19}{2}(a_1 + 103)$$
$$1102 = \frac{19}{2}a_1 + \frac{1957}{2}$$
$$\frac{247}{2} = \frac{19}{2}a_1$$
$$13 = a_1$$

Now find d.
$$a_n = a_1 + (n - 1)d$$
$$103 = 13 + (19 - 1)d$$
$$90 = 18d$$
$$5 = d$$

Now find a_2 and a_3.
$a_2 = 13 + 5$ or 18
$a_3 = 18 + 5$ or 23
The first three terms are 13, 18, and 23.

45. $a_1 = 2.65$, $d = 5.3$, and $n = 10$.
$$S_n = \frac{n}{2}[2a_1 + (n - 1)d]$$
$$S_{10} = \frac{10}{2}[2(2.65) + (10 - 1)(5.3)]$$
$$S_{10} = 5(53)$$
$$S_{10} = 265$$
The object would fall 265 feet.

46. True; for any series, $2a_1 + 2a_2 + 2a_3 + \ldots + 2a_n = 2(a_1 + a_2 + a_3 + \ldots + a_n)$.

47. False; for example, $7 + 10 + 13 + 16 = 46$, but $7 + 10 + 13 + 16 + 19 + 22 + 25 + 28 = 140$.

48. Arithmetic series can be used to find the seating capacity of an amphitheater. Answers should include the following.

- The sequence represents the numbers of seats in the rows. The sum of the first n terms of the series is the seating capacity of the first n rows.
- One method is to write out the terms and add them: $18 + 22 + 26 + 30 + 34 + 38 + 42 + 46 + 50 + 54 = 360$. Another method is to use the formula $S_n = \frac{n}{2}[2a_1 + (n - 1)d]$: $S_{10} = \frac{10}{2}[2(18) + (10 - 1)4]$ or 360.

49. C; $a_1 = 18$, $a_n = 50$, and $d = 4$. Find n.
$$a_n = a_1 + (n - 1)d$$
$$50 = 18 + (n - 1)(4)$$
$$50 = 18 + 4n - 4$$
$$50 = 14 + 4n$$
$$36 = 4n$$
$$9 = n$$
Find the sum.
$$S_n = \frac{n}{2}(a_1 + a_n)$$
$$S_9 = \frac{9}{2}(18 + 50)$$
$$S_9 = \frac{9}{2}(68)$$
$$S_9 = 306$$

50. C; $a_1 = 36$, $n = 3$, $S_n = 180$. Find a_3.
$$S_n = \frac{n}{2}(a_1 + a_n)$$
$$180 = \frac{3}{2}(36 + a_3)$$
$$180 = 54 + \frac{3}{2}a_3$$
$$126 = \frac{3}{2}a_3$$
$$84 = a_3$$
The largest angle measures 84°.

51. KEYSTROKES: 2nd [LIST] ▶ ▶ 5 2nd [LIST]
▶ 5 2 X,T,θ,n + 5 , X,T,θ,n , 21 ,
75 , 1)) ENTER
The sum is 5555.

52. KEYSTROKES: 2nd [LIST] ▶ ▶ 5 2nd [LIST]
▶ 5 3 X,T,θ,n − 1 , X,T,θ,n , 10 ,
50 , 1)) ENTER
The sum is 3649.

53. KEYSTROKES: 2nd [LIST] ▶ ▶ 5 2nd [LIST]
▶ 5 4 X,T,θ,n + 3 , X,T,θ,n , 20 ,
60 , 1)) ENTER
The sum is 6683.

Page 587   Maintain Your Skills

54. $a_n = a_1 + (n - 1)d$
$$a_{14} = 46 + (14 - 1)(5)$$
$$a_{14} = 46 + 13(5)$$
$$a_{14} = 46 + 65 \text{ or } 111$$

55. $a_n = a_1 + (n - 1)d$
$$a_{22} = 12 + (22 - 1)(-7)$$
$$a_{22} = 12 + 21(-7)$$
$$a_{22} = 12 + (-147) \text{ or } -135$$

56.
$$y = ae^{-0.1813t}$$
$$0.5a = ae^{-0.1813t}$$
$$0.5 = e^{-0.1813t}$$
$$\ln 0.5 = \ln e^{-0.1813t}$$
$$\ln 0.5 = -0.1813t$$
$$\frac{\ln 0.5}{-0.1813} = t$$
$$3.82 \approx t$$
The half-life of Radon-222 is about 3.82 days.

57.
$$x^2 + 9x + 20.25 = 0$$
$$(x + 4.5)^2 = 0$$
$$x + 4.5 = 0$$
$$x = -4.5 \text{ or } -\frac{9}{2}$$

58.
$$9x^2 + 96x + 256 = 0$$
$$x^2 + \frac{32}{3}x + \frac{256}{9} = 0$$
$$\left(x + \frac{16}{3}\right)^2 = 0$$
$$x + \frac{16}{3} = 0$$
$$x = -\frac{16}{3}$$

59.
$$x^2 - 3x - 20 = 0$$
$$x^2 - 3x = 20$$
$$x^2 - 3x + \frac{9}{4} = 20 + \frac{9}{4}$$
$$\left(x - \frac{3}{2}\right)^2 = \frac{89}{4}$$
$$x - \frac{3}{2} = \pm\sqrt{\frac{89}{4}}$$
$$x = \frac{3}{2} \pm \frac{\sqrt{89}}{2}$$
$$x = \frac{3 \pm \sqrt{89}}{2}$$

60. $5\sqrt{3} - 4\sqrt{3} = \sqrt{3}$

61.
$$\sqrt{26} \cdot \sqrt{39} \cdot \sqrt{14} = \sqrt{26 \cdot 39 \cdot 14}$$
$$= \sqrt{14{,}196}$$
$$= \sqrt{2^2 \cdot 13^2 \cdot 3 \cdot 7}$$
$$= \sqrt{2^2} \cdot \sqrt{13^2} \cdot \sqrt{3 \cdot 7}$$
$$= 2 \cdot 13\sqrt{21}$$
$$= 26\sqrt{21}$$

62. $(\sqrt{10} - \sqrt{6})(\sqrt{5} + \sqrt{3})$
$$= \sqrt{10} \cdot \sqrt{5} + \sqrt{10} \cdot \sqrt{3} - \sqrt{6} \cdot \sqrt{5} - \sqrt{6} \cdot \sqrt{3}$$
$$= \sqrt{10 \cdot 5} + \sqrt{10 \cdot 3} - \sqrt{6 \cdot 5} - \sqrt{6 \cdot 3}$$
$$= \sqrt{50} + \sqrt{30} - \sqrt{30} - \sqrt{18}$$
$$= \sqrt{5^2 \cdot 2} - \sqrt{3^2 \cdot 2}$$
$$= 5\sqrt{2} - 3\sqrt{2}$$
$$= 2\sqrt{2}$$

63. $a \cdot b^{n-1} = 1 \cdot 2^{5-1}$
$$= 2^4 \text{ or } 16$$

64. $a \cdot b^{n-1} = 2(-3)^{4-1}$
$$= 2(-3)^3$$
$$= 2(-27) \text{ or } -54$$

65. $a \cdot b^{n-1} = 18\left(\frac{1}{3}\right)^{6-1}$
$$= 18\left(\frac{1}{3}\right)^5$$
$$= 18\left(\frac{1}{243}\right) \text{ or } \frac{2}{27}$$

11-3   Geometric Sequences

Pages 590–591   Check for Understanding

1a. Geometric; since $\frac{-2}{1} = -2$, $\frac{4}{-2} = -2$, and $\frac{-8}{4} = -2$, the terms have a common ratio of -2.

1b. Arithmetic; since $-2 - 1 = -3$, $-5 - (-2) = -3$, and $-8 - (-5) = -3$, the terms have a common difference of -3.

2. Sample answer: $1, \frac{2}{3}, \frac{4}{9}, \frac{8}{27}, \ldots$

3. Marika; Lori divided in the wrong order when finding r.

4. First find the common ratio.

$r = \frac{30}{20}$ or 1.5

Multiply by 1.5.

$a_4 = 45(1.5)$ or 67.5

$a_5 = 67.5(1.5)$ or 101.25

The next two terms are 67.5 and 101.25.

5. Find the common ratio.

$r = \frac{\frac{1}{2}}{-\frac{1}{4}}$

$= \frac{1}{2}\left(-\frac{4}{1}\right)$ or -2

Multiply by -2.

$a_4 = -1 \cdot (-2)$ or 2

$a_5 = 2 \cdot (-2)$ or -4

The next two terms are 2 and -4.

6. Multiply by 3.

$a_2 = -2 \cdot 3$ or -6

$a_3 = -6 \cdot 3$ or -18

$a_4 = -18 \cdot 3$ or -54

$a_5 = -54 \cdot 3$ or -162

The first five terms are -2, -6, -18, -54, and -162.

7. $a_1 = 60$ and $r = \frac{30}{60}$ or $\frac{1}{2}$

$a_n = a_1 \cdot r^{n-1}$

$a_9 = 60\left(\frac{1}{2}\right)^{9-1}$

$= 60\left(\frac{1}{256}\right)$

$= \frac{15}{64}$

8. $a_n = a_1 \cdot r^{n-1}$

$a_4 = 7 \cdot 2^{4-1}$

$a_4 = 7 \cdot 8$

$a_4 = 56$

9. First find a_1.

$a_n = a_1 \cdot r^{n-1}$

$32 = a_1(-0.5)^{3-1}$

$32 = 0.25a_1$

$128 = a_1$

Now find a_6.

$a_n = a_1 \cdot r^{n-1}$

$a_6 = 128(-0.5)^{6-1}$

$a_6 = 128(-0.03125)$

$a_6 = -4$

10. $a_1 = 4$ and $r = \frac{8}{4}$ or 2

$a_n = a_1 \cdot r^{n-1}$

$a_n = 4 \cdot 2^{n-1}$

11. First find r.

$a_n = a_1 \cdot r^{n-1}$

$a_4 = 1 \cdot r^{4-1}$

$27 = r^3$

$3 = r$

Multiply by 3.

$a_2 = 1 \cdot 3$ or 3

$a_3 = 3 \cdot 3$ or 9

The geometric means are 3 and 9.

12. A; Find the common ratio.

$r = \frac{\frac{3}{4}}{\frac{9}{4}}$

$= \frac{3}{4} \cdot \frac{4}{9}$ or $\frac{1}{3}$

Multiply by $\frac{1}{3}$.

$a_5 = \frac{1}{12} \cdot \frac{1}{3}$ or $\frac{1}{36}$

The missing term is $\frac{1}{36}$.

Pages 591–592   Practice and Apply

13. First find the common ratio.

$r = \frac{135}{405}$ or $\frac{1}{3}$

Multiply by $\frac{1}{3}$.

$a_4 = 45 \cdot \frac{1}{3}$ or 15

$a_5 = 15 \cdot \frac{1}{3}$ or 5

The next two terms are 15 and 5.

14. First find the common ratio.

$r = \frac{108}{81}$ or $\frac{4}{3}$

Multiply by $\frac{4}{3}$.

$a_4 = 144 \cdot \frac{4}{3}$ or 192

$a_5 = 192 \cdot \frac{4}{3}$ or 256

The next two terms are 192 and 256.

15. First find the common ratio.

$r = \frac{24}{16}$ or $\frac{3}{2}$

Multiply by $\frac{3}{2}$.

$a_4 = 36 \cdot \frac{3}{2}$ or 54

$a_5 = 54 \cdot \frac{3}{2}$ or 81

The next two terms are 54 and 81.

16. First find the common ratio.

$r = \frac{108}{162}$ or $\frac{2}{3}$

Multiply by $\frac{2}{3}$.

$a_4 = 72 \cdot \frac{2}{3}$ or 48

$a_5 = 48 \cdot \frac{2}{3}$ or 32

The next two terms are 48 and 32.

17. First find the common ratio.

$r = \frac{\frac{5}{3}}{\frac{5}{2}}$

$= \frac{5}{3} \cdot \frac{2}{5}$ or $\frac{2}{3}$

Multiply by $\frac{2}{3}$.

$a_4 = \frac{10}{9} \cdot \frac{2}{3}$ or $\frac{20}{27}$

$a_5 = \frac{20}{27} \cdot \frac{2}{3}$ or $\frac{40}{81}$

The next two terms are $\frac{20}{27}$ and $\frac{40}{81}$.

18. First find the common ratio.

$$r = \dfrac{\frac{5}{6}}{\frac{1}{3}}$$

$$= \frac{5}{6} \cdot \frac{3}{1} \text{ or } \frac{5}{2}$$

Multiply by $\frac{5}{2}$.

$$a_4 = \frac{25}{12} \cdot \frac{5}{2} \text{ or } \frac{125}{24}$$

$$a_5 = \frac{125}{24} \cdot \frac{5}{2} \text{ or } \frac{625}{48}$$

The next two terms are $\frac{125}{24}$ and $\frac{625}{48}$.

19. First find the common ratio.

$$r = \frac{-1.5}{1.25} \text{ or } -1.2$$

Multiply by -1.2.

$a_4 = 1.8 \cdot (-1.2) \text{ or } -2.16$

$a_5 = -2.16 \cdot (-1.2) \text{ or } 2.592$

The next two terms are -2.16 and 2.592.

20. First find the common ratio.

$$r = \frac{-3.5}{1.4} \text{ or } -2.5$$

Multiply by -2.5.

$a_4 = 8.75 \cdot (-2.5) \text{ or } -21.875$

$a_5 = -21.875 \cdot (-2.5) \text{ or } 54.6875$

The next two terms are -21.875 and 54.6875.

21. Multiply by -3.

$a_2 = 2 \cdot (-3) \text{ or } -6$

$a_3 = -6 \cdot (-3) \text{ or } 18$

$a_4 = 18 \cdot (-3) \text{ or } -54$

$a_5 = -54 \cdot (-3) \text{ or } 162$

The first five terms are 2, -6, 18, -54, and 162.

22. Multiply by 4.

$a_2 = 1 \cdot 4 \text{ or } 4$

$a_3 = 4 \cdot 4 \text{ or } 16$

$a_4 = 16 \cdot 4 \text{ or } 64$

$a_5 = 64 \cdot 4 \text{ or } 256$

The first five terms are 1, 4, 16, 64, and 256.

23. Multiply by $\frac{1}{3}$.

$a_2 = 243 \cdot \frac{1}{3} \text{ or } 81$

$a_3 = 81 \cdot \frac{1}{3} \text{ or } 27$

$a_4 = 27 \cdot \frac{1}{3} \text{ or } 9$

$a_5 = 9 \cdot \frac{1}{3} \text{ or } 3$

The first five terms are 243, 81, 27, 9, and 3.

24. Multiply by $-\frac{1}{2}$.

$a_2 = 576 \cdot \left(-\frac{1}{2}\right) \text{ or } -288$

$a_3 = -288 \cdot \left(-\frac{1}{2}\right) \text{ or } 144$

$a_4 = 144 \cdot \left(-\frac{1}{2}\right) \text{ or } -72$

$a_5 = -72 \cdot \left(-\frac{1}{2}\right) \text{ or } 36$

The first five terms are 576, -288, 144, -72, and 36.

25. $a_n = 12\left(\frac{1}{2}\right)^{n-1}$

$a_7 = 12\left(\frac{1}{2}\right)^{7-1}$

$a_7 = 12\left(\frac{1}{64}\right)$

$a_7 = \frac{3}{16}$

26. $a_n = \frac{1}{3} \cdot 6^{n-1}$

$a_6 = \frac{1}{3} \cdot 6^{6-1}$

$a_6 = \frac{1}{3}(7776)$

$a_6 = 2592$

27. $a_n = a_1 \cdot r^{n-1}$

$a_8 = \frac{1}{3} \cdot 3^{8-1}$

$a_8 = \frac{1}{3}(2187)$

$a_8 = 729$

28. $a_n = a_1 \cdot r^{n-1}$

$a_9 = \frac{1}{64} \cdot 4^{9-1}$

$= \frac{1}{64}(65{,}536)$

$= 1024$

29. $a_n = a_1 \cdot r^{n-1}$

$a_6 = 16{,}807 \cdot \left(\frac{3}{7}\right)^{6-1}$

$a_6 = 16{,}807\left(\frac{243}{16{,}807}\right)$

$a_6 = 243$

30. $a_n = a_1 \cdot r^{n-1}$

$a_8 = 4096 \cdot \left(\frac{1}{4}\right)^{8-1}$

$a_8 = 4096\left(\frac{1}{16{,}384}\right)$

$a_8 = \frac{1}{4}$

31. Find a_1.

$a_n = a_1 \cdot r^{n-1}$

$a_4 = a_1 \cdot (0.5)^{4-1}$

$16 = 0.125\,a_1$

$128 = a_1$

Now find a_8.

$a_n = a_1 \cdot r^{n-1}$

$a_8 = 128 \cdot (0.5)^{8-1}$

$a_8 = 128(0.0078125)$

$a_8 = 1$

32. Find a_1.

$a_n = a_1 \cdot r^{n-1}$

$a_6 = a_1 \cdot 2^{6-1}$

$3 = 32a_1$

$\frac{3}{32} = a_1$

Now find a_{12}.

$a_n = a_1 \cdot r^{n-1}$

$a_{12} = \frac{3}{32} \cdot 2^{12-1}$

$a_{12} = \frac{3}{32}(2048)$

$a_{12} = 192$

33. Find the common ratio.

$r = \dfrac{1}{\frac{1}{5}}$

$= 1 \cdot \dfrac{5}{1}$ or 5

Now find a_9.

$a_n = a_1 \cdot r^{n-1}$

$a_9 = \dfrac{1}{5} \cdot 5^{9-1}$

$a_9 = \dfrac{1}{5}(390,625)$

$a_9 = 78,125$

34. Find the common ratio.

$r = \dfrac{\frac{1}{16}}{\frac{1}{32}}$

$= \dfrac{1}{16} \cdot \dfrac{32}{1}$ or 2

Now find a_7.

$a_n = a_1 \cdot r^{n-1}$

$a_7 = \dfrac{1}{32} \cdot 2^{7-1}$

$a_7 = \dfrac{1}{32}(64)$

$a_7 = 2$

35. Find the common ratio.

$r = \dfrac{-12}{4}$ or -3

Now find a_8.

$a_n = a_1 \cdot r^{n-1}$

$a_8 = 4 \cdot (-3)^{8-1}$

$a_8 = 4(-2187)$

$a_8 = -8748$

36. Find the common ratio.

$r = \dfrac{90}{540}$ or $\dfrac{1}{6}$

Now find a_6.

$a_n = a_1 \cdot r^{n-1}$

$a_6 = 540\left(\dfrac{1}{6}\right)^{6-1}$

$a_6 = 540\left(\dfrac{1}{7776}\right)$

$a_6 = \dfrac{5}{72}$

37. Since 1 ton = 2000 pounds, $a_1 = 2000$. Since the sculpture loses $\dfrac{1}{5}$ of its weight, it retains $\dfrac{4}{5}$, so $r = \dfrac{4}{5}$ or 0.8. After 5 hours, $n = 6$.

$a_n = a_1 \cdot r^{n-1}$

$a_6 = 2000 \cdot (0.8)^{6-1}$

$a_6 = 2000(0.32768)$

$a_6 = 655.36$

After 5 hours, the sculpture will weigh 655.36 pounds.

38. Find Geraldo's salary after the first 4% increase.

4% of 40,000 $= 0.04(40,000)$

$= 1600$

After the raise, his salary is 40,000 + 1600 or $41,600.

Find r.

$r = \dfrac{41,600}{40,000}$ or 1.04

Find the salary after the fourth increase.

$a_1 = 40,000$ and $n = 5$.

$a_n = a_1 \cdot r^{n-1}$

$a_5 = 40,000 \cdot 1.04^{5-1}$

$\approx 46,794.34$

Geraldo's salary will be about $46,794.34.

39. Find r.

$r = \dfrac{12}{36}$ or $\dfrac{1}{3}$

Write an equation.

$a_n = a_1 \cdot r^{n-1}$

$a_n = 36\left(\dfrac{1}{3}\right)^{n-1}$

40. Find r.

$r = \dfrac{16}{64}$ or $\dfrac{1}{4}$

Write an equation.

$a_n = a_1 \cdot r^{n-1}$

$a_n = 64\left(\dfrac{1}{4}\right)^{n-1}$

41. Find r.

$r = \dfrac{10}{-2}$ or -5

Write an equation.

$a_n = a_1 \cdot r^{n-1}$

$a_n = -2(-5)^{n-1}$

42. Find r.

$r = \dfrac{-12}{4}$ or -3

Write an equation.

$a_n = a_1 \cdot r^{n-1}$

$a_n = 4(-3)^{n-1}$

43. Find r.

$a_n = a_1 \cdot r^{n-1}$

$a_5 = 9 \cdot r^{5-1}$

$144 = 9r^4$

$16 = r^4$

$\pm 2 = r$

Use $r = 2$.

$a_2 = 9(2)$ or 18

$a_3 = 18(2)$ or 36

$a_4 = 36(2)$ or 72

Use $r = -2$.

$a_2 = 9(-2)$ or -18

$a_3 = -18(-2)$ or 36

$a_4 = 36(-2)$ or -72

The geometric means are 18, 36, and 72, or -18, 36, and -72.

44. Find r.

$a_n = a_1 \cdot r^{n-1}$

$a_5 = 4 \cdot r^{5-1}$

$324 = 4r^4$

$81 = r^4$

$\pm 3 = r$

Use $r = 3$.

$a_2 = 4(3)$ or 12

$a_3 = 12(3)$ or 36

$a_4 = 36(3)$ or 108

Use $r = -3$.

$a_2 = 4(-3)$ or -12

$a_3 = -12(-3)$ or 36

$a_4 = 36(-3)$ or -108

The geometric means are 12, 36, and 108, or -12, 36, and -108.

45. Find r.
$a_n = a_1 \cdot r^{n-1}$
$a_6 = 32 \cdot r^{6-1}$
$1 = 32r^5$
$\dfrac{1}{32} = r^5$
$\dfrac{1}{2} = r$

Find the geometric means.
$a_2 = 32\left(\dfrac{1}{2}\right)$ or 16
$a_3 = 16\left(\dfrac{1}{2}\right)$ or 8
$a_4 = 8\left(\dfrac{1}{2}\right)$ or 4
$a_5 = 4\left(\dfrac{1}{2}\right)$ or 2
The geometric means are 16, 8, 4, and 2.

46. Find r.
$a_n = a_1 \cdot r^{n-1}$
$a_6 = 3 \cdot r^{6-1}$
$96 = 3r^5$
$32 = r^5$
$2 = r$

Find the geometric means.
$a_2 = 3(2)$ or 6
$a_3 = 6(2)$ or 12
$a_4 = 12(2)$ or 24
$a_5 = 24(2)$ or 48
The geometric means are 6, 12, 24, and 48.

47. The half-life of Iodine-131 is 8 days.

48. $a_1 = 80$, $r = \dfrac{1}{2}$, and $n = 5$
$a_n = a_1 \cdot r^{n-1}$
$a_5 = 80\left(\dfrac{1}{2}\right)^{5-1}$
$a_5 = 80\left(\dfrac{1}{16}\right)$ or 5
There will be 5 mg of Iodine-131 left after 32 days.

49. False; the sequence 1, 4, 9, 16, ..., for example, is neither arithmetic nor geometric.

50. False; the sequence 1, 1, 1, 1, ..., for example, is arithmetic ($d = 0$) and geometric ($r = 1$).

51. The heights of the bounces of a ball and the heights from which a bouncing ball falls each form geometric sequences. Answers should include the following.
- 3, 1.8, 1.08, 0.648, 0.3888
- The common ratios are the same, but the first terms are different. The sequence of heights from which the ball falls is the sequence of heights of the bounces with the term 3 inserted at the beginning.

52. A; Find the common ratio.
$r = \dfrac{10}{-5}$ or -2
Find the fifth term.
$a_5 = 40(-2)$ or -80
The missing term is -80.

53. C; Find the common ratio.
$r = \dfrac{72}{144}$ or $\dfrac{1}{2}$
Find a_{10}.
$a_n = a_1 \cdot r^{n-1}$
$a_{10} = 144\left(\dfrac{1}{2}\right)^{10-1}$
$a_{10} = 144\left(\dfrac{1}{512}\right)$ or $\dfrac{9}{32}$

Page 592 Maintain Your Skills

54. $S_n = \dfrac{n}{2}(a_1 + a_n)$
$S_{23} = \dfrac{23}{2}(11 + 44)$
$S_{23} = \dfrac{23}{2}(55)$ or 632.5

55. $S_n = \dfrac{n}{2}[2a_1 + (n-1)d]$
$S_{14} = \dfrac{14}{2}[2(-5) + (14-1)(3)]$
$= 7(29)$ or 203

56. Find d.
$a_n = a_1 + (n-1)d$
$27 = 15 + (4-1)d$
$12 = 3d$
$4 = d$
Find the arithmetic means.
15 $\underset{+4}{\underset{\frown}{\quad}}$ 19 $\underset{+4}{\underset{\frown}{\quad}}$ 23
The arithmetic means are 19 and 23.

57. Find d.
$a_n = a_1 + (n-1)d$
$-24 = -8 + (5-1)d$
$-16 = 4d$
$-4 = d$
Find the arithmetic means.
$-8 \underset{+(-4)}{\underset{\frown}{\quad}} -12 \underset{+(-4)}{\underset{\frown}{\quad}} -16 \underset{+(-4)}{\underset{\frown}{\quad}} -20$
The arithmetic means are -12, -16, and -20.

58. Find the lengths of the sides.
With endpoints $(2, 4)$ and $(-1, 3)$:
$d = \sqrt{(x_2 - x_1)^2 + (y_2 - y_1)^2}$
$= \sqrt{(-1 - 2)^2 + (3 - 4)^2}$
$= \sqrt{(-3)^2 + (-1)^2}$
$= \sqrt{10}$
With endpoints $(-1, 3)$ and $(1, -3)$:
$d = \sqrt{(x_2 - x_1)^2 + (y_2 - y_1)^2}$
$= \sqrt{(1 - (-1))^2 + (-3 - 3)^2}$
$= \sqrt{2^2 + (-6)^2}$
$= \sqrt{40}$ or $2\sqrt{10}$
With endpoints $(1, -3)$ and $(2, 4)$:
$d = \sqrt{(x_2 - x_1)^2 + (y_2 - y_1)^2}$
$= \sqrt{(2 - 1)^2 + (4 - (-3))^2}$
$= \sqrt{1^2 + 7^2}$
$= \sqrt{50}$ or $5\sqrt{2}$
The perimeter is $\sqrt{10} + 2\sqrt{10} + 5\sqrt{2}$ or $5\sqrt{2} + 3\sqrt{10}$ units.

59. $\dfrac{1-2^7}{1-2} = \dfrac{1-128}{-1}$

$= \dfrac{-127}{-1}$ or 127

60. $\dfrac{1-\left(\frac{1}{2}\right)^6}{1-\left(\frac{1}{2}\right)} = \dfrac{1-\frac{1}{64}}{\frac{1}{2}}$

$= \dfrac{63}{64} \cdot \dfrac{2}{1}$ or $\dfrac{63}{32}$

61. $\dfrac{1-\left(-\frac{1}{3}\right)^5}{1-\left(-\frac{1}{3}\right)} = \dfrac{1-\left(-\frac{1}{243}\right)}{\frac{4}{3}}$

$= \dfrac{244}{243} \cdot \dfrac{3}{4}$ or $\dfrac{61}{81}$

Page 592   Practice Quiz 1

1. $a_n = a_1 + (n-1)d$

$a_{14} = 7 + (14-1)(3)$

$= 7 + 13(3)$

$= 7 + 39$ or 46

2. $a_n = a_1 + (n-1)d$

$a_8 = 2 + (8-1)\left(\dfrac{1}{2}\right)$

$= 2 + 7\left(\dfrac{1}{2}\right)$

$= 2 + \dfrac{7}{2}$ or $\dfrac{11}{2}$

3. $S_n = \dfrac{n}{2}(a_1 + a_n)$

$S_{11} = \dfrac{11}{2}(5 + 29)$

$S_{11} = \dfrac{11}{2}(34)$ or 187

4. Find d.

$d = 12 - 6$ or 6

Now find n.

$a_n = a_1 + (n-1)d$

$96 = 6 + (n-1)(6)$

$96 = 6 + 6n - 6$

$96 = 6n$

$16 = n$

Find the sum.

$S_n = \dfrac{n}{2}(a_1 + a_n)$

$S_{16} = \dfrac{16}{2}(6 + 96)$

$S_{16} = 8(102)$ or 816

5. Find r.

$r = \dfrac{-243}{729}$ or $-\dfrac{1}{3}$

Find a_7.

$a_n = a_1 \cdot r^{n-1}$

$a_7 = 729\left(-\dfrac{1}{3}\right)^{7-1}$

$a_7 = 729\left(\dfrac{1}{729}\right)$ or 1

Page 593   Graphing Calculator Investigation (Preview of Lesson 11-4)

1. KEYSTROKES: [STAT] [ENTER]

Position the cursor on L1.

[2nd] [LIST] [▶]5 [ALPHA] [N] [,] [ALPHA]

[N] [,] 1 [,] 10 [,] 1 [)] [ENTER]

Position the cursor on L2.

[2nd] [LIST] [▶]5 [(] 1 [÷] 2 [)] [^] [ALPHA]

[N] [,] [ALPHA] [N] [,] 1 [,] 10 [,] 1 [)]

[ENTER]

As n increases, the terms of the sequence get closer and closer to 0. This suggests that the limit of the sequence is 0.

2. KEYSTROKES: [STAT] [ENTER]

Position the cursor on L1.

[2nd] [LIST] [▶]5 [ALPHA] [N] [,] [ALPHA]

[N] [,] 1 [,] 10 [,] 1 [)] [ENTER]

Position the cursor on L2.

[2nd] [LIST] [▶]5 [(] [(-)] 1 [÷] 2 [)] [^]

[ALPHA] [N] [,] [ALPHA] [N] [,] 1 [,] 10 [,]

1 [)] [ENTER]

As n increases, the terms of the sequence get closer and closer to 0. This suggests that the limit of the sequence is 0.

3. KEYSTROKES: [STAT] [ENTER]

Position the cursor on L1.

[2nd] [LIST] [▶]5 [ALPHA] [N] [,] [ALPHA]

[N] [,] 1 [,] 10 [,] 1 [)] [ENTER]

Position the cursor on L2.

[2nd] [LIST] [▶]5 4 [^] [ALPHA] [N] [,]

[ALPHA] [N] [,] 1 [,] 10 [,] 1 [)] [ENTER]

As n increases, the terms of the sequence get larger and larger. This suggests that the limit of the sequence does not exist.

4. KEYSTROKES: [STAT] [ENTER]

Position the cursor on L1.

[2nd] [LIST] [▶]5 [ALPHA] [N] [,] [ALPHA]

[N] [,] 1 [,] 10 [,] 1 [)] [ENTER]

Position the cursor on L2.

[2nd] [LIST] [▶]5 1 [÷] [ALPHA] [N] [x^2] [,]

[ALPHA] [N] [,] 1 [,] 10 [,] 1 [)] [ENTER]

As n increases, the terms of the sequence get closer and closer to 0. This suggests that the limit of the sequence is 0.

5. KEYSTROKES: [STAT] [ENTER]

Position the cursor on L1.

[2nd] [LIST] [▶]5 [ALPHA] [N] [,] [ALPHA]
[N] [,] 1 [,] 10 [,] 1 [)] [ENTER]

Position the cursor on L2.

[2nd] [LIST] [▶]5 2 [∧] [ALPHA] [N] [÷] [(] 2
[∧] [ALPHA] [N] [+] 1 [)] [,] [ALPHA] [N]
[,] 1 [,] 10 [,] 1 [)] [ENTER]

As n increases, the terms of the sequence get closer and closer to 1. This suggests that the limit of the sequence is 1.

6. KEYSTROKES: [STAT] [ENTER]

Position the cursor on L1.

[2nd] [LIST] [▶]5 [ALPHA] [N] [,] [ALPHA]
[N] [,] 1 [,] 10 [,] 1 [)] [ENTER]

Position the cursor on L2.

[2nd] [LIST] [▶]5 [ALPHA] [N] [x^2] [÷] [(]
[ALPHA] [N] [+] 1 [)] [,] [ALPHA] [N] [,]
1 [,] 10 [,] 1 [)] [ENTER]

As n increases, the terms of the sequence get larger and larger. This suggests that the limit of the sequence does not exist.

11-4 | Geometric Series

Page 596–597   Check for Understanding

1. Sample answer: $4 + 2 + 1 + \frac{1}{2}$

2. The polynomial is a geometric series with first term 1, common ratio x, and 4 terms. The sum is $\frac{1(1-x^4)}{1-x} = \frac{x^4 - 1}{x - 1}$.

3. Sample answer: The first term is $a_1 = 2$. Divide the second term by the first to find that the common ratio is $r = 6$. Therefore, the nth term of the series is given by $2 \cdot 6^{n-1}$. There are five terms, so the series can be written as
$$\sum_{n=1}^{5} 2 \cdot 6^{n-1}.$$

4. $S_n = \frac{a_1 - a_n r}{1 - r}$
$= \frac{12 - 972(-3)}{1 - (-3)}$
$= \frac{2928}{4}$ or 732

5. $S_n = \frac{a_1 - a_n r}{1 - r}$
$= \frac{3 - 46{,}875(-5)}{1 - (-5)}$
$= \frac{234{,}378}{6}$ or 39,063

6. $S_n = \frac{a_1(1 - r^n)}{1 - r}$
$S_{14} = \frac{5(1 - 2^{14})}{1 - 2}$
$S_{14} = 81{,}915$

7. $S_n = \frac{a_1(1 - r^n)}{1 - r}$
$S_5 = \frac{243\left[1 - \left(-\frac{2}{3}\right)^5\right]}{1 - \left(-\frac{2}{3}\right)}$
$S_5 = 165$

8. Find r.
$r = \frac{36}{54}$ or $\frac{2}{3}$
Find the sum.
$S_n = \frac{a_1(1 - r^n)}{1 - r}$
$S_6 = \frac{54\left[1 - \left(\frac{2}{3}\right)^6\right]}{1 - \frac{2}{3}}$
$S_6 = \frac{1330}{9}$

9. Find r.
$r = \frac{-6}{3}$ or -2
Find the sum.
$S_n = \frac{a_1(1 - r^n)}{1 - r}$
$S_7 = \frac{3(1 - (-2)^7)}{1 - (-2)}$
$S_7 = 129$

10. $a_1 = \frac{1}{4}, r = 2, n = 5$
$S_n = \frac{a_1(1 - r^n)}{1 - r}$
$S_5 = \frac{\frac{1}{4}(1 - 2^5)}{1 - 2}$
$S_5 = \frac{31}{4}$

11. $a_1 = 81, r = \frac{1}{3}, n = 7$
$S_n = \frac{a_1(1 - r^n)}{1 - r}$
$S_7 = \frac{81\left[1 - \left(\frac{1}{3}\right)^7\right]}{1 - \frac{1}{3}}$
$S_7 = \frac{1093}{9}$

12. $S_n = \frac{a_1(1 - r^n)}{1 - r}$
$\frac{381}{64} = \frac{a_1\left[1 - \left(\frac{1}{2}\right)^7\right]}{1 - \frac{1}{2}}$
$\frac{381}{64} = \frac{\frac{127}{128}a_1}{\frac{1}{2}}$
$\frac{381}{64} = \frac{127}{64}a_1$
$3 = a_1$

13. $S_n = \frac{a_1 - a_n r}{1 - r}$
$33 = \frac{a_1 - 48(-2)}{1 - (-2)}$
$33 = \frac{a_1 + 96}{3}$
$99 = a_1 + 96$
$3 = a_1$

14. $a_1 = 3, r = 2, n = 5$

$$S_n = \frac{a_1(1 - r^n)}{1 - r}$$

$$S_5 = \frac{3(1 - 2^5)}{1 - 2}$$

$$S_5 = 93$$

The river rose 93 inches or 7 feet 9 inches in the first five days.

Pages 597–598   Practice and Apply

15. $S_n = \frac{a_1 - a_n r}{1 - r}$

$$S_6 = \frac{2 - 486(3)}{1 - 3}$$

$$= \frac{-1456}{-2} \text{ or } 728$$

16. $S_n = \frac{a_1 - a_n r}{1 - r}$

$$S_8 = \frac{3 - 384(2)}{1 - 2}$$

$$= \frac{-765}{-1} \text{ or } 765$$

17. $S_n = \frac{a_1 - a_n r}{1 - r}$

$$= \frac{1296 - 1\left(-\frac{1}{6}\right)}{1 - \left(-\frac{1}{6}\right)}$$

$$= \frac{1296\frac{1}{6}}{1\frac{1}{6}} \text{ or } 1111$$

18. $S_n = \frac{a_1 - a_n r}{1 - r}$

$$= \frac{343 - (-1)\left(-\frac{1}{7}\right)}{1 - \left(-\frac{1}{7}\right)}$$

$$= \frac{342\frac{6}{7}}{1\frac{1}{7}} \text{ or } 300$$

19. $S_n = \frac{a_1(1 - r^n)}{1 - r}$

$$S_5 = \frac{4(1 - (-3)^5)}{1 - (-3)}$$

$$S_5 = 244$$

20. $S_n = \frac{a_1(1 - r^n)}{1 - r}$

$$S_{12} = \frac{5(1 - 3^{12})}{1 - 3}$$

$$S_{12} = 1{,}328{,}600$$

21. $S_n = \frac{a_1(1 - r^n)}{1 - r}$

$$S_5 = \frac{2401\left[1 - \left(-\frac{1}{7}\right)^5\right]}{1 - \left(-\frac{1}{7}\right)}$$

$$S_5 = 2101$$

22. $S_n = \frac{a_1(1 - r^n)}{1 - r}$

$$S_5 = \frac{625\left[1 - \left(\frac{3}{5}\right)^5\right]}{1 - \frac{3}{5}}$$

$$S_5 = 1441$$

23. $S_n = \frac{a_1(1 - r^n)}{1 - r}$

$$S_6 = \frac{162\left[1 - \left(\frac{1}{3}\right)^6\right]}{1 - \frac{1}{3}}$$

$$S_6 = \frac{728}{3}$$

24. $S_n = \frac{a_1(1 - r^n)}{1 - r}$

$$S_7 = \frac{80\left[1 - \left(-\frac{1}{2}\right)^7\right]}{1 - \left(-\frac{1}{2}\right)}$$

$$S_7 = \frac{215}{4}$$

25. $S_n = \frac{a_1(1 - r^n)}{1 - r}$

$$S_8 = \frac{625(1 - 0.4^8)}{1 - 0.4}$$

$$S_8 = 1040.984$$

26. $S_n = \frac{a_1(1 - r^n)}{1 - r}$

$$S_8 = \frac{4(1 - 0.5^8)}{1 - 0.5}$$

$$S_8 = 7.96875$$

27. First find r.

$$a_5 = a_2 \cdot r^3$$
$$972 = -36r^3$$
$$-27 = r^3$$
$$-3 = r$$

Now find a_1.

$$a_2 = a_1 \cdot r$$
$$-36 = a_1(-3)$$
$$12 = a_1$$

Now find the sum.

$$S_n = \frac{a_1(1 - r^n)}{1 - r}$$
$$S_7 = \frac{12(1 - (-3)^7)}{1 - (-3)}$$
$$S_7 = 6564$$

28. First find r.

$$a_6 = a_3 \cdot r^3$$
$$-972 = -36r^3$$
$$27 = r^3$$
$$3 = r$$

Now find a_1.

$$a_3 = a_1 \cdot r^2$$
$$-36 = a_1 \cdot 3^2$$
$$-36 = 9a_1$$
$$-4 = a_1$$

Now find the sum.

$$S_n = \frac{a_1(1 - r^n)}{1 - r}$$
$$S_{10} = \frac{-4(1 - 3^{10})}{1 - 3}$$
$$S_{10} = -118{,}096$$

29. $a_1 = 5, r = 4, n = 10$

$$S_n = \frac{a_1(1 - r^n)}{1 - r}$$
$$S_{10} = \frac{5(1 - 4^{10})}{1 - 4}$$
$$S_{10} = 1{,}747{,}625$$

By the end of the tenth week, 1,747,625 people have been infected.

30. $a_1 = 0.01, r = 2, n = 30$

$$S_n = \frac{a_1(1 - r^n)}{1 - r}$$

$$S_{30} = \frac{0.01(1 - 2^{30})}{1 - 2}$$

$$S_{30} = 10{,}737{,}418.23$$

The second option would be worth $10,737,418.23.

31. Find r.

$$r = \frac{-512}{4096} \text{ or } -\frac{1}{8}$$

Find the sum.

$$S_n = \frac{a_1(1 - r^n)}{1 - r}$$

$$S_5 = \frac{4096\left[1 - \left(-\frac{1}{8}\right)^5\right]}{1 - \left(-\frac{1}{8}\right)}$$

$$S_5 = 3641$$

32. Find r.

$$r = \frac{21}{7} \text{ or } 3$$

Find the sum.

$$S_n = \frac{a_1(1 - r^n)}{1 - r}$$

$$S_{10} = \frac{7(1 - 3^{10})}{1 - 3}$$

$$S_{10} = 206{,}668$$

33. Find r.

$$r = \frac{\frac{1}{4}}{\frac{1}{16}} \text{ or } 4$$

Find the sum.

$$S_n = \frac{a_1(1 - r^n)}{1 - r}$$

$$S_7 = \frac{\frac{1}{16}(1 - 4^7)}{1 - 4}$$

$$S_7 = \frac{5461}{16}$$

34. Find r.

$$r = \frac{-\frac{1}{3}}{\frac{1}{9}} \text{ or } -3$$

Find the sum.

$$S_n = \frac{a_1(1 - r^n)}{1 - r}$$

$$S_6 = \frac{\frac{1}{9}(1 - (-3)^6)}{1 - (-3)}$$

$$S_6 = -\frac{182}{9}$$

35. $a_1 = 5, r = 2, n = 9$

$$S_n = \frac{a_1(1 - r^n)}{1 - r}$$

$$S_9 = \frac{5(1 - 2^9)}{1 - 2}$$

$$S_9 = 2555$$

36. $a_1 = 2, r = -3, n = 6$

$$S_n = \frac{a_1(1 - r^n)}{1 - r}$$

$$S_6 = \frac{2(1 - (-3)^6)}{1 - (-3)}$$

$$S_6 = -364$$

37. $a_1 = 144, r = -\frac{1}{2}, n = 7$

$$S_n = \frac{a_1(1 - r^n)}{1 - r}$$

$$S_7 = \frac{144\left[1 - \left(-\frac{1}{2}\right)^7\right]}{1 - \left(-\frac{1}{2}\right)}$$

$$S_7 = \frac{387}{4}$$

38. $a_1 = 64, r = \frac{3}{4}, n = 8$

$$S_n = \frac{a_1(1 - r^n)}{1 - r}$$

$$S_8 = \frac{64\left[1 - \left(\frac{3}{4}\right)^8\right]}{1 - \frac{3}{4}}$$

$$S_8 = \frac{58{,}975}{256}$$

39. $a_1 = 3, r = 2, n = 20$

$$S_n = \frac{a_1(1 - r^n)}{1 - r}$$

$$S_{20} = \frac{3(1 - 2^{20})}{1 - 2}$$

$$S_{20} = 3{,}145{,}725$$

40. $a_1 = 4, r = 3, n = 16$

$$S_n = \frac{a_1(1 - r^n)}{1 - r}$$

$$S_{16} = \frac{4(1 - 3^{16})}{1 - 3}$$

$$S_{16} = 86{,}093{,}440$$

41.

$$S_n = \frac{a_1 - a_n r}{1 - r}$$

$$165 = \frac{a_1 - 48\left(-\frac{2}{3}\right)}{1 - \left(-\frac{2}{3}\right)}$$

$$165 = \frac{a_1 + 32}{\frac{5}{3}}$$

$$275 = a_1 + 32$$

$$243 = a_1$$

42.

$$S_n = \frac{a_1 - a_n r}{1 - r}$$

$$688 = \frac{a_1 - 16\left(-\frac{1}{2}\right)}{1 - \left(-\frac{1}{2}\right)}$$

$$688 = \frac{a_1 + 8}{\frac{3}{2}}$$

$$1032 = a_1 + 8$$

$$1024 = a_1$$

43.

$$S_n = \frac{a_1(1 - r^n)}{1 - r}$$

$$-364 = \frac{a_1(1 - (-3)^6)}{1 - (-3)}$$

$$-364 = \frac{-728 a_1}{4}$$

$$-364 = -182 a_1$$

$$2 = a_1$$

44.

$$S_n = \frac{a_1(1 - r^n)}{1 - r}$$

$$1530 = \frac{a_1(1 - 2^8)}{1 - 2}$$

$$1530 = 255 a_1$$

$$6 = a_1$$

45. First find a_1.

$$S_n = \frac{a_1(1 - r^n)}{1 - r}$$

$$315 = \frac{a_1(1 - 0.5^6)}{1 - 0.5}$$

$$315 = 1.96875a_1$$

$$160 = a_1$$

Now find a_2.

$$a_2 = 160(0.5) \text{ or } 80$$

46. First find a_1.

$$S_n = \frac{a_1(1 - r^n)}{1 - r}$$

$$249.92 = \frac{a_1(1 - 0.2^5)}{1 - 0.2}$$

$$249.92 = 1.2496a_1$$

$$200 = a_1$$

Now find a_3.

$$a_2 = 200(0.2) \text{ or } 40$$

$$a_3 = 40(0.2) \text{ or } 8$$

47. $a_1 = 5$, $r = 0.30$, and $n = 5$

$$S_n = \frac{a_1(1 - r^n)}{1 - r}$$

$$S_5 = \frac{5(1 - 0.3^5)}{1 - 0.3}$$

$$S_5 = 7.1255$$

After five swings, he has driven the post about 7.13 inches into the ground.

48. If the first term and common ratio of a geometric series are integers, then all the terms of the series are integers. Therefore, the sum of the series is an integer.

49. If the number of people that each person sends the joke to is constant, then the total number of people who have seen the joke is the sum of a geometric series. Answers should include the following.
- The common ratio would change from 3 to 4.
- Increase the number of days that the joke circulates so that it is inconvenient to find and add all the terms of the series.

50. A; $a_1 = -1$, $r = -3$, and $S_n = 182$

$$S_n = \frac{a_1(1 - r^n)}{1 - r}$$

$$182 = \frac{-1(1 - (-3)^n)}{1 - (-3)}$$

$$182 = \frac{(-3)^n - 1}{4}$$

$$728 = (-3)^n - 1$$

$$729 = (-3)^n$$

$$6 = n \quad \text{since } (-3)^6 = 729$$

51. C; $n = 10$, $r = 0.5$, and $S_n = 511.5$

$$S_n = \frac{a_1(1 - r^n)}{1 - r}$$

$$511.5 = \frac{a_1(1 - 0.5^{10})}{1 - 0.5}$$

$$511.5 = 1.998046875a_1$$

$$256 = a_1$$

52. KEYSTROKES: 2nd [LIST] ▶ ▶ 5 2nd [LIST]
▶ 5 3 (((−) 2)) ∧ (ALPHA [N] − 1
) , ALPHA [N] , 1 , 20 , 1)
ENTER
The sum is −1,048,575.

53. KEYSTROKES: 2nd [LIST] ▶ ▶ 5 2nd [LIST]
▶ 5 2 ((1 ÷ 2)) ∧ (ALPHA [N] −
1) , ALPHA [N] , 1 , 15 , 1)
ENTER
The sum is about 3.99987793.

54. KEYSTROKES: 2nd [LIST] ▶ ▶ 5 2nd [LIST]
▶ 5 5 (0.2) ∧ (ALPHA [N] − 1
) , ALPHA [N] , 1 , 10 , 1)
ENTER
The sum is 6.24999936.

Page 598   Maintain Your Skills

55. First find r.

$$a_n = a_1 \cdot r^{n - 1}$$

$$a_5 = \frac{1}{24}r^{5 - 1}$$

$$54 = \frac{1}{24}r^4$$

$$1296 = r^4$$

$$\pm 6 = r$$

Use $r = 6$.

$$a_2 = \frac{1}{24}(6) \text{ or } \frac{1}{4}$$

$$a_3 = \frac{1}{4}(6) \text{ or } \frac{3}{2}$$

$$a_4 = \frac{3}{2}(6) \text{ or } 9$$

User $r = -6$.

$$a_2 = \frac{1}{24}(-6) \text{ or } -\frac{1}{4}$$

$$a_3 = -\frac{1}{4}(-6) \text{ or } \frac{3}{2}$$

$$a_4 = \frac{3}{2}(-6) \text{ or } -9$$

The geometric means are $\frac{1}{4}$, $\frac{3}{2}$, and 9, or $-\frac{1}{4}$, $\frac{3}{2}$, and -9.

56. First find r.

$$a_n = a_1 \cdot r^{n - 1}$$

$$a_6 = -2r^{6 - 1}$$

$$-\frac{243}{16} = -2r^5$$

$$\frac{243}{32} = r^5$$

$$\frac{3}{2} = r$$

Find the geometric means.

$$a_2 = -2\left(\frac{3}{2}\right) \text{ or } -3$$

$$a_3 = -3\left(\frac{3}{2}\right) \text{ or } -\frac{9}{2}$$

$$a_4 = -\frac{9}{2}\left(\frac{3}{2}\right) \text{ or } -\frac{27}{4}$$

$$a_5 = -\frac{27}{4}\left(\frac{3}{2}\right) \text{ or } -\frac{81}{8}$$

The geometric means are -3, $-\frac{9}{2}$, $-\frac{27}{4}$, and $-\frac{81}{8}$.

57. First find d.

$d = 44 - 50$ or -6

Next find n.

$a_n = a_1 + (n - 1)d$
$8 = 50 + (n - 1)(-6)$
$8 = 50 - 6n + 6$
$8 = 56 - 6n$
$-48 = -6n$
$8 = n$

Now find the sum.

$S_n = \dfrac{n}{2}(a_1 + a_n)$
$S_8 = \dfrac{8}{2}(50 + 8)$
$S_8 = 4(58)$
$S_8 = 232$

58. $a_1 = 2(1) + 3$ or 5, $a_{12} = 2(12) + 3$ or 27, and $n = 12$

$S_n = \dfrac{n}{2}(a_1 + a_n)$
$S_{12} = \dfrac{12}{2}(5 + 27)$
$S_{12} = 6(32)$
$S_{12} = 192$

59. Drive-In Movie Screens

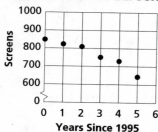

60. Sample answer using $(1, 826)$ and $(3, 750)$: First find the slope.

$m = \dfrac{y_2 - y_1}{x_2 - x_1}$
$m = \dfrac{750 - 826}{3 - 1}$
$m = \dfrac{-76}{2}$ or -38

Use the point-slope form.

$y - y_1 = m(x - x_1)$
$y - 826 = -38(x - 1)$
$y - 826 = -38x + 38$
$y = -38x + 864$

61. Sample answer using the prediction equation found in Exercise 60: The year 2010 is 15 years after 1995, so $x = 15$.

$y = -38x + 864$
$y = -38(15) + 864$
$y = 294$

There will be 294 screens in 2010.

62. $\dfrac{a}{1 - b} = \dfrac{1}{1 - \frac{1}{2}}$

$= \dfrac{1}{\frac{1}{2}}$

$= 2$

63. $\dfrac{a}{1 - b} = \dfrac{3}{1 - \left(-\frac{1}{2}\right)}$

$= \dfrac{3}{\frac{3}{2}}$

$= 3 \cdot \dfrac{2}{3}$ or 2

64. $\dfrac{a}{1 - b} = \dfrac{\frac{1}{3}}{1 - \left(-\frac{1}{3}\right)}$

$= \dfrac{\frac{1}{3}}{\frac{4}{3}}$

$= \dfrac{1}{3} \cdot \dfrac{3}{4}$ or $\dfrac{1}{4}$

65. $\dfrac{a}{1 - b} = \dfrac{\frac{1}{2}}{1 - \frac{1}{4}}$

$= \dfrac{\frac{1}{2}}{\frac{3}{4}}$

$= \dfrac{1}{2} \cdot \dfrac{4}{3}$ or $\dfrac{2}{3}$

66. $\dfrac{a}{1 - b} = \dfrac{-1}{1 - 0.5}$

$= \dfrac{-1}{0.5}$

$= -2$

67. $\dfrac{a}{1 - b} = \dfrac{0.9}{1 - (-0.5)}$

$= \dfrac{0.9}{1.5}$

$= 0.6$

11-5 Infinite Geometric Series

Page 602 Check for Understanding

1. Sample answer: $\displaystyle\sum_{n=1}^{\infty} \left(\dfrac{1}{2}\right)^n$

2. 0.999999... can be written as the infinite geometric series $\dfrac{9}{10} + \dfrac{9}{100} + \dfrac{9}{1000} + \cdots$. The first term of this series is $\dfrac{9}{10}$ and the common ratio is $\dfrac{1}{10}$, so the sum is $\dfrac{\frac{9}{10}}{1 - \frac{1}{10}}$ or 1.

3. Beth; the common ratio for the infinite geometric series is $-\dfrac{4}{3}$. Since $\left|-\dfrac{4}{3}\right| \geq 1$, the series does not have a sum and the formula $S = \dfrac{a_1}{1 - r}$ does not apply.

4. Since $\left|\dfrac{2}{3}\right| < 1$, the sum exists.

$S = \dfrac{a_1}{1 - r}$

$= \dfrac{36}{1 - \frac{2}{3}}$

$= \dfrac{36}{\frac{1}{3}}$ or 108

5. Since $|-1.5| > 1$, the sum does not exist.

6. First find r.

$r = \frac{24}{16}$ or $\frac{3}{2}$

Since $\left|\frac{3}{2}\right| > 1$, the sum does not exist.

7. First find r.

$r = \frac{\frac{1}{6}}{\frac{1}{4}}$ or $\frac{2}{3}$

Since $\left|\frac{2}{3}\right| < 1$, the sum exists.

$S = \frac{a_1}{1 - r}$

$\quad = \frac{\frac{1}{4}}{1 - \frac{2}{3}}$

$\quad = \frac{\frac{1}{4}}{\frac{1}{3}}$ or $\frac{3}{4}$

8. First find r.

$r = \frac{-2.4}{6}$ or -0.4

Since $|-0.4| < 1$, the sum exists.

$S = \frac{a_1}{1 - r}$

$\quad = \frac{6}{1 - (-0.4)}$

$\quad = \frac{6}{1.4}$ or $\frac{30}{7}$

9. $a_1 = 40$ and $r = \frac{3}{5}$

Since $\left|\frac{3}{5}\right| < 1$, the sum exists.

$S = \frac{a_1}{1 - r}$

$\quad = \frac{40}{1 - \frac{3}{5}}$

$\quad = \frac{40}{\frac{2}{5}}$ or 100

10. Write the decimal as a sum.

$0.\overline{5} = 0.555\ldots$

$\quad = 0.5 + 0.05 + 0.005 + \ldots$

$\quad = \frac{5}{10} + \frac{5}{100} + \frac{5}{1000} + \ldots$

$a_1 = \frac{5}{10}$ and $r = \frac{1}{10}$

$S = \frac{a_1}{1 - r}$

$\quad = \frac{\frac{5}{10}}{1 - \frac{1}{10}}$

$\quad = \frac{\frac{5}{10}}{\frac{9}{10}}$ or $\frac{5}{9}$

11. Write the decimal as a sum.

$0.\overline{73} = 0.737373\ldots$

$\quad = 0.73 + 0.0073 + 0.000073 + \ldots$

$\quad = \frac{73}{100} + \frac{73}{10,000} + \frac{73}{1,000,000} + \ldots$

$a_1 = \frac{73}{100}$ and $r = \frac{1}{100}$

$S = \frac{a_1}{1 - r}$

$\quad = \frac{\frac{73}{100}}{1 - \frac{1}{100}}$

$\quad = \frac{\frac{73}{100}}{\frac{99}{100}}$ or $\frac{73}{99}$

12. Write the decimal as a sum.

$0.\overline{175} = 0.175175175\ldots$

$\quad = 0.175 + 0.000175 + 0.000000175 + \ldots$

$\quad = \frac{175}{1000} + \frac{175}{1,000,000} + \frac{175}{1,000,000,000} + \ldots$

$a_1 = \frac{175}{1000}$ and $r = \frac{1}{1000}$

$S = \frac{a_1}{1 - r}$

$\quad = \frac{\frac{175}{1000}}{1 - \frac{1}{1000}}$

$\quad = \frac{\frac{175}{1000}}{\frac{999}{1000}}$ or $\frac{175}{999}$

13. $a_1 = 24$ and $r = \frac{18}{24}$ or 0.75

$S = \frac{a_1}{1 - r}$

$\quad = \frac{24}{1 - 0.75}$

$\quad = \frac{24}{0.25}$ or 96

The pendulum swings 96 cm.

Pages 602–603　Practice and Apply

14. Since $\left|\frac{5}{7}\right| < 1$, the sum exists.

$S = \frac{a_1}{1 - r}$

$\quad = \frac{4}{1 - \frac{5}{7}}$

$\quad = \frac{4}{\frac{2}{7}}$ or 14

15. Since $\left|\frac{7}{3}\right| > 1$, the sum does not exist.

16. Since $|-0.6| < 1$, the sum exists.

$S = \frac{a_1}{1 - r}$

$\quad = \frac{12}{1 - (-0.6)}$

$\quad = \frac{12}{1.6}$ or 7.5

17. Since $|0.6| < 1$, the sum exists.

$S = \frac{a_1}{1 - r}$

$\quad = \frac{18}{1 - 0.6}$

$\quad = \frac{18}{0.4}$ or 45

18. First find r.

$r = \dfrac{12}{16}$ or 0.75

Since $|0.75| < 1$, the sum exists.

$S = \dfrac{a_1}{1 - r}$

$= \dfrac{16}{1 - 0.75}$

$= \dfrac{16}{0.25}$ or 64

19. First find r.

$r = \dfrac{-4}{-8}$ or 0.5

Since $|0.5| < 1$, the sum exists.

$S = \dfrac{a_1}{1 - r}$

$= \dfrac{-8}{1 - 0.5}$

$= \dfrac{-8}{0.5}$ or -16

20. First find r.

$r = \dfrac{-18}{12}$ or -1.5

Since $|-1.5| > 1$, the sum does not exist.

21. First find r.

$r = \dfrac{-12}{18}$ or $-\dfrac{2}{3}$

Since $\left|-\dfrac{2}{3}\right| < 1$, the sum exists.

$S = \dfrac{a_1}{1 - r}$

$= \dfrac{18}{1 - \left(-\dfrac{2}{3}\right)}$

$= \dfrac{18}{\frac{5}{3}}$ or $\dfrac{54}{5}$

22. First find r.

$r = \dfrac{\frac{2}{3}}{1}$ or $\dfrac{2}{3}$

Since $\left|\dfrac{2}{3}\right| < 1$, the sum exists.

$S = \dfrac{a_1}{1 - r}$

$= \dfrac{1}{1 - \frac{2}{3}}$

$= \dfrac{1}{\frac{1}{3}}$ or 3

23. First find r.

$a_1 = \dfrac{5}{3}$ and $r = \dfrac{\frac{25}{3}}{\frac{5}{3}}$ or 5

Since $|5| > 1$, the sum does not exist.

24. First find r.

$r = \dfrac{\frac{10}{9}}{\frac{5}{3}}$ or $-\dfrac{2}{3}$

Since $\left|-\dfrac{2}{3}\right| < 1$, the sum exists.

$S = \dfrac{a_1}{1 - r}$

$= \dfrac{\frac{5}{3}}{1 - \left(-\dfrac{2}{3}\right)}$

$= \dfrac{\frac{5}{3}}{\frac{5}{3}}$ or 1

25. First find r.

$r = \dfrac{-\frac{3}{4}}{\frac{3}{2}}$ or $-\dfrac{1}{2}$

Since $\left|-\dfrac{1}{2}\right| < 1$, the sum exists.

$S = \dfrac{a_1}{1 - r}$

$= \dfrac{\frac{3}{2}}{1 - \left(-\dfrac{1}{2}\right)}$

$= \dfrac{\frac{3}{2}}{\frac{3}{2}}$ or 1

26. First find r.

$r = \dfrac{1.8}{3}$ or 0.6

Since $|0.6| < 1$, the sum exists.

$S = \dfrac{a_1}{1 - r}$

$= \dfrac{3}{1 - 0.6}$

$= \dfrac{3}{0.4}$ or 7.5

27. First find r.

$r = \dfrac{-0.5}{1}$ or -0.5

Since $|-0.5| < 1$, the sum exists.

$S = \dfrac{a_1}{1 - r}$

$= \dfrac{1}{1 - (-0.5)}$

$= \dfrac{1}{1.5}$ or $\dfrac{2}{3}$

28. $a_1 = 48$ and $r = \dfrac{2}{3}$

Since $\left|\dfrac{2}{3}\right| < 1$, the sum exists.

$S = \dfrac{a_1}{1 - r}$

$= \dfrac{48}{1 - \frac{2}{3}}$

$= \dfrac{48}{\frac{1}{3}}$ or 144

29. $a_1 = \frac{3}{8}$ and $r = \frac{3}{4}$

Since $\left|\frac{3}{4}\right| < 1$, the sum exists.

$S = \dfrac{a_1}{1 - r}$

$\quad = \dfrac{\frac{3}{8}}{1 - \frac{3}{4}}$

$\quad = \dfrac{\frac{3}{8}}{\frac{1}{4}}$ or $\dfrac{3}{2}$

30. $a_1 = 3$ and $r = 0.5$

Since $|0.5| < 1$, the sum exists.

$S = \dfrac{a_1}{1 - r}$

$\quad = \dfrac{3}{1 - 0.5}$

$\quad = \dfrac{3}{0.5}$ or 6

31. $a_1 = 1.5$ and $r = 0.25$

Since $|0.25| < 1$, the sum exists.

$S = \dfrac{a_1}{1 - r}$

$\quad = \dfrac{1.5}{1 - 0.25}$

$\quad = \dfrac{1.5}{0.75}$ or 2

32. $a_1 = 9$ and $r = 0.70$

$S = \dfrac{a_1}{1 - r}$

$\quad = \dfrac{9}{1 - 0.7}$

$\quad = \dfrac{9}{0.3}$ or 30

The swing traveled 30 feet.

33. The perimeter of each square is $\frac{\sqrt{2}}{2}$ times the perimeter of the next larger square. Thus, $a_1 = 40$ and $r = \frac{\sqrt{2}}{2}$.

$\displaystyle\sum_{n=1}^{\infty} 40\left(\frac{\sqrt{2}}{2}\right)^{n-1}$

$= 40 + 20\sqrt{2} + 20 + \ldots$

34. Since $\left|\frac{\sqrt{2}}{2}\right| < 1$, the sum exists.

$S = \dfrac{a_1}{1 - r}$

$\quad = \dfrac{40}{1 - \frac{\sqrt{2}}{2}}$

$\quad = \dfrac{40}{1 - \frac{\sqrt{2}}{2}} \cdot \dfrac{1 + \frac{\sqrt{2}}{2}}{1 + \frac{\sqrt{2}}{2}}$

$\quad = \dfrac{40 + 20\sqrt{2}}{1 - \frac{1}{2}}$

$\quad = \dfrac{40 + 20\sqrt{2}}{\frac{1}{2}}$ or $80 + 40\sqrt{2}$

The sum of the perimeters is $80 + 40\sqrt{2}$ or about 136.6 cm.

35. $a_1 = 90$ and $r = 0.90$

$S = \dfrac{a_1}{1 - r}$

$\quad = \dfrac{90}{1 - 0.9}$

$\quad = \dfrac{90}{0.1}$ or 900

The final height of the balloon is 900 feet.

36. $S = 81$ and $r = \frac{2}{3}$

$S = \dfrac{a_1}{1 - r}$

$81 = \dfrac{a_1}{1 - \frac{2}{3}}$

$81 = \dfrac{a_1}{\frac{1}{3}}$

$81 = 3a_1$

$27 = a_1$

Now find the next two terms.

$a_2 = 27\left(\frac{2}{3}\right)$ or 18

$a_3 = 18\left(\frac{2}{3}\right)$ or 12

The first three terms are 27, 18, and 12.

37. $S = 125$ and $r = 0.4$

$S = \dfrac{a_1}{1 - r}$

$125 = \dfrac{a_1}{1 - 0.4}$

$125 = \dfrac{a_1}{0.6}$

$75 = a_1$

Now find the next two terms.

$a_2 = 75(0.4)$ or 30

$a_3 = 30(0.4)$ or 12

The first three terms are 75, 30, and 12.

38. $S = 76\frac{4}{5}$ and $r = \frac{11}{16}$

$S = \dfrac{a_1}{1 - r}$

$76\frac{4}{5} = \dfrac{a_1}{1 - \frac{11}{16}}$

$\dfrac{384}{5} = \dfrac{a_1}{\frac{5}{16}}$

$24 = a_1$

Now find the next three terms.

$a_2 = 24\left(\frac{11}{16}\right)$ or $\frac{33}{2}$ or $16\frac{1}{2}$

$a_3 = \left(\frac{33}{2}\right)\left(\frac{11}{16}\right)$ or $\frac{363}{32}$ or $11\frac{11}{32}$

$a_4 = \left(\frac{363}{32}\right)\left(\frac{11}{16}\right)$ or $\frac{3993}{512}$ or $7\frac{409}{512}$

The first four terms are 24, $16\frac{1}{2}$, $11\frac{11}{32}$, and $7\frac{409}{512}$.

39. $a_1 = -8$ and $S = -13\frac{1}{3}$

$$S = \frac{a_1}{1-r}$$

$$-13\frac{1}{3} = \frac{-8}{1-r}$$

$$-\frac{40}{3}(1-r) = -8$$

$$1 - r = \frac{3}{5}$$

$$-r = -\frac{2}{5}$$

$$r = \frac{2}{5}$$

Now find the other terms.

$$a_2 = -8\left(\frac{2}{5}\right) \text{ or } -\frac{16}{5} \text{ or } -3\frac{1}{5}$$

$$a_3 = \left(-\frac{16}{5}\right)\left(\frac{2}{5}\right) \text{ or } -\frac{32}{25} \text{ or } -1\frac{7}{25}$$

$$a_4 = \left(-\frac{32}{25}\right)\left(\frac{2}{5}\right) \text{ or } -\frac{64}{125}$$

The first four terms are -8, $-3\frac{1}{3}$, $-1\frac{7}{25}$, and $-\frac{64}{125}$.

40. Write the decimal as a sum.

$$0.\overline{7} = 0.777\ldots$$

$$= 0.7 + 0.07 + 0.007 + \ldots$$

$$= \frac{7}{10} + \frac{7}{100} + \frac{7}{1000} + \ldots$$

$a_1 = \frac{7}{10}$ and $r = \frac{1}{10}$

$$S = \frac{a_1}{1-r}$$

$$= \frac{\frac{7}{10}}{1 - \frac{1}{10}}$$

$$= \frac{\frac{7}{10}}{\frac{9}{10}} \text{ or } \frac{7}{9}$$

41. Write the decimal as a sum.

$$0.\overline{1} = 0.111\ldots$$

$$= 0.1 + 0.01 + 0.001 + \ldots$$

$$= \frac{1}{10} + \frac{1}{100} + \frac{1}{1000} + \ldots$$

$a_1 = \frac{1}{10}$ and $r = \frac{1}{10}$

$$S = \frac{a_1}{1-r}$$

$$= \frac{\frac{1}{10}}{1 - \frac{1}{10}}$$

$$= \frac{\frac{1}{10}}{\frac{9}{10}} \text{ or } \frac{1}{9}$$

42. Write the decimal as a sum.

$$0.\overline{36} = 0.363636\ldots$$

$$= 0.36 + 0.0036 + 0.000036 + \ldots$$

$$= \frac{36}{100} + \frac{36}{10,000} + \frac{36}{1,000,000} + \ldots$$

$a_1 = \frac{36}{100}$ and $r = \frac{1}{100}$

$$S = \frac{a_1}{1-r}$$

$$= \frac{\frac{36}{100}}{1 - \frac{1}{100}}$$

$$= \frac{\frac{36}{100}}{\frac{99}{100}} \text{ or } \frac{4}{11}$$

43. Write the decimal as a sum.

$$0.\overline{82} = 0.828282\ldots$$

$$= 0.82 + 0.0082 + 0.000082 + \ldots$$

$$= \frac{82}{100} + \frac{82}{10,000} + \frac{82}{1,000,000} + \ldots$$

$a_1 = \frac{82}{100}$ and $r = \frac{1}{100}$

$$S = \frac{a_1}{1-r}$$

$$= \frac{\frac{82}{100}}{1 - \frac{1}{100}}$$

$$= \frac{\frac{82}{100}}{\frac{99}{100}} \text{ or } \frac{82}{99}$$

44. Write the decimal as a sum.

$$0.\overline{246} = 0.246246246246\ldots$$

$$= 0.246 + 0.000246 + 0.000000246 + \ldots$$

$$= \frac{246}{1000} + \frac{246}{1,000,000} + \frac{246}{1,000,000,000} + \ldots$$

$a_1 = \frac{246}{1000}$ and $r = \frac{1}{1000}$

$$S = \frac{a_1}{1-r}$$

$$= \frac{\frac{246}{1000}}{1 - \frac{1}{1000}}$$

$$= \frac{\frac{246}{1000}}{\frac{999}{1000}} \text{ or } \frac{82}{333}$$

45. Write the decimal as a sum.

$$0.\overline{427} = 0.427427427\ldots$$

$$= 0.427 + 0.000427 + 0.000000427 + \ldots$$

$$= \frac{427}{1000} + \frac{427}{1,000,000} + \frac{427}{1,000,000,000} + \ldots$$

$a_1 = \frac{427}{1000}$ and $r = \frac{1}{1000}$

$$S = \frac{a_1}{1-r}$$

$$= \frac{\frac{427}{1000}}{1 - \frac{1}{1000}}$$

$$= \frac{\frac{427}{1000}}{\frac{999}{1000}} \text{ or } \frac{427}{999}$$

46. Write the decimal as a sum.

$$0.\overline{45} = 0.454545\ldots$$

$$= 0.45 + 0.0045 + 0.000045 + \ldots$$

$$= \frac{45}{100} + \frac{45}{10,000} + \frac{45}{1,000,000} + \ldots$$

$a_1 = \frac{45}{100}$ and $r = \frac{1}{100}$

$$S = \frac{a_1}{1-r}$$

$$= \frac{\frac{45}{100}}{1 - \frac{1}{100}}$$

$$= \frac{\frac{45}{100}}{\frac{99}{100}} \text{ or } \frac{5}{11}$$

47. Write the decimal as a sum.

$0.2\overline{31} = 0.2313131...$

$= 0.2 + 0.031 + 0.00031 + 0.0000031 + ...$

$= \dfrac{2}{10} + \dfrac{31}{1000} + \dfrac{31}{100,000} + \dfrac{31}{10,000,000} + ...$

The infinite geometric series begins in the second term.

Thus, $a_1 = \dfrac{31}{1000}$ and $r = \dfrac{1}{100}$.

$S = \dfrac{2}{10} + \dfrac{a_1}{1 - r}$

$= \dfrac{2}{10} + \dfrac{\frac{31}{1000}}{1 - \frac{1}{100}}$

$= \dfrac{2}{10} + \dfrac{\frac{31}{1000}}{\frac{99}{100}}$

$= \dfrac{2}{10} + \dfrac{31}{990}$ or $\dfrac{229}{990}$

48.

$S = a_1 + a_1 r + a_1 r^2 + a_1 r^3 + \cdots$

$(-)rS = \quad\quad a_1 r + a_1 r^2 + a_1 r^3 + a_1 r^4 + \cdots$

$\overline{}$

$S - rS = a_1 + 0 \quad + 0 \quad + 0 \quad + 0 \quad + \cdots$

$S(1 - r) = a_1$

$S = \dfrac{a_1}{1 - r}$

49. The total distance that a ball bounces, both up and down, can be found by adding the sums of two infinite geometric series. Answers should include the following.

- $a_n = a_1 \cdot r^{n-1}, S_n = \dfrac{a_1(1 - r^n)}{1 - r}$, or $S = \dfrac{a_1}{1 - r}$
- The total distance the ball falls is given by the infinite geometric series
  $3 + 3(0.6) + 3(0.6)^2 + \ldots$.

The sum of this series is $\dfrac{3}{1 - 0.6}$ or 7.5. The total distance the ball bounces up is given by the infinite geometric series
$1.8(0.6) + 1.8(0.6)^2 + 1.8(0.6)^3 + \ldots$.

The sum of this series is $\dfrac{1.8(0.6)}{1 - 0.6}$ or 2.7. Thus, the total distance the ball travels is 7.5 + 2.7 or 10.2 feet.

50. D;

$S = \dfrac{a_1}{1 - r}$

$= \dfrac{6}{1 - \frac{1}{2}}$

$= \dfrac{6}{\frac{1}{2}}$ or 12

51. C; $a_1 = 2$ and $r = \dfrac{\frac{2}{3}}{2}$ or $\dfrac{1}{3}$

$S = \dfrac{a_1}{1 - r}$

$= \dfrac{2}{1 - \frac{1}{3}}$

$= \dfrac{2}{\frac{2}{3}}$ or 3

52. $S_n = \dfrac{a_1(1 - r^n)}{1 - r}$

$S_6 = \dfrac{1(1 - (-3)^6)}{1 - (-3)}$

$S_6 = \dfrac{-728}{4}$ or -182

53. $S_n = \dfrac{a_1(1 - r^n)}{1 - r}$

$S_7 = \dfrac{72\left[1 - \left(\frac{1}{3}\right)^7\right]}{1 - \frac{1}{3}}$

$S_7 = \dfrac{\frac{17,488}{243}}{\frac{2}{3}}$ or $\dfrac{8744}{81}$

54. Since the pump removes 20% of the previous amount of air with each stroke, 80% remains after each stroke. Thus, $r = 0.80$. Furthermore, $a_1 = 0.80$ since 80% of the original amount of air remains after the first stroke.

$a_n = a_1 \cdot r^{n-1}$

$a_5 = 0.8(0.8)^{5-1}$

$a_5 = 0.32768$

32.768% of the air remains after the fifth stroke.

55. $6^x = 216$

$6^x = 6^3$

$x = 3$

56. $2^{2x} = \dfrac{1}{8}$

$2^{2x} = 2^{-3}$

$2x = -3$

$x = -\dfrac{3}{2}$

57. $3^{x-2} \geq 27$

$3^{x-2} \geq 3^3$

$x - 2 \geq 3$

$x \geq 5$

58. $\dfrac{-2}{ab} + \dfrac{5}{a^2} = \dfrac{-2 \cdot a}{ab \cdot a} + \dfrac{5 \cdot b}{a^2 \cdot b}$

$= \dfrac{-2a}{a^2 b} + \dfrac{5b}{a^2 b}$

$= \dfrac{-2a + 5b}{a^2 b}$

59. $\dfrac{1}{x - 3} - \dfrac{2}{x + 1} = \dfrac{1 \cdot (x + 1)}{(x - 3) \cdot (x + 1)} - \dfrac{2 \cdot (x - 3)}{(x + 1) \cdot (x - 3)}$

$= \dfrac{(x + 1) - 2(x - 3)}{(x - 3)(x + 1)}$

$= \dfrac{x + 1 - 2x + 6}{(x - 3)(x + 1)}$

$= \dfrac{-x + 7}{(x - 3)(x + 1)}$

60. $\dfrac{1}{x^2 + 6x + 8} + \dfrac{3}{x + 4} = \dfrac{1}{(x + 4)(x + 2)} + \dfrac{3}{x + 4}$

$= \dfrac{1}{(x + 4)(x + 2)} + \dfrac{3 \cdot (x + 2)}{(x + 4) \cdot (x + 2)}$

$= \dfrac{1 + 3(x + 2)}{(x + 4)(x + 2)}$

$= \dfrac{1 + 3x + 6}{(x + 4)(x + 2)}$

$= \dfrac{3x + 7}{(x + 4)(x + 2)}$

61. $(x - h)^2 + (y - k)^2 = r^2$

$(x - 2)^2 + (y - 4)^2 = 6^2$

$(x - 2)^2 + (y - 4)^2 = 36$

62. Use the midpoint formula to find the center.

$$\left(\frac{x_1 + x_2}{2}, \frac{y_1 + y_2}{2}\right) = \left[\frac{7 + (-1)}{2}, \frac{3 + (-5)}{2}\right]$$
$$= \left(\frac{6}{2}, \frac{-2}{2}\right) \text{ or } (3, -1)$$

The center is $(3, -1)$. Use the distance formula to find the radius, the distance between the center and one of the points.

$$d = \sqrt{(x_2 - x_1)^2 + (y_2 - y_1)^2}$$
$$= \sqrt{(3 - 7)^2 + (-1 - 3)^2}$$
$$= \sqrt{(-4)^2 + (-4)^2}$$
$$= \sqrt{32} \text{ or } 4\sqrt{2}$$

The radius is $4\sqrt{2}$ units. Write the equation of the circle.

$$(x - h)^2 + (y - k)^2 = r^2$$
$$(x - 3)^2 + (y - (-1))^2 = (4\sqrt{2})^2$$
$$(x - 3)^2 + (y + 1)^2 = 32$$

63. $f(x) = 8x^3 - 36x^2 + 22x + 21$

Since there are two sign changes, the function has 2 or 0 positive real zeros.

$f(-x) = -8x^3 - 36x^2 - 22x + 21$

Since there is one sign change, the function has 1 negative real zero.

The possible rational zeros are $\pm 1, \pm 3, \pm 7, \pm 21,$ $\pm\frac{1}{2}, \pm\frac{3}{2}, \pm\frac{7}{2}, \pm\frac{21}{2}, \pm\frac{1}{4}, \pm\frac{3}{4}, \pm\frac{7}{4}, \pm\frac{21}{4}, \pm\frac{1}{8}, \pm\frac{3}{8}, \pm\frac{7}{8},$ and $\pm\frac{21}{8}$.

Use synthetic substitution to find a zero. We find that a zero occurs at $x = -\frac{1}{2}$, and the depressed polynomial is $8x^2 - 40x + 42$.

$$8x^2 - 40x + 42 = 0$$
$$2(4x^2 - 20x + 21) = 0$$
$$2(2x - 3)(2x - 7) = 0$$
$$2x - 3 = 0 \quad \text{or} \quad 2x - 7 = 0$$
$$2x = 3 \qquad\qquad 2x = 7$$
$$x = \frac{3}{2} \qquad\qquad x = \frac{7}{2}$$

The zeros are $-\frac{1}{2}, \frac{3}{2}$, and $\frac{7}{2}$.

64. $g(x) = 12x^4 + 4x^3 - 3x^2 - x$

Since there is one sign change, the function has 1 positive real zero.

$g(-x) = 12x^4 - 4x^3 - 3x^2 + x$

Since there are two sign changes, the function has 2 or 0 negative real zeros.

We find that a zero occurs at $x = 0$, and the depressed polynomial is $12x^3 + 4x^2 - 3x - 1$. The possible rational zeros are $\pm 1, \pm\frac{1}{2}, \pm\frac{1}{3}, \pm\frac{1}{4}, \pm\frac{1}{6},$ and $\pm\frac{1}{12}$. We find that another zero occurs at $x = \frac{1}{2}$, and the depressed polynomial is $12x^2 + 10x + 2$.

$$12x^2 + 10x + 2 = 0$$
$$2(6x^2 + 5x + 1) = 0$$
$$2(3x + 1)(2x + 1) = 0$$
$$3x + 1 = 0 \quad \text{or} \quad 2x + 1 = 0$$
$$3x = -1 \qquad\qquad 2x = -1$$
$$x = -\frac{1}{3} \qquad\qquad x = -\frac{1}{2}$$

The zeros are $-\frac{1}{2}, -\frac{1}{3}, 0$, and $\frac{1}{2}$.

65.
$$(x - p)(x - q) = 0$$
$$(x - 6)[x - (-6)] = 0$$
$$(x - 6)(x + 6) = 0$$
$$x^2 - 36 = 0$$

66.
$$(x - p)(x - q) = 0$$
$$[x - (-2)][x - (-7)] = 0$$
$$(x + 2)(x + 7) = 0$$
$$x^2 + 9x + 14 = 0$$

67.
$$(x - p)(x - q) = 0$$
$$(x - 6)(x - 4) = 0$$
$$x^2 - 10x + 24 = 0$$

68.
$$m = \frac{y_2 - y_1}{x_2 - x_1}$$
$$= \frac{3,648,384 - 4,190,557}{1999 - 1996}$$
$$= \frac{-542,173}{3} \text{ or about } -180,724$$

The average rate of change of the number of visitors from 1966 to 1999 was about $-180,724$ visitors per year.

69. Since the rate of change is negative, the number of visitors was decreasing.

70. $f(x) = 2x$
$$f(1) = 2(1)$$
$$= 2$$

71. $g(x) = 3x - 3$
$$g(2) = 3(2) - 3$$
$$= 6 - 3 \text{ or } 3$$

72. $h(x) = -2x + 2$
$$h(0) = -2(0) + 2$$
$$= 0 + 2 \text{ or } 2$$

73. $f(x) = 3x - 1$
$$f\left(\frac{1}{2}\right) = 3\left(\frac{1}{2}\right) - 1$$
$$= \frac{3}{2} - 1 \text{ or } \frac{1}{2}$$

74. $g(x) = x^2$
$$g(2) = 2^2$$
$$= 4$$

75. $h(x) = 2x^2 - 4$
$$h(0) = 2(0)^2 - 4$$
$$= 0 - 4 \text{ or } -4$$

Page 605   Spreadsheet Investigation
(Preview of Lesson 11–6)

1. $b_{n+1} = 1.0075b_n - 43.29$

2. $b_1 = 1.0075(495) - 43.29$ or 455.42
$b_2 = 1.0075(455.42) - 43.29$ or 415.55
$b_3 = 1.0075(415.55) - 43.29$ or 375.38
$b_4 = 1.0075(375.38) - 43.29$ or 334.91
$b_5 = 1.0075(334.91) - 43.29$ or 294.13
$b_6 = 1.0075(294.13) - 43.29$ or 253.05

The balance after six months is $253.05. This is about 51% of the loan.

3. $b_7 = 1.0075(253.05) - 43.29$ or 211.66
$b_8 = 1.0075(211.66) - 43.29$ or 169.96
$b_9 = 1.0075(169.96) - 43.29$ or 127.94
$b_{10} = 1.0075(127.94) - 43.29$ or 85.61
$b_{11} = 1.0075(85.61) - 43.29$ or 42.96
$b_{12} = 1.0075(42.96) - 43.29$ or -0.01
After 12 months, the balance is about $-\$0.01$; the balance is not exactly 0 due to rounding.

4. $b_{n+1} = 1.0075b_n - 50$
$b_1 = 1.0075(495) - 50$ or 448.71
$b_2 = 1.0075(448.71) - 50$ or 402.08
$b_3 = 1.0075(402.08) - 50$ or 355.10
$b_4 = 1.0075(355.10) - 50$ or 307.76
$b_5 = 1.0075(307.76) - 50$ or 260.07
$b_6 = 1.0075(260.07) - 50$ or 212.02
$b_7 = 1.0075(212.02) - 50$ or 163.61
$b_8 = 1.0075(163.61) - 50$ or 114.84
$b_9 = 1.0075(114.84) - 50$ or 65.70
$b_{10} = 1.0075(65.70) - 50$ or 16.19
$b_{11} = 1.0075(16.19) - 50$ or -33.69
The loan will be paid off after 11 months.

5. Changing the monthly payment only requires editing the amount subtracted in the formula in each cell.

6. The monthly interest will be $\frac{6\%}{12}$ or 0.5%.
$b_{n+1} = 1.005b_n - 365.06$
$b_1 = 1.005(12{,}000) - 365.06$ or $11{,}694.94$
$b_2 = 1.005(11{,}694.94) - 365.06$ or $11{,}388.36$
$b_3 = 1.005(11{,}388.36) - 365.06$ or $11{,}080.24$
$b_4 = 1.005(11{,}080.24) - 365.06$ or $10{,}770.58$
$b_5 = 1.005(10{,}770.58) - 365.06$ or $10{,}459.37$
$b_6 = 1.005(10{,}459.37) - 365.06$ or $10{,}146.61$
$b_7 = 1.005(10{,}146.61) - 365.06$ or 9832.28
$b_8 = 1.005(9832.28) - 365.06$ or 9516.38
$b_9 = 1.005(9516.38) - 365.06$ or 9198.90
$b_{10} = 1.005(9198.90) - 365.06$ or 8879.83
$b_{11} = 1.005(8879.83) - 365.06$ or 8559.17
$b_{12} = 1.005(8559.17) - 365.06$ or 8236.91
After 12 months, Jamie owes $\$8236.91$.

11-6 Recursion and Special Sequences

Page 607 Algebra Activity

1. Only one move is required to get the penny to the second circle.

2. (1) First move the penny to the second circle.
(2) Then move the nickel to the third circle.
(3) Finally, place the penny on the nickel in the third circle.
Three moves are necessary.

3. (1) First move the dime to the second circle.
(2) Then move the penny to the third circle.
(3) Place the dime on the penny in the third circle. (4) Move the nickel to the second circle. (5) Move the dime back to the first circle. (6) Place the penny on the nickel in the second circle. (7) Finally, place the dime on the penny and nickel.
Seven moves are required.

4. (1) First move the dime to the second circle.
(2) Then move the penny to the third circle.
(3) Place the dime on the penny in the third circle. (4) Move the nickel to the second circle. (5) Move the dime back to the first circle on the quarter. (6) Place the penny on the nickel in the second circle. (7) Then place the dime on the penny and nickel. (8) The third circle is vacant, so move the quarter to the third circle. (9) Place the dime on the quarter in the third circle. (10) The first circle is vacant, so move the penny to the first circle. (11) Move the dime to the first circle on the penny. (12) Place the nickel on the quarter in the third circle. (13) The second circle is vacant, so move the dime to the second circle. (14) Place the penny on the nickel and quarter in the third circle. (15) Finally, place the dime on the other three coins. Fifteen moves are required. Conjecture: $a_n = 2^n - 1$ moves are required to move a stack of n coins.

Page 608 Check for Understanding

1. arithmetic: $a_n = a_{n-1} + d$
geometric: $a_n = r \cdot a_{n-1}$

2. Sample answer: $a_n = 2a_{n-1} + a_{n-2}$

3. Sometimes; if $f(x) = x^2$ and $x_1 = 2$, then $x_2 = 2^2$ or 4, so $x_1 \neq x_2$. But if $x_1 = 1$, then $x_2 = 1$, so $x_2 = x_1$.

4. $a_{n+1} = a_n - 3$
$a_{1+1} = a_1 - 3$
$\quad a_2 = 12 - 3$ or 9
$a_{2+1} = a_2 - 3$
$\quad a_3 = 9 - 3$ or 6
$a_{3+1} = a_3 - 3$
$\quad a_4 = 6 - 3$ or 3
$a_{4+1} = a_4 - 3$
$\quad a_5 = 3 - 3$ or 0
The first five terms are 12, 9, 6, 3, and 0.

5. $a_{n+1} = a_n + n$
$a_{1+1} = a_1 + 1$
$\quad a_2 = -3 + 1$ or -2
$a_{2+1} = a_2 + 2$
$\quad a_3 = -2 + 2$ or 0
$a_{3+1} = a_3 + 3$
$\quad a_4 = 0 + 3$ or 3
$a_{4+1} = a_4 + 4$
$\quad a_5 = 3 + 4$ or 7
The first five terms are -3, -2, 0, 3, and 7.

547

6. $a_{n+1} = -2a_n - 4$

$a_{1+1} = -2a_1 - 4$

$\quad a_2 = -2(0) - 4$ or -4

$a_{2+1} = -2a_2 - 4$

$\quad a_3 = -2(-4) - 4$ or 4

$a_{3+1} = -2a_3 - 4$

$\quad a_4 = -2(4) - 4$ or -12

$a_{4+1} = -2a_4 - 4$

$\quad a_5 = -2(-12) - 4$ or 20

The first five terms are $0, -4, 4, -12$, and 20.

7. $a_{n+2} = 4a_{n+1} - 3a_n$

$a_{1+2} = 4a_{1+1} - 3a_1$

$\quad a_3 = 4a_2 - 3a_1$

$\quad a_3 = 4(2) - 3(1)$ or 5

$a_{2+2} = 4a_{2+1} - 3a_2$

$\quad a_4 = 4a_3 - 3a_2$

$\quad a_4 = 4(5) - 3(2)$ or 14

$a_{3+2} = 4a_{3+1} - 3a_3$

$\quad a_5 = 4a_4 - 3a_3$

$\quad a_5 = 4(14) - 3(5)$ or 41

The first five terms are $1, 2, 5, 14$, and 41.

8. $f(x) = 3x - 4$

$x_1 = f(x_0)$

$\quad = f(3)$

$\quad = 3(3) - 4$ or 5

$x_2 = f(x_1)$

$\quad = f(5)$

$\quad = 3(5) - 4$ or 11

$x_3 = f(x_2)$

$\quad = f(11)$

$\quad = 3(11) - 4$ or 29

The first three iterates are $5, 11$, and 29.

9. $f(x) = -2x + 5$

$x_1 = f(x_0)$

$\quad = f(2)$

$\quad = -2(2) + 5$ or 1

$x_2 = f(x_1)$

$\quad = f(1)$

$\quad = -2(1) + 5$ or 3

$x_3 = f(x_2)$

$\quad = f(3)$

$\quad = -2(3) + 5$ or -1

The first three iterates are $1, 3$, and -1.

10. $f(x) = x^2 + 2$

$x_1 = f(x_0)$

$\quad = f(-1)$

$\quad = (-1)^2 + 2$ or 3

$x_2 = f(x_1)$

$\quad = f(3)$

$\quad = 3^2 + 2$ or 11

$x_3 = f(x_2)$

$\quad = f(11)$

$\quad = 11^2 + 2$ or 123

The first three iterates are $3, 11$, and 123.

11. $b_n = 1.05b_{n-1} - 10$

12. $b_n = 1.05b_{n-1} - 10$

$b_1 = 1.05b_0 - 10$

$\quad = 1.05(1000) - 10$ or 1040

$b_2 = 1.05b_1 - 10$

$\quad = 1.05(1040) - 10$ or 1082

$b_3 = 1.05b_2 - 10$

$\quad = 1.05(1082) - 10$ or 1126.10

$b_4 = 1.05b_3 - 10$

$\quad = 1.05(1126.10) - 10$ or 1172.41

After four years, Rita will have $1172.41.

Pages 609–610   Practice and Apply

13. $a_{n+1} = a_n + 3$

$a_{1+1} = a_1 + 3$

$\quad a_2 = -6 + 3$ or -3

$a_{2+1} = a_2 + 3$

$\quad a_3 = -3 + 3$ or 0

$a_{3+1} = a_3 + 3$

$\quad a_4 = 0 + 3$ or 3

$a_{4+1} = a_4 + 3$

$\quad a_5 = 3 + 3$ or 6

The first five terms are $-6, -3, 0, 3$, and 6.

14. $a_{n+1} = a_n + 5$

$a_{1+1} = a_1 + 5$

$\quad a_2 = 13 + 5$ or 18

$a_{2+1} = a_2 + 5$

$\quad a_3 = 18 + 5$ or 23

$a_{3+1} = a_3 + 5$

$\quad a_4 = 23 + 5$ or 28

$a_{4+1} = a_4 + 5$

$\quad a_5 = 28 + 5$ or 33

The first five terms are $13, 18, 23, 28$, and 33.

15. $a_{n+1} = a_n - n$

$a_{1+1} = a_1 - 1$

$\quad a_2 = 2 - 1$ or 1

$a_{2+1} = a_2 - 2$

$\quad a_3 = 1 - 2$ or -1

$a_{3+1} = a_3 - 3$

$\quad a_4 = -1 - 3$ or -4

$a_{4+1} = a_4 - 4$

$\quad a_5 = -4 - 4$ or -8

The first five terms are $2, 1, -1, -4$, and -8.

16. $a_{n+1} = a_n + n + 3$

$a_{1+1} = a_1 + 1 + 3$

$\quad a_2 = 6 + 1 + 3$ or 10

$a_{2+1} = a_2 + 2 + 3$

$\quad a_3 = 10 + 2 + 3$ or 15

$a_{3+1} = a_3 + 3 + 3$

$\quad a_4 = 15 + 3 + 3$ or 21

$a_{4+1} = a_4 + 4 + 3$

$\quad a_5 = 21 + 4 + 3$ or 28

The first five terms are $6, 10, 15, 21$, and 28.

17. $a_{n+1} = 2a_n - 4$

$a_{1+1} = 2a_1 - 4$

$a_2 = 2(9) - 4$ or 14

$a_{2+1} = 2a_2 - 4$

$a_3 = 2(14) - 4$ or 24

$a_{3+1} = 2a_3 - 4$

$a_4 = 2(24) - 4$ or 44

$a_{4+1} = 2a_4 - 4$

$a_5 = 2(44) - 4$ or 84

The first five terms are 9, 14, 24, 44, and 84.

18. $a_{n+1} = 3a_n - 6$

$a_{1+1} = 3a_1 - 6$

$a_2 = 3(4) - 6$ or 6

$a_{2+1} = 3a_2 - 6$

$a_3 = 3(6) - 6$ or 12

$a_{3+1} = 3a_3 - 6$

$a_4 = 3(12) - 6$ or 30

$a_{4+1} = 3a_4 - 6$

$a_5 = 3(30) - 6$ or 84

The first five terms are 4, 6, 12, 30, and 84.

19. $a_{n+1} = a_n + a_{n-1}$

$a_{2+1} = a_2 + a_{2-1}$

$a_3 = a_2 + a_1$

$a_3 = 5 + (-1)$ or 4

$a_{3+1} = a_3 + a_{3-1}$

$a_4 = a_3 + a_2$

$a_4 = 4 + 5$ or 9

$a_{4+1} = a_4 + a_{4-1}$

$a_5 = a_4 + a_3$

$a_5 = 9 + 4$ or 13

The first five terms are -1, 5, 4, 9, and 13.

20. $a_{n+2} = a_{n+1} + 2a_n$

$a_{1+2} = a_{1+1} + 2a_1$

$a_3 = a_2 + 2a_1$

$a_3 = -3 + 2(4)$ or 5

$a_{2+2} = a_{2+1} + 2a_2$

$a_4 = a_3 + 2a_2$

$a_4 = 5 + 2(-3)$ or -1

$a_{3+2} = a_{3+1} + 2a_3$

$a_5 = a_4 + 2a_3$

$a_5 = -1 + 2(5)$ or 9

The first five terms are 4, -3, 5, -1, and 9.

21. $a_{n+1} = \frac{n}{n+1} \cdot a_n$

$a_{1+1} = \frac{1}{1+1} \cdot a_1$

$a_2 = \frac{1}{2}\left(\frac{7}{2}\right)$ or $\frac{7}{4}$

$a_{2+1} = \frac{2}{2+1} \cdot a_2$

$a_3 = \frac{2}{3}\left(\frac{7}{4}\right)$ or $\frac{7}{6}$

$a_{3+1} = \frac{3}{3+1} \cdot a_3$

$a_4 = \frac{3}{4}\left(\frac{7}{6}\right)$ or $\frac{7}{8}$

$a_{4+1} = \frac{4}{4+1} \cdot a_4$

$a_5 = \frac{4}{5}\left(\frac{7}{8}\right)$ or $\frac{7}{10}$

The first five terms are $\frac{7}{2}$, $\frac{7}{4}$, $\frac{7}{6}$, $\frac{7}{8}$, and $\frac{7}{10}$.

22. $a_{n+1} = \frac{n^2+1}{n} \cdot a_n$

$a_{1+1} = \frac{1^2+1}{1} \cdot a_1$

$a_2 = \frac{2}{1}\left(\frac{3}{4}\right)$ or $\frac{3}{2}$

$a_{2+1} = \frac{2^2+1}{2} \cdot a_2$

$a_3 = \frac{5}{2}\left(\frac{3}{2}\right)$ or $\frac{15}{4}$

$a_{3+1} = \frac{3^2+1}{3} \cdot a_3$

$a_4 = \frac{10}{3}\left(\frac{15}{4}\right)$ or $\frac{25}{2}$

$a_{4+1} = \frac{4^2+1}{4} \cdot a_4$

$a_5 = \frac{17}{4}\left(\frac{25}{2}\right)$ or $\frac{425}{8}$

The first five terms are $\frac{3}{4}$, $\frac{3}{2}$, $\frac{15}{4}$, $\frac{25}{2}$, and $\frac{425}{8}$.

23. $a_{n+1} = a_n + 12$

$a_{0+1} = a_0 + 12$

$a_1 = 7 + 12$ or 19

$a_{1+1} = a_1 + 12$

$a_2 = 19 + 12$ or 31

$a_{2+1} = a_2 + 12$

$a_3 = 31 + 12$ or 43

$a_{3+1} = a_3 + 12$

$a_4 = 43 + 12$ or 55

$a_{4+1} = a_4 + 12$

$a_5 = 55 + 12$ or 67

24. $a_{n+1} = -2.1$

$a_{3+1} = -2.1$

$a_4 = -2.1$

25. 1, 1, 2, 3, 5, ...

26. the Fibonacci sequence

27. $b_n = 1.006b_{n-1} - 678.79$

$b_1 = 1.006(100,000) - 678.79$ or $99,921.21$

After the first payment, the balance of the loan is $99,921.21.

$b_2 = 1.006(99,921.21) - 678.79$ or $99,841.95$

After the second payment, the balance of the loan is $99,841.95.

$b_3 = 1.006(99,841.95) - 678.79$ or $99,762.21$

After the third payment, the balance of the loan is $99,762.21.

$b_4 = 1.006(99,762.21) - 678.79$ or $99,681.99$

After the fourth payment, the balance of the loan is $99,681.99.

$b_5 = 1.006(99,681.99) - 678.79$ or $99,601.29$

After the fifth payment, the balance of the loan is $99,601.29.

$b_6 = 1.006(99,601.29) - 678.79$ or $99,520.11$

After the sixth payment, the balance of the loan is $99,520.11.

$b_7 = 1.006(99,520.11) - 678.79$ or $99,438.44$

After the seventh payment, the balance of the loan is $99,438.44.

$b_8 = 1.006(99,438.44) - 678.79$ or $99,356.28$

After the eighth payment, the balance of the loan is $99,356.28.

28. Count the number of dots in each figure.

1, 3, 6, 10, 15

29. The second triangular number is two more than the first. The third triangular number is three more than the second. The nth triangular number is n more than the previous triangular number.
$$t_n = t_{n-1} + n$$

30. The 200th triangular number can be represented by the following sum.
$$1 + 2 + 3 + \ldots + 200$$
Find the sum.
$$S_n = \frac{n}{2}(a_1 + a_n)$$
$$S_{200} = \frac{200}{2}(1 + 200)$$
$$= 100(201) \text{ or } 20{,}100$$
The 200th triangular number is 20,100.

31. $f(x) = 9x - 2$
$$\begin{aligned} x_1 &= f(x_0) \\ &= f(2) \\ &= 9(2) - 2 \text{ or } 16 \\ x_2 &= f(x_1) \\ &= f(16) \\ &= 9(16) - 2 \text{ or } 142 \\ x_3 &= f(x_3) \\ &= f(142) \\ &= 9(142) - 2 \text{ or } 1276 \end{aligned}$$
The first three iterates are 16, 142, and 1276.

32. $f(x) = 4x - 3$
$$\begin{aligned} x_1 &= f(x_0) \\ &= f(2) \\ &= 4(2) - 3 \text{ or } 5 \\ x_2 &= f(x_1) \\ &= f(5) \\ &= 4(5) - 3 \text{ or } 17 \\ x_3 &= f(x_2) \\ &= f(17) \\ &= 4(17) - 3 \text{ or } 65 \end{aligned}$$
The first three iterates are 5, 17, and 65.

33. $f(x) = 3x + 5$
$$\begin{aligned} x_1 &= f(x_0) \\ &= f(-4) \\ &= 3(-4) + 5 \text{ or } -7 \\ x_2 &= f(x_1) \\ &= f(-7) \\ &= 3(-7) + 5 \text{ or } -16 \\ x_3 &= f(x_2) \\ &= f(-16) \\ &= 3(-16) + 5 \text{ or } -43 \end{aligned}$$
The first three iterates are -7, -16, and -43.

34. $f(x) = 5x + 1$
$$\begin{aligned} x_1 &= f(x_0) \\ &= f(-1) \\ &= 5(-1) + 1 \text{ or } -4 \\ x_2 &= f(x_1) \\ &= f(-4) \\ &= 5(-4) + 1 \text{ or } -19 \\ x_3 &= f(x_2) \\ &= f(-19) \\ &= 5(-19) + 1 \text{ or } -94 \end{aligned}$$
The first three iterates are -4, -19, and -94.

35. $f(x) = 2x^2 - 5$
$$\begin{aligned} x_1 &= f(x_0) \\ &= f(-1) \\ &= 2(-1)^2 - 5 \text{ or } -3 \\ x_2 &= f(x_1) \\ &= f(-3) \\ &= 2(-3)^2 - 5 \text{ or } 13 \\ x_3 &= f(x_2) \\ &= f(13) \\ &= 2(13)^2 - 5 \text{ or } 333 \end{aligned}$$
The first three iterates are -3, 13, and 333.

36. $f(x) = 3x^2 - 4$
$$\begin{aligned} x_1 &= f(x_0) \\ &= f(1) \\ &= 3(1)^2 - 4 \text{ or } -1 \\ x_2 &= f(x_1) \\ &= f(-1) \\ &= 3(-1)^2 - 4 \text{ or } -1 \\ x_3 &= f(x_2) \\ &= f(-1) \\ &= 3(-1)^2 - 4 \text{ or } -1 \end{aligned}$$
The first three iterates are -1, -1, and -1.

37. $f(x) = 2x^2 + 2x + 1$
$$\begin{aligned} x_1 &= f(x_0) \\ &= f\left(\frac{1}{2}\right) \\ &= 2\left(\frac{1}{2}\right)^2 + 2\left(\frac{1}{2}\right) + 1 \text{ or } \frac{5}{2} \\ x_2 &= f(x_1) \\ &= f\left(\frac{5}{2}\right) \\ &= 2\left(\frac{5}{2}\right)^2 + 2\left(\frac{5}{2}\right) + 1 \text{ or } \frac{37}{2} \\ x_3 &= f(x_2) \\ &= f\left(\frac{37}{2}\right) \\ &= 2\left(\frac{37}{2}\right)^2 + 2\left(\frac{37}{2}\right) + 1 \text{ or } \frac{1445}{2} \end{aligned}$$
The first three iterates are $\frac{5}{2}$, $\frac{37}{2}$, and $\frac{1445}{2}$.

38. $f(x) = 3x^2 - 3x + 2$
$$\begin{aligned} x_1 &= f(x_0) \\ &= f\left(\frac{1}{3}\right) \\ &= 3\left(\frac{1}{3}\right)^2 - 3\left(\frac{1}{3}\right) + 2 \text{ or } \frac{4}{3} \\ x_2 &= f(x_1) \\ &= f\left(\frac{4}{3}\right) \\ &= 3\left(\frac{4}{3}\right)^2 - 3\left(\frac{4}{3}\right) + 2 \text{ or } \frac{10}{3} \\ x_3 &= f(x_2) \\ &= f\left(\frac{10}{3}\right) \\ &= 3\left(\frac{10}{3}\right)^2 - 3\left(\frac{10}{3}\right) + 2 \text{ or } \frac{76}{3} \end{aligned}$$
The first three iterates are $\frac{4}{3}$, $\frac{10}{3}$, and $\frac{76}{3}$.

39. $c(x) = 1.02x$

$x_1 = c(70)$
   $= 1.02(70)$ or 71.40

$x_2 = c(71.40)$
   $= 1.02(71.40)$ or 72.83

$x_3 = c(72.83)$
   $= 1.02(72.83)$ or 74.29

$x_4 = c(74.29)$
   $= 1.02(74.29)$ or 75.78

The cost will $75.78 in four years.

40. No; according to the first two iterates, $f(4) = 4$. According to the second and third iterates, $f(4) = 7$. Since $f(x)$ is a function, it cannot have two values when $x = 4$.

41. Under certain conditions, the Fibonacci sequence can be used to model the number of shoots on a plant. Answers should include the following.
- The 13th term of the sequence is 233, so there are 233 shoots on the plant during the 13th month.
- The Fibonacci sequence is not arithmetic because the differences $(0, 1, 1, 2, ...)$ of the terms are not constant. The Fibonacci sequence is not geometric because the ratios $\left(1, 2, \frac{3}{2}, ...\right)$ of the terms are not constant.

42. D; Use the percent proportion.

$\frac{8}{4a} = \frac{r}{100}$

$800 = 4ar$

$\frac{800}{4a} = r$

$\frac{200}{a} = r$

43. C; The area of a semicircle is given by $\frac{1}{2}\pi r^2$ where r is the radius.

$\text{area} = \frac{1}{2}\pi(6)^2 - \frac{1}{2}\pi(4)^2 + \frac{1}{2}\pi(2)^2$

$= \frac{1}{2}\pi(6^2 - 4^2 + 2^2)$

$= \frac{1}{2}\pi(24)$

$= 12\pi$

Page 610   Maintain Your Skills

44. First find r.

$r = \frac{6}{9}$ or $\frac{2}{3}$

Since $\left|\frac{2}{3}\right| < 1$, the sum exists.

$S = \frac{a_1}{1 - r}$

$= \frac{9}{1 - \frac{2}{3}}$

$= \frac{9}{\frac{1}{3}}$ or 27

45. First find r.

$r = \frac{\frac{1}{32}}{\frac{1}{8}}$ or $\frac{1}{4}$

Since $\left|\frac{1}{4}\right| < 1$, the sum exists.

$S = \frac{a_1}{1 - r}$

$= \frac{\frac{1}{8}}{1 - \frac{1}{4}}$

$= \frac{\frac{1}{8}}{\frac{3}{4}}$ or $\frac{1}{6}$

46. First find r.

$r = \frac{-\frac{8}{3}}{4}$ or $-\frac{2}{3}$

Since $\left|-\frac{2}{3}\right| < 1$, the sum exists.

$S = \frac{a_1}{1 - r}$

$= \frac{4}{1 - \left(-\frac{2}{3}\right)}$

$= \frac{4}{\frac{5}{3}}$ or $\frac{12}{5}$

47. First find r.

$r = \frac{-10}{2}$ or -5

Now find the sum.

$S_n = \frac{a_1(1 - r^n)}{1 - r}$

$S_6 = \frac{2(1 - (-5)^6)}{1 - (-5)}$

$S_6 = -5208$

48. First find r.

$r = \frac{1}{3}$

Now find the sum.

$S_n = \frac{a_1(1 - r^n)}{1 - r}$

$S_7 = \frac{3\left(1 - \left(\frac{1}{3}\right)^7\right)}{1 - \left(\frac{1}{3}\right)}$

$S_7 = \frac{1093}{243}$

49. Divide the area by the width to find the length.

$\frac{6x^2 + 38x + 56}{2x + 8} = \frac{(6x^2 + 38x + 56) \div 2}{(2x + 8) \div 2}$

$= \frac{3x^2 + 19x + 28}{x + 4}$

$= \frac{(3x + 7)(x + 4)}{x + 4}$

$= 3x + 7$

The length of the rectangle is $3x + 7$ units.

50. $5 \cdot 4 \cdot 3 \cdot 2 \cdot 1 = 120$

51. $7 \cdot 6 \cdot 5 \cdot 4 \cdot 3 \cdot 2 \cdot 1 = 5040$

52. $\frac{4 \cdot 3}{2 \cdot 1} = \frac{12}{2}$ or 6

53. $\frac{6 \cdot 5 \cdot 4}{3 \cdot 2 \cdot 1} = \frac{120}{6}$ or 20

54. $\frac{9 \cdot 8 \cdot 7 \cdot 6}{4 \cdot 3 \cdot 2 \cdot 1} = \frac{3024}{24}$ or 126

55. $\frac{10 \cdot 9 \cdot 8 \cdot 7 \cdot 6 \cdot 5}{6 \cdot 5 \cdot 4 \cdot 3 \cdot 2 \cdot 1} = \frac{151,200}{720}$ or 210

1.

Stage	1	2	3	4
Number of Segments	3	12	48	192
Length of Each Segment	9	3	1	$\frac{1}{3}$
Perimeter	27	36	48	64

2. $s_n = 4s_{n-1}$, $\ell_n = \frac{1}{3}\ell_{n-1}$, $P_n = \frac{4}{3}P_{n-1}$

3. $s_n = 3 \cdot 4^{n-1}$, $\ell_n = 9\left(\frac{1}{3}\right)^{n-1}$, $P_n = 27\left(\frac{4}{3}\right)^{n-1}$

4. The von Koch snowflake has infinite perimeter. As n increases, the perimeter P_n of Stage n increases without bound. That is, the limit of $27\left(\frac{4}{3}\right)^{n-1}$ is ∞.

5. Stage 1 is an equilateral triangle with sides of length 9 units, so its area is $\frac{81\sqrt{3}}{4}$ units^2. Each subsequent stage encloses $3 \cdot 4^{n-2}$ additional equilateral triangular regions of area $\frac{81\sqrt{3}}{4 \cdot 3^{2n-2}}$ units^2. Thus, the additional area at each stage is $3 \cdot 4^{n-2} \cdot \frac{81\sqrt{3}}{4 \cdot 3^{2n-2}}$ or $\frac{4^{n-3}\sqrt{3}}{3^{2n-7}}$ units^2. This is the general term of the series for $n \geq 2$.

6. Beginning with the second term, the terms of the series in Exercise 5 form an infinite geometric series with common ratio $\frac{4}{9}$. Therefore, the sum of the whole series in Exercise 5 is $\frac{81\sqrt{3}}{4} + \frac{\frac{27\sqrt{3}}{4}}{1 - \frac{4}{9}}$ or $\frac{162\sqrt{3}}{5}$. The area of the von Koch snowflake is $\frac{162\sqrt{3}}{5}$ units^2.

7. Sample answer: No, they show that it is possible for a figure with infinite perimeter to enclose only a finite amount of area.

11-7 The Binomial Theorem

Page 615 Check for Understanding

1. Write out Pascal's triangle to the row corresponding to $n = 8$.

$$
\begin{array}{ccccccccccccccccc}
&&&&&&&&1&&&&&&&&\\
&&&&&&&1&&1&&&&&&&\\
&&&&&&1&&2&&1&&&&&&\\
&&&&&1&&3&&3&&1&&&&&\\
&&&&1&&4&&6&&4&&1&&&&\\
&&&1&&5&&10&&10&&5&&1&&&\\
&&1&&6&&15&&20&&15&&6&&1&&\\
&1&&7&&21&&35&&35&&21&&7&&1&\\
1&&8&&28&&56&&70&&56&&28&&8&&1
\end{array}
$$

The coefficients are 1, 8, 28, 56, 70, 56, 28, 8, and 1.

2. According to the Binomial Theorem, the coefficient of $a^{n-1}b$ is $\frac{n!}{(n-1)!1!}$.

$\frac{n!}{(n-1)!1!} = \frac{n \cdot (n-1)!}{(n-1)!}$ or n

The coefficient is n.

---

3. Sample answer: $(5x + y)^4$
The first term of the expansion of $(5x + y)^4$ is $1 \cdot (5x)^4$ or $625x^4$.

4. $8! = 8 \cdot 7 \cdot 6 \cdot 5 \cdot 4 \cdot 3 \cdot 2 \cdot 1$ or 40,320

5. $\frac{13!}{9!} = \frac{13 \cdot 12 \cdot 11 \cdot 10 \cdot 9 \cdot 8 \cdot 7 \cdot 6 \cdot 5 \cdot 4 \cdot 3 \cdot 2 \cdot 1}{9 \cdot 8 \cdot 7 \cdot 6 \cdot 5 \cdot 4 \cdot 3 \cdot 2 \cdot 1}$
$= 13 \cdot 12 \cdot 11 \cdot 10$ or 17,160

6. $\frac{12!}{2!10!} = \frac{12 \cdot 11 \cdot 10 \cdot 9 \cdot 8 \cdot 7 \cdot 6 \cdot 5 \cdot 4 \cdot 3 \cdot 2 \cdot 1}{2 \cdot 1 \cdot 10 \cdot 9 \cdot 8 \cdot 7 \cdot 6 \cdot 5 \cdot 4 \cdot 3 \cdot 2 \cdot 1}$
$= \frac{12 \cdot 11}{2 \cdot 1}$ or 66

7. Use Pascal's triangle.
$(p + q)^5$
$= 1p^5q^0 + 5p^4q^1 + 10p^3q^2 + 10p^2q^3 + 5p^1q^4 + 1p^0q^5$
$= p^5 + 5p^4q + 10p^3q^2 + 10p^2q^3 + 5pq^4 + q^5$

8. Use Pascal's triangle.
$(t + 2)^6$
$= 1t^6(2)^0 + 6t^5(2)^1 + 15t^4(2)^2 + 20t^3(2)^3 + 15t^2(2)^4 + 6t^1(2)^5 + 1t^0(2)^6$
$= t^6 + 12t^5 + 60t^4 + 160t^3 + 240t^2 + 192t + 64$

9. Use the Binomial Theorem.
$(x - 3y)^4$
$= 1x^4(-3y)^0 + \frac{4}{1}x^3(-3y)^1 + \frac{4 \cdot 3}{1 \cdot 2}x^2(-3y)^2 + \frac{4 \cdot 3 \cdot 2}{1 \cdot 2 \cdot 3}x^1(-3y)^3 + 1x^0(-3y)^4$
$= x^4 - 12x^3y + 54x^2y^2 - 108xy^3 + 81y^4$

10. In the fourth term, $k = 3$.
$\frac{8!}{(8-3)!3!}a^{8-3}b^3 = \frac{8!}{5!3!}a^5b^3$
$= \frac{8 \cdot 7 \cdot 6}{3 \cdot 2 \cdot 1}a^5b^3$
$= 56a^5b^3$

11. In the fifth term, $k = 4$.
$\frac{10!}{(10-4)!4!}(2a)^{10-4}(3b)^4 = \frac{10!}{6!4!}(2a)^6(3b)^4$
$= \frac{10 \cdot 9 \cdot 8 \cdot 7}{4 \cdot 3 \cdot 2 \cdot 1}(64a^6)(81b^4)$
$= 1,088,640a^6b^4$

12. The coefficient of t^3f^2 in the expansion of $(t + f)^5$ gives the number of ways a student can answer the questions with three trues and two falses.
$\frac{5!}{(5-2)!2!}t^{5-2}f^2 = \frac{5!}{3!2!}t^3f^2$
$= \frac{5 \cdot 4}{2 \cdot 1}t^3f^2$
$= 10t^3f^2$
There are 10 ways.

Pages 615–616 Practice and Apply

13. $9! = 9 \cdot 8 \cdot 7 \cdot 6 \cdot 5 \cdot 4 \cdot 3 \cdot 2 \cdot 1$ or 362,880

14. $13! = 13 \cdot 12 \cdot 11 \cdot 10 \cdot 9 \cdot 8 \cdot 7 \cdot 6 \cdot 5 \cdot 4 \cdot 3 \cdot 2 \cdot 1$ or 6,227,020,800

15. $\frac{9!}{7!} = \frac{9 \cdot 8 \cdot 7 \cdot 6 \cdot 5 \cdot 4 \cdot 3 \cdot 2 \cdot 1}{7 \cdot 6 \cdot 5 \cdot 4 \cdot 3 \cdot 2 \cdot 1}$
$= 9 \cdot 8$ or 72

16. $\frac{7!}{4!} = \frac{7 \cdot 6 \cdot 5 \cdot 4 \cdot 3 \cdot 2 \cdot 1}{4 \cdot 3 \cdot 2 \cdot 1}$
$= 7 \cdot 6 \cdot 5$ or 210

17. $\frac{12!}{8!4!} = \frac{12 \cdot 11 \cdot 10 \cdot 9 \cdot 8 \cdot 7 \cdot 6 \cdot 5 \cdot 4 \cdot 3 \cdot 2 \cdot 1}{8 \cdot 7 \cdot 6 \cdot 5 \cdot 4 \cdot 3 \cdot 2 \cdot 1 \cdot 4 \cdot 3 \cdot 2 \cdot 1}$
$= \frac{12 \cdot 11 \cdot 10 \cdot 9}{4 \cdot 3 \cdot 2 \cdot 1}$ or 495

18. $\frac{14!}{5!9!} = \frac{14 \cdot 13 \cdot 12 \cdot 11 \cdot 10 \cdot 9 \cdot 8 \cdot 7 \cdot 6 \cdot 5 \cdot 4 \cdot 3 \cdot 2 \cdot 1}{5 \cdot 4 \cdot 3 \cdot 2 \cdot 1 \cdot 9 \cdot 8 \cdot 7 \cdot 6 \cdot 5 \cdot 4 \cdot 3 \cdot 2 \cdot 1}$
$= \frac{14 \cdot 13 \cdot 12 \cdot 11 \cdot 10}{5 \cdot 4 \cdot 3 \cdot 2 \cdot 1}$ or 2002

19. Use Pascal's triangle.

$(a - b)^3$
$$= 1a^3(-b)^0 + \tfrac{3}{1}a^2(-b)^1 + \tfrac{3 \cdot 2}{2 \cdot 1}a^1(-b)^2 + 1a^0(-b)^3$$
$$= a^3 - 3a^2b + 3ab^2 - b^3$$

20. Use Pascal's triangle.

$(m + n)^4$
$$= 1m^4n^0 + 4m^3n^1 + 6m^2n^2 + 4m^1n^3 + 1m^0n^4$$
$$= m^4 + 4m^3n + 6m^2n^2 + 4mn^3 + n^4$$

21. Use Pascal's triangle.

$(r + s)^8$
$$= 1r^8s^0 + 8r^7s^1 + 28r^6s^2 + 56r^5s^3 + 70r^4s^4 + 56r^3s^5 + 28r^2s^6 + 8r^1s^7 + 1r^0s^8$$
$$= r^8 + 8r^7s + 28r^6s^2 + 56r^5s^3 + 70r^4s^4 + 56r^3s^5 + 28r^2s^6 + 8rs^7 + s^8$$

22. Use the Binomial Theorem.

$(m - a)^5$
$$= 1m^5(-a)^0 + \tfrac{5}{1}m^4(-a)^1 + \tfrac{5 \cdot 4}{2 \cdot 1}m^3(-a)^2 + \tfrac{5 \cdot 4}{2 \cdot 1}m^2(-a)^3 + \tfrac{5}{1}m^1(-a)^4 + 1m^0(-a)^5$$
$$= m^5 - 5m^4a + 10m^3a^2 - 10m^2a^3 + 5ma^4 - a^5$$

23. Use the Binomial Theorem.

$(x + 3)^5$
$$= 1x^5(3)^0 + \tfrac{5}{1}x^4(3)^1 + \tfrac{5 \cdot 4}{2 \cdot 1}x^3(3)^2 + \tfrac{5 \cdot 4}{2 \cdot 1}x^2(3)^3 + \tfrac{5}{1}x^1(3)^4 + 1x^0(3)^5$$
$$= x^5 + 15x^4 + 90x^3 + 270x^2 + 405x + 243$$

24. Use the Binomial Theorem.

$(a - 2)^4$
$$= 1a^4(-2)^0 + \tfrac{4}{1}a^3(-2)^1 + \tfrac{4 \cdot 3}{2 \cdot 1}a^2(-2)^2 + \tfrac{4}{1}a^1(-2)^3 + 1a^0(-2)^4$$
$$= a^4 - 8a^3 + 24a^2 - 32a + 16$$

25. Use the Binomial Theorem.

$(2b - x)^4$
$$= 1(2b)^4(-x)^0 + \tfrac{4}{1}(2b)^3(-x)^1 + \tfrac{4 \cdot 3}{2 \cdot 1}(2b)^2(-x)^2 + \tfrac{4}{1}(2b)^1(-x)^3 + 1(2b)^0(-x)^4$$
$$= 16b^4 - 32b^3x + 24b^2x^2 - 8bx^3 + x^4$$

26. Use Pascal's triangle.

$(2a + b)^6$
$$= 1(2a)^6b^0 + 6(2a)^5b^1 + 15(2a)^4b^2 + 20(2a)^3b^3 + 15(2a)^2b^4 + 6(2a)^1b^5 + 1(2a)^0b^6$$
$$= 64a^6 + 192a^5b + 240a^4b^2 + 160a^3b^3 + 60a^2b^4 + 12ab^5 + b^6$$

27. Use Pascal's triangle.

$(3x - 2y)^5$
$$= 1(3x)^5(-2y)^0 + 5(3x)^4(-2y)^1 + 10(3x)^3(-2y)^2 + 10(3x)^2(-2y)^3 + 5(3x)^1(-2y)^4 + 1(3x)^0(-2y)^5$$
$$= 243x^5 - 810x^4y + 1080x^3y^2 - 720x^2y^3 + 240xy^4 - 32y^5$$

28. Use Pascal's triangle.

$(3x + 2y)^4$
$$= 1(3x)^4(2y)^0 + 4(3x)^3(2y)^1 + 6(3x)^2(2y)^2 + 4(3x)^1(2y)^3 + 1(3x)^0(2y)^4$$
$$= 81x^4 + 216x^3y + 216x^2y^2 + 96xy^3 + 16y^4$$

29. Use Pascal's triangle.

$\left(\dfrac{a}{2} + 2\right)^5$
$$= 1\left(\tfrac{a}{2}\right)^5(2)^0 + 5\left(\tfrac{a}{2}\right)^4(2)^1 + 10\left(\tfrac{a}{2}\right)^3(2)^2 + 10\left(\tfrac{a}{2}\right)^2(2)^3 + 5\left(\tfrac{a}{2}\right)^1(2)^4 + 1\left(\tfrac{a}{2}\right)^0(2)^5$$
$$= \dfrac{a^5}{32} + \dfrac{5a^4}{8} + 5a^3 + 20a^2 + 40a + 32$$

30. Use Pascal's triangle.

$\left(3 + \dfrac{m}{3}\right)^5$
$$= 1(3)^5\left(\tfrac{m}{3}\right)^0 + 5(3)^4\left(\tfrac{m}{3}\right)^1 + 10(3)^3\left(\tfrac{m}{3}\right)^2 + 10(3)^2\left(\tfrac{m}{3}\right)^3 + 5(3)^1\left(\tfrac{m}{3}\right)^4 + 1(3)^0\left(\tfrac{m}{3}\right)^5$$
$$= 243 + 135m + 30m^2 + \dfrac{10m^3}{3} + \dfrac{5m^4}{27} + \dfrac{m^5}{243}$$

31. The volume of the cube is $(3x + 2)^3$.

$(3x + 2)^3$
$$= 1(3x)^3(2)^0 + 3(3x)^2(2)^1 + 3(3x)^1(2)^2 + 1(3x)^0(2)^3$$
$$= 27x^3 + 54x^2 + 36x + 8$$

The volume of the cube is $27x^3 + 54x^2 + 36x + 8$ cubic centimeters.

32. At each nail or divider that a bearing encounters, it must go to the left ℓ or the right r. A bearing encounters one nail in each of the three rows of nails and one divider in the row of dividers, so there are four times that a bearing must go to the left or to the right. Expand $(\ell + r)^4$.

$(\ell + r)^4 = 1\ell^4r^0 + 4\ell^3r^1 + 6\ell^2r^2 + 4\ell^1r^3 + 1\ell^0r^4$
$$= \ell^4 + 4\ell^3r + 6\ell^2r^2 + 4\ell r^3 + r^4$$

The coefficent of ℓ^4 is the number of paths where a bearing always goes to the left, leading to the leftmost section. There is one such path. The coefficient of ℓ^3r is the number of paths where a bearing makes three lefts and one right, leading to the section second from the left. There are four such paths.

Thus, from left to right, the numbers of paths leading to each section are 1, 4, 6, 4, and 1.

33. The coefficient of k^8s^2 in the expansion of $(k + s)^{10}$ is the number of sequences of makes and misses that result in Ofelia making eight and missing two shots.

$$\dfrac{10!}{(10 - 2)!2!}k^{10 - 2}s^2 = \dfrac{10!}{8!2!}k^8s^2$$
$$= \dfrac{10 \cdot 9}{2 \cdot 1}k^8s^2$$
$$= 45k^8s^2$$

There are 45 such sequences.

34. In the sixth term, $k = 5$.

$$\dfrac{9!}{(9 - 5)!5!}x^{9 - 5}(-y)^5 = \dfrac{9!}{4!5!}x^4(-y)^5$$
$$= \dfrac{9 \cdot 8 \cdot 7 \cdot 6}{4 \cdot 3 \cdot 2 \cdot 1}x^4y^5$$
$$= -126x^4y^5$$

35. In the seventh term, $k = 6$.

$$\dfrac{12!}{(12 - 6)!6!}x^{12 - 6}y^6 = \dfrac{12!}{6!6!}x^6y^6$$
$$= \dfrac{12 \cdot 11 \cdot 10 \cdot 9 \cdot 8 \cdot 7}{6 \cdot 5 \cdot 4 \cdot 3 \cdot 2 \cdot 1}x^6y^6$$
$$= 924x^6y^6$$

36. In the fourth term, $k = 3$.

$$\dfrac{7!}{(7 - 3)!3!}x^{7 - 3}(2)^3 = \dfrac{7!}{4!3!}x^4(2)^3$$
$$= \dfrac{7 \cdot 6 \cdot 5}{3 \cdot 2 \cdot 1}x^4(8)$$
$$= 280x^4$$

37. In the fifth term, $k = 4$.

$$\dfrac{8!}{(8 - 4)!4!}a^{8 - 4}(-3)^4 = \dfrac{8!}{4!4!}a^4(-3)^4$$
$$= \dfrac{8 \cdot 7 \cdot 6 \cdot 5}{4 \cdot 3 \cdot 2 \cdot 1}a^4(81)$$
$$= 5670a^4$$

38. In the fifth term, $k = 4$.

$$\dfrac{10!}{(10 - 4)!4!}(2a)^{10 - 4}(3b)^4 = \dfrac{10!}{6!4!}(2a)^6(3b)^4$$
$$= \dfrac{10 \cdot 9 \cdot 8 \cdot 7}{4 \cdot 3 \cdot 2 \cdot 1}(64a^6)(81b^4)$$
$$= 1{,}088{,}640a^6b^4$$

39. In the fourth term, $k = 3$.

$$\frac{9!}{(9-3)!3!}(2x)^{9-3}(3y)^3 = \frac{9!}{6!3!}(2x)^6(3y)^3$$
$$= \frac{9 \cdot 8 \cdot 7}{3 \cdot 2 \cdot 1}(64x^6)(27y^3)$$
$$= 145{,}152x^6y^3$$

40. In the fourth term, $k = 3$.

$$\frac{7!}{(7-3)!3!}x^{7-3}\left(\frac{1}{3}\right)^3 = \frac{7!}{4!3!}x^4\left(\frac{1}{3}\right)^3$$
$$= \frac{7 \cdot 6 \cdot 5}{3 \cdot 2 \cdot 1}x^4\left(\frac{1}{27}\right)$$
$$= \frac{35}{27}x^4$$

41. In the sixth term, $k = 5$.

$$\frac{10!}{(10-5)!5!}x^{10-5}\left(-\frac{1}{2}\right)^5 = \frac{10!}{5!5!}x^5\left(-\frac{1}{2}\right)^5$$
$$= \frac{10 \cdot 9 \cdot 8 \cdot 7 \cdot 6}{5 \cdot 4 \cdot 3 \cdot 2 \cdot 1}x^5\left(-\frac{1}{32}\right)$$
$$= -\frac{63}{8}x^5$$

42. $\frac{12!}{7!5!}$ and $\frac{12!}{6!6!}$ represent the sixth and seventh entries in the row for $n = 12$ in Pascal's triangle. $\frac{13!}{7!6!}$ represents the seventh entry in the row for $n = 13$. Since $\frac{13!}{7!6!}$ is below $\frac{12!}{7!5!}$ and $\frac{12!}{6!6!}$ in Pascal's triangle, $\frac{12!}{7!5!} + \frac{12!}{6!6!} = \frac{13!}{7!6!}$.

43. The coefficients in a binomial expansion give the numbers of sequences of births resulting in given numbers of boys and girls. Answers should include the following.
  - $(b + g)^5 = b^5 + 5b^4g + 10b^3g^2 + 10b^2g^3 + 5bg^4 + g^5$; There is one sequence of births with all five boys, five sequences with four boys and one girl, ten sequences with three boys and two girls, ten sequences with two boys and three girls, five sequences with one boy and four girls, and one sequence with all five girls.
  - The number of sequences of births that have exactly k girls in a family of n children is the coefficient of $b^{n-k}g^k$ in the expansion of $(b + g)^n$. According to the Binomial Theorem, this coefficient is $\frac{n!}{(n-k)!k!}$.

44. D; Test $x = 6$.

$$x^2 < x + 20$$
$$6^2 < 6 + 20$$
$$36 < 26, \quad \text{false}$$

Since $x = 6$ is not a solution, we eliminate answer choice A. Now test $x = -4.5$.

$$x^2 < x + 20$$
$$(-4.5)^2 < -4.5 + 20$$
$$20.25 < 15.5, \quad \text{false}$$

Since $x = -4.5$ is not a solution, we eliminate answer choices B and C. This leaves answer choice D.

45. C; Consider the quadrilateral formed by the four lines. One interior angle of the quadrilateral is given as 75°. The other three interior angles are $x°$, $y°$, and 145°, since vertical angles have equal measures. The sum of the angles is 360°.

$$x + y + 145 + 75 = 360$$
$$x + y + 220 = 360$$
$$x + y = 140$$

46. $a_{n+1} = a_n - 2$

$$a_{1+1} = a_1 - 2$$
$$a_2 = 7 - 2 \text{ or } 5$$
$$a_{2+1} = a_2 - 2$$
$$a_3 = 5 - 2 \text{ or } 3$$
$$a_{3+1} = a_3 - 2$$
$$a_4 = 3 - 2 \text{ or } 1$$
$$a_{4+1} = a_4 - 2$$
$$a_5 = 1 - 2 \text{ or } -1$$

The first five terms are 7, 5, 3, 1, and -1.

47. $a_{n+1} = 2a_n - 1$

$$a_{1+1} = 2a_1 - 1$$
$$a_2 = 2(3) - 1 \text{ or } 5$$
$$a_{2+1} = 2a_2 - 1$$
$$a_3 = 2(5) - 1 \text{ or } 9$$
$$a_{3+1} = 2a_3 - 1$$
$$a_4 = 2(9) - 1 \text{ or } 17$$
$$a_{4+1} = 2a_4 - 1$$
$$a_5 = 2(17) - 1 \text{ or } 33$$

The first five terms are 3, 5, 9, 17, and 33.

48. $a_1 = 25$, $r = \frac{20}{25}$ or $\frac{4}{5}$

$$S = \frac{a_1}{1 - r}$$
$$S = \frac{25}{1 - \frac{4}{5}}$$
$$= \frac{25}{\frac{1}{5}} \text{ or } 125$$

The pendulum travels 125 cm before coming to a rest.

49. $\log_2 5 = \frac{\log 5}{\log 2}$
$$\approx 2.3219$$

50. $\log_3 10 = \frac{\log 10}{\log 3}$
$$= \frac{1}{\log 3}$$
$$\approx 2.0959$$

51. $\log_5 8 = \frac{\log 8}{\log 5}$
$$\approx 1.2920$$

52. Factor the denominator.
$$\frac{1}{x^2 + 5x + 6} = \frac{1}{(x + 3)(x + 2)}$$
The function is undefined for $x = -3$ and $x = -2$. Since the expression is simplified, $x = -3$ and $x = -2$ are vertical asymptotes.

53. Factor the denominator.
$$\frac{x + 2}{x^2 + 3x - 4} = \frac{x + 2}{(x + 4)(x - 1)}$$
The function is undefined for $x = -4$ and $x = 1$. Since the expression is simplified, $x = -4$ and $x = 1$ are vertical asymptotes.

54. Factor the numerator.
$$\frac{x^2 + 4x + 3}{x + 3} = \frac{(x + 3)(x + 1)}{x + 3}$$
The function is undefined for $x = -3$. Since $\frac{(x + 3)(x + 1)}{x + 3} = x + 1$, $x = -3$ represents a hole in the graph.

55. This is a hyperbola since A and C have opposite signs (the x^2 and y^2 terms have opposite signs).

56. This is a parabola since $A = 0$ (there is no x^2 term).

57. $[f \circ g](x) = f[g(x)]$ $\qquad$ $[g \circ f](x) = g[f(x)]$
$\qquad = f(x - 3)$ $\qquad\qquad\qquad = g(x + 3)$
$\qquad = (x - 3) + 3$ $\qquad\qquad = (x + 3) - 3$
$\qquad = x$ $\qquad\qquad\qquad\qquad = x$
The functions are inverses since both $[f \circ g](x)$ and $[g \circ f](x)$ equal x.

58. $[f \circ g](x) = f[g(x)]$
$\qquad = f\left(\dfrac{x + 1}{2}\right)$
$\qquad = 2\left(\dfrac{x + 1}{2}\right) + 1$
$\qquad = x + 1 + 1$
$\qquad = x + 2$
The functions are not inverses since $[f \circ g](x)$ does not equal x.

59. True; $\dfrac{1(1 + 1)}{2} = \dfrac{1(2)}{2}$ or 1.

60. False; $\dfrac{(1 + 1)(2 \cdot 1 + 1)}{2} = \dfrac{2(3)}{2}$ or 3.

61. True; $\dfrac{1^2(1 + 1)^2}{4} = \dfrac{1(4)}{4}$ or 1.

62. True; $3^1 - 1 = 2$, which is even.

Page 617 Practice Quiz 2

1. $S_n = \dfrac{a_1(1 - r^n)}{1 - r}$
$S_{12} = \dfrac{5(1 - 3^{12})}{1 - 3}$
$\qquad = 1,328,600$

2. $a_1 = 2, r = -3, n = 6$
$S_n = \dfrac{a_1(1 - r^n)}{1 - r}$
$S_6 = \dfrac{2(1 - (-3)^6)}{1 - (-3)}$
$\qquad = -364$

3. $a_1 = 8, r = \dfrac{2}{3}$
Since $\left|\dfrac{2}{3}\right| < 1$, the sum exists.
$S = \dfrac{a_1}{1 - r}$
$S = \dfrac{8}{1 - \frac{2}{3}}$
$\quad = \dfrac{8}{\frac{1}{3}}$ or 24

4. $a_1 = 5, r = \dfrac{1}{5}$
Since $\left|\dfrac{1}{5}\right| < 1$, the sum exists.
$S = \dfrac{a_1}{1 - r}$
$S = \dfrac{5}{1 - \frac{1}{5}}$
$\quad = \dfrac{5}{\frac{4}{5}}$ or $\dfrac{25}{4}$

5. $a_{n + 1} = 2a_n + 3$
$a_{1 + 1} = 2a_1 + 3$
$\quad a_2 = 2(1) + 3$ or 5
$a_{2 + 1} = 2a_2 + 3$
$\quad a_3 = 2(5) + 3$ or 13
$a_{3 + 1} = 2a_3 + 3$
$\quad a_4 = 2(13) + 3$ or 29
$a_{4 + 1} = 2a_4 + 3$
$\quad a_5 = 2(29) + 3$ or 61
The first five terms are 1, 5, 13, 29, and 61.

6. $a_{n + 1} = a_n + 2n$
$a_{1 + 1} = a_1 + 2(1)$
$\quad a_2 = 2 + 2$ or 4
$a_{2 + 1} = a_2 + 2(2)$
$\quad a_3 = 4 + 4$ or 8
$a_{3 + 1} = a_3 + 2(3)$
$\quad a_4 = 8 + 6$ or 14
$a_{4 + 1} = a_4 + 2(4)$
$\quad a_5 = 14 + 8$ or 22
The first five terms are 2, 4, 8, 14, and 22.

7. $f(x) = -3x + 2$
$x_1 = f(x_0)$
$\quad = f(-1)$
$\quad = -3(-1) + 2$ or 5
$x_2 = f(x_1)$
$\quad = f(5)$
$\quad = -3(5) + 2$ or -13
$x_3 = f(x_2)$
$\quad = f(-13)$
$\quad = -3(-13) + 2$ or 41
The first three iterates are 5, -13, and 41.

8. Use Pascal's triangle.
$(3x + y)^5$
$\quad = 1(3x)^5y^0 + 5(3x)^4y^1 + 10(3x)^3y^2 + 10(3x)^2y^3 + 5(3x)^1y^4 + 1(3x)^0y^5$
$\quad = 243x^5 + 405x^4y + 270x^3y^2 + 90x^2y^3 + 15xy^4 + y^5$

9. Use Pascal's triangle.
$(a + 2)^6$
$\quad = 1a^6(2)^0 + 6a^5(2)^1 + 15a^4(2)^2 + 20a^3(2)^3 + 15a^2(2)^4 + 6a^1(2)^5 + 1a^0(2)^6$
$\quad = a^6 + 12a^5 + 60a^4 + 160a^3 + 240a^2 + 192a + 64$

10. In the fifth term, $k = 4$.
$\dfrac{9!}{(9 - 4)!4!}(2a)^{9-4}b^4 = \dfrac{9 \cdot 8 \cdot 7 \cdot 6}{4 \cdot 3 \cdot 2 \cdot 1}(32a^5)b^4$
$\qquad\qquad\qquad\qquad = 4032a^5b^4$

11-8 Proof and Mathematical Induction

Pages 619–620 Check for Understanding

1. Sample answers: formulas for the sums of powers of the first n positive integers and statements that expressions involving exponents of n are divisible by certain numbers

2. Mathematical induction is used to show that a statement is true. A counterexample is used to show that a statement is false.

3. Sample answer: $3^n - 1$

4. Step 1: When $n = 1$, the left side of the given equation is 1. The right side is $\frac{1(1 + 1)}{2}$ or 1, so the equation is true for $n = 1$.

Step 2: Assume $1 + 2 + 3 + \ldots + k = \frac{k(k + 1)}{2}$ for some positive integer k.

Step 3: $1 + 2 + 3 + \ldots + k + (k + 1)$

$= \frac{k(k + 1)}{2} + (k + 1)$

$= \frac{k(k + 1) + 2(k + 1)}{2}$

$= \frac{k^2 + 3k + 2}{2}$

$= \frac{(k + 1)(k + 2)}{2}$

The last expression is the right side of the equation to be proved, where $n = k + 1$. Thus, the equation is true for $n = k + 1$.

Therefore, $1 + 2 + 3 + \ldots + n = \frac{n(n + 1)}{2}$ for all positive integers n.

5. Step 1: When $n = 1$, the left side of the given equation is $\frac{1}{2}$. The right side is $1 - \frac{1}{2}$ or $\frac{1}{2}$, so the equation is true for $n = 1$.

Step 2: Assume $\frac{1}{2} + \frac{1}{2^2} + \frac{1}{2^3} + \ldots + \frac{1}{2^k} = 1 - \frac{1}{2^k}$ for some positive integer k.

Step 3: $\frac{1}{2} + \frac{1}{2^2} + \frac{1}{2^3} + \ldots + \frac{1}{2^k} + \frac{1}{2^{k+1}}$

$= 1 - \frac{1}{2^k} + \frac{1}{2^{k+1}}$

$= 1 - \frac{2}{2^{k+1}} + \frac{1}{2^{k+1}}$

$= 1 - \frac{1}{2^{k+1}}$

The last expression is the right side of the equation to be proved, where $n = k + 1$. Thus, the equation is true for $n = k + 1$.

Therefore, $\frac{1}{2} + \frac{1}{2^2} + \frac{1}{2^3} + \ldots + \frac{1}{2^n} = 1 - \frac{1}{2^n}$ for all positive integers n.

6. Step 1: $4^1 - 1 = 3$, which is divisible by 3. The statement is true for $n = 1$.

Step 2: Assume that $4^k - 1$ is divisible by 3 for some positive integer k. This means that $4^k - 1 = 3r$ for some whole number r.

Step 3: $4^k - 1 = 3r$

$4^k = 3r + 1$

$4(4^k) = 4(3r + 1)$

$4^{k + 1} = 12r + 4$

$4^{k + 1} - 1 = 12r + 3$

$4^{k + 1} - 1 = 3(4r + 1)$

Since r is a whole number, $4r + 1$ is a whole number. Thus, $4^{k + 1} - 1$ is divisible by 3, so the statement is true for $n = k + 1$.

Therefore, $4^n - 1$ is divisible by 3 for all positive integers n.

7. Step 1: $5^1 + 3 = 8$, which is divisible by 4. The statement is true for $n = 1$.

Step 2: Assume that $5^k + 3$ is divisible by 4 for some positive integer k. This means that $5^k + 3 = 4r$ for some positive integer r.

Step 3: $5^k + 3 = 4r$

$5^k = 4r - 3$

$5(5^k) = 5(4r - 3)$

$5^{k + 1} = 20r - 15$

$5^{k + 1} + 3 = 20r - 12$

$5^{k + 1} + 3 = 4(5r - 3)$

Since r is a positive integer, $5r - 3$ is a positive integer. Thus, $5^{k + 1} + 3$ is divisible by 4, so the statement is true for $n = k + 1$.

Therefore, $5^n + 3$ is divisible by 4 for all positive integers n.

8. Sample answer: $n = 2$
For $n = 2$, the left side of the equation is $1 + 2$ or 3, and the right side is 2^2 or 4.

9. Sample answer: $n = 3$
For $n = 3$, $2^n + 2n$ is $2^3 + 2(3)$ or 14, which is not divisible by 4.

10. Step 1: After the first guest has arrived, no handshakes have taken place. $\frac{1(1 - 1)}{2} = 0$, so the formula is correct for $n = 1$.

Step 2: Assume that after k guests have arrived, a total of $\frac{k(k - 1)}{2}$ handshakes have taken place, for some positive integer k.

Step 3: When the $(k + 1)$st guest arrives, he or she shakes hands with the k guests already there, so the total number of handshakes that have then taken place is $\frac{k(k - 1)}{2} + k$.

$\frac{k(k - 1)}{2} + k = \frac{k(k - 1) + 2k}{2}$

$= \frac{k[(k - 1) + 2]}{2}$

$= \frac{k(k + 1)}{2}$ or $\frac{(k + 1)k}{2}$

The last expression is the formula to be proved, where $n = k + 1$. Thus, the formula is true for $n = k + 1$.

Therefore, the total number of handshakes is $\frac{n(n - 1)}{2}$ for all positive integers n.

Pages 620–621 Practice and Apply

11. Step 1: When $n = 1$, the left side of the given equation is 1. The right side is $1[2(1) - 1]$ or 1, so the equation is true for $n = 1$.

Step 2: Assume $1 + 5 + 9 + \ldots + (4k - 3) = k(2k - 1)$ for some positive integer k.

Step 3: $1 + 5 + 9 + \ldots + (4k - 3) + [4(k + 1) - 3]$

$= k(2k - 1) + [4(k + 1) - 3]$

$= 2k^2 - k + 4k + 4 - 3$

$= 2k^2 + 3k + 1$

$= (k + 1)(2k + 1)$

$= (k + 1)(2k + 2 - 1)$

$= (k + 1)[2(k + 1) - 1]$

The last expression is the right side of the equation to be proved, where $n = k + 1$. Thus, the equation is true for $n = k + 1$.

Therefore, $1 + 5 + 9 + \ldots + (4n - 3) = n(2n - 1)$ for all positive integers n.

12. Step 1: When $n = 1$, the left side of the given equation is 2. The right side is $\frac{1[3(1) + 1]}{2}$ or 2, so the equation is true for $n = 1$.

Step 2: Assume $2 + 5 + 8 + \ldots + (3k - 1) = \frac{k(3k + 1)}{2}$ for some positive integer k.

Step 3: $2 + 5 + 8 + \ldots + (3k - 1) + [3(k + 1) - 1]$
$$= \frac{k(3k + 1)}{2} + [3(k + 1) - 1]$$
$$= \frac{k(3k + 1) + 2[3(k + 1) - 1]}{2}$$
$$= \frac{3k^2 + k + 6k + 6 - 2}{2}$$
$$= \frac{3k^2 + 7k + 4}{2}$$
$$= \frac{(k + 1)(3k + 4)}{2}$$
$$= \frac{(k + 1)[3(k + 1) + 1]}{2}$$

The last expression is the right side of the equation to be proved, where $n = k + 1$. Thus, the equation is true for $n = k + 1$.

Therefore, $2 + 5 + 8 + \ldots + (3n - 1) = \frac{n(3n + 1)}{2}$ for all positive integers n.

13. Step 1: When $n = 1$, the left side of the given equation is 1^3 or 1. The right side is $\frac{1^2(1 + 1)^2}{4}$ or 1, so the equation is true for $n = 1$.

Step 2: Assume $1^3 + 2^3 + 3^3 + \ldots + k^3 = \frac{k^2(k + 1)^2}{4}$ for some positive integer k.

Step 3: $1^3 + 2^3 + 3^3 + \ldots + k^3 + (k + 1)^3$
$$= \frac{k^2(k + 1)^2}{4} + (k + 1)^3$$
$$= \frac{k^2(k + 1)^2 + 4(k + 1)^3}{4}$$
$$= \frac{(k + 1)^2[k^2 + 4(k + 1)]}{4}$$
$$= \frac{(k + 1)^2(k^2 + 4k + 4)}{4}$$
$$= \frac{(k + 1)^2(k + 2)^2}{4}$$
$$= \frac{(k + 1)^2[(k + 1) + 1]^2}{4}$$

The last expression is the right side of the equation to be proved, where $n = k + 1$. Thus, the equation is true for $n = k + 1$.

Therefore, $1^3 + 2^3 + 3^3 + \ldots + n^3 = \frac{n^2(n + 1)^2}{4}$ for all positive integers n.

14. Step 1: When $n = 1$, the left side of the given equation is 1^2 or 1. The right side is $\frac{1[2(1) - 1][2(1) + 1]}{3}$ or 1, so the equation is true for $n = 1$.

Step 2: Assume $1^2 + 3^2 + 5^2 + \ldots + (2k - 1)^2 = \frac{k(2k - 1)(2k + 1)}{3}$ for some positive integer k.

Step 3: $1^2 + 3^2 + 5^2 + \ldots + (2k - 1)^2 + [2(k + 1) - 1]^2$
$$= \frac{k(2k - 1)(2k + 1)}{3} + [2(k + 1) - 1]^2$$
$$= \frac{k(2k - 1)(2k + 1) + 3(2k + 1)^2}{3}$$
$$= \frac{(2k + 1)[k(2k - 1) + 3(2k + 1)]}{3}$$
$$= \frac{(2k + 1)(2k^2 - k + 6k + 3)}{3}$$
$$= \frac{(2k + 1)(2k^2 + 5k + 3)}{3}$$
$$= \frac{(2k + 1)(k + 1)(2k + 3)}{3}$$
$$= \frac{(k + 1)[2(k + 1) - 1][2(k + 1) + 1]}{3}$$

The last expression is the right side of the equation to be proved, where $n = k + 1$. Thus, the equation is true for $n = k + 1$.

Therefore, $1^2 + 3^2 + 5^2 + \ldots + (2n - 1)^2 = \frac{n(2n - 1)(2n + 1)}{3}$ for all positive integers n.

15. Step 1: When $n = 1$, the left side of the given equation is $\frac{1}{3}$. The right side is $\frac{1}{2}\left(1 - \frac{1}{3}\right)$ or $\frac{1}{3}$, so the equation is true for $n = 1$.

Step 2: Assume $\frac{1}{3} + \frac{1}{3^2} + \frac{1}{3^3} + \ldots + \frac{1}{3^k} = \frac{1}{2}\left(1 - \frac{1}{3^k}\right)$ for some positive integer k.

Step 3: $\frac{1}{3} + \frac{1}{3^2} + \frac{1}{3^3} + \ldots + \frac{1}{3^k} + \frac{1}{3^{k+1}}$
$$= \frac{1}{2}\left(1 - \frac{1}{3^k}\right) + \frac{1}{3^{k+1}}$$
$$= \frac{1}{2} - \frac{1}{2 \cdot 3^k} + \frac{1}{3^{k+1}}$$
$$= \frac{3^{k+1} - 3 + 2}{2 \cdot 3^{k+1}}$$
$$= \frac{3^{k+1} - 1}{2 \cdot 3^{k+1}}$$
$$= \frac{1}{2}\left(\frac{3^{k+1} - 1}{3^{k+1}}\right)$$
$$= \frac{1}{2}\left(1 - \frac{1}{3^{k+1}}\right)$$

The last expression is the right side of the equation to be proved, where $n = k + 1$. Thus, the equation is true for $n = k + 1$.

Therefore, $\frac{1}{3} + \frac{1}{3^2} + \frac{1}{3^3} + \ldots + \frac{1}{3^n} = \frac{1}{2}\left(1 - \frac{1}{3^n}\right)$ for all positive integers n.

16. Step 1: When $n = 1$, the left side of the given equation is $\frac{1}{4}$. The right side is $\frac{1}{3}\left(1 - \frac{1}{4}\right)$ or $\frac{1}{4}$, so the equation is true for $n = 1$.

Step 2: Assume $\frac{1}{4} + \frac{1}{4^2} + \frac{1}{4^3} + \ldots + \frac{1}{4^k}$
$= \frac{1}{3}\left(1 - \frac{1}{4^k}\right)$ for some positive integer k.

Step 3: $\frac{1}{4} + \frac{1}{4^2} + \frac{1}{4^3} + \ldots + \frac{1}{4^k} + \frac{1}{4^{k+1}}$
$= \frac{1}{3}\left(1 - \frac{1}{4^k}\right) + \frac{1}{4^{k+1}}$
$= \frac{1}{3} - \frac{1}{3 \cdot 4^k} + \frac{1}{4^{k+1}}$
$= \frac{4^{k+1} - 4 + 3}{3 \cdot 4^{k+1}}$
$= \frac{4^{k+1} - 1}{3 \cdot 4^{k+1}}$
$= \frac{1}{3}\left(\frac{4^{k+1} - 1}{4^{k+1}}\right)$
$= \frac{1}{3}\left(1 + \frac{1}{4^{k+1}}\right)$

The last expression is the right side of the equation to be proved, where $n = k + 1$. Thus, the equation is true for $n = k + 1$.

Therefore, $\frac{1}{4} + \frac{1}{4^2} + \frac{1}{4^3} + \ldots + \frac{1}{4^n} = \frac{1}{3}\left(1 - \frac{1}{4^n}\right)$ for all positive integers n.

17. Step 1: $8^1 - 1 = 7$, which is divisible by 7. The statement is true for $n = 1$.

Step 2: Assume that $8^k - 1$ is divisible by 7 for some positive integer k. This means that $8^k - 1 = 7r$ for some whole number r.

Step 3: $8^k - 1 = 7r$
$8^k = 7r + 1$
$8(8^k) = 8(7r + 1)$
$8^{k+1} = 56r + 8$
$8^{k+1} - 1 = 56r + 7$
$8^{k+1} - 1 = 7(8r + 1)$

Since r is a whole number, $8r + 1$ is a whole number. Thus, $8^{k+1} - 1$ is divisible by 7, so the statement is true for $n = k + 1$.

Therefore, $8^n - 1$ is divisible by 7 for all positive integers n.

18. Step 1: $9^1 - 1 = 8$, which is divisible by 8. The statement is true for $n = 1$.

Step 2: Assume that $9^k - 1$ is divisible by 8 for some positive integer k. This means that $9^k - 1 = 8r$ for some whole number r.

Step 3: $9^k - 1 = 8r$
$9^k = 8r + 1$
$9(9^k) = 9(8r + 1)$
$9^{k+1} = 72r + 9$
$9^{k+1} - 1 = 72r + 8$
$9^{k+1} - 1 = 8(9r + 1)$

Since r is a whole number, $9r + 1$ is a whole number. Thus, $9^{k+1} - 1$ is divisible by 8, so the statement is true for $n = k + 1$.

Therefore, $9^n - 1$ is divisible by 8 for all positive integers n.

19. Step 1: $12^1 + 10 = 22$, which is divisible by 11. The statement is true for $n = 1$.

Step 2: Assume that $12^k + 10$ is divisible by 11 for some positive integer k. This means that $12^k + 10 = 11r$ for some positive integer r.

Step 3: $12^k + 10 = 11r$
$12^k = 11r - 10$
$12(12^k) = 12(11r - 10)$
$12^{k+1} = 132r - 120$
$12^{k+1} + 10 = 132r - 110$
$12^{k+1} + 10 = 11(12r - 10)$

Since r is a positive integer, $12r - 10$ is a positive integer. Thus, $12^{k+1} + 10$ is divisible by 11, so the statement is true for $n = k + 1$.

Therefore, $12^n + 10$ is divisible by 11 for all positive integers n.

20. Step 1: $13^1 + 11 = 24$, which is divisible by 12. The statement is true for $n = 1$.

Step 2: Assume that $13^k + 11$ is divisible by 12 for some positive integer k. This means that $13^k + 11 = 12r$ for some positive integer r.

Step 3: $13^k + 11 = 12r$
$13^k = 12r - 11$
$13(13^k) = 13(12r - 11)$
$13^{k+1} = 156r - 143$
$13^{k+1} + 11 = 156r - 132$
$13^{k+1} + 11 = 12(13r - 11)$

Since r is a positive integer, $13r - 11$ is a positive integer. Thus, $13^{k+1} + 11$ is divisible by 12, so the statement is true for $n = k + 1$.

Therefore, $13^n + 11$ is divisible by 12 for all positive integers n.

21. Step 1: There are 6 bricks in the top row, and $1^2 + 5(1) = 6$, so the formula is true for $n = 1$.

Step 2: Assume that there are $k^2 + 5k$ bricks in the top k rows for some positive integer k.

Step 3: Since each row has 2 more bricks than the one above, the numbers of bricks in the rows form an arithmetic sequence. The number of bricks in the $(k + 1)$st row is $6 + [(k + 1) - 1](2)$ or $2k + 6$. Then the number of bricks in the top $k + 1$ rows is $k^2 + 5k + (2k + 6)$ or $k^2 + 7k + 6$.
$k^2 + 7k + 6 = (k + 1)^2 + 5(k + 1)$, which is the formula to be proved, where $n = k + 1$. Thus, the formula is true for $n = k + 1$.

Therefore, the number of bricks in the top n rows is $n^2 + 5n$ for all positive integers n.

22. Step 1: When $n = 1$, the left side of the given equation is a_1. The right side is $\frac{a_1(1 - r^1)}{1 - r}$ or a_1, so the equation is true for $n = 1$.

Step 2: Assume $a_1 + a_1 r + a_1 r^2 + \ldots + a_1 r^{k-1}$
$= \frac{a_1(1 - r^k)}{1 - r}$ for some positive integer k.

Step 3: $a_1 + a_1 r + a_1 r^2 + \ldots + a_1 r^{k-1} + a_1 r^k$
$$= \frac{a_1(1 - r^k)}{1 - r} + a_1 r^k$$
$$= \frac{a_1(1 - r^k) + (1 - r)a_1 r^k}{1 - r}$$
$$= \frac{a_1 - a_1 r^k + a_1 r^k - a_1 r^{k+1}}{1 - r}$$
$$= \frac{a_1 - a_1 r^{k+1}}{1 - r}$$
$$= \frac{a_1(1 - r^{k+1})}{1 - r}$$

The last expression is the right side of the equation to be proved, where $n = k + 1$. Thus, the equation is true for $n = k + 1$.

Therefore, $a_1 + a_1 r + a_1 r^2 + \ldots + a_1 r^{n-1}$
$= \frac{a_1(1 - r^n)}{1 - r}$ for all positive integers n.

23. Step 1: When $n = 1$, the left side of the given equation is a_1. The right side is $\frac{1}{2}[2a_1 + (1 - 1)d]$ or a_1, so the equation is true for $n = 1$.

Step 2: Assume $a_1 + (a_1 + d) + (a_1 + 2d) + \ldots + [a_1 + (k - 1)d] = \frac{k}{2}[2a_1 + (k - 1)d]$ for some positive integer k.

Step 3: $a_1 + (a_1 + d) + (a_1 + 2d) + \ldots + [a_1 + (k - 1)d] + [a_1 + (k + 1 - 1)d]$
$$= \frac{k}{2}[2a_1 + (k - 1)d] + [a_1 + (k + 1 - 1)d]$$
$$= \frac{k}{2}[2a_1 + (k - 1)d] + a_1 + kd$$
$$= \frac{k[2a_1 + (k - 1)d] + 2(a_1 + kd)}{2}$$
$$= \frac{k \cdot 2a_1 + (k^2 - k)d + 2a_1 + 2kd}{2}$$
$$= \frac{(k + 1)2a_1 + (k^2 - k + 2k)d}{2}$$
$$= \frac{(k + 1)2a_1 + k(k + 1)d}{2}$$
$$= \frac{k + 1}{2}(2a_1 + kd)$$
$$= \frac{k + 1}{2}[2a_1 + (k + 1 - 1)d]$$

The last expression is the right side of the formula to be proved, where $n = k + 1$. Thus, the formula is true for $n = k + 1$.

Therefore, $a_1 + (a_1 + d) + (a_1 + 2d) + \ldots + [a_1 + (n - 1)d] = \frac{n}{2}[2a_1 + (n - 1)d]$ for all positive integers n.

24. Step 1: The figure below shows how to cover a 2^1 by 2^1 board, so the statement is true for $n = 1$.

Step 2: Assume that a 2^k by 2^k board can be covered for some positive integer k.

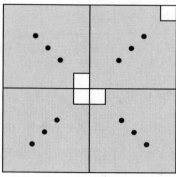

Step 3: Divide a 2^{k+1} by 2^{k+1} board into four quadrants. By the inductive hypothesis, the first quadrant can be covered. Rotate the design that covers Quadrant I 90° clockwise and use it to cover Quadrant II. Use the design that covers Quadrant I to cover Quadrant III. Rotate the design that covers Quadrant I 90° counterclockwise and use it to cover Quadrant IV. This leaves three empty squares near the center of the board, as shown. Use one more L-shaped tile to cover these 3 squares. Thus, a 2^{k+1} by 2^{k+1} board can be covered. The statement is true for $n = k + 1$.

Therefore, a 2^n by 2^n checkerboard with the top right square missing can be covered for all positive integers n.

25. Sample answer: $n = 3$
For $n = 3$, the left side of the equation is $1^2 + 2^2 + 3^2$ or 14, and the right side is $\frac{3[3(3) - 1]}{2}$ or 12.

26. Sample answer: $n = 4$
For $n = 4$, the left side of the equation is $1^3 + 3^3 + 5^3 + 7^3$ or 496, and the right side is $12(4)^3 - 23(4)^2 + 12(4)$ or 448.

27. Sample answer: $n = 2$
For $n = 2$, $3^n + 1$ is $3^2 + 1$ or 10, which is not divisible by 4.

28. Sample answer: $n = 3$
For $n = 3$, $2^n + 2n^2$ is $2^3 + 2(3)^2$ or 26, which is not divisible by 4.

29. Sample answer: $n = 11$
For $n = 11$, $n^2 - n + 11$ is $11^2 - 11 + 11$ or 121, which is not prime.

30. Sample answer: $n = 41$

For $n = 41$, $n^2 + n + 41$ is $41^2 + 41 + 41$ or 1763, which is not prime since 1763 can be factored as $41 \cdot 43$.

31. Write 7^n as $(6 + 1)^n$. Then use the Binomial Theorem.

$$7^n - 1 = (6 + 1)^n - 1$$
$$= 6^n + n \cdot 6^{n-1} + \frac{n(n-1)}{2} 6^{n-2} + \dots + n \cdot 6 + 1 - 1$$
$$= 6^n + n \cdot 6^{n-1} + \frac{n(n-1)}{2} 6^{n-2} + \dots + n \cdot 6$$

Since each term in the last expression is divisible by 6, the whole expression is divisible by 6. Thus, $7^n - 1$ is divisible by 6.

32. An analogy can be made between mathematical induction and a ladder with the positive integers on the steps. Answers should include the following.

- Showing that the statement is true for $n = 1$ (Step 1).
- Assuming that the statement is true for some positive integer k and showing that it is true for $k + 1$ (Steps 2 and 3).

33. C;

$$\frac{x - \frac{4}{x}}{1 - \frac{4}{x} + \frac{4}{x^2}} = \frac{\frac{x^2 - 4}{x}}{\frac{x^2 - 4x + 4}{x^2}}$$
$$= \frac{x^2 - 4}{x} \cdot \frac{x^2}{x^2 - 4x + 4}$$
$$= \frac{(x + 2)(x - 2)}{x} \cdot \frac{x^2}{(x - 2)(x - 2)}$$
$$= \frac{x(x + 2)}{x - 2} \quad \text{or} \quad \frac{x^2 + 2x}{x - 2}$$

34. A; Regardless of the length of $\overline{RS}$, the length of the diagonal $\overline{QS}$ is $\sqrt{2}$ times greater, so the quantity in Column B is $\sqrt{2}$, which is less than 2.

Page 621   Maintain Your Skills

35. $(x + y)^6$
$$= 1x^6y^0 + 6x^5y^1 + 15x^4y^2 + 20x^3y^3 + 15x^2y^4 + 6x^1y^5 + 1x^0y^6$$
$$= x^6 + 6x^5y + 15x^4y^2 + 20x^3y^3 + 15x^2y^4 + 6xy^5 + y^6$$

36. $(a - b)^7$
$$= 1a^7(-b)^0 + 7a^6(-b)^1 + 21a^5(-b)^2 + 35a^4(-b)^3 + 35a^3(-b)^4 + 21a^2(-b)^5 + 7a^1(-b)^6 + 1a^0(-b)^7$$
$$= a^7 - 7a^6b + 21a^5b^2 - 35a^4b^3 + 35a^3b^4 - 21a^2b^5 + 7ab^6 - b^7$$

37. $(2x + y)^8$
$$= 1(2x)^8y^0 + 8(2x)^7y^1 + 28(2x)^6y^2 + 56(2x)^5y^3 + 70(2x)^4y^4 + 56(2x)^3y^5 + 28(2x)^2y^6 + 8(2x)^1y^7 + 1(2x)^0y^8$$
$$= 256x^8 + 1024x^7y + 1792x^6y^2 + 1792x^5y^3 + 1120x^4y^4 + 448x^3y^5 + 112x^2y^6 + 16xy^7 + y^8$$

38. $f(x) = 3x - 2$
$$x_1 = f(x_0)$$
$$= f(2)$$
$$= 3(2) - 2 \text{ or } 4$$
$$x_2 = f(x_1)$$
$$= f(4)$$
$$= 3(4) - 2 \text{ or } 10$$
$$x_3 = f(x_2)$$
$$= f(10)$$
$$= 3(10) - 2 \text{ or } 28$$
The first three iterates are 4, 10, and 28.

39. $f(x) = 4x^2 - 2$
$$x_1 = f(x_0)$$
$$= f(1)$$
$$= 4(1)^2 - 2 \text{ or } 2$$
$$x_2 = f(x_1)$$
$$= f(2)$$
$$= 4(2)^2 - 2 \text{ or } 14$$
$$x_3 = f(x_2)$$
$$= f(14)$$
$$= 4(14)^2 - 2 \text{ or } 782$$
The first three iterates are 2, 14, and 782.

40. Let t represent the number of hours.
$$1 \cdot 2^t = 4096$$
$$2^t = 2^{12}$$
$$t = 12$$
It would take 12 hours.

41.
$$\frac{1}{y + 1} - \frac{3}{y - 3} = 2$$
$$(y + 1)(y - 3)\left(\frac{1}{y + 1} - \frac{3}{y - 3}\right) = 2(y + 1)(y - 3)$$
$$(y + 1)(y - 3)\left(\frac{1}{y + 1}\right) - (y + 1)(y - 3)\left(\frac{3}{y - 3}\right) = 2(y^2 - 2y - 3)$$
$$y - 3 - 3(y + 1) = 2y^2 - 4y - 6$$
$$y - 3 - 3y - 3 = 2y^2 - 4y - 6$$
$$-2y - 6 = 2y^2 - 4y - 6$$
$$0 = 2y^2 - 2y$$
$$0 = 2y(y - 1)$$
$$2y = 0 \quad \text{or} \quad y - 1 = 0$$
$$y = 0 \qquad \qquad y = 1$$
The solutions are 0 and 1.

42.
$$\frac{6}{a - 7} = \frac{a - 49}{a^2 - 7a} + \frac{1}{a}$$
$$a(a - 7)\left(\frac{6}{a - 7}\right) = a(a - 7)\left(\frac{a - 49}{a^2 - 7a} + \frac{1}{a}\right)$$
$$6a = a(a - 7)\left(\frac{a - 49}{a^2 - 7a}\right) + a(a - 7)\left(\frac{1}{a}\right)$$
$$6a = a - 49 + a - 7$$
$$6a = 2a - 56$$
$$4a = -56$$
$$a = -14$$
The solution is -14.

Chapter 11   Study Guide and Review

Page 622   Vocabulary and Concept Check

1. partial sum
2. geometric sequence
3. sigma notation
4. arithmetic means
5. Binomial Theorem
6. common ratio
7. arithmetic series
8. factorial

Pages 622–626   Lesson-by-Lesson Review

9. $a_n = a_1 + (n - 1)d$
$$a_5 = 6 + (5 - 1)(8)$$
$$a_5 = 38$$

10. $a_n = a_1 + (n - 1)d$
$a_{22} = -5 + (22 - 1)(7)$
$a_{22} = 142$

11. $a_n = a_1 + (n - 1)d$
$a_9 = 5 + (9 - 1)(-2)$
$a_9 = -11$

12. $a_n = a_1 + (n - 1)d$
$a_{15} = -2 + (15 - 1)(-3)$
$a_{15} = -44$

13. Find d.
$a_n = a_1 + (n - 1)d$
$a_5 = -7 + (5 - 1)d$
$9 = -7 + 4d$
$16 = 4d$
$4 = d$

Find a_2, a_3, and a_4.
$a_2 = -7 + 4$ or -3
$a_3 = -3 + 4$ or 1
$a_4 = 1 + 4$ or 5
The arithmetic means are -3, 1, and 5.

14. Find d.
$a_n = a_1 + (n - 1)d$
$a_4 = 12 + (4 - 1)d$
$4 = 12 + 3d$
$-8 = 3d$
$-\frac{8}{3} = d$
Find a_2 and a_3.
$a_2 = 12 + \left(-\frac{8}{3}\right)$ or $\frac{28}{3}$
$a_3 = \frac{28}{3} + \left(-\frac{8}{3}\right)$ or $\frac{20}{3}$

The arithmetic means are $\frac{28}{3}$ and $\frac{20}{3}$.

15. Find d.
$a_n = a_1 + (n - 1)d$.
$a_6 = 9 + (6 - 1)d$
$-6 = 9 + 5d$
$-15 = 5d$
$-3 = d$
Find a_2, a_3, a_4, and a_5.
$a_2 = 9 + (-3)$ or 6
$a_3 = 6 + (-3)$ or 3
$a_4 = 3 + (-3)$ or 0
$a_5 = 0 + (-3)$ or -3
The arithmetic means are 6, 3, 0, and -3.

16. Find d.
$a_n = a_1 + (n - 1)d$
$a_5 = 56 + (5 - 1)d$
$28 = 56 + 4d$
$-28 = 4d$
$-7 = d$
Find a_2, a_3, and a_4.
$a_2 = 56 + (-7)$ or 49
$a_3 = 49 + (-7)$ or 42
$a_4 = 42 + (-7)$ or 35
The arithmetic means are 49, 42, and 35.

17. $S_n = \frac{n}{2}(a_1 + a_n)$
$S_{36} = \frac{36}{2}(12 + 117)$
$S_{36} = 18(129)$ or 2322

18. First find d.
$d = 10 - 4$ or 6
Now find n.
$a_n = a_1 + (n - 1)d$
$106 = 4 + (n - 1)(6)$
$106 = 4 + 6n - 6$
$106 = 6n - 2$
$108 = 6n$
$18 = n$
Now find the sum.
$S_n = \frac{n}{2}(a_1 + a_n)$
$S_{18} = \frac{18}{2}(4 + 106)$
$S_{18} = 9(110)$ or 990

19. First find d.
$d = 4 - 10$ or -6
Now find n.
$a_n = a_1 + (n - 1)d$
$-50 = 10 + (n - 1)(-6)$
$-50 = 10 - 6n + 6$
$-50 = 16 - 6n$
$-66 = -6n$
$11 = n$
Now find the sum.
$S_n = \frac{n}{2}(a_1 + a_n)$
$S_{11} = \frac{11}{2}[10 + (-50)]$
$S_{11} = \frac{11}{2}(-40)$ or -220

20. There are 12 terms.
$a_1 = 3(2) + 1$ or 7
$a_{12} = 3(13) + 1$ or 40
Find the sum.
$S_n = \frac{n}{2}(a_1 + a_n)$
$S_{12} = \frac{12}{2}(7 + 40)$
$S_{12} = 6(47)$ or 282

21. $a_n = a_1 \cdot r^{n - 1}$
$a_5 = 2 \cdot 2^{5 - 1}$
$a_5 = 32$

22. $a_n = a_1 \cdot r^{n - 1}$
$a_4 = 7 \cdot 2^{4 - 1}$
$a_4 = 56$

23. $a_n = a_1 \cdot r^{n - 1}$
$a_5 = 243 \cdot \left(-\frac{1}{3}\right)^{5 - 1}$
$a_5 = 3$

24. First find r.
$r = \frac{\frac{4}{3}}{\frac{2}{3}}$ or 2
Now find a_6.
$a_n = a_1 \cdot r^{n - 1}$
$a_6 = \frac{2}{3} \cdot 2^{6 - 1}$
$a_6 = \frac{64}{3}$

25. Find r.

$a_n = a_1 \cdot r^{n-1}$

$a_4 = 3 \cdot r^{4-1}$

$24 = 3r^3$

$8 = r^3$

$2 = r$

Now find a_2 and a_3.

$a_2 = 3 \cdot 2$ or 6

$a_3 = 6 \cdot 2$ or 12

The geometric means are 6 and 12.

26. First find r.

$a_n = a_1 \cdot r^{n-1}$

$a_5 = 7.5 \cdot r^{5-1}$

$120 = 7.5r^4$

$16 = r^4$

$\pm 2 = r$

Use $r = 2$.

$a_2 = 7.5 \cdot 2$ or 15

$a_3 = 15 \cdot 2$ or 30

$a_4 = 30 \cdot 2$ or 60

Use $r = -2$.

$a_2 = 7.5 \cdot (-2)$ or -15

$a_3 = -15 \cdot (-2)$ or 30

$a_4 = 30 \cdot (-2)$ or -60

The geometric means are 15, 30, and 60, or -15, 30, and -60.

27. Find r.

$a_n = a_1 \cdot r^{n-1}$

$a_6 = 8 \cdot r^{6-1}$

$\frac{1}{4} = 8r^5$

$\frac{1}{32} = r^5$

$\frac{1}{2} = r$

Now find a_2, a_3, a_4, and a_5.

$a_2 = 8 \cdot \frac{1}{2}$ or 4

$a_3 = 4 \cdot \frac{1}{2}$ or 2

$a_4 = 2 \cdot \frac{1}{2}$ or 1

$a_5 = 1 \cdot \frac{1}{2}$ or $\frac{1}{2}$

The geometric means are 4, 2, 1, and $\frac{1}{2}$.

28. Find r.

$a_n = a_1 \cdot r^{n-1}$

$a_5 = 5 \cdot r^{5-1}$

$80 = 5r^4$

$16 = r^4$

$\pm 2 = r$

Use $r = 2$.

$a_2 = 5 \cdot 2$ or 10

$a_3 = 10 \cdot 2$ or 20

$a_4 = 20 \cdot 2$ or 40

Use $r = -2$.

$a_2 = 5 \cdot (-2)$ or -10

$a_3 = (-10) \cdot (-2)$ or 20

$a_4 = 20 \cdot (-2)$ or -40

The geometric means are 10, 20, and 40, or -10, 20, and -40.

29. $S_n = \dfrac{a_1(1 - r^n)}{1 - r}$

$S_5 = \dfrac{12(1 - 3^5)}{1 - 3}$

$S_5 = 1452$

30. $a_1 = 4$ and $r = \dfrac{-2}{4}$ or $-\dfrac{1}{2}$

$S_n = \dfrac{a_1(1 - r^n)}{1 - r}$

$S_6 = \dfrac{4\left(1 - \left(-\frac{1}{2}\right)^6\right)}{1 - \left(-\frac{1}{2}\right)}$

$S_6 = \dfrac{21}{8}$

31. $a_1 = 256$ and $r = \dfrac{192}{256}$ or $\dfrac{3}{4}$

$S_n = \dfrac{a_1(1 - r^n)}{1 - r}$

$S_7 = \dfrac{256\left(1 - \left(\frac{3}{4}\right)^7\right)}{1 - \frac{3}{4}}$

$S_7 = \dfrac{14{,}197}{16}$

32. $a_1 = 1$, $r = -\dfrac{1}{2}$, and $n = 5$

$S_n = \dfrac{a_1(1 - r^n)}{1 - r}$

$S_5 = \dfrac{1\left(1 - \left(-\frac{1}{2}\right)^5\right)}{1 - \left(-\frac{1}{2}\right)}$

$S_5 = \dfrac{11}{16}$

33. Since $\left|\dfrac{11}{12}\right| < 1$, the sum exists.

$S = \dfrac{a_1}{1 - r}$

$= \dfrac{6}{1 - \frac{11}{12}}$

$= \dfrac{6}{\frac{1}{12}}$ or 72

34. $r = \dfrac{-\frac{3}{16}}{\frac{1}{8}}$ or $-\dfrac{3}{2}$

Since $\left|-\dfrac{3}{2}\right| > 1$, the sum does not exist.

35. $a_1 = -2$ and $r = -\dfrac{5}{8}$

Since $\left|-\dfrac{5}{8}\right| < 1$, the sum exists.

$S = \dfrac{a_1}{1 - r}$

$= \dfrac{-2}{1 - \left(-\frac{5}{8}\right)}$

$= \dfrac{-2}{\frac{13}{8}}$ or $-\dfrac{16}{13}$

36. $a_{n+1} = a_n + 5$

$a_{1+1} = a_1 + 5$

$a_2 = -2 + 5$ or 3

$a_{2+1} = a_2 + 5$

$a_3 = 3 + 5$ or 8

$a_{3+1} = a_3 + 5$

$a_4 = 8 + 5$ or 13

$a_{4+1} = a_4 + 5$

$a_5 = 13 + 5$ or 18

The first five terms are -2, 3, 8, 13, and 18.

37. $a_{n+1} = 4a_n - 10$
$a_{1+1} = 4a_1 - 10$
$\quad a_2 = 4(3) - 10$ or 2
$a_{2+1} = 4a_2 - 10$
$\quad a_3 = 4(2) - 10$ or -2
$a_{3+1} = 4a_3 - 10$
$\quad a_4 = 4(-2) - 10$ or -18
$a_{4+1} = 4a_4 - 10$
$\quad a_5 = 4(-18) - 10$ or -82
The first five terms are 3, 2, -2, -18, and -82.

38. $a_{n+1} = a_n + 3n$
$a_{1+1} = a_1 + 3(1)$
$\quad a_2 = 2 + 3$ or 5
$a_{2+1} = a_2 + 3(2)$
$\quad a_3 = 5 + 6$ or 11
$a_{3+1} = a_3 + 3(3)$
$\quad a_4 = 11 + 9$ or 20
$a_{4+1} = a_4 + 3(4)$
$\quad a_5 = 20 + 12$ or 32
The first five terms are 2, 5, 11, 20, and 32.

39. $a_{n+2} = a_{n+1} + a_n$
$a_{1+2} = a_{1+1} + a_1$
$\quad a_3 = 3 + 1$ or 4
$a_{2+2} = a_{2+1} + a_2$
$\quad a_4 = 4 + 3$ or 7
$a_{3+2} = a_{3+1} + a_3$
$\quad a_5 = 7 + 4$ or 11
The first five terms are 1, 3, 4, 7, and 11.

40. $f(x) = -2x + 3$
$x_1 = f(x_0)$
$\quad = f(1)$
$\quad = -2(1) + 3$ or 1
$x_2 = f(x_1)$
$\quad = f(1)$
$\quad = -2(1) + 3$ or 1
$x_3 = f(x_2)$
$\quad = f(1)$
$\quad = -2(1) + 3$ or 1
The first three iterates are 1, 1, and 1.

41. $f(x) = 7x - 4$
$x_1 = f(x_0)$
$\quad = f(2)$
$\quad = 7(2) - 4$ or 10
$x_2 = f(x_1)$
$\quad = f(10)$
$\quad = 7(10) - 4$ or 66
$x_3 = f(x_2)$
$\quad = f(66)$
$\quad = 7(66) - 4$ or 458
The first three iterates are 10, 66, and 458.

42. $f(x) = x^2 - 6$
$x_1 = f(x_0)$
$\quad = f(-1)$
$\quad = (-1)^2 - 6$ or -5
$x_2 = f(x_1)$
$\quad = f(-5)$
$\quad = (-5)^2 - 6$ or 19
$x_3 = f(x_2)$
$\quad = f(19)$
$\quad = 19^2 - 6$ or 355
The first three iterates are -5, 19, and 355.

43. $f(x) = -2x^2 - x + 5$
$x_1 = f(x_0)$
$\quad = f(-2)$
$\quad = -2(-2)^2 - (-2) + 5$ or -1
$x_2 = f(x_1)$
$\quad = f(-1)$
$\quad = -2(-1)^2 - (-1) + 5$ or 4
$x_3 = f(x_2)$
$\quad = f(4)$
$\quad = -2(4)^2 - 4 + 5$ or -31
The first three iterates are -1, 4, and -31.

44. $(x + y)^3 = 1x^3y^0 + 3x^2y^1 + 3x^1y^2 + 1x^0y^3$
$\qquad\quad = x^3 + 3x^2y + 3xy^2 + y^3$

45. $(x - 2)^4$
$\quad = 1x^4(-2)^0 + 4x^3(-2)^1 + 6x^2(-2)^2 + 4x^1(-2)^3 + 1x^0(-2)^4$
$\quad = x^4 - 8x^3 + 24x^2 - 32x + 16$

46. $(3r + s)^5$
$\quad = 1(3r)^5s^0 + 5(3r)^4s^1 + 10(3r)^3s^2 + 10(3r)^2s^3 + 5(3r)^1s^4 + 1(3r)^0s^5$
$\quad = 243r^5 + 405r^4s + 270r^3s^2 + 90r^2s^3 + 15rs^4 + s^5$

47. In the fourth term, $k = 3$.
$$\frac{6!}{(6-3)!3!}x^{6-3}(2y)^3 = \frac{6!}{3!3!}x^3(2y)^3$$
$$= \frac{6\cdot5\cdot4}{3\cdot2\cdot1}x^3(8y^3)$$
$$= 160\,x^3y^3$$

48. In the second term, $k = 1$.
$$\frac{10!}{(10-1)!1!}(4x)^{10-1}(-5)^1 = \frac{10!}{9!1!}(4x)^9(-5)$$
$$= \frac{10}{1}(262{,}144x^9)(-5)$$
$$= -13{,}107{,}200x^9$$

49. Step 1: When $n = 1$, the left side of the given equation is 1. The right side is $2^1 - 1$ or 1, so the equation is true for $n = 1$.

Step 2: Assume $1 + 2 + 4 + \ldots + 2^{k-1} = 2^k - 1$ for some positive integer k.

Step 3: $1 + 2 + 4 + \ldots + 2^{k-1} + 2^{(k+1)-1}$
$\qquad = 2^k - 1 + 2^{(k+1)-1}$
$\qquad = 2^k - 1 + 2^k$
$\qquad = 2 \cdot 2^k - 1$
$\qquad = 2^{k+1} - 1$

The last expression is the right side of the equation to be proved, where $n = k + 1$.
Thus, the equation is true for $n = k + 1$.

Therefore, $1 + 2 + 4 + \ldots + 2^{n-1} = 2^n - 1$ for all positive integers n.

50. Step 1: $6^1 - 1 = 5$, which is divisible by 5. The statement is true for $n = 1$.

Step 2: Assume that $6^k - 1$ is divisible by 5 for some positive integer k. This means that $6^k - 1 = 5r$ for some whole number r.

Step 3:
$$6^k - 1 = 5r$$
$$6^k = 5r + 1$$
$$6(6^k) = 6(5r + 1)$$
$$6^{k+1} = 30r + 6$$
$$6^{k+1} - 1 = 30r + 5$$
$$6^{k+1} - 1 = 5(6r + 1)$$

Since r is a whole number, $6r + 1$ is a whole number. Thus, $6^{k+1} - 1$ is divisible by 5, so the statement is true for $n = k + 1$.

Therefore, $6^n - 1$ is divisible by 5 for all positive integers n.

Chapter 11 Practice Test

Page 627

1. arithmetic

2. series

3. Pascal's triangle

4. Find the common difference d.
$d = 37 - 42$ or -5
Add -5 four more times.
$a_4 = 32 + (-5)$ or 27
$a_5 = 27 + (-5)$ or 22
$a_6 = 22 + (-5)$ or 17
$a_7 = 17 + (-5)$ or 12
The next four terms are 27, 22, 17, and 12.

5. $a_n = a_1 + (n - 1)d$
$a_{27} = 2 + (27 - 1)(6)$ or 158

6. Find the common difference d.
$a_n = a_1 + (n - 1)d$
$a_5 = -4 + (5 - 1)d$
$16 = -4 + 4d$
$20 = 4d$
$5 = d$

Find the arithmetic means.
$a_2 = -4 + 5$ or 1
$a_3 = 1 + 5$ or 6
$a_4 = 6 + 5$ or 11
The arithmetic means are 1, 6, and 11.

7. $S_n = \frac{n}{2}(a_1 + a_n)$
$S_{31} = \frac{31}{2}(7 + 127)$
$S_{31} = \frac{31}{2}(134)$ or 2077

8. Find the common ratio r.
$r = \frac{\frac{1}{27}}{\frac{1}{81}}$ or 3

Multiply by 3 two more times.
$a_4 = \frac{1}{9} \cdot 3$ or $\frac{1}{3}$
$a_5 = \frac{1}{3} \cdot 3$ or 1
The next two terms are $\frac{1}{3}$ and 1.

9. $a_n = a_1 \cdot r^{n-1}$
$a_6 = 5 \cdot (-2)^{6-1}$ or -160

10. Find the common ratio r.
$a_n = a_1 \cdot r^{n-1}$
$a_4 = 7 \cdot r^{4-1}$
$189 = 7r^3$
$27 = r^3$
$3 = r$

Find the geometric means.
$a_2 = 7 \cdot 3$ or 21
$a_3 = 21 \cdot 3$ or 63
The geometric means are 21 and 63.

11. $S_n = \frac{a_1(1 - r^n)}{1 - r}$
$S_4 = \frac{125\left(1 - \left(\frac{2}{5}\right)^4\right)}{1 - \frac{2}{5}}$
$S_4 = 203$

12. This is an arithmetic series with 13 terms.
$a_1 = 14 - 2(3)$ or 8
$a_{13} = 14 - 2(15)$ or -16
Find the sum.
$S_n = \frac{n}{2}(a_1 + a_n)$
$S_{13} = \frac{13}{2}[8 + (-16)]$
$S_{13} = \frac{13}{2}(-8)$ or -52

13. This is a geometric series with an infinite number of terms. The common ratio r is -2. Since $|-2| > 1$, the sum does not exist.

14. This is an arithmetic series with common difference $85 - 91$ or -6. Find n.
$a_n = a_1 + (n - 1)d$
$-29 = 91 + (n - 1)(-6)$
$-29 = 91 - 6n + 6$
$-29 = 97 - 6n$
$-126 = -6n$
$21 = n$

Find the sum.
$S_n = \frac{n}{2}(a_1 + a_n)$
$S_{21} = \frac{21}{2}[91 + (-29)]$
$S_{21} = \frac{21}{2}(62)$ or 651

15. This is an infinite geometric series with common ratio $\frac{-6}{12}$ or $-\frac{1}{2}$. Since $\left|-\frac{1}{2}\right| < 1$, the sum exists.
$S = \frac{a_1}{1 - r}$
$S = \frac{12}{1 - \left(-\frac{1}{2}\right)}$
$S = \frac{12}{\frac{3}{2}}$ or 8

16. $a_{n+1} = a_n + 3$

$a_{1+1} = a_1 + 3$

    $a_2 = 1 + 3$ or 4

$a_{2+1} = a_2 + 3$

    $a_3 = 4 + 3$ or 7

$a_{3+1} = a_3 + 3$

    $a_4 = 7 + 3$ or 10

$a_{4+1} = a_4 + 3$

    $a_5 = 10 + 3$ or 13

The first five terms are 1, 4, 7, 10, and 13.

17. $a_{n+1} = a_n + n^2$

$a_{1+1} = a_1 + 1^2$

    $a_2 = -3 + 1$ or -2

$a_{2+1} = a_2 + 2^2$

    $a_3 = -2 + 4$ or 2

$a_{3+1} = a_3 + 3^2$

    $a_4 = 2 + 9$ or 11

$a_{4+1} = a_4 + 4^2$

    $a_5 = 11 + 16$ or 27

The first five terms are -3, -2, 2, 11, and 27.

18. $f(x) = x^2 - 3x$

$x_1 = f(x_0)$

    $= f(1)$

    $= 1^2 - 3(1)$ or -2

$x_2 = f(x_1)$

    $= f(-2)$

    $= (-2)^2 - 3(-2)$ or 10

$x_3 = f(x_2)$

    $= f(10)$

    $= 10^2 - 3(10)$ or 70

The first three iterates are -2, 10, and 70.

19. Use Pascal's triangle.

$(2s - 3t)^5$

    $= 1(2s)^5(-3t)^0 + 5(2s)^4(-3t)^1 + 10(2s)^3(-3t)^2 +$
       $10(2s)^2(-3t)^3 + 5(2s)^1(-3t)^4 + 1(2s)^0(-3t)^5$

    $= 32s^5 - 240s^4t + 720s^3t^2 - 1080s^2t^3 + 810st^4 - 243t^5$

20. In the third term, $k = 2$.

$\dfrac{10!}{(10-2)!2!} x^{10-2}y^2 = \dfrac{10!}{8!2!}x^8y^2$

              $= \dfrac{10 \cdot 9}{2 \cdot 1}x^8y^2$

              $= 45x^8y^2$

21. Step 1: When $n = 1$, the left side of the given equation is 1. The right side is 1^2 or 1, so the equation is true for $n = 1$.

Step 2: Assume $1 + 3 + 5 + \ldots + (2k - 1) = k^2$ for some positive integer k.

Step 3: $1 + 3 + 5 + \ldots + (2k - 1) + [2(k + 1) - 1]$

        $= k^2 + [2(k + 1) - 1]$

        $= k^2 + 2k + 2 - 1$

        $= k^2 + 2k + 1$

        $= (k + 1)^2$

The last expression is the right side of the equation to be proved, where $n = k + 1$. Thus, the equation is true for $n = k + 1$.

Therefore, $1 + 3 + 5 + \ldots + (2n - 1) = n^2$ for all positive integers n.

22. Step 1: $14^1 - 1 = 13$, which is divisible by 13. The statement is true for $n = 1$.

Step 2: Assume that $14^k - 1$ is divisible by 13 for some positive integer k. This means that $14^k - 1 = 13r$ for some whole number r.

Step 3: $14^k - 1 = 13r$

          $14^k = 13r + 1$

       $14(14^k) = 14(13r + 1)$

       $14^{k+1} = 182r + 14$

    $14^{k+1} - 1 = 182r + 13$

    $14^{k+1} - 1 = 13(14r + 1)$

Since r is a whole number, $14r + 1$ is a whole number. Thus, $14^{k+1} - 1$ is divisible by 13, so the statement is true for $n = k + 1$.

Therefore, $14^n - 1$ is divisible by 13 for all positive integers n.

23. $a_1 = 20$, $d = -3$, $a_n = 0$

$a_n = a_1 + (n - 1)d$

  $0 = 20 + (n - 1)(-3)$

  $0 = 20 - 3n + 3$

$3n = 23$

 $n = \dfrac{23}{3}$ or $7\dfrac{2}{3}$

There are 8 rows.

$S_n = \dfrac{n}{2}[2a_1 + (n - 1)d]$

$S_8 = \dfrac{7}{2}[2(20) + (7 - 1)(-3)]$

$S_8 = \dfrac{7}{2}(22)$ or 77

There are 77 red bricks.

24. $a_1 = 100$, $r = 0.5$, $n = 5$

$S_n = \dfrac{a_1(1 - r^n)}{1 - r}$

$S_5 = \dfrac{100(1 - 0.5^5)}{1 - 0.5}$

$S_5 = 193.75$

The balloon rises 193.75 feet in 5 minutes.

25. D; The common ratio is $\dfrac{6}{8}$ or $\dfrac{3}{4}$.

$a_5 = \dfrac{27}{8} \cdot \dfrac{3}{4}$ or $\dfrac{81}{32}$

Chapter 11 Standardized Test Practice

Pages 628–629

1. D; The greatest factor of 18 that is less than 18 is 9, so $x = 18 + 9$ or 27. The greatest factor of 27 that is less than 27 is also 9.

    $\boxed{x} = 27 + 9$ or 36

2. D; Use the percent proportion.

    $\dfrac{12}{6p} = \dfrac{r}{100}$

  $1200 = 6pr$

  $\dfrac{1200}{6p} = r$

   $\dfrac{200}{p} = r$

3. A; Let h represent the height of the new box. The length of the new box is 1.5(6) or 9 units, and the width is 1.5(8) or 12 units. The volume of the original box is $12 \cdot 6 \cdot 8$ or 576 cubic units.

$$9 \cdot 12 \cdot h = 576$$
$$108h = 576$$
$$h = \frac{576}{108} \text{ or about } 5.3$$

4. A; II and III are not true for $m = \frac{1}{2}$. The only answer choice that excludes both II and III is answer choice A.

5. D; $3kx - \frac{4s}{t} = 3ky$

$$3kx - 3ky = \frac{4s}{t}$$
$$3k(x - y) = \frac{4s}{t}$$
$$x - y = \frac{4s}{t} \cdot \frac{1}{3k}$$
$$x - y = \frac{4s}{3kt}$$

6. A; $m = \frac{y_2 - y_1}{x_2 - x_1}$

$$= \frac{-k - (-k)}{-n - 3n}$$
$$= \frac{0}{-4n} \text{ or } 0$$

7. C; The coefficients of x^2 and y^2 are equal, so the graph is a circle.

8. C; $\dfrac{x - \frac{9}{x}}{1 - \frac{6}{x} + \frac{9}{x^2}} = \dfrac{\frac{x^2 - 9}{x}}{\frac{x^2 - 6x + 9}{x^2}}$

$$= \frac{x^2 - 9}{x} \cdot \frac{x^2}{x^2 - 6x + 9}$$
$$= \frac{(x + 3)(x - 3)}{x} \cdot \frac{x^2}{(x - 3)(x - 3)}$$
$$= \frac{x(x + 3)}{x - 3} \text{ or } \frac{x^2 + 3x}{x - 3}$$

9. C; The positive even factors of 30 are 2, 6, 10, and 30. Their sum is 48.

10. D; The angle below the hypotenuse of the triangle where it meets ℓ_2 is 30° since it and the 150° angle are corresponding angles. Thus, the angle inside the triangle with vertex on ℓ_2 is 10° since this angle, the 140° angle, and the 30° angle form a straight angle. Thus, the remaining angle inside the right triangle is 80°, since the sum of the angles of a triangle is 180°. So, $x = 80$.

11. Since A is a digit and $A = 3B$, then B cannot be 4, 5, 6, 7, 8, or 9 since three times any of these numbers is a two-digit number.
If $B = 0$, then $A = 0$ and $00 + 00 = 00$, so 0 is a possible value of C.
If $B = 1$, then $A = 3$ and $33 + 11 = 44$, so 4 is a possible value of C.
If $B = 2$, then $A = 6$ and $66 + 22 = 88$, so 8 is a possible value of C.
If $B = 3$, then $A = 9$ and $99 + 33 = 132$, which is not of the form CC.
The possible values of C are 0, 4, and 8.

12. Let r represent the radius of the larger semicircle. Then $\frac{r}{4}$ is the radius of the smaller semicircle. Their areas are $\frac{1}{2}\pi r^2$ and $\frac{1}{2}\pi\left(\frac{r}{4}\right)^2$, respectively.

$$\frac{\frac{1}{2}\pi\left(\frac{r}{4}\right)^2}{\frac{1}{2}\pi r^2} = \frac{\frac{r^2}{16}}{r^2} \text{ or } \frac{1}{16}$$

The ratio is $\frac{1}{16}$.

13. Let t represent the time it takes until they meet. Using the formula $d = rt$, the peoples' distances are $4t$ and $3t$. The total distance $4t + 3t$ is equal to 17.5 miles.

$$4t + 3t = 17.5$$
$$7t = 17.5$$
$$t = 2.5$$

They will meet after 2.5 or $\frac{5}{2}$ hours.

14.

$$\frac{x + y}{x} = \frac{5}{4}$$
$$1 + \frac{y}{x} = \frac{5}{4}$$
$$\frac{y}{x} = \frac{1}{4} \text{ or } 0.25$$

15. Let x be the number of gallons the tank holds.

$$\frac{1}{2}x + 7 = \frac{3}{4}x$$
$$7 = \frac{1}{4}x$$
$$28 = x$$

The tank holds 28 gallons.

16. $3a + 3b = 3(15 - b) + 3b$
$$= 45 - 3b + 3b$$
$$= 45$$

17. First solve the second equation for $\frac{1}{y}$.

$$x^7 = \frac{1}{5y}$$
$$5x^7 = \frac{1}{y}$$

Now substitute into the first equation.

$$x^9 = \frac{45}{y}$$
$$x^9 = 45 \cdot \frac{1}{y}$$
$$x^9 = 45 \cdot 5x^7$$
$$x^9 = 225x^7$$
$$x^9 - 225x^7 = 0$$
$$x^7(x^2 - 225) = 0$$
$$x^7 = 0 \text{ or } x^2 - 225 = 0$$
$$x = 0 \qquad\quad x^2 = 225$$
$$x = \pm 15$$

Since x is positive, $x = 15$.

18. C; In both cases, x is the median of an odd number of integers, making it the one in the middle. The mean of three consecutive integers is
$$\frac{m + (m + 1) + (m + 2)}{3} = \frac{3m + 3}{3} \text{ or } m + 1.$$
The mean of five consecutive integers is
$$\frac{n + (n + 1) + (n + 2) + (n + 3) + (n + 4)}{5} = \frac{5n + 10}{5} \text{ or } n + 2.$$

In both cases, the mean is the middle integer or the median x of the integers. Thus the quantities are equal.

19. C; If the area of Square B is nine times the area of Square A, then the length of a side of Square B is three times the length of a side of Square A. Thus, three times the perimeter of Square A equals the perimeter of Square B. The quantities are equal.

20. C; The value in Column A is $8(8 + 1)$ or 72 since 8 is even. The value in Column B is $9(9 - 1)$ or 72 since 9 is odd. Thus, the quantities are equal.

21. A; Using a calculator to evaluate the expressions, the quantity in Column A is about 0.5359, and the quantity in Column B is -2. The quantity in Column A is greater.

22. B; Since the hypotenuse is the longest side of a right triangle, $z > y$.

$$z > y$$
$$x + z > x + y$$
$$\frac{x + z}{2} > \frac{x + y}{2}$$

The quantity in Column B is greater.

Page 631 Getting Started

1. There is 1 face with a 2 and 6 total faces on the die.

$$P(2) = \frac{1}{6}$$
$$\approx 0.167\%$$

The probability of rolling a 2 is $\frac{1}{6}$ or about 16.7%.

2. There is 1 face with a 5 and 6 total faces on the die.

$$P(5) = \frac{1}{6}$$
$$\approx 0.167$$

The probability of rolling a 5 is $\frac{1}{6}$ or about 16.7%.

3. There are 3 faces with even numbers and 6 total faces on the die.

$$P(\text{even number}) = \frac{3}{6}$$
$$= \frac{1}{2}$$
$$= 0.5$$

The probability of rolling an even number is $\frac{1}{2}$ or 50%.

4. There are 3 faces with odd numbers and 6 total faces on the die.

$$P(\text{odd number}) = \frac{3}{6}$$
$$= \frac{1}{2}$$
$$= 0.5$$

The probability of rolling an odd number is $\frac{1}{2}$ or 50%.

5. There are 4 faces with numbers less than 5 and 6 total faces on the die.

$$P(\text{number less than 5}) = \frac{4}{6}$$
$$= \frac{2}{3}$$
$$\approx 0.667$$

The probability of rolling a number less than 5 is $\frac{2}{3}$ or 66.7%.

6. There are 5 faces with numbers greater than 1 and 6 total faces on the die.

$$P(\text{number greater than 1}) = \frac{5}{6}$$
$$\approx 0.833$$

The probability of rolling a number greater than 1 is $\frac{5}{6}$ or 83.3%.

7. Step 1 Find the least and greatest number. Then draw a number line that covers the range of the data. In this case, the least value is 21, and the greatest value is 40.

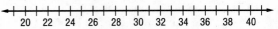

Step 2 Find the median, the extreme values, and the upper and lower quartiles. Mark the points above the number line.

21, 23, 24, 26, 31, 32, 33, 37, 38, 38, 39, 40

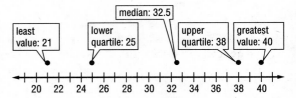

$$LQ = \frac{24 + 26}{2} \text{ or } 25 \qquad M = \frac{32 + 33}{2} \text{ or } 32.5 \qquad UQ = \frac{38 + 38}{2} \text{ or } 38$$

median: 32.5

least value: 21 | lower quartile: 25 | upper quartile: 38 | greatest value: 40

Step 3 Draw a box and the whiskers.

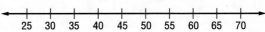

8. Step 1 Find the least and greatest number. Then draw a number line that covers the range of the data. In this case, the least value is 25, and the greatest value is 68.

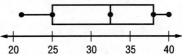

Step 2 Find the median, the extreme values, and the upper and lower quartiles. Mark the points above the number line.

25, 29, 31, 39, 43, 46, 48, 53, 59, 64, 68

$$LQ = 31 \qquad M = 46 \qquad UQ = 59$$

least value: 25 | lower quartile: 31 | median: 46 | upper quartile: 59 | greatest value: 68

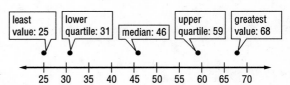

Step 3 Draw a box and the whiskers.

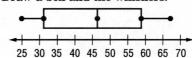

9. Step 1 Find the least and greatest number. Then draw a number line that covers the range of the data. In this case, the least value is 23, and the greatest value is 81.

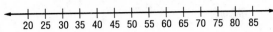

Step 2 Find the median, the extreme values, and the upper and lower quartiles. Mark the points above the number line.

23, 27, 39, 46, 46, 51, 53, 54, 55, 60, 69, 81

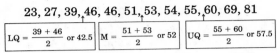

$$LQ = \frac{39 + 46}{2} \text{ or } 42.5 \qquad M = \frac{51 + 53}{2} \text{ or } 52 \qquad UQ = \frac{55 + 60}{2} \text{ or } 57.5$$

least value: 23 | lower quartile: 42.5 | median: 52 | upper quartile: 57.5 | greatest value: 81

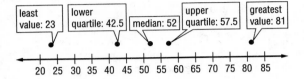

Step 3 Draw a box and the whiskers.

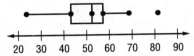

10. Step 1 Find the least and greatest number. Then draw a number line that covers the range of the data. In this case, the least value is 13.6, and the greatest value is 16.3.

Step 2 Find the median, the extreme values, and the upper and lower quartiles. Mark the points above the number line.

13.6, 13.8, 14.1, 14.3, 14.9, 15.1, 15.7, 16.0, 16.3

$$LQ = \frac{38.8 + 14.1}{2} \text{ or } 13.95 \qquad M = 14.9 \qquad UQ = \frac{15.7 + 16.0}{2} \text{ or } 15.85$$

median: 14.9

least value: 13.6 | lower quartile: 13.95 | upper quartile: 15.85 | greatest value: 16.3

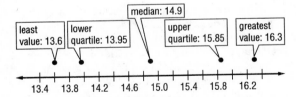

Step 3 Draw a box and the whiskers.

11.
$$\sqrt{\frac{(a-b)^2 + (c-b)^2}{d}} = \sqrt{\frac{(4-7)^2 + (1-7)^2}{5}}$$
$$= \sqrt{\frac{(-3)^2 + (-6)^2}{5}}$$
$$= \sqrt{\frac{9 + 36}{5}}$$
$$= \sqrt{\frac{45}{5}}$$
$$= \sqrt{9}$$
$$= 3$$

The value is 3.

12.
$$\sqrt{\frac{(a-b)^2 + (c-b)^2}{d}} = \sqrt{\frac{(2-6)^2 + (9-6)^2}{5}}$$
$$= \sqrt{\frac{(-4)^2 + (3)^2}{5}}$$
$$= \sqrt{\frac{16 + 9}{5}}$$
$$= \sqrt{\frac{25}{5}}$$
$$= \sqrt{5}$$

The value is $\sqrt{5}$.

13.
$$\sqrt{\frac{(a-b)^2 + (c-b)^2}{d}} = \sqrt{\frac{(5-1)^2 + (7-1)^2}{4}}$$
$$= \sqrt{\frac{(4)^2 + (6)^2}{4}}$$
$$= \sqrt{\frac{16 + 36}{4}}$$
$$= \sqrt{\frac{52}{4}}$$
$$= \sqrt{13}$$

The value is $\sqrt{13}$.

14.
$$\sqrt{\frac{(a-b)^2 + (c-b)^2}{d}} = \sqrt{\frac{(3-4)^2 + (11-4)^2}{10}}$$
$$= \sqrt{\frac{(-1)^2 + (7)^2}{10}}$$
$$= \sqrt{\frac{1 + 49}{10}}$$
$$= \sqrt{\frac{50}{10}}$$
$$= \sqrt{5}$$

The value is $\sqrt{5}$.

15. $(a + b)^3 = 1a^3b^0 + \frac{3}{1}a^2b^1 + \frac{3 \cdot 2}{1 \cdot 2}a^1b^2 + 1a^0b^3$
$$= a^3 + 3a^2b + 3ab^2 + b^3$$

16. $(c + d)^4 = 1c^4d^0 + \frac{4}{1}c^3d^1 + \frac{4 \cdot 3}{1 \cdot 2}c^2d^2 + \frac{4 \cdot 3 \cdot 2}{1 \cdot 2 \cdot 3}c^1d^3 + 1c^0d^4$
$$= c^4 + 4c^3d + 6c^2d^2 + 4cd^3 + d^4$$

17. $(m - n)^5 = 1m^5(-n)^0 + \frac{5}{1}m^4(-n)^1 + \frac{5 \cdot 4}{1 \cdot 2}m^3(-n)^2 +$
$$\frac{5 \cdot 4 \cdot 3}{1 \cdot 2 \cdot 3}m^2(-n)^3 + \frac{5 \cdot 4 \cdot 3 \cdot 2}{1 \cdot 2 \cdot 3 \cdot 4}m^1(-n)^4 +$$
$$1m^0(-n)^5$$
$$= m^5 - 5m^4n + 10m^3n^2 - 10m^2n^3 +$$
$$5mn^4 - n^5$$

18. $(x + y)^6 = 1x^6y^0 + \frac{6}{1}x^5y^1 + \frac{6 \cdot 5}{1 \cdot 2}x^4y^2 + \frac{6 \cdot 5 \cdot 4}{1 \cdot 2 \cdot 3}x^3y^3 +$
$$\frac{6 \cdot 5 \cdot 4 \cdot 3}{1 \cdot 2 \cdot 3 \cdot 4}x^2y^4 + \frac{6 \cdot 5 \cdot 4 \cdot 3 \cdot 2}{1 \cdot 2 \cdot 3 \cdot 4 \cdot 5}x^1y^5 + 1x^0y^6$$
$$= x^6 + 6x^5y + 15x^4y^2 + 20x^3y^3 + 15x^2y^4 +$$
$$6xy^5 + y^6$$

Page 634 Check for Understanding

1. The outcome of each toss does not affect the outcomes of the other two tosses, so these events are independent. Let H represent tossing a head and T represent tossing a tail.

First Toss   H   T

Second Toss   H   T   H   T

Third Toss   H T H T   H T H T

Possible Outcomes   HHH HHT HTH HTT THH THT TTH TTT

2. Sample answer: buying a shirt that comes in 3 sizes and 6 colors

3. Sample answer: The available colors for the car could be different from those for the truck.

4. The choice of the color does not affect the choice of the size of the pair of shoes, so these events are independent.

5. When the winner of a dog show is chosen, that dog is not considered in the choice for the runner-up. Therefore, the choices of winner and runner-up at a dog show are dependent events.

6. The choice of cone does not affect the choice of flavor of ice cream, so these events are independent. There are 2 possible choices of cone and 15 possible choices of ice cream flavors. So, there are $2 \cdot 15$ or 30 possible 1-scoop ice cream cones.

7. The choice of answer for each question does not affect the other seven questions, so the choices of the answers are independent events. There are 2 possible answers for each of the eight questions. So, there are $2 \cdot 2 \cdot 2 \cdot 2 \cdot 2 \cdot 2 \cdot 2 \cdot 2$ or 256 possible completions of the eight question test.

8. When Macawi selects the topic for the short essay, she cannot pick the same topic for the long essay. Therefore, the choices of which topics to pick for the two essays are dependent events. There are 5 topics Macawi can pick for her short essay. That leaves 4 topics she can pick for her long essay. There are $5 \cdot 4$ or 20 choices of topics for the two essays.

9. D; The choice of biography does not affect the choice of mystery novel, so these events are independent. There are 4 ways to choose a biography, and there are 5 ways to choose a mystery novel. By the fundamental Counting Principle, there are $4 \cdot 5$ or 20 total ways to choose one book of each type.

Pages 635–636 Practice and Apply

10. When a person is chosen for a position, that person is not considered in the choice for the other positions. Therefore, the choices of which person to hold which office are dependent events.

11. The choice of which fiction book does not affect the choice of which nonfiction book, so these events are independent.

12. Each person's guess does not affect the other five people's guesses, so the guesses of the game's score are independent events.

13. When a letter is selected, it is not replaced, so it can not be selected again. Therefore, the selections of letters without replacement are dependent events.

14. The choice of album does not affect the choice of format, so these events are independent. There are 3 possible choices of album and 2 possible choices of format. So, there are $3 \cdot 2$ or 6 possible combinations of album and format that Tim can choose.

15. The choice of new release does not affect the choice of format, so these events are independent. There are 8 possible choices of new release and 2 possible choices of format. So, there are $8 \cdot 2$ or 16 possible combinations of new release and format that a customer can choose.

16. When Carlos chooses which subject's homework to do and completes it, he will not choose that subject's homework again. Therefore, the choices of which homework to do first, second, and third are dependent events. There are 3 homework assignments he can do first. That leaves 2 homework assignments he can do second and 1 homework assignment he can do third. There are $3 \cdot 2 \cdot 1$ or 6 orders in which he can do his homework.

17. The choice of any course does not affect the choice of the other two courses, so the choices of the courses are independent events. There are 2 possible types of salad, 5 possible main courses, and 3 possible desserts. So, there are $2 \cdot 5 \cdot 3$ or 30 combinations of salad, main course and dessert.

18. The choice of any characteristic or part of the golf club does not affect the choice of the other three characteristics or parts, so the choices of the characteristics or parts are independent events. There are 4 possible shaft lengths, 3 possible lofts, 2 possible grips, and 2 possible materials for the club head. So, there are $4 \cdot 3 \cdot 2 \cdot 2$ or 48 combinations possible to make a golf club.

19. The choice of answer for each question does not affect the other four questions, so the choices of the answers are independent events. There are 4 possible answers for each of the five questions. So, there are $4 \cdot 4 \cdot 4 \cdot 4 \cdot 4$ or 1024 possible completions of the five question quiz.

20. When a book is placed in a certain location, it is not considered for the other locations. Therefore, the choices of which location to place each book are dependent events. There are 2 ends where the dictionary can be placed. That leaves 5 books to be placed in the next location. After the first two locations are determined, there are 4 remaining books for the third location, and so on. There are $2 \cdot 5 \cdot 4 \cdot 3 \cdot 2 \cdot 1$ or 240 arrangements possible on the shelf.

21. When an actor's name is listed in a certain position in the credits, it is not considered for the other positions. Therefore, the choices of which position to place each actor's name are dependent events. There are 2 positions, first or last, where the lead actor's name can be placed. That leaves 7 names to be placed in the next position considered. After the first two positions considered are determined, there are 6 remaining names for the third position considered, and so on. There are $2 \cdot 7 \cdot 6 \cdot 5 \cdot 4 \cdot 3 \cdot 2 \cdot 1$ or 10,080 orders possible in the opening credits.

22. When a numeral is selected as one of the digits in the password, it is not considered for the other digits in the password. Therefore, the choices of numerals for each digit are dependent events. There are 10 numerals to choose from for the first digit. That leaves 9 numerals to choose from for the second digit. After the first two digits are chosen, there are 8 remaining choices for the third digit, and so on. There are $10 \cdot 9 \cdot 8 \cdot 7 \cdot 6 \cdot 5$ or 151,200 passwords allowed.

23. When a book is placed in a certain location, it is not considered for the other locations. Therefore, the choices of which location to place each book are dependent events. There are 9 books to choose from for the first location on the shelf. That leaves 8 books to choose from for the next location. After the first two locations are determined, there are 7 remaining books for the third location, and so on. There are $9 \cdot 8 \cdot 7 \cdot 6 \cdot 5 \cdot 4 \cdot 3 \cdot 2 \cdot 1$ or 362,880 arrangements possible on the shelf.

24. When a person is chosen for a position, that person is not considered in the choice for the other position. Therefore, the choices of which person to hold which office are dependent events. Let n = the number of people in the Math Club. There are n people to choose from for the president. That leaves $n - 1$ people to choose from for the vice-president. There are $n \cdot (n - 1)$ ways to fill the positions. Thus, solve $n \cdot (n - 1) = 272$ for n.

$$n(n - 1) = 272$$
$$n^2 - n = 272$$
$$n^2 - n - 272 = 0$$
$$(n + 16)(n - 17) = 0$$
$$n + 16 = 0 \quad \text{or} \quad n - 17 = 0$$
$$n = -16 \qquad n = 17$$

Since the number of people in the Math Club cannot be negative, there are 17 people in the Math Club.

25. When a numeral is chosen for a specific digit, it is not considered for the other digits. Therefore, the choices of numerals for each digit are dependent events. There are 9 numerals to choose from for the first digit. With the addition of 0, that leaves 9 numerals to choose from for the second digit. After the first two digits are determined, there are 8 remaining numerals for the third digit, and so on. There are $9 \cdot 9 \cdot 8 \cdot 7 \cdot 6$ or 27,216 5-digit codes possible.

26. The choice of any digit does not affect the other two digits, so the choices of the digits are independent events. There are 8 possible first digits in the code, 2 possible second digits, and 10 possible third digits. So, there were $8 \cdot 2 \cdot 10$ or 160 possible different area codes before 1995.

27. The choice of any digit does not affect the other two digits, so the choices of the digits are independent events. Now there are 8 possible first digits in the code, 10 possible second digits, and 10 possible third digits. So, there are now $8 \cdot 10 \cdot 10$ or 800 possible different area codes.

28. See students' work.

29. The maximum number of license plates is a product with factors of 26s and 10s, depending on how many letters are used and how many digits are used. Answers should include the following.
- There are 26 choices for the first letter, 26 for the second, and 26 for the third. There are 10 choices for the first number, 10 for the second, and 10 for the third. By the Fundamental Counting Principle, there are $26^3 \cdot 10^3$ or 17,576,000 possible license plates.
- Replace positions containing numbers with letters.

30. A; The choice of any digit does not affect the other two digits, so the choices of the digits are independent events. There are 9 possible first digits in the number, 1 possible second digit, and 10 possible third digits. So, there are $9 \cdot 1 \cdot 10$ or 90 possible numbers.

31. C; The outcome of each toss does not affect the outcome of the other three tosses, so these events are independent. There are 2 possible outcomes for each toss. So, there are $2 \cdot 2 \cdot 2 \cdot 2$ or 16 possible sequences.

32. Since each edge connects two vertices, first determine the number of ways to arrange two different vertices. Then, since each combination of two different vertices can be chosen in two orders, A then B or B then A, divide by 2. When a vertex is chosen, it is not considered again. Therefore, the choices of vertices are dependent events. There are 10 vertices that can be chosen first. That leaves 9 vertices that can be chosen second. There are $10 \cdot 9$ or 90 arrangements of two different vertices. Thus, there are $90 \div 2$ or 45 edges in the graph.

33. Draw 5 points, and label the points Greenville, Roseburg, Bluemont, Whiteston, and Red Rock. Draw a line to represent each route in the table, and label the lines with the distance of each route.

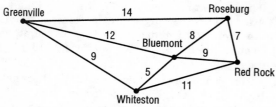

The graph shows the shortest route is through Whiteston and is 20 miles long.

Page 637   Maintain Your Skills

34. Step 1 When $n = 1$, the left side of the given equation is $3(1) + 1$ or 4. The right side is $\frac{(1)[3(1) + 5]}{2}$ or 4. Thus, the equation is true for $n = 1$.

Step 2 Assume $4 + 7 + 10 + \cdots + (3k + 1) = \frac{k(3k + 5)}{2}$ for a positive integer k.

Step 3 Show that the given equation is true for $n = k + 1$.

$4 + 7 + 10 + \ldots + (3k + 1) + [3(k + 1) + 1]$
$= \frac{k(3k + 5)}{2} + [3(k + 1) + 1]$
$= \frac{k(3k + 5) + 2[3(k + 1) + 1]}{2}$
$= \frac{3k^2 + 5k + 6k + 6 + 2}{2}$
$= \frac{3k^2 + 11k + 8}{2}$
$= \frac{(k + 1)(3k + 8)}{2}$
$= \frac{(k + 1)[3(k + 1) + 5]}{2}$

Thus, the equation is true for $n = k + 1$. This proves the equation for all positive integers n.

35. First, use the Binomial Theorem to write the expression in sigma notation.

$(x + y)^8 = \sum_{k=0}^{8} \frac{8!}{(8 - k)!k!} x^{8 - k} y^k$

In the third term, $k = 2$.

$\frac{8!}{(8 - k)!k!} x^{8 - k} y^k = \frac{8!}{(8 - 2)!2!} x^{8 - 2} y^2$
$= \frac{8 \cdot 7}{2 \cdot 1} x^6 y^2$
$= 28 x^6 y^2$

36. First, use the Bionomial Theorem to write the expression in sigma notation.

$(2a - b)^7 = \sum_{k=0}^{7} \frac{7!}{(7 - k)!k!} (2a)^{7 - k} (-b)^k$

In the fifth term, $k = 4$.

$\frac{7!}{(7 - k)!k!} (2a)^{7 - k} (-b)^k = \frac{7!}{(7 - 4)!4!} (2a)^{7 - 4} (-b)^4$
$= \frac{7 \cdot 6 \cdot 5 \cdot 4}{4 \cdot 3 \cdot 2 \cdot 1} 2^3 a^3 b^4$
$= 280 a^3 b^4$

37. $\log_2 128 = y$
$128 = 2^y$
$2^7 = 2^y$
$7 = y$
So, $\log_2 128 = 7$.

38. $\log_3 243 = y$
$243 = 3^y$
$3^5 = 3^y$
$5 = y$
So, $\log_3 243 = 5$.

39. $\log_9 3 = y$
$3 = 9^y$
$9^{\frac{1}{2}} = 9^y$
$\frac{1}{2} = y$
So, $\log_9 3 = \frac{1}{2}$.

40. $-\dfrac{x^2 - y^2}{x + y} \cdot \dfrac{1}{x - y} = -\dfrac{\cancel{(x + y)}(x \cancel{- y})}{\cancel{x + y}} \cdot \dfrac{1}{\cancel{x - y}}$
$= -1$

41. $\dfrac{\frac{x^2}{x^2 - 25y^2}}{\frac{x}{5y - x}} = \dfrac{x^2}{x^2 - 25y^2} \div \dfrac{x}{5y - x}$
$= \dfrac{x^2}{x^2 - 25y^2} \cdot \dfrac{5y - x}{x}$
$= \dfrac{\cancel{x} \cdot x(-1)(x \cancel{- 5y})}{(x + 5y)(x \cancel{- 5y})\cancel{x}}$
$= \dfrac{-x}{x + 5y}$
$= -\dfrac{x}{x + 5y}$

42. $d = \sqrt{(x_2 - x_1)^2 + (y_2 - y_1)^2}$
$= \sqrt{(12 - 9)^2 + (5 - 3)^2}$
$= \sqrt{3^2 + 2^2}$
$= \sqrt{9 + 4}$
$= \sqrt{13}$
≈ 3.6

Since each unit on the map represents 10 miles, The distance between Edison and Kettering is about 3.6(10) or 36 miles.

43. $x^4 - 5x^2 + 4 = 0$
$(x^2)^2 - 5(x^2) + 4 = 0$
$(x^2 - 4)(x^2 - 1) = 0$
$(x - 2)(x + 2)(x - 1)(x + 1) = 0$

$x - 2 = 0$ or $x + 2 = 0$
$x = 2$ $x = -2$

or $x - 1 = 0$ or $x + 1 = 0$
$x = 1$ $x = -1$

The solutions are $-2, -1, 1,$ and 2.

44. $y^4 + 4y^3 + 4y^2 = 0$
$y^2(y^2 + 4y + 4) = 0$
$y^2(y + 2)(y + 2) = 0$

$y^2 = 0$ or $y + 2 = 0$ or $y + 2 = 0$
$y = 0$ $y = -2$ $y = -2$

The solutions are -2 and 0.

45. $h = 3$ and $k = 2$. Let $x = 5$ and $y = 6$. Substitute these values into the vertex form of the equation and solve for a.

$y = a(x - h)^2 + k$
$6 = a(5 - 3)^2 + 2$
$6 = a(4) + 2$
$4 = 4a$
$1 = a$

The equation is $y = (x - 3)^2 + 2$.

46. $h = -1$ and $k = 4$. Let $x = -2$ and $y = 2$. Substitute these values into the vertex form of the equation and solve for a.

$y = a(x - h)^2 + k$
$2 = a[-2 - (-1)]^2 + 4$
$2 = a(1) + 4$
$-2 = a$

The equation is $y = -2(x + 1)^2 + 4$.

47. $h = 0$ and $k = 8$. Let $x = 4$ and $y = 0$. Substitute these values into the vertex form of the equation and solve for a.

$y = a(x - h)^2 + k$
$0 = a(4 - 0)^2 + 8$
$0 = a(16) + 8$
$-8 = 16a$
$-\frac{1}{2} = a$

The equation is $y = -\frac{1}{2}(x - 0)^2 + 8$ or

$y = -\frac{1}{2}x^2 + 8$.

48.
$\sqrt{2x + 1} = 3$
$(\sqrt{2x + 1})^2 = 3^2$
$2x + 1 = 9$
$2x = 8$
$x = 4$

Check: $\sqrt{2x + 1} = 3$
$\sqrt{2(4) + 1} \stackrel{?}{=} 3$
$\sqrt{9} \stackrel{?}{=} 3$
$3 = 3$ ✓

The solution is 4.

49. $3 + \sqrt{x + 1} = 5$
$\sqrt{x + 1} = 2$
$(\sqrt{x + 1})^2 = 2^2$
$x + 1 = 4$
$x = 3$

Check: $3 + \sqrt{x + 1} = 5$
$3 + \sqrt{3 + 1} \stackrel{?}{=} 5$
$3 + \sqrt{4} \stackrel{?}{=} 5$
$3 + 2 \stackrel{?}{=} 5$
$5 = 5$ ✓

The solution is 3.

50. $\sqrt{x} + \sqrt{x + 5} = 5$
$\sqrt{x + 5} = 5 - \sqrt{x}$
$(\sqrt{x + 5})^2 = (5 - \sqrt{x})^2$
$x + 5 = 25 - 10\sqrt{x} + x$
$-20 = -10\sqrt{x}$
$2 = \sqrt{x}$
$2^2 = (\sqrt{x})^2$
$4 = x$

Check: $\sqrt{x} + \sqrt{x + 5} = 5$
$\sqrt{4} + \sqrt{4 + 5} \stackrel{?}{=} 5$
$2 + \sqrt{9} \stackrel{?}{=} 5$
$2 + 3 \stackrel{?}{=} 5$
$5 = 5$ ✓

The solution is 4.

51. Find the value of the determinant.

$\begin{vmatrix} 3 & 1 \\ -4 & 1 \end{vmatrix} = 3 - (-4) = 7$

Since the determinant does not equal 0, the inverse exists.

$\frac{1}{ad - bc}\begin{bmatrix} d & -b \\ -c & a \end{bmatrix} = \frac{1}{3(1) - (1)(-4)}\begin{bmatrix} 1 & -1 \\ 4 & 3 \end{bmatrix}$

$= \frac{1}{7}\begin{bmatrix} 1 & -1 \\ 4 & 3 \end{bmatrix}$

52. Find the value of the determinant.

$\begin{vmatrix} 4 & -5 \\ 2 & -1 \end{vmatrix} = -4 - (-10) = 6$

Since the determinant does not equal 0, the inverse exists.

$\frac{1}{ad - bc}\begin{bmatrix} d & -b \\ -c & a \end{bmatrix} = \frac{1}{4(-1) - (-5)(2)}\begin{bmatrix} -1 & 5 \\ -2 & 4 \end{bmatrix}$

$= \frac{1}{6}\begin{bmatrix} -1 & 5 \\ -2 & 4 \end{bmatrix}$

53. Find the value of the determinant.

$\begin{vmatrix} -3 & 2 \\ -6 & 4 \end{vmatrix} = -12 - (-12) = 0$

Since the determinant equals 0, the inverse does not exist.

54. From the graph, we see that the line goes through points $(0, -2)$ and $(-1, 0)$.
Find the slope.

$m = \frac{y_2 - y_1}{x_2 - x_1}$
$= \frac{0 - (-2)}{-1 - 0}$
$= \frac{2}{-1}$
$= -2$

Use the point-slope form to find the equation.

$y - y_1 = m(x - x_1)$
$y - (-2) = -2(x - 0)$
$y + 2 = -2x$
$y = -2x - 2$

The equation in slope-intercept form is

$y = -2x - 2$.

55. From the graph, we see that the line goes through points (1, 1) and (4, 3).

Find the slope.

$$m = \frac{y_2 - y_1}{x_2 - x_1}$$
$$= \frac{3 - 1}{4 - 1}$$
$$= \frac{2}{3}$$

Use the point-slope form to find the equation.

$$y - y_1 = m(x - x_1)$$
$$y - 1 = \frac{2}{3}(x - 1)$$
$$y - 1 = \frac{2}{3}x - \frac{2}{3}$$
$$y = \frac{2}{3}x + \frac{1}{3}$$

The equation in slope-intercept form is

$$y = \frac{2}{3}x + \frac{1}{3}.$$

56. $\frac{5!}{2!} = \frac{5 \cdot 4 \cdot 3 \cdot 2 \cdot 1}{2 \cdot 1}$
$= 5 \cdot 4 \cdot 3$
$= 60$

57. $\frac{6!}{4!} = \frac{6 \cdot 5 \cdot 4 \cdot 3 \cdot 2 \cdot 1}{4 \cdot 3 \cdot 2 \cdot 1}$
$= 6 \cdot 5$
$= 30$

58. $\frac{7!}{3!} = \frac{7 \cdot 6 \cdot 5 \cdot 4 \cdot 3 \cdot 2 \cdot 1}{3 \cdot 2 \cdot 1}$
$= 7 \cdot 6 \cdot 5 \cdot 4$
$= 840$

59. $\frac{6!}{1!} = \frac{6 \cdot 5 \cdot 4 \cdot 3 \cdot 2 \cdot 1}{1}$
$= 6 \cdot 5 \cdot 4 \cdot 3 \cdot 2$
$= 720$

60. $\frac{4!}{2!2!} = \frac{4 \cdot 3 \cdot 2 \cdot 1}{2 \cdot 1 \cdot 2 \cdot 1}$
$= \frac{4 \cdot 3}{2 \cdot 1}$
$= 6$

61. $\frac{6!}{2!4!} = \frac{6 \cdot 5 \cdot 4 \cdot 3 \cdot 2 \cdot 1}{2 \cdot 1 \cdot 4 \cdot 3 \cdot 2 \cdot 1}$
$= \frac{6 \cdot 5}{2 \cdot 1}$
$= 15$

62. $\frac{8!}{3!5!} = \frac{8 \cdot 7 \cdot 6 \cdot 5 \cdot 4 \cdot 3 \cdot 2 \cdot 1}{3 \cdot 2 \cdot 1 \cdot 5 \cdot 4 \cdot 3 \cdot 2 \cdot 1}$
$= \frac{8 \cdot 7 \cdot 6}{3 \cdot 2 \cdot 1}$
$= 56$

63. $\frac{5!}{5!0!} = \frac{5 \cdot 4 \cdot 3 \cdot 2 \cdot 1}{5 \cdot 4 \cdot 3 \cdot 2 \cdot 1 \cdot 1}$
$= \frac{1}{1}$
$= 1$

12-2 Permutations and Combinations

Page 641 Check for Understanding

1. Sample answer: There are six people in a contest. How many ways can the first, second, and third prizes be awarded?

2. $C(n, n - r) = \frac{n!}{[n - (n - r)]!(n - r)!}$
$= \frac{n!}{r!(n - r)!}$
$= \frac{n!}{(n - r)!r!}$
$= C(n, r)$

3. Sometimes; the statement is only true when $r = 1$.

4. $P(5, 3) = \frac{5!}{(5 - 3)!}$
$= \frac{5!}{2!}$
$= \frac{5 \cdot 4 \cdot 3 \cdot 2!}{2!}$
$= 60$

5. $P(6, 3) = \frac{6!}{(6 - 3)!}$
$= \frac{6!}{3!}$
$= \frac{6 \cdot 5 \cdot 4 \cdot 3!}{3!}$
$= 120$

6. $C(4, 2) = \frac{4!}{(4 - 2)!2!}$
$= \frac{4!}{2!2!}$
$= 6$

7. $C(6, 1) = \frac{6!}{(6 - 1)!1!}$
$= \frac{6!}{5!1!}$
$= 6$

8. Since the order in which the toppings are chosen is not important, find the number of combinations of 6 toppings taken 2 at a time.

$C(6, 2) = \frac{6!}{(6 - 2)!2!}$
$= \frac{6!}{4!2!}$
$= 15$

There are 15 possible ways to choose the two toppings.

9. Since each shopper is in a different position in line, order is important. Find the number of permutations of 7 things taken 7 at a time.

$P(7, 7) = \frac{7!}{(7 - 7)!}$
$= \frac{7!}{0!}$
$= 5040$

The line of 7 shoppers can be formed 5040 ways.

10. Since each letter is in a different position in each arrangement, order is important. Find the number of permutations of 9 things of which 5 are different, 2 are alike, and 2 others are alike.

$\frac{9!}{2!2!} = \frac{9 \cdot 8 \cdot 7 \cdot 6 \cdot 5 \cdot 4 \cdot 3 \cdot 2!}{2!2!}$
$= 90{,}720$

There are 90,720 ways to arrange the letters.

11. Since the order in which the students are chosen is not important, find the number of combinations of 9 students taken 6 at a time.

$C(9, 6) = \frac{9!}{(9 - 6)!6!}$
$= \frac{9!}{3!6!}$
$= 84$

There are 84 possible ways to choose the six students.

Pages 641–642 Practice and Apply

12. $P(8, 2) = \frac{8!}{(8 - 2)!}$
$= \frac{8!}{6!}$
$= \frac{8 \cdot 7 \cdot 6!}{6!}$
$= 56$

13. $P(9, 1) = \frac{9!}{(9 - 1)!}$
$= \frac{9!}{8!}$
$= \frac{9 \cdot 8!}{8!}$
$= 9$

14. $P(7, 5) = \frac{7!}{(7 - 5)!}$
$= \frac{7!}{2!}$
$= \frac{7 \cdot 6 \cdot 5 \cdot 4 \cdot 3 \cdot 2!}{2!}$
$= 2520$

15. $P(12, 6) = \frac{12!}{(12 - 6)!}$
$= \frac{12!}{6!}$
$= \frac{12 \cdot 11 \cdot 10 \cdot 9 \cdot 8 \cdot 7 \cdot 6!}{6!}$
$= 665{,}280$

16. $C(5, 2) = \frac{5!}{(5-2)!2!}$

$= \frac{5!}{3!2!}$

$= 10$

17. $C(8, 4) = \frac{8!}{(8-4)!4!}$

$= \frac{8!}{4!4!}$

$= 70$

18. $C(12, 7) = \frac{12!}{(12-7)!7!}$

$= \frac{12!}{5!7!}$

$= 792$

19. $C(10, 4) = \frac{10!}{(10-4)!4!}$

$= \frac{10!}{6!4!}$

$= 210$

20. $C(12, 4) \cdot C(8, 3) = \frac{12!}{(12-4)!4!} \cdot \frac{8!}{(8-3)!3!}$

$= \frac{12!}{8!4!} \cdot \frac{8!}{5!3!}$

$= 495 \cdot 56$

$= 27{,}720$

21. $C(9, 3) \cdot C(6, 2) = \frac{9!}{(9-3)!3!} \cdot \frac{6!}{(6-2)!2!}$

$= \frac{9!}{6!3!} \cdot \frac{6!}{4!2!}$

$= 84 \cdot 15$

$= 1260$

22. Since each finishing position is different, order is important. Find the number of permutations of 10 things taken 4 at a time.

$P(10, 4) = \frac{10!}{(10-4)!}$

$= \frac{10!}{6!}$

$= \frac{10 \cdot 9 \cdot 8 \cdot 7 \cdot 6!}{6!}$

$= 5040$

The contestants can finish in 5040 ways.

23. Since the order in which the employees are selected is not important, find the number of combinations of 8 employees taken 2 at a time.

$C(8, 2) = \frac{8!}{(8-2)!2!}$

$= \frac{8!}{6!2!}$

$= 28$

There are 28 possible ways to choose the two employees.

24. Since each letter is in a different position in each arrangement, order is important. Find the number of permutations of 7 things of which 5 are different and 2 are alike.

$\frac{7!}{2!} = \frac{7 \cdot 6 \cdot 5 \cdot 4 \cdot 3 \cdot 2!}{2!}$

$= 2520$

There are 2520 ways to arrange the letters.

25. Since each position on the shelf is different, order is important. Find the number of permutations of 5 things taken 5 at a time.

$P(5, 5) = \frac{5!}{(5-5)!}$

$= \frac{5!}{0!}$

$= 120$

The books can be placed on the shelf 120 ways.

26. Since the order in which the books are selected is not important, find the number of combinations of 12 books taken 9 at a time.

$C(12, 9) = \frac{12!}{(12-9)!9!}$

$= \frac{12!}{3!9!}$

$= 220$

There are 220 possible ways to choose the nine books.

27. Since each letter is in a different position in each arrangement, order is important. Find the number of permutations of 8 things of which 3 are different, 2 are alike, and 3 others are alike.

$\frac{8!}{2!3!} = \frac{8 \cdot 7 \cdot 6 \cdot 5 \cdot 4 \cdot 3!}{2!3!}$

$= 3360$

There are 3360 ways to arrange the letters.

28. Since the order in which the CDs are chosen is not important, find the number of combinations of 10 CDs taken 2 at a time.

$C(10, 2) = \frac{10!}{(10-2)!2!}$

$= \frac{10!}{8!2!}$

$= 45$

There are 45 possible ways to choose the two CDs.

29. Since the order in which the flavors are chosen is not important, find the number of combinations of 15 flavors taken 3 at a time.

$C(15, 3) = \frac{15!}{(15-3)!3!}$

$= \frac{15!}{12!3!}$

$= 455$

There are 455 possible ways to choose the three flavors.

30. Since the seating in each room is different, order is important. Find the number of permutations of 12 things taken 4 at a time.

$P(12, 4) = \frac{12!}{(12-4)!}$

$= \frac{12!}{8!}$

$= 11{,}880$

The movies can be shown in 11,880 ways.

31. Since each letter is in a different position in each arrangement, order is important. Find the number of permutations of 5 things of which 3 are different and 2 are alike.

$\frac{5!}{2!} = \frac{5 \cdot 4 \cdot 3 \cdot 2!}{2!}$

$= 60$

There are 60 ways to arrange the letters.

32. Since the order in which the senators are chosen is not important, find the number of combinations of 100 senators taken 5 at a time.

$C(100, 5) = \frac{100!}{(100-5)!5!}$

$= \frac{100!}{95!5!}$

$= 75{,}287{,}520$

There are 75,287,520 possible ways to choose the five senators.

33. Only the cards in the hand matter, not the order in which they were drawn, so use combinations.

$C(13, 4)$ Four of 13 cards of the same suit are to be drawn.

$C(4, 1)$ The four cards are from 1 of 4 suits.

$C(13, 1)$ One of 13 cards of another suit is to be drawn.

$C(3, 1)$ The one card is from 1 of 3 suits.

$C(13, 4) \cdot C(4, 1) \cdot C(13, 1) \cdot C(3, 1)$

$= \dfrac{13!}{(13-4)!\,4!} \cdot \dfrac{4!}{(4-1)!\,1!} \cdot \dfrac{13!}{(13-1)!\,1!} \cdot \dfrac{3!}{(3-1)!\,1!}$

$= \dfrac{13!}{9!\,4!} \cdot \dfrac{4!}{3!\,1!} \cdot \dfrac{13!}{12!\,1!} \cdot \dfrac{3!}{2!\,1!}$

$= 715 \cdot 4 \cdot 13 \cdot 3$

$= 111{,}540$

There are 111,540 hands consisting of 4 cards from one suit and 1 card from another suit.

34. Only the cards in the hand matter, not the order in which they were drawn, so use combinations.

$C(13, 3)$ Three of 13 cards of the same suit are to be drawn.

$C(4, 1)$ The three cards are from 1 of 4 suits.

$C(13, 2)$ Two of 13 cards of another suit are to be drawn.

$C(3, 1)$ The two cards are from 1 of 3 suits.

$C(13, 3) \cdot C(4, 1) \cdot C(13, 2) \cdot C(3, 1)$

$= \dfrac{13!}{(13-3)!\,3!} \cdot \dfrac{4!}{(4-1)!\,1!} \cdot \dfrac{13!}{(13-2)!\,2!} \cdot \dfrac{3!}{(3-1)!\,1!}$

$= \dfrac{13!}{10!\,3!} \cdot \dfrac{4!}{3!\,1!} \cdot \dfrac{13!}{11!\,2!} \cdot \dfrac{3!}{2!\,1!}$

$= 286 \cdot 4 \cdot 78 \cdot 3$

$= 267{,}696$

There are 267,696 hands consisting of 3 cards from one suit and 2 cards from another suit.

35. Only the balls drawn matter, not the order in which they were drawn, so use combinations.

$C(49, 5)$ Five of 49 white balls are to be drawn.

$C(42, 1)$ One of 42 red balls is to be drawn.

$C(49, 5) \cdot C(42, 1) = \dfrac{49!}{(49-5)!\,5!} \cdot \dfrac{42!}{(42-1)!\,1!}$

$= \dfrac{49!}{44!\,5!} \cdot \dfrac{42!}{41!\,1!}$

$= 1{,}906{,}884 \cdot 42$

$= 80{,}089{,}128$

There are 80,089,128 ways to fill out a lottery ticket.

36. Only the cards in the hand matter, not the order in which they were drawn, so use combinations.

$C(4, 3)$ Three of 4 cards of the same suit are to be drawn.

$C(12, 1)$ The three cards are from 1 of 12 suits.

$C(4, 4)$ Four of 4 cards of another suit are to be drawn.

$C(11, 1)$ The four cards are from 1 of 11 suits.

$C(4, 3) \cdot C(12, 1) \cdot C(4, 4) \cdot C(11, 1)$

$= \dfrac{4!}{(4-3)!\,3!} \cdot \dfrac{12!}{(12-1)!\,1!} \cdot \dfrac{4!}{(4-4)!\,4!} \cdot \dfrac{11!}{(11-1)!\,1!}$

$= 4 \cdot 12 \cdot 1 \cdot 11$

$= 528$

There are 528 hands consisting of 3 cards from one suit and 4 cards from another suit.

37. $C(n-1, r) + C(n-1, r-1)$

$= \dfrac{(n-1)!}{[(n-1)-r]!\,r!} + \dfrac{(n-1)!}{[(n-1)-(r-1)]!\,(r-1)!}$

$= \dfrac{(n-1)!}{(n-r-1)!\,r!} + \dfrac{(n-1)!}{(n-r)!\,(r-1)!}$

$= \dfrac{(n-1)!}{(n-r-1)!\,r!} \cdot \dfrac{n-r}{n-r} + \dfrac{(n-1)!}{(n-r)!\,(r-1)!} \cdot \dfrac{r}{r}$

$= \dfrac{(n-1)!(n-r)}{(n-r)!\,r!} + \dfrac{(n-1)!\,r}{(n-r)!\,r!}$

$= \dfrac{(n-1)!(n-r+r)}{(n-r)!\,r!}$

$= \dfrac{(n-1)!\,n}{(n-r)!\,r!}$

$= \dfrac{n!}{(n-r)!\,r!}$

$= C(n, r)$

38. Permutations and combinations can be used to find the number of different lineups. Answers should include the following.

• There are 9! different 9-person lineups available: 9 choices for the first player, 8 choices for the second player, 7 for the third player, and so on. So, there are 362,880 different lineups.

• There are $C(16, 9)$ ways to choose 9 players from 16: $C(16, 9) = \dfrac{16!}{7!\,9!}$ or 11,440.

39. D; Since each finishing position is different, order is important. Find the number of permutations of 8 things taken 3 at a time.

$P(8, 3) = \dfrac{8!}{(8-3)!}$

$= \dfrac{8!}{5!}$

$= 336$

40. A; A diagonal connects two nonadjacent vertices, and an edge connects two adjacent vertices. To determine the number of diagonals, determine how many ways to choose 2 of the 5 vertices, then subtract the number of edges. Since the order in which the two vertices are chosen is not important, use a combination.

$C(5, 2) - 5 = \dfrac{5!}{(5-2)!\,2!} - 5$

$= 10 - 5$

$= 5$

41. Let $n = 5$.

$\dfrac{n!}{n} = \dfrac{5!}{5}$

$= \dfrac{5 \cdot 4!}{5}$

$= 4!$

$= 24$

42. Let $n = 4$.

$\dfrac{n!}{n} = \dfrac{4!}{4}$

$= \dfrac{4 \cdot 3!}{4}$

$= 3!$

$= 6$

43. Let $n = 6$.

$\dfrac{n!}{n} = \dfrac{6!}{6}$

$= \dfrac{6 \cdot 5!}{6}$

$= 5!$

$= 120$

44. Each choice does not affect the other two choices, so these events are independent. There are 2 ways he can choose a writing instrument, 2 ways to choose a type of paper, and 2 ways to choose which sides to use. There are $2 \cdot 2 \cdot 2$ or 8 total ways he can prepare his homework.

45. Each choice does not affect the other two choices, so these events are independent. There are 10 ways to choose a flavor of ice cream, 4 ways to choose a flavor of sauce, and 2 ways to choose a cherry or not. There are $10 \cdot 4 \cdot 2$ or 80 different sundaes possible.

46. Sample answer: $n = 3$
$1 + 2 + 3 = 6$, but $2(3) - 1 = 5$.

47. Sample answer: $n = 2$
$5^n + 1 = 5^2 + 1$ or 26, and 26 is not divisible by 6.

48. $3e^x + 1 = 2$
$$3e^x = 1$$
$$e^x = \frac{1}{3}$$
$$\ln e^x = \ln\frac{1}{3}$$
$$x = \ln\frac{1}{3}$$
$$x \approx -1.0986$$
The solution is about -1.0986.

49. $e^{2x} > 5$
$$\ln e^{2x} > \ln 5$$
$$2x > \ln 5$$
$$x > \frac{1}{2}\ln 5$$
$$x > 0.8047$$
The solution is approximately all numbers greater than 0.8047.

50. $\ln(x - 1) = 3$
$$e^{\ln(x - 1)} = e^3$$
$$x - 1 = e^3$$
$$x = e^3 + 1$$
$$x \approx 21.0855$$
The solution is about 21.0855.

51. Let x = the number of days it would take the painter to do the job alone.

In 1 day, the painter could complete $\frac{1}{x}$ of the job.

In 6 days, the painter could complete $\frac{1}{x} \cdot 6$ or $\frac{6}{x}$ of the job.

In 10 days, the painter could complete $\frac{1}{x} \cdot 10$ or $\frac{10}{x}$ of the job.

Likewise, in 6 days, the associate could complete $\frac{1}{30} \cdot 6$ or $\frac{1}{5}$ of the job. Together they completed the whole job.

Part completed in 10 days	plus	part completed in 6 more days	equals	entire job.
$\frac{10}{x}$	$+$	$\left(\frac{6}{x} + \frac{1}{5}\right)$	$=$	1

Solve the equation.
$$\frac{10}{x} + \frac{6}{x} + \frac{1}{5} = 1$$
$$\frac{16}{x} + \frac{1}{5} = 1$$
$$\frac{16}{x} = \frac{4}{5}$$
$$16(5) = x(4)$$
$$80 = 4x$$
$$20 = x$$
It would take the painter 20 days to do the job alone.

52. The length of the major axis is the distance from $(-4, 0)$ to $(4, 0)$ or 8 units.
$$2a = 8$$
$$a = 4$$
The length of the minor axis is the distance from $(0, -3)$ to $(0, 3)$ or 6 units.
$$2b = 6$$
$$b = 3$$
Since the major axis is horizontal, substitute 16 for a^2 and 9 for b^2 in the form $\frac{x^2}{a^2} + \frac{y^2}{b^2} = 1$. An equation of the ellipse is $\frac{x^2}{16} + \frac{y^2}{9} = 1$.

53. The center of the ellipse is $(4, 4)$. So, $h = 4$ and $k = 4$. The length of the major axis is the distance from $(4, 1)$ to $(4, 7)$ or 6 units.
$$2a = 6$$
$$a = 3$$
The length of the minor axis is the distance from $(2, 4)$ to $(6, 4)$ or 4 units.
$$2b = 4$$
$$b = 2$$
Since the major axis is vertical substitute 9 for a^2 and 4 for b^2 in the form $\frac{(y - k)^2}{a^2} + \frac{(x - h)^2}{b^2} = 1$ where $h = 4$ and $k = 4$. An equation of the ellipse is $\frac{(y - 4)^2}{9} + \frac{(x - 4)^2}{4} = 1$.

54. $p(x) = \frac{1}{2}x^2 + 3x - 1$
$$p(-1) = \frac{1}{2}(-1)^2 + 3(-1) - 1$$
$$= \frac{1}{2} - 3 - 1$$
$$= -\frac{7}{2}$$
$$p(5) = \frac{1}{2}(5)^2 + 3(5) - 1$$
$$= \frac{25}{2} + 15 - 1$$
$$= \frac{53}{2}$$

55. $p(x) = x^4 - 4x^3 + 2x - 7$
$$p(-1) = (-1)^4 - 4(-1)^3 + 2(-1) - 7$$
$$= 1 + 4 - 2 - 7$$
$$= -4$$
$$p(5) = (5)^4 - 4(5)^3 + 2(5) - 7$$
$$= 625 - 500 + 10 - 7$$
$$= 128$$

56. $x^2 - 16 = 0$
$(x - 4)(x + 4) = 0$

$x - 4 = 0$ or $x + 4 = 0$
$x = 4$ $x = -4$

The solution set is $\{-4, 4\}$.

57. $x^2 - 3x - 10 = 0$
$(x - 5)(x + 2) = 0$

$x - 5 = 0$ or $x + 2 = 0$
$x = 5$ $x = -2$

The solution set is $\{-2, 5\}$.

58. $3x^2 + 8x - 3 = 0$
$(x + 3)(3x - 1) = 0$

$x + 3 = 0$ or $3x - 1 = 0$
$x = -3$ $3x = 1$
                             $x = \frac{1}{3}$

The solution set is $\left\{-3, \frac{1}{3}\right\}$.

59. $\sqrt{128} = \sqrt{2^6 \cdot 2}$
$= \sqrt{2^6} \cdot \sqrt{2}$
$= 2^3\sqrt{2}$
$= 8\sqrt{2}$

60. $\sqrt{3x^6y^4} = \sqrt{3 \cdot (x^3)^2 \cdot (y^2)^2}$
$= \sqrt{3} \cdot \sqrt{(x^3)^2} \cdot \sqrt{(y^2)^2}$
$= \sqrt{3} \cdot |x^3| \cdot y^2$
$= |x^3|y^2\sqrt{3}$

61. $\sqrt{20} + 2\sqrt{45} - \sqrt{80}$
$= \sqrt{2^2 \cdot 5} + 2\sqrt{3^2 \cdot 5} - \sqrt{4^2 \cdot 5}$
$= \sqrt{2^2} \cdot \sqrt{5} + 2\sqrt{3^2} \cdot \sqrt{5} - \sqrt{4^2} \cdot \sqrt{5}$
$= 2 \cdot \sqrt{5} + 2 \cdot 3 \cdot \sqrt{5} - 4 \cdot \sqrt{5}$
$= 2\sqrt{5} + 6\sqrt{5} - 4\sqrt{5}$
$= 4\sqrt{5}$

62. The matrix equation is $\begin{bmatrix} 1 & 2 \\ 3 & -3 \end{bmatrix} \cdot \begin{bmatrix} x \\ y \end{bmatrix} = \begin{bmatrix} 5 \\ -12 \end{bmatrix}$,

when $A = \begin{bmatrix} 1 & 2 \\ 3 & -3 \end{bmatrix}$, $X = \begin{bmatrix} x \\ y \end{bmatrix}$, and $B = \begin{bmatrix} 5 \\ -12 \end{bmatrix}$.

Step 1 Find the inverse of the coefficient matrix.

$A^{-1} = \frac{1}{-3 - 6}\begin{bmatrix} -3 & -2 \\ -3 & 1 \end{bmatrix}$

$= -\frac{1}{9}\begin{bmatrix} -3 & -2 \\ -3 & 1 \end{bmatrix}$

Step 2 Multiply each side of the matrix equation by the inverse matrix.

$-\frac{1}{9}\begin{bmatrix} -3 & -2 \\ -3 & 1 \end{bmatrix} \cdot \begin{bmatrix} 1 & 2 \\ 3 & -3 \end{bmatrix} \cdot \begin{bmatrix} x \\ y \end{bmatrix} = -\frac{1}{9}\begin{bmatrix} -3 & -2 \\ -3 & 1 \end{bmatrix} \cdot \begin{bmatrix} 5 \\ -12 \end{bmatrix}$

$\begin{bmatrix} 1 & 0 \\ 0 & 1 \end{bmatrix} \cdot \begin{bmatrix} x \\ y \end{bmatrix} = -\frac{1}{9}\begin{bmatrix} 9 \\ -27 \end{bmatrix}$

$\begin{bmatrix} x \\ y \end{bmatrix} = \begin{bmatrix} -1 \\ 3 \end{bmatrix}$

The solution is $(-1, 3)$.

63. The matrix equation is $\begin{bmatrix} 5 & 2 \\ -3 & 1 \end{bmatrix} \cdot \begin{bmatrix} a \\ b \end{bmatrix} = \begin{bmatrix} 4 \\ 2 \end{bmatrix}$,

when $A = \begin{bmatrix} 5 & 2 \\ -3 & 1 \end{bmatrix}$, $X = \begin{bmatrix} a \\ b \end{bmatrix}$, and $B = \begin{bmatrix} 4 \\ 2 \end{bmatrix}$.

Step 1 Find the inverse of the coefficient matrix.

$A^{-1} = \frac{1}{5 + 6}\begin{bmatrix} 1 & -2 \\ 3 & 5 \end{bmatrix}$

$= \frac{1}{11}\begin{bmatrix} 1 & -2 \\ 3 & 5 \end{bmatrix}$

Step 2 Multiply each side of the matrix equation by the inverse matrix.

$\frac{1}{11}\begin{bmatrix} 1 & -2 \\ 3 & 5 \end{bmatrix} \cdot \begin{bmatrix} 5 & 2 \\ -3 & 1 \end{bmatrix} \cdot \begin{bmatrix} a \\ b \end{bmatrix} = \frac{1}{11}\begin{bmatrix} 1 & -2 \\ 3 & 5 \end{bmatrix} \cdot \begin{bmatrix} 4 \\ 2 \end{bmatrix}$

$\begin{bmatrix} 1 & 0 \\ 0 & 1 \end{bmatrix} \cdot \begin{bmatrix} a \\ b \end{bmatrix} = \frac{1}{11}\begin{bmatrix} 0 \\ 22 \end{bmatrix}$

$\begin{bmatrix} a \\ b \end{bmatrix} = \begin{bmatrix} 0 \\ 2 \end{bmatrix}$

The solution is $(0, 2)$.

64. $m = \frac{y_2 - y_1}{x_2 - x_1}$
$= \frac{-3 - 1}{5 - 2}$
$= \frac{-4}{3}$
$= -\frac{4}{3}$

The slope of the line is $-\frac{4}{3}$.

65. $m = \frac{y_2 - y_1}{x_2 - x_1}$
$= \frac{-2 - 4}{7 - 0}$
$= \frac{-6}{7}$
$= -\frac{6}{7}$

The slope of the line is $-\frac{6}{7}$.

66. $m = \frac{y_2 - y_1}{x_2 - x_1}$
$= \frac{3 - 3}{2 - 5}$
$= \frac{0}{-3}$
$= 0$

The slope of the line is 0.

67. Case 1: $a = b$ or   Case 2: $a = -b$
           $x - 4 = 11$ $x - 4 = -11$
               $x = 15$ $x = -7$

Check $|x - 4| = 11$ $|x - 4| = 11$
$|15 - 4| \overset{?}{=} 11$ $|-7 - 4| \overset{?}{=} 11$
$|11| \overset{?}{=} 11$ $|-11| \overset{?}{=} 11$
$11 = 11 \checkmark$ $11 = 11 \checkmark$

The solutions are -7 and 15.

68. This equation is never true. So the solution set is $\varnothing$.

69. $\frac{x}{x + y} = \frac{3}{3 + 2}$
$= \frac{3}{5}$

70. $\frac{x}{x + y} = \frac{4}{4 + 4}$
$= \frac{4}{8}$
$= \frac{1}{2}$

71. $\frac{x}{x + y} = \frac{2}{2 + 8}$
$= \frac{2}{10}$
$= \frac{1}{5}$

72. $\frac{x}{x + y} = \frac{5}{5 + 10}$
$= \frac{5}{15}$
$= \frac{1}{3}$

Page 647   Check for Understanding

1. Sample answer: The event *July comes before June* has a probability of 0. The event *June comes before July* has a probability of 1.

2. **Step 1** Identify s and f.

   Odds $= 3:2$

   $\qquad = s:f \quad s = 3, f = 2$

   Step 2 Find the probability.

   $$P(\text{event occurs}) = \frac{s}{s+f}$$
   $$= \frac{3}{3+2}$$
   $$= \frac{3}{5}$$

   So, the probability of the event occurring is $\frac{3}{5}$.

3. There are $6 \cdot 6$ or 36 possible outcomes for the two dice. Only 1 outcome, 1 and 1, results in a sum of 2, so $P(2) = \frac{1}{36}$. There are 2 outcomes, 1 and 2 as well as 2 and 1, that result in a sum of 3, so $P(3) = \frac{2}{36}$ or $\frac{1}{18}$.

4. **Step 1** Determine how many 2-letter selections meet the conditions.

   $C(3, 2)$ Select 2 of the 3 vowels. Their order does not matter.

   Step 2 Find the number of successes.

   $$C(3, 2) = \frac{3!}{(3-2)!\,2!}$$
   $$= \frac{3!}{1!\,2!}$$
   $$= 3$$

   Step 3 Find the total number, $s + f$, of possible 2-letter selections.

   $$C(7, 2) = \frac{7!}{(7-2)!\,2!}$$
   $$= \frac{7!}{5!\,2!}$$
   $$= 21$$

   Step 4 Determine the probability.

   $$P(\text{2 vowels}) = \frac{s}{s+f}$$
   $$= \frac{3}{21}$$
   $$= \frac{1}{7}$$

   The probability of selecting 2 vowels is $\frac{1}{7}$.

5. **Step 1** Determine how many 2-letter selections meet the conditions.

   $C(4, 2)$ Select 2 of the 4 consonants. Their order does not matter.

   Step 2 Find the number of successes.

   $$C(4, 2) = \frac{4!}{(4-2)!\,2!}$$
   $$= \frac{4!}{2!\,2!}$$
   $$= 6$$

   Step 3 Find the total number, $s + f$, of possible 2-letter selections.

   $$C(7, 2) = \frac{7!}{(7-2)!\,2!}$$
   $$= \frac{7!}{5!\,2!}$$
   $$= 21$$

Step 4 Determine the probability.

$$P(\text{2 consonants}) = \frac{s}{s+f}$$
$$= \frac{6}{21}$$
$$= \frac{2}{7}$$

The probability of selecting 2 consonants is $\frac{2}{7}$.

6. **Step 1** Determine how many 2-letter selections meet the conditions.

   $C(3, 1)$ Select 1 vowel.

   $C(4, 1)$ Select 1 consonant.

   Step 2 Find the number of successes.

   $$C(3, 1) \cdot C(4, 1) = \frac{3!}{(3-1)!\,1!} \cdot \frac{4!}{(4-1)!\,1!}$$
   $$= \frac{3!}{2!\,1!} \cdot \frac{4!}{3!\,1!}$$
   $$= 3 \cdot 4$$
   $$= 12$$

   Step 3 Find the total number, $s + f$, of possible 2-letter selections.

   $$C(7, 2) = \frac{7!}{(7-2)!\,2!}$$
   $$= \frac{7!}{5!\,2!}$$
   $$= 21$$

   Step 4 Determine the probability.

   $$P(\text{1 vowel, 1 consonant}) = \frac{s}{s+f}$$
   $$= \frac{12}{21}$$
   $$= \frac{4}{7}$$

   The probability of selecting 1 vowel and 1 consonant is $\frac{4}{7}$.

7. **Step 1** Identify s and f.

   $$P(\text{event occurs}) = \frac{8}{9}$$
   $$= \frac{s}{s+f} \quad s = 8, f = 1$$

   Step 2 Find the odds.

   Odds $= s:f$

   $\qquad = 8:1$

   So, the odds of the event occurring are $8:1$.

8. **Step 1** Identify s and f.

   $$P(\text{event occurs}) = \frac{1}{6}$$
   $$= \frac{s}{s+f} \quad s = 1, f = 5$$

   Step 2 Find the odds.

   Odds $= s:f$

   $\qquad = 1:5$

   So, the odds of the event occurring are $1:5$.

9. **Step 1** Identify s and f.

   $$P(\text{event occurs}) = \frac{2}{9}$$
   $$= \frac{s}{s+f} \quad s = 2, f = 7$$

   Step 2 Find the odds.

   Odds $= s:f$

   $\qquad = 2:7$

   So, the odds of the event occurring are $2:7$.

10. Step 1 Identify s and f.

Odds = 6:5

$= s{:}f \qquad s = 6, f = 5$

Step 2 Find the probability.

$$P(\text{event occurs}) = \frac{s}{s+f}$$

$$= \frac{6}{6+5}$$

$$= \frac{6}{11}$$

So, the probability of the event occurring is $\frac{6}{11}$.

11. Step 1 Identify s and f.

Odds = 10:1

$= s{:}f \qquad s = 10, f = 1$

Step 2 Find the probability.

$$P(\text{event occurs}) = \frac{s}{s+f}$$

$$= \frac{10}{10+1}$$

$$= \frac{10}{11}$$

So, the probability of the event occurring is $\frac{10}{11}$.

12. Step 1 Identify s and f.

Odds = 2:5

$= s{:}f \qquad s = 2, f = 5$

Step 2 Find the probability.

$$P(\text{event occurs}) = \frac{s}{s+f}$$

$$= \frac{2}{2+5}$$

$$= \frac{2}{7}$$

So, the probability of the event occurring is $\frac{2}{7}$.

13. According to the table, the probability of tossing 0 heads is $\frac{1}{8}$.

14. According to the table, the probability of tossing 2 heads is $\frac{3}{8}$.

15. The map shows that there are 5 states next to the Pacific Ocean. Thus, there are 5 outcomes that are successes, so $s = 5$. The other 45 outcomes are failures, so $f = 45$.

$$P(\text{next to the Pacific Ocean}) = \frac{s}{s+f}$$

$$= \frac{5}{5+45}$$

$$= \frac{5}{50}$$

$$= \frac{1}{10}$$

16. The map shows that there are 21 states that have at least five neighboring states. Thus, there are 21 outcomes that are successes, so $s = 21$. The other 29 outcomes are failures, so $f = 29$.

$$P(\text{has at least five neighboring states}) = \frac{s}{s+f}$$

$$= \frac{21}{21+29}$$

$$= \frac{21}{50}$$

17. The map shows that there are 4 states that border Mexico. Thus, There are 4 outcomes that are successes, so $s = 4$. The other 46 outcomes are failures, so $f = 46$.

$$P(\text{borders Mexico}) = \frac{s}{s+f}$$

$$= \frac{4}{4+46}$$

$$= \frac{4}{50}$$

$$= \frac{2}{25}$$

18. The map shows that there is 1 state that is surrounded by water. Thus, there is 1 outcome that is a success, so $s = 1$. The other 49 outcomes are failures, so $f = 49$.

$$P(\text{is surrounded by water}) = \frac{s}{s+f}$$

$$= \frac{1}{1+49}$$

$$= \frac{1}{50}$$

Pages 648–649   Practice and Apply

19. Step 1 Determine how many 2-kitten selections meet the conditions.

$C(4, 2)$ Select 2 of the 4 male kittens. Their order does not matter.

Step 2 Find the number of successes.

$$C(4, 2) = \frac{4!}{(4-2)!\,2!}$$

$$= \frac{4!}{2!\,2!}$$

$$= 6$$

Step 3 Find the total number, $s + f$, of possible 2-kitten selections.

$$C(11, 2) = \frac{11!}{(11-2)!\,2!}$$

$$= \frac{11!}{9!\,2!}$$

$$= 55$$

Step 4 Determine the probability.

$$P(2\text{ male}) = \frac{s}{s+f}$$

$$= \frac{6}{55}$$

The probability of selecting 2 male kittens is $\frac{6}{55}$.

20. Step 1 Determine how many 2-kitten selections meet the conditions.

$C(7, 2)$ Select 2 female kittens. Their order does not matter.

Step 2 Find the number of successes.

$$C(7, 2) = \frac{7!}{(7-2)!\,2!}$$

$$= \frac{7!}{5!\,2!}$$

$$= 21$$

Step 3 Find the total number, $s + f$, of possible 2-kitten selections.

$$C(11, 2) = \frac{11!}{(11-2)!\,2!}$$

$$= \frac{11!}{9!\,2!}$$

$$= 55$$

Step 4 Determine the probability.

$$P(2\text{ female}) = \frac{s}{s+f}$$

$$= \frac{21}{55}$$

The probability of selecting 2 female kittens is $\frac{21}{55}$.

21. Step 1 Determine how many 2-kitten selections meet the conditions.

$C(4, 1)$ Select one male kitten.

$C(7, 1)$ Select one female kitten.

Step 2 Find the number of successes.

$$C(4, 1) \cdot C(7, 1) = \frac{4!}{(4-1)!\,1!} \cdot \frac{7!}{(7-1)!\,1!}$$
$$= \frac{4!}{3!\,1!} \cdot \frac{7!}{6!\,1!}$$
$$= 4 \cdot 7$$
$$= 28$$

Step 3 Find the total number, $s + f$, of possible 2-kitten selections.

$$C(11, 2) = \frac{11!}{(11-2)!\,2!}$$
$$= \frac{11!}{9!\,2!}$$
$$= 55$$

Step 4 Determine the probability.

$$P(1 \text{ of each}) = \frac{s}{s+f}$$
$$= \frac{28}{55}$$

The probability of selecting 1 male and 1 female kitten is $\frac{28}{55}$.

22. Step 1 Determine how many 3-CD selections meet the conditions.

$C(8, 3)$ Select three jazz CDs.

Step 2 Find the number of successes.

$$C(8, 3) = \frac{8!}{(8-3)!\,3!}$$
$$= \frac{8!}{5!\,3!}$$
$$= 56$$

Step 3 Find the total number, $s + f$, of possible 3-CD selections.

$$C(25, 3) = \frac{25!}{(25-3)!\,3!}$$
$$= \frac{25!}{22!\,3!}$$
$$= 2300$$

Step 4 Determine the probability.

$$P(3 \text{ jazz}) = \frac{s}{s+f}$$
$$= \frac{56}{2300}$$
$$= \frac{14}{575}$$

The probability of selecting 3 jazz CDs is $\frac{14}{575}$.

23. Step 1 Determine how many 3-CD selections meet the conditions.

$C(12, 3)$ Select three rock CDs.

Step 2 Find the number of successes.

$$C(12, 3) = \frac{12!}{(12-3)!\,3!}$$
$$= \frac{12!}{9!\,3!}$$
$$= 220$$

Step 3 Find the total number, $s + f$, of possible 3-CD selections.

$$C(25, 3) = \frac{25!}{(25-3)!\,3!}$$
$$= \frac{25!}{22!\,3!}$$
$$= 2300$$

Step 4 Determine the probability.

$$P(3 \text{ rock}) = \frac{s}{s+f}$$
$$= \frac{220}{2300}$$
$$= \frac{11}{115}$$

The probability of selecting 3 rock CDs is $\frac{11}{115}$.

24. Step 1 Determine how many 3-CD selections meet the conditions.

$C(5, 1)$ Select one classical CD.

$C(8, 2)$ Select two jazz CDs.

Step 2 Find the number of successes.

$$C(5, 1) \cdot C(8, 2) = \frac{5!}{(5-1)!\,1!} \cdot \frac{8!}{(8-2)!\,2!}$$
$$= \frac{5!}{4!\,1!} \cdot \frac{8!}{6!\,2!}$$
$$= 5 \cdot 28$$
$$= 140$$

Step 3 Find the total number, $s + f$, of possible 3-CD selections.

$$C(25, 3) = \frac{25!}{(25-3)!\,3!}$$
$$= \frac{25!}{22!\,3!}$$
$$= 2300$$

Step 4 Determine the probability.

$$P(1 \text{ classical, 2 jazz}) = \frac{s}{s+f}$$
$$= \frac{140}{2300}$$
$$= \frac{7}{115}$$

The probability of selecting 1 classical and 2 jazz CDs is $\frac{7}{115}$.

25. Step 1 Determine how many 3-CD selections meet the conditions.

$C(5, 2)$ Select two classical CDs.

$C(12, 1)$ Select one rock CD.

Step 2 Find the number of successes.

$$C(5, 2) \cdot C(12, 1) = \frac{5!}{(5-2)!\,2!} \cdot \frac{12!}{(12-1)!\,1!}$$
$$= \frac{5!}{3!\,2!} \cdot \frac{12!}{11!\,1!}$$
$$= 10 \cdot 12$$
$$= 120$$

Step 3 Find the total number, $s + f$, of possible 3-CD selections.

$$C(25, 3) = \frac{25!}{(25-3)!\,3!}$$
$$= \frac{25!}{22!\,3!}$$
$$= 2300$$

Step 4 Determine the probability.

$$P(2 \text{ classical, 1 rock}) = \frac{s}{s+f}$$
$$= \frac{120}{2300}$$
$$= \frac{6}{115}$$

The probability of selecting 2 classical and 1 rock CD is $\frac{6}{115}$.

26. Step 1 Determine how many 3-CD selections meet the conditions.

$C(8, 1)$ Select one jazz CD.
$C(12, 2)$ Select two rock CDs.

Step 2 Find the number of successes.

$$C(8, 1) \cdot C(12, 2) = \frac{8!}{(8-1)!\,1!} \cdot \frac{12!}{(12-2)!\,2!}$$
$$= \frac{8!}{7!\,1!} \cdot \frac{12!}{10!\,2!}$$
$$= 8 \cdot 66$$
$$= 528$$

Step 3 Find the total number, $s + f$, of possible 3-CD selections.

$$C(25, 3) = \frac{25!}{(25-3)!\,3!}$$
$$= \frac{25!}{22!\,3!}$$
$$= 2300$$

Step 4 Determine the probability.

$$P(1\text{ jazz, 2 rock}) = \frac{s}{s+f}$$
$$= \frac{528}{2300}$$
$$= \frac{132}{575}$$

The probability of selecting 1 jazz and 2 rock CDs is $\frac{132}{575}$.

27. Step 1 Determine how many 3-CD selections meet the conditions.

$C(5, 1)$ Select one classical CD.
$C(8, 1)$ Select one jazz CD.
$C(12, 1)$ Select one rock CD.

Step 2 Find the number of successes.

$$C(5, 1) \cdot C(8, 1) \cdot C(12, 1)$$
$$= \frac{5!}{(5-1)!\,1!} \cdot \frac{8!}{(8-1)!\,1!} \cdot \frac{12!}{(12-1)!\,1!}$$
$$= \frac{5!}{4!\,1!} \cdot \frac{8!}{7!\,1!} \cdot \frac{12!}{11!\,1!}$$
$$= 5 \cdot 8 \cdot 12$$
$$= 480$$

Step 3 Find the total number, $s + f$, of possible 3-CD selections.

$$C(25, 3) = \frac{25!}{(25-3)!\,3!}$$
$$= \frac{25!}{22!\,3!}$$
$$= 2300$$

Step 4 Determine the probability.

$$P(1\text{ classical, 1 jazz, 1 rock}) = \frac{s}{s+f}$$
$$= \frac{480}{2300}$$
$$= \frac{24}{115}$$

The probability of selecting 1 classical, 1 jazz and 1 rock CD is about $\frac{24}{115}$.

28. Step 1 Determine how many 4-CD selections meet the conditions.

$C(12, 2)$ Select two rock CDs.
$C(5, 2)$ Select two classical CDs.

Step 2 Find the number of successes.

$$C(12, 2) \cdot C(5, 2) = \frac{12!}{(12-2)!\,2!} \cdot \frac{5!}{(5-2)!\,2!}$$
$$= \frac{12!}{10!\,2!} \cdot \frac{5!}{3!\,2!}$$
$$= 66 \cdot 10$$
$$= 660$$

Step 3 Find the total number, $s + f$, of possible 4-CD selections.

$$C(25, 4) = \frac{25!}{(25-4)!\,4!}$$
$$= \frac{25!}{21!\,4!}$$
$$= 12{,}650$$

Step 4 Determine the probability.

$$P(2\text{ rock, 2 classical}) = \frac{s}{s+f}$$
$$= \frac{660}{12{,}650}$$
$$= \frac{6}{115}$$

The probability of selecting 2 rock and 2 classical CDs is $\frac{6}{115}$.

29. Bob has only rock, jazz, and classical CDs in his collection. Therefore, he cannot select a reggae CD. This is an event that cannot occur. Thus, $P(2\text{ jazz, 1 reggae}) = 0$.

30. There are $C(53, 6)$ or 22,957,480 possible outcomes. Only one of these outcomes is a success, so $s = 1$. The other 22,957,479 outcomes are failures, so $f = 22{,}957{,}479$.

$$P(\text{all 6 numbers}) = \frac{s}{s+f}$$
$$= \frac{1}{1 + 22{,}957{,}479}$$
$$= \frac{1}{22{,}957{,}480}$$

31. The table shows there are $15{,}819 + 963 + 179 + 2770 + 2482 + 1431 + 1761$ or 25,405 possible outcomes. Only 179 of these outcomes are successes, so $s = 179$. The other $15{,}819 + 963 + 2770 + 2482 + 1431 + 1761$ or 25,226 outcomes are failures, so $f = 25{,}226$.

$$P(\text{math or statistics}) = \frac{s}{s+f}$$
$$= \frac{179}{179 + 25{,}226}$$
$$= \frac{179}{25{,}405}$$
$$\approx 0.007$$

32. The table shows there are $15{,}819 + 963 + 179 + 2770 + 2482 + 1431 + 1761$ or 25,405 possible outcomes. Only 15,819 of these outcomes are successes, so $s = 15{,}819$. The other $963 + 179 + 2770 + 2482 + 1431 + 1761$ or 9586 outcomes are failures, so $f = 9586$.

$$P(\text{biological sciences}) = \frac{s}{s+f}$$
$$= \frac{15{,}819}{15{,}819 + 9586}$$
$$= \frac{15{,}819}{25{,}405}$$
$$\approx 0.623$$

33. The table shows there are $15{,}819 + 963 + 179 + 2770 + 2482 + 1431 + 1761$ or $25{,}405$ possible outcomes. Only 2770 of these outcomes are successes, so $s = 2770$. The other $15{,}819 + 963 + 179 + 2482 + 1431 + 1761$ or $22{,}635$ outcomes are failures, so $f = 22{,}635$.

$$P(\text{physical sciences}) = \frac{s}{s+f}$$
$$= \frac{2770}{2770 + 22{,}635}$$
$$= \frac{2770}{25{,}405}$$
$$\approx 0.109$$

34. Step 1 Identify s and f.
$$P(\text{event occurs}) = \frac{1}{2}$$
$$= \frac{s}{s+f} \qquad s = 1, f = 1$$

Step 2 Find the odds.
$$\text{Odds} = s{:}f$$
$$= 1{:}1$$
So, the odds of the event occurring are $1{:}1$.

35. Step 1 Identify s and f.
$$P(\text{event occurs}) = \frac{3}{8}$$
$$= \frac{s}{s+f} \qquad s = 3, f = 5$$

Step 2 Find the odds.
$$\text{Odds} = s{:}f$$
$$= 3{:}5$$
So, the odds of the event occurring are $3{:}5$.

36. Step 1 Identify s and f.
$$P(\text{event occurs}) = \frac{11}{12}$$
$$= \frac{s}{s+f} \qquad s = 11, f = 1$$

Step 2 Find the odds.
$$\text{Odds} = s{:}f$$
$$= 11{:}1$$
So, the odds of the event occurring are $11{:}1$.

37. Step 1 Identify s and f.
$$P(\text{event occurs}) = \frac{5}{8}$$
$$= \frac{s}{s+f} \qquad s = 5, f = 3$$

Step 2 Find the odds.
$$\text{Odds} = s{:}f$$
$$= 5{:}3$$
So, the odds of the event occurring are $5{:}3$.

38. Step 1 Identify s and f.
$$P(\text{event occurs}) = \frac{4}{7}$$
$$= \frac{s}{s+f} \qquad s = 4, f = 3$$

Step 2 Find the odds.
$$\text{Odds} = s{:}f$$
$$= 4{:}3$$
So, the odds of the event occurring are $4{:}3$.

39. Step 1 Identify s and f.
$$P(\text{event occurs}) = \frac{1}{5}$$
$$= \frac{s}{s+f} \qquad s = 1, f = 4$$

Step 2 Find the odds.
$$\text{Odds} = s{:}f$$
$$= 1{:}4$$
So, the odds of the event occurring are $1{:}4$.

40. Step 1 Identify s and f.
$$P(\text{event occurs}) = \frac{4}{11}$$
$$= \frac{s}{s+f} \qquad s = 4, f = 7$$

Step 2 Find the odds.
$$\text{Odds} = s{:}f$$
$$= 4{:}7$$
So, the odds of the event occurring are $4{:}7$.

41. Step 1 Identify s and f.
$$P(\text{event occurs}) = \frac{3}{4}$$
$$= \frac{s}{s+f} \qquad s = 3, f = 1$$

Step 2 Find the odds.
$$\text{Odds} = s{:}f$$
$$= 3{:}1$$
So, the odds of the event occurring are $3{:}1$.

42. Step 1 Identify s and f.
$$\text{Odds} = 6{:}1$$
$$= s{:}f \qquad s = 6, f = 1$$

Step 2 Find the probability.
$$P(\text{event occurs}) = \frac{s}{s+f}$$
$$= \frac{6}{6+1}$$
$$= \frac{6}{7}$$
So, the probability of the event occurring is $\frac{6}{7}$.

43. Step 1 Identify s and f.
$$\text{Odds} = 3{:}7$$
$$= s{:}f \qquad s = 3, f = 7$$

Step 2 Find the probability.
$$P(\text{event occurs}) = \frac{s}{s+f}$$
$$= \frac{3}{3+7}$$
$$= \frac{3}{10}$$
So, the probability of the event occurring is $\frac{3}{10}$.

44. Step 1 Identify s and f.
$$\text{Odds} = 5{:}6$$
$$= s{:}f \qquad s = 5, f = 6$$

Step 2 Find the probability.
$$P(\text{event occurs}) = \frac{s}{s+f}$$
$$= \frac{5}{5+6}$$
$$= \frac{5}{11}$$
So, the probability of the event occurring is $\frac{5}{11}$.

45. Step 1 Identify s and f.
$$\text{Odds} = 4{:}5$$
$$= s{:}f \qquad s = 4, f = 5$$

Step 2 Find the probability.
$$P(\text{event occurs}) = \frac{s}{s+f}$$
$$= \frac{4}{4+5}$$
$$= \frac{4}{9}$$
So, the probability of the event occurring is $\frac{4}{9}$.

46. Step 1 Identify s and f.

$$\text{Odds} = 9{:}8$$
$$= s{:}f \quad s = 9, f = 8$$

Step 2 Find the probability.

$$P(\text{event occurs}) = \frac{s}{s+f}$$
$$= \frac{9}{9+8}$$
$$= \frac{9}{17}$$

So, the probability of the event occurring is $\frac{9}{17}$.

47. Step 1 Identify s and f.

$$\text{Odds} = 1{:}8$$
$$= s{:}f \quad s = 1, f = 8$$

Step 2 Find the probability.

$$P(\text{event occurs}) = \frac{s}{s+f}$$
$$= \frac{1}{1+8}$$
$$= \frac{1}{9}$$

So, the probability of the event occurring is $\frac{1}{9}$.

48. Step 1 Identify s and f.

$$\text{Odds} = 7{:}9$$
$$= s{:}f \quad s = 7, f = 9$$

Step 2 Find the probability.

$$P(\text{event occurs}) = \frac{s}{s+f}$$
$$= \frac{7}{7+9}$$
$$= \frac{7}{16}$$

So, the probability of the event occurring is $\frac{7}{16}$.

49. Step 1 Identify s and f.

$$\text{Odds} = 3{:}2$$
$$= s{:}f \quad s = 3, f = 2$$

Step 2 Find the probability.

$$P(\text{event occurs}) = \frac{s}{s+f}$$
$$= \frac{3}{3+2}$$
$$= \frac{3}{5}$$

So, the probability of the event occurring is $\frac{3}{5}$.

50. Step 1 Identify s and f.

$$\text{Odds} = 1{:}9$$
$$= s{:}f \quad s = 1, f = 9$$

Step 2 Find the probability.

$$P(\text{an American is of English ancestry})$$
$$= \frac{s}{s+f}$$
$$= \frac{1}{1+9}$$
$$= \frac{1}{10}$$

So, the probability that an American is of English ancestry is $\frac{1}{10}$.

51. Eight out of 100 males will have some form of color blindness, so the number of successes is 8. The number of failures is $100 - 8$ or 92.

$$\text{odds of a male being color-blind} = s{:}f$$
$$= 8{:}92$$
$$= 2{:}23$$

The odds of a male being color-blind are $2{:}23$.

52. One out of 1000 females will have some form of color blindness, so the number of successes is 1. The number of failures is $1000 - 1$ or 999.

$$\text{odds of a female being color-blind} = s{:}f$$
$$= 1{:}999$$

The odds of a female being color-blind are $1{:}999$.

53. Step 1 Identify s and f.

$$P(\text{college scholarship}) = \frac{4}{5}$$
$$= \frac{s}{s+f} \quad s = 4, f = 1$$

Step 2 Find the odds.

$$\text{odds she will not earn a scholarship} = f{:}s$$
$$= 1{:}4$$

So, the odds she will not earn a scholarship are $1{:}4$.

54. Step 1 Determine how many 5-card euchre hands meet the conditions.

$C(4, 1)$ Select one suit to have two cards.
$C(6, 2)$ Select two cards of the first suit.
$C(6, 1)$ Select one card of the second suit.
$C(6, 1)$ Select one card of the third suit.
$C(6, 1)$ Select one card of the fourth suit.

Step 2 Find the number of successes.

$$C(4, 1) \cdot C(6, 2) \cdot C(6, 1) \cdot C(6, 1) \cdot C(6, 1)$$
$$= \frac{4!}{(4-1)!\,1!} \cdot \frac{6!}{(6-2)!\,2!} \cdot \frac{6!}{(6-1)!\,1!} \cdot$$
$$\frac{6!}{(6-1)!\,1!} \cdot \frac{6!}{(6-1)!\,1!}$$
$$= \frac{4!}{3!\,1!} \cdot \frac{6!}{4!\,2!} \cdot \frac{6!}{5!\,1!} \cdot \frac{6!}{5!\,1!} \cdot \frac{6!}{5!\,1!}$$
$$= 4 \cdot 15 \cdot 6 \cdot 6 \cdot 6$$
$$= 12{,}960$$

Step 3 Find the total number, $s + f$, of possible 5-card euchre hands.

$$C(24, 5) = \frac{24!}{(24-5)!\,5!}$$
$$= \frac{24!}{19!\,5!}$$
$$= 42{,}504$$

Step 4 Determine the probability.

$$P(\text{all four suits}) = \frac{s}{s+f}$$
$$= \frac{12{,}960}{42{,}504}$$
$$= \frac{540}{1771}$$

The probability of being dealt a 5-card euchre hand containing all four suits is $\frac{540}{1771}$.

55. According to the table, the probability of 0 sophomores being chosen is $\frac{1}{20}$.

56. According to the table, the probability of 1 sophomore being chosen is $\frac{9}{20}$.

57. According to the table, the probability of 2 sophomores being chosen is $\frac{9}{20}$.

58. According to the table, the probability of 3 sophomores being chosen is $\frac{1}{20}$.

59. Selecting 2 juniors out of 3 students means that 1 sophomore is selected. Thus, $P(2 \text{ juniors}) = P(1 \text{ sophomore})$. According to the table, the probability of 1 sophomore being chosen is $\frac{9}{20}$.

60. Selecting 1 junior out of 3 students means that 2 sophomores are selected. Thus, $P(1\text{ junior})$ $= P(2\text{ sophomores})$. According to the table, the probability of 2 sophomores being chosen is $\frac{9}{20}$.

61. There are $P(5, 5)$ or 120 ways in which the 5 entries can be ordered. Only one of these orders is a success, so $s = 1$. The other 119 orders are failures, so $f = 119$.

$$P(\text{alphabetical order}) = \frac{s}{s+f}$$
$$= \frac{1}{1+119}$$
$$= \frac{1}{120}$$

The probability that the entries are in alphabetical order is $\frac{1}{120}$.

62. Step 1 Determine the area of the shaded region.

Area of the circle	minus	the area of the triangle.
$\pi(4)^2$	$-$	$\frac{1}{2}(8)(4)$

Find the area of the shaded region.
$$\pi(4)^2 - \frac{1}{2}(8)(4) = 16\pi - 4(4)$$
$$= 16\pi - 16$$

Step 2 Find the total area, $s + f$, of the circle.
$$\pi(4)^2 = \pi(16)$$
$$= 16\pi$$

Step 3 Determine the probability.
$$P(\text{in the shaded region}) = \frac{s}{s+f}$$
$$= \frac{16\pi - 16}{16\pi}$$
$$= \frac{16(\pi - 1)}{16\pi}$$
$$= \frac{\pi - 1}{\pi}$$

The probability a point chosen at random in the figure is in the shaded region is $\frac{\pi - 1}{\pi}$ or about 68%.

63. Probability and odds are good tools for assessing risk. Answers should include the following.

- $P(\text{struck by lightning}) = \frac{s}{s+f} = \frac{1}{750,000}$, so Odds $= 1:(750,000 - 1)$ or $1:749,999$.

  $P(\text{surviving a lightning strike}) = \frac{s}{s+f} = \frac{3}{4}$, so Odds $= 3:(4 - 3)$ or $3:1$.

- In this case, success is being struck by lightning or surviving the lightning strike. Failure is not being struck by lightning or not surviving the lightning strike.

64. C; $\frac{6!}{2!} = \frac{6 \cdot 5 \cdot 4 \cdot 3 \cdot 2!}{2!}$
$$= 6 \cdot 5 \cdot 4 \cdot 3$$
$$= 360$$

65. D; There are $4 + 3 + 2$ or 9 possible outcomes. Only $4 + 2$ or 6 of these outcomes are successes, so $s = 6$. The other 3 are failures, so $f = 3$.

$$P(\text{not green}) = \frac{s}{s+f}$$
$$= \frac{6}{6+3}$$
$$= \frac{6}{9}$$

$$= \frac{2}{3}$$

66. Since mathematical methods and assumptions about the fairness of the dice will be used, this probability is theoretical. There are $6 \cdot 6$ or 36 possible outcomes. Only one of these outcomes is a success, so $s = 1$. The other 35 outcomes are failures, so $f = 35$.

$$P(12) = \frac{s}{s+f}$$
$$= \frac{1}{1+35}$$
$$= \frac{1}{36}$$

The probability the sum will be 12 is $\frac{1}{36}$.

67. Since an experiment was repeatedly performed and the outcomes will be used, this probability is experimental. There were 410 total outcomes. Only 126 of these outcomes are successes, so $s = 126$. The other 284 outcomes are failures, so $f = 284$.

$$P(\text{hit}) = \frac{s}{s+f}$$
$$= \frac{126}{126 + 284}$$
$$= \frac{126}{410}$$
$$= \frac{63}{205}$$

The probability he gets a hit in his next at-bat is $\frac{63}{205}$ or about 0.307.

68. Since an experiment was performed and the outcome will be used, this probability is experimental. There were 25 possible outcomes. Only 5 of these outcomes are successes, so $s = 5$. The other 20 outcomes are failures, so $f = 20$.

$$P(\text{red}) = \frac{s}{s+f}$$
$$= \frac{5}{5 + 20}$$
$$= \frac{5}{25}$$
$$= \frac{1}{5}$$

The probability that the next bird is red is $\frac{1}{5}$.

69. Since mathematical methods and assumptions about the fairness of the deck of cards will be used, this probability is theoretical. There are $C(52, 2)$ or 1326 possible outcomes. Only $C(13, 2)$ or 78 of these outcomes are successes, so $s = 78$. The other 1248 outcomes are failures, so $f = 1248$.

$$P(2\text{ clubs}) = \frac{s}{s+f}$$
$$= \frac{78}{78 + 1248}$$
$$= \frac{78}{1326}$$
$$= \frac{1}{17}$$

The probability that both cards are clubs is $\frac{1}{17}$.

70. Since each book is in a different position on the shelf, order is important. Find the number of permutations of 5 things taken 5 at a time.

$$P(5, 5) = \frac{5!}{(5-5)!}$$
$$= \frac{5!}{0!}$$
$$= \frac{5 \cdot 4 \cdot 3 \cdot 2 \cdot 1}{1}$$
$$= 120$$

There are 120 ways to arrange the books.

71. Since each letter is in a different position in each arrangement, order is important. Find the number of permutations of 7 things of which 3 are different, 2 are alike, and 2 others are alike.

$$P(7, 7) = \frac{7!}{2!2!}$$
$$= \frac{7 \cdot 6 \cdot 5 \cdot 4 \cdot 3 \cdot 2!}{2! \, 2!}$$
$$= 1260$$

There are 1260 ways to arrange the letters.

72. Since the order in which the apples are chosen is not important, find the number of combinations of 7 apples taken 3 at a time.

$$C(7, 3) = \frac{7!}{(7-3)!3!}$$
$$= \frac{7!}{4!3!}$$
$$= 35$$

There are 35 ways to choose the 3 apples.

73. The choice of each computer component does not affect the other two choices, so the choices of the computer components are independent events. There are 4 possible choices of memory, 2 possible choices of hard drives, and 2 possible choices of monitors. So, there are $4 \cdot 2 \cdot 2$ or 16 possible systems.

74. When a gift is placed in a gift bag, that gift is not considered in the choice for the other gift bags. Therefore, the choices of which gift to place in which gift bag are dependent events. There are 4 gifts to pick from for the first gift bag. That leaves 3 gifts to pick from for the second gift bag. After the first two gifts are chosen, there are 2 remaining gifts to pick from for the third gift bag, and so on. There are $4 \cdot 3 \cdot 2 \cdot 1$ or 24 ways to place the gifts in the gift bags.

75. The graph appears to be a direct variation since it is a straight line passing through the origin.

76. The graph has a starting point and curves in one direction. The graph represents a square root function.

77. Since the matrices are equal, the corresponding elements are equal.

$$x = y$$
$$y = 4$$

To find the value for x, substitute 4 for y in the first equation.

$$x = y$$
$$x = 4$$

The solution is (4, 4).

78. Since the matrices are equal, the corresponding elements are equal.

$$3y = x + 8$$
$$2x = y - x$$

This system can be solved using substitution. Solve the second equation for y.

$$2x = y - x$$
$$3x = y$$

Substitute $3x$ for y in the first equation.

$$3y = x + 8$$
$$3(3x) = x + 8$$
$$9x = x + 8$$
$$8x = 8$$
$$x = 1$$

Substitute 1 for x in either equation and solve for y.

$$3y = x + 8$$
$$3y = 1 + 8$$
$$3y = 9$$
$$y = 3$$

The solution is (1, 3).

79. $ab = \left(\frac{3}{5}\right)\left(\frac{2}{7}\right)$
$= \frac{6}{35}$

80. $bc = \left(\frac{2}{7}\right)\left(\frac{3}{4}\right)$
$= \frac{6}{28}$
$= \frac{3}{14}$

81. $cd = \left(\frac{3}{4}\right)\left(\frac{1}{3}\right)$
$= \frac{3}{12}$
$= \frac{1}{4}$

82. $bd = \left(\frac{2}{7}\right)\left(\frac{1}{3}\right)$
$= \frac{2}{21}$

83. $ac = \left(\frac{3}{5}\right)\left(\frac{3}{4}\right)$
$= \frac{9}{20}$

Page 650   Practice Quiz 1

1. The choice of each topping or cooking duration does not affect the other three choices, so the choices of what to have on your hamburger and how to cook it are independent events. There are 2 possible choices of cheese, 2 possible choices of onions, 2 possible choices of pickles, and 3 possible choices of cooking duration. So, there are $2 \cdot 2 \cdot 2 \cdot 3$ or 24 ways to order your hamburger.

2. The choice of each option for the model of car does not affect the other three choices, so the choices of what options to include are independent events. There are 3 possible engines, 2 possible stereos, 18 possible body colors, and 7 possible upholstery colors. So, there are $3 \cdot 2 \cdot 18 \cdot 7$ or 756 possibilities available for that model.

3. When a digit is chosen it cannot be used again. Therefore, the choices of the three digits are dependent events. There are 26 choices for the letter, and 10 choices for the first of the three digits. That leaves 9 choices for the second digit and 8 choices for the third digit. There are $26 \cdot 10 \cdot 9 \cdot 8$ or 18,720 codes that are possible.

4. $P(12, 3) = \frac{12!}{(12-3)!}$

$= \frac{12!}{9!}$

$= \frac{12 \cdot 11 \cdot 10 \cdot 9!}{9!}$

$= 12 \cdot 11 \cdot 10$

$= 1320$

5. $C(8, 3) = \frac{8!}{(8-3)!\,3!}$

$= \frac{8!}{5!\,3!}$

$= 56$

6. Since each car is in a different position next to the curb, order is important. Find the number of permutations of 8 things taken 8 at a time.

$P(8, 8) = \frac{8!}{(8-8)!}$

$= \frac{8!}{0!}$

$= \frac{8 \cdot 7 \cdot 6 \cdot 5 \cdot 4 \cdot 3 \cdot 2 \cdot 1}{1}$

$= 40{,}320$

There are 40,320 ways to park the cars.

7. Since the order in which the cards are chosen is not important, find the number of combinations of 52 cards taken 6 at a time.

$C(52, 6) = \frac{52!}{(52-6)!\,6!}$

$= \frac{52!}{46!\,6!}$

$= 20{,}358{,}520$

There are 20,358,520 possible 6-card hands.

8. Step 1 Determine how many 2-card selections meet the conditions.

$C(4, 2)$ Select two aces.

Step 2 Find the number of successes.

$C(4, 2) = \frac{4!}{(4-2)!\,2!}$

$= \frac{4!}{2!\,2!}$

$= 6$

Step 3 Find the total number, $s + f$, of possible 2-card selections.

$C(52, 2) = \frac{52!}{(52-2)!\,2!}$

$= \frac{52!}{50!\,2!}$

$= 1326$

Step 4 Determine the probability.

$P(2 \text{ aces}) = \frac{s}{s+f}$

$= \frac{6}{1326}$

$= \frac{1}{221}$

The probability of selecting 2 aces is about $\frac{1}{221}$.

9. Step 1 Determine how many 2-card selections meet the conditions.

$C(13, 1)$ Select one heart.

$C(13, 1)$ Select one club.

Step 2 Find the number of successes.

$C(13, 1) \cdot C(13, 1) = \frac{13!}{(13-1)!\,1!} \cdot \frac{13!}{(13-1)!\,1!}$

$= \frac{13!}{12!\,1!} \cdot \frac{13!}{12!\,1!}$

$= 13 \cdot 13$

$= 169$

Step 3 Find the total number, $s + f$, of possible 2-card selections.

$C(52, 2) = \frac{52!}{(52-2)!\,2!}$

$= \frac{52!}{50!\,2!}$

$= 1326$

Step 4 Determine the probability.

$P(1 \text{ heart}, 1 \text{ club}) = \frac{s}{s+f}$

$= \frac{169}{1326}$

$= \frac{13}{102}$

The probability of selecting 1 heart and 1 club is $\frac{13}{102}$.

10. Step 1 Determine how many 2-card selections meet the conditions.

$C(4, 1)$ Select one queen.

$C(4, 1)$ Select one king.

Step 2 Find the number of successes.

$C(4, 1) \cdot C(4, 1) = \frac{4!}{(4-1)!\,1!} \cdot \frac{4!}{(4-1)!\,1!}$

$= \frac{4!}{3!\,1!} \cdot \frac{4!}{3!\,1!}$

$= 4 \cdot 4$

$= 16$

Step 3 Find the total number, $s + f$, of possible 2-card selections.

$C(52, 2) = \frac{52!}{(52-2)!\,2!}$

$= \frac{52!}{50!\,2!}$

$= 1326$

Step 4 Determine the probability.

$P(1 \text{ queen}, 1 \text{ king}) = \frac{s}{s+f}$

$= \frac{16}{1326}$

$= \frac{8}{663}$

The probability of selecting 1 queen and 1 king is $\frac{8}{663}$.

12-4   Multiplying Probabilities

Page 651   Algebra Activity

1. The area of rectangle A is $\left(\frac{2}{3}\right)\left(\frac{3}{4}\right)$ or $\frac{1}{2}$; it represents the probability of drawing a silver clip and a blue clip. The area of rectangle B is $\left(\frac{2}{3}\right)\left(\frac{1}{4}\right)$ or $\frac{1}{6}$; it represents the probability of drawing a silver clip and a red clip. The area of rectangle C is $\left(\frac{1}{3}\right)\left(\frac{3}{4}\right)$ or $\frac{1}{4}$; it represents the probability of drawing a gold clip and a blue clip. The area of rectangle D is $\left(\frac{1}{3}\right)\left(\frac{1}{4}\right)$ or $\frac{1}{12}$; it represents the probability of drawing a gold clip and a red clip.

2. From the area diagram the probability of choosing a red clip and a silver clip would be the area of rectangle B which is $\left(\frac{2}{3}\right)\left(\frac{1}{4}\right)$ or $\frac{1}{6}$.

3. The length of the whole square is $\frac{3}{4} + \frac{1}{4} = 1$. The width of the whole square is $\frac{2}{3} + \frac{1}{3} = 1$. Thus, the area of the whole square is $1 \cdot 1 = 1$. The area of the whole square represents the sum of the probabilities, and the sum of the probabilities must be 1.

4. Draw a rectangle made up of six smaller rectangles and label as shown.

Spinner 2

	blue $\frac{3}{4}$	red $\frac{1}{4}$
green $\frac{1}{2}$	A	B
yellow $\frac{1}{3}$	C	D
purple $\frac{1}{6}$	E	F

Spinner 1

The area of rectangle A represents the probability of spinning green and blue. The area of rectangle B represents the probability of spinning green and red. The area of rectangle C represents the probability of spinning yellow and blue. The area of rectangle D represents the probability of spinning yellow and red. The area of rectangle E represents the probability of spinning purple and blue. The area of rectangle F represents the probability of spinning purple and red.

Pages 654–655   Check for Understanding

1. Sample answer: putting on your socks and then your shoes

2. Since A, B, C, and D are all independent, we know that $P(A, B, C,$ and $D) = P(A) \cdot P(B) \cdot P(C) \cdot P(D)$.

3. Mario; the probabilities of rolling a 4 and rolling a 2 are both $\frac{1}{6}$.

4. $P(5, \text{ then } 1) = P(5) \cdot P(1)$
$$= \frac{1}{6} \cdot \frac{1}{6}$$
$$= \frac{1}{36}$$

The probability is $\frac{1}{36}$ or about 0.028.

5. $P(\text{two even numbers})$
$= P(\text{an even number}) \cdot P(\text{an even number})$
$$= \frac{3}{6} \cdot \frac{3}{6}$$
$$= \frac{9}{36}$$
$$= \frac{1}{4}$$

The probability is $\frac{1}{4}$ or 0.25.

6. $P(\text{two hearts})$
$= P(\text{a heart}) \cdot P(\text{a heart following a heart})$
$$= \frac{13}{52} \cdot \frac{12}{51}$$
$$= \frac{156}{2652}$$
$$= \frac{1}{17}$$

The probability is $\frac{1}{17}$ or about 0.059.

7. $P(\text{ace, then king})$
$= P(\text{ace}) \cdot P(\text{king following an ace})$
$$= \frac{4}{52} \cdot \frac{4}{51}$$
$$= \frac{16}{2652}$$
$$= \frac{4}{663}$$

The probability is $\frac{4}{663}$ or about 0.006.

8. $P(\text{2 action DVDs})$
$= P(\text{action DVD})$
$\quad \cdot P(\text{action DVD following action DVD})$
$$= \frac{8}{16} \cdot \frac{7}{15}$$
$$= \frac{56}{240}$$
$$= \frac{7}{30}$$

The probability is $\frac{7}{30}$ or about 0.233.

9. $P(\text{2 action DVDs}) = P(\text{action DVD}) \cdot P(\text{action DVD})$
$$= \frac{8}{16} \cdot \frac{8}{16}$$
$$= \frac{64}{256}$$
$$= \frac{1}{4}$$

The probability is $\frac{1}{4}$ or about 0.25.

10. $P(\text{romantic DVD, then children's DVD})$
$= P(\text{romantic DVD})$
$\quad \cdot P(\text{Children's DVD following romantic DVD})$
$$= \frac{3}{16} \cdot \frac{5}{15}$$
$$= \frac{15}{240}$$
$$= \frac{1}{16}$$

The probability is $\frac{1}{16}$ or about 0.063.

11. Because the pens are not replaced, the events are dependent.

$P(\text{Blue, Black, Blue})$
$= P(\text{Blue}) \cdot P(\text{Black following Blue})$
$\quad \cdot P(\text{Blue following Blue and Black})$
$$= \frac{7}{12} \cdot \frac{3}{11} \cdot \frac{6}{10}$$
$$= \frac{126}{1320}$$
$$= \frac{21}{220}$$

The probability is $\frac{21}{220}$ or about 0.096.

12. These events are independent since the number rolled on one die does not affect the number rolled on the other die.

P(3 on black, 5 on white)

$\quad = P$(3 on black) $\cdot$ P(5 on white)

$\quad = \frac{1}{6} \cdot \frac{1}{6}$

$\quad = \frac{1}{36}$

The probability is $\frac{1}{36}$ or about 0.028.

13. Because the first name chosen is not replaced, the events are dependent.

P(Malik, then Sonia)

$\quad = P$(Malik) $\cdot$ P(Sonia following Malik)

$\quad = \frac{1}{4} \cdot \frac{1}{3}$

$\quad = \frac{1}{12}$

The probability is $\frac{1}{12}$ or about 0.083.

Pages 655–657 Practice and Apply

14. P(2, then 3) $= P(2) \cdot P(3)$

$\quad = \frac{1}{6} \cdot \frac{1}{6}$

$\quad = \frac{1}{36}$

The probability is $\frac{1}{36}$ or about 0.028.

15. P(no 6s) $= P$(no 6) $\cdot$ P(no 6)

$\quad = \frac{5}{6} \cdot \frac{5}{6}$

$\quad = \frac{25}{36}$

The probability is $\frac{25}{36}$ or about 0.694.

16. P(two 4s) $= P(4) \cdot P(4)$

$\quad = \frac{1}{6} \cdot \frac{1}{6}$

$\quad = \frac{1}{36}$

The probability is $\frac{1}{36}$ or about 0.028.

17. P(1, then any number) $= P(1) \cdot P$(any number)

$\quad = \frac{1}{6} \cdot \frac{6}{6}$

$\quad = \frac{1}{6}$

The probability is $\frac{1}{6}$ or about 0.167.

18. P(two of the same number)

$\quad = P$(any number) $\cdot$ P(same number)

$\quad = \frac{6}{6} \cdot \frac{1}{6}$

$\quad = \frac{1}{6}$

The probability is $\frac{1}{6}$ or about 0.167.

19. P(two different numbers)

$\quad = P$(any number) $\cdot$ P(a different number)

$\quad = \frac{6}{6} \cdot \frac{5}{6}$

$\quad = \frac{5}{6}$

The probability is $\frac{5}{6}$ or about 0.833.

20. $P(R$, then $S) = P(R) \cdot P(S$ following $R)$

$\quad = \frac{1}{7} \cdot \frac{1}{6}$

$\quad = \frac{1}{42}$

The probability is $\frac{1}{42}$ or about 0.024.

21. $P(A$, then $M) = P(A) \cdot P(M)$

$\quad = \frac{1}{7} \cdot \frac{1}{7}$

$\quad = \frac{1}{49}$

The probability is $\frac{1}{49}$ or about 0.020.

22. P(2 consonants) $= P$(consonant) $\cdot$ P(consonant)

$\quad = \frac{5}{7} \cdot \frac{5}{7}$

$\quad = \frac{25}{49}$

The probability is $\frac{25}{49}$ or about 0.510.

23. P(2 consonants)

$\quad = P$(consonant) $\cdot$ P(consonant following consonant)

$\quad = \frac{5}{7} \cdot \frac{4}{6}$

$\quad = \frac{20}{42}$

$\quad = \frac{10}{21}$

The probability is $\frac{10}{21}$ or about 0.476.

24. $P(B$, then $D) = P(B) \cdot P(D)$

$\quad = \frac{1}{7} \cdot \frac{0}{6}$

$\quad = 0$

The probability is 0.

25. P(same letter twice)

$\quad = P$(any letter) $\cdot$ P(same letter following the letter)

$\quad = \frac{7}{7} \cdot \frac{0}{6}$

$\quad = 0$

The probability is 0.

26. P(2 vases) $= P$(vase) $\cdot$ P(vase following vase)

$\quad = \frac{3}{10} \cdot \frac{2}{9}$

$\quad = \frac{6}{90}$

$\quad = \frac{1}{15}$

The probability is $\frac{1}{15}$ or about 0.067.

27. P(2 statues)

$\quad = P$(statue) $\cdot$ P(statue following statue)

$\quad = \frac{4}{10} \cdot \frac{3}{9}$

$\quad = \frac{12}{90}$

$\quad = \frac{2}{15}$

The probability is $\frac{2}{15}$ or about 0.133.

28. P(frame, then vase)

$\quad = P$(frame) $\cdot$ P(vase following frame)

$\quad = \frac{3}{10} \cdot \frac{3}{9}$

$\quad = \frac{9}{90}$

$\quad = \frac{1}{10}$

The probability is $\frac{1}{10}$ or 0.1.

29. P(statue, frame)

$= P$(statue) $\cdot$ P(frame following statue)

$= \frac{4}{10} \cdot \frac{3}{9}$

$= \frac{12}{90}$

$= \frac{2}{15}$

The probability is $\frac{2}{15}$ or about 0.133.

30. Because the 2 candies are chosen together, there is no replacement. The events are dependent.

P(2 chocolate bars)

$= P$(chocolate bar)

$\cdot$ P(chocolate bar following chocolate bar)

$= \frac{3}{8} \cdot \frac{2}{7}$

$= \frac{6}{56}$

$= \frac{3}{28}$

The probability is $\frac{3}{28}$ or about 0.107.

31. The events are independent since Maxine replaced the first piece of fruit that she removed.

P(2 apricots) $= P$(apricot) $\cdot$ P(apricot)

$= \frac{5}{9} \cdot \frac{5}{9}$

$= \frac{25}{81}$

The probability is $\frac{25}{81}$ or about 0.309.

32. The events are independent since replacement occurs each time.

P(Blue, Yellow, Red)

$= P$(Blue) $\cdot$ P(Yellow) $\cdot$ P(Red)

$= \frac{4}{17} \cdot \frac{6}{17} \cdot \frac{7}{17}$

$= \frac{168}{4913}$

The probability is $\frac{168}{4913}$ or about 0.034.

33. Because the bills are not replaced, the events are dependent.

P($10, $5, $1)

$= P$($10) $\cdot$ P($5 following $10)

$\cdot$ P($1 following $10 and $5)

$= \frac{2}{9} \cdot \frac{4}{8} \cdot \frac{3}{7}$

$= \frac{24}{504}$

$= \frac{1}{21}$

The probability is $\frac{1}{21}$ or about 0.048.

34. These events are independent since the outcome of any toss does not affect the outcomes of the other four tosses.

$P(H, H, H, H, H)$

$= P(H) \cdot P(H) \cdot P(H) \cdot P(H) \cdot P(H)$

$= \frac{1}{2} \cdot \frac{1}{2} \cdot \frac{1}{2} \cdot \frac{1}{2} \cdot \frac{1}{2}$

$= \frac{1}{32}$

The probability is $\frac{1}{32}$ or about 0.031.

35. Find the probability that Diego reaches the highest level.

odds $= 3:4$

$= s:f$ $s = 3, f = 4$

P(highest level) $= \frac{s}{s+f}$

$= \frac{3}{3+4}$

$= \frac{3}{7}$

The events are independent since reaching the highest level during one game does not affect reaching the highest level during a different game.

P(highest level next four times)

$= P$(highest level) $\cdot$ P(highest level)

$\cdot$ P(highest level) $\cdot$ P(highest level)

$= \frac{3}{7} \cdot \frac{3}{7} \cdot \frac{3}{7} \cdot \frac{3}{7}$

$= \frac{81}{2401}$

The probability is $\frac{81}{2401}$ or about 0.034.

36. Let R stand for red, B stand for blue, and Y stand for yellow.

$P(R$, then $B) = P(R) \cdot P(B)$

$= \frac{1}{3} \cdot \frac{1}{3}$

$= \frac{1}{9}$

The probability is $\frac{1}{9}$.

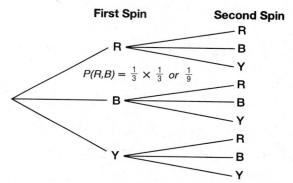

37. Draw a square made up of nine smaller squares and label as shown.

		First Spin	
		blue $\frac{1}{3}$	yellow $\frac{1}{3}$	red $\frac{1}{3}$
Second Spin	blue $\frac{1}{3}$	BB $\frac{1}{9}$	BY $\frac{1}{9}$	BR $\frac{1}{9}$
	yellow $\frac{1}{3}$	YB $\frac{1}{9}$	YY $\frac{1}{9}$	YR $\frac{1}{9}$
	red $\frac{1}{3}$	RB $\frac{1}{9}$	RY $\frac{1}{9}$	RR $\frac{1}{9}$

38. P(same color on both spins)

= P(any color) $\cdot$ P(same color)

= $\frac{3}{3} \cdot \frac{1}{3}$

= $\frac{1}{3}$

The probability of getting the same color is $\frac{1}{3}$.

39. P(red on both spins) = P(red) $\cdot$ P(red)

= $\frac{1}{3} \cdot \frac{1}{3}$

= $\frac{1}{9}$

The probability of getting red both spins is $\frac{1}{9}$.

40. P(all clubs)

= P(club) $\cdot$ P(club following club)

$\cdot$ P(club following 2 clubs)

$\cdot$ P(club following 3 clubs)

$\cdot$ P(club following 4 clubs)

$\cdot$ P(club following 5 clubs)

$\cdot$ P(club following 6 clubs)

$\cdot$ P(club following 7 clubs)

$\cdot$ P(club following 8 clubs)

$\cdot$ P(club following 9 clubs)

$\cdot$ P(club following 10 clubs)

$\cdot$ P(club following 11 clubs)

$\cdot$ P(club following 12 clubs)

= $\frac{13}{52} \cdot \frac{12}{51} \cdot \frac{11}{50} \cdot \frac{10}{49} \cdot \frac{9}{48} \cdot \frac{8}{47} \cdot \frac{7}{46} \cdot \frac{6}{45} \cdot \frac{5}{44} \cdot$

$\frac{4}{43} \cdot \frac{3}{42} \cdot \frac{2}{41} \cdot \frac{1}{40}$

= $\frac{6,227,020,800}{3,954,242,643,911,239,680,000}$

= $\frac{1}{635,013,559,600}$

The probability of drawing all clubs is

$\frac{1}{635,013,559,600}$.

41. P(all black cards)

= P(black) $\cdot$ P(black following black) $\cdot$ ...

$\cdot$ P(black following 12 blacks)

= $\frac{26}{52} \cdot \frac{25}{51} \cdot \frac{24}{50} \cdot \frac{23}{49} \cdot \frac{22}{48} \cdot \frac{21}{47} \cdot \frac{20}{46} \cdot \frac{19}{45} \cdot \frac{18}{44} \cdot$

$\frac{17}{43} \cdot \frac{16}{42} \cdot \frac{15}{41} \cdot \frac{14}{40}$

= $\frac{64,764,752,532,480,000}{3,954,242,643,911,239,680,000}$

= $\frac{19}{1,160,054}$

The probability of drawing all black cards is

$\frac{19}{1,160,054}$.

42. P(all one suit)

= P(any suit) $\cdot$ P(same suit following the suit)

$\cdot$ ... $\cdot$ P(same suit following 12 of the suit)

= $\frac{4}{4} \cdot \frac{12}{51} \cdot \frac{11}{50} \cdot \frac{10}{49} \cdot \frac{9}{48} \cdot \frac{8}{47} \cdot \frac{7}{46} \cdot \frac{6}{45} \cdot \frac{5}{44} \cdot$

$\frac{4}{43} \cdot \frac{3}{42} \cdot \frac{2}{41} \cdot \frac{1}{40}$

= $\frac{1,916,006,400}{304,172,511,070,095,360,000}$

= $\frac{1}{158,753,389,900}$

The probability of drawing all cards of the same

suit is $\frac{1}{158,753,389,900}$.

43. P(no aces)

= P(no ace) $\cdot$ P(no ace following no ace)

$\cdot$ ... $\cdot$ P(no ace following 12 no aces)

= $\frac{48}{52} \cdot \frac{47}{51} \cdot \frac{46}{50} \cdot \frac{45}{49} \cdot \frac{44}{48} \cdot \frac{43}{47} \cdot \frac{42}{46} \cdot \frac{41}{45} \cdot \frac{40}{44} \cdot$

$\frac{39}{43} \cdot \frac{38}{42} \cdot \frac{37}{41} \cdot \frac{36}{40}$

= $\frac{6327}{20,825}$

The probability of drawing no aces is $\frac{6327}{20,825}$.

44. Since the probability of failure for any one pump

is $\frac{1}{100}$, a pump will fail 1 out of every 100 uses.

Thus, the pump does not fail 99 out of every 100 uses. The probability of no failure for any one

pump is $\frac{99}{100}$.

P(no failure through 4 pumps)

= P(no failure) $\cdot$ P(no failure) $\cdot$ P(no failure)

$\cdot$ P(no failure)

= $\frac{99}{100} \cdot \frac{99}{100} \cdot \frac{99}{100} \cdot \frac{99}{100}$

= $\frac{96,059,601}{100,000,000}$

≈ 0.96

The probability is $\frac{96,059,601}{100,000,000}$ or about 0.96.

45. Since the probability of spelling any given word correctly is 93%, the contestant spells 93 out of 100 words correctly. Thus, the contestant spells 7 out of 100 words incorrectly. The probability the

contestant will misspell any given word is $\frac{7}{100}$

or 7%.

P(5 words spelled correctly, then 1 word spelled incorrectly)

= P(spelled correctly) $\cdot$ P(spelled correctly)

$\cdot$ P(spelled correctly) $\cdot$ P(spelled correctly)

$\cdot$ P(spelled correctly) $\cdot$ P(misspelled)

= $\frac{93}{100} \cdot \frac{93}{100} \cdot \frac{93}{100} \cdot \frac{93}{100} \cdot \frac{93}{100} \cdot \frac{7}{100}$

= $\frac{48,698,185,851}{1,000,000,000,000}$

≈ 0.0487

The probability is $\frac{48,698,185,851}{1,000,000,000,000}$ or about 4.87%.

46. P(3 correct hats)

= P(1 correct hat)

$\cdot$ P(1 correct hat following 1 correct hat)

$\cdot$ P(1 correct hat following 2 correct hats)

= $\frac{1}{12} \cdot \frac{1}{11} \cdot \frac{1}{10}$

= $\frac{1}{1320}$

The probability of the first three men choosing

their own hats is $\frac{1}{1320}$.

47. No, going through the cycle 10 times does not mean that you have drawn 10 different marbles.

48. No, going through the cycle 50 times does not mean that you have drawn each of the 10 marbles.

49. Sample answer: As the number of trials increases, the results become more reliable. However, you cannot be absolutely certain that there are no black marbles in the bag without looking at all of the marbles.

50. $P(1 \text{ bulb works}) = 99.5\%$ or $\frac{995}{1000}$.

$P(2 \text{ bulbs work})$
$= P(1 \text{ bulb works}) \cdot P(1 \text{ bulb works})$
$= \frac{995}{1000} \cdot \frac{995}{1000}$
$= \left(\frac{995}{1000}\right)^2$

$P(3 \text{ bulbs work})$
$= P(1 \text{ bulb works}) \cdot P(1 \text{ bulb works})$
$\quad \cdot P(1 \text{ bulb works})$
$= \frac{995}{1000} \cdot \frac{995}{1000} \cdot \frac{995}{1000}$
$= \left(\frac{995}{1000}\right)^3$

Likewise,

$P(n \text{ bulbs work}) = \left(\frac{995}{1000}\right)^n$.

Find the largest n such that $\left(\frac{995}{1000}\right)^n \geq 0.90$.

$\left(\frac{995}{1000}\right)^n \geq 0.90$

$\log\left(\frac{995}{1000}\right)^n \geq \log(0.90)$

$n \log\left(\frac{995}{1000}\right) \geq \log(0.90)$

$n \leq \frac{\log(0.90)}{\log\left(\frac{995}{1000}\right)}$

$n \leq 21.01938$

Therefore, the maximum number of lights is 21.

51. Probability can be used to analyze the chances of a player making 0, 1, or 2 free throws when he or she goes to the foul line to shoot 2 free throws. Answers should include the following.

- One of the decimals in the table could be used as the value of p, the probability that a player makes a given free throw. The probability that a player misses both free throws is $(1 - p)(1 - p)$ or $(1 - p)^2$. The probability that a player makes both free throws is pp or p^2. Since the sum of the probabilities of all the possible outcomes is 1, the probability that a player makes exactly 1 of the 2 free throws is $1 - (1 - p)^2 - p^2$ or $2p(1 - p)$.

- The result of the first free throw could affect the player's confidence on the second free throw. For example, if the player makes the first free throw, the probability of he or she making the second free throw might increase. Or, if the player misses the first free throw, the probability that he or she makes the second free throw might decrease.

52. D; $P(2, 2, 2, 2) = P(2) \cdot P(2) \cdot P(2) \cdot P(2)$
$= \frac{1}{4} \cdot \frac{1}{4} \cdot \frac{1}{4} \cdot \frac{1}{4}$
$= \frac{1}{256}$

The probability is $\frac{1}{256}$.

53. C; $P(\text{head}, 3) = P(\text{head}) \cdot P(3)$
$= \frac{1}{2} \cdot \frac{1}{6}$
$= \frac{1}{12}$

The probability is $\frac{1}{12}$.

Page 657   Maintain Your Skills

54. Step 1 Determine how many 3-gumball selections meet the conditions.

$C(7, 3)$ Select 3 of the red gumballs.

Step 2 Find the number of successes.

$C(7, 3) = \frac{7!}{(7 - 3)! \, 3!}$
$= \frac{7!}{4! \, 3!}$
$= 35$

Step 3 Find the total number, $s + f$, of possible 3-gumball selections.

$C(36, 3) = \frac{36!}{(36 - 3)! \, 3!}$
$= \frac{36!}{33! \, 3!}$
$= 7140$

Step 4 Determine the probability.

$P(3 \text{ red}) = \frac{s}{s + f}$
$= \frac{35}{7140}$
$= \frac{1}{204}$

The probability of buying 3 red gumballs is $\frac{1}{204}$.

55. Step 1 Determine how many 3-gumball selections meet the conditions.

$C(7, 2)$ Select two of the white gumballs.
$C(9, 1)$ Select one of the purple gumballs.

Step 2 Find the number of successes.

$C(7, 2) \cdot C(9, 1) = \frac{7!}{(7 - 2)! \, 2!} \cdot \frac{9!}{(9 - 1)! \, 1!}$
$= \frac{7!}{5! \, 2!} \cdot \frac{9!}{8! \, 1!}$
$= 21 \cdot 9$
$= 189$

Step 3 Find the total number, $s + f$, of possible 3-gumball selections.

$C(36, 3) = \frac{36!}{(36 - 3)! \, 3!}$
$= \frac{36!}{33! \, 3!}$
$= 7140$

Step 4 Determine the probability.

$P(2 \text{ white}, 1 \text{ purple}) = \frac{s}{s + f}$
$= \frac{189}{7140}$
$= \frac{9}{340}$

The probability of buying 2 white gumballs and 1 purple gumball is $\frac{9}{340}$.

56. Step 1 Determine how many 3-gumball selections meet the conditions.

$C(9, 1)$ Select one of the purple gumballs.

$C(8, 1)$ Select one of the orange gumballs.

$C(5, 1)$ Select one of the yellow gumballs.

Step 2 Find the number of successes.

$$C(9, 1) \cdot C(8, 1) \cdot C(5, 1)$$
$$= \frac{9!}{(9-1)!1!} \cdot \frac{8!}{(8-1)!1!} \cdot \frac{5!}{(5-1)!1!}$$
$$= \frac{9!}{8!1!} \cdot \frac{8!}{7!1!} \cdot \frac{5!}{4!1!}$$
$$= 9 \cdot 8 \cdot 5$$
$$= 360$$

Step 3 Find the total number, $s + f$, of possible 3-gumball selections.

$$C(36, 3) = \frac{36!}{(36-3)!3!}$$
$$= \frac{36!}{33!3!}$$
$$= 7140$$

Step 4 Determine the probability.

$$P(1 \text{ purple}, 1 \text{ orange}, 1 \text{ yellow}) = \frac{s}{s+f}$$
$$= \frac{360}{7140}$$
$$= \frac{6}{119}$$

The probability of buying 1 purple gumball, 1 orange gumball, and 1 yellow gumball is $\frac{6}{119}$.

57. The number of arrangements of the 8 people in a row with the restriction of the bride and groom in the 2 middle spots is equal to the number of arrangements of the bride and groom in the 2 middle spots times the number of arrangements of the other 6 people in the other 6 spots. Since each person is in a different location in each arrangement, order is important. Find the number of permutations of 2 things taken 2 at a time times the number of permutations of 6 things taken 6 at a time.

$$P(2, 2) \cdot P(6, 6) = \frac{2!}{(2-2)!} \cdot \frac{6!}{(6-6)!}$$
$$= 2! \cdot 6!$$
$$= 1440$$

There are 1440 possible arrangements of the 8 people in a row.

58.
$$\log_5 5 + \log_5 x = \log_5 30$$
$$\log_5 5x = \log_5 30$$
$$5x = 30$$
$$x = 6$$

The solution is 6.

59.
$$\log_{16} c - 2\log_{16} 3 = \log_{16} 4$$
$$\log_{16} c - \log_{16} 9 = \log_{16} 4$$
$$\log_{16} \frac{c}{9} = \log_{16} 4$$
$$\frac{c}{9} = 4$$
$$c = 36$$

The solution is 36.

60. Use synthetic division.

$$\begin{array}{r|rrrr} -3 & 1 & -1 & -10 & 6 \\ & & -3 & 12 & -6 \\ \hline & 1 & -4 & 2 & 0 \end{array}$$

The polynomial $x^3 - x^2 - 10x + 6$ can be factored as $(x + 3)(x^2 - 4x + 2)$. The depressed polynomial $x^2 - 4x + 2$ is prime.

So, $x^3 - x^2 - 10x + 6 = (x + 3)(x^2 - 4x + 2)$, and $x^2 - 4x + 2$ is the remaining factor.

61. Use synthetic division.

$$\begin{array}{r|rrrr} 3 & 1 & -7 & 12 & 0 \\ & & 3 & -12 & 0 \\ \hline & 1 & -4 & 0 & 0 \end{array}$$

The polynomial $x^3 - 7x^2 + 12x$ can be factored as $(x - 3)(x^2 - 4x)$. Factor the depressed polynomial $x^2 - 4x$.

$$x^2 - 4x = x(x - 4)$$

So, $x^3 - 7x^2 + 12x = x(x - 3)(x - 4)$, and $x(x - 4)$ are the remaining factors.

62. Step 1 Graph the related quadratic equation, $y = x^2 + x - 2$. Since the inequality symbol is $\leq$, the parabola should be solid.

Step 2 Test $(0, 0)$.

$$y \leq x^2 + x - 2$$
$$0 \overset{?}{\leq} 0^2 + 0 - 2$$
$$0 \leq -2 \quad ✗$$

So, $(0, 0)$ is not a solution of the inequality.

Step 3 Shade the region outside the parabola.

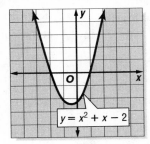

63. Step 1 Graph the related quadratic equation, $y = x^2 - 4$. Since the inequality symbol is $<$, the parabola should be dashed.

Step 2 Test $(0, 0)$.

$$y < x^2 - 4$$
$$0 \overset{?}{<} 0^2 - 4$$
$$0 < -4 \quad ✗$$

So, $(0, 0)$ is not a solution of the inequality.

Step 3 Shade the region outside the parabola.

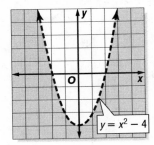

64. Step 1 Graph the related quadratic equation, $y = x^2 - 3x$. Since the inequality symbol is $>$, the parabola should be dashed.

Step 2 Test $(1, 0)$.
$$y > x^2 - 3x$$
$$0 \overset{?}{>} 1^2 - 3(1)$$
$$0 \overset{?}{>} 1 - 3$$
$$0 > -2 \quad \checkmark$$
So, $(1, 0)$ is a solution of the inequality.

Step 3 Shade the region inside the parabola.

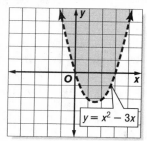

$y = x^2 - 3x$

65. $\sqrt{(153)^2} = 153$

66. $\sqrt[3]{-729} = \sqrt[3]{(-9)^3}$
$$= -9$$

67. $\sqrt[16]{b^{16}} = |b|$

68. $\sqrt{25a^8b^6} = \sqrt{(5a^4b^3)^2}$
$$= 5a^4|b^3|$$

69. Substitute $4y - 2$ for z in the second equation and solve for y.
$$z = -y + 3$$
$$4y - 2 = -y + 3$$
$$5y - 2 = 3$$
$$5y = 5$$
$$y = 1$$
Substitute 1 for y in either original equation and solve for z.
$$z = -y + 3$$
$$z = -1 + 3$$
$$z = 2$$
The solution is $(1, 2)$.

70. Add the equations to eliminate the k variable.
$$\begin{array}{r} j - k = \ \ 4 \\ (+)\ 2j + k = 35 \\ \hline 3j \quad\quad = 39 \\ j = 13 \end{array}$$

Replace j with 13 and solve for k.
$$2j + k = 35$$
$$2(13) + k = 35$$
$$26 + k = 35$$
$$k = 9$$
The solution is $(13, 9)$.

71. Solve the second equation for y in terms of x.
$$2y = -4x$$
$$y = -2x$$
Substitute $-2x$ for y in the first equation and solve for x.
$$3x + 1 = -y - 1$$
$$3x + 1 = -(-2x) - 1$$
$$3x + 1 = 2x - 1$$
$$x + 1 = -1$$
$$x = -2$$
Substitute -2 for x in either original equation and solve for y.
$$2y = -4x$$
$$2y = -4(-2)$$
$$2y = 8$$
$$y = 4$$
The solution is $(-2, 4)$.

72. $a + b = \frac{1}{2} + \frac{1}{6}$
$$= \frac{3}{6} + \frac{1}{6}$$
$$= \frac{4}{6}$$
$$= \frac{2}{3}$$

73. $b + c = \frac{1}{6} + \frac{2}{3}$
$$= \frac{1}{6} + \frac{4}{6}$$
$$= \frac{5}{6}$$

74. $a + d = \frac{1}{2} + \frac{3}{4}$
$$= \frac{2}{4} + \frac{3}{4}$$
$$= \frac{5}{4}$$
$$= 1\frac{1}{4}$$

75. $b + d = \frac{1}{6} + \frac{3}{4}$
$$= \frac{2}{12} + \frac{9}{12}$$
$$= \frac{11}{12}$$

76. $c + a = \frac{2}{3} + \frac{1}{2}$
$$= \frac{4}{6} + \frac{3}{6}$$
$$= \frac{7}{6}$$
$$= 1\frac{1}{6}$$

77. $c + d = \frac{2}{3} + \frac{3}{4}$
$$= \frac{8}{12} + \frac{9}{12}$$
$$= \frac{17}{12}$$
$$= 1\frac{5}{12}$$

12-5 Adding Probabilities

Pages 660–661 Check for Understanding

1. Sample answer: mutually exclusive events: tossing a coin and rolling a die; inclusive events: drawing a 7 and a diamond from a standard deck of cards

2. Draw two circles in a rectangle, one to represent the group of students taking French, and the other to represent the group of students taking algebra. The two circles should overlap to represent the group of students taking both French and algebra. Label each region and include the number of students in each group.

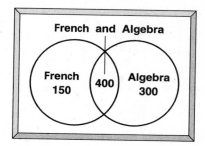

French and Algebra

French 150 · 400 · Algebra 300

3. The events are not mutually exclusive, so the chance of rain is less than 100%.

4. These are mutually exclusive events, since the outcome cannot be both 1 and 6.

$P(1 \text{ or } 6) = P(1) + P(6)$
$$= \frac{1}{6} + \frac{1}{6}$$
$$= \frac{1}{3}$$

The probability of rolling a 1 or 6 is $\frac{1}{3}$.

5. Rolling at least 5 means rolling 5 or 6. These are mutually exclusive events, since the outcome cannot be both 5 and 6.

$P(5 \text{ or } 6) = P(5) + P(6)$
$$= \frac{1}{6} + \frac{1}{6}$$
$$= \frac{1}{3}$$

The probability of rolling at least 5 is $\frac{1}{3}$.

6. Rolling less than 3 means rolling 1 or 2. These are mutually exclusive events, since the outcome cannot be both 1 and 2.

$P(1 \text{ or } 2) = P(1) + P(2)$
$$= \frac{1}{6} + \frac{1}{6}$$
$$= \frac{1}{3}$$

The probability of rolling less than 3 is $\frac{1}{3}$.

7. Rolling a prime means rolling 2, 3, or 5. These are mutually exclusive events, since the outcome cannot be 2, 3, and 5 all at the same time.

$P(2, 3, \text{ or } 5) = P(2) + P(3) + P(5)$
$$= \frac{1}{6} + \frac{1}{6} + \frac{1}{6}$$
$$= \frac{1}{2}$$

The probability of rolling a prime number is $\frac{1}{2}$.

8. Since one outcome is both even and prime, the events are inclusive. There are three even outcomes, rolling a 2, 4, or 6, three prime outcomes, rolling a 2, 3, or 5, and one outcome that is both even and prime, 2.

$P(\text{even}) = \frac{3}{6}$

$P(\text{prime}) = \frac{3}{6}$

$P(\text{even and prime}) = \frac{1}{6}$

$P(\text{even or prime})$
$$= P(\text{even}) + P(\text{prime}) - P(\text{even and prime})$$
$$= \frac{3}{6} + \frac{3}{6} - \frac{1}{6}$$
$$= \frac{5}{6}$$

The probability of rolling an even or prime number is $\frac{5}{6}$.

9. Since one outcome is both a multiple of 2 and of 3, the events are inclusive. There are three outcomes that are a multiple of 2, rolling a 2, 4, or 6, two outcomes that are a multiple of 3, rolling a 3 or 6, and one outcome that is both a multiple of 2 and of 3, 6.

$P(\text{multiple of } 2) = \frac{3}{6}$

$P(\text{multiple of } 3) = \frac{2}{6}$

$P(\text{multiple of } 2 \text{ and } 3) = \frac{1}{6}$

$P(\text{multiple of } 2 \text{ or } 3)$
$$= P(\text{multiple of } 2) + P(\text{multiple of } 3)$$
$$\quad - P(\text{multiple of } 2 \text{ and } 3)$$
$$= \frac{3}{6} + \frac{2}{6} - \frac{1}{6}$$
$$= \frac{2}{3}$$

The probability of rolling a multiple of 2 or 3 is $\frac{2}{3}$.

10. These are mutually exclusive events, since the card cannot be both a 6 or a king.

$P(6 \text{ or king}) = P(6) + P(\text{king})$
$$= \frac{4}{52} + \frac{4}{52}$$
$$= \frac{2}{13}$$

The probability of drawing a 6 or king is $\frac{2}{13}$.

11. Since one card is both a queen and a spade, the events are inclusive.

$P(\text{queen}) = \frac{4}{52}$

$P(\text{spade}) = \frac{13}{52}$

$P(\text{queen and spade}) = \frac{1}{52}$

$P(\text{queen or spade})$
$$= P(\text{queen}) + P(\text{spade}) - P(\text{queen and spade})$$
$$= \frac{4}{52} + \frac{13}{52} - \frac{1}{52}$$
$$= \frac{4}{13}$$

The probability of drawing a queen or a spade is $\frac{4}{13}$.

12. Since a student cannot be both a senior and not a senior, these events are mutually exclusive. There are 3 seniors, so there are $(8 + 8) - 3$ or 13 students that are not seniors.

$P(\text{not a senior}) = \frac{s}{s + f}$
$$= \frac{13}{13 + 3}$$
$$= \frac{13}{16}$$

The probability that a person selected from the student senate is not a senior is $\frac{13}{16}$.

Pages 661–662   Practice and Apply

13. Selecting 2 silver means selecting 2 silver and 1 gold, and selecting 2 gold means selecting 1 silver and 2 gold. These are mutually exclusive events, since Lisa cannot select both 2 silver and 2 gold.

$P(2 \text{ silver or } 2 \text{ gold}) = P(2 \text{ silver}) + P(2 \text{ gold})$
$$= \frac{C(4, 2) \cdot C(5, 1)}{C(9, 3)} + \frac{C(4, 1) \cdot C(5, 2)}{C(9, 3)}$$
$$= \frac{6 \cdot 5}{84} + \frac{4 \cdot 10}{84}$$
$$= \frac{30}{84} + \frac{40}{84}$$
$$= \frac{5}{6}$$

The probability Lisa selects 2 silver or 2 gold is $\frac{5}{6}$.

14. Selecting all gold means selecting 3 gold and 0 silver, and selecting all silver means selecting 0 gold and 3 silver. These are mutually exclusive events, since Lisa cannot select both all gold and all silver.

P(all gold or all silver)

$$= P(\text{all gold}) + P(\text{all silver})$$
$$= \frac{C(5,3) \cdot C(4,0)}{C(9,3)} + \frac{C(5,0) \cdot C(4,3)}{C(9,3)}$$
$$= \frac{10 \cdot 1}{84} + \frac{1 \cdot 4}{84}$$
$$= \frac{10}{84} + \frac{4}{84}$$
$$= \frac{1}{6}$$

The probability Lisa selects all gold or all silver is $\frac{1}{6}$.

15. Selecting at least 2 gold means selecting 2 gold and 1 silver or selecting 3 gold and 0 silver. These are mutually exclusive events, since Lisa cannot select both 2 gold and 3 gold.

$P(\text{at least 2 gold}) = P(2\text{ gold}) + P(3\text{ gold})$
$$= \frac{C(5,2) \cdot C(4,1)}{C(9,3)} + \frac{C(5,3) \cdot C(4,0)}{C(9,3)}$$
$$= \frac{10 \cdot 4}{84} + \frac{10 \cdot 1}{84}$$
$$= \frac{40}{84} + \frac{10}{84}$$
$$= \frac{25}{42}$$

The probability Lisa selects at least 2 gold is $\frac{25}{42}$.

16. Selecting at least 1 silver means selecting 1 silver and 2 gold, 2 silver and 1 gold, or 3 silver and 0 gold. These are mutually exclusive events, since Lisa cannot select 1 silver, 2 silver, and 3 silver all at the same time.

$P(\text{at least 1 silver})$
$$= P(1\text{ silver}) + P(2\text{ silver}) + P(3\text{ silver})$$
$$= \frac{C(4,1) \cdot C(5,2)}{C(9,3)} + \frac{C(4,2) \cdot C(5,1)}{C(9,3)} + \frac{C(4,3) \cdot C(5,0)}{C(9,3)}$$
$$= \frac{4 \cdot 10}{84} + \frac{6 \cdot 5}{84} + \frac{4 \cdot 1}{84}$$
$$= \frac{40}{84} + \frac{30}{84} + \frac{4}{84}$$
$$= \frac{37}{42}$$

The probability Lisa selects at least 1 silver is $\frac{37}{42}$.

17. Helping 4 girls means helping 4 girls and 1 boy, and helping 4 boys means helping 1 girl and 4 boys. These are mutually exclusive events, since the salespeople cannot help both 4 girls and 4 boys.

$P(4\text{ girls or }4\text{ boys}) = P(4\text{ girls}) + P(4\text{ boys})$
$$= \frac{C(7,4) \cdot C(6,1)}{C(13,5)} + \frac{C(7,1) \cdot C(6,4)}{C(13,5)}$$
$$= \frac{35 \cdot 6}{1287} + \frac{7 \cdot 15}{1287}$$
$$= \frac{210}{1287} + \frac{105}{1287}$$
$$= \frac{35}{143}$$

The probability the salespeople help 4 girls or 4 boys is $\frac{35}{143}$.

18. Helping 3 girls means helping 3 girls and 2 boys, and helping 3 boys means helping 2 girls and 3 boys. These are mutually exclusive events, since the salespeople cannot help both 3 girls and 3 boys.

$P(3\text{ girls or }3\text{ boys}) = P(3\text{ girls}) + P(3\text{ boys})$
$$= \frac{C(7,3) \cdot C(6,2)}{C(13,5)} + \frac{C(7,2) \cdot C(6,3)}{C(13,5)}$$
$$= \frac{35 \cdot 15}{1287} + \frac{21 \cdot 20}{1287}$$
$$= \frac{525}{1287} + \frac{420}{1287}$$
$$= \frac{105}{143}$$

The probability the salespeople help 3 girls or 3 boys is $\frac{105}{143}$.

19. Helping all girls means helping 5 girls and 0 boys, and helping all boys means helping 0 girls and 5 boys. These are mutually exclusive events, since the salespeople cannot help both all girls and all boys.

$P(\text{all girls or all boys}) = P(\text{all girls}) + P(\text{all boys})$
$$= \frac{C(7,5) \cdot C(6,0)}{C(13,5)} + \frac{C(7,0) \cdot C(6,5)}{C(13,5)}$$
$$= \frac{21 \cdot 1}{1287} + \frac{1 \cdot 6}{1287}$$
$$= \frac{21}{1287} + \frac{6}{1287}$$
$$= \frac{3}{143}$$

The probability the salespeople help all girls or all boys is $\frac{3}{143}$.

20. Helping at least 3 girls means helping 3 girls and 2 boys, 4 girls and 1 boy, or 5 girls and 0 boys. These are mutually exclusive events, since the salespeople cannot help 3 girls, 4 girls, and 5 girls all at the same time.

$P(\text{at least 3 girls})$
$$= P(3\text{ girls}) + P(4\text{ girls}) + P(5\text{ girls})$$
$$= \frac{C(7,3) \cdot C(6,2)}{C(13,5)} + \frac{C(7,4) \cdot C(6,1)}{C(13,5)} + \frac{C(7,5) \cdot C(6,0)}{C(13,5)}$$
$$= \frac{35 \cdot 15}{1287} + \frac{35 \cdot 6}{1287} + \frac{21 \cdot 1}{1287}$$
$$= \frac{525}{1287} + \frac{210}{1287} + \frac{21}{1287}$$
$$= \frac{84}{143}$$

The probability the salespeople help at least 3 girls is $\frac{84}{143}$.

21. Helping at least 4 girls means helping 4 girls and 1 boy or 5 girls and 0 boys, and helping at least 4 boys means helping 1 girl and 4 boys or 0 girls and 5 boys. These are mutually exclusive events, since the salespeople cannot help 0 girls, 1 girl, 4 girls, and 5 girls all at the same time.

$P(\text{at least 4 girls or at least 4 boys})$
$$= P(0\text{ girls}) + P(1\text{ girl}) + P(4\text{ girls})$$
$$\quad + P(5\text{ girls})$$
$$= \frac{C(7,0) \cdot C(6,5)}{C(13,5)} + \frac{C(7,1) \cdot C(6,4)}{C(13,5)} + \frac{C(7,4) \cdot C(6,1)}{C(13,5)}$$
$$\quad + \frac{C(7,5) \cdot C(6,0)}{C(13,5)}$$
$$= \frac{1 \cdot 6}{1287} + \frac{7 \cdot 15}{1287} + \frac{35 \cdot 6}{1287} + \frac{21 \cdot 1}{1287}$$
$$= \frac{6}{1287} + \frac{105}{1287} + \frac{210}{1287} + \frac{21}{1287}$$
$$= \frac{38}{143}$$

The probability the salespeople help at least 4 girls or at least 4 boys is $\frac{38}{143}$.

22. Helping at least 2 boys means helping 2 boys and 3 girls, 3 boys and 2 girls, 4 boys and 1 girl, or 5 boys and 0 girls. These are mutually exclusive events, since the salespeople cannot help 2 boys, 3 boys, 4 boys, and 5 boys all at the same time.

P(at least 2 boys)

$$= P(\text{2 boys}) + P(\text{3 boys}) + P(\text{4 boys}) + P(\text{5 boys})$$

$$= \frac{C(6,2) \cdot C(7,3)}{C(13,5)} + \frac{C(6,3) \cdot C(7,2)}{C(13,5)} + \frac{C(6,4) \cdot C(7,1)}{C(13,5)} + \frac{C(6,5) \cdot C(7,0)}{C(13,5)}$$

$$= \frac{15 \cdot 35}{1287} + \frac{20 \cdot 21}{1287} + \frac{15 \cdot 7}{1287} + \frac{6 \cdot 1}{1287}$$

$$= \frac{525}{1287} + \frac{420}{1287} + \frac{105}{1287} + \frac{6}{1287}$$

$$= \frac{32}{39}$$

The probability the salespeople help at least 2 boys is $\frac{32}{39}$.

23. These are mutually exclusive events, since the book cannot be both a literature book and an algebra book.

P(literature or algebra)

$$= P(\text{literature}) + P(\text{algebra})$$

$$= \frac{3}{9} + \frac{4}{9}$$

$$= \frac{7}{9}$$

The probability of selecting a literature book or an algebra book is $\frac{7}{9}$.

24. Since 5 is a number greater than 3, the events are inclusive.

$P(5) = \frac{1}{6}$

$P(\text{greater than 3}) = \frac{3}{6}$

$P(\text{5 and greater than 3}) = \frac{1}{6}$

P(5 or greater than 3)

$$= P(5) + P(\text{greater than 3})$$

$$- P(\text{5 and greater than 3})$$

$$= \frac{1}{6} + \frac{3}{6} - \frac{1}{6}$$

$$= \frac{1}{2}$$

The probability of rolling a 5 or a number greater than 3 is $\frac{1}{2}$.

25. Since some students are both a boy and a senior, the events are inclusive.

$P(\text{boy}) = \frac{14}{34}$

$P(\text{senior}) = \frac{11}{34}$

$P(\text{boy and senior}) = \frac{4}{34}$

P(boy or senior)

$$= P(\text{boy}) + P(\text{senior}) - P(\text{boy and senior})$$

$$= \frac{14}{34} + \frac{11}{34} - \frac{4}{34}$$

$$= \frac{21}{34}$$

The probability of selecting a boy or a senior is $\frac{21}{34}$.

26. These are mutually exclusive events, since the card cannot be both an ace and a face card.

P(ace or face card) $= P(\text{ace}) + P(\text{face card})$

$$= \frac{4}{52} + \frac{12}{52}$$

$$= \frac{4}{13}$$

The probability of drawing an ace or a face card is $\frac{4}{13}$.

27. Since some letters are both a vowel and from the word *equation*, the events are inclusive.

$P(\text{vowel}) = \frac{5}{26}$

$P(\text{from } equation) = \frac{8}{26}$

$P(\text{vowel and from } equation) = \frac{5}{26}$

P(vowel or from *equation*)

$$= P(\text{vowel}) + P(\text{from } equation)$$

$$- P(\text{vowel and from } equation)$$

$$= \frac{5}{26} + \frac{8}{26} - \frac{5}{26}$$

$$= \frac{4}{13}$$

The probability of selecting a vowel or a letter from the word equation is $\frac{4}{13}$.

28. Since some of the numbers from 1 to 30 are both a multiple of 2 and a multiple of 3, the events are inclusive.

$P(\text{multiple of 2}) = \frac{15}{30}$

$P(\text{multiple of 3}) = \frac{10}{30}$

$P(\text{multiple of 2 and 3}) = \frac{5}{30}$

P(multiple of 2 or 3)

$$= P(\text{multiple of 2}) + P(\text{multiple of 3})$$

$$- P(\text{multiple of 2 and 3})$$

$$= \frac{15}{30} + \frac{10}{30} - \frac{5}{30}$$

$$= \frac{2}{3}$$

The probability of selecting a number that is a multiple of 2 or a multiple of 3 is $\frac{2}{3}$.

29. Since some cards are both a king and black, the events are inclusive.

$P(\text{both kings}) = \frac{C(4,2) \cdot C(48,0)}{C(52,2)}$

$$= \frac{1}{221}$$

$P(\text{both black}) = \frac{C(26,2) \cdot C(26,0)}{C(52,2)}$

$$= \frac{25}{102}$$

$P(\text{both kings and both black}) = \frac{C(2,2) \cdot C(50,0)}{C(52,2)}$

$$= \frac{1}{1326}$$

P(both kings or both black)

$$= P(\text{both kings}) + P(\text{both black})$$

$$- P(\text{both kings and both black})$$

$$= \frac{1}{221} + \frac{25}{102} - \frac{1}{1326}$$

$$= \frac{55}{221}$$

The probability of drawing two cards that are both kings or both black is $\frac{55}{221}$.

30. Since some cards are both a king and a face card, the events are inclusive.

$P(\text{both kings}) = \dfrac{C(4, 2) \cdot C(48, 0)}{C(52, 2)}$

$= \dfrac{1}{221}$

$P(\text{both face cards}) = \dfrac{C(12, 2) \cdot C(40, 0)}{C(52, 2)}$

$= \dfrac{11}{221}$

$P(\text{both kings and both face cards}) = \dfrac{C(4, 2) \cdot C(48, 0)}{C(52, 2)}$

$= \dfrac{1}{221}$

$P(\text{both kings or both face cards})$
$= P(\text{both kings}) + P(\text{both face cards})$
$\quad - P(\text{both kings and both face cards})$
$= \dfrac{1}{221} + \dfrac{11}{221} - \dfrac{1}{221}$
$= \dfrac{11}{221}$

The probability of drawing two cards that are both kings or both face cards is $\dfrac{11}{221}$.

31. Since some cards are both a face card and red, the events are inclusive.

$P(\text{both face cards}) = \dfrac{C(12, 2) \cdot C(40, 0)}{C(52, 2)}$

$= \dfrac{11}{221}$

$P(\text{both red}) = \dfrac{C(26, 2) \cdot C(26, 0)}{C(52, 2)}$

$= \dfrac{25}{102}$

$P(\text{both face cards and both red}) = \dfrac{C(6, 2) \cdot C(46, 0)}{C(52, 2)}$

$= \dfrac{5}{442}$

$P(\text{both face cards or both red})$
$= P(\text{both face cards}) + P(\text{both red})$
$\quad - P(\text{both face cards and both red})$
$= \dfrac{11}{221} + \dfrac{25}{102} - \dfrac{5}{442}$
$= \dfrac{188}{663}$

The probability of drawing two cards that are both face cards or both red is $\dfrac{188}{663}$.

32. Since some cards are both red and a king, the events are inclusive. There are 26 red cards, 4 kings, and 2 red kings. Thus, there are $26 + 4 - 2$ or 28 cards that are red or a king. Drawing a card that is red or a king, and then drawing another card that is red or a king are dependent events, since once a red card or king is drawn it is not replaced.

$P(\text{both either red or king})$
$= P(\text{red or king})$
$\quad \cdot P(\text{red or king following red or king})$
$= \dfrac{28}{52} \cdot \dfrac{27}{51}$
$= \dfrac{63}{221}$

The probability of drawing two cards that are both either red or a king is $\dfrac{63}{221}$.

33. There are $2 \cdot 2 \cdot 2$ or 8 possible outcomes for the three cane dice. Only 1 outcome results in three round sides up, so $s = 1$. The other 7 outcomes are failures, so $f = 7$.

$P(\text{advancing 2 lines}) = \dfrac{s}{s + f}$
$= \dfrac{1}{1 + 7}$
$= \dfrac{1}{8}$

The probability of advancing 2 lines is $\dfrac{1}{8}$.

34. There are $2 \cdot 2 \cdot 2$ or 8 possible outcomes for the three cane dice. Only 1 outcome results in three flat sides up, so $s = 1$. The other 7 outcomes are failures, so $f = 7$.

$P(\text{advancing 1 line}) = \dfrac{s}{s + f}$
$= \dfrac{1}{1 + 7}$
$= \dfrac{1}{8}$

The probability of advancing 1 line is $\dfrac{1}{8}$.

35. Advancing at least 1 line means advancing 1 line or advancing 2 lines. These are mutually exclusive events, since the player cannot advance both 1 line and 2 lines.

$P(\text{advancing at least 1 line})$
$= P(\text{advancing 1 line}) + P(\text{advancing 2 lines})$
$= \dfrac{1}{8} + \dfrac{1}{8}$
$= \dfrac{1}{4}$

The probability of advancing at least 1 line is $\dfrac{1}{4}$.

36. There are $2 \cdot 2 \cdot 2$ or 8 possible outcomes for the three cane dice. Only 6 outcomes result in a combination of round sides and flat sides, so $s = 6$. The other 2 outcomes are failures, so $f = 2$.

$P(\text{losing a turn}) = \dfrac{s}{s + f}$
$= \dfrac{6}{6 + 2}$
$= \dfrac{6}{8}$
$= \dfrac{3}{4}$

The probability of losing a turn is $\dfrac{3}{4}$.

37. Since a ball cannot be in both cages, these are independent events.

$P(\text{each is a 25})$
$= P(\text{25 from first cage}) \cdot P(\text{25 from second cage})$
$= \dfrac{1}{30} \cdot \dfrac{1}{26}$
$= \dfrac{1}{780}$

The probability that each ball chosen is 25 is $\dfrac{1}{780}$.

38. Since a ball cannot be in both cages, these are independent events.

$P(\text{neither is a 20}) = P(\text{not 20 from first cage})$
$\quad \cdot P(\text{not 20 from second cage})$
$= \dfrac{29}{30} \cdot \dfrac{25}{26}$
$= \dfrac{725}{780}$
$= \dfrac{145}{156}$

The probability that neither ball chosen is 20 is $\dfrac{145}{156}$.

39. Exactly one is a 30 means 30 is chosen from the first cage or 30 is chosen from the second cage, but 30 is not chosen from both cages. These are mutually exclusive events, since the outcome of choosing 30 and 30 is not a success.

P(exactly one is a 30)

$= P(\text{30 and not 30}) + P(\text{not 30 and 30})$

$= \dfrac{1}{30} \cdot \dfrac{25}{26} + \dfrac{29}{30} \cdot \dfrac{1}{26}$

$= \dfrac{25}{780} + \dfrac{29}{780}$

$= \dfrac{9}{130}$

The probability of choosing exactly one 30 is $\dfrac{9}{130}$.

40. None of the balls in the first cage has the number 40. Thus, exactly one is a 40 means that any number is chosen from the first cage and 40 is chosen from the second cage. These are independent events.

P(exactly one is a 40)

$= P(\text{any number from first cage})$
$\quad \cdot P(\text{40 from second cage})$

$= \dfrac{30}{30} \cdot \dfrac{1}{26}$

$= \dfrac{1}{26}$

The probability of choosing exactly one 40 is $\dfrac{1}{26}$.

41. Only the numbers 20 through 30 appear on balls in both cages. The numbers are equal means that one of the numbers from 20 to 30 is chosen from the first cage, then the same number is chosen from the second cage. These are independent events.

P(the numbers are equal)

$= P(\text{from 20 to 30 from first cage})$
$\quad \cdot P(\text{same number from second cage})$

$= \dfrac{11}{30} \cdot \dfrac{1}{26}$

$= \dfrac{11}{780}$

The probability that the numbers are equal is $\dfrac{11}{780}$.

42. Since there are only certain numbers in each of the cages, the sum is 30 means that one of the numbers from 1 to 10 is chosen from the first cage, then the number needed to sum to 30, from 20 to 29, is chosen from the second cage. These are independent events.

P(the sum is 30)

$= P(\text{from 1 to 10 from first cage})$
$\quad \cdot P(\text{number needed from second cage})$

$= \dfrac{10}{30} \cdot \dfrac{1}{26}$

$= \dfrac{1}{78}$

The probability that the sum is 30 is $\dfrac{1}{78}$.

43. Since some members of the community would recycle both aluminum and glass, the events are inclusive.

$P(\text{aluminum}) = \dfrac{134}{300}$

$P(\text{glass}) = \dfrac{108}{300}$

$P(\text{aluminum and glass}) = \dfrac{62}{300}$

$P(\text{aluminum or glass})$
$\quad = P(\text{aluminum}) + P(\text{glass}) - P(\text{aluminum and glass})$
$\quad = \dfrac{134}{300} + \dfrac{108}{300} - \dfrac{62}{300}$
$\quad = \dfrac{3}{5}$

The probability that a member of the community would recycle aluminum or glass is $\dfrac{3}{5}$.

44. Since some students take both drama and music, the events are inclusive.

$P(\text{drama}) = \dfrac{89}{324}$

$P(\text{music}) = \dfrac{93}{324}$

$P(\text{drama and music}) = \dfrac{23}{324}$

$P(\text{drama or music})$
$\quad = P(\text{drama}) + P(\text{music}) - P(\text{drama and music})$
$\quad = \dfrac{89}{324} + \dfrac{93}{324} - \dfrac{23}{324}$
$\quad = \dfrac{53}{108}$

The probability that a student participates in drama or music is $\dfrac{53}{108}$.

45. Since some students participate in both drama and athletics, the events are inclusive.

$P(\text{drama}) = \dfrac{89}{324}$

$P(\text{athletics}) = \dfrac{142}{324}$

$P(\text{drama and athletics}) = \dfrac{27}{324}$

$P(\text{drama or athletics})$
$\quad = P(\text{drama}) + P(\text{athletics})$
$\quad\quad - P(\text{drama and athletics})$
$\quad = \dfrac{89}{324} + \dfrac{142}{324} - \dfrac{27}{324}$
$\quad = \dfrac{17}{27}$

The probability that a student participates in drama or athletics is $\dfrac{17}{27}$.

46. Since some students participate in athletics, drama, and music, the events are inclusive.

$P(\text{athletics and drama}) = \dfrac{27}{324}$

$P(\text{music and athletics}) = \dfrac{19}{324}$

$P(\text{athletics and drama and music}) = \dfrac{12}{324}$

$P(\text{athletics and drama, or music and athletics})$
$\quad = P(\text{athletics and drama}) + P(\text{music and athletics})$
$\quad\quad - P(\text{athletics and drama and music})$
$\quad = \dfrac{27}{324} + \dfrac{19}{324} - \dfrac{12}{324}$
$\quad = \dfrac{17}{162}$

The probability that a student participates in athletics and drama, or in music and athletics is $\dfrac{17}{162}$.

47. Subtracting $P(A \text{ and } B)$ from each side and adding $P(A \text{ or } B)$ to each side results in the equation $P(A \text{ or } B) = P(A) + P(B) - P(A \text{ and } B)$. This is the equation for the probability of inclusive events. If A and B are mutually exclusive, then $P(A \text{ and } B) = 0$, so the equation simplifies to $P(A \text{ or } B) = P(A) + P(B)$, which is the equation for the probability of mutually exclusive events. Therefore, the equation is correct in either case.

48. Probability can be used to estimate the percents of people who do the same things before going to bed. Answers should include the following.

- The events are inclusive because some people brush their teeth and set their alarm. Also, you know that the events are inclusive because the sum of the percents is not 100%.

- According to the information in the text and the table, $P(\text{read book}) = \frac{38}{100}$ and $P(\text{brush teeth}) = \frac{81}{100}$. Since the events are inclusive,

  $P(\text{read book or brush teeth})$
  $= P(\text{read book}) + P(\text{brush teeth})$
  $\quad - P(\text{read book and brush teeth})$
  $= \frac{38}{100} + \frac{81}{100} - \frac{600}{2000}$
  $= \frac{89}{100}.$

49. C; The ratio of 5:4 means that there are 4 red gumballs for every group of $5 + 4$ or 9 gumballs. There are $180 \div 9$ or 20 groups of 9 gumballs. Thus, there are $20 \cdot 4$ or 80 red gumballs.

50. A; $\langle\!\langle 7 \rangle\!\rangle + \langle\!\langle 18 \rangle\!\rangle = 2(7) + \frac{1}{2}(18)$
$= 14 + 9$
$= 23$

Page 663 Maintain Your Skills

51. $P(1, \text{ then } 2, \text{ then } 3) = P(1) \cdot P(2) \cdot P(3)$
$= \frac{1}{6} \cdot \frac{1}{6} \cdot \frac{1}{6}$
$= \frac{1}{216}$

The probability is $\frac{1}{216}$ or about 0.005.

52. $P(\text{no 4s}) = P(\text{no 4}) \cdot P(\text{no 4}) \cdot P(\text{no 4})$
$= \frac{5}{6} \cdot \frac{5}{6} \cdot \frac{5}{6}$
$= \frac{125}{216}$

The probability is $\frac{125}{216}$ or about 0.579.

53. $P(\text{three 1s}) = P(1) \cdot P(1) \cdot P(1)$
$= \frac{1}{6} \cdot \frac{1}{6} \cdot \frac{1}{6}$
$= \frac{1}{216}$

The probability is $\frac{1}{216}$ or about 0.005.

54. $P(\text{three even numbers})$
$= P(\text{even}) \cdot P(\text{even}) \cdot P(\text{even})$
$= \frac{3}{6} \cdot \frac{3}{6} \cdot \frac{3}{6}$
$= \frac{27}{216}$
$= \frac{1}{8}$

The probability is $\frac{1}{8}$ or about 0.125.**55. Step 1** Identify s and f.

$P(\text{event}) = \frac{4}{5}$
$\qquad = \frac{s}{s+f} \quad s = 4, \ f = 1$

Step 2 Find the odds.
$\text{Odds} = s : f$
$\qquad = 4 : 1$
So, the odds of the event occurring are $4 : 1$.

56. Step 1 Identify s and f.

$P(\text{event}) = \frac{1}{9}$
$\qquad = \frac{s}{s+f} \quad s = 1, \ f = 8$

Step 2 Find the odds.
$\text{Odds} = s : f$
$\qquad = 1 : 8$
So, the odds of the event occurring are $1 : 8$.

57. Step 1 Identify s and f.

$P(\text{event}) = \frac{2}{7}$
$\qquad = \frac{s}{s+f} \quad s = 2, f = 5$

Step 2 Find the odds.
$\text{Odds} = s : f$
$\qquad = 2 : 5$
So, the odds of the event occurring are $2 : 5$.

58. Step 1 Identify s and f.

$P(\text{event}) = \frac{5}{8}$
$\qquad = \frac{s}{s+f} \quad s = 5, \ f = 3$

Step 2 Find the odds.
$\text{Odds} = s : f$
$\qquad = 5 : 3$
So, the odds of the event occurring are $5 : 3$.

59. The sum is a geometric series with $a_1 = 2$, $r = 2$, and $a_n = 128$.
$s_n = \frac{a_1 - a_n r}{1 - r}$
$\quad = \frac{2 - (128)(2)}{1 - 2}$
$\quad = \frac{-254}{-1}$
$\quad = 254$

60. $\displaystyle\sum_{n=1}^{3}(5n - 2) = (5 \cdot 1 - 2) + (5 \cdot 2 - 2) + (5 \cdot 3 - 2)$
$= 3 + 8 + 13$
$= 24$

61. Use substitution to solve the system.
$y^2 = x^2 + 36$
$(-10)^2 = x^2 + 36$
$100 = x^2 + 36$
$64 = x^2$
$\pm\sqrt{64} = \sqrt{x^2}$
$\pm 8 = x$

The solutions are $(-8, -10)$ and $(8, -10)$.

62. Use substitution to solve the system. First solve the first equation for x.

$$x^2 = 144$$
$$\sqrt{x^2} = \pm\sqrt{144}$$
$$x = \pm 12$$

Substitute ± 12 for x in the second equation and solve for y.

$x^2 + y^2 = 169$	$x^2 + y^2 = 169$
$(12)^2 + y^2 = 169$	$(-12)^2 + y^2 = 169$
$144 + y^2 = 169$	$144 + y^2 = 169$
$y^2 = 25$	$y^2 = 25$
$y = \pm 5$	$y = \pm 5$

The solutions are $(12, 5)$, $(-12, 5)$, $(-12, -5)$, and $(12, -5)$.

63. The graph of $f(x)$ touches the x-axis at -1 and crosses the x-axis at 1. Use the factor theorem and synthetic division to find all of the factors.

```
1 | 1   1   0   0  -1  -1
  |     1   2   2   2   1
  -------------------------
    1   2   2   2   1 | 0
```

$x^5 + x^4 - x - 1 = (x - 1)(x^4 + 2x^3 + 2x^2 + 2x + 1)$

```
-1 | 1   2   2   2   1
   |    -1  -1  -1  -1
   ---------------------
     1   1   1   1 | 0
```

$x^4 + 2x^3 + 2x^2 + 2x + 1 = (x + 1)(x^3 + x^2 + x + 1)$

```
-1 | 1   1   1   1
   |    -1   0  -1
   ------------------
     1   0   1 | 0
```

$x^3 + x^2 + x + 1 = (x + 1)(x^2 + 1)$

So, $x^5 + x^4 - x - 1 = (x - 1)(x + 1)^2(x^2 + 1)$.

64. Enter $y = x^3 + 2x^2 - 5$ in the Y = list of a graphing calculator and graph the function. Use the maximum and minimum options from the CALC menu to find the coordinates of the relative maxima and relative minima.

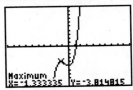

[10, −10] scl: 1 by [10, −10] scl: 1

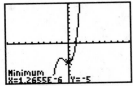

[10, −10] scl: 1 by [10, −10] scl: 1

The relative maximum is $(-1.33, -3.81)$, and the relative minimum is $(0, -5)$.

65. Enter $y = x^3 + 3x^2 + 2x + 1$ in the Y = list of a graphing calculator and graph the function. Use the maximum and minimum options from the CALC menu of find the coordinates of the relative maxima and relative minima.

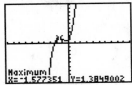

[10, −10] scl: 1 by [10, −10] scl: 1

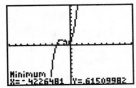

[10, −10] scl: 1 by [10, −10] scl: 1

The relative maximum is $(-1.58, 1.38)$, and the relative minimum is $(-0.42, 0.62)$.

66. Step 1 Find the vertices of the region. Graph the inequalities.

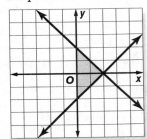

The polygon formed is a triangle with vertices at $(0, 2)$, $(0, -2)$, and $(2, 0)$.

Step 2 Use a table to find the maximum and minimum values of $f(x, y)$. Substitute the coordinates of the vertices into the function.

(x, y)	$3x + y$	$f(x, y)$
$(0, 2)$	$3(0) + 2$	2
$(0, -2)$	$3(0) + (-2)$	-2
$(2, 0)$	$3(2) + 0$	6

The maximum value is 6 at $(2, 0)$.
The minimum value is -2 at $(0, -2)$.

67. Step 1 Find the vertices of the region. Graph the inequalities.

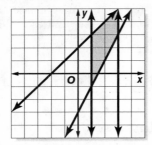

The polygon formed is a quadrilateral with vertices at $(1, -1)$, $(1, 3)$, $(3, 3)$, and $(3, 5)$.

Step 2 Use a table to find the maximum and minimum values of $f(x, y)$. Substitute the coordinates of the vertices into the function.

(x, y)	$x + 4y$	$f(x, y)$
$(1, -1)$	$1 + 4(-1)$	-3
$(1, 3)$	$1 + 4(3)$	13
$(3, 3)$	$3 + 4(3)$	15
$(3, 5)$	$3 + 4(5)$	23

The maximum value is 23 at $(3, 5)$.

The minimum value is -3 at $(1, -1)$.

68. Let t be her time and let d be the distance she has skated. Use the slope $m = 12.79$ and the point $(0, 0)$ with the point-slope form to write an equation.

$$d - d_1 = m(t - t_1)$$
$$d - 0 = 12.79(t - 0)$$
$$d = 12.79t$$

The equation is $d = 12.79t$.

69. Since the equation is a linear equation that can be expressed in the form $y = kx$, this equation is a direct variation.

70. mean $= \dfrac{\text{sum of the data}}{\text{number of items in data set}}$

$$= \frac{298 + 256 + 399 + 388 + 276}{5}$$
$$= \frac{1617}{5}$$
$$= 323.4$$

The mean is 323.4.

To find the median, order the numbers from least to greatest. The median is in the middle.

256   276   298   388   399

The median is 298.

Since each number in the set occurs only once, there is no mode.

The greatest value is 399 and the least value is 256. So, the range is $399 - 256$ or 143.

71. mean $= \dfrac{\text{sum of the data}}{\text{number of items in data set}}$

$$= \frac{3 + 75 + 58 + 7 + 34}{5}$$
$$= \frac{177}{5}$$
$$= 35.4$$

The mean is 35.4.

To find the median, order the numbers from least to greatest. The median is in the middle.

3   7   34   58   75

The median is 34.

Since each number in the set occurs only once, there is no mode.

The greatest value is 75, and the least value is 3. So, the range is $75 - 3$ or 72.

72. mean $= \dfrac{\text{sum of the data}}{\text{number of items in data set}}$

$$= \frac{4.8 + 5.7 + 2.1 + 2.1 + 4.8 + 2.1}{6}$$
$$= \frac{21.6}{6}$$
$$= 3.6$$

The median is 21.6.

To find the median, order the numbers from least to greatest. The median is in the middle.

2.1   2.1   2.1   4.8   4.8   5.7

$$\frac{2.1 + 4.8}{2} = 3.45$$

The mean is 3.45.

Since 2.1 occurs 3 times and the other numbers occur only once each, the mode is 2.1.

The greatest value is 5.7, and the least value is 2.1. So, the range is $5.7 - 2.1$ or 3.6.

73. mean $= \dfrac{\text{sum of the data}}{\text{number of items in data set}}$

$$= \frac{80 + 50 + 65 + 55 + 70 + 65 + 75 + 50}{8}$$
$$= \frac{510}{8}$$
$$= 63.75$$

The mean is 63.75.

To find the median, order the numbers from least to greatest. The median is in the middle.

50   50   55   65   65   70   75   80

$$\frac{65 + 65}{2} = 65$$

The median is 65.

Since 50 and 65 occurs twice each and the other numbers occur only once each, there are two modes, 50 and 65.

The greatest value is 80, and the least value is 50. So, the range is $80 - 50$ or 30.

74. mean $= \dfrac{\text{sum of the data}}{\text{number of items in data set}}$

$= \dfrac{61 + 89 + 93 + 102 + 45 + 89}{6}$

$= \dfrac{479}{6}$

≈ 79.83

The mean is 79.83.

To find the median, order the numbers from least to greatest. The median is in the middle.

$$45 \quad 61 \quad \underbrace{89 \quad 89}\quad 93 \quad 102$$

$$\dfrac{89 + 89}{2} = 89$$

The median is 89.

Since 89 occurs 2 times and the other numbers occur only once each, the mode is 89.

The greatest value is 102, and the least value is 45. So, the range is $102 - 45$ or 57.

75. mean $= \dfrac{\text{sum of the data}}{\text{number of items in data set}}$

$= \dfrac{13.3 + 15.4 + 12.5 + 10.7}{4}$

$= \dfrac{51.9}{4}$

≈ 12.98

The mean is 12.98.

To find the median, order the numbers from least to greatest. The median is in the middle.

$$10.7 \quad \underbrace{12.5 \quad 13.3}\quad 15.4$$

$$\dfrac{12.5 + 13.3}{2} = 12.9$$

The median is 12.9.

Since each number in the set occurs only once, there is no mode.

The greatest value is 15.4, and the least value is 10.7. So, the range is $15.4 - 10.7$ or 4.7.

12-6 | Statistical Measures

Page 666 Graphing Calculator Investigation

1. Since the standard deviation is the square root of the variance and the standard deviation is about 5.6, the variance is about $(5.6)^2$ or about 31.36.

2.
```
1-Var Stats
 x̄=4.06
 Σx=40.6
 Σx²=306.32
 Sx=3.964901568
 σx=3.761435896
↓n=10
```

The mean $\overline{x}$ is 4.06, the median is 2.35, and the standard deviation, σx, is about 3.8.

3. By deleting the outlier, 19.0, the mean changed from 5.4 to 4.06, which is a difference of $5.4 - 4.06$ or 1.34. The median changed from 3.4 to 2.35, which is a difference of $3.4 - 2.35$ or 1.05. In this situation, the median changed less.

Pages 666–667 Check for Understanding

1. Sample answer: $\{10, 10, 10, 10, 10, 10\}$

2. Sample answer: The variance of the set $\{0, 1\}$ is 0.25, and the standard deviation is 0.5.

3. We can use sigma notation to rewrite the numerator of the fraction.

$$(x_1 - \overline{x})^2 + (x_2 - \overline{x})^2 + \dots + (x_n - \overline{x})^2 = \sum_{i=1}^{n}(x_i - \overline{x})^2$$

$$\sigma = \sqrt{\dfrac{(x_1 - \overline{x})^2 + (x_2 - \overline{x})^2 + \dots + (x_n - \overline{x})^2}{n}}$$

$$\sigma = \sqrt{\dfrac{1}{n} \cdot [(x_1 - \overline{x})^2 + (x_2 - \overline{x})^2 + \dots + (x_n - \overline{x})^2]}$$

$$\sigma = \sqrt{\dfrac{1}{n}\sum_{i=1}^{n}(x_i - \overline{x})^2}$$

4. **Step 1** Find the mean.

$$\overline{x} = \dfrac{48 + 36 + 40 + 29 + 45 + 51 + 38 + 47 + 39 + 37}{10}$$

$$= 41$$

Step 2 Find the variance.

$$\sigma^2 = \dfrac{(x_1 - \overline{x})^2 + (x_2 - \overline{x})^2 + \dots + (x_n - \overline{x})^2}{n}$$

$$= \dfrac{(48 - 41)^2 + (36 - 41)^2 + \dots + (39 + 41)^2 + (37 - 41)^2}{10}$$

$$= \dfrac{400}{10}$$

$$= 40$$

The variance is 40.

Step 3 Find the standard deviation.

$$\sigma^2 = 40$$

$$\sigma \approx 6.32455532$$

The standard deviation is about 6.3.

5. **Step 1** Find the mean.

$$\overline{x} = \dfrac{\begin{array}{c}321 + 322 + 323 + 324 + 325 + \\ 326 + 327 + 328 + 329 + 330\end{array}}{10}$$

$$= 325.5$$

Step 2 Find the variance.

$$\sigma^2 = \dfrac{(x_1 - \overline{x})^2 + (x_2 - \overline{x})^2 + \dots + (x_n - \overline{x})^2}{n}$$

$$= \dfrac{\begin{array}{c}(321 - 325.5)^2 + (322 - 325.5)^2 + \dots + \\ (329 - 325.5)^2 + (330 - 325.5)^2\end{array}}{10}$$

$$= \dfrac{82.5}{10}$$

$$= 8.25$$

The variance is about 8.3.

Step 3 Find the standard deviation.

$$\sigma^2 = 8.25$$

$$\sigma \approx 2.872281323$$

The standard deviation is about 2.9.

6. Step 1 Find the mean.

$$\bar{x} = \frac{\begin{array}{c}43 + 56 + 78 + 81 + 47 + 42 + 34 + 22 + 78 +\\ 98 + 38 + 46 + 54 + 67 + 58 + 92 + 55\end{array}}{17}$$

$$\approx 58.2$$

Step 2 Find the variance.

$$\sigma^2 = \frac{(x_1 - \bar{x})^2 + (x_2 - \bar{x})^2 + \ldots + (x_n - \bar{x})^2}{n}$$

$$\approx \frac{\begin{array}{c}(43 - 58.2)^2 + (56 - 58.2)^2 + \ldots +\\ (92 - 58.2)^2 + (55 - 58.2)^2\end{array}}{17}$$

$$\approx \frac{7212.48}{17}$$

$$\approx 424.2635294$$

The variance is about 424.3.

Step 3 Find the standard deviation.

$$\sigma^2 \approx 424.3$$

$$\sigma \approx 20.59$$

The standard deviation is about 20.6.

7. Find the mean for the Pacific states.

$$\bar{x} = \frac{\$10{,}650 + \$5345 + \$6488 + \$6719}{4}$$

$$= \$7300.50$$

Find the mean for the southwest central states.

$$\bar{x} = \frac{\$6291 + \$5222 + \$5194 + \$4634}{4}$$

$$= \$5335.25$$

8. The mean is more representative for the southwest central states because the data for the Pacific states contains the most extreme value, $10,650.

Pages 667–669   Practice and Apply

9. Step 1 Find the mean.

$$\bar{x} = \frac{400 + 300 + 325 + 275 + 425 + 375 + 350}{7}$$

$$= 350$$

Step 2 Find the variance.

$$\sigma^2 = \frac{(x_1 - \bar{x})^2 + (x_2 - \bar{x})^2 + \ldots + (x_n - \bar{x})^2}{n}$$

$$= \frac{\begin{array}{c}(400 - 350)^2 + (300 - 350)^2 + \ldots +\\ (375 - 350)^2 + (350 - 350)^2\end{array}}{7}$$

$$= \frac{17{,}500}{7}$$

$$= 2500$$

The variance is 2500.

Step 3 Find the standard deviation.

$$\sigma^2 = 2500$$

$$\sigma = 50$$

The standard deviation is 50.

10. Step 1 Find the mean.

$$\bar{x} = \frac{\begin{array}{c}5 + 4 + 5 + 5 + 5 + 5 + 6 + 6 +\\ 6 + 6 + 7 + 7 + 7 + 7 + 8 + 9\end{array}}{16}$$

$$= 6.125$$

Step 2 Find the variance.

$$\sigma^2 = \frac{(x_1 - \bar{x})^2 + (x_2 - \bar{x})^2 + \ldots + (x_n - \bar{x})^2}{n}$$

$$= \frac{\begin{array}{c}(5 - 6.125)^2 + (4 - 6.125)^2 + \ldots +\\ (8 - 6.125)^2 + (9 - 6.125)^2\end{array}}{16}$$

$$= \frac{25.75}{16}$$

$$\approx 1.609375$$

The variance is about 1.6.

Step 3 Find the standard deviation.

$$\sigma^2 \approx 1.6$$

$$\sigma \approx 1.26$$

The standard deviation is about 1.3.

11. Step 1 Find the mean.

$$\bar{x} = \frac{2.4 + 5.6 + 1.9 + 7.1 + 4.3 + 2.7 + 4.6 + 1.8 + 2.4}{9}$$

$$\approx 3.6$$

Step 2 Find the variance.

$$\sigma^2 = \frac{(x_1 - \bar{x})^2 + (x_2 - \bar{x})^2 + \ldots + (x_n - \bar{x})^2}{n}$$

$$\approx \frac{\begin{array}{c}(2.4 - 3.6)^2 + (5.6 - 3.6)^2 + \ldots +\\ (1.8 - 3.6)^2 + (2.4 - 3.6)^2\end{array}}{9}$$

$$\approx \frac{27.56}{9}$$

$$\approx 3.06$$

The variance is about 3.1.

Step 3 Find the standard deviation.

$$\sigma^2 \approx 3.06$$

$$\sigma \approx 1.749$$

The standard deviation is about 1.7.

12. Step 1 Find the mean.

$$\bar{x} = \frac{\begin{array}{c}4.3 + 6.4 + 2.9 + 3.1 + 8.7 +\\ 2.8 + 3.6 + 1.9 + 7.2\end{array}}{9}$$

$$\approx 4.5$$

Step 2 Find the variance.

$$\sigma^2 = \frac{(x_1 - \bar{x})^2 + (x_2 - \bar{x})^2 + \ldots + (x_n - \bar{x})^2}{n}$$

$$\approx \frac{\begin{array}{c}(4.3 - 4.5)^2 + (6.4 - 4.5)^2 + \ldots +\\ (1.9 - 4.5)^2 + (7.2 - 4.5)^2\end{array}}{9}$$

$$\approx \frac{43.5}{9}$$

$$\approx 4.84$$

The variance is about 4.84.

Step 3 Find the standard deviation.

$$\sigma^2 \approx 4.84$$

$$\sigma \approx 2.2$$

The standard deviation is about 2.2.

13. Step 1 Find the mean.

$$\overline{x} = \frac{\begin{array}{c}234 + 345 + 123 + 368 + 279 + \\ 876 + 456 + 235 + 333 + 444\end{array}}{10}$$

$$= 369.3$$

Step 2 Find the variance.

$$\sigma^2 = \frac{(x_1 - \overline{x})^2 + (x_2 - \overline{x})^2 + \ldots + (x_n - \overline{x})^2}{n}$$

$$= \frac{\begin{array}{c}(234 - 369.3)^2 + (345 - 369.3)^2 + \ldots + \\ (333 - 369.3)^2 + (444 - 369.3)^2\end{array}}{10}$$

$$= \frac{376{,}912}{10}$$

$$= 37{,}691.2$$

The variance is about 37,691.2.

Step 3 Find the standard deviation.

$$\sigma^2 = 37{,}691.2$$

$$\sigma \approx 194.1422$$

The standard deviation is about 194.1.

14. Step 1 Find the mean.

$$\overline{x} = \frac{\begin{array}{c}13 + 14 + 15 + 16 + 17 + 18 + 19 + 20 + \\ 21 + 23 + 67 + 56 + 34 + 99 + 44 + 55\end{array}}{16}$$

$$\approx 33.2$$

Step 2 Find the variance.

$$\sigma^2 = \frac{(x_1 - \overline{x})^2 + (x_2 - \overline{x})^2 + \ldots + (x_n - \overline{x})^2}{n}$$

$$\approx \frac{\begin{array}{c}(13 - 33.2)^2 + (14 - 33.2)^2 + \ldots + \\ (44 - 33.2)^2 + (55 - 33.2)^2\end{array}}{16}$$

$$\approx \frac{9110.4}{16}$$

$$\approx 569.4$$

The variance is about 569.4.

Step 3 Find the standard deviation.

$$\sigma^2 \approx 569.4$$

$$\sigma \approx 23.9$$

The standard deviation is about 23.9.

15. Step 1 Find the mean.

$$\overline{x} = \frac{\begin{array}{c}44 + 45 + 46 + 47 + 47 + 53 + 55 + 56 + 57 + \\ 58 + 59 + 67 + 67 + 68 + 69 + 69 + 69\end{array}}{17}$$

$$\approx 57.4$$

Step 2 Find the variance.

$$\sigma^2 = \frac{(x_1 - \overline{x})^2 + (x_2 - \overline{x})^2 + \ldots + (x_n - \overline{x})^2}{n}$$

$$\approx \frac{\begin{array}{c}(44 - 57.4)^2 + (45 - 57.4)^2 + \ldots + \\ (69 - 57.4)^2 + (69 - 57.4)^2\end{array}}{17}$$

$$\approx \frac{1410.1}{17}$$

$$\approx 82.94$$

The variance is about 82.9.

Step 3 Find the standard deviation.

$$\sigma^2 \approx 82.94$$

$$\sigma \approx 9.1075$$

The standard deviation is about 9.1.

16. Step 1 Find the mean.

$$\overline{x} = \frac{\begin{array}{c}57 + 57 + 57 + 58 + 59 + 63 + 64 + 65 + \\ 65 + 66 + 67 + 72 + 73 + 74 + 75 + 76\end{array}}{16}$$

$$= 65.5$$

Step 2 Find the variance.

$$\sigma^2 = \frac{(x_1 - \overline{x})^2 + (x_2 - \overline{x})^2 + \ldots + (x_n - \overline{x})^2}{n}$$

$$= \frac{\begin{array}{c}(57 - 65.5)^2 + (57 - 65.5)^2 + \ldots + \\ (75 - 65.5)^2 + (76 - 65.5)^2\end{array}}{16}$$

$$= \frac{698}{16}$$

$$= 43.625$$

The variance is about 43.6.

Step 3 Find the standard deviation.

$$\sigma^2 = 43.625$$

$$\sigma \approx 6.604922407$$

The standard deviation is about 6.6.

17. $\text{mean} = \dfrac{\text{sum of the data}}{\text{number of items in data set}}$

$$= \frac{\begin{array}{c}306 + 179 + 205 + 194 + 105 + \\ 55 + 122 + 32 + 23 + 16 + 23\end{array}}{11}$$

$$= \frac{1260}{11}$$

$$\approx 114.5$$

The mean is 114.5.

To find the median, order the numbers from least to greatest. The median is in the middle.

16 23 23 32 55 105 122 179 194 205 306

The median is 105.

Since 23 occurs 2 times and the other numbers occur only once each, the mode is 23.

18. The mean and median both seem to represent the center of the data.

19. The mean since it is the highest.

20. The mode since it is lower and is what most employees make. It reflects the most representative worker.

21. $\text{mean} = \dfrac{\text{sum of the data}}{\text{number of items in data set}}$

$$= \frac{\begin{array}{c}\$1200 + \$999 + \$1499 + \$895 + \\ \$695 + \$1100 + \$1300 + \$695\end{array}}{8}$$

$$= \frac{\$8383}{8}$$

$$\approx \$1047.88$$

The mean is $1047.88.

To find the median, order the numbers from least to greatest. The median is in the middle.

$695 $695 $895 $999 $1100 $1200 $1300 $1499

$$\frac{\$999 + \$1100}{2} = \$1049.50$$

The median is $1049.50.

Since $695 occurs 2 times and the other numbers occur only once each, the mode is $695.

22. Mode; it is the least expensive price.

23. Mean or median; they are nearly equal and are more representative of the prices than the mode.

24. mean $= \dfrac{\text{sum of the data}}{\text{number of items in data set}}$

$= \dfrac{3{,}000{,}000 + 2{,}918{,}236 + \ldots + 2{,}000{,}000 + 2{,}000{,}000}{12}$

$= \dfrac{27{,}484{,}840}{12}$

$\approx 2{,}290{,}403.333$

The mean is about 2,290,403.

To find the median, order the numbers from least to greatest. The median is in the middle.

2,000,000 2,000,000 ... 2,100,000 2,200,000 ... 2,918,236 3,000,000

$\dfrac{2{,}100{,}000 + 2{,}200{,}000}{2} = 2{,}150{,}000$

The median is 2,150,000.

Since 2,000,000 occurs 3 times and the other numbers occur only once each, the mode is 2,000,000.

25. The mode since it is lowest.

26. The mean since it is highest.

27. Step 1 Find the mean.

$\bar{x} = \dfrac{170 + 165 + 140 + 188 + 195}{5}$

$= 171.6$

Step 2 Find the variance.

$\sigma^2 = \dfrac{(x_1 - \bar{x})^2 + (x_2 - \bar{x})^2 + \ldots + (x_n - \bar{x})^2}{n}$

$= \dfrac{(170 - 171.6)^2 + (165 - 171.6)^2 + \ldots + (188 - 171.6)^2 + (195 - 171.6)^2}{5}$

$= \dfrac{1861.2}{5}$

$= 372.24$

Step 3 Find the standard deviation.

$\sigma^2 \approx 372.24$

$\sigma \approx 19.29352223$

The standard deviation is about 19.3.

28. Step 1 Find the mean.

$\bar{x} = \dfrac{144 + 177 + 215 + 225 + 197}{5}$

$= 191.6$

Step 2 Find the variance.

$\sigma^2 = \dfrac{(x_1 - \bar{x})^2 + (x_2 - \bar{x})^2 + \ldots + (x_n - \bar{x})^2}{n}$

$= \dfrac{(144 - 191.6)^2 + (177 - 191.6)^2 + \ldots + (225 - 191.6)^2 (197 - 191.6)^2}{5}$

$= \dfrac{4171.2}{5}$

$= 834.24$

Step 3 Find the standard deviation.

$\sigma^2 = 834.24$

$\sigma \approx 28.88321312$

The standard deviation is about 28.9.

29. Step 1 Find the mean.

$\bar{x} = \dfrac{166 + 175 + 196 + 206 + 219}{5}$

$= 192.4$

Step 2 Find the variance.

$\sigma^2 = \dfrac{(x_1 - \bar{x})^2 + (x_2 - \bar{x})^2 + \ldots + (x_n - \bar{x})^2}{n}$

$= \dfrac{(166 - 192.4)^2 + (175 - 192.4)^2 + \ldots + (206 - 192.4)^2 + (219 - 192.4)^2}{5}$

$= \dfrac{1905.2}{5}$

$= 381.04$

Step 3 Find the standard deviation.

$\sigma^2 = 381.04$

$\sigma \approx 19.5202459$

The standard deviation is about 19.5.

30. The team from Washington High School since the standard deviation of their weights is greatest. See students' work.

31. Step 1 Find the mean.

$\bar{x} = \dfrac{90(3) + 85(2) + 80(3) + 75(5) + 70(6) + 65(4)}{3 + 2 + 3 + 7 + 6 + 4}$

$= \dfrac{1885}{25}$

$= 75.4$

Step 2 Find the variance. Let f_n represent the frequency of the nth score.

$\sigma^2 = \dfrac{f_1(x_1 - \bar{x})^2 + f_2(x_2 - \bar{x})^2 + \ldots + f_n(x_n - \bar{x})^2}{f_1 + f_2 + \ldots + f_n}$

$= \dfrac{3(90 - 75.4)^2 + 2(85 - 75.4)^2 + \ldots + 6(70 - 75.4)^2 + 4(65 - 75.4)^2}{3 + 2 + \ldots + 6 + 4}$

$= \dfrac{1496}{25}$

$= 59.84$

The variance is about 59.8.

Step 3 Find the standard deviation.

$\sigma^2 = 59.84$

$\sigma \approx 7.735631842$

The standard deviation is about 7.7.

32. Within one standard deviation of the mean means greater than $75.4 - 7.7$ or 67.7 and less than $75.4 + 7.7$ or 83.1. There are $6 + 7 + 3$ or 16 scores that are in the interval from 67.7 to 83.1. The percent of scores that are within one standard deviation of the mean is $\frac{16}{25}$ or 64%.

33. Within two standard deviations of the mean means greater than $75.4 - 2(7.7)$ or 60 and less than $75.4 + 2(7.7)$ or 90.8. All of the scores are in the interval from 60 to 90.8. The percent of scores that are within two standard deviations of the mean is 100%.

34. Different scales are used on the vertical axes.

35. Sample answer: The first graph might be used by a sales manager to show a salesperson that he or she does not deserve a big raise. It appears that sales are steady but not increasing fast enough to warrant a big raise.

36. Sample answer: The second graph might be shown by the company owner to a prospective buyer of the company. It looks like there is a dramatic rise in sales.

37. Set A:

Step 1 Find the mean.

$$\bar{x} = \frac{1+2+2+2+2+3+3+3+3+4}{10}$$

$$= 2.5$$

The mean is 2.5.

Step 2 Find the median. Order the numbers from least to greatest. The median is in the middle.

$$1 \quad 2 \quad 2 \quad 2 \quad \underbrace{2 \quad 3}\quad 3 \quad 3 \quad 3 \quad 4$$

$$\frac{2+3}{2} = 2.5$$

The median is 2.5.

Step 3 Find the variance.

$$\sigma^2 = \frac{(x_1 - \bar{x})^2 + (x_2 - \bar{x})^2 + \ldots + (x_n - \bar{x})^2}{n}$$

$$= \frac{(1-2.5)^2 + (2-2.5)^2 + \cdots + (3-2.5)^2 + (4-2.5)^2}{10}$$

$$= \frac{6.5}{10}$$

$$= 0.65$$

The variance is about 0.7.

Step 4 Find the standard deviation.

$$\sigma^2 = 0.65$$

$$\sigma \approx 0.8062257748$$

The standard deviation is about 0.8.

Set B:

Step 1 Find the mean.

$$\bar{x} = \frac{1+1+2+2+2+3+3+3+4+4}{10}$$

$$= 2.5$$

The mean is 2.5.

Step 2 Find the median. Order the numbers from least to greatest. The median is in the middle.

$$1 \quad 1 \quad 2 \quad 2 \quad \underbrace{2 \quad 3}\quad 3 \quad 3 \quad 4 \quad 4$$

$$\frac{2+3}{2} = 2.5$$

The median is 2.5.

Step 3 Find the variance.

$$\sigma^2 = \frac{(x_1 - \bar{x})^2 + (x_2 - \bar{x})^2 + \ldots + (x_n - \bar{x})^2}{n}$$

$$= \frac{(1-2.5)^2 + (1-2.5)^2 + \cdots + (4-2.5)^2 + (4-2.5)^2}{10}$$

$$= \frac{10.5}{10}$$

$$= 1.05$$

The variance is about 1.1.

Step 4 Find the standard deviation.

$$\sigma^2 = 1.05$$

$$\sigma \approx 1.024695077$$

The standard deviation is about 1.0.

38. The first histogram is lower in the middle and higher on the ends, so it represents data that are more spread out. Since set B has the greater standard deviation, set B corresponds to the first histogram, and set A corresponds to the second.

39. The statistic(s) that best represent a set of test scores depends on the distribution of the particular set of scores. Answers should include the following.
- mean, 73.9; median, 76.5; mode, 94
- The mode is not representative at all because it is the highest score. The median is more representative than the mean because it is influenced less than the mean by the two very low scores of 34 and 19.

40. A; mean $= \dfrac{\text{sum of the data}}{\text{number of items in data set}}$

$$= \frac{(x+1) + (3x-2) + (2x-5)}{3}$$

$$= \frac{6x-6}{3}$$

$$= 2x - 2$$

The mean is $2x - 2$.

41. D; Let x represent Manuel's score on the fourth test.

$$\text{mean} = \frac{\text{sum of the scores}}{\text{number of scores}}$$

$$90 = \frac{92 + 85 + 84 + x}{4}$$

$$90 = \frac{261 + x}{4}$$

$$360 = 261 + x$$

$$99 = x$$

Manuel needs a score of 99 on the fourth test.

42. **Step 1** Find the mean.

$$\bar{x} = \frac{95 + 91 + 88 + 86}{4}$$

$$= 90$$

Step 2 Find the mean deviation.

$$MD = \frac{|x_1 - \bar{x}| + |x_2 - \bar{x}| + \ldots + |x_n - \bar{x}|}{n}$$

$$= \frac{|95 - 90| + |91 - 90| + |88 - 90| + |86 - 90|}{4}$$

$$= \frac{12}{4}$$

$$= 3$$

The mean deviation is 3.

43. **Step 1** Find the mean.

$$\bar{x} = \frac{10.4 + 11.4 + 16.2 + 14.9 + 13.5}{5}$$

$$= 13.28$$

Step 2 Find the mean deviation.

$$MD = \frac{|x_1 - \bar{x}| + |x_2 - \bar{x}| + \ldots + |x_n - \bar{x}|}{n}$$

$$= \frac{|10.4 - 13.28| + |11.4 - 13.28| + \ldots + |14.9 - 13.28| + |13.5 - 13.28|}{5}$$

$$= \frac{9.52}{5}$$

$$= 1.904$$

The mean deviation is about 1.9.

44. The mean deviation would be greater for the group of data that has the greater standard deviation and lower for the group of data that has the smaller standard deviation.

45. Since there is a card that is a 5 and a spade, the events are inclusive.

$P(5) = \frac{4}{52}$

$P(\text{spade}) = \frac{13}{52}$

$P(5 \text{ and spade}) = \frac{1}{52}$

$P(5 \text{ or spade}) = P(5) + P(\text{spade}) - P(5 \text{ and spade})$

$= \frac{4}{52} + \frac{13}{52} - \frac{1}{52}$

$= \frac{4}{13}$

The probability that a card drawn is a 5 or a spade is $\frac{4}{13}$.

46. These are mutually exclusive events, since the coin cannot be both a nickel and a dime.

$P(\text{nickel or dime}) = P(\text{nickel}) + P(\text{dime})$

$= \frac{10}{42} + \frac{8}{42}$

$= \frac{3}{7}$

The probability that the coin is a nickel or a dime is $\frac{3}{7}$.

47. $P(\text{ace, then king }) = P(\text{ace}) \cdot P(\text{king})$

$= \frac{4}{52} \cdot \frac{4}{52}$

$= \frac{1}{169}$

The probability is $\frac{1}{169}$.

48. $P(\text{ace, then king}) = P(\text{ace}) \cdot P(\text{king following ace})$

$= \frac{4}{52} \cdot \frac{4}{51}$

$= \frac{4}{663}$

The probability is $\frac{4}{663}$.

49. $P(\text{heart, then club})$

$= P(\text{heart}) \cdot P(\text{club following heart})$

$= \frac{13}{52} \cdot \frac{13}{51}$

$= \frac{13}{204}$

The probability is $\frac{13}{204}$.

50. $P(\text{heart, then club}) = P(\text{heart}) \cdot P(\text{club})$

$= \frac{13}{52} \cdot \frac{13}{52}$

$= \frac{1}{16}$

The probability is $\frac{1}{16}$.

51. The center of this hyperbola is at the origin. According to the equation, $a^2 = 81$ and $b^2 = 25$, so $a = 9$ and $b = 5$. The coordinates of the vertices are $(0, 9)$ and $(0, -9)$.

$c^2 = a^2 + b^2$

$c^2 = 9^2 + 5^2$

$c^2 = 106$

$c = \sqrt{106}$

The foci are at $(0, \sqrt{106})$ and $(0, -\sqrt{106})$.

The equations of the asymptotes are $y = \pm\frac{a}{b}x$ or $y = \pm\frac{9}{5}x$. Thus, the slopes of the asymptotes are $\pm\frac{9}{5}$.

52. $f[g(-1)] = f[4(-1)^2]$

$= f(4)$

$= 4 - 7$

$= -3$

53. $h[f(15)] = h[15 - 7]$

$= h(8)$

$= 2(8) + 1$

$= 17$

54. $[f \circ h](2) = f[h(2)]$

$= f[2(2) + 1]$

$= f(5)$

$= 5 - 7$

$= -2$

55. The volume of the rectangular tank is $(x - 1)(x + 3)(x - 2)$ or $x^3 - 7x + 6$. To find the amount unbottled divide $x^3 - 7x + 6$ by $x - 3$. Use synthetic division.

$$\begin{array}{r|rrrr} 1 & 1 & 0 & -7 & 6 \\ & & 3 & 9 & 6 \\ \hline & 1 & 3 & 2 & \mid 12 \end{array}$$

Since the remainder is 12, the amount left unbottled is 12 cubic centimeters.

56. $x = \dfrac{\begin{vmatrix} e & b \\ f & d \end{vmatrix}}{\begin{vmatrix} a & b \\ c & d \end{vmatrix}}$ $\qquad$ $y = \dfrac{\begin{vmatrix} a & e \\ c & f \end{vmatrix}}{\begin{vmatrix} a & b \\ c & d \end{vmatrix}}$

$= \dfrac{\begin{vmatrix} 28 & 6 \\ -20 & -4 \end{vmatrix}}{\begin{vmatrix} 2 & 6 \\ -1 & -4 \end{vmatrix}}$ $\qquad$ $= \dfrac{\begin{vmatrix} 2 & 28 \\ -1 & -20 \end{vmatrix}}{\begin{vmatrix} 2 & 6 \\ -1 & -4 \end{vmatrix}}$

$= \dfrac{28(-4) - (-20)(6)}{2(-4) - (-1)(6)}$ $\qquad$ $= \dfrac{2(-20) - (-1)(28)}{2(-4) - (-1)(6)}$

$= \dfrac{8}{-2}$ $\qquad$ $= \dfrac{-12}{-2}$

$= -4$ $\qquad$ $= 6$

The solution is $(-4, 6)$.

57. $x = \dfrac{\begin{vmatrix} e & b \\ f & d \end{vmatrix}}{\begin{vmatrix} a & b \\ c & d \end{vmatrix}}$ $\qquad$ $y = \dfrac{\begin{vmatrix} a & e \\ c & f \end{vmatrix}}{\begin{vmatrix} a & b \\ c & d \end{vmatrix}}$

$= \dfrac{\begin{vmatrix} -8 & -3 \\ 9 & 1 \end{vmatrix}}{\begin{vmatrix} 7 & -3 \\ 4 & 1 \end{vmatrix}}$ $\qquad$ $= \dfrac{\begin{vmatrix} 7 & -8 \\ 4 & 9 \end{vmatrix}}{\begin{vmatrix} 7 & -3 \\ 4 & 1 \end{vmatrix}}$

$= \dfrac{-8(1) - 9(-3)}{7(1) - 4(-3)}$ $\qquad$ $= \dfrac{7(9) - 4(-8)}{7(1) - 4(-3)}$

$= \dfrac{19}{19}$ $\qquad$ $= \dfrac{95}{19}$

$= 1$ $\qquad$ $= 5$

The solution is $(1, 5)$.

58. $x = \dfrac{\begin{vmatrix} e & b \\ f & d \end{vmatrix}}{\begin{vmatrix} a & b \\ c & d \end{vmatrix}}$ $\qquad$ $y = \dfrac{\begin{vmatrix} a & e \\ c & f \end{vmatrix}}{\begin{vmatrix} a & b \\ c & d \end{vmatrix}}$

$= \dfrac{\begin{vmatrix} -7 & -2 \\ -4 & 1 \end{vmatrix}}{\begin{vmatrix} 1 & -2 \\ -3 & 1 \end{vmatrix}}$ $\qquad$ $= \dfrac{\begin{vmatrix} 1 & -7 \\ -3 & -4 \end{vmatrix}}{\begin{vmatrix} 1 & -2 \\ -3 & 1 \end{vmatrix}}$

$= \dfrac{-7(1) - (-4)(-2)}{1(1) - (-3)(-2)}$ $\qquad$ $= \dfrac{1(-4) - (-3)(-7)}{1(1) - (-3)(-2)}$

$= \dfrac{-15}{-5}$ $\qquad$ $= \dfrac{-25}{-5}$

$= 3$ $\qquad$ $= 5$

The solution is $(3, 5)$.

59. $\underbrace{68\%}_{} \ \underbrace{\text{of}}_{} \ \underbrace{200}_{}$
$0.68 \cdot 200 = 136$

60. $\underbrace{68\%}_{} \ \underbrace{\text{of}}_{} \ \underbrace{500}_{}$
$0.68 \cdot 500 = 340$

61. $\underbrace{95\%}_{} \ \underbrace{\text{of}}_{} \ \underbrace{400}_{}$
$0.95 \cdot 400 = 380$

62. $\underbrace{95\%}_{} \ \underbrace{\text{of}}_{} \ \underbrace{500}_{}$
$0.95 \cdot 500 = 475$

63. $\underbrace{99\%}_{} \ \underbrace{\text{of}}_{} \ \underbrace{400}_{}$
$0.99 \cdot 400 = 396$

64. $\underbrace{99\%}_{} \ \underbrace{\text{of}}_{} \ \underbrace{500}_{}$
$0.99 \cdot 500 = 495$

Page 670　Practice Quiz 2

1. $P(\text{red, then green}) = P(\text{red}) \cdot P(\text{green})$
$$= \frac{5}{10} \cdot \frac{3}{10}$$
$$= \frac{3}{20}$$
The probability is $\frac{3}{20}$.

2. $P(\text{red, then green}) = P(\text{red}) \cdot P(\text{green following red})$
$$= \frac{5}{10} \cdot \frac{3}{9}$$
$$= \frac{1}{6}$$
The probability is $\frac{1}{6}$.

3. $P(2 \text{ red}) = P(\text{red}) \cdot P(\text{red following red})$
$$= \frac{5}{10} \cdot \frac{4}{9}$$
$$= \frac{2}{9}$$
The probability is $\frac{2}{9}$.

4. $P(2 \text{ red}) = P(\text{red}) \cdot P(\text{red})$
$$= \frac{5}{10} \cdot \frac{5}{10}$$
$$= \frac{1}{4}$$
The probability is $\frac{1}{4}$.

5. These are mutually exclusive events, since the outcome cannot be both 4 and 5.
$P(4 \text{ or } 5) = P(4) + P(5)$
$$= \frac{1}{12} \cdot \frac{1}{12}$$
$$= \frac{1}{6}$$
The probability of rolling a 4 or 5 is $\frac{1}{6}$.

6. Since there are outcomes that are both even and a multiple of 3, the events are inclusive.
$P(\text{even}) = \frac{6}{12}$
$P(\text{multiple of 3}) = \frac{4}{12}$
$P(\text{even and multiple of 3}) = \frac{2}{12}$
$P(\text{even or multiple of 3})$
$\quad = P(\text{even}) + P(\text{multiple of 3})$
$\quad\quad - P(\text{even and multiple of 3})$
$\quad = \frac{6}{12} + \frac{4}{12} - \frac{2}{12}$
$\quad = \frac{2}{3}$
The probability of rolling an even number or a multiple of 3 is $\frac{2}{3}$.

7. These are mutually exclusive events, since the outcome cannot be both odd and a multiple of 4.
$P(\text{odd or multiple of 4})$
$\quad = P(\text{odd}) + P(\text{multiple of 4})$
$\quad = \frac{6}{12} + \frac{3}{12}$
$\quad = \frac{3}{4}$
The probability of rolling an odd number or a multiple of 4 is $\frac{3}{4}$.

8. Step 1 Find the mean.
$$\bar{x} = \frac{5 + 8 + 2 + 9 + 4}{5}$$
$$= 5.6$$
Step 2 Find the variance.
$$\sigma^2 = \frac{(x_1 - \bar{x})^2 + (x_2 - \bar{x})^2 + \ldots + (x_n - \bar{x})^2}{n}$$
$$= \frac{(5 - 5.6)^2 + (8 - 5.6)^2 + \ldots + (9 - 5.6)^2 + (4 - 5.6)^2}{5}$$
$$= \frac{33.2}{5}$$
$$= 6.64$$
The variance is about 6.6.
Step 3 Find the standard deviation.
$\sigma^2 = 6.64$
$\sigma \approx 2.576819745$
The standard deviation is about 2.6.

9. Step 1 Find the mean.
$$\bar{x} = \frac{16 + 22 + 18 + 31 + 25 + 22}{6}$$
$$\approx 22.3$$
Step 2 Find the variance.
$$\sigma^2 = \frac{(x_1 - \bar{x})^2 + (x_2 - \bar{x})^2 + \ldots + (x_n - \bar{x})^2}{n}$$
$$\approx \frac{(16 - 22.3)^2 + (22 - 22.3)^2 + \ldots + (25 - 22.3)^2 + (22 - 22.3)^2}{6}$$
$$\approx \frac{141.3}{6}$$
$$\approx 23.55$$
The variance is about 23.6.
Step 3 Find the standard deviation.
$\sigma^2 \approx 23.55$
$\sigma \approx 4.853$
The standard deviation is about 4.9.

10. Step 1 Find the mean.

$$\bar{x} = \frac{425 + 400 + 395 + 415 + 420}{5}$$

$$= 411$$

Step 2 Find the variance.

$$\sigma^2 = \frac{(x_1 - \bar{x})^2 + (x_2 - \bar{x})^2 + \ldots + (x_n - \bar{x})^2}{n}$$

$$= \frac{(425 - 411)^2 + (400 - 411)^2 + \ldots + (415 - 411)^2 + (420 - 411)^2}{5}$$

$$= \frac{670}{5}$$

$$= 134$$

The variance is 134.

Step 3 Find the standard deviation.

$$\sigma^2 = 134$$

$$\sigma \approx 11.5758369$$

The standard deviation is about 11.6.

12-7 | The Normal Distribution

Page 673   Check for Understanding

1. Sample answer:

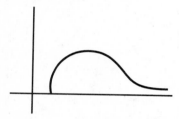

The use of cassettes since CDs were introduced.

2. The mean of the three graphs is the same, but the standard deviations are different. The first graph has the least standard deviation, the standard deviation of the middle graph is slightly greater, and the standard deviation of the last graph is greatest.

3. Since 99% of the data is within 3 standard deviations of the mean, 1% of the data is more than 3 standard deviations from the mean. By symmetry, half of this, or 0.5%, is more than 3 standard deviations above the mean.

4. Use a table to make a histogram.

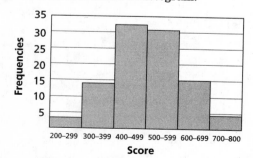

Since the histogram is high in the middle and low on both ends, the data appear to be normally distributed.

5. The values 82 and 88 are 1 standard deviation below and above the mean, respectively. Therefore, about 68% of the data are between 82 and 88.

6. The values 88 and 91 are 1 and 2 standard deviations above the mean, respectively. Therefore, about 13.5% of the data are between 88 and 91.

7. The values 79 and 91 are 2 standard deviations below and above the mean, respectively. Since about 95% of the data are less than 2 standard deviations away from the mean, the probability that a student chosen at random scored between 79 and 91 is about 95% or 0.95.

8. The values 25,000 and 35,000 are 1 standard deviation below and above the mean, respectively. Therefore, about 68% of the data are between 25,000 and 35,000.

$$10,000 \times 68\% = 6800$$

About 6800 tires will last between 25,000 and 35,000 miles.

9. The value 40,000 is 2 standard deviations above the mean. You know about 100% − 95% or 5% of the data are more than 2 standard deviations away from the mean. By the symmetry of the normal curve, half of 5%, or 2.5%, of the data are more than 2 standard deviations above the mean.

$$10,000 \times 2.5\% = 250$$

About 250 tires will last more than 40,000 miles.

10. The value 25,000 is 1 standard deviation below the mean. You know about 100% − 68% or 32% of the data are more than 1 standard deviation away from the mean. By the symmetry of the normal curve, half of 32%, or 16%, of the data are more than 1 standard deviation below the mean.

$$10,000 \times 16\% = 1600$$

About 1600 tires will last less than 25,000 miles.

11. The value 20,000 is 2 standard deviations below the mean. You know about 95% of the data are less than 2 standard deviations away from the mean. By the symmetry of the normal curve, half of 95%, or 47.5%, of the data are less than 2 standard deviations below the mean. The value 35,000 is 1 standard deviation above the mean. You know about 68% of the data are less than 1 standard deviation away from the mean. By the symmetry of the normal curve, half of 68%, or 34%, of the data are less than 1 standard deviation above the mean. The probability that a tire will last between 20,000 and 35,000 miles is about 47.5% + 34% or 81.5%.

12. Use a table to make a histogram.

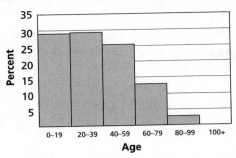

Since the histogram is high at the left and has a tail to the right, the data appear to be positively skewed.

13. Use a table to make a histogram.

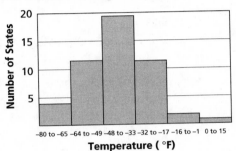

Since the histogram is high in the middle and low on both ends, the data appear to be normally distributed.

14. Use a table to make a histogram.

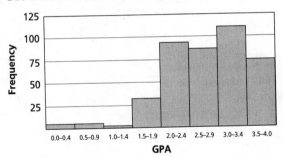

Since the histogram is high at the right and has a tail to the left, the data appear to be negatively skewed.

15. The values 9 and 15 are 1 standard deviation below and above the mean, respectively. Therefore, about 68% of the data are between 9 and 15. Thus, about 68% of the products last between 9 and 15 days.

16. The value 15 is 1 standard deviation above the mean. You know about 68% of the data are less than 1 standard deviation away from the mean. By the symmetry of the normal curve, half of 68%, or 34% of the data are less than 1 standard deviation above the mean. Thus, about 34% of the products last between 12 and 15 days.

17. The value 3 is 3 standard deviations below the mean. You know about 100% − 99% or 1% of the data are more than 3 standard deviations away from the mean. By the symmetry of the normal curve, half of 1%, or 0.5% of the data are more than 3 standard deviations below the mean. Thus, about 0.5% of the products last less than 3 days.

18. The value 15 is 1 standard deviation above the mean. You know about 100% − 68% or 32% of the data are more than 1 standard deviation away from the mean. By the symmetry of the normal curve, half of 32%, or 16% of the data are more than 1 standard deviation above the mean. Thus, about 16% of the products last more than 15 days.

19. The value 6 is the mean. By the symmetry of the normal curve, half of 100%, or 50% of the data are more than the mean. Thus, about 50% of the time you get more than 6 ounces.

20. The value 6 is the mean. By the symmetry of the normal curve, half of 100%, or 50% of the data are less than the mean. Thus, about 50% of the time you get less than 6 ounces.

21. The values 5.6 and 6.4 are 2 standard deviations below and above the mean, respectively. Therefore, about 95% of the data are between 5.6 and 6.4. Thus, about 95% of the time you get between 5.6 and 6.4 ounces.

22. The value 120 is the mean. By the symmetry of the normal curve, half of 100%, or 50% of the data are more than the mean. Thus, about 50% of the CDs are greater than 120 millimeters.

23. The value 119 is 1 standard deviation below the mean. You know about 68% of the data are less than 1 standard deviation away from the mean. By the symmetry of the normal curve, half of 68%, or 34% of the data are less than 1 standard deviation below the mean.
$1000 \times 34\% = 340$
The value 122 is 2 standard deviations above the mean. You know about 95% of the data are less than 2 standard deviations away from the mean. By the symmetry of the normal curve, half of 95% or 47.5% of the data are less than 2 standard deviations above the mean.
$1000 \times 47.5\% = 475$
Thus, about 340 + 475 or 815 CDs would be between 119 and 122 millimeters.

24. Too large to fit in the drives means larger than 122 millimeters. The value 122 is 2 standard deviations above the mean. You know about 100% − 95% or 5% of the data are more than 2 standard deviations away from the mean. By the symmetry of the normal curve, half of 5%, or 2.5% of the data are more than 2 standard deviations above the mean.
$1000 \times 2.5\% = 25$
Thus, about 25 CDs would be too large to fit in the drives.

25. The value 108 is 1 standard deviation below the mean. You know about 100% − 68% or 32% of the data are more than 1 standard deviation away from the mean. By the symmetry of the normal curve, half of 32%, or 16% of the data are more than 1 standard deviation below the mean. Thus, about 16% of the students have blood pressures below 108.

26. The value 108 is 1 standard deviation below the mean. You know about 68% of the data are less than 1 standard deviation away from the mean. By the symmetry of the normal curve, half of 68%, or 34% of the data are less than 1 standard deviation below the mean.

$800 \times 34\% = 272$

The value 144 is 2 standard deviations above the mean. You know about 95% of the data are less than 2 standard deviations away from the mean. By the symmetry of the normal curve, half of 95% or 47.5% of the data are less than 2 standard deviations above the mean.

$800 \times 47.5\% = 380$

Thus, about 272 + 380 or 652 students have blood pressures between 108 and 144.

27. The mean would increase by 25; the standard deviation would not change; and the graph would be translated 25 units to the right.

28. If a large enough group of athletes is studied, some of the characteristics may be normally distributed; others may have skewed distributions. Answers should include the following.

-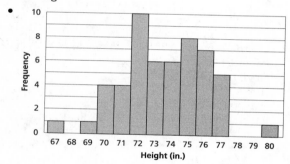

- Since the histogram has two peaks, the data may not be normally distributed. This may be because athletes who play certain positions tend to be of similar large sizes while athletes who play other positions tend to be of similar small sizes.

29. A; $x^2 + y^2 = x^2 + 2xy + y^2 - 2xy$
$= (x + y)^2 - 2(xy)$
$= 5^2 - 2(6)$
$= 25 - 12$
$= 13$

30. D; $0.04 = (0.2)^2$
$0.16 = (0.4)^2$
$\frac{4}{9} = \left(\frac{2}{3}\right)^2$
$\frac{2}{3} = \left(\sqrt{\frac{2}{3}}\right)^2$
$= \left(\frac{\sqrt{2}}{\sqrt{3}}\right)^2$

$\sqrt{2}$ and $\sqrt{3}$ are not rational. Thus $\sqrt{\frac{2}{3}}$ is not rational.

Page 675 Maintain Your Skills

31. Step 1 Find the mean.
$$\bar{x} = \frac{7 + 16 + 9 + 4 + 12 + 3 + 9 + 4}{8}$$
$$= 8$$

Step 2 Find the variance.
$$\sigma^2 = \frac{(x_1 - \bar{x})^2 + (x_2 - \bar{x})^2 + \ldots + (x_n - \bar{x})^2}{n}$$
$$= \frac{(7 - 8)^2 + (16-8)^2 + \ldots +}{8}$$
$$= \frac{(9 - 8)^2 + (4 - 8)^2}{8}$$
$$= \frac{140}{8}$$
$$= 17.5$$

The variance is 17.5.

Step 3 Find the standard deviation.
$\sigma^2 = 17.5$
$\sigma \approx 4.183300133$

The standard deviation is about 4.2.

32. Step 1 Find the mean.
$$\bar{x} = \frac{12 + 14 + 28 + 19 + 11 + 7 + 10}{7}$$
$$\approx 14.4$$

Step 2 Find the variance.
$$\sigma^2 = \frac{(x_1 - \bar{x})^2 + (x_2 - \bar{x})^2 + \ldots + (x_n - \bar{x})^2}{n}$$
$$\approx \frac{(12 - 14.4)^2 + (14 - 14.4)^2 + \ldots +}{7}$$
$$\approx \frac{(7 - 14.4)^2 + (10 - 14.4)^2}{7}$$
$$\approx \frac{297.7}{7}$$
$$\approx 42.53$$

The variance is about 42.5.

Step 3 Find the standard deviation.
$\sigma^2 \approx 42.53$
$\sigma \approx 6.521$

The standard deviation is about 6.5.

33. These are mutually exclusive events, since the card cannot be both a jack and a queen.
$P(\text{jack or queen}) = P(\text{jack}) + P(\text{queen})$
$$= \frac{4}{52} + \frac{4}{52}$$
$$= \frac{2}{13}$$

The probability of drawing a jack or a queen is $\frac{2}{13}$.

34. Since one card is an ace and a heart, the events are inclusive.

$P(\text{ace}) = \frac{4}{52}$

$P(\text{heart}) = \frac{13}{52}$

$P(\text{ace and heart}) = \frac{1}{52}$

$P(\text{ace or heart})$
$= P(\text{ace}) + P(\text{heart}) - P(\text{ace and heart})$
$= \frac{4}{52} + \frac{13}{52} - \frac{1}{52}$
$= \frac{4}{13}$

The probability of drawing an ace or a heart is $\frac{4}{13}$.

35. These are mutually exclusive events, since the card cannot be both a 2 and a face card.

$P(2 \text{ or face card}) = P(2) + P(\text{face card})$
$= \frac{4}{52} + \frac{12}{52}$
$= \frac{4}{13}$

The probability of drawing a 2 or a face card is $\frac{4}{13}$.

36. There are exactly 3 complex roots. According to Descartes' Rule of Signs, there is 1 positive real root, and 1 negative real root.

Factor $x^3 + 4x^2 - 5x$.
$x^3 + 4x^2 - 5x = 0$
$x(x^2 + 4x - 5) = 0$
$x(x + 5)(x - 1) = 0$
$x = 0 \quad \text{or} \quad x + 5 = 0 \quad \text{or} \quad x - 1 = 0$
$\phantom{x = 0 \quad \text{or} \quad} x = -5 \phantom{\quad \text{or} \quad} x = 1$

The rational zeros are -5, 0, and 1.

37. There are exactly 3 complex roots. According to Descartes' Rule of Signs, there are 2 or 0 positive real roots, and 1 negative real root. The possible rational zeros are $\pm 1, \pm 2, \pm 3, \pm 4, \pm 6, \pm 8, \pm 12,$ and ± 24. Make a table and test some possible rational zeros.

$\frac{p}{q}$	1	−3	−10	24
1	1	−2	−12	12
2	1	−1	−12	0

Since $p(2) = 0$, you know that $x = 2$ is a zero. The depressed polynomial is $x^2 - x - 12$.

Factor $x^2 - x - 12$.
$x^2 - x - 12 = 0$
$(x + 3)(x - 4) = 0$
$x + 3 = 0 \quad \text{or} \quad x - 4 = 0$
$x = -3 \phantom{\quad \text{or} \quad} x = 4$

The rational zeros are -3, 2, and 4.

38. There are exactly 4 complex roots. According to Descart's Rule of Signs, there are 2 or 0 positive real roots, and 2 or 0 negative real roots.
A possible rational zero is 1. Make a table and test some possible rational zeros.

$\frac{p}{q}$	1	0	−2	0	1
1	1	1	−1	−1	0

Since $h(1) = 0$, you know that $x = 1$ is a zero. The depressed polynomial is $x^3 + x^2 - x - 1$.

Factor $x^3 + x^2 - x - 1$.
$x^3 + x^2 - x - 1 = 0$
$(x^3 + x^2) + (-x - 1) = 0$
$x^2(x + 1) - 1(x + 1) = 0$
$(x^2 - 1)(x + 1) = 0$
$(x - 1)(x + 1)(x + 1) = 0$
$x - 1 = 0 \quad \text{or} \quad x + 1 = 0 \quad \text{or} \quad x + 1 = 0$
$x = 1 \phantom{\quad \text{or} \quad} x = -1 \phantom{\quad \text{or} \quad} x = -1$

The rational zeros are -1 and 1.

39. There are exactly 4 complex roots. According to Descartes' Rule of Signs, there are 3 or 1 positive real roots, and 1 negative real root. The possible rational zeros are $\pm 1, \pm 2, \pm 3, \pm 6, \ldots$. Make a table and test some possible rational zeros.

$\frac{p}{q}$	4	−13	−13	28	−6
1	4	−9	−22	6	0

Since $f(1) = 0$, you know that $x = 1$ is a zero. The depressed polynomial is $4x^3 - 9x^2 - 22x + 6$. The possible rational zeros of the depressed polynomial are the same as for the original polynomial. Make another table and test some possible rational zeros.

$\frac{p}{q}$	4	−9	−22	6
1	4	−5	−27	−21
$\frac{1}{4}$	4	−8	−24	0

Since $f\left(\frac{1}{4}\right) = 0$, you know that $x = \frac{1}{4}$ is a zero. The new depressed polynomial is $4x^2 - 8x - 24$. This polynomial does not factor. The rational zeros are $\frac{1}{4}$ and 1.

40. Graph $y = 216t^2 - 5^3$.

x	−1	$-\frac{1}{2}$	0	$\frac{1}{2}$	1
y	91	−71	−125	−71	91

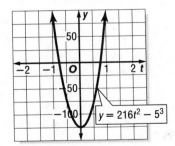

From the graph, we see that the zeros are between -1 and $-\frac{1}{2}$, and $\frac{1}{2}$ and 1. We estimate that the storm lasts about 45 minutes.

613

41. Substitute 5 for d in the equation and solve for t.

$$216t^2 = d^3$$
$$216t^2 = 5^3$$
$$216t^2 = 125$$
$$t^2 = \frac{125}{216}$$
$$t = \sqrt{\frac{125}{216}}$$
$$t \approx \pm 0.7607257743$$

Since the time cannot be negative, the storm lasts for about 0.76 hour or about 45.6 minutes. This is very close to our answer in Exercise 40.

42. Use the Binomial Theorem to write the expansion in sigma notation.

$$(a + b)^7 = \sum_{k=0}^{7} \frac{7!}{(7-k)!k!} a^{7-k} b^k$$

In the third term, $k = 2$.

$$\frac{7!}{(7-k)!k!} a^{7-k} b^k = \frac{7!}{(7-2)!2!} a^{7-2} b^2$$
$$= \frac{7 \cdot 6}{2 \cdot 1} a^5 b^2$$
$$= 21 a^5 b^2$$

43. Use the Binomial Theorem to write the expansion in sigma notation.

$$(c + d)^8 = \sum_{k=0}^{8} \frac{8!}{(8-k)!k!} c^{8-k} d^k$$

In the fourth term, $k = 3$.

$$\frac{8!}{(8-k)!k!} c^{8-k} d^k = \frac{8!}{(8-3)!3!} c^{8-3} d^3$$
$$= \frac{8 \cdot 7 \cdot 6}{3 \cdot 2 \cdot 1} c^5 d^3$$
$$= 56 c^5 d^3$$

44. Use the Binomial Theorem to write the expansion in sigma notation.

$$(x + y)^9 = \sum_{k=0}^{9} \frac{9!}{(9-k)!k!} x^{9-k} y^k$$

In the fifth term, $k = 4$.

$$\frac{9!}{(9-k)!k!} x^{9-k} y^k = \frac{9!}{(9-4)!4!} x^{9-4} y^4$$
$$= \frac{9 \cdot 8 \cdot 7 \cdot 6}{4 \cdot 3 \cdot 2 \cdot 1} x^5 y^4$$
$$= 126\, x^5 y^4$$

12-8 Binomial Experiments

Page 678   Check for Understanding

1. Sample answer: In a 5-card hand, what is the probability that at least 2 cards are hearts?

2. RRRWW, RRWRW, RRWWR, RWRRW, RWRWR, RWWRR, WRRRW, WRRWR, WRWRR, WWRRR

3a. Each trial has more than two possible outcomes.

3b. The number of trials is not fixed.

3c. The trials are not independent.

4. The probability of tossing a head is $\frac{1}{2}$. The probability of tossing a tail is $\frac{1}{2}$. There are $C(3, 2)$ ways to toss 2 heads in three tosses.

$$P(\text{exactly 2 heads}) = C(3, 2)\left(\frac{1}{2}\right)^2 \left(\frac{1}{2}\right)^1$$
$$= 3\left(\frac{1}{2}\right)^2 \left(\frac{1}{2}\right)$$
$$= \frac{3}{8}$$

The probability of tossing exactly 2 heads is $\frac{3}{8}$.

5. The probability of tossing a head is $\frac{1}{2}$. The probability of tossing a tail is $\frac{1}{2}$. There are $C(3, 0)$ ways to toss 0 heads in three tosses.

$$P(\text{0 heads}) = C(3, 0)\left(\frac{1}{2}\right)^0 \left(\frac{1}{2}\right)^3$$
$$= 1\left(\frac{1}{2}\right)^3$$
$$= \frac{1}{8}$$

The probability of tossing 0 heads is $\frac{1}{8}$.

6. Instead of adding the probabilities of getting exactly 1, 2, and 3 heads, it is easier to subtract the probability of getting exactly 0 heads from 1.

$$P(\text{at least 1 head}) = 1 - P(\text{0 heads})$$
$$= 1 - C(3, 0)\left(\frac{1}{2}\right)^0 \left(\frac{1}{2}\right)^3$$
$$= 1 - \frac{1}{8}$$
$$= \frac{7}{8}$$

The probability of tossing at least 1 head is $\frac{7}{8}$.

7. The probability of drawing a jack is $\frac{1}{13}$. The probability of not drawing a jack is $\frac{12}{13}$. There are $C(4, 4)$ ways to draw 4 jacks in four draws.

$$P(\text{4 jacks}) = C(4, 4)\left(\frac{1}{13}\right)^4 \left(\frac{12}{13}\right)^0$$
$$= 1\left(\frac{1}{13}\right)^4$$
$$= \frac{1}{28,561}$$

The probability of drawing 4 jacks is $\frac{1}{28,561}$.

8. The probability of drawing a jack is $\frac{1}{13}$. The probability of not drawing a jack is $\frac{12}{13}$. There are $C(4, 3)$ ways to draw 3 jacks in four draws.

$$P(\text{exactly 3 jacks}) = C(4, 3)\left(\frac{1}{13}\right)^3 \left(\frac{12}{13}\right)$$
$$= 4\left(\frac{1}{13}\right)^3 \left(\frac{12}{13}\right)$$
$$= \frac{48}{28,561}$$

The probability of drawing exactly 3 jacks is $\frac{48}{28,561}$.

9. Add the probabilities of drawing exactly 0 or 1 jacks.

$$P(\text{at most 1 jack})$$
$$= P(\text{0 jacks}) + P(\text{1 jack})$$
$$= C(4, 0)\left(\frac{1}{13}\right)^0 \left(\frac{12}{13}\right)^4 + C(4, 1)\left(\frac{1}{13}\right)^1 \left(\frac{12}{13}\right)^3$$
$$= \frac{20,736}{28,561} + \frac{6912}{28,561}$$
$$= \frac{27,648}{28,561}$$

The probability of drawing at most 1 jack is $\frac{27,648}{28,561}$.

10. The probability that she gets a hit in a given at-bat is 0.475. The probability that she does not get a hit in a given at-bat is 0.525. There are $C(4, 4)$ ways to get the 4 hits in 4 at-bats.

$$P(\text{4 hits}) = C(4, 4)(0.475)^4 (0.525)^0$$
$$= 1(0.475)^4$$
$$\approx 0.0509066406$$

The probability that she gets 4 hits in 4 at-bats is about 0.05.

11. The probability that she gets a hit in a given at-bat is 0.475. The probability that she does not get a hit in a given at-bat is 0.525. There are $C(4, 2)$ ways to get the 2 hits in 4 at-bats.

$$P(\text{exactly 2 hits}) = C(4, 2)(0.475)^2(0.525)^2$$
$$= \frac{4 \cdot 3}{2}(0.475)^2(0.525)^2$$
$$\approx 0.3731273438$$

The probability that she gets exactly 2 hits in 4 at-bats is about 0.37.

Pages 678–680 **Practice and Apply**

12. There are $C(4, 4)$ ways to toss 4 tails in 4 tosses.

$$P(4 \text{ tails}) = C(4, 4)\left(\frac{1}{2}\right)^4\left(\frac{1}{2}\right)^0$$
$$= 1\left(\frac{1}{2}\right)^4$$
$$= \frac{1}{16}$$

The probability of tossing 4 tails is $\frac{1}{16}$.

13. There are $C(4, 0)$ ways to toss 0 tails in 4 tosses.

$$P(0 \text{ tails}) = C(4, 0)\left(\frac{1}{2}\right)^0\left(\frac{1}{2}\right)^4$$
$$= 1\left(\frac{1}{2}\right)^4$$
$$= \frac{1}{16}$$

The probability of tossing 0 tails is $\frac{1}{16}$.

14. There are $C(4, 2)$ ways to toss 2 tails in 4 tosses.

$$P(\text{exactly 2 tails}) = C(4, 2)\left(\frac{1}{2}\right)^2\left(\frac{1}{2}\right)^2$$
$$= \frac{4 \cdot 3}{2}\left(\frac{1}{2}\right)^2\left(\frac{1}{2}\right)^2$$
$$= \frac{3}{8}$$

The probability of tossing exactly 2 tails is $\frac{3}{8}$.

15. There are $C(4, 1)$ ways to toss 1 tail in 4 tosses.

$$P(\text{exactly 1 tail}) = C(4, 1)\left(\frac{1}{2}\right)^1\left(\frac{1}{2}\right)^3$$
$$= 4\left(\frac{1}{2}\right)\left(\frac{1}{2}\right)^3$$
$$= \frac{1}{4}$$

The probability of tossing exactly 1 tail is $\frac{1}{4}$.

16. Add the probabilities of tossing exactly 3 or 4 tails.

$P(\text{at least 3 tails})$
$$= P(3 \text{ tails}) + P(4 \text{ tails})$$
$$= C(4, 3)\left(\frac{1}{2}\right)^3\left(\frac{1}{2}\right)^1 + C(4, 4)\left(\frac{1}{2}\right)^4\left(\frac{1}{2}\right)^0$$
$$= \frac{4}{16} + \frac{1}{16}$$
$$= \frac{5}{16}$$

The probability of tossing at least 3 tails is $\frac{5}{16}$.

17. Add the probabilities of tossing exactly 0, 1, or 2 tails.

$P(\text{at most 2 tails})$
$$= P(0 \text{ tails}) + P(1 \text{ tail}) + P(2 \text{ tails})$$
$$= C(4, 0)\left(\frac{1}{2}\right)^0\left(\frac{1}{2}\right)^4 + C(4, 1)\left(\frac{1}{2}\right)^1\left(\frac{1}{2}\right)^3 +$$
$$C(4, 2)\left(\frac{1}{2}\right)^2\left(\frac{1}{2}\right)^2$$
$$= \frac{1}{16} + \frac{4}{16} + \frac{6}{16}$$
$$= \frac{11}{16}$$

The probability of tossing at most 2 tails is $\frac{11}{16}$.

18. There are $C(5, 1)$ ways to roll one 5 in 5 rolls.

$$P(\text{exactly one 5}) = C(5, 1)\left(\frac{1}{6}\right)^1\left(\frac{5}{6}\right)^4$$
$$= 5\left(\frac{1}{6}\right)\left(\frac{5}{6}\right)^4$$
$$= \frac{3125}{7776}$$

The probability of rolling exactly one 5 is $\frac{3125}{7776}$.

19. There are $C(5, 3)$ ways to roll three 5s in 5 rolls.

$$P(\text{exactly three 5s}) = C(5, 3)\left(\frac{1}{6}\right)^3\left(\frac{5}{6}\right)^2$$
$$= \frac{5 \cdot 4}{2}\left(\frac{1}{6}\right)^3\left(\frac{5}{6}\right)^2$$
$$= \frac{125}{3888}$$

The probability of rolling exactly three 5s is $\frac{125}{3888}$.

20. Add the probabilities of rolling exactly zero, one, or two 5s.

$P(\text{at most two 5s})$
$$= P(\text{zero 5s}) + P(\text{one 5}) + P(\text{two 5s})$$
$$= C(5, 0)\left(\frac{1}{6}\right)^0\left(\frac{5}{6}\right)^5 + C(5, 1)\left(\frac{1}{6}\right)^1\left(\frac{5}{6}\right)^4$$
$$+ C(5, 2)\left(\frac{1}{6}\right)^2\left(\frac{5}{6}\right)^3$$
$$= \frac{3125}{7776} + \frac{3125}{7776} + \frac{1250}{7776}$$
$$= \frac{625}{648}$$

The probability of rolling at most two 5s is $\frac{625}{648}$.

21. Add the probabilities of rolling exactly three, four, or five 5s.

$P(\text{at least three 5s})$
$$= P(\text{three 5s}) + P(\text{four 5s}) + P(\text{five 5s})$$
$$= C(5, 3)\left(\frac{1}{6}\right)^3\left(\frac{5}{6}\right)^2 + C(5, 4)\left(\frac{1}{6}\right)^4\left(\frac{5}{6}\right)^1 +$$
$$C(5, 5)\left(\frac{1}{6}\right)^5\left(\frac{5}{6}\right)^0$$
$$= \frac{250}{7776} + \frac{25}{7776} + \frac{1}{7776}$$
$$= \frac{23}{648}$$

The probability of rolling at least three 5s is $\frac{23}{648}$.

22. The probability she selects the correct key is $\frac{1}{4}$. The probability she does not select the correct key is $\frac{3}{4}$. There are $C(5, 0)$ ways to never select the correct key if she selects a key five times.

$$P(\text{never the correct key}) = C(5, 0)\left(\frac{1}{4}\right)^0\left(\frac{3}{4}\right)^5$$
$$= 1\left(\frac{3}{4}\right)^5$$
$$= \frac{243}{1024}$$

The probability of never selecting the correct key is $\frac{243}{1024}$.

23. There are $C(5, 5)$ ways to always select the correct key if she selects a key five times.

$$\begin{aligned}P(\text{always the correct key}) &= C(5, 5)\left(\frac{1}{4}\right)^5\left(\frac{3}{4}\right)^0\\ &= 1\left(\frac{1}{4}\right)^5\\ &= \frac{1}{1024}\end{aligned}$$

The probability of always selecting the correct key is $\frac{1}{1024}$.

24. There are $C(5, 4)$ ways to select the correct key 4 times if she selects a key five times.

$$\begin{aligned}P(\text{correct exactly 4 times}) &= C(5, 4)\left(\frac{1}{4}\right)^4\left(\frac{3}{4}\right)^1\\ &= 5\left(\frac{1}{4}\right)^4\left(\frac{3}{4}\right)\\ &= \frac{15}{1024}\end{aligned}$$

The probability of selecting the correct key exactly four times is $\frac{15}{1024}$.

25. There are $C(5, 2)$ ways to select the correct key 2 times if she selects a key five times.

$$\begin{aligned}P(\text{correct exactly 2 times}) &= C(5, 2)\left(\frac{1}{4}\right)^2\left(\frac{3}{4}\right)^3\\ &= \frac{5\cdot 4}{2}\left(\frac{1}{4}\right)^2\left(\frac{3}{4}\right)^3\\ &= \frac{135}{512}\end{aligned}$$

The probability of selecting the correct key exactly two times is $\frac{135}{512}$.

26. Add the probabilities of selecting the correct key exactly 0, 1, or 2 times.

$$\begin{aligned}P(&\text{no more than 2 times correct})\\ &= P(\text{correct 0 times}) + P(\text{correct 1 time}) +\\ &\quad P(\text{correct 2 times})\\ &= C(5, 0)\left(\frac{1}{4}\right)^0\left(\frac{3}{4}\right)^5 + C(5, 1)\left(\frac{1}{4}\right)^1\left(\frac{3}{4}\right)^4 +\\ &\quad C(5, 2)\left(\frac{1}{4}\right)^2\left(\frac{3}{4}\right)^3\\ &= 1\left(\frac{3}{4}\right)^5 + 5\left(\frac{1}{4}\right)\left(\frac{3}{4}\right)^4 + \frac{5\cdot 4}{2}\left(\frac{1}{4}\right)^2\left(\frac{3}{4}\right)^3\\ &= \frac{243}{1024} + \frac{405}{1024} + \frac{270}{1024}\\ &= \frac{459}{512}\end{aligned}$$

The probability of selecting the correct key no more than 2 times is $\frac{459}{512}$.

27. Add the probabilities of selecting the correct key exactly 3, 4, or 5 times.

$$\begin{aligned}P(&\text{at least 3 times correct})\\ &= P(\text{correct 3 times}) + P(\text{correct 4 times}) + P(\text{correct 5 times})\\ &= C(5, 3)\left(\frac{1}{4}\right)^3\left(\frac{3}{4}\right)^2 + C(5, 4)\left(\frac{1}{4}\right)^4\left(\frac{3}{4}\right)^1 + C(5, 5)\left(\frac{1}{4}\right)^5\left(\frac{3}{4}\right)^0\\ &= \frac{5\cdot 4}{2}\left(\frac{1}{4}\right)^3\left(\frac{3}{4}\right)^2 + 5\left(\frac{1}{4}\right)^4\left(\frac{3}{4}\right) + 1\left(\frac{1}{4}\right)^5\\ &= \frac{90}{1024} + \frac{15}{1024} + \frac{1}{1024}\\ &= \frac{53}{512}\end{aligned}$$

The probability of selecting the correct key at least 3 times is $\frac{53}{512}$.

28. The probability of answering a true/false question correctly is $\frac{1}{2}$. The probability of answering a true/false question incorrectly is $\frac{1}{2}$. There are $C(10, 6)$ ways to choose the 6 questions that are correct.

$$\begin{aligned}P(\text{exactly 6 correct}) &= C(10, 6)\left(\frac{1}{2}\right)^6\left(\frac{1}{2}\right)^4\\ &= \frac{10\cdot 9\cdot 8\cdot 7}{4\cdot 3\cdot 2}\left(\frac{1}{2}\right)^6\left(\frac{1}{2}\right)^4\\ &= \frac{105}{512}\end{aligned}$$

The probability of answering exactly 6 correctly is $\frac{105}{512}$.

29. There are $C(10, 4)$ ways to choose the 4 questions that are correct.

$$\begin{aligned}P(\text{exactly 4 correct}) &= C(10, 4)\left(\frac{1}{2}\right)^4\left(\frac{1}{2}\right)^6\\ &= \frac{10\cdot 9\cdot 8\cdot 7}{4\cdot 3\cdot 2}\left(\frac{1}{2}\right)^4\left(\frac{1}{2}\right)^6\\ &= \frac{105}{512}\end{aligned}$$

The probability of answering exactly 4 correctly is $\frac{105}{512}$.

30. Add the probabilities of answering exactly 0, 1, 2, 3, 4, or 5 questions correctly.

$$\begin{aligned}P(&\text{at most half correct})\\ &= P(0\text{ correct}) + P(1\text{ correct}) + P(2\text{ correct}) +\\ &\quad P(3\text{ correct}) + P(4\text{ correct}) + P(5\text{ correct})\\ &= C(10, 0)\left(\frac{1}{2}\right)^0\left(\frac{1}{2}\right)^{10} + C(10, 1)\left(\frac{1}{2}\right)^1\left(\frac{1}{2}\right)^9 +\\ &\quad C(10, 2)\left(\frac{1}{2}\right)^2\left(\frac{1}{2}\right)^8 + C(10, 3)\left(\frac{1}{2}\right)^3\left(\frac{1}{2}\right)^7 +\\ &\quad C(10, 4)\left(\frac{1}{2}\right)^4\left(\frac{1}{2}\right)^6 + C(10, 5)\left(\frac{1}{2}\right)^5\left(\frac{1}{2}\right)^5\\ &= \frac{1}{1024} + \frac{10}{1024} + \frac{45}{1024} + \frac{120}{1024} + \frac{210}{1024} + \frac{252}{1024}\\ &= \frac{319}{512}\end{aligned}$$

The probability of answering at most half of the questions correctly is $\frac{319}{512}$.

31. Add the probabilities of answering exactly 5, 6, 7, 8, 9, or 10 questions correctly.

$$\begin{aligned}P(&\text{at least half correct})\\ &= P(5\text{ correct}) + P(6\text{ correct}) + P(7\text{ correct}) +\\ &\quad P(8\text{ correct}) + P(9\text{ correct}) + P(10\text{ correct})\\ &= C(10, 5)\left(\frac{1}{2}\right)^5\left(\frac{1}{2}\right)^5 + C(10, 6)\left(\frac{1}{2}\right)^6\left(\frac{1}{2}\right)^4 +\\ &\quad C(10, 7)\left(\frac{1}{2}\right)^7\left(\frac{1}{2}\right)^3 + C(10, 8)\left(\frac{1}{2}\right)^8\left(\frac{1}{2}\right)^2 +\\ &\quad C(10, 9)\left(\frac{1}{2}\right)^9\left(\frac{1}{2}\right)^1 + C(10, 10)\left(\frac{1}{2}\right)^{10}\left(\frac{1}{2}\right)^0\\ &= \frac{252}{1024} + \frac{210}{1024} + \frac{120}{1024} + \frac{45}{1024} + \frac{10}{1024} + \frac{1}{1024}\\ &= \frac{319}{512}\end{aligned}$$

The probability of answering at least half of the questions correctly is $\frac{319}{512}$.

32. Add the probabilities of getting exactly 9, 10, 11, or 12 points up.

P(at least 9 points up)

$\quad = P(9 \text{ points up}) + P(10 \text{ points up}) +$
$\quad\quad P(11 \text{ points up}) + P(12 \text{ points up})$

$\quad = C(12, 9)(0.4)^9(0.6)^3 + C(12, 10)(0.4)^{10}(0.6)^2 +$
$\quad\quad C(12, 11)(0.4)^{11}(0.6)^1 + C(12, 12)(0.4)^{12}(0.6)^0$

$\quad \approx 0.0125 + 0.0025 + 0.0003 + 0.0000$

$\quad \approx 0.02$

The probability of getting at least 9 points up is about 0.02.

33. Add the probabilities of getting exactly 0, 1, 2, 3, or 4 points up.

P(at most 4 points up)

$\quad = P(0 \text{ points up}) + P(1 \text{ point up}) +$
$\quad\quad P(2 \text{ points up}) + P(3 \text{ points up}) +$
$\quad\quad P(4 \text{ points up})$

$\quad = C(12, 0)(0.4)^0(0.6)^{12} + C(12, 1)(0.4)^1(0.6)^{11} +$
$\quad\quad C(12, 2)(0.4)^2(0.6)^{10} + C(12, 3)(0.4)^3(0.6)^9 +$
$\quad\quad C(12, 4)(0.4)^4(0.6)^8$

$\quad \approx 0.0022 + 0.0174 + 0.0639 + 0.1419 + 0.2128$

$\quad \approx 0.44$

The probability of getting at most 4 points up is about 0.44.

34. The probability that a new car is leased is $\frac{1}{3}$. The probability that a new car is not leased is $\frac{2}{3}$. There are $C(7, 3)$ ways to choose which 3 of 7 new cars are leased.

$P(\text{exactly 3 leased}) = C(7, 3)\left(\frac{1}{3}\right)^3\left(\frac{2}{3}\right)^4$

$\quad\quad = \frac{7 \cdot 6 \cdot 5}{3 \cdot 2}\left(\frac{1}{3}\right)^3\left(\frac{2}{3}\right)^4$

$\quad\quad = \frac{560}{2187}$

The probability that 3 of 7 new cars are leased is $\frac{560}{2187}$.

35. The probability that a U.S. adult uses the Internet is 32.5%. The probability that a U.S. adult does not use the Internet is 67.5%. There are $C(5, 2)$ ways to choose which 2 of 5 U.S. adults use the Internet.

$P(\text{exactly 2 use}) = C(5, 2)(0.325)^2(0.675)^3$

$\quad\quad = \frac{5 \cdot 4}{2}(0.325)^2(0.675)^3$

$\quad\quad \approx 0.3248$

The probability that exactly 2 of 5 U.S. adults use the Internet is about 0.32.

36. The probability of tossing a black face is $\frac{1}{2}$.

The probability of tossing a neutral face is $\frac{1}{2}$.

$P(6 \text{ black}) = C(6, 6)\left(\frac{1}{2}\right)^6\left(\frac{1}{2}\right)^0$

$\quad\quad = 1\left(\frac{1}{2}\right)^6$

$\quad\quad = \frac{1}{64}$

$P(5 \text{ black}) = C(6, 5)\left(\frac{1}{2}\right)^5\left(\frac{1}{2}\right)^1$

$\quad\quad = 6\left(\frac{1}{2}\right)^5\left(\frac{1}{2}\right)$

$\quad\quad = \frac{3}{32}$

$P(4 \text{ black}) = C(6, 4)\left(\frac{1}{2}\right)^4\left(\frac{1}{2}\right)^2$

$\quad\quad = \frac{6 \cdot 5}{2}\left(\frac{1}{2}\right)^4\left(\frac{1}{2}\right)^2$

$\quad\quad = \frac{15}{64}$

$P(3 \text{ black}) = C(6, 3)\left(\frac{1}{2}\right)^3\left(\frac{1}{2}\right)^3$

$\quad\quad = \frac{6 \cdot 5 \cdot 4}{3 \cdot 2}\left(\frac{1}{2}\right)^3\left(\frac{1}{2}\right)^3$

$\quad\quad = \frac{5}{16}$

$P(2 \text{ black}) = C(6, 2)\left(\frac{1}{2}\right)^2\left(\frac{1}{2}\right)^4$

$\quad\quad = \frac{6 \cdot 5}{2}\left(\frac{1}{2}\right)^2\left(\frac{1}{2}\right)^4$

$\quad\quad = \frac{15}{64}$

$P(1 \text{ black}) = C(6, 1)\left(\frac{1}{2}\right)^1\left(\frac{1}{2}\right)^5$

$\quad\quad = 6\left(\frac{1}{2}\right)\left(\frac{1}{2}\right)^5$

$\quad\quad = \frac{3}{32}$

$P(0 \text{ black}) = C(6, 0)\left(\frac{1}{2}\right)^0\left(\frac{1}{2}\right)^6$

$\quad\quad = 1\left(\frac{1}{2}\right)^6$

$\quad\quad = \frac{1}{64}$

Use the probabilities to fill in the table.

Outcome	Points	Probability
6 black	5	$\frac{1}{64}$
5 black, 1 neutral	1	$\frac{3}{32}$
4 black, 2 neutral	0	$\frac{15}{64}$
3 black, 3 neutral	0	$\frac{5}{16}$
2 black, 4 neutral	0	$\frac{15}{64}$
1 black, 5 neutral	1	$\frac{3}{32}$
6 neutral	5	$\frac{1}{64}$

37. Add the probabilities of getting exactly 6, 5, 1, or 0 blacks.

P(at least 1 point)

$\quad = P(6 \text{ black}) + P(5 \text{ black}) + P(1 \text{ black}) +$
$\quad\quad P(0 \text{ black})$

$\quad = C(6, 6)\left(\frac{1}{2}\right)^6\left(\frac{1}{2}\right)^0 + C(6, 5)\left(\frac{1}{2}\right)^5\left(\frac{1}{2}\right)^1 +$
$\quad\quad C(6, 1)\left(\frac{1}{2}\right)^1\left(\frac{1}{2}\right)^5 + C(6, 0)\left(\frac{1}{2}\right)^0\left(\frac{1}{2}\right)^6$

$\quad = \frac{1}{64} + \frac{6}{64} + \frac{6}{64} + \frac{1}{64}$

$\quad = \frac{7}{32}$

The probability of getting at least 1 point is $\frac{7}{32}$.

38. The probability of a success is p. The probability of a failure is $1 - p$. There are $C(n, m)$ ways to have m successes in n trials.
$P(\text{exactly } m \text{ successes}) = C(n, m)p^m(1 - p)^{n-m}$

39. Getting a right answer and a wrong answer are the outcomes of a binomial experiment. The probability is far greater that guessing will result in a low grade than in a high grade. Answers should include the following.
- Use $(r + w)^5 = r^5 + 5r^4w + 10r^3w^2 + 10r^2w^3 + 5rw^4 + w^5$ and the chart on page 676 to determine the probabilities of each combination of right and wrong.
- $P(5 \text{ right}): r^5 = \left(\frac{1}{4}\right)^5 = \frac{1}{1024}$ or about 0.098%;

  $P(4 \text{ right, 1 wrong}): 5r^4w = 5\left(\frac{1}{4}\right)^4\left(\frac{3}{4}\right)^1 = \frac{15}{1024}$ or about 1.5%;

  $P(3 \text{ right, 2 wrong}): 10r^3w^2 = 10\left(\frac{1}{4}\right)^3\left(\frac{3}{4}\right)^2 = \frac{45}{512}$ or about 8.8%;

  $P(2 \text{ right, 3 wrong}): 10r^2w^3 = 10\left(\frac{1}{4}\right)^2\left(\frac{3}{4}\right)^3 = \frac{135}{512}$ or about 26.4%;

  $P(1 \text{ right, 4 wrong}): 5r^1w^4 = 5\left(\frac{1}{4}\right)^1\left(\frac{3}{4}\right)^4 = \frac{405}{1024}$ or about 39.6%;

  $P(5 \text{ wrong}): w^5 = \left(\frac{3}{4}\right)^5 = \frac{243}{1024}$ or about 23.7%.

40. 2; From the Pythagorean Theorem, $(DE)^2 = (BD)^2 + (BE)^2$. $\triangle ABE$ and $\triangle BCD$ are both isosceles triangles. Thus, the area of $\triangle ABE$ is given by $\frac{1}{2}(AE)(BE)$ or $\frac{1}{2}(BE)^2$. Also, the area of $\triangle BCD$ is given by $\frac{1}{2}(BD)(CD)$ or $\frac{1}{2}(BD)^2$.

$$\frac{1}{2}(BE)^2 + \frac{1}{2}(BD)^2 = \frac{1}{2}[(BE)^2 + (BD)^2]$$
$$= \frac{1}{2}(DE)^2$$
$$= \frac{1}{2}(2)^2$$
$$= 2$$

Therefore, the sum is 2.

41. B; $\$340.60 - 5\%(\$340.60) = \$340.60 - \$17.03$
$$= \$323.57$$

42. See students' work.

43. As n increases, the graph has a symmetrical shape that is high in the middle and low on both ends. This resembles a normal distribution.

Page 680 Maintain Your Skills

44. The values 67 and 83 are 1 standard deviation below and above the mean, respectively.

Therefore, about 68% of the data are between 67 and 83.

45. The value 91 is 2 standard deviations above the mean. You know that about $100\% - 95\%$ or 5% of the data are more than 2 standard deviations away from the mean. By the symmetry of the normal curve, half of 5%, or 2.5%, of the data are more than 2 standard deviations above the mean.
$400 \times 2.5\% = 10$
About 10 of the test scores are greater than 91.

46. The value 67 is 1 standard deviation below the mean. You know that about $100\% - 68\%$ or 32% of the data are more than 1 standard deviation away from the mean. By the symmetry of the normal curve, half of 32%, or 16%, of the data are more than 1 standard deviation below the mean.

47. The mean since it is the highest.

48. The boundary is the graph of $x = -3$. Since the inequality symbol is $\geq$, the boundary will be solid. Test $(0, 0)$.

$x \geq -3$
$0 \overset{?}{\geq} -3$
$0 \geq -3$ ✓

Shade the region that does contain $(0, 0)$.

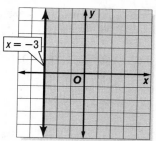

49. The boundary is the graph of $x + y = 4$. Since the inequality symbol is $\leq$, the boundary will be solid. Test $(0, 0)$.

$x + y \leq 4$
$0 + 0 \overset{?}{\leq} 4$
$0 \leq 4$ ✓

Shade the region that does contain $(0, 0)$.

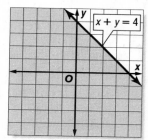

50. Since the inequality symbol is $>$, the graph of the related equation $y = |5x|$ is dashed. Test $(0, 1)$.

$y > |5x|$
$1 \overset{?}{>} |5(0)|$
$1 \overset{?}{>} |0|$
$1 > 0$ ✓

Shade the region that includes $(0, 1)$.

51. $2\sqrt{\dfrac{p(1-p)}{n}} = 2\sqrt{\dfrac{(0.5)(1-0.5)}{100}}$

$\qquad\qquad = 2\sqrt{0.0025}$

$\qquad\qquad = 2(0.05)$

$\qquad\qquad = 0.1$

52. $2\sqrt{\dfrac{p(1-p)}{n}} = 2\sqrt{\dfrac{(0.5)(1-0.5)}{400}}$

$\qquad\qquad = 2\sqrt{0.000625}$

$\qquad\qquad = 2(0.025)$

$\qquad\qquad = 0.05$

53. $2\sqrt{\dfrac{p(1-p)}{n}} = 2\sqrt{\dfrac{0.25(1-0.25)}{500}}$

$\qquad\qquad = 2\sqrt{0.000375}$

$\qquad\qquad \approx 2(0.0193649167)$

$\qquad\qquad \approx 0.039$

54. $2\sqrt{\dfrac{p(1-p)}{n}} = 2\sqrt{\dfrac{(0.75)(1-0.75)}{1000}}$

$\qquad\qquad = 2\sqrt{0.0001875}$

$\qquad\qquad \approx 2(0.0136930639)$

$\qquad\qquad \approx 0.027$

55. $2\sqrt{\dfrac{p(1-p)}{n}} = 2\sqrt{\dfrac{(0.3)(1-0.3)}{500}}$

$\qquad\qquad = 2\sqrt{0.00042}$

$\qquad\qquad \approx 2(0.0204939015)$

$\qquad\qquad \approx 0.041$

56. $2\sqrt{\dfrac{p(1-p)}{n}} = 2\sqrt{\dfrac{0.6(1-0.6)}{1000}}$

$\qquad\qquad = 2\sqrt{0.00024}$

$\qquad\qquad \approx 2(0.0154919334)$

$\qquad\qquad \approx 0.031$

**Page 681   Algebra Activity
(Follow-Up of Lesson 12-8)**

1. Sample answer:

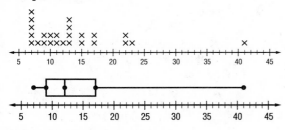

2. Step 1 Find the mean.

$\qquad \bar{x} = \dfrac{7 + 7 + 7 + \ldots + 22 + 23 + 41}{25}$

$\qquad\quad = 13.56$

The mean is 13.56.

Step 2 Find the median. Order the numbers from least to greatest. The median is in the middle.

$\qquad 7 \quad 7 \quad 7 \quad \ldots \quad 11 \quad \underbrace{12}_{12} \quad 13 \quad \ldots \quad 22 \quad 23 \quad 41$

The median is 12.

Step 3 The maximum is 41, and the minimum is 7.

Step 4 Find the variance.

$\qquad \sigma^2 = \dfrac{(x_1 - \bar{x})^2 + (x_2 - \bar{x})^2 + \ldots + (x_n - \bar{x})^2}{n}$

$\qquad\quad = \dfrac{\begin{array}{c}(7 - 13.56)^2 + (7 - 13.56)^2 + \ldots + \\ (23 - 13.56)^2 + (41 - 13.56)^2\end{array}}{25}$

$\qquad\quad = \dfrac{1342.16}{25}$

$\qquad\quad = 53.6864$

Step 5 Find the standard deviation.

$\qquad \sigma^2 = 53.6864$

$\qquad \sigma \approx 7.327100381$

The standard deviation is about 7.3.

3. See students' work.

4. Probably not; the outcomes of the trials are random since you are rolling a die

5. The class results should be better since it is a much larger set of data.

6. If the number of prizes increases, you will need to buy more boxes of cereal.

7. Sample answer: Put 20 marbles—5 red, 3 yellow, 3 blue, 3 green, 3 orange, and 3 black—into a bag. The red will represent Amazing Amy, and the other colors will represent each of the other prizes.

12-9   Sampling and Error

Pages 683–684   Check for Understanding

1. Sample answer: If a sample is not random, the results of a survey may not be valid.

2. Sample answer for good sample: doing a random telephone poll to rate the mayor's performance; bad sample: conducting a survey on how much the average person reads at a bookstore

3. The margin of sampling error decreases when the size of the sample n increases. As n increases, $\dfrac{p(1-p)}{n}$ decreases.

4. Yes; the last digits of social security numbers are random.

5. No; these students probably study more than average.

6. $ME = 2\sqrt{\dfrac{p(1-p)}{n}}$

$\qquad\;\; = 2\sqrt{\dfrac{0.72(1-0.72)}{100}}$

$\qquad\;\; \approx 0.0897997773$

The margin of error is about 9%.

7. $ME = 2\sqrt{\dfrac{p(1-p)}{n}}$

$\qquad\;\; = 2\sqrt{\dfrac{0.31(1-0.31)}{500}}$

$\qquad\;\; \approx 0.0413666532$

The margin of error is about 4%.

8. $ME = 2\sqrt{\dfrac{p(1-p)}{n}}$

$\qquad\;\; = 2\sqrt{\dfrac{0.68(1-0.68)}{520}}$

$\qquad\;\; \approx 0.040912665$

The margin of error is about 4%.

9. The probability is 0.95 that the percent of Americans ages 12 and older who listen to the radio every day is between 77% − 5% or 72% and 77% + 5% or 82%.

10.
$$ME = 2\sqrt{\frac{p(1 - p)}{n}}$$
$$0.05 = 2\sqrt{\frac{0.77(1 - 0.77)}{n}}$$
$$0.025 = \sqrt{\frac{0.77(0.23)}{n}}$$
$$0.000625 = \frac{0.77(0.23)}{n}$$
$$n = \frac{0.77(0.23)}{0.000625}$$
$$n = 283.36$$

About 283 people were surveyed.

Pages 684–685   Practice and Apply

11. No; you would tend to point toward the middle of the page.

12. Yes; all seniors would have the same chance of being selected.

13. Yes; a wide variety of people would be called since almost everyone has a phone.

14. No; freshmen are more likely than older students to still be growing, so a sample of freshmen would not give representative heights for the whole school.

15. $ME = 2\sqrt{\frac{p(1 - p)}{n}}$
$$= 2\sqrt{\frac{0.81(1 - 0.81)}{100}}$$
$$\approx 0.078460181$$

The margin of error is about 8%.

16. $ME = 2\sqrt{\frac{p(1 - p)}{n}}$
$$= 2\sqrt{\frac{0.16(1 - 0.16)}{400}}$$
$$\approx 0.0366606056$$

The margin of error is about 4%.

17. $ME = 2\sqrt{\frac{p(1 - p)}{n}}$
$$= 2\sqrt{\frac{0.54(1 - 0.54)}{500}}$$
$$\approx 0.0445780215$$

The margin of error is about 4%.

18. $ME = 2\sqrt{\frac{p(1 - p)}{n}}$
$$= 2\sqrt{\frac{0.48(1 - 0.48)}{1000}}$$
$$\approx 0.0315974683$$

The margin of error is about 3%.

19. $ME = 2\sqrt{\frac{p(1 - p)}{n}}$
$$= 2\sqrt{\frac{0.33(1 - 0.33)}{1000}}$$
$$\approx 0.0297388635$$

The margin of error is about 3%.

20. $ME = 2\sqrt{\frac{p(1 - p)}{n}}$
$$= 2\sqrt{\frac{0.67(1 - 0.67)}{1500}}$$
$$\approx 0.0242816803$$

The margin of error is about 2%.

21. $ME = 2\sqrt{\frac{p(1 - p)}{n}}$
$$= 2\sqrt{\frac{0.46(1 - 0.46)}{800}}$$
$$\approx 0.0352420204$$

The margin of error is about 4%.

22. $ME = 2\sqrt{\frac{p(1 - p)}{n}}$
$$= 2\sqrt{\frac{0.33(1 - 0.33)}{2406}}$$
$$\approx 0.0191724033$$

The margin of error is about 2%.

23. $ME = 2\sqrt{\frac{p(1 - p)}{n}}, p = \frac{367}{425} \approx 0.86$
$$\approx 2\sqrt{\frac{0.86(1 - 0.86)}{425}}$$
$$\approx 0.033$$

The margin of error is about 3%.

24. $ME = 2\sqrt{\frac{p(1 - p)}{n}}, p = \frac{934}{2150} \approx 0.43$
$$\approx 2\sqrt{\frac{0.43(1 - 0.43)}{2150}}$$
$$\approx 0.0213$$

The margin of error is about 2%.

25. $ME = 2\sqrt{\frac{p(1 - p)}{n}}$
$$= 2\sqrt{\frac{0.83(1 - 0.83)}{1020}}$$
$$\approx 0.0235230384$$

The margin of error is about 2%.

26. $ME = 2\sqrt{\frac{p(1 - p)}{n}}$
$$= 2\sqrt{\frac{0.61(1 - 0.61)}{1010}}$$
$$\approx 0.0306949217$$

The margin of error is about 3%.

27.
$$ME = 2\sqrt{\frac{p(1 - p)}{n}}$$
$$0.03 = 2\sqrt{\frac{0.33(1 - 0.33)}{n}}$$
$$0.015 = \sqrt{\frac{0.33(0.67)}{n}}$$
$$0.000225 = \frac{0.33(0.67)}{n}$$
$$n = \frac{0.33(0.67)}{0.000225}$$
$$n \approx 982.66667$$

About 983 people were surveyed.

28.
$$ME = 2\sqrt{\frac{p(1-p)}{n}}$$
$$0.096 = 2\sqrt{\frac{p(1-p)}{100}}$$
$$0.048 = \sqrt{\frac{p(1-p)}{100}}$$
$$0.002304 = \frac{p(1-p)}{100}$$
$$0.2304 = p(1-p)$$
$$0.2304 = p - p^2$$
$$p^2 - p + 0.2304 = 0$$
$$p = \frac{-b \pm \sqrt{b^2 - 4ac}}{2a}$$
$$p = \frac{-(-1) \pm \sqrt{(-1)^2 - 4(1)(0.2304)}}{2(1)}$$
$$p = \frac{1 \pm \sqrt{0.0784}}{2}$$
$$p = \frac{1 \pm 0.28}{2}$$
$$p = \frac{1 + 0.28}{2} \quad \text{or} \quad p = \frac{1 - 0.28}{2}$$
$$p = 0.64 \qquad\qquad p = 0.36$$

Either $0.36(100) = 36$ or $0.64(100) = 64$ people said "yes."

29. A political candidate can use the statistics from an opinion poll to analyze his or her standing and to help plan the rest of the campaign. Answers should include the following.
- The candidate could decide to skip areas where he or she is way ahead or way behind, and concentrate on areas where the polls indicate the race is close.
- about 3.5%
- The margin of error indicates that with a probability of 0.95 the percent of the Florida population that favored Bush was between 43.5% and 50.5%. The margin of error for Gore was also about 3.5%, so with probability 0.95 the percent that favored Gore was between 40.5% and 47.5%. Therefore, it was possible that the percent of the Florida population that favored Bush was less than the percent that favored Gore.

30. A; measure $\angle ABD = 90°$
$$\text{measure } \angle ABD = (90 - x)° + z° + (90 - y)°$$
$$90 = (90 - x) + z + (90 - y)$$
$$90 = 180 + z - x - y$$
$$0 = 90 + z - x - y$$
$$x + y = 90 + z$$

31. C; Since $xy^{-2} + y^{-1} = y^{-2}$ is equivalent to $\frac{x}{y^2} + \frac{1}{y} = \frac{1}{y^2}$, then $y \neq 0$.
$$\frac{x}{y^2} + \frac{1}{y} = \frac{1}{y^2}$$
$$y^2\left(\frac{x}{y^2} + \frac{1}{y}\right) = \left(\frac{1}{y^2}\right)y^2$$
$$x + y = 1$$
$$x = 1 - y$$
If $y = 0$, then $x = 1 - 0$ or 1. Thus $x \neq 1$.

32. The probability of a correct answer for any one question is $\frac{1}{2}$. The probability of an incorrect answer for any one question is $\frac{1}{2}$. There are $C(5, 5)$ ways to answer all 5 questions correctly.
$$P(\text{all 5 correct}) = C\left(5, 5\left(\frac{1}{2}\right)^5\left(\frac{1}{2}\right)^0\right)$$
$$= 1\left(\frac{1}{2}\right)^5$$
$$= \frac{1}{32}$$

The probability that a student answers all 5 questions correctly is $\frac{1}{32}$.

33. There are $C(5, 4)$ ways to answer exactly 4 questions correctly.
$$P(\text{exactly 4 correct}) = C\left(5, 4\right)\left(\frac{1}{2}\right)^4\left(\frac{1}{2}\right)^1$$
$$= 5\left(\frac{1}{2}\right)^4\left(\frac{1}{2}\right)$$
$$= \frac{5}{32}$$

The probability that a student answers exactly 4 questions correctly is $\frac{5}{32}$.

34. Add the probabilities of answering exactly 3, 4, or 5 questions correctly.
$$P(\text{at least 3 correct})$$
$$= P(\text{3 correct}) + P(\text{4 correct}) + P(\text{5 correct})$$
$$= C\left(5, 3\right)\left(\frac{1}{2}\right)^3\left(\frac{1}{2}\right)^2 + C\left(5, 4\right)\left(\frac{1}{2}\right)^4\left(\frac{1}{2}\right)^1 +$$
$$C\left(5, 5\right)\left(\frac{1}{2}\right)^5\left(\frac{1}{2}\right)^0$$
$$= \frac{5 \cdot 4}{2}\left(\frac{1}{2}\right)^3\left(\frac{1}{2}\right)^2 + 5\left(\frac{1}{2}\right)^4\left(\frac{1}{2}\right)^1 + 1\left(\frac{1}{2}\right)^5$$
$$= \frac{10}{32} + \frac{5}{32} + \frac{1}{32}$$
$$= \frac{1}{2}$$

The probability that a student answers at least 3 questions correctly is $\frac{1}{2}$.

35. The values 39 and 61 are 2 standard deviations below and above the mean, respectively. Therefore, about 95% of the data are between 39 and 61.

36. The value 55.5 is 1 standard deviation above the mean. You know that about $100\% - 68\%$ or 32% of the data are more than one standard deviation away from the mean. By the symmetry of the normal curve, half of 32%, or 16%, of the data are more than one standard deviation above the mean.
$$250 \times 16\% = 40$$
About 40 data values are greater than 55.5. Thus, about $250 - 40$ or 210 data values are less than 55.5.

37. The value 39 is 2 standard deviations below the mean. You know that about $100\% - 95\%$ or 5% of the data are more than two standard deviations away from the mean. By the symmetry of the normal curve, half of 5%, or 2.5%, of the data are more than two standard deviations below the mean. The probability that a data value selected is less than 39 is 2.5%. Thus, the probability that a data value selected is greater than 39 is $100\% - 2.5\%$ or 97.5%.

38. Use synthetic division.

$$\begin{array}{r|rrrr} -2 & 1 & -3 & -4 & 12 \\ & & -2 & 10 & -12 \\ \hline & 1 & -5 & 6 & \,|\ 0 \end{array}$$

The depressed polynomial is $x^2 - 5x + 6$.
$x^2 - 5x + 6 = (x - 2)(x - 3)$
So, $x^3 - 3x^2 - 4x + 12 = (x + 2)(x - 2)(x - 3)$, and the remaining factors are $x - 2$ and $x - 3$.

Page 686 Algebra Activity
(Follow-Up of Lesson 12-9)

1. H_0: Playing classical music during a math test will cause the average test score $\neq 73$.

H_1: Playing classical music during a math test will cause the average test score $= 73$.

2. H_0: Using robots on an assembly line will cause the mean number of defects per 1000 items < 18.

H_1: Using robots on an assembly line will cause the mean number of defects per 1000 items ≥ 18.

3. H_0: Taking medication will cause the mean pulse rate for the population > 82 beats per minute.

H_1: Taking medication will cause the mean pulse rate for the population ≤ 82 beats per minute.

4. See students' work.

Chapter 12 Study Guide and Review

Page 687 Vocabulary and Concept Check

1. c; probability

2. b; combination

3. a; dependent events

4. g; unbiased sample

5. d; permutation

6. e; mutually exclusive events

7. f; odds

8. The choice of any letter does not affect the other five letters, so the choices of the digits are independent events. There are 6 possible first letters in the code, 6 possible second letters in the code, 6 possible third letters in the code, 6 possible fourth letters in the code, 6 possible fifth letters in the code, and 6 possible sixth letters in the code. So, there are $6 \cdot 6 \cdot 6 \cdot 6 \cdot 6 \cdot 6$ or 46,656 possible passwords.

9. When a numeral is used for one of the digits, it is not considered for the other three digits. Therefore, the choices of numerals for each digit are dependent events. There are 10 numerals that can be used for the first digit. That leaves 9 numerals for the second digit. After two numerals are used for the first two digits, there are 8 remaining numerals that can be used for the third digit, and so on. There are $10 \cdot 9 \cdot 8 \cdot 7$ or 5040 possible codes.

10. This involves the product of two combinations.
$$C(2, 2) \cdot C(2, 1) = \frac{2!}{(2 - 2)!2!} \cdot \frac{2!}{(2 - 1)!1!}$$
$$= 1 \cdot 2$$
$$= 2$$

There are 2 committees that contain 2 boys and 1 girl.

11. This involves the product of two combinations.
$$C(4, 4) \cdot C(4, 1) = \frac{4!}{(4 - 4)!4!} \cdot \frac{4!}{(4 - 1)!1!}$$
$$= 1 \cdot 4$$
$$= 4$$

There are 4 hands that consist of 4 queens and 1 king.

12. This involves the product of three combinations
$$C(4, 2) \cdot C(2, 1) \cdot C(3, 1)$$
$$= \frac{4!}{(4 - 2)!2!} \cdot \frac{2!}{(2 - 1)!1!} \cdot \frac{3!}{(3 - 1)!1!}$$
$$= 6 \cdot 2 \cdot 3$$
$$= 36$$

There are 36 ways to choose the pencils from the box.

13. Step 1 Identify s and f.
$$P(\text{event}) = \frac{1}{4}$$
$$= \frac{s}{s + f} \quad s = 1, f = 3$$

Step 2 Find the odds.
$$\text{Odds} = s : f$$
$$= 1 : 3$$

So, the odds of the event occurring are $1 : 3$.

14. Step 1 Identify s and f.
$$P(\text{event}) = \frac{5}{8}$$
$$= \frac{s}{s + f} \quad s = 5, f = 3$$

Step 2 Find the odds.
$$\text{Odds} = s : f$$
$$= 5 : 3$$

So, the odds of the event occurring are $5 : 3$.

15. Step 1 Identify s and f.
$$P(\text{event}) = \frac{7}{12}$$
$$= \frac{s}{s+f} \quad s = 7, f = 5$$
Step 2 Find the odds.
$$\text{Odds} = s:f$$
$$= 7:5$$
So, the odds of the event occurring are 7:5.

16. Step 1 Identify s and f.
$$P(\text{event}) = \frac{3}{7}$$
$$= \frac{s}{s+f} \quad s = 3, f = 4$$
Step 2 Find the odds.
$$\text{Odds} = s:f$$
$$= 3:4$$
So, the odds of the event occurring are 3:4.

17. Step 1 Identify s and f.
$$P(\text{event}) = \frac{2}{5}$$
$$= \frac{s}{s+f} \quad s = 2, f = 3$$
Step 2 Find the odds.
$$\text{Odds} = s:f$$
$$= 2:3$$
So, the odds of the event occurring are 2:3.

18. According to the table, the probability of three heads occurring when 4 coins are tossed is $\frac{1}{4}$.

19. These events are independent since the outcome of the first die does not affect the outcome of the second die.
$$P(\text{two 4s}) = P(4) \cdot P(4)$$
$$= \frac{1}{6} \cdot \frac{1}{6}$$
$$= \frac{1}{36}$$
The probability is $\frac{1}{36}$.

20. Since the cards are not replaced, the events are dependent.
$$P(\text{heart, then club})$$
$$= P(\text{heart}) \cdot P(\text{club, following heart})$$
$$= \frac{13}{52} \cdot \frac{13}{51}$$
$$= \frac{13}{204}$$
The probability is $\frac{13}{204}$.

21. Since the marbles are not replaced, the events are dependent.
$$P(\text{white, then blue})$$
$$= P(\text{white}) \cdot P(\text{blue, following white})$$
$$= \frac{2}{7} \cdot \frac{3}{6}$$
$$= \frac{1}{7}$$
The probability is $\frac{1}{7}$.

22. These are mutually exclusive events, since the book cannot be both a math book and a chemistry book.
$$P(\text{math or chemistry}) = P(\text{math}) + P(\text{chemistry})$$
$$= \frac{2}{10} + \frac{3}{10}$$
$$= \frac{1}{2}$$
The probability of selecting a math or chemistry book is $\frac{1}{2}$.

23. These are mutually exclusive events, since you cannot roll a 6 and a number less than 4.
$$P(6 \text{ or less than } 4) = P(6) + P(\text{less than } 4)$$
$$= \frac{1}{6} + \frac{3}{6}$$
$$= \frac{2}{3}$$
The probability of rolling a 6 or a number less than 4 is $\frac{2}{3}$.

24. Since 6 is greater than 4, the events are inclusive.
$$P(6) = \frac{1}{6}$$
$$P(\text{greater than } 4) = \frac{2}{6}$$
$$P(6 \text{ and greater than } 4) = \frac{1}{6}$$
$$P(6 \text{ or greater than } 4)$$
$$= P(6) + P(\text{greater than } 4)$$
$$- P(6 \text{ and greater than } 4)$$
$$= \frac{1}{6} + \frac{2}{6} - \frac{1}{6}$$
$$= \frac{1}{3}$$
The probability of rolling a 6 or a number greater than 4 is $\frac{1}{3}$.

25. Since there are red kings, the events are inclusive.
$$P(\text{king}) = \frac{4}{52}$$
$$P(\text{red}) = \frac{26}{52}$$
$$P(\text{king and red}) = \frac{2}{52}$$
$$P(\text{king or red})$$
$$= P(\text{king}) + P(\text{red}) - P(\text{king and red})$$
$$= \frac{4}{52} + \frac{26}{52} - \frac{2}{52}$$
$$= \frac{7}{13}$$
The probability of drawing a king or a red card is $\frac{7}{13}$.

26. Step 1 Find the mean.
$$\bar{x} = \frac{56 + 56 + 57 + 58 + 58 + 58 + 59 + 61}{8}$$
$$= \frac{463}{8}$$
$$= 57.875$$
Step 2 Find the variance.
$$\sigma^2 = \frac{(x_1 - \bar{x})^2 + (x_2 - \bar{x})^2 + \ldots + (x_n - \bar{x})^2}{n}$$
$$= \frac{\begin{array}{c}(56 - 57.875)^2 + (56 - 57.875)^2 + \ldots + \\ (59 - 57.875)^2 + (61 - 57.875)^2\end{array}}{8}$$
$$= \frac{18.875}{8}$$
$$= 2.359375$$
The variance is about 2.4.
Step 3 Find the standard deviation.
$$\sigma^2 = 2.359375$$
$$\sigma \approx 1.536025716$$
The standard deviation is about 1.5.

27. Step 1 Find the mean.

$$\bar{x} = \frac{302 + 310 + 331 + 298 + 348 + 305 + 314 + 284 + 321 + 337}{10}$$

$$= \frac{3150}{10}$$

$$= 315$$

Step 2 Find the variance.

$$\sigma^2 = \frac{(x_1 - \bar{x})^2 + (x_2 - \bar{x})^2 + \ldots + (x_n - \bar{x})^2}{n}$$

$$= \frac{(302 - 315)^2 + (310 - 315)^2 + \ldots + (321 - 315)^2 + (337 - 315)^2}{10}$$

$$= \frac{3410}{10}$$

$$= 341$$

The variance is 341.

Step 3 Find the standard deviation.

$$\sigma^2 = 341$$

$$\sigma \approx 18.46618531$$

The standard deviation is about 18.5.

28. Step 1 Find the mean.

$$\bar{x} = \frac{3.4 + 4.2 + 8.6 + 5.1 + 3.6 + 2.8 + 7.1 + 4.4 + 5.2 + 5.6}{10}$$

$$= \frac{50}{10}$$

$$= 5$$

Step 2 Find the variance.

$$\sigma^2 = \frac{(x_1 - \bar{x})^2 + (x_2 - \bar{x})^2 + \ldots + (x_n - \bar{x})^2}{n}$$

$$= \frac{(3.4 - 5)^2 + (4.2 - 5)^2 + \ldots + (5.2 - 5)^2 + (5.6 - 5)^2}{10}$$

$$= \frac{28.14}{10}$$

$$= 2.814$$

The variance is about 2.8.

Step 3 Find the standard deviation.

$$\sigma^2 = 2.814$$

$$\sigma \approx 1.677498137$$

The standard deviation is about 1.7.

29. The values \$164 and \$196 are 1 standard deviation below and above the mean, respectively. Therefore, about 68% of the data are between \$164 and \$196.

$5000 \times 68\% = 3400$

About 3400 bills were between \$164 and \$196.

30. The value \$212 is 2 standard deviations above the mean. You know that about 100% − 95% or 5% of the data are more than two standard deviations away from the mean. By the symmetry of the normal curve, half of 5%, or 2.5%, of the data are more than two standard deviations above the mean.

$5000 \times 2.5\% = 125$

About 125 bills were more than \$212.

31. The value \$164 is 1 standard deviation below the mean. You know that about 100% − 68% or 32% of the data are more than one standard deviation away from the mean. By the symmetry of the normal curve, half of 32%, or 16%, of the data are more than one standard deviation below the mean.

$5000 \times 16\% = 800$

About 800 bills were less than \$164.

32. The value \$164 is 1 standard deviation below the mean. You know that about 68% of the data are less than one standard deviation away from the mean. By the symmetry of the normal curve, half of 68%, or 34%, of the data are less than one standard deviation below the mean. The probability that a household has a bill between \$164 and \$180 is 34%.

33. There are $C(8, 7)$ ways to get 7 heads in 8 tosses.

$$P(7 \text{ heads}) = C(8, 7)\left(\frac{1}{2}\right)^7\left(\frac{1}{2}\right)^1$$

$$= 8\left(\frac{1}{2}\right)^7\left(\frac{1}{2}\right)^1$$

$$= \frac{1}{32}$$

The probability of getting 7 heads in 8 tosses is $\frac{1}{32}$.

34. There are $C(7, 5)$ ways to have 5 boys in a family with 7 children.

$$P(5 \text{ boys}) = C(7, 5)\left(\frac{1}{2}\right)^5\left(\frac{1}{2}\right)^2$$

$$= \frac{7 \cdot 6}{2}\left(\frac{1}{2}\right)^5\left(\frac{1}{2}\right)^2$$

$$= \frac{21}{128}$$

The probability of having 5 boys in a family with 7 children is $\frac{21}{128}$.

35. There are $C(12, 12)$ ways to get twelve 3s in twelve rolls.

$$P(\text{twelve 3s}) = C(12, 12)\left(\frac{1}{6}\right)^{12}\left(\frac{5}{6}\right)^0$$

$$= 1\left(\frac{1}{6}\right)^{12}$$

$$= \frac{1}{2,176,782,336}$$

The probability of getting twelve 3s is $\frac{1}{2,176,782,336}$.

36. There are $C(12, 1)$ ways to get exactly one 3 in twelve rolls.

$$P(\text{exactly one 3}) = C(12, 1)\left(\frac{1}{6}\right)^1\left(\frac{5}{6}\right)^{11}$$

$$= 12\left(\frac{1}{6}\right)\left(\frac{5}{6}\right)^{11}$$

$$= \frac{48,828,125}{181,398,528}$$

The probability of getting exactly one 3 is $\frac{48,828,125}{181,398,528}$.

37. There are $C(12, 6)$ ways to get six 3s in twelve rolls.

$$P(\text{six 3s}) = C(12, 6)\left(\frac{1}{6}\right)^6\left(\frac{5}{6}\right)^6$$

$$= \frac{12 \cdot 11 \cdot 10 \cdot 9 \cdot 8 \cdot 7}{6 \cdot 5 \cdot 4 \cdot 3 \cdot 2}\left(\frac{1}{6}\right)^6\left(\frac{5}{6}\right)^6$$

$$= \frac{14,437,500}{2,176,782,336}$$

The probability of getting six 3s is $\frac{14,437,500}{2,176,782,336}$.

38. $ME = 2\sqrt{\frac{p(1-p)}{n}}$

$= 2\sqrt{\frac{0.51(1 - 0.51)}{625}}$

≈ 0.0399919992

The margin of error is about 4%.

39. $ME = 2\sqrt{\frac{p(1-p)}{n}}$

$0.045 = 2\sqrt{\frac{0.63(1 - 0.63)}{n}}$

$0.0225 = \sqrt{\frac{0.63(0.37)}{n}}$

$0.00050625 = \frac{0.63(0.37)}{n}$

$n = \frac{0.63(0.37)}{0.00050625}$

$n \approx 460.44444$

About 460 mothers were surveyed.

Chapter 12 Practice Test

Page 693

1. c; normal distribution
2. b; measures of variation
3. a; measures of central tendency

4. $P(7, 3) = \frac{7!}{(7 - 3)!}$

$= \frac{7!}{4!}$

$= 7 \cdot 6 \cdot 5$

$= 210$

5. $C(7, 3) = \frac{7!}{(7 - 3)!3!}$

$= \frac{7!}{4!3!}$

$= \frac{7 \cdot 6 \cdot 5}{3 \cdot 2 \cdot 1}$

$= 35$

6. $P(13, 5) = \frac{13!}{(13 - 5)!}$

$= \frac{13!}{8!}$

$= 13 \cdot 12 \cdot 11 \cdot 10 \cdot 9$

$= 154,440$

7. There are 9 balls which can be chosen for the first location. That leaves 8 balls which can be chosen for the second location. After the first two locations are filled, there are 7 remaining balls which can be chosen for the third location, and so on. There are $9 \cdot 8 \cdot 7 \cdot 6 \cdot 5 \cdot 4 \cdot 3 \cdot 2 \cdot 1$ or 362,880 ways to arrange the 9 bowling balls on the rack.

8. There are 11 possible skirts, 9 possible blouses, 3 possible belts, and 7 possible pairs of shoes. So, there are $11 \cdot 9 \cdot 3 \cdot 7$ or 2079 different outfits.

9. You need to find the number of permutations of 11 letters of which 7 are different, 2 are the same, and 2 others are the same.

$\frac{11!}{2!2!} = \frac{11 \cdot 10 \cdot 9 \cdot 8 \cdot 7 \cdot 6 \cdot 5 \cdot 4 \cdot 3 \cdot 2!}{2!2!}$

$= 9,979,200$

There are 9,979,200 ways to arrange the letters.

10. Since the order in which they choose the players is not important, you must find the number of combinations of 18 players taken 11 at a time.

$C(18, 11) = \frac{18!}{(18 - 11)!11!}$

$= \frac{18!}{7!11!}$

$= 31,824$

There are 31,824 possible ways to choose the 11 players.

11. Since each car will occupy a different space, order is important. You must find the number of permutations of 10 spaces taken 4 at a time.

$P(10, 4) = \frac{10!}{(10 - 4)!}$

$= \frac{10!}{6!}$

$= 10 \cdot 9 \cdot 8 \cdot 7$

$= 5040$

The 4 cars can be parked in 5040 ways.

12. Since the order they choose the points is not important, you must find the number of combinations of 11 points taken 5 at a time.

$C(11, 5) = \frac{11!}{(11 - 5)!5!}$

$= \frac{11!}{6!5!}$

$= 462$

There are 462 possible ways to choose the 5 points.

13. There are 100 possible outcomes. Only 15 of these outcomes is a success, so $s = 15$. The other 85 outcomes are failures, so $f = 85$.

$P(\text{less than } 16) = \frac{s}{s + f}$

$= \frac{15}{15 + 85}$

$= \frac{15}{100}$

$= \frac{3}{20}$

The probability is $\frac{3}{20}$.

14. Because the first card is not replaced, the events are dependent.

$P(\text{two cards} > 2 \text{ and} < 9)$

$= P(> 2 \text{ and} < 9) \cdot P(> 2 \text{ and} < 9 \text{ following} > 2 \text{ and} < 9)$

$= \frac{24}{52} \cdot \frac{23}{51}$

$= \frac{46}{221}$

The probability is $\frac{46}{221}$.

15. At least 2 of the defective sets means 2 defective sets or 3 defective sets.

$C(3, 2) \cdot C(7, 2) + C(3, 3) \cdot C(7, 1)$

$= \frac{3!}{(3 - 2)!2!} \cdot \frac{7!}{(7 - 2)!2!} + \frac{3!}{(3 - 3)!3!} \cdot \frac{7!}{(7 - 1)!1!}$

$= 3 \cdot 21 + 1 \cdot 7$

$= 70$

There are 70 possible ways to choose at least 2 defective sets.

16. The probability that William Tell will hit an apple on a given shot is $\frac{9}{10}$. The probability that William Tell will miss an apple on a given shot is $\frac{1}{10}$. There are $C(7, 4)$ ways to choose the 4 times that he hit an apple out of the 7 shots.

$$P(\text{exactly 4}) = C(7, 4)\left(\frac{9}{10}\right)^4\left(\frac{1}{10}\right)^3$$
$$= \frac{7 \cdot 6 \cdot 5}{3 \cdot 2}\left(\frac{9}{10}\right)^4\left(\frac{1}{10}\right)^3$$
$$= \frac{45,927}{2,000,000}$$

The probability is $\frac{45,927}{2,000,000}$.

17. Since there are 10 people and 11 seats, there will be one person missing from one of the cars. If the person is missing from the 5-passenger car, you need to find the number of permutations of 10 people of which 4 are the same (in the same car), 2 others are the same, and 4 others are the same.

$$\frac{10!}{4!2!4!} = \frac{10 \cdot 9 \cdot 8 \cdot 7 \cdot 6 \cdot 5 \cdot 4!}{4!2!4!}$$
$$= 3150$$

If the person is missing from the 2-passenger car, you need to find the number of permutations of 10 people of which 5 are the same (in the same car), 1 other is the same, and 4 others are the same.

$$\frac{10!}{5!1!4!} = \frac{10 \cdot 9 \cdot 8 \cdot 7 \cdot 6 \cdot 5!}{5!1!4!}$$
$$= 1260$$

If the person is missing from the 4-passenger car, you need to find the number of permutations of 10 people of which 5 are the same (in the same car), 2 others are the same, and 3 others are the same.

$$\frac{10!}{5!2!3!} = \frac{10 \cdot 9 \cdot 8 \cdot 7 \cdot 6 \cdot 5!}{5!2!3!}$$
$$= 2520$$

There are $3150 + 1260 + 2520$ or 6930 ways to arrange the 10 people in the 3 cars.

18. These events are independent since the golf balls are replaced after each draw.

$$P(\text{3 same color}) = P(\text{3 white}) + P(\text{3 red})$$
$$= P(\text{white}) \cdot P(\text{white}) \cdot P(\text{white})$$
$$\quad + P(\text{red}) \cdot P(\text{red}) \cdot P(\text{red})$$
$$= \frac{5}{8} \cdot \frac{5}{8} \cdot \frac{5}{8} + \frac{3}{8} \cdot \frac{3}{8} \cdot \frac{3}{8}$$
$$= \frac{152}{512}$$
$$= \frac{19}{64}$$

The probability is $\frac{19}{64}$.

19. The probability that a given question is answered correctly is $\frac{1}{4}$. The probability that a given question is answered incorrectly is $\frac{3}{4}$. There are $C(10, 6)$ ways to choose which 6 of the 10 questions are answered correctly.

$$P(\text{6 correct}) = C(10, 6)\left(\frac{1}{4}\right)^6\left(\frac{3}{4}\right)^4$$
$$= \frac{10 \cdot 9 \cdot 8 \cdot 7}{4 \cdot 3 \cdot 2}\left(\frac{1}{4}\right)^6\left(\frac{3}{4}\right)^4$$
$$= \frac{8505}{524,288}$$

The probability that 6 questions are answered correctly is $\frac{8505}{524,288}$.

20. Add the probabilities of answering exactly 8, 9, or 10 questions correctly.

$P(\text{at least 8 correct})$
$$= P(\text{8 correct}) + P(\text{9 correct}) + P(\text{10 correct})$$
$$= C(10, 8)\left(\frac{1}{4}\right)^8\left(\frac{3}{4}\right)^2 + C(10, 9)\left(\frac{1}{4}\right)^9\left(\frac{3}{4}\right)^1 +$$
$$\quad C(10, 10)\left(\frac{1}{4}\right)^{10}\left(\frac{3}{4}\right)^0$$
$$= \frac{10 \cdot 9}{2}\left(\frac{1}{4}\right)^8\left(\frac{3}{4}\right)^2 + 10\left(\frac{1}{4}\right)^9\left(\frac{3}{4}\right) + 1\left(\frac{1}{4}\right)^{10}$$
$$= \frac{405}{1,048,576} + \frac{30}{1,048,576} + \frac{1}{1,048,576}$$
$$= \frac{109}{262,144}$$

The probability that at least 8 questions are answered correctly is $\frac{109}{262,144}$.

21. Subtract the probabilities of answering exactly 8, 9, or 10 questions correctly from 1.

$P(\text{fewer than 8 correct})$
$$= 1 - [P(\text{8 correct}) + P(\text{9 correct}) +$$
$$\quad P(\text{10 correct})]$$
$$= 1 - \left[C(10, 8)\left(\frac{1}{4}\right)^8\left(\frac{3}{4}\right)^2 + C(10, 9)\left(\frac{1}{4}\right)^9\left(\frac{3}{4}\right)^1 +\right.$$
$$\quad \left.C(10, 10)\left(\frac{1}{4}\right)^{10}\left(\frac{3}{4}\right)^0\right]$$
$$= 1 - \left[\frac{10 \cdot 9}{2}\left(\frac{1}{4}\right)^8\left(\frac{3}{4}\right)^2 + 10\left(\frac{1}{4}\right)^9\left(\frac{3}{4}\right) + 10\left(\frac{1}{4}\right)^{10}\right]$$
$$= 1 - \left[\frac{405}{1,048,576} + \frac{30}{1,048,576} + \frac{1}{1,048,576}\right]$$
$$= 1 - \frac{109}{262,144}$$
$$= \frac{262,035}{262,144}$$

The probability that fewer than 8 questions are answered correctly is $\frac{262,035}{262,144}$.

22. D; There are 6 possible outcomes. Only one of the outcomes is a success, rolling the same number, so $s = 1$. The other five outcomes are failures, so $f = 5$.

$$P(\text{same number}) = \frac{s}{s + f}$$
$$= \frac{1}{1 + 5}$$
$$= \frac{1}{6}$$

Chapter 12 Standardized Test Practice

Pages 694–695

1. C; The ratio of red gumdrops to green gumdrops is 7 to 3, which means 3 out of every $7 + 3$ or 10 gumdrops is green. Since there are 15 groups of 10 in 150, there are $15 \cdot 3$ or 45 green gumdrops.

2. B; $\langle 16 \rangle + \langle 11 \rangle = \frac{1}{2}(16) + 2(11)$
$$= 8 + 22$$
$$= 30$$

3. D; Since $ABCD$ is a rhombus, line segment $\overline{AB}$ is parallel to line segment $\overline{DC}$. So, line segment $\overline{AC}$ is a transversal cutting accross two parallel lines. Thus, $\angle s$ and $\angle x$ are congruent since they are alternating interior angles. Since $ABCD$ is a rhombus, $\triangle ABD$ is congruent to $\triangle CBD$. Thus, $\angle t$ and $\angle v$ are congruent since corresponding parts of congruent triangles are congruent. Line segment $\overline{BD}$ is also a transversal cutting accross two parallel lines, so $\angle z$ and $\angle v$ are alternating interior angles and are congruent. By the transitive property of congruence $\angle z$ and $\angle t$ are congruent.

4. B; Since the length of the hypotenuse is $3\sqrt{2}$ units, the length of each leg is $3\sqrt{2} \div \sqrt{2}$ or 3 units. Thus the area is $\frac{1}{2} \cdot 3 \cdot 3$ or 4.5 square units.

5. D; $\quad t(t + 7) = 18$
$$t^2 + 7t = 18$$
$$t^2 + 7t - 18 = 0$$
$$(t + 9)(t - 2) = 0$$
$$t + 9 = 0 \quad \text{or} \quad t - 2 = 0$$
$$t = -9 \qquad\qquad t = 2$$
The solution set is $\{-9, 2\}$.

6. B; $3x - 8 = 5x^2 - y$
$$0 = 5x^2 - 3x - y + 8$$
$A = 5$. Since there is no y^2 term, $C = 0$.
The equation represents a parabola.

7. B; Solve the first equation for y to obtain $y = \pm\sqrt{16 - x^2}$. Enter the functions $y = \sqrt{16 - x^2}$, $y = -\sqrt{16 - x^2}$, and $y = x^2 + 4$ on the Y = screen. The graph indicates that the circle and parabola intersect in one point.

8. A; There are 20 numbers in the set. Only 3 of the numbers are both odd and divisible by 3. Thus, there are 3 successes, so $s = 3$. The other 17 outcomes are failures, so $f = 17$.

$$P(\text{odd and divisible by 3}) = \frac{s}{s + f}$$
$$= \frac{3}{3 + 17}$$
$$= \frac{3}{20}$$

The probability is $\frac{3}{20}$.

9. A; $\quad 3 = 1 \cdot 3$
$$4 = 2 \cdot 2$$
$$5 = 1 \cdot 5$$
$$6 = 2 \cdot 3$$
Thus, the least common multiple is $2 \cdot 2 \cdot 3 \cdot 5$ or 60.

10. C; If $x + 7 = 13$, then $x = 6$. Substitute 6 for x in the first equation and solve for y.
$$4y - 5x + 6xy - 50 = 0$$
$$4y - 5(6) + 6(6)y - 50 = 0$$
$$4y - 30 + 36y - 50 = 0$$
$$40y - 80 = 0$$
$$40(y - 2) = 0$$
$$y - 2 = 0$$
$$y - 2 + 7 = 0 + 7$$
$$y + 5 = 7$$
The value of $y + 5$ is 7.

11. The number of students who take math or art is equal to the number of students who take math plus the number of students who take art minus the number of students who take both math and art. Let $x =$ the number of students who take both math and art.
$$280 = 250 + 50 - x$$
$$280 = 300 - x$$
$$-20 = -x$$
$$20 = x$$
20 students take both math and art.

12. The greatest possible value for x occurs when the least possible value for y occurs. The least integer value for y is 21. Substitute 21 for y in the equation $y + 2x = 180$ and solve for x.
$$y + 2x = 180$$
$$21 + 2x = 180$$
$$2x = 159$$
$$x = 79.5$$
Since 79.5 is not an integer, substitute 22 for y in the equation $y + 2x = 180$ and solve for x.
$$y + 2x = 180$$
$$22 + 2x = 180$$
$$2x = 158$$
$$x = 79$$
The greatest possible value for x is 79.

13. mean $= \frac{\text{sum of the data}}{\text{number of items in data}}$

$$45 = \frac{\text{sum of first three numbers} + 34}{4}$$
$$180 = \text{sum of first three numbers} + 34$$
$$146 = \text{sum of first three numbers}$$
The sum of the other three numbers is 146.

14. Let $n =$ the even positive integer. Then $n + 2 =$ the next greater even integer.
$$\frac{1}{2}n + \frac{3}{4}(n + 2) = 24$$
$$4\left[\frac{1}{2}n + \frac{3}{4}(n + 2)\right] = 4(24)$$
$$2n + 3(n + 2) = 96$$
$$2n + 3n + 6 = 96$$
$$5n + 6 = 96$$
$$5n = 90$$
$$n = 18$$
$$n + 2 = 18 + 2 \quad \text{or} \quad 20$$
$$\text{mean} = \frac{18 + 20}{2}$$
$$= \frac{38}{2}$$
$$= 19$$
The mean of the two integers is 19.

15. When a tile is chosen it cannot be used elsewhere in the arrangement. The choices of tiles are dependent events. A and F must be used. There are $C(4, 1)$ ways to choose the third tile used. There are $C(2, 1)$ ways to position the A tile, and $C(1, 1)$ ways to position the F tile.

$C(4, 1) \cdot C(2, 1) \cdot C(1, 1)$

$= \dfrac{4!}{(4-1)!1!} \cdot \dfrac{2!}{(2-1)!1!} \cdot \dfrac{1!}{(1-1)!1!}$

$= \dfrac{4!}{3!1!} \cdot \dfrac{2!}{1!1!} \cdot \dfrac{1!}{0!1!}$

$= 4 \cdot 2 \cdot 1$

$= 8$

There are 8 arrangements that Shane can create.

16. B;
$\begin{array}{ll} x < 0 & x < 0 \\ x - 2 < 0 - 2 & -x > 0 \\ x - 2 < -2 & 2 - x > 2 + 0 \\ & 2 - x > 2 \end{array}$

Thus, $x - 2 < -2 < 2 < 2 - x$ or $x - 2 < 2 - x$.

17. C; Since $ABCD$ is a rectangle, $x + 60 = 180$ and $y + 30 = 90$. Add the two equations and solve for $x + y$.

$\begin{array}{r} x + 60 = 180 \\ (+)\, y + 30 = 90 \\ \hline x + y + 90 = 270 \\ x + y = 180 \end{array}$

18. B;
$\begin{array}{ll} x > y & w < z \\ \dfrac{1}{z}(x) > \dfrac{1}{z}(y) & \dfrac{1}{w} > \dfrac{1}{z} \\ \dfrac{x}{z} > \dfrac{y}{z} & x\left(\dfrac{1}{w}\right) > x\left(\dfrac{1}{z}\right) \\ & \dfrac{x}{w} > \dfrac{x}{z} \end{array}$

Thus, $\dfrac{y}{z} < \dfrac{x}{z} < \dfrac{x}{w}$ or $\dfrac{y}{z} < \dfrac{x}{w}$.

19. A; $\langle 2 \rangle = \dfrac{2^2 - 1}{2}$ $\qquad \langle -2 \rangle = \dfrac{(-2)^2 - 1}{-2}$

$\qquad\qquad = \dfrac{4 - 1}{2}$ $\qquad\qquad\qquad = \dfrac{4 - 1}{-2}$

$\qquad\qquad = \dfrac{3}{2}$ $\qquad\qquad\qquad\quad = -\dfrac{3}{2}$

Thus, $\langle 2 \rangle > \langle -2 \rangle$.

20. C; $\langle 1 \rangle = \dfrac{1^2 - 1}{1}$ $\qquad \langle -1 \rangle = \dfrac{(-1)^2 - 1}{1}$

$\qquad\qquad = \dfrac{1 - 1}{1}$ $\qquad\qquad\qquad = \dfrac{1 - 1}{-1}$

$\qquad\qquad = \dfrac{0}{1}$ $\qquad\qquad\qquad\quad = \dfrac{0}{1}$

$\qquad\qquad = 0$ $\qquad\qquad\qquad\quad = 0$

Thus, $\langle 1 \rangle = \langle -1 \rangle$.

21. A; $\begin{array}{ll} y^2 = (-3)^2 & y^{-2} = (-3)^{-2} \\ = 9 & \phantom{y^{-2}} = \dfrac{1}{(-3)^2} \\ & \phantom{y^{-2}} = \dfrac{1}{9} \end{array}$

Thus, $y^2 < y^{-2}$.

Chapter 13 Trigonometric Functions

Page 699 Getting Started

1. $a^2 + b^2 = c^2$
$8^2 + 6^2 = x^2$
$64 + 36 = x^2$
$100 = x^2$
$\sqrt{100} = x$
$10 = x$

2. $a^2 + b^2 = c^2$
$9^2 + 5^2 = x^2$
$81 + 25 = x^2$
$106 = x^2$
$\sqrt{106} = x$
$10.3 \approx x$

3. $a^2 + b^2 = c^2$
$x^2 + 11^2 = 20^2$
$x^2 + 121 = 400$
$x^2 = 279$
$x = \sqrt{279}$
$x \approx 16.7$

4. $a^2 + b^2 = c^2$
$x^2 + 10^2 = 24^2$
$x^2 + 100 = 576$
$x^2 = 476$
$x^2 = \sqrt{476}$
$x \approx 21.8$

5. $x = 7$ since one leg measures 7 and the legs of a 45°-45°-90° triangle are equal in measure. By the Pythagorean Theorem, $c = \sqrt{a^2 + b^2}$.
$y = \sqrt{7^2 + 7^2}$
$y = \sqrt{2(7^2)}$
$y = 7\sqrt{2}$

6. By the Pythagorean Theorem, $a^2 + b^2 = c^2$.
$x^2 + x^2 = 21^2$
$2x^2 = 21^2$
$x^2 = \frac{21^2}{2}$
$x = \sqrt{\frac{21^2}{2}}$
$x = \frac{21}{\sqrt{2}}$
$x = \frac{21\sqrt{2}}{2}$

7. Since this is a 30°-60°-90° triangle and the short leg is 4, then $x = 4\sqrt{3}$ and $y = 2(4) = 8$.

8. Since this is a 30°-60°-90° triangle and the long leg is 9, then
$x = \frac{9}{\sqrt{3}} = \frac{9 \cdot \sqrt{3}}{\sqrt{3} \cdot \sqrt{3}} = \frac{9\sqrt{3}}{3} = 3\sqrt{3}$
and $y = 2 \cdot 3\sqrt{3} = 6\sqrt{3}$.

9. $f(x) = x + 3$
$y = x + 3$
Interchange x and y.
$x = y + 3$
$x - 3 = y$
$f^{-1}(x) = x - 3$

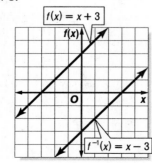

10. $f(x) = \frac{x - 2}{5}$
$y = \frac{x - 2}{5}$
Interchange x and y.
$x = \frac{y - 2}{5}$
$5x = y - 2$
$5x + 2 = y$
$f^{-1}(x) = 5x + 2$

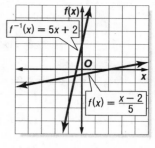

11. $f(x) = x^2 - 4$
$y = x^2 - 4$
Interchange x and y.
$x = y^2 - 4$
$x + 4 = y^2$
$\pm\sqrt{x + 4} = y$
$f^{-1}(x) = \pm\sqrt{x + 4}$

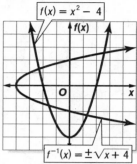

12. $f(x) = -7x - 9$
$y = -7x - 9$
Interchange x and y.
$x = -7y - 9$
$x + 9 = -7y$
$\frac{-x - 9}{7} = y$
$f^{-1}(x) = \frac{-x - 9}{7}$

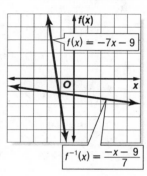

Page 700 Spreadsheet Investigation
(Preview of Lesson 13-1)

1.

	A	B	C	D	E	F
1	a	b	c	b/a	b/c	a/c
2	1	=SQRT (C2^2 - A2^2)	2	=B2/A2	=B2/C2	=A2/C2
3	2	=SQRT (C3^2 - A3^2)	4	=B3/A3	=B3/C3	=A3/C3
4	3	=SQRT (C4^2 - A4^2)	6	=B4/A4	=B4/C4	=A4/C4
5	4	=SQRT (C5^2 - A5^2)	8	=B5/A5	=B5/C5	=A5/C5
6	5	=SQRT (C6^2 - A6^2)	10	=B6/A6	=B6/C6	=A6/C6

2. The triangles are all similar.

3. All of the ratios of side b to side a are approximately 1.73. All of the ratios of side b to side c are approximately 0.87. All of the ratios of side a to side c are 0.5.

13-1 Right Triangle Trigonometry

Page 706 Check for Understanding

1. Trigonometry is the study of the relationships between the angles and sides of a right triangle.

2.

3. Given only the measures of the angles of a right triangle, you cannot find the measures of its sides.

4. opp = 8, adj = 15, hyp = $\sqrt{8^2 + 15^2} = \sqrt{289} = 17$

$$\sin \theta = \frac{\text{opp}}{\text{hyp}} = \frac{8}{17} \qquad \csc \theta = \frac{\text{hyp}}{\text{opp}} = \frac{17}{8}$$

$$\cos \theta = \frac{\text{adj}}{\text{hyp}} = \frac{15}{17} \qquad \sec \theta = \frac{\text{hyp}}{\text{adj}} = \frac{17}{15}$$

$$\tan \theta = \frac{\text{opp}}{\text{adj}} = \frac{8}{15} \qquad \cot \theta = \frac{\text{adj}}{\text{opp}} = \frac{15}{8}$$

5. adj = 6, hyp = 11, opp = $\sqrt{11^2 - 6^2} = \sqrt{85}$

$$\sin \theta = \frac{\text{opp}}{\text{hyp}} = \frac{\sqrt{85}}{11} \quad \csc \theta = \frac{\text{hyp}}{\text{opp}} = \frac{11}{\sqrt{85}} = \frac{11\sqrt{85}}{85}$$

$$\cos \theta = \frac{\text{adj}}{\text{hyp}} = \frac{6}{11} \quad \sec \theta = \frac{\text{hyp}}{\text{adj}} = \frac{11}{6}$$

$$\tan \theta = \frac{\text{opp}}{\text{adj}} = \frac{\sqrt{85}}{6} \quad \cot \theta = \frac{\text{adj}}{\text{opp}} = \frac{6}{\sqrt{85}} = \frac{6\sqrt{85}}{85}$$

6. opp = 10, hyp = 12, adj = $\sqrt{12^2 - 10^2} = \sqrt{44}$
   $= 2\sqrt{11}$

$$\sin \theta = \frac{\text{opp}}{\text{hyp}} = \frac{10}{12} = \frac{5}{6}$$

$$\cos \theta = \frac{\text{adj}}{\text{hyp}} = \frac{2\sqrt{11}}{12} = \frac{\sqrt{11}}{6}$$

$$\tan \theta = \frac{\text{opp}}{\text{adj}} = \frac{10}{2\sqrt{11}} = \frac{5\sqrt{11}}{11}$$

$$\csc \theta = \frac{\text{hyp}}{\text{opp}} = \frac{12}{10} = \frac{6}{5}$$

$$\sec \theta = \frac{\text{hyp}}{\text{adj}} = \frac{12}{2\sqrt{11}} = \frac{6\sqrt{11}}{11}$$

$$\cot \theta = \frac{\text{adj}}{\text{opp}} = \frac{2\sqrt{11}}{10} = \frac{\sqrt{11}}{5}$$

7. $\cos \theta = \frac{\text{adj}}{\text{hyp}}$

$$\cos 23° = \frac{32}{x}$$

$$x = \frac{32}{\cos 23°}$$

$$x \approx 34.8$$

8. $\tan \theta = \frac{\text{opp}}{\text{adj}}$

$$\tan x° = \frac{15}{21}$$

$$x \approx 36$$

9. $45° + B = 90°$
$$B = 45°$$
Since this is a 45°-45°-90° triangle and $b = 6$, then $a = 6$ and $c = \sqrt{6^2 + 6^2} = \sqrt{72} \approx 8.5$.

10. $A + 56° = 90°$
$$A = 34°$$

$$\sin B = \frac{b}{c}$$

$$\sin 56° = \frac{b}{16}$$

$$b \approx 13.3$$

$$\cos B = \frac{a}{c}$$

$$\cos 56° = \frac{a}{16}$$

$$a \approx 8.9$$

11. $a^2 + b^2 = c^2$
$$a^2 + 7^2 = 18^2$$
$$a^2 = 18^2 - 7^2$$
$$a^2 = 275$$
$$a \approx 16.6$$

$$\sin B = \frac{b}{c}$$

$$\sin B = \frac{7}{18}$$

$$B \approx 23°$$

$$\cos A = \frac{b}{c}$$

$$\cos A = \frac{7}{18}$$

$$A \approx 67°$$

12. $c^2 = a^2 + b^2$
$$c^2 = 14^2 + 13^2$$
$$c = \sqrt{365}$$
$$c \approx 19.1$$

$$\tan B = \frac{b}{a}$$

$$\tan B = \frac{13}{14}$$

$$B \approx 43°$$

$$\tan A = \frac{a}{b}$$

$$\tan A = \frac{14}{13}$$

$$A \approx 47°$$

13.   6 miles = 6 · 5280 feet = 31,680 feet
$$\tan \theta = \frac{\text{opp}}{\text{adj}}$$

$$\tan 3° = \frac{x}{31,680}$$

$$31,680 \tan 3° = x$$
$$1660 \approx x$$
The altitude is 1660 feet.

14. B; $\tan \theta = \frac{\text{opp}}{\text{adj}}$

$$\tan \theta = \frac{3}{1}$$

$$\text{opp} = 3, \text{adj} = 1$$
$$\text{hyp} = \sqrt{3^2 + 1^2} = \sqrt{10}$$

$$\sin \theta = \frac{\text{opp}}{\text{hyp}}$$

$$\sin \theta = \frac{3}{\sqrt{10}}$$

$$\sin \theta = \frac{3\sqrt{10}}{10}$$

Pages 706-708   Practice and Apply

15. opp = 4, hyp = 11, adj = $\sqrt{11^2 - 4^2} = \sqrt{105}$

$$\sin \theta = \frac{\text{opp}}{\text{hyp}} = \frac{4}{11}$$

$$\cos \theta = \frac{\text{adj}}{\text{hyp}} = \frac{\sqrt{105}}{11}$$

$$\tan \theta = \frac{\text{opp}}{\text{adj}} = \frac{4}{\sqrt{105}} = \frac{4\sqrt{105}}{105}$$

$$\csc \theta = \frac{\text{hyp}}{\text{opp}} = \frac{11}{4}$$

$$\sec \theta = \frac{\text{hyp}}{\text{adj}} = \frac{11}{\sqrt{105}} = \frac{11\sqrt{105}}{105}$$

$$\cot \theta = \frac{\text{adj}}{\text{opp}} = \frac{\sqrt{105}}{4}$$

16. opp = 21, adj = 28, hyp = $\sqrt{21^2 + 28^2} = \sqrt{1225} = 35$

$\sin \theta = \frac{\text{opp}}{\text{hyp}} = \frac{21}{35} = \frac{3}{5}$ $\csc \theta = \frac{\text{hyp}}{\text{opp}} = \frac{35}{21} = \frac{5}{3}$

$\cos \theta = \frac{\text{adj}}{\text{hyp}} = \frac{28}{35} = \frac{4}{5}$ $\sec \theta = \frac{\text{hyp}}{\text{adj}} = \frac{35}{28} = \frac{5}{4}$

$\tan \theta = \frac{\text{opp}}{\text{adj}} = \frac{21}{28} = \frac{3}{4}$ $\cot \theta = \frac{\text{adj}}{\text{opp}} = \frac{28}{21} = \frac{4}{3}$

17. adj = 12, hyp = 16, opp = $\sqrt{16^2 - 12^2} = \sqrt{112} = 4\sqrt{7}$

$\sin \theta = \frac{\text{opp}}{\text{hyp}} = \frac{4\sqrt{7}}{16} = \frac{\sqrt{7}}{4}$

$\cos \theta = \frac{\text{adj}}{\text{hyp}} = \frac{12}{16} = \frac{3}{4}$

$\tan \theta = \frac{\text{opp}}{\text{adj}} = \frac{4\sqrt{7}}{12} = \frac{\sqrt{7}}{3}$

$\csc \theta = \frac{\text{hyp}}{\text{opp}} = \frac{16}{4\sqrt{7}} = \frac{4\sqrt{7}}{7}$

$\sec \theta = \frac{\text{hyp}}{\text{adj}} = \frac{16}{12} = \frac{4}{3}$

$\cot \theta = \frac{\text{adj}}{\text{opp}} = \frac{12}{4\sqrt{7}} = \frac{3\sqrt{7}}{7}$

18. adj = 5, opp = 9, hyp = $\sqrt{9^2 + 5^2} = \sqrt{106}$

$\sin \theta = \frac{\text{opp}}{\text{hyp}} = \frac{9}{\sqrt{106}} = \frac{9\sqrt{106}}{106}$

$\cos \theta = \frac{\text{adj}}{\text{hyp}} = \frac{5}{\sqrt{106}} = \frac{5\sqrt{106}}{106}$

$\tan \theta = \frac{\text{opp}}{\text{adj}} = \frac{9}{5}$

$\csc \theta = \frac{\text{hyp}}{\text{opp}} = \frac{\sqrt{106}}{9}$

$\sec \theta = \frac{\text{hyp}}{\text{adj}} = \frac{\sqrt{106}}{5}$

$\cot \theta = \frac{\text{adj}}{\text{opp}} = \frac{5}{9}$

19. opp = 2, hyp = $2\sqrt{5}$, adj = $\sqrt{(2\sqrt{5})^2 - 2^2} = \sqrt{16} = 4$

$\sin \theta = \frac{\text{opp}}{\text{hyp}} = \frac{2}{2\sqrt{5}} = \frac{\sqrt{5}}{5}$

$\cos \theta = \frac{\text{adj}}{\text{hyp}} = \frac{4}{2\sqrt{5}} = \frac{2\sqrt{5}}{5}$

$\tan \theta = \frac{\text{opp}}{\text{adj}} = \frac{2}{4} = \frac{1}{2}$

$\csc \theta = \frac{\text{hyp}}{\text{opp}} = \frac{2\sqrt{5}}{2} = \sqrt{5}$

$\sec \theta = \frac{\text{hyp}}{\text{adj}} = \frac{2\sqrt{5}}{4} = \frac{\sqrt{5}}{2}$

$\cot \theta = \frac{\text{adj}}{\text{opp}} = \frac{4}{2} = 2$

20. opp = $\sqrt{15}$, adj = 7, hyp = $\sqrt{7^2 + (\sqrt{15})^2} = \sqrt{64} = 8$

$\sin \theta = \frac{\text{opp}}{\text{hyp}} = \frac{\sqrt{15}}{8}$ $\csc \theta = \frac{\text{hyp}}{\text{opp}} = \frac{8}{\sqrt{15}} = \frac{8\sqrt{15}}{15}$

$\cos \theta = \frac{\text{adj}}{\text{hyp}} = \frac{7}{8}$ $\sec \theta = \frac{\text{hyp}}{\text{adj}} = \frac{8}{7}$

$\tan \theta = \frac{\text{opp}}{\text{adj}} = \frac{\sqrt{15}}{7}$ $\cot \theta = \frac{\text{adj}}{\text{opp}} = \frac{7}{\sqrt{15}} = \frac{7\sqrt{15}}{15}$

21. $\tan \theta = \frac{\text{opp}}{\text{adj}}$

$\tan 30° = \frac{x}{10}$

$10 \tan 30° = x$

$5.8 \approx x$

22. $\cos \theta = \frac{\text{adj}}{\text{hyp}}$

$\cos 60° = \frac{3}{x}$

$x = \frac{3}{\cos 60°}$

$x = 6$

23. $\sin \theta = \frac{\text{opp}}{\text{hyp}}$

$\sin 54° = \frac{17.8}{x}$

$x = \frac{17.8}{\sin 54°}$

$x \approx 22.0$

24. $\tan \theta = \frac{\text{opp}}{\text{adj}}$

$\tan 17.5° = \frac{x}{23.7}$

$23.7 \tan 17.5° = x$

$7.5 \approx x$

25. $\cos \theta = \frac{\text{adj}}{\text{hyp}}$

$\cos x° = \frac{15}{36}$

$x \approx 65$

26. $\sin \theta = \frac{\text{opp}}{\text{hyp}}$

$\sin x° = \frac{16}{22}$

$x \approx 47$

27a. $\sin 30° = \frac{\text{opp}}{\text{hyp}}$ *sine ratio*

$\sin 30° = \frac{x}{2x}$ *Replace opp with x and hyp with 2x.*

$\sin 30° = \frac{1}{2}$ *Simplify.*

27b. $\cos 30° = \frac{\text{adj}}{\text{hyp}}$ *cosine ratio*

$\cos 30° = \frac{\sqrt{3}x}{2}$ *Replace adj with $\sqrt{3}x$ and hyp with 2x.*

$\cos 30° = \frac{\sqrt{3}}{2}$ *Simplify.*

27c. $\sin 60° = \frac{\text{opp}}{\text{hyp}}$ *sine ratio*

$\sin 60° = \frac{\sqrt{3}x}{2x}$ *Replace opp with $\sqrt{3}x$ and hyp with 2x.*

$\sin 60° = \frac{\sqrt{3}}{2}$ *Simplify.*

28a. $\sin 45° = \frac{\text{opp}}{\text{hyp}}$ *sine ratio*

$\sin 45° = \frac{x}{\sqrt{2}x}$ *Replace opp with x and hyp with $\sqrt{2}x$.*

$\sin 45° = \frac{1}{\sqrt{2}}$ *Simplify.*

$\sin 45° = \frac{\sqrt{2}}{2}$ *Rationalize the denominator.*

28b. $\cos 45° = \frac{\text{adj}}{\text{hyp}}$ *cosine ratio*

$\cos 45° = \frac{x}{\sqrt{2}x}$ *Replace adj with x and hyp with $\sqrt{2}x$.*

$\cos 45° = \frac{1}{\sqrt{2}}$ *Simplify.*

$\cos 45° = \frac{\sqrt{2}}{2}$ *Rationalize the denominator.*

28c. $\tan 45° = \frac{\text{opp}}{\text{adj}}$ *tangent ratio*

      $\tan 45° = \frac{x}{x}$ *Replace opp with x and adj with x.*

      $\tan 45° = 1$ *Simplify.*

29. $16° + B = 90°$

        $B = 74°$

      $\cos A = \frac{b}{c}$

      $\cos 16° = \frac{b}{14}$

  $14 \cos 16° = b$

      $13.5 \approx b$

      $\sin A = \frac{a}{c}$

      $\sin 16° = \frac{a}{14}$

  $14 \sin 16° = a$

      $3.9 \approx a$

30. $A + 27° = 90°$

        $A = 63°$

      $\sin B = \frac{b}{c}$

      $\sin 27° = \frac{7}{c}$

         $c = \frac{7}{\sin 27°}$

         $c \approx 15.4$

      $\cos B = \frac{a}{c}$

      $\cos 27° \approx \frac{a}{15.4}$

  $15.4 \cos 27° \approx a$

      $13.7 \approx a$

31. $34° + B = 90°$

        $B = 56°$

      $\sin A = \frac{a}{c}$

      $\sin 34° = \frac{10}{c}$

         $c = \frac{10}{\sin 34°}$

         $c \approx 17.9$

      $\cos A = \frac{b}{c}$

      $\cos 34° \approx \frac{b}{17.9}$

  $17.9 \cos 34° \approx b$

      $14.8 \approx b$

32. $A + 15° = 90°$

        $A = 75°$

      $\sin B = \frac{b}{c}$

      $\sin 15° = \frac{b}{25}$

  $25 \sin 15° = b$

      $6.5 \approx b$

      $\cos B = \frac{a}{c}$

      $\cos 15° = \frac{a}{25}$

  $25 \cos 15° = a$

      $24.1 \approx a$

33. $A + 30° = 90°$

      $A = 60°$

Since this is a 30°-60°-90° triangle and $b = 11$, then $a = 11\sqrt{3} \approx 19.1$ and $c = 2(11) = 22$.

---

34. $45° + B = 90°$

      $B = 45°$

Since this is a 45°-45°-90° triangle and $c = 7\sqrt{2}$, then $a = 7$ and $b = 7$.

35. $A + 18° = 90°$

        $A = 72°$

      $\cos B = \frac{a}{c}$

      $\cos 18° = \frac{\sqrt{15}}{c}$

         $c = \frac{\sqrt{15}}{\cos 18°}$

         $c \approx 4.1$

      $\cos A = \frac{b}{c}$

      $\cos 72° \approx \frac{b}{4.1}$

  $4.1 \cos 72° \approx b$

      $1.3 \approx b$

36. $10° + B = 90°$

        $B = 80°$

      $\cos A = \frac{b}{c}$

      $\cos 10° = \frac{15}{c}$

         $c = \frac{15}{\cos 10°}$

         $c \approx 15.2$

      $\sin A = \frac{a}{c}$

      $\sin 10° \approx \frac{a}{15.2}$

  $15.2 \sin 10° \approx a$

      $2.6 \approx a$

37. $a^2 + b^2 = c^2$

    $a^2 + 6^2 = 13^2$

        $a^2 = 133$

        $a \approx 11.5$

    $\cos A = \frac{b}{c}$

    $\cos A = \frac{6}{13}$

        $A \approx 63°$

    $\sin B = \frac{b}{c}$

    $\sin B = \frac{6}{13}$

        $B \approx 27°$

38. $a^2 + b^2 = c^2$

    $4^2 + b^2 = 9^2$

        $b^2 = 65$

        $b \approx 8.1$

    $\sin A = \frac{a}{c}$

    $\sin A = \frac{4}{9}$

        $A \approx 26°$

    $\cos B = \frac{a}{c}$

    $\cos B = \frac{4}{9}$

        $B \approx 64°$

39. $\tan B = \frac{b}{a} = \frac{7}{8}, a = 8$

$\tan B = \frac{7}{8}$

$B \approx 41°$

$A + 41° \approx 90°$

$A \approx 49°$

$\cos B = \frac{a}{c}$

$\cos 41° \approx \frac{8}{c}$

$c \approx \frac{8}{\cos 41°}$

$c \approx 10.6$

40. $\sin A = \frac{1}{3}$

$A \approx 19°$

$19° + B \approx 90°$

$B \approx 71°$

$\sin A = \frac{1}{3} = \frac{a}{c}$

$\frac{1}{3} = \frac{5}{c}$

$c = 15$

$c^2 = a^2 + b^2$

$15^2 = 5^2 + b^2$

$b^2 = 200$

$b \approx 14.1$

41. Since this is a 30°-60°-90° triangle and $x = 173$, then $x\sqrt{3} = 173\sqrt{3} \approx 300$. The distance from the boat to the base of the falls is about 300 feet.

42. Let x be the height.

$\tan 55° = \frac{x}{100}$

$100 \tan 55° = x$

$142.8 \approx x$

The building is about 142.8 feet high.

43. Let $x°$ be the angle.

$\tan x° = \frac{10}{100}$

$x \approx 6$

The treadmill is set at about a 6° angle.

44. Let $x°$ be the angle.

$\tan x° = \frac{8}{100}$

$x \approx 4.57$

Now let v be the vertical rise.

$\sin 4.57° \approx \frac{v}{40}$

$40 \sin 4.57° \approx v$

$3.2 \approx v$

The vertical rise is about 3.2 inches.

45. $\theta = \frac{360°}{12} = 30°$

$\tan \theta = \frac{\text{opp}}{\text{adj}}$

$\tan 30° = \frac{3}{x}$

$\frac{\sqrt{3}}{3} = \frac{3}{x}$

$x = 3\sqrt{3}$

Area of small right triangle $= \frac{1}{2}(3)(3\sqrt{3}) = \frac{9\sqrt{3}}{2}$

Area of regular hexagon $= 12\left(\frac{9\sqrt{3}}{2}\right) =$

$54\sqrt{3} \approx 93.53$

The area is about 93.53 units^2.

46. $\tan 40° = \frac{h}{x}, h = x \tan 40°$

$\tan 34° = \frac{h}{x + 0.5}, h = (x + 0.5) \tan 34°$

Solve for x.

$x \tan 40° = (x + 0.5) \tan 34°$

$x \tan 40° = x \tan 34° + 0.5 \tan 34°$

$x(\tan 40° - \tan 34°) = 0.5 \tan 34°$

$x = \frac{0.5 \tan 34°}{\tan 40° - \tan 34°}$

$x \approx 2.05$

Solve for h.

$h \approx 2.05 \tan 40°$

$h \approx 1.7$

The top of the mountain is about 1.7 km high.

47. The sine and cosine ratios of acute angles of right triangles each have the longest measure of the triangle, the hypotenuse, as their denominator. A fraction whose denominator is greater than its numerator is less than 1. The tangent ratio of an acute angle of a right triangle does not involve the measure of the hypotenuse, $\frac{\text{opp}}{\text{adj}}$. If the measure of the opposite side is greater than the measure of the adjacent side, the tangent ratio is greater than 1. If the measure of the opposite side is less than the measure of the adjacent side, the tangent ratio is less than 1.

48. When construction involves right triangles, including building ramps, designing buildings, or surveying land before building, trigonometry is likely to be used. Answers should include the following.

- If you view the ramp from the side then the vertical rise is opposite the angle that the ramp makes with the horizontal. Similarly, the horizontal run is the adjacent side. So the tangent of the angle is the ratio of the rise to the run or the slope of the ramp.
- Given the ratio of the slope of ramp, you can find the angle of inclination by calculating $\tan^{-1}$ of this ratio.

49. C; $\sec \theta = \frac{\text{hyp}}{\text{adj}} = \frac{25}{7}$

$\text{hyp} = 25, \text{adj} = 7$

$25^2 = 7^2 + \text{opp}^2$

$\text{opp}^2 = 576$

$\text{opp} = 24$

$\sin \theta = \frac{\text{opp}}{\text{hyp}} = \frac{24}{25}$

50. Let x be the length of the ramp.

$\sin 15° = \frac{2}{x}$

$x = \frac{2}{\sin 15°}$

$x \approx 7.7$

The ramp is 7.7 feet long, to the nearest tenth of a foot.

Page 708   Maintain Your Skills

51. No; band members may be more likely to like the same kinds of music.

52. Yes; this sample is random since different kinds of people go to the post office.

53. $P(\text{exactly 2 heads}) = C(4, 2)\left(\frac{1}{2}\right)^2\left(\frac{1}{2}\right)^2$

$$= 6\left(\frac{1}{4}\right)\left(\frac{1}{4}\right)$$

$$= \frac{3}{8}$$

54. $P(4 \text{ heads}) = C(4, 4)\left(\frac{1}{2}\right)^4\left(\frac{1}{2}\right)^0$

$$= 1\left(\frac{1}{16}\right)(1)$$

$$= \frac{1}{16}$$

55. $P(\text{at least 1 heads}) = 1 - P(0 \text{ heads})$

$$= 1 - C(4, 0)\left(\frac{1}{2}\right)^0\left(\frac{1}{2}\right)^4$$

$$= 1 - \frac{1}{16}$$

$$= \frac{15}{16}$$

56.
$$y^4 - 64 = 0$$
$$(y^2 - 8)(y^2 + 8) = 0$$

$y^2 - 8 = 0$ or $y^2 + 8 = 0$
$\quad y^2 = 8 \qquad\qquad\qquad y^2 = -8$
$\quad\quad y = \pm\sqrt{8} \qquad\qquad y = \pm\sqrt{-8}$
$\quad\quad y = \pm 2\sqrt{2} \qquad\qquad y = \pm 2i\sqrt{2}$
$\{\pm 2\sqrt{2}, \pm 2i\sqrt{2}\}$

57. $x^5 - 5x^3 + 4x = 0$
$\quad x(x^4 - 5x^2 + 4) = 0$
$\quad x(x^2 - 4)(x^2 - 1) = 0$

$x = 0$ or $x^2 - 4 = 0$ or $x^2 - 1 = 0$
$\qquad\qquad\qquad x^2 = 4 \qquad\qquad x^2 = 1$
$\qquad\qquad\qquad x = \pm 2 \qquad\qquad x = \pm 1$

$\{-2, -1, 0, 1, 2\}$

58.
$$d + \sqrt{d} - 132 = 0$$
$$(\sqrt{d})^2 + \sqrt{d} - 132 = 0$$
$$(\sqrt{d} + 12)(\sqrt{d} - 11) = 0$$

$\sqrt{d} + 12 = 0$ or $\sqrt{d} - 11 = 0$
$\quad\quad \sqrt{d} = -12 \qquad\qquad \sqrt{d} = 11$
The principal square $d = 121$
root cannot be negative.
$\{121\}$

59. 5 gallons $\left(\frac{4 \text{ quarts}}{1 \text{ gallon}}\right) = 5 \cdot 4$ quarts $= 20$ quarts

60. 6.8 miles $\left(\frac{5280 \text{ feet}}{1 \text{ mile}}\right) = 6.8(5280)$ feet $= 35,904$ feet

61. $\left(\frac{2 \text{ square meters}}{5 \text{ dollars}}\right)$ 30 dollars $= \frac{2 \cdot 30}{5}$ square meters $=$ 12 square meters

62. $\left(\frac{4 \text{ liters}}{5 \text{ minutes}}\right)$ 60 minutes $= \frac{4 \cdot 60}{5}$ liters $= 48$ liters

---

13-2 | Angles and Angle Measure

Page 712   Check for Understanding

1. Angle measures belong to the set of real numbers.

2. In a circle of radius r units, one radian is the measure of an angle whose rays intercept an arc length of r units.

3.
$$\theta = -70°$$
$$360° - 70° = 290°$$

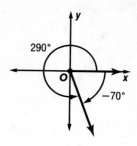

4. Draw the terminal side of the angle 70° counterclockwise from the positive x-axis.

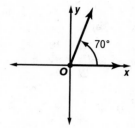

5. $300° = 360° - 60°$
Draw the terminal side of the angle 60° clockwise from the positive x-axis.

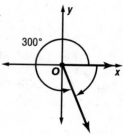

6. $570° - 360° = 210°$
$\qquad\qquad 210° = 180° + 30°$
Draw the terminal side of the angle 30° counterclockwise past the negative x-axis.

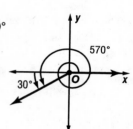

7. Draw the terminal side of the angle 45° clockwise from the positive x-axis.

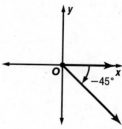

8. $130° = 130°\left(\frac{\pi \text{ radians}}{180°}\right)$

$\qquad = \frac{130\pi}{180}$ radians or $\frac{13\pi}{18}$

9. $-10° = -10°\left(\frac{\pi \text{ radians}}{180°}\right)$

$\qquad = \frac{-10\pi}{180}$ radians or $-\frac{\pi}{18}$

10. $485° = 485°\left(\frac{\pi \text{ radians}}{180°}\right)$

$\qquad\quad = \frac{485\pi}{180}$ radians or $\frac{97\pi}{36}$

11. $\frac{3\pi}{4} = \left(\frac{3\pi}{4} \text{ radians}\right)\left(\frac{180°}{\pi \text{ radians}}\right)$

$= \frac{540°}{4}$ or $135°$

12. $-\frac{\pi}{6} = \left(-\frac{\pi}{6} \text{ radians}\right)\left(\frac{180°}{\pi \text{ radians}}\right)$

$= -\frac{180°}{6}$ or $-30°$

13. $\frac{19\pi}{3} = \left(\frac{19\pi}{3} \text{ radians}\right)\left(\frac{180°}{\pi \text{ radians}}\right)$

$= \frac{3420°}{3}$ or $1140°$

14. A positive angle is $60° + 360° = 420°$.

A negative angle is $60° - 360° = -300°$.

15. A positive angle is $425° + 360° = 785°$.

A negative angle is $425° - 2(360°) = -295°$.

16. A positive angle is $\frac{\pi}{3} + 2\pi = \frac{7\pi}{3}$.

A negative angle is $\frac{\pi}{3} - 2\pi = -\frac{5\pi}{3}$.

17. 24 hr for $360°$

$\frac{24 \text{ hr}}{360°} \cdot 315° = \frac{24 \cdot 315}{360} \text{ hr} = 21 \text{ hr}$

It takes Earth 21 hr to rotate $315°$.

18. 24 hr for 2π radians

$\frac{24 \text{ hr}}{2\pi} \cdot \frac{\pi}{6} = \frac{24}{2 \cdot 6} \text{ hr} = 2 \text{ hr}$

It takes Earth 2 hr to rotate $\frac{\pi}{6}$ radians.

Pages 712–714   Practice and Apply

19. $235° = 180° + 55°$
Draw the terminal side of
the angle $55°$
counterclockwise past the
negative x-axis.

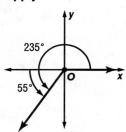

20. $270° = 180° + 90°$
Draw the terminal side of
the angle $90°$
counterclockwise past the
negative x-axis (coincides
with negative y-axis).

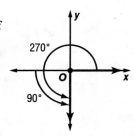

21. $790° = 2(360°) + 70°$
Draw the terminal side of
the angle $70°$
counterclockwise from the
positive x-axis.

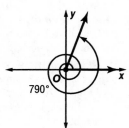

22. $380° = 360° + 20°$
Draw the terminal side of
the angle $20°$
counterclockwise from the
positive x-axis.

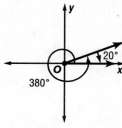

23. $-150° = -180° + 30°$
Draw the terminal side of
the angle $30°$
counterclockwise from the
negative x-axis.

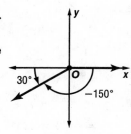

24. Draw the terminal side of
the angle $50°$ clockwise
from the positive x-axis.

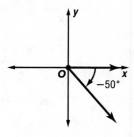

25. Draw the terminal side of
the angle to coincide with
the negative x-axis
(i.e., $\frac{1}{2}$ of a full revolution).

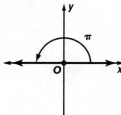

26. $-\frac{2\pi}{3} = -\pi + \frac{\pi}{3}$
Draw the terminal side of
the angle $\frac{\pi}{3}$

(or $\frac{\pi}{3} \cdot \frac{180°}{\pi} = 60°$)

counterclockwise from the
negative x-axis.

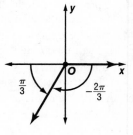

27. $120° = 120°\left(\frac{\pi \text{ radians}}{180°}\right)$

$= \frac{120\pi}{180} \text{ radians or } \frac{2\pi}{3}$

28. $60° = 60°\left(\frac{\pi \text{ radians}}{180°}\right)$

$= \frac{60\pi}{180} \text{ radians or } \frac{\pi}{3}$

29. $-15° = -15°\left(\frac{\pi \text{ radians}}{180°}\right)$

$= \frac{-15\pi}{180} \text{ radians or } -\frac{\pi}{12}$

30. $-225° = -225°\left(\frac{\pi \text{ radians}}{180°}\right)$

$= \frac{-225\pi}{180} \text{ radians or } -\frac{5\pi}{4}$

31. $660° = 660°\left(\frac{\pi \text{ radians}}{180°}\right)$

$= \frac{660\pi}{180}$ radians or $\frac{11\pi}{3}$

32. $570° = 570°\left(\frac{\pi \text{ radians}}{180°}\right)$

$= \frac{570\pi}{180}$ radians or $\frac{19\pi}{6}$

33. $158° = 158°\left(\frac{\pi \text{ radians}}{180°}\right)$

$= \frac{158\pi}{180}$ radians or $\frac{79\pi}{90}$

34. $260° = 260°\left(\frac{\pi \text{ radians}}{180°}\right)$

$= \frac{260\pi}{180}$ radians or $\frac{13\pi}{9}$

35. $\frac{5\pi}{6} = \left(\frac{5\pi}{6} \text{ radians}\right)\left(\frac{180°}{\pi \text{ radians}}\right)$

$= \frac{900°}{6}$ or $150°$

36. $\frac{11\pi}{4} = \left(\frac{11\pi}{4} \text{ radians}\right)\left(\frac{180°}{\pi \text{ radians}}\right)$

$= \frac{1980°}{4}$ or $495°$

37. $-\frac{\pi}{4} = \left(-\frac{\pi}{4} \text{ radians}\right)\left(\frac{180°}{\pi \text{ radians}}\right)$

$= -\frac{180°}{4}$ or $-45°$

38. $-\frac{\pi}{3} = \left(-\frac{\pi}{3} \text{ radians}\right)\left(\frac{180°}{\pi \text{ radians}}\right)$

$= -\frac{180°}{3} = -60°$

39. $\frac{29\pi}{4} = \left(\frac{29\pi}{4} \text{ radians}\right)\left(\frac{180°}{\pi \text{ radians}}\right)$

$= \frac{5220°}{4}$ or $1305°$

40. $\frac{17\pi}{6} = \left(\frac{17\pi}{6} \text{ radians}\right)\left(\frac{180°}{\pi \text{ radians}}\right)$

$= \frac{3060°}{6}$ or $510°$

41. $9 = (9 \text{ radians})\left(\frac{180°}{\pi \text{ radians}}\right)$

$= \frac{1620°}{\pi} \approx 515.7°$

42. $3 = (3 \text{ radians})\left(\frac{180°}{\pi \text{ radians}}\right)$

$= \frac{540°}{\pi} \approx 171.9°$

43. A positive angle is $225° + 360° = 585°$.
A negative angle is $225° - 360° = -135°$.

44. A positive angle is $30° + 360° = 390°$.
A negative angle is $30° - 360° = -330°$.

45. A positive angle is $-15° + 360° = 345°$.
A negative angle is $-15° - 360° = -375°$.

46. A positive angle is $-140° + 360° = 220°$.
A negative angle is $-140° - 360° = -500°$.

47. A positive angle is $368° - 360° = 8°$.
A negative angle is $368° - 2(360°) = -352°$.

48. A positive angle is $760° - 360° = 400°$.
A negative angle is $760° - 3(360°) = -320°$.

49. A positive angle is $\frac{3\pi}{4} + 2\pi = \frac{11\pi}{4}$.

A negative angle is $\frac{3\pi}{4} - 2\pi = -\frac{5\pi}{4}$.

50. A positive angle is $\frac{7\pi}{6} + 2\pi = \frac{19\pi}{6}$.

A negative angle is $\frac{7\pi}{6} - 2\pi = -\frac{5\pi}{6}$.

51. A positive angle is $-\frac{5\pi}{4} + 2\pi = \frac{3\pi}{4}$.

A negative angle is $-\frac{5\pi}{4} - 2\pi = -\frac{13\pi}{4}$.

52. A positive angle is $-\frac{2\pi}{3} + 2\pi = \frac{4\pi}{3}$.

A negative angle is $-\frac{2\pi}{3} - 2\pi = -\frac{8\pi}{3}$.

53. A positive angle is $\frac{9\pi}{2} + 2\pi = \frac{13\pi}{2}$.

A negative angle is $\frac{9\pi}{2} - 3(2\pi) = -\frac{3\pi}{2}$.

54. A positive angle is $\frac{17\pi}{4} + 2\pi = \frac{25\pi}{4}$.

A negative angle is $\frac{17\pi}{4} - 3(2\pi) = -\frac{7\pi}{4}$.

55. Convert miles per hour to inches per second.

$\frac{40 \text{ mi}}{\text{hr}} \cdot \frac{5280 \text{ ft}}{\text{mi}} \cdot \frac{12 \text{ in}}{1 \text{ ft}} \cdot \frac{1 \text{ hr}}{60 \text{ min}} \cdot \frac{1 \text{ min}}{60 \text{ sec}} = 704 \text{ in./sec}$

360° is one revolution, where
$\quad\quad$ circumference $= 2\pi r = 2\pi(15) = 30\pi$ in.

$704 \text{ in./sec} \cdot \left(\frac{360°}{30\pi \text{ in.}}\right) \approx 2689°$ per second

$2689° \cdot \left(\frac{\pi \text{ radians}}{180°}\right) \approx 47$ radians per second

56. $A = \frac{1}{2}r^2\theta$

$A = \frac{1}{2}(10 \text{ in.})^2\left(\frac{4\pi}{3}\right)$

$A \approx 209.4 \text{ in}^2$

57. $150° = 150°\left(\frac{\pi}{180°}\right) = \frac{5\pi}{6}$

$A = \frac{1}{2}r^2\theta$

$A = \frac{1}{2}(12 \text{ m})^2\left(\frac{5\pi}{6}\right)$

$A \approx 188.5 \text{ m}^2$

58. The gondolas are spaced $\frac{2\pi}{40} = \frac{\pi}{20}$ radians apart.

The wheel rotates $\frac{47\pi}{10} = 2(2\pi) + 14\left(\frac{\pi}{20}\right)$ or

2 revolutions plus 14 gondola positions.
Since you were at number 3, the gondola that used
to be in your new position is number $3 + 14 = 17$.

59. $\quad\quad\quad 135° = 135°\left(\frac{\pi}{180°}\right) = \frac{3\pi}{4}$

Swept area = Total area − Small area at
$\quad\quad\quad\quad\quad\quad\quad\quad\quad\quad$ base

Total area $= \frac{1}{2}r^2\theta = \frac{1}{2}(16 + 9)^2\left(\frac{3\pi}{4}\right)$

$\quad\quad\quad\quad \approx 736.31$

Small area at base $= \frac{1}{2}r^2\theta = \frac{1}{2}(9)^2\left(\frac{3\pi}{4}\right) \approx 95.43$

Swept area $\approx 736.31 - 95.43 = 640.88$
The area swept by the wiper is about 640.88 in².

60a. $a^2 + (-b)^2 = a^2 + b^2 = 1$

60b. $b^2 + a^2 = a^2 + b^2 = 1$

60c. $b^2 + (-a)^2 = a^2 + b^2 = 1$

61. Student answers should include the following.

- An angle with a measure of more than 180°
  gives an indication of motion in a circular path
  that ended at a point more than halfway
  around the circle from where it started.

- Negative angles convey the same meaning as
  positive angles, but in an opposite direction.
  The standard convention is that negative
  angles represent rotations in a clockwise
  direction.

- Rates over 360° per minute indicate that an
  object is rotating or revolving more than one
  revolution per minute.

62. C; Convert radians to degrees.

$\frac{14\pi}{45} \cdot \left(\frac{180°}{\pi}\right) = 56°$

The quantities are equal.

63. D; $\omega = \frac{\theta}{t}$

$\omega = \frac{2(2\pi)}{3}$

$\omega = \frac{4\pi}{3}$

Pages 714-715   Maintain Your Skills

64. $34° + B = 90°$

$B = 56°$

$\cos A = \frac{b}{c}$

$\cos 34° = \frac{5}{c}$

$c \approx 6.0$

$\sin A = \frac{a}{c}$

$\sin 34° \approx \frac{a}{6.0}$

$a \approx 3.4$

65. $A + 68° = 90°$

$A = 22°$

$\sin B = \frac{b}{c}$

$\sin 68° = \frac{14.7}{c}$

$c \approx 15.9$

$\tan A = \frac{a}{b}$

$\tan 22° = \frac{a}{14.7}$

$a \approx 5.9$

66. $A + 55° = 90°$

$A = 35°$

$\cos B = \frac{a}{c}$

$\cos 55° = \frac{a}{16}$

$a \approx 9.2$

$\sin B = \frac{b}{c}$

$\sin 55° = \frac{b}{16}$

$b \approx 13.1$

67. $c^2 = a^2 + b^2$

$c^2 = 0.4^2 + (0.4\sqrt{3})^2$

$c^2 = \sqrt{0.64}$

$c = 0.8$

$\sin A = \frac{a}{c}$

$\sin A = \frac{0.4}{0.8}$

$A = 30°$

$30° + B = 90°$

$B = 60°$

68. $ME = 2\sqrt{\frac{p(1-p)}{n}}$

$= 2\sqrt{\frac{0.72(1-0.72)}{100}}$

≈ 0.0898

The margin of sampling error is about 8.98%.

69. $ME = 2\sqrt{\frac{p(1-p)}{n}}$

$= 2\sqrt{\frac{0.5(0.5)}{200}}$

≈ 0.0707

The margin of sampling error is about 7.07%.

70. In this arrangement, order is important, so this is a permutation.

$P(n, r) = \frac{n!}{(n-r)!}$

$P(30, 5) = \frac{30!}{(30-5)!}$

$= \frac{30!}{25!}$

$= \frac{30 \cdot 29 \cdot 28 \cdot 27 \cdot 26 \cdot 25!}{25!}$

$= 17,100,720$

71. This is a combination since order is not important.

$C(n, r) = \frac{n!}{(n-r)!r!}$

$C(7, 3) = \frac{7!}{(7-3)!\,3!}$

$= \frac{7!}{4!3!}$

$= \frac{7 \cdot 6 \cdot 5 \cdot 4!}{4! \cdot 6}$

$= 35$

72. $g(x) = 2x, h(x) = 3x - 4$

$[g \circ h](x) = g[h(x)]$

$= g(3x - 4)$

$= 2(3x - 4)$

$= 6x - 8$

$[h \circ g](x) = h[g(x)]$

$= h(2x)$

$= 3(2x) - 4$

$= 6x - 4$

73. $g(x) = 2x + 5, h(x) = 2x^2 - 3x + 9$

$[g \circ h](x) = g[h(x)]$

$= g(2x^2 - 3x + 9)$

$= 2(2x^2 - 3x + 9) + 5$

$= 4x^2 - 6x + 18 + 5$

$= 4x^2 - 6x + 23$

$[h \circ g](x) = h[g(x)]$

$= h(2x + 5)$

$= 2(2x + 5)^2 - 3(2x + 5) + 9$

$= 2(4x^2 + 20x + 25) - 3(2x + 5) + 9$

$= 8x^2 + 40x + 50 - 6x - 15 + 9$

$= 8x^2 + 34x + 44$

74. Let $x = 2006 - 1996 = 10$.

10	7.8	16.6	95.8
		78.0	946
	7.8	94.6	1041.8

The number of sports radio stations for 2006 is estimated to be 1041.8.

75.

12	7.8	16.6	95.8
		93.6	1322.4
	7.8	110.2	1418.2

$1996 + 12 = 2008$

The number of sports radio stations in 2008 is estimated to be about 1418.

76. $\frac{2}{\sqrt{3}} = \frac{2}{\sqrt{3}} \cdot \frac{\sqrt{3}}{\sqrt{3}} = \frac{2\sqrt{3}}{3}$

77. $\frac{3}{\sqrt{5}} = \frac{3}{\sqrt{5}} \cdot \frac{\sqrt{5}}{\sqrt{5}} = \frac{3\sqrt{5}}{5}$

78. $\frac{4}{\sqrt{6}} = \frac{4}{\sqrt{6}} \cdot \frac{\sqrt{6}}{\sqrt{6}} = \frac{4\sqrt{6}}{6} = \frac{2\sqrt{6}}{3}$

79. $\frac{5}{\sqrt{10}} = \frac{5}{\sqrt{10}} \cdot \frac{\sqrt{10}}{\sqrt{10}} = \frac{5\sqrt{10}}{10} = \frac{\sqrt{10}}{2}$

80. $\frac{\sqrt{7}}{\sqrt{2}} = \frac{\sqrt{7}}{\sqrt{2}} \cdot \frac{\sqrt{2}}{\sqrt{2}} = \frac{\sqrt{14}}{2}$

81. $\frac{\sqrt{5}}{\sqrt{8}} = \frac{\sqrt{5}}{2\sqrt{2}} = \frac{\sqrt{5}}{2\sqrt{2}} \cdot \frac{\sqrt{2}}{\sqrt{2}} = \frac{\sqrt{10}}{4}$

Page 715 Practice Quiz 1

1. $48° + B = 90°$
$B = 42°$
$\cos A = \frac{b}{c}$
$\cos 48° = \frac{12}{c}$
$c \approx 17.9$
$\tan A = \frac{a}{b}$
$\tan 48° = \frac{a}{12}$
$12 \tan 48° = a$
$13.3 \approx a$

2. $a^2 + b^2 = c^2$
$18^2 + b^2 = 21^2$
$b^2 = 117$
$b \approx 10.8$
$\sin A = \frac{a}{c}$
$\sin A = \frac{18}{21}$
$A \approx 59°$
$\cos B = \frac{a}{c}$
$\cos B = \frac{18}{21}$
$B \approx 31°$

3. Draw the terminal side of the angle 60° clockwise from the positive x-axis.

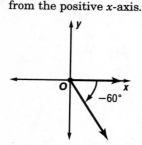

4. opp = 10, adj = 7, hyp = $\sqrt{10^2 + 7^2} = \sqrt{149}$

$\sin \theta = \frac{\text{opp}}{\text{hyp}} = \frac{10}{\sqrt{149}} = \frac{10\sqrt{149}}{149}$

$\cos \theta = \frac{\text{adj}}{\text{hyp}} = \frac{7}{\sqrt{149}} = \frac{7\sqrt{149}}{149}$

$\tan \theta = \frac{\text{opp}}{\text{adj}} = \frac{10}{7}$

$\csc \theta = \frac{\text{hyp}}{\text{opp}} = \frac{\sqrt{149}}{10}$

$\sec \theta = \frac{\text{hyp}}{\text{adj}} = \frac{\sqrt{149}}{7}$

$\cot \theta = \frac{\text{adj}}{\text{opp}} = \frac{7}{10}$

5. $190° = 190°\left(\frac{\pi \text{ radians}}{180°}\right)$
$= \frac{190\pi}{180}$ radians or $\frac{19\pi}{18}$

6. $450° = 50°\left(\frac{\pi \text{ radians}}{180°}\right)$
$= \frac{450\pi}{180}$ radians or $\frac{5\pi}{2}$

7. $\frac{7\pi}{6} = \left(\frac{7\pi}{6} \text{ radians}\right)\left(\frac{180°}{\pi \text{ radians}}\right)$
$= \frac{1260°}{6}$ or $210°$

8. $-\frac{11\pi}{5} = \left(-\frac{11\pi}{5} \text{ radians}\right)\left(\frac{180°}{\pi \text{ radians}}\right)$
$= -\frac{1980°}{5}$ or $-396°$

9. A positive angle is $-55° + 360° = 305°$.
A negative angle is $-55° - 360° = -415°$.

10. A positive angle is $\frac{11\pi}{3} - 2\pi = \frac{5\pi}{3}$.
A negative angle is $\frac{11\pi}{3} - 4\pi = -\frac{\pi}{3}$.

Page 716 Algebra Activity (Follow-Up of Lesson 13-2)

1.

Number of Sides, n	θ	a
3	60	0.50
4	45	0.71
5	36	0.81
6	30	0.87
7	≈ 26	0.90
8	22.5	0.92
9	20	0.94
10	18	0.95

2. The measure of θ decreases.

3. The length of the apothem increase as the number of sides increases.

4. The measure of angle θ is $\frac{360°}{2(20)} = 9°$.

5. $\theta = 360° \div 2n$ or $\theta = 180° \div n$

6. $a = \cos \theta$

7. To find the length of the apothem, you need to write this equation: $\cos \theta = \frac{a}{\text{length of radius}}$.
If the radius is 1, then $\cos \theta = a$. If the radius is not 1, then $a = \text{length of radius} \cdot \cos \theta$.

Trigonometric Function of General Angles

Page 722 Check for Understanding

1. The statement is false.

$\sec 0° = \frac{r}{r}$ or 1 and

$\tan 0° = \frac{0}{r}$ or 0.

2. The sines of angles in Quadrants III and IV are negative. Sample answer: 190°, since 190° is in Quadrant III.

3. To find the value of a trigonometric function of θ, where θ is greater than 90°, find the value of the trigonometric function for θ', then use the quadrant in which the terminal side of θ lies to determine the sign of the trigonometric function value of θ.

4. $x = -15, y = 8, r = \sqrt{(-15)^2 + 8^2} = 17$

$\sin \theta = \frac{y}{r} = \frac{8}{17}$ $\csc \theta = \frac{r}{y} = \frac{17}{8}$

$\cos \theta = \frac{x}{r} = \frac{-15}{17}$ or $-\frac{15}{17}$ $\sec \theta = \frac{r}{x} = \frac{17}{-15}$ or $-\frac{17}{15}$

$\tan \theta = \frac{y}{x} = \frac{8}{-15}$ or $-\frac{8}{15}$ $\cot \theta = \frac{x}{y} = \frac{-15}{8}$ or $-\frac{15}{8}$

5. $x = -3, y = 0, r = \sqrt{(-3)^2 + 0^2} = 3$

$\sin \theta = \frac{y}{r} = \frac{0}{3} = 0$ $\csc \theta = \frac{r}{y} = \frac{3}{0}$ is undefined.

$\cos \theta = \frac{x}{r} = \frac{-3}{3} = -1$ $\sec \theta = \frac{r}{x} = 3 \backslash -3 = -1$

$\tan \theta = \frac{y}{x} = \frac{0}{-3} = 0$ $\cot \theta = \frac{x}{y} = \frac{-3}{0}$ is undefined.

6. $x = 4, y = 4, r = \sqrt{4^2 + 4^2} = 4\sqrt{2}$

$\sin \theta = \frac{y}{r} = \frac{4}{4\sqrt{2}} = \frac{\sqrt{2}}{2}$ $\csc \theta = \frac{r}{y} = \frac{4\sqrt{2}}{4} = \sqrt{2}$

$\cos \theta = \frac{x}{r} = \frac{4}{4\sqrt{2}} = \frac{\sqrt{2}}{2}$ $\sec \theta = \frac{r}{x} = \frac{4\sqrt{2}}{4} = \sqrt{2}$

$\tan \theta = \frac{y}{x} = \frac{4}{4} = 1$ $\cot \theta = \frac{x}{y} = \frac{4}{4} = 1$

7. The terminal side of 235° lies in Quadrant III.

$\theta' = 235° - 180° = 55°$

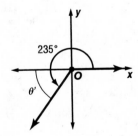

8. The terminal side of $\frac{7\pi}{4}$ lies in Quadrant IV.

$\theta' = 2\pi - \frac{7\pi}{4} = \frac{\pi}{4}$

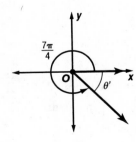

9. a coterminal angle of $-240°$ is $360° - 240° = 120°$. The terminal side of 120° lies in Quadrant II. $\theta' = 180° - 120° = 60°$

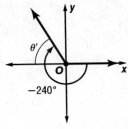

10. The terminal side of 300° lies in Quadrant IV, so $\theta' = 360° - 300° = 60°$.

The sine function is negative in Quadrant IV;

$\sin 300° = -\sin 60° = -\frac{\sqrt{3}}{2}$.

11. The terminal side of 180° lies on the negative x-axis, so $\cos 180° = -1$.

12. The terminal side of $\frac{5\pi}{3}$ lies in Quadrant IV, so

$\theta' = 2\pi - \frac{5\pi}{3} = \frac{\pi}{3}$.

The tangent function is negative in Quadrant IV;

$\tan \frac{5\pi}{3} = -\tan \frac{\pi}{3} = -\tan 60° = -\sqrt{3}$.

13. The terminal side of $\frac{7\pi}{6}$ lies in Quadrant III, so

$\theta' = \frac{7\pi}{6} - \pi = \frac{\pi}{6}$.

The secant function is negative in Quadrant III;

$\sec \frac{7\pi}{6} = -\sec \frac{\pi}{6} = -\sec 30° = -\frac{2\sqrt{3}}{3}$.

14. $\cos \theta = -\frac{1}{2}$

$\frac{x}{r} = -\frac{1}{2}$

θ is in Quadrant II, so $x = -1, r = 2$, and $y = \sqrt{2^2 - (-1)^2} = \sqrt{3}$.

$\sin \theta = \frac{y}{r} = \frac{\sqrt{3}}{2}$

$\tan \theta = \frac{y}{x} = \frac{\sqrt{3}}{-1} = -\sqrt{3}$

$\csc \theta = \frac{r}{y} = \frac{2}{\sqrt{3}} = \frac{2\sqrt{3}}{3}$

$\sec \theta = \frac{r}{x} = \frac{2}{-1} = -2$

$\cot \theta = \frac{x}{y} = \frac{-1}{\sqrt{3}} = -\frac{\sqrt{3}}{3}$

15. $\cot \theta = -\frac{\sqrt{2}}{2}$

$\frac{x}{y} = -\frac{\sqrt{2}}{2} = -\frac{1}{\sqrt{2}}$

θ is in Quadrant IV, so $x = 1, y = -\sqrt{2}$, and $r = \sqrt{1^2 + (-\sqrt{2})^2} = \sqrt{3}$.

$\sin \theta = \frac{y}{r} = \frac{-\sqrt{2}}{\sqrt{3}} = -\frac{\sqrt{6}}{3}$

$\cos \theta = \frac{x}{r} = \frac{1}{\sqrt{3}} = \frac{\sqrt{3}}{3}$

$\tan \theta = \frac{y}{x} = \frac{-\sqrt{2}}{1} = -\sqrt{2}$

$\csc \theta = \frac{r}{y} = \frac{\sqrt{3}}{-\sqrt{2}} = -\frac{\sqrt{6}}{2}$

$\sec \theta = \frac{r}{x} = \frac{\sqrt{3}}{1} = \sqrt{3}$

16. $H = \frac{V_0^2 (\sin \theta)^2}{64}$

$H = \frac{30^2 (\sin 70°)^2}{64}$

$H \approx 12.4$

The maximum height is about 12.4 feet.

17. $x = 7, y = 24, r = \sqrt{7^2 + 24^2} = 25$

$\sin \theta = \frac{y}{r} = \frac{24}{25}$ $\csc \theta = \frac{r}{y} = \frac{25}{24}$

$\cos \theta = \frac{x}{r} = \frac{7}{25}$ $\sec \theta = \frac{r}{x} = \frac{25}{7}$

$\tan \theta = \frac{y}{x} = \frac{24}{7}$ $\cot \theta = \frac{x}{y} = \frac{7}{24}$

18. $x = 2, y = 1, r = \sqrt{2^2 + 1^2} = \sqrt{5}$

$\sin \theta = \frac{y}{r} = \frac{1}{\sqrt{5}} = \frac{\sqrt{5}}{5}$ $\csc \theta = \frac{r}{y} = \frac{\sqrt{5}}{1} = \sqrt{5}$

$\cos \theta = \frac{x}{r} = \frac{2}{\sqrt{5}} = \frac{2\sqrt{5}}{5}$ $\sec \theta = \frac{r}{x} = \frac{\sqrt{5}}{2}$

$\tan \theta = \frac{y}{x} = \frac{1}{2}$ $\cot \theta = \frac{x}{y} = \frac{2}{1} = 2$

19. $x = 5, y = -8, r = \sqrt{5^2 + (-8)^2} = \sqrt{89}$

$\sin \theta = \frac{y}{r} = \frac{-8}{\sqrt{89}}$ or $-\frac{8\sqrt{89}}{89}$ $\csc \theta = \frac{r}{y} = \frac{\sqrt{89}}{-8}$ or $-\frac{\sqrt{89}}{8}$

$\cos \theta = \frac{x}{r} = \frac{5}{\sqrt{89}} = \frac{5\sqrt{89}}{89}$ $\sec \theta = \frac{r}{x} = \frac{\sqrt{89}}{5}$

$\tan \theta = \frac{y}{x} = \frac{-8}{5}$ or $-\frac{8}{5}$ $\cot \theta = \frac{x}{y} = \frac{5}{-8}$ or $-\frac{5}{8}$

20. $x = 4, y = -3, r = \sqrt{4^2 + (-3)^2} = 5$

$\sin \theta = \frac{y}{r} = \frac{-3}{5}$ or $-\frac{3}{5}$ $\csc \theta = \frac{r}{y} = \frac{5}{-3}$ or $-\frac{5}{3}$

$\cos \theta = \frac{x}{r} = \frac{4}{5}$ $\sec \theta = \frac{r}{x} = \frac{5}{4}$

$\tan \theta = \frac{y}{x} = \frac{-3}{4}$ or $-\frac{3}{4}$ $\cot \theta = \frac{x}{y} = \frac{4}{-3}$ or $-\frac{4}{3}$

21. $x = 0, y = -6, r = \sqrt{0^2 + (-6)^2} = 6$

$\sin \theta = \frac{y}{r} = \frac{-6}{6} = -1$

$\cos \theta = \frac{x}{r} = \frac{0}{6} = 0$

$\tan \theta = \frac{y}{x} = \frac{-6}{0}$ is undefined.

$\csc \theta = \frac{r}{y} = \frac{6}{-6} = -1$

$\sec \theta = \frac{r}{x} = \frac{6}{0}$ is undefined.

$\cot \theta = \frac{x}{y} = \frac{0}{-6} = 0$

22. $x = -1, y = 0, r = \sqrt{(-1)^2 + 0^2} = 1$

$\sin \theta = \frac{y}{r} = \frac{0}{1} = 0$ $\csc \theta = \frac{r}{y} = \frac{1}{0}$ is undefined.

$\cos \theta = \frac{x}{r} = \frac{-1}{1} = -1$ $\sec \theta = \frac{r}{x} = \frac{1}{-1} = -1$

$\tan \theta = \frac{y}{x} = \frac{0}{-1} = 0$ $\cot \theta = \frac{x}{y} = \frac{-1}{0}$ is undefined.

23. $x = \sqrt{2}, y = -\sqrt{2}, r = \sqrt{(\sqrt{2})^2 + (-\sqrt{2})^2} = 2$

$\sin \theta = \frac{y}{r} = -\frac{\sqrt{2}}{2}$ or $-\frac{\sqrt{2}}{2}$

$\cos \theta = \frac{x}{r} = \frac{\sqrt{2}}{2}$

$\tan \theta = \frac{y}{x} = \frac{-\sqrt{2}}{\sqrt{2}} = -1$

$\csc \theta = \frac{r}{y} = \frac{2}{-\sqrt{2}} = -\sqrt{2}$

$\sec \theta = \frac{r}{x} = \frac{2}{\sqrt{2}} = \sqrt{2}$

$\cot \theta = \frac{x}{y} = \frac{\sqrt{2}}{-\sqrt{2}} = -1$

24. $x = -\sqrt{3}, y = -\sqrt{6}, r = \sqrt{(-\sqrt{3})^2 + (-\sqrt{6})^2} = 3$

$\sin \theta = \frac{y}{r} = \frac{-\sqrt{6}}{3}$ or $-\frac{\sqrt{6}}{3}$

$\cos \theta = \frac{x}{r} = \frac{-\sqrt{3}}{3}$ or $-\frac{\sqrt{3}}{3}$

$\tan \theta = \frac{y}{x} = \frac{-\sqrt{6}}{-\sqrt{3}} = \sqrt{2}$

$\csc \theta = \frac{r}{y} = \frac{3}{-\sqrt{6}} = -\frac{\sqrt{6}}{2}$

$\sec \theta = \frac{r}{x} = \frac{3}{-\sqrt{3}} = -\sqrt{3}$

$\cot \theta = \frac{x}{y} = \frac{-\sqrt{3}}{-\sqrt{6}} = \frac{\sqrt{2}}{2}$

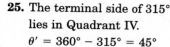

25. The terminal side of 315°
lies in Quadrant IV.
$\theta' = 360° - 315° = 45°$

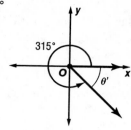

26. The terminal side of 240°
lies in Quadrant III.
$\theta' = 240° - 180° = 60°$

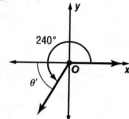

27. A coterminal angle of −210°
is $360° - 210° = 150°$.
The terminal side of 150°
lies in Quadrant II.
$\theta' = 180° - 150° = 30°$

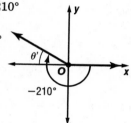

28. A coterminal angle
of −125° is
$360° - 125° = 235°$.
The terminal side of 235°
lies in Quadrant III.
$\theta' = 235° - 180° = 55°$

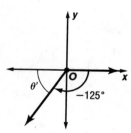

29. The terminal side of $\frac{5\pi}{4}$
lies in Quadrant III.
$\theta' = \frac{5\pi}{4} - \pi = \frac{\pi}{4}$

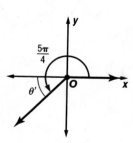

30. The terminal side of $\frac{5\pi}{6}$
lies in Quadrant II.
$\theta' = \pi - \frac{5\pi}{6} = \frac{\pi}{6}$

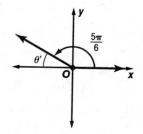

31. The terminal side of $\frac{13\pi}{7}$ lies in Quadrant IV.

$\theta' = 2\pi - \frac{13\pi}{7} = \frac{\pi}{7}$

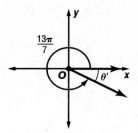

32. A coterminal angle of $-\frac{2\pi}{3}$ is $2\pi - \frac{2\pi}{3} = \frac{4\pi}{3}$.

The terminal side of $\frac{4\pi}{3}$ lies in Quadrant III.

$\theta' = \frac{4\pi}{3} - \pi = \frac{\pi}{3}$

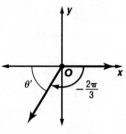

33. The terminal side of 240° lies in Quadrant III, so $\theta' = 240° - 180° = 60°$.

The sine function is negative in Quadrant III;
$\sin 240° = -\sin 60° = -\frac{\sqrt{3}}{2}$

34. The terminal side of 120° lies in Quadrant II, so $\theta' = 180° - 120° = 60°$.

The secant function is negative in Quadrant II; $\sec 120° = -\sec 60° = -2$.

35. The terminal side of 300° lies in Quadrant IV, so $\theta' = 360° - 300° = 60°$.

The tangent function is negative in Quadrant IV; $\tan 300° = -\tan 60° = -\sqrt{3}$.

36. The terminal side of 510° lies in Quadrant II $(510° - 360° = 150°)$, so $\theta' = 180° - 150° = 30°$.

The cotangent function is negative in Quadrant II; $\cot 510° = -\cot 30° = -\sqrt{3}$.

37. The terminal side of 5400° lies on the positive x-axis. $(5400° - 15 \cdot 360° = 0°)$ $\csc 0°$ is undefined.

38. The terminal side of $\frac{11\pi}{3}$ lies in Quadrant IV $\left(\frac{11\pi}{3} - 2\pi = \frac{5\pi}{3}\right)$, so $\theta' = 2\pi - \frac{5\pi}{3} = \frac{\pi}{3}$.

The cosine function is positive in Quadrant IV; $\cos \frac{11\pi}{3} = \cos \frac{\pi}{3} = \frac{1}{2}$.

39. The terminal side of $-\frac{5\pi}{6}$ lies in Quadrant III $\left(2\pi - \frac{5\pi}{6} = \frac{7\pi}{6}\right)$, so $\theta' = \frac{7\pi}{6} - \pi = \frac{\pi}{6}$.

The cotangent function is positive in Quadrant III; $\cot\left(-\frac{5\pi}{6}\right) = \cot \frac{\pi}{6} = \sqrt{3}$.

40. The terminal side of $\frac{3\pi}{4}$ lies in Quadrant II, so $\theta' = \pi - \frac{3\pi}{4} = \frac{\pi}{4}$.

The sine function is positive in Quadrant II; $\sin \frac{3\pi}{4} = \sin \frac{\pi}{4} = \frac{\sqrt{2}}{2}$.

41. The terminal side of $\frac{3\pi}{2}$ lies on the negative y-axis, so $\sec \frac{3\pi}{2}$ is undefined.

42. The terminal side of $\frac{17\pi}{6}$ lies in Quadrant II $\left(\frac{17\pi}{6} - 2\pi = \frac{5\pi}{6}\right)$, so $\theta' = \pi - \frac{5\pi}{6} = \frac{\pi}{6}$.

The cosecant function is positive in Quadrant II; $\csc \frac{17\pi}{6} = \csc \frac{\pi}{6} = 2$.

43. The terminal side of $-30°$ lies in Quadrant IV $(360° - 30° = 330°)$, so $\theta' = 360° - 330° = 30°$.

The cosine function is positive in Quadrant IV; $\cos(-30°) = \cos 30° = \frac{\sqrt{3}}{2}$.

44. The terminal side of $-\frac{5\pi}{4}$ lies in Quadrant II $\left(2\pi - \frac{5\pi}{4} = \frac{3\pi}{4}\right)$, so $\theta' = \pi - \frac{3\pi}{4} = \frac{\pi}{4}$.

The tangent function is negative in Quadrant II; $\tan\left(-\frac{5\pi}{4}\right) = -\tan \frac{\pi}{4} = -1$.

45.

t	$\theta_R = 0.2 \cos \pi t$ (radians)	$\theta_D = \theta_R\left(\frac{180°}{\pi}\right)$ (degrees)
0	$0.2 \cos 0 = 0.2$	$0.2\left(\frac{180°}{\pi}\right) \approx 11.5°$
0.5	$0.2 \cos \frac{\pi}{2} = 0$	$0\left(\frac{180°}{\pi}\right) = 0°$
1	$0.2 \cos \pi = -0.2$	$-0.2\left(\frac{180°}{\pi}\right) \approx -11.5°$
1.5	$0.2 \cos \frac{3\pi}{2} = 0$	$0\left(\frac{180°}{\pi}\right) = 0°$
2	$0.2 \cos 2\pi = 0.2$	$0.2\left(\frac{180°}{\pi}\right) \approx 11.5°$
2.5	$0.2 \cos \frac{5\pi}{2} = 0$	$0\left(\frac{180°}{\pi}\right) = 0°$
3	$0.2 \cos 3\pi = -0.2$	$-0.2\left(\frac{180°}{\pi}\right) \approx -11.5°$

46. $6077 - 31 \cos 2\theta = 6077 - 31 \cos 2(60°)$
$$= 6077 - 31 \cos 120°$$
$$= 6077 - 31\left(-\frac{1}{2}\right)$$
$$= 6092.5$$

The nautical mile is 6092.5 feet at 60° latitude.

47. $\cos \theta = \frac{3}{5}$

$\frac{x}{r} = \frac{3}{5}$

θ is in Quadrant IV, so $x = 3, r = 5$, and $y = -\sqrt{5^2 - 3^2} = -4$.

$\sin \theta = \frac{y}{r} = \frac{-4}{5}$ or $-\frac{4}{5}$

$\tan \theta = \frac{y}{x} = \frac{-4}{3}$ or $-\frac{4}{3}$

$\csc \theta = \frac{r}{y} = \frac{5}{-4}$ or $-\frac{5}{4}$

$\sec \theta = \frac{r}{x} = \frac{5}{3}$

$\cot \theta = \frac{x}{y} = \frac{3}{-4}$ or $-\frac{3}{4}$

48. $\tan \theta = -\frac{1}{5}$

$\frac{y}{x} = -\frac{1}{5}$

θ is in Quadrant II, so $x = -5$, $y = 1$, and $r = \sqrt{(-5)^2 + 1^2} = \sqrt{26}$.

$\sin \theta = \frac{y}{r} = \frac{1}{\sqrt{26}} = \frac{\sqrt{26}}{26}$

$\cos \theta = \frac{x}{r} = \frac{-5}{\sqrt{26}}$ or $-\frac{5\sqrt{26}}{26}$

$\csc \theta = \frac{r}{y} = \frac{\sqrt{26}}{1} = \sqrt{26}$

$\sec \theta = \frac{r}{x} = \frac{\sqrt{26}}{-5}$ or $-\frac{\sqrt{26}}{5}$

$\cot \theta = \frac{x}{y} = \frac{-5}{1} = -5$

49. $\sin \theta = \frac{1}{3}$

$\frac{y}{r} = \frac{1}{3}$

θ is in Quadrant II, so $y = 1$, $r = 3$, and $x = -\sqrt{3^2 - 1^2} = -\sqrt{8} = -2\sqrt{2}$.

$\cos \theta = \frac{x}{r} = \frac{-2\sqrt{2}}{3}$ or $-\frac{2\sqrt{2}}{3}$

$\tan \theta = \frac{y}{x} = \frac{1}{-2\sqrt{2}} = -\frac{\sqrt{2}}{4}$

$\csc \theta = \frac{r}{y} = \frac{3}{1} = 3$

$\sec \theta = \frac{r}{x} = \frac{3}{-2\sqrt{2}} = -\frac{3\sqrt{2}}{4}$

$\cot \theta = \frac{x}{y} = \frac{-2\sqrt{2}}{1} = -2\sqrt{2}$

50. $\cot \theta = \frac{1}{2}$

$\frac{x}{y} = \frac{1}{2}$

θ is in Quadrant III, so $x = -1$, $y = -2$, and $r = \sqrt{(-1)^2 + (-2)^2} = \sqrt{5}$.

$\sin \theta = \frac{y}{r} = \frac{-2}{\sqrt{5}} = -\frac{2\sqrt{5}}{5}$

$\cos \theta = \frac{x}{r} = \frac{-1}{\sqrt{5}} = -\frac{\sqrt{5}}{5}$

$\tan \theta = \frac{y}{x} = \frac{-2}{-1} = 2$

$\csc \theta = \frac{r}{y} = -\frac{\sqrt{5}}{2}$

$\sec \theta = \frac{r}{x} = \frac{\sqrt{5}}{-1} = -\sqrt{5}$

51. $\sec \theta = -\sqrt{10}$

$\frac{r}{x} = -\sqrt{10} = \frac{\sqrt{10}}{-1}$

θ is in Quadrant III, so $x = -1$, $r = \sqrt{10}$, and $y = -\sqrt{(\sqrt{10})^2 - (1)^2} = -3$.

$\sin \theta = \frac{y}{r} = \frac{-3}{\sqrt{10}} = -\frac{3\sqrt{10}}{10}$

$\cos \theta = \frac{x}{r} = \frac{-1}{\sqrt{10}} = -\frac{\sqrt{10}}{10}$

$\tan \theta = \frac{y}{x} = \frac{-3}{-1} = 3$

$\csc \theta = \frac{r}{y} = \frac{\sqrt{10}}{-3}$ or $-\frac{\sqrt{10}}{3}$

$\cot \theta = \frac{x}{y} = \frac{-1}{-3} = \frac{1}{3}$

52. $\csc \theta = -5$

$\frac{r}{y} = -5 = \frac{5}{-1}$

θ is in Quadrant IV, so $y = -1$, $r = 5$, and $x = \sqrt{5^2 - (-1)^2} = \sqrt{24} = 2\sqrt{6}$.

$\sin \theta = \frac{y}{r} = \frac{-1}{5} = -\frac{1}{5}$

$\cos \theta = \frac{x}{r} = \frac{2\sqrt{6}}{5}$

$\tan \theta = \frac{y}{x} = \frac{-1}{2\sqrt{6}} = -\frac{\sqrt{6}}{12}$

$\sec \theta = \frac{r}{x} = \frac{5}{2\sqrt{6}} = \frac{5\sqrt{6}}{12}$

$\cot \theta = \frac{x}{y} = \frac{2\sqrt{6}}{-1} = -2\sqrt{6}$

53. $R = \frac{V_0{}^2 \sin 2\theta}{32}$

$R = \frac{80^2 \sin 2(30°)}{32}$

$R = \frac{80^2 \sin 60°}{32}$

$R = \frac{80^2 \left(\frac{\sqrt{3}}{2}\right)}{32}$

$R \approx 173.2$

The ball was hit about 173.2 feet.

54. An angle of 45° will result in the greatest distance because $2 \times 45° = 90°$, which yields the greatest value for $\sin 2\theta$.

55. Find the value of x at 240°, then add $|x|$ to 7 m (3 m + 4 m).

$\theta' = 240° - 180° = 60°$

At 240°, $x = -\frac{1}{2}(4) = -2$ and $y = -\frac{\sqrt{3}}{2}(4) = -2\sqrt{3}$.

$|-2 \text{ m}| + 7 \text{ m} = 9 \text{ m}$

His brother will be 9 m from the fence.

56. The sine function is positive in Quadrants I and II.

57. The sine function is positive in Quadrants I and II. The cosine function is negative in Quadrants II and III. So, $\sin \theta > 0$ and $\cos \theta < 0$ in Quadrant II.

58. The tangent function is positive in Quadrants I and III. The cosine function is negative in Quadrants II and III. So, $\tan \theta > 0$ and $\cos \theta < 0$ in Quadrant III.

59. Answers should include the following.
- The cosine of any angle is defined as $\frac{x}{r}$, where x is the x-coordinate of any point on the terminal ray of the angle and r is the distance from the origin to that point. This means that for angles with terminal sides to the left of the y-axis, the cosine is negative, and for those with terminal sides to the right of the y-axis, the cosine is positive. Therefore the cosine function can be used to model real-world data that oscillate between being positive and negative.
- If we knew the length of the cable we could find the vertical distance from the top of the tower to the rider. Then if we knew the height of the tower we could subtract from it the vertical distance calculated previously. This will leave the height of the rider from the ground.

60. C; $\cot \theta = \frac{x}{y} = 1$

$\tan \theta = \frac{y}{x} = 1$

61. The terminal side of $\frac{5\pi}{3}$ lies in Quadrant IV.

$\theta' = 2\pi - \frac{5\pi}{3} = \frac{\pi}{3}$

At $\frac{\pi}{3}$, $x = \frac{1}{2}$, $y = \frac{\sqrt{3}}{2}$ on a unit circle.

At $\frac{5\pi}{3}$, $x = \frac{1}{2}(5) = \frac{5}{2}$, $y = -\frac{\sqrt{3}}{2}(5) = -\frac{5\sqrt{3}}{2}$ on a circle of radius 5.

The coordinates are $\left(\frac{5}{2}, -\frac{5\sqrt{3}}{2}\right)$.

Page 724   Maintain Your Skills

62. $90° = 90°\left(\frac{\pi \text{ radians}}{180°}\right)$

$= \frac{90\pi}{180}$ radians or $\frac{\pi}{2}$

63. $\frac{5\pi}{3} = \left(\frac{5\pi}{3} \text{ radians}\right)\left(\frac{180°}{\pi \text{ radians}}\right)$

$= \frac{900°}{3}$ or $300°$

64. $5 = (5 \text{ radians})\left(\frac{180°}{\pi \text{ radians}}\right)$

$= \frac{900°}{\pi}$ or $\approx 286.5°$

65. $\sin\theta = \frac{\text{opp}}{\text{hyp}}$

$\sin 28° = \frac{x}{12}$

$12 \sin 28° = x$

$5.6 \approx x$

66. $\cos\theta = \frac{\text{adj}}{\text{hyp}}$

$\cos 43° = \frac{x}{83}$

$83 \cos 43° = x$

$60.7 \approx x$

67. $\sin\theta = \frac{\text{opp}}{\text{hyp}}$

$\sin x° = \frac{5}{13}$

$x \approx 23$

68. $S_n = \frac{a_1(1 - r^n)}{1 - r}$, where $r \neq 1$.

As a result, $S_7 = \frac{5(1 - 2^7)}{1 - 2} = \frac{5(1 - 128)}{-1} = \frac{5(-127)}{-1} =$

635.

69. $3x - 4y = 13$

$-2x + 5y = -4$

$x = \frac{\begin{vmatrix} e & b \\ f & d \end{vmatrix}}{\begin{vmatrix} a & b \\ c & d \end{vmatrix}} = \frac{\begin{vmatrix} 13 & -4 \\ -4 & 5 \end{vmatrix}}{\begin{vmatrix} 3 & -4 \\ -2 & 5 \end{vmatrix}} = \frac{13(5) - (-4)(-4)}{3(5) - (-2)(-4)} = \frac{49}{7} = 7$

$y = \frac{\begin{vmatrix} a & e \\ c & f \end{vmatrix}}{\begin{vmatrix} a & b \\ c & d \end{vmatrix}} = \frac{\begin{vmatrix} 3 & 13 \\ -2 & -4 \end{vmatrix}}{\begin{vmatrix} 3 & -4 \\ -2 & 5 \end{vmatrix}} = \frac{3(-4) - (-2)(13)}{3(5) - (-2)(-4)} = \frac{14}{7} = 2$

The solution is $(7, 2)$.

70. $5x + 7y = 1$

$3x + 5y = 3$

$x = \frac{\begin{vmatrix} e & b \\ f & d \end{vmatrix}}{\begin{vmatrix} a & b \\ c & d \end{vmatrix}} = \frac{\begin{vmatrix} 1 & 7 \\ 3 & 5 \end{vmatrix}}{\begin{vmatrix} 5 & 7 \\ 3 & 5 \end{vmatrix}} = \frac{1(5) - 3(7)}{5(5) - 3(7)} = \frac{-16}{4} = -4$

$y = \frac{\begin{vmatrix} a & e \\ c & f \end{vmatrix}}{\begin{vmatrix} a & b \\ c & d \end{vmatrix}} = \frac{\begin{vmatrix} 5 & 1 \\ 3 & 3 \end{vmatrix}}{\begin{vmatrix} 5 & 7 \\ 3 & 5 \end{vmatrix}} = \frac{5(3) - 3(1)}{5(5) - 3(7)} = \frac{12}{4} = 3$

The solution is $(-4, 3)$.

71. $2x + 3y = -2$

$-6x + y = -34$

$x = \frac{\begin{vmatrix} e & b \\ f & d \end{vmatrix}}{\begin{vmatrix} a & b \\ c & d \end{vmatrix}} = \frac{\begin{vmatrix} -2 & 3 \\ -34 & 1 \end{vmatrix}}{\begin{vmatrix} 2 & 3 \\ -6 & 1 \end{vmatrix}} = \frac{-2(1) - (-34)(3)}{2(1) - (-6)(3)} = \frac{100}{20} = 5$

$y = \frac{\begin{vmatrix} a & e \\ c & f \end{vmatrix}}{\begin{vmatrix} a & b \\ c & d \end{vmatrix}} = \frac{\begin{vmatrix} 2 & -2 \\ -6 & -34 \end{vmatrix}}{\begin{vmatrix} 2 & 3 \\ -6 & 1 \end{vmatrix}} = \frac{2(-34) - (-6)(-2)}{2(1) - (-6)(3)}$

$= \frac{-80}{20} = -4$

The solution is $(5, -4)$.

72. $\frac{a}{\sin 32°} = \frac{8}{\sin 65°}$

$a = \frac{8 \sin 32°}{\sin 65°}$

$a \approx 4.7$

73. $\frac{b}{\sin 45°} = \frac{21}{\sin 100°}$

$b = \frac{21 \sin 45°}{\sin 100°}$

$b \approx 15.1$

74. $\frac{c}{\sin 60°} = \frac{3}{\sin 75°}$

$c = \frac{3 \sin 60°}{\sin 75°}$

$c \approx 2.7$

75. $\frac{\sin A}{14} = \frac{\sin 104°}{25}$

$\sin A = \frac{14 \sin 104°}{25}$

$A \approx 32.9°$

76. $\frac{\sin B}{3} = \frac{\sin 55°}{7}$

$\sin B = \frac{3 \sin 55°}{7}$

$B \approx 20.6°$

77. $\frac{\sin C}{10} = \frac{\sin 35°}{9}$

$\sin C = \frac{10 \sin 35°}{9}$

$C \approx 39.6°$

13-4   Law of Sines

Pages 729–730   Check for Understanding

1. Sometimes; only when A is acute, $a = b \sin A$ or $a > b$ and when A is obtuse, $a > b$.

2. Sample answer: $A = 42°$, $a = 2.6$ cm, $b = 3.2$ cm

$b > a > b \sin A$

$3.2 > 2.6 > 3.2 \sin 42°$

$3.2 > 2.6 > \approx 2.1$

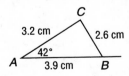   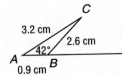

643   Chapter 13

3. Gabe said there is not enough information to do this problem. That is not correct.

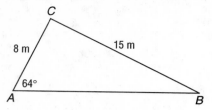

By using the Law of Sines, he can find $\angle B$. Therefore, you can find $\angle C$.

$\angle C = 180° - (64° + \angle B)$.

Once $\angle C$ is found, $A = \frac{1}{2} \cdot b \cdot a \cdot \sin C$ will yield the area of the triangle.

4. Area $= \frac{1}{2} bc \sin A$

$= \frac{1}{2} (15)(10) \sin 50°$

≈ 57.5

To the nearest tenth, the area is 57.5 in².

5. Area $= \frac{1}{2}ac \sin B$

$= \frac{1}{2}(6)(3) \sin 135°$

≈ 6.4

To the nearest tenth, the area is 6.4 cm².

6. $70° + 80° + C = 180°$

$C = 30°$

$\dfrac{\sin A}{a} = \dfrac{\sin B}{b}$

$\dfrac{\sin 70°}{a} = \dfrac{\sin 80°}{3}$

$a = \dfrac{3 \sin 70°}{\sin 80°}$

$a \approx 2.9$

$\dfrac{\sin C}{c} = \dfrac{\sin B}{b}$

$\dfrac{\sin 30°}{c} = \dfrac{\sin 80°}{3}$

$c = \dfrac{3 \sin 30°}{\sin 80°}$

$c \approx 1.5$

Therefore, $C = 30°$, $a \approx 2.9$, and $c \approx 1.5$.

7. $75° + B + 25° = 180°$

$B = 80°$

$\dfrac{\sin A}{a} = \dfrac{\sin C}{c}$

$\dfrac{\sin 75°}{a} = \dfrac{\sin 25°}{14}$

$a = \dfrac{14 \sin 75°}{\sin 25°}$

$a \approx 32.0$

$\dfrac{\sin B}{b} = \dfrac{\sin C}{c}$

$\dfrac{\sin 80°}{b} = \dfrac{\sin 25°}{14}$

$b = \dfrac{14 \sin 80°}{\sin 25°}$

$b \approx 32.6$

Therefore, $B = 80°$, $a \approx 32.0$, and $b \approx 32.6$.

8.

$\dfrac{\sin B}{b} = \dfrac{\sin C}{c}$

$\dfrac{\sin B}{20} = \dfrac{\sin 140°}{38}$

$\sin B = \dfrac{20 \sin 140°}{38}$

$\sin B \approx 0.3383$

$B \approx 19.8° \approx 20°$

$A + 19.8° + 140° \approx 180°$

$A \approx 20.2° \approx 20°$

$\dfrac{\sin A}{a} = \dfrac{\sin C}{c}$

$\dfrac{\sin 20.2°}{a} \approx \dfrac{\sin 140°}{38}$

$a \approx \dfrac{38 \sin 20.2°}{\sin 140°}$

$a \approx 20.4$

Therefore, $A \approx 20°$, $B \approx 20°$, and $a \approx 20.4$.

9. $A = 123°$, $a = 12$, $b = 23$

Since angle A is obtuse and $a \leq b$, there is no solution.

10. $A = 30°$, $a = 3$, $b = 4$

Since angle A is acute, find $b \sin A$ and compare it with a.

$b \sin A = 4 \sin 30° = 2$

Since $4 > 3 > 2$, there are two solutions.

Case 1: Acute angle B

$\dfrac{\sin B}{b} = \dfrac{\sin A}{a}$

$\dfrac{\sin B}{4} = \dfrac{\sin 30°}{3}$

$\sin B = \dfrac{4 \sin 30°}{3}$

$\sin B = \dfrac{2}{3}$

$B \approx 41.8°$

$C \approx 180° - (30° + 41.8°) = 108.2°$

$\dfrac{\sin C}{c} = \dfrac{\sin A}{a}$

$\dfrac{\sin 108.2°}{c} \approx \dfrac{\sin 30°}{3}$

$c \approx \dfrac{3 \sin 108.2°}{\sin 30°}$

$c \approx 5.7$

Therefore, $B \approx 42°$, $C \approx 108°$, and $c \approx 5.7$.

Case 2: Obtuse angle B

$B \approx 180 - 41.8° = 138.2°$

$C \approx 180° - (30° + 138.2°) = 11.8°$

$\dfrac{\sin C}{c} = \dfrac{\sin A}{a}$

$\dfrac{\sin 11.8°}{c} \approx \dfrac{\sin 30°}{3}$

$c \approx \dfrac{3 \sin 11.8°}{\sin 30°}$

$c \approx 1.2$

Therefore, $B \approx 138°$, $C \approx 12°$, and $c \approx 1.2$.

11. $A = 55°$, $a = 10$, $b = 5$

Since angle A is acute and $a > b$, there is one solution.

$$\frac{\sin B}{b} = \frac{\sin A}{a}$$

$$\frac{\sin B}{5} = \frac{\sin 55°}{10}$$

$$\sin B = \frac{5 \sin 55°}{10} = \frac{\sin 55°}{2}$$

$$\sin B \approx 0.4096$$

$$B \approx 24.2°$$

$$C \approx 180° - (55° + 24.2°) \approx 100.8°$$

$$\frac{\sin 100.8°}{c} \approx \frac{\sin 55°}{10}$$

$$c \approx \frac{10 \sin 100.8°}{\sin 55°}$$

$$c \approx 12.0$$

Therefore, $B \approx 24°$, $C \approx 101°$, and $c \approx 12.0$.

12. $A = 145°$, $a = 18$, $b = 10$

Since A is obtuse and $a > b$, there is one solution.

When solving this problem by the Law of Sines, angle measures were rounded to the nearest tenth of a degree until the final step of the solution.

$$\frac{\sin B}{b} = \frac{\sin A}{a}$$

$$\frac{\sin B}{10} = \frac{\sin 145°}{18}$$

$$\sin B = \frac{10 \sin 145°}{18} = \frac{5 \sin 145°}{9}$$

$$\sin B \approx 0.3187$$

$$B \approx 18.6° \approx 19°$$

$$C \approx 180° - (145° + 18.6°) = 16.4°$$

$$\frac{\sin C}{c} = \frac{\sin A}{a}$$

$$\frac{\sin 16.4°}{c} \approx \frac{\sin 145°}{18}$$

$$c \approx \frac{18 \sin 16.4°}{\sin 145°}$$

$$c \approx 8.9$$

Therefore, $B \approx 19°$, $C \approx 16°$, and $c \approx 8.9$.

13. When solving this problem by the Law of Sines, angle measures were rounded to the nearest tenth of a degree until the final step of the solution.

$$\frac{\sin 75°}{7} = \frac{\sin A}{6}$$

$$A \approx 55.9°$$

$$C \approx 180° - (75° + 55.9°) = 49.1°$$

$$\frac{\sin 49.1°}{c} \approx \frac{\sin 75°}{7}$$

$$c \approx 5.5$$

Latisha should cut the third beam to be 5.5 m.

Pages 730-732   Practice and Apply

14. Area $= \frac{1}{2}bc \sin A$

$= \frac{1}{2}(12)(9) \sin 127°$

≈ 43.1

To the nearest tenth, the area is 43.1 m^2.

15. Area $= \frac{1}{2}ab \sin C$

$= \frac{1}{2}(7)(8) \sin 44°$

≈ 19.5

To the nearest tenth, the area is 19.5 yd^2.

16. Area $= \frac{1}{2}ac \sin B$

$= \frac{1}{2}(50)(23) \sin 85°$

≈ 572.8

To the nearest tenth, the area is 572.8 ft^2.

17. Area $= \frac{1}{2}bc \sin A$

$= \frac{1}{2}(12)(12) \sin 60°$

≈ 62.4

To the nearest tenth, the area is 62.4 cm^2.

18. Area $= \frac{1}{2}ab \sin C$

$= \frac{1}{2}(3)(4) \sin 136°$

$= 4.2$

To the nearest tenth, the area is 4.2 m^2.

19. Area $= \frac{1}{2}ac \sin B$

$= \frac{1}{2}(11)(5) \sin 32°$

$= 14.6$

To the nearest tenth, the area is 14.6 mi^2.

20. $17° + B + 62° = 180°$

$$B = 101°$$

$$\frac{\sin C}{c} = \frac{\sin A}{a}$$

$$\frac{\sin 62°}{c} = \frac{\sin 17°}{1}$$

$$c = \frac{\sin 62°}{\sin 17°}$$

$$c \approx 3.0$$

$$\frac{\sin B}{b} = \frac{\sin A}{a}$$

$$\frac{\sin 101°}{b} = \frac{\sin 17°}{1}$$

$$b = \frac{\sin 101°}{\sin 17°}$$

$$b \approx 3.4$$

Therefore, $B \approx 101°$, $b \approx 3.4$, and $c \approx 3.0$.

21. $59° + 48° + C = 180°$

$$C = 73°$$

$$\frac{\sin A}{a} = \frac{\sin C}{c}$$

$$\frac{\sin 59°}{a} = \frac{\sin 73°}{62}$$

$$a = \frac{62 \sin 59°}{\sin 73°}$$

$$a \approx 55.6$$

$$\frac{\sin B}{b} = \frac{\sin C}{c}$$

$$\frac{\sin 48°}{b} = \frac{\sin 73°}{62}$$

$$b = \frac{62 \sin 48°}{\sin 73°}$$

$$b \approx 48.2$$

Therefore, $C = 73°$, $a \approx 55.6$, and $b \approx 48.2$.

22. When solving this problem by the Law of Sines, angle measures were rounded to the nearest tenth of a degree until the final step of the solution.

$$\frac{\sin C}{c} = \frac{\sin A}{a}$$
$$\frac{\sin C}{22} = \frac{\sin 122°}{31}$$
$$\sin C = \frac{22 \sin 122°}{31}$$
$$\sin C \approx 0.6018$$
$$C \approx 37.0°$$
$$122° + B + 37.0° \approx 180°$$
$$B \approx 21.0°$$
$$\frac{\sin B}{b} = \frac{\sin A}{a}$$
$$\frac{\sin 21°}{b} \approx \frac{\sin 122°}{31}$$
$$b \approx \frac{31 \sin 21°}{\sin 122°}$$
$$b \approx 13.1$$

Therefore, $B \approx 21°$, $C \approx 37°$, and $b \approx 13.1$.

23. When solving this problem by the Law of Sines, angle measures were rounded to the nearest hundredth of a degree until the final step of the solution.

$$\frac{\sin B}{b} = \frac{\sin A}{a}$$
$$\frac{\sin B}{4} = \frac{\sin 65°}{5}$$
$$\sin B = \frac{4 \sin 65°}{5}$$
$$\sin B \approx 0.7250$$
$$B \approx 46.47°$$
$$65° + 46.47° + C \approx 180°$$
$$C \approx 68.53°$$
$$\frac{\sin C}{c} = \frac{\sin A}{a}$$
$$\frac{\sin 68.5°}{c} \approx \frac{\sin 65°}{5}$$
$$c = \frac{5 \sin 68.5°}{\sin 65°}$$
$$c \approx 5.1$$

Therefore, $B \approx 46°$, $C \approx 69°$, and $c \approx 5.1$.

24.
$$20° + 63° + C = 180°$$
$$C = 97°$$
$$\frac{\sin A}{a} = \frac{\sin C}{c}$$
$$\frac{\sin 20°}{a} = \frac{\sin 97°}{16}$$
$$a = \frac{16 \sin 20°}{\sin 97°}$$
$$a \approx 5.5$$
$$\frac{\sin B}{b} = \frac{\sin C}{c}$$
$$\frac{\sin 63°}{b} = \frac{\sin 97°}{16}$$
$$b = \frac{16 \sin 63°}{\sin 97°}$$
$$b \approx 14.4$$

Therefore, $C = 97°$, $a \approx 5.5$, and $b \approx 14.4$.

25. When solving this problem by the Law of Sines, angle measures were rounded to the nearest tenth of a degree until the final step of the solution.

$$\frac{\sin A}{a} = \frac{\sin C}{c}$$
$$\frac{\sin A}{2} = \frac{\sin 75°}{3}$$
$$\sin A = \frac{2 \sin 75°}{3}$$
$$\sin A \approx 0.6440$$
$$A \approx 40.1°$$
$$40.1° + B + 75° \approx 180°$$
$$B \approx 64.9°$$
$$\frac{\sin B}{b} = \frac{\sin C}{c}$$
$$\frac{\sin 64.9°}{b} = \frac{\sin 75°}{3}$$
$$b = \frac{3 \sin 64.9°}{\sin 75°}$$
$$b \approx 2.8$$

Therefore, $A \approx 40°$, $B \approx 65°$, and $b \approx 2.8$.

26. When solving this problem by the Law of Sines, angle measures were rounded to the nearest tenth of a degree until the final step of the solution.

$$\frac{\sin C}{c} = \frac{\sin A}{a}$$
$$\frac{\sin C}{3} = \frac{\sin 50°}{2.5}$$
$$\sin C = \frac{3 \sin 50°}{2.5}$$
$$\sin C \approx 0.9193$$
$$C \approx 66.8°$$
$$50° + B + 66.8° \approx 180°$$
$$B \approx 63.2°$$
$$\frac{\sin B}{b} = \frac{\sin A}{a}$$
$$\frac{\sin 63.2°}{b} \approx \frac{\sin 50°}{2.5}$$
$$b \approx \frac{2.5 \sin 63.2°}{\sin 50°}$$
$$b \approx 2.9$$

Therefore, $C \approx 67°$, $B \approx 63°$, and $b \approx 2.9$.

27.
$$A + 18° + 142° = 180°$$
$$A = 20°$$
$$\frac{\sin A}{a} = \frac{\sin B}{b}$$
$$\frac{\sin 20°}{a} = \frac{\sin 18°}{20}$$
$$a = \frac{20 \sin 20°}{\sin 18°}$$
$$a \approx 22.1$$
$$\frac{\sin C}{c} = \frac{\sin B}{b}$$
$$\frac{\sin 142°}{c} = \frac{\sin 18°}{20}$$
$$c = \frac{20 \sin 142°}{\sin 18°}$$
$$c \approx 39.8$$

Therefore, $A = 20°$, $a \approx 22.1$, and $c \approx 39.8$.

28. $A = 124°$, $a = 1$, $b = 2$

Since angle A is obtuse and $a \leq b$, there is no solution.

29. When solving this problem by the Law of Sines, angle measures were rounded to the nearest tenth of a degree until the final step of the solution.

$A = 99°$, $a = 2.5$, $b = 1.5$

Since angle A is obtuse and $a > b$, there is one solution.

$$\frac{\sin B}{b} = \frac{\sin A}{a}$$
$$\frac{\sin B}{1.5} = \frac{\sin 99°}{2.5}$$
$$\sin B = \frac{1.5 \sin 99°}{2.5}$$
$$\sin B \approx 0.5926$$
$$B \approx 36.3°$$
$$99° + 36.3° + C \approx 180°$$
$$C \approx 44.7°$$
$$\frac{\sin C}{c} = \frac{\sin A}{a}$$
$$\frac{\sin 44.7°}{c} \approx \frac{\sin 99°}{2.5}$$
$$c \approx \frac{2.5 \sin 44.7°}{\sin 99°}$$
$$c \approx 1.8$$

Therefore, $B \approx 36°$, $C \approx 45°$, and $c \approx 1.8$.

30. $A = 33°$, $a = 2$, $b = 3.5$

Since angle A is acute, find $b \sin A$ and compare it with a.

$b \sin A = 3.5 \sin 33° \approx 1.9$

Since $3.5 > 2 > 1.9$, there are two solutions. When solving this problem by the Law of Sines, angle measures were rounded to the nearest tenth of a degree until the final step of the solution.

Case 1: Acute angle B

$$\frac{\sin B}{b} = \frac{\sin A}{a}$$
$$\frac{\sin B}{3.5} = \frac{\sin 33°}{2}$$
$$\sin B = \frac{3.5 \sin 33°}{2}$$
$$\sin B = 0.9531$$
$$B \approx 72.4°$$
$$33° + 72.4° + C \approx 180°$$
$$C \approx 74.6°$$
$$\frac{\sin C}{c} = \frac{\sin A}{a}$$
$$\frac{\sin 74.6°}{c} \approx \frac{\sin 33°}{2}$$
$$c \approx \frac{2 \sin 74.6°}{\sin 33°}$$
$$c \approx 3.5$$

Therefore, $B \approx 72°$, $C \approx 75°$, and $c \approx 3.5$.

Case 2: Obtuse angle B

$$B \approx 180° - 72.4° = 107.6°$$
$$C \approx 180° - (33° + 107.6°) = 39.4°$$
$$\frac{\sin C}{c} = \frac{\sin A}{a}$$
$$\frac{\sin 39.4°}{c} \approx \frac{\sin 33°}{2}$$
$$c \approx \frac{2 \sin 39.4°}{\sin 33°}$$
$$c \approx 2.3$$

Therefore, $B \approx 108°$, $C \approx 39°$, and $c \approx 2.3$.

31. $A = 68°$, $a = 3$, $b = 5$

Since angle A is acute, find $b \sin A$ and compare it with a.

$b \sin A = 5 \sin 68° \approx 4.6$

Since $3 < 4.6$, there is no solution.

32. $A = 30°$, $a = 14$, $b = 28$

Since angle A is acute, find $b \sin A$ and compare it with a.

$b \sin A = 28 \sin 30° = 14$

Since $a = b \sin A$, there is one solution.

$$\frac{\sin B}{b} = \frac{\sin A}{a}$$
$$\frac{\sin B}{28} = \frac{\sin 30°}{14}$$
$$\sin B = \frac{28 \sin 30°}{14}$$
$$\sin B = 1$$
$$B = 90°$$
$$30° + 90° + C = 180°$$
$$C = 60°$$
$$\frac{\sin C}{c} = \frac{\sin A}{a}$$
$$\frac{\sin 60°}{c} = \frac{\sin 30°}{14}$$
$$c = \frac{14 \sin 60°}{\sin 30°}$$
$$c \approx 24.2$$

Therefore, $B = 90°$, $C = 60°$, and $c \approx 24.2$.

33. When solving this problem by the Law of Sines, angle measures were rounded to the nearest tenth of a degree until the final step of the solution.

$A = 61°$, $a = 23$, $b = 8$

Since angle A is acute and $a > b$, there is one solution.

$$\frac{\sin B}{b} = \frac{\sin A}{a}$$
$$\frac{\sin B}{8} = \frac{\sin 61°}{23}$$
$$\sin B = \frac{8 \sin 61°}{23}$$
$$\sin B = 0.3042$$
$$B \approx 17.7°$$
$$61° + 17.7° + C \approx 180°$$
$$C \approx 101.3°$$
$$\frac{\sin C}{c} = \frac{\sin A}{a}$$
$$\frac{\sin 101.3°}{c} \approx \frac{\sin 61°}{23}$$
$$c \approx \frac{23 \sin 101.3°}{\sin 61°}$$
$$c \approx 25.8$$

Therefore, $B \approx 18°$, $C \approx 101°$, and $c \approx 25.8$.

34. $A = 52°$, $a = 190$, $b = 200$

Since angle A is acute, find $b \sin A$ and compare it with a.

$b \sin A = 200 \sin 52° \approx 157.6$

Since $200 > 190 > 157.6$, there are two solutions.

When solving this problem by the Law of Sines, angle measures were rounded to the nearest tenth of a degree until the final step of the solution.

Case 1: Acute angle B

$$\frac{\sin B}{b} = \frac{\sin A}{a}$$

$$\frac{\sin B}{200} = \frac{\sin 52°}{190}$$

$$\sin B = \frac{200 \sin 52°}{190}$$

$$\sin B \approx 0.8295$$

$$B \approx 56.0°$$

$$52° + 56.0° + C \approx 180°$$

$$C \approx 72°$$

$$\frac{\sin C}{c} = \frac{\sin A}{a}$$

$$\frac{\sin 72°}{c} \approx \frac{\sin 52°}{190}$$

$$c \approx \frac{190 \sin 72°}{\sin 52°}$$

$$c \approx 229.3$$

Therefore, $B \approx 56°$, $C \approx 72°$, and $c \approx 229.3$.

Case 2: Obtuse angle B

$$B \approx 180° - 56° = 124°$$

$$C \approx 180° - (52° + 124°) = 4°$$

$$\frac{\sin C}{c} = \frac{\sin A}{a}$$

$$\frac{\sin 4°}{c} = \frac{\sin 52°}{190}$$

$$c = \frac{190 \sin 4°}{\sin 52°}$$

$$c \approx 16.8$$

Therefore, $B \approx 124°$, $C \approx 4°$, and $c \approx 16.8$.

35. $A = 80°$, $a = 9$, $b = 9.1$

Since angle A is acute, find $b \sin A$ and compare it with a.

$b \sin A = 9.1 \sin 80° \approx 8.96$

Since $9.1 > 9 > 8.96$, there are two solutions.

When solving this problem by the Law of Sines, angle measures were rounded to the nearest tenth of a degree until the final step of the solution.

Case 1: Acute angle B

$$\frac{\sin B}{b} = \frac{\sin A}{a}$$

$$\frac{\sin B}{9.1} = \frac{\sin 80°}{9}$$

$$\sin B = \frac{9.1 \sin 80°}{9}$$

$$\sin B \approx 0.9958$$

$$B \approx 84.7°$$

$$C \approx 180° - (80° + 84.7°) = 15.3°$$

$$\frac{\sin C}{c} = \frac{\sin A}{a}$$

$$\frac{\sin 15.3°}{c} \approx \frac{\sin 80°}{9}$$

$$c \approx \frac{9 \sin 15.3°}{\sin 80°}$$

$$c \approx 2.4$$

Therefore, $B \approx 85°$, $C \approx 15°$, and $c \approx 2.4$.

Case 2: Obtuse angle B

$$B \approx 180° - 84.7° \approx 95.3°$$

$$C \approx 180° - (80° + 95.3°) \approx 4.7°$$

$$\frac{\sin C}{c} = \frac{\sin A}{a}$$

$$\frac{\sin 4.7°}{c} \approx \frac{\sin 80°}{9}$$

$$c \approx \frac{9 \sin 4.7°}{\sin 80°}$$

$$c \approx 0.7$$

Therefore, $B \approx 95°$, $C \approx 5°$, and $c \approx 0.7$.

36. When solving this problem by the Law of Sines, angle measures were rounded to the nearest tenth of a degree until the final step of the solution.

$A = 28°$, $a = 8.5$, $b = 7.2$

Since angle A is acute and $a > b$, there is one solution.

$$\frac{\sin B}{b} = \frac{\sin A}{a}$$

$$\frac{\sin B}{7.2} = \frac{\sin 28°}{8.5}$$

$$\sin B = \frac{7.2 \sin 28°}{8.5}$$

$$\sin B \approx 0.3977$$

$$B \approx 23.43° = 23.4°$$

$$C \approx 180° - (28° + 23.43°) = 128.6°$$

$$\frac{\sin C}{c} = \frac{\sin A}{a}$$

$$\frac{\sin 128.6°}{c} \approx \frac{\sin 28°}{8.5}$$

$$c \approx \frac{8.5 \sin 128.6°}{\sin 28°}$$

$$c \approx 14.1$$

Therefore, $B \approx 23°$, $C \approx 129°$, and $c \approx 14.1$.

37. $A = 47°$, $a = 67$, $b = 83$

Since angle A is acute, find $b \sin A$ and compare it with a.

$b \sin A = 83 \sin 47° \approx 60.7$

Since $83 > 67 > 60.7$, there are two solutions.

When solving this problem by the Law of Sines, angle measures were rounded to the nearest tenth of a degree until the final step of the solution.

Case 1: Acute angle B

$$\frac{\sin B}{b} = \frac{\sin A}{a}$$

$$\frac{\sin B}{83} = \frac{\sin 47°}{67}$$

$$\sin B = \frac{83 \sin 47°}{67}$$

$$\sin B \approx 0.9060$$

$$B \approx 65.0°$$

$$C \approx 180° - (47° + 65.0°) = 68°$$

$$\frac{\sin C}{c} = \frac{\sin A}{a}$$

$$\frac{\sin 68°}{c} \approx \frac{\sin 47°}{67}$$

$$c \approx \frac{67 \sin 68°}{\sin 47°}$$

$$c \approx 85.0$$

Therefore, $B \approx 65°$, $C \approx 68°$, and $c \approx 84.9$.

Case 2: Obtuse angle B

$$B \approx 180° - 65.0° = 115.0°$$

$$C \approx 180° - (47° + 115.0°) = 18°$$

$$\frac{\sin C}{c} = \frac{\sin A}{a}$$

$$\frac{\sin 18°}{c} = \frac{\sin 47°}{67}$$

$$c \approx \frac{67 \sin 18°}{\sin 47°}$$

$$c \approx 28.3$$

Therefore, $B \approx 115°$, $C \approx 18°$, and $c \approx 28.3$.

38. Let x = miles between intersection and closest distance.

Let y = miles between intersection and farthest distance.

Large triangle:

$$\frac{\sin A}{8} = \frac{\sin 35°}{5}$$

$$\sin A \approx \frac{8 \sin 35°}{5}$$

$$\sin A \approx 0.9177$$

$$A \approx 66.6°$$

$$B \approx 180° - (35° + 66.6°) = 78.4°$$

$$\frac{\sin 78.4°}{y} = \frac{\sin 35°}{5}$$

$$y \approx 8.5$$

Small triangle:

$$A' \approx 180° - 66.6° \approx 113.4°$$

$$B' \approx 180° - (35 + 113.4°) \approx 31.6°$$

$$\frac{\sin 31.6°}{x} \approx \frac{\sin 35°}{5}$$

$$x \approx \frac{5 \sin 31.6°}{\sin 35°}$$

$$x \approx 4.6$$

The two distances are 4.6 miles and 8.5 miles.

39. Let Ranger A's angle be $A = 38°$ (then side b is distance to fire) and Ranger B's angle be $B = 63°$ (then side a is distance to fire).

$$C = 180° - (38° + 63°) = 79°$$

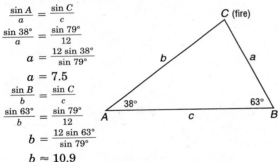

$$\frac{\sin A}{a} = \frac{\sin C}{c}$$

$$\frac{\sin 38°}{a} = \frac{\sin 79°}{12}$$

$$a = \frac{12 \sin 38°}{\sin 79°}$$

$$a = 7.5$$

$$\frac{\sin B}{b} = \frac{\sin C}{c}$$

$$\frac{\sin 63°}{b} = \frac{\sin 79°}{12}$$

$$b = \frac{12 \sin 63°}{\sin 79°}$$

$$b \approx 10.9$$

The fire is 7.5 miles from Ranger B, and 10.9 miles from Ranger A.

40. Angle 1 $= 180° - 64° = 116°$

Angle 2 $= 7°$

Remaining angle $= 64° - 7° = 57°$

$$\frac{\sin 57°}{5280} = \frac{\sin 7°}{\text{hyp}}$$

$$\text{hyp} \approx 767.3$$

$$\sin 64° = \frac{\text{opp}}{\text{hyp}} \approx \frac{\text{opp}}{767.3}$$

$$\text{opp} \approx 690$$

The balloon is 690 feet high, to the nearest foot.

41.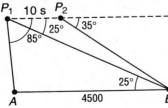

$$\angle A = 180° - (25° + 60°) = 95°$$

$$\frac{\sin 95°}{P_1 B} = \frac{\sin 60°}{4500}, \quad P_1 B \approx 5176.4$$

$$\frac{\sin(180° - 35°)}{5176.4} \approx \frac{\sin(35° - 25°)}{P_1 P_2}, \quad P_1 P_2 \approx 1567.1$$

$$\frac{1567.1 \text{ feet}}{10 \text{ seconds}} \cdot \frac{1 \text{ mile}}{5280 \text{ feet}} \cdot \frac{60 \text{ minutes}}{1 \text{ hour}} \cdot \frac{60 \text{ seconds}}{1 \text{ minute}} \approx$$

$$106.8 \text{ miles/hour}$$

The plane is flying 107 mph.

42a. $a = 20, B = 47°$

For two solutions,

$$a \sin B < b < a$$

$$20 \sin 47° < b < 20$$

$$14.63 < b < 20.$$

42b. For one solution,

$$b = a \sin B$$

$$b = 14.63$$

or $b \geq a$

$$b \geq 20.$$

42c. For no solution,

$$b < a \sin B$$

$$b < 14.63.$$

43. Answers should include the following.

- If the height of the triangle is not given, but the measure of two sides and their included angle are given, then the formula for the area of a triangle using the sine function should be used.

- You might use this formula to find the area of a triangular piece of land, since it might be easier to measure two sides and use surveying equipment to measure the included angle than to measure the perpendicular distance from one vertex to its opposite side.

- The area of $\triangle ABC$ is $\frac{1}{2}ah$.

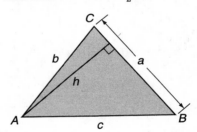

$$\sin B = \frac{h}{c} \text{ or } h = c \sin B$$

$$\text{Area} = \frac{1}{2}ah \text{ or Area} = \frac{1}{2}a(c \sin B)$$

44. D; The two base angles are equal.

$$A = \frac{1}{2}(180° - 36°) = 72°$$

$$\frac{\sin 72°}{a} = \frac{\sin 36°}{22}$$

$$a = \frac{22 \sin 72°}{\sin 36°}$$

$$a \approx 35.6$$

Perimeter $\approx 2(35.6) + 22 = 93.2$ cm.

45. Let $b = 67, A = 47°, C = 55°$

$$B = 180° - (47° + 55°) = 78°$$

$$\frac{\sin A}{a} = \frac{\sin B}{b}$$

$$\frac{\sin 47°}{a} = \frac{\sin 78°}{67}$$

$$a = \frac{67 \sin 47°}{\sin 78°}$$

$$a \approx 50.1$$

$$\frac{\sin C}{c} = \frac{\sin B}{b}$$

$$\frac{\sin 55°}{c} = \frac{\sin 78°}{67}$$

$$c = \frac{67 \sin 55°}{\sin 78°}$$

$$c \approx 56.1$$

Therefore, $B = 78°, a \approx 50.1$, and $c \approx 56.1$.

Page 732   Maintain Your Skills

46. $\cos 30° = \dfrac{\sqrt{3}}{2}$

47. $\cot\left(\dfrac{\pi}{3}\right) = \dfrac{\frac{1}{2}}{\frac{\sqrt{3}}{2}} = \dfrac{1}{\sqrt{3}} = \dfrac{\sqrt{3}}{3}$

48. $\csc\left(\dfrac{\pi}{4}\right) = \dfrac{1}{\sin\left(\frac{\pi}{4}\right)} = \dfrac{1}{\frac{\sqrt{2}}{2}} = \dfrac{2}{\sqrt{2}} = \sqrt{2}$

49. A positive angle is $300° + 360° = 660°$.
A negative angle is $300° - 360° = -60°$.

50. A positive angle is $47° + 360° = 407°$.
A negative angle is $47° - 360° = -313°$.

51. A positive angle is $\dfrac{5\pi}{6} + 2\pi = \dfrac{17\pi}{6}$.
A negative angle is $\dfrac{5\pi}{6} - 2\pi = -\dfrac{7\pi}{6}$.

52. P(both 5s or both spades)
$= P$(both 5s) $+ P$(both spades) $- P$(1 card is the 5 of spades)

$$= \frac{4}{52} \cdot \frac{3}{51} + \frac{13}{52} \cdot \frac{12}{51} - \frac{1}{52} \cdot \frac{12}{51}$$

$$= \frac{1}{221} + \frac{1}{17} - \frac{1}{221} = \frac{1}{17}$$

53. P(both 7s or both red)
$= P$(both 7s) $+ P$(both red) $- P$(both red 7s)

$$= \left(\frac{4}{52}\right)\left(\frac{3}{51}\right) + \left(\frac{26}{52}\right)\left(\frac{25}{51}\right) - \left(\frac{2}{52}\right)\left(\frac{1}{51}\right)$$

$$= \frac{55}{221}$$

54. $a_1 = 20, d = 40$

$$a_n = a_1 + (n - 1)d$$

$$a_{20} = 20 + (20 - 1)(40)$$

$$a_{20} = 780$$

The rocket rises 780 feet in the 20th second.

55. $a^2 = 3^2 + 5^2 - 2(3)(5) \cos 85°$

$$a^2 = 34 - 30 \cos 85°$$

$$a \approx 5.6$$

56. $c^2 = 12^2 + 10^2 - 2(12)(10) \cos 40°$

$$c^2 = 244 - 240 \cos 40°$$

$$c \approx 7.8$$

57. $7^2 = 11^2 + 9^2 - 2(11)(9) \cos B°$

$$\cos B° = \frac{7^2 - 11^2 - 9^2}{-2(11)(9)} = \frac{17}{22}$$

$$B \approx 39.4$$

58. $13^2 = 8^2 + 6^2 - 2(8)(6) \cos A°$

$$\cos A° = \frac{13^2 - 8^2 - 6^2}{-2(8)(6)} = -\frac{23}{32}$$

$$A \approx 136.0$$

13-5 | Law of Cosines

Pages 735-736   Maintain Your Skills

1. Mateo; the angle given is not between the two sides; therefore the Law of Sines should be used.

2a. Use the Law of Cosines to find the measure of one angle. Then use the Law of Sines or the Law of Cosines to find the measure of a second angle. Finally, subtract the sum of these two angles from 180° to find the measure of the third angle.

2b. Use the Law of Cosines to find the measure of the third side. Then use the Law of Sines or the Law of Cosines to find the measure of a second angle. Finally, subtract the sum of these two angles from 180° to find the measure of the third angle.

3. Sample answer:

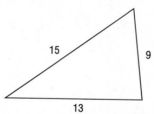

4. Begin with the Law of Cosines, since the measures of two sides and the included angle are given.

$$c^2 = a^2 + b^2 - 2ab \cos C$$

$$c^2 = 11^2 + 10.5^2 - 2(11)(10.5) \cos 35°$$

$$c^2 = 231.25 - 231 \cos 35°$$

$$c \approx 6.48 \approx 6.5$$

When solving this problem by the Law of Sines, angle measures were rounded to the nearest tenth of a degree until the final step of the solution.

$$\frac{\sin A}{a} = \frac{\sin C}{c}$$

$$\frac{\sin A}{11} \approx \frac{\sin 35°}{6.48}$$

$$\sin A \approx \frac{11 \sin 35°}{6.48}$$

$$\sin A \approx 0.9733$$

$$A \approx 76.7°$$

$$B \approx 180° - (76.7° + 35°) \approx 68.3°$$

Therefore, $c \approx 6.5, A \approx 77°$, and $B \approx 68°$.

5. Begin with the Law of Sines, since the measure of a side and two angles are given.

$$\frac{\sin A}{a} = \frac{\sin C}{c}$$

$$\frac{\sin 40°}{a} = \frac{\sin 70°}{14}$$

$$a = \frac{14 \sin 40°}{\sin 70°}$$

$$a \approx 9.6$$

$$B = 180° - (40° + 70°) = 70°$$

Since angles B and C are equal, so are sides b and c.

$$b = 14$$

Therefore, $B = 70°$, $a \approx 9.6$, and $b = 14$.

6. Begin with the Law of Sines, since the measures of two sides and the angle opposite one of them are given.

When solving this problem by the Law of Sines, angle measures were rounded to the nearest tenth of a degree until the final step of the solution.

$$\frac{\sin B}{b} = \frac{\sin A}{a}$$

$$\frac{\sin B}{57} = \frac{\sin 42°}{63}$$

$$\sin B = \frac{57 \sin 42°}{63}$$

$$\sin B \approx 0.6054$$

$$B \approx 37.3° \approx 37°$$

$$C \approx 180° - (42° + 37.3°) \approx 100.7° \approx 101°$$

$$\frac{\sin C}{c} = \frac{\sin A}{a}$$

$$\frac{\sin 100.7°}{c} \approx \frac{\sin 42°}{63}$$

$$c \approx 92.5$$

Therefore, $B \approx 37°$, $C \approx 101°$, and $c \approx 92.5$.

7. Begin with the Law of Cosines, since the measures of three sides are given.

$$a^2 = b^2 + c^2 - 2bc \cos A$$

$$5^2 = 12^2 + 13^2 - 2(12)(13) \cos A$$

$$\cos A = \frac{12}{13}$$

$$A \approx 22.6° \approx 23°$$

When solving this problem by the Law of Sines, angle measures were rounded to the nearest tenth of a degree until the final step of the solution.

$$\frac{\sin B}{b} = \frac{\sin A}{a}$$

$$\frac{\sin B}{12} \approx \frac{\sin 22.6°}{5}$$

$$\sin B \approx \frac{12 \sin 22.6°}{5}$$

$$\sin B \approx 0.9223$$

$$B \approx 67.3°$$

$$C \approx 180° - (22.6° + 67.3°) \approx 90.1°$$

Therefore, $A \approx 23°$, $B \approx 67°$, and $C = 90°$.

8. Let h = distance from the pitcher's mound to first base.

The angle opposite side h is $\frac{1}{2}(90°)$ or $H = 45°$.

$$h^2 = b^2 + p^2 - 2bp \cos H$$

$$h^2 = 18^2 + 27.5^2 - 2(18)(27.5) \cos 45°$$

$$h^2 = 1080.25 - 990 \cos 45°$$

$$h \approx 19.5$$

The distance is 19.5 meters.

9. Using $h \approx 19.5$ from Problem 8, we have:

$$\frac{\sin P}{p} = \sin H \backslash h$$

$$\frac{\sin P}{27.5} \approx \frac{\sin 45°}{19.5}$$

$$\sin P \approx \frac{27.5 \sin 45°}{19.5}$$

$$\sin P \approx 0.9972$$

$$P \approx 85.7$$

But since P is obtuse, we know $P \approx 180° - 85.7° = 94.3°$.

Therefore, the angle is 94.3°.

10. Begin with the Law of Sines, since the measures of two angles and a side are given.

$$A = 180° - (72° + 48°) = 60°$$

$$\frac{\sin B}{b} = \frac{\sin A}{a}$$

$$\frac{\sin 72°}{b} = \frac{\sin 60°}{13}$$

$$b = \frac{13 \sin 72°}{\sin 60°}$$

$$b \approx 14.3$$

$$\frac{\sin C}{c} = \frac{\sin A}{a}$$

$$\frac{\sin 48°}{c} = \frac{\sin 60°}{13}$$

$$c = \frac{13 \sin 48°}{\sin 60°}$$

$$c \approx 11.2$$

Therefore, $A = 60°$, $b \approx 14.3$, and $c \approx 11.2$.

11. Begin with the Law of Cosines, since the measures of three sides are given.

$$a^2 = b^2 + c^2 - 2bc \cos A$$

$$15^2 = 18^2 + 19^2 - 2(18)(19) \cos A$$

$$\cos A = \frac{115}{171}$$

$$A \approx 47.7°$$

When solving this problem by the Law of Sines, angle measures were rounded to the nearest tenth of a degree until the final step of the solution.

$$\frac{\sin C}{c} = \frac{\sin A}{a}$$

$$\frac{\sin C}{19} = \frac{\sin 47.7°}{15}$$

$$\sin C = \frac{19 \sin 47.7°}{15}$$

$$\sin C \approx 0.9369$$

$$C \approx 69.7°$$

$$B \approx 180° - (47.7° + 69.5°) \approx 62.8°$$

Therefore, $A \approx 48°$, $B \approx 63°$, and $C \approx 70°$.

12. Begin with the Law of Cosines, since the measures of three sides are given.

$$c^2 = a^2 + b^2 - 2ab \cos C$$
$$166^2 = 140^2 + 185^2 - 2(140)(185) \cos C$$
$$\cos C \approx 0.5071$$
$$C \approx 59.5° \approx 60°$$

When solving this problem by the law of Sines, angle measures were rounded to the nearest tenth of a degree until the final step of the solution.

$$\frac{\sin B}{b} = \frac{\sin C}{c}$$
$$\frac{\sin B}{185} = \frac{\sin 59.5°}{166}$$
$$\sin B = \frac{185 \sin 59.5°}{166}$$
$$\sin B \approx 0.9602$$
$$B \approx 73.8°$$
$$A \approx 180° - (73.8° + 59.5°) = 46.7°$$

Therefore, $A \approx 47°$, $B \approx 74°$, and $C \approx 60°$.

13. Begin with the Law of Sines, since the measures of two sides and the angle opposite one of them are given.

When solving this problem by the Law of Sines, angle measures were rounded to the nearest tenth of a degree until the final step of the solution.

$$\frac{\sin C}{c} = \frac{\sin A}{a}$$
$$\frac{\sin C}{15} = \frac{\sin 34°}{12}$$
$$\sin C = \frac{15 \sin 34°}{12}$$
$$\sin C \approx 0.6990$$
$$C \approx 44.3°$$
$$B \approx 180° - (34° + 44.3°) = 101.7°$$
$$\frac{\sin B}{b} = \frac{\sin A}{a}$$
$$\frac{\sin 101.7°}{b} \approx \frac{\sin 34°}{12}$$
$$b \approx \frac{12 \sin 101.7°}{\sin 34°}$$
$$b \approx 21.0$$

Therefore, $B \approx 102°$, $C \approx 44°$, and $b \approx 21.0$.

14. Begin with the Law of Cosines, since the measures of two sides and the angle between them are given.

$$c^2 = a^2 + b^2 - 2ab \cos C$$
$$c^2 = 11^2 + 17^2 - 2(11)(17) \cos 42°$$
$$c^2 = 410 - 374 \cos 42°$$
$$c \approx 11.5$$

When solving this problem by the Law of Sines, angle measures were rounded to the nearest tenth of a degree until the final step of the solution.

$$\frac{\sin B}{b} = \frac{\sin C}{c}$$
$$\frac{\sin B}{17} \approx \frac{\sin 42°}{11.5}$$
$$\sin B \approx \frac{17 \sin 42°}{11.5}$$
$$\sin B \approx 0.9891$$
$$B \approx 81.5°$$
$$A \approx 180° - (81.5° + 42°) = 56.5°$$

Therefore, $c \approx 11.5$, $A \approx 57°$, and $B \approx 82°$.

15. Begin with the Law of Sines, since the measures of two angles and a side are given.

$$A = 180° - (71° + 29°) = 80°$$
$$\frac{\sin A}{a} = \frac{\sin B}{b}$$
$$\frac{\sin 80°}{a} = \frac{\sin 71°}{10.5}$$
$$a = \frac{10.5 \sin 80°}{\sin 71°}$$
$$a \approx 10.9$$
$$\frac{\sin C}{c} = \frac{\sin B}{b}$$
$$c = \frac{10.5 \sin 29°}{\sin 71°}$$
$$\frac{\sin 29°}{c} = \frac{\sin 71°}{10.5}$$
$$c \approx 5.4$$

Therefore, $A = 80°$, $a \approx 10.9$, and $c \approx 5.4$.

16. Begin with the Law of Cosines, since the measures of two sides and the angle between them are given.

$$b^2 = a^2 + c^2 - 2ac \cos B$$
$$b^2 = 20^2 + 24^2 - 2(20)(24) \cos 47°$$
$$b^2 = 976 - 960 \cos 47°$$
$$b \approx 17.9$$

When solving this problem by the Law of Sines, angle measures were rounded to the nearest tenth of a degree until the final step of the solution.

$$\frac{\sin A}{a} = \frac{\sin B}{b}$$
$$\frac{\sin A}{20} \approx \frac{\sin 47°}{17.9}$$
$$\sin A = \frac{20 \sin 47°}{17.9}$$
$$\sin A \approx 0.8172$$
$$A \approx 54.8°$$
$$C \approx 180° - (54.8° + 47°) = 78.2°$$

Therefore, $b \approx 17.9$, $A \approx 55°$, and $C \approx 78°$.

17. Begin with the Law of Cosines, since the measures of three sides are given.

$$a^2 = b^2 + c^2 - 2bc \cos A$$
$$345^2 = 648^2 + 442^2 - 2(648)(442) \cos A$$
$$\cos A = 0.8663$$
$$A \approx 30.0°$$

When solving this problem by the Law of Sines, angle measures were rounded to the nearest tenth of a degree until the final step of the solution.

$$\frac{\sin C}{c} = \frac{\sin A}{a}$$
$$\frac{\sin C}{442} \approx \frac{\sin 30.0°}{345}$$
$$\sin C \approx \frac{442 \sin 30.0°}{345}$$
$$C \approx 39.8°$$
$$B \approx 180° - (30° + 39.8°) = 110.2°$$

Therefore, $A \approx 30°$, $B \approx 110°$, and $C \approx 40°$.

18. $A = 36°$, $a = 10$, $b = 19$

Since angle A is acute and $a < b \sin A$ ($10 < 19 \sin 36° \approx 11.2$), there is no solution.

19. Begin with the Law of Sines, since the measures of two angles and a side are given.

$$\frac{\sin B}{b} = \frac{\sin A}{a}$$
$$\frac{\sin 78°}{b} = \frac{\sin 25°}{13.7}$$
$$b = \frac{13.7 \sin 78°}{\sin 25°}$$
$$b \approx 31.7$$
$$C = 180° - (25° + 78°) = 77°$$
$$\frac{\sin C}{c} = \frac{\sin A}{a}$$
$$\frac{\sin 77°}{c} = \frac{\sin 25°}{13.7}$$
$$c = \frac{13.7 \sin 77°}{\sin 25°}$$
$$c \approx 31.6$$

Therefore, $C = 77°$, $b \approx 31.7$, and $c \approx 31.6$.

20. Begin with the Law of Cosines, since the measures of three sides are given.

$$a^2 = b^2 + c^2 - 2bc \cos A$$
$$21.5^2 = 16.7^2 + 10.3^2 - 2(16.7)(10.3) \cos A$$
$$\cos A \approx -0.2246$$
$$A \approx 103.0°$$

When solving this problem by the Law of Sines, angle measures were rounded to the nearest tenth of a degree until the final step of the solution.

$$\frac{\sin B}{b} = \frac{\sin A}{a}$$
$$\frac{\sin B}{16.7} \approx \frac{\sin 103.0°}{21.5}$$
$$\sin B \approx \frac{16.7 \sin 103.0°}{21.5}$$
$$B \approx 49.2°$$
$$C \approx 180° - (103.0° + 49.2°) = 27.8°$$

Therefore, $A \approx 103°$, $B \approx 49°$, and $C \approx 28°$.

21. Begin with the Law of Cosines, since the measures of three sides are given.

$$a^2 = b^2 + c^2 - 2bc \cos A$$
$$16^2 = 24^2 + 41^2 - 2(24)(41) \cos A$$
$$\cos A \approx 1.0168$$

Since the cosine function cannot be greater than 1, there is no solution. Also, note more directly that the given information violates the triangle inequality, since $c > a + b$.

22. Begin with the Law of Cosines, since the measures of three sides are given.

$$a^2 = b^2 + c^2 - 2bc \cos A$$
$$8^2 = 24^2 + 18^2 - 2(24)(18) \cos A$$
$$\cos A = \frac{209}{216}$$
$$A \approx 14.6° \approx 15°$$

When solving this problem by the Law of Sines, angle measures were rounded to the nearest tenth of a degree until the final step of the solution.

$$\frac{\sin C}{c} = \frac{\sin A}{a}$$
$$\frac{\sin C}{18} \approx \frac{\sin 14.6°}{8}$$
$$\sin C \approx \frac{9 \sin 14.6°}{4}$$
$$C \approx 34.6°$$
$$B \approx 180° - (15° + 34.6°) \approx 130.4°$$

Therefore, $A \approx 15°$, $B \approx 130°$, and $C \approx 35°$.

23. Begin with the Law of Cosines, since the measures of two sides and the included angle are given.

$$b^2 = a^2 + c^2 - 2ac \cos B$$
$$b^2 = 51^2 + 61^2 - 2(51)(61) \cos 19°$$
$$b \approx 21.0$$

When solving this problem by the Law of Sines, angle measures were rounded to the nearest tenth of a degree until the final step of the solution.

$$\frac{\sin A}{a} = \frac{\sin B}{b}$$
$$\frac{\sin A}{51} \approx \frac{\sin 19°}{21.0}$$
$$\sin A \approx \frac{51 \sin 19°}{21.0}$$
$$A \approx 52.2°$$
$$C \approx 180° - (52.2° + 19°) \approx 108.8°$$

Therefore, $b \approx 21.0$, $A \approx 52°$, and $C \approx 109°$.

24. Begin with the Law of Sines, since the measures two angles and a side are given.

$$\frac{\sin B}{b} = \frac{\sin A}{a}$$
$$\frac{\sin 22°}{b} = \frac{\sin 56°}{12.2}$$
$$b = \frac{12.2 \sin 22°}{\sin 56°}$$
$$b \approx 5.5$$
$$C = 180° - (56° + 22°) = 102°$$
$$\frac{\sin C}{c} = \frac{\sin A}{a}$$
$$\frac{\sin 102°}{c} = \frac{\sin 56°}{12.2}$$
$$c = \frac{12.2 \sin 102°}{\sin 56°}$$
$$c \approx 14.4$$

Therefore, $b \approx 5.5$, $c \approx 14.4$, and $C \approx 102°$.

25. Begin with the Law of Cosines, since the measures of three sides are given.

$$a^2 = b^2 + c^2 - 2bc \cos A$$
$$4^2 = 8^2 + 5^2 - 2(8)(5) \cos A$$
$$\cos A = \frac{73}{80}$$
$$A \approx 24.1°$$

When solving this problem by the Law of Sines, angle measures were rounded to the nearest tenth of a degree until the final step of the solution.

$$\frac{\sin C}{c} = \frac{\sin A}{a}$$
$$\frac{\sin C}{5} \approx \frac{\sin 24.1°}{4}$$
$$\sin C \approx \frac{5 \sin 24.1°}{4}$$
$$C \approx 30.7°$$
$$B \approx 180° - (24.1° + 30.7°) \approx 125.2°$$

Therefore, $A \approx 24°$, $B \approx 125°$, and $C \approx 31°$.

26. Begin with the Law of Cosines, since the measures of two sides and the included angle are given.

$$c^2 = a^2 + b^2 - 2ab \cos C$$
$$c^2 = 21.5^2 + 13^2 - 2(21.5)(13) \cos 38°$$
$$c^2 = 631.25 - 559 \cos 38°$$
$$c \approx 13.8$$

When solving this problem by the Law of Sines, angle measures were rounded to the nearest tenth of a degree until the final step of the solution.

$$\frac{\sin B}{b} = \frac{\sin C}{c}$$
$$\frac{\sin B}{13} \approx \frac{\sin 38°}{13.8}$$
$$\sin B \approx \frac{13 \sin 38°}{13.8}$$
$$B \approx 35.4°$$
$$A \approx 180° - (35.4° + 38°) \approx 106.6°$$

Therefore, $c \approx 13.8$, $B \approx 35°$, and $A \approx 107°$.

27. Begin with the Law of Sines, since the measures of two sides and an angle are given.

When solving this problem by the Law of Sines, angle measures were rounded to the nearest tenth of a degree until the final step of the solution.

$$\frac{\sin A}{a} = \frac{\sin B}{b}$$
$$\frac{\sin 40°}{6} = \frac{\sin B}{7}$$
$$\sin B = \frac{7 \sin 40°}{6}$$
$$B \approx 0.87°$$
$$C \approx 180° - (40° + 0.87°) \approx 139.13°$$
$$\frac{\sin A}{a} = \frac{\sin C}{c}$$
$$\frac{\sin 40°}{6} = \frac{\sin 139.13°}{c}$$
$$c \approx \frac{6 \sin 139.13°}{\sin 40°}$$
$$c \approx 6.3$$

Therefore, $B \approx 1°$, and $C \approx 139°$, $c \approx 6.3$.

28. $\text{stride}^2 = \text{pace}^2 + \text{pace}^2 - 2(\text{pace})(\text{pace}) \cos \theta$
$$3.15^2 = 1.6^2 + 1.6^2 - 2(1.6)^2 \cos \theta$$
$$\cos \theta = -\frac{1921}{2048}$$
$$\theta \approx 159.7°$$

The step angle is about 159.7°.

29. $\text{stride}^2 = \text{pace}^2 + \text{pace}^2 - 2(\text{pace})(\text{pace}) \cos \theta$
$$2.73^2 = 1.78^2 + 1.78^2 - 2(1.78)^2 \cos \theta$$
$$\cos \theta = -0.1761$$
$$\theta \approx 100.1°$$

The step angle is about 100.1°.

30. Since the step angle for the carnivore is closer to 180°, it appears as though the carnivore made more forward progress with each step than the herbivore did.

31. $(AC)^2 = 5^2 + 5^2 - 2(5)(5) \cos 52°$
$$(AC)^2 = 50 - 50 \cos 52°$$
$$AC \approx 4.4 \text{ cm}$$

The measure of $\angle BCD = 180° - 52° = 128°$
$$(DB)^2 = 5^2 + 5^2 - 2(5)(5) \cos 128°$$
$$(DB)^2 = 50 - 50 \cos 128°$$
$$DB \approx 9.0 \text{ cm}$$

32. remaining side
$$= \sqrt{425^2 + 550^2 - 2(425)(550) \cos 44.5°}$$
remaining side ≈ 387

The perimeter is about 425 ft + 550 ft + 387 ft = 1362 ft.

$$\text{Area} = \frac{1}{2}bc \sin A$$
$$= \frac{1}{2}(425)(550) \sin 44.5°$$
$$\approx 81{,}919$$

The area is about 81,919 ft².

33. $c^2 = a^2 + b^2 - 2ab \cos C$
$$117^2 = 42^2 + 108^2 - 2(42)(108) \cos C$$
$$\cos C = -\frac{29}{1008}$$
$$C \approx 91.6°$$

34. Since $\cos 90° = 0$, $a^2 = b^2 + c^2 - 2bc \cos A$ becomes $a^2 = b^2 + c^2$.

35. Answers should include the following.

- The Law of Cosines can be used when you know all three sides of a triangle or when you know two sides and the included angle. It can even be used with two sides and the nonincluded angle. This set of conditions leaves a quadratic equation to be solved. It may have one, two, or no solution just like the SSA case with the Law of Sines.

- Given the latitude of a point on the surface of Earth, you can use the radius of Earth and the orbiting height of a satellite in geosynchronous orbit to create a triangle. This triangle will have two known sides and the measure of the included angle. Find the third side using the Law of Cosines and then use the Law of Sines to determine the angles of the triangle. Subtract 90 degrees from the angle with its vertex on Earth's surface to find the angle at which to aim the receiver dish.

36. B; $(\sqrt{115})^2 = 11^2 + 5^2 - 2(11)(5) \cos \theta$
$$\cos \theta = \frac{31}{110}$$
$$\theta \approx 74°$$

37. B; Speed of truck $B = x$, then speed of truck $A = 2x$. Distance traveled by truck $B = 4x$, then distance traveled by truck $A = 8x$.

$$350^2 = (4x)^2 + (8x)^2 = 2(4x)(8x) \cos 100°$$
$$350^2 = 16x^2 + 64x^2 - 64x^2 \cos 100°$$
$$350^2 = x^2 (16 + 64 - 64 \cos 100°)$$
$$x^2 = \frac{350^2}{16 + 64 - 64 \cos 100°}$$
$$x \approx 37 \text{ mph}$$

38. $c^2 = a^2 + b^2 - 2ab \cos C$
$$\cos C = \frac{c^2 - a^2 - b^2}{-2ab}$$
$$\cos C = \frac{20^2 - 17^2 - 8^2}{-2(17)(8)}$$
$$C \approx 100.0°$$

39. $a^2 = b^2 + c^2 - 2bc \cos A$

$\cos A = \dfrac{a^2 - b^2 - c^2}{-2bc}$

$\cos A = \dfrac{17^2 - 8^2 - 20^2}{-2(8)(20)}$

$A \approx 56.8°$

When solving this problem by the Law of Sines, angle measures were rounded to the nearest tenth of a degree until the final step of the solution.

$\dfrac{\sin C}{c} = \dfrac{\sin A}{a}$

$\sin C = \dfrac{c \sin A}{a}$

$\sin C \approx \dfrac{20 \sin 56.8°}{17}$

$C \approx 79.9°$

C is obtuse, so $C \approx 180° - 79.9° = 100.1°$.

40. By finding the measure of angle C in one step using the Law of Cosines, only the given information was used. By finding this angle measure using the Law of Cosines and then the Law of Sines, a calculated value that was not exact was introduced; 100.0°.

Page 738   Maintain Your Skills

41. $A = 55°, a = 8, b = 7$

Since angle A is acute and $a > b$ ($8 > 7$), there is one solution.

When solving this problem by the Law of Sines, angle measures were rounded to the nearest tenth of a degree until the final step of the solution.

$\dfrac{\sin B}{b} = \dfrac{\sin A}{a}$

$\dfrac{\sin B}{7} = \dfrac{\sin 55°}{8}$

$\sin B = 7 \sin 55° \backslash 8$

$B \approx 45.8°$

$C \approx 180° - (55° + 45.8°) = 79.2°$

$\dfrac{\sin C}{c} = \dfrac{\sin A}{a}$

$\dfrac{\sin 79.2°}{c} \approx \dfrac{\sin 55°}{8}$

$c \approx \dfrac{8 \sin 79.2°}{\sin 55°}$

$c \approx 9.6$

Therefore, $B \approx 46°$, $C \approx 79°$, and $c \approx 9.6$.

42. $A = 70°, a = 7, b = 10$

Since angle A is acute, find $b \sin A$ and compare it with a.

$b \sin A = 10 \sin 70° \approx 9.4$

Since $a < b \sin A$ ($7 < 9.4$), there is no solution.

43. $x = 5, y = 12, r = \sqrt{5^2 + 12^2} = 13$

$\sin \theta = \dfrac{y}{r} = \dfrac{12}{13}$ $\csc \theta = \dfrac{r}{y} = \dfrac{13}{12}$

$\cos \theta = \dfrac{x}{r} = \dfrac{5}{13}$ $\sec \theta = \dfrac{r}{x} = \dfrac{13}{5}$

$\tan \theta = \dfrac{y}{x} = \dfrac{12}{5}$ $\cot \theta = \dfrac{x}{y} = \dfrac{5}{12}$

44. $x = 4, y = 7, r = \sqrt{4^2 + 7^2} = \sqrt{65}$

$\sin \theta = \dfrac{y}{r} = \dfrac{7}{\sqrt{65}} = \dfrac{7\sqrt{65}}{65}$

$\cos \theta = \dfrac{x}{r} = \dfrac{4}{\sqrt{65}} = \dfrac{4\sqrt{65}}{65}$

$\tan \theta = \dfrac{y}{x} = \dfrac{7}{4}$

$\csc \theta = \dfrac{r}{y} = \dfrac{\sqrt{65}}{7}$

$\sec \theta = \dfrac{r}{x} = \dfrac{\sqrt{65}}{4}$

$\cot \theta = \dfrac{x}{y} = \dfrac{4}{7}$

45. $x = \sqrt{10}, y = \sqrt{6}, r = \sqrt{(\sqrt{10})^2 + (\sqrt{6})^2} = 4$

$\sin \theta = \dfrac{y}{r} = \dfrac{\sqrt{6}}{4}$

$\cos \theta = \dfrac{x}{r} = \dfrac{\sqrt{10}}{4}$

$\tan \theta = \dfrac{y}{x} = \dfrac{\sqrt{6}}{\sqrt{10}} = \dfrac{\sqrt{15}}{5}$

$\csc \theta = \dfrac{r}{y} = \dfrac{4}{\sqrt{6}} = \dfrac{2\sqrt{6}}{3}$

$\sec \theta = \dfrac{r}{x} = \dfrac{4}{\sqrt{10}} = \dfrac{2\sqrt{10}}{5}$

$\cot \theta = \dfrac{x}{y} = \dfrac{\sqrt{10}}{\sqrt{6}} = \dfrac{\sqrt{15}}{3}$

46. $e^x + 5 = 9$

$e^x = 4$

$\ln(e^x) = \ln 4$

$x = \ln 4$

$x \approx 1.3863$

47. $4e^x - 3 > -1$

$4e^x > 2$

$e^x > \dfrac{1}{2}$

$\ln(e^x) > \ln\left(\dfrac{1}{2}\right)$

$x > \ln\left(\dfrac{1}{2}\right)$

$x > -0.6931$

$\{x \mid x > -0.6931\}$

48. $\ln(x + 3) = 2$

$e^{\ln(x + 3)} = e^2$

$x + 3 = e^2$

$x = e^2 - 3$

$x \approx 4.3891$

49. A positive angle is $45° + 360° = 405°$.
A negative angle is $45° - 360° = -315°$.

50. A positive angle is $30° + 360° = 390°$.
A negative angle is $30° - 360° = -330°$.

51. A positive angle is $180° + 360° = 540°$
A negative angle is $180° - 360° = -180°$.

52. A positive angle is $\dfrac{\pi}{2} + 2\pi = \dfrac{5\pi}{2}$.
A negative angle is $\dfrac{\pi}{2} - 2\pi = -\dfrac{3\pi}{2}$.

53. A positive angle is $\dfrac{7\pi}{6} + 2\pi = \dfrac{19\pi}{6}$.
A negative angle is $\dfrac{7\pi}{6} - 2\pi = -\dfrac{5\pi}{6}$.

54. A positive angle is $\dfrac{4\pi}{3} + 2\pi = \dfrac{10\pi}{3}$.
A negative angle is $\dfrac{4\pi}{3} - 2\pi = -\dfrac{2\pi}{3}$.

1. $x = -2, y = 3, r = \sqrt{(-2)^2 + 3^2} = \sqrt{13}$.

$\sin \theta = \frac{y}{r} = \frac{3}{\sqrt{13}} = \frac{3\sqrt{13}}{13}$

$\cos \theta = \frac{x}{r} = \frac{-2}{\sqrt{13}} = -\frac{2\sqrt{13}}{13}$

$\tan \theta = \frac{y}{x} = \frac{3}{-2}$ or $-\frac{3}{2}$

$\csc \theta = \frac{r}{y} = \frac{\sqrt{13}}{3}$

$\sec \theta = \frac{r}{x} = \frac{\sqrt{13}}{-2}$ or $-\frac{\sqrt{13}}{2}$

$\cot \theta = \frac{x}{y} = \frac{-2}{3}$ or $-\frac{2}{3}$

2. The terminal side of $\frac{5\pi}{3}$ lies in Quadrant IV, so

$\theta' = 2\pi - \frac{5\pi}{3} = \frac{\pi}{3}$.

The cosecant function is negative in Quadrant IV;

$\csc \frac{5\pi}{3} = -\csc \frac{\pi}{3} = -\frac{1}{\sin \frac{\pi}{3}} = -\frac{1}{\frac{\sqrt{3}}{2}} = -\frac{2\sqrt{3}}{3}$.

3. Area $= \frac{1}{2} ef \sin D$

$= \frac{1}{2}(11)(6) \sin 57°$

≈ 27.7

To the nearest tenth, the area is 27.7 m^2.

4. $A = 22°, a = 15, b = 18$

Since angle A is acute, find $b \sin A$ and compare it with a.

$b \sin A = 18 \sin 22° \approx 6.7$

Since $b > a > b \sin A$ ($18 > 15 > 6.7$), there are two solutions.

When solving this problem by the Law of Sines, angle measures were rounded to the nearest tenth of a degree until the final step of the solution.

Case 1: Acute angle B

$\frac{\sin B}{b} = \frac{\sin A}{a}$

$\frac{\sin B}{18} = \frac{\sin 22°}{15}$

$\sin B = \frac{18 \sin 22°}{15}$

$B \approx 26.7 \approx 27°$

$C \approx 180° - (22° + 26.7°) \approx 131.3°$

$\frac{\sin C}{c} = \frac{\sin A}{a}$

$\frac{\sin 131.3°}{c} \approx \frac{\sin 22°}{15}$

$c \approx \frac{15 \sin 131.3°}{\sin 22°}$

$c \approx 30.1$

Therefore, $B \approx 27°, C \approx 131°$, and $c \approx 30.1$.

Case 2: Obtuse angle B

$B \approx 180° - 26.7° \approx 153.3°$

$C \approx 180° - (22° + 153.3°) \approx 4.7° \approx 5°$

$\frac{\sin C}{c} = \frac{\sin A}{a}$

$\frac{\sin 4.7°}{c} \approx \frac{\sin 22°}{15}$

$c \approx \frac{15 \sin 4.7°}{\sin 22°}$

$c \approx 3.3$

Therefore, $B \approx 153°, C \approx 5°$, and $c \approx 3.3$.

5. Begin with the Law of Cosines since the measures of two sides and the included angle are given.

$a^2 = b^2 + c^2 - 2bc \cos A$

$a^2 = 11^2 + 14^2 - 2(11)(14) \cos 78°$

$a^2 = 317 - 308 \cos 78°$

$a \approx 15.9$

When solving this problem by the Law of Sines, angle measures were rounded to the nearest tenth of a degree until the final step of the solution.

$\frac{\sin B}{b} = \frac{\sin A}{a}$

$\frac{\sin B}{11} \approx \frac{\sin 78°}{15.9}$

$\sin B \approx \frac{11 \sin 78°}{15.9}$

$B \approx 42.6°$

$C \approx 180° - (78° + 42.6°) \approx 59.4°$

Therefore, $a \approx 15.9, B \approx 43°$, and $C \approx 59°$.

13-6   Circular Functions

Page 740   Graphing Calculator Investigation

1. T represents the angle θ.
The x value represents $\cos \theta$.
The y value represents $\sin \theta$.

2. $\sin 0° = 0, \cos 0° = 1$;
$\sin 90° = 1, \cos 90° = 0$;
$\sin 180° = 0, \cos 180° = -1$;
$\sin 270° = -1, \cos 270° = 0$

3. For $0° \le \theta \le 90°$, $\sin \theta$ increases from 0 to 1. For $90° \le \theta \le 270°$, $\sin \theta$ decreases from 1 to -1. For $270° \le \theta \le 360°$, $\sin \theta$ increases from -1 to 0. For $0° \le \theta \le 180°$, $\cos \theta$ decreases from 1 to -1. For $180° \le \theta \le 270°$, $\cos \theta$ increases from -1 to 1.

Pages 742-743   Check for Understanding

1. The terminal side of the angle θ in standard position must intersect the unit circle at $P(x, y)$.

2. Sample answer: the motion of the minute hand on a clock; the period is 60 s.

3. Sample answer: The graphs have the same shape, but cross the x-axis at different points.

4. $P\left(\frac{5}{13}, -\frac{12}{13}\right) = P(\cos \theta, \sin \theta)$,

so $\sin \theta = -\frac{12}{13}$ and $\cos \theta = \frac{5}{13}$.

5. $P\left(\frac{\sqrt{2}}{2}, \frac{\sqrt{2}}{2}\right) = P(\cos \theta, \sin \theta)$,

so $\sin \theta = \frac{\sqrt{2}}{2}$ and $\cos \theta = \frac{\sqrt{2}}{2}$.

6. $\sin -240° = \sin(-240° + 360°)$

$= \sin 120°$

$= \frac{\sqrt{3}}{2}$

7. $\cos \frac{10\pi}{3} = \cos \left(\frac{10\pi}{3} - 2\pi\right)$

$= \cos \frac{4\pi}{3}$

$= -\frac{1}{2}$

8. Notice in the graph that the values of the function for 0° and 720° are both 0 and that every 720° the function repeats its values. Therefore, the period is 720°.

9. The function will repeat itself every 2 seconds, so the period is 2 seconds.

10. Plot some points to give an idea of the graph of the function.

At $t = 0$, $h = -2$;
$t = 2$, $h = -2$;
$t = \frac{2+0}{2} = 1$, $h = 2$;
$t = \frac{1+0}{2} = \frac{1}{2}$, $h = 0$;
$t = \frac{2+1}{2} = \frac{3}{2}$, $h = 0$.

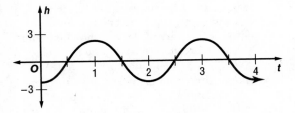

Pages 743-745 Practice and Apply

11. $P\left(-\frac{3}{5}, \frac{4}{5}\right) = P(\cos\theta, \sin\theta)$,
so $\sin\theta = \frac{4}{5}$ and $\cos\theta = -\frac{3}{5}$.

12. $P\left(-\frac{12}{13}, -\frac{5}{13}\right) = P(\cos\theta, \sin\theta)$,
so $\sin\theta = -\frac{5}{13}$ and $\cos\theta = -\frac{12}{13}$.

13. $P\left(\frac{8}{17}, \frac{15}{17}\right) = P(\cos\theta, \sin\theta)$,
so $\sin\theta = \frac{15}{17}$ and $\cos\theta = \frac{8}{17}$.

14. $P\left(\frac{\sqrt{3}}{2}, -\frac{1}{2}\right) = P(\cos\theta, \sin\theta)$,
so $\sin\theta = -\frac{1}{2}$ and $\cos\theta = \frac{\sqrt{3}}{2}$.

15. $P\left(-\frac{1}{2}, \frac{\sqrt{3}}{2}\right) = P(\cos\theta, \sin\theta)$,
so $\sin\theta = \frac{\sqrt{3}}{2}$ and $\cos\theta = -\frac{1}{2}$.

16. $P(0.6, 0.8) = P(\cos\theta, \sin\theta)$,
so $\sin\theta = 0.8$ and $\cos\theta = 0.6$.

17. $\sin 690° = \sin (690° - 360°)$
$= \sin 330°$
$= -\frac{1}{2}$

18. $\cos 750° = \cos [750° - 2(360°)]$
$= \cos 30°$
$= \frac{\sqrt{3}}{2}$

19. $\cos 5\pi = \cos [5\pi - 2(2\pi)]$
$= \cos \pi$
$= -1$

20. $\sin\left(\frac{14\pi}{6}\right) = \sin\left[\frac{14\pi}{6} - 2\pi\right]$
$= \sin \frac{\pi}{3}$
$= \frac{\sqrt{3}}{2}$

21. $\sin\left(-\frac{3\pi}{2}\right) = \sin\left(-\frac{3\pi}{2} + 2\pi\right)$
$= \sin \frac{\pi}{2}$
$= 1$

22. $\cos (-225°) = \cos (-225° + 360°)$
$= \cos 135°$
$= -\frac{\sqrt{2}}{2}$

23. $\frac{\cos 60° + \sin 30°}{4} = \frac{\frac{1}{2} + \frac{1}{2}}{4}$
$= \frac{1}{4}$

24. $3(\sin 60°)(\cos 30°) = 3\left(\frac{\sqrt{3}}{2}\right)\left(\frac{\sqrt{3}}{2}\right)$
$= 3\left(\frac{3}{4}\right)$
$= \frac{9}{4}$

25. $\sin 30° - \sin 60° = \frac{1}{2} - \frac{\sqrt{3}}{2}$
$= \frac{1 - \sqrt{3}}{2}$

26. $\frac{4\cos 330° + 2\sin 60°}{3} = \frac{4\left(\frac{\sqrt{3}}{2}\right) + 2\left(\frac{\sqrt{3}}{2}\right)}{3}$
$= \frac{2\sqrt{3} + \sqrt{3}}{3}$
$= 3\frac{\sqrt{3}}{3}$
$= \sqrt{3}$

27. $12(\sin 150°)(\cos 150°) = 12\left(\frac{1}{2}\right)\left(-\frac{\sqrt{3}}{2}\right)$
$= 12\left(-\frac{\sqrt{3}}{4}\right)$
$= -3\sqrt{3}$

28. $(\sin 30°)^2 + (\cos 30°)^2 = \left(\frac{1}{2}\right)^2 + \left(\frac{\sqrt{3}}{2}\right)^2$
$= \frac{1}{4} + \frac{3}{4}$
$= \frac{4}{4}$
$= 1$

29. Notice in the graph that the values of the function for $\theta = 0$ and $\theta = 6$ are both 0 and that every 6 units the function repeats its values. Therefore, the period is 6.

30. Notice in the graph that the values of the function for $x = 0$ and $x = 9$ are both 0 and that every 9 units the function repeats itself. Therefore, the period is 9.

31. Notice in the graph that the values of the function for $\theta = 0$ and $\theta = 2\pi$ are both 1 and that every 2π units the function repeats itself. Therefore, the period is 2π.

32. Notice in the graph that the values of the function for $x = 0$ and $x = 8$ are both 0 and that every 8 units the function repeats itself. Therefore, the period is 8.

33. If the string vibrates 440 cycles per second, then it goes through one cycle every $\frac{1}{440}$ second. Therefore, the period is $\frac{1}{440}$ second.

34.

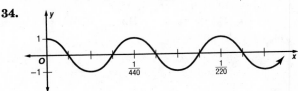

35. Divide 360° into 6 equal parts; $\frac{360°}{6} = 60°$;

Each vertex is at a multiple of 60°.

Vertex 1 at 0° or (1, 0).

Vertex 2 at 60° or $\left(\frac{1}{2}, \frac{\sqrt{3}}{2}\right)$.

Vertex 3 at 2(60°) = 120° or $\left(-\frac{1}{2}, \frac{\sqrt{3}}{2}\right)$.

Vertex 4 at 3(60°) = 180° or (−1, 0).

Vertex 5 at 4(60°) = 240° or $\left(-\frac{1}{2}, -\frac{\sqrt{3}}{2}\right)$.

Vertex 6 at 5(60°) = 300° or $\left(\frac{1}{2}, -\frac{\sqrt{3}}{2}\right)$.

36. $\sin 0 = 0$ ($R = 425$) when $\frac{\pi}{365}(d - 60) = 0$ or $d = 60$;

$\sin \frac{\pi}{2} = 1$ ($R = 625$, maximum) when $\frac{\pi}{365}(d - 60) = \frac{\pi}{2}$ or $d = 242.5$;

$\sin \pi = 0$ ($R = 425$) when $\frac{\pi}{365}(d - 60) = \pi$ or $d = 425$;

$\sin \frac{3\pi}{2} = -1$ ($R = 225$, minimum) when $\frac{\pi}{365}(d - 60) = \frac{3\pi}{2}$ or $d = 607.5$;

$d = 60$ is 60th day of year;

$d = 242.5$ is 242.5 day of year or August/September;

$d = 425$ (425 − 365 = 60) is 60th day of following year;

$d = 607.5$ (607.5 − 365 = 242.5) is August/September of following year;

The population is around 425 near the 60th day of the year. It rises to around 625 in August/September. It falls to around 425 again the 60th day of the following year. It continues to drop to around 225 in August/September of the same following year.

37. slope $= \frac{\text{rise}}{\text{run}} = \frac{y}{x}$

38. $\tan \theta = \frac{y}{x}$

39. product of perpendicular slopes is −1;

$\left(\frac{y}{x}\right)\left(-\frac{x}{y}\right) = -1$;

slope of any line perpendicular to $\overline{OP} = -\frac{x}{y}$

40. $-\cot \theta = \frac{x}{y}$

41. $\tan 60° = \frac{y}{x} = \frac{\frac{\sqrt{3}}{2}}{\frac{1}{2}} = \sqrt{3}$

42. $-\cot 60° = -\frac{x}{y} = -\frac{\frac{1}{2}}{\frac{\sqrt{3}}{2}} = -\frac{1}{\sqrt{3}} = -\frac{\sqrt{3}}{3}$

43. For the sine function,
Domain = {all reals} and
Range = {−1 ≤ y ≤ 1};
For the cosine function,
Domain = {all reals} and
Range = {−1 ≤ y ≤ 1}.

44. Answers should include the following.
- Over the course of one period both the sine and cosine function attain their maximum value once and their minimum value once. From the maximum to the minimum the functions decrease slowly at first, then decrease more quickly and return to a slow rate of change as they come into the minimum. Similarly, the functions rise slowly from their minimum. They begin to increase more rapidly as they pass the halfway point, and then begin to rise more slowly as they increase into the maximum. Annual temperature fluctuations behave in exactly the same manner.
- The maximum value of the sine function is 1 so the maximum temperature would be 50 + 25(1) or 75°F. Similarly, the minimum value would be 50 + 25(−1) or 25°F. The average temperature over this time period occurs when the sine function takes on a value of 0. In this case that would be 50°F.

45. A; $\overline{AC} = 5$

$\sin \theta = \frac{\text{opp}}{\text{hyp}} = \frac{\overline{AC}}{\overline{AD}}$

$\sin 45° = \frac{5}{\overline{AD}}$

$\overline{AD} = \frac{5}{\sin 45°} = \frac{5}{\frac{\sqrt{2}}{2}} = \frac{10}{\sqrt{2}} = \frac{10\sqrt{2}}{2} = 5\sqrt{2}$

46. $\tan 1830° = \tan [1830° - 5(360°)]$

$= \tan 30°$

$= \frac{\frac{1}{2}}{\frac{\sqrt{3}}{2}}$

$= \frac{\sqrt{3}}{3}$

Page 745 Maintain Your Skills

47. Begin with the Law of Cosines, since the measures of two sides and the included angle are given.

$c^2 = a^2 + b^2 - 2ab \cos C$

$c^2 = 17^2 + 15^2 - 2(17)(15) \cos 45°$

$c^2 = 514 - 255\sqrt{2}$

$c \approx 12.4$

$\frac{\sin A}{a} = \frac{\sin C}{c}$

$\frac{\sin A}{17} \approx \frac{\sin 45°}{12.4}$

$\sin A \approx \frac{17 \sin 45°}{12.4}$

$A \approx 76°$

$B \approx 180° - (76° + 45°) \approx 59°$

Therefore, $c \approx 12.4$, $A \approx 76°$, and $B \approx 59°$.

48. Begin with the Law of Cosines, since the measures of three sides are given.

$$a^2 = b^2 + c^2 - 2bc \cos A$$
$$5^2 = 8^2 + 9^2 - 2(8)(9) \cos A$$
$$\cos A = \frac{5}{6}$$
$$A \approx 33.6° \approx 34°$$

When solving this problem by the Law of Sines, angle measures were rounded to the nearest tenth of a degree until the final step of the solution.

$$\frac{\sin B}{b} = \frac{\sin A}{a}$$
$$\frac{\sin B}{8} \approx \frac{\sin 33.6°}{5}$$
$$\sin B \approx \frac{8 \sin 33.6°}{5}$$
$$B \approx 62°$$
$$C \approx 180° - (34° + 62°) \approx 84°$$

Therefore, $A \approx 34°$, $B \approx 62°$, and $C \approx 84°$.

49. Area $= \frac{1}{2}ac \sin B$

$= \frac{1}{2}(11)(5) \sin 79°$

≈ 27.0

To the nearest tenth, the area is 27.0 in^2.

50. Area $= \frac{1}{2}bc \sin A$

$= \frac{1}{2}(4)(7) \sin 63°$

≈ 12.5

To the nearest tenth, the area is 12.5 m^2.

51. $300 - 260 = 40$
$340 - 300 = 40$
The values 260 and 340 are one standard deviation below and above the mean, respectively. Therefore, about 68% of the data are between 260 and 340.
$0.68(10,000) = 6800$
6800 light bulbs will last between 260 and 340 days.

52. $300 - 220 = 80 = 2(40)$
$380 - 300 = 80 = 2(40)$
The values 220 and 380 are two standard deviations below and above the mean, respectively. Therefore, about 95% of the data are between 220 and 380.
$0.95(10,000) = 9500$
9500 light bulbs will last between 220 and 380 days.

53. The value 300 is at the mean. Therefore, 50% of the data are below 300.
$0.50(10,000) = 5000$
5000 light bulbs will last fewer than 300 days.

54. The value 300 is at the mean. Therefore, 50% of the data are above 300.
$0.50(10,000) = 5000$
5000 light bulbs will last more than 300 days.

55. $680 - 300 = 80 = 2(40)$
The value 380 is two standard deviations above the mean. Therefore, about 2.5% of the data are more than 380.
$0.025(10,000) = 250$
250 light bulbs will last more than 380 days.

56. $300 - 180 = 120 = 3(40)$
The value 180 is three standard deviations below the mean. Therefore, about 0.5% of the data are less than 180.
$0.005(10,000) = 50$
50 light bulbs last fewer than 180 days.

57. $a_1 = 3$, $r = 1.2$
An infinite geometric series for which $|r| \geq 1$ does not have a sum.

58. $16, 4, 1, \frac{1}{4}, \ldots$

$a_1 = 16$, $r = \frac{4}{16} = \frac{1}{4}$

$S = \frac{a_1}{1 - r} = \frac{16}{1 - \frac{1}{4}} = \frac{16}{\frac{3}{4}} = 16 \cdot \frac{4}{3} = \frac{64}{3}$

The sum of the series is $\frac{64}{3}$.

59. $\sum_{n=1}^{\infty} 13(-0.625)^{n-1}$

$a_1 = 13$, $r = -0.625$

$S = \frac{a_1}{1 - r} = \frac{13}{1 - (-0.625)} = 8$

Thus, $\sum_{n=1}^{\infty} 13(-0.625)^{n-1} = 8$.

60.

$$\begin{array}{r|rrr} 2 & 4 & -13 & 10 \\ & & 8 & -10 \\ \hline & 4 & -5 & 0 \end{array}$$

$(4x^2 - 13x + 10) \div (x - 2) = 4x - 5$

61.

$$\begin{array}{r|rrr} -6 & 2 & 21 & 54 \\ & & -12 & -54 \\ \hline & 2 & 9 & 0 \end{array}$$

$(2x^2 + 21x + 54) \div (x + 6) = 2x + 9$

62.

$$\begin{array}{r|rrrr} -1 & 5 & 1 & 0 & -7 \\ & & -5 & 4 & -4 \\ \hline & 5 & -4 & 4 & -11 \end{array}$$

$(5y^3 + y^2 - 7) \div (y + 1) = 5y^2 - 4y + 4 - \frac{11}{y + 1}$

63.

$$\begin{array}{r|rrr} 3 & 2 & 1 & -16 \\ & & 6 & 21 \\ \hline & 2 & 7 & 5 \end{array}$$

$(2y^2 + y - 16) \div (y - 3) = 2y + 7 + \frac{5}{y - 3}$

64. $\sin \theta = 0.3420$
$\theta \approx 20°$

65. $\cos \theta = -0.3420$
$\theta \approx 110°$

66. $\tan \theta = 3.2709$
$\theta \approx 73°$

67. $\tan \theta = 5.6713$
$\theta \approx 80°$

68. $\sin \theta = 0.8290$
$\theta \approx 56°$

69. $\cos \theta = 0.0175$
$\theta \approx 89°$

13-7 Inverse Trigonometric Functions

Page 749 Check for Understanding

1. Restricted domains are denoted with a capital letter.

2. Sample answer:

$\text{Cos } 45° = \frac{\sqrt{2}}{2}$;

$\text{Cos}^{-1} \frac{\sqrt{2}}{2} = 45°$

3. They are inverses of each other.

4. $\tan \theta = x$

$\theta = \text{Arctan } x$

5. $\cos \alpha = 0.5$

$\alpha = \text{Arccos } 0.5$

6. $x = \text{Cos}^{-1} \frac{\sqrt{2}}{2}$

x is the value between 0° and 180° whose cosine is $\frac{\sqrt{2}}{2}$.

$x = 45°$

7. $\text{Arctan } 0 = x$

x is the value between −90° and 90° whose tangent is 0.

$x = 0°$

8. KEYSTROKES: $\boxed{\text{2nd}}$ [TAN^{-1}] $\boxed{(-)}$ $\boxed{\text{2nd}}$ [$\sqrt{}$] 3 $\boxed{)}$

$\boxed{\div}$ 3 $\boxed{)}$ $\boxed{\text{ENTER}}$ −.5235987756

$\text{Tan}^{-1}\left(-\frac{\sqrt{3}}{3}\right) = -\frac{\pi}{6} \approx -0.52$

9. KEYSTROKES: $\boxed{\text{2nd}}$ [COS^{-1}] $\boxed{(-)}$ 1 $\boxed{)}$ $\boxed{\text{ENTER}}$

3.141592654

$\text{Cos}^{-1}(-1) = \pi \approx 3.14$

10. KEYSTROKES: $\boxed{\text{COS}}$ $\boxed{\text{2nd}}$ [COS^{-1}] 2 $\boxed{\div}$ 9 $\boxed{)}$

$\boxed{)}$ $\boxed{\text{ENTER}}$ .2222222222

$\cos\left(\text{Cos}^{-1}\frac{2}{9}\right) = \frac{2}{9} \approx 0.22$

11. KEYSTROKES: $\boxed{\text{SIN}}$ $\boxed{\text{2nd}}$ [SIN^{-1}] 3 $\boxed{\div}$ 4 $\boxed{)}$

$\boxed{)}$ $\boxed{\text{ENTER}}$ .75

$\sin\left(\text{Sin}^{-1}\frac{3}{4}\right) = \frac{3}{4} = 0.75$

12. KEYSTROKES: $\boxed{\text{SIN}}$ $\boxed{\text{2nd}}$ [COS^{-1}] 3 $\boxed{\div}$ 4 $\boxed{)}$

$\boxed{)}$ $\boxed{\text{ENTER}}$ .6614378278

$\sin\left(\text{Cos}^{-1}\frac{3}{4}\right) \approx 0.66$

13. KEYSTROKES: $\boxed{\text{TAN}}$ $\boxed{\text{2nd}}$ [SIN^{-1}] 1 $\boxed{\div}$ 2 $\boxed{)}$

$\boxed{)}$ $\boxed{\text{ENTER}}$ .5773502692

$\tan\left(\text{Sin}^{-1}\frac{1}{2}\right) \approx 0.58$

14. $\text{Sin } \theta = \frac{\text{opp}}{\text{hyp}}$

$\text{Sin } \theta = \frac{9}{18}$

$\text{Sin } \theta = \frac{1}{2}$

$\theta = \text{Sin}^{-1}\left(\frac{1}{2}\right)$

$\theta = 30°$

Pages 749–751 Practice and Apply

15. $\alpha = \text{Sin } \beta$

$\beta = \text{Arcsin } \alpha$

16. $\text{Tan } a = b$

$a = \text{Arctan } b$

17. $\text{Cos } y = x$

$y = \text{Arccos } x$

18. $\text{Sin } 30° = \frac{1}{2}$

$30° = \text{Arcsin } \frac{1}{2}$

19. $\text{Cos } 45° = y$

$\text{Arccos } y = 45°$

20. $-\frac{4}{3} = \text{Tan } x$

$\text{Arctan}\left(-\frac{4}{3}\right) = x$

21. $x = \text{Cos}^{-1} \frac{1}{2}$

x is the value between 0° and 180° whose cosine is $\frac{1}{2}$.

$x = 60°$

22. $\text{Sin}^{-1} \frac{1}{2} = x$

x is the value between −90° and 90° whose sine is $\frac{1}{2}$.

$x = 30°$

23. $\text{Arctan } 1 = x$

x is the value between −90° and 90° whose tangent is 1.

$x = 45°$

24. $x = \text{Arctan } \frac{\sqrt{3}}{3}$

x is the value between −90° and 90° whose tangent is $\frac{\sqrt{3}}{3}$.

$x = 30°$

25. $x = \text{Sin}^{-1} \frac{1}{\sqrt{2}}$

x is the value between −90° and 90° whose sine is $\frac{1}{\sqrt{2}}$.

$x = 45°$

26. $x = \text{Cos}^{-1} 0$

x is the value between 0° and 180° whose cosine is 0.

$x = 90°$

27. KEYSTROKES: $\boxed{\text{2nd}}$ [COS^{-1}] $\boxed{(-)}$ 1 $\boxed{\div}$ 2 $\boxed{)}$

$\boxed{\text{ENTER}}$ 2.094395102

$\text{Cos}^{-1}\left(-\frac{1}{2}\right) \approx 2.09$

28. KEYSTROKES: $\boxed{\text{2nd}}$ [SIN^{-1}] $\boxed{\text{2nd}}$ [π] $\boxed{\div}$ 2 $\boxed{)}$

$\boxed{\text{ENTER}}$ ERR

$\text{Sin}^{-1} \frac{\pi}{2}$ does not exist.

29. KEYSTROKES: $\boxed{\text{2nd}}$ [TAN^{-1}] $\boxed{\text{2nd}}$ [$\sqrt{}$] 3 $\boxed{)}$ $\boxed{\div}$

3 $\boxed{)}$ $\boxed{\text{ENTER}}$ .5235987756

$\text{Arctan } \frac{\sqrt{3}}{3} \approx 0.52$

30. KEYSTROKES: $\boxed{\text{2nd}}$ [COS^{-1}] $\boxed{\text{2nd}}$ [$\sqrt{}$] 3 $\boxed{)}$

$\boxed{\div}$ 2 $\boxed{)}$ $\boxed{\text{ENTER}}$ .5235987756

$\text{Arccos } \frac{\sqrt{3}}{2} \approx 0.52$

31. KEYSTROKES: SIN 2nd [SIN⁻¹] 1 ÷ 2)
) ENTER .5

$$\sin\left(\text{Sin}^{-1}\frac{1}{2}\right) = 0.5$$

32. KEYSTROKES: 1 ÷ (TAN 2nd [SIN⁻¹] 5
÷ 6)))) ENTER
.6633249581

$$\cot\left(\text{Sin}^{-1}\frac{5}{6}\right) \approx 0.66$$

33. KEYSTROKES: TAN 2nd [COS⁻¹] 6 ÷ 7)
) ENTER .6009252126

$$\tan\left(\text{Cos}^{-1}\frac{6}{7}\right) \approx 0.60$$

34. KEYSTROKES: SIN 2nd [TAN⁻¹] 2nd [√] 3
) ÷ 3)) ENTER .5

$$\text{Sin}\left(\text{Arctan }\frac{\sqrt{3}}{3}\right) = 0.5$$

35. KEYSTROKES: COS 2nd [SIN⁻¹] 3 ÷ 5)
) ENTER .8

$$\cos\left(\text{Arcsin }\frac{3}{5}\right) = 0.8$$

36. KEYSTROKES: 1 ÷ (TAN 2nd [SIN⁻¹] 7
÷ 9)))) ENTER
.8081220356

$$\cot\left(\text{Sin}^{-1}\frac{7}{9}\right) \approx 0.81$$

37. KEYSTROKES: COS 2nd [TAN⁻¹] 2nd [√] 3
))) ENTER .5

$$\cos(\text{Tan}^{-1}\sqrt{3}) = 0.5$$

38. KEYSTROKES: TAN 2nd [TAN⁻¹] 3))
ENTER 3

$$\tan(\text{Arctan } 3) = 3$$

39. KEYSTROKES: COS 2nd [COS⁻¹] (−) 1 ÷ 2
)) ENTER −.5

$$\cos\left[\text{Arccos}\left(-\frac{1}{2}\right)\right] = -0.5$$

40. KEYSTROKES: 2nd [SIN⁻¹] TAN 2nd [π] ÷ 4
)) ENTER 1.570796327

$$\text{Sin}^{-1}\left(\tan\frac{\pi}{4}\right) = \frac{\pi}{2} \approx 1.57$$

41. KEYSTROKES: COS 2nd [COS⁻¹] 2nd [√] 2
) ÷ 2) (−) 2nd [π] ÷ 2
) ENTER .7071067812

$$\cos\left(\text{Cos}^{-1}\frac{\sqrt{2}}{2} - \frac{\pi}{2}\right) = \frac{\sqrt{2}}{2} \approx 0.71$$

42. KEYSTROKES: 2nd [COS⁻¹] 2nd [SIN⁻¹] 90)
) ENTER ERR

$$\text{Cos}^{-1}(\text{Sin}^{-1} 90) \text{ does not exist.}$$

43. KEYSTROKES: SIN 2 2nd [COS⁻¹] 3 ÷ 5)
) ENTER .96

$$\sin\left(2\,\text{Cos}^{-1}\frac{3}{5}\right) = 0.96$$

44. KEYSTROKES: SIN 2 2nd [SIN⁻¹] 1 ÷ 2)
) ENTER .8660254038

$$\sin\left(2\,\text{Sin}^{-1}\frac{1}{2}\right) = \frac{\sqrt{3}}{2} \approx 0.87$$

45. $\cos\theta = 0.5$
$\theta = \cos^{-1} 0.5$
$\theta = 60°$
The rescue boat should travel 60° south of west.

46. $\frac{H}{D} = \frac{1}{4}\tan\theta$

$2 = \frac{1}{4}\tan\theta$

$8 = \tan\theta$

$\theta = \text{Tan}^{-1} 8$

$\theta \approx 83°$

The angle should be 83°.

47. No; with this point on the terminal side of the throwing angle θ, the measure of θ is found by solving the equation $\tan\theta = \frac{17}{18}$. Thus $\theta = \tan^{-1}\frac{17}{18}$ or about 43.3°, which is greater than the 40° requirement.

48. $\cos\theta = \sqrt{\frac{I_t}{I_0}}$

$\cos\theta = \sqrt{\frac{1}{4}}$

$\cos\theta = \frac{1}{2}$

$\theta = \text{Cos}^{-1}\frac{1}{2}$

$\theta = 60°$

The transmission axis of the filter makes a 60° angle with the horizontal.

49. $3x + 5y = 7$

$y = -\frac{3}{5}x + \frac{7}{5}$

$m = -\frac{3}{5}$

$\tan\theta = -\frac{3}{5}$

$\theta = \text{Tan}^{-1}\left(-\frac{3}{5}\right)$

$\theta \approx -31°$

The angle is 31°.

50. $2x + 5y = 8$ or $y = -\frac{2}{5}x + \frac{8}{5}$; $m = -\frac{2}{5}$

$6x - y = -8$ or $y = 6x + 8$; $m = 6$

$\theta = \text{Tan}^{-1}\left(-\frac{2}{5}\right) - \text{Tan}^{-1}(6)$

$\theta \approx -102°$

The obtuse angle is 102°.

661

51. Suppose $P(x_1, y_1)$ and $Q(x_2, y_2)$ lie on the line $y = mx + b$. Then $m = \frac{y_2 - y_1}{x_2 - x_1}$. The tangent of the angle θ the line makes with the positive x-axis is equal to the ratio $\frac{\text{opp}}{\text{adj}}$ or $\frac{y_2 - y_1}{x_2 - x_1}$. Thus $\tan \theta = m$.

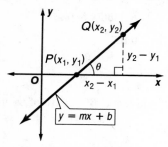

52. Trigonometry is used to determine proper banking angles. Answer should include the following.

- Knowing the velocity of the cars to be traveling on a road and the radius of the curve to be built, then the banking angle can be determined. First find the ratio of the square of the velocity to the product of the acceleration due to gravity and the radius of the curve. Then determine the angle that has this ratio as its tangent. This will be the banking angle for the turn.

- If the speed limit were increased and the banking angle remained the same, then in order to maintain a safe road the curvature would have to be decreased. That is, the radius of the curve would also have to increase, which would make the road less curved.

53. $\tan \theta = \frac{\text{opp}}{\text{adj}}$

$\tan \theta = \frac{10 - 4}{24 - 8 - 8} = \frac{6}{8} = \frac{3}{4}$

$\theta = \text{Tan}^{-1} \frac{3}{4}$

$\theta \approx 37°$

The angle of depression is 37°.

54. D; $\sin \theta = \frac{2}{3}$

$\theta = \text{Sin}^{-1} \frac{2}{3}$

$\cos 2\theta = \cos \left(2 \, \text{Sin}^{-1} \frac{2}{3} \right) = 0.\overline{1} = \frac{1}{9}$

55.

x	0	$\frac{1}{2}$	$\frac{\sqrt{2}}{2}$	$\frac{\sqrt{3}}{2}$	1	$-\frac{1}{2}$	$-\frac{\sqrt{2}}{2}$	$-\frac{\sqrt{3}}{2}$	-1
y	$\frac{\pi}{2}$	$\frac{\pi}{2}$	$\frac{\pi}{2}$	$\frac{\pi}{2}$	$\frac{\pi}{2}$	$\frac{\pi}{2}$	$\frac{\pi}{2}$	$\frac{\pi}{2}$	$\frac{\pi}{2}$

56. $\text{Sin}^{-1} x + \text{Cos}^{-1} x = \frac{\pi}{2}$ for all values of x.

57. From a right triangle perspective, if an acute angle θ has a given sine, say x, then the complementary angle $\frac{\pi}{2} - \theta$ has that same value as its cosine. This can be verified by looking at a right triangle. Therefore, the sum of the angle whose sine is x and the angle whose cosine is x should be $\frac{\pi}{2}$.

58. $\sin(-660°) = \sin [-660 + 2(360°)]$

$= \sin 60°$

$= \frac{\sqrt{3}}{2}$

59. $\cos 25\pi = \cos [25\pi - 12(2\pi)]$

$= \cos \pi$

$= -1$

60. $(\sin 135°)^2 + (\cos -675°)^2$

$= (\sin 135°)^2 + [\cos (-675 + 2 \cdot 360°)]^2$

$= (\sin 135°)^2 + (\cos 45°)^2$

$= \left(-\frac{\sqrt{2}}{2} \right)^2 + \left(\frac{\sqrt{2}}{2} \right)^2$

$= \frac{1}{2} + \frac{1}{2}$

$= 1$

61. $a = 3.1, b = 5.8, A = 30°$

Begin with the Law of Sines, since the measures of two sides and the angle opposite one of them are given.

$\frac{\sin B}{b} = \frac{\sin A}{a}$

$\frac{\sin B}{5.8} = \frac{\sin 30°}{3.1}$

$\sin B = \frac{5.8 \sin 30°}{3.1}$

$\sin B = \frac{2.9}{3.1}$

$B \approx 69°$

$C \approx 180° - (30° + 69°) \approx 81°$

$\frac{\sin C}{c} = \frac{\sin A}{a}$

$\frac{\sin 81°}{c} \approx \frac{\sin 30°}{3.1}$

$c \approx \frac{3.1 \sin 81°}{\sin 30°}$

$c \approx 6.1$

Therefore, $B \approx 69°$, $C \approx 81°$, and $c \approx 6.1$.

62. $a = 9, b = 40, c = 41$

Begin with the Law of Cosines, since the measures of three sides are given.

$a^2 = b^2 + c^2 - 2bc \cos A$

$9^2 = 40^2 + 41^2 - 2(40)(41) \cos A$

$\cos A = \frac{40}{41}$

$A \approx 12.68° \approx 13°$

When solving this problem by the Law of Sines, angle measures were rounded to the nearest tenth of a degree until the final step of the solution.

$\frac{\sin B}{b} = \frac{\sin A}{a}$

$\frac{\sin B}{40} \approx \frac{\sin 12.68°}{9}$

$\sin B \approx \frac{40 \sin 12.68°}{9}$

$B \approx 77°$

$C \approx 180° - (13° + 77°) \approx 90°$

Therefore, $A \approx 13°$, $B \approx 77°$, and $C \approx 90°$.

63. $f(x) = 5x^2 + 6x - 17$

$$\begin{array}{c|rrr} 3 & 5 & 6 & -17 \\ & & 15 & 63 \\ \hline & 5 & 21 & \boxed{46} \end{array}$$

$f(3) = 46$

$$\begin{array}{c|rrr} -4 & 5 & 6 & -17 \\ & & -20 & 56 \\ \hline & 5 & -14 & \boxed{39} \end{array}$$

$f(-4) = 39$

64. $f(x) = -3x^2 + 2x - 1$

$$\begin{array}{c|rrr} 3 & -3 & 2 & -1 \\ & & -9 & -21 \\ \hline & -3 & -7 & \boxed{-22} \end{array}$$

$f(3) = -22$

$$\begin{array}{c|rrr} -4 & -3 & 2 & -1 \\ & & 12 & -56 \\ \hline & -3 & 14 & \boxed{-57} \end{array}$$

$f(-4) = -57$

65. $f(x) = 4x^2 - 10x + 5$

$$\begin{array}{c|rrr} 3 & 4 & -10 & 5 \\ & & 12 & 6 \\ \hline & 4 & 2 & \boxed{11} \end{array}$$

$f(3) = 11$

$$\begin{array}{c|rrr} -4 & 4 & -10 & 5 \\ & & -16 & 104 \\ \hline & 4 & -26 & \boxed{109} \end{array}$$

$f(-4) = 109$

66.
$$h(t) = -16t^2 + 80t + 200$$
$$300 = -16t^2 + 80t + 200$$
$$16t^2 - 80t + 100 = 0$$
$$a = 16, b = -80, c = 100$$
$$t = \frac{-(-80) \pm \sqrt{(-80)^2 - 4(16)(100)}}{2(16)}$$
$$t = \frac{80 \pm 0}{32}$$
$$t = 2.5$$

The rocket reaches its maximum height in 2.5 seconds.

Chapter 13 Study Guide and Review

Page 752 Vocabulary and Concept Check

1. False; coterminal
2. True
3. True
4. False; sec θ
5. True
6. False; law of cosines
7. False; 0°, 90°, 180°, 270°, 360°, or any multiple of these
8. False; 360°
9. False; terminal

Pages 752–756 Lesson–by–Lesson Review

10. $a^2 + b^2 = c^2$
$7^2 + b^2 = 16^2$
$b^2 = 207$
$b \approx 14.4$
$\sin A = \dfrac{a}{c}$
$\sin A = \dfrac{7}{16}$
$A \approx 26°$
$26° + B \approx 90°$
$B \approx 64°$
Therefore, $b \approx 14.4$, $A \approx 26°$, and $B \approx 64°$

11. $25° + B = 90°$
$B = 65°$
$\sin A = \dfrac{a}{c}$
$\sin 25° = \dfrac{a}{6}$
$a = 6 \sin 25°$
$a \approx 2.5$
$\sin B = \dfrac{b}{c}$
$\sin 65° = \dfrac{b}{6}$
$b = 6 \sin 65°$
$b \approx 5.4$
Therefore, $B = 65°$, $a \approx 2.5$, and $b \approx 5.4$.

12. $A + 45° = 90°$
$A = 45°$
$\sin A = \dfrac{a}{c}$
$\sin 45° = \dfrac{a}{12}$
$a = 12 \sin 45°$
$a = 6\sqrt{2}$
$a \approx 8.5$
$\sin B = \dfrac{b}{c}$
$\sin 45° = \dfrac{b}{12}$
$b = 12 \sin 45°$
$b = 6\sqrt{2}$
$b \approx 8.5$
Therefore, $A = 45°$, $a \approx 8.5$, and $b \approx 8.5$.

13. $A + 83° = 90°$
$A = 7°$
$\cos A = \dfrac{b}{c}$
$\cos 7° = \dfrac{\sqrt{31}}{c}$
$c = \dfrac{\sqrt{31}}{\cos 7°}$
$c \approx 5.6$
$\tan B = \dfrac{b}{a}$
$\tan 83° = \dfrac{\sqrt{31}}{a}$
$a = \dfrac{\sqrt{31}}{\tan 83°}$
$a \approx 0.7$
Therefore, $A = 7°$, $a \approx 0.7$, and $c \approx 5.6$.

14. $A + 49° = 90°$
$A = 41°$
$\sin A = \dfrac{a}{c}$
$\sin 41° = \dfrac{9}{c}$
$c = \dfrac{9}{\sin 41°}$
$c \approx 13.7$
$\tan B = \dfrac{b}{a}$
$\tan 49° = \dfrac{b}{9}$
$b = 9 \tan 49°$
$b \approx 10.4$
Therefore, $A = 41°$, $b \approx 10.4$, and $c \approx 13.7$.

15. $\cos A = \dfrac{1}{4}$
$A \approx 76°$
$76° + B \approx 90°$
$B \approx 14°$
$\sin A = \dfrac{a}{c}$
$\sin 76° \approx \dfrac{4}{c}$
$c \approx \dfrac{4}{\sin 76°}$
$c \approx 4.1$
$\tan A = \dfrac{a}{b}$
$\tan 76° \approx \dfrac{4}{b}$
$b \approx \dfrac{4}{\tan 76°}$
$b \approx 1.0$
Therefore, $A \approx 76°$, $B \approx 14°$, $b \approx 1.0$, and $c \approx 4.1$.

16. $255° = 255°\left(\dfrac{\pi \text{ radians}}{180°}\right)$
$= \dfrac{255\pi}{180}$ radians or $\dfrac{17\pi}{12}$

17. $-210° = -210°\left(\dfrac{\pi \text{ radians}}{180°}\right)$
$= -\dfrac{210\pi}{180}$ radians or $-\dfrac{7\pi}{6}$

18. $\dfrac{7\pi}{4} = \left(\dfrac{7\pi}{4} \text{ radians}\right)\left(\dfrac{180°}{\pi \text{ radians}}\right)$
$= \dfrac{1260°}{4}$ or $315°$

19. $-4\pi = (-4\pi \text{ radians})\left(\dfrac{180°}{\pi \text{ radians}}\right)$
$= -720°$

20. A positive angle is $205° + 360° = 565°$.
A negative angle is $205° - 360° = -155°$.

21. A positive angle is $-40° + 360° = 320°$.
A negative angle is $-40° - 360° = 400°$.

22. A positive angle is $\dfrac{4\pi}{3} + 2\pi = \dfrac{10\pi}{3}$.
A negative angle is $\dfrac{4\pi}{3} - 2\pi = -\dfrac{2\pi}{3}$.

23. A positive angle is $-\dfrac{7\pi}{4} + 2\pi = \dfrac{\pi}{4}$.
A negative angle is $-\dfrac{7\pi}{4} - 2\pi = -\dfrac{15\pi}{4}$.

24. $x = 2, y = 5, r = \sqrt{2^2 + 5^2} = \sqrt{29}$
$\sin \theta = \dfrac{y}{r} = \dfrac{5}{\sqrt{29}} = \dfrac{5\sqrt{29}}{29}$
$\cos \theta = \dfrac{x}{r} = \dfrac{2}{\sqrt{29}} = \dfrac{2\sqrt{29}}{29}$
$\tan \theta = \dfrac{y}{x} = \dfrac{5}{2}$
$\csc \theta = \dfrac{r}{y} = \dfrac{\sqrt{29}}{5}$
$\sec \theta = \dfrac{r}{x} = \dfrac{\sqrt{29}}{2}$
$\cot \theta = \dfrac{x}{y} = \dfrac{2}{5}$

25. $x = 15, y = -8, r = \sqrt{(15)^2 + (-8)^2} = 17$
$\sin \theta = \dfrac{y}{r} = \dfrac{-8}{17}$ or $-\dfrac{8}{17}$ $\qquad \csc \theta = \dfrac{r}{y} = \dfrac{17}{-8}$ or $-\dfrac{17}{8}$
$\cos \theta = \dfrac{x}{r} = \dfrac{15}{17}$ $\qquad\qquad\quad \sec \theta = \dfrac{r}{x} = \dfrac{17}{15}$
$\tan \theta = \dfrac{y}{x} = \dfrac{-8}{15}$ or $-\dfrac{8}{15}$ $\qquad \cot \theta = \dfrac{x}{y} = \dfrac{15}{-8}$ or $-\dfrac{15}{8}$

26. The terminal side of 3π lies on the negative
x-axis, so $\cos 3\pi = -1$

27. The terminal side of $120°$ lies in Quadrant II , so
$\theta' = 180° - 120° = 60°$.
The tangent function is negative in Quadrant II;
$\tan 120° = -\tan 60° = -\sqrt{3}$.

28. The terminal side of $\dfrac{5\pi}{4}$ lies in Quadrant III, so
$\theta' = \dfrac{5\pi}{4} - \pi = \dfrac{\pi}{4}$.
The sine function is negative in Quadrant III;
$\sin \dfrac{5\pi}{4} = -\sin \dfrac{\pi}{4} = -\dfrac{\sqrt{2}}{2}$.

29. The terminal side of $-30°$ lies in Quadrant IV, so
$\theta' = 30°$.
The secant function is positive in Quadrant IV;
$\sec(-30°) = \sec(30°) = \dfrac{1}{\cos(30°)} = \dfrac{1}{\frac{\sqrt{3}}{2}} = \dfrac{2\sqrt{3}}{3}$.

30. $a = 24, b = 36, A = 64°$
Since angle A is acute, find $b \sin A$ and compare it with a.
$b \sin A = 36 \sin 64° \approx 32.4$
Since $a < b \sin A$ $(24 < 32.4)$, there is no solution.

31. $A = 40°$, $b = 10$, $a = 8$

Since angle A is acute, find $b \sin A$ and compare it with a.

$b \sin A = 10 \sin 40° \approx 6.4$

Since $b > a > b \sin A$ $(10 > 8 > 6.4)$, there are two solutions.

When solving this problem by the Law of Sines, angle measures were rounded to the nearest hundredth of a degree until the final step of the solution.

Case :1 Acute angle B

$$\frac{\sin B}{b} = \frac{\sin A}{a}$$
$$\frac{\sin b}{10} = \frac{\sin 40°}{8}$$
$$\sin B = \frac{5 \sin 40°}{4}$$
$$B \approx 53.46° \approx 53°$$
$$C \approx 180° - (40° + 53.46°) \approx 86.54°$$
$$\frac{\sin C}{c} = \frac{\sin A}{a}$$
$$\frac{\sin 86.54°}{c} \approx \frac{\sin 40°}{8}$$
$$c \approx \frac{8 \sin 86.54°}{\sin 40°}$$
$$c \approx 12.4$$

Therefore, $B \approx 53°$, $C \approx 87°$, and $c \approx 12.4$.

Case 2: Obtuse angle B

$$B \approx 180° - 53.46° = 126.54° \approx 127°$$
$$C \approx 180° - (40° + 126.54°) \approx 13.46° \approx 13°$$
$$\frac{\sin C}{c} = \frac{\sin A}{a}$$
$$\frac{\sin 13.46°}{c} \approx \frac{\sin 40°}{8}$$
$$C \approx \frac{8 \sin 13.46°}{\sin 40°}$$
$$C \approx 2.9$$

Therefore, $B \approx 127°$, $C \approx 13°$, and $c \approx 2.9$.

32. $b = 10$, $c = 15$, $C = 66°$

Since angle C is acute and $c > b$ $(15 > 10)$, there is one solution.

When solving this problem by the Law of Sines, angle measures were rounded to the nearest hundredth of a degree until the final step of the solution.

$$\frac{\sin B}{b} = \frac{\sin C}{c}$$
$$\frac{\sin B}{10} = \frac{\sin 66°}{15}$$
$$\sin B = \frac{2 \sin 66°}{3}$$
$$B \approx 37.52° \approx 38°$$
$$A \approx 180° - (37.52° + 66°) \approx 76.48° \approx 76°$$
$$\frac{\sin A}{a} = \frac{\sin C}{c}$$
$$\frac{\sin 76.48°}{a} \approx \frac{\sin 66°}{15}$$
$$a \approx \frac{15 \sin 76.48°}{\sin 66°}$$
$$a \approx 16.0$$

Therefore $A \approx 76°$, $B \approx 38°$, and $a \approx 16.0$.

33. $A = 82°$, $a = 9$, $b = 12$

Since angle A is acute, find $b \sin A$ and compare it with a.

$b \sin A = 12 \sin 82° \approx 11.9$

Since $a < b \sin A$ $(9 < 11.9)$, there is no solution.

34. $A = 105°$, $a = 18$, $b = 14$

Since angle A is obtuse and $a > b$ $(18 > 14)$, there is one solution.

When solving this problem by the Law of Sines, angle measures were rounded to the nearest tenth of a degree until the final step of the solution.

$$\frac{\sin B}{b} = \frac{\sin A}{a}$$
$$\frac{\sin B}{14} = \frac{\sin 105°}{18}$$
$$\sin B = \frac{7 \sin 105°}{9}$$
$$B \approx 48.7° \approx 49°$$
$$C \approx 180° - (105° + 48.7°) \approx 26.3° \approx 26°$$
$$\frac{\sin C}{c} = \frac{\sin A}{a}$$
$$\frac{\sin 26.3°}{c} \approx \frac{\sin 105°}{18}$$
$$c \approx \frac{18 \sin 26.3°}{\sin 105°}$$
$$c \approx 8.3$$

Therefore, $B \approx 49°$, $C \approx 26°$, and $c \approx 8.3$.

35. $B = 46°$, $C = 83°$, $b = 65$

Since two angles are given, there is one solution.

$$A = 180° - (46° + 83°) = 51°$$
$$\frac{\sin A}{a} = \frac{\sin B}{b}$$
$$\frac{\sin 51°}{a} = \frac{\sin 46°}{65}$$
$$a = \frac{65 \sin 51°}{\sin 46°}$$
$$a \approx 70.2$$
$$\frac{\sin C}{c} = \frac{\sin B}{b}$$
$$\frac{\sin 83°}{c} = \frac{\sin 46°}{65}$$
$$c = \frac{65 \sin 83°}{\sin 46°}$$
$$c \approx 89.7$$

Therefore, $A = 51°$, $a \approx 70.2$, and $c \approx 89.7$.

36. Begin with the Law of Cosines, since the measures of two sides and the included angle are given.

$$c^2 = a^2 + b^2 - 2ab \cos C$$
$$c^2 = 8^2 + 7^2 - 2(8)(7) \cos 35°$$
$$c^2 = 113 - 112 \cos 35°$$
$$c \approx 4.6$$

When solving this problem by the Law of Sines, angle measures were rounded to the nearest tenth of a degree until the final step of the solution.

$$\frac{\sin B}{b} = \frac{\sin C}{c}$$
$$\frac{\sin B}{7} \approx \frac{\sin 35°}{4.6}$$
$$\sin B \approx \frac{7 \sin 35°}{4.6}$$
$$B \approx 60.8°$$
$$A \approx 180° - (60.8° + 35°) \approx 84.2°$$

Therefore, $c \approx 4.6$, $A \approx 84°$, and $B \approx 61°$.

37. Begin with the Law of Sines, since the measures of two angles and a side are given.

$$\frac{\sin A}{a} = \frac{\sin B}{b}$$
$$\frac{\sin 45°}{a} = \frac{\sin 30°}{20}$$
$$a = \frac{20 \sin 45°}{\sin 30°}$$
$$a = 20\sqrt{2}$$
$$a \approx 28.3$$
$$C = 180° - (45° + 30°) = 105°$$
$$\frac{\sin C}{c} = \frac{\sin B}{b}$$
$$\frac{\sin 105°}{c} = \frac{\sin 30°}{20}$$
$$c = \frac{20 \sin 105°}{\sin 30°}$$
$$c = 40 \sin 105°$$
$$c \approx 38.6$$

Therefore, $C = 105°$, $a \approx 28.3$, and $c \approx 38.6$.

38. Begin with the Law of Cosines, since the measures of three sides are given.

$$b^2 = a^2 + c^2 - 2ac \cos B$$
$$13^2 = 11^2 + 15^2 - 2(11)(15)\cos B$$
$$\cos B = \frac{177}{330}$$
$$B \approx 57.56° \approx 58°$$

When solving this problem by the Law of Sines, angle measures were rounded to the nearest hundredth of a degree until the final step of the solution.

$$\frac{\sin C}{c} = \frac{\sin B}{b}$$
$$\frac{\sin C}{15} \approx \frac{\sin 57.56°}{13}$$
$$\sin C \approx \frac{15 \sin 57.56°}{13}$$
$$C \approx 76.85°$$
$$A \approx 180° - (57.56° + 76.85°) \approx 45.59°$$

Therefore, $A \approx 46°$, $B \approx 58°$, and $C \approx 77°$.

39. Begin with the Law of Cosines, since the measures of two sides and the included angle are given.

$$c^2 = a^2 + b^2 - 2ab \cos C$$
$$c^2 = 4^2 + 7^2 - 2(4)(7) \cos 65°$$
$$c^2 = 65 - 56 \cos 65°$$
$$c \approx 6.43 \approx 6.4$$

When solving this problem by the Law of Sines, angle measures were rounded to the nearest tenth of a degree until the final step of the solution.

$$\frac{\sin B}{b} = \frac{\sin C}{c}$$
$$\frac{\sin B}{7} \approx \frac{\sin 65°}{6.43}$$
$$\sin B \approx \frac{7 \sin 65°}{6.43}$$
$$B \approx 80.6°$$
$$A \approx 180° - (80.6° + 65°) \approx 34.4°$$

Therefore, $c \approx 6.4$, $A \approx 34°$, and $B \approx 81°$.

40. Since A is acute and $b \sin A = 8 \sin 36° \approx 4.7$ where $b > a > b \sin A$ $(8 > 6 > 4.7)$, there are two solutions. Begin with the Law of Sines, since the measures of two sides and the angle opposite one of them are given.

When solving this problem by the Law of Sines, angle measures were rounded to the nearest tenth of a degree until the final step of the solution.

Case 1: Acute angle B

$$\frac{\sin B}{b} = \frac{\sin A}{a}$$
$$\frac{\sin B}{8} = \frac{\sin 36°}{6}$$
$$\sin B = \frac{4 \sin 36°}{3}$$
$$B \approx 51.6° \approx 52°$$
$$C \approx 180° - (36° + 51.6°) \approx 92.4°$$
$$\frac{\sin C}{c} = \frac{\sin A}{a}$$
$$\frac{\sin 92.4°}{c} \approx \frac{\sin 36°}{6}$$
$$c \approx \frac{6 \sin 92.4°}{\sin 36°}$$
$$c \approx 10.2$$

Therefore, $B \approx 52°$, $C \approx 92°$, and $c \approx 10.2$.

Case 2: Obtuse angle B

$$B \approx 180° - 51.6° \approx 128.4° \approx 128°$$
$$C \approx 180° - (36° + 128.4°) \approx 15.6° \approx 16°$$
$$\frac{\sin C}{c} = \frac{\sin A}{a}$$
$$\frac{\sin 15.6°}{c} \approx \frac{\sin 36°}{6}$$
$$c \approx \frac{6 \sin 15.6°}{\sin 36°}$$
$$c \approx 2.7$$

Therefore, $B \approx 128°$, $C \approx 16°$, and $c \approx 2.7$.

41. Begin with the Law of Cosines, since the measures of two sides and the included angle are given.

$$a^2 = b^2 + c^2 - 2bc \cos A$$
$$a^2 = 7.6^2 + 14.1^2 - 2(7.6)(14.1) \cos 29°$$
$$a^2 = 256.57 - 214.32 \cos 29°$$
$$a \approx 8.3$$

When solving this problem by the Law of Sines, angle measures were rounded to the nearest tenth of a degree until the final step of the solution.

$$\frac{\sin B}{b} = \frac{\sin A}{a}$$
$$\frac{\sin B}{7.6} \approx \frac{\sin 29°}{8.3}$$
$$\sin B \approx \frac{7.6 \sin 29}{8.3}$$
$$B \approx 26.4°$$
$$C \approx 180° - (29° + 26.4°) \approx 124.6°$$

Therefore, $a \approx 8.3$, $B \approx 26°$, and $C \approx 125°$.

42.
$$\sin(-150°) = \sin(-150° + 360°)$$
$$= \sin 210°$$
$$= -\frac{1}{2}$$

43. $\cos 300° = \frac{1}{2}$

44.
$$(\sin 45°)(\sin 225°) = \left(\frac{\sqrt{2}}{2}\right)\left(-\frac{\sqrt{2}}{2}\right)$$
$$= -\frac{2}{4}$$
$$= -\frac{1}{2}$$

45. $\sin \frac{5\pi}{4} = -\frac{\sqrt{2}}{2}$

46. $(\sin 30°)^2 + (\cos 30°)^2 = \left(\frac{1}{2}\right)^2 + \left(\frac{\sqrt{3}}{2}\right)^2$

$$= \frac{1}{4} + \frac{3}{4}$$

$$= 1$$

47. $\dfrac{4\cos 150° + 2\sin 300°}{3} = \dfrac{4\left(-\frac{\sqrt{3}}{2}\right) + 2\left(-\frac{\sqrt{3}}{2}\right)}{3}$

$$= \frac{-2\sqrt{3} - \sqrt{3}}{3}$$

$$= \frac{-3\sqrt{3}}{3}$$

$$= -\sqrt{3}$$

48. KEYSTROKES: [2nd] [SIN⁻¹] [(−)] 1 [)] [ENTER]
-1.570796327

$\operatorname{Sin}^{-1}(-1) = -\frac{\pi}{2} \approx -1.57$

49. KEYSTROKES: [2nd] [TAN⁻¹] [2nd] [√] 3 [)] [)]
[ENTER] 1.047197551

$\operatorname{Tan}^{-1}\sqrt{3} = \frac{\pi}{3} \approx 1.05$

50. KEYSTROKES: [TAN] [2nd] [SIN⁻¹] 3 [÷] 5 [)]
[)] [ENTER] .75

$\tan\left(\operatorname{Arcsin}\frac{3}{5}\right) = 0.75$

51. KEYSTROKES: [COS] [2nd] [SIN⁻¹] 1 [)] [)]
[ENTER] 0

$\cos(\operatorname{Sin}^{-1} 1) = 0$

Chapter 13 Practice Test

Page 757

1.

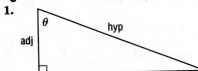

2. Sample answer: $\dfrac{\sin A}{a} = \dfrac{\sin B}{b} = \dfrac{\sin C}{c}$

3. Sample answer: when the measures of two sides and the included angle are given

4. $a = 7, A = 49°$

$49° + B = 90°$

$B = 41°$

$\sin A = \dfrac{a}{c}$

$\sin 49° = \dfrac{7}{c}$

$c = \dfrac{7}{\sin 49°}$

$c \approx 9.3$

$\tan A = \dfrac{a}{b}$

$\tan 49° = \dfrac{7}{b}$

$b = \dfrac{7}{\tan 49°}$

$b \approx 6.1$

Therefore, $B = 41°, b \approx 6.1$, and $c \approx 9.3$.

5. $B = 75°, b = 6$

$A + 75° = 90°$

$A = 15°$

$\sin B = \dfrac{b}{c}$

$\sin 75° = \dfrac{6}{c}$

$c = \dfrac{6}{\sin 75°}$

$c \approx 6.2$

$\tan A = \dfrac{a}{b}$

$\tan 15° = \dfrac{a}{6}$

$a = 6\tan 15°$

$a \approx 1.6$

Therefore, $A = 15°, c \approx 6.2$ and $a \approx 1.6$.

6. $A = 22°, c = 8$

$22° + B = 90°$

$b = 68°$

$\operatorname{Sin} A = \dfrac{a}{c}$

$\sin 22° = \dfrac{a}{8}$

$a = 8\sin 22°$

$a \approx 3.0$

$\cos A = \dfrac{b}{c}$

$\cos 22° = \dfrac{b}{8}$

$b = 8\cos 22°$

$b \approx 7.4$

Therefore, $B = 68°, a \approx 3.0$, and $b \approx 7.4$.

7. $a = 7, c = 16$

$a^2 + b^2 = c^2$

$7^2 + b^2 = 16^2$

$b^2 = 207$

$b \approx 14.4$

$\sin A = \dfrac{a}{c}$

$\sin A = \dfrac{7}{16}$

$A \approx 26°$

$B \approx 90° - 26° \approx 64°$

Therefore, $b \approx 14.4, A \approx 26°$ and $B \approx 64°$.

8. $275° = 275°\left(\dfrac{\pi \text{ radians}}{180°}\right)$

$= \dfrac{275\pi}{180}$ radians or $\dfrac{55\pi}{36}$

9. $-\dfrac{\pi}{6} = \left(-\dfrac{\pi}{6}\text{ radians}\right)\left(\dfrac{180°}{\pi \text{ radians}}\right)$

$= -\dfrac{180°}{6}$ or $-30°$

10. $\dfrac{11\pi}{2} = \left(\dfrac{11\pi}{2}\text{ radians}\right)\left(\dfrac{180°}{\pi \text{ radians}}\right)$

$= \dfrac{1980°}{2}$ or $990°$

11. $330° = 330°\left(\dfrac{\pi \text{ radians}}{180°}\right)$

$= \dfrac{330\pi}{180}$ radians or $\dfrac{11\pi}{6}$

12. $-600° = -600°\left(\dfrac{\pi \text{ radians}}{180°}\right)$

$= \dfrac{-600\pi}{180}$ radians or $-\dfrac{10\pi}{3}$

13. $-\dfrac{7\pi}{4} = \left(-\dfrac{7\pi}{4}\text{ radians}\right)\left(\dfrac{180°}{\pi \text{ radians}}\right)$

$= -\dfrac{1260°}{4}$ or $-315°$

14. $\cos(-120°) = \cos(-120° + 360°)$
$= \cos 240°$
$= -\frac{1}{2}$

15. $\sin \frac{7\pi}{4} = -\frac{\sqrt{2}}{2}$

16. $\cot 300° = \frac{\cos 300°}{\sin 300°} = \frac{\frac{1}{2}}{-\frac{\sqrt{3}}{2}} = -\frac{1}{\sqrt{3}} = -\frac{\sqrt{3}}{3}$

17. $\sec\left(-\frac{7\pi}{6}\right) = \sec\left(-\frac{7\pi}{6} + 2\pi\right)$
$= \sec \frac{5\pi}{6}$
$= \frac{1}{\cos \frac{5\pi}{6}}$
$= \frac{1}{-\frac{\sqrt{3}}{2}}$
$= -\frac{2}{\sqrt{3}}$
$= -\frac{2\sqrt{3}}{3}$

18. KEYSTROKES: [2nd] [SIN⁻¹] [(−)] [2nd] [√] 3 [ )]
[÷] 2 [ )] [ENTER] −60
$\text{Sin}^{-1}\left(-\frac{\sqrt{3}}{2}\right) = -60°$

19. KEYSTROKES: [2nd] [TAN⁻¹] 1 [ )] [ENTER] 45
$\text{Arctan } 1 = 45°$

20. $\tan 135° = \frac{\sin 135°}{\cos 135°} = \frac{\frac{\sqrt{2}}{2}}{-\frac{\sqrt{2}}{2}} = -1$

21. $\csc \frac{5\pi}{6} = \frac{1}{\sin \frac{5\pi}{6}}$
$= \frac{1}{\frac{1}{2}}$
$= 2$

22. $A = 40°, b = 10, a = 14$
Since angle A is acute and $a > b$ ($14 > 10$), there is one solution.

When solving this problem by the Law of Sines, angle measures were rounded to the nearest tenth of a degree until the final step of the solution.
$\frac{\sin B}{b} = \frac{\sin A}{a}$
$\frac{\sin B}{10} = \frac{\sin 40°}{14}$
$\sin B = \frac{5 \sin 40°}{7}$
$B \approx 27.3° \approx 27°$
$C \approx 180° - (40° + 27.3°) \approx 112.7° \approx 113°$
$\frac{\sin C}{c} = \frac{\sin A}{a}$
$\frac{\sin 112.7°}{c} \approx \frac{\sin 40°}{14}$
$c \approx \frac{14 \sin 112.7°}{\sin 40°}$
$c \approx 20.1$
Therefore, $B \approx 27°$, $C \approx 113°$, and $c \approx 20.1$.

23. $\cos \theta = -\frac{\sqrt{3}}{2}$
$\frac{x}{r} = -\frac{\sqrt{3}}{2} = \frac{-\sqrt{3}}{2}$
Since the terminal side of θ lies in Quadrant II, $x = -\sqrt{3}$, $r = 2$, and $y = \sqrt{2^2 - (-\sqrt{3})^2} = 1$.
$\sin \theta = \frac{y}{r} = \frac{1}{2}$

$\tan \theta = \frac{y}{x} = \frac{1}{-\sqrt{3}} = -\frac{\sqrt{3}}{3}$
$\csc \theta = \frac{r}{y} = \frac{2}{1} = 2$
$\sec \theta = \frac{r}{x} = \frac{2}{-\sqrt{3}} = -\frac{2\sqrt{3}}{3}$
$\cot \theta = \frac{x}{y} = \frac{-\sqrt{3}}{1} = -\sqrt{3}$

24. Let x = distance.
$\tan \theta = \frac{\text{opp}}{\text{adj}}$
$\tan 70° = \frac{50}{x}$
$x = \frac{50}{\tan 70°}$
$x \approx 18.2$
The riverbed is 18.2 meters from the base of the cliff.

25. C; $A = 90° - 30° = 60°$
Since this is a 30°-60°-90° triangle and the longer leg is 6 units, then the shorter leg is $\frac{6}{\sqrt{3}}$ or $2\sqrt{3}$ units.
Area $= \frac{1}{2}bh$
$= \frac{1}{2}(2\sqrt{3} \text{ units})(6 \text{ units})$
$= 6\sqrt{3} \text{ units}^2$

Chapter 13 Standardized Test Practice

Pages 758-759
1. C; If n is a positive even integer, then $3n$ is a positive even integer. Then k, or $30 - 3n$ is an even integer.
Also $30 - 3n = 3(10 - n)$, so k is divisible by 3. k may be greater than 20 (consider $n = 2$, then $k = 24$).

2. C; $4x^2 + 5x = 80$ or $4x^2 = 80 - 5x$
$4x^2 - 5y = 30$ or $4x^2 = 30x + 5y$
Then by substitution,
$80 - 5x = 30 + 5y$
$5x + 5y = 50$
$5(x + y) = 5(10)$
$x + y = 10$
$6(x + y) = 6(10)$
$6x + 6y = 60$

3. B; $a = b + cb$
$a = b(1 + c)$
$1 = \frac{b(1 + c)}{a}$
$\frac{1}{1 + c} = \frac{b}{a}$

4. D; $\sum_{n=1}^{5} 3n^2 = 3(1)^2 + 3(2)^2 + 3(3)^2 + 3(4)^2 + 3(5)^2$
$= 3 + 12 + 27 + 48 + 75$
$= 165$

5. D; $P(\text{yellow}) = \frac{6}{24} = \frac{1}{4}$

To double the probability, it must be $\frac{1}{2}$. Let x be the number of additional yellow marbles.

$P(\text{yellow}) = \frac{6+x}{24+x} = \frac{1}{2}$

$12 + 2x = 24 + x$

$x = 12$

6. D; Let x = height of cliff

$\tan \theta = \frac{\text{opp}}{\text{adj}}$

$\tan 12° = \frac{x}{3}$

$x = 3 \tan 12°$

7. C; Since $x + y = 90°$, then

$\cos x = \sin y$, so $\frac{\cos x}{\sin y} = 1$.

8. A; Let x = height of kite from the child. Then add x to 4 for final answer.

$\sin \theta = \frac{\text{opp}}{\text{hyp}}$

$\sin 35° = \frac{x}{40}$

$x = 40 \sin 35°$

height of kite off the ground = $4 + 40 \sin 35°$

9. B; What angle between 180° and 270° has a sine of $-\frac{1}{2}$? $\sin 210° = -\frac{1}{2}$

10. C; $\cos \theta = \frac{8}{17}$

$\frac{x}{r} = \frac{8}{17}$

The angle is in Quadrant IV, so $x = 8, r = 17$, and $y = -\sqrt{17^2 - 8^2} = -15$.

$\sin \theta = \frac{y}{r} = \frac{-15}{17}$ or $-\frac{15}{17}$

11. Let AB = height = h,
AD = width = w,
and DE = length = ℓ.

Area of $ABCD = hw = 18, h = \frac{18}{w}$

Area of $CDEF = h\ell = 21, h = \frac{21}{\ell}$

What integer greater than 1 is a factor of 18 and 21? Try $h = 3$.
Then $w = 6$ and $\ell = 7$.

$V = \ell wh = 7(6)(3) = 126$

The volume of the box is 126 units³.

12. One of the integers must be 0, and since the integers are consecutive, the next five must be 1, 2, 3, 4 and 5. So the greatest possible sum is $0 + 1 + 2 + 3 + 4 + 5 = 15$.

13. The sum of 20 of the players is $20(7) = 1400$. The sum for all 25 players is $25n$. So, the remaining 5 players can have scores as low as 60, sum = $5(60)$, or as high as 100, sum = $5(100)$. Therefore, the possible values for n are:

least: $25n = 5(60) + 1400, \quad n = 68$
greatest: $25n = 5(100) + 1400, \quad n = 76$
difference = $76 - 68 = 8$

The difference between the greatest and least possible values of n is 8.

14. $a = 2,$
$b = 12,$
$c = 25,$
$d = 2(25) + (12 - 1) = 61$
$e = 2(61) + (25 - 1) = 146$

15. $t° + (t - v)° + (t + v)° = 180°$
$\qquad\qquad\qquad\qquad 3t° = 180°$
$\qquad\qquad\qquad\qquad\quad t° = 60°$

Since $t = 2v$, then $2v = 60$ or $v = 30$.

$x° + (t - v)° = 180°$
$x° + (60 - 30)° = 180°$
$\qquad\qquad x° = 150°$
$\qquad\qquad x = 150$

16. Start with the second equation and substitute 4 for b and solve for c.

$2b + 4c = 12$
$2(4) + 4c = 12$
$8 + 4c = 12$
$4c = 4$
$c = 1$

Substitute 4 for b and 1 for c in the first equation and solve for a.

$3a + 4b + 2c = 33$
$3a + 4(4) + 2(1) = 33$
$3a + 16 + 2 = 33$
$3a = 15$
$a = 5$

17. Start with one woman (3 ways to choose), then one man (3 ways to choose), then one woman (now only 2 ways to choose), then one man (also only 2 ways to choose), then seat the remaining woman and man (only 1 way to choose each).

ways to start with a woman = $3(3)(2)(2)(1)(1) = 36$

There are the same number of ways to start with a man, so the total number of ways is $2(36) = 72$.

18. B; The highest probability that can be obtained in Column A is 100%, so 200% is greater.

19. A; The quantity in Column B is:

$\left(4 \cdot \frac{1}{4}\right)^4 + \frac{\frac{1}{4}}{4} = 1^4 + \frac{1}{16}$
$\qquad\qquad\qquad = 1 + \frac{1}{16}$
$\qquad\qquad\qquad = \frac{17}{16}$

The quantity in column A is greater, $5 > \frac{1}{4}$.

20. B; Side of square = $\sqrt{64} = 8$

diameter of circle = $\sqrt{8^2 + 8^2} = 8\sqrt{2}$

radius of circle = $r = \frac{8\sqrt{2}}{2} = 4\sqrt{2}$

area of circle = πr^2
$\qquad\qquad\qquad = \pi(4\sqrt{2})^2 \approx 100.5$ units²

Since $192 > 100.5$, the answer is B.

21. B; $QS = \sqrt{(RS)^2 + (QR)^2} = \sqrt{2(RS)^2}$
(note: $QR = RS$, since it is a square)

$\frac{QS}{RS} = \frac{RS\sqrt{2}}{RS} = \sqrt{2}$

Since $2 > \sqrt{2}$, the answer is B.

Chapter 14 Trigonometric Graphs and Identities

Page 761 Getting Started

1. Because the terminal side of 135° lies in Quadrant II, the reference angle θ' is $180° - 135°$ or 45°. The sine function is positive in Quadrant II, so $\sin 135° = \sin 45°$ or $\frac{\sqrt{2}}{2}$.

2. Because the terminal side of 315° lies in Quadrant IV, the reference angle θ' is $360° - 315°$ or 45°. The tangent function is negative in Quadrant IV, so $\tan 315° = -\tan 45°$ or -1.

3. Because the terminal side of 90° lies on the positive y-axis, a point on the terminal side of 90° is of the form $(0, r)$.
$$\cos 90° = \frac{x}{r}$$
$$= \frac{0}{r} \text{ or } 0$$

4. Because the terminal side of 45° lies in Quadrant I, the reference angle θ' is 45°. The tangent function is positive in Quadrant I, so $\tan 45° = 1$.

5. Because the terminal side of $\frac{5\pi}{4}$ lies in Quadrant III, the reference angle θ' is $\frac{5\pi}{4} - \pi$ or $\frac{\pi}{4}$. The sine function is negative in Quadrant III.
$$\sin \frac{5\pi}{4} = -\sin \frac{\pi}{4}$$
$$= -\sin 45°$$
$$= -\frac{\sqrt{2}}{2}$$

6. Because the terminal side of $\frac{7\pi}{6}$ lies in Quadrant III, the reference angle θ' is $\frac{7\pi}{6} - \pi$ or $\frac{\pi}{6}$. The cosine function is negative in Quadrant III.
$$\cos \frac{7\pi}{6} = -\cos \frac{\pi}{6}$$
$$= -\cos 30°$$
$$= -\frac{\sqrt{3}}{2}$$

7. Because the terminal side of $\frac{11\pi}{6}$ lies in Quadrant IV, the reference angle θ' is $\pi - \frac{11\pi}{6}$ or $\frac{\pi}{6}$. The sine function is negative in Quadrant IV.
$$\sin \frac{11\pi}{6} = -\sin \frac{\pi}{6}$$
$$= -\sin 30°$$
$$= -\frac{1}{2}$$

8. Because the terminal side of $\frac{3\pi}{2}$ lies on the negative y-axis, a point on the terminal side of $\frac{3\pi}{2}$ is of the form $(0, -r)$.
$$\tan \frac{3\pi}{2} = \frac{y}{x}$$
$$= \frac{-r}{0} \text{ or undefined}$$

9. $\cos(-150°) = \cos(-150° + 360°)$
$$= \cos 210°$$
$$= -\frac{\sqrt{3}}{2}$$

10. $\sin 510° = \sin(510° - 360°)$
$$= \sin 150°$$
$$= \frac{1}{2}$$

11. $\cot \frac{9\pi}{4} = \cot\left(\frac{9\pi}{4} - 2\pi\right)$
$$= \cot \frac{\pi}{4}$$
$$= 1$$

12. $\sec \frac{13\pi}{6} = \sec\left(\frac{13\pi}{6} - 2\pi\right)$
$$= \sec \frac{\pi}{6}$$
$$= \frac{2\sqrt{3}}{3}$$

13. $\tan\left(-\frac{3\pi}{2}\right) = \tan\left(-\frac{3\pi}{2} + 2\pi\right)$
$$= \tan \frac{\pi}{2}$$
undefined

14. $\csc(-720°) = \csc(-720° + 360°)$
$$= \csc(-360°)$$
$$= \csc(-360° + 360°)$$
$$= \csc 0°$$
undefined

15. $\cos \frac{7\pi}{3} = \cos\left(\frac{7\pi}{3} - 2\pi\right)$
$$= \cos \frac{\pi}{3}$$
$$= \frac{1}{2}$$

16. $\tan \frac{8\pi}{3} = \tan\left(\frac{8\pi}{3} - 2\pi\right)$
$$= \tan \frac{2\pi}{3}$$
$$= -\sqrt{3}$$

17. $-15x^2 - 5x = (-5x \cdot 3x) + (-5x \cdot 1)$
$$= -5x(3x + 1)$$

18. $2x^4 - 4x^2 = (2x^2 \cdot x^2) - (2x^2 \cdot 2)$
$$= 2x^2(x^2 - 2)$$

19. $x^3 + 4$ is prime.

20. $x^2 - 6x + 8 = x^2 - 4x - 2x + 8$
$$= (x^2 - 4x) + (-2x + 8)$$
$$= x(x - 4) - 2(x - 4)$$
$$= (x - 2)(x - 4)$$

21. $2x^2 - 3x - 2 = 2x^2 - 4x + x - 2$
$$= (2x^2 - 4x) + (x - 2)$$
$$= 2x(x - 2) + (x - 2)$$
$$= (2x + 1)(x - 2)$$

22. $3x^3 - 2x^2 - x = x(3x^2 - 2x - 1)$
$$= x(3x^2 - 3x + x - 1)$$
$$= x[3x(x - 1) + (x - 1)]$$
$$= x(3x + 1)(x - 1)$$

23. $x^2 - 5x - 24 = 0$
$(x + 3)(x - 8) = 0$
$x + 3 = 0 \qquad \text{or} \qquad x - 8 = 0$
$\ x = -3 \qquad\qquad\qquad x = 8$
$\{-3, 8\}$

24. $x^2 - 2x - 48 = 0$
$(x + 6)(x - 8) = 0$

$x + 6 = 0$ or $x - 8 = 0$
$x = -6$ $x = 8$
$\{-6, 8\}$

25. $x^2 + 3x - 40 = 0$
$(x + 8)(x - 5) = 0$

$x + 8 = 0$ or $x - 5 = 0$
$x = -8$ $x = 5$
$\{-8, 5\}$

26. $x^2 - 12x = 0$
$x(x - 12) = 0$

$x = 0$ or $x - 12 = 0$
                       $x = 12$

$\{0, 12\}$

27. $-2x^2 - 11x - 12 = 0$
$-(2x^2 + 11x + 12) = 0$
$2x^2 + 11x + 12 = 0$
$(2x + 3)(x + 4) = 0$

$2x + 3 = 0$ or $x + 4 = 0$
$2x = -3$ $x = -4$
$x = -\frac{3}{2}$

$\left\{-4, -\frac{3}{2}\right\}$

28. $x^2 - 16 = 0$
$(x + 4)(x - 4) = 0$

$x + 4 = 0$ or $x - 4 = 0$
$x = -4$ $x = 4$
$\{-4, 4\}$

14-1 Graphing Trigonometric Functions

Page 764   Graphing Calculator Investigation

1. For each function, the maximum value is 1.

2. In the viewing rectangle shown, $y = \sin x$ reaches its maximum value 2 times, and $y = \sin 2x$ reaches its maximum value four times.

3. The maximum value of $y = \sin\left(\frac{x}{2}\right)$ is 1. The function reaches its maximum value one time.

4. The greater the value of b, the smaller the period. b has no effect on the maximum value.

5. The maximum value of $y = \sin x$ is 1. The maximum value of $y = 2 \sin x$ is 2. For each function, the period is 360°.

6. The maximum value of $y = \frac{1}{2} \sin x$ is $\frac{1}{2}$. The period is 360°.

7. When a is positive, the amplitude is a. When a is negative, the amplitude is $|a|$. a has no effect on the period.

Pages 766–767   Check for Understanding

1. Sample answer: Amplitude is half the difference between the maximum and minimum values of a graph; $y = \tan \theta$ has no maximum or minimum value.

2. Sample answer: The graph repeats itself every 180°.

3. Jamile; The amplitude is 3 and the period is 3π.

4. $y = \frac{1}{2} \sin \theta$

Amplitude: $|a| = \left|\frac{1}{2}\right|$
            $= \frac{1}{2}$

Period: $\frac{360°}{|b|} = \frac{360°}{|1|}$
            $= 360°$ or 2π

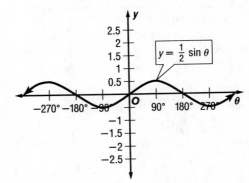

5. $y = 2 \sin \theta$

Amplitude: $|a| = |2|$
            $= 2$

Period: $\frac{360°}{|b|} = \frac{360°}{|1|}$
            $= 360°$ or 2π

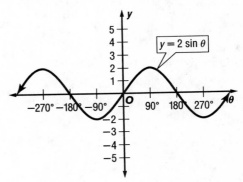

6. $y = \frac{2}{3} \cos \theta$

Amplitude: $|a| = \left|\frac{2}{3}\right|$
            $= \frac{2}{3}$

Period: $\frac{360°}{|b|} = \frac{360°}{1}$
            $= 360°$ or 2π

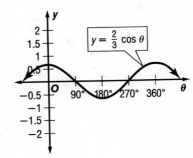

7. $y = \frac{1}{4} \tan \theta$

The tangent function has no amplitude.

Period: $\frac{180°}{|b|} = \frac{180°}{|1|}$

$= 180°$ or π

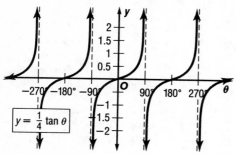

$y = \frac{1}{4} \tan \theta$

8. $y = \csc 2\theta$

The cosecant function has no amplitude.

Period: $\frac{360°}{|b|} = \frac{360°}{|2|}$

$= 180°$ or π

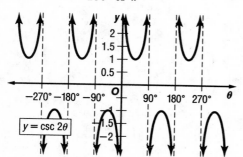

$y = \csc 2\theta$

9. $y = 4 \sin 2\theta$

Amplitude: $|a| = |4|$

$= 4$

Period: $\frac{360°}{|b|} = \frac{360°}{|2|}$

$= 180°$ or π

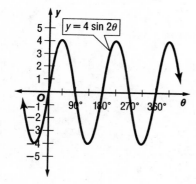

$y = 4 \sin 2\theta$

10. $y = 4 \cos \frac{3}{4}\theta$

Amplitude: $|a| = |4|$

$= 4$

Period: $\frac{360°}{|b|} = \frac{360°}{\left|\frac{3}{4}\right|}$

$= 480°$ or $\frac{8\pi}{3}$

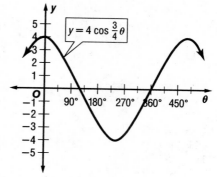

$y = 4 \cos \frac{3}{4}\theta$

11. $y = \frac{1}{2} \sec 3\theta$

The secant function has no amplitude.

Period: $\frac{360°}{|b|} = \frac{360°}{|3|}$

$= 120°$ or $\frac{2\pi}{3}$

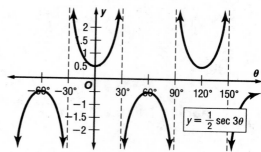

$y = \frac{1}{2} \sec 3\theta$

12. $y = \frac{3}{4} \cos \frac{1}{2}\theta$

Amplitude: $|a| = \left|\frac{3}{4}\right|$

$= \frac{3}{4}$

Period: $\frac{360°}{|b|} = \frac{360°}{\left|\frac{1}{2}\right|}$

$= 720°$ or 4π

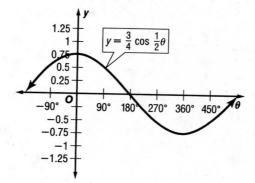

$y = \frac{3}{4} \cos \frac{1}{2}\theta$

13. Period: $\frac{2\pi}{|b|} =$

$$= 12$$

The period of the function is 12 months.
Sample answer: The pattern in the population
will repeat itself every 12 months.

14. Amplitude: $|a| = |1250|$
$$= 1250$$

The maximum number of mice is 3000 + 1250 or
4250. This occurs three months after March 1 or
June 1.

Pages 767–768   Practice and Apply

15. $y = 3 \sin \theta$
   Amplitude: $|a| = |3|$ or 3
   Period: $\frac{360°}{|b|} = \frac{360°}{|1|}$
   $$= 360° \text{ or } 2\pi$$

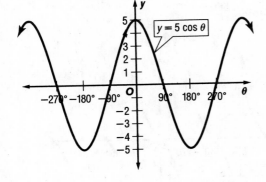

16. $y = 5 \cos \theta$
   Amplitude: $|a| = |5|$ or 5
   Period: $\frac{360°}{|b|} = \frac{360°}{|1|}$
   $$= 360° \text{ or } 2\pi$$

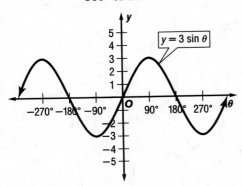

17. $y = 2 \csc \theta$
   The cosecant function has no amplitude.
   Period: $\frac{360°}{|b|} = \frac{360°}{|1|}$
   $$= 360° \text{ or } 2\pi$$

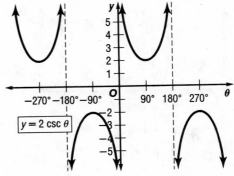

18. $y = 2 \tan \theta$
   The tangent function has no amplitude.
   Period: $\frac{180°}{|b|} = \frac{180°}{|1|}$
   $$= 180° \text{ or } \pi$$

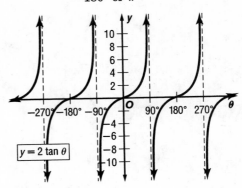

19. $y = \frac{1}{5} \sin \theta$
   Amplitude: $|a| = \left|\frac{1}{5}\right|$ or $\frac{1}{5}$
   Period: $\frac{360°}{|b|} = \frac{360°}{|1|}$
   $$= 360° \text{ or } 2\pi$$

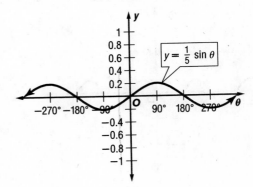

20. $y = \frac{1}{3} \sec \theta$

The secant function has no amplitude.

Period: $\frac{360°}{|b|} = \frac{360°}{|1|}$

$\qquad = 360°$ or 2π

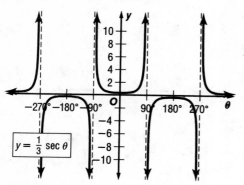

$y = \frac{1}{3} \sec \theta$

21. $y = \sin 4\theta$

Amplitude: $|a| = |1|$ or 1

Period: $\frac{360°}{|b|} = \frac{360°}{|4|}$

$\qquad = 90°$ or $\frac{\pi}{2}$

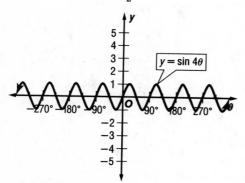

$y = \sin 4\theta$

22. $y = \sin 2\theta$

Amplitude: $|a| = |1|$ or 1

Period: $\frac{360°}{|b|} = \frac{360°}{|2|}$

$\qquad = 180°$ or π

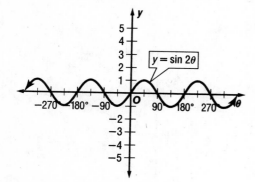

$y = \sin 2\theta$

23. $y = \sec 3\theta$

The secant function has no amplitude.

Period: $\frac{360°}{|b|} = \frac{360°}{|3|}$

$\qquad = 120°$ or $\frac{2\pi}{3}$

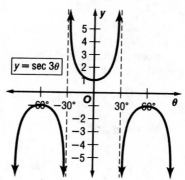

$y = \sec 3\theta$

24. $y = \cot 5\theta$

The cotangent function has no amplitude.

Period: $\frac{180°}{|b|} = \frac{180°}{|5|}$

$\qquad = 36°$ or $\frac{\pi}{5}$

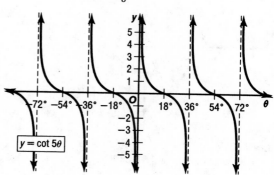

$y = \cot 5\theta$

25. $y = 4 \tan \frac{1}{3}\theta$

The tangent function has no amplitude.

Period: $\frac{180°}{|b|} = \frac{180°}{\left|\frac{1}{3}\right|}$

$\qquad = 540°$ or 3π

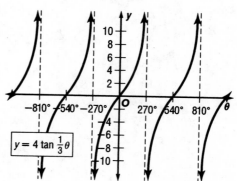

$y = 4 \tan \frac{1}{3}\theta$

26. $y = 2 \cot \frac{1}{2}\theta$

The cotangent function has no amplitude.

Period: $\frac{180°}{|b|} =$

$$= 360° \text{ or } 2\pi$$

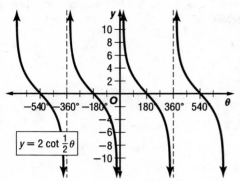

$y = 2 \cot \frac{1}{2}\theta$

27. $y = 6 \sin \frac{2}{3}\theta$

Amplitude: $|a| = |6|$ or 6

Period: $\frac{360°}{|b|} = \frac{360°}{\left|\frac{2}{3}\right|}$

$$= 540° \text{ or } 3\pi$$

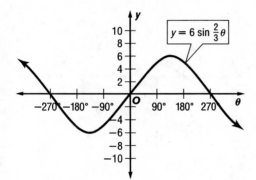

$y = 6 \sin \frac{2}{3}\theta$

28. $y = 3 \cos \frac{1}{2}\theta$

Amplitude: $|a| = |3|$ or 3

Period: $\frac{360°}{|b|} = \frac{360°}{\left|\frac{1}{2}\right|}$

$$= 720° \text{ or } 4\pi$$

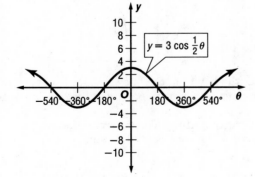

$y = 3 \cos \frac{1}{2}\theta$

29. $y = 3 \csc \frac{1}{2}\theta$

The cosecant function has no amplitude.

Period: $\frac{360°}{|b|} = \frac{360°}{\left|\frac{1}{2}\right|}$

$$= 720° \text{ or } 4\pi$$

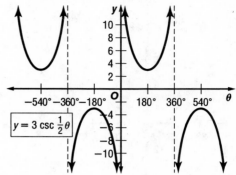

$y = 3 \csc \frac{1}{2}\theta$

30. $y = \frac{1}{2} \cot 2\theta$

The cotangent function has no amplitude.

Period: $\frac{180°}{|b|} = \frac{180°}{|2|}$

$$= 90° \text{ or } \frac{\pi}{2}$$

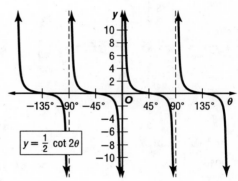

$y = \frac{1}{2} \cot 2\theta$

31. $2y = \tan \theta$

$y = \frac{1}{2} \tan \theta$

The tangent function has no amplitude.

Period: $\frac{180°}{|b|} = \frac{180°}{|1|}$

$$= 180° \text{ or } \pi$$

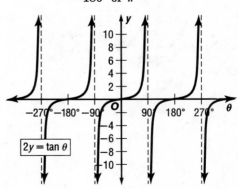

$2y = \tan \theta$

32. $\frac{3}{4}y = \frac{2}{3} \sin \frac{3}{5}\theta$

$y = \frac{8}{9} \sin \frac{3}{5}\theta$

Amplitude: $|a| = \left|\frac{8}{9}\right|$ or $\frac{8}{9}$

Period: $\frac{360°}{|b|} = \frac{360°}{\left|\frac{3}{5}\right|}$

$= 600°$ or $\frac{10\pi}{3}$

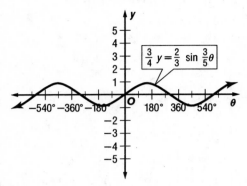

33.

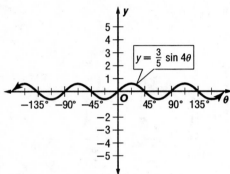

$a = \frac{3}{5}$; find the value of b.

$\frac{360°}{|b|} = 90°$

$b = 4$

The equation is $y = \frac{3}{5} \sin 4\theta$.

34.

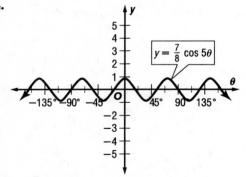

$a = \frac{7}{8}$; find the value of b.

$\frac{2\pi}{|b|} = \frac{2\pi}{5}$

$b = 5$

The equation is $y = \frac{7}{8} \cos 5\theta$.

35. $\frac{2\pi}{|b|} = \frac{2\pi}{|10^7 \cdot 2\pi|}$

$= \frac{1}{10^7}$

36. For all three equations, $a = 0.25$. When the frequency is 64 Hertz, the period is $\frac{1}{64}$. Find b.

$\frac{2\pi}{|b|} = \frac{1}{64}$

$b = 128\pi$

When the frequency is 64 Hertz, the equation is $y = 0.25 \sin 128\pi t$. When the frequency is 256 Hertz, the period is $\frac{1}{256}$. Find b.

$\frac{2\pi}{|b|} = \frac{1}{256}$

$b = 512\pi$

When the frequency is 256 Hertz, the equation is $y = 0.25 \sin 512\pi t$. When the frequency is 512 Hertz, the period is $\frac{1}{512}$. Find b.

$\frac{2\pi}{|b|} = \frac{1}{512}$

$b = 1024\pi$

When the frequency is 512 Hertz, the equation is $y = 0.25 \sin 1024\pi t$.

37. Sample answer: The amplitudes are the same. As the frequency increases, the period decreases.

38. $f(x) = \cos x$ and $f(x) = \sec x$ are even functions.

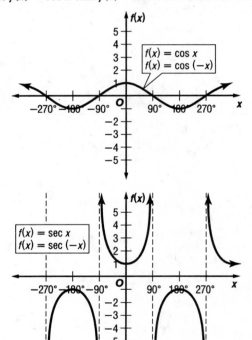

39. Since the height of the buoy is 0 at $t = 0$, use the sine function $y = a \sin bt$, where t is the time in seconds.

Find the amplitude. The difference between the highest and lowest point is 4 feet.

$a = \frac{4}{2}$ or 2

Find the value of b. The period is 10 seconds.

$\frac{2\pi}{|b|} = 10$

$b = \frac{2\pi}{10}$ or $\frac{\pi}{5}$

The equation is $y = 2 \sin \frac{\pi}{5}t$.

40.

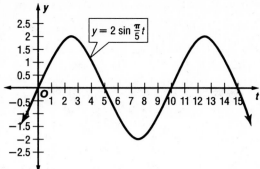

$y = 2 \sin \frac{\pi}{5} t$

41. $y = 2 \sin \frac{\pi}{5} t$

$= 2 \sin\left(\frac{\pi}{5} \cdot 12\right)$

≈ 1.9

After 12 seconds, the height of the buoy is about 1.9 feet.

42. Sample answer: Tides display periodic behavior. This means that their pattern repeats at regular intervals. Answers should include the following information.

- Tides rise and fall in a periodic manner, similar to the sine function.
- To determine the amplitude, subtract the minimum value from the maximum value and divide the difference by 2.

43. A; $\frac{360°}{|b|} = \frac{360°}{|3|}$ or 120°

43. C; The graph rises less than 0.5 unit above the x-axis. Thus, we can eliminate answer choices A, B, and D, whose amplitudes are $\frac{1}{2}$, 2, and 4, respectively.

Page 768 Maintain Your Skills

45. $x = \text{Sin}^{-1} 1$

KEYSTROKES: [2nd] [SIN⁻¹] 1 [ )] [ENTER] 90

$x = 90°$

46. Arcsin $(-1) = y$

KEYSTROKES: [2nd] [SIN⁻¹] [(−)] 1 [ )] [ENTER]
−90

$y = -90°$

47. Arccos $\frac{\sqrt{2}}{2} = x$

KEYSTROKES: [2nd] [COS⁻¹] [2nd] [√] 2 [ )]
[÷] 2 [ )] [ENTER] 45

$x = 45°$

48. $\sin 390° = \sin(30° + 360°)$

$= \sin 30°$

$= \frac{1}{2}$

49. $\sin (-315°) = \sin(45° - 360°)$

$= \sin 45°$

$= \frac{\sqrt{2}}{2}$

50. $\cos 405° = \cos(45° + 360°)$

$= \cos 45°$

$= \frac{\sqrt{2}}{2}$

51. There are 16 total boys and girls on the committee, of which 16 − 3 or 13 are not juniors.

$P(\text{not a junior}) = \frac{13}{16}$

52. $a_{n + 1} = 2a_n + 5$

$a_{1 + 1} = 2a_1 + 5$

$a_2 = 2(3) + 5$ or 11

$a_{2 + 1} = 2a_2 + 5$

$a_3 = 2(11) + 5$ or 27

$a_{3 + 1} = 2a_3 + 5$

$a_4 = 2(27) + 5$ or 59

$a_{4 + 1} = 2a_4 + 5$

$a_5 = 2(59) + 5$ or 123

The first five terms are 3, 11, 27, 59, and 123.

53.

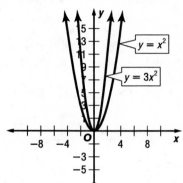

$y = x^2$

$y = 3x^2$

54.

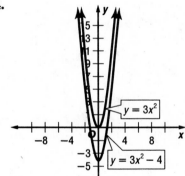

$y = 3x^2$

$y = 3x^2 - 4$

55.

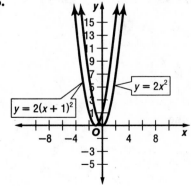

$y = 2x^2$

$y = 2(x + 1)^2$

56.

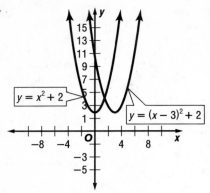

$y = x^2 + 2$

$y = (x - 3)^2 + 2$

Page 769   Graphing Calculator Investigation

1. The graph of $y = \sin(x - 30)$ is shifted 30° to the right of the graph of $y = \sin x$.

2. The graph of $y = \sin(x + 60)$ is shifted 60° to the left of the graph of $y = \sin x$.

3. Sample answer: When h is positive the graph shifts right h units. When h is negative the graph shifts left h units.

4.

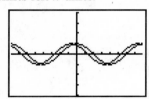

[−360, 360] scl: 45 by [−5, 5] scl:

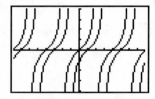

[−360, 360] scl: 45 by [−4, 4] scl: 1

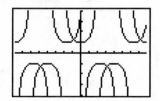

[−360, 360] scl: 45 by [−4, 4] scl: 1

The conjecture holds.

Page 774   Check for Understanding

1. vertical shift: 15; amplitude: 3; period: 180°; phase shift: 90°

2. The midline of a trigonometric function is the line about which the graph of the function oscillates after a vertical shift.

3. Sample answer: $y = \sin(\theta + 45°)$

---

4. $y = \sin\left(\theta - \frac{\pi}{2}\right)$

Amplitude: $|a| = |1|$ or 1

Period: $\frac{2\pi}{|b|} = \frac{2\pi}{|1|}$ or 2π

Phase shift: $h = \frac{\pi}{2}$

The phase shift is to the right.

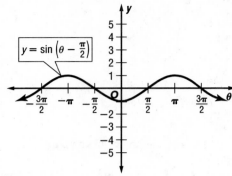

$y = \sin\left(\theta - \frac{\pi}{2}\right)$

5. $y = \tan(\theta + 60°)$

The tangent function has no amplitude.

Period: $\frac{180°}{|b|} = \frac{180°}{|1|}$ or 180°

Phase shift: $h = -60°$

The phase shift is to the left.

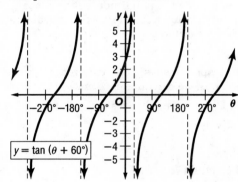

$y = \tan(\theta + 60°)$

6. $y = \cos(\theta - 45°)$

Amplitude: $|a| = |1|$ or 1

Period: $\frac{360°}{|b|} = \frac{360°}{|1|}$ or 360°

Phase shift: $h = 45°$

The phase shift is to the right.

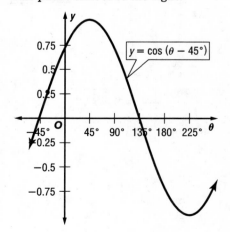

$y = \cos(\theta - 45°)$

---

7. $y = \sec\left(\theta + \frac{\pi}{3}\right)$

The secant function has no amplitude.

Period: $\frac{2\pi}{|b|} = \frac{2\pi}{|1|}$ or 2π

Phase shift: $h = -\frac{\pi}{3}$

The phase shift is to the left.

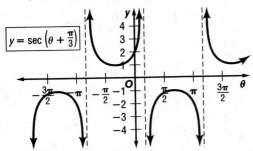

8. $y = \cos\theta + \frac{1}{4}$

Vertical shift: $\frac{1}{4}$

Equation of Midline: $y = \frac{1}{4}$

Amplitude: $|a| = |1|$ or 1

Period: $\frac{360°}{|b|} = \frac{360°}{|1|}$ or $360°$

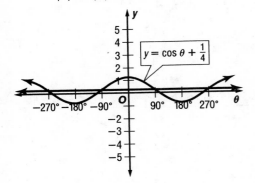

9. $y = \sec\theta - 5$

Vertical shift: -5

Equation of Midline: $y = -5$

The secant function has no amplitude.

Period: $\frac{360°}{|b|} = \frac{360°}{|1|}$ or $360°$

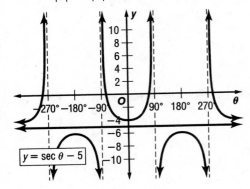

10. $y = \tan\theta + 4$

Vertical shift: 4

Equation of Midline: $y = 4$

The tangent function has no amplitude.

Period: $\frac{180°}{|b|} = \frac{180°}{|1|}$ or $180°$

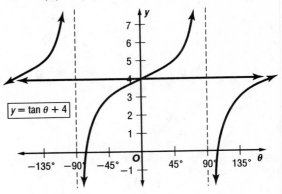

11. $y = \sin\theta + 0.25$

Vertical shift: 0.25

Equation of Midline: $y = 0.25$

Amplitude: $|a| = |1|$ or 1

Period: $\frac{360°}{|b|} = \frac{360°}{|1|}$ or $360°$

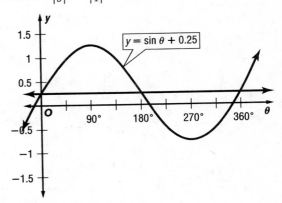

12. $y = 3\sin[2(\theta - 30°)] + 10$

Vertical shift: 10

Amplitude: $|a| = |3|$ or 3

Period: $\frac{360°}{|b|} = \frac{360°}{|2|}$ or $180°$

Phase shift: $30°$ to the right

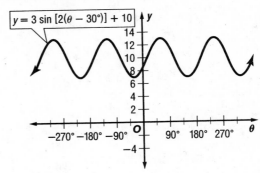

13. $y = 2\cot(3\theta + 135°) - 6$
$y = 2\cot[3(\theta + 45°)] - 6$
Vertical shift: -6
The cotangent function has no amplitude.
Period: $\frac{180°}{|b|} = \frac{180°}{|3|}$ or $60°$
Phase shift: $45°$ to the left

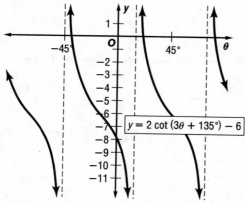

14. $y = \frac{1}{2}\sec\left[4\left(\theta - \frac{\pi}{4}\right)\right] + 1$
Vertical shift: 1
The secant function has no amplitude.
Period: $\frac{2\pi}{|b|} = \frac{2\pi}{|4|}$ or $\frac{\pi}{2}$
Phase shift: $\frac{\pi}{4}$ to the right

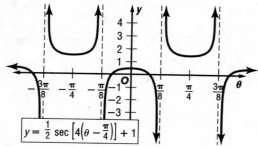

15. $y = \frac{2}{3}\cos\left[\frac{1}{2}\left(\theta + \frac{\pi}{6}\right)\right] - 2$
Vertical shift: -2
Amplitude: $|a| = \left|\frac{2}{3}\right|$ or $\frac{2}{3}$
Period: $\frac{2\pi}{|b|} = \frac{2\pi}{\left|\frac{1}{2}\right|}$ or 4π
Phase shift: $\frac{\pi}{6}$ to the left

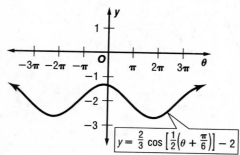

16. Vertical shift: 4 feet
Amplitude: 1 foot
Period: 4 seconds

17. Find b.
$\frac{2\pi}{|b|} = 4$
$b = \frac{\pi}{2}$ or $90°$
The equation is $h = 4 - \cos\frac{\pi}{2}t$
or $h = 4 - \cos 90°t$.

18.

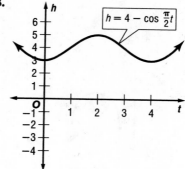

Pages 774–776   Practice and Apply

19. $y = \cos(\theta + 90°)$
Amplitude: $|a| = |1|$ or 1
Period: $\frac{360°}{|b|} = \frac{360°}{|1|}$ or $360°$
Phase shift: $90°$ to the left

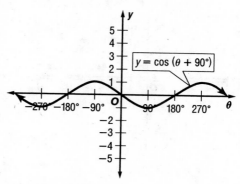

20. $y = \cot(\theta - 30°)$
The cotangent function has no amplitude.
Period: $\frac{180°}{|b|} = \frac{180°}{|1|}$ or $180°$
Phase shift: $30°$ to the right

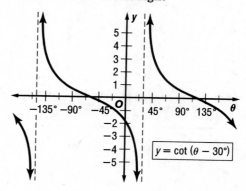

21. $y = \sin\left(\theta - \frac{\pi}{4}\right)$

Amplitude: $|a| = |1|$ or 1

Period: $\frac{2\pi}{|b|} = \frac{2\pi}{|1|}$ or 2π

Phase shift: $\frac{\pi}{4}$ to the right

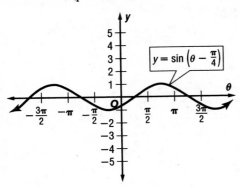

22. $y = \cos\left(\theta + \frac{\pi}{3}\right)$

Amplitude: $|a| = |1|$ or 1

Period: $\frac{2\pi}{|b|} = \frac{2\pi}{|1|}$ or 2π

Phase shift: $\frac{\pi}{3}$ to the left

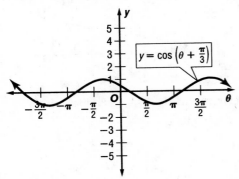

23. $y = \frac{1}{4}\tan(\theta + 22.5°)$

The tangent function has no amplitude.

Period: $\frac{180°}{|b|} = \frac{180°}{|1|}$ or $180°$

Phase shift: $22.5°$ to the left

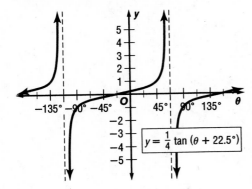

24. $y = 3\sin(\theta - 75°)$

Amplitude: $|a| = |3|$ or 3

Period: $\frac{360°}{|b|} = \frac{360°}{|1|}$ or $360°$

Phase shift: $75°$ to the right

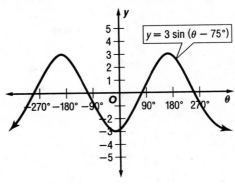

25. $y = \sin\theta - 1$

Vertical shift: -1

Equation of the Midline: $y = -1$

Amplitude: $|a| = |1|$ or 1

Period: $\frac{360°}{|b|} = \frac{360°}{|1|}$ or $360°$

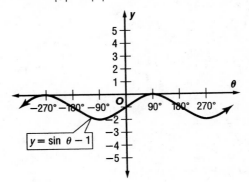

26. $y = \sec\theta + 2$

Vertical shift: 2

Equation of the Midline: $y = 2$

The secant function has no amplitude.

Period: $\frac{360°}{|b|} = \frac{360°}{|1|}$ or $360°$

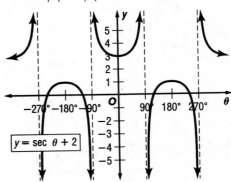

27. $y = \cos \theta - 5$

Vertical shift: -5

Equation of the Midline: $y = -5$

Amplitude: $|a| = |1|$ or 1

Period: $\frac{360°}{|b|} = \frac{360°}{|1|}$ or 360°

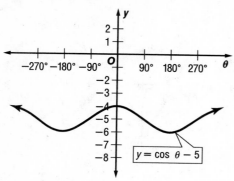

28. $y = \csc \theta - \frac{3}{4}$

Vertical shift: $-\frac{3}{4}$

Equation of the Midline: $y = -\frac{3}{4}$

The cosecant function has no amplitude.

Period: $\frac{360°}{|b|} = \frac{360°}{|1|}$ or 360°

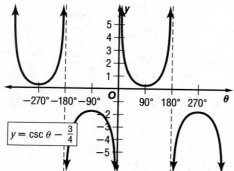

29. $y = \frac{1}{2} \sin \theta + \frac{1}{2}$

Vertical shift: $\frac{1}{2}$

Equation of the Midline: $y = \frac{1}{2}$

Amplitude: $|a| = \left|\frac{1}{2}\right|$ or $\frac{1}{2}$

Period: $\frac{360°}{|b|} = \frac{360°}{|1|}$ or 360°

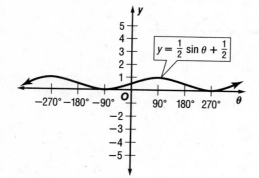

30. $y = 6 \cos \theta + 1.5$

Vertical shift: 1.5

Equation of the Midline: $y = 1.5$

Amplituds: $|a| = |6|$ or 6

Period: $\frac{360°}{|b|} = \frac{360°}{|1|}$ or 360°

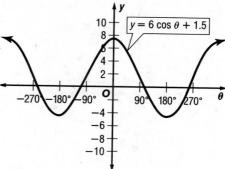

31.

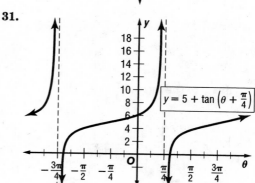

The parent function is translated $\frac{\pi}{4}$ unit to the left and 5 units up.

32.

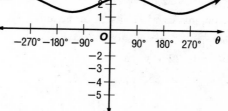

This is a translation 50° to the right and 2 units up with an amplitude of $\frac{2}{3}$ unit.

33. $y = 2 \sin[3(\theta - 45°)] + 1$
Vertical Shift: 1
Amplitude: $|a| = |2|$ or 2
Period: $\frac{360°}{|b|} = \frac{360°}{|3|}$ or 120°
Phase shift: 45° to the right

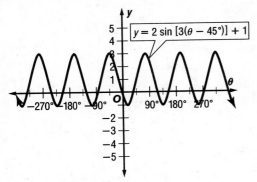

34. $y = 4 \cos[2(\theta + 30°)] - 5$
Vertical shift: −5
Amplitude: $|a| = |4|$ or 4
Period: $\frac{360°}{|b|} = \frac{360°}{|2|}$ or 180°
Phase shift: 30° to the left

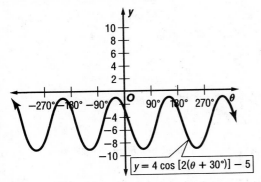

35. $y = 3 \csc\left[\frac{1}{2}(\theta + 60°)\right] - 3.5$
Vertical shift: −3.5
The cosecant function has no amplitude.
Period: $\frac{360°}{|b|} = \frac{360°}{\left|\frac{1}{2}\right|}$ or 720°
Phase shift: 60° to the left

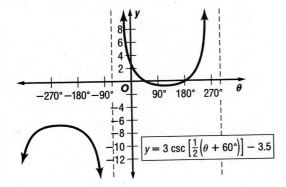

36. $y = 6 \cot\left[\frac{2}{3}(\theta - 90°)\right] + 0.75$
Vertical shift: 0.75
The cotangent function has no amplitude.
Period: $\frac{180°}{|b|} = \frac{180°}{\left|\frac{2}{3}\right|}$ or 270°
Phase shift: 90° to the right

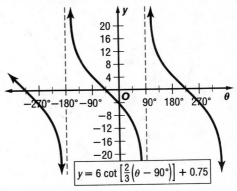

37. $y = \frac{1}{4} \cos(2\theta - 150°) + 1$
$y = \frac{1}{4} \cos[2(\theta - 75°)] + 1$
Vertical shift: 1
Amplitude: $|a| = \left|\frac{1}{4}\right|$ or $\frac{1}{4}$
Period: $\frac{360°}{|b|} = \frac{360°}{|2|}$ or 180°
Phase shift: 75° to the right

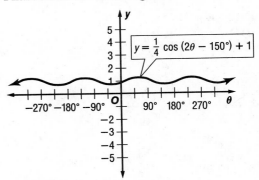

38. $y = \frac{2}{5} \tan(6\theta + 135°) - 4$
$y = \frac{2}{5} \tan[6(\theta + 22.5)] - 4$
Vertical shift: −4
The tangent function has no amplitude.
Period: $\frac{180°}{|b|} = \frac{180°}{|6|}$ or 30°
Phase shift: 22.5° to the left

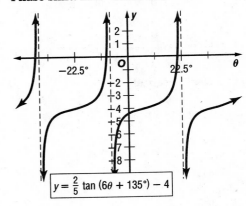

39. $y = 3 + 2 \sin\left[2\left(\theta + \frac{\pi}{4}\right)\right]$

Vertical shift: 3

Amplitude: $|a| = |2|$ or 2

Period: $\frac{2\pi}{|b|} = \frac{2\pi}{|2|}$ or π

Phase shift: $\frac{\pi}{4}$ to the left

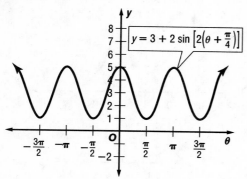

40. $y = 4 + 5 \sec\left[\frac{1}{3}\left(\theta + \frac{2\pi}{3}\right)\right]$

Vertical shift: 4

The secant function has no amplitude.

Period: $\frac{2\pi}{|b|} = \frac{2\pi}{\left|\frac{1}{3}\right|}$ or 6π

Phase shift: $\frac{2\pi}{3}$ to the left

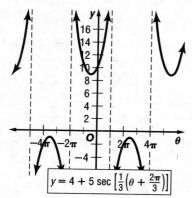

41.

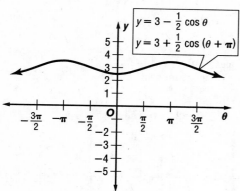

The graphs are identical.

42.

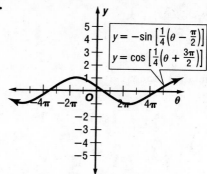

The graphs are identical.

43. c; Find b.

$$\frac{2\pi}{|b|} = \frac{1}{440}$$
$$b = 880\pi$$

44. The maximum value of $\sin\left(\frac{\pi}{10}t\right)$ is 1, so the maximum value of O is $150 + 30(1)$ or 180. The value of $\sin\left(\frac{\pi}{10}t\right)$ is 1 when $\frac{\pi}{10}t = \frac{\pi}{2}$ or $t = 5$.

The maximum number of owls is 180 and occurs after 5 years.

45. The minimum value of $\sin\left(\frac{\pi}{10}t + \frac{\pi}{20}\right)$ is -1, so the minimum value of M is $600 + 300(-1)$ or 300.

The value of $\sin\left(\frac{\pi}{10}t + \frac{\pi}{20}\right)$ is -1 when $\frac{\pi}{10}t + \frac{\pi}{20}$ is $\frac{3\pi}{2}$.

$$\frac{\pi}{10}t + \frac{\pi}{20} = \frac{3\pi}{2}$$
$$2\pi t + \pi = 30\pi$$
$$2\pi t = 29\pi$$
$$t = \frac{29}{2} \text{ or } 14.5$$

The minimum number of mice is 300 and occurs after 14.5 years.

46. Sample answer: When the prey (mouse) population is at its greatest the predator will consume more and the predator population will grow while the prey population falls.

47. First find the midline.

$y = \frac{15 + 3}{2}$ or 9

The vertical shift is 9.

Since the tide reaches extremes 6 feet above and below the midline, the amplitude is 6.

The period is 18 hours. Find b.

$\frac{2\pi}{|b|} = 18$

$b = \frac{\pi}{9}$

To find the phase shift, solve

$h = 9 + 6 \sin\left[\frac{\pi}{9}(t - p)\right]$ for p when $t = 6$ and $h = 15$.

$15 = 9 + 6 \sin\left[\frac{\pi}{9}(6 - p)\right]$

$6 = 6 \sin\left[\frac{\pi}{9}(6 - p)\right]$

$1 = \sin\left[\frac{\pi}{9}(6 - p)\right]$

$\frac{\pi}{2} = \frac{\pi}{9}(6 - p)$

$4.5 = 6 - p$

$-1.5 = -p$

$1.5 = p$

The equation is $h = 9 + 6 \sin\left[\frac{\pi}{9}(t - 1.5)\right]$.

48. The periods of the cotangent and tangent functions are the same, so $b = 1$.

If $h = \frac{\pi}{2}$, the x-intercept of $y = \tan x$ at the origin would be translated to $x = \frac{\pi}{2}$, an x-intercept of the cotangent function.

Finally, the graph needs to be reflected across the x-axis. This is accomplished by letting $a = -1$.

49. Sample answer: You can use changes in amplitude and period along with vertical and horizontal shifts to show an animal population's starting point and display changes to that population over a period of time. Answers should include the following information.

- The equation shows a rabbit population that begins at 1200, increases to a maximum of 1450 then decreases to a minimum of 950 over a period of 4 years.
- Relative to $y = a \cos bx$, $y = a \cos bx + k$ would have a vertical shift of k units, while $y = a \cos [b(x - h)]$ has a horizontal shift of h units.

50. B; The graph is the graph of $y = \cot \theta$ shifted 45° to the right.

51. D; Since the phase shift is 20° to the left, we can eliminate answer choices A and B where the shift is to the right. Find b.

$\frac{360°}{|b|} = 90°$

$b = 4$

The correct answer choice is D.

Page 776　Maintain Your Skills

52. $y = 3 \csc \theta$

The cosecant function has no amplitude.

Period: $\frac{360°}{|b|} = \frac{360°}{|1|}$

$= 360°$ or 2π

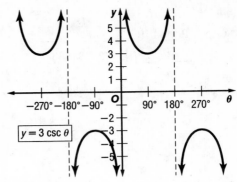

53. $y = \sin \frac{\theta}{2}$

Amplitude: $|a| = |1|$ or 1

Period: $\frac{360°}{|b|} = \frac{360°}{\left|\frac{1}{2}\right|}$

$= 720°$ or 4π

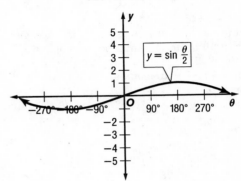

54. $y = 3 \tan \frac{2}{3}\theta$

The tangent function has no amplitude.

Period: $\frac{180°}{|b|} = \frac{180°}{\left|\frac{2}{3}\right|}$

$= 270°$ or $\frac{3\pi}{2}$

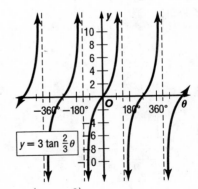

55. $\sin\left(\text{Cos}^{-1} \frac{2}{3}\right)$

KEYSTROKES: SIN 2nd [COS^{-1}] 2 ÷ 3)

) ENTER .7453559925

$\sin\left(\text{Cos}^{-1} \frac{2}{3}\right) \approx 0.75$

56. $\cos\left(\text{Cos}^{-1} \frac{4}{7}\right)$

KEYSTROKES: COS 2nd [COS^{-1}] 4 ÷ 7)

) ENTER .5714285714

$\cos\left(\text{Cos}^{-1} \frac{4}{7}\right) \approx 0.57$

57. $\sin^{-1}\left(\sin\frac{5}{6}\right)$

KEYSTROKES: [2nd] [SIN^{-1}] [SIN] 5 [÷] 6 [)]
[)] [ENTER] .8333333333

$\sin^{-1}\left(\sin\frac{5}{6}\right) \approx 0.83$

58. $\cos\left(\text{Tan}^{-1}\frac{3}{4}\right)$

KEYSTROKES: [COS] [2nd] [TAN^{-1}] 3 [÷] 4 [)]
[)] [ENTER] .8

$\cos\left(\text{Tan}^{-1}\frac{3}{4}\right) = 0.8$

59. First count the total number of ways you can connect two vertices of the decagon with a line segment.

$C(n, r) = \frac{n!}{(n-r)!\,r!}$

$C(10, 2) = \frac{10!}{(10-2)!\,2!}$

$= \frac{10!}{8!\,2!}$ or 45

This number includes the sides of the decagon. Subtract 10 to find the number of diagonals.

$45 - 10 = 35$

A decagon has 35 diagonals.

60.
$4^x = 24$
$\log 4^x = \log 24$
$x \log 4 = \log 24$
$x = \frac{\log 24}{\log 4}$
$x \approx 2.29$

61.
$4.3^{3x+1} = 78.5$
$\log 4.3^{3x+1} = \log 78.5$
$(3x+1)\log 4.3 = \log 78.5$
$3x + 1 = \frac{\log 78.5}{\log 4.3}$
$3x = \frac{\log 78.5}{\log 4.3} - 1$
$x = \frac{1}{3}\left(\frac{\log 78.5}{\log 4.3} - 1\right)$
$x \approx 0.66$

62.
$7^{x-2} = 53^{-x}$
$\log 7^{x-2} = \log 53^{-x}$
$(x-2)\log 7 = (-x)\log 53$
$x\log 7 - 2\log 7 = -x\log 53$
$x\log 7 + x\log 53 = 2\log 7$
$x(\log 7 + \log 53) = 2\log 7$
$x = \frac{2\log 7}{\log 7 + \log 53}$
$x \approx 0.66$

63. $\frac{3}{a-2} + \frac{2}{a-3} = \frac{3(a-3)}{(a-2)(a-3)} + \frac{2(a-2)}{(a-3)(a-2)}$

$= \frac{3(a-3) + 2(a-2)}{(a-2)(a-3)}$

$= \frac{3a - 9 + 2a - 4}{(a-2)(a-3)}$

$= \frac{5a - 13}{(a-2)(a-3)}$

64. $\frac{w+12}{4w-16} - \frac{w+4}{2w-8} = \frac{w+12}{4(w-4)} - \frac{w+4}{2(w-4)}$

$= \frac{w+12}{4(w-4)} - \frac{(w+4)(2)}{2(w-4)(2)}$

$= \frac{(w+12) - (2)(w+4)}{4(w-4)}$

$= \frac{w + 12 - 2w - 8}{4(w-4)}$

$= \frac{-w + 4}{4(w-4)}$

$= \frac{-1(w - 4)}{4(w - 4)}$ or $-\frac{1}{4}$

65. $\frac{3y+1}{2y-10} + \frac{1}{y^2 - 2y - 15} = \frac{3y+1}{2(y-5)} + \frac{1}{(y-5)(y+3)}$

$= \frac{(3y+1)(y+3)}{2(y-5)(y+3)} + \frac{1(2)}{(y-5)(y+3)(2)}$

$= \frac{(3y+1)(y+3) + 2}{2(y-5)(y+3)}$

$= \frac{3y^2 + 9y + y + 3 + 2}{2(y-5)(y+3)}$

$= \frac{3y^2 + 10y + 5}{2(y-5)(y+3)}$

66. $\cos 150°$

Because the terminal side of 150° lies in Quadrant II, the reference angle θ' is $180° - 150°$ or 30°. The cosine function is negative in Quadrant II, so $\cos 150° = -\cos 30°$ or $-\frac{\sqrt{3}}{2}$.

67. $\tan 135°$

Because the terminal side of 135° lies in Quadrant II, the reference angel θ' is $180° - 135°$ or 45°. The tangent function is negative in Quadrant II, so $\tan 135° = -\tan 45°$ or -1.

68. $\sin\frac{3\pi}{2}$

Because the terminal side of $\frac{3\pi}{2}$ lies on the negative y-axis, a point on the terminal side of $\frac{3\pi}{2}$ is of the form $(0, -r)$.

$\sin\frac{3\pi}{2} = \frac{y}{r}$

$= \frac{-r}{r}$ or -1

69. $\cos\left(-\frac{\pi}{3}\right)$

A coterminal angle of $-\frac{\pi}{3}$ is $2\pi - \frac{\pi}{3}$ or $\frac{5\pi}{3}$. Because the terminal side of $\frac{5\pi}{3}$ lies in Quadrant IV, the reference angle θ' is $2\pi - \frac{5\pi}{3}$ or $\frac{\pi}{3}$. The cosine function is positive in Quadrant IV, so $\cos\left(-\frac{\pi}{3}\right) = \cos\frac{\pi}{3}$ or $\frac{1}{2}$.

70. $\sin(-\pi)$

A coterminal angle of $-\pi$ is $2\pi - \pi$ or π. Because the terminal side of π lies on the negative x-axis, a point on the terminal side of π is of the form $(-r, 0)$.

$\sin(-\pi) = \frac{y}{r}$

$= \frac{0}{r}$ or 0

71. $\tan\left(-\frac{5\pi}{6}\right)$

A coterminal angle of $-\frac{5\pi}{6}$ is $2\pi - \frac{5\pi}{6}$ or $\frac{7\pi}{6}$.
Because the terminal side of $\frac{7\pi}{6}$ lies in
Quadrant III, the reference angle θ' is $\frac{7\pi}{6} - \pi$
or $\frac{\pi}{6}$. The tangent function is positive in
Quadrant III, so $\tan\left(-\frac{5\pi}{6}\right) = \tan\frac{\pi}{6}$ or $\frac{\sqrt{3}}{3}$.

72. $\cos 225°$
Because the terminal side of $225°$ lies in
Quadrant III, the reference angle θ' is
$225° - 180°$ or $45°$. The cosine function is
negative in Quadrant III, so $\cos 225° = -\cos 45°$
or $-\frac{\sqrt{2}}{2}$.

73. $\tan 405°$
A coterminal angle of $405°$ is $405° - 360°$ or $45°$,
so $\tan 405° = \tan 45°$ or 1.

14-3 Trigonometric Identities

Page 779 Check for Understanding

1. Sample answer: The sine function is negative in
the third and fourth quadrants. Therefore, the
terminal side of the angle must lie in one of those
two quadrants.

2. Sample answer: Pythagorean identities are
derived by applying the Pythagorean Theorem to
trigonometric concepts.

3. Sample answer: Simplifying a trigonometric
expression means writing the expression as a
numerical value or in terms of a single
trigonometric function, if possible.

4. First find $\cos\theta$.
$$\cos^2\theta + \sin^2\theta = 1$$
$$\cos^2\theta = 1 - \sin^2\theta$$
$$\cos^2\theta = 1 - \left(\frac{1}{2}\right)^2$$
$$\cos^2\theta = 1 - \frac{1}{4}$$
$$\cos^2\theta = \frac{3}{4}$$
$$\cos\theta = \pm\frac{\sqrt{3}}{2}$$

Since θ is in the second quadrant, $\cos\theta$ is
negative. Thus, $\cos\theta = -\frac{\sqrt{3}}{2}$.

Now find $\tan\theta$.
$$\tan\theta = \frac{\sin\theta}{\cos\theta}$$
$$= \frac{\frac{1}{2}}{-\frac{\sqrt{3}}{2}}$$
$$= \frac{1}{2} \cdot \left(-\frac{2}{\sqrt{3}}\right) \text{ or } -\frac{1}{\sqrt{3}} \text{ or } -\frac{\sqrt{3}}{3}$$

5. First find $\sin\theta$.
$$\cos^2\theta + \sin^2\theta = 1$$
$$\sin^2\theta = 1 - \cos^2\theta$$
$$\sin^2\theta = 1 - \left(-\frac{3}{5}\right)^2$$
$$\sin^2\theta = 1 - \frac{9}{25}$$
$$\sin^2\theta = \frac{16}{25}$$
$$\sin\theta = \pm\frac{4}{5}$$

Since θ is in the third quadrant, $\sin\theta$ is negative.
Thus, $\sin\theta = -\frac{4}{5}$.

Now find $\csc\theta$.
$$\csc\theta = \frac{1}{\sin\theta}$$
$$= \frac{1}{-\frac{4}{5}} \text{ or } -\frac{5}{4}$$

6. Find $\cos\theta$.
$$\cos^2\theta + \sin^2\theta = 1$$
$$\cos^2\theta = 1 - \sin^2\theta$$
$$\cos^2\theta = 1 - \left(\frac{4}{5}\right)^2$$
$$\cos^2\theta = 1 - \frac{16}{25}$$
$$\cos^2\theta = \frac{9}{25}$$
$$\cos\theta = \pm\frac{3}{5}$$

Since θ is in the first quadrant, $\cos\theta$ is positive.
Thus, $\cos\theta = \frac{3}{5}$.

7. Find $\sec\theta$.
$$\tan^2\theta + 1 = \sec^2\theta$$
$$(-1)^2 + 1 = \sec^2\theta$$
$$1 + 1 = \sec^2\theta$$
$$2 = \sec^2\theta$$
$$\pm\sqrt{2} = \sec\theta$$
Since θ is in the fourth quadrant, $\sec\theta$ is positive.
Thus, $\sec\theta = \sqrt{2}$.

8. $\csc\theta\cos\theta\tan\theta = \frac{1}{\sin\theta} \cdot \cos\theta \cdot \frac{\sin\theta}{\cos\theta}$
$$= \frac{\cos\theta}{\sin\theta} \cdot \frac{\sin\theta}{\cos\theta}$$
$$= 1$$

9. $\sec^2\theta - 1 = (\tan^2\theta + 1) - 1$
$$= \tan^2\theta$$

10. $\frac{\tan\theta}{\sin\theta} = \frac{\frac{\sin\theta}{\cos\theta}}{\frac{\sin\theta}{1}}$
$$= \frac{\sin\theta}{\cos\theta} \cdot \frac{1}{\sin\theta}$$
$$= \frac{1}{\cos\theta}$$
$$= \sec\theta$$

11. $\sin\theta(1 + \cot^2\theta) = \sin\theta\csc^2\theta$
$$= \sin\theta \cdot \frac{1}{\sin^2\theta}$$
$$= \frac{1}{\sin\theta}$$
$$= \csc\theta$$

12. $\tan\theta = \frac{v^2}{gR}$
$$\frac{\sin\theta}{\cos\theta} = \frac{v^2}{gR}$$
$$\sin\theta = \frac{v^2}{gR}\cos\theta$$

13. Find $\tan \theta$.

$$\cot \theta = \frac{1}{\tan \theta}$$
$$\frac{1}{\cot \theta} = \tan \theta$$
$$\frac{1}{2} = \tan \theta$$

14. Find $\sin \theta$.

$$\cos^2 \theta + \sin^2 \theta = 1$$
$$\sin^2 \theta = 1 - \cos^2 \theta$$
$$\sin^2 \theta = 1 - \left(\frac{2}{3}\right)^2$$
$$\sin^2 \theta = 1 - \frac{4}{9}$$
$$\sin^2 \theta = \frac{5}{9}$$
$$\sin \theta = \pm \frac{\sqrt{5}}{3}$$

Since θ is in the first quadrant, $\sin \theta$ is positive. Thus, $\sin \theta = \frac{\sqrt{5}}{3}$.

15. Find $\sec \theta$.

$$\tan^2 \theta + 1 = \sec^2 \theta$$
$$(-2)^2 + 1 = \sec^2 \theta$$
$$4 + 1 = \sec^2 \theta$$
$$5 = \sec^2 \theta$$
$$\pm \sqrt{5} = \sec \theta$$

Since θ is in the second quadrant, $\sec \theta$ is negative. Thus, $\sec \theta = -\sqrt{5}$.

16. Find $\tan \theta$.

$$\tan^2 \theta + 1 = \sec^2 \theta$$
$$\tan^2 \theta = \sec^2 \theta - 1$$
$$\tan^2 \theta = (-3)^2 - 1$$
$$\tan^2 \theta = 9 - 1$$
$$\tan^2 \theta = 8$$
$$\tan \theta = \pm \sqrt{8} \text{ or } \pm 2\sqrt{2}$$

Since θ is in the third quadrant, $\tan \theta$ is positive. Thus, $\tan \theta = 2\sqrt{2}$.

17. First find $\sin \theta$.

$$\cos^2 \theta + \sin^2 \theta = 1$$
$$\sin^2 \theta = 1 - \cos^2 \theta$$
$$\sin^2 \theta = 1 - \left(-\frac{3}{5}\right)^2$$
$$\sin^2 \theta = 1 - \frac{9}{25}$$
$$\sin^2 \theta = \frac{16}{25}$$
$$\sin \theta = \pm \frac{4}{5}$$

Since θ is in the second quadrant, $\sin \theta$ is positive. Thus, $\sin \theta = \frac{4}{5}$.

Now find $\csc \theta$.

$$\csc \theta = \frac{1}{\sin \theta}$$
$$= \frac{1}{\frac{4}{5}} \text{ or } \frac{5}{4}$$

18. Find $\cos \theta$.

$$\sec \theta = \frac{1}{\cos \theta}$$
$$\frac{1}{\sec \theta} = \cos \theta$$
$$\frac{1}{\frac{5}{3}} = \cos \theta$$
$$\frac{3}{5} = \cos \theta$$

19. Find $\cos \theta$.

$$\cos^2 \theta + \sin^2 \theta = 1$$
$$\cos^2 \theta = 1 - \sin^2 \theta$$
$$\cos^2 \theta = 1 - \left(\frac{1}{2}\right)^2$$
$$\cos^2 \theta = 1 - \frac{1}{4}$$
$$\cos^2 \theta = \frac{3}{4}$$
$$\cos \theta = \pm \frac{\sqrt{3}}{2}$$

Since θ is in the first quadrant, $\cos \theta$ is positive. Thus, $\cos \theta = \frac{\sqrt{3}}{2}$.

20. First find $\sin \theta$.

$$\cos^2 \theta + \sin^2 \theta = 1$$
$$\sin^2 \theta = 1 - \cos^2 \theta$$
$$\sin^2 \theta = 1 - \left(-\frac{2}{3}\right)^2$$
$$\sin^2 \theta = 1 - \frac{4}{9}$$
$$\sin^2 \theta = \frac{5}{9}$$
$$\sin \theta = \pm \frac{\sqrt{5}}{3}$$

Since θ is in the third quadrant, $\sin \theta$ is negative. Thus, $\sin \theta = -\frac{\sqrt{5}}{3}$.

Now find $\csc \theta$.

$$\csc \theta = \frac{1}{\sin \theta}$$
$$= \frac{1}{-\frac{\sqrt{5}}{3}}$$
$$= -\frac{3}{\sqrt{5}} \text{ or } -\frac{3\sqrt{5}}{5}$$

21. First find $\sin \theta$.

$$\cos^2 \theta + \sin^2 \theta = 1$$
$$\sin^2 \theta = 1 - \cos^2 \theta$$
$$\sin^2 \theta = 1 - \left(\frac{4}{5}\right)^2$$
$$\sin^2 \theta = 1 - \frac{16}{25}$$
$$\sin^2 \theta = \frac{9}{25}$$
$$\sin \theta = \pm \frac{3}{5}$$

Since θ is in the third quadrant, $\sin \theta$ is positive. Thus, $\sin \theta = \frac{3}{5}$.

Now find $\tan \theta$.

$$\tan \theta = \frac{\sin \theta}{\cos \theta}$$
$$= \frac{\frac{3}{5}}{\frac{4}{5}}$$
$$= \frac{3}{5} \cdot \frac{5}{4} \text{ or } \frac{3}{4}$$

22. First find $\sin \theta$.

$\csc \theta = \dfrac{1}{\sin \theta}$

$-\dfrac{5}{3} = \dfrac{1}{\sin \theta}$

$-\dfrac{3}{5} = \sin \theta$

Now find $\cos \theta$.

$\cos^2 \theta + \sin^2 \theta = 1$

$\cos^2 \theta = 1 - \sin^2 \theta$

$\cos^2 \theta = 1 - \left(-\dfrac{3}{5}\right)^2$

$\cos^2 \theta = 1 - \dfrac{9}{25}$

$\cos^2 \theta = \dfrac{16}{25}$

$\cos \theta = \pm\dfrac{4}{5}$

Since θ is in the fourth quadrant, $\cos \theta$ is positive.

Thus, $\cos \theta = \dfrac{4}{5}$.

23. First find $\cos \theta$.

$\cos^2 \theta + \sin^2 \theta = 1$

$\cos^2 \theta = 1 - \sin^2 \theta$

$\cos^2 \theta = 1 - \left(\dfrac{3}{4}\right)^2$

$\cos^2 \theta = 1 - \dfrac{9}{16}$

$\cos^2 \theta = \dfrac{7}{16}$

$\cos \theta = \pm\dfrac{\sqrt{7}}{4}$

Since θ is in the second quadrant, $\cos \theta$ is negative. Thus, $\cos \theta = -\dfrac{\sqrt{7}}{4}$.

Now find $\sec \theta$.

$\sec \theta = \dfrac{1}{\cos \theta}$

$= \dfrac{1}{-\frac{\sqrt{7}}{4}}$

$= -\dfrac{4}{\sqrt{7}}$ or $-\dfrac{4\sqrt{7}}{4}$

24. First find $\sec \theta$.

$\tan^2 \theta + 1 = \sec^2 \theta$

$4^2 + 1 = \sec^2 \theta$

$16 + 1 = \sec^2 \theta$

$17 = \sec^2 \theta$

$\pm\sqrt{17} = \sec \theta$

Since θ is in the third quadrant, $\sec \theta$ is negative. Thus, $\sec \theta = -\sqrt{17}$.

Now find $\cos \theta$.

$\sec \theta = \dfrac{1}{\cos \theta}$

$\dfrac{1}{\sec \theta} = \cos \theta$

$\dfrac{1}{-\sqrt{17}} = \cos \theta$

$-\dfrac{\sqrt{17}}{17} = \cos \theta$

Finally, find $\sin \theta$.

$\cos^2 \theta + \sin^2 \theta = 1$

$\sin^2 \theta = 1 - \cos^2 \theta$

$\sin^2 \theta = 1 - \left(-\dfrac{\sqrt{17}}{17}\right)^2$

$\sin^2 \theta = 1 - \dfrac{17}{289}$

$\sin^2 \theta = \dfrac{272}{289}$

$\sin \theta = \pm\dfrac{\sqrt{272}}{17}$ or $\pm\dfrac{4\sqrt{17}}{17}$

Since θ is in the third quadrant, $\sin \theta$ is negative.

Thus, $\sin \theta = -\dfrac{4\sqrt{17}}{17}$.

25. $\cos \theta \csc \theta = \dfrac{\cos \theta}{1} \cdot \dfrac{1}{\sin \theta}$

$= \dfrac{\cos \theta}{\sin \theta}$

$= \cot \theta$

26. $\tan \theta \cot \theta = \dfrac{\sin \theta}{\cos \theta} \cdot \dfrac{\cos \theta}{\sin \theta}$

$= 1$

27. $\sin \theta \cot \theta = \dfrac{\sin \theta}{1} \cdot \dfrac{\cos \theta}{\sin \theta}$

$= \cos \theta$

28. $\cos \theta \tan \theta = \dfrac{\cos \theta}{1} \cdot \dfrac{\sin \theta}{\cos \theta}$

$= \sin \theta$

29. $2(\csc^2 \theta - \cot^2 \theta) = 2[(\cot^2 \theta + 1) - \cot^2 \theta]$

$= 2(1)$

$= 2$

30. $3(\tan^2 \theta - \sec^2 \theta) = 3[\tan^2 \theta - (\tan^2 \theta + 1)]$

$= 3(-1)$

$= -3$

31. $\dfrac{\cos \theta \csc \theta}{\tan \theta} = \dfrac{\frac{\cos \theta}{1} \cdot \frac{1}{\sin \theta}}{\frac{\sin \theta}{\cos \theta}}$

$= \dfrac{\cos \theta}{\sin \theta} \cdot \dfrac{\cos \theta}{\sin \theta}$

$= \cot \theta \cdot \cot \theta$

$= \cot^2 \theta$

32. $\dfrac{\sin \theta \csc \theta}{\cot \theta} = \dfrac{\frac{\sin \theta}{1} \cdot \frac{1}{\sin \theta}}{\frac{\cos \theta}{\sin \theta}}$

$= 1 \cdot \dfrac{\sin \theta}{\cos \theta}$

$= \tan \theta$

33. $\dfrac{1 - \cos^2 \theta}{\sin^2 \theta} = \dfrac{(\cos^2 \theta + \sin^2 \theta) - \cos^2 \theta}{\sin^2 \theta}$

$= \dfrac{\sin^2 \theta}{\sin^2 \theta}$

$= 1$

34. $\dfrac{1 - \sin^2 \theta}{\sin^2 \theta} = \dfrac{(\cos^2 \theta + \sin^2 \theta) - \sin^2 \theta}{\sin^2 \theta}$

$= \dfrac{\cos^2 \theta}{\sin^2 \theta}$

$= \left(\dfrac{\cos \theta}{\sin \theta}\right)^2$

$= \cot^2 \theta$

35. $\dfrac{\sin^2 \theta + \cos^2 \theta}{\sin^2 \theta} = \dfrac{\cos^2 \theta + \sin^2 \theta}{\sin^2 \theta}$

$= \dfrac{1}{\sin^2 \theta}$

$= \left(\dfrac{1}{\sin \theta}\right)^2$

$= \csc^2 \theta$

36. $\dfrac{\tan^2 \theta - \sin^2 \theta}{\tan^2 \theta \sin^2 \theta} = \dfrac{\tan^2 \theta}{\tan^2 \theta \sin^2 \theta} - \dfrac{\sin^2 \theta}{\tan^2 \theta \sin^2 \theta}$

$= \dfrac{1}{\sin^2 \theta} - \dfrac{1}{\tan^2 \theta}$

$= \csc^2 \theta - \cot^2 \theta$

$= (\cot^2 \theta + 1) - \cot^2 \theta$

$= 1$

37. Find $\text{Sin}^{-1} \dfrac{1}{5}$.

KEYSTROKES: 【2nd】 [SIN⁻¹] 1 【÷】 5 【)】 【ENTER】

11.53695903

The angle of inclination is about 11.5°.

38. First find $\cos \theta$.

$$\cos^2 \theta + \sin^2 \theta = 1$$
$$\cos^2 \theta = 1 - \sin^2 \theta$$
$$\cos^2 \theta = 1 - \left(\frac{1}{5}\right)^2$$
$$\cos^2 \theta = 1 - \frac{1}{25}$$
$$\cos^2 \theta = \frac{24}{25}$$
$$\cos \theta = \pm \frac{\sqrt{24}}{5} \text{ or } \pm \frac{2\sqrt{6}}{5}$$

Assuming θ is in the first quadrant, $\cos \theta$ is positive. Thus, $\cos \theta = \frac{2\sqrt{6}}{5}$.

Now use the result of Exercise 12 to find v.

$$\sin \theta = \frac{v^2}{gR} \cos \theta$$
$$\frac{1}{5} = \frac{v^2}{(9.8)(8)} \cdot \frac{2\sqrt{6}}{5}$$
$$\frac{1}{5} = \frac{\sqrt{6}}{196} v^2$$
$$\frac{196}{5\sqrt{6}} = v^2$$
$$\pm\sqrt{\frac{196}{5\sqrt{6}}} = v$$

Assuming the velocity is positive, the velocity of the merry-go-round is $\sqrt{\frac{196}{5\sqrt{6}}}$ or about 4 meters per second.

39. Find the tangent of the angle of inclination.

$$\tan \theta = \frac{v^2}{gR}$$
$$\tan \theta = \frac{3.6^2}{(9.8)(8)}$$
$$\tan \theta = \frac{12.96}{78.4} \text{ or } \frac{81}{490}$$

KEYSTROKES: [2nd] [TAN^{-1}] 81 [÷] 490 [ )]
[ENTER] 9.386458923

The angle of inclination is about 9.4°.

40.
$$\sec \theta = \frac{I}{ER^2}$$
$$E \sec \theta = \frac{I}{R^2}$$
$$E = \frac{I}{R^2 \sec \theta} \text{ or } \frac{I \cos \theta}{R^2}$$

41. No;
$$R^2 = \frac{I \tan \theta \cos \theta}{E}$$
$$R^2 = \frac{I \cdot \frac{\sin \theta}{\cos \theta} \cdot \frac{\cos \theta}{1}}{E}$$
$$ER^2 = I \sin \theta$$
$$E = \frac{I \sin \theta}{R^2}$$

42. $P = I^2 R - I^2 R \cos^2(2ft\pi)$
$P = I^2 R[1 - \cos^2(2ft\pi)]$
$P = I^2 R \sin^2(2ft\pi)$

43. $P = I^2 R - I^2 R \cos^2 (2ft\pi)$
$$P = I^2 R - I^2 R \cdot \frac{1}{\sec^2(2ft\pi)}$$
$$P = I^2 R - \frac{I^2 R}{1 + \tan^2(2ft\pi)}$$

44.
$$\frac{\sin \beta \sec \beta}{\cot \beta} = \frac{\frac{\sin \beta}{1} \cdot \frac{1}{\cos \beta}}{\frac{\cos \beta}{\sin \beta}}$$
$$= \frac{\sin \beta}{\cos \beta} \cdot \frac{\sin \beta}{\cos \beta}$$
$$= \tan \beta \cdot \tan \beta$$
$$= \frac{3}{4} \cdot \frac{3}{4}$$
$$= \frac{9}{16}$$

45. Sample answer: You can use equations to find the height and the horizontal distance of a baseball after it has been hit. The equations involve using the initial angle the ball makes with the ground with the sine function. Answers should include the following information.
- Both equations are quadratic in nature with a leading negative coefficient. Thus, both are inverted parabolas which model the path of a baseball.
- model rockets, hitting a golf ball, kicking a rock

46. B; First find $\cos x$.
$$\cos^2 x + \sin^2 x = 1$$
$$\cos^2 x = 1 - \sin^2 x$$
$$\cos^2 x = 1 - m^2$$
$$\cos x = \pm\sqrt{1 - m^2}$$

Since the terminal side of x is in the first quadrant, $\cos x$ is positive. Thus,
$\cos x = \sqrt{1 - m^2}$.
Now find $\tan x$.
$$\tan x = \frac{\sin x}{\cos x}$$
$$= \frac{m}{\sqrt{1 - m^2}}$$

47. A;
$$\frac{1}{1 + \sin x} + \frac{1}{1 - \sin x}$$
$$= \frac{1(1 - \sin x)}{(1 + \sin x)(1 - \sin x)} + \frac{1(1 + \sin x)}{(1 - \sin x)(1 + \sin x)}$$
$$= \frac{(1 - \sin x) + (1 + \sin x)}{(1 + \sin x)(1 - \sin x)}$$
$$= \frac{2}{1 - \sin^2 x}$$
$$= \frac{2}{\cos^2 x}$$
$$= 2 \sec^2 x$$

Page 781   Maintain Your Skills

48. $v = \sin \theta - 1$
Vertical Shift: -1
Equation of Midline: $y = -1$
Amplitude: $|a| = |1|$ or 1
Period: $\frac{360°}{|b|} = \frac{360°}{|1|}$ or 360°

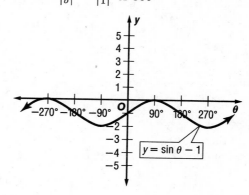

49. $y = \tan \theta + 12$
  Vertical shift: 12.
  Equation of Midline: $y = 12$.
  The tangent function has no amplitude.
  Period: $\frac{180°}{|b|} = \frac{180°}{|1|}$ or $180°$

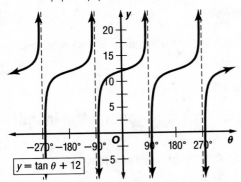

$y = \tan \theta + 12$

50. $y = \csc 2\theta$
  The cosecant function has no amplitude.
  Period: $\frac{360°}{|b|} = \frac{360°}{|2|}$
  $ = 180°$ or π

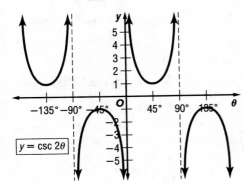

$y = \csc 2\theta$

51. $y = \cos 3\theta$
  Amplitude: $|a| = |1|$ or 1
  Period: $\frac{360°}{|b|} = \frac{360°}{|3|}$
  $ = 120°$ or $\frac{2\pi}{3}$

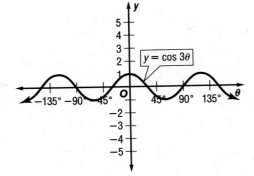

$y = \cos 3\theta$

52. $y = \frac{1}{3} \cot 5\theta$
  The cotangent function has no amplitude.
  Period: $\frac{180°}{|b|} = \frac{180°}{|5|}$
  $ = 36°$ or $\frac{\pi}{5}$

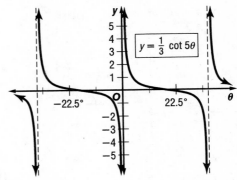

$y = \frac{1}{3} \cot 5\theta$

53. First find n.
$$a_n = a_1 \cdot r^{n-1}$$
$$3 = 48\left(\frac{1}{2}\right)^{n-1}$$
$$\frac{1}{16} = \left(\frac{1}{2}\right)^{n-1}$$
$$4 = n - 1$$
$$5 = n$$

Now find S_5.
$$S_n = \frac{a_1(1 - r^n)}{1 - r}$$
$$S_5 = \frac{48\left(1 - \left(\frac{1}{2}\right)^5\right)}{1 - \frac{1}{2}}$$
$$= 93$$
The sum is 93.

54. The focus is $(11, -1)$, so $h = 11$ and $k + \frac{1}{4a} = -1$.

The directrix is $y = 2$, so $k - \frac{1}{4a} = 2$. Add these two equations.
$$k + \frac{1}{4a} = -1$$
$$\underline{k - \frac{1}{4a} = 2}$$
$$2k \phantom{ + \frac{1}{4a}} = 1$$
$$k = \frac{1}{2}$$

Replace k with $\frac{1}{2}$ in one equation and solve for a.
$$k + \frac{1}{4a} = -1$$
$$\frac{1}{2} + \frac{1}{4a} = -1$$
$$\frac{1}{4a} = -\frac{3}{2}$$
$$\frac{1}{a} = -6$$
$$a = -\frac{1}{6}$$

Now write the equation.
$$y = a(x - h)^2 + k$$
$$y = -\frac{1}{6}(x - 11)^2 + \frac{1}{2}$$

55. Symmetric Property of Equality
56. Subtraction Property of Equality
57. Multiplication Property of Equality
58. Substitution Property of Equality

1. $y = \frac{3}{4} \sin \frac{1}{2}\theta$

Amplitude: $|a| = \left|\frac{3}{4}\right|$ or $\frac{3}{4}$

Period: $\frac{360°}{|b|} = \frac{360°}{\left|\frac{1}{2}\right|}$

$\qquad\qquad = 720°$ or 4π

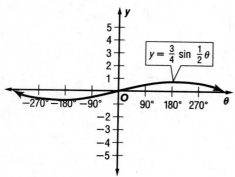

2. $y = 2 \cos\left[\frac{1}{4}\left(\theta - \frac{\pi}{4}\right)\right] - 5$

Vertical shift: -5

Amplitude: $|a| = |2|$ or 2

Period: $\frac{2\pi}{|b|} = \frac{2\pi}{\left|\frac{1}{4}\right|}$ or 8π

Phase shift: $\frac{\pi}{4}$ to the right

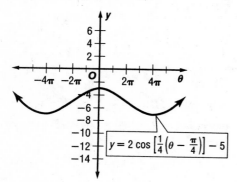

3. Find $\cos \theta$.

$\cos^2 \theta + \sin^2 \theta = 1$

$\qquad \cos^2 \theta = 1 - \sin^2 \theta$

$\qquad \cos^2 \theta = 1 - \left(\frac{4}{5}\right)^2$

$\qquad \cos^2 \theta = 1 - \frac{16}{25}$

$\qquad \cos^2 \theta = \frac{9}{25}$

$\qquad \cos \theta = \pm\frac{3}{5}$

Since θ is in the second quadrant, $\cos \theta$ is negative. Thus, $\cos \theta = -\frac{3}{5}$.

4. Find $\csc \theta$.

$\cot^2 \theta + 1 = \csc^2 \theta$

$\left(-\frac{2}{3}\right) + 1 = \csc^2 \theta$

$\qquad \frac{4}{9} + 1 = \csc^2 \theta$

$\qquad \frac{13}{9} = \csc^2 \theta$

$\qquad \pm\frac{\sqrt{13}}{3} = \csc \theta$

Since θ is in the fourth quadrant, $\csc \theta$ is negative. Thus, $\csc \theta = -\frac{\sqrt{13}}{3}$.

5. Find $\sec \theta$.

$\tan^2 \theta + 1 = \sec^2 \theta$

$\left(\frac{1}{2}\right)^2 + 1 = \sec^2 \theta$

$\qquad \frac{1}{4} + 1 = \sec^2 \theta$

$\qquad \frac{5}{4} = \sec^2 \theta$

$\qquad \pm\frac{\sqrt{5}}{2} = \sec \theta$

Since θ is in the first quadrant, $\sec \theta$ is positive. Thus, $\sec \theta = \frac{\sqrt{5}}{2}$.

14-4 Verifying Trigonometric Identities

Page 784   Check for Understanding

1. $\sin \theta \tan \theta \overset{?}{=} \sec \theta - \cos \theta$

$\sin \theta \tan \theta \overset{?}{=} \dfrac{1}{\cos \theta} - \cos \theta \quad sec\ \theta = \frac{1}{\cos \theta}$

$\sin \theta \tan \theta \overset{?}{=} \dfrac{1}{\cos \theta} - \dfrac{\cos^2 \theta}{\cos \theta} \quad$ *Multiply by the LCD, $\cos \theta$.*

$\sin \theta \tan \theta \overset{?}{=} \dfrac{1 - \cos^2 \theta}{\cos \theta} \quad$ *Subtract.*

$\sin \theta \tan \theta \overset{?}{=} \dfrac{\sin^2 \theta}{\cos \theta} \quad 1 - \cos^2 \theta = \sin^2 \theta$

$\sin \theta \tan \theta \overset{?}{=} \sin \theta \cdot \dfrac{\sin \theta}{\cos \theta} \quad$ *Factor.*

$\sin \theta \tan \theta = \sin \theta \tan \theta \quad \frac{sin}{\cos \theta} = tan\ \theta$

2. Sample answer: Use various identities, multiply or divide terms to form an equivalent expression, factor, and simplify rational expressions.

3. Sample answer: $\sin^2 \theta = 1 + \cos^2 \theta$, it is not an identity because $\sin^2 \theta = 1 - \cos^2 \theta$.

4. $\tan \theta (\cot \theta + \tan \theta) \overset{?}{=} \sec^2 \theta$

$\qquad 1 + \tan^2 \theta \overset{?}{=} \sec^2 \theta$

$\qquad\qquad \sec^2 \theta = \sec^2 \theta$

5. $\tan^2 \theta \cos^2 \theta \overset{?}{=} 1 - \cos^2 \theta$

$\dfrac{\sin^2 \theta}{\cos^2 \theta} \cdot \cos^2 \theta \overset{?}{=} \sin^2 \theta$

$\qquad\quad \sin^2 \theta = \sin^2 \theta$

6.

$\qquad \dfrac{\cos^2 \theta}{1 - \sin \theta} \overset{?}{=} 1 + \sin \theta$

$\qquad \dfrac{1 - \sin^2 \theta}{1 - \sin \theta} \overset{?}{=} 1 + \sin \theta$

$\dfrac{(1 - \sin \theta)(1 + \sin \theta)}{1 - \sin \theta} \overset{?}{=} 1 + \sin \theta$

$\qquad\quad 1 + \sin \theta = 1 + \sin \theta$

7.

$\qquad \dfrac{1 + \tan^2 \theta}{\csc^2 \theta} \overset{?}{=} \tan^2 \theta$

$\qquad\quad \dfrac{\sec^2 \theta}{\csc^2 \theta} \overset{?}{=} \tan^2 \theta$

$\qquad\quad \dfrac{\frac{1}{\cos^2 \theta}}{\frac{1}{\sin^2 \theta}} \overset{?}{=} \tan^2 \theta$

$\dfrac{1}{\cos^2 \theta} \cdot \sin^2 \theta \overset{?}{=} \tan^2 \theta$

$\qquad\quad \tan^2 \theta = \tan^2 \theta$

8. $\dfrac{\sin \theta}{\sec \theta} \stackrel{?}{=} \dfrac{1}{\tan \theta + \cot \theta}$

$\dfrac{\sin \theta}{\sec \theta} \stackrel{?}{=}$

$\dfrac{\sin \theta}{\sec \theta} \stackrel{?}{=}$

$\dfrac{\sin \theta}{\sec \theta} \stackrel{?}{=} \dfrac{\sin \theta \cos \theta}{\sin^2 \theta + \cos^2 \theta}$

$\dfrac{\sin \theta}{\sec \theta} \stackrel{?}{=} \dfrac{\sin \theta \cos \theta}{1}$

$\dfrac{\sin \theta}{\sec \theta} = \dfrac{\sin \theta}{\sec \theta}$

9. $\dfrac{\sec \theta + 1}{\tan \theta} \stackrel{?}{=} \dfrac{\tan \theta}{\sec \theta - 1}$

$\dfrac{\sec \theta + 1}{\tan \theta} \stackrel{?}{=} \dfrac{\tan \theta}{\sec \theta - 1} \cdot \dfrac{\sec \theta + 1}{\sec \theta + 1}$

$\dfrac{\sec \theta + 1}{\tan \theta} \stackrel{?}{=} \dfrac{\tan \theta \cdot (\sec \theta + 1)}{}$

$\dfrac{\sec \theta + 1}{\tan \theta} \stackrel{?}{=} \dfrac{\tan \theta \cdot (\sec \theta + 1)}{}$

$\dfrac{\sec \theta + 1}{\tan \theta} = \dfrac{\sec \theta + 1}{\tan \theta}$

10. D; $\dfrac{\sec \theta + \csc \theta}{1 + \tan \theta} = \dfrac{\frac{1}{\cos \theta} + \frac{1}{\sin \theta}}{1 + \frac{\sin \theta}{\cos \theta}}$

$= \dfrac{\frac{\sin \theta + \cos \theta}{\cos \theta \sin \theta}}{\frac{\cos \theta + \sin \theta}{\cos \theta}}$

$= \dfrac{\sin \theta + \cos \theta}{\cos \theta \sin \theta} \cdot \dfrac{\cos \theta}{\cos \theta + \sin \theta}$

$= \dfrac{1}{\sin \theta}$

$= \csc \theta$

Pages 784–785 Practice and Apply

11. $\cos^2 \theta + \tan^2 \theta \cos^2 \theta \stackrel{?}{=} 1$

$\cos^2 \theta + \dfrac{\sin^2 \theta}{\cos^2 \theta} \cdot \cos^2 \theta \stackrel{?}{=} 1$

$\cos^2 \theta + \sin^2 \theta \stackrel{?}{=} 1$

$1 = 1$

12. $\cot \theta \, (\cot \theta + \tan \theta) \stackrel{?}{=} \csc^2 \theta$

$\cot^2 + \cot \theta \tan \theta \stackrel{?}{=} \csc^2 \theta$

$\cot^2 \theta + \dfrac{\cos \theta}{\sin \theta} \cdot \dfrac{\sin \theta}{\cos \theta} \stackrel{?}{=} \csc^2 \theta$

$\cot^2 \theta + 1 \stackrel{?}{=} \csc^2 \theta$

$\csc^2 \theta = \csc^2 \theta$

13. $1 + \sec^2 \theta \sin^2 \theta \stackrel{?}{=} \sec^2 \theta$

$1 + \dfrac{1}{\cos^2 \theta} \cdot \sin^2 \theta \stackrel{?}{=} \sec^2 \theta$

$1 + \tan^2 \theta \stackrel{?}{=} \sec^2 \theta$

$\sec^2 \theta = \sec^2 \theta$

14. $\sin \theta \sec \theta \cot \theta \stackrel{?}{=} 1$

$\sin \theta \cdot \dfrac{1}{\cos \theta} \cdot \dfrac{\cos \theta}{\sin \theta} \stackrel{?}{=} 1$

$1 = 1$

15. $\dfrac{1 - \cos \theta}{1 + \cos \theta} \stackrel{?}{=} (\csc \theta - \cot \theta)^2$

$\dfrac{1 - \cos \theta}{1 + \cos \theta} \stackrel{?}{=} \csc^2 \theta - 2 \cot \theta \csc \theta + \cot^2 \theta$

$\dfrac{1 - \cos \theta}{1 + \cos \theta} \stackrel{?}{=} \dfrac{1}{\sin^2 \theta} - 2 \cdot \dfrac{\cos \theta}{\sin \theta} \cdot \dfrac{1}{\sin \theta} + \dfrac{\cos^2 \theta}{\sin^2 \theta}$

$\dfrac{1 - \cos \theta}{1 + \cos \theta} \stackrel{?}{=} \dfrac{1}{\sin^2 \theta} - \dfrac{2 \cos \theta}{\sin^2 \theta} + \dfrac{\cos^2 \theta}{\sin^2 \theta}$

$\dfrac{1 - \cos \theta}{1 + \cos \theta} \stackrel{?}{=} \dfrac{1 - 2 \cos \theta + \cos^2 \theta}{}$

$\dfrac{1 - \cos \theta}{1 + \cos \theta} \stackrel{?}{=} \dfrac{(1 - \cos \theta)(1 - \cos \theta)}{}$

$\dfrac{1 - \cos \theta}{1 + \cos \theta} \stackrel{?}{=} \dfrac{(1 - \cos \theta)(1 - \cos \theta)}{}$

$\dfrac{1 - \cos \theta}{1 + \cos \theta} = \dfrac{1 - \cos \theta}{1 + \cos \theta}$

16. $\dfrac{1 - 2 \cos^2 \theta}{\sin \theta \cos \theta} \stackrel{?}{=} \tan \theta - \cot \theta$

$\dfrac{(1 - \cos^2 \theta) - \cos^2 \theta}{} \stackrel{?}{=} \tan \theta - \cot \theta$

$\dfrac{\sin^2 \theta - \cos^2 \theta}{\sin \theta \cos \theta} \stackrel{?}{=} \tan \theta - \cot \theta$

$\dfrac{\sin^2 \theta}{\sin \theta \cos \theta} - \dfrac{\cos^2 \theta}{\sin \theta \cos \theta} \stackrel{?}{=} \tan \theta - \cot \theta$

$\dfrac{\sin \theta}{\cos \theta} - \dfrac{\cos \theta}{\sin \theta} \stackrel{?}{=} \tan \theta - \cot \theta$

$\tan \theta - \cot \theta = \tan \theta - \cot \theta$

17. $\cot \theta \csc \theta \stackrel{?}{=} \dfrac{\cot \theta + \csc \theta}{}$

$\cot \theta \csc \theta \stackrel{?}{=} \dfrac{\frac{\cos \theta}{\sin \theta} + \frac{1}{\sin \theta}}{\frac{\sin \theta + \sin \theta}{\cos \theta}}$

$\cot \theta \csc \theta \stackrel{?}{=} \dfrac{\frac{\cos \theta + 1}{\sin \theta}}{\frac{\sin \theta \cos \theta + \sin \theta}{\cos \theta}}$

$\cot \theta \csc \theta \stackrel{?}{=} \dfrac{\frac{\cos \theta + 1}{\sin \theta}}{\frac{\sin \theta (\cos \theta + 1)}{\cos \theta}}$

$\cot \theta \csc \theta \stackrel{?}{=} \dfrac{\cos \theta + 1}{\sin \theta} \cdot \dfrac{\cos \theta}{\sin \theta (\cos \theta + 1)}$

$\cot \theta \csc \theta \stackrel{?}{=} \dfrac{\cos \theta}{\sin \theta} \cdot \dfrac{1}{\sin \theta}$

$\cot \theta \csc \theta = \cot \theta \csc \theta$

18. $\sin \theta + \cos \theta \stackrel{?}{=} \dfrac{1 + \tan \theta}{\sec \theta}$

$\sin \theta + \cos \theta \stackrel{?}{=} \dfrac{1 + \frac{\sin \theta}{\cos \theta}}{\frac{1}{\cos \theta}}$

$\sin \theta + \cos \theta \stackrel{?}{=} \dfrac{\frac{\sin \theta + \cos \theta}{\cos \theta}}{\frac{1}{\cos \theta}}$

$\sin \theta + \cos \theta \stackrel{?}{=} \dfrac{\sin \theta + \cos \theta}{\cos \theta} \cdot \cos \theta$

$\sin \theta + \cos \theta = \sin \theta + \cos \theta$

19. $\dfrac{\sec \theta}{\sin \theta} - \dfrac{\sin \theta}{\cos \theta} \stackrel{?}{=} \cot \theta$

$\dfrac{1}{\frac{\cos \theta}{\sin \theta}} - \dfrac{\sin \theta}{\cos \theta} \stackrel{?}{=} \cot \theta$

$\dfrac{1}{\sin \theta \cos \theta} - \dfrac{\sin^2 \theta}{\sin \theta \cos \theta} \stackrel{?}{=} \cot \theta$

$\dfrac{1 - \sin^2 \theta}{\sin \theta \cos \theta} \stackrel{?}{=} \cot \theta$

$\dfrac{\cos^2 \theta}{\sin \theta \cos \theta} \stackrel{?}{=} \cot \theta$

$\dfrac{\cos \theta}{\sin \theta} \stackrel{?}{=} \cot \theta$

$\cot \theta = \cot \theta$

20. $\dfrac{\sin \theta}{1 - \cos \theta} + \dfrac{1 - \cos \theta}{\sin \theta} \stackrel{?}{=} 2 \csc \theta$

$\dfrac{\sin \theta}{\sin \theta} \cdot \dfrac{\sin}{1 - \cos \theta} + \dfrac{1 - \cos \theta}{1 - \cos \theta} \cdot \dfrac{1 - \cos \theta}{\sin \theta} \stackrel{?}{=} 2 \csc \theta$

$\dfrac{\sin^2 \theta}{\sin \theta (1 - \cos \theta)} + \dfrac{1 - 2 \cos \theta + \cos^2 \theta}{\sin \theta (1 - \cos \theta)} \stackrel{?}{=} 2 \csc \theta$

$\dfrac{\sin^2 \theta + \cos^2 \theta + 1 - 2 \cos \theta}{\sin \theta (1 - \cos \theta)} \stackrel{?}{=} 2 \csc \theta$

$\dfrac{2 - 2 \cos \theta}{\sin \theta (1 - \cos \theta)} \stackrel{?}{=} 2 \csc \theta$

$\dfrac{2 (1 - \cos \theta)}{\sin \theta (1 - \cos \theta)} \stackrel{?}{=} 2 \csc \theta$

$\dfrac{2}{\sin \theta} \stackrel{?}{=} 2 \csc \theta$

$2 \csc \theta = 2 \csc \theta$

21. $\dfrac{1+\sin\theta}{\sin\theta} \overset{?}{=} \dfrac{\cot^2\theta}{\csc\theta-1}$

$\dfrac{1+\sin\theta}{\sin\theta} \overset{?}{=} \dfrac{\cot^2\theta}{\csc\theta-1} \cdot \dfrac{\csc\theta+1}{\csc\theta+1}$

$\dfrac{1+\sin\theta}{\sin\theta} \overset{?}{=} \dfrac{\cot^2\theta(\csc\theta+1)}{\csc^2\theta-1}$

$\dfrac{1+\sin\theta}{\sin\theta} \overset{?}{=} \dfrac{\cot^2\theta(\csc\theta+1)}{\cot^2\theta}$

$\dfrac{1+\sin\theta}{\sin\theta} \overset{?}{=} \csc\theta+1$

$\dfrac{1+\sin\theta}{\sin\theta} \overset{?}{=} \dfrac{1}{\sin\theta} + \dfrac{\sin\theta}{\sin\theta}$

$\dfrac{1+\sin\theta}{\sin\theta} = \dfrac{1+\sin\theta}{\sin\theta}$

22.

$\dfrac{1+\tan\theta}{1+\cot\theta} \overset{?}{=} \dfrac{\sin\theta}{\cos\theta}$

$\dfrac{1+\frac{\sin\theta}{\cos\theta}}{\frac{1+\cos\theta}{\sin\theta}} \overset{?}{=} \dfrac{\sin\theta}{\cos\theta}$

$\dfrac{\frac{\sin\theta+\cos\theta}{\cos\theta}}{\frac{\sin\theta+\cos\theta}{\sin\theta}} \overset{?}{=} \dfrac{\sin\theta}{\cos\theta}$

$\dfrac{\sin\theta+\cos\theta}{\cos\theta} \cdot \dfrac{\sin\theta}{\sin\theta+\cos\theta} \overset{?}{=} \dfrac{\sin\theta}{\cos\theta}$

$\dfrac{\sin\theta}{\cos\theta} = \dfrac{\sin\theta}{\cos\theta}$

23. $\dfrac{1}{\sec^2\theta} + \dfrac{1}{\csc^2\theta} \overset{?}{=} 1$

$\cos^2\theta + \sin^2\theta \overset{?}{=} 1$

$1 = 1$

24. $1 + \dfrac{1}{\cos\theta} \overset{?}{=} \dfrac{\tan^2\theta}{\sec\theta-1}$

$1 + \dfrac{1}{\cos\theta} \overset{?}{=} \dfrac{\tan^2\theta}{\sec\theta-1} \cdot \dfrac{\sec\theta+1}{\sec\theta+1}$

$1 + \dfrac{1}{\cos\theta} \overset{?}{=} \dfrac{\tan^2\theta(\sec\theta+1)}{\sec^2\theta-1}$

$1 + \dfrac{1}{\cos\theta} \overset{?}{=} \dfrac{\tan^2\theta(\sec\theta+1)}{\tan^2\theta}$

$1 + \dfrac{1}{\cos\theta} \overset{?}{=} \sec\theta+1$

$1 + \dfrac{1}{\cos\theta} = 1 + \dfrac{1}{\cos\theta}$

25. $1 - \tan^4\theta \overset{?}{=} 2\sec^2\theta - \sec^4\theta$

$(1-\tan^2\theta)(1+\tan^2\theta) \overset{?}{=} \sec^2\theta(2-\sec^2\theta)$

$[1-(\sec^2\theta-1)](\sec^2\theta) \overset{?}{=} (2-\sec^2\theta)(\sec^2\theta)$

$(2-\sec^2\theta)(\sec^2\theta) = (2-\sec^2\theta)(\sec^2\theta)$

26. $\cos^4\theta - \sin^4\theta \overset{?}{=} \cos^2\theta - \sin^2\theta$

$(\cos^2\theta-\sin^2\theta)(\cos^2\theta+\sin^2\theta) \overset{?}{=} \cos^2\theta-\sin^2\theta$

$(\cos^2\theta-\sin^2\theta)\cdot 1 \overset{?}{=} \cos^2\theta-\sin^2\theta$

$\cos^2\theta-\sin^2\theta = \cos^2\theta-\sin^2\theta$

27.

$\dfrac{1-\cos\theta}{\sin\theta} \overset{?}{=} \dfrac{\sin\theta}{1+\cos\theta}$

$\dfrac{1-\cos\theta}{\sin\theta} \cdot \dfrac{1+\cos\theta}{1+\cos\theta} \overset{?}{=} \dfrac{\sin\theta}{1+\cos\theta}$

$\dfrac{1-\cos^2\theta}{\sin\theta(1+\cos\theta)} \overset{?}{=} \dfrac{\sin\theta}{1+\cos\theta}$

$\dfrac{\sin^2\theta}{\sin\theta(1+\cos\theta)} \overset{?}{=} \dfrac{\sin\theta}{1+\cos\theta}$

$\dfrac{\sin\theta}{1+\cos\theta} = \dfrac{\sin\theta}{1+\cos\theta}$

28.

$\dfrac{\cos\theta}{1+\sin\theta} + \dfrac{\cos\theta}{1-\sin\theta} \overset{?}{=} 2\sec\theta$

$\dfrac{\cos\theta}{1+\sin\theta}\cdot\dfrac{1-\sin\theta}{1-\sin\theta} + \dfrac{\cos\theta}{1-\sin\theta}\cdot\dfrac{1+\sin\theta}{1+\sin\theta} \overset{?}{=} 2\sec\theta$

$\dfrac{\cos\theta(1-\sin\theta)+\cos\theta(1+\sin\theta)}{(1+\sin\theta)(1-\sin\theta)} \overset{?}{=} 2\sec\theta$

$\dfrac{\cos\theta-\sin\theta\cos\theta+\cos\theta+\sin\theta\cos\theta}{1-\sin^2\theta} \overset{?}{=} 2\sec\theta$

$\dfrac{2\cos\theta}{\cos^2\theta} \overset{?}{=} 2\sec\theta$

$\dfrac{2}{\cos\theta} \overset{?}{=} 2\sec\theta$

$2\sec\theta = 2\sec\theta$

29. $\tan\theta\sin\theta\cos\theta\csc^2\theta \overset{?}{=} 1$

$\dfrac{\sin\theta}{\cos\theta}\cdot\sin\theta\cdot\cos\theta\cdot\dfrac{1}{\sin^2\theta} \overset{?}{=} 1$

$1 = 1$

30.

$\dfrac{\sin^2\theta}{1-\cos\theta} \overset{?}{=} 1+\cos\theta$

$\dfrac{\sin^2\theta}{1-\cos\theta}\cdot\dfrac{1+\cos\theta}{1+\cos\theta} \overset{?}{=} 1+\cos\theta$

$\dfrac{\sin^2\theta(1+\cos\theta)}{1-\cos^2\theta} \overset{?}{=} 1+\cos\theta$

$\dfrac{\sin^2\theta(1+\cos\theta)}{\sin^2\theta} \overset{?}{=} 1+\cos\theta$

$1+\cos\theta = 1+\cos\theta$

31. $\dfrac{v^2\tan^2\theta}{2g\sec^2\theta} = \dfrac{v^2\frac{\sin^2\theta}{\cos^2\theta}}{2g\frac{1}{\cos^2\theta}}$

$= \dfrac{v^2}{2g}\cdot\dfrac{\sin^2\theta}{\cos^2\theta}\cdot\dfrac{\cos^2\theta}{1}$

$= \dfrac{v^2\sin^2\theta}{2g}$

32. $h = \dfrac{v^2\sin^2\theta}{2g}$

$= \dfrac{(110)^2\sin^2 80°}{2(9.8)}$

≈ 598.7

The maximum height of the rocket is about 598.7 meters.

33. Sample answer: Consider a right triangle ABC with right angle at C. If an angle, say A, has a sine of x, then angle B must have a cosine of x. Since A and B are both in a right triangle and neither is the right angle, their sum must be $\dfrac{\pi}{2}$.

34. Sample answer: Trigonometric identities are verified in a similar manner to proving theorems in geometry before using them. Answers should include the following.

- The expressions have not yet been shown to be equal, so you could not use the properties of equality on them.
- To show two expressions you must transform one, or both independently.
- Graphing two expressions could result in identical graphs for a set interval, that are different elsewhere.

35. D; $\tan\theta\csc\theta = \dfrac{\sin\theta}{\cos\theta}\cdot\dfrac{1}{\sin\theta}$

$= \dfrac{1}{\cos\theta}$

36. B; $\sin\theta + \cot\theta\cos\theta = \sin\theta + \dfrac{\cos\theta}{\sin\theta}\cdot\cos\theta$

$= \dfrac{\sin^2\theta}{\sin\theta} + \dfrac{\cos^2\theta}{\sin\theta}$

$= \dfrac{\sin^2\theta+\cos^2\theta}{\sin\theta}$

$= \dfrac{1}{\sin\theta}$

37.

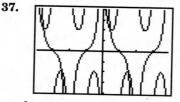

[−360, 360] scl: 90 by [−5, 5] scl:

The graphs do not match. The equation is not an identity.

38.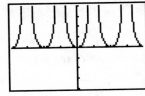

$[-360, 360]$ scl: 90 by $[-5, 5]$ scl: 1

The graphs coincide; the equation may be an identity.

39.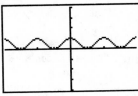

$[-360, 360]$ scl: 90 by $[-5, 5]$ scl: 1

The graphs coincide; the equation may be an identity.

40.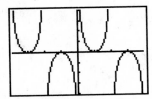

$[-360, 360]$ scl: 90 by $[-5, 5]$ scl: 1

The graphs coincide; the equation may be an identity.

41.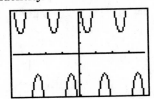

$[-360, 360]$ scl: 90 by $[-5, 5]$ scl: 1

The graphs coincide; the equation may be an identity.

42.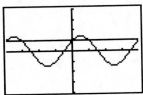

$[-360, 360]$ scl: 90 by $[-5, 5]$ scl: 1

The graphs do not match. The equation is not an identity.

Page 785   Maintain Your Skills

43. Find sec θ.

$$\sec^2 \theta = \tan^2 \theta + 1$$
$$\sec^2 \theta = \left(\frac{1}{2}\right)^2 + 1$$
$$\sec^2 \theta = \frac{1}{4} + 1$$
$$\sec^2 \theta = \frac{5}{4}$$
$$\sec \theta = \pm\frac{\sqrt{5}}{2}$$

Since θ is in the first quadrant, sec θ is positive. Thus, $\sec \theta = \frac{\sqrt{5}}{2}$.

44. Find cos θ.

$$\cos^2 \theta + \sin^2 \theta = 1$$
$$\cos^2 \theta = 1 - \sin^2 \theta$$
$$\cos^2 \theta = 1 - \left(-\frac{2}{3}\right)^2$$
$$\cos^2 \theta = 1 - \frac{4}{9}$$
$$\cos^2 \theta = \frac{5}{9}$$
$$\cos \theta = \pm\frac{\sqrt{5}}{3}$$

Since θ is in the third quadrant, cos θ is negative. Thus, $\cos \theta = -\frac{\sqrt{5}}{3}$.

45. Find csc θ.

$$\csc^2 \theta = \cot^2 \theta + 1$$
$$\csc^2 \theta = \left(-\frac{7}{12}\right)^2 + 1$$
$$\csc^2 \theta = \frac{49}{144} + 1$$
$$\csc^2 \theta = \frac{193}{144}$$
$$\csc \theta = \pm\frac{\sqrt{193}}{12}$$

Since θ is in the second quadrant, csc θ is positive. Thus, $\csc \theta = \frac{\sqrt{193}}{12}$.

46. Find sin θ.

$$\cos^2 \theta + \sin^2 \theta = 1$$
$$\sin^2 \theta = 1 - \cos^2 \theta$$
$$\sin^2 \theta = 1 - \left(\frac{3}{4}\right)^2$$
$$\sin^2 \theta = 1 - \frac{9}{16}$$
$$\sin^2 \theta = \frac{7}{16}$$
$$\sin \theta = \pm\frac{\sqrt{7}}{4}$$

Since θ is in the fourth quadrant, sin θ is negative. Thus, $\sin \theta = -\frac{\sqrt{7}}{4}$.

47. $y = \cos(\theta - 30°)$

Amplitude $= |a| = |1|$ or 1

Period: $\frac{360°}{|b|} = \frac{360°}{|1|}$ or 360°

Phase shift: $h = 30°$

The phase shift is to the right.

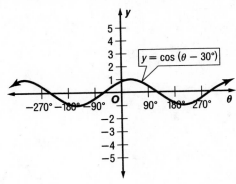

48. $y = \sin(\theta - 45°)$

Amplitude $= |a| = |1|$ or 1

Period: $\frac{360°}{|b|} = \frac{360°}{|1|}$ or 360°

Phase shift: $h = 45°$

The phase shift is to the right.

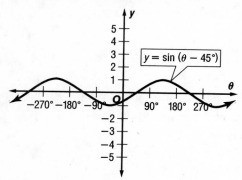

49. $y = 3\cos\left(\theta + \frac{\pi}{2}\right)$

Amplitude $= |a| = |3|$ or 3

Period: $\frac{2\pi}{|b|} = \frac{2\pi}{|1|}$ or 2π

Phase shift: $h = -\frac{\pi}{2}$

The phase shift is to the left.

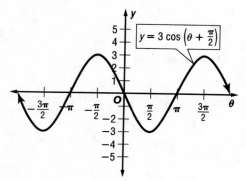

50. The probability is $\frac{5}{5+1}$ or $\frac{5}{6}$.

51. $\frac{\sqrt{3}}{2} \cdot \frac{\sqrt{2}}{2} = \frac{\sqrt{3 \cdot 2}}{4}$

$\qquad = \frac{\sqrt{6}}{4}$

52. $\frac{1}{2} \cdot \frac{\sqrt{2}}{2} = \frac{\sqrt{2}}{4}$

53. $\frac{\sqrt{6}}{4} + \frac{\sqrt{2}}{2} = \frac{\sqrt{6}}{4} + \frac{2\sqrt{2}}{4}$

$\qquad = \frac{\sqrt{6} + 2\sqrt{2}}{4}$

54. $\frac{1}{2} - \frac{\sqrt{3}}{4} = \frac{2}{4} - \frac{\sqrt{3}}{4}$

$\qquad = \frac{2 - \sqrt{3}}{4}$

14-5 Sum and Difference of Angles Formulas

Pages 788–789 Check for Understanding

1. $\sin(45° + 45°) = \sin 90°$

$\qquad\qquad\qquad = 1$

$\sin 45° + \sin 45° = \frac{\sqrt{2}}{2} + \frac{\sqrt{2}}{2}$

$\qquad\qquad\qquad = \sqrt{2}$

Thus, $\sin(\alpha + \beta) \neq \sin\alpha + \sin\beta$.
The equation is not an identity.
Or: $\sin(\alpha + \beta) \stackrel{?}{=} \sin\alpha + \sin\beta$
$\sin\alpha\cos\beta + \cos\alpha\sin\beta \neq \sin\alpha + \sin\beta$

2. Use the formula $\sin(\alpha + \beta) = \sin\alpha\cos\beta + \cos\alpha\sin\beta$. Since $\sin 105° = \sin(60° + 45°)$, replace α with 60° and β with 45° to get $\sin 60°\cos 45° + \cos 60°\sin 45°$. By finding the sum of the products of the values, the result is $\frac{\sqrt{6} + \sqrt{2}}{4}$ or about 0.9659.

3. Sometimes; sample answer: The cosine function can equal 1.

4. $\sin 75° = \sin(30° + 45°)$

$\qquad = \sin 30°\cos 45° + \cos 30°\sin 45°$

$\qquad = \left(\frac{1}{2} \cdot \frac{\sqrt{2}}{2}\right) + \left(\frac{\sqrt{3}}{2} \cdot \frac{\sqrt{2}}{2}\right)$

$\qquad = \frac{\sqrt{2}}{4} + \frac{\sqrt{6}}{4}$

$\qquad = \frac{\sqrt{2} + \sqrt{6}}{4}$ or $\frac{\sqrt{6} + \sqrt{2}}{4}$

5. $\sin 165° = \sin(120° + 45°)$

$\qquad = \sin 120°\cos 45° + \cos 120°\sin 45°$

$\qquad = \left(\frac{\sqrt{3}}{2} \cdot \frac{\sqrt{2}}{2}\right) + \left(-\frac{1}{2} \cdot \frac{\sqrt{2}}{2}\right)$

$\qquad = \frac{\sqrt{6}}{4} + \left(-\frac{\sqrt{2}}{4}\right)$

$\qquad = \frac{\sqrt{6} - \sqrt{2}}{4}$

6. $\cos 255° = \cos(210° + 45°)$

$\qquad = \cos 210°\cos 45° - \sin 210°\sin 45°$

$\qquad = \left(-\frac{\sqrt{3}}{2} \cdot \frac{\sqrt{2}}{2}\right) + \left(-\frac{1}{2} \cdot \frac{\sqrt{2}}{2}\right)$

$\qquad = -\frac{\sqrt{6}}{4} - \left(-\frac{\sqrt{2}}{4}\right)$

$\qquad = \frac{-\sqrt{6} + \sqrt{2}}{4}$ or $\frac{\sqrt{2} - \sqrt{6}}{4}$

7. $\cos(-30°) = \cos(60° - 90°)$

$\qquad = \cos 60°\cos 90° + \sin 60°\sin 90°$

$\qquad = \left(\frac{1}{2} \cdot 0\right) + \left(\frac{\sqrt{3}}{2} \cdot 1\right)$

$\qquad = 0 + \frac{\sqrt{3}}{2}$

$\qquad = \frac{\sqrt{3}}{2}$

8. $\sin(-240°) = \sin(30° - 270°)$

$\qquad = \sin 30°\cos 270° - \cos 30°\sin 270°$

$\qquad = \left(\frac{1}{2}\right)(0) - \left(\frac{\sqrt{3}}{2}\right)(-1)$

$\qquad = 0 - \left(-\frac{\sqrt{3}}{2}\right)$

$\qquad = \frac{\sqrt{3}}{2}$

9. $\cos(-120°) = \cos(60° - 180°)$
$= \cos 60° \cos 180° + \sin 60° \sin 180°$
$= \left(\frac{1}{2}\right)(-1) + \left(\frac{\sqrt{3}}{2}\right)(0)$
$= -\frac{1}{2} + 0$
$= -\frac{1}{2}$

10.
$$\cos(270° - \theta) \stackrel{?}{=} -\sin \theta$$
$$\cos 270° \cos \theta + \sin 270° \sin \theta \stackrel{?}{=} -\sin \theta$$
$$(0 \cdot \cos \theta) + (-1 \cdot \sin \theta) \stackrel{?}{=} -\sin \theta$$
$$-\sin \theta = -\sin \theta$$

11.
$$\sin\left(\theta + \frac{\pi}{2}\right) \stackrel{?}{=} \cos \theta$$
$$\sin \theta \cos \frac{\pi}{2} + \cos \theta \sin \frac{\pi}{2} \stackrel{?}{=} \cos \theta$$
$$\sin \theta \cdot 0 + \cos \theta \cdot 1 \stackrel{?}{=} \cos \theta$$
$$\cos \theta = \cos \theta$$

12.
$$\sin(\theta + 30°) + \cos(\theta + 60°) \stackrel{?}{=} \cos \theta$$
$$\sin \theta \cos 30° + \cos \theta \sin 30° + \cos \theta \cos 60° - \sin \theta \sin 60° \stackrel{?}{=} \cos \theta$$
$$\frac{\sqrt{3}}{2} \sin \theta + \frac{1}{2} \cos \theta + \frac{1}{2} \cos \theta - \frac{\sqrt{3}}{2} \sin \theta \stackrel{?}{=} \cos \theta$$
$$\cos \theta = \cos \theta$$

13.
$$\tan(\alpha + 60°) = \frac{40}{8}$$
$$\frac{\sin(\alpha + 60°)}{\cos(\alpha + 60°)} = 5$$
$$\sin(\alpha + 60°) = 5 \cos(\alpha + 60°)$$
$$\sin \alpha \cos 60° + \cos \alpha \sin 60° = 5(\cos \alpha \cos 60° - \sin \alpha \sin 60°)$$
$$\frac{1}{2} \sin \alpha + \frac{\sqrt{3}}{2} \cos \alpha = 5\left(\frac{1}{2} \cos \alpha - \frac{\sqrt{3}}{2} \sin \alpha\right)$$
$$\sin \alpha + \sqrt{3} \cos \alpha = 5 \cos \alpha - 5\sqrt{3} \sin \alpha$$
$$\sin \alpha + 5\sqrt{3} \sin \alpha = 5 \cos \alpha - \sqrt{3} \cos \alpha$$
$$(1 + 5\sqrt{3})\sin \alpha = (5 - \sqrt{3})\cos \alpha$$
$$\frac{\sin \alpha}{\cos \alpha} = \frac{5 - \sqrt{3}}{1 + 5\sqrt{3}}$$
$$\tan \alpha = \frac{5 - \sqrt{3}}{1 + 5\sqrt{3}}$$

Pages 789–790 Practice and Apply

14. $\sin 135° = \sin(90° + 45°)$
$= \sin 90° \cos 45° + \cos 90° \sin 45°$
$= 1 \cdot \frac{\sqrt{2}}{2} + 0 \cdot \frac{\sqrt{2}}{2}$
$= \frac{\sqrt{2}}{2} + 0$
$= \frac{\sqrt{2}}{2}$

15. $\cos 105° = \cos(60° + 45°)$
$= \cos 60° \cos 45° - \sin 60° \sin 45°$
$= \frac{1}{2} \cdot \frac{\sqrt{2}}{2} - \frac{\sqrt{3}}{2} \cdot \frac{\sqrt{2}}{2}$
$= \frac{\sqrt{2}}{4} - \frac{\sqrt{6}}{4}$
$= \frac{\sqrt{2} - \sqrt{6}}{4}$

16. $\sin 285° = \sin(240° + 45°)$
$= \sin 240° \cos 45° + \cos 240° \sin 45°$
$= -\frac{\sqrt{3}}{2} \cdot \frac{\sqrt{2}}{2} + \left(-\frac{1}{2}\right) \cdot \frac{\sqrt{2}}{2}$
$= -\frac{\sqrt{6}}{4} + \left(-\frac{\sqrt{2}}{4}\right)$
$= \frac{-\sqrt{6} - \sqrt{2}}{4}$

17. $\cos 165° = \cos(120° + 45°)$
$= \cos 120° \cos 45° - \sin 120° \sin 45°$
$= -\frac{1}{2} \cdot \frac{\sqrt{2}}{2} - \frac{\sqrt{3}}{2} \cdot \frac{\sqrt{2}}{2}$
$= -\frac{\sqrt{2}}{4} - \frac{\sqrt{6}}{4}$
$= \frac{-\sqrt{2} - \sqrt{6}}{4}$ or $\frac{-\sqrt{6} - \sqrt{2}}{4}$

18. $\cos 195° = \cos(135° + 60°)$
$= \cos 135° \cos 60° - \sin 135° \sin 60°$
$= -\frac{\sqrt{2}}{2} \cdot \frac{1}{2} - \frac{\sqrt{2}}{2} \cdot \frac{\sqrt{3}}{2}$
$= -\frac{\sqrt{2}}{4} - \frac{\sqrt{6}}{4}$
$= \frac{-\sqrt{2} - \sqrt{6}}{4}$ or $\frac{-\sqrt{6} - \sqrt{2}}{4}$

19. $\sin 255° = \sin(120° + 135°)$
$= \sin 120° \cos 135° + \cos 120° \sin 135°$
$= \frac{\sqrt{3}}{2} \cdot \left(-\frac{\sqrt{2}}{2}\right) + \left(-\frac{1}{2}\right) \cdot \frac{\sqrt{2}}{2}$
$= -\frac{\sqrt{6}}{4} - \frac{\sqrt{2}}{4}$
$= \frac{-\sqrt{6} - \sqrt{2}}{4}$

20. $\cos 225° = \cos(180° + 45°)$
$= \cos 180° \cos 45° - \sin 180° \sin 45°$
$= -1 \cdot \frac{\sqrt{2}}{2} - 0 \cdot \frac{\sqrt{2}}{2}$
$= -\frac{\sqrt{2}}{2} - 0$
$= -\frac{\sqrt{2}}{2}$

21. $\sin 315° = \sin(270° + 45°)$
$= \sin 270° \cos 45° + \cos 270° \sin 45°$
$= -1 \cdot \frac{\sqrt{2}}{2} + 0 \cdot \frac{\sqrt{2}}{2}$
$= -\frac{\sqrt{2}}{2} + 0$
$= -\frac{\sqrt{2}}{2}$

22. $\sin(-15°) = \sin(30° - 45°)$
$= \sin 30° \cos 45° - \cos 30° \sin 45°$
$= \frac{1}{2} \cdot \frac{\sqrt{2}}{2} - \frac{\sqrt{3}}{2} \cdot \frac{\sqrt{2}}{2}$
$= \frac{\sqrt{2}}{4} - \frac{\sqrt{6}}{4}$
$= \frac{\sqrt{2} - \sqrt{6}}{4}$

23. $\cos(-45°) = \cos(45° - 90°)$
$= \cos 45° \cos 90° + \sin 45° \sin 90°$
$= \frac{\sqrt{2}}{2} \cdot 0 + \frac{\sqrt{2}}{2} \cdot 1$
$= 0 + \frac{\sqrt{2}}{2}$
$= \frac{\sqrt{2}}{2}$

24. $\cos(-150°) = \cos(30° - 180°)$
$= \cos 30° \cos 180° + \sin 30° \sin 180°$
$= \frac{\sqrt{3}}{2} \cdot (-1) + \frac{1}{2} \cdot 0$
$= -\frac{\sqrt{3}}{2} + 0$
$= -\frac{\sqrt{3}}{2}$

25. $\sin(-165°) = \sin(60° - 225°)$

$\qquad = \sin 60° \cos 225° - \cos 60° \sin 225°$

$\qquad = \dfrac{\sqrt{3}}{2} \cdot \left(-\dfrac{\sqrt{2}}{2}\right) - \dfrac{1}{2} \cdot \left(-\dfrac{\sqrt{2}}{2}\right)$

$\qquad = -\dfrac{\sqrt{6}}{4} - \left(-\dfrac{\sqrt{2}}{4}\right)$

$\qquad = -\dfrac{\sqrt{6} + \sqrt{2}}{4}$ or $\dfrac{\sqrt{2} - \sqrt{6}}{4}$

26. $\sin 75° - \sin 15°$

$\qquad = \sin(45° + 30°) - \sin(45° - 30°)$

$\qquad = (\sin 45° \cos 30° + \cos 45° \sin 30°)$

$\qquad\quad - (\sin 45° \cos 30° - \cos 45° \sin 30°)$

$\qquad = 2 \cos 45° \sin 30°$

$\qquad = 2 \cdot \dfrac{\sqrt{2}}{2} \cdot \dfrac{1}{2}$

$\qquad = \dfrac{\sqrt{2}}{2}$

27. $\cos 105° + \cos 225°$

$\qquad = \cos(60° + 45°) + \cos(180° + 45°)$

$\qquad = (\cos 60° \cos 45° - \sin 60° \sin 45°)$

$\qquad\quad + (\cos 180° \cos 45° - \sin 180° \sin 45°)$

$\qquad = \dfrac{1}{2} \cdot \dfrac{\sqrt{2}}{2} - \dfrac{\sqrt{3}}{2} \cdot \dfrac{\sqrt{2}}{2} + (-1) \cdot \dfrac{\sqrt{2}}{2} - 0 \cdot \dfrac{\sqrt{2}}{2}$

$\qquad = \dfrac{\sqrt{2}}{4} - \dfrac{\sqrt{6}}{4} - \dfrac{\sqrt{2}}{2} - 0$

$\qquad = -\dfrac{\sqrt{6}}{4} - \dfrac{\sqrt{2}}{4}$

$\qquad = \dfrac{-\sqrt{6} - \sqrt{2}}{4}$

28. $\sin(270° - \theta) \overset{?}{=} \sin 270° \cos \theta - \cos 270° \sin \theta$

$\qquad\qquad \overset{?}{=} -\cos \theta - 0$

$\qquad\qquad = -\cos \theta$

29. $\cos(90° + \theta) \overset{?}{=} \cos 90° \cos \theta - \sin 90° \sin \theta$

$\qquad\qquad \overset{?}{=} 0 - \sin \theta$

$\qquad\qquad = -\sin \theta$

30. $\cos(90° - \theta) \overset{?}{=} \cos 90° \cos \theta + \sin 90° \sin \theta$

$\qquad\qquad \overset{?}{=} 0 \cdot \cos \theta + 1 \cdot \sin \theta$

$\qquad\qquad = \sin \theta$

31.

$\qquad\qquad \sin(90° - \theta) \overset{?}{=} \cos \theta$

$\sin 90° \cos \theta - \cos 90° \sin \theta \overset{?}{=} \cos \theta$

$\qquad 1 \cdot \cos \theta - 0 \cdot \sin \theta \overset{?}{=} \cos \theta$

$\qquad\qquad \cos \theta - 0 \overset{?}{=} \cos \theta$

$\qquad\qquad\qquad \cos \theta = \cos \theta$

32.

$\qquad\qquad \sin\left(\theta + \dfrac{3\pi}{2}\right) \overset{?}{=} -\cos \theta$

$\sin \theta \cos \dfrac{3\pi}{2} + \cos \theta \sin \dfrac{3\pi}{2} \overset{?}{=} -\cos \theta$

$\qquad \sin \theta \cdot 0 + \cos \theta \cdot (-1) \overset{?}{=} -\cos \theta$

$\qquad\qquad 0 + (-\cos \theta) \overset{?}{=} -\cos \theta$

$\qquad\qquad\qquad -\cos \theta = -\cos \theta$

33.

$\qquad\qquad \cos(\pi - \theta) \overset{?}{=} -\cos \theta$

$\cos \pi \cos \theta + \sin \pi \sin \theta \overset{?}{=} -\cos \theta$

$\quad -1 \cdot \cos \theta + 0 \cdot \sin \theta \overset{?}{=} -\cos \theta$

$\qquad\qquad -\cos \theta + 0 \overset{?}{=} -\cos \theta$

$\qquad\qquad\qquad -\cos \theta = -\cos \theta$

34.

$\qquad\qquad \cos(2\pi + \theta) \overset{?}{=} \cos \theta$

$\cos 2\pi \cos \theta - \sin 2\pi \sin \theta \overset{?}{=} \cos \theta$

$\quad 1 \cdot \cos \theta - 0 \cdot \sin \theta \overset{?}{=} \cos \theta$

$\qquad\qquad \cos \theta - 0 \overset{?}{=} \cos \theta$

$\qquad\qquad\qquad \cos \theta = \cos \theta$

35.

$\qquad\qquad \sin(\pi - \theta) \overset{?}{=} \sin \theta$

$\sin \pi \cos \theta - \cos \pi \sin \theta \overset{?}{=} \sin \theta$

$0 \cdot \cos \theta - [(-1) \cdot \sin \theta] \overset{?}{=} \sin \theta$

$\qquad\qquad 0 + \sin \theta \overset{?}{=} \sin \theta$

$\qquad\qquad\qquad \sin \theta = \sin \theta$

36.

$\qquad\qquad \sin(60° + \theta) + \sin(60° - \theta) \overset{?}{=} \sqrt{3} \cos \theta$

$(\sin 60° \cos \theta + \cos 60° \sin \theta) + (\sin 60° \cos \theta - \cos 60° \sin \theta) \overset{?}{=} \sqrt{3} \cos \theta$

$\qquad\qquad 2 \sin 60° \cos \theta \overset{?}{=} \sqrt{3} \cos \theta$

$\qquad\qquad 2 \cdot \dfrac{\sqrt{3}}{2} \cdot \cos \theta \overset{?}{=} \sqrt{3} \cos \theta$

$\qquad\qquad \sqrt{3} \cos \theta = \sqrt{3} \cos \theta$

37.

$\qquad\qquad \sin\left(\theta + \dfrac{\pi}{3}\right) - \cos\left(\theta + \dfrac{\pi}{6}\right) \overset{?}{=} \sin \theta$

$\left(\sin \theta \cos \dfrac{\pi}{3} + \cos \theta \sin \dfrac{\pi}{3}\right) - \left(\cos \theta \cos \dfrac{\pi}{6} - \sin \theta \sin \dfrac{\pi}{6}\right) \overset{?}{=} \sin \theta$

$\sin \theta \cdot \dfrac{1}{2} + \cos \theta \cdot \dfrac{\sqrt{3}}{2} - \cos \theta \cdot \dfrac{\sqrt{3}}{2} + \sin \theta \cdot \dfrac{1}{2} \overset{?}{=} \sin \theta$

$\qquad\qquad \dfrac{1}{2} \sin \theta + \dfrac{1}{2} \sin \theta \overset{?}{=} \sin \theta$

$\qquad\qquad\qquad \sin \theta = \sin \theta$

38. $\sin(\alpha + \beta) \sin(\alpha - \beta)$

$\qquad \overset{?}{=} (\sin \alpha \cos \beta + \cos \alpha \sin \beta)(\sin \alpha \cos \beta - \cos \alpha \sin \beta)$

$\qquad \overset{?}{=} \sin^2 \alpha \cos^2 \beta - \cos^2 \alpha \sin^2 \beta$

$\qquad \overset{?}{=} \sin^2 \alpha(1 - \sin^2 \beta) - (1 - \sin^2 \alpha)\sin^2 \beta$

$\qquad \overset{?}{=} \sin^2 \alpha - \sin^2 \alpha \sin^2 \beta - \sin^2 \beta + \sin^2 \alpha \sin^2 \beta$

$\qquad\quad \sin^2 \alpha - \sin^2 \beta$

39. $\cos(\alpha + \beta) \overset{?}{=} \dfrac{1 - \tan \alpha \tan \beta}{\sec \alpha \sec \beta}$

$\qquad \cos(\alpha + \beta) \overset{?}{=} \dfrac{1 - \dfrac{\sin \alpha}{\cos \alpha} \cdot \dfrac{\sin \beta}{\cos \beta}}{\dfrac{1}{\cos \alpha} \cdot \dfrac{1}{\cos \beta}}$

$\qquad \cos(\alpha + \beta) \overset{?}{=} \dfrac{1 - \dfrac{\sin \alpha}{\cos \alpha} \cdot \dfrac{\sin \beta}{\cos \beta}}{\dfrac{1}{\cos \alpha} \cdot \dfrac{1}{\cos \beta}} \cdot \dfrac{\cos \alpha \cos \beta}{\cos \alpha \cos \beta}$

$\qquad \cos(\alpha + \beta) \overset{?}{=} \dfrac{\cos \alpha \cos \beta - \sin \alpha \sin \beta}{1}$

$\qquad \cos(\alpha + \beta) = \cos(\alpha + \beta)$

40. Add the equations.

$v + d = 10 \sin(2t - 30°) + 10 \cos(2t + 60°)$

$\qquad = 10(\sin 2t \cos 30° - \cos 2t \sin 30°)$

$\qquad\quad + 10(\cos 2t \cos 60° - \sin 2t \sin 60°)$

$\qquad = 10\left(\dfrac{\sqrt{3}}{2} \sin 2t - \dfrac{1}{2} \cos 2t\right)$

$\qquad\quad + 10\left(\dfrac{1}{2} \cos 2t - \dfrac{\sqrt{3}}{2} \sin 2t\right)$

$\qquad = 0$

$y = 10 \sin (2t - 30) + 10 \cos (2t + 60)$

41. Destructive; the resulting graph has a smaller amplitude than the two initial graphs.

42. $\sin(113.5° + \phi)$

$\qquad = \sin 113.5° \cos \phi + \cos 113.5° \sin \phi$

$\qquad = \sin 113.5° \cos 44.9° + \cos 113.5° \sin 44.9°$

$\qquad \approx 0.9171 \cdot 0.7083 + (-0.3987) \cdot 0.7059$

$\qquad \approx 0.3681$

In Salem, OR, the maximum light energy per square foot is $0.3681 \, E$.

43. $\sin(113.5° + \phi)$
$= \sin 113.5° \cos \phi + \cos 113.5° \sin \phi$
$= \sin 113.5° \cos 41.8° + \cos 113.5° \sin 41.8°$
$\approx 0.9171 \cdot 0.7455 + (-0.3987) \cdot 0.6665$
≈ 0.4180

In Chicago, IL, the maximum light energy per square foot is $0.4180\ E$.

44. $\sin(113.5° + \phi)$
$= \sin 113.5° \cos \phi + \cos 113.5° \sin \phi$
$= \sin 113.5° \cos 28.5° + \cos 113.5° \sin 28.5°$
$\approx 0.9171 \cdot 0.8788 + (-0.3987) \cdot 0.4772$
≈ 0.6157

In Charleston, SC, the maximum light energy per square foot is $0.6157\ E$.

45. $\sin(113.5° + \phi)$
$= \sin 113.5° \cos \phi + \cos 113.5° \sin \phi$
$= \sin 113.5° \cos 32.7° + \cos 113.5° \sin 32.7°$
$\approx 0.9171 \cdot 0.8415 + (-0.3987) \cdot 0.5402$
≈ 0.5564

In San Diego, CA, the maximum light energy per square foot is $0.5564\ E$.

46. $\tan(\alpha + \beta) = \dfrac{\sin(\alpha + \beta)}{\cos(\alpha + \beta)}$
$= \dfrac{\sin \alpha \cos \beta + \cos \alpha \sin \beta}{\cos \alpha \cos \beta - \sin \alpha \sin \beta}$
$= \dfrac{\frac{\sin \alpha \cos \beta}{\cos \alpha \cos \beta} + \frac{\cos \alpha \sin \beta}{\cos \alpha \cos \beta}}{\frac{\cos \alpha \cos \beta}{\cos \alpha \cos \beta} - \frac{\sin \alpha \sin \beta}{\cos \alpha \cos \beta}}$
$= \dfrac{\tan \alpha + \tan \beta}{1 - \tan \alpha \tan \beta}$

$\tan(\alpha - \beta) = \dfrac{\sin(\alpha - \beta)}{\cos(\alpha - \beta)}$
$= \dfrac{\sin \alpha \cos \beta - \cos \alpha \sin \beta}{\cos \alpha \cos \beta + \sin \alpha \sin \beta}$
$= \dfrac{\frac{\sin \alpha \cos \beta}{\cos \alpha \cos \beta} - \frac{\cos \alpha \sin \beta}{\cos \alpha \cos \beta}}{\frac{\cos \alpha \cos \beta}{\cos \alpha \cos \beta} + \frac{\sin \alpha \sin \beta}{\cos \alpha \cos \beta}}$
$= \dfrac{\tan \alpha - \tan \beta}{1 + \tan \alpha \tan \beta}$

47. Sample answer: To determine communication interference, you need to determine the sine or cosine of the sum or difference of two angles. Answers should include the following information.

- Interference occurs when waves pass through the space at the same time. When the combined waves have a greater amplitude, constructive interference results and when the combined waves have a smaller amplitude, destructive interference results.

48. A; $\sin \theta = \sin(75° + 45°)$
$= \sin 120°$
$= \dfrac{\sqrt{3}}{2}$

49. C; $\cos(-210°)$
$= \cos(150° - 360°)$
$= \cos 150° \cos 360° + \sin 150° \sin 360°$
$= -\dfrac{\sqrt{3}}{2} \cdot 1 + \dfrac{1}{2} \cdot 0$
$= -\dfrac{\sqrt{3}}{2}$

50. $\cot \theta + \sec \theta \stackrel{?}{=} \dfrac{\cos^2 \theta + \sin \theta}{\sin \theta \cos \theta}$
$\cot \theta + \sec \theta \stackrel{?}{=} \dfrac{\cos^2 \theta}{\sin \theta \cos \theta} + \dfrac{\sin \theta}{\sin \theta \cos \theta}$
$\cot \theta + \sec \theta \stackrel{?}{=} \dfrac{\cos \theta}{\sin \theta} + \dfrac{1}{\cos \theta}$
$\cot \theta + \sec \theta = \cot \theta + \sec \theta$

51. $\sin^2 \theta + \tan^2 \theta \stackrel{?}{=} (1 - \cos^2 \theta) + \dfrac{\sec^2 \theta}{\csc^2 \theta}$
$\sin^2 \theta + \tan^2 \theta \stackrel{?}{=} \sin^2 \theta + \dfrac{\sec^2 \theta}{\csc^2 \theta}$
$\sin^2 \theta + \tan^2 \theta \stackrel{?}{=} \sin^2 \theta + \dfrac{1}{\cos^2 \theta} \div \dfrac{1}{\sin^2 \theta}$
$\sin^2 \theta + \tan^2 \theta \stackrel{?}{=} \sin^2 \theta + \dfrac{\sin^2 \theta}{\cos^2 \theta}$
$\sin^2 \theta + \tan^2 \theta = \sin^2 \theta + \tan^2 \theta$

52. $\sin \theta(\sin \theta + \csc \theta) \stackrel{?}{=} 2 - \cos^2 \theta$
$\sin^2 \theta + 1 \stackrel{?}{=} 2 - \cos^2 \theta$
$1 - \cos^2 \theta + 1 \stackrel{?}{=} 2 - \cos^2 \theta$
$2 - \cos^2 \theta = 2 - \cos^2 \theta$

53. $\dfrac{\sec \theta}{\tan \theta} \stackrel{?}{=} \csc \theta$
$\dfrac{1}{\cos \theta} \div \dfrac{\sin \theta}{\cos \theta} \stackrel{?}{=} \csc \theta$
$\dfrac{1}{\cos \theta} \cdot \dfrac{\cos \theta}{\sin \theta} \stackrel{?}{=} \csc \theta$
$\dfrac{1}{\sin \theta} \stackrel{?}{=} \csc \theta$
$\csc \theta = \csc \theta$

54. $\dfrac{\tan \theta \csc \theta}{\sec \theta} = \dfrac{\frac{\sin \theta}{\cos \theta} \cdot \frac{1}{\sin \theta}}{\sec \theta}$
$= \dfrac{\frac{1}{\cos \theta}}{\sec \theta}$
$= \dfrac{\sec \theta}{\sec \theta}$
$= 1$

55. $4\left(\sec^2 \theta - \dfrac{\sin^2 \theta}{\cos^2 \theta}\right) = 4\left(\dfrac{1}{\cos^2 \theta} - \dfrac{\sin^2 \theta}{\cos^2 \theta}\right)$
$= 4\left(\dfrac{1 - \sin^2 \theta}{\cos^2 \theta}\right)$
$= 4\left(\dfrac{\cos^2 \theta}{\cos^2 \theta}\right)$
$= 4$

56. $(\cot \theta + \tan \theta)\sin \theta = \left(\dfrac{\cos \theta}{\sin \theta} + \dfrac{\sin \theta}{\cos \theta}\right)\sin \theta$
$= \cos \theta + \dfrac{\sin^2 \theta}{\cos \theta}$
$= \dfrac{\cos^2 \theta + \sin^2 \theta}{\cos \theta}$
$= \dfrac{1}{\cos \theta}$
$= \sec \theta$

57. $\csc \theta \tan \theta + \sec \theta = \dfrac{1}{\sin \theta} \cdot \dfrac{\sin \theta}{\cos \theta} + \sec \theta$
$= \dfrac{1}{\cos \theta} + \sec \theta$
$= \sec \theta + \sec \theta$
$= 2 \sec \theta$

58. $r = \sqrt{x^2 + y^2}$
$\quad = \sqrt{5^2 + (-3)^2}$
$\quad = \sqrt{25 + 9}$
$\quad = \sqrt{34}$

$\sin \theta = \frac{y}{r}$
$\quad = \frac{-3}{\sqrt{34}} \text{ or } -\frac{3\sqrt{34}}{34}$

$\cos \theta = \frac{x}{r}$
$\quad = \frac{5}{\sqrt{34}} \text{ or } \frac{5\sqrt{34}}{34}$

$\tan \theta = \frac{y}{x}$
$\quad = \frac{-3}{5} \text{ or } -\frac{3}{5}$

$\csc \theta = \frac{r}{y}$
$\quad = \frac{\sqrt{34}}{-3} \text{ or } -\frac{\sqrt{34}}{3}$

$\sec \theta = \frac{r}{x}$
$\quad = \frac{\sqrt{34}}{5}$

$\cot \theta = \frac{x}{y}$
$\quad = \frac{5}{-3} \text{ or } -\frac{5}{3}$

59. $r = \sqrt{x^2 + y^2}$
$\quad = \sqrt{(-3)^2 + (-4)^2}$
$\quad = \sqrt{9 + 16}$
$\quad = \sqrt{25} \text{ or } 5$

$\sin \theta = \frac{y}{r}$
$\quad = \frac{-4}{5} \text{ or } -\frac{4}{5}$

$\cos \theta = \frac{x}{r}$
$\quad = \frac{-3}{5} \text{ or } -\frac{3}{5}$

$\tan \theta = \frac{y}{x}$
$\quad = \frac{-4}{-3} \text{ or } \frac{4}{3}$

$\csc \theta = \frac{r}{y}$
$\quad = \frac{5}{-4} \text{ or } -\frac{5}{4}$

$\sec \theta = \frac{r}{x}$
$\quad = \frac{5}{-3} \text{ or } -\frac{5}{3}$

$\cot \theta = \frac{x}{y}$
$\quad = \frac{-3}{-4} \text{ or } \frac{3}{4}$

60. $r = \sqrt{0^2 + 2^2}$
$\quad = \sqrt{4} \text{ or } 2$

$\sin \theta = \frac{y}{r}$
$\quad = \frac{2}{2} \text{ or } 1$

$\cos \theta = \frac{x}{r}$
$\quad = \frac{0}{2} \text{ or } 0$

$\tan \theta = \frac{y}{x}$
$\quad = \frac{2}{0} \text{ or undefined}$

$\csc \theta = \frac{r}{y}$
$\quad = \frac{2}{2} \text{ or } 1$

$\sec \theta = \frac{r}{x}$
$\quad = \frac{2}{0} \text{ or undefined}$

$\cot \theta = \frac{x}{y}$
$\quad = \frac{0}{2} \text{ or } 0$

61. $P(n, r) = \frac{n!}{(n - r)!}$
$\quad P(6, 4) = \frac{6!}{(6 - 4)!}$
$\quad\quad = \frac{6!}{2!}$
$\quad\quad = \frac{6 \cdot 5 \cdot 4 \cdot 3 \cdot 2!}{2!}$
$\quad\quad = 6 \cdot 5 \cdot 4 \cdot 3$
$\quad\quad = 360$

62. $P(n, r) = \frac{n!}{(n - r)!}$
$\quad P(12, 7) = \frac{12!}{(12 - 7)!}$
$\quad\quad = \frac{12!}{5!}$
$\quad\quad = \frac{12 \cdot 11 \cdot 10 \cdot 9 \cdot 8 \cdot 7 \cdot 6 \cdot 5!}{5!}$
$\quad\quad = 12 \cdot 11 \cdot 10 \cdot 9 \cdot 8 \cdot 7 \cdot 6$
$\quad\quad = 3{,}991{,}680$

63. $C(n, r) = \frac{n!}{(n - r)! \, r!}$
$\quad C(8, 3) = \frac{8!}{(8 - 3)! \, 3!}$
$\quad\quad = \frac{8!}{5! \, 3!}$
$\quad\quad = \frac{8 \cdot 7 \cdot 6 \cdot 5!}{5! \, 3!}$
$\quad\quad = \frac{8 \cdot 7 \cdot 6}{3 \cdot 2 \cdot 1}$
$\quad\quad = 56$

64. $C(n, r) = \frac{n!}{(n - r)! \, r!}$
$\quad C(10, 4) = \frac{10!}{(10 - 4)! \, 4!}$
$\quad\quad = \frac{10!}{6! \, 4!}$
$\quad\quad = \frac{10 \cdot 9 \cdot 8 \cdot 7 \cdot 6!}{6! \, 4!}$
$\quad\quad = \frac{10 \cdot 9 \cdot 8 \cdot 7}{4 \cdot 3 \cdot 2 \cdot 1}$
$\quad\quad = 210$

65. Let c be the unknown distance. Use the Law of Cosines with $a = 300$, $b = 75$, and $C = 15°$.
$c^2 = a^2 + b^2 - 2ab \cos C$
$c^2 = 300^2 + 75^2 - 2(300)(75)\cos 15°$
$c^2 \approx 52{,}158$
$c \approx 228$
She is about 228 miles from Columbus.

66. $6y^2 - 34x^2 = 204$
$\quad \frac{6y^2}{204} - \frac{34x^2}{204} = \frac{204}{204}$
$\quad \frac{y^2}{34} - \frac{x^2}{6} = 1$

67. $x^2 = \frac{20}{16}$
$\quad x = \pm\sqrt{\frac{20}{16}}$
$\quad = \pm\frac{2\sqrt{5}}{4} \text{ or } \pm\frac{\sqrt{5}}{5}$

68. $x^2 = \frac{9}{25}$
$\quad x = \pm\sqrt{\frac{9}{25}} \text{ or } \pm\frac{3}{5}$

69. $x^2 = \frac{5}{25}$
$\quad x = \pm\sqrt{\frac{5}{25}} \text{ or } \pm\frac{\sqrt{5}}{5}$

70. $x^2 = \frac{18}{32}$

$\quad x = \pm\sqrt{\frac{18}{32}}$

$\quad\ \ = \pm\frac{3\sqrt{2}}{4\sqrt{2}}$ or $\pm\frac{3}{4}$

71. $x^2 - 1 = \frac{1}{2}$

$\quad\ \ x^2 = \frac{3}{2}$

$\quad\ \ \ x = \pm\sqrt{\frac{3}{2}}$ or $\pm\frac{\sqrt{6}}{2}$

72. $x^2 - 1 = \frac{4}{5}$

$\quad\ \ x^2 = \frac{9}{5}$

$\quad\ \ \ x = \pm\sqrt{\frac{9}{5}}$ or $\pm\frac{3\sqrt{5}}{5}$

73. $x^2 = \frac{\sqrt{3}}{2} - \frac{1}{2}$

$\quad x^2 = \frac{\sqrt{3}-1}{2}$

$\quad\ x = \pm\sqrt{\frac{\sqrt{3}-1}{2}}$

$\quad\ \ \ = \pm\frac{\sqrt{\sqrt{2}(\sqrt{3}-1)}}{2}$

$\quad\ \ \ = \pm\frac{\sqrt{\sqrt{6}-\sqrt{2}}}{2}$

74. $x^2 = \frac{\sqrt{2}}{2} - 1$

$\quad x^2 = \frac{\sqrt{2}-2}{2}$

$\quad\ x = \pm\sqrt{\frac{\sqrt{2}-2}{2}}$

$\quad\ \ \ = \pm\frac{\sqrt{\sqrt{2}(\sqrt{2}-2)}}{2}$

$\quad\ \ \ = \pm\frac{\sqrt{2-2\sqrt{2}}}{2}$

14-6 Double-Angle and Half-Angle Formulas

Pages 794–795 Check for Understanding

1. Sample answer: If x is in the third quadrant, then $\frac{x}{2}$ is between 90° and 135°. Use the half-angle formula for cosine knowing that the value is negative.

2. Sample answer: 45°; $\cos 2(45°) = \cos 90°$ or 0, $2\cos 45° = 2 \cdot \frac{\sqrt{2}}{2}$ or $\sqrt{2}$

3. Sample answer: The identity used for $\cos 2\theta$ depends on whether you know the value of $\sin\theta$, $\cos\theta$ or both values.

4. First find $\sin\theta$.

$\sin^2\theta = 1 - \cos^2\theta$

$\sin^2\theta = 1 - \left(\frac{3}{5}\right)^2$

$\sin^2\theta = \frac{16}{25}$

$\ \sin\theta = \pm\frac{4}{5}$

Since θ is in the first quadrant, $\sin\theta = \frac{4}{5}$.

$\sin 2\theta = 2\sin\theta\cos\theta$

$\qquad\ \ = 2\left(\frac{4}{5}\right)\left(\frac{3}{5}\right)$

$\qquad\ \ = \frac{24}{25}$

$\cos 2\theta = 2\cos^2\theta - 1$

$\qquad\ \ = 2\left(\frac{3}{5}\right)^2 - 1$

$\qquad\ \ = -\frac{7}{25}$

$\sin\frac{\theta}{2} = \pm\sqrt{\frac{1-\cos\theta}{2}}$

$\qquad = \pm\sqrt{\frac{1-\frac{3}{5}}{2}}$

$\qquad = \pm\sqrt{\frac{1}{5}}$

$\qquad = \pm\frac{\sqrt{5}}{5}$

Since θ is between 0° and 90°, $\frac{\theta}{2}$ is between 0° and 45°. Thus, $\sin\frac{\theta}{2} = \frac{\sqrt{5}}{5}$.

$\cos\frac{\theta}{2} = \pm\sqrt{\frac{1+\cos\theta}{2}}$

$\qquad = \pm\sqrt{\frac{1+\frac{3}{5}}{2}}$

$\qquad = \pm\sqrt{\frac{4}{5}}$

$\qquad = \pm\frac{2\sqrt{5}}{5}$

Since θ is between 0° and 90°, $\frac{\theta}{2}$ is between 0° and 45°. Thus, $\cos\frac{\theta}{2} = \frac{2\sqrt{5}}{5}$.

5. First find $\sin\theta$.

$\sin^2\theta = 1 - \cos^2\theta$

$\sin^2\theta = 1 - \left(-\frac{2}{3}\right)^2$

$\sin^2\theta = \frac{5}{9}$

$\ \sin\theta = \pm\frac{\sqrt{5}}{3}$

Since θ is in the third quadrant, $\sin\theta = -\frac{\sqrt{5}}{3}$.

$\sin 2\theta = 2\sin\theta\cos\theta$

$\qquad\ \ = 2\left(-\frac{\sqrt{5}}{3}\right)\left(-\frac{2}{3}\right)$

$\qquad\ \ = \frac{4\sqrt{5}}{9}$

$\cos 2\theta = 2\cos^2\theta - 1$

$\qquad\ \ = 2\left(-\frac{2}{3}\right)^2 - 1$

$\qquad\ \ = -\frac{1}{9}$

$\sin\frac{\theta}{2} = \pm\sqrt{\frac{1-\cos\theta}{2}}$

$\qquad = \pm\sqrt{\frac{1-\left(-\frac{2}{3}\right)}{2}}$

$\qquad = \pm\sqrt{\frac{5}{6}}$

$\qquad = \pm\frac{\sqrt{30}}{6}$

Since θ is between 180° and 270°, $\frac{\theta}{2}$ is between 90° and 135°. Thus, $\sin\frac{\theta}{2} = \frac{\sqrt{30}}{6}$.

$\cos\frac{\theta}{2} = \pm\sqrt{\frac{1+\cos\theta}{2}}$

$\qquad = \pm\sqrt{\frac{1+\left(-\frac{2}{3}\right)}{2}}$

$\qquad = \pm\sqrt{\frac{1}{6}}$

$\qquad = \pm\frac{\sqrt{6}}{6}$

Since θ is between 180° and 270°, $\frac{\theta}{2}$ is between 90° and 135°. Thus, $\cos\frac{\theta}{2} = -\frac{\sqrt{6}}{6}$.

6. First find $\cos \theta$.

$\cos^2 \theta = 1 - \sin^2 \theta$

$\cos^2 \theta = 1 - \left(\frac{1}{2}\right)^2$

$\cos^2 \theta = \frac{3}{4}$

$\cos \theta = \pm \frac{\sqrt{3}}{2}$

Since θ is in the first quadrant, $\cos \theta = \frac{\sqrt{3}}{2}$.

$\sin 2\theta = 2 \sin \theta \cos \theta$

$ = 2\left(\frac{1}{2}\right)\left(\frac{\sqrt{3}}{2}\right)$

$ = \frac{\sqrt{3}}{2}$

$\cos 2\theta = 1 - 2\sin^2 \theta$

$ = 1 - 2\left(\frac{1}{2}\right)^2$

$ = \frac{1}{2}$

$\sin \frac{\theta}{2} = \pm\sqrt{\frac{1 - \cos \theta}{2}}$

$\phantom{\sin \frac{\theta}{2}} = \pm\sqrt{\frac{1 - \frac{\sqrt{3}}{2}}{2}}$

$\phantom{\sin \frac{\theta}{2}} = \pm\sqrt{\frac{2 - \sqrt{3}}{4}}$

$\phantom{\sin \frac{\theta}{2}} = \pm\frac{\sqrt{2 - \sqrt{3}}}{2}$

Since θ is between 0° and 90°, $\frac{\theta}{2}$ is between 0° and 45°. Thus, $\sin \frac{\theta}{2} = \frac{\sqrt{2 - \sqrt{3}}}{2}$.

$\cos \frac{\theta}{2} = \pm\sqrt{\frac{1 + \cos \theta}{2}}$

$\phantom{\cos \frac{\theta}{2}} = \pm\sqrt{\frac{1 + \frac{\sqrt{3}}{2}}{2}}$

$\phantom{\cos \frac{\theta}{2}} = \pm\sqrt{\frac{2 + \sqrt{3}}{4}}$

$\phantom{\cos \frac{\theta}{2}} = \pm\frac{\sqrt{2 + \sqrt{3}}}{2}$

Since θ is between 0° and 90°, $\frac{\theta}{2}$ is between 0° and 45°. Thus, $\cos \frac{\theta}{2} = \frac{\sqrt{2 + \sqrt{3}}}{2}$.

7. First find $\cos \theta$.

$\cos^2 \theta = 1 - \sin^2 \theta$

$\cos^2 \theta = 1 - \left(-\frac{3}{4}\right)^2$

$\cos^2 \theta = \frac{7}{16}$

$\cos \theta = \pm\frac{\sqrt{7}}{4}$

Since θ is in the fourth quadrant, $\cos \theta = \frac{\sqrt{7}}{4}$.

$\sin 2\theta = 2 \sin \theta \cos \theta$

$ = 2\left(-\frac{3}{4}\right)\left(\frac{\sqrt{7}}{4}\right)$

$ = -\frac{3\sqrt{7}}{8}$

$\cos 2\theta = 1 - 2\sin^2 \theta$

$ = 1 - 2\left(-\frac{3}{4}\right)^2$

$ = -\frac{1}{8}$

$\sin \frac{\theta}{2} = \pm\sqrt{\frac{1 - \cos \theta}{2}}$

$\phantom{\sin \frac{\theta}{2}} = \pm\sqrt{\frac{1 - \frac{\sqrt{7}}{4}}{2}}$

$\phantom{\sin \frac{\theta}{2}} = \pm\sqrt{\frac{8 - 2\sqrt{7}}{16}}$

$\phantom{\sin \frac{\theta}{2}} = \pm\frac{\sqrt{8 - 2\sqrt{7}}}{4}$

Since θ is between 270° and 360°, $\frac{\theta}{2}$ is between 135° and 180°. Thus, $\sin \frac{\theta}{2} = \frac{\sqrt{8 - 2\sqrt{7}}}{4}$.

$\cos \frac{\theta}{2} = \pm\sqrt{\frac{1 + \cos \theta}{2}}$

$\phantom{\cos \frac{\theta}{2}} = \pm\sqrt{\frac{1 + \frac{\sqrt{7}}{4}}{2}}$

$\phantom{\cos \frac{\theta}{2}} = \pm\sqrt{\frac{8 + 2\sqrt{7}}{16}}$

$\phantom{\cos \frac{\theta}{2}} = \pm\frac{\sqrt{8 + 2\sqrt{7}}}{4}$

Since θ is between 270° and 360°, $\frac{\theta}{2}$ is between 135° and 180°. Thus, $\cos \frac{\theta}{2} = \frac{\sqrt{8 + 2\sqrt{7}}}{4}$.

8. $\sin 195° = \sin \frac{390°}{2}$

$ = -\sqrt{\frac{1 - \cos 390°}{2}}$

$ = -\sqrt{\frac{1 - \frac{\sqrt{3}}{2}}{2}}$

$ = -\sqrt{\frac{2 - \sqrt{3}}{4}}$

$ = -\frac{\sqrt{2 - \sqrt{3}}}{2}$

9. $\cos \frac{19\pi}{12} = \cos \frac{\frac{19\pi}{6}}{2}$

$\phantom{\cos \frac{19\pi}{12}} = \sqrt{\frac{1 + \cos \frac{19\pi}{6}}{2}}$

$\phantom{\cos \frac{19\pi}{12}} = \sqrt{\frac{1 + \left(-\frac{\sqrt{3}}{2}\right)}{2}}$

$\phantom{\cos \frac{19\pi}{12}} = \sqrt{\frac{2 - \sqrt{3}}{4}}$

$\phantom{\cos \frac{19\pi}{12}} = \frac{\sqrt{2 - \sqrt{3}}}{2}$

10. $\cot x \overset{?}{=} \frac{\sin 2x}{1 - \cos 2x}$

$\cot x \overset{?}{=} \frac{2 \sin x \cos x}{1 - (1 - 2\sin^2 x)}$

$\cot x \overset{?}{=} \frac{2 \sin x \cos x}{2 \sin^2 x}$

$\cot x \overset{?}{=} \frac{\cos x}{\sin x}$

$\cot x = \cot x$

11. $\cos^2 2x + 4 \sin^2 x \cos^2 x \overset{?}{=} 1$

$ \cos^2 2x + \sin^2 2x \overset{?}{=} 1$

$ 1 = 1$

12. $\sin \frac{\theta}{2} = \frac{1}{M}$

$ \sin \frac{75°}{2} = \frac{1}{M}$

$M \sin 37.5° = 1$

$ M = \frac{1}{\sin 37.5°}$

$ M \approx 1.64$

The Mach number is 1.64.

13. First find $\cos \theta$.

$$\cos^2 \theta = 1 - \sin^2 \theta$$

$$\cos^2 \theta = 1 - \left(\frac{5}{13}\right)^2$$

$$\cos^2 \theta = \frac{144}{169}$$

$$\cos \theta = \pm\frac{12}{13}$$

Since θ is in the second quadrant, $\cos \theta = -\frac{12}{13}$.

$$\sin 2\theta = 2 \sin \theta \cos \theta$$

$$= 2\left(\frac{5}{13}\right)\left(-\frac{12}{13}\right)$$

$$= -\frac{120}{169}$$

$$\cos 2\theta = 1 - 2 \sin^2 \theta$$

$$= 1 - 2\left(\frac{5}{13}\right)^2$$

$$= \frac{119}{169}$$

$$\sin \frac{\theta}{2} = \pm\sqrt{\frac{1 - \cos \theta}{2}}$$

$$= \pm\sqrt{\frac{1 - \left(-\frac{12}{13}\right)}{2}}$$

$$= \pm\sqrt{\frac{25}{26}}$$

$$= \pm\frac{5\sqrt{26}}{26}$$

Since θ is between 90° and 180°, $\frac{\theta}{2}$ is between 45° and 90°. Thus, $\sin \frac{\theta}{2} = \frac{5\sqrt{26}}{26}$.

$$\cos \frac{\theta}{2} = \pm\sqrt{\frac{1 + \cos \theta}{2}}$$

$$= \pm\sqrt{\frac{1 + \left(-\frac{12}{13}\right)}{2}}$$

$$= \pm\sqrt{\frac{1}{26}}$$

$$= \pm\frac{\sqrt{26}}{26}$$

Since θ is between 90° and 180°, $\frac{\theta}{2}$ is between 45° and 90°. Thus, $\cos \frac{\theta}{2} = \frac{\sqrt{26}}{26}$.

14. First find $\sin \theta$.

$$\sin^2 \theta = 1 - \cos^2 \theta$$

$$\sin^2 \theta = 1 - \left(\frac{1}{5}\right)^2$$

$$\sin^2 \theta = \frac{24}{25}$$

$$\sin \theta = \pm\frac{2\sqrt{6}}{5}$$

Since θ is in the fourth quadrant, $\sin \theta = -\frac{2\sqrt{6}}{5}$.

$$\sin 2\theta = 2 \sin \theta \cos \theta$$

$$= 2\left(-\frac{2\sqrt{6}}{5}\right)\left(\frac{1}{5}\right)$$

$$= -\frac{4\sqrt{6}}{25}$$

$$\cos 2\theta = 2 \cos^2 \theta - 1$$

$$= 2\left(\frac{1}{5}\right)^2 - 1$$

$$= -\frac{23}{25}$$

$$\sin \frac{\theta}{2} = \pm\sqrt{\frac{1 - \cos \theta}{2}}$$

$$= \pm\sqrt{\frac{1 - \frac{1}{5}}{2}}$$

$$= \pm\sqrt{\frac{2}{5}}$$

$$= \pm\frac{\sqrt{10}}{5}$$

Since θ is between 270° and 360°, $\frac{\theta}{2}$ is between 135° and 180°. Thus, $\sin \frac{\theta}{2} = \frac{\sqrt{10}}{5}$.

$$\cos \frac{\theta}{2} = \pm\sqrt{\frac{1 + \cos \theta}{2}}$$

$$= \pm\sqrt{\frac{1 + \frac{1}{5}}{2}}$$

$$= \pm\sqrt{\frac{3}{5}}$$

$$= \pm\frac{\sqrt{15}}{5}$$

Since θ is between 270° and 360°, $\frac{\theta}{2}$ is between 135° and 180°. Thus, $\cos \frac{\theta}{2} = -\frac{\sqrt{15}}{5}$.

15. First find $\sin \theta$.

$$\sin^2 \theta = 1 - \cos^2 \theta$$

$$\sin^2 \theta = 1 - \left(-\frac{1}{3}\right)^2$$

$$\sin^2 \theta = \frac{8}{9}$$

$$\sin \theta = \pm\frac{2\sqrt{2}}{3}$$

Since θ is in the third quadrant, $\sin \theta = -\frac{2\sqrt{2}}{3}$.

$$\sin 2\theta = 2 \sin \theta \cos \theta$$

$$= 2\left(-\frac{2\sqrt{2}}{3}\right)\left(-\frac{1}{3}\right)$$

$$= \frac{4\sqrt{2}}{9}$$

$$\cos 2\theta = 2 \cos^2 \theta - 1$$

$$= 2\left(-\frac{1}{3}\right)^2 - 1$$

$$= -\frac{7}{9}$$

$$\sin \frac{\theta}{2} = \pm\sqrt{\frac{1 - \cos \theta}{2}}$$

$$= \pm\sqrt{\frac{1 - \left(-\frac{1}{3}\right)}{2}}$$

$$= \pm\sqrt{\frac{2}{3}}$$

$$= \pm\frac{\sqrt{6}}{3}$$

Since θ is between 180° and 270°, $\frac{\theta}{2}$ is between 90° and 135°. Thus, $\sin \frac{\theta}{2} = -\frac{\sqrt{6}}{3}$.

$$\cos \frac{\theta}{2} = \pm\sqrt{\frac{1 + \cos \theta}{2}}$$

$$= \pm\sqrt{\frac{1 + \left(-\frac{1}{3}\right)}{2}}$$

$$= \pm\sqrt{\frac{1}{3}}$$

$$= \pm\frac{\sqrt{3}}{3}$$

Since θ between 180° and 270°, $\frac{\theta}{2}$ is between 90° and 135°. Thus, $\cos \frac{\theta}{2} = -\frac{\sqrt{3}}{3}$.

16. First find $\cos \theta$.

$\cos^2 \theta = 1 - \sin^2 \theta$

$\cos^2 \theta = 1 - \left(-\frac{3}{5}\right)^2$

$\cos^2 \theta = \frac{16}{25}$

$\cos \theta = \pm \frac{4}{5}$

Since θ is in the third quadrant, $\cos \theta = -\frac{4}{5}$.

$\sin 2\theta = 2 \sin \theta \cos \theta$

$= 2\left(-\frac{3}{5}\right)\left(-\frac{4}{5}\right)$

$= \frac{24}{25}$

$\cos 2\theta = 2 \cos^2 \theta - 1$

$= 2\left(-\frac{4}{5}\right)^2 - 1$

$= \frac{7}{25}$

$\sin \frac{\theta}{2} = \pm\sqrt{\frac{1 - \cos \theta}{2}}$

$= \pm\sqrt{\frac{1 - \left(-\frac{4}{5}\right)}{2}}$

$= \pm\sqrt{\frac{9}{10}}$

$= \pm\frac{3\sqrt{10}}{10}$

Since θ is between 180° and 270°, $\frac{\theta}{2}$ is between 90° and 135°. Thus, $\sin \frac{\theta}{2} = \frac{3\sqrt{10}}{10}$.

$\cos \frac{\theta}{2} = \pm\sqrt{\frac{1 + \cos \theta}{2}}$

$= \pm\sqrt{\frac{1 + \left(-\frac{4}{5}\right)}{2}}$

$= \pm\sqrt{\frac{1}{10}}$

$= \pm\frac{\sqrt{10}}{10}$

Since θ is between 180° and 270°, $\frac{\theta}{2}$ is between 90° and 135°. Thus, $\cos \frac{\theta}{2} = -\frac{\sqrt{10}}{10}$.

17. First find $\cos \theta$.

$\cos^2 \theta = 1 - \sin^2 \theta$

$\cos^2 \theta = 1 - \left(-\frac{3}{8}\right)^2$

$\cos^2 \theta = \frac{55}{64}$

$\cos \theta = \pm\frac{\sqrt{55}}{8}$

Since θ is in the fourth quadrant, $\cos \theta = \frac{\sqrt{55}}{8}$.

$\sin 2\theta = 2 \sin \theta \cos \theta$

$= 2\left(-\frac{3}{8}\right)\left(\frac{\sqrt{55}}{8}\right)$

$= -\frac{3\sqrt{55}}{32}$

$\cos 2\theta = 2 \cos^2 \theta - 1$

$= 2\left(\frac{\sqrt{55}}{8}\right)^2 - 1$

$= \frac{23}{32}$

$\sin \frac{\theta}{2} = \pm\sqrt{\frac{1 - \cos \theta}{2}}$

$= \pm\sqrt{\frac{1 - \frac{\sqrt{55}}{8}}{2}}$

$= \pm\sqrt{\frac{8-\sqrt{55}}{16}}$

$= \pm\frac{\sqrt{8 - \sqrt{55}}}{4}$

Since θ is between 270° and 360°, $\frac{\theta}{2}$ is between 135°, and 180°. Thus, $\sin \frac{\theta}{2} = \frac{\sqrt{8 - \sqrt{55}}}{4}$.

$\cos \frac{\theta}{2} = \pm\sqrt{\frac{1 + \cos \theta}{2}}$

$= \pm\sqrt{\frac{1 + \frac{\sqrt{55}}{8}}{2}}$

$= \pm\sqrt{\frac{8 + \sqrt{55}}{16}}$

$= \pm\frac{\sqrt{8 + \sqrt{55}}}{4}$

Since θ is between 270° and 360°, $\frac{\theta}{2}$ is between 135° and 180°. Thus, $\cos \frac{\theta}{2} = -\frac{\sqrt{8 + \sqrt{55}}}{4}$.

18. First find $\sin \theta$.

$\sin^2 \theta = 1 - \cos^2 \theta$

$\sin^2 \theta = 1 - \left(-\frac{1}{4}\right)^2$

$\sin^2 \theta = \frac{15}{16}$

$\sin \theta = \pm\frac{\sqrt{15}}{4}$

Since θ is in the second quadrant, $\sin \theta = \frac{\sqrt{15}}{4}$.

$\sin 2\theta = 2 \sin \theta \cos \theta$

$= 2\left(\frac{\sqrt{15}}{4}\right)\left(-\frac{1}{4}\right)$

$= -\frac{\sqrt{15}}{8}$

$\cos 2\theta = 2 \cos^2 \theta - 1$

$= 2\left(-\frac{1}{4}\right)^2 - 1$

$= -\frac{7}{8}$

$\sin \frac{\theta}{2} = \pm\sqrt{\frac{1 - \cos \theta}{2}}$

$= \pm\sqrt{\frac{1 - \left(-\frac{1}{4}\right)}{2}}$

$= \pm\sqrt{\frac{5}{8}}$

$= \pm\frac{\sqrt{10}}{4}$

Since θ is between 90° and 180°, $\frac{\theta}{2}$ is between 45° and 90°. Thus, $\sin \frac{\theta}{2} = \frac{\sqrt{10}}{4}$.

$\cos \frac{\theta}{2} = \pm\sqrt{\frac{1 + \cos \theta}{2}}$

$= \pm\sqrt{\frac{1 + \left(-\frac{1}{4}\right)}{2}}$

$= \pm\sqrt{\frac{3}{8}}$

$= \pm\frac{\sqrt{6}}{4}$

Since θ is between 90° and 180°, $\frac{\theta}{2}$ is between 45° and 90°. Thus, $\cos \frac{\theta}{2} = \frac{\sqrt{6}}{4}$.

19. First find $\sin \theta$.

$\sin^2 \theta = 1 - \cos^2 \theta$

$\sin^2 \theta = 1 - \left(\frac{1}{6}\right)^2$

$\sin^2 \theta = \frac{35}{36}$

$\sin \theta = \pm \frac{\sqrt{35}}{6}$

Since θ is in the first quadrant, $\sin \theta = \frac{\sqrt{35}}{6}$.

$\sin 2\theta = 2 \sin \theta \cos \theta$

$\quad = 2\left(\frac{\sqrt{35}}{6}\right)\left(\frac{1}{6}\right)$

$\quad = \frac{\sqrt{35}}{18}$

$\cos 2\theta = 2 \cos^2 \theta - 1$

$\quad = 2\left(\frac{1}{6}\right)^2 - 1$

$\quad = -\frac{17}{18}$

$\sin \frac{\theta}{2} = \pm \sqrt{\frac{1 - \cos \theta}{2}}$

$\quad = \pm \sqrt{\frac{1 - \frac{1}{6}}{2}}$

$\quad = \pm \sqrt{\frac{5}{12}}$

$\quad = \pm \frac{\sqrt{15}}{6}$

Since θ is between 0° and 90°, $\frac{\theta}{2}$ is between 0° and 45°. Thus, $\sin \frac{\theta}{2} = \frac{\sqrt{15}}{6}$.

$\cos \frac{\theta}{2} = \pm \sqrt{\frac{1 + \cos \theta}{2}}$

$\quad = \pm \sqrt{\frac{1 + \frac{1}{6}}{2}}$

$\quad = \pm \sqrt{\frac{7}{12}}$

$\quad = \pm \frac{\sqrt{21}}{6}$

Since θ is between 0° and 90°, $\frac{\theta}{2}$ is between 0° and 45°. Thus, $\cos \frac{\theta}{2} = \frac{\sqrt{21}}{6}$.

20. First find $\sin \theta$.

$\sin^2 \theta = 1 - \cos^2 \theta$

$\sin^2 \theta = 1 - \left(-\frac{12}{13}\right)^2$

$\sin^2 \theta = \frac{25}{169}$

$\sin \theta = \pm \frac{5}{13}$

Since θ is in the third quadrant, $\sin \theta = -\frac{5}{13}$.

$\sin 2\theta = 2 \sin \theta \cos \theta$

$\quad = 2\left(-\frac{5}{13}\right)\left(-\frac{12}{13}\right)$

$\quad = \frac{120}{169}$

$\cos 2\theta = 2 \cos^2 \theta - 1$

$\quad = 2\left(-\frac{12}{13}\right)^2 - 1$

$\quad = \frac{119}{169}$

$\sin \frac{\theta}{2} = \pm \sqrt{\frac{1 - \cos \theta}{2}}$

$\quad = \pm \sqrt{\frac{1 - \left(-\frac{12}{13}\right)}{2}}$

$\quad = \pm \sqrt{\frac{25}{26}}$

$\quad = \pm \frac{5\sqrt{26}}{26}$

Since θ is between 180° and 270°, $\frac{\theta}{2}$ is between 90° and 135°. Thus, $\sin \frac{\theta}{2} = \frac{5\sqrt{26}}{26}$.

$\cos \frac{\theta}{2} = \pm \sqrt{\frac{1 + \cos \theta}{2}}$

$\quad = \pm \sqrt{\frac{1 + \left(-\frac{12}{13}\right)}{2}}$

$\quad = \pm \sqrt{\frac{1}{26}}$

$\quad = \pm \frac{\sqrt{26}}{26}$

Since θ is between 180° and 270°, $\frac{\theta}{2}$ is between 90° and 135°. Thus, $\cos \frac{\theta}{2} = -\frac{\sqrt{26}}{26}$.

21. First find $\cos \theta$.

$\cos^2 \theta = 1 - \sin^2 \theta$

$\cos^2 \theta = 1 - \left(-\frac{1}{3}\right)^2$

$\cos^2 \theta = \frac{8}{9}$

$\cos \theta = \pm \frac{2\sqrt{2}}{3}$

Since θ is in the fourth quadrant, $\cos \theta = \frac{2\sqrt{2}}{3}$.

$\sin 2\theta = 2 \sin \theta \cos \theta$

$\quad = 2\left(-\frac{1}{3}\right)\left(\frac{2\sqrt{2}}{3}\right)$

$\quad = -\frac{4\sqrt{2}}{9}$

$\cos 2\theta = 2 \cos^2 \theta - 1$

$\quad = 2\left(\frac{2\sqrt{2}}{3}\right)^2 - 1$

$\quad = \frac{7}{9}$

$\sin \frac{\theta}{2} = \pm \sqrt{\frac{1 - \cos \theta}{2}}$

$\quad = \pm \sqrt{\frac{1 - \frac{2\sqrt{2}}{3}}{2}}$

$\quad = \pm \sqrt{\frac{18 - 12\sqrt{2}}{36}}$

$\quad = \pm \frac{\sqrt{18 - 12\sqrt{2}}}{6}$

Since θ is between 270° and 360°, $\frac{\theta}{2}$ is between 135° and 180°. Thus, $\sin \frac{\theta}{2} = \frac{\sqrt{18 - 12\sqrt{2}}}{6}$.

$\cos \frac{\theta}{2} = \pm \sqrt{\frac{1 + \cos \theta}{2}}$

$\quad = \pm \sqrt{\frac{1 + \frac{2\sqrt{2}}{3}}{2}}$

$\quad = \pm \sqrt{\frac{18 + 12\sqrt{2}}{36}}$

$\quad = \pm \frac{\sqrt{18 + 12\sqrt{2}}}{6}$

Since θ is between 270° and 360°, $\frac{\theta}{2}$ is between 135° and 180°. Thus, $\cos \frac{\theta}{2} = -\frac{\sqrt{18 + 12\sqrt{2}}}{6}$.

22. First find $\cos\theta$.

$$\cos^2\theta = 1 - \sin^2\theta$$
$$\cos^2\theta = 1 - \left(-\frac{1}{4}\right)^2$$
$$\cos^2\theta = \frac{15}{16}$$
$$\cos\theta = \pm\frac{\sqrt{15}}{4}$$

Since θ is in the third quadrant, $\cos\theta = -\frac{\sqrt{15}}{4}$.

$$\sin 2\theta = 2\sin\theta\cos\theta$$
$$= 2\left(-\frac{1}{4}\right)\left(-\frac{\sqrt{15}}{4}\right)$$
$$= \frac{\sqrt{15}}{8}$$
$$\cos 2\theta = 1 - 2\sin^2\theta$$
$$= 1 - 2\left(-\frac{1}{4}\right)^2$$
$$= \frac{7}{8}$$
$$\sin\frac{\theta}{2} = \pm\sqrt{\frac{1-\cos\theta}{2}}$$
$$= \pm\sqrt{\frac{1-\left(-\frac{\sqrt{15}}{4}\right)}{2}}$$
$$= \pm\sqrt{\frac{8+2\sqrt{15}}{16}}$$
$$= \pm\frac{\sqrt{8+2\sqrt{15}}}{4}$$

Since θ is between $180°$ and $270°$, $\frac{\theta}{2}$ is between $90°$ and $135°$. Thus, $\sin\frac{\theta}{2} = \frac{\sqrt{8+2\sqrt{15}}}{4}$.

$$\cos\frac{\theta}{2} = \pm\sqrt{\frac{1+\cos\theta}{2}}$$
$$= \pm\sqrt{\frac{1+\left(-\frac{\sqrt{15}}{4}\right)}{2}}$$
$$= \pm\sqrt{\frac{8-2\sqrt{15}}{16}}$$
$$= \pm\frac{\sqrt{8-2\sqrt{15}}}{4}$$

Since θ is between $180°$ and $270°$, $\frac{\theta}{2}$ is between $90°$ and $135°$. Thus, $\cos\frac{\theta}{2} = -\frac{\sqrt{8-2\sqrt{15}}}{4}$.

23. First find $\sin\theta$.

$$\sin^2\theta = 1 - \cos^2\theta$$
$$\sin^2\theta = 1 - \left(\frac{2}{3}\right)^2$$
$$\sin^2\theta = \frac{5}{9}$$
$$\sin\theta = \pm\frac{\sqrt{5}}{3}$$

Since θ is in the first quadrant, $\sin\theta = \frac{\sqrt{5}}{3}$.

$$\sin 2\theta = 2\sin\theta\cos\theta$$
$$= 2\left(\frac{\sqrt{5}}{3}\right)\left(\frac{2}{3}\right)$$
$$= \frac{4\sqrt{5}}{9}$$
$$\cos 2\theta = 2\cos^2\theta - 1$$
$$= 2\left(\frac{2}{3}\right)^2 - 1$$
$$= -\frac{1}{9}$$
$$\sin\frac{\theta}{2} = \pm\sqrt{\frac{1-\cos\theta}{2}}$$
$$= \pm\sqrt{\frac{1-\frac{2}{3}}{2}}$$
$$= \pm\sqrt{\frac{1}{6}}$$
$$= \pm\frac{\sqrt{6}}{6}$$

Since θ is between $0°$ and $90°$, $\frac{\theta}{2}$ is between $0°$ and $45°$. Thus, $\sin\frac{\theta}{2} = \frac{\sqrt{6}}{6}$.

$$\cos\frac{\theta}{2} = \pm\sqrt{\frac{1+\cos\theta}{2}}$$
$$= \pm\sqrt{\frac{1+\frac{2}{3}}{2}}$$
$$= \pm\sqrt{\frac{5}{6}}$$
$$= \pm\frac{\sqrt{30}}{6}$$

Since θ is between $0°$ and $90°$, $\frac{\theta}{2}$ is between $0°$ and $45°$. Thus, $\cos\frac{\theta}{2} = \frac{\sqrt{30}}{6}$.

24. First find $\cos\theta$.

$$\cos^2\theta = 1 - \sin^2\theta$$
$$\cos^2\theta = 1 - \left(\frac{2}{5}\right)^2$$
$$\cos^2\theta = \frac{21}{25}$$
$$\cos\theta = \pm\frac{\sqrt{21}}{5}$$

Since θ is in the second quadrant, $\cos\theta = -\frac{\sqrt{21}}{5}$.

$$\sin 2\theta = 2\sin\theta\cos\theta$$
$$= 2\left(\frac{2}{5}\right)\left(-\frac{\sqrt{21}}{5}\right)$$
$$= -\frac{4\sqrt{21}}{25}$$
$$\cos 2\theta = 1 - 2\sin^2\theta$$
$$= 1 - 2\left(\frac{2}{5}\right)^2$$
$$= \frac{17}{25}$$
$$\sin\frac{\theta}{2} = \pm\sqrt{\frac{1-\cos\theta}{2}}$$
$$= \pm\sqrt{\frac{1+\left(-\frac{\sqrt{21}}{5}\right)}{2}}$$
$$= \pm\sqrt{\frac{50+10\sqrt{21}}{100}}$$
$$= \pm\frac{\sqrt{50+10\sqrt{21}}}{10}$$

Since θ is between $90°$ and $180°$, $\frac{\theta}{2}$ is between $45°$ and $90°$.

Thus, $\sin\frac{\theta}{2} = \frac{\sqrt{50+10\sqrt{21}}}{10}$ or $\frac{\sqrt{5\sqrt{2}+10\sqrt{21}}}{10}$.

$$\cos\frac{\theta}{2} = \pm\sqrt{\frac{1+\cos\theta}{2}}$$
$$= \pm\sqrt{\frac{1+\left(-\frac{\sqrt{21}}{5}\right)}{2}}$$
$$= \pm\sqrt{\frac{50-10\sqrt{21}}{100}}$$
$$= \pm\frac{\sqrt{50-10\sqrt{21}}}{10}$$

Since θ is between $90°$ and $180°$, $\frac{\theta}{2}$ is between $45°$ and $90°$. Thus, $\cos\frac{\theta}{2} = \frac{\sqrt{50-10\sqrt{21}}}{10}$ or $\frac{\sqrt{5\sqrt{2}-10\sqrt{21}}}{10}$.

25. $\cos 165° = \cos \dfrac{330°}{2}$

$\quad = -\sqrt{\dfrac{1 + \cos 330°}{2}}$

$\quad = -\sqrt{\dfrac{1 + \frac{\sqrt{3}}{2}}{2}}$

$\quad = -\sqrt{\dfrac{2 + \sqrt{3}}{4}}$

$\quad = -\dfrac{\sqrt{2 + \sqrt{3}}}{2}$

26. $\sin 22\tfrac{1}{2}° = \sin \dfrac{45°}{2}$

$\quad = \sqrt{\dfrac{1 - \cos 45°}{2}}$

$\quad = \sqrt{\dfrac{1 - \frac{\sqrt{2}}{2}}{2}}$

$\quad = \sqrt{\dfrac{2 - \sqrt{2}}{4}}$

$\quad = \dfrac{\sqrt{2 - \sqrt{2}}}{2}$

27. $\cos 157\tfrac{1}{2}° = \cos \dfrac{315°}{2}$

$\quad = -\sqrt{\dfrac{1 + \cos 315°}{2}}$

$\quad = -\sqrt{\dfrac{1 + \frac{\sqrt{2}}{2}}{2}}$

$\quad = -\sqrt{\dfrac{2 + \sqrt{2}}{4}}$

$\quad = -\dfrac{\sqrt{2 + \sqrt{2}}}{2}$

28. $\sin 345° = \sin \dfrac{690°}{2}$

$\quad = -\sqrt{\dfrac{1 - \cos 690°}{2}}$

$\quad = -\sqrt{\dfrac{1 - \frac{\sqrt{3}}{2}}{2}}$

$\quad = -\sqrt{\dfrac{2 - \sqrt{3}}{4}}$

$\quad = -\dfrac{\sqrt{2 - \sqrt{3}}}{2}$

29. $\sin \dfrac{7\pi}{8} = \sin \dfrac{\frac{7\pi}{4}}{2}$

$\quad = \sqrt{\dfrac{1 - \cos \frac{7\pi}{4}}{2}}$

$\quad = \sqrt{\dfrac{1 - \frac{\sqrt{2}}{2}}{2}}$

$\quad = \sqrt{\dfrac{2 - \sqrt{2}}{4}}$

$\quad = \dfrac{\sqrt{2 - \sqrt{2}}}{2}$

30. $\cos \dfrac{7\pi}{12} = \cos \dfrac{\frac{7\pi}{6}}{2}$

$\quad = -\sqrt{\dfrac{1 + \cos \frac{7\pi}{4}}{2}}$

$\quad = -\sqrt{\dfrac{1 + \left(-\frac{\sqrt{3}}{2}\right)}{2}}$

$\quad = -\sqrt{\dfrac{2 - \sqrt{3}}{4}}$

$\quad = -\dfrac{\sqrt{2 - \sqrt{3}}}{2}$

31. $\sin 2x \overset{?}{=} 2 \cot x \sin^2 x$

$\quad \sin 2x \overset{?}{=} 2 \cdot \dfrac{\cos x}{\sin x} \cdot \sin^2 x$

$\quad \sin 2x \overset{?}{=} 2 \cos x \sin x$

$\quad \sin 2x = \sin 2x$

32. $2 \cos^2 \dfrac{x}{2} \overset{?}{=} 1 + \cos x$

$\quad 2\left(\pm\sqrt{\dfrac{1 + \cos x}{2}}\right)^2 \overset{?}{=} 1 + \cos x$

$\quad 2\left(\dfrac{1 + \cos x}{2}\right) \overset{?}{=} 1 + \cos x$

$\quad 1 + \cos x = 1 + \cos x$

33. $\sin^4 x - \cos^4 x \overset{?}{=} 2 \sin^2 x - 1$

$\quad (\sin^2 x - \cos^2 x)(\sin^2 x + \cos^2 x) \overset{?}{=} 2 \sin^2 x - 1$

$\quad (\sin^2 x - \cos^2 x) \cdot 1 \overset{?}{=} 2 \sin^2 x - 1$

$\quad [\sin^2 x - (1 - \sin^2 x)] \cdot 1 \overset{?}{=} 2 \sin^2 x - 1$

$\quad \sin^2 x - 1 + \sin^2 x \overset{?}{=} 2 \sin^2 x - 1$

$\quad 2 \sin^2 x - 1 = 2 \sin^2 x - 1$

34. $\sin^2 x \overset{?}{=} \dfrac{1}{2}(1 - \cos 2x)$

$\quad \sin^2 x \overset{?}{=} \dfrac{1}{2}[1 - (1 - 2 \sin^2 x)]$

$\quad \sin^2 x \overset{?}{=} \dfrac{1}{2}(2 \sin^2 x)$

$\quad \sin^2 x = \sin^2 x$

35. $\tan^2 \dfrac{x}{2} \overset{?}{=} \dfrac{1 - \cos x}{1 + \cos x}$

$\quad \dfrac{\sin^2 \frac{x}{2}}{\cos^2 \frac{x}{2}} \overset{?}{=} \dfrac{1 - \cos x}{1 + \cos x}$

$\quad \dfrac{\left(\pm\sqrt{\frac{1 - \cos x}{2}}\right)^2}{\left(\pm\sqrt{\frac{1 + \cos x}{2}}\right)^2} \overset{?}{=} \dfrac{1 - \cos x}{1 + \cos x}$

$\quad \dfrac{1 - \cos x}{1 + \cos x} = \dfrac{1 - \cos x}{1 + \cos x}$

36. $\dfrac{1}{\sin x \cos x} - \dfrac{\cos x}{\sin x} \overset{?}{=} \tan x$

$\quad \dfrac{1 - \cos^2 x}{\sin x \cos x} \overset{?}{=} \tan x$

$\quad \dfrac{\sin^2 x}{\sin x \cos x} \overset{?}{=} \tan x$

$\quad \dfrac{\sin x}{\cos x} \overset{?}{=} \tan x$

$\quad \tan x = \tan x$

37. $n = \dfrac{\sin\left[\frac{1}{2}(\alpha + \beta)\right]}{\sin \frac{\alpha}{2}}$

$\quad 2 = \dfrac{\sin\left[\frac{1}{2}(40° + \beta)\right]}{\sin \frac{40°}{2}}$

$\quad 2 \sin 20° = \sin\left(20° + \tfrac{1}{2}\beta\right)$

$\quad 43.16° \approx 20° + \tfrac{1}{2}\beta$

$\quad 23.16° \approx \tfrac{1}{2}\beta$

$\quad 46.32° \approx \beta$

The angle of deviation is about 46.3°.

38. $\tan\left(45° + \dfrac{L}{2}\right) = \dfrac{\sin\left(45° + \dfrac{L}{2}\right)}{\cos\left(45° + \dfrac{L}{2}\right)}$

$= \dfrac{\sin 45° \cos \dfrac{L}{2} + \cos 45° \sin \dfrac{L}{2}}{\cos 45° \cos \dfrac{L}{2} - \sin 45° \sin \dfrac{L}{2}}$

$= \dfrac{\dfrac{\sqrt{2}}{2}\cos \dfrac{L}{2} + \dfrac{\sqrt{2}}{2}\sin \dfrac{L}{2}}{\dfrac{\sqrt{2}}{2}\cos \dfrac{L}{2} - \dfrac{\sqrt{2}}{2}\sin \dfrac{L}{2}}$

$= \dfrac{\cos \dfrac{L}{2} + \sin \dfrac{L}{2}}{\cos \dfrac{L}{2} - \sin \dfrac{L}{2}}$

$= \dfrac{\pm\sqrt{\dfrac{1+\cos L}{2}} \pm \sqrt{\dfrac{1-\cos L}{2}}}{\pm\sqrt{\dfrac{1+\cos L}{2}} \pm \sqrt{\dfrac{1-\cos L}{2}}}$

$= \dfrac{\pm\sqrt{1+\cos L} \pm \sqrt{1-\cos L}}{\pm\sqrt{1+\cos L} \pm \sqrt{1-\cos L}}$

$= \dfrac{1 \pm \sqrt{\dfrac{1-\cos L}{1+\cos L}}}{1 \mp \sqrt{\dfrac{1-\cos L}{1+\cos L}}}$

39. $\dfrac{1 + \sqrt{\dfrac{1-\cos L}{1+\cos L}}}{1 - \sqrt{\dfrac{1-\cos L}{1+\cos L}}} = \dfrac{1 + \sqrt{\dfrac{1-\cos 60°}{1+\cos 60°}}}{1 - \sqrt{\dfrac{1-\cos 60°}{1+\cos 60°}}}$

$= \dfrac{1 + \sqrt{\dfrac{1-\dfrac{1}{2}}{1+\dfrac{1}{2}}}}{1 - \sqrt{\dfrac{1-\dfrac{1}{2}}{1+\dfrac{1}{2}}}}$

$= \dfrac{1 + \sqrt{\dfrac{1}{3}}}{1 - \sqrt{\dfrac{1}{3}}}$

$= \dfrac{\sqrt{3}+1}{\sqrt{3}-1} \cdot \dfrac{\sqrt{3}+1}{\sqrt{3}+1}$

$= \dfrac{4 + 2\sqrt{3}}{2}$ or $2 + \sqrt{3}$

40. $\dfrac{2}{g}v^2(\tan\theta - \tan\theta \sin^2\theta) \overset{?}{=} \dfrac{2}{g}v^2 \tan\theta(1 - \sin^2\theta)$

$\overset{?}{=} \dfrac{2}{g}v^2 \tan\theta \cos^2\theta$

$\overset{?}{=} \dfrac{2}{g}v^2 \sin\theta \cos\theta$

$= \dfrac{v^2 \sin 2\theta}{g}$

41. $\dfrac{h}{d} = \dfrac{\dfrac{v^2 \sin^2\theta}{2g}}{\dfrac{v^2 \sin 2\theta}{g}}$

$= \dfrac{v^2 \sin^2\theta}{2g} \cdot \dfrac{g}{v^2 \sin 2\theta}$

$= \dfrac{\sin^2\theta}{2 \sin 2\theta}$

$= \dfrac{\sin^2\theta}{2(2\sin\theta\cos\theta)}$

$= \dfrac{\sin\theta}{4\cos\theta}$

$= \dfrac{1}{4}\tan\theta$

42.

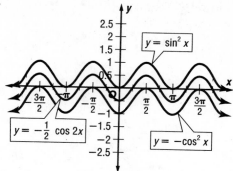

Sample answer: They all have the same shape and are vertical translations of each other.

43. The maxima occur at $x = \pm\dfrac{\pi}{2}$ and $\pm\dfrac{3\pi}{2}$. The maxima occur at $x = 0$, $\pm\pi$ and $\pm 2\pi$.

44.

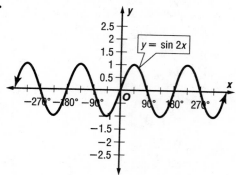

45. The graph of $f(x)$ crosses the x-axis at the points specified in Exercise 43.

46. The graph of $g(x)$ is the graph of $h(x)$ shifted up 1 unit, so $g(x) = h(x) + 1$. Thus, $c = 1$.

The graph of $g(x)$ is the graph of $k(x)$ shifted up 0.5 unit, so $g(x) = k(x) + 0.5$. Thus, $d = 0.5$.

47. Sample answer: The sound waves associated with music can be modeled using trigonometric functions. Answers should include the following information.

• In moving from one harmonic to the next, the number of vibrations that appear as sine waves increase by 1.

• The period of the function as you move from the nth harmonic to the $(n+1)$th harmonic decreases from $\dfrac{2\pi}{n}$ to $\dfrac{2\pi}{n+1}$.

48. D; $\cos 2\theta = 1 - 2\sin^2\theta$

$= 1 - 2\left(\dfrac{-\sqrt{5}}{3}\right)^2$

$= -\dfrac{1}{9}$ or $\dfrac{-1}{9}$

49. B; $\sin\dfrac{\theta}{2} = \pm\sqrt{\dfrac{1-\cos\theta}{2}}$

$= \pm\sqrt{\dfrac{1-\dfrac{\sqrt{3}}{2}}{2}}$

$= \pm\sqrt{\dfrac{2-\sqrt{3}}{4}}$

$= \pm\dfrac{\sqrt{2-\sqrt{3}}}{2}$

Since θ is between 0° and 90°, $\dfrac{\theta}{2}$ is between 0° and 45°. Thus, $\sin\theta = \dfrac{\sqrt{2-\sqrt{3}}}{2}$.

50. $\cos 15° = \cos(45° - 30°)$
$\quad\quad\quad = \cos 45° \cos 30° + \sin 45° \sin 30°$
$\quad\quad\quad = \frac{\sqrt{2}}{2} \cdot \frac{\sqrt{3}}{2} + \frac{\sqrt{2}}{2} \cdot \frac{1}{2}$
$\quad\quad\quad = \frac{\sqrt{6}}{4} + \frac{\sqrt{2}}{4}$ or $\frac{\sqrt{6} + \sqrt{2}}{4}$

51. $\sin 15° = \sin(45° - 30°)$
$\quad\quad\quad = \sin 45° \cos 30° - \cos 45° \sin 30°$
$\quad\quad\quad = \frac{\sqrt{2}}{2} \cdot \frac{\sqrt{3}}{2} - \frac{\sqrt{2}}{2} \cdot \frac{1}{2}$
$\quad\quad\quad = \frac{\sqrt{6}}{4} - \frac{\sqrt{2}}{4}$ or $\frac{\sqrt{6} - \sqrt{2}}{4}$

52. $\sin(-135°) = \sin(45° - 180°)$
$\quad\quad\quad\quad = \sin 45° \cos 180° - \cos 45° \sin 180°$
$\quad\quad\quad\quad = \frac{\sqrt{2}}{2} \cdot (-1) - \frac{\sqrt{2}}{2} \cdot 0$
$\quad\quad\quad\quad = -\frac{\sqrt{2}}{2} - 0$ or $-\frac{\sqrt{2}}{2}$

53. $\cos 150° = \cos(90° + 60°)$
$\quad\quad\quad = \cos 90° \cos 60° - \sin 90° \sin 60°$
$\quad\quad\quad = 0 \cdot \frac{1}{2} - 1 \cdot \frac{\sqrt{3}}{2}$
$\quad\quad\quad = 0 - \frac{\sqrt{3}}{2}$ or $-\frac{\sqrt{3}}{2}$

54. $\sin 105° = \sin(60° + 45°)$
$\quad\quad\quad = \sin 60° \cos 45° + \cos 60° \sin 45°$
$\quad\quad\quad = \frac{\sqrt{3}}{2} \cdot \frac{\sqrt{2}}{2} + \frac{1}{2} \cdot \frac{\sqrt{2}}{2}$
$\quad\quad\quad = \frac{\sqrt{6}}{4} + \frac{\sqrt{2}}{4}$ or $\frac{\sqrt{6} + \sqrt{2}}{4}$

55. $\cos(-300°) = \cos(60° - 360°)$
$\quad\quad\quad\quad = \cos 60° \cos 360° + \sin 60° \sin 360°$
$\quad\quad\quad\quad = \frac{1}{2} \cdot 1 + \frac{\sqrt{3}}{2} \cdot 0$
$\quad\quad\quad\quad = \frac{1}{2} + 0$ or $\frac{1}{2}$

56. $\cot^2 \theta - \sin^2 \theta \stackrel{?}{=} \frac{\cos^2 \theta \csc^2 \theta - \sin^2 \theta}{\sin^2 \theta \csc^2 \theta}$

$\cot^2 \theta - \sin^2 \theta \stackrel{?}{=} \frac{\cos^2 \theta \frac{1}{\sin^2 \theta} - \sin^2 \theta}{\sin^2 \theta \frac{1}{\sin^2 \theta}}$

$\cot^2 \theta - \sin^2 \theta \stackrel{?}{=} \frac{\cot^2 \theta - \sin^2 \theta}{1}$

$\cot^2 \theta - \sin^2 \theta = \cot^2 \theta - \sin^2 \theta$

57. $\cos \theta(\cos \theta + \cot \theta) \stackrel{?}{=} \cot \theta \cos \theta(\sin \theta + 1)$

$\cos \theta(\cos \theta + \cot \theta) \stackrel{?}{=} \frac{\cos \theta}{\sin \theta} \cos \theta \sin \theta + \cot \theta \cos \theta$

$\cos \theta(\cos \theta + \cot \theta) \stackrel{?}{=} \cos^2 \theta + \cot \theta \cos \theta$

$\cos \theta(\cos \theta + \cot \theta) = \cos \theta(\cos \theta + \cot \theta)$

58. $9.5 - 8.5 = 1$, so the 1960 Chile earthquake was 10^1 or 10 times as great.

59. $9.2 - 6.7 = 2.5$, so the aftershock was $10^{2.5}$ or about 316 times as great.

60. $(x + 6)(x - 5) = 0$
$\quad x + 6 = 0 \quad$ or $\quad x - 5 = 0$
$\quad\quad\quad x = -6 \quad\quad\quad\quad\quad x = 5$
The solutions are -6 and 5.

61. $(x - 1)(x + 1) = 0$
$\quad x - 1 = 0 \quad$ or $\quad x + 1 = 0$
$\quad\quad\quad x = 1 \quad\quad\quad\quad\quad x = -1$
The solutions are 1 and -1.

62. $x(x + 2) = 0$
$\quad x = 0 \quad$ or $\quad x + 2 = 0$
$\quad\quad\quad\quad\quad\quad\quad\quad x = -2$
The solutions are 0 and -2.

63. $(2x - 5)(x + 2) = 0$
$\quad 2x - 5 = 0 \quad$ or $\quad x + 2 = 0$
$\quad\quad 2x = 5 \quad\quad\quad\quad\quad x = -2$
$\quad\quad\quad x = \frac{5}{2}$
The solutions are $\frac{5}{2}$ and -2.

64. $(2x + 1)(2x - 1) = 0$
$\quad 2x + 1 = 0 \quad$ or $\quad 2x - 1 = 0$
$\quad\quad 2x = -1 \quad\quad\quad\quad 2x = 1$
$\quad\quad\quad x = -\frac{1}{2} \quad\quad\quad\quad x = \frac{1}{2}$
The solutions are $-\frac{1}{2}$ and $\frac{1}{2}$.

65. $x^2(2x + 1) = 0$
$\quad x^2 = 0 \quad$ or $\quad 2x + 1 = 0$
$\quad x = 0 \quad\quad\quad\quad\quad 2x = -1$
$\quad\quad\quad\quad\quad\quad\quad\quad x = -\frac{1}{2}$

The solutions are 0 and $-\frac{1}{2}$.

Page 797   Practice Quiz 2

1. $\sin \theta \sec \theta \stackrel{?}{=} \tan \theta$

$\quad \sin \theta \cdot \frac{1}{\cos \theta} \stackrel{?}{=} \tan \theta$

$\quad\quad \frac{\sin \theta}{\cos \theta} \stackrel{?}{=} \tan \theta$

$\quad\quad \tan \theta = \tan \theta$

2. $\quad\quad \sec \theta - \cos \theta \stackrel{?}{=} \sin \theta \tan \theta$

$\frac{1}{\cos \theta} - \cos \theta \cdot \frac{\cos \theta}{\cos \theta} \stackrel{?}{=} \sin \theta \tan \theta$

$\quad \frac{1}{\cos \theta} - \frac{\cos^2 \theta}{\cos \theta} \stackrel{?}{=} \sin \theta \tan \theta$

$\quad\quad \frac{1 - \cos^2 \theta}{\cos \theta} \stackrel{?}{=} \sin \theta \tan \theta$

$\quad\quad\quad \frac{\sin^2 \theta}{\cos \theta} \stackrel{?}{=} \sin \theta \tan \theta$

$\quad\quad \sin \theta \frac{\sin \theta}{\cos \theta} \stackrel{?}{=} \sin \theta \tan \theta$

$\quad\quad \sin \theta \tan \theta = \sin \theta \tan \theta$

3. $\sin \theta + \tan \theta \stackrel{?}{=} \frac{\sin \theta (\cos \theta + 1)}{\cos \theta}$

$\sin \theta + \tan \theta \stackrel{?}{=} \frac{\sin \theta \cos \theta + \sin \theta}{\cos \theta}$

$\sin \theta + \tan \theta \stackrel{?}{=} \frac{\sin \theta \cos \theta}{\cos \theta} + \frac{\sin \theta}{\cos \theta}$

$\sin \theta + \tan \theta = \sin \theta + \tan \theta$

4. $\quad\quad\quad \sin(90° + \theta) \stackrel{?}{=} \cos \theta$

$\sin 90° \cos \theta + \cos 90° \sin \theta \stackrel{?}{=} \cos \theta$

$\quad 1 \cdot \cos \theta + 0 \cdot \sin \theta \stackrel{?}{=} \cos \theta$

$\quad\quad\quad \cos \theta + 0 \stackrel{?}{=} \cos \theta$

$\quad\quad\quad\quad \cos \theta = \cos \theta$

5. $\quad\quad\quad \cos\left(\frac{3\pi}{2} - \theta\right) \stackrel{?}{=} -\sin \theta$

$\cos \frac{3\pi}{2} \cos \theta + \sin \frac{3\pi}{2} \sin \theta \stackrel{?}{=} -\sin \theta$

$\quad 0 \cdot \cos \theta + (-1) \cdot \sin \theta \stackrel{?}{=} -\sin \theta$

$\quad\quad\quad 0 - \sin \theta \stackrel{?}{=} -\sin \theta$

$\quad\quad\quad\quad -\sin \theta = -\sin \theta$

6. $\quad\quad \sin(\theta + 30°) + \cos(\theta + 60°) \stackrel{?}{=} \cos \theta$

$(\sin \theta \cos 30° + \cos \theta \sin 30°)$
$\quad + (\cos \theta \cos 60° - \sin \theta \sin 60°) \stackrel{?}{=} \cos \theta$

$\frac{\sqrt{3}}{2} \sin \theta + \frac{1}{2} \cos \theta + \frac{1}{2} \cos \theta - \frac{\sqrt{3}}{2} \sin \theta \stackrel{?}{=} \cos \theta$

$\quad\quad\quad\quad\quad\quad\quad\quad \cos \theta \stackrel{?}{=} \cos \theta$

7. First find $\sin \theta$.

$$\sin^2 \theta = 1 - \cos^2 \theta$$
$$\sin^2 \theta = 1 - \left(-\frac{\sqrt{3}}{2}\right)^2$$
$$\sin^2 \theta = \frac{1}{4}$$
$$\sin \theta = \pm \frac{1}{2}$$

Since θ is in the third quadrant, $\sin \theta = -\frac{1}{2}$.

$$\sin 2\theta = 2 \sin \theta \cos \theta$$
$$= 2\left(-\frac{1}{2}\right)\left(-\frac{\sqrt{3}}{2}\right)$$
$$= \frac{\sqrt{3}}{2}$$

8. First find $\cos \theta$.

$$\cos^2 \theta = 1 - \sin^2 \theta$$
$$\cos^2 \theta = 1 - \left(-\frac{9}{41}\right)^2$$
$$\cos^2 \theta = \frac{1600}{1681}$$
$$\cos \theta = \pm \frac{40}{41}$$

Since θ is in the fourth quadrant, $\cos \theta = \frac{40}{41}$.

$$\cos \frac{\theta}{2} = \pm \sqrt{\frac{1 + \cos \theta}{2}}$$
$$= \pm \sqrt{\frac{1 + \frac{40}{41}}{2}}$$
$$= \pm \sqrt{\frac{81}{82}}$$
$$= \pm \frac{9\sqrt{82}}{82}$$

Since θ is between $270°$ and $360°$, $\frac{\theta}{2}$ is between $135°$ and $180°$. Thus, $\cos \frac{\theta}{2} = -\frac{9\sqrt{82}}{82}$.

9. $\sin 165° = \sin \frac{330°}{2}$
$$= \sqrt{\frac{1 - \cos 330°}{2}}$$
$$= \sqrt{\frac{1 - \frac{\sqrt{3}}{2}}{2}}$$
$$= \sqrt{\frac{2 - \sqrt{3}}{4}}$$
$$= \frac{\sqrt{2 - \sqrt{3}}}{2}$$

10. $\cos \frac{5\pi}{8} = \cos \frac{\frac{5\pi}{4}}{2}$
$$= -\sqrt{\frac{1 + \cos \frac{5\pi}{4}}{2}}$$
$$= -\sqrt{\frac{1 + \left(-\frac{\sqrt{2}}{2}\right)}{2}}$$
$$= -\sqrt{\frac{2 - \sqrt{2}}{4}}$$
$$= -\frac{\sqrt{2 - \sqrt{2}}}{2}$$

Page 798 Graphing Calculator Investigation (Preview of Lesson 14-7)

1. Graph the functions $y = \sin x$ and $y = 0.8$ in the indicated interval. There are two points of intersection. The approximate solutions are $53.1°$ and $126.9°$.

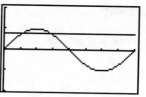

[0, 360] scl: 45 by [−2, 2] scl: 1

2. Graph the functions $y = \tan x$ and $y = \sin x$ in the indicated interval. There are two points of intersection. The solutions are $0°$ and $180°$.

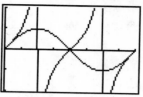

[0, 360] scl: 45 by [−2, 2] scl: 1

3. Graph the functions $y = 2 \cos x + 3$ and $y = 0$ in the indicated interval. There are no points of intersection. There are no solutions in this interval.

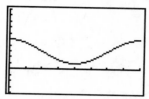

[0, 360] scl: 45 by [−5, 10] scl: 1

4. Graph the functions $y = 0.5 \cos x$ and $y = 1.4$ in the indicated interval. There are no points of intersection. There are no solutions in this interval.

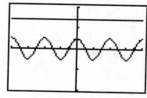

[−720, 720] scl: 90 by [−2, 2] scl: 1

5. Graph the functions $y = \sin 2x$ and $y = \sin x$ in the indicated interval. There are four points of intersection. The solutions are $0°$, $60°$, $180°$, and $300°$.

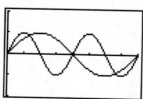

[0, 360] scl: 45 by [−2, 2] scl: 1

6. Graph the functions $y = \sin 2x - 3 \sin x$ and $y = 0$ in the indicated interval. There are four points of intersection. The solutions are $-360°$, $-180°$, $0°$ and $180°$.

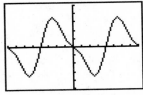

$[-360, 360]$ scl: 45 by $[-5, 5]$ scl: 1

14-7 | Solving Trigonometric Equations

Page 802   Check for Understanding

1. Sample answer: If $\sec \theta = 0$ then $\frac{1}{\cos \theta} = 0$. Since no value of θ makes $\frac{1}{\cos \theta} = 0$, there are no solutions.

2. Sample answer: The function is periodic with two solutions in each of its infinite number of periods.

3. Sample answer: $\sin \theta = 2$

4.
$$4 \cos^2 \theta = 1$$
$$4 \cos^2 \theta - 1 = 0$$
$$(2 \cos \theta + 1)(2 \cos \theta - 1) = 0$$

$2 \cos \theta + 1 = 0$ or $2 \cos \theta - 1 = 0$
$\quad 2 \cos \theta = -1$ $2 \cos \theta = 1$
$\quad\quad \cos \theta = -\frac{1}{2}$ $\cos \theta = \frac{1}{2}$
$\quad\quad\quad \theta = 120°$ or $240°$ $\theta = 60°$ or $300°$

The solutions are $60°$, $120°$, $240°$, and $300°$.

5. $2 \sin^2 \theta - 1 = 0$
$$2 \sin^2 \theta = 1$$
$$\sin^2 \theta = \frac{1}{2}$$
$$\sin \theta = \pm\sqrt{\frac{1}{2}} \text{ or } \pm\frac{\sqrt{2}}{2}$$

$\sin \theta = \frac{\sqrt{2}}{2}$ or $\sin \theta = -\frac{\sqrt{2}}{2}$
$\quad \theta = 135°$ $\theta = 225°$

The solutions are $135°$ and $225°$.

6.
$$\sin 2\theta = \cos \theta$$
$$2 \sin \theta \cos \theta = \cos \theta$$
$$2 \sin \theta \cos \theta - \cos \theta = 0$$
$$\cos \theta(2 \sin \theta - 1) = 0$$

$\cos \theta = 0$ or $2 \sin \theta - 1 = 0$
$\quad \theta = \frac{\pi}{2}$ or $\frac{3\pi}{2}$ $2 \sin \theta = 1$
$\quad\quad\quad\quad\quad\quad\quad\quad\quad \sin \theta = \frac{1}{2}$
$\quad\quad\quad\quad\quad\quad\quad\quad\quad\quad \theta = \frac{\pi}{6}$ or $\frac{5\pi}{6}$

The solutions are $\frac{\pi}{6}$, $\frac{\pi}{2}$, $\frac{5\pi}{6}$, and $\frac{3\pi}{2}$.

7.
$$3 \sin^2 \theta - \cos^2 \theta = 0$$
$$3(1 - \cos^2 \theta) - \cos^2 \theta = 0$$
$$3 - 4 \cos^2 \theta = 0$$
$$-4 \cos^2 \theta = -3$$
$$\cos^2 \theta = \frac{3}{4}$$
$$\cos \theta = \pm\frac{\sqrt{3}}{2}$$

$\cos \theta = \frac{\sqrt{3}}{2}$ or $\cos \theta = -\frac{\sqrt{3}}{2}$
$\theta = \frac{\pi}{6}$

The solution is $\frac{\pi}{6}$.   no solutions

8.
$$2 \cos \theta = \cos \theta$$
$$2 \cos^2 \theta - 1 = \cos \theta$$
$$2 \cos^2 \theta - \cos \theta - 1 = 0$$
$$(2 \cos \theta + 1)(\cos \theta - 1) = 0$$

$2 \cos \theta + 1 = 0$ or $\cos \theta - 1 = 0$
$\quad 2 \cos \theta = -1$ $\cos \theta = 1$
$\quad\quad \cos \theta = -\frac{1}{2}$ $\theta = 0$
$\quad\quad\quad \theta = \frac{2\pi}{3}$ or $\frac{4\pi}{3}$

The solutions are $0 + \frac{2k\pi}{3}$.

9. $\sin \theta + \sin \theta \cos \theta = 0$
$$\sin \theta(1 + \cos \theta) = 0$$

$\sin \theta = 0$ or $1 + \cos \theta = 0$
$\quad \theta = 0$ or π $\cos \theta = -1$
$\quad\quad\quad\quad\quad\quad\quad\quad \theta = \pi$

The solutions are $0 + k\pi$.

10.
$$\sin \theta = 1 + \cos \theta$$
$$\sin^2 \theta = (1 + \cos \theta)^2$$
$$1 - \cos^2 \theta = 1 + 2 \cos \theta + \cos^2 \theta$$
$$0 = 2 \cos \theta + 2 \cos^2 \theta$$
$$0 = 2 \cos \theta(1 + \cos \theta)$$

$2 \cos \theta = 0$ $1 + \cos \theta = 0$
$\quad \cos \theta = 0$ $\cos \theta = -1$
$\quad\quad \theta = 90°$ or $270°$ $\theta = 180°$

Check:
$\sin \theta = 1 + \cos \theta$ $\sin \theta = 1 + \cos \theta$
$\sin 90° \stackrel{?}{=} 1 + \cos 90°$ $\sin 180° = 1 + \cos 180°$
$\quad 1 \stackrel{?}{=} 1 + 0$ $0 = 1 + (-1)$
$\quad 1 = 1$ ✓ $0 = 0$ ✓

$\sin \theta = 1 + \cos \theta$
$\sin 270° \stackrel{?}{=} 1 + \cos 270°$
$\quad -1 \stackrel{?}{=} 1 + 0$
$\quad -1 \neq 1$

$270°$ is not a solution.
The solutions are $90° + k \cdot 360°$ and $180° + k \cdot 360°$.

11.
$$2 \cos^2 \theta + 2 = 5 \cos \theta$$
$$2 \cos^2 \theta - 5 \cos \theta + 2 = 0$$
$$(2 \cos \theta - 1)(\cos \theta - 2) = 0$$

$2 \cos \theta - 1 = 0$ or $\cos \theta - 2 = 0$
$\quad 2 \cos \theta = 1$ $\cos \theta = 2$
$\quad\quad \cos \theta = \frac{1}{2}$ no solutions
$\quad\quad\quad \theta = 60°$ or $300°$

The solutions are $60° + k \cdot 360°$ and $300° + k \cdot 360°$.

12. $2\sin^2\theta - 3\sin\theta - 2 = 0$
$(2\sin\theta + 1)(\sin\theta - 2) = 0$

$2\sin\theta + 1 = 0 \qquad$ or $\quad \sin\theta - 2 = 0$
$\quad 2\sin\theta = -1 \qquad\qquad\qquad \sin\theta = 2$
$\qquad \sin\theta = -\frac{1}{2} \qquad\qquad\quad$ no solutions
$\qquad\qquad \theta = \frac{7\pi}{6}$ or $\frac{11\pi}{6}$

The solutions are $\frac{7\pi}{6} + 2k\pi$ and $\frac{11\pi}{6} + 2k\pi$ or $210° + k \cdot 360°$ and $330° + k \cdot 360°$.

13. $2\cos^2\theta + 3\sin\theta - 3 = 0$
$2(1 - \sin^2\theta) + 3\sin\theta - 3 = 0$
$-2\sin^2\theta + 3\sin\theta - 1 = 0$
$2\sin^2\theta - 3\sin\theta + 1 = 0$
$(2\sin\theta - 1)(\sin\theta - 1) = 0$

$2\sin\theta - 1 = 0 \qquad$ or $\quad \sin\theta - 1 = 0$
$\quad 2\sin\theta = 1 \qquad\qquad\qquad \sin\theta = 1$
$\qquad \sin\theta = \frac{1}{2} \qquad\qquad\qquad\quad \theta = \frac{\pi}{2}$
$\qquad\qquad \theta = \frac{\pi}{6}$ or $\frac{5\pi}{6}$

The solutions are $\frac{\pi}{6} + 2k\pi$, $\frac{\pi}{2} + 2k\pi$, and $\frac{5\pi}{6} + 2k\pi$ or $30° + k \cdot 360°$, $90° + k \cdot 360°$, and $150° + k \cdot 360°$.

14. $\sin\alpha = 1.33\sin\beta$
$\sin\alpha = 1.33\sin 23°$
$\sin\alpha \approx 0.5197$
$\alpha \approx 31.3°$
The beam of light enters the water at an angle of about 31.3°.

Pages 803–804 Practice and Apply

15. $2\cos\theta - 1 = 0$
$\quad 2\cos\theta = 1$
$\qquad \cos\theta = \frac{1}{2}$
$\qquad\qquad \theta = 60°$ or $300°$
The solutions are 60° and 300°.

16. $2\sin\theta = -\sqrt{3}$
$\quad \sin\theta = -\frac{\sqrt{3}}{2}$
$\qquad \theta = 240°$ or $300°$
The solutions are 240° and 300°.

17. $4\sin^2\theta = 1$
$4\sin^2\theta - 1 = 0$
$(2\sin\theta - 1)(2\sin\theta + 1) = 0$

$2\sin\theta - 1 = 0 \quad$ or $\quad 2\sin\theta + 1 = 0$
$\quad 2\sin\theta = 1 \qquad\qquad\quad 2\sin\theta = -1$
$\qquad \sin\theta = \frac{1}{2} \qquad\qquad\quad \sin\theta = -\frac{1}{2}$
no solutions $\qquad\qquad\qquad \theta = 210°$ or $330°$
The solutions are 210° and 330°.

18. $4\cos^2\theta = 3$
$\quad \cos^2\theta = \frac{3}{4}$
$\quad \cos\theta = \pm\frac{\sqrt{3}}{2}$

$\cos\theta = \frac{\sqrt{3}}{2} \qquad$ or $\quad \cos\theta = -\frac{\sqrt{3}}{2}$
$\quad \theta = 30°$ or $330° \qquad\qquad \theta = 150°$ or $210°$
The solutions are 30°, 150°, 210°, and 330°.

19. $2\cos^2\theta = \sin\theta + 1$
$2(1 - \sin^2\theta) = \sin\theta + 1$
$2 - 2\sin^2\theta = \sin\theta + 1$
$0 = 2\sin^2\theta + \sin\theta - 1$
$0 = (2\sin\theta - 1)(\sin\theta + 1)$

$2\sin\theta - 1 = 0 \qquad$ or $\quad \sin\theta + 1 = 0$
$\quad 2\sin\theta = 1 \qquad\qquad\qquad \sin\theta = -1$
$\qquad \sin\theta = \frac{1}{2} \qquad\qquad\qquad\quad \theta = \frac{3\pi}{2}$
$\qquad\qquad \theta = \frac{\pi}{6}$ or $\frac{5\pi}{6}$

The solutions are $\frac{\pi}{6}, \frac{5\pi}{6}$, and $\frac{3\pi}{2}$.

20. $\sin^2\theta - 1 = \cos^2\theta$
$\sin^2\theta - 1 = 1 - \sin^2\theta$
$2\sin^2\theta = 2$
$\sin^2\theta = 1$
$\sin\theta = \pm 1$

$\sin\theta = 1 \qquad$ or $\quad \sin\theta = -1$
$\quad \theta = \frac{\pi}{2} \qquad\qquad\qquad$ no solution

The solution is $\frac{\pi}{2}$.

21. $2\sin^2\theta + \sin\theta = 0$
$\sin\theta(2\sin\theta + 1) = 0$

$\sin\theta = 0 \qquad$ or $\quad 2\sin\theta + 1 = 0$
no solution $\qquad\qquad\quad 2\sin\theta = -1$
$\qquad\qquad\qquad\qquad\quad \sin\theta = -\frac{1}{2}$
$\qquad\qquad\qquad\qquad\qquad \theta = \frac{7\pi}{6}$ or $\frac{11\pi}{6}$

The solutions are $\frac{7\pi}{6}$ and $\frac{11\pi}{6}$.

22. $2\cos^2\theta = -\cos\theta$
$2\cos^2\theta + \cos\theta = 0$
$\cos\theta(2\cos\theta + 1) = 0$

$\cos\theta = 0 \qquad$ or $\quad 2\cos\theta + 1 = 0$
$\quad \theta = \frac{\pi}{2}$ or $\frac{3\pi}{2} \qquad\qquad 2\cos\theta = -1$
$\qquad\qquad\qquad\qquad\quad \cos\theta = -\frac{1}{2}$
$\qquad\qquad\qquad\qquad\qquad \theta = \frac{2\pi}{3}$ or $\frac{4\pi}{3}$

The solutions are $\frac{\pi}{2}, \frac{2\pi}{3}, \frac{4\pi}{3}$, and $\frac{3\pi}{2}$.

23. $\cos 2\theta + 3\cos\theta - 1 = 0$
$(2\cos^2\theta - 1) + 3\cos\theta - 1 = 0$
$2\cos^2\theta + 3\cos\theta - 2 = 0$
$(2\cos\theta - 1)(\cos\theta + 2) = 0$

$2\cos\theta - 1 = 0 \qquad$ or $\quad \cos\theta + 2 = 0$
$\quad 2\cos\theta = 1 \qquad\qquad\qquad \cos\theta = -2$
$\qquad \cos\theta = \frac{1}{2} \qquad\qquad\quad$ no solution
$\qquad\qquad \theta = \frac{\pi}{3}$ or $\frac{5\pi}{3}$

The solutions are $\frac{\pi}{3} + 2k\pi$ and $\frac{5\pi}{3} + 2k\pi$.

24.
$$2\sin^2\theta - \cos\theta - 1 = 0$$
$$2(1 - \cos^2\theta) - \cos\theta - 1 = 0$$
$$-2\cos^2\theta - \cos\theta + 1 = 0$$
$$2\cos^2\theta + \cos\theta - 1 = 0$$
$$(2\cos\theta - 1)(\cos\theta + 1) = 0$$

$2\cos\theta - 1 = 0$ or $\cos\theta + 1 = 0$
$$2\cos\theta = 1 \qquad\qquad \cos\theta = -1$$
$$\cos\theta = \tfrac{1}{2} \qquad\qquad\qquad \theta = \pi$$
$$\theta = \tfrac{\pi}{3} \text{ or } \tfrac{5\pi}{3}$$

The solutions are $\tfrac{\pi}{3} + 2k\pi$, $\pi + 2k\pi$, and $\tfrac{5\pi}{3} + 2k\pi$.

25. $\cos^2\theta - \tfrac{5}{2}\cos\theta - \tfrac{3}{2} = 0$
$$2\cos^2\theta - 5\cos\theta - 3 = 0$$
$$(2\cos\theta + 1)(\cos\theta - 3) = 0$$

$2\cos\theta + 1 = 0$ or $\cos\theta - 3 = 0$
$$2\cos\theta = -1 \qquad\qquad \cos\theta = 3$$
$$\cos\theta = -\tfrac{1}{2} \qquad\qquad \text{no solution}$$
$$\theta = \tfrac{2\pi}{3} \text{ or } \tfrac{4\pi}{3}$$

The solutions are $\tfrac{2\pi}{3} + 2k\pi$ and $\tfrac{4\pi}{3} + 2k\pi$.

26. $\cos\theta = 3\cos\theta - 2$
$$-2\cos\theta = -2$$
$$\cos\theta = 1$$
$$\theta = 0$$
The solutions are $0 + 2k\pi$.

27. $4\cos^2\theta - 4\cos\theta + 1 = 0$
$$(2\cos\theta - 1)^2 = 0$$
$$2\cos\theta - 1 = 0$$
$$2\cos\theta = 1$$
$$\cos\theta = \tfrac{1}{2}$$
$$\theta = \tfrac{\pi}{3} \text{ or } \tfrac{5\pi}{3}$$

The solutions are $\tfrac{\pi}{3} + 2k\pi$ and $\tfrac{5\pi}{3} + 2k\pi$.

28. $\cos 2\theta = 1 - \sin\theta$
$$1 - 2\sin^2\theta = 1 - \sin\theta$$
$$0 = 2\sin^2\theta - \sin\theta$$
$$0 = \sin\theta(2\sin\theta - 1)$$

$\sin\theta = 0$ or $2\sin\theta - 1 = 0$
$\theta = 0$ or π $2\sin\theta = 1$
$$\sin\theta = \tfrac{1}{2}$$
$$\theta = \tfrac{\pi}{6} \text{ or } \tfrac{5\pi}{6}$$

The solutions are $0 + k\pi$, $\tfrac{\pi}{6} + 2k\pi$, and $\tfrac{5\pi}{6} + 2k\pi$.

29. $\sin\theta = \cos\theta$
$$\sin^2\theta = \cos^2\theta$$
$$\sin^2\theta = 1 - \sin^2\theta$$
$$2\sin^2\theta = 1$$
$$\sin^2\theta = \tfrac{1}{2}$$
$$\sin\theta = \pm\sqrt{\tfrac{1}{2}} \text{ or } \pm\tfrac{\sqrt{2}}{2}$$

$\sin\theta = \tfrac{\sqrt{2}}{2}$ or $\sin\theta = -\tfrac{\sqrt{2}}{2}$
$\theta = 45°$ or $135°$ $\theta = 225°$ or $315°$

Check:
$\sin\theta = \cos\theta$ $\sin\theta = \cos\theta$
$\sin 45° \stackrel{?}{=} \cos 45°$ $\sin 225° \stackrel{?}{=} \cos 225°$
$\tfrac{\sqrt{2}}{2} = \tfrac{\sqrt{2}}{2}$ ✓ $-\tfrac{\sqrt{2}}{2} = -\tfrac{\sqrt{2}}{2}$ ✓

$\sin\theta = \cos\theta$ $\sin\theta = \cos\theta$
$\sin 135° \stackrel{?}{=} \cos 135°$ $\sin 315° \stackrel{?}{=} \cos 315°$
$\tfrac{\sqrt{2}}{2} \neq -\tfrac{\sqrt{2}}{2}$ $-\tfrac{\sqrt{2}}{2} \neq \tfrac{\sqrt{2}}{2}$

135° is not a solution. 315° is not a solution.
The solutions are $45° + k \cdot 180°$.

30. $\tan\theta = \sin\theta$
$$\tfrac{\sin\theta}{\cos\theta} - \sin\theta = 0$$
$$\sin\theta\left(\tfrac{1}{\cos\theta} - 1\right) = 0$$

$\sin\theta = 0$ or $\tfrac{1}{\cos\theta} - 1 = 0$
$\theta = 0°$ or $180°$ $\tfrac{1}{\cos\theta} = 1$
$$\cos\theta = 1$$
$$\theta = 0°$$

The solutions are $0° + k \cdot 180°$.

31. $\sin^2\theta - 2\sin\theta - 3 = 0$
$$(\sin\theta - 3)(\sin\theta + 1) = 0$$

$\sin\theta - 3 = 0$ or $\sin\theta + 1 = 0$
$\sin\theta = 3$ $\sin\theta = -1$
no solution $\theta = 270°$
The solutions are $270° + k \cdot 360°$.

32. $4\sin^2\theta - 4\sin\theta + 1 = 0$
$$(2\sin\theta - 1)^2 = 0$$
$$2\sin\theta - 1 = 0$$
$$2\sin\theta = 1$$
$$\sin\theta = \tfrac{1}{2}$$
$$\theta = 30° \text{ or } 150°$$

The solutions are $30° + k \cdot 360°$ and $150° \ k \cdot 360°$.

33. $\tan^2\theta - \sqrt{3}\tan\theta = 0$
$$\tan\theta(\tan\theta - \sqrt{3}) = 0$$

$\tan\theta = 0$ or $\tan\theta - \sqrt{3} = 0$
$\theta = 0°$ or $180°$ $\tan\theta = \sqrt{3}$
$$\theta = 60° \text{ or } 240°$$

The solutions are $0° + k \cdot 180°$ and $60° + k \cdot 180°$.

34. $\cos^2\theta - \tfrac{7}{2}\cos\theta - 2 = 0$
$$2\cos^2\theta - 7\cos\theta - 4 = 0$$
$$(2\cos\theta + 1)(\cos\theta - 4) = 0$$

$2\cos\theta + 1 = 0$ or $\cos\theta - 4 = 0$
$2\cos\theta = -1$ $\cos\theta = 4$
$\cos\theta = -\tfrac{1}{2}$ no solution
$$\theta = 120° \text{ or } 240°$$

The solutions are $120° + k \cdot 360°$ and $240° + k \cdot 360°$.

35. $\sin^2\theta + \cos 2\theta - \cos\theta = 0$
$$(1 - \cos^2\theta) + (2\cos^2\theta - 1) - \cos\theta = 0$$
$$\cos^2\theta - \cos\theta = 0$$
$$\cos\theta(\cos\theta - 1) = 0$$

$\cos\theta = 0$ or $\cos\theta - 1 = 0$
$\theta = \tfrac{\pi}{2}$ or $\tfrac{3\pi}{2}$ $\cos\theta = 1$
$$\theta = 0$$

The solutions are $0 + 2k\pi$ and $\tfrac{\pi}{2} + k\pi$
or $0° + k \cdot 360°$ and $90° + k \cdot 180°$.

36. $2 \sin^2 \theta - 3 \sin \theta - 2 = 0$
$(2 \sin \theta + 1)(\sin \theta - 2) = 0$

$2 \sin \theta + 1 = 0$ or $\sin \theta - 2 = 0$
$2 \sin \theta = -1$ $\sin \theta = 2$
$\sin \theta = -\frac{1}{2}$ no solution
$\theta = \frac{7\pi}{6}$ or $\frac{11\pi}{6}$

The solutions are $\frac{7\pi}{6} + 2k\pi$ and $\frac{11\pi}{6} + 2k\pi$
or $210° + k \cdot 360°$ and $330° + k \cdot 360°$.

37. $\sin^2 \theta = \cos^2 \theta - 1$
$\sin^2 \theta = (1 - \sin^2 \theta) - 1$
$\sin^2 \theta = -\sin^2 \theta$
$2 \sin^2 \theta = 0$
$\sin^2 \theta = 0$
$\sin \theta = 0$
$\theta = 0$ or π
The solutions are $0 + k \cdot \pi$ or $0° + k \cdot 180°$.

38. $2 \cos^2 \theta + \cos \theta = 0$
$\cos \theta (2 \cos \theta + 1) = 0$

$\cos \theta = 0$ or $2 \cos \theta + 1 = 0$
$\theta = \frac{\pi}{2}$ or $\frac{3\pi}{2}$ $\cos \theta = -\frac{1}{2}$
                        $2 \cos \theta = -1$
                        $\theta = \frac{2\pi}{3}$ or $\frac{4\pi}{3}$

The solutions are $\frac{\pi}{2} + k\pi$, $\frac{2\pi}{3} + 2k\pi$, and
$\frac{4\pi}{3} + 2k\pi$ or $90° + k \cdot 180°$, $120° + k \cdot 360°$,
and $240° + k \cdot 360°$.

39. $\sin \frac{\theta}{2} + \cos \theta = 1$

$\sin \frac{\theta}{2} = 1 - \cos \theta$
$\sqrt{\frac{1 - \cos \theta}{2}} = 1 - \cos \theta$
$\frac{1 - \cos \theta}{2} = 1 - 2 \cos \theta + \cos^2 \theta$
$1 - \cos \theta = 2 - 4 \cos \theta + 2 \cos^2 \theta$
$0 = 1 - 3 \cos \theta + 2 \cos^2 \theta$
$0 = (1 - 2 \cos \theta)(1 - \cos \theta)$

$1 - 2 \cos \theta = 0$ or $1 - \cos \theta = 0$
$-2 \cos \theta = -1$ $-\cos \theta = -1$
$\cos \theta = \frac{1}{2}$ $\cos \theta = 1$
$\theta = \frac{\pi}{3}$ or $\frac{5\pi}{3}$ $\theta = 0$

Check:

$\sin \frac{\theta}{2} + \cos \theta = 1$ $\sin \frac{\theta}{2} + \cos \theta = 1$
$\sin \frac{\pi}{6} + \cos \frac{\pi}{3} \overset{?}{=} 1$ $\sin 0 + \cos 0 \overset{?}{=} 1$
$\frac{1}{2} + \frac{1}{2} \overset{?}{=} 1$ $0 + 1 \overset{?}{=} 1$
$1 = 1$ ✓ $1 = 1$ ✓

$\sin \frac{\theta}{2} + \cos \theta = 1$
$\sin \frac{5\pi}{6} + \cos \frac{3\pi}{3} \overset{?}{=} 1$
$\frac{1}{2} + \frac{1}{2} \overset{?}{=} 1$
$1 = 1$ ✓

The solutions are $0 + 2k\pi$, $\frac{\pi}{3} + 2k\pi$, and
$\frac{5\pi}{3} + 2k\pi$ or $0° + k \cdot 360°$, $60° + k \cdot 360°$, and
$300° + k \cdot 360°$.

40. $\sin \frac{\theta}{2} + \cos \frac{\theta}{2} = \sqrt{2}$
$\sin^2 \frac{\theta}{2} + 2 \sin \frac{\theta}{2} \cos \frac{\theta}{2} + \cos^2 \frac{\theta}{2} = 2$
$1 + 2 \sin \frac{\theta}{2} \cos \frac{\theta}{2} = 2$
$2 \sin \frac{\theta}{2} \cos \frac{\theta}{2} = 1$
$2 \sqrt{\frac{1 - \cos \theta}{2}} \cdot \sqrt{\frac{1 + \cos \theta}{2}} = 1$
$1 - \cos^2 \theta = 1$
$-\cos^2 \theta = 0$
$\cos^2 \theta = 0$
$\cos \theta = 0$
$\theta = \frac{\pi}{2}, \frac{3\pi}{2}, \frac{5\pi}{2}$, or $\frac{7\pi}{2}$

Check:

$\sin \frac{\theta}{2} + \cos \frac{\theta}{2} = \sqrt{2}$ $\sin \frac{\theta}{2} + \cos \frac{\theta}{2} = \sqrt{2}$
$\sin \frac{\pi}{4} + \cos \frac{\pi}{4} \overset{?}{=} \sqrt{2}$ $\sin \frac{3\pi}{4} + \cos \frac{3\pi}{4} \overset{?}{=} \sqrt{2}$
$\frac{\sqrt{2}}{2} + \frac{\sqrt{2}}{2} \overset{?}{=} \sqrt{2}$ $\frac{\sqrt{2}}{2} + \left(-\frac{\sqrt{2}}{2}\right) \overset{?}{=} \sqrt{2}$
$\sqrt{2} = \sqrt{2}$ ✓ $0 \neq \sqrt{2}$

                    $\frac{3\pi}{2}$ is not a solution.

$\sin \frac{\theta}{2} + \cos \frac{\theta}{2} = \sqrt{2}$ $\sin \frac{\theta}{2} + \cos \frac{\theta}{2} = \sqrt{2}$
$\sin \frac{5\pi}{4} + \cos \frac{5\pi}{4} \overset{?}{=} \sqrt{2}$ $\sin \frac{7\pi}{4} + \cos \frac{7\pi}{4} \overset{?}{=} \sqrt{2}$
$\left(-\frac{\sqrt{2}}{2}\right) + \left(-\frac{\sqrt{2}}{2}\right) \overset{?}{=} \sqrt{2}$ $\left(-\frac{\sqrt{2}}{2}\right) + \frac{\sqrt{2}}{2} \overset{?}{=} \sqrt{2}$
$-\sqrt{2} \neq \sqrt{2}$ $0 \neq \sqrt{2}$

$\frac{5\pi}{2}$ is not a solution. $\frac{7\pi}{2}$ is not a solution.

The solutions are $\frac{\pi}{2} + 4k\pi$ or $90° + k \cdot 720°$.

41. $\tan \theta = \frac{352}{S}$
$S \tan \theta = 352$
$S = \frac{352}{\tan \theta}$ or $S = 352 \cot \theta$

42. $\tan \theta = \frac{352}{560}$
$\theta \approx 32°$
The angle of inclination is about 32°.

43. $y = \frac{1}{2}h + \frac{1}{2}h \sin \frac{2\pi t}{P}$
$y = \frac{1}{2}(3) + \frac{1}{2}(3)\sin \frac{2\pi t}{2}$
$y = \frac{3}{2} + \frac{3}{2} \sin \pi t$

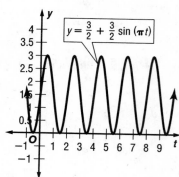

44. From the graph, we see that the wave is one foot high 10 times.

45. Write an equation for x'.
$x' = x \cos \theta - y \sin \theta$
$3 = x \cos 60° - y \sin 60°$
$3 = \frac{1}{2}x - \frac{\sqrt{3}}{2}y$
Write an equation for y'.
$y' = x \sin \theta + y \cos \theta$
$4 = x \sin 60° + y \cos 60°$
$4 = \frac{\sqrt{3}}{2}x + \frac{1}{2}y$
Solve the system of two equations.

$3 = \frac{1}{2}x - \frac{\sqrt{3}}{2}y \longrightarrow \qquad 3 = \frac{1}{2}x - \frac{\sqrt{3}}{2}y$

$4 = \frac{\sqrt{3}}{2}x + \frac{1}{2}y$ Multiply by $\sqrt{3}$. $(+)\ 4\sqrt{3} = \frac{3}{2}x + \frac{\sqrt{3}}{2}y$

$$3 + 4\sqrt{3} = 2x$$
$$3 + \frac{4\sqrt{3}}{2} = x$$
$$4.964 \approx x$$

$$3 = \frac{1}{2}x - \frac{\sqrt{3}}{2}y$$
$$3 \approx \frac{1}{2}(4.964) - \frac{\sqrt{3}}{2}y$$
$$3 \approx 2.482 - \frac{\sqrt{3}}{2}y$$
$$0.518 \approx -\frac{\sqrt{3}}{2}y$$
$$-\frac{2}{\sqrt{3}} \cdot 0.518 \approx y$$
$$-0.598 \approx y$$

The coordinates of the preimage point are about $(4.964, -0.598)$.

46. Sample answer: Temperatures are cyclic and can be modeled by trigonometric functions. Answers should include the following information.
 - A temperature could occur twice in a given period such as when the temperature rises in the spring and falls in autumn.

47. D; $\tan \frac{5\pi}{2}$ is undefined.

48. B; Since the point $\left(\frac{\pi}{3}, 1\right)$ is on the graph, $\frac{\pi}{3}$ is a solution of the equation. Thus, $\frac{\pi}{3} + 2 \cdot 2\pi$ or $\frac{13\pi}{3}$ is also a solution.

Page 804   Maintain Your Skills

49. First find $\cos \theta$.
$\cos^2 \theta = 1 - \sin^2 \theta$
$\cos^2 \theta = 1 - \left(\frac{3}{5}\right)^2$
$\cos^2 \theta = \frac{16}{25}$
$\cos \theta = \pm\frac{4}{5}$
Since θ is in the first quadrant, $\cos \theta = \frac{4}{5}$.
$\sin 2\theta = 2 \sin \theta \cos \theta$
$\qquad = 2\left(\frac{3}{5}\right)\left(\frac{4}{5}\right)$
$\qquad = \frac{24}{25}$
$\cos 2\theta = 1 - 2 \sin^2 \theta$
$\qquad = 1 - 2\left(\frac{3}{5}\right)^2$
$\qquad = \frac{7}{25}$

$\sin \frac{\theta}{2} = \pm\sqrt{\dfrac{1 - \cos \theta}{2}}$
$\qquad = \pm\sqrt{\dfrac{1 - \frac{4}{5}}{2}}$
$\qquad = \pm\sqrt{\dfrac{1}{10}}$
$\qquad = \pm\dfrac{\sqrt{10}}{10}$

Since θ is between $0°$ and $90°$, $\frac{\theta}{2}$ is between $0°$ and $45°$. Thus, $\sin \frac{\theta}{2} = \frac{\sqrt{10}}{10}$.

$\cos \frac{\theta}{2} = \pm\sqrt{\dfrac{1 + \cos \theta}{2}}$
$\qquad = \pm\sqrt{\dfrac{1 + \frac{4}{5}}{2}}$
$\qquad = \pm\sqrt{\dfrac{9}{10}}$
$\qquad = \pm\dfrac{3\sqrt{10}}{10}$

Since θ is between $0°$ and $90°$, $\frac{\theta}{2}$ is between $0°$ and $45°$. Thus, $\cos \frac{\theta}{2} = \frac{3\sqrt{10}}{10}$.

50. First find $\sin \theta$.
$\sin^2 \theta = 1 - \cos^2 \theta$
$\sin^2 \theta = 1 - \left(\frac{1}{2}\right)^2$
$\sin^2 \theta = \frac{3}{4}$
$\sin \theta = \pm\frac{\sqrt{3}}{2}$
Since θ is in the first quadrant, $\sin \theta = \frac{\sqrt{3}}{2}$.
$\sin 2\theta = 2 \sin \theta \cos \theta$
$\qquad = 2\left(\frac{\sqrt{3}}{2}\right)\left(\frac{1}{2}\right)$
$\qquad = \frac{\sqrt{3}}{2}$
$\cos 2\theta = 2 \cos^2 \theta - 1$
$\qquad = 2\left(\frac{1}{2}\right)^2 - 1$
$\qquad = -\frac{1}{2}$

$\sin \frac{\theta}{2} = \pm\sqrt{\dfrac{1 - \cos \theta}{2}}$
$\qquad = \pm\sqrt{\dfrac{1 - \frac{1}{2}}{2}}$
$\qquad = \pm\sqrt{\dfrac{1}{4}}$
$\qquad = \pm\dfrac{1}{2}$

Since θ is between $0°$ and $90°$, $\frac{\theta}{2}$ is between $0°$ and $45°$. Thus, $\sin \frac{\theta}{2} = \frac{1}{2}$.

$\cos \frac{\theta}{2} = \pm\sqrt{\dfrac{1 + \cos \theta}{2}}$
$\qquad = \pm\sqrt{\dfrac{1 + \frac{1}{2}}{2}}$
$\qquad = \pm\sqrt{\dfrac{3}{4}}$
$\qquad = \pm\dfrac{\sqrt{3}}{2}$

Since θ is between $0°$ and $90°$, $\frac{\theta}{2}$ is between $0°$ and $45°$. Thus, $\cos \frac{\theta}{2} = \frac{\sqrt{3}}{2}$.

51. First find $\sin \theta$.

$\sin^2 \theta = 1 - \cos^2 \theta$

$\sin^2 \theta = 1 - \left(\frac{5}{6}\right)^2$

$\sin^2 \theta = \frac{11}{36}$

$\sin \theta = \pm \frac{\sqrt{11}}{6}$

Since θ is in the first quadrant, $\sin \theta = \frac{\sqrt{11}}{6}$.

$\sin 2\theta = 2 \sin \theta \cos \theta$

$= 2\left(\frac{\sqrt{11}}{6}\right)\left(\frac{5}{6}\right)$

$= \frac{5\sqrt{11}}{18}$

$\cos 2\theta = 2 \cos^2 \theta - 1$

$= 2\left(\frac{5}{6}\right)^2 - 1$

$= \frac{7}{18}$

$\sin \frac{\theta}{2} = \pm \sqrt{\frac{1 - \cos \theta}{2}}$

$= \pm \sqrt{\frac{1 - \frac{5}{6}}{2}}$

$= \pm \sqrt{\frac{1}{12}}$

$= \pm \frac{\sqrt{3}}{6}$

Since θ is betweem 0° and 90°, $\frac{\theta}{2}$ is between 0° and 45°. Thus, $\sin \frac{\theta}{2} = \frac{\sqrt{3}}{6}$.

$\cos \frac{\theta}{2} = \pm \sqrt{\frac{1 + \cos \theta}{2}}$

$= \pm \sqrt{\frac{1 + \frac{5}{6}}{2}}$

$= \pm \sqrt{\frac{11}{12}}$

$= \pm \frac{\sqrt{33}}{6}$

Since θ is between 0° and 90°, $\frac{\theta}{2}$ is between 0° and 45°. Thus, $\cos \frac{\theta}{2} = \frac{\sqrt{33}}{6}$.

52. First find $\cos \theta$.

$\cos^2 \theta = 1 - \sin^2 \theta$

$\cos^2 \theta = 1 - \left(\frac{4}{5}\right)^2$

$\cos^2 \theta = \frac{9}{25}$

$\cos \theta = \pm \frac{3}{5}$

Since θ is in the first quadrant, $\cos \theta = \frac{3}{5}$.

$\sin 2\theta = 2 \sin \theta \cos \theta$

$= 2\left(\frac{4}{5}\right)\left(\frac{3}{5}\right)$

$= \frac{24}{25}$

$\cos 2\theta = 1 - 2 \sin^2 \theta$

$= 1 - 2\left(\frac{4}{5}\right)^2$

$= -\frac{7}{25}$

$\sin \frac{\theta}{2} = \pm \sqrt{\frac{1 - \cos \theta}{2}}$

$= \pm \sqrt{\frac{1 - \frac{3}{5}}{2}}$

$= \pm \sqrt{\frac{1}{5}}$

$= \pm \frac{\sqrt{5}}{5}$

Since θ is between 0° and 90°, $\frac{\theta}{2}$ is between 0° and 45°. Thus, $\sin \frac{\theta}{2} = \frac{\sqrt{5}}{5}$.

$\cos \frac{\theta}{2} = \pm \sqrt{\frac{1 + \cos \theta}{2}}$

$= \pm \sqrt{\frac{1 + \frac{3}{5}}{2}}$

$= \pm \sqrt{\frac{4}{5}}$

$= \pm \frac{2\sqrt{5}}{5}$

Since θ is between 0° and 90°, $\frac{\theta}{2}$ is between 0° and 45°. Thus, $\cos \frac{\theta}{2} = \frac{2\sqrt{5}}{5}$.

53. $\sin 240° = \sin(180° + 60°)$

$= \sin 180° \cos 60° + \cos 180° \sin 60°$

$= 0 \cdot \frac{1}{2} + (-1) \cdot \frac{\sqrt{3}}{2}$

$= 0 - \frac{\sqrt{3}}{2}$

$= -\frac{\sqrt{3}}{2}$

54. $\cos 315° = \cos(360° - 45°)$

$= \cos 360° \cos 45° + \sin 360° \sin 45°$

$= 1 \cdot \frac{\sqrt{2}}{2} + 0 \cdot \frac{\sqrt{2}}{2}$

$= \frac{\sqrt{2}}{2} + 0$

$= \frac{\sqrt{2}}{2}$

55. First, find the measure of the third angle.

$40° + 62° + C = 180°$

$C = 78°$

Now find b.

$\frac{\sin B}{b} = \frac{\sin A}{a}$

$\frac{\sin 62°}{b} = \frac{\sin 40°}{8}$

$b = \frac{8 \sin 62°}{\sin 40°}$

$b = 11.0$

Now find c.

$\frac{\sin C}{c} = \frac{\sin A}{a}$

$\frac{\sin 78°}{c} = \frac{\sin 40°}{8}$

$c = \frac{8 \sin 78°}{\sin 40°}$

$c \approx 12.2$

Chapter 14 Study Guide and Review

Page 805   Vocabulary and Concept Check

1. h; phase shift
2. b; midline
3. d; vertical shift
4. f; half-angle formula
5. e; double-angle formula
6. c; period
7. g; difference of angles formula
8. a; amplitude

9. $y = -\frac{1}{2} \cos \theta$

Amplitude: $|a| = \left|-\frac{1}{2}\right|$ or $\frac{1}{2}$

Period: $\frac{360°}{|b|} = \frac{360°}{|1|}$ or $360°$ or 2π

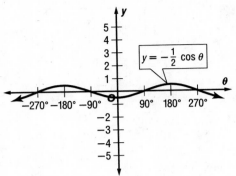

10. $y = 4 \sin 2\theta$

Amplitude: $|a| = |4|$ or 4

Period: $\frac{360°}{|b|} = \frac{360°}{|2|}$ or $180°$ or π

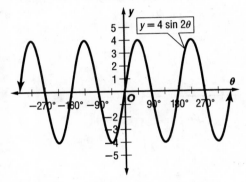

11. $y = \sin \frac{1}{2}\theta$

Amplitude: $|a| = |1|$ or 1

Period: $\frac{360°}{|b|} = \frac{360°}{\left|\frac{1}{2}\right|}$ or $720°$ or 4π

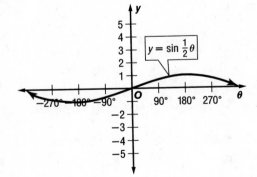

12. $y = 5 \sec \theta$

The secant function has no amplitude.

Period: $\frac{360°}{|b|} = \frac{360°}{|1|}$ or $360°$ or 2π

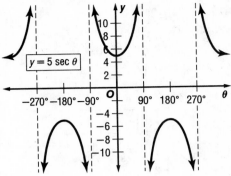

13. $y = \frac{1}{2} \csc \frac{2}{3}\theta$

The cosecant function has no amplitude.

Period: $\frac{360°}{|b|} =$ or $540°$ or 3π

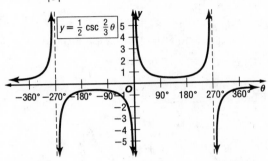

14. $y = \tan 4\theta$

The tangent function has no amplitude.

Period: $\frac{180°}{|b|} = \frac{180°}{|4|}$ or $45°$ or $\frac{\pi}{4}$

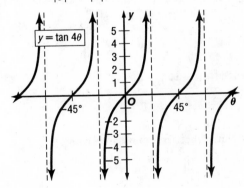

15. $y = \frac{1}{2} \sin[2(\theta - 60°)] - 1$

    Vertical shift: -1

    Amplitude: $|a| = \left|\frac{1}{2}\right|$ or $\frac{1}{2}$

    Period: $\frac{360°}{|b|} = \frac{360°}{|2|}$ or $180°$

    Phase shift: $60°$

    The phase shift is to the right.

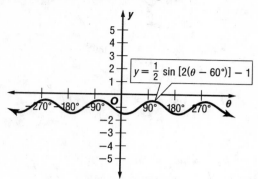

$y = \frac{1}{2} \sin[2(\theta - 60°)] - 1$

16. $y = 2 \tan\left[\frac{1}{4}(\theta - 90°)\right] + 3$

    Vertical shift: 3

    The tangent function has no amplitude.

    Period: $\frac{180°}{|b|} = \frac{180°}{\left|\frac{1}{4}\right|}$ or $720°$

    Phase shift: $90°$

    The phase shift is to the right.

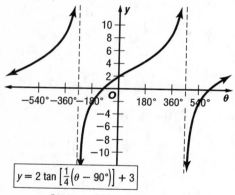

$y = 2 \tan\left[\frac{1}{4}(\theta - 90°)\right] + 3$

17. $y = 3 \sec\left[\frac{1}{2}\left(\theta + \frac{\pi}{4}\right)\right] + 1$

    Vertical shift: 1

    The secant function has no amplitude.

    Period: $\frac{2\pi}{|b|} = \frac{2\pi}{\left|\frac{1}{2}\right|}$ or 4π

    Phase shift: $-\frac{\pi}{4}$

    The phase shift is to the left.

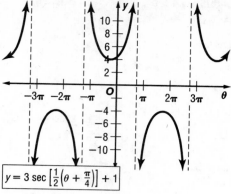

$y = 3 \sec\left[\frac{1}{2}\left(\theta + \frac{\pi}{4}\right)\right] + 1$

18. $y = \frac{1}{3} \cos\left[\frac{1}{3}\left(\theta - \frac{2\pi}{3}\right)\right] - 2$

    Vertical shift: -2

    Amplitude: $|a| = \left|\frac{1}{3}\right|$ or $\frac{1}{3}$

    Period: $\frac{2\pi}{|b|} =$ or 6π

    Phase shift: $\frac{2\pi}{3}$

    The phase shift is to the right.

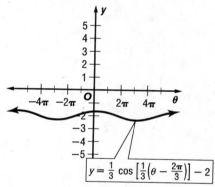

$y = \frac{1}{3} \cos\left[\frac{1}{3}\left(\theta - \frac{2\pi}{3}\right)\right] - 2$

19. $\cot^2 \theta + 1 = \csc^2 \theta$

    $\cot^2 \theta = \csc^2 \theta - 1$

    $\cot^2 \theta = \left(-\frac{5}{3}\right)^2 - 1$

    $\cot^2 \theta = \frac{16}{9}$

    $\cot \theta = \pm\frac{4}{3}$

    Since θ is in the fourth quadrant, $\cot \theta$ is negative. Thus, $\cot \theta = -\frac{4}{3}$.

20. First find $\cos \theta$.

    $\cos^2 \theta + \sin^2 \theta = 1$

    $\cos^2 \theta = 1 - \sin^2 \theta$

    $\cos^2 \theta = 1 - \left(\frac{1}{2}\right)^2$

    $\cos^2 \theta = \frac{3}{4}$

    $\cos \theta = \pm\frac{\sqrt{3}}{2}$

    Since θ is in the first quadrant, $\cos \theta$ is positive. Thus, $\cos \theta = \frac{\sqrt{3}}{2}$.

    Now find $\sec \theta$.

    $\sec \theta = \frac{1}{\cos \theta}$

    $= \frac{1}{\frac{\sqrt{3}}{2}}$

    $= \frac{2}{\sqrt{3}}$ or $\frac{2\sqrt{3}}{3}$

21. $\sin\theta\csc\theta - \cos^2\theta = \sin\theta\cdot\frac{1}{\sin\theta} - \cos^2\theta$
$$= 1 - \cos^2\theta$$
$$= \sin^2\theta$$

22. $\cos^2\theta\sec\theta\csc\theta = \cos^2\theta\cdot\frac{1}{\cos\theta}\cdot\frac{1}{\sin\theta}$
$$= \frac{\cos\theta}{\sin\theta}$$
$$= \cot\theta$$

23. $\cos\theta + \sin\theta\tan\theta = \cos\theta + \sin\theta\cdot\frac{\sin\theta}{\cos\theta}$
$$= \frac{\cos^2\theta + \sin^2\theta}{\cos\theta}$$
$$= \frac{1}{\cos\theta}$$
$$= \sec\theta$$

24.
$$\frac{\sin\theta}{\tan\theta} + \frac{\cos\theta}{\cot\theta} \overset{?}{=} \cos\theta + \sin\theta$$
$$\frac{\sin\theta}{\frac{\sin\theta}{\cos\theta}} + \frac{\cos\theta}{\frac{\cos\theta}{\sin\theta}} \overset{?}{=} \cos\theta + \sin\theta$$
$$\sin\theta\cdot\frac{\cos\theta}{\sin\theta} + \cos\theta\cdot\frac{\sin\theta}{\cos\theta} \overset{?}{=} \cos\theta + \sin\theta$$
$$\cos\theta + \sin\theta = \cos\theta + \sin\theta$$

25. $\frac{\sin\theta}{1-\cos\theta} \overset{?}{=} \cos\theta + \cot\theta$
$$\frac{\sin\theta}{1-\cos\theta} \overset{?}{=} \frac{1}{\sin\theta} + \frac{\cos\theta}{\sin\theta}$$
$$\frac{\sin\theta}{1-\cos\theta} \overset{?}{=} \frac{1+\cos\theta}{\sin\theta}$$
$$\frac{\sin\theta}{1-\cos\theta} \overset{?}{=} \frac{1+\cos\theta}{\sin\theta}\cdot\frac{1-\cos\theta}{1-\cos\theta}$$
$$\frac{\sin\theta}{1-\cos\theta} \overset{?}{=} \frac{1-\cos^2\theta}{\sin\theta(1-\cos\theta)}$$
$$\frac{\sin\theta}{1-\cos\theta} \overset{?}{=} \frac{\sin^2\theta}{\sin\theta(1-\cos\theta)}$$
$$\frac{\sin\theta}{1-\cos\theta} = \frac{\sin\theta}{1-\cos\theta}$$

26. $\cot^2\theta\sec^2\theta \overset{?}{=} 1 + \cot^2\theta$
$$\frac{\cos^2\theta}{\sin^2\theta}\cdot\frac{1}{\cos^2\theta} \overset{?}{=} 1 + \cot^2\theta$$
$$\frac{1}{\sin^2\theta} \overset{?}{=} 1 + \cot^2\theta$$
$$\csc^2\theta \overset{?}{=} 1 + \cot^2\theta$$
$$1 + \cot^2\theta = 1 + \cot^2\theta$$

27. $\sec\theta(\sec\theta - \cos\theta) \overset{?}{=} \tan^2\theta$
$$\frac{1}{\cos\theta}\left(\frac{1}{\cos\theta} - \cos\theta\right) \overset{?}{=} \tan^2\theta$$
$$\frac{1}{\cos^2\theta} - 1 \overset{?}{=} \tan^2\theta$$
$$\sec^2\theta - 1 \overset{?}{=} \tan^2\theta$$
$$\tan^2\theta = \tan^2\theta$$

28. $\cos 15° = \cos(45° - 30°)$
$$= \cos 45°\cos 30° + \sin 45°\sin 30°$$
$$= \frac{\sqrt{2}}{2}\cdot\frac{\sqrt{3}}{2} + \frac{\sqrt{2}}{2}\cdot\frac{1}{2}$$
$$= \frac{\sqrt{6}}{4} + \frac{\sqrt{2}}{4} \text{ or } \frac{\sqrt{6}+\sqrt{2}}{4}$$

29. $\cos 285° = \cos(240° + 45°)$
$$= \cos 240°\cos 45° - \sin 240°\sin 45°$$
$$= -\frac{1}{2}\cdot\frac{\sqrt{2}}{2} - \left(\frac{\sqrt{3}}{2}\right)\cdot\frac{\sqrt{2}}{2}$$
$$= -\frac{\sqrt{2}}{4} + \frac{\sqrt{6}}{4} \text{ or } \frac{\sqrt{6}-\sqrt{2}}{4}$$

30. $\sin 150° = \sin(180° - 30°)$
$$= \sin 180°\cos 30° - \cos 180°\sin 30°$$
$$= 0\cdot\frac{\sqrt{3}}{2} - (-1)\cdot\frac{1}{2}$$
$$= 0 + \frac{1}{2} \text{ or } \frac{1}{2}$$

31. $\sin 195° = \sin(135° + 60°)$
$$= \sin 135°\cos 60° + \cos 135°\sin 60°$$
$$= \frac{\sqrt{2}}{2}\cdot\frac{1}{2} + \left(-\frac{\sqrt{2}}{2}\right)\cdot\frac{\sqrt{3}}{2}$$
$$= \frac{\sqrt{2}}{4} - \frac{\sqrt{6}}{4} \text{ or } \frac{\sqrt{2}-\sqrt{6}}{4}$$

32. $\cos(-210°) = \cos(60° - 270°)$
$$= \cos 60°\cos 270° + \sin 60°\sin 270°$$
$$= \frac{1}{2}\cdot 0 + \frac{\sqrt{3}}{2}\cdot(-1)$$
$$= 0 - \frac{\sqrt{3}}{2} \text{ or } -\frac{\sqrt{3}}{2}$$

33. $\sin(-105°) = \sin(45° - 150°)$
$$= \sin 45°\cos 150° - \cos 45°\sin 150°$$
$$= \frac{\sqrt{2}}{2}\cdot\left(-\frac{\sqrt{3}}{2}\right) - \frac{\sqrt{2}}{2}\cdot\frac{1}{2}$$
$$= -\frac{\sqrt{6}}{4} - \frac{\sqrt{2}}{4} \text{ or } -\frac{\sqrt{6}-\sqrt{2}}{4}$$

34.
$$\cos(90° + \theta) \overset{?}{=} -\sin\theta$$
$$\cos 90°\cos\theta - \sin 90°\sin\theta \overset{?}{=} -\sin\theta$$
$$0\cdot\cos\theta - 1\cdot\sin\theta \overset{?}{=} -\sin\theta$$
$$-\sin\theta = -\sin\theta$$

35.
$$\sin(30 - \theta) \overset{?}{=} \cos(60 + \theta)$$
$$\sin 30°\cos\theta - \cos 30°\sin\theta \overset{?}{=} \cos 60°\cos\theta - \sin 60°\sin\theta$$
$$\frac{1}{2}\cos\theta - \frac{\sqrt{3}}{2}\sin\theta = \frac{1}{2}\cos\theta - \frac{\sqrt{3}}{2}\sin\theta$$

36.
$$\sin(\theta + \pi) \overset{?}{=} -\sin\theta$$
$$\sin\theta\cos\pi + \cos\theta\sin\pi \overset{?}{=} -\sin\theta$$
$$(\sin\theta)(-1) + (\cos\theta)(0) \overset{?}{=} -\sin\theta$$
$$-\sin\theta = -\sin\theta$$

37. $-\cos\theta \overset{?}{=} \cos(\pi + \theta)$
$$-\cos\theta \overset{?}{=} \cos\pi\cos\theta - \sin\pi\sin\theta$$
$$-\cos\theta \overset{?}{=} -1\cdot\cos\theta - 0\cdot\sin\theta$$
$$-\cos\theta = -\cos\theta$$

38. First find $\cos\theta$.
$$\cos^2\theta = 1 - \sin^2\theta$$
$$\cos^2\theta = 1 - \left(\frac{1}{4}\right)^2$$
$$\cos^2\theta = \frac{15}{16}$$
$$\cos\theta = \pm\frac{\sqrt{15}}{4}$$

Since θ is in the first quadrant, $\cos\theta = \frac{\sqrt{15}}{4}$.

$$\sin 2\theta = 2\sin\theta\cos\theta \qquad \cos 2\theta = 1 - 2\sin^2\theta$$
$$= 2\left(\frac{1}{4}\right)\left(\frac{\sqrt{15}}{4}\right) \qquad\qquad = 1 - 2\left(\frac{1}{4}\right)^2$$
$$= \frac{\sqrt{15}}{8} \qquad\qquad\qquad = \frac{7}{8}$$

$$\sin\frac{\theta}{2} = \pm\sqrt{\frac{1-\cos\theta}{2}}$$
$$= \pm\sqrt{\frac{1-\frac{\sqrt{15}}{4}}{2}}$$
$$= \pm\sqrt{\frac{8-2\sqrt{15}}{16}}$$
$$= \pm\frac{\sqrt{8-2\sqrt{15}}}{4}$$

Since θ is between $0°$ and $90°$, $\frac{\theta}{2}$ is between $0°$ and $45°$. Thus, $\sin\frac{\theta}{2} = \frac{\sqrt{8-2\sqrt{15}}}{4}$.

$$\cos\frac{\theta}{2} = \pm\sqrt{\frac{1+\cos\theta}{2}}$$
$$= \pm\sqrt{\frac{1+\frac{\sqrt{15}}{4}}{2}}$$
$$= \pm\sqrt{\frac{8+2\sqrt{5}}{16}}$$
$$= \pm\frac{\sqrt{8+2\sqrt{5}}}{4}$$

Since θ is between $0°$ and $90°$, $\frac{\theta}{2}$ is between $0°$ and $45°$. Thus, $\cos\frac{\theta}{2} = \frac{\sqrt{8+2\sqrt{5}}}{4}$.

39. First find $\cos \theta$.

$\cos^2 \theta = 1 - \sin^2 \theta$

$\cos^2 \theta = 1 - \left(-\frac{5}{13}\right)^2$

$\cos^2 \theta = \frac{144}{169}$

$\cos \theta = \pm \frac{12}{13}$

Since θ is in the third quadrant, $\cos \theta = -\frac{12}{13}$.

$\sin 2\theta = 2 \sin \theta \cos \theta$

$\quad = 2\left(-\frac{5}{13}\right)\left(-\frac{12}{13}\right)$

$\quad = \frac{120}{169}$

$\cos 2\theta = 1 - 2 \sin^2 \theta$

$\quad = 1 - 2\left(-\frac{5}{13}\right)^2$

$\quad = \frac{119}{169}$

$\sin \frac{\theta}{2} = \pm \sqrt{\frac{1 - \cos \theta}{2}}$

$\quad = \pm \sqrt{\frac{1 - \left(-\frac{12}{13}\right)}{2}}$

$\quad = \pm \sqrt{\frac{25}{26}}$

$\quad = \pm \frac{5\sqrt{26}}{26}$

Since θ is between 180° and 270°, $\frac{\theta}{2}$ is between 90° and 135°.

Thus, $\sin \frac{\theta}{2} = \frac{5\sqrt{26}}{26}$.

$\cos \frac{\theta}{2} = \pm \sqrt{\frac{1 + \cos \theta}{2}}$

$\quad = \pm \sqrt{\frac{1 + \left(-\frac{12}{13}\right)}{2}}$

$\quad = \pm \sqrt{\frac{1}{26}}$

$\quad = \pm \frac{\sqrt{26}}{26}$

Since θ is between 180° and 270°, $\frac{\theta}{2}$ is between 90° and 135°. Thus, $\cos \frac{\theta}{2} = -\frac{\sqrt{26}}{26}$.

40. First find $\sin \theta$.

$\sin^2 \theta = 1 - \cos^2 \theta$

$\sin^2 \theta = 1 - \left(-\frac{5}{17}\right)^2$

$\sin^2 \theta = \frac{264}{289}$

$\sin \theta = \pm \frac{2\sqrt{66}}{17}$

Since θ is in the second quadrant, $\sin \theta = \frac{2\sqrt{66}}{17}$.

$\sin 2\theta = 2 \sin \theta \cos \theta$

$\quad = 2\left(\frac{2\sqrt{66}}{17}\right)\left(-\frac{5}{17}\right)$

$\quad = -\frac{20\sqrt{66}}{289}$

$\cos 2\theta = 2 \cos^2 \theta - 1$

$\quad = 2\left(-\frac{5}{17}\right)^2 - 1$

$\quad = -\frac{239}{289}$

$\sin \frac{\theta}{2} = \pm \sqrt{\frac{1 - \cos \theta}{2}}$

$\quad = \pm \sqrt{\frac{1 - \left(-\frac{5}{17}\right)}{2}}$

$\quad = \pm \frac{11}{17}$

$\quad = \pm \frac{\sqrt{187}}{17}$

Since θ is between 90° and 180°, $\frac{\theta}{2}$ is between 45° and 90°. Thus, $\sin \frac{\theta}{2} = \frac{\sqrt{187}}{17}$.

$\cos \frac{\theta}{2} = \pm \sqrt{\frac{1 + \cos \theta}{2}}$

$\quad = \pm \sqrt{\frac{1 + \left(-\frac{5}{17}\right)}{2}}$

$\quad = \pm \sqrt{\frac{6}{17}}$

$\quad = \pm \frac{\sqrt{102}}{17}$

Since θ is between 90° and 180°, $\frac{\theta}{2}$ is between 45° and 90°. Thus, $\cos \frac{\theta}{2} = \frac{\sqrt{102}}{17}$.

41. First find $\sin \theta$.

$\sin^2 \theta = 1 - \cos^2 \theta$

$\sin^2 \theta = 1 - \left(\frac{12}{13}\right)^2$

$\sin^2 \theta = \frac{25}{169}$

$\sin \theta = \pm \frac{5}{13}$

Since θ is in the fourth quadrant, $\sin \theta = -\frac{5}{13}$.

$\sin 2\theta = 2 \sin \theta \cos \theta$

$\quad = 2\left(-\frac{5}{13}\right)\left(\frac{12}{13}\right)$

$\quad = -\frac{120}{169}$

$\cos 2\theta = 2 \cos^2 \theta - 1$

$\quad = 2\left(\frac{12}{13}\right)^2 - 1$

$\quad = \frac{119}{169}$

$\sin \frac{\theta}{2} = \pm \sqrt{\frac{1 - \cos \theta}{2}}$

$\quad = \pm \sqrt{\frac{1 - \frac{12}{13}}{2}}$

$\quad = \pm \sqrt{\frac{1}{26}}$

$\quad = \pm \frac{\sqrt{26}}{26}$

Since θ is between 270° and 360°, $\frac{\theta}{2}$ is between 135° and 180°. Thus, $\sin \frac{\theta}{2} = \frac{\sqrt{26}}{26}$.

$\cos \frac{\theta}{2} = \pm \sqrt{\frac{1 + \cos \theta}{2}}$

$\quad = \pm \sqrt{\frac{1 + \frac{12}{13}}{2}}$

$\quad = \pm \sqrt{\frac{25}{26}}$

$\quad = \pm \frac{5\sqrt{26}}{26}$

Since θ is between 270° and 360°, $\frac{\theta}{2}$ is between 135° and 180°. Thus, $\cos \frac{\theta}{2} = -\frac{5\sqrt{26}}{26}$.

42. $2 \sin 2\theta = 1$

$\sin 2\theta = \frac{1}{2}$

$2\theta = 30°, 150°, 390°,$ or $510°$

$\theta = 15°, 75°, 195°,$ or $255°$.

The solutions are 15°, 75°, 195°, and 255°

43.
$$2\cos^2\theta + \sin^2\theta = 2\cos\theta$$
$$2\cos^2\theta + (1 - \cos^2\theta) = 2\cos\theta$$
$$\cos^2\theta + 1 = 2\cos\theta$$
$$\cos^2\theta - 2\cos\theta + 1 = 0$$
$$(\cos\theta - 1)^2 = 0$$
$$\cos\theta - 1 = 0$$
$$\cos\theta = 1$$
$$\theta = 0°$$

The solution is 0°.

44.
$$6\sin^2\theta - 5\sin\theta - 4 = 0$$
$$(3\sin\theta - 4)(2\sin\theta + 1) = 0$$

$$3\sin\theta - 4 = 0 \quad \text{or} \quad 2\sin\theta + 1 = 0$$
$$3\sin\theta = 4 \qquad\qquad 2\sin\theta = -1$$
$$\sin\theta = \frac{4}{3} \qquad\qquad \sin\theta = -\frac{1}{2}$$
no solutions $\qquad\qquad \theta = \frac{7\pi}{6} \text{ or } \frac{11\pi}{6}$

The solutions are $\frac{7\pi}{6} + 2k\pi$ and $\frac{11\pi}{6} + 2k\pi$.

45.
$$2\cos^2\theta = 3\sin\theta$$
$$2(1 - \sin^2\theta) = 3\sin\theta$$
$$2 - 2\sin^2\theta = 3\sin\theta$$
$$0 = 2\sin^2\theta + 3\sin\theta - 2$$
$$0 = (2\sin\theta - 1)(\sin\theta + 2)$$

$$2\sin\theta - 1 = 0 \quad \text{or} \quad \sin\theta + 2 = 0$$
$$2\sin\theta = 1 \qquad\qquad \sin\theta = -2$$
$$\sin\theta = \frac{1}{2} \qquad\qquad \text{no solution}$$
$$\theta = \frac{\pi}{6} \text{ or } \frac{5\pi}{6}$$

The solutions are $\frac{\pi}{6} + 2k\pi$ and $\frac{5\pi}{6} + 2k\pi$.

Chapter 14 Practice Test

Page 809

1. period

2. vertical shift

3. $\frac{1}{3}$

4. cosecant

5. $y = \frac{2}{3}\sin 2\theta + 5$

Vertical Shift: 5

Amplitude: $|a| = \left|\frac{2}{3}\right|$ or $\frac{2}{3}$

Period: $\frac{360°}{|b|} = \frac{360°}{|2|}$ or 180°

There is no phase shift.

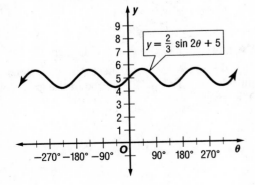

6. $y = 4\cos\left[\frac{1}{2}(\theta + 30°)\right] - 1$

Vertical Shift: -1

Amplitude: $|a| = |4|$ or 4

Period: $\frac{360°}{|b|} = \frac{360°}{\left|\frac{1}{2}\right|}$ or 720°

Phase Shift $-30°$

The phase shift is to the left.

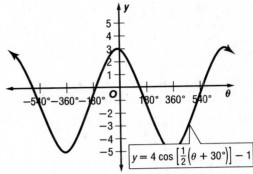

7. First find $\cos\theta$.
$$\cos^2\theta + \sin^2\theta = 1$$
$$\cos^2\theta = 1 - \sin^2\theta$$
$$\cos^2\theta = 1 - \left(\frac{1}{2}\right)^2$$
$$\cos^2\theta = \frac{3}{4}$$
$$\cos\theta = \pm\frac{\sqrt{3}}{2}$$

Since θ is in the second quadrant, $\cos\theta$ is negative. Thus, $\cos\theta = -\frac{\sqrt{3}}{2}$.

$$\tan\theta = \frac{\sin\theta}{\cos\theta}$$
$$= \frac{\frac{1}{2}}{-\frac{\sqrt{3}}{2}}$$
$$= -\frac{1}{\sqrt{3}} \text{ or } -\frac{\sqrt{3}}{3}$$

8. First find $\tan\theta$.
$$\tan\theta = \sqrt{\frac{1}{\cos\theta}}$$
$$= \frac{1}{3} \text{ or } \frac{4}{3}$$

Now find $\sec\theta$.
$$\sec^2\theta = \tan^2\theta + 1$$
$$\sec^2\theta = \left(\frac{4}{3}\right)^2 + 1$$
$$\sec^2\theta = \frac{25}{9}$$
$$\sec\theta = \pm\frac{5}{3}$$

Since θ is in the third quadrant, $\sec\theta$ is negative. Thus, $\sec\theta = -\frac{5}{3}$.

9.
$$(\sin\theta - \cos\theta)^2 \overset{?}{=} 1 - \sin 2\theta$$
$$\sin^2\theta - 2\sin\theta\cos\theta + \cos^2\theta \overset{?}{=} 1 - \sin 2\theta$$
$$(\sin^2\theta + \cos^2\theta) - 2\sin\theta\cos\theta \overset{?}{=} 1 - \sin 2\theta$$
$$1 - \sin 2\theta = 1 - \sin 2\theta$$

10.
$$\frac{\cos\theta}{1 - \sin^2\theta} \overset{?}{=} \sec\theta$$
$$\frac{\cos\theta}{\cos^2\theta} \overset{?}{=} \sec\theta$$
$$\frac{1}{\cos\theta} \overset{?}{=} \sec\theta$$
$$\sec\theta = \sec\theta$$

11.
$$\frac{\sec \theta}{\sin \theta} - \frac{\sin \theta}{\cos \theta} \overset{?}{=} \cot \theta$$
$$\frac{\frac{1}{\sin \theta \cos \theta} - \frac{\sin \theta}{\cos \theta}}{} \overset{?}{=} \cot \theta$$
$$\frac{1}{\sin \theta \cos \theta} - \frac{\sin^2 \theta}{\sin \theta \cos \theta} \overset{?}{=} \cot \theta$$
$$\frac{\cos^2 \theta}{\sin \theta \cos \theta} \overset{?}{=} \cot \theta$$
$$\frac{\cos \theta}{\sin \theta} \overset{?}{=} \cot \theta$$
$$\cot \theta = \cot \theta$$

12.
$$\frac{1 + \tan^2 \theta}{\cos^2 \theta} \overset{?}{=} \sec^4 \theta$$
$$\frac{\sec^2 \theta}{\cos^2 \theta} \overset{?}{=} \sec^4 \theta$$
$$\sec^2 \theta \sec^2 \theta \overset{?}{=} \sec^4 \theta$$
$$\sec^4 \theta = \sec^4 \theta$$

13. $\cos 285° = \cos(240° + 45°)$
$$= \cos 240° \cos 45° - \sin 240° \sin 45°$$
$$= -\frac{1}{2} \cdot \frac{\sqrt{2}}{2} - \left(-\frac{\sqrt{3}}{2}\right) \cdot \frac{\sqrt{2}}{2}$$
$$= -\frac{\sqrt{2}}{4} + \frac{\sqrt{6}}{4} \text{ or } \frac{\sqrt{6} - \sqrt{2}}{4}$$

14. $\sin 345° = \sin(300° + 45°)$
$$= \sin 300° \cos 45° + \cos 300° \sin 45°$$
$$= -\frac{\sqrt{3}}{2} \cdot \frac{\sqrt{2}}{2} + \frac{1}{2} \cdot \frac{\sqrt{2}}{2}$$
$$= -\frac{\sqrt{6}}{4} + \frac{\sqrt{2}}{4} \text{ or } \frac{\sqrt{2} - \sqrt{6}}{4}$$

15. $\sin(-225°) = \sin(45° - 270°)$
$$= \sin 45° \cos 270° - \cos 45° \sin 270°$$
$$= \frac{\sqrt{2}}{2} \cdot 0 - \frac{\sqrt{2}}{2} \cdot (-1)$$
$$= 0 + \frac{\sqrt{2}}{2} \text{ or } \frac{\sqrt{2}}{2}$$

16. $\cos 480° = \cos(2 \cdot 240°)$
$$= 2 \cos^2 240° - 1$$
$$= 2\left(-\frac{1}{2}\right)^2 - 1$$
$$= -\frac{1}{2}$$

17. $\cos 67.5° = \cos \frac{135°}{2}$
$$= \sqrt{\frac{1 + \cos 135°}{2}}$$
$$= \sqrt{\frac{1 + \left(-\frac{\sqrt{2}}{2}\right)}{2}}$$
$$= \sqrt{\frac{2 - \sqrt{2}}{4}}$$
$$= \frac{\sqrt{2 - \sqrt{2}}}{2}$$

18. $\sin 75° = \sin(45° + 30°)$
$$= \sin 45° \cos 30° + \cos 45° \sin 30°$$
$$= \frac{\sqrt{2}}{2} \cdot \frac{\sqrt{3}}{2} + \frac{\sqrt{2}}{2} \cdot \frac{1}{2}$$
$$= \frac{\sqrt{6}}{4} + \frac{\sqrt{2}}{4} \text{ or } \frac{\sqrt{6} + \sqrt{2}}{4}$$

19.
$$\sec \theta = 1 + \tan \theta$$
$$\sec^2 \theta = (1 + \tan \theta)^2$$
$$\tan^2 \theta + 1 = 1 + 2 \tan \theta + \tan^2 \theta$$
$$0 = 2 \tan \theta$$
$$0 = \tan \theta$$
$$\theta = 0° \text{ or } 180°$$

Check:
$$\sec \theta = 1 + \tan \theta \qquad\qquad \sec \theta = 1 + \tan \theta$$
$$\sec 0° \overset{?}{=} 1 + \tan 0° \qquad\qquad \sec 180° \overset{?}{=} 1 + \tan 180°$$
$$1 \overset{?}{=} 1 + 0 \qquad\qquad\qquad -1 = 1 + 0$$
$$1 = 1 \checkmark \qquad\qquad\qquad\quad -1 \neq 1$$
$$\qquad\qquad\qquad\qquad\qquad 180° \text{ is not a solution.}$$
The solutions are $0° + k \cdot 360°$.

20.
$$\cos 2\theta = \cos \theta$$
$$2 \cos^2 \theta - 1 = \cos \theta$$
$$2 \cos^2 \theta - \cos \theta - 1 = 0$$
$$(2 \cos \theta + 1)(\cos \theta - 1) = 0$$
$$2 \cos \theta + 1 = 0 \qquad\qquad \text{or} \quad \cos \theta - 1 = 0$$
$$2 \cos \theta = -1 \qquad\qquad\qquad\qquad \cos \theta = 1$$
$$\cos \theta = -\frac{1}{2} \qquad\qquad\qquad\qquad \theta = 0°$$
$$\theta = 120° \text{ or } 240°$$
The solutions are $0° + k \cdot 360°$, $120° + k \cdot 360°$, and $240° + k \cdot 360°$.

21.
$$\cos 2\theta + \sin \theta = 1$$
$$(1 - 2 \sin^2 \theta) + \sin \theta = 1$$
$$-2 \sin^2 \theta + \sin \theta = 0$$
$$-\sin \theta (2 \sin \theta - 1) = 0$$
$$-\sin \theta = 0 \qquad\qquad \text{or} \quad 2 \sin \theta - 1 = 0$$
$$\sin \theta = 0 \qquad\qquad\qquad\qquad 2 \sin \theta = 1$$
$$\theta = 0° \text{ or } 180° \qquad\qquad\qquad \sin \theta = \frac{1}{2}$$
$$\qquad\qquad\qquad\qquad\qquad\qquad \theta = 30° \text{ or } 150°$$
The solutions are $0° + k \cdot 180°$, $30° + k \cdot 360°$, and $150° + k \cdot 360°$.

22.
$$\sin \theta = \tan \theta$$
$$\sin \theta = \frac{\sin \theta}{\cos \theta}$$
$$\sin \theta \cos \theta = \sin \theta$$
$$\sin \theta \cos \theta - \sin \theta = 0$$
$$\sin \theta (\cos \theta - 1) = 0$$
$$\sin \theta = 0 \qquad\qquad \text{or} \quad \cos \theta - 1 = 0$$
$$\theta = 0° \text{ or } 180° \qquad\qquad\qquad \cos \theta = 1$$
$$\qquad\qquad\qquad\qquad\qquad\qquad \theta = 0°$$

Check:
$$\sin \theta = \tan \theta \qquad\qquad \sin \theta = \tan \theta$$
$$\sin 0° \overset{?}{=} \tan 0° \qquad\qquad \sin 180° \overset{?}{=} \tan 180°$$
$$0 = 0 \checkmark \qquad\qquad\qquad 0 = 0 \checkmark$$
The solutions are $0° + k \cdot 180°$.

23. $d = \frac{v_0{}^2}{g} \sin 2\theta$
$$= \frac{100^2}{32} \sin(2 \cdot 60°)$$
$$\approx 270.6$$
The ball travels about 270.6 feet.

24.
$$d = \frac{v_0{}^2}{g} \sin 2\theta$$
$$312.5 = \frac{100^2}{32} \sin 2\theta$$
$$\frac{32}{100^2} \cdot 312.5 = \sin 2\theta$$
$$1 = \sin 2\theta$$
$$2\theta = 90°$$
$$\theta = 45°$$
The ball made a 45° angle with the ground.

25. B; The amplitude of the graph is less than $\frac{1}{2}$, so we can eliminate answer choices A and C, whose amplitudes are both 3. The period of the graph is π. Of answer choices B and D, only B has period π.

Chapter 14 Standardized Test Practice

Pages 810–811

1. D; $(0.5)(0.007) = 0.0035$ or 3.5×10^{-3}

2. B; Let $n, n + 2, n + 4, n + 6$, and $n + 8$ represent the five conscutive odd integers.
$$n + (n + 2) + (n + 4) + (n + 6) + (n + 8) = 55$$
$$5n + 20 = 55$$
$$5n = 35$$
$$n = 7$$
$$n + 8 = 15$$
The greatest of the integers is 15, and the least is 7. The sum is $15 + 7$ or 22.

3. D; Each banana costs $\frac{a}{8}$ cents and each orange costs $\frac{b}{6}$ cents.

   Thus, 2 bananas and 2 oranges cost $2\left(\frac{a}{8}\right) + 2\left(\frac{b}{6}\right)$ cents.
   $$2\left(\frac{a}{8}\right) + 2\left(\frac{b}{6}\right) = \frac{a}{4} + \frac{b}{3} \text{ or } \frac{3a + 4b}{12}$$

4. C; There are 7 cherry candies left and a total of 28 candies.
   $$P(\text{cherry}) = \frac{7}{28} \text{ or } \frac{1}{4}$$

5. B; $\dfrac{\sin \frac{\pi}{6}}{\cos \frac{2\pi}{3}} = \dfrac{\frac{1}{2}}{-\frac{1}{2}}$ or -1

6. D; $\tan R = \frac{\text{opp}}{\text{adj}}$ or $\frac{24}{7}$

7. B; KEYSTROKES: $\boxed{\text{SIN}}$ $\boxed{\text{2nd}}$ $[\text{COS}^{-1}]$ 1 $\boxed{\div}$ 3 $\boxed{)}$ $\boxed{\text{ENTER}}$
   $$\sin\left(\cos^{-1} \frac{1}{3}\right) \approx 0.9428$$
   $$\frac{2\sqrt{2}}{3} \approx 0.928$$

8. C; The minimum value of $y = \sin 2x$ is -1.
   $$y = \sin 2x$$
   $$-1 = \sin 2x$$
   $$\frac{3\pi}{2} = 2x$$
   $$\frac{3\pi}{4} = x$$

9. A; $\dfrac{\sin^2 \theta + \cos^2 \theta}{\sin^2 \theta} = \dfrac{1}{\sec^2 \theta}$
   $$= \cos^2 \theta$$

10. D; First find $\sin \theta$.
    $$\cos^2 \theta + \sin^2 \theta = 1$$
    $$\sin^2 \theta = 1 - \cos^2 \theta$$
    $$\sin^2 \theta = 1 - \left(-\frac{1}{2}\right)^2$$
    $$\sin^2 \theta = \frac{3}{4}$$
    $$\sin \theta = \pm \frac{\sqrt{3}}{2}$$
    Since θ is in the second quadrant, $\sin \theta$ is positive.
    Thus, $\sin \theta = \frac{\sqrt{3}}{2}$.
    $$\sin 2\theta = 2 \sin \theta \cos \theta$$
    $$= 2\left(\frac{\sqrt{3}}{2}\right)\left(-\frac{1}{2}\right)$$
    $$= -\frac{\sqrt{3}}{2}$$

11. List the values of $7k + 3$ less than 50, where k is a positive integer.
    $k = 1: 7k + 1 = 7(1) + 3$ or 10
    $k = 2: 7k + 1 = 7(2) + 3$ or 17
    $k = 3: 7k + 1 = 7(3) + 3$ or 24
    $k = 4: 7k + 1 = 7(4) + 3$ or 31
    $k = 5: 7k + 1 = 7(5) + 3$ or 38
    $k = 6: 7k + 1 = 7(6) + 3$ or 45
    The only prime values of $7k + 3$ less than 50 are 17 and 31.

12. $8 + 200\%$ of $8 = 8 + 2.00(8)$ or 24
    The selling price will be \$24.

13. Let x represent the sum of the remaining four numbers.
    $$\frac{-9 + x}{7} = 0$$
    $$-9 + x = 0$$
    $$x = 9$$
    The sum of the remaining four numbers is 9.

14. Solve $4a - 6b = 0$ for a.
    $$4a - 6b = 0$$
    $$4a = 6b$$
    $$a = \frac{6b}{4} \text{ or } \frac{3b}{2}$$
    Now find the ratio.
    $$\frac{a}{c} = \frac{\frac{3b}{2}}{9b}$$
    $$= \frac{3b}{2} \cdot \frac{1}{9b}$$
    $$= \frac{1}{6}$$

15. $$\frac{3^3 \cdot 3}{\sqrt{81}} = 3^x$$
    $$\frac{3^4}{9} = 3^x$$
    $$\frac{3^4}{3^2} = 3^x$$
    $$3^2 = 3^x$$
    $$2 = x$$

16. There are 13 children. In order from youngest to oldest, the seventh child is 7 years old. Thus, $N = 7$.
    The most frequent age is 7. Thus, $m = 7$.
    $N - m = 7 - 7$ or 0

17. Since the area of the square is 16, the length of each side of the square is 4. Since D and H are the midpoints of their respective sides of the square, both segment CD and segment CH have length 2. Since C is the midpoint of segment BD and the length of segment CD is 2, the length of segment BC is also 2. Thus, the length of segment BD is 4.

    Since triangles ABD and HCD are similar, the length of segment AB is equal to the length of segment BD because the corresponding parts of triangle HCD have equal lengths. Thus, the length of segment AB is 4.

    Use the formula for the area of a trapezoid.
    $$A = \frac{1}{2}(b_1 + b_2)h$$
    $$= \frac{1}{2}(4 + 2)(2)$$
    $$= 6$$
    The area of quadrilateral $ABCH$ is 6.

18. Use the slope formula.

$$m = \frac{y_2 - y_1}{x_2 - x_1}$$

$$\frac{3}{8} = \frac{n - 4n}{0 - 6}$$

$$\frac{3}{8} = \frac{-3n}{-6}$$

$$\frac{3}{8} = \frac{n}{2}$$

$$\frac{3}{4} = n$$

19. Since $\cos^2 \theta + \sin^2 \theta = 1$ for all angles θ, $\sin^2 30° + \cos^2 30° = 1$. The value of $\sin 60°$ is unnecessary information.

20. A; The length of each side of the square is 10. Use the Pythagorean Theorem to show that the length of the diagonal is $10\sqrt{2}$. Use the Pythagorean Theorem to show that the length of a diagonal of the rectangle is 10.

21. B; The value in Column A is $1^2 + \frac{2}{1} - 2$ or 1. The value in Column B is $2^2 + \frac{2}{2} - 2$ or 3.

22. D; The quantities are equal when $w = x = 0$. The quantity in Column A is greater when $w = 2$ and $x = 1$. The quantity in Column B is greater when $w = -2$ and $x = -1$.

23. C; Simplify the given equation.

$$(a + b)^2 = a^2 + b^2$$

$$a^2 + 2ab + b^2 = a^2 + b^2$$

$$2ab = 0$$

Now simplify $(a - b)^2$ replacing $2ab$ with 0.

$$(a - b)^2 = a^2 - 2ab + b^2$$
$$= a^2 - 0 + b^2$$
$$= a^2 + b^2$$

24. B; $\tan \beta = \frac{\text{opp}}{\text{adj}}$ or $\frac{3}{4}$ and $\sin \alpha = \frac{\text{opp}}{\text{hyp}}$ or $\frac{4}{5}$